FEATURES AND BENEFITS
ALGEBRA 2: Integration, Applications, Connections

1. **Integration**   Integration helps students to view mathematics as a whole and not as compartmentalized areas of instruction. *Lessons* that connect the various areas of mathematics to algebra are included as they are appropriate (see Lesson 2-5). This integration also occurs *within* algebra lessons. *Lesson Openers* often reflect integration (see page 141), as do *Examples* (see Example 2 on page 200) and *Exercises* (see Exercise 58 on page 383).

2. **Applications**   Because the ability to grasp concepts and skills is greatly enhanced when they are tied to applications, most lessons open with a real-world application (see page 160). This is strengthened by including *Applications and Problem Solving* in every set of exercises (see page 145), as well as in *Examples* (see Example 1 on page 195).

3. **Connections**   Connections to *interdisciplinary areas*, such as science, geography, history, music, and so on, enhance learning while increasing student interest. These connections appear as *Lesson Openers* (see page 64), *Examples* (see Example 7 on page 258), and as *Exercises* (see Exercise 48 on page 272).

4. **Technology**   Although this program is *not* dependent upon graphing calculators, the graphing calculator is integrated throughout the program in various ways.

Graphing Technology Lessons	See Lesson 3-1A.
Graphing Calculator Explorations	See page 127.
Graphing Calculator Programs	See Exercise 46 on page 272.
Graphing Calculator Exercises	See Exercises 23–25 on page 158.

   Spreadsheets also play a role in the program, particularly with the integration of statistics (see Example 2 on page 188). *Technology Tips* are provided as appropriate.

5. **Modeling**   Students have the opportunity to bridge the gap between the concrete and the abstract through *hands-on experiences* in the *Modeling Mathematics* activities.

Modeling Mathematics Lessons	See Lesson 7-4A.
Modeling Mathematics Activities	See page 416.
Modeling Mathematics Exercises	See Exercise 4 on page 419.

6. **Problem Solving**   Problem-solving strategies are *integrated* within lessons (see *solve a simpler problem* in Example 3 on page 156). *Applications and Problem Solving* and *Critical Thinking* in *every* set of exercises illustrate the ongoing attention to problem solving (see Exercises 26–31 on pages 158–159).

7. **Graphing**   Graphing is the unifying theme, with students graphing a variety of relations and functions.

Linear Functions	See Lesson 2-2.
Quadratic Functions	See Lesson 6-1.
Conic Sections	See Chapter 7.
Polynomial Functions	See Lesson 8-3.
Rational Functions	See Lesson 9-1.
Exponential and Logarithmic Functions	See Lessons 10-1 and 10-2.
Trigonometric Functions	See Lesson 14-1.

D1088728

Glencoe
Algebra 2

Handbook for **Texas Teachers**

**Helping You Be Your
Professional Best**

Cindy J. Boyd, Author

CONTENTS

ISBN: 0-02-825182-2

Features for Texas Teachers

Glencoe *Algebra 2* provides a variety of handy, effective teaching tools for making sure that your students have a successful learning experience.

Texas Essential Knowledge and Skills (TEKS)

New for the 1998-1999 school year, the Texas Essential Knowledge and Skills (TEKS), which replaced the Essential Elements, were approved in 1996. The TEKS include overall Basic Understandings, Knowledge and Skills statements, and Performance Descriptions for each Texas mathematics course.

The study of **functions** provides the foundation for Algebra 1 and 2. Students are provided with opportunities to solve problems in real-life situations. Although there are few specific references to technology in the TEKS, its use is assumed, much as it will be in the workplace of the future.

Correlations to the Knowledge and Skills statements are provided for individual lessons on Teacher's Wraparound Edition pages and on the chapter overview pages, making it easy for you to be sure that you have covered the Algebra 2 TEKS. In addition, a complete correlation in this handbook gives you an overview of TEKS coverage.

Texas Teacher Resources

Glencoe's *Algebra 2* provides a number of resources for use by teachers in Texas.

● ***Texas Teacher's Wraparound Edition***

Includes:
- Correlation to TEKS in chapter planning guide
- Correlation to TEKS in relevant lessons

● ***Texas Lesson Planning Guide***

● ***Texas Block Scheduling Booklet***

Both include:
- Correlation to TEKS
- Correlation to Mindjogger Videoquizzes

● ***Algebra 1 End-of-Course Examination (EOC) Practice and Sample Test Masters***

● ***Texas Assessment of Academic Skills (TAAS) Practice and Sample Test Masters***

Both include:
- Practice for each objective
- Sample tests

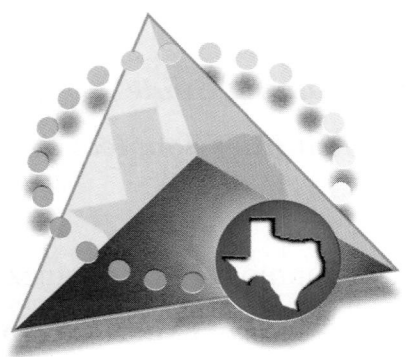

Meet Our Texas Authors and Consultants

To meet the goal of creating a program that serves the unique needs of students in Texas, the Glencoe Algebra-Geometry series has seven authors and consultants from Texas. They are profiled below.

CINDY J. BOYD is a high school mathematics teacher from Abilene, Texas, and the author of *Skit-So-Phrenia!: Educational Skits Based on Mathematical Concepts.* She has been recognized as the Texas Academy of Science's Outstanding Mathematics Educator for 1995 and has received the Walt Disney American Teacher Award in 1995 and the Texas Presidential State Awards in 1994, 1995, and 1996. She is also an author of *Glencoe Geometry.*

BEATRICE MOORE-HARRIS is a mathematics coordinator for the Houston Independent School District.

EVA GATES is an independent mathematics consultant in Pearland, Texas. She was formerly the mathematics supervisor for the Pasadena Independent School District.

ROBBIE BONNEVILLE is the mathematics coordinator for the La Joya Independent School District.

MELISSA McCLURE is a mathematics consultant with Teaching for Tomorrow in Fort Worth, Texas. She was formerly a high school and middle school teacher in Mansfield, Texas.

Various chapters in Glencoe's *Algebra 2* were also reviewed by **Nancy Barr,** Lubbock, Texas, **Susan L. Harder,** Plano, Texas, **Chris Johnson,** Lewisville, Texas, **Nancy Lee King,** Midland, Texas, **Frank LaFuente, Sr.,** San Antonio, Texas, and **Dee Mattox-Hall,** Galena Park, Texas.

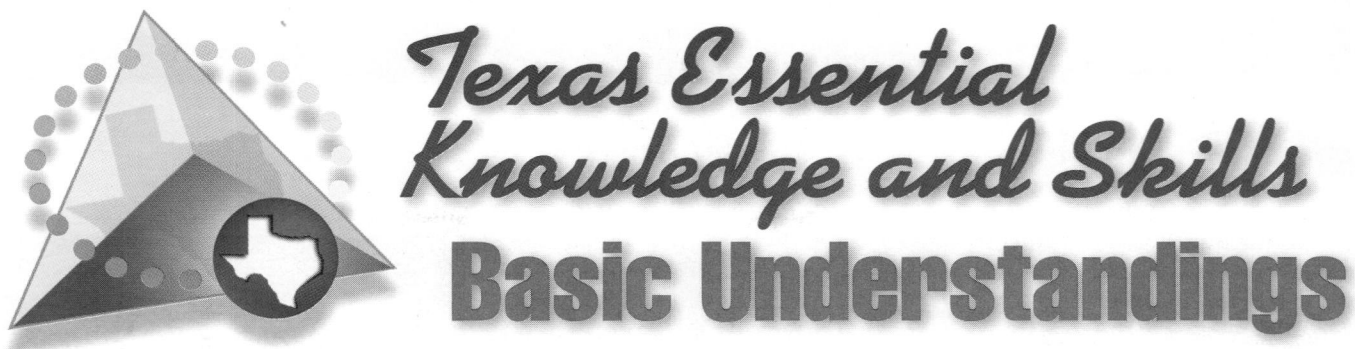

Texas Essential Knowledge and Skills
Basic Understandings

A **Foundation Concepts for High School Mathematics**

As presented in grades K-8, the Basic Understandings of Number, Operation, and Quantitative Reasoning; Patterns, Relationships, and Algebraic Thinking; Geometry; Measurement; and Probability and Statistics are essential foundations for all work in high school mathematics. Students continue to build on this foundation as they expand their understanding through other mathematical experiences.

B **Algebraic Thinking and Symbolic Reasoning**

Symbolic reasoning plays a critical role in algebra; symbols provide powerful ways to represent mathematical situations and to express generalizations. Students use symbols in a variety of ways to study relationships among quantities.

C **Function Concepts**

Functions represent the systematic dependence of one quantity on another. Students use functions to represent and model problem situations and to analyze and interpret relationships.

D **Relationship between Equations and Functions**

Equations arise as a way of asking and answering questions involving functional relationships. Students work in many situations to set up equations and use a variety of methods to solve these equations.

E **Tools for Algebraic Thinking**

Techniques for working with functions and equations are essential in understanding underlying relationships. Students use a variety of representations (concrete, numerical, algorithmic, graphical), tools, and technology, including, but not limited to, powerful and accessible hand-held calculators and computers with graphing capabilities and model mathematical situations to solve meaningful problems.

F **Underlying Mathematical Processes**

Many processes underlie all content areas in mathematics. As they do mathematics, students continually use problem solving, computation in problem-solving contexts, language and communication, connections within and outside mathematics, and reasoning, as well as multiple representations, applications and modeling, and justification and proof.

Glencoe's correlation to the Texas Essential Knowledge and Skills (TEKS) is based upon the numbering and lettering system approved by the Texas State Board of Education on July 12, 1996. Subsequently, after publication of this Teacher's Wraparound Edition, a different numbering and lettering system may have been disseminated. However, Glencoe's statement of the approved TEKS (the Basic Understandings, the Knowledge and Skills statements, and the Performance Descriptors) are exact duplicates of the TEKS approved by the Texas State Board of Education.

Algebra 2 TEKS to Glencoe *Algebra 2*

Knowledge and Skills and Performance Descriptions	Glencoe *Algebra 2* Student Edition (Lesson)
Objective 1: The student uses properties and attributes of functions and applies functions to problem situations.	
a. For a variety of situations, the student identifies the mathematical domains and ranges and determines reasonable domain and range values for given situations.	2-1, 2-2, 6-6, 8-1, 8-8, 8-8B, 9-1, 9-5, 10-1A, 10-1, 11-1, 13-1, 13-3, 13-6, 13-7
b. In solving problems, the student collects data and records results, organizes the data, makes scatterplots, fits the curves to the appropriate parent function, interprets the results, and proceeds to model, predict, and make decisions and critical judgments.	2-5, 2-5B, 2-6, 6-6, 8-3B, 10-1B, 11-1A, 11-3, Inv. (pp. 60-61, 100, 108, 140, 159, 174), Inv. (pp. 180-181, 193, 231, 273, 302, 322), Inv. (pp. 474-475, 501, 538, 555, 575, 584), Inv. (pp. 590-591, 616, 630, 655, 682, 702), Inv. (pp. 768-769, 785, 810, 834, 859, 868)
Objective 2: The student understands the importance of the skills required to manipulate symbols in order to solve problems and uses the necessary algebraic skills to simplify algebraic expressions and solve equations and inequalities in problem situations.	
a. The student uses tools including matrices, factoring, and properties of exponents to simplify expressions and transform and solve equations.	1-1A, 1-1, 1-2, 1-4, 1-5A, 1-5, 2-2B, 2-7A, 2-7, 4-1, 4-2, 4-3, 4-4, 4-5, 4-6, 4-7, 5-1, 5-4, 5-7, 5-8, 6-1A, 6-1, 6-2, 6-3, 6-4, 6-7A, 6-7, 8-6, 9-5, 10-1, 10-2, 10-3, 10-6, 14-6, Inv. (pp. 180-181, 193, 231, 273, 302, 322)
b. The student uses complex numbers to describe the solutions of quadratic equations.	6-3, 6-4
c. The student connects the function notation of $y =$ and $f(x) =$.	2-1
Objective 3: The student formulates systems of equations and inequalities from problem situations, uses a variety of methods to solve them, and analyzes the solutions in terms of the situations.	
a. The student analyzes situations and formulates systems of equations or inequalities in two or more unknowns to solve problems.	3-1, 3-2, 3-3, 3-4, 3-5, 3-6, 3-7, 7-7
b. The student uses algebraic methods, graphs, tables, or matrices to solve systems of equations or inequalities.	3-1A, 3-1, 3-2, 3-3, 3-4, 3-5, 3-6, 3-7, 4-6, 4-7, 7-7A, 7-7
c. For given contexts, the student interprets and determines the reasonableness of solutions to systems of equations or inequalities.	3-1, 3-2, 3-3, 3-7, 4-6, 4-7, 7-7A, 7-7
Objective 4: The student connects algebraic and geometric representations of functions.	
a. The student identifies and sketches graphs of parent functions, including linear $(y = x)$, quadratic $(y = x^2)$, square root $(y = \sqrt{x})$, inverse $\left(y = \frac{1}{x}\right)$, exponential $(y = a^x)$, and logarithmic $(y = \log_a x)$ functions.	2-2, 2-3, 2-6, 6-1, 6-6A, 6-6, 8-1, 8-8B, 9-1A, 9-1, 10-1, 10-2, 13-6, 13-7

Knowledge and Skills and Performance Descriptions	Glencoe *Algebra 2* Student Edition (Lesson)
b. The student extends parent functions with parameters such as *m* in $y = mx$ and describes parameter changes on the graphs of parent functions.	2-3, 2-6, 6-6A, 8-1, 10-1A, 10-1
c. The student recognizes inverse relationships between various functions.	8-8, 10-2, 13-7, Inv. (pp. 474-475, 501, 538, 555, 575, 584)
Objective 5: The student knows the relationship between the geometric and algebraic descriptions of conic sections.	
a. The student describes a conic section as the intersection of a plane and a cone.	7-2, 7-6
b. In order to sketch graphs of conic sections, the student relates simple parameter changes in the equation to corresponding changes in the graph.	7-2, 7-3, 7-4, 7-5, 7-6, Inv. (pp. 328-329, 340, 375, 422, 455, 468)
c. The student identifies symmetries from graphs of conic sections.	7-2, 7-3, 7-4, 7-5, 7-6
d. The student identifies the conic section from a given equation.	7-6
e. The student uses the method of completing the square.	6-3, 7-2, 7-3, 7-4, 7-5, 7-6
Objective 6: The student understands that quadratic functions can be represented in different ways and translates among their various representations.	
a. For given contexts, the student determines the reasonable domain and range values of quadratic functions, as well as interprets and determines the reasonableness of solutions to quadratic equations and inequalities.	6-1A, 6-2, 6-3, 6-4, 6-5, 6-6, 6-7
b. The student relates representations of quadratic functions, such as algebraic, tabular, graphical, and verbal descriptions.	6-1A, 6-1, 6-2, 6-3, 6-4, 6-5, 6-6A, 6-6, 6-7, 7-2, Inv. (pp. 328-329, 340, 375, 422, 455, 468)
c. The student determines a quadratic function(s) from its roots or a graph.	6-5, 6-6, 7-2
Objective 7: The student interprets and describes the effects of changes in the parameters of quadratic functions in applied and mathematical situations.	
a. The student uses characteristics of the quadratic parent function to sketch the related graphs and connects between the $y = ax^2 + bx + c$ and the $y = a(x - h)^2 + k$ symbolic representations of quadratic functions.	6-6A, 6-6, 7-2
b. The student uses the parent function to investigate, describe, and predict the effects of changes in *a*, *h*, and *k* on the graphs of $y = a(x - h)^2 + k$ form of a function in applied and purely mathematical situations.	6-6A, 6-6, 7-2

Algebra 2 TEKS to Glencoe *Algebra 2*

Knowledge and Skills and Performance Descriptions	Glencoe *Algebra 2* Student Edition (Lesson)
Objective 8: The student formulates equations and inequalities based on quadratic functions, uses a variety of methods to solve them, and analyzes the solutions in terms of the situation.	
a. The student analyzes situations involving quadratic functions and formulates quadratic equations or inequalities to solve problems.	6-1, 6-2, 6-3, 6-4, 6-5, 6-6, 6-7A, 6-7, 7-2
b. The student analyzes and interprets the solutions of quadratic equations using discriminants and solves quadratic equations using the quadratic formula.	6-4, 8-6
c. The student compares and translates between algebraic and graphical solutions of quadratic equations.	6-1, 6-2, 6-3, 6-4, 7-2
d. The student solves quadratic equations and inequalities.	6-2, 6-4, 6-5, 6-7A, 6-7, 7-2, 8-6
Objective 9: The student formulates equations and inequalities based on square root functions, uses a variety of methods to solve them, and analyzes the solutions in terms of the situation.	
a. The student uses the parent function to investigate, describe, and predict the effects of parameter changes on the graphs of square root functions and describes limitations on the domains and ranges.	5-6, 8-8B
b. The student relates representations of square root functions, such as algebraic, tabular, graphical, and verbal descriptions.	5-6, 8-8B
c. For given contexts, the student determines the reasonable domain and range values of square root functions, as well as interprets and determines the reasonableness of solutions to square root equations and inequalities.	5-6, 5-8, 8-8B
d. The student solves square root equations and inequalities using graphs, tables, and algebraic methods.	5-6, 5-8, 8-8B
e. The student analyzes situations modeled by square root functions, formulates equations or inequalities, selects a method, and solves problems.	5-6, 8-8B
f. The student expresses inverses of quadratic functions using square root functions.	8-8, 8-8B
Objective 10: The student formulates equations and inequalities based on rational functions, uses a variety of methods to solve them, and analyzes the solutions in terms of the situation.	
a. The student uses quotients to describe the graphs of rational functions, describes limitations on the domains and ranges, and examines asymptotic behavior.	9-1A, 9-1

Knowledge and Skills and Performance Descriptions	Glencoe *Algebra 2* Student Edition (Lesson)
b. The student analyzes various representations of rational functions with respect to problem situations.	9-1
c. For given contexts, the student determines the reasonable domain and range values of rational functions, as well as interprets and determines the reasonableness of solutions to rational equations and inequalities.	9-1A, 9-1, 9-5
d. The student solves rational equations and inequalities using graphs, tables, and algebraic methods.	9-1A, 9-5
e. The student analyzes a situation modeled by a rational function, formulates an equation or inequality composed of a linear or quadratic function, and solves the problem.	9-1, 9-4, 9-5
f. The student uses direct and inverse variation functions as models to make predictions in problem situations.	2-6, 9-2
Objective 11: The student formulates equations and inequalities based on exponential and logarithmic functions, uses a variety of methods to solve them, and analyzes the solutions in terms of the situation.	
a. The student develops the definition of logarithms by exploring and describing the relationship between exponential functions and their inverses.	10-1A, 10-2
b. The student uses the parent functions to investigate, describe, and predict the effects of parameter changes on the graphs of exponential and logarithmic functions, describes limitations on the domains and ranges, and examines asymptotic behavior.	10-1A, 10-1, 10-2
c. For given contexts, the student determines the reasonable domain and range values of exponential and logarithmic functions, as well as interprets and determines the reasonableness of solutions to exponential and logarithmic equations and inequalities.	10-1A, 10-1, 10-2, 10-3, 10-6, 10-7
d. The student solves exponential and logarithmic equations and inequalities using graphs, tables, and algebraic methods.	10-1A, 10-1, 10-2, 10-3, 10-6, 10-7
e. The student analyzes a situation modeled by an exponential function, formulates an equation or inequality, and solves the problem.	10-1, 10-1B, 10-2, 10-3, 10-6, 10-7, 11-3, Inv. (pp. 590-591, 616, 630, 655, 682, 702)

Glencoe *Algebra 2* to TEKS

Student Edition Lesson	TEKS
Chapter 1 Analyzing Equations and Inequalities	
1-1A	2.a.
1-1	2.a.
1-2	2.a.
1-3	
1-4	2.a.
1-5A	2.a.
1-5	2.a.
1-6	
1-7	
Inv., pp. 60-61, 100, 108, 140, 159, 174	1.b.
Chapter 2 Graphing Linear Relations and Functions	
2-1	1.a., 2.c.
2-2	1.a., 4.a.
2-2B	2.a.
2-3	4.a., 4.b.
2-4	
2-5	1.b.
2-5B	1.b.
2-6	1.b., 4.a., 4.b., 10.f.
2-7A	2.a.
2-7	2.a.
Chapter 3 Solving Systems of Linear Equations and Inequalities	
3-1A	3.b.
3-1	3.a., 3.b., 3.c.
3-2	3.a., 3.b., 3.c.
3-3	3.a., 3.b., 3.c.
3-4	3.a., 3.b.
3-5	3.a., 3.b.
3-6	3.a., 3.b.
3-7	3.a., 3.b., 3.c.
Inv., pp. 180-181, 193, 231, 273, 302, 322	1.b., 2.a.
Chapter 4 Using Matrices	
4-1	2.a.
4-2	2.a.
4-3	2.a.
4-4	2.a.
4-5	2.a.
4-6	2.a., 3.b., 3.c.

KEY: Inv. = Investigations (Long-Term Projects)

Student Edition Lesson	TEKS
4-7	2.a., 3.b., 3.c.
4-8	
Chapter 5 Exploring Polynomials and Radical Expressions	
5-1	2.a.
5-2	
5-3	
5-4	2.a.
5-5	
5-6	9.a., 9.b., 9.c., 9.d., 9.e.
5-7	2.a.
5-8	2.a., 9.c., 9.d.
5-9	
5-10	
Inv., pp. 328-329, 340, 375, 422, 455, 468	5.b., 6.b.
Chapter 6 Exploring Quadratic Functions and Inequalities	
6-1A	2.a., 4.a., 6.a., 6.b.
6-1	2.a., 6.b., 8.a., 8.c.
6-2	2.a., 6.a., 6.b., 8.a., 8.c., 8.d.
6-3	2.a., 2.b., 5.e., 6.a., 6.b., 8.a., 8.c.
6-4	2.b., 6.a., 6.b., 8.a., 8.b., 8.c., 8.d.
6-5	6.a., 6.b., 6.c., 8.a., 8.d.
6-6A	4.a., 4.b., 6.b., 7.a., 7.b.
6-6	1.a., 1.b., 4.a., 6.a., 6.b., 6.c., 7.a., 7.b., 8.a.
6-7A	2.a., 8.a., 8.d.
6-7	2.a., 6.a., 6.b., 8.a., 8.d.
Chapter 7 Analyzing Conic Sections	
7-1	
7-2	5.a., 5.b., 5.c., 5.e., 6.b., 6.c., 7.a., 7.b., 8.a., 8.c., 8.d.
7-3	5.b., 5.c., 5.e.
7-4	5.b., 5.c., 5.e.
7-5	5.b., 5.c., 5.e.
7-6	5.a., 5.b., 5.c., 5.d., 5.e.
7-7A	3.b., 3.c.
7-7	3.a., 3.b., 3.c.
Inv., pp. 474-475, 501, 538, 555, 575, 584	1.b., 4.c.
Chapter 8 Exploring Polynomial Functions	
8-1	1.a., 4.a., 4.b.
8-2	
8-3	

Glencoe *Algebra 2* to TEKS

Student Edition Lesson	TEKS
8-3B	1.b.
8-4	
8-5	
8-6	2.a., 8.b., 8.d.
8-7	
8-8	1.a., 4.c., 9.f.
8-8B	1.a., 4.a., 9.a., 9.b., 9.c., 9.d., 9.e., 9.f.
Chapter 9 Exploring Rational Expressions	
9-1A	4.a., 10.a., 10.c., 10.d.
9-1	1.a., 4.a., 10.a., 10.b., 10.c., 10.e.
9-2	10.f.
9-3	
9-4	10.e.
9-5	1.a., 2.a., 10.c., 10.d., 10.e.
Inv., pp. 590-591, 616, 630, 655, 682, 702	1.b., 11.e.
Chapter 10 Exploring Exponential and Logarithmic Functions	
10-1A	1.a., 4.b., 11.a., 11.b., 11.c., 11.d.
10-1	1.a., 2.a., 4.a., 4.b., 11.b., 11.c., 11.d., 11.e.
10-1B	1.b., 11.e.
10-2	2.a., 4.a., 4.c., 11.a., 11.b., 11.c., 11.d., 11.e.
10-3	2.a., 11.c., 11.d., 11.e.
10-4	
10-5	
10-6	2.a., 11.c., 11.d., 11.e.
10-7	11.c., 11.d., 11.e.
Chapter 11 Investigating Sequences and Series	
11-1A	1.b.
11-1	1.a.
11-2	
11-3	1.b., 11.e.
11-4	
11-5	
11-6	
11-7	
11-8	
Chapter 12 Investigating Discrete Mathematics and Probability	
12-1	
12-2	
12-3	
12-4	

Student Edition Lesson	TEKS
12-5	
12-6	
12-7	
12-8	
Inv., pp. 768-769, 785, 810, 834, 859, 868	1.b.
Chapter 13 Exploring Trigonometric Functions	
13-1	1.a.
13-2	
13-3	1.a.
13-4	
13-5	
13-6	1.a., 4.a.
13-7	1.a., 4.a., 4.c.
Chapter 14 Using Trigonometric Graphs and Identities	
14-1	
14-2	
14-3	
14-4	
14-5	
14-6	2.a.

Glencoe Algebra 2

COMPONENTS LIST

⊕ **Texas Student Edition**	0-02-825179-2
⊕ **Texas Teacher's Wraparound Edition**	0-02-825182-2
⊕ **Algebra 1 End-of-Course Examination (EOC)**	0-02-825341-8
Practice and Sample Test Masters	
⊕ **Texas Assessment of Academic Skills (TAAS)**	0-02-825342-6
Practice and Sample Test Master	
⊕ **Texas Teacher's Classroom Resources**	0-02-825185-7

Applications
Investigations and Projects Masters
Multicultural Activity Masters
🌀 Real World Applications Transparencies
Tech Prep Applications Masters
Science and Math Lab Manual
Problem-of-the-Week Cards

Teaching Aids
Answer Key Masters
Texas Block Scheduling Booklet
Texas Lesson Planning Guide
Solutions Manual
🌀 Transparencies A: 5-Minute Checks
🌀 Transparencies B: Teaching Transparencies

Meeting Individual Needs
Enrichment Masters
Practice Masters
Study Guide Masters

Technology and Multimedia
Graphing Calculator Masters
Teacher's Guide for Software Resources
Graphing Calculators in the Mathematics
Classroom

Assessment and Evaluation
Assessment and Evaluation Masters
SAT/ACT Study Guide

Manipulatives and Modeling
Modeling Mathematics Masters

● **High School Mathematics Manipulative Kit**	0-02-824847-3
▭ **MindJogger Videoquizzes**	0-02-825172-5
▣ **Interactive Math Tools Software**	
Macintosh Version	0-02-825142-3
Windows Version	0-02-825166-0
▣ **Test and Review Software**	
Macintosh & IBM	0-02-825146-6
◉ **Algebra 2 Multimedia CD-ROM**	
Macintosh & Windows	0-02-825165-2
● **Teacher's Handbook**	0-02-824885-6

Notes

Notes

Glencoe
Algebra 2

Handbook for
Texas Students

Cindy J. Boyd, Author

CONTENTS

ISBN: 0-02-825179-2

Your Student Edition

WELCOME TO ALGEBRA 2

Glencoe's *Algebra 2* is a program that is uniquely designed for you. The program has the following goals.

- To make algebra accessible to you and all students.

- To answer the question, "When am I ever going to use this?"

- To use technology: graphing and scientific calculators, computers, CD-ROM, the Internet, and application software like word processors and spreadsheets.

- To use a variety of methods: reading, writing, speaking, making charts and graphs, using manipulatives, and completing long-term projects.

- To help you achieve success in algebra.

- To bring algebra to life by showing how it relates to your world.

Remember...

We don't just help you cover the math, we help you uncover it!

WITHIN THESE PAGES

The goals of this Handbook for Texas Students are as follows.

- To acquaint you with the philosophy of the book.

- To introduce you to educators from Texas who helped plan your coursework for the coming year.

- To provide an opportunity for you to practice the skills you'll need for success in first-year algebra.

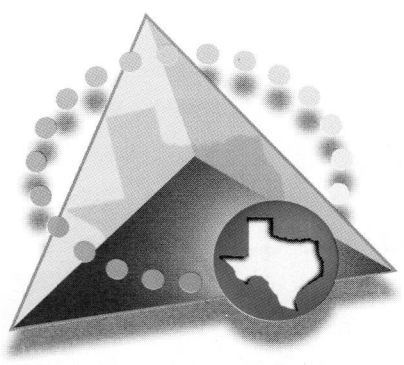

Meet Our Texas Authors and Consultants

To meet the goal of creating a program that serves the unique needs of students in Texas, the Glencoe Algebra-Geometry series has five authors and consultants from Texas. They are profiled below.

CINDY J. BOYD is a high school mathematics teacher from Abilene, Texas, and the author of *Skit-So-Phrenia!: Educational Skits Based on Mathematical Concepts.* She has been recognized as the Texas Academy of Science's Outstanding Mathematics Educator for 1995 and has received the Walt Disney American Teacher Award in 1995 and the Texas Presidential State Awards in 1994, 1995, and 1996. She is also an author of *Glencoe Geometry.*

BEATRICE MOORE-HARRIS is a mathematics coordinator for the Houston Independent School District.

EVA GATES is an independent mathematics consultant in Pearland, Texas. She was formerly the mathematics supervisor for the Pasadena Independent School District.

ROBBIE BONNEVILLE is the mathematics coordinator for the La Joya Independent School District.

MELISSA McCLURE is a mathematics consultant with Teaching for Tomorrow in Fort Worth, Texas. She was formerly a high school and middle school teacher in Mansfield, Texas.

Various chapters in Glencoe's *Algebra 2* were also reviewed by **Nancy Barr,** Lubbock, Texas, **Susan L. Harder,** Plano, Texas, **Chris Johnson,** Lewisville, Texas, **Nancy Lee King,** Midland, Texas, **Frank LaFuente, Sr.,** San Antonio, Texas, and **Dee Mattox-Hall,** Galena Park, Texas.

You can order copies of Cindy Boyd's *Skit-So-Phrenia!* materials from:

Cindy Boyd
2502 Rountree
Abilene, TX 79601-2033
phone: (915) 672-2654
FAX: (915) 672-2312
e-mail: cjboyd@tenet.edu

Book 1: *Quadnet* (special quadrilaterals), *One Function to Live* (functions), *Triangle Trek* (similar triangles)

Book 2: *Leave it to Olive* (Pythagorean theorem, identifying the hypotenuse), *As the Triangle Turns* (Pythagorean theorem), *Old McOlive* (constructions)

Book 3: *The Days of Your Lines* (graphing inequalities), *Toast Riders in the Sky* (cylinders, area and volume), *Polyhedron Delight* (polyhedrons, spheres as limit of pyramids)

Book 4: *All My Circles* (circles and their parts), *Solid Gold* (polyhedrons and solids in everyday life), *Night of the Living Trapezoids* (trapezoids)

Book 5: *Beverly Hills Op* (operations with positive and negative numbers), *Attack of the Killer Zucchini* (complementary and supplementary angles, complements of congruent angles)

Skit
Algebra Lite

by Cindy J. Boyd

Olive: Hello, Ms. Boyd!

Ms. B: Hello, Olive!

Olive: Guess what, Ms. Boyd! I got a job!

Ms. B: What kind of job, Olive?

Olive: I make pink cookies!

Ms. B: Pink cookies!?!

Olive: Yes! For that new bakery, Think Pink. My recipe makes 70 dozen.

Ms. B: 70 dozen! That's a lot of dough!

Olive: Well, I put a lot into these cookies. The recipe calls for:

3	lb powdered sugar
4	lb shortening
$1\frac{1}{2}$	oz salt
$\frac{1}{2}$	oz baking soda
$1\frac{1}{2}$	lb chopped pecans
1	pint eggs
1	pint milk
1	oz vanilla
$\frac{1}{2}$	bottle lemon flavoring
$\frac{1}{2}$	bottle red food coloring
$7\frac{1}{2}$	lb cake flour

I made some the other day. Then, as I was taking the cookies out of the oven, I dropped the pan and all of the cookies broke into little pieces.

Ms. B: Well Olive, that's the way the cookie crumbles!

Olive: Well, I only had enough ingredients to make $3\frac{1}{2}$ dozen. This recipe calls for:

1 c xxx sugar
1 c shortening
$\frac{1}{2}$ tsp salt
$\frac{3}{4}$ c chopped pecans
1 egg
$\frac{1}{4}$ c milk
1 tsp vanilla
$\frac{1}{2}$ tsp lemon flavoring
$\frac{1}{2}$ tsp red food coloring
4 c cake flour

I was in a hurry when I wrote this recipe, so I substituted xxx sugar for powdered sugar.

Ms. B: So you made the cookies?

Olive: Yes, but I had a little trouble. I used my 1-cup measure to measure the shortening and then I couldn't use the same cup to measure the powdered sugar and flour. Also, I couldn't find my teaspoon or $\frac{1}{2}$-teaspoon measuring spoon. I didn't know what I was going to do. Then I realized that I could use my $\frac{1}{2}$-cup measuring cup two times to equal 1 cup and eight times to equal 4 cups. Also, I could use the $\frac{1}{4}$-cup measure three times to measure $\frac{3}{4}$ cup of pecans. And, I used the $\frac{1}{4}$-tsp measure four times to equal 1 teaspoon.

Ms. B: Olive, I can't believe this !

Olive: What?

Ms. B: It can't be!

Olive: What!?!

Ms. B: This is a perfect example of ALGEBRA!

Olive: You're right. I don't believe it! Please explain.

Ms. B: Well, when you wrote your recipe, you substituted a symbol for powdered sugar. Then when you mixed the dough, you substituted two half-cups of powdered sugar for one cup of powdered sugar. Since two half cups equal one cup, you did not change anything in the recipe; you just changed the way the ingredients were packaged.

Olive: Are you telling me that this substitution is an example of algebra?

Ms. B: Yes, we use it when we solve a system of equations. Look at these steps:

1. Solve *one* equation for the variable.
2. Substitute the resulting expression in the *other* equation.
3. Solve this equation.
4. Substitute back into either equation and solve for the other variable.

Let's try this on a system, Olive.

$-4x + 3y = -15$
$x + 5y = -2$

What would be the easiest variable to solve for?

Olive: The x in the second equation.

Ms. B: That's right, Olive. Solve for x.

Olive: I can subtract $5y$ from each side and get $x = -5y - 2$.

Ms. B: Now substitute this back into the other equation everywhere you have an x.

Olive: So, $-4x + 3y = -15$ becomes $-4(-5y - 2) + 3y = -15$.

Ms. B: You're on a roll, Olive! What's next?

Olive: Next, I'll solve this equation. I'll get $20y + 8 + 3y = -15$. I can combine like terms on the left and get $23y + 8 = -15$, then subtract 8 from each side and get $23y = -23$. After I divide each side by 23, I get $y = -1$.

Ms. B: Are we through?

Olive: No, now we take $y = -1$ and substitute back in either original equation to find x. $x = -5y - 2$, so $x = -5(-1) - 2$.

Ms. B: Watch your signs!

Olive: O.K. Well, $x = +5 - 2$ or $x = 3$.

Ms. B: So, your final answer is (3, −1). Olive, I feel a song in the air!

(Tune: Ghostbusters)

There's something in
My math that's strange!
What ya gonna do?
Substitution!

There's something weird.
It's an interchange.
What ya gonna do?
Substitution!

I ain't afraid of no x!

If you're seein' y's
Running through your brain,
What ya gonna do?
Substitution!

Replacing x
Can relieve that pain!
What ya gonna do?
Substitution!

I ain't afraid of no x!

You have math problems!
Freaky math problems!
You better do—Substitution!
If your y is loose
Just use this ruse
And do—Substitution!

I ain't afraid of no x!

Olive: I'm glad I understand this now, Ms. Boyd. I want to pass algebra so I can graduate, get out of high school, and get a really good job.

Ms. B: That's right, Olive. NO PA$$—NO PAY. And that really is...

The End

Glencoe

Algebra 2

Integration
Applications
Connections

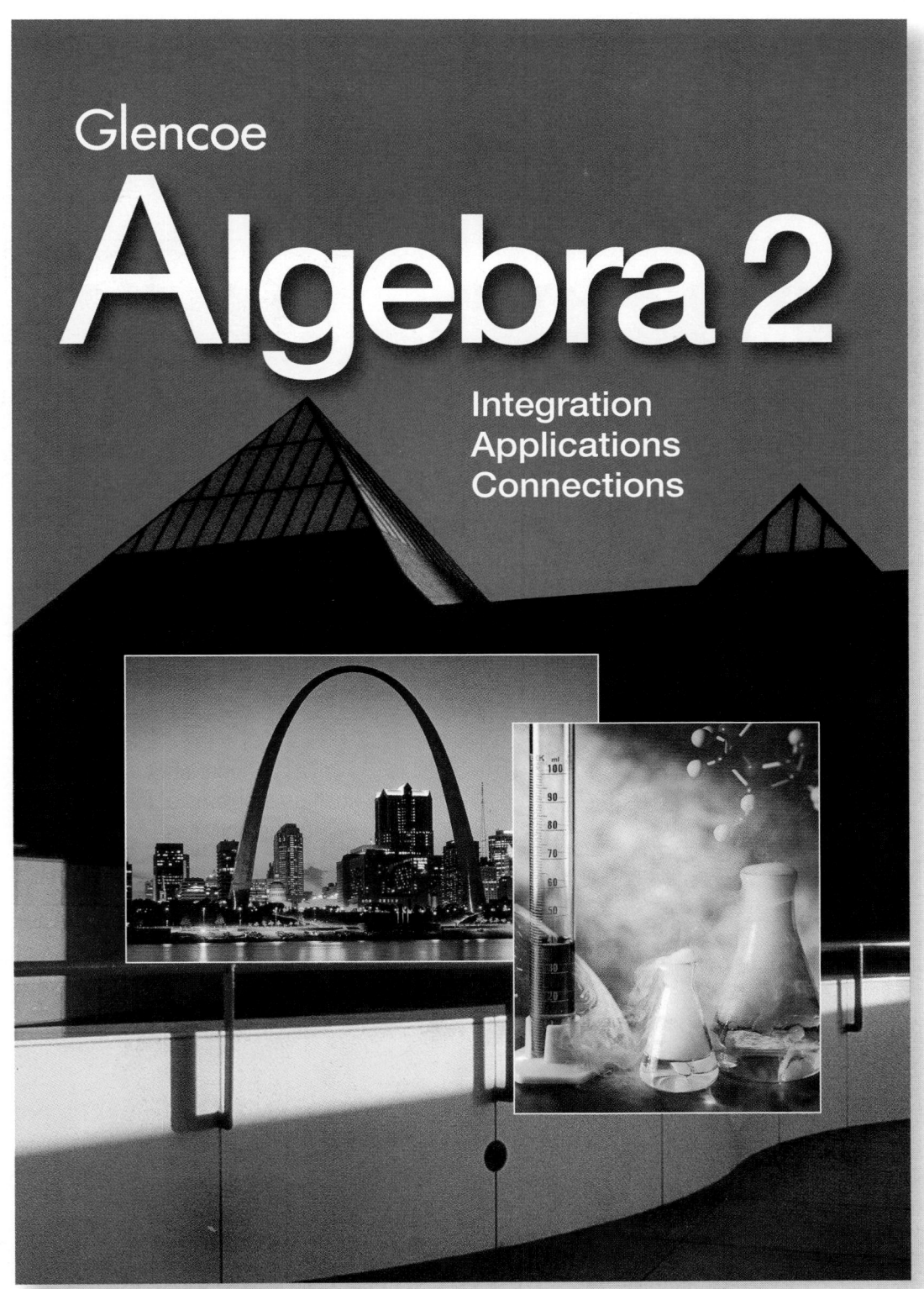

GLENCOE
McGraw-Hill

New York, New York   Columbus, Ohio   Mission Hills, California   Peoria, Illinois

Visit the Glencoe Mathematics Internet Home Page at...

glencoe.com

For teachers, you will find classroom resources and information about *Algebra 2* and the entire Glencoe Mathematics Series. You'll also find ordering information, toll-free numbers for customer service, and links to information about NCTM conferences.

For students and parents, there are challenging activities such as problems of the week and group activities.

**Come see us at
http://www.glencoe.com/sec/math**

Glencoe/McGraw-Hill

*A Division of The **McGraw·Hill** Companies*

Copyright © 1998 by The McGraw-Hill Companies, Inc. All rights reserved. Printed in the United States of America. Except as permitted under the United States Copyright Act, no part of this publication may be reproduced or distributed in any form or by any means, or stored in a database or retrieval system, without prior written permission of the publisher.

Send all inquiries to:
Glencoe/McGraw-Hill
936 Eastwind Drive
Westerville, OH 43081-3374

ISBN: 0-02-825178-4 (Student Edition)
        0-02-825181-4 (Teacher's Wraparound Edition)
        0-02-825179-2 (Texas Student Edition)
        0-02-825182-2 (Texas Teacher's Wraparound Edition)

1 2 3 4 5 6 7 8 9 10 VH/LP 04 03 02 01 00 99 98 97

Table of Contents
Algebra ②

INTEGRATION ● APPLICATIONS ● CONNECTIONS

Glencoe Brings Algebra ② to Life!

INTEGRATION ● **APPLICATIONS** ● **CONNECTIONS**

Students relate and apply algebraic concepts to geometry, statistics, data analysis, probability, and discrete mathematics.

Realistic and relevant applications help answer the question "When am I ever going to use this stuff?" Sports, space, world cultures, and consumerism are just a few of the real-life problem settings that students explore.

Students connect mathematics to other topics they are studying, like biology, geography, art, history, and health, through problems that are rich in algebraic content.

TECHNOLOGY

Graphing calculators, interactive computer software, and CD-ROM multimedia technology provide tools for both problem solving and discovery. The variety of integrated technology supports diverse learning styles.

HANDS-ON ACTIVITIES

Modeling Mathematics activities and multi-day Investigations engage students with manipulatives and mathematical models. Both college-bound and tech-prep students find meaningful hands-on activities that relate to life and work.

ASSESSMENT

A broad spectrum of evaluation and assessment tools, ranging from short-response questions to open-ended problems, lets all students demonstrate what they have learned.

ACCESSIBILITY

Practical strategies meet the needs of students with differing ability levels, rates of learning, and learning styles. Modeling, journal writing, cooperative learning projects, and technology tools help all students experience success.

NCTM STANDARDS

The sequence of topics, the content emphasis, integration with other mathematics areas, hands-on activities, and technology combine to form a program that reflects the NCTM Curriculum, Teaching, and Assessment Standards.

Glencoe's Dynamic Lesson Structure

Each lesson follows a straightforward format —

> Objective
> Application/Connection/Integration
> Examples
> Check for Understanding
> Exercises

— that focuses on concepts and applications.

● OBJECTIVE

The lesson objectives help students quickly see what performance is indicated and expected. "After studying this lesson, you should be able to...."

● APPLICATION/CONNECTION/INTEGRATION

A motivating lesson opener introduces the concept by posing a real-world application, an interdisciplinary connection, or a mathematical integration.

● EXAMPLES

A set of completely worked-out examples with clear explanations supports the objectives and mirrors the exercises in the Guided Practice and Practice sections that follow.

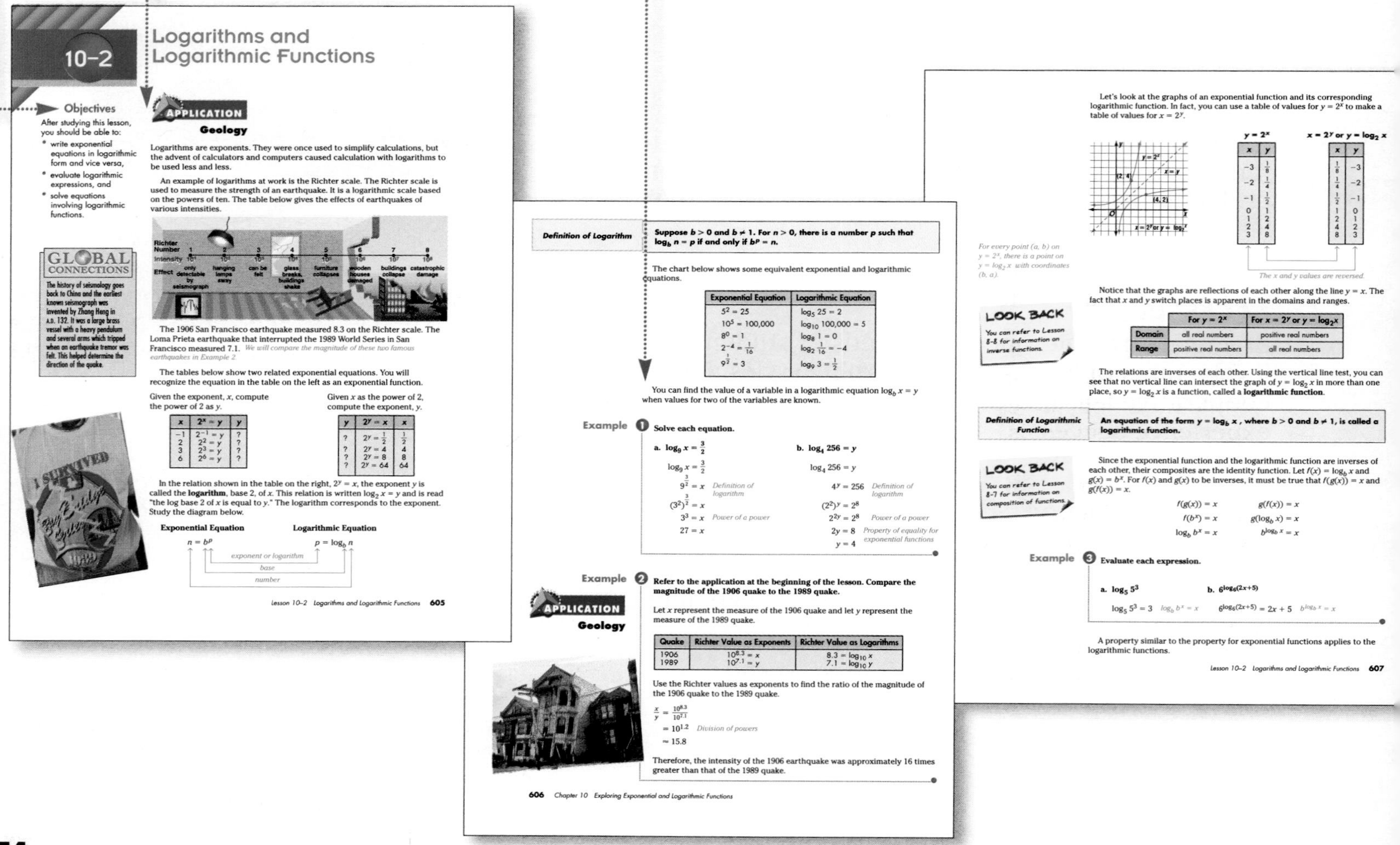

10-2 Logarithms and Logarithmic Functions

Objectives

After studying this lesson, you should be able to:
* write exponential equations in logarithmic form and vice versa,
* evaluate logarithmic expressions, and
* solve equations involving logarithmic functions.

APPLICATION

Geology

Logarithms are exponents. They were once used to simplify calculations, but the advent of calculators and computers caused calculation with logarithms to be used less and less.

An example of logarithms at work is the Richter scale. The Richter scale is used to measure the strength of an earthquake. It is a logarithmic scale based on the powers of ten. The table below gives the effects of earthquakes of various intensities.

GLOBAL CONNECTIONS

The history of seismology goes back to China and the earliest known seismograph was invented by Zhang Heng in A.D. 132. It was a large brass vessel with a heavy pendulum and several arms which tripped when an earthquake tremor was felt. This helped determine the direction of the quake.

The 1906 San Francisco earthquake measured 8.3 on the Richter scale. The Loma Prieta earthquake that interrupted the 1989 World Series in San Francisco measured 7.1. *We will compare the magnitude of these two famous earthquakes in Example 2.*

The tables below show two related exponential equations. You will recognize the equation in the table on the left as an exponential function.

Given the exponent, x, compute the power of 2 as y.

Given x as the power of 2, compute the exponent, y.

In the relation shown in the table on the right, $2^y = x$, the exponent y is called the **logarithm**, base 2, of x. This relation is written $\log_2 x = y$ and is read "the log base 2 of x is equal to y." The logarithm corresponds to the exponent. Study the diagram below.

Exponential Equation   Logarithmic Equation

$$n = b^p \qquad p = \log_b n$$

Lesson 10-2 Logarithms and Logarithmic Functions **605**

Definition of Logarithm

Suppose $b > 0$ and $b \neq 1$. For $n > 0$, there is a number p such that $\log_b n = p$ if and only if $b^p = n$.

The chart below shows some equivalent exponential and logarithmic equations.

Exponential Equation	Logarithmic Equation
$5^2 = 25$	$\log_5 25 = 2$
$10^5 = 100,000$	$\log_{10} 100,000 = 5$
$8^0 = 1$	$\log_8 1 = 0$
$2^{-4} = \frac{1}{16}$	$\log_2 \frac{1}{16} = -4$
$9^{\frac{1}{2}} = 3$	$\log_9 3 = \frac{1}{2}$

You can find the value of a variable in a logarithmic equation $\log_b x = y$ when values for two of the variables are known.

Example 1 Solve each equation.

a. $\log_9 x = \frac{3}{2}$

$\log_9 x = \frac{3}{2}$

$9^{\frac{3}{2}} = x$ *Definition of logarithm*

$(3^2)^{\frac{3}{2}} = x$

$3^3 = x$ *Power of a power*

$27 = x$

b. $\log_4 256 = y$

$\log_4 256 = y$

$4^y = 256$ *Definition of logarithm*

$(2^2)^y = 2^8$

$2^{2y} = 2^8$ *Power of a power*

$2y = 8$ *Property of equality for exponential functions*

$y = 4$

Example 2 Refer to the application at the beginning of the lesson. Compare the magnitude of the 1906 quake to the 1989 quake.

APPLICATION

Geology

Let x represent the measure of the 1906 quake and let y represent the measure of the 1989 quake.

Quake	Richter Value as Exponents	Richter Value as Logarithms
1906	$10^{8.3} = x$	$8.3 = \log_{10} x$
1989	$10^{7.1} = y$	$7.1 = \log_{10} y$

Use the Richter values as exponents to find the ratio of the magnitude of the 1906 quake to the 1989 quake.

$\frac{x}{y} = \frac{10^{8.3}}{10^{7.1}}$

$= 10^{1.2}$ *Division of powers*

≈ 15.8

Therefore, the intensity of the 1906 earthquake was approximately 16 times greater than that of the 1989 quake.

606 *Chapter 10 Exploring Exponential and Logarithmic Functions*

Let's look at the graphs of an exponential function and its corresponding logarithmic function. In fact, you can use a table of values for $y = 2^x$ to make a table of values for $x = 2^y$.

$y = 2^x$

x	y
-3	$\frac{1}{8}$
-2	$\frac{1}{4}$
-1	$\frac{1}{2}$
0	1
1	2
2	4
3	8

$x = 2^y$ or $y = \log_2 x$

x	y
$\frac{1}{8}$	-3
$\frac{1}{4}$	-2
$\frac{1}{2}$	-1
1	0
2	1
4	2
8	3

For every point (a, b) on $y = 2^x$, there is a point on $y = \log_2 x$ with coordinates (b, a).

The x and y values are reversed.

Notice that the graphs are reflections of each other along the line $y = x$. The fact that x and y switch places is apparent in the domains and ranges.

LOOK BACK

You can refer to Lesson 8–8 for information on inverse functions.

	For $y = 2^x$	For $x = 2^y$ or $y = \log_2 x$
Domain	all real numbers	positive real numbers
Range	positive real numbers	all real numbers

The relations are inverses of each other. Using the vertical line test, you can see that no vertical line can intersect the graph of $y = \log_2 x$ in more than one place, so $y = \log_2 x$ is a function, called a **logarithmic function**.

Definition of Logarithmic Function

An equation of the form $y = \log_b x$, where $b > 0$ and $b \neq 1$, is called a logarithmic function.

LOOK BACK

You can refer to Lesson 8–7 for information on composition of functions.

Since the exponential function and the logarithmic function are inverses of each other, their composites are the identity function. Let $f(x) = \log_b x$ and $g(x) = b^x$. For $f(x)$ and $g(x)$ to be inverses, it must be true that $f(g(x)) = x$ and $g(f(x)) = x$.

$f(g(x)) = x \qquad g(f(x)) = x$

$f(b^x) = x \qquad g(\log_b x) = x$

$\log_b b^x = x \qquad b^{\log_b x} = x$

Example 3 Evaluate each expression.

a. $\log_5 5^3$

$\log_5 5^3 = 3$ *$\log_b b^x = x$*

b. $6^{\log_6(2x+5)}$

$6^{\log_6(2x+5)} = 2x + 5$ *$b^{\log_b x} = x$*

A property similar to the property for exponential functions applies to the logarithmic functions.

Lesson 10-2 Logarithms and Logarithmic Functions **607**

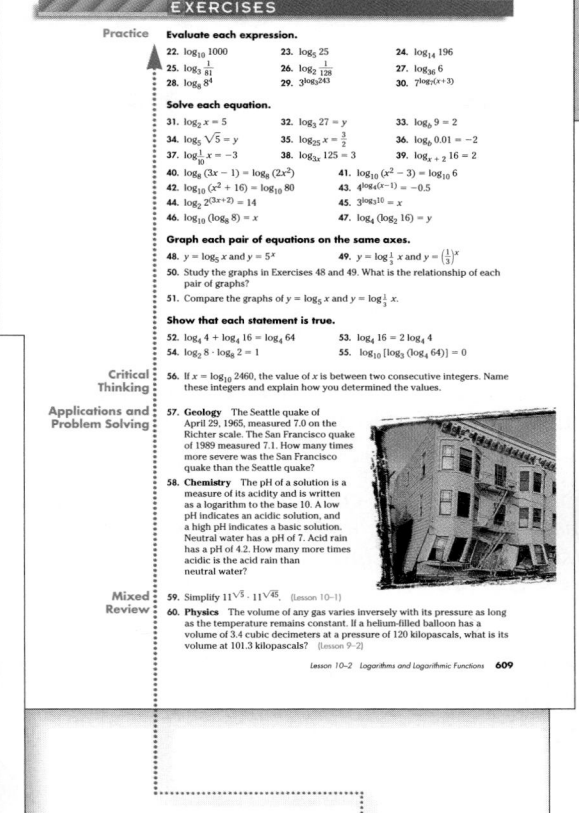

Practice | **Evaluate each expression.**

22. $\log_{10} 1000$ 23. $\log_5 25$ 24. $\log_{14} 196$
25. $\log_3 \frac{1}{81}$ 26. $\log_2 \frac{1}{128}$ 27. $\log_{36} 6$
28. $\log_8 8^4$ 29. $3^{\log_3 243}$ 30. $7^{\log_7(x+3)}$

Solve each equation.

31. $\log_2 x = 5$ 32. $\log_5 27 = y$ 33. $\log_b 9 = 2$
34. $\log_5 \sqrt{5} = y$ 35. $\log_{25} x = \frac{3}{2}$ 36. $\log_6 0.01 = -2$
37. $\log_{\frac{1}{3}} x = 3$ 38. $\log_{3x} 125 = 3$ 39. $\log_{x+2} 16 = 2$
40. $\log_8 (3x - 1) = \log_8 (2x^2)$ 41. $\log_{10} (x^2 - 3) = \log_{10} 6$
42. $\log_{10} (x^2 + 16) = \log_{10} 80$ 43. $4^{\log_4(x-1)} = -0.5$
44. $\log_2 2^{(3x+2)} = 14$ 45. $3^{\log_3 10} = x$
46. $\log_{10} (\log_8 8) = x$ 47. $\log_4 (\log_3 16) = y$

Graph each pair of equations on the same axes.

48. $y = \log_5 x$ and $y = 5^x$ 49. $y = \log_{\frac{1}{3}} x$ and $y = \left(\frac{1}{3}\right)^x$
50. Study the graphs in Exercises 48 and 49. What is the relationship of each pair of graphs?
51. Compare the graphs of $y = \log_5 x$ and $y = \log_{\frac{1}{5}} x$.

Show that each statement is true.

52. $\log_4 4 + \log_4 16 = \log_4 64$ 53. $\log_4 16 = 2 \log_4 4$
54. $\log_2 8 \cdot \log_8 2 = 1$ 55. $\log_{10} [\log_3 (\log_4 64)] = 0$

Critical Thinking

56. If $x = \log_{10} 2460$, the value of x is between two consecutive integers. Name these integers and explain how you determined the values.

Applications and Problem Solving

57. **Geology** The Seattle quake of April 29, 1965, measured 7.0 on the Richter scale. The San Francisco quake of 1989 measured 7.1. How many times more severe was the San Francisco quake than the Seattle quake?

58. **Chemistry** The pH of a solution is a measure of its acidity and is written as a logarithm to the base 10. A low pH indicates an acidic solution, and a high pH indicates a basic solution. Neutral water has a pH of 7. Acid rain has a pH of 4.2. How many more times acidic is the acid rain than neutral water?

Mixed Review

59. Simplify $11^{\sqrt{3}} \cdot 11^{\sqrt{45}}$. (Lesson 10-1)
60. **Physics** The volume of any gas varies inversely with its pressure as long as the temperature remains constant. If a helium-filled balloon has a volume of 3.4 cubic decimeters at a pressure of 120 kilopascals, what is its volume at 101.3 kilopascals? (Lesson 9-2)

Lesson 10-2 Logarithms and Logarithmic Functions **609**

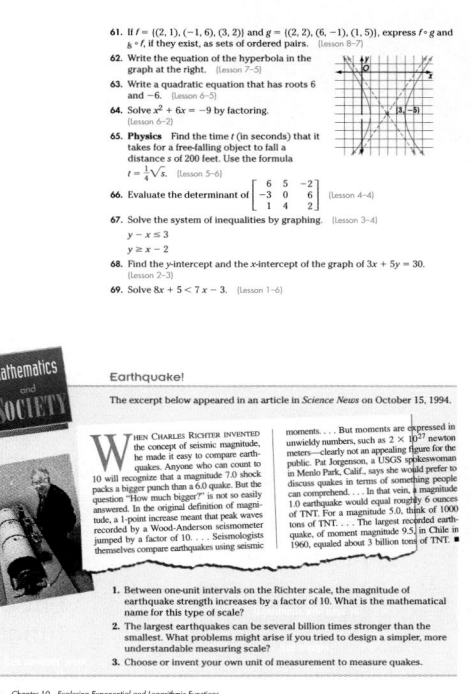

61. If $f = \{(2, 1), (-1, 6), (3, 2)\}$ and $g = \{(2, 2), (6, -1), (1, 5)\}$, express $f \circ g$ and $g \circ f$, if they exist, as sets of ordered pairs. (Lesson 8-7)
62. Write the equation of the hyperbola in the graph at the right. (Lesson 7-5)
63. Write a quadratic equation that has roots 6 and -6. (Lesson 6-5)
64. Solve $x^2 + 6x = -9$ by factoring. (Lesson 6-2)
65. **Physics** Find the time t (in seconds) that it takes for a free-falling object to fall a distance s of 200 feet. Use the formula $t = \frac{1}{4}\sqrt{s}$. (Lesson 5-6)
66. Evaluate the determinant of $\begin{bmatrix} 6 & 5 & -2 \\ -3 & 0 & 6 \\ 1 & 4 & 2 \end{bmatrix}$ (Lesson 4-4)
67. Solve the system of inequalities by graphing. (Lesson 3-4)
$y - x \le 3$
$y \ge x - 2$
68. Find the y-intercept and the x-intercept of the graph of $3x + 5y = 30$. (Lesson 2-3)
69. Solve $8x + 5 < 7x - 3$. (Lesson 1-6)

Mathematics and Society

Earthquake!

The excerpt below appeared in an article in *Science News* on October 15, 1994.

WHEN CHARLES RICHTER INVENTED the concept of seismic magnitude, he made it easy to compare earthquakes. Anyone who can count to 10 will recognize that a magnitude 8.0 shock packs a bigger punch than a 6.0 quake. But the question "How much bigger?" is not so easily answered. In the original definition of magnitude, a 1-point increase meant that peak waves recorded by a Wood-Anderson seismometer jumped by a factor of 10. . . . Seismologists themselves compare earthquakes using seismic moments . . . But moments are expressed in unwieldy numbers, such as 2×10^{27} newton meters—clearly not an appealing figure for the public. Pat Jorgenson, a USGS spokeswoman in Menlo Park, Calif., says she would prefer to discuss quakes in terms of something people can comprehend. . . . In that vein, a magnitude 1.0 earthquake would equal roughly 6 ounces of TNT. For a magnitude 5.0, think of 1000 tons of TNT. . . . The largest recorded earthquake, of moment magnitude 9.5, in Chile in 1960, equaled about 3 billion tons of TNT.

1. Between one-unit intervals on the Richter scale, the magnitude of earthquake strength increases by a factor of 10. What is the mathematical name for this type of scale?
2. The largest earthquakes can be several billion times stronger than the smallest. What problems might arise if you tried to design a simpler, more understandable measuring scale?
3. Choose or invent your own unit of measurement to measure quakes.

610 *Chapter 10 Exploring Exponential and Logarithmic Functions*

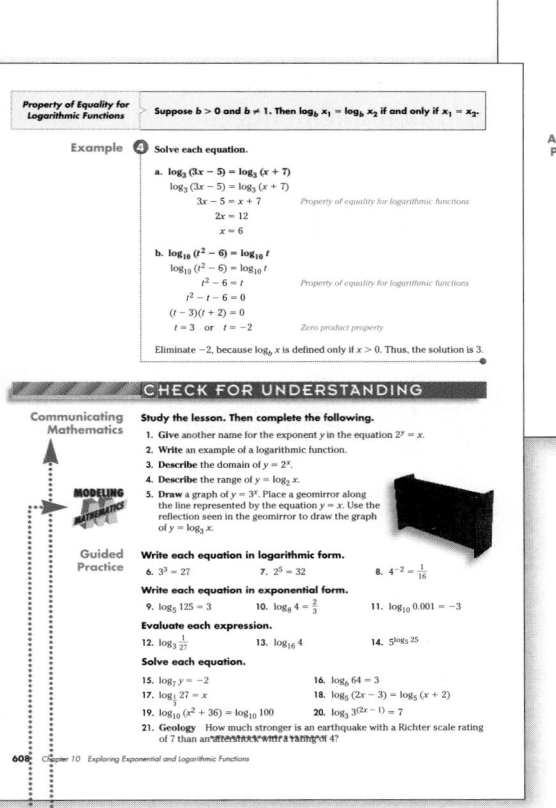

Property of Equality for Logarithmic Functions | Suppose $b > 0$ and $b \ne 1$. Then $\log_b x_1 = \log_b x_2$ if and only if $x_1 = x_2$.

Example 4 Solve each equation.

a. $\log_3 (3x - 5) = \log_3 (x + 7)$
$\log_3 (3x - 5) = \log_3 (x + 7)$
$3x - 5 = x + 7$ *Property of equality for logarithmic functions*
$2x = 12$
$x = 6$

b. $\log_{10} (t^2 - 6) = \log_{10} t$
$\log_{10} (t^2 - 6) = \log_{10} t$
$t^2 - 6 = t$ *Property of equality for logarithmic functions*
$t^2 - t - 6 = 0$
$(t - 3)(t + 2) = 0$
$t = 3$ or $t = -2$ *Zero product property*

Eliminate -2, because $\log_b x$ is defined only if $x > 0$. Thus, the solution is 3.

CHECK FOR UNDERSTANDING

Communicating Mathematics | Study the lesson. Then complete the following.

1. Give another name for the exponent y in the equation $2^y = x$.
2. Write an example of a logarithmic function.
3. Describe the domain of $y = 2^x$.
4. Describe the range of $y = \log_2 x$.
5. Draw a graph of $y = 3^x$. Place a geomirror along the line represented by the equation $y = x$. Use the reflection seen in the geomirror to draw the graph of $y = \log_3 x$.

Guided Practice | Write each equation in logarithmic form.

6. $3^3 = 27$ 7. $2^5 = 32$ 8. $4^{-2} = \frac{1}{16}$

Write each equation in exponential form.

9. $\log_5 125 = 3$ 10. $\log_8 4 = \frac{2}{3}$ 11. $\log_{10} 0.001 = -3$

Evaluate each expression.

12. $\log_3 \frac{1}{27}$ 13. $\log_{16} 4$ 14. $5^{\log_5 25}$

Solve each equation.

15. $\log_7 y = -2$ 16. $\log_b 64 = 3$
17. $\log_{\frac{1}{3}} 27 = x$ 18. $\log_5 (2x - 3) = \log_5 (x + 2)$
19. $\log_{10} (x^2 + 36) = \log_{10} 100$ 20. $\log_3 3^{(2x-1)} = 7$
21. **Geology** How much stronger is an earthquake with a Richter scale rating of 7 than an earthquake with a rating of 4?

608 *Chapter 10 Exploring Exponential and Logarithmic Functions*

● **EXERCISES**

The Exercises always include **Practice, Critical Thinking, Applications and Problem Solving,** and **Mixed Review.**

Practice
The Practice exercises are separated into A, B, and C sections, indicated only in the Teacher's Wraparound Edition. The A and B sections generally match the Guided Practice exercises in a 3:1 ratio. The C section offers challenging, thought-provoking questions.

Critical Thinking
Each lesson contains critical thinking exercises, in which students explain, evaluate, and justify mathematical concepts and relationships.

Applications and Problem Solving
Students find numerous opportunities to apply concepts to both real-life and mathematical problem situations.

Mixed Review
This spiraled, cumulative review comprises about 15% of the total number of exercises in each lesson and includes at least one application, connection, or integration problem.

● **CHECK FOR UNDERSTANDING**
This section ensures that all students are engaged in the lesson and understand the concepts.

Communicating Mathematics
Students work in small groups or as a whole class to define, explain, describe, make lists, draw models, use symbols, or create graphs.

Modeling Mathematics and **Math Journal** activities, which further strengthen communication skills, appear frequently.

Guided Practice
Keyed to the lesson objectives, the Guided Practice exercises present a representative sample of the exercises in the Practice section.

Glencoe's Algebra ② Exemplifies the NCTM Standards

CONTENT EMPHASIS

Algebra 2: Integration, Applications, and Connections implements the shift from just manipulative skills to algebra as a means of representation.

> *"The proposed algebra curriculum will move away from a tight focus on manipulative facility to include a greater emphasis on conceptual understanding, on algebra as a means of representation, and on algebraic methods as a problem-solving tool." NCTM Standards, page 150, 1989.*

In each chapter, students explore the language of algebra in verbal, tabular, graphical, and symbolic forms. Problem-solving activities and applications encourage students to model patterns and relationships with variables and functions.

> *"The primary role of algebra at the school level is to develop confidence and facility in using variables and functions to model numerical patterns and quantitative relations." NCTM Statement on Algebra, February 1994.*

Each lesson opener motivates students to master the content they need to solve the application, connection, or integration. Additional applications, connections, and integration in the exercises enable students to apply what they have learned.

Glencoe's ***Algebra 2*** incorporates graphing-calculator and computer-software activities for discovery, problem solving, and modeling. The program deemphasizes paper-and-pencil methods of transforming, simplifying, and solving symbolic expressions, while retaining those procedures that students need for algebraic understanding.

> *"Development of algebra should use technology to explore ideas and methods from at least three connected perspectives—graphic, numeric, and symbolic." NCTM Statement on Algebra, February 1994.*

Examples, exercises, and assessment activities in Glencoe's ***Algebra 2*** integrate algebra topics with statistics, geometry, and discrete mathematics.

> *"Refocusing algebra on modeling...serves to break down artificial barriers between algebra and statistics, between algebra and geometry, and between algebra and discrete mathematics." NCTM Statement on Algebra, February 1994.*

Applications, modeling activities, and open-ended projects encourage a diversity of approaches and engage today's students in Algebra 2.

ASSESSMENT

The wide and varied collection of assessment tools and materials that accompany Glencoe's *Algebra 2* support the NCTM Assessment Standards. *[Note: The bulleted headings and quotations below are taken from the Assessment Standards for School Mathematics, NCTM, 1995, pages 11, 13, 15, 17, 19, and 21.]*

● **The Mathematics Standard** — "Assessment should reflect the mathematics that all students need to know and be able to do."
> Skills, procedural knowledge, factual knowledge, reasoning, applying mathematics, and problem solving are assessed through a broad range of short-response exercises and longer-term, open-ended activities.

● **The Learning Standard** — "Assessment should enhance mathematics learning."
> Assessment is an integral part of the Communicating Mathematics, Guided Practice, and Exercises sections of each Glencoe's *Algebra 2* lesson. Students are able to evaluate their own learning by writing in their math journals and selecting portfolio items.

● **The Equity Standard** — "Assessment should promote equity."
> The wide variety of assessment tools enable all students to demonstrate what they know and can do. Performance Assessment tasks for each chapter include a scoring guide.

● **The Openness Standard** — "Assessment should be an open process."
> Learning objectives tell students what they are expected to learn in each lesson. The examples, activities, and assessment match those objectives. Guided Practice prepares students to successfully complete the Exercises.

● **The Inferences Standard** — "Assessment should promote valid inferences about mathematics learning."
> The assortment of assessment tools provide many sources of evidence. Exercises, Mixed Review, and Chapter Tests are all correlated to the learning objectives and practice activities.

● **The Coherence Standard** — "Assessment should be a coherent process."
> The numerous, varied assessment tools are carefully designed to complement each other. They enable you to easily construct the assessment program that best fits your needs.

Learning Objectives & NCTM Standards Correlation

Lesson	Lesson Objectives	NCTM Standards
1-1A	Use a graphing calculator to evaluate expressions.	1-5
1-1	Use the order of operations to evaluate expressions. Use formulas.	1-5
1-2	Determine the sets of numbers to which a number belongs. Use the properties of real numbers to simplify expressions.	1-5
1-3	Represent and interpret data using line plots and stem-and-leaf plots. Find and use the median, mode, and mean to interpret data.	1-4, 10
1-4	Translate verbal expressions and sentences into algebraic expressions and equations. Solve equations by using the properties of equalities. Solve equations for a specific variable.	1-5
1-5A	Use a graphing calculator to estimate solutions to equations by building tables of values.	1-5
1-5	Solve equations containing absolute value. Solve problems by making lists.	1-5
1-6	Solve inequalities and graph the solution sets.	1-5
1-7	Solve compound inequalities using and and or. Solve inequalities involving absolute value and graph the solutions.	1-5
2-1	Graph a relation, state its domain and range, and determine if it is a function. Find values of functions for given elements of the domain.	1-6
2-2A	Use a graphing calculator to graph linear equations.	1-6
2-2	Identify equations that are linear and graph them. Write linear equations in standard form. Determine the intercepts of a line and use them to graph an equation.	1-6
2-2B	Use a graphing calculator to approximate solutions to equations with one variable.	1-6
2-3	Determine the slope of a line. Use slope and a point to graph an equation. Determine if two lines are parallel, perpendicular, or neither. Solve problems by identifying and using a pattern.	1-6
2-4	Write an equation of a line in slope-intercept form given the slope and one or two points. Write an equation of a line that is parallel or perpendicular to the graph of a given equation.	1-6
2-5	Draw scatter plots. Find and use prediction equations.	1-6
2-5B	Use a graphing calculator to graph lines of regression.	1-6
2-6	Identify and graph special functions.	1-6
2-7A	Use a graphing calculator to graph linear inequalities.	1-5
2-7	Draw graphs of inequalities in two variables.	1-5
3-1A	Use a graphing calculator to graph and solve systems of linear equations.	1-5
3-1	Solve systems of equations by graphing.	1-5
3-2	Use the substitution and elimination methods to solve systems of equations.	1-5
3-3	Find the values of second-order determinants. Solve systems of equations by using Cramer's rule.	1-5
3-4A	Use a graphing calculator to graph and solve systems of linear inequalities.	1-5
3-4	Solve systems of inequalities by graphing.	1-5, 8
3-5	Find the maximum and minimum values of a function over a region using linear programming techniques. Solve problems by solving a simpler problem.	1-6

Lesson	Lesson Objectives	NCTM Standards
3-6	Solve problems involving maximum and minimum values by using linear programming techniques.	1-6
3-7	Solve a system of three equations in three variables.	1-5
3-7B	Determine the octant in which a point in space is located. Graph linear equations in space and determine the intercepts.	1-5, 8
4-1A	Use a graphing calculator to perform operations with matrices and find determinants and inverses.	1-4, 12
4-1	Perform scalar multiplication on a matrix. Solve matrices for variables. Solve problems using matrix logic.	1-4, 8, 12
4-2	Add and subtract matrices.	1-4, 8, 12
4-3	Multiply matrices.	1-4, 8, 12
4-4	Evaluate the determinant of a 3×3 matrix. Find the area of a triangle, given the coordinates of its vertices.	1-4, 8, 12
4-5	Write the identity matrix for any square matrix. Find the inverse of a 2×2 matrix.	1-4, 12
4-6	Solve systems of linear equations by using inverse matrices.	1-5, 12
4-7	Solve systems of linear equations by using augmented matrices.	1-5, 12
4-7B	Use a graphing calculator to solve systems of linear equations.	1-5, 12
4-8	Find the range, quartiles, and interquartile range for a set of data. Determine if any values in a set of data are outliers. Represent data using box-and-whisker plots.	1-4, 10
5-1	Multiply and divide monomials. Represent numbers in scientific notation. Multiply and divide expressions written in scientific notation.	1-5
5-2	Add, subtract, and multiply polynomials.	1-5
5-3	Divide polynomials using long division. Divide polynomials by binomials using synthetic division.	1-5
5-4	Factor polynomials. Use factoring to simplify polynomial quotients.	1-5
5-5	Simplify radicals having various indices. Use a calculator to estimate roots of numbers.	1-5
5-6	Simplify radical expressions. Rationalize the denominator of a fraction containing a radical expression. Add, subtract, multiply, and divide radical expressions.	1-5
5-7	Solve problems by identifying and achieving subgoals. Write expressions with radical exponents in simplest radical form and vice versa. Evaluate expressions in either exponential or radical form.	1-5
5-8	Solve equations containing radicals.	1-5
5-9	Simplify square roots containing negative radicands. Solve quadratic equations that have pure imaginary solutions. Add, subtract, and multiply complex numbers.	1-5
5-10	Simplify rational expressions containing complex numbers in the denominator.	1-5
6-1A	Use a graphing calculator to graph and solve quadratic equations.	1-6
6-1	Write functions in quadratic form. Graph quadratic functions. Solve quadratic equations by graphing.	1-6
6-2	Solve problems by using the guess-and-check strategy. Solve quadratic equations by factoring.	1-5
6-3	Solve quadratic equations by completing the square.	1-5
6-4	Solve quadratic equations by using the quadratic formula. Use discriminants to determine the nature of the roots of quadratic equations.	1-5
6-5	Find the sum and product of the roots of quadratic equations. Find a quadratic equation to fit a given condition.	1-5
6-6A	Use a graphing calculator to graph and explore similarities between parabolas.	1-6
6-6	Graph quadratic equations of the form $y = a(x - h)^2 + k$. Determine the equation of a parabola by using points on its graph.	1-6
6-7A	Use a graphing calculator to graph and solve quadratic inequalities.	1-5

Lesson	Lesson Objectives	NCTM Standards
6-7	Graph quadratic inequalities. Solve quadratic inequalities in one variable.	1-5
6-8	Find the standard deviation for a set of data.	1-4, 10
6-9	Solve problems involving normally-distributed data.	1-4, 10
7-1	Find the distance between two points in the coordinate plane. Find the midpoint of a line segment in the coordinate plane.	1-5, 8
7-2	Write equations of parabolas. Graph parabolas having certain properties.	1-5
7-3	Write equations of circles. Graph circles having certain properties.	1-5
7-4A	Draw an ellipse using simple materials.	1-5
7-4	Write equations of ellipses. Graph ellipses having certain properties.	1-5
7-5	Write equations of hyperbolas. Graph hyperbolas having certain properties.	1-5
7-6A	Use a graphing calculator to graph conic sections.	1-5
7-6	Write equations of conic sections in standard form. Identify conic sections from their equations. Use simulation to solve problems.	1-5
7-6B	Draw conic sections using conic graph paper.	1-5
7-7A	Use a graphing calculator to solve systems of quadratic equations and inequalities by graphing.	1-5
7-7	Solve systems of equations involving quadratics graphically and algebraically. Solve systems of inequalities involving quadratics graphically.	1-5
8-1	Evaluate polynomial functions. Identify general shapes of the graphs of polynomial functions.	1-5
8-2	Find factors of polynomials by using the factor theorem and synthetic division.	1-5
8-3A	Use a graphing calculator to graph polynomial functions and approximate the real zeros of the functions.	1-5
8-3	Approximate the real zeros of polynomial functions. Find maxima and minima of polynomial functions. Graph polynomial functions.	1-5
8-3B	Use a graphing calculator to model data whose curve of best fit is a polynomial function.	1-5
8-4	Find the number and type of zeros of a polynomial function.	1-5
8-5	Identify all possible rational zeros of a polynomial function by using the rational zero theorem. Find zeros of polynomial functions.	1-5
8-6	Solve nonquadratic equations by using quadratic techniques.	1-5
8-7	Find the composition of functions.	1-5
8-7B	Graph the iterations of a function.	1-5
8-8	Determine the inverse of a function or relation. Graph functions and their inverses. Work backward to solve problems.	1-5
8-8B	Graph and analyze square root functions. Graph square root inequalities.	1-6
9-1A	Use a graphing calculator to explore graphs of rational functions.	1-6, 13
9-1	Graph rational functions.	1-6, 13
9-2	Solve problems involving direct, inverse, and joint variation.	1-6, 13
9-3	Simplify rational expressions. Simplify complex fractions.	1-5, 7
9-4	Find the least common denominator of two or more algebraic expressions. Add and subtract rational expressions.	1-5
9-5	Solve rational equations and inequalities.	1-5
10-1A	Use a graphing calculator to draw graphs of exponential functions.	1-6
10-1	Simplify expressions and solve equations and inequalities involving real exponents.	1-6
10-1B	Use a graphing calculator to fit a curve to a scatter plot of real-world data.	1-6, 10
10-2	Write exponential equations in logarithmic form and vice versa. Evaluate logarithmic expressions. Solve equations and inequalities involving logarithmic functions.	1-6
10-3	Simplify and evaluate expressions using properties of logarithms. Solve equations involving logarithms.	1-6
10-4	Identify the characteristic and the mantissa of a logarithm. Find common logarithms and antilogarithms.	1-6
10-5	Find natural logarithms of numbers.	1-6

Lesson	Lesson Objectives	NCTM Standards
10-6	Solve equations with variable exponents by using logarithms.	1-6
10-7	Use logarithms to solve problems involving growth and decay.	1-6
11-1A	Use a graphing calculator to investigate sequences.	1-5, 12
11-1	Find the next term in a sequence by looking for a pattern. Find the nth term of an arithmetic sequence. Find the position of a given term in an arithmetic sequence. Find arithmetic means.	1-5, 12
11-2	Find sums of arithmetic series. Find specific terms in an arithmetic series. Use sigma notation to express sums.	1-5, 12
11-3	Find the nth term of a geometric sequence. Find the position of a given term in a geometric sequence. Find geometric means.	1-5, 8, 12
11-4	Find sums of geometric series. Find specific terms in a geometric series. Use sigma notation to express sums.	1-5, 12
11-5	Find sums of infinite geometric series.	1-5, 8, 12, 13
11-6	Study special sequences. Iterate functions.	1-6, 12
11-7	Define and draw fractals. Write a recursive formula for the perimeter or area of a fractal.	1-5, 7, 12
11-8	Expand powers of binomials by using Pascal's triangle and the binomial theorem. Find specific terms of binomial expansions.	1-5, 11, 12, 14
12-1	Solve problems using the fundamental counting principle. Solve problems by using the strategy of solving a simpler problem.	1-4, 12
12-2	Solve problems involving linear and circular permutations.	1-4, 12
12-3	Solve problems involving combinations.	1-4, 12
12-4	Find the probability of an event. Determine the odds of success and failure of an event.	1-4, 11
12-5	Find the probability of two or more independent or dependent events.	1-4, 11
12-6	Find the probability of mutually exclusive or inclusive events.	1-4, 11
12-7	Use binomial experiments to find probabilities. Use simulation to solve various probability problems.	1-4, 11-12
12-8	Determine an unbiased sample. Find margins of sampling error. Test hypotheses by designing and conducting experiments.	1-4, 11-12
13-1	Find values of trigonometric functions for acute angles. Solve problems involving right triangles.	1-6, 7, 9
13-2	Change radian measure to degree measure and vice versa. Identify coterminal angles.	1-5, 9
13-3	Find values of trigonometric functions for general angles. Use trigonometric identities to find values of trigonometric functions.	1-6, 9
13-4	Solve triangles by using the law of sines.	1-6, 7, 9
13-5	Solve triangles by using the law of cosines.	1-6, 7, 9
13-6	Define and use the trigonometric functions based on the unit circle.	1-6, 9
13-7	Find values of expressions involving inverse trigonometric functions.	1-6, 9
14-1A	Use a graphing calculator to graph trigonometric functions.	1-4, 6, 8-9
14-1	Graph trigonometric functions. Find the amplitude and period for variations of the sine and cosine functions.	1-6, 8-9
14-2	Use trigonometric identities to simplify or evaluate expressions.	1-6, 8-9
14-3A	Use a graphing calculator to verify trigonometric identities.	1-6, 8-9
14-3	Verify trigonometric identities. Solve problems by working backward.	1-6, 9
14-4	Find values of sine and cosine involving sum and difference formulas. Verify identities by using the sum and difference formulas.	1-6, 9
14-5	Find values of sine and cosine involving double and half angles. Verify identities by using double- and half-angle formulas.	1-6, 9
14-6A	Use a graphing calculator to solve trigonometric equations.	1-6, 8-9
14-6	Solve trigonometric equations.	1-6, 9

Planning Your Algebra 2 Course

40- TO 50-MINUTE CLASS PERIODS

The chart below gives suggested pacing guides for two options, Standard and Honors, for four 9-week grading periods. The Standard option covers Chapters 1-12 while the Honors option covers Chapters 1-14. Generally, one day is allotted for each lesson including the Graphing Technology and Modeling Mathematics lessons, one day for the Chapter Study Guide and Assessment, and one day for a chapter test. *A pacing guide that addresses both of these options is provided in each lesson of the Teacher's Wraparound Edition.*

The total days suggested for each option is about 165 days. This allows for teacher flexibility in planning due to school cancellation or shortened class periods.

Grading Period	Standard		Honors	
	Chapter	Days	Chapter	Days
1	1	12	1	12
	2	14	2	13
	3	14	3	12
			4-1 to 4-3	
2	4	14	4-4 to end	8
	5	16	5	12
	6-1 to 6-7	12	6	14
			7-1 to 7-5	6
3	6-8 to end	5	7-6A to end	7
	7	15	8	14
	8	15	9	9
	9	10	10	11
4	10	12	11	11
	11	14	12	10
	12	12	13	9
			14	11

BLOCK SCHEDULE, 90-MINUTE CLASS PERIODS

The chart below gives a suggested pacing guides for teaching Glencoe's
Algebra 2 using block scheduling in 1 semester (classes meet everyday)
or 1 year (classes meet about 85 days). The guide is based on teaching
Chapters 1-14. It is suggested that Graphing Technology and Modeling
Mathematics lessons be paired with their corresponding lessons for one
class period while most other lessons be taught individually. *The pacing
guide in each lesson of the Teacher's Wraparound Edition also addresses
block scheduling.*

Chapter	Class Periods
1	6
2	7
3	6
4	7
5	6
6	7
7-1 to 7-5	4
7-6 to end	3
8	7
9	4
10	5
11	7
12	6
13	6
14	6

 For day-by-day lesson plans, please refer to
Glencoe's Algebra 2 Block Scheduling Booklet.

Classroom Vignettes

Glencoe's unique **Classroom Vignettes** are classroom-tested teaching suggestions made by experienced mathematics educators. Each vignette was written by a teacher who uses Glencoe's *Algebra 2* or by a Glencoe reviewer, consultant, or author. Glencoe thanks these outstanding mathematics educators for their unique contributions.

Noreen Allen (p. 560)
George Washington High School
Charleston, West Virginia

Carol Baden (p. 18)
The Galloway School
Atlanta, Georgia

Nancy Barr (p. 380)
Monterey High School
Lubbock, Texas

Nancy Berkley (p. 337)
North Stafford High School
Stafford, Virginia

Cindy Boyd (pp. 451, 736)
Abilene High School
Abilene, Texas

Martha Britton (p. 104)
Cabell Midland High School
Ona, West Virginia

Susan Creekmore (pp. 9, 775, 830)
Marion High School
Marion, Arkansas

William Crosby (p. 355)
Riverside High School
Parsons, Tennessee

Sara Davis (p. 494)
Riverton High School
Riverton, Kansas

Robert Deml (p. 429)
Onalaska High School
Onalaska, Wisconsin

Charlotte Duis (p. 105)
Brookville High School
Lynchburg, Virginia

Gail Gardner (p. 510)
New Bern High School
New Bern, North Carolina

Eva Gates (pp. 96, 255, 275)
Independent Mathematics Consultant
Pearland, Texas

Joan Gell (p. 207)
Palos Verdes High School
Palos Verdes Estates, California

Scott Hendrickson (p. 617)
American Fork High School
American Fork, Utah

Nancy Lee King (p. 416)
Greenwood High School
Midland, Texas

Richard Kyes (p. 429)
Onalaska High School
Onalaska, Wisconsin

Anne Licciardi (p. 371)
Foxborough High School
Foxborough, Massachusetts

Linda Matthews (p. 149)
Egg Harbor Township High School
Pleasantville, New Jersey

Carol Ann VanGalder (p. 318)
Milton High School
Milton, Wisconsin

Suzy Ward (p. 81)
Jeffersontown High School
Louisville, Kentucky

Bonnie Wicker (p. 334)
Munford High School
Munford, Tennessee

Leah Wisnewski (p. 429)
Onalaska High School
Onalaska, Wisconsin

Peggy Yountz (p. 23)
Cary-Grove Community High School
Cary, Illinois

People in the News

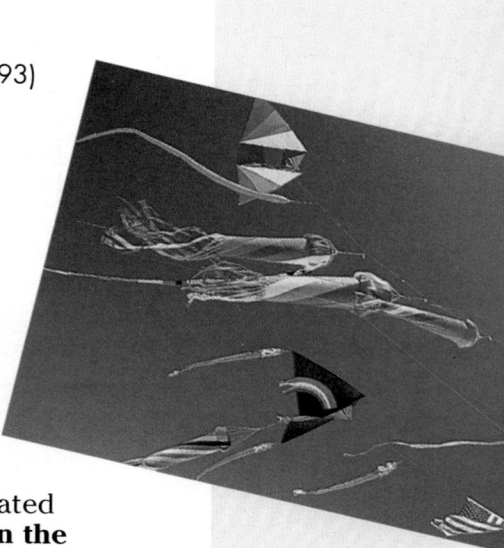

Glencoe's unique **People in the News** features young people from across the United States who have appeared "in the news" because of a noteworthy accomplishment. Glencoe congratulates these exceptional citizens.

Internet Connections

Glencoe's unique **Internet Connection** is a source for more information related to the **Chapter Project** and the interests of the person featured in **People in the News.**

The sites referenced in Glencoe's **Internet Connections** are not under the control of Glencoe. Therefore, Glencoe can make no representation concerning the content of these sites. Extreme care has been taken to list only reputable links by using educational and government sites whenever possible. Internet searches have been used that return only sites that contained no content apparently intended for mature audiences. The following list of mathematics Internet sites may prove helpful. Useful search tools include http://webcrawler.com/, http://www.yahoo.com/search.html, and http://www.microsoft.com/search.

Internet Site	Comments
http://www.yahoo.com/science/mathematics	An ideal starting point that has links to other math sites.
http://www.tc.cornell.edu/Edu/MathSciGateway	Provides links to math and science resources; for grades 9-12.
http://forum.swarthmore.edu/dr.math/	Students in grades K-12 can ask Dr. Math their own questions.
http://www.enc.org/	This is the Eisenhower clearinghouse for K-2 math and science instructional materials.
http://forum.swarthmore.edu/mathmagic	K-12 telecommunications project in Texas that uses computers to increase problem-solving and communication skills.

Glencoe's Algebra ② Research Activities

Glencoe's *Algebra 2: Integration, Applications, and Connections*, as well as the entire Glencoe Mathematics Series, is the product of ongoing, classroom-oriented research that involves students, teachers, curriculum supervisors, administrators, parents, and college-level mathematics educators.

The programs that make up the Glencoe Mathematics Series are currently being used by millions of students and tens of thousands of teachers. The key reason that Glencoe Mathematics programs are so successful in the classroom is the fact that each Glencoe author team is a mix of practicing classroom teachers, curriculum supervisors, and college-level mathematics educators. Glencoe's balanced author teams help ensure that Glencoe Mathematics programs are both practical and progressive.

Prior to publication of a Glencoe program, typical research activities include:

- a review of educational research and recommendations made by groups such as NCTM
- mail surveys of mathematics educators
- discussion groups involving mathematics teachers, department heads, and supervisors
- focus groups involving mathematics educators
- face-to-face interviews with mathematics educators
- telephone surveys of mathematics educators
- in-depth analyses of manuscript by a wide range of reviewers and consultants
- field tests in which students and teachers use pre-publication manuscript in the classroom

Feedback from teachers, curriculum supervisors, and even students who currently use Glencoe mathematics programs is also incorporated as Glencoe plans and publishes new and revised programs. For example, Classroom Vignettes, which are printed in the Teacher's Wraparound Editions, are one result of this feedback.

All of this research and information is used by Glencoe's authors and editors to publish the best instructional resources possible.

WHY IS ALGEBRA IMPORTANT?

Algebra is a tool that you'll be able to use throughout your life.

Algebra 2 is designed to illustrate how you'll be using algebra in the real world. This goal is accomplished through **integration, applications,** and **connections.**

INTEGRATION
Geometry

In addition to algebra, you'll study many other math topics. You'll learn how different branches of mathematics, such as geometry and statistics, are interrelated.

You'll use matrices to perform geometric transformations such as dilations. (Lesson 4-1, page 190)

APPLICATION
Space Science

Mathematics can usually be related to real-life events, even the making of a hit movie. Relevant, real-world uses of mathematics are featured throughout this book.

You'll learn how quadratic equations and parabolas are related to the making of the hit movie *Apollo 13*. (Lesson 6-1, page 334)

CONNECTION
Literature

Many authors incorporate their interest in math in their writing. Mathematics topics are connected to other subjects that you study, even literature.

You'll use Edgar Allen Poe's *The Pit and the Pendulum* to evaluate expressions with rational exponents. (Lesson 5-7, page 296)

iii

Authors

WILLIAM COLLINS teaches mathematics at James Lick High School in San Jose, California. He has served as the mathematics department chairperson at James Lick and Andrew Hill High Schools. Mr. Collins received his B.A. in mathematics and philosophy from Herbert H. Lehman College in Bronx, New York, and his M.S. in mathematics education from California State University, Hayward. Mr. Collins is a member of the Association of Supervision and Curriculum Development and the National Council of Teachers of Mathematics, and is active in several professional mathematics organizations at the state level. He is also currently serving on the Teacher Advisory Panel of the *Mathematics Teacher*.

"In this era of educational reform and change, it is good to be part of a program that will set the pace for others to follow. This program integrates the ideas of the NCTM Standards with real tools for the classroom, so that algebra teachers and students can expect success every day."

GILBERT CUEVAS is a professor of mathematics education at the University of Miami in Miami, Florida. Dr. Cuevas received his B.A. in mathematics and M.Ed. and Ph.D., both in educational research, from the University of Miami. He also holds a M.A.T. in mathematics from Tulane University. Dr. Cuevas is a member of many mathematics, science, and research associations on the local, state, and national levels and has been an author and editor of several National Council of Teachers of Mathematics (NCTM) publications. He is also a frequent speaker at NCTM conferences, particularly on the topics of equity and mathematics for all students.

ALAN G. FOSTER is a former mathematics teacher and department chairperson at Addison Trail High School in Addison, Illinois. He obtained his B.S. from Illinois State University and his M.A. in mathematics from the University of Illinois. Mr. Foster is a past president of the Illinois Council of Teachers of Mathematics (ICTM) and was a recipient of the ICTM's T.E. Rine Award for Excellence in the Teaching of Mathematics. He also was a recipient of the 1987 Presidential Award for Excellence in the Teaching of Mathematics for Illinois. Mr. Foster was the chairperson of the MATHCOUNTS question writing committee in 1990 and 1991. He frequently speaks and conducts workshops on the topic of cooperative learning.

BERCHIE GORDON is the mathematics/science coordinator for the Northwest Local School District in Cincinnati, Ohio. Dr. Gordon has taught mathematics at every level from junior high school to college. She received her B.S. in mathematics from Emory University in Atlanta, Georgia, her M.A.T. in education from Northwestern University in Evanston, Illinois, and her Ph.D. in curriculum and instruction at the University of Cincinnati. Dr. Gordon has developed and conducted numerous inservice workshops in mathematics and computer applications. She has also served as a consultant for IBM, and has traveled throughout the country making presentations on graphing calculators to teacher groups.

"Using this textbook, you will learn to think mathematically for the 21st century, solve a variety of problems based on real-world applications, and learn the appropriate use of technological devices so you can use them as tools for problem solving."

BEATRICE MOORE-HARRIS is an educational specialist at the Region IV Education Service Center in Houston, Texas. She is also the Southwest Regional Director of the Benjamin Banneker Association. Ms. Moore-Harris received her B.A. from Prairie View A&M University in Prairie View, Texas. She has also done graduate work there, at Texas Southern University in Houston, Texas, and at Tarleton State University in Stephenville, Texas. Ms. Moore-Harris is a consultant for the National Council of Teachers of Mathematics (NCTM) and serves on the Editorial Board of the NCTM's *Mathematics Teaching in the Middle School.*

"This program will bring algebra to life by engaging you in motivating, challenging, and worthwhile mathematical tasks that mirror real-life situations. Opportunities to use technology, manipulatives, language, and a variety of other tools are an integral part of this program, which allows all students full access to the algebra curriculum."

JAMES RATH has 30 years of classroom experience in teaching mathematics at every level of the high school curriculum. He is a former mathematics teacher and department chairperson at Darien High School in Darien, Connecticut. Mr. Rath earned his B.A. in philosophy from The Catholic University of America and his M.Ed. and M.A. in mathematics from Boston College. He has also been a Visiting Fellow in the mathematics department at Yale University in New Haven, Connecticut.

DORA SWART is a mathematics teacher at W.F. West High School in Chehalis, Washington. She received her B.A. in the mathematics education at Eastern Washington University in Cheney, Washington, and has done graduate work at Central Washington University in Ellensburg, Washington, and Seattle Pacific University in Seattle, Washington. Ms. Swart is a member of the National Council of Teachers of Mathematics, the Western Washington Mathematics Curriculum Leaders, and the Association of Supervision and Curriculum Development. She has developed and conducted numerous inservices and presentations to teachers in the Pacific Northwest.

"Glencoe's algebra series provides the best opportunity for you to learn algebra well. It explores mathematics through hands-on learning, technology, applications, and connections to the world around us. Mathematics can unlock the door to your success—this series is the key."

LESLIE J. WINTERS is the former secondary mathematics specialist for the Los Angeles Unified School District and is currently supervising student teachers at California State University, Northridge. Mr. Winters received bachelor's degrees in mathematics and secondary education from Pepperdine University and the University of Dayton, and master's degrees from the University of Southern California and Boston College. He is a past president of the California Mathematics Council-Southern Section, and received the 1983 Presidential Award for Excellence in the Teaching of Mathematics and the 1988 George Polya Award for being the Outstanding Mathematics Teacher in the state of California.

Consultants, Writers, and Reviewers

Consultants

Cindy J. Boyd
Mathematics Teacher
Abilene High School
Abilene, Texas

Eva Gates
Independent Mathematics
    Consultant
Pearland, Texas

Melissa McClure
Consultant, Tech Prep
Mathematics Consultant
Teaching for Tomorrow
Fort Worth, Texas

Gail Burrill
National Center for Research/
    Mathematical & Science Education
University of Wisconsin
Madison, Wisconsin

Joan Gell
Mathematics Department Chairman
Palos Verdes High School
Palos Verdes Estates, California

Dr. Luis Ortiz-Franco
Consultant, Diversity
Associate Professor of Mathematics
Chapman University
Orange, California

David Foster
Glencoe Author and Mathematics
    Consultant
Morgan Hill, California

Daniel Marks
Consultant, Real-World Applications
Associate Professor of Mathematics
Auburn University at Montgomery
Montgomery, Alabama

Writers

Gail Burrill
Writer, Statistics
National Center for
    Research/Mathematical & Science
    Education
University of Wisconsin
Madison, Wisconsin

Jeri Nichols-Riffle
Writer, Graphing Technology
Assistant Professor
Teacher Education/Mathematics and
    Statistics
Wright State University
Dayton, Ohio

Carol Damian
Writer, Investigations
Physics Teacher
Dublin Scioto High School
Dublin, Ohio

David Foster
Writer, Investigations
Glencoe Author and Mathematics
    Consultant
Morgan Hill, California

Reviewers

Jacqueline L. Austin
Mathematics Teacher
Henry Clay High School
Lexington, Kentucky

Bill Bernhardt
Mathematics Teacher
Moses Lake High School
Moses Lake, Washington

Melody L. Boring
Mathematics Department Chairperson
Lafayette High School
St. Joseph, Missouri

Judy L. Buchholtz
Mathematics Department Chairperson
Dublin Scioto High School
Dublin, Ohio

Linda R. Baker
Mathematics Teacher
New Hanover High School
Wilmington, North Carolina

Gary Boe
Mathematics Teacher
Platteview High School
Springfield, Nebraska

Sabina Wade Bradberry
Mathematics Teacher
Hueytown High School
Hueytown, Alabama

Judith A. Fish
Mathematics Department
    Chairperson/Teacher
West Deptford High School
West Deptford, New Jersey

Nancy Barr
Mathematics Teacher
Monterey High School
Lubbock, Texas

Paul J. Bohney
Supervisor of Mathematics/Science
Gary Community School Corporation
Gary, Indiana

Teresa Call Brown
Mathematics Teacher
Western Guilford High School
Greensboro, North Carolina

Robert Gillham
Mathematics Department Chairperson
Huffman High School
Birmingham, Alabama

Charles Hall
Mathematics Teacher
John F. Kennedy High School
Granada Hills, California

Marilyn Hanson
Mathematics Teacher
Ames High School
Ames, Iowa

Susan L. Harder
Algebra Team Leader
Clark High School
Plano, Texas

Scott J. Hendrickson
Mathematics Chairperson
American Fork High School
American Fork, Utah

Karl R. Hiester
Mathematics Department Chairperson
Governor Mifflin Senior High School
Shillington, Pennsylvania

Vickie L. Inge
Mathematics Coordinator
Stafford County Public Schools
Stafford, Virginia

Allen L. Janes
Mathematics Teacher
Red River High School
Grand Forks, North Dakota

Sonja Jernigan
Mathematics Teacher
Northview High School
Dothan, Alabama

Chris Johnson
Mathematics Teacher
Lewisville High School
Lewisville, Texas

Nancy Lee King
Mathematics Teacher
Greenwood High School
Midland, Texas

James Kinsella
Mathematics Teacher
Irondequoit High School
Rochester, New York

Frank LaFuente, Sr.
Mathematics Teacher
East Central High School
San Antonio, Texas

Rebecca Gibbons Lane
Mathematics Teacher
West Florence High School
Florence, South Carolina

Dr. Gerald E. Martau
Deputy Superintendent (Retired)
Lakewood City Schools
Lakewood, Ohio

Ross A. Martin
Mathematics Department Chairperson
Bethel High School
Bethel, Connecticut

Dee Mattox-Hall
Mathematics Coordinator
Galena Park ISD
Galena Park, Texas

Donna McLeish
Mathematics and Science Secondary
  Curriculum Coordinator
Vigo County School Corporation
Terre Haute, Indiana

Jane E. Morey
Mathematics Department
  Chairperson
Washington High School
Sioux Falls, South Dakota

Patricia Neighbors
Mathematics Department
  Chairperson
Clover Park High School
Lakewood, Washington

Harry Oldweiler
Secondary Mathematics Coordinator
Columbia Public Schools
Columbia, Missouri

Angela S. Pasquariello
Mathematics Teacher
Pompton Lakes High School
Pompton Lakes, New Jersey

Marshall Ranson
Mathematics Specialist
Volusia County Schools
Daytona Beach, Florida

William A. Reid
Mathematics Teacher
Shelby County High School
Columbiana, Alabama

Judy M. Renegar
Mathematics Department Chairperson
Independence High School
Charlotte, North Carolina

Treasa A. Coleman Robinson
Mathematics Department Chairperson
Pike County Central High School
Pikeville, Kentucky

Doug Sanford
Mathematics Department Chairperson
Bothell High School
Bothell, Washington

Garry Taylor
Mathematics Supervisor
Mercer County Schools
Princeton, West Virginia

Vicki Tribul
Mathematics Department Chairperson
Carmel High School
Carmel, Indiana

Susan Ward
Mathematics Teacher
Jeffersontown High School
Louisville, Kentucky

Andrew Wildes
Mathematics Teacher
Pentucket High School
West Newbury, Massachusetts

Laura S. Winters
Mathematics Teacher
John F. Kennedy High School
Granada Hills, California

Edith Sloan Woods
Mathematics Department Chairperson
Benton Harbor High School
Benton Harbor, Michigan

Tyrus E. Woodward
Mathematics Teacher
Hampton City Schools
Hampton, Virginia

Table of Contents

CHAPTER 2 **Graphing Linear Relations and Functions** **62**

CHAPTER 3 **Solving Systems of Linear Equations and Inequalities** **122**

INTEGRATION

Content Integration

What does geometry have to do with algebra? Believe it or not, you can study most math topics from more than one point of view. Here are some examples.

Geometry You'll use your skills with matrices to find the coordinates of the vertices of a parallelogram.
(Lesson 3–3, pages 141 and 143)

Look Back features refer you to skills and concepts that have been taught earlier in the book.

Discrete Mathematics ▲
You'll use permutations to find out why certain movies are shown at some theaters but not others. (Lesson 12–2, page 718)

LOOK BACK

You can refer to Lesson 1-5 for information about absolute value equations.

(Lesson 2–6, page 104)

▲ Problem Solving
You'll solve real-world problems by using matrix logic.
(Lesson 4–1, page 187)

▼ Number Theory You'll learn how complex numbers are used in building houses. (Lesson 5–9, pages 310 and 313)

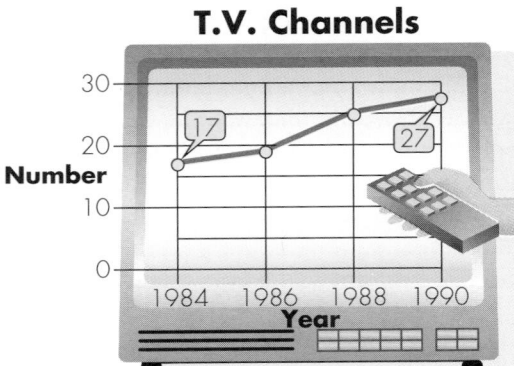

T.V. Channels

◄ Statistics You'll learn how to draw scatter plots and from the scatter plots to determine prediction equations.
(Lesson 2–5, pages 95–100)

Probability You'll model the behavior of mice by using probability and transition matrices. (Lesson 4–3, page 200)

CHAPTER 5 Exploring Polynomials and Radical Expressions **252**

APPLICATIONS

Real-Life Applications

Have you ever wondered if you'll ever actually use math? Every lesson in this book is designed to help show you where and when math is used in the real world. Since you'll explore many interesting topics, we believe you'll discover that math is relevant and exciting. Here are some examples.

Top Five List, FYI, and **Fabulous Firsts** contain interesting facts that enhance the applications.

Auto Racing You'll use racing data from the Indianapolis 500 in your study of the slope of lines. (Lesson 2–3, pages 80–81)

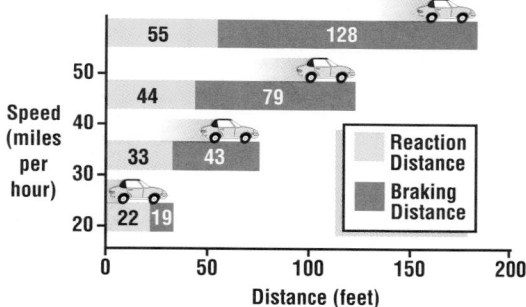

◀ Solar Energy You'll learn how to write an equation of a parabola that models the shape of a mirror used to harness solar energy. (Lesson 7–2, page 418)

Cryptography You'll learn how matrices can be used to encode secret messages. (Lesson 4–5, pages 212–213)

Singles of All Time in the U.S.

1. *White Christmas,* Bing Crosby, 1942
2. *I Want to Hold Your Hand,* Beatles, 1964
3. *Hound Dog/Don't Be Cruel,* Elvis Presley, 1956
4. *It's Now or Never,* Elvis Presley, 1960
5. *I Will Always Love You,* Whitney Houston, 1992

(Lesson 12–2, page 721)

BRAKING DISTANCES
(after driver sees danger)

FYI

The strongest earthquake in American history measured 8.4 on the Richter scale. It occurred on March 27, 1964 near Prince William Sound, Alaska. It killed 131 people and caused an estimated $750 million in property damage.

(Lesson 7–3, page 423)

▲ Law Enforcement You'll evaluate a radical expression that police officers often use at the scene of an auto accident. (Lesson 5–6, page 288)

World Cultures You'll relate the solution of a number puzzle to the study of functions and their inverses. (Lesson 8–8, page 528)

Mae Carol Jemison (1956–)

Mae Carol Jemison was the first African-American woman astronaut. She was the computer engineer and physician aboard the space shuttle Endeavor, launched September 12, 1992.

(Lesson 3–4, page 148)

Divine Mathematics

Did you know that the great American poet Henry Wadsworth Longfellow enjoyed math? Reprints of actual articles or works of literature illustrate how mathematics is a part of our society. (Lesson 5–6, page 295)

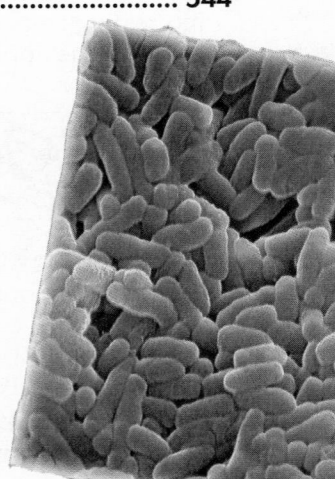

CHAPTER **10** **Exploring Exponential and Logarithmic Functions** **592**

CHAPTER **11** **Investigating Sequences and Series** **644**

CONNECTIONS

Interdisciplinary Connections

Some people believe that mathematics has very little use in other subjects such as chemistry or music. Of course, this isn't true. In this textbook, mathematics is frequently connected to other subjects that you are studying.

Global Connections features introduce you to a variety of world cultures. ▼

GLOBAL CONNECTIONS

Malaysian foot tennis is a very popular sport in Malaysia and other countries in the Far East. It is played by teams of two using a volleyball-type net. A ball woven from rattan must be kept in the air using only feet, knees, or thighs.

CAREER CHOICES

Engineers apply the principles of science and mathematics to solve practical technical problems. **Electrical engineers** design, develop, test, and supervise the manufacturing of electrical and electronic equipment. They comprise more than one fourth of all engineers. A bachelor's degree in engineering is the minimum requirement.

For more information, contact:

Institute of Electrical and Electronic Engineers 1828 L St. NW, Suite 1202 Washington, DC 20036

Physics You'll model speed of sound data by using a linear equation. (Lesson 2–2, page 73)

Chemistry You'll solve a problem involving Avogadro's constant. (Lesson 5–1, page 258)

▲ **Biology** You'll model the shape of a deadly frog's leap by using an equation of a parabola. (Lesson 6–6, page 370)

Health You'll evaluate a polynomial that is a model for the number of people who are likely to get the flu. (Lesson 5–3, page 272)

◄ **Career Choices** features include information on interesting careers.

◄ **Literature** You'll solve a Sherlock Holmes mystery. (Lesson 13–1, page 772)

Geography The growth of the population of Arizona is used to introduce mathematical relations. (Lesson 2–1, page 64)

Math Journal exercises give you the opportunity to assess yourself and write about your understanding of key math concepts. (Lesson 3–1, Exercise 6)

MATH JOURNAL

6. **Write** a paragraph explaining how to identify whether the graph of a system of linear equations would be two intersecting lines, two distinct parallel lines, or two coincident lines.

CHAPTER  **12** **Investigating Discrete Mathematics and Probability** **710**

Modeling Mathematics
Activities **733, 739, 755, 760**
Mathematics and Society
"Fowl" Advertising **731**

CHAPTER **13** **Exploring Trigonometric Functions** **770**

Long-Term Investigation
Scream Machines! **768–769**
• Working on the Investigation **785, 810**
Technology
Explorations **774, 788, 806**
Mathematics and Society
The Channel Tunnel **804**

TECHNOLOGY

Do you know how to use computers and graphing calculators? If you do, you'll have a much better chance of being successful in today's society and workplace.

GRAPHING CALCULATORS

There are several ways in which graphing calculators are integrated.

- **Introduction to Graphing Calculators**   On pages 2–3, you'll get acquainted with the basic features and functions of a graphing calculator.

- **Graphing Technology Lessons**   In Lesson 3–1A, you'll learn how to solve a system of linear equations using a graphing calculator.

- **Graphing Calculator Explorations**   You'll learn how to use a graphing calculator to model sun intensity using a quadratic equation in Lesson 6–6.

- **Graphing Calculator Programs**   In Lesson 5–3, Exercise 46 includes a graphing calculator program that performs synthetic division.

- **Graphing Calculator Exercises**   Many exercises are designed to be solved using a graphing calculator. For example, see Exercise 45 in Lesson 2–3.

COMPUTER SOFTWARE

- **Spreadsheets**   On page 188 of Lesson 4–1, a spreadsheet is used to help manage a small business.

- **BASIC Programs**   The program on page 143 of Lesson 3–3 is designed to solve systems of equations using Cramer's Rule.

- **Graphing Software**   The graphing software Exploration on page 571 of Lesson 9–4 involves simplifying rational expressions.

Technology Tips, such as this one on page 207 of Lesson 4–4, are designed to help you make more efficient use of technology through practical hints and suggestions.

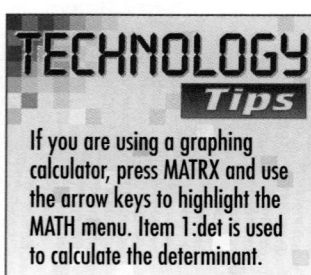

TECHNOLOGY *Tips*

If you are using a graphing calculator, press MATRX and use the arrow keys to highlight the MATH menu. Item 1:det is used to calculate the determinant.

CHAPTER **14** **Using Trigonometric Graphs and Identities** **822**

Long-Term Investigation
Scream Machines!
Technology
Mathematics and Society

SYMBOLS AND MEASURES

Symbols

$=$	is equal to
$\neq$	is not equal to
$>$	is greater than
$<$	is less than
$\geq$	is greater than or equal to
$\leq$	is less than or equal to
$\approx$	is approximately equal to
$\sim$	is similar to
$\times$ or $\cdot$	times
$\div$	divided by
$-$	negative or minus
$+$	positive or plus
$\pm$	positive or negative
$-a$	opposite or additive inverse of a
$\lvert a \rvert$	absolute value of a
$a \overset{?}{=} b$	Does a equal b?
$a : b$	ratio of a to b
$\sqrt{a}$	square root of a
$[a]$	greatest integer not greater than a
O	origin
$\varnothing$	empty set
i	imaginary unit
x	mean of a set of data
$\sigma_{\bar{x}}$	standard deviation of a set of data

$!$	factorial
$\log_b x$	logarithm, base b, of x
$P(A)$	probability of A
$f(x)$	f of x, the value of f at x
$f^{-1}(x)$	f inverse of x, inverse of $f(x)$
(a, b)	ordered pair a, b
$\overline{AB}$	line segment AB
$\overset{\frown}{AB}$	arc AB
$\overrightarrow{AB}$	ray AB
$\overleftrightarrow{AB}$	line AB
AB	measure of $\overline{AB}$
$\angle$	angle
Δ	triangle
$\cos A$	cosine of A
$\sin A$	sine of A
$\tan A$	tangent of A
$\sec A$	secant of A
$\csc A$	cosecant of A
$\cot A$	cotangent of A
$(\ )$	parentheses; *also* ordered pairs
$[\ ]$	brackets; *also* matrices
$\{\ \}$	braces; *also* sets
$^\circ$	degree
$'$	minute

Measures

mm	millimeter
cm	centimeter
m	meter
km	kilometer
g	gram
kg	kilogram
mL	milliliter
L	liter

in.	inch
ft	foot
yd	yard
mi	mile
in^2 or sq in.	square inch
s	second
min	minute
h	hour

Greek Letters

α	alpha
β	beta
ϕ	phi
π	pi

θ	theta
σ	sigma
ω	omega
Σ	capital sigma

GETTING ACQUAINTED WITH THE GRAPHING CALCULATOR

What is it?
What does it do?
How is it going to help me learn math?

These are just a few of the questions many students ask themselves when they first see a graphing calculator. Some students may think, "Oh, no! Do we *have* to use one?", while others may think, "All right! We get to use these neat calculators!" There are as many thoughts and feelings about graphing calculators as there are students, but one thing is for sure: a graphing calculator *can* help you learn mathematics.

So what is a graphing calculator? Very simply, it is a calculator that draws graphs. This means that it will do all of the things that a "regular" calculator will do, *plus* it will draw graphs of simple or very complex equations. In algebra, this capability is nice to have because the graphs of some complex equations take a lot of time to sketch by hand. Some are even considered impossible to draw by hand. This is where a graphing calculator can be very useful.

But a graphing calculator can do more than just calculate and draw graphs. You can program it, work with matrices, and make statistical graphs and computations, just to name a few things. If you need to generate random numbers, you can do that on the graphing calculator. If you need to find the absolute value of numbers, you can do that, too. It's really a very powerful tool—so powerful that it is often called a pocket computer. But don't let that intimidate you. A graphing calculator can save you time and make doing mathematics easier.

As you may have noticed, graphing calculators have some keys that other calculators do not. The Texas Instruments TI-82 will be used throughout this text. The keys located on the bottom half of the calculator are probably familiar to you as they are the keys found on basic scientific calculators. The keys located just below the screen are the graphing keys. You will also notice the up, down, left, and right arrow keys. These allow you to move the cursor around on the screen and to "trace" graphs that have been plotted. The other keys located on the top half of the calculator access the special features such as statistical and matrix computations.

There are some keystrokes that can save you time when using the graphing calculator. A few of them are listed below.

- Any light blue commands written above the calculator keys are accessed with the 2nd key. Similarly, any gray characters above the keys are accessed with the ALPHA key.

- 2nd ENTRY copies the previous calculation so you can edit and use it again.

- Pressing ON while the calculator is graphing stops the calculator from completing the graph.

- 2nd QUIT will return you to the home (or text) screen.

- 2nd A-LOCK locks the ALPHA key, which is like pressing "shift lock" or "caps lock" on a typewriter or computer. The result is that all caps will be typed and you do not have to hold the shift key down. (This is handy for programming.)

- 2nd OFF turns the calculator off.

Graphing on the TI–82

Before graphing, we must instruct the calculator how to set up the axes in the coordinate plane. To do this, we define a **viewing window.** The viewing window for a graph is the portion of the coordinate grid that is displayed on the **graphics screen** of the calculator. The viewing window is written as [left, right] by [bottom, top] or [Xmin, Xmax] by [Ymin, Ymax]. A viewing window of $[-10, 10]$ by $[-10, 10]$ is called the **standard viewing window** and is a good viewing window to start with to graph an equation. The standard viewing window can be easily obtained by pressing ZOOM 6. Try this. Move the arrow keys around and observe what happens. You are seeing a portion of the coordinate plane that includes the region from -10 to 10 on the x-axis and from -10 to 10 on the y-axis. Move the cursor, and you can see the coordinates of the points for the current position of the cursor.

Any viewing window can be set manually by pressing the WINDOW key. The window screen will appear and display the current settings for your viewing window. First press ENTER. Then, using the arrow and ENTER keys, move the cursor to edit the window settings. Xscl and Yscl refer to the x-scale and y-scale. This is the number of tick marks placed on the x- and y-axes. Xscl=1 means that there will be a tick mark for every unit of one along the x-axis. In the standard viewing window both the Xscl and Yscl are 1.

Graphing equations is as simple as defining a viewing window, entering the equations in the Y= list, and pressing GRAPH. It is often important to view enough of a graph so you can see all of the important characteristics of the graph and understand its behavior. The term **complete graph** refers to a graph that shows all of the important characteristics such as intercepts or maximum and minimum values.

Example: Graph $y = x + 20$ in the standard viewing window.

Enter: **Y=**

X,T,θ **+**

20 **GRAPH**

It appears that nothing happens. Why?

The graph of $y = x + 20$ is a line whose y-intercept is 20 and whose x-intercept is -20. The graph is plotted off the screen and is not complete. A better viewing window for this graph would be $[-25, 25]$ by $[-25, 25]$, which includes both intercepts.

Graphing calculators allow you to analyze graphs by approximating the coordinates of individual points. Suppose we wanted to determine the x-intercept of the graph of $y = x^2 - 2$. Begin by graphing the equation in the standard viewing window.

Enter: **Y=**

X,T,θ **x²**

— 2 **ZOOM** 6

We will use a process called zoom-in to approximate the intercepts. The ZOOM IN feature of the calculator is very useful for determining the coordinates of any point, such as an intercept, with greater accuracy. Use the TRACE function and the arrow keys to determine an approximation for the x-coordinate of the left-most intercept. Begin by placing the cursor on the left-most intercept and observing the x-coordinate. Now, ZOOM IN by entering **ZOOM** 2 **ENTER** .

TRACE to position the cursor at the intercept again. Observe the coordinates. Now move the cursor one time to the left or right. Any digits that remain unchanged as you move are accurate. Repeat the process of zooming and checking digits until you have the number of accurate digits that you desire.
$x \approx -1.414214$

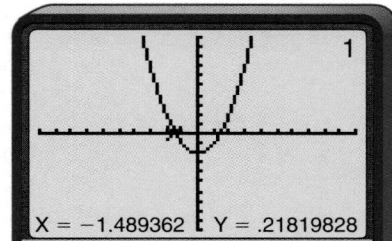

X = -1.489362   Y = .21819828

Programming on the TI–82

The TI–82 has programming features that allow us to write and execute a series of commands to perform tasks that may be too complex or cumbersome to perform otherwise. Each program is given a name. Commands begin with a colon (:) followed by an expression or an instruction. Most of the features of the calculator are accessible from program mode.

When you press **PRGM** , you see three menus: EXEC, EDIT, and NEW. EXEC allows you to execute a stored program by selecting the name of the program from the menu. EDIT allows you to edit or change an existing program and NEW allows you to create a new program. To break during program execution, press **ON** . The following example illustrates how to create and execute a new program that stores an expression as Y and evaluates the expression for a designated value of X.

1. Enter **PRGM** **▶** **▶** **ENTER** to create a new program.

2. Type EVAL **ENTER** to name the program. (Make sure that the caps lock is on.) You are now in the program editor, which allows you to enter commands. The colon (:) in the first column of the line indicates that this is the beginning of the command line.

3. The first command lines will ask the user to designate a value for x. Enter **PRGM** **▶** 3 **2nd** **A-LOCK** **"** ENTER THE VALUE FOR X **"** **ALPHA** **ENTER** **PRGM** **▶** 1 **X,T,θ** **ENTER** .

4. The expression to be evaluated for the value of x is $3x^2 - \sqrt{x}$. To store the expression as Y, enter 3 **X,T,θ** **x²** **—** **2nd** **√** **X,T,θ** **STO▶** **ALPHA** **Y** **ENTER** .

5. Finally, we want to display the value for the expression. Enter **PRGM** **▶** 3 **ALPHA** **Y** **ENTER** .

6. Now press **2nd** **QUIT** to return to the home screen.

7. To execute the program, enter **PRGM** **ENTER** **ENTER** . The program asks for a value for x. You will input any value for which the expression is defined and press **ENTER** . To immediately re-execute the program, simply press **ENTER** when Done appears on the screen.

While a graphing calculator cannot do everything, it can make some things easier. To prepare for whatever lies ahead, you should try to learn as much as you can. The future will definitely involve technology, and using a graphing calculator is a good start toward becoming familiar with technology. Who knows? Maybe one day you will be designing the next satellite, building the next skyscraper, or helping students learn mathematics with the aid of a graphing calculator!

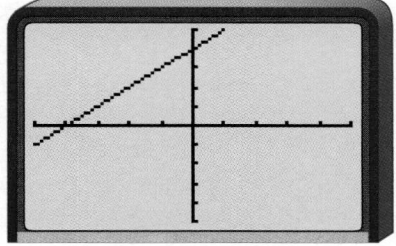

Analyzing Equations and Inequalities

PREVIEWING THE CHAPTER

This chapter provides a review of essential skills and concepts in algebraic and statistical settings. Students survey evaluating expressions, the properties of real numbers, the use of line and stem-and-leaf plots to represent data, and the use of measures of central tendency to interpret and describe sets of data. Then, the procedures for solving linear equations are presented and extended to solving inequalities. The number line is used as a mathematical model to review absolute value, and equations involving absolute values are solved. The chapter ends with solving compound sentences and inequalities involving absolute values.

Lesson (Pages)	Lesson Objectives	NCTM Standards	State/Local Objectives
1-1A (6)	Use a graphing calculator to evaluate expressions.	1–5	2.a.
1-1 (7–12)	Use the order of operations to evaluate expressions. Use formulas.	1–5	2.a.
1-2 (13–18)	Determine the sets of numbers to which a number belongs. Use the properties of real numbers to simplify expressions.	1–5, 14	2.a.
1-3 (19–26)	Represent and interpret data using line plots and stem-and-leaf plots. Find and use the median, mode, and mean to interpret data.	1–4, 10	
1-4 (27–34)	Translate verbal expressions and sentences into algebraic expressions and equations. Solve equations by using the properties of equality. Solve equations for a specific variable.	1–5	2.a.
1-5A (35–36)	Use a graphing calculator to estimate solutions to equations by building tables of values.	1–5	2.a.
1-5 (37–42)	Solve equations containing absolute value. Solve problems by making lists.	1–5	2.a.
1-6 (43–48)	Solve inequalities and graph the solution sets.	1–5	
1-7 (49–54)	Solve compound inequalities using *and* and *or*. Solve inequalities involving absolute value and graph the solutions.	1–5	

ORGANIZING THE CHAPTER

You may want to refer to the **Course Planning Calendar** on page T12 for detailed information on pacing.
PACING: Standard—12 days; **Honors**—12 days; **Block**—6 days

LESSON PLANNING CHART

| Lesson (Pages) | Materials/ Manipulatives | Extra Practice (Student Edition) | BLACKLINE MASTERS | | | | | | | | | | Real-World Applications | Interactive Mathematics Tools Software | Teaching Transparencies |
			Study Guide	Practice	Enrichment	Assessment and Evaluation	Modeling Mathematics	Multicultural Activity	Tech Prep Applications	Graphing Calculator	Science and Math Lab Manual			
1-1A (6)	graphing calculator									pp. 15, 16				
1-1 (7–12)	graphing calculator	p. 876	p. 1	p. 1	p. 1			p. 1	p. 1		pp. 63–68	1		1-1A 1-1B
1-2 (13–18)		p. 876	p. 2	p. 2	p. 2	p. 16		p. 2					1-2	1-2A 1-2B
1-3 (19–26)	graphing calculator	p. 876	p. 3	p. 3	p. 3							2	1-3.1 1-3.2	1-3A 1-3B
1-4 (27–34)		p. 877	p. 4	p. 4	p. 4	pp. 15, 16	pp. 25–27		p. 2				1-4.1 1-4.2 1-4.3	1-4A 1-4B
1-5A (35–36)	graphing calculator									pp. 17, 18				
1-5 (37–42)	graphing calculator	p. 877	p. 5	p. 5	p. 5									1-5A 1-5B
1-6 (43–48)	graphing calculator	p. 877	p. 6	p. 6	p. 6	p. 17				p. 1		3		1-6A 1-6B
1-7 (49–54)		p. 878	p. 7	p. 7	p. 7	p. 17	p. 61							1-7A 1-7B
Study Guide/ Assessment (55–59)						pp. 1–14, 18–20								

ORGANIZING THE CHAPTER

OTHER CHAPTER RESOURCES

Student Edition
Chapter Opener, pp. 4–5
Mathematics and Society, p. 26

Teacher's Classroom Resources
Investigations and Projects Masters, pp. 25–28

Technology
Teacher's Guide for Software Resources
Test and Review Software (IBM and Macintosh)
CD-ROM Interactions (Windows and Macintosh)

Professional Publications
Block Scheduling Booklet
Glencoe Mathematics Professional Series

OUTSIDE RESOURCES

Books/Periodicals
Dalton, LeRoy, *Algebra in the Real World*, Dale Seymour Publications
Schadler, Reuben, *Algebra Problem: One Step Beyond*, Dale Seymour Publications

Software
Algebraic Patterns, Sunburst
Math Connections: Algebra II, Sunburst

Videos/CD-ROMs
Futures, ITSCO
How to Take the Mystery Out of Algebra, ETA

See the *Teacher's Guide for Software Resources* for software addresses.

ASSESSMENT RESOURCES

Student Edition
Math Journal, pp. 23, 52
Mixed Review, pp. 18, 26, 33, 42, 48, 54
Self Test, p. 34
Chapter Highlights, p. 55
Chapter Study Guide and Assessment, pp. 56–58
Alternative Assessment, p. 59
Portfolio, p. 59

Teacher's Wraparound Edition
5-Minute Check, pp. 7, 13, 19, 27, 37, 43, 49
Check for Understanding, pp. 10, 16, 22, 30, 40, 46, 52
Closing Activity, pp. 12, 18, 26, 34, 42, 48, 54
Cooperative Learning, pp. 8, 44

Assessment and Evaluation Masters
Multiple-Choice Tests, Forms 1A (Honors), 1B (Average), 1C (Basic), pp. 1–6
Free-Response Tests, Forms 2A (Honors), 2B (Average), 2C (Basic), pp. 7–12
Calculator-Based Test, p. 13
Performance Assessment, p. 14
Mid-Chapter Test, p. 15
Quizzes A–D, pp. 16–17
Standardized Test Practice, p. 18
Cumulative Review, pp. 19–20

Examples of some of the materials for enhancing Chapter 1 are shown below.

DIVERSITY

Multicultural Activity Masters, pp. 1, 2

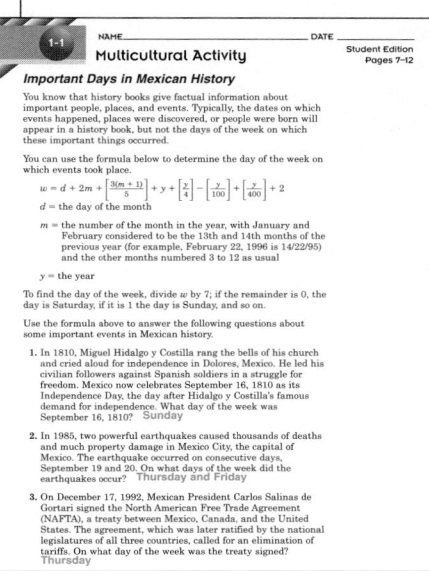

APPLICATIONS

Real-World Applications, 1, 2, 3

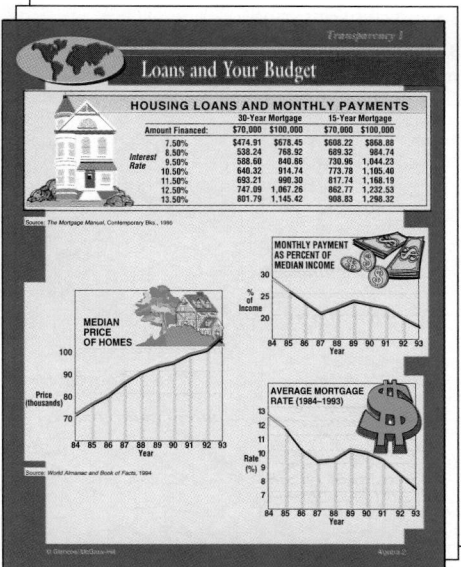

TECHNOLOGY

Graphing Calculator Masters, p. 1

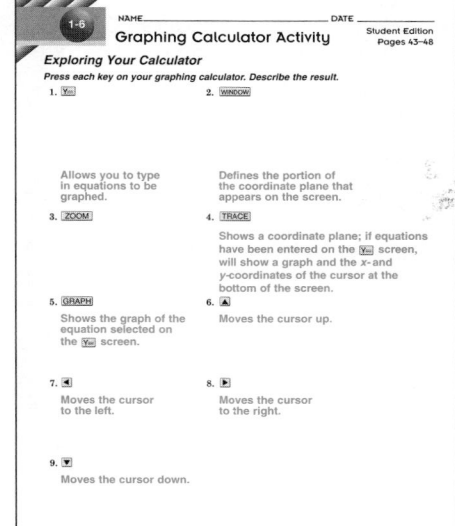

TECH PREP

Tech Prep Applications Masters, pp. 1, 2

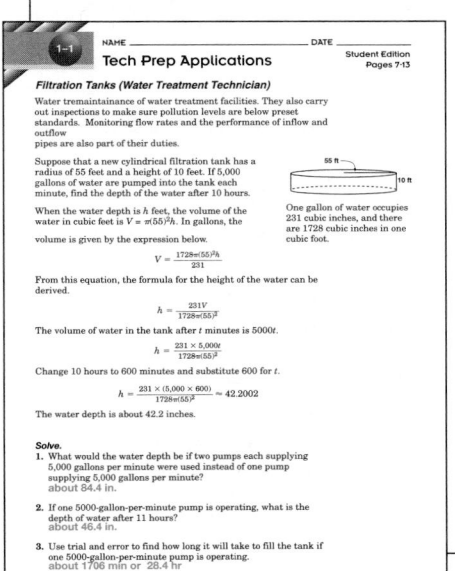

CONNECTIONS

Science and Math Lab Manual, pp. 63–68

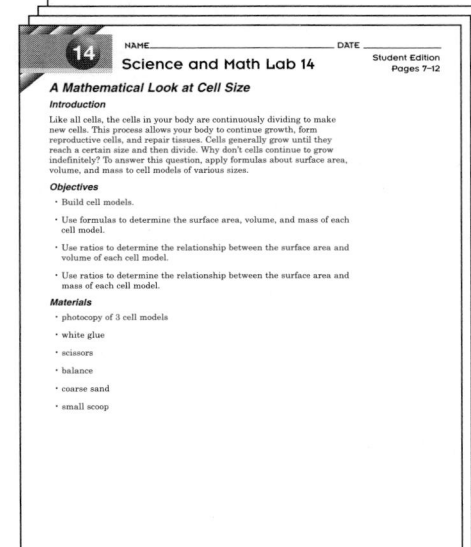

PROBLEM SOLVING

Problem of the Week Cards, 1, 2, 3

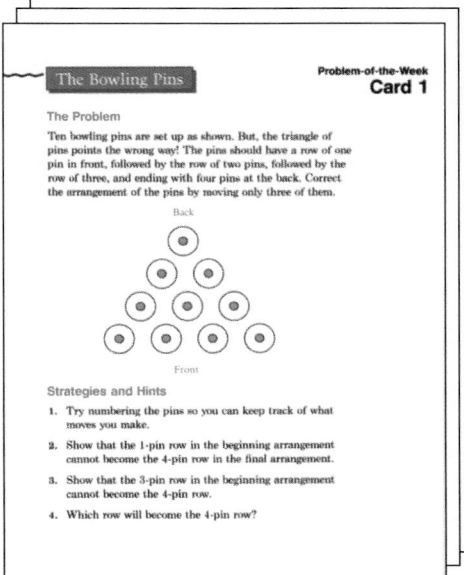

MAKING MATHEMATICS RELEVANT

This two-page introduction to the chapter provides students with an opportunity to explore contemporary topics and their applications to mathematics.

Background Information

Outdoors Activities Students might find it helpful to organize the activities into different categories and reevaluate the results. For example, under a category called "Nature Appreciation Activities," students would include *Wildlife Viewing, Hiking,* and *Camping.* Students might also create categories such as *Watersports, Motorsports,* and so on. Caution students that adding the numbers in each category is not exact, since many people engage in more than one of the activities.

CHAPTER 1

Analyzing Equations and Inequalities

Objectives

In this chapter, you will:

*   evaluate and simplify expressions,
*   display and interpret data using line plots and stem-and-leaf plots,
*   solve equations, and
*   solve and graph inequalities.

Outdoor Activities

Percentage of Americans who said they participated in each activity. Respondents could cite more than one activity.

Activity	Percentage
Driving for pleasure	40%
Swimming	35%
Picnicking	33%
Fishing	26%
Bicycling (on -road)	21%
Running/Jogging	19%
Hiking	18%
Wildlife viewing	18%
Camping	16%
Photography	15%

Source: *New York Times*

In American culture, sports are very important. Our sports heroes have fame and fortune. Why does American society place so much emphasis on sports? Why is so much money spent on spectator sports such as football and baseball? Should more emphasis be placed on participation than on passive viewing? What benefits do each provide an individual? What are your views on these issues?

TIME *Line*

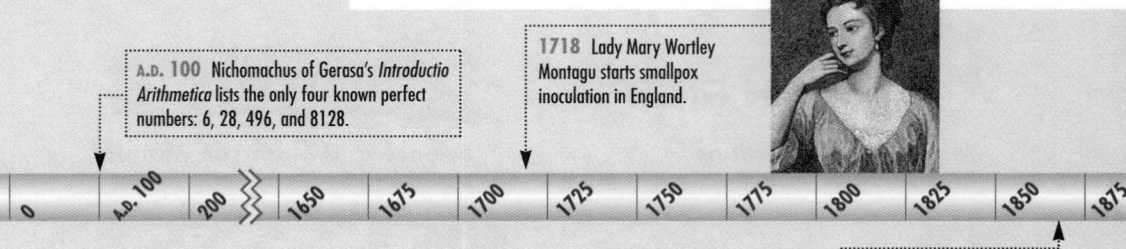

A.D. 100 Nichomachus of Gerasa's *Introductio Arithmetica* lists the only four known perfect numbers: 6, 28, 496, and 8128.

1718 Lady Mary Wortley Montagu starts smallpox inoculation in England.

0	A.D. 100	200	1650	1675	1700	1725	1750	1775	1800	1825	1850	1875

1869 First college football game between Rutgers and College of New Jersey.

TIME *Line*

Have students explain what a "perfect number" is. Students could research and give reports on other types of numbers such as composite, prime, and imaginary.

inter**NET** CONNECTION

Check out "The Great Outdoor Recreation Page." It features information on outdoor activities such as hiking, biking, and so on.

World Wide Web
http://www.gorp.com/

Chapter Project

Sports statistics involve data that are often easy to display and interpret. Look at the topics below. Research to find the data for each. Then display the data in a graphical format such as a line plot, stem-and-leaf plot, bar graph, circle graph, or line graph that best represents the data. Present the data to the class.

- Find the winning times for the gold medal in the women's

100-meter freestyle in the last eight Olympic Games.

- Find the dollar amounts for the top twenty money winners on the men's PGA tour last year.

- Pick a professional baseball team and find the final batting averages at the end of last season. Show this data for each player and also show the averages listed by positions.

Eldrick "Tiger" Woods of Cypress, California, has been playing golf for as long as he can remember. At the age of 9 months, he was introduced to golf, and at age 6, he made his first hole-in-one.

Today Tiger is busy winning tournaments. In August of 1996, he won the U.S. Amateur Golf Championship for the third time at the age of 20. His first U.S. amateur title in 1994 made him the youngest winner ever, the first black player to win, and the only player to have won both the Amateur and the U.S. Junior Amateur Championships, a title he won in 1991, 1992, and 1993.

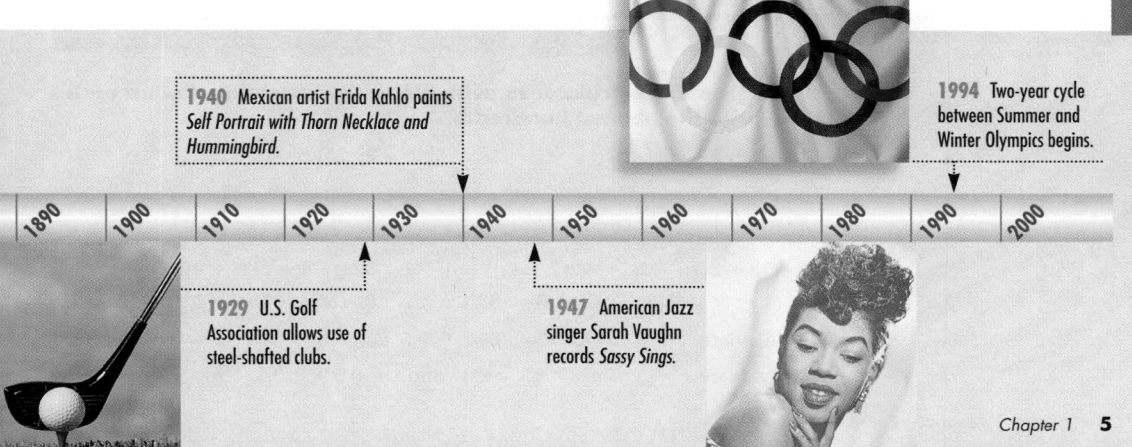

1940 Mexican artist Frida Kahlo paints *Self Portrait with Thorn Necklace and Hummingbird.*

1994 Two-year cycle between Summer and Winter Olympics begins.

1929 U.S. Golf Association allows use of steel-shafted clubs.

1947 American Jazz singer Sarah Vaughn records *Sassy Sings.*

Chapter 1 **5**

Alternative Chapter Projects

Two other chapter projects are included in the *Investigations and Projects Masters.* In Chapter 1 Project A, pp. 25–26, students extend the topic in the chapter opener. In Chapter 1 Project B, pp. 27–28, students investigate temperature control in their school.

Tiger's father, Earl, was determined to make Tiger a great golfer. He introduced him to golf at the age of 18 months and even had him hypnotized at age 13 to help him focus on the golf course.

Chapter Project

Cooperative Learning Groups of four are best for this project. Three students can research the three sports; the fourth student is responsible for creating the graphs. Before constructing the graphs, the entire group should meet to discuss what type of graph is best to represent the data for each sport.

Investigations and Projects Masters, p. 25

Good Sports

1. Work in a small group to explore some ways to use the tools of statistics to describe and analyze sporting events. Do research to find the following.
   - the winning times in the last twenty Indianapolis 500 automobile races
   - the earnings of the top ten male and female players in professional tennis last year
   - the winning distances in the men's long jump event in the last eight Olympic Games
2. Decide on the best way to present each set of sports data in graphical form. For example, your group might decide to make a stem-and-leaf plot or a line plot.
3. Find the mean, median, and mode of each set of data in exercise 1. Decide which measure your group will use as the "average" for each set of data.
4. Write a report summarizing your group's work on this project. Explain how the group completed steps 1, 2, and 3.
5. Exchange graphs and reports with another group. Note similarities and differences in the way each group completed the project. Discuss what, if anything, you would do differently if you could redo the project.

NCTM Standards: 1–5

Objective
Use a graphing calculator to evaluate expressions.

Recommended Time
15 minutes

Instructional Resources
Graphing Calculator Masters,
pp. 15 and 16

These masters provide keystroking instruction for this lesson for the TI-81 and Casio graphing calculators.

1 FOCUS

Motivating the Lesson
Give students five minutes to play with the calculator. Have them write down three questions that arise in that five-minute time period. Then work on answering some of the simpler questions.

2 TEACH

Teaching Tip If students are having problems with parentheses or order of operations, start with simple problems and work up to more difficult ones. Have them state each step in solving an expression. This can give you an insight into possible errors.

3 PRACTICE/APPLY

Assignment Guide

Core: 1–10
Enriched: 1–10

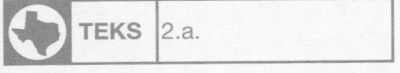 TEKS | 2.a.

4 ASSESS

Observing students working with technology is an excellent method of assessment.

1–1A Graphing Technology
Expressions

A Preview of Lesson 1–1

The Graphing Technology lessons in this text will use the TI-82 graphing calculator. In these lessons, you will be introduced to keying sequences that will allow you to perform mathematical computations, graph equations, and utilize other features of the calculator.

Remember that, as with any scientific calculator, graphing calculators follow the order of operations.

Example ❶ Evaluate $39 - 3^3 \cdot 2 + \frac{5^2 + 9}{4}$.

Enter: 39 ⊟ 3 ⌃ 3 ⌧ 2 ⊞ ⟮ 5 $\boxed{x^2}$ ⊞ 9 ⟯ ÷ 4 $\boxed{\text{ENTER}}$ −6.5

You may enter 5^2 as 5 ⌃ 2 or as 5 $\boxed{x^2}$.

Use parentheses for all grouping symbols on a graphing calculator.

Occasionally, you will need to evaluate an algebraic expression for several different values of a variable. This can be done efficiently using the $\boxed{\text{STO▶}}$ and $\boxed{\text{ENTRY}}$ features.

Example ❷ Evaluate $6x(14 - x)^2$ for $x = -6, 11,$ and 1.25.

Enter: $\boxed{(-)}$ 6 $\boxed{\text{STO▶}}$ $\boxed{\text{X,T,}\theta}$ *Stores -6 as x.*

$\boxed{\text{2nd}}$ $\boxed{:}$ 6 $\boxed{\text{X,T,}\theta}$ ⟮ 14 *Evaluates the expression.*

⊟ $\boxed{\text{X,T,}\theta}$ ⟯ $\boxed{x^2}$ $\boxed{\text{ENTER}}$ −14400

Now press $\boxed{\text{2nd}}$ $\boxed{\text{ENTRY}}$ and use the editing features of the calculator to change the value for x. Move the cursor with the arrow keys to the -6 and change it to 11. The new value is 594 and is computed when you press $\boxed{\text{ENTER}}$. Repeat for $x = 1.25$.

EXERCISES

Use a graphing calculator to evaluate each expression. Round each answer to the nearest hundredth.

1. $5 \times \frac{4 + 7}{6}$ 9.17

2. 231.5^6 1.54×10^{14}

3. $(52 \times 4)^3 + \frac{76}{6}$ 8,998,924.67

4. $3\left[\frac{4 + \frac{3(4 + 6)}{5}}{4}\right] + 11$ 18.5

5. 72

5. $112 - 2\{16 + 2[14 - 2(7 + 1)]\} - 4^2$

6. $[(-4 + 11)^2 \div 4]3$ 36.75

7. $(1.12 \times 10^4)(3.65 \times 10^{-3})$ 40.88

8. $(5.24 \times 10^{-6})(3.24 \times 10^4)$ 0.17

9. 10, 0, −17.78, −20.56, 26.67

9. Evaluate $\frac{5}{9}(F - 32)$ for $F = 50, 32, 0, -5,$ and 80.

10. Evaluate $x^2 - y^2$ for $x = 15, y = 13$ and $x = 0.8, y = 0.4$.   56, 0.48

Using Technology
This lesson offers an excellent opportunity for using technology in your algebra classroom. For more information on using technology, see *Graphing Calculators in the Mathematics Classroom,* one of the titles in the Glencoe Mathematics Professional Series.

1-1

Expressions and Formulas

What YOU'LL LEARN

- To use the order of operations to evaluate expressions, and
- to use formulas.

Why IT'S IMPORTANT

You can use expressions to solve problems involving exercise, baseball, and geometry.

APPLICATION

Exercise

Chris Edwards of Escondido, California, earned his nickname "Airman" by soaring 13 feet off of a ramp while on in-line skates. He has been in-line skating since he was 13 years old and is currently a member of Team Rollerblade, a group that performs shows around the country.

According to a recent study by the University of Massachusetts, you burn as many Calories in-line skating at moderate speeds or faster as you do running. The chart below shows the Calories burned per minute for various body weights and skating speeds.

F Y I

In 1993, there were more than 12.5 million in-line skaters in the United States. This was a third more than there were in 1992 and double the number in 1991.

Calories Burned per Minute While In-Line Skating								
Weight	8 mph	9 mph	10 mph	11 mph	12 mph	13 mph	14 mph	15 mph
120 lb	4.2	5.8	7.4	8.9	10.5	12.1	13.6	15.2
140 lb	5.1	6.7	8.3	9.9	11.4	13.0	14.6	16.1
160 lb	6.1	7.7	9.2	10.8	12.4	13.9	15.5	17.1
180 lb	7.0	8.6	10.2	11.7	13.3	14.9	16.4	18.0
200 lb	7.9	9.5	11.2	12.6	14.2	15.8	17.3	18.9

To determine your skating speed in miles per hour, divide 60 (the number of minutes in an hour) by the number of minutes you skated. Then multiply that number by the number of miles you skated. You can represent this by the expression $(60 \div t) \times d$, where t represents the time skated in minutes and d represents the distance traveled in miles.

Maya works out each day by in-line skating. She skates about three miles in 20 minutes, and she weighs 140 pounds. About how many Calories does she burn during a workout?

First, find how fast Maya was skating.

$$(60 \div t) \times d = (60 \div 20) \times 3 \quad \text{\textit{t = 20 and d = 3}}$$

How do you evaluate $(60 \div 20) \times 3$? What do you do first? Do you multiply or divide? A numerical expression must have exactly one value. In order to find that value, you must follow an **order of operations.**

Order of Operations

> 1. **Simplify the expressions inside grouping symbols, such as parentheses, brackets, braces, and fraction bars.**
> 2. **Evaluate all powers.**
> 3. **Do all multiplications and divisions from left to right.**
> 4. **Do all additions and subtractions from left to right.**

Using the rules above, evaluate the expression.

$$(60 \div 20) \times 3 = 3 \times 3 \quad \text{\textit{Perform the operation inside the parentheses first.}}$$
$$= 9 \quad \text{\textit{Multiply.}}$$

Maya skated at an average speed of 9 mph during her 20-minute workout.

F Y I

How many in-line skaters were there in 1992? In 1991? **9.4 million; 6.25 million**

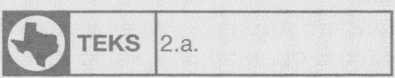 **TEKS** | 2.a.

1-1 LESSON NOTES

NCTM Standards: 1–5

Instructional Resources

- Study Guide Master 1-1
- Practice Master 1-1
- Enrichment Master 1-1
- Multicultural Activity Masters, p. 1
- Real-World Applications, 1
- Science and Math Lab Manual, pp. 63–68
- Tech Prep Applications Masters, p. 1

 Transparency 1-1A contains the 5-Minute Check for this lesson; **Transparency 1-1B** contains a teaching aid for this lesson.

Recommended Pacing	
Standard Pacing	Day 2 of 12
Honors Pacing	Day 2 of 12
Block Scheduling*	Day 1 of 6

 *For more information on pacing and possible lesson plans, refer to the *Block Scheduling Booklet*.

1 FOCUS

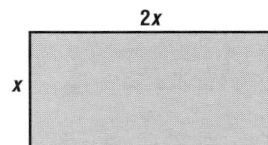

5-Minute Check

1. Evaluate $(12 - 9)^3$. **27**

2. Simplify $3(a + 2) + 5a$. **$8a + 6$**

3. Simplify $\frac{4an + 2}{3am} + \frac{8an + 1}{3am}$. **$\frac{4n}{m} + \frac{1}{am}$**

Use the diagram below for Exercises 4 and 5.

[diagram: rectangle with width $2x$ and height x]

4. Write an expression for the area. **$2x^2$**

5. Write an expression for the perimeter. **$6x$**

Motivating the Lesson

Situational Problem You invest $2000 for 2 years. What is the simple interest rate if the interest is $500? What is the formula for simple interest? **12.5%; prt = I**

2 TEACH

Teaching Tip Ask students how they should key in the equation on page 7 on a nonscientific calculator. Explain that they must key the numbers by grouping them. For example, $4 + 3.7 \times 3$ should be keyed in as $3.7 \times 3 + 4$.

In-Class Examples

For Example 1
Find the value of
$[9 \div (4^2 - 7)] - 8.$ **−7**

For Example 2

a. Evaluate $a^2[b\,(a^2 + a)]$
if $a = 2$ and $b = 3.$ **72**

b. Evaluate $\dfrac{x}{2a^2 - b}$ if $x = 4,$
$a = 3,$ and $b = 2.$ **0.25**

EXPLORATION

In this Exploration, students discover the importance of parentheses. They will see that the value of an expression can often depend on how terms are grouped with parentheses.

Answers for the Exploration

b. **Multiply 5 by 2. Add 3. Subtract 1.**
c. **They performed the operations in order from left to right.**
d. **1010; Find 18^2. Add 711. Subtract result from 2045.**
e. **No; you would then find 18^2. Subtract from 2045. Add 711.**
f. **Multiply 10 by 8. Add result to 135. Find 16^2. Subtract result of previous operations from this number.**

To determine how many Calories Maya burns, find her weight on the chart. Then go across to the column with her average speed of 9 mph. Maya burns 6.7 Calories per minute during her 20-minute workout. So, she burns a total of 20×6.7 or 134 Calories.

As in the expression $(60 \div 20) \times 3$, grouping symbols can be used to change or clarify the order of operations. Frequently-used grouping symbols are parentheses, ( ), brackets, [ ], braces, { }, and fraction bars, as in $\frac{2 + 4}{3}$. When calculating the value of an expression, begin with the operation in the innermost set of grouping symbols.

Example **Find the value of $[(3 + 6)^2 \div 3] \cdot 4.$**

$$
\begin{aligned}
[(3 + 6)^2 \div 3] \cdot 4 &= [(9)^2 \div 3] \cdot 4 && \textit{First add 3 and 6.} \\
&= (81 \div 3) \cdot 4 && \textit{Then find } 9^2. \\
&= 27 \cdot 4 && \textit{Divide 81 by 3.} \\
&= 108 && \textit{Multiply 27 by 4.}
\end{aligned}
$$

The value is 108.

Scientific calculators follow the order of operations.

EXPLORATION — SCIENTIFIC CALCULATORS

Your Turn b–f. See margin.

a. Simplify $3 + 5 \times 2 - 1$ using a scientific calculator. **12**

b. Explain how your calculator arrived at the answer.

c. Suppose someone concluded that $3 + 5 \times 2 - 1 = 15$. How is this possible?

d. Evaluate $2045 - (18^2 + 711)$ using your calculator. Explain how the answer was calculated.

e. If you remove the parentheses in part d above, would the solution remain the same? Explain.

f. Write a set of directions for someone to find the value of $16^2 - (135 + 10 \times 8)$ without a scientific calculator.

Algebraic expressions contain at least one variable. You can evaluate an algebraic expression by replacing each variable with a value and then applying the rules for the order of operations.

Example **a.** Evaluate $a[b^2(b + a)]$ if $a = 12$ and $b = 0.5.$

$$
\begin{aligned}
a[b^2(b+a)] &= 12[(0.5)^2\,(0.5 + 12)] && \textit{Replace a with 12 and b with 0.5.} \\
&= 12[0.25(0.5 + 12)] && \textit{Find } (0.5)^2. \\
&= 12[0.25(12.5)] && \textit{Add 0.5 and 12.} \\
&= 12[3.125] && \textit{Multiply 0.25 by 12.5.} \\
&= 37.5 && \textit{Multiply 12 by 3.125.}
\end{aligned}
$$

The value is 37.5.

 Alternative Teaching Strategies

Reading Algebra When we use the order of operations, we find that we always get a unique answer. Discuss what *unique* means.

 Cooperative Learning

Group Discussion Separate students into pairs. Have one student write a complex equation and the other student evaluate it. Then have each pair trade equations with another pair and together evaluate the equation. For more information on the group discussion strategy, see *Cooperative Learning in the Mathematics Classroom,* one of the titles in the Glencoe Mathematics Professional Series, page 31.

b. Evaluate $\dfrac{y^3}{3ab + 2}$ if $y = 4$, $a = -2$, and $b = -5$.

The fraction bar, which indicates division, is a grouping symbol. Evaluate the expressions in the numerator and denominator separately before dividing.

$$\frac{y^3}{3ab + 2} = \frac{4^3}{3(-2)(-5) + 2} \quad \textit{Replace y with 4, a with } -2\textit{, and b with } -5.$$

$$= \frac{64}{3(10) + 2} \quad \textit{Evaluate the numerator and denominator separately.}$$

$$= \frac{64}{32} \quad \textit{Divide.}$$

$$= 2$$

The value is 2.

A **formula** is a mathematical sentence that expresses the relationship between certain quantities. If you know a value for every variable in the formula except one, you can find the value of the remaining variable.

Pythagoras

One formula you may use is the **Pythagorean theorem,** which was developed by the Greek mathematician Pythagoras. In a right triangle, the side opposite the right angle is called the **hypotenuse.** This side is always the longest side of a right triangle. The other two sides are called the **legs** of the right triangle. The Pythagorean theorem states that in a right triangle, if a and b are the measures of the legs and c is the measure of the hypotenuse, then $c^2 = a^2 + b^2$.

Example ③

INTEGRATION
Geometry

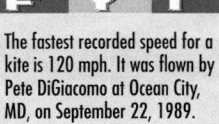

The fastest recorded speed for a kite is 120 mph. It was flown by Pete DiGiacomo at Ocean City, MD, on September 22, 1989.

Suppose the distance from a person flying a kite to the ground directly below the kite is 100 meters, and the length of the string from the person to the kite is 125 meters. Use the Pythagorean theorem to find the height of the kite.

You can think of the kite and the ground as a right triangle as shown at the right.

$$c^2 = a^2 + b^2$$
$$125^2 = 100^2 + b^2 \quad \textit{Substitute.}$$
$$15{,}625 = 10{,}000 + b^2 \quad \textit{Evaluate all powers.}$$
$$b^2 = 5625 \quad \textit{Subtract.}$$
$$b = \sqrt{5625} \quad \textit{Take the square root of each side.}$$
$$b = 75$$

The kite is 75 meters high.

Lesson 1–1 Expressions and Formulas **9**

In-Class Example

For Example 3
If the wind picks up and the kite string is now 175 meters long but the ground distance is still the same, how high is the kite? **approximately 144 meters**

F Y I

The origin of the kite is shrouded in mystery. Some maintain that it was invented by the Greek scientist Archytus in the fifth century B.C. Others maintain that Asian peoples had kites long before the time of Archytus.

Classroom Vignette

"During the first few weeks of school, I like to motivate the students with the following assignment. 'Design a mathematical bumper sticker. Be as creative as you can. Write your own slogan, and design your own message.'"

Susan Justus Creekmore

Susan Creekmore
Marion High School
Marion, Arkansas

Check for Understanding

Exercises 1–17 are designed to help you assess your students' understanding through reading, writing, speaking, and modeling. You should work through Exercises 1–5 with your students and then monitor their work on Exercises 6–17.

Error Analysis

Students sometimes misinterpret the fraction bar to mean only division, as in $\frac{10-4}{2}$. They may also focus on the operations and want to divide before subtracting. $\frac{10-4}{2}$ means $(10-4) \div 2$, not $10 - 4 \div 2$. The fraction bar is a sign of division and a symbol of inclusion.

Additional Answers

1. The operation with the innermost group is evaluated first.
2. First, solve the parenthesis to get 66. Multiply 66 and 12 to get 792. Divide 792 by 2 to get 396. Then subtract 396 from $\frac{1}{3}$ to get $-395\frac{2}{3}$.
5. Both formulas will work to find the volume of $V = 3690 \text{ cm}^3$.

Study Guide Masters, p. 1

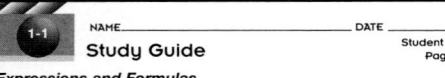

| 1-1 | NAME_____ DATE_____ |
| Study Guide | Student Edition Pages 7–13 |

Expressions and Formulas

To find the value of a numerical expression, you must follow the established order of operations. Always remember to do operations within grouping symbols first. Study the chart below.

Evaluate $8 - 4 \div 2 + 3 \cdot 2^3$	Order of Operations
$8 - 4 \div 2 + 3 \cdot 2^3 = 8 - 4 \div 2 + 3 \cdot 8$ $= 8 - 2 + 24$ $= 6 + 24$ $= 30$	1. Evaluate all powers. 2. Do all multiplications and divisions from left to right. 3. Do all additions and subtractions from left to right.
The value is 30.	

Find the value of each expression.

1. $7 + 6 - 4$ 9
2. $9(3^2 + 6)$ 135
3. $11 - (3 + 2)^2$ −14
4. $14 + (6 \div 2)$ 17
5. $[18 - (6 + 4)] \div 2$ 4
6. $(7 - 2)(3 + 8)$ 55
7. $7 + 2^3 - 18 \div 3$ 9
8. $6 \cdot 7 + 4 \div 4 - 5$ 38
9. $2 + (4 - 2)^3 - 6$ 4

Evaluate each expression if $a = 12$, $b = 4$, $c = 5$, $x = \frac{1}{2}$, and $y = 3$.

10. $y - a \div b$ 0
11. $cb \div xb$ 160
12. $8y + b^2 (ay)$ 600
13. $\frac{(abc \div x) - (6b^2 - 4)}{776}$ 0.5
14. $\frac{1}{3}(y - x)^2$ $\frac{25}{12}$
15. $x \div \frac{a + b}{b^2}$ $\frac{1}{2}$

Communicating Mathematics

Study the lesson. Then complete the following. 1–2, 5. See margin.

1. **Explain** which operation to perform first when evaluating an expression that has both brackets and parentheses.

2. **Describe** how you would evaluate the expression $\frac{1}{3} - \frac{12(77-11)}{2}$.

3–4. See students' work.

3. **List** three formulas that you have used before.

4. **Write** three examples of algebraic expressions.

5. **You Decide** To find the volume of a cone, you multiply the area of the base by the height, then divide by 3. Andrea developed the formula $V = \frac{1}{3}\pi r^2 h$ to find the volume of a cone while Lorenzo developed the formula $V = \frac{\pi r^2 h}{3}$. The cone has a height of 16.3 centimeters, and its base has a radius of 14.7 centimeters. Explain which formula will work, and why.

Guided Practice

Find the value of each expression.

6. $7 - 6 \div 3$ 5
7. $9(4 + 2)$ 54
8. $18 \cdot 6 + 12$ 120
9. $25 \cdot 2 - 3$ 47
10. $\frac{45(4 + 32)}{10}$ 162
11. $(4 - 3)5 \cdot 9$ 9

Evaluate each expression if $a = 3$, $b = -4$, and $c = 5$.

12. $a + b - c$ −6
13. $a + c^2$ 28
14. $a(b + c)$ 3

The relationship between Celsius temperature C and Fahrenheit temperature F is given by $C = \frac{5(F - 32)}{9}$. Find the Celsius temperature for each Fahrenheit temperature.

15. normal body temperature, 98.6° 37°C
16. freezing point of water, 32° 0°C
17. **Geometry** Write a formula to represent the area A of the rectangle shown at the right.
$A = (a + 6)(a - 6)$ in^2

$(a + 6)$ in.

$(a - 6)$ in.

Practice

Find the value of each expression. 27. $-\frac{17}{6}$, $-2.8\overline{3}$

A

18. $4(3^2 + 3)$ 48
19. $2(9 + 2) - 3$ 19
20. $(7 + 5)3 - 3$ 33
21. $4 + 2^2 - 15 + 4$ −3
22. $10 + 16 \div 4 + 8$ 22
23. $5 + 9(3) \div 3 - 8$ 6
24. $7 - [4 + (6 \cdot 5)]$ −27
25. $[21 - (9 - 2)] \div 2$ 7
26. $4 + [9 \div (9 - 2(4))]$ 13
27. $[(-7 + 4) \times 5 - 2] \div 6$

Reteaching

Translating Expressions Write each series of instructions as a single algebraic phrase. Use x to represent the number at the start of each set of instructions.

1. Multiply a number by 6. Add 8.
   Divide by 2. $\frac{(6x + 8)}{2}$

2. Add 8 to a number. Multiply by 6.
   Divide by 2. $\frac{(x + 8)6}{2}$

28. $\frac{1}{2}(5^2 + 3)$ 14

29. $\frac{14(8 - 15)}{2}$ -49

30. $-3(2^2 + 3)$ -21

31. $4 + (49 \div 7) \times 8 \div 2$ 32

32. $0.4(0.6 + 3.2) \div 2$ 0.76

33. $0.5(2.3 + 25) \div 1.5$ 9.1

B **34.** $3 + [8 \div (9 + 2(-4))]$ 11

35. $\frac{1}{3} - \frac{12(77 \div 11)}{9}$ -9

Evaluate each expression if $a = -5$, $b = 0.25$, $c = \frac{1}{2}$, and $d = 4$.

36. $d(3 + c)$ 14

37. $a + b + d$ -0.75

C **38.** $a + 2b - c$ -5

39. $a + 10 \div c$ 15

40. $2^d + a$ 11

41. $\frac{3ab}{cd}$ -1.875

42. $\frac{3a + 4c}{2c}$ -13

43. $(a + c)^2 - bd$ 19.25

44. Geometry The formula for the area A of a
triangle is $A = \frac{1}{2}bh$ where b is the measure of the
base and h is the measure of the height. Write an
expression to represent the area of the triangle
at the right. $A = 0.5(x + 4)(x + 8)$ ft^2

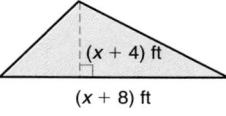
$(x + 4)$ ft
$(x + 8)$ ft

The formula for the area of a trapezoid is
$A = \frac{h}{2}(b_1 + b_2)$. A represents the area, h
represents the measure of the altitude, and
b_1 and b_2 represent the measures of the
bases. Find the area of each trapezoid given
the following values.

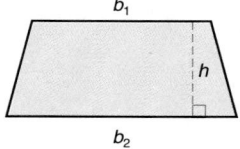
b_1
h
b_2

45. $h = 6, b_1 = 22, b_2 = 17$ 117

46. $h = 10, b_2 = 17, b_1 = 52$ 345

47. $b_2 = 6.25, b_1 = 12.50, h = 4$ 37.5

48. $h = \frac{5}{8}, b_1 = \frac{3}{4}, b_2 = \frac{1}{2}$ $\frac{25}{64}$

Simple interest is the amount paid or earned for the use of money
for a unit of time. It is calculated using the formula $I = prt$ where p
represents the principal in dollars, r represents the annual interest
rate, and t represents the time in years. Find the simple interest I
given each of the following values.

49. $p = \$1500, r = 6.5\%, t = 3$ years $292.50

50. $p = \$2500, r = 7.25\%, t = 2$ years $362.50

51. $p = \$20,005, r = 7.9\%, t = 2$ years, 3 months $3555.89

52. $p = \$65,283.21, r = 9.32\%, t = 78$ months $39,548.57

Programming

53. The graphing calculator program at the right
finds the area of a trapezoid once the height
and lengths of the two bases are entered.

**Run the program to find the area of
each trapezoid.**

a. $h = 8, b_1 = 112, b_2 = 20$

b. $h = 7, b_1 = 4, b_2 = 11$

c. $h = 4.8, b_1 = 5.6, b_2 = 6.4$

53a. 528
53b. 52.5
53c. 28.8

```
PROGRAM:AREA
: Disp "HEIGHT =?"
: Input H
: Disp "B1 ="
: Input B
: Disp "B2 = "
: Input C
: Disp "AREA ="
H(B+C)/2
```

(continued on the next page)

For **Extra Practice,** see p. 876.

The red A, B, and C flags, printed
only in the Teacher's Wraparound
Edition, indicate the level of
difficulty of the exercises.

**Using the Programming
Exercises** The program given in
Exercise 53 is for use with a TI-82
graphing calculator. For other
programmable calculators, have
students consult their owner's
manual for commands similar to
those presented here.

Practice Masters, p. 1

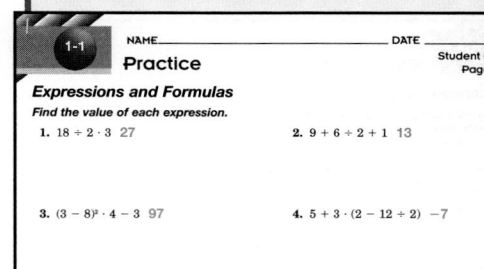

1-1   NAME_____ DATE _____
Practice   Student Edition
Pages 7–13

Expressions and Formulas
Find the value of each expression.

1. $18 \div 2 \cdot 3$ 27

2. $9 + 6 \div 2 + 1$ 13

3. $(3 - 8)^2 \cdot 4 - 3$ 97

4. $5 + 3 \cdot (2 - 12 \div 2)$ -7

5. $1 + 2 - 3 \cdot 4 \div 5$ $\frac{3}{5}$

6. $12 - [20 - 2(6^2 \div 3 \cdot 2^3)]$ 88

Evaluate each expression if $a = \frac{3}{4}$, $b = -8$, $c = -2$, $d = 3$, and $e = \frac{1}{3}$.

7. $ab^2 - d$ 45

8. $(c + d)b$ -8

9. $\frac{ae}{c} + d^2$ $\frac{71}{8}$

10. $\frac{d(b - c)}{ac}$ 12

11. $(a - ce)c^2$ $\frac{17}{3}$

12. $a^2c^3 - be^2$ $-\frac{65}{18}$

13. $-b[a + (c - d)^2]$ 206

14. $\frac{a^2c^4}{d^2} - \frac{c}{e^2}$ $\frac{73}{4}$

Closing Activity

Writing Have students write a paragraph explaining why it is important to have an order of operations.

Additional Answers

57a. 2, 3, 5, 7, 11, 13, 17, 19, 23, 29, 31, 37, 41, 43, 47, 53, 57, 59, 61, 67, 71, 73, 79, 83, 89

57b. Answers will vary; sample answers are 2, 3, 5, 7.

58c. To find the salary for 1970, use −5; for 1965, use −10.

Enrichment Masters, p. 1

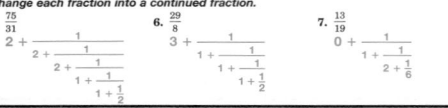

Alter the program to find the area of a triangle if the formula is $A = \frac{1}{2}bh$, where b is the measure of the base (in cm) and h is the measure of the height (in cm). Find the area of each triangle.

d. $b = 6.7, h = 13.8$ **46.23 cm²**   e. $b = 127.2, h = 82.6$ **5253.36 cm²**

Critical Thinking

54. Insert grouping symbols as needed to make each statement true.
   a. $1 + 3 \cdot 2^2 = 16$ $(1 + 3) \cdot 2^2$
   b. $1 + 3 \cdot 2^2 = 49$ $[1 + (3 \cdot 2)]^2$
   c. $1 + 3 \cdot 2^2 = 13$ $1 + 3 \cdot 2^2$
   d. $1 + 3 \cdot 2^2 = 37$ $1 + (3 \cdot 2)^2$

55. **Geometry** Study the rectangular prism at the right.
   a. Create a formula that will determine the total surface area of this rectangular prism. $S = 22a^2 + 24a$
   b. What is the surface area if $a = 4$?   **448 square units**
   c. What is the surface area if $a = 6.2$?   **994.48 square units**

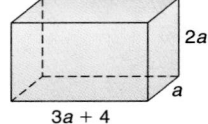

Applications and Problem Solving

56. **Medicine** Dosages of medicine are based upon the weight and/or age of a patient. Suppose an asthma patient must take a medicine that is dispensed in 100-milligram tablets. The dosage is 5 milligrams per kilogram of body weight and is given every six hours.
   a. If the patient weighs 20 kilograms, what dosage should he receive?   **100 mg**
   b. How many tablets would be needed for a 30-day supply?   **120 tablets**

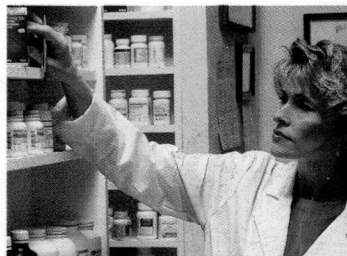

57a–b. See margin.

57. **Number Theory** The sum of the factors of 6 that are less than 6 is $1 + 2 + 3$, or 6. Thus, 6 is called a **perfect number** because the number 6 equals the sum of its factors, excluding itself. 28 is also a perfect number because the sum of the factors, $1 + 2 + 4 + 7 + 14$, is equal to 28. The formula for generating perfect numbers is $p = (2^{n-1})(2^n - 1)$. In order for the formula to work, both n and $(2^n - 1)$ must be prime numbers.
   a. List the first 25 prime numbers. Recall that a prime number is an integer greater than 1 whose only positive factors are 1 and itself.
   b. Find four prime numbers n where $2^n - 1$ is also prime.
   c. Find the next two perfect numbers after 28.   **496, 8128**

58. **Baseball** The graph at the right gives the average salary of a major-league baseball player. The expression $2.9t^2 + 5.8t + 50$, where t is the time in years since 1975, closely models the graph. Evaluating the expression gives the average salary in thousands of dollars.

58a. about $50,000
58b. about $1,207,100

   a. What was the average salary in 1975?
   b. What was the average salary in the strike-shortened 1994 season?
   c. Explain how to find the salary for 1970 and 1965.   **See margin.**

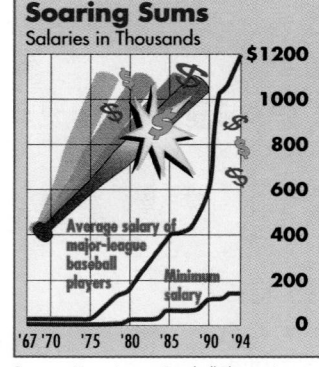

Soaring Sums
Salaries in Thousands

Source: Major League Baseball Players Assoc.

Extension ▬▬▬

Connections Suppose you invest $5000 at 8% simple interest. How many years will it take to accumulate $10,000 if you reinvest the interest each year?   **10 years** Discuss what formula you would use. Can you write a procedure to solve this equation?

Tech Prep

Medical Assistant Students who are interested in medicine may wish to do further research on the data given in Exercise 56 and explore the potential growth of this career. For more information on tech prep, see the *Teacher's Handbook*.

Properties of Real Numbers

What YOU'LL LEARN

- To determine the sets of numbers to which a given number belongs, and
- to use the properties of real numbers to simplify expressions.

Why IT'S IMPORTANT

You can use the properties of real numbers to evaluate expressions and solve equations.

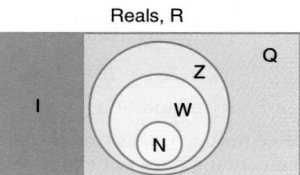

INTEGRATION

Statistics

Tables, charts, and graphs are used to represent data in a manner that is easy to read and understand.

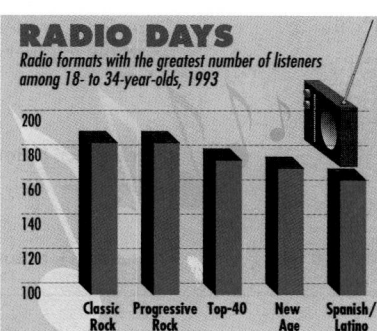

RADIO DAYS
Radio formats with the greatest number of listeners among 18- to 34-year-olds, 1993

Source: American Demographics

POPULAR SPORTS ACTIVITIES
Top sports of Americans 7 years and older, 1994
Participation (in millions):

70.8 — Exercising/Walking
60.3 — Swimming
49.8 — Bicycling
45.7 — Fishing
43.8 — Exercising with Equipment

Source: National Sporting Goods Association

Both of the figures above use numbers to convey their message to the reader. All of the numbers that you use in everyday life are **real numbers.** Each real number corresponds to exactly one point on the number line, and every point on the number line represents exactly one real number.

$$-5 \quad -4 \quad -3 \quad -2 \quad -1 \quad 0 \quad 1 \quad 2 \quad 3 \quad 4 \quad 5$$

Every real number can be classified as either **rational** or **irrational.** A rational number can be expressed as a ratio $\frac{m}{n}$, where m and n are integers and n is not zero. The decimal form of a rational number is either a terminating or repeating decimal. Some examples of rational numbers are $\frac{1}{3}$, $1.\overline{34}$, 5.8, -6, and 0. Any real number that is not rational is irrational. $\sqrt{2}$, π, and $\sqrt{7}$ are irrational numbers.

The sets of natural numbers, $\{1, 2, 3, 4, 5, \ldots\}$, whole numbers, $\{0, 1, 2, 3, 4, \ldots\}$, and integers, $\{\ldots, -3, -2, -1, 0, 1, 2, \ldots\}$ are all subsets of the rational numbers.

Reals, R

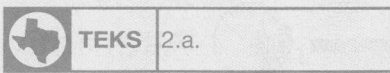

The Venn diagram at the left shows the relationship among these sets of numbers.

R = reals   Q = rationals
I = irrationals   Z = integers
W = wholes   N = naturals

TEKS 2.a.

1-2 LESSON NOTES

NCTM Standards: 1–5, 14

Instructional Resources

- Study Guide Master 1-2
- Practice Master 1-2
- Enrichment Master 1-2
- Assessment and Evaluation Masters, p. 16
- Multicultural Activity Masters, p. 2

Transparency 1-2A contains the 5-Minute Check for this lesson; **Transparency 1-2B** contains a teaching aid for this lesson.

Recommended Pacing	
Standard Pacing	Day 3 of 12
Honors Pacing	Day 3 of 12
Block Scheduling*	Day 2 of 6 (along with Lesson 1-3)

*For more information on pacing and possible lesson plans, refer to the *Block Scheduling Booklet.*

1 FOCUS

5-Minute Check
(over Lesson 1-1)

Find the value of each expression.

1. $3^2 - 2(4 - 2)$ 5
2. $[(8 + 3) \times 3 - 12] \div 7$ 3
3. $\frac{5(12 + 6)}{10} - 2^2$ 5

Evaluate each expression if $a = 0.5$, $b = 6$, and $c = -3$.

4. $ac - bc + a$ 17
5. $a(b + c) + ab^2$ 19.5

Motivating the Lesson

Questioning Give examples of irrational numbers. Have students determine whether addition, subtraction, multiplication, and division of two irrational numbers always results in an irrational number. If not, give a counterexample.

Teaching Tip Note that any number that is not a perfect square has an irrational square root.

In-Class Examples

For Example 1
Find the value of each expression. Then name the sets of numbers to which each value belongs.

a. -5.2×10 -52; Z, Q, R

b. $\sqrt{25 - 4}$
$\sqrt{21}$ or about 4.58; I, R

For Example 2
Name the property illustrated by each equation.

a. $(3 + a) + 2b = 3 + (a + 2b)$
associative (+)

b. $3(x + 8) = (x + 8)3$
commutative ($\times$)

Example 1 Find the value of each expression. Then name the sets of numbers to which each value belongs.

a. $\sqrt{17}$
$\sqrt{17} = 4.1231056 \ldots$ reals (R), irrationals (I)

b. $8 \div 4$
$8 \div 4 = 2$ reals (R), rationals (Q), integers (Z), whole numbers (W), natural numbers (N)

c. 0.25×0
$0.25 \times 0 = 0$ reals (R), rationals (Q), integers (Z), whole numbers (W)

d. $10 - 25$
$10 - 25 = -15$ reals (R), rationals (Q), integers (Z)

e. $6 \div 10$
$6 \div 10 = 0.6$ or $\frac{3}{5}$ reals (R), rationals (Q)

Operations with real numbers have several important properties. The chart below summarizes the properties of real numbers for addition and multiplication.

—a is read "the opposite of a".

For any real numbers a, b, and c:		
	Addition	**Multiplication**
Commutative	$a + b = b + a$	$a \cdot b = b \cdot a$
Associative	$(a + b) + c = a + (b + c)$	$(a \cdot b) \cdot c = a \cdot (b \cdot c)$
Identity	$a + 0 = a = 0 + a$	$a \cdot 1 = a = 1 \cdot a$
Inverse	$a + (-a) = 0 = (-a) + a$	If $a \neq 0$, then $a \cdot \frac{1}{a} = 1 = \frac{1}{a} \cdot a$.
Distributive	$a(b + c) = ab + ac$ and $(b + c)a = ba + ca$	

Example 2 Name the property illustrated by each equation.

a. $(3 + 4a)2 = 2(3 + 4a)$
commutative property of multiplication
The commutative property says that the order in which you multiply does not change the product.

b. $62 + (38 + 75) = (62 + 38) + 75$
associative property of addition
The associative property says that the way you group three numbers when adding does not change their sum.

 ## Alternative Learning Styles

Visual Give students a rectangular piece of paper that measures 11 centimeters by 5 centimeters. Ask them to use the rectangle to illustrate the distributive property. For example, you can find the area of the rectangle in two different ways.

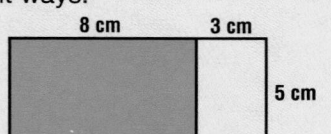

Method 1: Multiply the length by the width.
$A = 5(8 + 3)$
$ = 5(11)$
$ = 55$

Method 2: Add the areas of the smaller rectangles.
$A = 5(8) + 5(3)$
$ = 40 + 15$
$ = 55$

Example **Name the additive inverse and multiplicative inverse for each number.**

a. $\frac{3}{8}$

Since $\frac{3}{8} + \left(-\frac{3}{8}\right) = 0$, the additive inverse of $\frac{3}{8}$ is $-\frac{3}{8}$.

Since $\left(\frac{3}{8}\right)\left(\frac{8}{3}\right) = 1$, the multiplicative inverse of $\frac{3}{8}$ is $\frac{8}{3}$.

b. -2.5

Since $-2.5 + 2.5 = 0$, the additive inverse of -2.5 is 2.5.

To find the multiplicative inverse of -2.5, find $\frac{1}{-2.5}$.

Enter: 1 [÷] 2.5 [+/−] [=]   *−0.4*

The multiplicative inverse of -2.5 is -0.4.

You can use properties to simplify algebraic expressions.

Example **4** **Simplify $4(2b - 6c) + 2(3b + c)$.**

$4(2b - 6c) + 2(3b + c)$

$\quad = 4(2b) - 4(6c) + 2(3b) + 2(c)$ *Use the distributive property.*

$\quad = 8b - 24c + 6b + 2c$ *Multiply.*

$\quad = 14b - 22c$ *Combine like terms.*

The distributive property is often used in real-world applications.

Example **5** Taco Bell® is offering its new Border Lights™ Light Taco Supreme for a special introductory price of 99¢ to attract customers who would like a healthier choice. The number of Light Taco Supremes sold each day for 5 days in one restaurant are given in the table below. What was the average income from the sale of the tacos during each day?

APPLICATION
Consumerism

Monday	Tuesday	Wednesday	Thursday	Friday
182	341	246	303	378

An average is calculated by adding to find the total amount, then dividing the total amount by the number of items. In this case, it would be the total dollar amount divided by the number of days, 5.

There are two ways to find the total dollar amount.

Method 1

Multiply each daily amount by 0.99 and then add.

$T = 0.99(182) + 0.99(341) + 0.99(246) + 0.99(303) + 0.99(378)$

$\quad = 180.18 + 337.59 + 243.54 + 299.97 + 374.22$

$\quad = 1435.50$

(continued on the next page)

Teaching Tip Point out that a number and its multiplication inverse have the same sign.

In-Class Examples

For Example 3
Name the additive inverse and multiplicative inverse for each number.

a. $-\frac{2}{3}$ $\frac{2}{3}, -\frac{3}{2}$

b. 1.3 $-1.3, \frac{10}{13}$

For Example 4
Simplify $2(2x - 3y) - 8(x + 4y)$.
$-4x - 38y$

For Example 5
José makes \$8 an hour mowing lawns. He worked 2 hours one day and 3.5 hours the next day. How much did he earn for both days? **\$44**

GLENCOE *Technology*

Interactive Mathematics Tools Software

This multimedia software provides an interactive lesson with a game where students find the difference between two positive and/or negative integers. A **Computer Journal** gives students an opportunity to write about what they have learned.

For Windows & Macintosh

Check for Understanding

Exercises 1–19 are designed to help you assess your students' understanding through reading, writing, speaking, and modeling. You should work through Exercises 1–5 with your students and then monitor their work on Exercises 6–19.

Additional Answers

2. Natural numbers belong in the set of whole numbers, which are in the set of integers, which are in the set of rational numbers.

3. Sample answer: Rational numbers: $30, -8, \frac{1}{2}, \sqrt{9}, 4\frac{1}{3}$; Irrational numbers: $\sqrt{2}, \pi, \sqrt{11}, \sqrt{15}, \sqrt{17}$

4. Use the commutative property when you can switch the order of the numbers around the operation without affecting the answer. Use the associative property when you can move the parentheses or regroup the numbers in a given problem without affecting the answer.

Study Guide Masters, p. 2

1-2
NAME_____ DATE _____
Study Guide
Student Edition Pages 14–20

Properties of Real Numbers

You should be familiar with the following sets of numbers.
- natural numbers: $N = \{1, 2, 3, 4, 5, 6, 7, 8, 9, 10, \cdots\}$
- whole numbers: $W = \{0, 1, 2, 3, 4, 5, 6, 7, 8, 9, 10, \cdots\}$
- integers: $Z = \{\cdots, -4, -3, -2, -1, 0, 1, 2, 3, 4, \cdots\}$
- rational numbers: $Q = \{$all numbers that can be expressed in the form $\frac{m}{n}$, where m and n are integers and n is not zero$\}$
- irrational numbers: $I = \{$all nonterminating, nonrepeating decimals$\}$
- real numbers: $R = \{$all rationals and irrationals$\}$

You should also be familiar with the basic properties that hold for addition and multiplication of real numbers.

Property	Addition	Multiplication
Commutative	$a + b = b + a$	$a \cdot b = b \cdot a$
Associative	$(a + b) + c = a + (b + c)$	$(a \cdot b) \cdot c = a \cdot (b \cdot c)$
Identity	$a + 0 = a = 0 + a$	$a \cdot 1 = a = 1 \cdot a$
Inverse	$a + (-a) = 0 = (-a) + a$	If a is not zero, then $a \cdot \frac{1}{a} = 1 = \frac{1}{a} \cdot a$
Distributive	Addition and Multiplication $a(b + c) = ab + ac$ and $(b + c)a = ba + ca$	

For any real numbers a, b, and c.

Name the sets of numbers to which each number belongs.

1. $-\frac{11}{3}$ Q, R 2. $-\sqrt{81}$ Z, Q, R 3. -12 Z, Q, R
4. 0 W, Z, Q, R 5. 7.22 Q, R 6. $\sqrt{15}$ I, R
7. $\sqrt{25}$ N, W, Z, Q, R 8. π I, R 9. $-4.\overline{17}$ Q, R
10. 20 N, W, Z, Q, R 11. $5.\overline{44}$ Q, R 12. $\frac{3}{5}$ Q, R

State the property illustrated in each equation.

13. $7 + (2.4 + 9) = (7 + 2.4) + 9$ associative +
14. $4(1 + 7) = 4(1) + 4(7)$ distributive
15. $9(3 - 5) = (3 - 5)9$ commutative × 16. $(19a + 11b) + 0 = 19a + 11b$ identity +
17. $1 = 11^2 \cdot \frac{1}{11^2}$ inverse × 18. $(8 + (-8)) - 9 = 0 - 9$ inverse +

Simplify each expression.

19. $9x + 3y + 12y - 0.9x$ 8.1x + 15y 20. $2a + 7b + 8a - 3b + 4a$ 14a + 4b
21. $10(6g + 3h) + 4(5g - h)$ 80g + 26h 22. $9(7e - 4f) - 0.6(e + 5f)$ 62.4e − 39f
23. $2(15 + 45c) + \frac{5}{6}(12 + 18c)$ 40 + 105c 24. $4(20 - 4p) - \frac{3}{4}(4 - 16p)$ 77 − 4p

---

Method 2

Add the daily amounts and then multiply the total by 0.99.

$T = 0.99(182 + 341 + 246 + 303 + 378)$
$= 0.99(1450)$
$= 1435.50$

Now find the mean or average by dividing the total by 5.

$1435.50 \div 5 = 287.10$

The average daily income from Light Taco Supremes was $287.10.

The two methods of calculating the average income illustrate the distributive property of multiplication over addition.

CHECK FOR UNDERSTANDING

Communicating Mathematics

1. It is irrational because it is neither a repeating nor a terminating decimal.

Study the lesson. Then complete the following. 2–4. See margin.

1. **Explain** how you know π is an irrational number given that the digits of π never end and never repeat a pattern.

2. **Examine** the Venn diagram on page 13 that shows the relationships among all real numbers. Explain why natural numbers are enclosed by whole numbers, integers, and rationals.

3. **List** five rational numbers and five irrational numbers.

4. **Explain** the difference between the commutative and associative properties.

MODELING MATHEMATICS

5. You can model algebraic expressions with algebra tiles. The unit tile $\boxed{1}$₁ represents 1. The x tile $\boxed{}$₁ represents x.
   a. Model $x + 1$ with algebra tiles. a–c. See students' work.
   b. Model $2(x + 1)$ with algebra tiles.
   c. Use algebra tiles to show that $2(x + 1) = 2x + 2$.

Guided Practice

6. 1;R,Q,Z,W,N
7. −1;R,Q,Z
8. 1.5;R,Q
9. 7.550;R,I

Find the value of each expression. Then name the sets of numbers to which each value belongs.

6. $7 - 6$ 7. $6 - 7$ 8. $6 \div 2^2$ 9. $\sqrt{49 + 8}$

Determine whether each statement is true or false. If false, give an example of a number that shows the statement is false.

10. Every integer is a whole number. false; −1
11. Every whole number is an integer. true

Name the property illustrated by each equation.

12. comm. (×)
13. additive inverse
14. comm. (+)

12. $8(4) = 4(8)$ 13. $2 + (-2) = 0$ 14. $6 + (0 + 4) = 6 + (4 + 0)$

Name the additive inverse and the multiplicative inverse of each number.

15. 7 $-7, \frac{1}{7}$ 16. $-\frac{2}{3}$ $\frac{2}{3}; -\frac{3}{2}$

Simplify each expression.

17. $2(4c + 5d) + 6(2c - d)$ 20c + 4d 18. $3x + 5y + 7x - 3y$ 10x + 2y

16 Chapter 1 *Analyzing Equations and Inequalities*

Reteaching

Classification Which of the numbers $2, 5.2, -3, -0.6, \frac{9}{17}, 0, \sqrt{5}, -\frac{7}{5}, \pi, \frac{\sqrt{7}}{2}, \frac{\pi}{3}, 0.4, 0.\overline{28}, \sqrt{9}$ are:

a. natural numbers? 2
b. whole numbers? 2, 0
c. integers? 2, −3, 0, $\sqrt{9}$

d. rational numbers? 2, 5.2, −3, −0.6, $\frac{9}{17}$, 0, $-\frac{7}{5}$, 0.4, 0.$\overline{28}$, $\sqrt{9}$
e. irrational numbers? $\sqrt{5}$, π, $\frac{\sqrt{7}}{2}$, $\frac{\pi}{3}$
f. real numbers? all

19. Baby-sitting Maria baby-sat for 5 hours on Friday night and 7 hours on Saturday night to earn money for band camp. She charges $3 per hour. How much money did Maria earn for band camp? $36.00

EXERCISES

Practice

Find the value of each expression. Then name the sets of numbers to which each value belongs. 20–31. See margin.

20. $2.9 + 3.7$ **21.** $-56 \div 8$ **22.** $58 \div 100$ **23.** -4.2×10

24. $1 - 5$ **25.** $\sqrt{25} - 6$ **26.** $3^3 + 2^2$ **27.** $1\frac{1}{2} + \frac{3}{4}$

28. $10 \times (-3.9)$ **29.** $4 \div 2^3$ **30.** $-81 \div (-9)$ **31.** $\sqrt{64} + 3$

Determine whether each statement is *true* or *false*. If *false,* give an example of a number that shows the statement is false.

32. Every real number is irrational. false; 1.5

33. Every integer is a rational number. true

34. Every rational number is an integer. false; 1.5

35. Every irrational number is a real number. true

36. Every natural number is an integer. true

37. Every real number is either a rational number or an irrational number. true

Name the property illustrated by each equation.

38. distributive

39. comm. (+)

41. add. inv.

42. distributive

38. $m(4 - 3) = m \cdot 4 - m \cdot 3$ **39.** $(5 + 9) + 13 = 13 + (5 + 9)$

40. $s + t + 0 = s + t$ add. iden.   **41.** $(a + b) + [-(a + b)] = 0$

42. $(3 + 9) \cdot 5 = 3(5) + 9(5)$ **43.** $(48)3 = 3(48)$ comm. ($\times$)

44. $\frac{4}{5}(1) = \frac{4}{5}$ mult. iden.   **45.** $\left(\frac{1}{4}\right)4 = 1$ mult. inv.

Name the additive inverse and the multiplicative inverse of each number.

46. 8 $-8; \frac{1}{8}$ **47.** 0.2 $-0.2; 5$ **48.** -1.25 $1.25; -0.8$

49. -1 $1; -1$ **50.** $\frac{5}{6}$ $-\frac{5}{6}; \frac{6}{5}$ **51.** $-3\frac{5}{7}$ $3\frac{5}{7}; \frac{7}{26}$

53. $32c - 46d$

54. $4 + 10x$

55. $\frac{11}{6}x - \frac{7}{4}y$

56. $12 + 20a$

57. $4.4m - 2.9n$

Simplify each expression.

52. $6x - 2y - 3x + 2y$ $3x$ **53.** $4(14c - 10d) - 6(d + 4c)$

54. $\frac{1}{2}(17 - 4x) - \frac{3}{4}(6 - 16x)$ **55.** $\frac{3}{4}(2x - 5y) + \frac{1}{2}\left(\frac{2}{3}x + 4y\right)$

56. $\frac{1}{4}(12 + 20a) + \frac{3}{4}(12 + 20a)$ **57.** $7(0.2m + 0.3n) + 5(0.6m - n)$

Lesson 1–2   Properties of Real Numbers   **17**

Extension

Reasoning Below is a proof that $2.\overline{9} = 3$. Does this statement contradict the statement "each real number corresponds to exactly one point on the number line"? Let $n = 2.\overline{9}$.

$$
\begin{aligned}
10n &= 29.\overline{9} \\
-n &= -2.\overline{9} \\
\hline
9n &= 27 \\
n &= 3
\end{aligned}
$$

Assignment Guide

Core: 21–57 odd, 58, 59, 61–71
Enriched: 20–56 even, 58–71

For **Extra Practice**, see p. 876.

The red A, B, and C flags, printed only in the Teacher's Wraparound Edition, indicate the level of difficulty of the exercises.

Additional Answers

20. 6.6; R, Q
21. -7; R, Q, Z
22. 0.58; R, Q
23. -42; R, Q, Z
24. -4; R, Q, Z
25. -1; R, Q, Z
26. 31; R, Q, Z, W, N
27. $2\frac{1}{4}$; R, Q
28. -39; R, Q, Z
29. $\frac{1}{2}$; R, Q
30. 9; R, Q, Z, W, N
31. $\sqrt{67}$; R, I

Practice Masters, p. 2

1-2 NAME_____ DATE _____

Practice Student Edition
Pages 14–20

Properties of Real Numbers

Name the sets of numbers to which each number belongs.

1. 6425 N, W, Z, Q, R   **2.** $\sqrt{7}$ I, R   **3.** π I, R   **4.** 0 W, Z, Q, R

5. $\sqrt{\frac{25}{36}}$ Q, R   **6.** $-\sqrt{16}$ Z, Q, R   **7.** -35 Z, Q, R   **8.** -31.8 Q, R

Name the property illustrated by each equation.

9. $5x + (4y + 3x) = 5x + (3x + 4y)$ commutative +   **10.** $7x + (9x + 8) = (7x + 9x) + 8$ associative +

11. $5(3x + y) = 5(3x + 1y)$ identity $\times$ **12.** $7n + 2n = (7 + 2)n$ distributive

13. $3(2x)y = 3 \cdot 2(xy)$ associative $\times$ **14.** $3x \cdot 2y = 3 \cdot 2 \cdot x \cdot y$ associative $\times$

15. $(6 + -6)y = 0y$ inverse +   **16.** $\frac{1}{4} \cdot 4y = 1y$ inverse $\times$

17. $5(x + y) = 5x + 5y$ distributive   **18.** $4n + 0 = 4n$ identity +

Simplify each expression.

19. $5x - 3y - 2x + 3y$ $3x$ **20.** $-11a - 13b + 7a - 3b$ $-4a - 16b$

21. $8xy - 7y - (3 - 6y)$ $8xy - y - 3$ **22.** $4c - 2c^2 - (4c + 2c^2)$ $-4c^2$

23. $3(r - 10s) - 4(7s + 2r)$ $-5r - 58s$ **24.** $\frac{1}{5}(10a - 4) + \frac{1}{2}(8 + 4a)$ $4a + \frac{16}{5}$

25. $2x(4 - 2x + y) - 5x(y^2 + x - y)$ $-5xy^2 + 7xy - 9x^2 + 8x$ **26.** $\frac{5}{6}\left(\frac{3}{10}x + 12y\right) - \frac{1}{4}(2x - 3y)$ $\frac{-x + 43y}{4}$

Closing Activity

Modeling Have students cut paper to represent examples of reals, rationals, wholes, integers, and naturals. Are there examples of some of these groups that they cannot represent? Can they represent any irrationals? Why or why not?

Chapter 1, Quiz A (Lessons 1-1 and 1-2), is available in the *Assessment and Evaluation Masters,* p. 16.

Additional Answer

59c. This method works because the difference between a number and the number whose digits are reversed is 9.

Enrichment Masters, p. 2

NAME_____ DATE _____
1-2   Enrichment   Student Edition
                                      Pages 14–20

Equivalence Relations

A relation R on a set A is an *equivalence relation* if it has the following properties.

Reflexive Property   For any element *a* of set A, *a* R *a*.
Symmetric Property   For all elements *a* and *b* of set A, if *a* R *b*, then *b* R *a*.
Transitive Property   For all elements *a*, *b*, and *c* of set A, if *a* R *b* and *b* R *c*, then *a* R *c*.

Equality on the set of all real numbers is reflexive, symmetric, and transitive. Therefore, it is an equivalence relation.

In each of the following, a relation and a set are given. Write yes if the relation is an equivalence relation on the given set. If it is not, tell which of the properties it fails to exhibit.

1. <, {all numbers} no; reflexive, symmetric

2. ≅, {all triangles in a plane} yes

3. is the sister of, {all women in Tennessee} no; reflexive

4. ≥, {all numbers} no; symmetric

5. is a factor of, {all nonzero integers} no; symmetric

6. ~, {all polygons in a plane} yes

7. is the spouse of, {all people in Roanoke, Virginia} no; reflexive, transitive

8. ⊥, {all lines in a plane} no; reflexive, transitive

9. is a multiple of, {all integers} no; symmetric

10. is the square of, {all numbers} no; reflexive, symmetric, transitive

11. ||, {all lines in a plane} no; reflexive

12. has the same color eyes as, {all members of the Cleveland Symphony Orchestra} yes

13. is the greatest integer not greater than, {all numbers} no; reflexive, symmetric, transitive

14. is the greatest integer not greater than, {all integers} yes

---

Critical Thinking

58b. $\frac{1}{a}$; multiplicative inverse of *a*

58. Use the properties of real numbers to answer these questions.
 a. If $a + b = a$, what is the value of *b*? 0
 b. If $ab = 1$, what is the value of *b*? What is *b* called?
 c. If $ab = a$, what is the value of *b*? 1

Applications and Problem Solving

59. Accounting A number is divisible by 9 if the sum of its digits is divisible by 9. This fact is used by accountants to check figures in double entry books. If the totals of the credit and debit columns do not match, and the difference between the totals is divisible by 9, then the error was probably made when two digits were reversed in one of the entries. Explain whether the errors in the following might have come from reversing the digits of an entry. **c. See margin.**
 a. credit = \$638, debit = \$577 no
 b. credit = \$1050, debit = \$1095 yes
 c. Why does this error check work?

60. Geometry Find the area of the tennis court at the right in two different ways. **Methods will vary, but $A = 2808$ ft².**

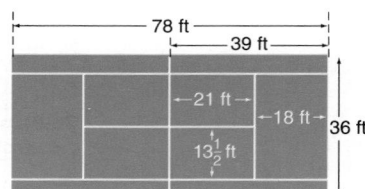

Mixed Review

Find the value of each expression. (Lesson 1–1)

61. $0.2(0.5 + 2.2) \div 6$ **0.09**

62. $8 - [21 - (3 \cdot 5)]$ **2**

63. $3(13 - 7) + (7 - 5)2$ **22**

64. $17 - [22 \div (21 - 2(5))]$ **15**

65. Evaluate the expression $\frac{3a + 4c}{b}$ if $a = -3$, $b = 2$, and $c = 0.5$. (Lesson 1–1) **−3.5**

66. Evaluate the expression $d - [c \div (a - b(a))]$ if $a = -1$, $b = 5$, $c = 12$, and $d = 17$. (Lesson 1–1) **14**

67. Human Body Humans blink their eyes about once every 5 seconds. About how many times do humans blink their eyes in two hours? (Lesson 1–1) **1440 times**

68. Geometry The formula for the area of a trapezoid is $A = \frac{h}{2}(b_1 + b_2)$. Find the area of a trapezoid with height 3 and bases 4 and 8. (Lesson 1–1) **18**

69. Use the formula $I = prt$ to find the simple interest if $p = \$2500$, $r = 7.37\%$, and $t = 4$ years. (Lesson 1–1) **\$737**

70. 492 yd, 484.67 yd

70. Buildings The Sears Tower, located in Chicago, Illinois, is the tallest building in the United States. It is 1454 feet tall, only 22 feet shorter than the Petronas Towers in Kuala Lumpur, Malaysia, the tallest buildings in the world. Use the formula $Y = \frac{F}{3}$ to find the height of both buildings in yards if *Y* is the height in yards and *F* is the height in feet. (Lesson 1–1)

71. Evaluate $12 + 18 \div 6 + 7$. (Lesson 1–1) **22**

Petronas Towers

Classroom Vignette

"At the beginning of the school year, I ask students to write, design, illustrate, and make a pop-up book using a math theme. A book of real-number properties is especially effective. This project allows students to be creative while they learn and enjoy math. I require a minimum of four different pop-ups."

Carol Baden
The Galloway School
Atlanta, Georgia

Carol Baden

Integration: Statistics
Graphs and Measures of Central Tendency

APPLICATION
Education

What YOU'LL LEARN

- To represent and interpret data using line plots and stem-and-leaf plots, and
- to find and use the median, mode, and mean to interpret data.

Why IT'S IMPORTANT

Measures of central tendency can help you easily describe a set of data.

CAREER CHOICES

Statisticians collect, analyze, and present data for surveys and experiments. Their work is very important in the fields of economics, biology, engineering, medicine, and psychology.

A bachelor's degree with a major in statistics or mathematics is required to enter the field.

For more information, contact:
American Statistics Association
1429 Duke St.
Alexandria, VA 22314

The average salaries for teachers in 1993–94 are listed in the table below. How do teacher salaries in your state compare with other states?

\multicolumn{8}{c}{Average Teacher Salaries (1993–94)}							
State	Salary	State	Salary	State	Salary	State	Salary
AL	$28,705	IN	$35,711	NE	$29,564	SC	$29,566
AK	$46,581	IA	$30,760	NV	$33,955	SD	$25,059
AZ	$31,800	KS	$33,919	NH	$34,121	TN	$30,514
AR	$27,873	KY	$31,640	NJ	$44,693	TX	$30,519
CA	$40,289	LA	$26,285	NM	$27,922	UT	$28,056
CO	$33,826	ME	$30,996	NY	$45,772	VT	$34,517
CT	$49,910	MD	$39,463	NC	$29,727	VA	$33,063
DE	$37,469	MA	$40,852	ND	$25,506	WA	$35,855
FL	$31,944	MI	$42,500	OH	$35,684	WV	$30,549
GA	$30,527	MN	$36,146	OK	$27,009	WI	$35,990
HI	$36,564	MS	$25,153	OR	$37,590	WY	$30,952
ID	$27,756	MO	$30,324	PA	$42,411		
IL	$39,387	MT	$28,200	RI	$39,261		

Source: NEA Research

The answer to this question is not immediately obvious from the table. You are familiar with statistical graphs such as *bar graphs, line graphs,* and *circle graphs* that are used to organize and illustrate data. Another way to display statistical data such as that provided in the table above is on a number line called a **line plot.** Like other statistical graphs, line plots can help you see patterns and variability in data.

To make a line plot, determine a scale that includes all of the data and appropriate intervals. Then plot each number using a symbol to represent the data. The teacher salaries data ranges from 25,059 to 49,910. Round each salary to the nearest thousand. Let's use a scale of 25,000 to 50,000 with intervals of 2500 and denote each salary with an "×."

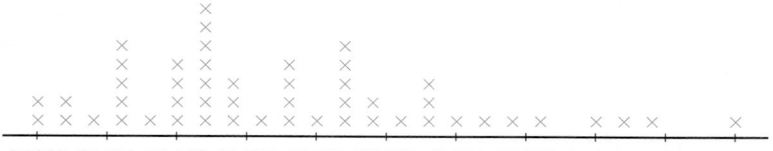

Locate your state's data on the line plot. Now it should be easy to see how teachers' salaries in your state compare with those in other states.

CAREER CHOICES

The average annual salary for statisticians in the federal government was $51,893 in 1993. Statisticians who hold advanced degrees and work in private industry generally have higher salaries.

NCTM Standards: 1–4, 10

Instructional Resources
- Study Guide Master 1-3
- Practice Master 1-3
- Enrichment Master 1-3
- Real-World Applications, 2

Transparency 1-3A contains the 5-Minute Check for this lesson; **Transparency 1-3B** contains a teaching aid for this lesson.

\multicolumn{2}{c}{Recommended Pacing}	
Standard Pacing	Day 4 of 12
Honors Pacing	Day 4 of 12
Block Scheduling*	Day 2 of 6 (along with Lesson 1-2)

*For more information on pacing and possible lesson plans, refer to the *Block Scheduling Booklet.*

1 FOCUS

5-Minute Check
(over Lesson 1-2)

1. Evaluate $\sqrt{25}$. To which sets of numbers does it belong? **N, W, Z, Q, R**
2. To which sets of numbers does $\frac{2}{3}$ belong? **Q, R**

Name the property illustrated by each equation.

3. $a + (4 + c) = (a + 4) + c$
   associative (+)
4. $3(4 + 0.2) = 3(4) + 3(0.2)$
   distributive
5. Simplify $(2c)(3d) + c + 5cd + 3c^2$. $11cd + c + 3c^2$

Motivating the Lesson
Hands-On Activity Bring a foliage plant to class. Ask students what the relationship is between the stems and the leaves. Develop the concept that, although the leaves may be different, several may come off the same stem.

Teaching Tip In Example 1, encourage students to plot the numbers as they appear in the data and then reorder the data in ascending or descending order in a second stem-and-leaf plot.

In-Class Examples

For Example 1
Each student in Mrs. Fogg's class walks to school. The times, in minutes, for each student are 27, 25, 5, 23, 7, 18, 23, 13, 14, 8, 10, 17, 12, 19, 19, 30, 18, 19, 14, 23, 9, 15, 23, 13, 29, 16, 27, 19, 22, 15, 16, 33. Make a stem-and-leaf plot of the times.

Stem	Leaf
0	5 7 8 9
1	0 2 3 3 4 4 5 5 6 6 7
•	8 8 9 9 9 9
2	2 3 3 3 3 5 7 7 9
3	0 3

$2|2 = 22$ minutes

For Example 2
Make a back-to-back stem-and-leaf plot of the percent of TV households viewing network programs and special programs.

Top 5 Regularly Scheduled Network Programs, 12/95	% of TV Households
Seinfeld	27.7
Home Improvement	27.3
Frasier	24.6
Friends	23.9
Coach	22.1

Top 5 TV Specials, 12/95	% of TV Households
Rudolph the Red-Nosed Reindeer	23.1
National Geographic: Cyclone	21.8
Football: Raiders vs. Chargers	21.6
NBC Movie: Shadow of a Doubt	20.4
NBC Movie: Visitors of the Night	18.7

Network		Stem	Specials	
0.3	0.7	27		
	0.6	24		
	0.9	23	0.1	
	0.1	22		
		21	0.8	0.6
		20	0.4	
		18	0.7	

$|27|0.3 = 27.3\%$

A **stem-and-leaf plot** can also be used to display data in a compact way. When making a stem-and-leaf plot, each item of data is separated into two parts. The *stems* usually consist of the digits in the greatest common place value of each item of data. The *leaves* contain the other digits of each item of data. For example, if the greatest common place value is thousands, then the stem for 1573 is 1, and the leaf is 573.

If data values have many digits, you may want to round each item of data before you plot it in a stem-and-leaf plot. This way each leaf will have only one digit. If 1573 is rounded to 1600, then the stem is 1 and the leaf is 6.

Example  **① Refer to the application at the beginning of the lesson. Make a stem-and-leaf plot of the rounded salaries.**

APPLICATION
Education

Round each item of data to the nearest thousand.
So, using rounded data, $3|0 = 29,500$ to $30,499$, inclusive.

Stem	Leaf
2	
•	5 5 6 6 7 8 8 8 8 8 9
3	0 0 0 0 1 1 1 1 1 1 1 2 2 2 3 4 4 4 4
•	5 6 6 6 6 6 7 7 8 9 9 9
4	0 1 2 3 3
•	5 6 7
5	0

To make the plot easier to interpret, the stems have been broken into two parts. $4| = \$40,000$ to $\$44,000$ and $\cdot| = \$45,000$ to $\$49,000$

A **back-to-back stem-and-leaf plot** is sometimes used to compare two sets of data or rounded values of the same set of data. In a back-to-back plot, the same stem is used for the leaves of both plots.

Example  **② The number of Republicans and Democrats in the U.S. Senate from 1965–1995 is given in the table below.**
a. Make a back-to-back stem-and-leaf plot of the data.
b. Compare the number of Republican and Democratic senators since 1965.

CONNECTION
Civics

fabulous
FIRSTS

Nydia M. Velazquez (1953–)

In 1992, Nydia Velazquez became the first Puerto Rican woman elected to the U.S. House of Representatives. She earned a master's degree from New York University and served on the City Council of New York City.

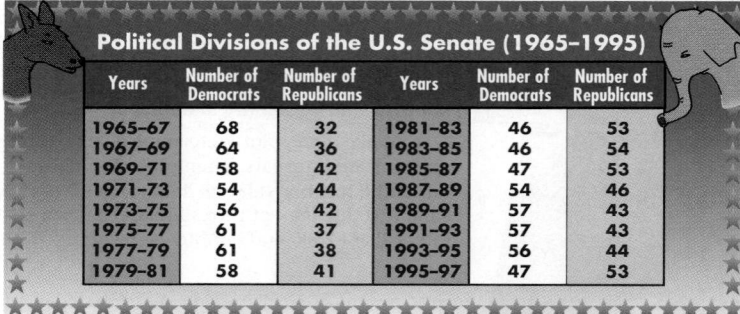

Political Divisions of the U.S. Senate (1965–1995)

Years	Number of Democrats	Number of Republicans	Years	Number of Democrats	Number of Republicans
1965–67	68	32	1981–83	46	53
1967–69	64	36	1983–85	46	54
1969–71	58	42	1985–87	47	53
1971–73	54	44	1987–89	54	46
1973–75	56	42	1989–91	57	43
1975–77	61	37	1991–93	57	43
1977–79	61	38	1993–95	56	44
1979–81	58	41	1995–97	47	53

Source: *World Almanac, 1995*

a.

Democrats	Stem	Republicans
	3	2 6 7 8
6 6 7 7	4	1 2 2 3 3 4 4 6
4 4 6 6 7 7 8 8	5	3 3 3 4
1 1 4 8	6	

fabulous
FIRSTS

Nydia Velazquez represents the 12th New York district in the U.S. House of Representatives.

b. The stem-and-leaf plot shows that there have usually been more Democratic senators than Republican senators. The number of Democratic senators ranged from 46 to 68, while the number of Republican senators ranged from 32 to 54.

Teaching Tip Point out that the median divides the data so that there is an equal number of values above and below it.

Sometimes it is convenient to have one number that describes a set of data. This number is called a **measure of central tendency** because it represents the center or middle of the data. The most commonly-used measures of central tendency are the **median, mode,** and **mean.**

Teaching Tip A set of data has no mode if there are no repeated data. For example, the set {0, 1, 5, 3, −2} has no mode.

Teaching Tip The term *mean* is commonly referred to as the *average* or *arithmetic mean*.

Definition of Median, Mode, and Mean	
Median:	The median of a set of data is the middle value. If there are two middle values, it is the mean of the two middle values.
Mode:	The mode of a set of data is the most frequent value. Some sets of data have multiple modes and others have no mode.
Mean:	The mean of a set of data is the sum of all the values divided by the number of values.

Example ③

APPLICATION
Consumerism

Over the years, jeans have become very popular with consumers. Some prices for these jeans are listed below. Find the median, mode, and mean prices.

$44.99	$39.99	$39.99	$27.99	$32.00	$34.99
$29.99	$32.99	$44.99	$29.99	$24.99	$44.99

Median: To find the median of the jean data, arrange the dollar values in order.

44.99 44.99 44.99 39.99 39.99 34.99 32.99 32.00 29.99 29.99 27.99 24.99

If there were an odd number of dollar values, the middle one would be the median. However, since there is an even number of dollar values, the median is the average of the two middle values, 34.99 and 32.99.

$$\text{median} = \frac{34.99 + 32.99}{2}$$
$$= \frac{67.98}{2}$$
$$= 33.99$$

The median is $33.99. Notice that the number of values that are greater than the median is the same as the number of values that are less than the median.

Mode: To find the mode of the jean data, look for the number that occurs most often. In this set, $44.99 appears three times. Thus, the mode of the data is $44.99.

Mean: To find the mean of the jean data, find the sum of the dollar values and divide by 12, the number of values in the set.

$$\text{mean} = \frac{44.99 + 44.99 + 44.99 + \ldots + 24.99}{12}$$
$$= \frac{427.89}{12}$$
$$= 35.6575$$

The mean of the data is approximately $35.66.

In-Class Example

For Example 3
Two partners in a company have salaries of $50,000 each. Of their eight employees, two earn $12,700 each, two earn $9600 each, and four earn $8700 each. Find the mean, median, and mode for the ten wages. {50,000;50,000;12,700; 12,700;9600;9600;8700; 8700;8700;8700}
mean: $17,940; median: $9600; mode: $8700

GLENCOE *Technology*

Interactive Mathematics Tools Software

This multimedia software allows students to investigate the effects of changing data on box-and-whisker plots and histograms and relationships among the mean, mode, and median. **Computer Journals** give students an opportunity to write about what they have learned.

For Windows & Macintosh

In-Class Example

For Example 4
The times that it took five students to complete a science experiment are listed in the table below. Find the mean, median, and mode.

Students	Time (minutes)
Yvette	6
Jason	8
Marta	9
Alex	12
Eric	did not finish

Since there was not a time for Eric, a mean for all five students could not be determined. The mean for the four students who completed the experiment is $\frac{35}{4}$ or 8.75 minutes. Since there was not a time that appeared most often, a mode could not be determined. The median time of 9 minutes could be determined since the times were ordered.

3 PRACTICE/APPLY

Check for Understanding
Exercises 1–9 are designed to help you assess your students' understanding through reading, writing, speaking, and modeling. You should work through Exercises 1–5 with your students and then monitor their work on Exercises 6–9.

Additional Answer
1. The number of overall scores for the floor exercises of the Buckeye Gymnastics team members is closer to the higher marks of 8.5 to 10.

As you can see, the median, mode, and mean are not always the same number. In Example 3, the mode is greater than both the median and the mean. This means that more of the jeans cost $44.99 than any other price. In this example, the mean is the most representative average of the prices. If you buy any pair of jeans in the set of data, you will pay an average of $35.66.

Extreme values are those data values that vary greatly from the central group of data values. Every data value affects the value of the mean, so when extreme values are included in a set of data, the mean may become less representative of the set. However, the values of the median and the mode are not affected by extreme values in the set.

Example ④ **APPLICATION Business**

The amounts of money spent per student in 1992 in two regions of the U.S. are listed below. Determine the mean of the values in each column. To what extent is each mean representative of the data?

Pacific States		Southwest Central States	
State	Expenditures Per Student	State	Expenditures Per Student
Alaska	$8450	Texas	$4632
California	4746	Arkansas	4031
Washington	5271	Louisiana	4354
Oregon	5913	Oklahoma	4078

Source: *World Almanac*, 1995

$$\text{mean} = \frac{8450 + 4746 + 5271 + 5913}{4}$$
$$= \frac{24,380}{4} \text{ or } 6095$$

$8450 is an extreme value. In this case, the mean is not representative of the data.

$$\text{mean} = \frac{4632 + 4031 + 4354 + 4078}{4}$$
$$= \frac{17,095}{4} \text{ or } 4273.75$$

There are no extreme values in this set. In this case, the mean is representative of the data.

CHECK FOR UNDERSTANDING

Communicating Mathematics

Study the lesson. Then complete the following. 1. See margin.

1. **Describe** what the line plot below tells you about the overall scores for the floor exercises of the Buckeye Gymnastics team members.

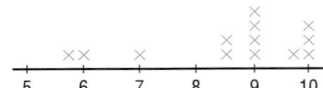

				×	
			×	×	
				×	× ×
	× ×	×		×	× ×
5	6	7	8	9	10

2. **Explain** how the number 98.6 would be plotted on a stem-and-leaf plot if 54.6 is plotted using stem 5 and leaf 4. **stem 9, leaf 8**

3. **Explain** what an extreme value does to the median. **It does not affect it.**

4. **Tell** which measure, the median, mode, or mean, must be a member of the set of data. **mode**

Reteaching

Using Models Give students a list of test scores. Have them make a stem-and-leaf plot for the data. Then have them make a line plot for the same data. Put in cutoff lines for letter grades. Finally, have students find the median, mode, and mean of the data.

MATH JOURNAL

5. Assess Yourself List the main advantages and disadvantages for using the median, mode, and mean to describe a set of data. **See students' work.**

Guided Practice

Find the median, mode, and mean for each set of data.

7. 8; no mode; 7.8

6. 0, 2, 2, 3, 4 **2; 2; 2.2**   7. 4, 5, 8, 10, 12

8. 7, 7, 7, 7, 7, 7 **7; 7; 7**

9. The table at the right shows the salary offers to graduating college students with bachelor's degrees in mathematics- and science-related fields of study in 1992.

Field of Study	Bachelor's Degree
Accounting	$27,179
Business, general	24,305
Marketing	23,914
Engineering:	
Civil	29,376
Chemical	39,203
Computer	32,848
Electrical	33,754
Mechanical	34,462
Nuclear	34,447
Petroleum	40,679
Engineering tech.	31,051
Chemistry	27,557
Mathematics	28,434
Physics	29,019
Humanities	22,941
Social sciences	21,623
Computer science	30,523

a. Make a stem-and-leaf plot of the data rounded to the nearest thousand. **See margin.**

9b. about $30,059
9c. $29,000
9d. $34,000

b. What is the mean salary?

c. What is the median salary?

d. Which is the mode salary?

e. Write three questions that can be answered using this data. **See students' work.**

EXERCISES

Practice

10–18. See margin.

Find the median, mode, and mean for each set of data.

A 10. 298, 256, 399, 388, 276   11. 3, 75, 58, 7, 34

12. 4.8, 5.7, 2.1, 2.1, 4.8, 2.1   13. 80, 50, 65, 55, 70, 65, 75, 50

14. 61, 89, 93, 102, 45, 89   15. 13.3, 15.4, 12.5, 10.7

16. 101, 192, 121, 153, 101   17. 43, 43, 55, 43, 54, 42, 51

B 18. 2301, 2324, 2000, 1999, 2738, 1947, 1989, 2004, 2938

19. Find the median, mode, and mean for the stem-and-leaf plot at the right. Round to the nearest whole number if necessary.
71; 71 and 88; 73

Stem	Leaf
5	5 5
6	0 4 5 6 7 8
7	0 1 1 1 2 2 5 6 6
8	0 5 6 8 8 8 *8|5 = 85*

C 20. In Mrs. Elizondo's algebra class, report card averages are based on 100 points. Tests and quizzes account for $\frac{2}{3}$ of the final average. Homework, classwork, and journals account for $\frac{1}{3}$ of the final average. Jennifer's test and quiz scores are 100, 100, 88, 76, 95, 88, and 93. What is Jennifer's average on tests and quizzes? **91.4**

21. The Millersburg school board is negotiating a pay raise with the teacher's union. Three of the administrators have salaries of $80,000 each. However, a majority of the teachers have salaries of about $35,000 per year.

a. You are a member of the school board and would like to show that the current salaries are reasonable. Would you quote the median, mode, or mean as the "average" salary to justify your claim? Explain.

b. You are the head of the teacher's union and maintain that a pay raise is in order. Which of the median, mode, or mean would you quote to justify your claim? Explain your reasoning. **a–b. See margin.**

Lesson 1–3 **INTEGRATION** *Statistics Graphs and Measures of Central Tendency* **23**

Classroom Vignette

"Taking an active part in their learning helps students retain the measures of central tendency. Have students gather data, such as each other's height in centimeters, and then find the mode, median, and mean."

Peggy Yountz
Cary-Grove Community High School
Cary, Illinois

Assignment Guide

Core: 11–29 odd, 30–35
Enriched: 10–22 even, 23–35

For **Extra Practice**, see p. 876.

The red A, B, and C flags, printed only in the Teacher's Wraparound Edition, indicate the level of difficulty of the exercises.

Additional Answers

9a.

Stem	Leaf
2	2 3 4 4 7 8 8 9 9
3	1 1 3 4 4 4 9
4	1

3\|1 = 31,000

10. 298; no mode; 323.4
11. 34; no mode; 35.4
12. 3.45; 2.1; 3.6
13. 65; 50 and 65; about 63.8
14. 89; 89; 79.8̄3̄
15. 12.9; no mode; 12.975
16. 121; 101; 133.6
17. 43; 43; about 47.29
18. 2004; no mode; 2248.8̄
21a. Mean; it is higher.
21b. Mode; it is lower and is what most employees make. It reflects the most representative worker.

Additional Answers

23a. The graphs of the data look different because a different scale is used in each graph.

23b. Sample answer: Graph A might be used by an employer to show an employee she cannot get a big raise. It appears that sales are steady but not rising drastically enough to warrant a big raise.

23c. Sample answer: Graph B might be used by a company owner to show a prospective buyer. It looks like there is a dramatic rise in sales.

25a.

Employed	Stem	Unemployed
	0	2 2 2 3 3
	•	3 4 4 6 6
	1	2
	2	
0 4 8	3	
6	4	
3 4 7	5	
4	6	
	7	
0 8	8	
	•	
	•	
	•	
4		14

$1|2 = 1,200,000$

Study Guide Masters, p. 3

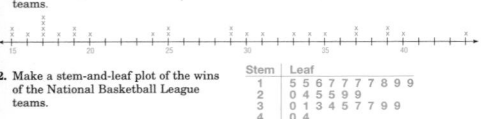

NAME_____ DATE _____

Student Edition
Pages 21–27

1-3 Study Guide

Integration: Statistics
Graphs and Measures of Central Tendency

Two ways to display data are a **stem-and-leaf plot** and a **line plot**.

Example: Display the following scores from an algebra quiz using a line plot and a stem-and-leaf plot.
82, 95, 74, 82, 95, 73, 88, 76, 90, 82

Stem	Leaf
7	3 4 6
8	2 2 2 8
9	0 5 5

The most commonly used averages are the **median, mode,** and **mean.** These terms are described in the chart below.

Term	Definition	Example for 10, 11, 12, 12, 13, 13, 15
Median	The **median** of a set of data is the middle value. If there are two middle values, it is the number halfway between them.	The median is 12.
Mode	The **mode** of a set of data is the most frequent value. Some sets of data have multiple modes and others have no mode.	There are two modes, 12 and 13.
Mean	The **mean** of a set of data is the sum of all the values divided by the number of values.	mean = (10 + 11 + 12 + 12 + 13 + 13 + 15)/7 The mean is approximately 12.3.

Each number below is the number of games won by a member team of the National Basketball League prior to the All Star Break.

39	37	34	30	25	19	16	39	29	25
19	17	18	37	33	31	20	17	17	15
44	40	35	29	24	17	15			

1. Make a line plot of the wins of National Basketball League teams.

2. Make a stem-and-leaf plot of the wins of the National Basketball League teams.

Stem	Leaf
1	5 5 6 7 7 7 7 8 9 9
2	0 4 5 5 9 9
3	0 1 3 4 5 7 7 9 9
4	0 4

Find the median, mode, and mean for each set of data.

3. {1, 4, 8, 3, 4, 5, 2, 2, 2, 5}
3.5, 2, 3.6

5. {299, 302, 500, 115, 89, 432}
300.5, no mode, 289.5

4. {95, 67, 22, 36, 67}
67, 67, 57.4

6. {23, 30, 23, 68, 91, 81, 12, 75}
49, 23, 50.375

22. Use a graphing calculator to find the mean and median for each set of data below. Access the LIST MATH function by pressing [2nd] [LIST] [▶]. Then choose 3, for mean or 4, for median. Enter the numbers by first pressing [2nd] [{] and ending with [2nd] [}], a right parenthesis, and [ENTER].

a. 3, 5, 7, 5, 3, 8, 2
4.714285714; 5

b. 45.7, 64.8, 33.2, 66.1, 54.4, 64.5
54.783; 59.45

Critical Thinking

23a–c. See margin.

23. Statistics can sometimes be misleading if an incorrect representation of the data leads to wrong conclusions. Study the two graphs below.

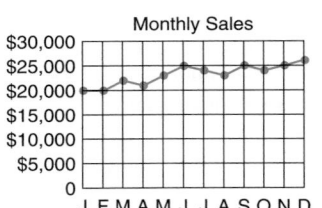

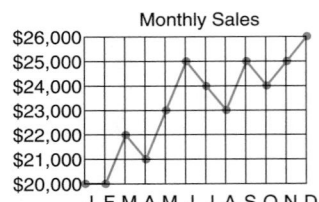

a. Explain why the graphs made from the same data look different.

b. Explain a situation where graph A might be used.

c. Explain a situation where graph B might be used.

24. Choose five whole numbers from 1 to 10 for each situation below. Numbers may be used more than once.   a–c. See students' work.

a. Construct a set of data in which the median, mode, and mean are the same number.

b. Find the median of a set of data with the greatest possible mean.

c. Construct a set of data in which the median and mean are the same number and there is no mode.

Applications and Problem Solving

25. Employment   The table below lists the employment figures for 11 states during October, 1994.   a–d. See margin.

Employment, October 1994		
State	**Employed**	**Unemployed**
California	14,411,000	1,197,000
Florida	6,384,000	445,000
Illinois	5,672,000	378,000
Massachusetts	2,979,000	205,000
Michigan	4,570,000	247,000
New Jersey	3,830,000	277,000
New York	8,048,000	561,000
North Carolina	3,443,000	180,000
Ohio	5,282,000	274,000
Pennsylvania	5,428,000	344,000
Texas	8,842,000	555,000

Source: USA Today

a. Round each number to the nearest hundred thousand. Make a back-to-back stem-and-leaf plot of the data.

b. What observations can you make from the data?

c. How could you calculate the unemployment rate for each state?

d. Calculate the approximate unemployment rate for each state.

Additional Answers

25b. Answers will vary. Sample answer: The number of employed people in these states is much higher than the number of unemployed people.

25c. Divide the number of unemployed people by the total number of employed and unemployed people.

25d.	
California	7.7%
Florida	6.5%
Illinois	6.2%
Massachusetts	6.4%
Michigan	5.1%
New Jersey	6.7%
New York	6.5%
North Carolina	5.0%
Ohio	4.9%
Pennsylvania	6.0%
Texas	5.9%

26. Advertising Cordless Camera placed an ad in the newspaper showing five videocameras for sale. The ad says, "Our videocameras average $695." The prices of the videocameras are $1200, $999, $1499, $895, $695, $1100, $1300, and $695. **a–c. See margin.**

a. Find the median, mode, and mean of the prices.

b. Which measure was Cordless Camera using in its ad? Why did they choose this measure?

c. As a consumer, which measure would you want to see advertised? Explain your reasoning.

27. See margin.

27. Business The minimum start-up costs for the fastest-growing franchises in 1993 are listed below. Find the median, mode, and mean for the costs. Which average is the most representative of the data? Explain.

Company	Business	Minimum Start-up Cost
7-Eleven Convenience Stores	convenience stores	$12,500
Subway	submarine sandwiches	38,900
Snap-On Tools	retail hardware	12,600
Maico Tools	retail hardware	42,500
McDonald's	hamburgers	varies
Chem-Dry Carpet Drapery & Upholstery Cleaning	carpet, upholstery, and drapery services	3,550
Little Caesar's Pizza	pizza	170,000
Burger King Corp.	hamburgers	73,000
Coverall North America Inc.	commercial cleaning services	3,250
Mail Boxes Etc.	postal and business services	28,180
CleanNet USA Inc.	commercial cleaning services	425
Jani-King	commercial cleaning services	2,500
Dunkin' Donuts	donuts	175,000

Source: Reprinted with permission from *Entrepreneur* Magazine, January 1994

28a. 2,150,000; 2,000,000; about 2,290,403

28. Shopping Malls The table below shows the largest U.S. shopping malls.

	Mall	Gross Leasable Area (sq ft)
1	Del Amo Fashion Center, Torrance, California	3,000,000
2	South Coast Plaza/Crystal Court, Costa Mesa, California	2,918,236
3	Mall of America, Bloomington, Minnesota	2,472,500
4	Lakewood Center Mall, Lakewood, California	2,390,000
5	Roosevelt Field Mall, Garden City, New York	2,300,000
6	Gurnee Mills, Gurnee, Illinois	2,200,000
7	The Galleria, Houston, Texas	2,100,000
8	Randall Park Mall, North Randall, Ohio	2,097,416
9	Oakbrook Shopping Center, Oak Brook, Illinois	2,006,688
10	Sawgrass Mills, Sunrise, Florida	2,000,000
10	The Woodlands Mall, The Woodlands, Texas	2,000,000
10	Woodfield, Schaumburg, Illinois	2,000,000

Source: Blackburn Marketing Service

a. Find the median, mode, and mean of the gross leasable area.

b. You are a realtor who is trying to lease mall space in different areas of the country to a large retailer. Which measure would you talk about if the customer felt that the price per square foot was expensive to lease? Explain. **Mode; it is lower.**

c. Which measure would you talk about if the customer had lots of inventory to display? Explain. **Mean; it is higher.**

Lesson 1–3   *Statistics* Graphs and Measures of Central Tendency **25**

Extension

Connections Have students refer to a page from a reading book to make a data table listing the frequency of use of each letter of the alphabet. Have students determine the mean, the median, and the mode for the set of frequencies.

Additional Answers
26a. $1049.50; $695; $1047.88
26b. Mode; it is the least expensive price.
26c. Mean; it is the most representative of the prices of the cameras.
27. $20,390; no mode; $46,867.08; The median is most representative of the data since there is such a wide range of costs.

Practice Masters, p. 3

1-3   NAME _____ DATE _____

Practice   Student Edition Pages 21–27

Integration: Statistics
Graphs and Measures of Central Tendency

The following tables give the number of games bowled and total points scored for two bowling teams for the season.

Pin Struck

Player	No. of games	Points
Bob	111	17,316
Cindy	93	11,625
Steve	87	11,832
Cheri	110	15,070
Juan	108	19,008

Bowl Downers

Player	No. of games	Points
Kiko	96	10,752
Paul	84	12,348
Clarice	111	14,319
Bethany	105	10,290
Jarrod	99	16,731

1. Make a stem-and-leaf plot of the number of games bowled by the 10 players.

Stem	Leaf
8	4 7
9	3 6 9
10	5 8
11	0 1 1

2. Who had the highest total points? Juan

3. Who had the lowest total points? Bethany

4. Find the mode of the number of games played. 111

Each number below represents the weight of a person in Mr. Miller's math class.

134 116 146 152 124 110 137 108 110 132
98 221 86 143 114 104 121 127 137 110

5. Make a line plot of the weights of the people in the class.

6. What is the weight of the heaviest person? 221

7. Which weight(s) occur most frequently? 110

8. Find the median of the data. 122.5

9. Find the mean of the data. 126.5

4 ASSESS

Closing Activity

Modeling Have students gather strips of paper of various lengths and use a ruler to determine the mean, median, and mode of the lengths of the strips.

Additional Answers

29a.

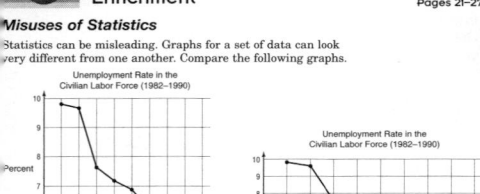

29b. 79.5; 91; 77.58

29c.

29d. They each increase by 5 since the temperature increased by 5 degrees; different.

29e. All points on the original line plot would be shifted 5 to the right to obtain the new line plot.

Enrichment Masters, p. 3

1-3   NAME_____ DATE _____
Enrichment   Student Edition
                                Pages 21–27

Misuses of Statistics

Statistics can be misleading. Graphs for a set of data can look very different from one another. Compare the following graphs.

Notice that the two graphs show the same data, but the spacing in the vertical and horizontal scales differs. Scales can be cramped or spread out to make a graph that gives a certain impression. Which graph would you use to give the impression that the unemployment rate dropped dramatically from 1983 to 1990? **the first graph**

Suppose that a car company claims, "75% of people surveyed say that our car is better than the competition." If four people were asked which car they preferred and 75% agreed, how many people thought that *Our Car* was better? **3 people**

The advertisement was misleading in other ways as well. For example, who was surveyed—were the people company employees, or impartial buyers?

Suppose an advertiser claims that 90% of all of one brand of car sold in the last 10 years are still on the road.

1. If 10,000 cars were sold, how many are   **2.** If 1000 cars were sold, how many are
still on the road? **9,000**   still on the road? **900**

3. Find an example to show how you think averages could be used in a misleading way. **See students' work.**

4. A survey of a large sample of people who own small computers revealed that 85% of the people thought the instruction manuals should be better written. A manufacturer of small computers claimed that it surveyed many of the same people and found that all of them liked their manuals. Discuss the possible discrepancy in the results. **See students' work.**

26 Chapter 1

29. Weather The average monthly temperatures for Mobile, Alabama, are listed below.   **a–e. See margin.**

January, 59.7°	May, 84.6°	September, 86.9°
February, 63.6°	June, 90.0°	October, 79.5°
March, 70.9°	July, 91.3°	November, 70.3°
April, 78.5°	August, 90.5°	December, 62.9°

a. Make a line plot. Round each temperature to the nearest degree.

b. Use the line plot to find the median, mode, and mean.

c. Suppose each of the average monthly temperatures rose 5°. Make a line plot of these new temperatures.

d. How do the two line plots compare? Are the median, mode, and mean the same or different? Explain.

e. How could you make the new line plot from the original line plot?

Mixed Review

30. Name the property illustrated by $5 + (2 + x) = (2 + x) + 5$.   (Lesson 1–2)

31. Simplify $a(3 + 5) - 6(3a - 1)$.   (Lesson 1–2) $-10a + 6$

32. Simplify $\frac{2}{3}(6a - 18) + 3(2a - 9)$.   (Lesson 1–2) $10a - 39$

33. Evaluate $\frac{7(3 + 2)}{4 - 9}$.   (Lesson 1–1) -7

34. Evaluate $(r + 7) \div s$ if $r = 20$ and $s = 3$.   (Lesson 1–1) 9

35. Chemistry The boiling point of the metal zinc is 787.1°F. Use the formula $C = \frac{5(F - 32)}{9}$ to find the equivalent Celsius temperature.   (Lesson 1–1)

30. comm. (+)
35. 419.5°C

Mathematics and SOCIETY

What, No Census?

The article below appeared in *Business Week* on November 28, 1994.

SINCE 1790, THE GOVERNMENT HAS FAITHfully tried to count every resident once a decade. Now, a panel of statisticians has a blunt message for the Census Bureau: Give up. For 2000, a National Academy of Sciences committee says a "fundamentally redesigned" census should rely heavily on statistical sampling and estimation. The committee says that these methods can produce a more accurate—and far less costly—count of residents who don't respond to the census' mail-in questionnaire, especially minority groups. Congress, angered by the inaccuracy and expense of the 1990 census, is likely to embrace the committee's proposal. ∎

1–3. See Solutions Manual.

1. Each census compiles large amounts of data about us, including age, sex, race, education, home address, household size and composition, and income level. What uses could the government make of the census data? Who else might be interested in the data?

2. Why would a census using statistical sampling and estimation be less expensive than the past method of trying to count everyone by using questionnaires?

3. Describe how you might use statistical sampling to study a group of people that you want to learn more about. What factors would you want to consider in planning your procedures?

26   Chapter 1   *Analyzing Equations and Inequalities*

Tech Prep

Publicist Students who are interested in publicity may wish to do further research on the information given in Exercise 29 and explore the potential growth of this career. For more information on tech prep, see the *Teacher's Handbook*.

Mathematics and SOCIETY

The earliest census was taken for the purposes of taxation and military service. The Bible includes accounts of a census of military men by the Israelites around 1500 B.C., but the Chinese took a census at regular intervals from 2275 B.C. to A.D. 1712. This was a count of taxpaying households. In 1712 they began counting individuals.

Solving Equations

CONNECTION
History

What YOU'LL LEARN

- To translate verbal expressions and sentences into algebraic expressions and equations,
- to solve equations by using the properties of equality, and
- to solve equations for a specific variable.

Why IT'S IMPORTANT

You can use equations to solve problems involving history, astronomy, and travel.

Have you ever thought it would have been great to live 4500 years ago in Babylon because you wouldn't have had algebra homework? Those teenagers may not have had shopping malls, CD-ROMS, or TVs, but they did have algebra homework!

Babylonian students wrote their assignments on clay tablets with little sticks used to make wedge-shaped marks. They didn't use letters for unknown values in equations because today's alphabet hadn't been invented. Instead, they drew pictures to stand for the unknowns.

A Greek mathematician named Diophantus introduced algebraic symbols to write equations. The chart below shows examples of his equations along with today's algebraic form.

Diophantine Equation	Modern Meaning
ζισβ	$x = 2$
ζγισθ	$x + 3 = 9$
ζγβισθ	$3x + 2 = 9$
ζθΛγισβ	$9x - 3 = 2$
ζβΛθισζγ	$2x - 9 = x + 3$

GLOBAL CONNECTIONS

Diophantus of Alexandria, who lived about A.D. 250, was famous for his work in algebra. His main work was titled *Arithmetica* and introduced symbolism to Greek algebra as well as propositions in number theory and polygonal numbers.

The language of today's algebra provides a powerful way to translate word expressions into algebraic or mathematical expressions. **Variables** are used to represent numbers that are not known. Any letter can be used as a variable.

Verbal Expression	Algebraic Expression
• *a number* increased by 4	$x + 4$
• twice the cube of *a number*	$2n^3$
• the square of *a number* decreased by the cube of the *same number*	$c^2 - c^3$
• three times the sum of *a number* and 6	$3(b + 6)$

Sentences with variables to be replaced, such as $4x - 8 = 32$ and $2x + 4 > 9$, are called **open sentences.** An open sentence that states that two mathematical expressions are equal is called an **equation.** Equations can be used to represent verbal mathematical sentences.

Verbal Sentence	Equation
• Nine is equal to five plus four.	$9 = 5 + 4$
• A *number* decreased by 6 is −3.	$m - 6 = -3$
• A *number* divided by 3 is equal to $\frac{3}{4}$.	$\frac{x}{3} = \frac{3}{4}$

GLOBAL CONNECTIONS

Before this time, algebra problems and their solution methods were written out in natural language. A completely symbolic language for mathematics evolved over a long period of time.

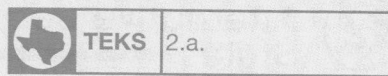
TEKS 2.a.

1-4 LESSON NOTES

NCTM Standards: 1–5

Instructional Resources

- Study Guide Master 1-4
- Practice Master 1-4
- Enrichment Master 1-4
- Assessment and Evaluation Masters, pp. 15–16
- Modeling Mathematics Masters, pp. 25–27
- Tech Prep Applications Masters, p. 2

Transparency 1-4A contains the 5-Minute Check for this lesson; **Transparency 1-4B** contains a teaching aid for this lesson.

Recommended Pacing	
Standard Pacing	Day 5 of 12
Honors Pacing	Day 5 of 12
Block Scheduling*	Day 3 of 6

*For more information on pacing and possible lesson plans, refer to the *Block Scheduling Booklet.*

1 FOCUS

5-Minute Check
(over Lesson 1-3)

1. List the data displayed in the line plot. 10, 14, 14, 20, 20, 20, 24, 26, 28

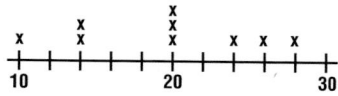

Use the stem-and-leaf plot to answer each question.

Stem	Leaf
8	3 7
9	4 4 8 8 9
10	0 5
11	1 8|3 = 83

2. What is the difference between the greatest value and least value? 28
3. Which value(s) appear most frequently? 94, 98

Find the median of each set of data.

4. 3, 5, 8, 2, 1 3
5. 22, 45, 67, 3, 98 45
6. 146, 232, 79, 182 164

Questioning Have a student pick a number. Instruct the student to perform the following operations. Increase the number by 10. Next, find half of the new number. Decrease the number by five. Finally, double the result. What number results? Have several students try the sequence. Have students explain what happens.

2 TEACH

In-Class Examples

For Example 1
Name the property illustrated by each statement.
a. $x + 9 = 6 + 9$
    $6 + 9 = 15$
    $x + 9 = 15$ transitive
b. $28 = 6y + 4$
    $6y + 4 = 28$ symmetric
c. $r + (6 + 9) = 32$
    $r + 15 = 32$ substitution

For Example 2
Solve $y - 25 = 13.4$. $y = 38.4$

To solve an equation, you find replacements for the variables that make the equation true. Each of these replacements is called a **solution** of the equation.

We can use certain properties of equality to solve equations or open sentences. Some of those properties are listed below.

Reflexive Property of Equality	For any real number a, $a = a$.
Symmetric Property of Equality	For all real numbers a and b, if $a = b$, then $b = a$.
Transitive Property of Equality	For all real numbers a, b, and c, if $a = b$ and $b = c$, then $a = c$.
Substitution Property of Equality	If $a = b$, then a may be replaced by b.

Example Name the property illustrated by each statement.
a. If $1.5(7.5) = 11.25$, then $11.25 = 1.5(7.5)$.
  symmetric property of equality

b. If $7 = 1 + 2 + 4$ and $1 + 2 + 4 = 4 + 3$, then $7 = 4 + 3$.
  transitive property of equality

Sometimes an equation can be solved by adding or subtracting the same number on each side.

Addition and Subtraction Properties of Equality	For any numbers a, b, and c, if $a = b$, then $a + c = b + c$ and $a - c = b - c$.

Example ② Solve $x + 54.57 = 78$.   *Estimate:* $80 - 55 = 25$
$$x + 54.57 = 78$$
$$x + 54.57 - 54.57 = 78 - 54.57 \quad \text{\small\textit{Subtract 54.57 from each side.}}$$
$$x = 23.43$$

Check: $x + 54.57 = 78$
  $23.43 + 54.57 \overset{?}{=} 78$ *Replace x with 23.43.*
  $78 = 78$ ✓

The solution is 23.43.

Some equations may be solved by multiplying or dividing each side by the same number.

Multiplication and Division Properties of Equality	For any real numbers a, b, and c, if $a = b$, then $a \cdot c = b \cdot c$ and, if $c \neq 0$, $\dfrac{a}{c} = \dfrac{b}{c}$.

 Alternative Learning Styles

Kinesthetic Separate students into groups, giving each group a balance scale. Have students use different weights to illustrate how to solve equations. The students should write down the combinations of weights used.

 GLENCOE *Technology*

Interactive Mathematics Tools Software

This multimedia software allows students to use counters to solve one-step equations with addition or subtraction. Another lesson examines the relationship between cricket chirps and the temperature. **Computer Journals** give students an opportunity to write about what they have learned.
For Windows & Macintosh

Example ③ **Solve each equation.**

a. $4x = -12$

$4x = -12$

$\frac{1}{4}(4x) = \frac{1}{4}(-12)$ *Multiply each side by $\frac{1}{4}$,*

$x = -3$ *the reciprocal of 4.*

The solution is -3.

This equation could also be solved by dividing each side by 4.

Check:

$4x = -12$

$4(-3) \overset{?}{=} -12$

$-12 = -12$ ✓

b. $-\frac{3}{4}t = 15$

$-\frac{3}{4}t = 15$

$-\frac{4}{3}\left(-\frac{3}{4}\right)t = \left(-\frac{4}{3}\right)(15)$ *Multiply each side by $-\frac{4}{3}$,*

$t = -20$ *the reciprocal of $-\frac{3}{4}$.*

The solution is -20.

Check:

$-\frac{3}{4}t = 15$

$-\frac{3}{4}(-20) \overset{?}{=} 15$

$15 = 15$ ✓

In order to solve some equations, it may be necessary to apply more than one property.

Example ④ **Solve $3(2a + 25) - 2(a - 1) = 78$.**

$3(2a + 25) - 2(a - 1) = 78$

$6a + 75 - 2a + 2 = 78$ *Distributive and substitution properties*

$4a + 77 = 78$ *Commutative, distributive, and substitution properties*

$4a = 1$ *Subtraction and substitution properties*

$a = \frac{1}{4}$ *Division and substitution properties*

The solution is $\frac{1}{4}$. *Check this result.*

Sometimes you need to solve an equation or formula for a variable.

Example ⑤

INTEGRATION
Geometry

The formula for the volume of a cylinder is $V = \pi r^2 h$, where V is the volume, r represents the radius of the circular base and top and h represents the height of the cylinder. Solve the formula for h.

$V = \pi r^2 h$

$\frac{V}{\pi r^2} = \frac{\pi r^2 h}{\pi r^2}$ *Divide each side by πr^2.*

$\frac{V}{\pi r^2} = h$

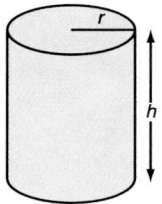

Lesson 1–4 Solving Equations **29**

In-Class Examples

For Example 3
Solve each equation.

a. $9y = 63$ $y = 7$

b. $\frac{2}{3}d = 1$ $\frac{3}{2}$

For Example 4
Solve $5\left(\frac{y}{6} - 2\right) = 2y + 4$.

$y = -12$

For Example 5
The formula for the tension of a string is $T = \sqrt{\frac{\ell}{g}}$, where ℓ represents the length of the string and g is the acceleration due to gravity. Solve the formula for ℓ. $\ell = gT^2$

Alternative Teaching Strategies ▬▬▬

Student Diversity Given the equation $4 = 5 + x$, express the equation in words three different ways. Use a problem or a verbal sentence.
Do the same for each equation.
1. $x = 2(4)$
2. $15 = 2(x + 3)$

In-Class Example

For Example 6
Mrs. Campbell wants to put up new cabinets in her kitchen. She needs 1.5 feet for each cabinet, and she has 10.5 feet of wall to put the cabinets on. How many cabinets can she put up? **7 cabinets**

3 PRACTICE/APPLY

Check for Understanding

Exercises 1–18 are designed to help you assess your students' understanding through reading, writing, speaking, and modeling. You should work through Exercises 1–5 with your students and then monitor their work on Exercises 6–18.

Error Analysis
Students may check their answers to verbal problems by substituting the answer back into the equation. The check requires that all conditions in the original problem have been met and students should not assume the answer is correct. To help students complete checks to verbal problems, give students a set of verbal problems with a proposed answer to each problem. Students are to determine if the proposed answers are correct without solving the problem.

Additional Answer

3. An equation has an equals sign in it; it conveys a complete mathematical sentence. An expression does not have an equals sign in it; it is only part of a mathematical sentence.

You can use a four-step **problem-solving plan** to help you solve problems.

Problem-Solving Plan ▷
1. **Explore the problem.**
2. **Plan the solution.**
3. **Solve the problem.**
4. **Examine the solution.**

Example ⑥  **INTEGRATION**
Geometry

The perimeter of a parallelogram is 48 inches. What is the length of the longer side if the shorter side measures 9 inches?

Explore   Draw a diagram and let ℓ represent the measure of the longer side.

Plan   The perimeter equals the sum of the lengths of the sides. So, we can write the following equation.

$$2(9) + 2(\ell) = 48$$

Solve $$2(9) + 2(\ell) = 48$$
$$18 + 2\ell = 48$$
$$\ell = 15$$

The length of the longer side is 15 inches.

Examine   If one of the two longer sides has length 15 inches and one of the shorter sides has length 9 inches, the perimeter is $15 + 15 + 9 + 9 = 48$ inches. Thus, the answer is correct.

CHECK FOR UNDERSTANDING

Communicating Mathematics

Study the lesson. Then complete the following.

1. **Write** two verbal expressions and two verbal sentences containing unknown quantities. Write each as an algebraic expression or equation.   See students' work.

2. **Summarize** the properties you studied in this lesson. Exchange summaries with another student. Discuss your summaries and make any necessary revisions.   See students' work.

3. See margin.

3. **Explain** the difference between an equation and an expression.

4. **Write** an equation to find the length of a side of a regular pentagon if its perimeter is 250 inches. $5s = 250$

5. **You Decide**   Was this equation solved correctly? If not, explain what error was made. Then show how to solve the equation correctly.   yes

$$4(a + 5) - 2(a + 6) = a + 16$$
$$4a + 20 - 2a - 12 = a + 16$$
$$2a + 8 = a + 16$$
$$a = 8$$

Reteaching

Logical Thinking Decide if each relation is reflexive, symmetric, or transitive. Use *N* for no or *Y* for yes in the chart.

Relation	R	S	T
factor of	Y	N	Y
parallel	N	Y	Y
perpendicular	N	Y	N
congruent	Y	Y	Y
is less than	N	N	Y

Guided Practice

8. subtraction ($=$)
9. multiplication ($=$)
12. 2.5
14. 7.5

Write an algebraic expression to represent each verbal expression.

6. three decreased by twice a number $3 - 2n$
7. five times a number decreased by three $5x - 3$

Name the property illustrated by each statement.

8. If $r + 2 = 8$, then $r = 6$.
9. If $4x = 16$, then $12x = 48$.

Solve each equation.

10. $10 + 5x = 110$ **20**
11. $-2(a + 4) = 2$ **−5**
12. $3b + 4b + 5b = 30$
13. $7 + 5n = -58$ **−13**
14. $-1.4t + 3 = -7.5$
15. $-\frac{2}{3}k = 14$ **−21**

Solve each equation or formula for the variable specified.

16. $2x - 3m = 6$, for x $x = \frac{6 + 3m}{2}$
17. $V = \frac{1}{3}\pi r^2 h$, for h $\frac{3V}{\pi r^2} = h$

Define a variable, write an equation, and solve the problem. Then check your solution.

18. Marisa is 16 years old. Her parents are both the same age. The three of them have lived a total of 100 years. How old are Marisa's parents?
   $16 + 2x = 100$; $x = 42$

EXERCISES

Practice

Write an algebraic expression to represent each verbal expression.

19. fourteen decreased by the square of a number $14 - x^2$
20. twice the sum of a number and 11 $2(n + 11)$
21. four times the sum of a number and its square $4(n + n^2)$
22. the product of the square of a number and five $5x^2$
23. the sum of 7 and three times a number $7 + 3n$
24. the square of the sum of a number and 13 $(x + 13)^2$

Name the property illustrated by each statement.

25. $(5 + 6) + 7 = (5 + 6) + 7$ reflexive ($=$)

26. If $4 + 8 = 12$, then $12 = 4 + 8$.   symmetric ($=$)
27. If $3x = 10$, then $3x + 6 = 10 + 6$.   addition ($=$)
28. If $3m = 5n$ and $5n = 10p$, then $3m = 10p$.   transitive ($=$)
29. If $7 + s = 21$, then $s = 14$.   subtraction ($=$)
30. If $q + (8 + 5) = 32$, then $q + 13 = 32$.   substitution ($=$)

Solve each equation.

31. $3y + 16 = 22$ **2**
32. $14 - x = -7$ **21**
33. $34 - 10w = 6w + 2$ **2**
34. $t + 2t + 3t + 4t + 5t = 45$ **3**
35. $\frac{1}{8} - \frac{3}{4}x = \frac{1}{16}$ $\frac{1}{12}$
36. $\frac{3}{4} - \frac{3}{5}x = \frac{2}{5}x + \frac{2}{4}$ $\frac{1}{4}$
37. $5 = -5(y + 3)$ **−4**
38. $2d + 5 = 8d + 2$ $\frac{1}{2}$
39. $280 - 26f = 1098$ $-\frac{409}{13}$
40. $3(4 - 5k) = 2k - 4$ $\frac{16}{17}$
41. $4m - 9 = 5m + 7$ **−16**
42. $32g + 245 = 3829$ **112**
43. $12x - 24 = -14x + 28$ **2**
44. $18 = -6(p + 5)$ **−8**
45. $4.5(b + 1) - 2 = 4(b + 3)$ **19**
46. $2.3n + 1 = 1.3n + 7$ **6**
47. $\frac{5}{7}x - 4 = \frac{3}{7}x + 1$ $\frac{35}{2}$
48. $\frac{3}{4}n - 2 = \frac{1}{2}n + 7$ **36**

Assignment Guide

Core: 19–63 odd, 64–76
Enriched: 20–58 even, 59–76
All: Self Test, 1–10

For **Extra Practice,** see p. 877.

The red A, B, and C flags, printed only in the Teacher's Wraparound Edition, indicate the level of difficulty of the exercises.

Additional Answers

59. the product of twice a number and the sum of the number and four added to twice the sum of the number and six

61. The last day's trip will take him only 10.2 hours, which will bring the driver's total time to 64.95 hours.

Solve each equation or formula for the variable specified.

49. $x(y + 2) = z$, for y $\dfrac{z}{x} - 2$

50. $I = prt$, for t $\dfrac{I}{pr}$

51. $5a - 6b = 9$, for b $\dfrac{5a - 9}{6}$

52. $de - 4f = 5g$, for e $\dfrac{5g + 4f}{d}$

53. $F = G\dfrac{Mm}{r^2}$, for M $\dfrac{Fr^2}{Gm}$

54. $qr + s = t$, for q $\dfrac{t - s}{r}$

Define a variable, write an equation, and solve the problem. Then check your solution.

55. The high school principal has given Mrs. Diaz $420 to buy tickets to *Phantom of the Opera* for her English class and chaperones. The school requires that there be one adult chaperone for every five students on such a trip. How many $15.00 student tickets and $30.00 adult tickets can she order? $30x + 15(5x) = 420$; **four adult tickets, twenty student tickets**

56. Hearthstone Toyota's price for a Toyota Camry is $18,999. Sheila Rayburn offered the dealership a price of $17,099. Sheila's price is what percent of the dealership's price? $\dfrac{17,099}{18,999} = \dfrac{x}{100}$; **90%**

57. You have $32 to spend on supplies for your science fair project. If you buy two plants for experiments, you will have $18 left for other supplies. How much is each plant? $2x + 18 = 32$; **$7**

58. **Geometry**   The perimeter of an isosceles triangle is 116 centimeters. The length of the base is 36 cm. What is the length of one of the equal sides?   **40 cm**

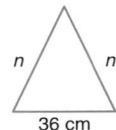

n n

36 cm

Critical Thinking

59. Write a verbal expression to represent the algebraic expression $2x(x + 4) + 2(x + 6)$.   **See margin.**

Applications and Problem Solving

60. **Packaging**   Two designs for a tuna can are shown at the right. If each can holds the same amount of tuna, what is the height of can A?   **4 units**

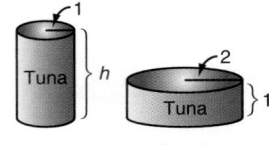

Can A   Can B

61. **Transportation**   The U.S. Department of Transportation regulations prohibit a truck driver from driving more than 70 hours in any 8-day period. Over the past 7 days, a driver has accumulated 54.75 hours of driving time. Does he have enough hours available on the eighth day to deliver freight if he must drive 510 miles at a speed of 50 mph? Explain.   **Yes; see margin for explanation.**

62. **Astronomy**   Earth is about 93,000,000 miles from the sun. When Venus is on the opposite side of the sun from Earth, it is about 69,000,000 from the sun. What is the distance from Earth to Venus?   **162,000,000 miles**

63. **Travel**   The distance by water from New York City to San Francisco by way of Cape Horn is about 13,200 miles. By going through the Panama Canal, the distance is only 5280 miles. How many miles does a ship save by going through the Panama Canal?   **7920 miles**

Scene from Phantom of the Opera

Study Guide Masters, p. 4

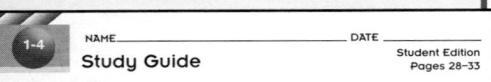

1-4   NAME_____   DATE _____

Study Guide

Student Edition Pages 28–33

Solving Equations

Many equations can be solved by using addition, subtraction, multiplication, or division.

| Addition and Subtraction Properties of Equality | For any real numbers a, b, and c, if $a = b$, then $a + c = b + c$ and $a - c = b - c$. |
| Multiplication and Division Properties of Equality | For any real numbers a, b, and c, if $a = b$, then $a \cdot c = b \cdot c$ and, if c is not zero, $\dfrac{a}{c} = \dfrac{b}{c}$. |

Example: Solve $8x - 13 = 43$.

$8x - 13 = 43$
$8x - 13 + 13 = 43 + 13$
$8x = 56$
$x = 7$

Solve each equation.

1. $3s = 45$ 15

2. $17 = 9 - a$ -8

3. $5t - 1 = 6t - 5$ 4

4. $\dfrac{2}{3}m = \dfrac{1}{2}$ $\dfrac{3}{4}$

5. $7 - \dfrac{1}{2}x = 3$ 8

6. $-8 = -2(z + 7)$ -3

Define a variable, write an equation, and solve the problem.

7. A number decreased by 11 is 46. Find the number.   57

8. The sum of three times a number and 6 is 39. Find the number.   11

9. Mrs. Chin bought some $0.20 stamps and an equal number of $0.32 stamps. She paid a total of $5.20 for all the stamps. How many of each type of stamp did Mrs. Chin buy?   10 stamps

10. Enrique Romero bought a refrigerator for $50 more than half its original price. He paid $525 for the refrigerator. What was the original price of the refrigerator? $950

32   Chapter 1

Mixed Review

64. Animals The table at the right lists major U.S. zoological parks and the number of species at each park. (Lesson 1–3)

a. Make a stem-and-leaf plot of the data. Round each number to the nearest ten.

b. Find the median, mode, and mean of the data. **450; 560; 470.90**

a. See margin.

Zoo	Species
Bronx	670
Cleveland	563
Dallas	329
Detroit	413
Houston	596
Memphis	445
Minnesota	311
Philadelphia	560
Phoenix	324
San Antonio	700
San Francisco	270

65. Statistics Find the median, mode, and mean for the following set of data. (Lesson 1–3) **217.5; 399; about 265.3**

216, 399, 219, 179, 180, 399

66. Hockey Use the line plot below to answer each question. (Lesson 1–3)

Most NHL Goals in a Season

```
                  X X        X
          X X X X              X
     X  X X X X X X X   X                       X X X            X
    +--+--+--+--+--+--+--+--+--+--+--+--+--+--+--+--+--+--+--+--+
      65      70      75      80      85      90      95
```

a. What is the greatest number of goals scored in a season? **92**

b. In the 1992–93 season, Mario Lemieux scored 69 goals. In the 1988–89 season, he scored 85 goals. How many scores were greater than Mario's in 1992–93 but less than Mario's in 1988–89? **10**

Mario Lemieux

67. Weather The average monthly temperatures in selected cities for January and July are given in the table below. Make a back-to-back stem-and-leaf plot of the temperatures of the cities rounded to the nearest degree. (Lesson 1–3) **See margin.**

City	January Temperature	July Temperature
Baton Rouge, LA	50.8	82.1
Caribou, ME	10.7	65.1
Charlotte, NC	40.5	78.5
Chicago, IL	21.4	73.0
Dallas, TX	44.0	86.3
Denver, CO	29.5	73.4
Indianapolis, IN	26.0	75.1
Jacksonville, FL	53.2	81.3
Juneau, AK	21.8	55.7
Roswell, NM	41.4	77.7
San Diego, CA	56.8	70.3
Tulsa, OK	35.2	83.2

Source: U.S. National Oceanic and Atmospheric Administration

Extension

Reasoning Solve the equation.
$$5(3x - 2) + 2(1 - x) = 3(7 + 3x) - 4(6 - x)$$
no solution
Explain the steps taken to solve the equation.

Additional Answers

64a.

Stem	Leaf
2	7
3	1 2 3
4	1 5
5	6 6
6	0 7
7	0

$2|7 = 270$

67.

January	Stem	July
1	1	
1 2 6	2	
0 5	3	
1 1 4	4	
1 3 7	5	6
	6	5
	7	0 3 3 5 8 9
	8	1 2 3 6

$|3|5 = 35°$

Practice Masters, p. 4

1-4 NAME_____ DATE_____
Practice Student Edition Pages 28–33

Solving Equations

Solve each equation.

1. $13 = 8 - 6r$ $-\frac{5}{6}$

2. $9 + 4n = -59$ -17

3. $\frac{3}{8}y = 2\frac{3}{4}$ $\frac{22}{3}$

4. $-6 = \frac{4x}{7} + 2$ -14

5. $\frac{3}{4} - \frac{1}{2}n = \frac{4}{5}$ $-\frac{1}{10}$

6. $\frac{5}{6}s + \frac{3}{8} = \frac{2}{3}$ $\frac{7}{20}$

7. $-1.6r + 5 = -7.8$ 8

8. $6x - 5 = 7 - 9x$ $\frac{4}{5}$

9. $5(6 - 4v) = v + 21$ $\frac{3}{7}$

10. $-4(6y - 5) = 23 - 3(8y + 1)$ all reals

Define a variable, write an equation, and solve the problem.

11. Fourteen less than twice some number is 154. Find the number. **84**

12. The length of a rectangle is 9 centimeters more than half the width. Find the length if the perimeter is 60 centimeters. **16 cm**

13. In an evening, a sporting goods store sold twice as many T-shirts as shorts. T-shirts are $9 each, and shorts are $14 each. The total amount of money taken in for both items was $256. Find the number of each that was sold. **8 shorts, 16 T-shirts**

Closing Activity

Speaking Have students explain how to solve an equation. Have several students take an equation and explain the steps to be taken as well as the reasons for the steps.

Chapter 10, Quiz B (Lessons 1-3 and 1-4), is available in the *Assessment and Evaluation Masters,* p. 16.

Mid-Chapter Test (Lessons 1-1 through 1-4) is available in the *Assessment and Evaluation Masters,* p. 15.

Enrichment Masters, p. 4

---

68. Statistics Find the median, mode, and mean for the following set of data. (Lesson 1–3)   **12; 12 and 13; about 12.3**

$$11, 10, 13, 12, 12, 13, 15$$

69. Simplify $2(9a - 2) - 3(5 + a)$. (Lesson 1–2)   **$15a - 19$**

Name the property illustrated by each equation. (Lesson 1–2)

70. comm. (+)
71. add. iden.

70. $11(3a + 2b) = 11(2b + 3a)$ **71.** $a + b + 0 = a + b$

72. Evaluate $\sqrt{9 \div 3}$ and name the sets of numbers to which it belongs. (Lesson 1–2) $\sqrt{3};$ **I, R**

73. Banking Find the interest earned in 6 years on a savings account containing $20,000 if the interest rate is 14.5%. (Lesson 1–1)   **$17,400**

74. Evaluate $3^b - a + c$ if $a = 13$, $b = 2$ and $c = 9$. (Lesson 1–1)   **5**

75. Evaluate $4 - [32 \div (16 - 12)]$. (Lesson 1–1)   **−4**

76. Evaluate $[18 - (5 + 22)] \times 2$. (Lesson 1–1)   **−18**

SELF TEST

Evaluate each expression if $m = 2$, $n = -3$, and $p = 4$. (Lesson 1–1)

1. $m + n - p$ **−5**   **2.** $m(n + p)$ **2**

Find the value of each expression. Then name the sets of numbers to which each value belongs. (Lesson 1–2)

3. $7 - 8$ **−1; R, Q, Z**   **4.** $3.9 + 2.6$ **6.5; R, Q**   **5.** $\sqrt{36 + 5}$ $\sqrt{41}$, **6.403; R, I**

6. Consumerism The Super Shoes catalog contains 29 pairs of shoes that can be ordered through the mail. The prices are $53, $42, $49, $38, $39, $48, $37, $48, $37, $39, $58, $59, $32, $50, $59, $37, $36, $30, $40, $33, $30, $45, $40, $30, $35, $48, $37, $48, and $50. (Lesson 1–3)
   a. Make a stem-and-leaf plot of the shoe prices.   **See margin.**
   b. Find the median, mode, and mean of the prices.   **40; 37 and 48; 42.3**

Solve each equation. (Lesson 1–4)

7. $4.5 - 3.9m = 20.1$ **−4**   **8.** $9 = 16d + 51$ **−2.625**

9. $2y - 8 = 14 - 9y$ **2**   **10.** $285 - 38x = 2033$ **−46**

34   Chapter 1   *Analyzing Equations and Inequalities*

SELF TEST

The Self Test provides students with a brief review of the concepts and skills in Lessons 1-1 through 1-4. Lesson numbers are given to the right of exercises or instruction lines so students can review concepts not yet mastered.

Answer for the Self Test

6a.

Stem	Leaf
3	0 0 0 2 3 5 6 7 7 7 7 8 9 9
4	0 0 2 5 8 8 8 8 9
5	0 0 3 8 9 9

$4|8 = \$48$

NAME_____ DATE_____
1-4   Student Edition
Enrichment   Pages 28–32

Significant Digits

All measurements are approximations. The **significant digits** of an approximate number are those which indicate the results of a measurement. For example, the mass of an object, measured to the nearest gram, is 210 grams. The measurement 21\underline{0} g has 3 significant digits. The mass of the same object, measured to the nearest 100 g, is 200 g. The measurement 200 g has one significant digit.

1. Nonzero digits and zeros between significant digits are significant. For example, the measurement 9.071 m has 4 significant digits, 9, 0, 7, and 1.

2. Zeros at the end of a decimal fraction are significant. The measurement 0.050 mm has 2 significant digits, 5 and 0.

3. Underlined zeros in whole numbers are significant. The measurement 104,\underline{0}00 km has 5 significant digits, 1, 0, 4, 0, and 0.

In general, a computation involving multiplication or division of measurements *cannot* be more accurate than the least accurate measurement in the computation. Thus, the result of computation involving multiplication or division of measurements should be rounded to the number of significant digits in the least accurate measurement.

Example: The mass of 37 quarters if 21\underline{0} g is the mass of one quarter.

mass of 1 quarter = 21\underline{0} g ÷ 37   21\underline{0} has 3 significant digits.
                                           37 does not represent a measurement.
        = 5.68 g   Round the result to 3 significant digits.
                                           Why?

Write the number of significant digits for each measurement.

1. 8314.20 m   2. 30.70 cm   3. 0.01 mm   4. 0.0605 mg
   6   4   1   3

5. 370,000 km   6. 370,\underline{0}00 km   7. 9.7 × 10⁴ g   8. 3.20 × 10⁻¹ g
   3   5   2   3

Solve. Round each result to the correct number of significant digits.

9. 23 m × 1.54 m   10. 12,000 ft ÷ 52\underline{0} ft   11. 2.5 cm × 25
   35 m²   23.1   63 cm

12. 11.01 mm × 11   13. 908 yd ÷ 0.5   14. 38.6 m × 4.0 m
    121.1 mm   1820 yd   150 m²

1–5A Graphing Technology
Using Tables to Estimate Solutions

A Preview of Lesson 1–5

You can use a graphing calculator to estimate solutions to equations by building tables of values.

Example **Estimate the solution of $12x - 3 = 5$ to the nearest hundredth.**

Rewrite the equation in an equivalent form to get 0 on one side.

$$12x - 3 = 5 \quad \rightarrow \quad 12x - 8 = 0$$

To estimate the solution means to find a value for x so that $12x - 8$ is very close to 0. Let $y = 12x - 8$ and make a table of values for x and y. First, enter $y = 12x - 8$.

Enter: [Y=] 12 [X,T,θ] [−] 8

Then, set up a table of values for x and y. You must enter a starting value for x and an increment for successive values. Let's start with $x = 0$ and use increments of 1.

Enter: [2nd] [TblSet] 0 [ENTER]

　　　1 [2nd] [Table]

We need to find the value of x when $y = 0$. From the table, we can see that x is a value between 0 and 1. To get a better approximation for x, create a new table that starts at $x = 0$ and use increments of 0.1.

X	Y₁
0	−8
1	4
2	16
3	28
4	40
5	52
6	64

X=0

Enter: [2nd] [TblSet] 0 [ENTER]

　　　.1 [2nd] [Table]

Use the arrow keys to scroll down the table to determine where $y = 0$. The solution is between 0.6 and 0.7. Continue to adjust the estimated value for x.

X	Y₁
.2	−5.6
.3	−4.4
.4	−3.2
.5	−2
.6	−.8
.7	.4
.8	1.6

X=.7

Enter: [2nd] [TblSet] .6 [ENTER]

　　　.01 [2nd] [Table]

Repeating this process one more time, we see that the solution is between 0.666 and 0.667. Thus, the solution is about 0.67.

X	Y₁
.62	−.56
.63	−.44
.64	−.32
.65	−.2
.66	−.08
.67	.04
.68	.16

X=.66

NCTM Standards: 1–5

Objective
Use a graphing calculator to estimate solutions of equations by building tables of values.

Recommended Time
25 minutes

Instructional Resources
Graphing Calculator Masters, pp. 17 and 18

These masters provide keystroking instruction for this lesson for the TI-81 and Casio graphing calculators.

1 FOCUS

Motivating the Lesson
On a number line, locate the point 3 and all points at a distance of 2 units from the point 3.

2 TEACH

Teaching Tip For Example 2, you may want to review the concept of absolute value.

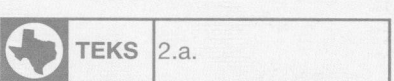

TEKS	2.a.

3 PRACTICE/APPLY

Assignment Guide

Core: 1–10
Enriched: 1–10

4 ASSESS

Observing students working with technology is an excellent method of assessment.

Example 2 involves an absolute value equation.

Example **Estimate the solutions of $|1.5x - 3| = 0.7$ to the nearest hundredth.**

Rewrite the equation as $|1.5x - 3| - 0.7 = 0$. Then, enter the equation and set up the table. Let's start with $x = 0$ and then use increments of 1 for the x values.

Enter: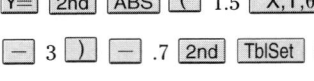

X	Y₁
0	2.3
1	.8
2	−.7
3	.8
4	2.3
5	3.8
6	5.3
X=1	

We need to find the value of x when $y = 0$. From the table, we can see that x is a value between 1 and 2 and also between 2 and 3. Begin to adjust your estimate by repeating the process.

Enter: 2nd TblSet 1 ENTER .1 2nd
Table

X	Y₁
1	.8
1.1	.65
1.2	.5
1.3	.35
1.4	.2
1.5	.05
1.6	−.1
X=1	

The solution is between 1.5 and 1.6. Continue the process to estimate the first solution. Then adjust your estimate for the second solution.

Enter: 2nd TblSet 2 ENTER .1
2nd Table

X	Y₁
2	−.7
2.1	−.55
2.2	−.4
2.3	−.25
2.4	−.1
2.5	.05
2.6	.2
X=2	

The solution is between 2.4 and 2.5. Continue the process to estimate the second solution.

The solutions are about 1.53 and 2.47.

EXERCISES

Use the TABLE feature to estimate the solution(s) of each equation to the nearest hundredth. 8. −0.84, −7.2

1. $4x + 6 = 9$ **0.75**
2. $3.5x + 7 = 11$ **1.14**
3. $-1.25 - 0.3x = 8$ **−30.83**
4. $5(x - 3) = -2$ **2.6**
5. $2x + 1 = 12 - x$ **3.67**
6. $|6x + 4| - 7 = 2$ **0.83, −2.17**
7. $|3 - x| = 5$ **−2, 8**
8. $|2.21 + 0.55x| = 1.75$
9. $\left|\frac{1}{2}x - 5\right| = 17$ **44, −24**
10. $40 = \frac{5}{9}(x - 32)$ **104**

Using Technology

This lesson offers an excellent opportunity for using technology in your algebra classroom. For more information on using technology, see *Graphing Calculators in the Mathematics Classroom,* one of the titles in the Glencoe Mathematics Professional Series.

Solving Absolute Value Equations

1-5

What YOU'LL LEARN

- To solve equations containing absolute value, and
- to solve problems by making lists.

Why IT'S IMPORTANT

You can use absolute value equations to solve problems involving travel and manufacturing.

APPLICATION
Time Zones

Joan Haghiri works as a consultant. Her job consists of providing or developing training for businesses or organizations to help their employees perform better. Joan travels frequently as a part of her job and often goes from one time zone to another.

Joan lives in El Paso, Texas. One week she flew to New York City to give a presentation. She called home the first night to talk to her 6-year-old son. She called at 10:00 P.M. to be in time for his 8:00 P.M. bedtime. Since New York is in the Eastern time zone and El Paso is in the Mountain time zone, it is two hours later in New York City than in El Paso.

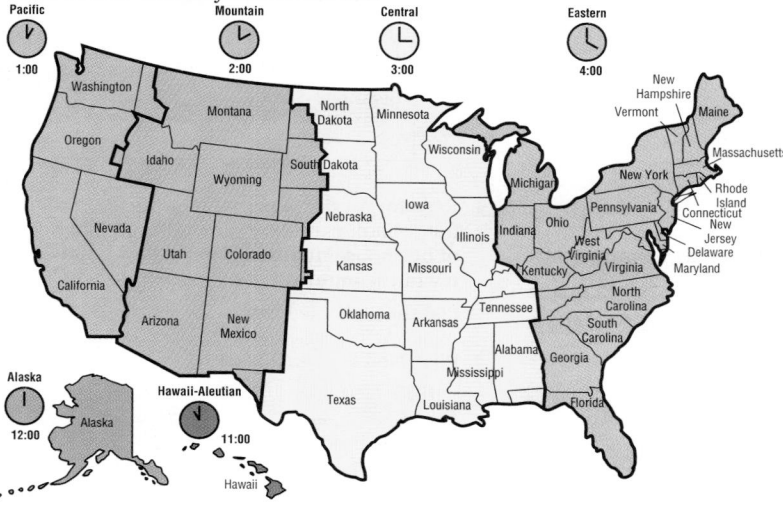

While in Fairbanks, Alaska, the next week, Joan had to remember to call her son at 6:00 P.M. Alaska time. This is because it is two hours later in El Paso.

On a number line, the time zone for El Paso is the starting point and corresponds to 0. New York City is at +2, while Fairbanks is at −2.

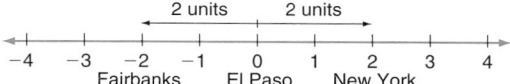

Certainly −2 and 2 are quite different, but they do have something in common. They are the same distance from 0 on the number line.

We say that −2 and 2 have the same **absolute value.** The absolute value of a number is the number of units it is from 0 on the number line. We use the symbol $|x|$ to represent the absolute value of a number x.

The absolute value of −2 is 2.   The absolute value of 2 is 2.
$$|-2| = 2$$ $$|2| = 2$$

Lesson 1–5   Solving Absolute Value Equations **37**

TEKS 2.a.

1-5 LESSON NOTES

NCTM Standards: 1–5

Instructional Resources
- Study Guide Master 1-5
- Practice Master 1-5
- Enrichment Master 1-5

Transparency 1-5A contains the 5-Minute Check for this lesson; **Transparency 1-5B** contains a teaching aid for this lesson.

Recommended Pacing

Standard Pacing	Day 7 of 12
Honors Pacing	Day 7 of 12
Block Scheduling*	Day 4 of 6

*For more information on pacing and possible lesson plans, refer to the *Block Scheduling Booklet.*

1 FOCUS

5-Minute Check
(over Lesson 1-4)

1. Choose a variable and write an expression to represent the phrase three times the sum of a number and its square. $3(x + x^2)$
2. Write an equation and solve the problem. If you add 23 to a number, the result is 64. Find the number.
$n + 23 = 64;$ 41

Solve each equation.

3. $12f - 4 = 7 + f$ $f = 1$
4. $8(2n + 3) = 12$ $n = -\frac{3}{4}$
5. $6y + 1 = 3\left(2y - \frac{1}{3}\right)$
no solution

Motivating the Lesson

Questioning Describe the outside environment at −40°F. What would you wear for that temperature? Describe the outside environment at 40°F. What would you wear for that temperature? Is there a difference in how you would feel at each temperature? What do the two temperatures have in common?

Teaching Tip In the definition of *absolute value*, the second statement implies that *a* is negative. If *a* is negative, then absolute value must be opposite of that value. Therefore, the absolute value of *a* is $-a$.

In-Class Examples

For Example 1
Find each absolute value.
a. $|10|$ 10
b. $|-4|$ 4

For Example 2
Jason Nies is a teller for Happy Valley Bank. He received three receipts for deposits and noticed that they did not add up to the total amount deposited into the customer's account. He thinks some of the numbers were transposed when they were entered into the bank's computer. If all three deposits were two digits, how many combinations must he try in order to check his theory?   7

For Example 3
Find the absolute value of $x + 5$.
$x + 5$ if $x \geq -5$ and $-x - 5$ if $x < -5$

Teaching Tip Discuss with students possible reasons for combining letters and numbers for personal identification numbers.

We can also define absolute value in the following way.

Absolute Value	For any real number *a*: if $a \geq 0$, then $|a| = a$; if $a < 0$, then $|a| = -a$.

The symbol $\geq$ means "is greater than or equal to."

Example 1 Find each absolute value.
a. $|9|$ b. $|-14|$

$|9| = 9$ $|-14| = -(-14)$ or 14

You will solve certain kinds of problems by using the strategy **list possibilities**. List possibilities is one of many *problem-solving strategies* that you can use to solve problems. Here are some other problem-solving strategies.

Problem-Solving Strategies	
draw a diagram	solve a simpler (or a similar) problem
make a table or chart	eliminate the possibilities
make a model	look for a pattern
guess and check	act it out
check for hidden assumptions	work backward
use a graph	identify subgoals

Example 2

PROBLEM SOLVING
List Possibilities

Rosa forgot the personal identification number (PIN) for her automatic teller bank card. She remembered that her PIN is the rearranged digits of her house number. If her house number is 1256, what PINs should she try in the automatic teller machine?

List the possible PINs.

Possible PINs starting with 1:   Possible PINs starting with 2:
  1265   1526   1562 *Why isn't*   2156   2165   2516
  1625   1652   *1256 listed?*   2561   2615   2651

Possible PINs starting with 5:   Possible PINs starting with 6:
  5126   5162   5216   6125   6152   6215
  5261   5612   5621   6251   6512   6521

These are the 23 possible PINs that Rosa should try in the automatic teller machine.

You can list the possibilities to help you find absolute values.

Example 3 Find the absolute value of $x - 15$.
Make a list of the possible cases.
Case 1: If *x* is 15 or greater, then $x - 15 \geq 0$.
    So, $|x - 15| = x - 15$.
Case 2: If *x* is less than 15, then $x - 15 < 0$.
    So, $|x - 15| = -(x - 15)$ or $15 - x$.

Alternative Learning Styles

Auditory Have students discuss how they would solve the equation $4 - |x + 12| = 3$. Ask them how they would deal with the second step where $-|x + 12| = -1$. Explain that this expression is saying to take the opposite of the absolute value. Why does it have a solution?

You can evaluate expressions that contain absolute values. The absolute value bars can be grouping symbols.

Example 4 Evaluate $|3x - 6| + 3.2$ if $x = -2$.

$|3x - 6| + 3.2 = |3(-2) - 6| + 3.2$ *Replace x with -2.*

$\qquad\qquad\quad = |-6 - 6| + 3.2$ *Simplify within absolute value bars first.*

$\qquad\qquad\quad = |-12| + 3.2$

$\qquad\qquad\quad = 12 + 3.2$

$\qquad\qquad\quad = 15.2$

The value is 15.2.

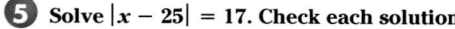

Some equations contain absolute value expressions. The definition of absolute value is used in solving the equations. When an equation has more than one solution, the solutions are often written as a set, $\{a, b\}$.

Example 5 Solve $|x - 25| = 17$. Check each solution.

$|x - 25| = 17$ means $x - 25 = 17$ or $-(x - 25) = 17$.

$$x - 25 = 17 \qquad \text{or} \qquad -(x - 25) = 17$$
$$x - 25 + 25 = 17 + 25 \qquad\qquad x - 25 = -17$$
$$x = 42 \qquad\qquad x - 25 + 25 = -17 + 25$$
$$\qquad\qquad\qquad\qquad x = 8$$

Check:
$$|x - 25| = 17 \qquad\qquad |x - 25| = 17$$
$$|42 - 25| \overset{?}{=} 17 \quad \text{or} \quad |8 - 25| \overset{?}{=} 17$$
$$|17| \overset{?}{=} 17 \qquad\qquad |-17| \overset{?}{=} 17$$
$$17 = 17 \checkmark \qquad\qquad 17 = 17 \checkmark$$

The solutions are 42 and 8. Thus, the solution set is $\{42, 8\}$.

Example 6

CONNECTION

Health

Hypothermia and *hyperthermia* are similar words but have opposite meanings. Hypothermia is defined as a lowered body temperature. Hyperthermia means an extremely high body temperature. Both are potentially dangerous conditions and occur when a person's body temperature is more than 8° above or below the normal body temperature of 98.6°F. At what temperatures do these conditions begin to occur?

Let b = normal body temperature. Then solve $|b - 98.6| = 8$.

$$|b - 98.6| = 8$$

$$b - 98.6 = 8 \qquad \text{or} \qquad b - 98.6 = -8$$
$$b = 106.6 \qquad\qquad b = 90.6$$

The solutions are 106.6 and 90.6. Hypothermia occurs when the body temperature is below 90.6°F. Hyperthermia occurs when the body temperature is above 106.6°F.

For Example 4
Evaluate $|-8a - 3|$ if $a = -2$.
$|-8(-2) - 3| = |13|$ or 13

For Example 5
Solve $|k + 6| = 9$.
$k + 6 = 9$ or $k + 6 = -9$
$\quad k = 3 \qquad\qquad k = -15$
{3, 15}

For Example 6
A school contest is being run by the Booster Club. To win, you must guess the number of jelly beans in a jar within 5 of the actual number. If there are 498 jelly beans in the jar, what are the highest and lowest guesses that will win?
Let n = number guessed.
$|486 - n| = 5$
$486 - n = 5$ or $486 - n = -5$
$\quad n = 481 \qquad\qquad n = 491$

Teaching Tip If students use a calculator to solve any of the examples, they may make the mistake of changing the sign when they see the first negative number in the display. Make sure they realize that they use the key only after the expression in the absolute value is completely evaluated.

In-Class Examples

For Example 7

Solve $-2|x + 3| = 6$. $\varnothing$

For Example 8

Solve $|x + 6| = 2x$.
$x = 6$ or $x = -2$
Check: $|6 + 6| = |12| = 12$
$\qquad 2(6) = 12$ yes
$\qquad |-2 + 6| = |4| = 4$
$\qquad 2(-2) = -4$ no
$\{6\}$

3 PRACTICE/APPLY

Check for Understanding

Exercises 1–15 are designed to help you assess your students' understanding through reading, writing, speaking, and modeling. You should work through Exercises 1–5 with your students and then monitor their work on Exercises 6–15.

Additional Answers

1. Absolute value represents the number of units x is away from zero.

2. $|x - 7| = -4$ can have no solution because an absolute value cannot have a negative solution.

Study Guide Masters, p. 5

NAME	DATE

1-5
Study Guide

Student Edition
Pages 36–41

Solving Absolute Value Equations

The absolute value of a number is the number of units it is from 0 on the number line. Absolute value can also be defined as shown in the box to the right.

Definition of Absolute Value
For any real number a:
If $a \geq 0$, then $|a| = a$.
If $a < 0$, then $|a| = -a$.

The definition of absolute value is used in solving absolute value equations.

Example: Solve $|x - 5| = 10$. Check each solution.

$$|x - 5| = 10$$

If $x - 5$ is positive or zero, then $|x - 5| = x - 5$.	If $x - 5$ is negative, then $|x - 5| = -(x - 5)$.
$x - 5 = 10$	$-(x - 5) = 10$
$x = 15$	$x - 5 = -10$
	$x = -5$

Check: $|x - 5| = 10$ or $|-5 - 5| \stackrel{?}{=} 10$
$\quad |15 - 5| \stackrel{?}{=} 10 \qquad |-10| \stackrel{?}{=} 10$
$\quad |10| \stackrel{?}{=} 10 \qquad\quad 10 = 10 ✔$
$\quad 10 = 10 ✔$

The solutions are -5 and 15.

Solve each equation.

1. $|x + 15| = 37$ $-52, 22$
2. $|t - 4| - 5 = 0$ $-1, 9$
3. $|m + 3| = 12 - 2m$ 3

4. $|x - 5| = 45$ $-40, 50$
5. $|5x + 9| = 16$ $-5, \frac{7}{5}$
6. $|8 + 5a| = 14 - a$ 1

7. $2|x - \frac{6}{3}| = 8$ $-2, 6$
8. $|x - \frac{4}{3}| = 8$ $-\frac{20}{3}, \frac{28}{3}$
9. $|\frac{1}{3}x + 3| = 0$ -9

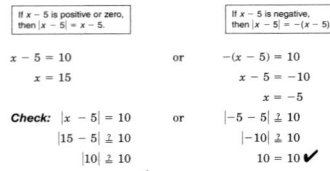

Sometimes an equation has no solution. For example, $|x| = -6$ is never true. Since the absolute value of a number is always positive or zero, there is no replacement for x that will make that sentence true. The solution set has no members. It is called the **empty set** and is symbolized by $\{\ \}$ or $\varnothing$.

Example **7** **Solve $|2x + 7| + 5 = 0$.**

$$|2x + 7| + 5 = 0$$
$$|2x + 7| = -5$$

This sentence is *never* true, so the solution set is $\varnothing$.

It is important to check your answers when solving absolute value equations. Even if the correct procedure for solving the equations is used, the answers may not be actual solutions to the original equation.

Example **8** **Solve $|x - 2| = 2x - 10$.**

$|x - 2| = 2x - 10$ means $x - 2 = 2x - 10$ or $x - 2 = -(2x - 10)$.

$x - 2 = 2x - 10$ or $x - 2 = -(2x - 10)$
$\quad -2 = x - 10 \qquad\qquad x - 2 = -2x + 10$
$\qquad 8 = x \qquad\qquad\qquad 3x = 12$
$\qquad\qquad\qquad\qquad\qquad\quad x = 4$

Check: $|x - 2| = 2x - 10 \qquad\qquad |x - 2| = 2x - 10$
$\quad |8 - 2| \stackrel{?}{=} 2(8) - 10 \quad$ or $\quad |4 - 2| \stackrel{?}{=} 2(4) - 10$
$\qquad |6| \stackrel{?}{=} 16 - 10 \qquad\qquad\quad |2| \stackrel{?}{=} 8 - 10$
$\qquad\quad 6 = 6 ✓ \qquad\qquad\qquad\quad 2 \neq -2$

The only solution is 8.

CHECK FOR UNDERSTANDING

Communicating Mathematics

Study the lesson. Then complete the following. 1–4. See margin.

1. **Explain** why an absolute value equation can have two solutions.

2. **Write** a convincing argument for why $|x - 7| + 4 = 0$ has no solution.

3. **You Decide** Janelle says that $-a$ is always negative in the definition of absolute value. (If $a < 0$, then $|a| = -a$.) Bobby says that even $-a$ can be positive. Who is correct, and why?

4. **Determine** whether $-x < x$ is always true, sometimes true, or never true. Explain your reasoning.

5. **Write** an absolute value equation that has no solution.
   See students' work.

Guided Practice

Evaluate each expression if $x = 2.5$.

6. $|x + 6|$ 8.5
7. $|-2x|$ 5
8. $-|x + 10|$ -12.5

Solve each equation.

9. $|x + 5| = 18$ 13, -23
10. $|x + 9| = 25$ 16, -34
11. $|x - 6| = 12$ 18, -6
12. $|x - 3| = 15$ 18, -12
13. $|3 + x| = 45$ 42, -48
14. $6|5x + 2| = 312$ 10, -10.8

40 Chapter 1 *Analyzing Equations and Inequalities*

Reteaching

Using Alternative Methods At Pete's Pizza there are three possible toppings: pepperoni, mushroom, and onions. List all 8 different types of pizza that can be made at Pete's Pizza. Use initials of toppings to abbreviate answers. For example, MP is a mushroom-pepperoni pizza.

Additional Answers

3. Explanations will vary; $-a$ could be a positive number if the original a is negative; $-(-a) = a$.

4. sometimes true; true if x is positive, false if x is 0 or negative

15. Manufacturing A machine is to fill each of several boxes with 16 ounces of sugar. After the boxes are filled, another machine weighs the boxes. If the box is more than 0.2 ounces above or below the desired weight, the box is rejected.

a. Write an absolute value equation to find the heaviest and lightest box the machine will approve. $|x - 16| = 0.2$

b. Solve the equation. $x = 16.2, x = 15.8$

EXERCISES

Practice

Evaluate each expression if $x = -4$, $y = 5$, and $z = 1.2$.

16. $|-4x|$ 16
17. $|2y - 5|$ 5
18. $|3z|$ 3.6
19. $|x + 5|$ 1
20. $|-2y|$ 10
21. $-|2z - 4|$ -1.6
22. $6 - |4y + 10|$ -24 23. $7 - |3z + 10|$ -6.6 24. $3|x + 4| + |3x|$ 12

Solve each equation.

25. $|x - 3| = 17$ 20, -14
26. $|x + 6| = 18$ 12, -24
27. $|x + 11| = 42$ 31, -53
28. $3|x + 6| = 36$ 6, -18
29. $11|x - 9| = 121$ 20, -2
30. $|2x + 9| = 30$ 10.5, -19.5
31. $8|x - 3| = 88$ 14, -8
32. $|2x + 7| = 0$ $-\frac{7}{2}$
33. $|4x - 3| = -27$ no solution
34. $8|4x - 3| = 64$ $\frac{11}{4}, -\frac{5}{4}$
35. $3|3x + 2| = 51$ 5, $-\frac{19}{3}$
36. $5|x + 4| = 45$ 5, -13
37. $4|6x - 1| = 29$ $\frac{11}{8}, -\frac{25}{24}$
38. $|3t - 5| = 2t$ 1, 5
39. $|2a + 7| = a - 4$ no solution
40. $|x - 3| + 7 = 2$ no solution
41. $3|x + 6| = 9x - 6$ 4
42. $5|3x - 4| = x + 1$ $\frac{3}{2}, \frac{19}{16}$

Programming

43. The graphing calculator program at the right tests decimal values to estimate the solution for $|x^2 - 2| = 0$. Enter a possible solution for x. The program will test it, give you the value of $|x^2 - 2|$, and tell you if you need to try again. If you guess correctly, the program will give you both solutions.

```
PROGRAM:ABSVALUE
:Prompt X
:Disp "abs(X²−2)=",abs(X²−2)
:If abs(X²−2)=0
:Then
:Goto 1
:End
:Disp "TRY AGAIN"
:Disp "PRESS ENTER"
:Stop
:Lbl 1
:Disp "SOLUTIONS ARE",X
:Disp "AND",−X
```

Use the program to approximate to the nearest tenth the solutions for each equation. You will need to enter the equation into Y₁ on the Y= list for each exercise. All solutions are between −10 and 10.

a. $x^2 - 2x - 4 = 0$; 2 solutions $-2.4, 2.4$
b. $x^3 - 3x = 0$; 3 solutions $-1.7, 0, 1.7$
c. $|3x - 2| - 4 = 0$; 2 solutions $-0.7, 2$
d. $5x^3 + 3x^2 - 25x - 15 = 0$; 3 solutions $-2.2, -0.6, 2.2$

Assignment Guide

Core: 17–43 odd, 44, 45, 47–56

Enriched: 16–42 even, 43–56

For **Extra Practice,** see p. 877.

The red A, B, and C flags, printed only in the Teacher's Wraparound Edition, indicate the level of difficulty of the exercises.

Using the Programming Exercises The program given in Exercise 43 is for use with a TI-82 graphing calculator. For other programmable calculators, have students consult their owner's manual for commands similar to those presented here.

Practice Masters, p. 5

1-5   NAME _____   DATE _____

Practice   Student Edition Pages 36–41

Solving Absolute Value Equations

Solve each equation.

1. $|n - 4| = 13$ $-9, 17$
2. $7|x + 3| = 42$ $-9, 3$
3. $|2y - 3| = 29$ $-13, 16$
4. $|x - \frac{3}{8}| = 2$ $-\frac{13}{8}, \frac{19}{8}$
5. $|\frac{2}{3}u - 6| = 42$ $-54, 72$
6. $|5x - 4| = -6$ no solution
7. $-3|4x - 9| = 24$ no solution
8. $-6|5 - 2y| = -9$ $\frac{7}{4}, \frac{13}{4}$
9. $|8 + p| = 2p - 3$ 11
10. $5|4w - 1| = 5w + 40$ $-\frac{7}{5}, 3$
11. $4|2y - 7| + 5 = 9$ 3, 4
12. $-2|7 - 3y| - 6 = -14$ 1, $\frac{11}{3}$

List possibilities to answer each problem.

13. In how many ways can a clerk give a customer 25¢ in change? **13 ways**

14. In how many ways can you select three numbers from the set {1, 2, 3, 4, 5, 6, 7, 8} so that the numbers could represent the measures of the sides of a triangle? Remember that the sum of the measures of any two sides of a triangle must be greater than the measure of the other side. **22 ways**

Closing Activity

Modeling Give students counters in five colors. Have the students model the combinations with one of the colors staying in the first place. Can they conjecture how many cases there will be from this one case?

Additional Answer

47. TAW, TAX, TAY, TBW, TBX, TBY, TCW, TCX, TCY, UAW, UAX, UAY, UBW, UBX, UBY, UCW, UCX, UCY, VAW, VAX, VAY, VBW, VBX, VBY, VCW, VCX, VCY

Enrichment Masters, p. 5

NAME_____ DATE _____

1-5
Enrichment

Student Edition
Pages 36–41

Venn Diagrams

Relationships among sets can be shown using Venn diagrams.
Study the diagrams below. The circles represent sets A and B,
which are subsets of set S.

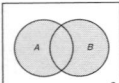 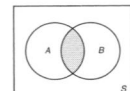 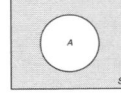

The union of A and B consists of all elements in *either* A or B.
The intersection of A and B consists of all elements in *both* A and B.
The complement of A consists of all elements *not* in A.

You can combine the operations of union, intersection, and finding
the complement.

Example: Shade the region (A ∩ B)′.

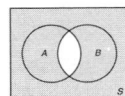

(A ∩ B)′ means the complement of the
intersection of A and B.
First find the intersection of A and B.
Then find its complement.

Draw a Venn diagram and shade the region indicated. See students' diagrams.

1. $A′ \cap B$ 2. $A′ \cup B$
3. $A \cap B′$ 4. $A′ \cup B′$
5. $(A \cup B)′$ 6. $A \cap B′$

**Draw a Venn diagram and three overlapping circles. Then
shade the region indicated.** See students' diagrams.

7. $(A \cup B) \cup C′$ 8. $(A \cup B)′ \cap C′$
9. $A \cup (B \cup C)$ 10. $(A \cup B) \cup C$
11. Is the union operation associative? yes
12. Is the intersection operation associative? yes

Critical Thinking

44. Solve $|x + 2| = |2x - 4|$ and explain your method of solution.
$6, \frac{2}{3}$; See students' work for explanations.

Applications and Problem Solving

45. **Contests** Foust Honda is having a contest to win a new Honda Civic. To win a chance at the car, you must guess the number of keys in a jar within 5 of the actual number. The people who are within this range get to try a key in the ignition of the Civic. Suppose there are 697 keys in the jar.
   a. Write an equation to determine the highest and lowest guesses that will win a chance at the car. $|x - 697| = 5$
   b. Solve the equation. $x = 702$ or $x = 692$

46. **Chemistry** For hydrogen to be a liquid, its temperature must be within 2°C of −257°C.
   a. Write an equation to determine the least and greatest temperatures for this substance to remain a liquid. $|x + 257°| = 2°$
   b. Solve the equation. $x = -259°C, x = -255°C$

47. **List Possibilities** The telephone number of a local business is 555-1829. They are trying to make a word from the last three digits of their number so that customers will remember it easily. The digit 8 can be T, U, or V; 2 can be A, B, or C; 9 can be W, X, or Y. List the possible combinations of letters that their number can represent. See margin.

Mixed Review

48. Write an algebraic expression to represent *four plus three times a number*. (Lesson 1–4) $4 + 3x$

49. Solve $3 - 2x = 18$. (Lesson 1–4) $-\frac{15}{2}$

50. **Geometry** The perimeter of a square is 42 inches. Find the length of one side of the square. (Lesson 1–4) **10.5 inches**

51. **Zoology** The population of gorillas at a zoo was decreased when five of them were moved to another zoo. Write an expression to represent the original number of gorillas at the zoo if there are p gorillas there now. (Lesson 1–4) $p + 5$

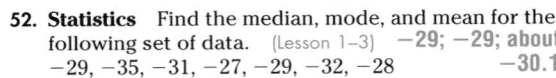

52. **Statistics** Find the median, mode, and mean for the following set of data. (Lesson 1–3) **−29; −29; about −30.1**
   $-29, -35, -31, -27, -29, -32, -28$

53. **Statistics** Find the median, mode, and mean for the stem-and-leaf plot at the right.

Stem	Leaf
13	0 2 3 3 5 7
14	1 1 1 5 7 8 9 9
15	5 6 7 7 $14|5 = 145$

   (Lesson 1–3) **143; 141; about 143.7**

54. Name the property illustrated by $\frac{3}{8}(1) = \frac{3}{8}$. (Lesson 1–2) **mult. iden.**

55. Evaluate -2.4×10. Then name the sets of numbers to which it belongs. (Lesson 1–2) **−24; Z, Q, R**

56. Find the value of $12a^2 + bc$ if $a = 3, b = 7$, and $c = -2$. (Lesson 1–1) **94**

Extension

Communication Given the equation $3n + 24 = 105$, write a problem that fits the equation. Then explain in writing, without using another equation, how to solve the problem. Make sure to list the strategy and explain why it was chosen.

Solving Inequalities

1-6

What YOU'LL LEARN

* To solve inequalities and graph the solution sets.

Why IT'S IMPORTANT

You can use inequalities to solve problems involving health, school, and shopping.

CONNECTION
Health

Kristin read in a magazine about an effective way for women to calculate the optimal daily Calorie intake, which is the number of Calories used while at rest. The steps are listed below.

1. Multiply your weight in pounds w by 4.3.
2. Multiply your height in inches h by 4.7.
3. Add the numbers.
4. Add 655 to your result from step 3.
5. Multiply your age a times 4.7.
6. Subtract the product in step 5 from the expression in step 4.

The expression for optimal Calorie intake is $4.3w + 4.7h + 655 - 4.7a$. To find the number of Calories you burn with moderate activity, multiply the expression by 1.3. This gives you the number of Calories per day to maintain your weight.

$$1.3(4.3w + 4.7h + 655 - 4.7a)$$

If you keep your daily Calorie intake between the two numbers, you should lose weight. If you take in fewer Calories than you burn at rest, your metabolism will slow down and you may lose less weight.

A 30-year old woman weighing 130 pounds and 65 inches tall burns about 1400 Calories a day at rest and about 1800 Calories with moderate activity. If she eats 1800 Calories per day, she should maintain her weight. Her actual intake will either be greater than, less than, or equal to her optimal intake of 1800 Calories.

Let x represent her optimal intake and a represent her actual intake. You can compare the optimal and actual intakes using an inequality or an equation.

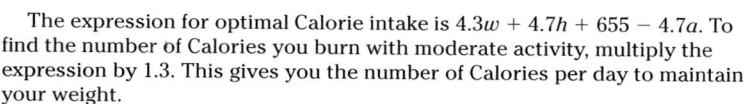

$$x > a \qquad\qquad x < a \qquad\qquad x = a$$

This is an illustration of the **trichotomy property**.

Trichotomy Property	For any two real numbers, a and b, exactly one of the following statements is true. $$a < b \qquad a = b \qquad a > b$$

Adding the same number to each side of an inequality does not change the truth of the inequality.

Addition and Subtraction Properties for Inequalities	For any real numbers, a, b, and c: 1. if $a > b$, then $a + c > b + c$ and $a - c > b - c$; 2. if $a < b$, then $a + c < b + c$ and $a - c < b - c$.

These properties can be used to solve inequalities. The solution sets of inequalities can then be graphed on number lines.

GLENCOE *Technology*

CD-ROM Interaction

A multimedia simulation uses collecting and graphing data to explore the ocean floor. A blackline master activity with teacher's notes provides a follow-up to the CD-ROM simulation.

For Windows & Macintosh

1-6 LESSON NOTES

NCTM Standards: 1–5

Instructional Resources

* Study Guide Master 1-6
* Practice Master 1-6
* Enrichment Master 1-6
* Assessment and Evaluation Masters, p. 17
* Graphing Calculator Masters, p. 1
* Real-World Applications, 3

Transparency 1-6A contains the 5-Minute Check for this lesson; **Transparency 1-6B** contains a teaching aid for this lesson.

Recommended Pacing	
Standard Pacing	Day 8 of 12
Honors Pacing	Day 8 of 12
Block Scheduling*	Day 5 of 6 (along with Lesson 1-7)

*For more information on pacing and possible lesson plans, refer to the *Block Scheduling Booklet*.

1 FOCUS

5-Minute Check
(over Lesson 1-5)

1. Evaluate $|4x + 1|$ if $x = -2$. **7**

Solve each equation.

2. $|x + 10| = 12$ **2, −22**
3. $2|2x + 1| = -10$
   no solution
4. $5|x - 2| = 2x + 11$ **7, $-\frac{1}{7}$**

Use the strategy of listing possibilities to solve.

5. Maggie forgot her locker combination. She knows the first digit is 2 and the second digit is 6 or 9, but she cannot remember the last digit. If the digits can range from 0–9, how many possibilities of locker combinations can she try? **20**

Motivating the Lesson

Questioning Here are two inequalities.

$-5 < -4$ $8 > 5$

Is each inequality still true if you:

1. add 2 to each side?
2. add -2 to each side?
3. multiply each side by 2?
4. multiply each side by -2?

2 TEACH

Teaching Tip For Example 1, to check inequalities, first check the boundary point for the variable and see if the two sides are equivalent. To make sure the direction of the inequality is correct, check a point on each side of the boundary point.

In-Class Example

For Example 1
Solve $y + 6 > 3$. Graph the solution set. $y > -3$

$-4\ -3\ -2\ -1\ \ 0\ \ 1\ \ 2\ \ 3\ \ 4\ \ 5$

Example ❶ **Solve $6x + 3 > 5x - 2$. Graph the solution set.**

$$6x + 3 > 5x - 2$$

$$-5x + 6x + 3 > -5x + 5x - 2 \quad \textit{Add } -5x \textit{ to each side.}$$

$$x + 3 > -2$$

$$x + 3 + (-3) > -2 + (-3) \quad \textit{Add } -3 \textit{ to each side.}$$

$$x > -5$$

A circle means that this point is not included.

$-7\ -6\ -5\ -4\ -3\ -2\ -1\ \ 0\ \ 1\ \ 2\ \ 3\ \ 4$

Any real number greater than -5 is a solution.

Check: Substitute -5 for x in $6x + 3 > 5x - 2$. The two sides should be equal. Then substitute a number greater than -5. The inequality should be true.

You know that $12 > -3$ is a true inequality. What happens if you multiply the numbers on each side by a positive number or by a negative number? Is it still true?

Multiply by 6.

$$12 > -3$$
$$6(12) \overset{?}{>} 6(-3)$$
$$72 > -18 \quad \text{true}$$

Multiply the inequality by other positive numbers. Do you think that the inequality will always remain true?

Multiply by $-\frac{1}{3}$.

$$12 > -3$$
$$-\frac{1}{3}(12) \overset{?}{>} -\frac{1}{3}(-3)$$
$$-4 > 1 \quad \text{false}$$

If you reverse the inequality, the statement is true.
$$-4 < 1 \quad \text{true}$$
Try other negative numbers as multipliers.

This suggests that when you multiply each side of an inequality by a negative number, the order of the inequality must be reversed.

These and other examples suggest the following properties.

Multiplication and Division Properties for Inequalities	**For any real numbers a, b, and c:**
	1. if c is positive and $a < b$, then $ac < bc$ and $\frac{a}{c} < \frac{b}{c}$;
	2. if c is positive and $a > b$, then $ac > bc$ and $\frac{a}{c} > \frac{b}{c}$;
	3. if c is negative and $a < b$, then $ac > bc$ and $\frac{a}{c} > \frac{b}{c}$;
	4. if c is negative and $a > b$, then $ac < bc$ and $\frac{a}{c} < \frac{b}{c}$.

Cooperative Learning

Co-op Co-op Have students work in small groups. Their task is to develop a flowchart for solving inequalities. Make one flowchart for inequalities involving addition and one flowchart for inequalities involving multiplication. Each student should develop a problem and solve it by following the flowchart.

For more information on the co-op co-op strategy, see *Cooperative Learning in the Mathematics Classroom,* one of the titles in the Glencoe Mathematics Professional Series, page 32.

Examples 2 and 3 show how to use these properties when solving inequalities.

Example Solve $-0.4p > 10$. Graph the solution set.

$$-0.4p > 10$$

$$\frac{-0.4p}{-0.4} < \frac{10}{-0.4}$$ *Reverse the inequality sign because each side is divided by a negative number.*

$$p < -25$$

$$\begin{array}{c} \xleftarrow{\hspace{4cm}} \circ \xrightarrow{\hspace{1.5cm}} \\ {\scriptstyle -33\,-32\,-31\,-30\,-29\,-28\,-27\,-26\,-25\,-24\,-23\,-22\,-21} \end{array}$$

Any real number less than -25 is a solution.

The solution in Example 2 can be written using set-builder notation. This solution set can be written as $\{p \mid p < -25\}$. This is read as *the set of all numbers p such that p is less than -25.*

Example Solve $-y \geq \dfrac{y+6}{7}$.

$$-y \geq \frac{y+6}{7}$$

$$-7y \geq y + 6 \quad \text{\textit{Multiply each side by 7.}}$$

$$-8y \geq 6 \quad \text{\textit{Add } -y \text{ \textit{to each side.}}}$$

$$y \leq -\frac{3}{4} \quad \text{\textit{Divide each side by } -8, \text{ \textit{reversing the inequality sign.}}}$$

A dot means that this point is included.

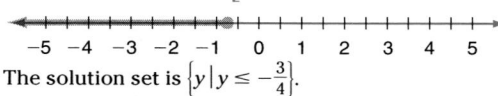

$$\begin{array}{c} \xleftarrow{\hspace{3cm}} \bullet \xrightarrow{\hspace{4cm}} \\ {\scriptstyle -5 \quad -4 \quad -3 \quad -2 \quad -1 \quad 0 \quad 1 \quad 2 \quad 3 \quad 4 \quad 5} \end{array}$$

The solution set is $\left\{ y \mid y \leq -\dfrac{3}{4} \right\}$.

You can use a graphing calculator to find the solution of an inequality graphically.

EXPLORATION

GRAPHING CALCULATORS

You can use the inequality symbols in the TEST menu on the TI-82 graphing calculator to find the solution to an inequality in one variable. Use the standard viewing window.

Your Turn a–c. See students' work.

a. Clear the Y= list. Enter $8x + 5 < 6x - 3$ as Y1. Press GRAPH. Describe what you see. (The symbol $<$ is item 5 on the TEST menu.)

b. Use the TRACE function to scan the values along the graph. What values of x are on the graph? What do you notice about the values of Y on the graph?

c. Solve the inequality algebraically. How does your solution compare to the pattern you noticed in part b?

In-Class Examples

For Example 2
Solve $-3x > 27$. Graph the solution set. $x < -9$

$$\begin{array}{c} \xleftarrow{\hspace{2cm}} \circ \xrightarrow{\hspace{3cm}} \\ {\scriptstyle -18\,-15\,-12\,-9\,\,-6\,\,-3\,\,\,0\,\,\,3\,\,\,6\,\,\,9} \end{array}$$

For Example 3
Solve $\dfrac{3y}{4} + 6 \geq 3$. $y \geq -4$

EXPLORATION

Students will be introduced to the TEST option on the TI-82.

Teaching Tip

Teaching Tip For Example 4, show that $\neq$ means "$>$ or $<$"; thus, $6x \neq 18$ means "$6x > 18$ or $6x < 18$." Point out that $\not>$ means "is not greater than," and $\not<$ means "is not less than."

In-Class Example

For Example 4

Mr. and Mrs. Brubaker want to buy a used car that costs $9000. They don't want to spend more than $3000 in interest over 4 years. Use the formula $I = prt$ to find the interest rates they can afford.

$r \le 8\frac{1}{3}\%$

3 PRACTICE/APPLY

Check for Understanding

Exercises 1–13 are designed to help you assess your students' understanding through reading, writing, speaking, and modeling. You should work through Exercises 1–3 with your students and then monitor their work on Exercises 4–13.

Study Guide Masters, p. 6

1-6

NAME_____ DATE _____

Student Edition
Pages 42–48

Study Guide

Solving Inequalities

The following properties can be used to solve inequalities.

Addition and Subtraction Properties for Inequalities

For any real numbers a, b, and c:
1. If $a > b$, then $a + c > b + c$ and $a - c > b - c$.
2. If $a < b$, then $a + c < b + c$ and $a - c < b - c$.

Multiplication and Division Properties for Inequalities

For any real numbers a, b, and c:
1. If c is positive and $a < b$, then $ac < bc$ and $\frac{a}{c} < \frac{b}{c}$.
2. If c is positive, and $a > b$, then $ac > bc$ and $\frac{a}{c} > \frac{b}{c}$.
3. If c is negative and $a < b$, then $ac > bc$ and $\frac{a}{c} > \frac{b}{c}$.
4. If c is negative and $a > b$, then $ac < bc$ and $\frac{a}{c} < \frac{b}{c}$.

Solve each inequality.

1. $3a - 15 > 6$
   $\{a | a > 7\}$
2. $2x + 4 > 36$
   $\{x | x > 16\}$
3. $7(7a - 9) \le 84$
   $\{a | a \le 3\}$

4. $17 - 3w \ge 35$
   $\{w | w \le -6\}$
5. $2 + 3(n + 5) \ge 4(n + 3)$
   $\{n | n \le 5\}$
6. $4s - 12 < 20$
   $\{s | s < 8\}$

7. $4(b - 7) + 6 \ge 22$
   $\{b | b \ge 11\}$
8. $3(9z + 4) > 35z - 4$
   $\{z | z < 2\}$
9. $4(m - 5) > 5 - m$
   $\{m | m > 5\}$

10. $4p + 7 > 5p + 1(16 - 2p)$
    $\{p | p > 9\}$
11. $32 + 11r^2 < 17(r + r^2) - 6r^2$
    $\left\{r | r > \frac{32}{17}\right\}$
12. $4x - 2 > -7(4x - 2)$
    $\left\{x | x > \frac{1}{2}\right\}$

Inequalities can be used to solve many verbal problems. You can solve problems with inequalities in the same way you solve problems with equations.

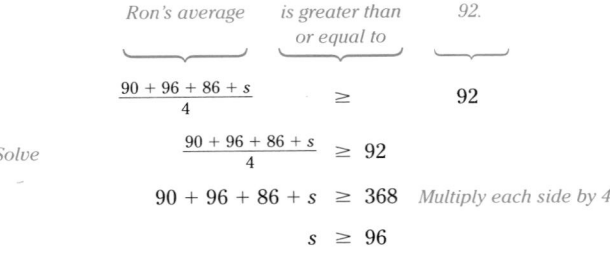

Example 4

APPLICATION
School

Ron's scores on the first three of four 100-point chemistry tests were 90, 96, and 86. What score must he receive on the fourth test to have an average of at least 92 for all the tests?

Explore Let s represent the score needed on the fourth test. *The phrase at least 92 means greater than or equal to 92.*

Plan The average of Ron's test scores is their sum divided by 4. This number must be greater than or equal to 92. Write an inequality. Let s represent the score on the fourth test.

Ron's average	is greater than or equal to	92.
$\dfrac{90 + 96 + 86 + s}{4}$	$\ge$	92

Solve

$$\frac{90 + 96 + 86 + s}{4} \ge 92$$

$$90 + 96 + 86 + s \ge 368 \quad \textit{Multiply each side by 4.}$$

$$s \ge 96$$

Examine Ron must score at least 96 on the fourth test to average at least 92 for all the tests.

CHECK FOR UNDERSTANDING

Communicating Mathematics

Study the lesson. Then complete the following.

1. **Draw** a graph that shows the solution set $\{x | x > -2\}$.   **See margin.**

2. **Write** *half of five times a number is less than or equal to 10* as an inequality. $\frac{1}{2}(5x) \le 10$

3. **Solve** the following problems.

   a. Choose the correct symbol ($<$, $>$, or $=$) to make each statement true.

      $6 \underline{\ ?\ } 3 \quad 6 \underline{\ ?\ } -3 \quad -6 \underline{\ ?\ } 3 \quad -6 \underline{\ ?\ } -3$
      $\quad > \qquad\quad > \qquad\quad < \qquad\quad <$

   b. Divide each side of each inequality above by 2. Record each result. Are the inequalities still true?   **yes**

   c. Divide each side of the original inequalities by -2. Are the inequalities still true? Explain your results.   **See margin.**

Reteaching

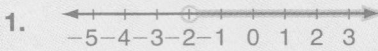

Using Substeps Have students list the first two steps they would take to solve the inequalities. Then have them solve each inequality.

1. $3 - 2x < 9$ $x > -3$
2. $4x + 7 \ge 3(x + 2)$ $x \ge -1$
3. $3x > 4x$ $x < 0$
4. $2x > x + 1 + x$ $\varnothing$
5. $3(x + 2) < 3x + 8$ **all reals**
6. $4x + 3 \le -33$ $x \le -9$

Additional Answers

1.
   $-5\ -4\ -3\ -2\ -1\ \ 0\ \ 1\ \ 2\ \ 3$

3c. No; when you multiply both sides of an inequality by a negative number, the inequality sign must by reversed to keep the inequality true.

Guided Practice

4–11. See margin for graphs.

Solve each inequality. Graph the solution set.

4. $x > 4.5$ $\{x \mid x > 4.5\}$

5. $7 \le 4a$ $\{a \mid a \ge 1.75\}$

6. $7 - b \ge 5$ $\{b \mid b \le 2\}$

7. $3x + 4 \ge 19$ $\{x \mid x \ge 5\}$

8. $2c + 15 \ge 3$ $\{c \mid c \ge -6\}$

9. $\frac{d}{10} - 2 \le 0$ $\{d \mid d \le 20\}$

10. $-0.5y < 6$ $\{y \mid y > -12\}$

11. $\frac{7x + 1}{8} > \frac{7x}{8} + 1$ $\varnothing$

Define a variable and write an inequality for each problem. Then solve.

12. Four times a number is less than 32. $4x < 32$

13. A number plus fifteen is greater than or equal to 27. $n + 15 \ge 27$

14–37. See Solutions Manual for graphs.

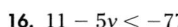

EXERCISES

Practice

Solve each inequality. Graph the solution set.

A

14. $6x < 30$ $\{x \mid x < 5\}$

15. $-5r > 25$ $\{r \mid r < -5\}$

16. $11 - 5y < -77$ $\{y \mid y > 17.6\}$

17. $0.06 + x < 2$ $\{x \mid x < 1.94\}$

18. $15 - 5t \ge 55$ $\{t \mid t \le -8\}$

19. $6x + 4 \ge 34$ $\{x \mid x \ge 5\}$

20. $3(4x + 7) < 21$ $\{x \mid x < 0\}$

21. $8x + 5 \ge 10$ $\left\{x \mid x \ge \frac{5}{8}\right\}$

22. $40 \le -6(5r - 7)$ $\left\{r \mid r \ge \frac{1}{15}\right\}$

23. $7x - 5 > 3x + 4$ $\{x \mid x > 2.25\}$

24. $9(2x + 3) > 10$ $\left\{x \mid x > -\frac{17}{18}\right\}$

25. $5(3z - 3) \le 60$ $\{z \mid z \le 5\}$

27. $\left\{m \mid m > \frac{4}{9}\right\}$

26. $7 - 2m \ge 0$ $\{m \mid m \le 3.5\}$

27. $2(m - 5) - 3(2m - 5) < 5m + 1$

B

28. $0.01x - 4.23 \ge 0$ $\{x \mid x \ge 423\}$

29. $3b - 2(b - 5) < 2(b + 4)$ $\{b \mid b > 2\}$

30. $0.75x - 0.5 < 0$ $\left\{x \mid x < \frac{2}{3}\right\}$

31. $2.55x - 4.24 \le 0$ $\{x \mid x \le 1.66\}$

32. $\frac{2x + 3}{5} \le 0.03$ $\{x \mid x \le 1.425\}$

33. $\frac{3x - 3}{5} < \frac{6(x - 1)}{10}$ $\varnothing$

34. $\frac{4x + 2}{5} \ge -0.04$ $\{x \mid x \ge -0.55\}$

35. $-x \ge \frac{x + 4}{7}$ $\left\{x \mid x \le -\frac{1}{2}\right\}$

36. $\frac{x + 8}{4} - 1 > \frac{x}{3}$ $\{x \mid x < 12\}$

37. $20\left(\frac{1}{5} - \frac{w}{4}\right) \ge -2w$ $\left\{w \mid w \le \frac{4}{3}\right\}$

Define a variable and write an inequality for each problem. Then solve. 38–43. See Solutions Manual for solutions.

C

38. The product of 11 and a number is less than 53. $11x < 53$

39. Three fourths of a number decreased by 25 is at least 8. $\frac{3}{4}x - 25 \ge 8$

40. The opposite of five times a number is less than 321. $-5x < 321$

41. Fifty-seven is greater than one-half a number. $57 > 0.5x$

42. Ninety decreased by 5 is greater than or equal to the product of a number and 10. $90 - 5 \ge 10x$

43. Sixty-two is less than the opposite of 6 times a number. $62 < -6x$

Assignment Guide

Core: 15–47 odd, 48, 49, 51–59
Enriched: 14–46 even, 48–59

For **Extra Practice,** see p. 877.

The red A, B, and C flags, printed only in the Teacher's Wraparound Edition, indicate the level of difficulty of the exercises.

Additional Answers

4.

5.

6.

7.

8.

9.

10.

11. $\varnothing$

Practice Masters, p. 6

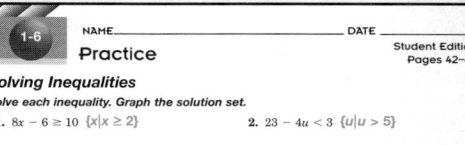

NAME _____ DATE _____
1-6 Practice
Student Editio
Pages 42–4

Solving Inequalities

Solve each inequality. Graph the solution set.

1. $8x - 6 \ge 10$ $\{x \mid x \ge 2\}$

2. $23 - 4u < 3$ $\{u \mid u > 5\}$

3. $-3(4w - 1) > -12$ $\left\{w \mid w < \frac{5}{4}\right\}$

4. $5(2x + 3) \le 4$ $\left\{x \mid x \le -\frac{11}{10}\right\}$

Solve each inequality.

5. $9x - 11 > 4x + 12$ $\left\{x \mid x > \frac{23}{5}\right\}$

6. $1 - 8u \le 3u - 10$ $\{u \mid u \ge 1\}$

7. $16 - 10r \ge 0$ $\left\{r \mid r \le \frac{8}{5}\right\}$

8. $9(2r - 5) - 3 < 7r - 4$ $\{r \mid r < 4\}$

9. $1 + 5(x - 8) \le 2 - (x + 5)$ $\{x \mid x \le 6\}$

10. $4n - 5(n - 3) > 3(n + 1) - 20$ $\{n \mid n < 8\}$

11. $17.5 < 19 - 2.5x$ $\{x \mid x < 0.6\}$

12. $\frac{5x}{8} - \frac{3}{4} < \frac{1}{5}$ $\left\{x \mid x < \frac{38}{25}\right\}$

13. $-6\left(\frac{1}{2} + \frac{2w}{3}\right) > 2w$ $\left\{w \mid w < -\frac{1}{2}\right\}$

14. $\frac{4x - 3}{2} \ge -1.9$ $\{x \mid x \ge -0.2\}$

Closing Activity

Writing Have students explain in writing why the division properties for inequality do not have restrictions about dividing by zero. Also, have students explain why each property works.

Chapter 1, Quiz C (Lessons 1-5 and 1-6), is available in the *Assessment and Evaluation Masters,* p. 17.

Enrichment Masters, p. 6

NAME_____ DATE _____

1-6 Enrichment

Student Edition
Pages 42–48

Properties of a Group

A set of numbers forms a group with respect to an operation if for that operation the set has (1) the closure property, (2) the associative property, (3) a member which is an identity, and (4) an inverse for each member of the set.

Example 1: Does the set {0, 1, 2, 3, ···} form a group with respect to addition?

Closure property: For all numbers in the set, is $a + b$ in the set? $0 + 1 = 1$, and 1 is in the set; $0 + 2 = 2$, and 2 is in the set; and so on. The set has closure for addition.

Associative property: For all numbers in the set, does $a + (b + c) = (a + b) + c$? $0 + (1 + 2) = (0 + 1) + 2$; $1 + (2 + 3) = (1 + 2) + 3$; and so on. The set is associative for addition.

Identity: Is there some number, i, in the set such that $i + a = a = a + i$ for all a? $0 + 1 = 1 = 1 + 0$; $0 + 2 = 2 = 2 + 0$; and so on. The identity for addition is 0.

Inverse: Does each number, a, have an inverse, a', such that $a' + a = a = a + a' = i$? The integer inverse of 3 is -3 since $-3 + 3 = 0$, and 0 is the identity for addition. But the set does not contain -3. Therefore, there is no inverse for 3.

The set is not a group with respect to addition because only three of the four properties hold.

Example 2: Is the set {-1, 1} a group with respect to multiplication?

Closure property: $(-1)(-1) = 1$; $(-1)(1) = -1$; $(1)(-1) = -1$; $(1)(1) = 1$. The set has closure for multiplication.

Associative property: $(-1)[(-1)(-1)] = (-1)(1) = -1$; and so on. The set is associative for multiplication.

Identity: $1(-1) = -1$; $1(1) = 1$. The identity for multiplication is 1.

Inverse: -1 is the inverse of -1 since $(-1)(-1) = 1$, and 1 is the identity. 1 is the inverse of 1 since $(1)(1) = 1$, and 1 is the identity. Each member has an inverse.

The set {-1, 1} is a group with respect to multiplication because all four properties hold.

Tell whether the set forms a group with respect to the given operation.

1. {integers}, addition **yes**
2. {integers}, multiplication **no**
3. {$\frac{1}{2}, \frac{2}{2}, \frac{3}{2}, \cdots$}, addition **no**
4. {multiples of 5}, multiplication **no**
5. {$x, x^2, x^3, x^4, \cdots$} addition **no**
6. {$\sqrt{1}, \sqrt{2}, \sqrt{3}, \cdots$}, multiplication **no**
7. {irrational numbers}, addition **no**
8. {rational numbers}, addition **yes**

Graphing Calculator

Use a graphing calculator to solve each inequality.

44. $-49 > 7(2x + 3)$ {$x \mid x < -5$}
45. $8r + 3(2 + 7.5) < 25$ {$r \mid r < 0.4375$}
46. $2(3k + 4) - 3 \le 2(-1)$ {$k \mid k \le -1.1\overline{6}$}
47. $-5s + 4(3 - 5) < 7$ {$s \mid s > -3$}

Critical Thinking

48. Find the set of all numbers that satisfy $3x - 2 \ge 0$ and $5x - 1 \le 0$. $\varnothing$

Applications and Problem Solving

49. **Health** The National Heart Association recommends that less than 30% of a person's total daily caloric intake come from fat. One gram of fat yields nine Calories. Jason is a healthy 21-year old male whose average daily caloric intake is between 2500 and 3300 Calories. **a. $750 < x < 990$**

   a. Write an inequality that represents the suggested fat intake for Jason.

   b. What is the greatest suggested fat intake for Jason? **990 calories**

50. **Consumerism** Tala is buying holiday gifts for her family early this year to take advantage of sales. Best Buy has a select group of CDs on sale for $4.99 each. Tala finds 2 jazz CDs for her father, who loves jazz. If she has $75 to spend on her family, write an inequality that tells how much money Tala has to spend on her other family members. **$2(4.99) + x \le 75$**

Mixed Review

Solve each equation. (Lesson 1–5)

51. $|x - 4| = 11$ **15, −7**
52. $|x - 8| = 3x - 4$ **3**
53. Evaluate $|2x - 4| + 1.2$ if $x = -3$. (Lesson 1–5) **11.2**
54. **Geometry** A piece of wire was cut into two pieces. One was bent into a square and the other was bent into an equilateral triangle. The side of the equilateral triangle has the same whole-number length (in cm) as the side of the square. If the length of the piece of wire is less than 50 cm, find all possible measurements for the sides of the figures. (Lesson 1–4) **1 cm, 2 cm, 3 cm, 4 cm, 5 cm, 6 cm, 7 cm**
55. Use a calculator to solve $68x + 373 = 802$. (Lesson 1–4) **about 6.309**
56. **Statistics** Find the median, mode, and mean for the following set of data. 2, 56, 8, 43, 44 (Lesson 1–3) **43; no mode; 30.6**
57. Name the property illustrated by $x(7 - 5) = x \cdot 7 - x \cdot 5$. (Lesson 1–2) **distributive**
58. Simplify $5(3m - 7n) + 3(4m + n)$. (Lesson 1–2) **$27m - 32n$**
59. **Electricity** Find the amount of current I (in amperes) produced if the electromotive force E is 1.5 volts, the circuit resistance R is 2.35 ohms, and the resistance r within a battery is 0.15 ohms, using the formula $I = \dfrac{E}{R + r}$. (Lesson 1–1) **0.6 amperes**

Extension

Problem Solving Jim plans to make an antifreeze solution by mixing some 30% antifreeze with some 90% antifreeze. How much 30% solution can he use to make 50 quarts of a solution that is at least 60% antifreeze and at most 75% antifreeze?

$12.5 < x < 25$

Solving Absolute Value Inequalities

What YOU'LL LEARN

- To solve compound inequalities using *and* and *or*, and
- to solve inequalities involving absolute value and graph the solutions.

Why IT'S IMPORTANT

You can use absolute value inequalities to solve problems involving entertainment and education.

APPLICATION
Postal Service

In January 1995, the postage for a first-class stamp rose from $0.29 to $0.32. The table below shows the past and present postage rates.

Postal Rates		
Item	**Before January 1995**	**After January 1995**
Postcard	$0.19	$0.20
Birthday card (1 oz)	$0.29	$0.32
Heavy letter (2 oz)	$0.52	$0.55
Bank statement (3 oz)	$0.75	$0.78
Insured mail ($50)	$0.75	$0.75
Parcel post (2 lb)	$1.74	$2.10
Priority mail (1 lb)	$2.90	$3.00
Registered mail ($500)	$4.85	$5.40
Express mail (8 oz)	$9.95	$10.75

Source: U.S. Postal Service

If you were to mail an oversized birthday card, you would expect to pay at least $0.32 but no more than $0.55. Let c stand for the cost of mailing the card. The two inequalities, $c \geq 0.32$ and $c \leq 0.55$, describe the cost of mailing the card. A sentence like this is called a **compound inequality.** A compound inequality containing *and* is true only if both parts of it are true.

Another way of writing $c \geq 0.32$ and $c \leq 0.55$ is $0.32 \leq c \leq 0.55$. This inequality is read *c is greater than or equal to 0.32 and is less than or equal to 0.55.*

To solve a compound inequality, you must solve each part of the inequality. Thus, the graph of a compound inequality containing *and* is the **intersection** of the graphs of the two inequalities. The intersection can be found by graphing the two inequalities and then determining where these graphs overlap or intersect.

Most popular types of greeting cards mailed in the U.S.
1. Christmas
2. Valentine's Day
3. Easter
4. Mother's Day
5. Father's Day

Greeting cards as we know them first appeared in Europe in the Middle Ages. These were mostly woodcuts and engravings.

1-7 LESSON NOTES

NCTM Standards: 1–5

Instructional Resources

- Study Guide Master 1-7
- Practice Master 1-7
- Enrichment Master 1-7
- Assessment and Evaluation Masters, p. 17
- Modeling Mathematics Masters, p. 61

Transparency 1-7A contains the 5-Minute Check for this lesson; **Transparency 1-7B** contains a teaching aid for this lesson.

Recommended Pacing	
Standard Pacing	Days 9 & 10 of 12
Honors Pacing	Days 9 & 10 of 12
Block Scheduling*	Day 5 of 6 (along with Lesson 1-6)

*For more information on pacing and possible lesson plans, refer to the *Block Scheduling Booklet.*

1 FOCUS

5-Minute Check
(over Lesson 1-6)

Solve each inequality.

1. $3x + 7 > 43$ {$x \mid x > 12$}
2. $3(3w + 1) \geq 48$ {$w \mid w \geq 5$}
3. $7 + 3y > 2(y + 3) - 2(-1 - y)$ {$y \mid y < -1$}
4. $3 + 2x > 3(x - 1)$ {$x \mid x < 6$}

Solve.

5. Tom makes $4.50 an hour. He worked 12 hours one week. If at least one third of his pay is taken out in taxes and other deductions, what is the greatest amount he will receive in his paycheck? $36.00

Motivating the Lesson

Situational Problem Have students work in cooperative groups of four and write an inequality. Collect the problems and randomly return the problems to the groups. Have each student solve the problem given to his or her group. The group should then discuss the solutions. Choose a student from each group to explain the problem and the solution.

In-Class Examples

For Example 1
Solve $8 \leq m + 6 \leq 14$. Then graph the solution set.
$\{m \mid 2 \leq m \leq 8\}$

For Example 2
Solve $-3 \leq 2y + 9$ or $18 > 4y - 10$. Then graph the solution set.
$\{y \mid -6 \leq y < 7\}$

Example **Solve $9 < 3x + 6 < 15$. Then graph the solution set.**

Method 1	**Method 2**
Write the compound inequality using the word *and*. Then solve each part.	Solve both parts at the same time by adding -6 to each part of the inequality. Then divide each part by 3.

Method 1
$$9 < 3x + 6 \quad \text{and} \quad 3x + 6 < 15$$
$$3 < 3x \qquad\qquad\qquad 3x < 9$$
$$1 < x \qquad\qquad\qquad\quad x < 3$$

Method 2
$$9 < \quad 3x + 6 \quad < 15$$
$$9 + (-6) < 3x + 6 + (-6) < 15 + (-6)$$
$$3 \div 3 < \quad 3x \div 3 \quad < 9 \div 3$$
$$1 < \quad x \quad < 3$$

Graph each inequality and find the intersection.

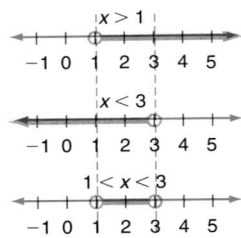

The solution set is $\{x \mid 1 < x < 3\}$.

Another type of compound inequality contains the word *or* instead of *and*. A compound inequality containing *or* is true if one or more of the inequalities is true. The graph of a compound inequality containing *or* is the **union** of the graphs of the two inequalities.

Example **Solve $x - 3 > 1$ or $x + 2 < 1$. Then graph the solution set.**

Solve each part separately.
$$x - 3 > 1 \qquad \text{or} \qquad x + 2 < 1$$
$$x > 4 \qquad\qquad\qquad\quad x < -1$$

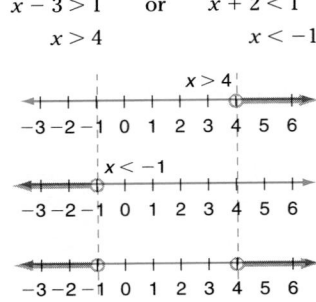

The last graph shows the solution set, $\{x \mid x > 4 \text{ or } x < -1\}$.

There is no short way to write an inequality containing "or."

Recall that the absolute value of a number is its distance from 0 on the number line. You can use this idea to solve inequalities involving absolute value.

Example **Solve $|y| < 7$.**

$|y| < 7$ means that the distance between y and 0 is less than 7 units. To make $|y| < 7$ true, you must substitute values for y that are less than 7 units from 0. *Note that $|y| < 7$ is the same as $y < 7$ and $y > -7$.*

$$\begin{array}{c} \leftarrow\!+\!\!\!+\!\!|\!\!\oplus\!\!+\!\!+\!\!+\!\!+\!\!+\!\!+\!\!+\!\!+\!\!+\!\!+\!\!+\!\!+\!\!+\!\!+\!\!\oplus\!\!|\!\!+\!\!+\!\!\rightarrow \\ -9\,\text{-}8\,\text{-}7\,\text{-}6\,\text{-}5\,\text{-}4\,\text{-}3\,\text{-}2\,\text{-}1\ \ 0\ \ 1\ \ 2\ \ 3\ \ 4\ \ 5\ \ 6\ \ 7\ \ 8\ \ 9 \end{array}$$

All of the numbers between -7 and 7 are less than 7 units from 0. The solution set is $\{y \mid -7 < y < 7\}$.

Example **Solve $|2x + 4| \geq 12$. Graph the solution set.**

This inequality says that $2x + 4$ is greater than or equal to 12 units from 0.

$$\begin{array}{ccc} 2x + 4 \geq 12 & \text{or} & 2x + 4 \leq -12 \\ 2x \geq 8 & & 2x \leq -16 \\ x \geq 4 & & x \leq -8 \end{array}$$

$$\begin{array}{c} \leftarrow\!+\!\!+\!\!|\!\!+\!\!+\!\!\oplus\!\!+\!\!+\!\!+\!\!+\!\!+\!\!+\!\!+\!\!+\!\!+\!\!+\!\!+\!\!+\!\!\oplus\!\!+\!\!|\!\!+\!\!\rightarrow \\ -11\,\text{-}10\,\text{-}9\,\text{-}8\,\text{-}7\,\text{-}6\,\text{-}5\,\text{-}4\,\text{-}3\,\text{-}2\,\text{-}1\ \ 0\ \ 1\ \ 2\ \ 3\ \ 4\ \ 5\ \ 6\ \ 7 \end{array}$$

The solution set is $\{x \mid x \geq 4 \text{ or } x \leq -8\}$.

Example **Steven Spielberg is the most successful filmmaker in history. The ten top-grossing movies he has directed are listed below.**

APPLICATION
Entertainment

Movie	Year	North American Gross (millions)
E.T.	1982	$399
Jurassic Park	1993	345
Jaws	1975	260
Raiders of the Lost Ark	1981	260
Indiana Jones and the Last Crusade	1989	197
Indiana Jones and the Temple of Doom	1984	180
Close Encounters of the Third Kind	1977	165
Hook	1991	116
The Color Purple	1985	94
Schindler's List	1993	75

Source: *The Guinness Book of Records, 1995*

a. Write a compound inequality that expresses the range of the grosses from Steven Spielberg's movies.

b. Suppose Mr. Spielberg wanted his next film to gross within $3 million of the average gross of his movies, $210.3 million. Write and solve an absolute value inequality for the difference between the gross of the next film and the average.

(continued on the next page)

In-Class Examples

For Example 3
Solve $|8x| \leq 24$.
$\{x \mid -3 \leq x \leq 3\}$

For Example 4
Solve $|x + 2| > 5$. Graph the solution set.
$\{x \mid x > 3 \text{ or } x < -7\}$

$$\begin{array}{c} \leftarrow\!+\!\!\oplus\!\!+\!\!+\!\!+\!\!+\!\!+\!\!+\!\!+\!\!\oplus\!\!+\!\!+\!\!\rightarrow \\ -8\ \ -6\ \ -4\ \ -2\ \ \ 0\ \ \ 2\ \ \ 4\ \ \ 6 \end{array}$$

For Example 5
One camera lens can focus clearly up to 10 yards away. Another lens can focus from 16 to 40 yards away. Write an inequality that describes where you can stand to take a focused picture.
$d \leq 10 \text{ or } 16 \leq d \leq 40$

Teaching Tip In Example 4, remind the students that an open circle means the point is not included and a closed circle means the point is included.

Check for Understanding

Exercises 1–14 are designed to help you assess your students' understanding through reading, writing, speaking, and modeling. You should work through Exercises 1–4 with your students and then monitor their work on Exercises 5–14.

Additional Answers

4. A compound inequality containing *and* is true only if both inequalities are true. A compound inequality containing *or* is true if one or more of the inequalities is true.

9.

0 1 2 3 4 5 6 7 8 9 10

10.

−5−4−3−2−1 0 1 2 3 4 5

11.

−6−5−4−3−2−1 0 1 2

12.

2 3 4 5 6 7 8 9 10

13.

−18−9 0 5 10

14.

−10 0 10

Study Guide Masters, p. 7

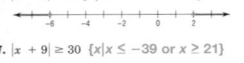

NAME_____ DATE _____

1-7 **Study Guide** Student Edition Pages 49–54

Solving Absolute Value Inequalities

The absolute value of a number represents its distance from zero on the number line. You can often use this idea to solve absolute value inequalities.

Example: Solve $|x - 3| \leq 2$. Graph the solution set.

$|x - 3| \leq 2$ means that $x - 3$ is no more than 2 units from 0 on the number line.

$x - 3 \geq -2$ and $x - 3 \leq 2$
$x \geq 1$ and $x \leq 5$

The solution set is $\{x | 1 \leq x \leq 5\}$.

−3 −2 −1 0 1 2 3 4 5 6 7

Solve each inequality.

1. $3y - 2 < -6$ or $2y + 4 \geq 6$
$\left\{ y | y < -\frac{4}{3} \text{ or } y \geq 1 \right\}$

2. $p + 7 > -2$ or $p - 4 < 8$
all reals

3. $1 < z - 4 < 9$
$\{z | 5 < z < 13\}$

4. $6a \leq 8 + 2a$ or $10 - 2a > 4$
$\{a | a < 3\}$

Solve each inequality. Graph each solution set.

5. $|x + 2| > 4$ $\{x | x > 2 \text{ or } x < -6\}$

−8 −4 0 4 8

6. $|4x| + 1 > 27$ $\left\{ x | x < -\frac{13}{2} \text{ or } x > \frac{13}{2} \right\}$

−8 −4 0 4 8

7. $|x + 9| \geq 30$ $\{x | x \leq -39 \text{ or } x \geq 21\}$

−50 −40 −30 −20 −10 0 10 20

8. $|5x + 2| < 28$ $\left\{ x | -6 < x < \frac{26}{5} \right\}$

−8 −4 0 4 8

Solve.

9. The Vikings play 36 games this year. At midseason, they had won 16 games. How many of the remaining games must they win in order to win at least 80% of *all* their games?
at least 13 games

10. The city parking lot charges $2.50 for the first hour and $0.25 for each additional hour. If the most you can pay is $6.50, how long can you park your car?
at most 17 hours

a. Let *r* represent the range of the films' grosses.

$$75 \leq r \leq 399$$

b. $|x - 210.3| \leq 3$

$x - 210.3 \leq 3$ and $x - 210.3 \geq -3$
$x \leq 3 + 210.3$ $\qquad$ $x \geq -3 + 210.3$
$x \leq 213.3$ $\qquad$ $x \geq 207.3$

The solution set is $\{x | x \geq 207.3 \text{ and } x \leq 213.3\}$, which may be written as $\{x | 207.3 \leq x \leq 213.3\}$. Spielberg wanted his next movie to gross between $207.3 and $213.3 million.

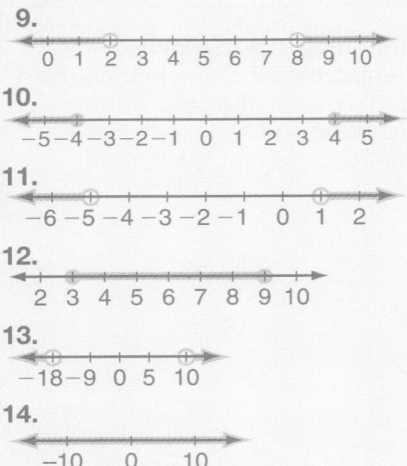

Some absolute value inequalities have no solution. For example, $|4x - 3| < -6$ is never true. Since the absolute value of a number is never negative, there is no replacement for *x* that will make this sentence true. So, the solution set to this inequality is the empty set.

Other absolute value inequalities are always true. One such inequality is $|x + 5| > -10$. The solution set of this inequality is all real numbers. Can you see why? *Think of the definition of absolute value.*

CHECK FOR UNDERSTANDING

Communicating Mathematics

Study the lesson. Then complete the following.

1. **Give** an example of an absolute value inequality whose solution set is the empty set. **Sample answer:** $|x + 9| < -2$

2. **State** an absolute value inequality for all numbers less than 5 and greater than −5. $|x| < 5$

3. **Explain** why $|x + 2| \geq -4$ has all real numbers as its solution set. **Because the absolute value of $x + 2 \geq 0$ and $0 > -4$.**

4. Explain the difference between a compound inequality containing the word *or* and the word *and*. **See margin.**

Guided Practice

State an absolute value inequality for each of the following. Then graph each solution set. 5–6. See Solutions Manual for graphs.

5. all numbers less than 18 and greater than −18 $|x| < 18$

6. all numbers between −3 and 3 $|x| < 3$

State an absolute value inequality for each graph.

9–14. See margin for graphs.

7.

−5−4−3−2−1 0 1 2 3 4 5

$|x| < 4$

8.

−5−4−3−2−1 0 1 2 3 4 5

$|x| \leq 2$

Solve each inequality. Graph the solution set.

9. $3x + 1 < 7$ or $7 < 2x - 9$ $\{x | x < 2 \text{ or } x > 8\}$

10. $|x| \geq 4$ $\{x | x \leq -4 \text{ or } x \geq 4\}$

11. $|x + 2| > 3$ $\{x | x > 1 \text{ or } x > -5\}$

12. $1 \leq x - 2 \leq 7$ $\{x | 3 \leq x \leq 9\}$

13. $|3x + 12| > 42$ $\{x | x < -18 \text{ or } x > 10\}$

14. $|x| \geq x$ all reals

Reteaching

Using Substeps Have students list the first two steps they would take to solve the open sentences. Then have them solve each open sentence.

1. $-5 < 0.5x + 1 \leq 4$
$\{x | -12 < x \leq 6\}$

2. $3 + x < 1$ or $x - 2 > -1$
$\{x | x < -2 \text{ or } x > 1\}$

3. $|x + 5| > 4$
$\{x | x < -9 \text{ or } x > -1\}$

4. $|x - 3| \leq 5$
$\{x | -2 \leq x \leq 8\}$

5. $|4 - 3x| < 1$
$\left\{ x | 1 < x < \frac{5}{3} \right\}$

6. $|6 - x| \geq 4$
$\{x | x \leq 2 \text{ or } x \geq 10\}$

Sample answers for substeps of Exercise 1: Add −1 to each part of the inequality; multiply each part by 2.

Practice

State an absolute value inequality for each of the following. Then graph each solution set. 15–20. See margin for graphs.

16. $|x| \le 15$

18. $|x| \le 5$

20. $|x| \le 10$

15. all numbers less than 7 and greater than -7 $|x| < 7$
16. all numbers less than or equal to 15, and greater than or equal to -15
17. all numbers greater than 11 or less than -11 $|x| > 11$
18. all numbers less than or equal to 5, and greater than or equal to -5
19. all numbers between -8 and 8 $|x| < 8$
20. all numbers greater than or equal to -10, and less than or equal to 10

State an absolute value inequality for each graph.

21. $|x| < 3$
22. $|x| \le 1$
23. $|x| \ge 4$
24. $|x| < 2.8$
25. $|x + 1| > 2$
26. $|x - 1| < 1$

21.
-5-4-3-2-1 0 1 2 3 4 5
22.
-5-4-3-2-1 0 1 2 3 4 5
23.
-5-4-3-2-1 0 1 2 3 4 5
24.
-5.6 -4.2 -2.8 -1.4 0 1.4 2.8 4.2
25.
-6-5-4-3-2-1 0 1 2 3 4
26.
-4-3-2-1 0 1 2 3 4 5 6

27–44. See Solutions Manual for graphs.

27. $\left\{ x \mid -\dfrac{5}{4} \le x \le \dfrac{5}{4} \right\}$

31. $\left\{ x \mid x \ge \dfrac{7}{3} \text{ or } x \le -\dfrac{7}{3} \right\}$

33. $\left\{ x \mid x > \dfrac{1}{2} \text{ or } \right.$
$\left. x < -\dfrac{1}{2} \right\}$

34. all reals

37. $\left\{ x \mid x < -4 \text{ or } \right.$
$\left. x > -\dfrac{10}{3} \right\}$

39. all reals

42. $\{x \mid -14.8 < x < 17.6\}$

Solve each inequality. Graph the solution set.

27. $|8x| \le 10$
28. $|2x| < 6$ $\{x \mid -3 < x < 3\}$
29. $|x| > 5$ $\{x \mid x < -5 \text{ or } x > 5\}$
30. $|2x - 9| \le 27$ $\{x \mid -9 \le x \le 18\}$
31. $|3x| \ge 7$
32. $|5x| < -25$ $\varnothing$
33. $|2x| > 1$
34. $x - 4 < 1 \text{ or } x + 2 > 1$
35. $|x - 6| \le -12$ $\varnothing$
36. $-1 < 3x + 2 < 14$ $\{x \mid -1 < x < 4\}$
37. $|3x + 11| > 1$
38. $|x| \le x$ $\{x \mid x \ge 0\}$
39. $x + 6 \ge -1 \text{ or } x - 2 \le 4$
40. $-4 \le 4x + 24 \le 4$ $\{x \mid -7 \le x \le -5\}$
41. $|3x| + 3 \le 0$ $\varnothing$
42. $|5x - 7| < 81$
43. $2x - 1 < -5 \text{ or } 3x + 2 \ge 5$
$\{x \mid x < -2 \text{ or } x \ge 1\}$
44. $|x + 2| - x \ge 0$ all reals

Critical Thinking

45. Solve $|x + 1| + |x - 1| \le 2$. $\{x \mid -1 \le x \le 1\}$

Applications and Problem Solving

46. **Transportation**   On some interstate highways, the maximum speed a car may drive is 65 miles per hour. A tractor-trailer may not drive more than 55 miles per hour. The minimum speed for all vehicles is 45 miles per hour.

   a. Write an inequality to represent the allowable speed for a car on an interstate highway. $45 \le s \le 65$

46b. $45 \le s \le 55$

   b. Write an inequality to represent the speed at which a tractor-trailer may travel on an interstate highway.

Lesson 1–7   Solving Absolute Value Inequalities   **53**

Assignment Guide

Core: 15–47 odd, 49–57
Enriched: 16–44 even, 45–57

For **Extra Practice,** see p. 878.

The red A, B, and C flags, printed only in the Teacher's Wraparound Edition, indicate the level of difficulty of the exercises.

Additional Answers

15.
-7 0 7

16.
-15 0 15

17.
-11 0 11

18.
-10 -5 0 5 10

19.
-8 0 8

20.
-10 0 10

Practice Masters, p. 7

Closing Activity

Writing Explain the difference between *and* and *or* in inequalities. Use examples in your paragraph.

Chapter 1, Quiz D (Lesson 1-7), is available in the *Assessment and Evaluation Masters,* p. 17.

Additional Answers

49.

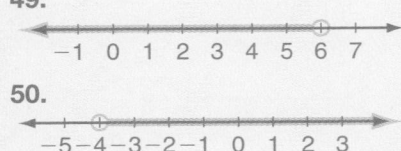

-1 0 1 2 3 4 5 6 7

50.

-5 -4 -3 -2 -1 0 1 2 3

Enrichment Masters, p. 7

NAME_____ DATE _____

1-7 **Enrichment**

Student Edition
Pages 49–54

Conjunctions and Disjunctions

An absolute value inequality may be solved as a compound sentence.

Example: Solve $|2x| < 10$.
$|2x| < 10$ means $2x < 10$ and $2x > -10$.

Solve each inequality.　$x < 5$ and $x > -5$.

Every solution for $|2x| < 10$ is a replacement for x
that makes both $x < 5$ and $x > -5$ true.

A compound sentence that combines two statements by the word
and is a *conjunction.*

Example: Solve $|3x - 7| \geq 11$.
$|3x - 7| \geq 11$ means $3x - 7 \geq 11$ or $3x - 7 \leq -11$.

Solve each inequality.　$3x \geq 18$ or $3x \leq -4$
$x \geq 6$ or $x \leq -\frac{4}{3}$

Every solution for the inequality is a replacement for
x that makes either $x \geq 6$ or $x \leq -\frac{4}{3}$ true.

A compound sentence that combines two statements by the word
or is a *disjunction.*

Solve each inequality. Then write whether the solution is a conjunction or disjunction.

1. $|4x| > 24$
$x > 6$ or $x < -6$; disjunction

2. $|x - 7| \leq 8$
$x \leq 15$ and $x \geq -1$; conjunction

3. $|2x + 5| < 1$
$x < -2$ and $x > -3$; conjunction

4. $|x - 1| \geq 1$
$x \geq 2$ or $x \leq 0$; disjunction

5. $|3x - 1| \leq x$
$x \leq \frac{1}{2}$ and $x \geq \frac{1}{4}$; conjunction

6. $7 - |2x| > 5$
$x < 1$ and $x > -1$; conjunction

7. $|\frac{x}{2} + 1| \geq 7$
$x \geq 12$ or $x \leq -16$; disjunction

8. $|\frac{x-4}{3}| < 4$
$x < 16$ and $x > -8$; conjunction

9. $|8 - x| > 2$
$x < 6$ or $x > 10$; disjunction

10. $|5 - 2x| \leq 3$
$x \geq 1$ and $x \leq 4$; conjunction

47. Education　Use the chart below to answer the following questions.

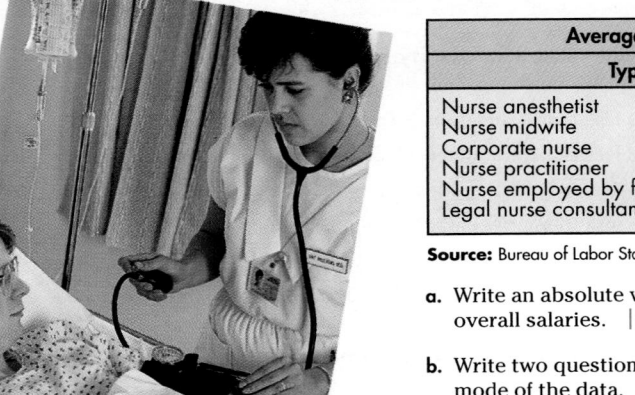

Average Nursing Salaries	
Type	**Salary**
Nurse anesthetist	$76,000
Nurse midwife	57,000
Corporate nurse	47,000
Nurse practitioner	43,600
Nurse employed by federal government	43,200
Legal nurse consultant at law firm	40,000

Source: Bureau of Labor Statistics

a. Write an absolute value inequality that describes the range in overall salaries.　$|x - 58{,}000| \leq 18{,}000$

b. Write two questions that can be answered using the mean and mode of the data.　**See students' work.**

48. Consumerism　Marcus is buying his first tank of gasoline since he got his driver's license. Where he lives, gasoline is selling for between $1.20 and $1.40 per gallon. If he has $10.50 to spend on gas, how many gallons can he buy?　**7.5 to 8.75 gal**

Mixed Review

Solve each inequality. Then graph the solution set.　(Lesson 1–6)

49. $9(x + 2) < 72$　$\{x \mid x < 6\}$

50. $3(3x + 2) > 7x - 2$　$\{x \mid x > -4\}$

49–50. See margin for graphs.

51. Solve $8x + 5 < 7x - 3$.　(Lesson 1–6)　$x < -8$

52. Solve $-4(3m - 7) - (3 - m) < 13$.　(Lesson 1–6)　$m > \frac{12}{11}$

53. Solve $|3x - 4| = -1$.　(Lesson 1–5)　$1, \frac{5}{3}$

54. Find the value of $|7(-3) + 10|$.　(Lesson 1–5)　**11**

55. Consumerism　Beto has gone to a doughnut shop with $10 his father gave him. He needs to buy 6 glazed doughnuts at $0.50 each for his father. He can then buy some frosted cake doughnuts for himself at $0.35 each. (Lesson 1–4)

a. Let x represent the number of frosted cake doughnut Beto buys. Translate "Beto bought 6 glazed doughnuts and some frosted cake doughnuts for $10.00" into an equation.　$(0.50)6 + (0.35)x = 10$

b. Solve the equation to find out how many frosted cake doughnuts Beto can buy.　**20**

56. Solve $y = 8(0.3) + 1.2$.　(Lesson 1–4)　**3.6**

57. Olympics　The time in seconds of 15 Olympic Games Champions' scores for the 200-meter run are listed below. Find the median, mode, and mean for these scores. 22.2, 21.6, 22.6, 21.7, 22, 21.6, 21.8, 20.7, 20.7, 20.5, 20.3, 20.01, 19.80, 20.19, 19.75　(Lesson 1–3)　**20.7; 21.6 and 20.7; 21.03**

54　Chapter 1　Analyzing Equations and Inequalities

Extension

Reasoning Solve $|x - 6| + |x + 6| \leq |3x|$. What do you need to do first? Explain why you need to have different choices.

$\{x \mid x \geq 4 \text{ or } x \leq -4\}$

VOCABULARY

After completing this chapter, you should be able to define each term, property, or phrase and give an example or two of each.

Algebra
absolute value   (p. 37)
addition property of equality   (p. 28)
addition property of inequality   (p. 43)
algebraic expressions (p. 8)
associative properties (p. 14)
commutative properties (p. 14)
compound inequality (p. 49)
distributive properties (p. 14)
division property of equality   (p. 28)
division property of inequality   (p. 44)
empty set   (p. 40)
equation   (p. 27)
formula   (p. 9)
identity properties   (p. 14)
intersection   (p. 49)

inverse properties   (p. 14)
irrational number   (p. 13)
multiplication property of equality   (p. 28)
multiplication property of inequality   (p. 44)
open sentences   (p. 27)
order of operations   (p. 7)
perfect number   (p. 12)
rational number   (p. 13)
real numbers   (p. 13)
reflexive property of equality (p. 28)
solution   (p. 28)
substitution property of equality (p. 28)
subtraction property of equality (p. 28)
subtraction property of inequality (p. 43)
symmetric property of equality (p. 28)
transitive property of equality (p. 28)
trichotomy property   (p. 43)

union   (p. 50)
variables   (p. 27)

Geometry
hypotenuse   (p. 9)
legs   (p. 9)
Pythagorean theorem   (p. 9)

Problem Solving
list possibilities   (p. 38)
problem-solving plan   (p. 30)
problem-solving strategies (p. 38)

Statistics
back-to-back stem-and-leaf plot (p. 20)
extreme values   (p. 22)
line plot   (p. 19)
mean   (p. 21)
measure of central tendency (p. 21)
median   (p. 21)
mode   (p. 21)
stem-and-leaf plot   (p. 20)

UNDERSTANDING AND USING THE VOCABULARY

Choose the letter that best matches each description.

1. $-b = -b$ j
2. $(4x) \cdot 1 = 4x$ h
3. $8(4x - 1) = 32x - 8$ f
4. $x = 4$, then $4 = x$ k
5. $4x + 6(y - 5x) - 3z$ b
6. $10 > t > 4.5$ e
7. $x = 4y, 4y = 12$, then $x = 12$ l
8. $5a - 7(a - 6) = 12$ g
9. $9 + (4 + 7) = (9 + 4) + 7$ c
10. $|-3m|$ a
11. $-5 + 5 = 0$ i
12. $xy = yx$ d

a.   absolute value
b.   algebraic expression
c.   associative property
d.   commutative property
e.   compound inequality
f.   distributive property
g.   equation
h.   identity property
i.   inverse property
j.   reflexive property
k.   symmetric property
l.   transitive property

Chapter 1   Highlights   **55**

Using the CHAPTER HIGHLIGHTS

The Chapter Highlights begins with a listing of the new terms, properties, and phrases that were introduced in this chapter. Have students define each term and provide an example or two of it, if appropriate.

Assessment and Evaluation Masters, pp. 3–4

NAME_____ DATE _____

1

Chapter 1 Test, Form 1B

Write the letter for the correct answer in the blank at the right of each problem.

1. Find the value of $5 + 8 \cdot 2 \div 4 - 11$.
   A. $-5\frac{3}{4}$ B. $-5\frac{1}{2}$ C. 2   D. -2 **1. D**

2. Evaluate $(a - y)^2 + 2y^3$ if $a = 2$ and $y = -3$.
   A. -29 B. 43   C. 79   D. -8 **2. A**

3. The formula $A = \frac{180(n-2)}{n}$ relates the measure, A, of an interior angle of a regular polygon to the number of sides, n. If an interior angle measures 120°, find the number of sides.
   A. 5   B. 6   C. 8   D. 10   **3. B**

4. Name *all* the sets of numbers to which -28 belongs.
   A. integers   B. integers, reals
   C. integers, rationals   D. integers, rationals, reals   **4. D**

5. State the property illustrated in the equation $5n + (3t + 8n) = (5n + 3t) + 8n$.
   A. associative property of addition
   B. inverse property of addition
   C. distributive property
   D. commutative property of addition   **5. A**

6. Simplify $\frac{1}{3}(6x + 1) - 4(3x - 2)$.
   A. $-10x + 8\frac{1}{3}$ B. $-9x + 8\frac{1}{3}$ C. $25 - 30x$ D. $-9x - 7\frac{2}{3}$ **6. A**

Chris's scores on six weekly quizzes are 10, 8, 7, 9, 10, and 10.

7. What is the mode of the data?
   A. 8   B. 9   C. 9.5   D. 10   **7. D**

8. What is the median of the data?
   A. 8   B. 9   C. 9.5   D. 10   **8. C**

9. What is the mean of the data?
   A. 8.5   B. 9   C. 9.5   D. 10   **9. B**

Solve each equation.

10. $\frac{2}{5}y = \frac{3}{14}$
    A. $\frac{28}{15}$ B. $\frac{35}{3}$ C. $\frac{3}{35}$ D. $\frac{15}{28}$ **10. D**

11. $3(5x - 1) = 3x + 3$
    A. $\frac{1}{2}$ B. 2   C. -2 D. $-\frac{1}{2}$ **11. A**

NAME_____ DATE _____

1

Chapter 1 Test, Form 1B (continued)

12. $3|x - 5| = 12$
    A. 9   B. 1   C. 1, 9   D. Ø   **12. C**

13. $|y - 8| + 6 = 15$
    A. 17   B. -1 C. $17, -1$ D. Ø   **13. C**

Solve each inequality.

14. $-3(r - 11) + 15 \geq 9$
    A. $\{r \,|\, r \leq 13\}$ B. $\{r \,|\, r \geq 13\}$ C. $\{r \,|\, r \leq -13\}$ D. $\{r \,|\, r \geq -13\}$ **14. A**

15. $|3w - 7| \leq 2$
    A. $\{w \,|\, \frac{5}{3} \leq w \leq 3\}$ B. $\{w \,|\, -3 \leq w \leq 3\}$
    C. $\{w \,|\, w \leq 3\}$ D. {real numbers}   **15. A**

16. Which equation could be used to solve the following problem? 55 minus 3 times a number is 22. Find the number.
    A. $n(55 - 3) = 22$ B. $3n - 22 = 55$
    C. $55n - 3 = 22$ D. $55 - 3n = 22$ **16. D**

17. The digits 3, 4, and 5 are used to form a three-digit code. No repeated digits are allowed. How many codes are possible?
    A. 60   B. 12   C. 9   D. 6   **17. D**

18. Sarah has $328.17 in her checking account. The bank does not charge for checks if there is a balance of $250 or more in the account. What is the greatest check Sarah can write without paying a check charge?
    A. $78.16   B. $78.17   C. $78.18   D. $250   **18. A**

19. Which of the following is the solution set of $2x - 5 \leq 10$ or $33 - 4x > 5$?
    A. $\{x \,|\, x \leq 7\frac{1}{2} \text{ or } x < 7\}$ B. $\{x \,|\, 7 < x \leq 7\frac{1}{2}\}$
    C. {real numbers}   D. Ø   **19. A**

20. Identify the graph of $8.5 > 6.1 + 0.6y$.
    A. [number line graph]   B. [number line graph]
    C. [number line graph]   D. [number line graph]   **20. D**

Bonus Solve $|x| - x > 0$.
    A. $\{x \,|\, x < 0\}$ B. {all reals}   C. {0}   D. $\{x \,|\, x > 0\}$ **Bonus A**

Instructional Resources

Three multiple-choice tests and three free-response tests are provided in the *Assessment and Evaluation Masters*. Forms 1A and 2A are for honors pacing, and Forms 1B, 1C, 2B, and 2C are for average pacing. Chapter 1 Test, Form 1B is shown at the right. Chapter 1 Test, Form 2B is shown on the next page.

Using the
STUDY GUIDE AND ASSESSMENT

Skills and Concepts Encourage students to refer to the objectives and examples on the left as they complete the review exercises on the right.

Assessment and Evaluation Masters, pp. 9–10

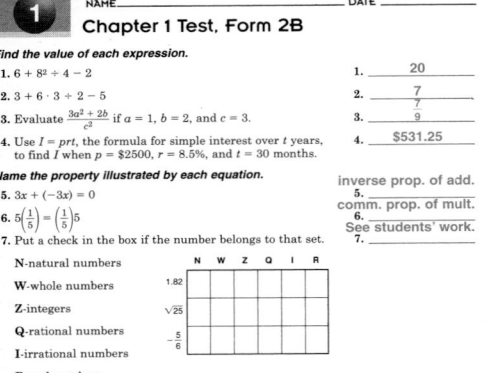

1 NAME_____ DATE _____

Chapter 1 Test, Form 2B

Find the value of each expression.

1. $6 + 8^2 \div 4 - 2$ 1. _____20_____

2. $3 + 6 \cdot 3 \div 2 - 5$ 2. _____$\frac{7}{7}$_____

3. Evaluate $\frac{3a^2 + 2b}{c^2}$ if $a = 1$, $b = 2$, and $c = 3$.   3. _____9_____

4. Use $I = prt$, the formula for simple interest over t years, to find I when $p = \$2500$, $r = 8.5\%$, and $t = 30$ months.   4. _____\$531.25_____

Name the property illustrated by each equation.

5. $3x + (-3x) = 0$ inverse prop. of add. 5.

6. $5\left(\frac{1}{5}\right) = \left(\frac{1}{5}\right)5$ comm. prop. of mult. 6.

7. Put a check in the box if the number belongs to that set.   See students' work. 7.

	N	W	Z	Q	I	R
N-natural numbers						
W-whole numbers	1.82					
Z-integers	$\sqrt{25}$					
Q-rational numbers	$-\frac{5}{6}$					
I-irrational numbers						
R-real numbers						

8. Simplify $\frac{1}{4}(12v - 8) + \frac{2}{3}(6v + 1)$.   8. _____$7v - 1\frac{1}{3}$_____

The chart below shows the average per-person expenditures (in dollars) for state and district lotteries for a recent year.

Arizona	43	Maryland	170	Oregon	37
California	52	Massachusetts	260	Pennsylvania	113
Colorado	35	Michigan	110	Rhode Island	59
Connecticut	153	Missouri	34	Vermont	47
Delaware	72	New Hampshire	56	Washington	43
Illinois	113	New Jersey	147	Washington, D.C.	194
Iowa	33	New York	82	West Virginia	35
Maine	49	Ohio	99		

9. Find the mean to the nearest tenth.   9. _____88.5_____

10. Find the median.   10. _____59_____

11. Find the mode.   11. _____35, 43, 113_____

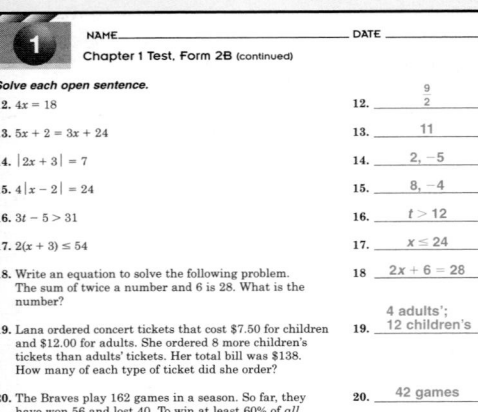

1 NAME_____ DATE _____

Chapter 1 Test, Form 2B (continued)

Solve each open sentence.

12. $4x = 18$ 12. _____$\frac{9}{2}$_____

13. $5x + 2 = 3x + 24$ 13. _____11_____

14. $|2x + 3| = 7$ 14. _____2, −5_____

15. $4|x - 2| = 24$ 15. _____8, −4_____

16. $3t - 5 > 31$ 16. _____$t > 12$_____

17. $2(x + 3) \le 54$ 17. _____$x \le 24$_____

18. Write an equation to solve the following problem. The sum of twice a number and 6 is 28. What is the number?   18. _____$2x + 6 = 28$_____

19. Lana ordered concert tickets that cost \$7.50 for children and \$12.00 for adults. She ordered 8 more children's tickets than adults' tickets. Her total bill was \$138. How many of each type of ticket did she order?   19. _____4 adults'; 12 children's_____

20. The Braves play 162 games in a season. So far, they have won 56 and lost 40. To win at least 60% of *all* games, how many more games must they win?   20. _____42 games_____

21. A quiz has four true-false questions. How many different patterns of answers are possible?   21. _____16_____

Solve each compound sentence.

22. $-5 < 6n - 17 \le 13$ 22. _____$2 < n \le 5$_____

23. $7v + 6 \le -22$ or $11 - v < 19$ 23. _____all reals_____

Solve each inequality. Graph the solution set.

24. $|x - 2| > 4$ 24. _____$x > 6$ or $x < -2$; see students' graphs._____

25. $|2x + 3| \le 5$ 25. _____$-4 \le x \le 1$; see students' graphs._____

Bonus Find the value of k so that the equation below has the solution set $\{-5\}$. $4(x + 3) = x(3 - k)$ Bonus _____$\frac{7}{5}$_____

OBJECTIVES AND EXAMPLES	REVIEW EXERCISES

Upon completing this chapter, you should be able to:

Use these exercises to review and prepare for the chapter test.

- use the order of operations to evaluate expressions   (Lesson 1–1)

$$5 - 8(3 - 6) \div 2^2 + 10 = 5 - 8(-3) \div 4 + 10$$
$$= 5 - (-24) \div 4 + 10$$
$$= 5 - (-6) + 10$$
$$= 5 + 6 + 10$$
$$= 21$$

Find the value of each expression.

13. $6(5 - 8) \div 9 + 4$ **2**

14. $(3 + 7)^2 - 16 \div 2$ **92**

15. $(6 + 5)4 - 3$ **41**

16. $-7 + [28 \div (18 - 7(2))]$ **0**

Evaluate each expression if $a = 4$, $b = 5$, $c = -0.5$, and $d = -3$.

17. $\frac{8c + ab}{a}$ **4**   18. $(a - d + b) \div c$ **−24**

- determine the sets of numbers to which a given number belongs   (Lesson 1–2)

Find the value of $3(-4.5)$. Then name the sets of numbers to which this value belongs.

$$3(-4.5) = -13.5$$

rationals, reals

Find the value of each expression. Then name the sets of numbers to which each value belongs.   22. 18, N, W, Z, Q, R

19. $4 - 12$ **−8, Z, Q, R**   20. $42 \div 8$ **5.25, Q, R**

21. $\sqrt{2 + 3}$ $\sqrt{5}$, **I, R**   22. $2^3 + 10$

23. $2\pi(8.75)$ **54.978, I, R**   24. $-20 \div 2^2$ **−5, Z, Q, R**

- use the properties of real numbers to simplify expressions   (Lesson 1–2)

$$2a(5.4 - 4b) - 4a(3.1 + 8b)$$
$$= 10.8a - 8ab - 12.4a - 32ab$$
$$= -1.6a - 40ab$$

Name the property illustrated by each equation.

25. $7 \cdot \frac{1}{7} = 1$ 26. $4(3 \cdot 5.5) = (4 \cdot 3) 5.5$

multiplicative inverse   associative ($\times$)

Simplify each expression.

27. $7a + 2b - 5a - 6b$ **$2a - 4b$**

28. $3(a + 4b) - 2(4a + 2b)$ **$-5a + 8b$**

- find and use the median, mode, and mean to interpret data   (Lesson 1–3)

Find the median, mode, and mean of 78, 67, 73, 69, 84, 68, 74, 76, 66, 78, 70.

66, 67, 68, 69, 70, 73, 74, 76, 78, 78, 84

median: 6th value $= 73$

mode: 78

mean: $\dfrac{66 + 67 + 68 + \ldots + 78 + 84}{11} = 73$

Find the median, mode, and mean for each set of data.

29. 5, 92, 64, 18, 25   **25; no mode; 40.8**

30. 66, 48, 35, 52, 48, 41, 59, 61   **50; 48; 51.25**

31. 4.6, 6.1, 8.9, 3.6, 6.1, 10, 2.9   **6.1; 6.1; 6.0**

32. 3, 6, 7, 10, 7, 14, 19, 21, 10, 10, 31, 17, 16, 9, 7, 17, 20, 14, 7, 10, 13, 10   **10; 10; about 12.6**

GLENCOE Technology

Test and Review Software

You may use this software, a combination of an item generator and item bank, to create your own tests or worksheets. Types of items include free response, multiple choice, short answer, and open ended.

For IBM & Macintosh

Additional Answers

53.

0 1 2 3 4 5 6 7 8

54.

11 12 13 14 15 16 17 18 19

55.

6 7 8 9 10 11 12 13 14

56.

−0.60   −0.58   −0.56   −0.54
   −0.59   −0.57   −0.55

57.

−37 −36 −35 −34 −33 −32

58.

−1 0 1 2 3 4 5 6 7

59.

1 2 3 4 5 6 7 8 9

60.

−2.0   −1.8   −1.6   −1.4
   −1.9   −1.7   −1.5   −1.3

OBJECTIVES AND EXAMPLES

- solve equations by using the properties of equality (Lesson 1–4)

Solve $2(a - 1) = 8a - 6$.

$2(a - 1) = 8a - 6$

$2a - 2 = 8a - 6$ *Distributive property*

$-2 = 6a - 6$ *Subtract 2a from each side.*

$4 = 6a$ *Add 6 to each side.*

$\frac{2}{3} = a$ *Divide each side by 6.*

- solve equations for a specific variable (Lesson 1–4)

Solve $3(x - 2) = y$ for x.

$3(x - 2) = y$

$3x - 6 = y$ *Distributive property*

$3x = y + 6$ *Add 6 to each side.*

$x = \frac{y + 6}{3}$ *Divide each side by 3.*

- solve equations containing absolute value (Lesson 1–5)

Solve $|r + 14| = 23$.

$|r + 14| = 23$

$r + 14 = 23$ or $r + 14 = -23$

$r = 9$ $r = -37$

- solve inequalities and graph the solution sets. (Lesson 1–6)

Solve $3 - 4x \le 6x - 2$.

$3 - 4x \le 6x - 2$

$3 \le 10x - 2$ *Add 4x to each side.*

$5 \le 10x$ *Add 2 to each side.*

$\frac{1}{2} \le x$ *Divide each side by 10.*

REVIEW EXERCISES

Solve each equation.   **33.** −21   **37.** −20

33. $12z + 36 = 8z - 48$ **34.** $4.2x + 6.4 = 40$ 8

35. $14y - 3 = 25$ 2   **36.** $7w + 2 = 3w + 94$ 23

37. $4 - 2(1 - w) = -38$ **38.** $4y - \frac{1}{10} = 3y + \frac{4}{5}$ $\frac{9}{10}$

39. $48 + 5y = 96 - 3y$ 6   **40.** $\frac{x}{3} + \frac{x}{2} = \frac{3}{4}$ $\frac{9}{10}$

Solve each equation or formula for the variable specified.

41. $A = p + prt$ for t $\frac{A - p}{pr}$

42. $df - 3g = 4h$ for f $\frac{4h + 3g}{d}$

43. $\frac{3a^2 - 1}{2b} = c$ for b $\frac{3a^2 - 1}{2c}$

44. $s = \frac{1}{2}gt^2$ for g $\frac{2s}{t^2}$

Solve each equation.

45. $|y - 5| - 2 = 10$ 17, −7

46. $|5y - 8| = 12$ 4, $-\frac{4}{5}$

47. $|2x - 36| = 14$ 11, 25

48. $|x + 4| + 3 = 17$ −18, 10

49. $|q - 3| + 7 = 2$ no solution

50. $4|3x + 4| = 4x + 8$ −1, $-\frac{3}{2}$

51. $2|w + 6| = 10$ −11, −1

52. $5|6 - 5x| = 15x - 35$ no solution

Solve each inequality. Graph the solution set.   **53–60. See margin for graphs.**

53. $5z - 6 > 14$ $\{z \mid z > 4\}$

54. $5(x - 2) < 75$ $\{x \mid x < 17\}$

55. $57 - 4t \ge 13$ $\{t \mid t \le 11\}$

56. $-3(2x + 5) > 13x - 4$ $\{x \mid x < -0.58\}$

57. $18 - 2(y + 6) < 76$ $\{y \mid y > -35\}$

58. $3(6 - 5x) \le 12x - 36$ $\{x \mid x \ge 2\}$

59. $2 - 3z \ge 7(8 - 2z) + 12$ $\{z \mid z \ge 6\}$

60. $8(2x - 1) > 11x - 17$ $\{x \mid x > -1.8\}$

61.
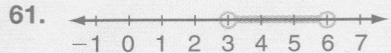
-1 0 1 2 3 4 5 6 7

62.
-3 -2 -1 0 1 2 3 4 5

63.
0 1 2 3 4 5 6 7 8

64.
-2 -1 0 1 2 3 4 5

65.
-7 -6 -5 -4 -3 -2 -1 0 1

66.
-10 0 10

68.
-11 0 11

69.
-9 0 9

70.
-11 -8 -5 0 5 8 11

Applications and Problem Solving Encourage students to work through the exercises in the Applications and Problem Solving section to strengthen their problem-solving skills.

CHAPTER 1   STUDY GUIDE AND ASSESSMENT

OBJECTIVES AND EXAMPLES	REVIEW EXERCISES
• solve compound inequalities using *and* and *or* (Lesson 1–7)	**Solve each inequality. Graph the solution set.** 62. $\{x\,|\,x < 0 \text{ or } x \geq 1\}$

$$-2 \leq x - 4 < 3$$
$$-2 \leq x - 4 \text{ and } x - 4 < 3$$
$$2 \leq x \qquad x < 7$$
$$2 \leq x < 7$$

61. $11 < 3x + 2 < 20$ $\{x\,|\,3 < x < 6\}$
62. $4x - 10 < -10 \text{ or } 6x + 4 \geq 10$
63. $-1 < 3(y - 2) \leq 9$ $\left\{y\,|\,\frac{5}{3} < y \leq 5\right\}$
64. $5y - 4 > 16 \text{ or } 3y + 2 < 1$ $\left\{y\,|\,y > 4 \text{ or } y < -\frac{1}{3}\right\}$

61–70. See margin for graphs.

• solve inequalities involving absolute value and graph the solutions   (Lesson 1–7)

$$|3x + 7| \geq 26$$
$$3x + 7 \geq 26 \text{ or } 3x + 7 \leq -26$$
$$3x \geq 19 \qquad 3x \leq -33$$
$$x \geq \frac{19}{3} \qquad x \leq -11$$
$$x \geq \frac{19}{3} \text{ or } x \leq -11$$

Solve each inequality. Graph the solution set.

65. $|2x + 6| \leq 4$ $\{x\,|\,-5 \leq x \leq -1\}$
66. $7 + |9 - 5x| > 1$ **all reals**
67. $|4x| + 3 \leq 0$ $\varnothing$
68. $|x| + 1 < 12$ $\{x\,|\,-11 < x < 11\}$
69. $|3x| < 27$ $\{x\,|\,-9 < x < 9\}$
70. $|2x + 3| - 6 \geq 7$ $\{x\,|\,x \leq -8 \text{ or } x \geq 5\}$

APPLICATIONS AND PROBLEM SOLVING

71. Geometry   The perimeter of a rectangle is 150 centimeters. The length is 15 centimeters greater than the width. Find the dimensions of the rectangle.   (Lesson 1–1)   **30 cm by 45 cm**

72. Car Expenses   Rafael spent $2011 to operate his car last year. He drove 7400 miles. He also paid $972 for insurance and $114 for the registration fee. Rafael's only other expense was for gasoline. How much did the gasoline cost per mile?   (Lesson 1–4)   **12.5¢**

73. Test Scores   Your quiz scores are 73, 75, 89, and 91. What is the lowest score you can obtain on the last quiz and still achieve an average of at least 85?   (Lesson 1–6)   **97**

74. Bowling   Bowling at Sunset Lanes cost Danny and Zorina $9. This included shoe rental of $0.75 a pair. How much did each game cost if Danny bowled 3 games and Zorina bowled 2 games?   (Lesson 1–4)   **$1.50**

75. Oceans   The depths, in meters, of certain points of the oceans and seas of the world are: 10918, 9219, 7455, 5625, 4632, 5016, 4773, 3787, 3658, 2782, 3742, 3777, 660, 22, 421, 6946, and 183. Find the median, mode, and mean for this set.   (Lesson 1–3)   **3777, none, 4330.4**

A practice test for Chapter 1 is provided on page 912.

ALTERNATIVE ASSESSMENT

COOPERATIVE LEARNING PROJECT

Chicken Farming
In this project, you will complete a chicken and egg math problem. Janice flew to Iowa to visit her grandparents on their chicken farm for a week in the summer. She was raised in the city so it was quite a treat for her to be on a farm. One night as she and her grandfather were sitting at the table enjoying lemonade, her grandfather pulled out a piece of paper that he had been working on to give her.

The following is what was on the paper. Answer all the questions.

If a chicken and a half lays an egg and a half in a day and a half, then

a. how many eggs will nine chickens lay in ten days?

b. how many eggs will c chickens lay in twelve days?

c. how many eggs will twelve chickens lay in d days?

d. how many days will it take c chickens to lay twelve eggs?

e. how many days will it take twelve chickens to lay e eggs?

f. how many chickens will it take to lay e eggs in twelve days?

g. how many chickens will it take to lay twelve eggs in d days?

Suppose you want all of the answers in parts d–g to be whole numbers. Then what must be true about c, d, and e?

Follow these steps to accomplish your task.

• Construct a pattern for this situation.

• Read and reread each of the verbal sentences in order to understand them.

• Determine what each of the variables stands for and how they should be used.

• Write a paragraph describing the problem and your solution.

THINKING CRITICALLY

• Translate each of the following into at least two different word phrases that mean the same thing.

$$x + 8, n - 3, \text{ and } 2w$$

• When, if ever, is $|a + b| = |a| + |b|$ true?

PORTFOLIO

Translating word expressions into algebraic expressions requires reading the words and determining their meaning mathematically. Another way to enhance this skill is to do the opposite—translate mathematical symbols and numbers into words.

Write a mathematical expression or equation and create a story about it. Be creative and make it fun to read. Then exchange your story with someone else's story and translate the story into a mathematical expression or equation. Place your story in your portfolio.

SELF EVALUATION

There are five steps to solid reasoning.

1. *Clarify*—Determine precisely what must be decided.

2. *Evaluate*—Determine the facts and assumptions.

3. *Decide*—Determine what information should be used and what is not relevant.

4. *Implement*—Develop a plan of how to implement the decision.

5. *Monitor and Modify*—Watch the conclusions of the decision and be prepared to revise the plan or take a different course of action based on new information.

Assess yourself. Do you use these five steps in your reasoning? Determine a problem or situation that you have had recently, or think you will have in the future, and use these steps to reason your way through it.

Assessment and Evaluation Masters, pp. 14, 25

NAME_____ DATE_____

Chapter 1 Performance Assessment

Instructions: *Demonstrate your knowledge by giving a clear, concise solution to each problem. Be sure to include all relevant drawings and justify your answers. You may show your solution in more than one way or investigate beyond the requirements of the problem.*

1. a. The height of a ball thrown upward at 50 feet per second is given by the formula $h = 6 + (50 - 6t)t$. Find the height of the ball at $t = 2$ seconds in at least two ways. Explain each step.

b. Find the height of the ball when $t = 0$. Name the properties of real numbers used to obtain the answer.

c. Explain how the height of the ball may not be zero when $t = 0$.

d. Simplify the formula in part a. Name the property used.

2. a. Explain the meaning of $|x| = 9$.

b. Explain the meaning of $|x - 5| \geq 7$.

c. Write a compound sentence for the inequality in part b. Solve and graph the solution set.

d. Explain the meaning of $|2x + 5| < 11$.

e. Write a compound sentence for the inequality in part d. Solve and graph the solution set.

3. a. Write a word problem for the equation $2(x - 2) = x + 6$.

b. Solve and give the meaning of the answer.

4. The Marion High School Giants played 22 basketball games last season. The number of points they scored in each of their games was 76, 78, 69, 80, 70, 77, 80, 78, 81, 76, 81, 78, 88, 82, 80, 79, 73, 68, 72, 78, 73, and 77.

a. Find two measures of central tendency.

b. What is the purpose of a measure of central tendency?

Scoring Guide
Chapter 1
Performance Assessment

Level	Specific Criteria
3 Superior	• Shows thorough understanding of the concepts *order of operations, properties of real numbers, absolute value, solving equations and inequalities,* and *measures of central tendency.* • Uses appropriate strategies to solve problems. • Computations are correct. • Written explanations are exemplary. • Word problem concerning equation is appropriate and makes sense. • Graphs are accurate and appropriate. • Goes beyond requirements of problem.
2 Satisfactory, with Minor Flaws	• Shows understanding of the concepts *order of operations, properties of real numbers, absolute value, solving equations and inequalities,* and *measures of central tendency.* • Uses appropriate strategies to solve problems. • Computations are mostly correct. • Written explanations are effective. • Word problem concerning equation is appropriate and makes sense. • Graphs are mostly accurate and appropriate. • Satisfies all requirements of problem.
1 Nearly Satisfactory, with Serious Flaws	• Shows understanding of most of the concepts *order of operations, properties of real numbers, absolute value, solving equations and inequalities,* and *measures of central tendency.* • May not use appropriate strategies to solve problems. • Computations are mostly correct. • Written explanations are satisfactory. • Word problem concerning equation is mostly appropriate and sensible. • Graphs are mostly accurate and appropriate. • Satisfies most requirements of problem.
0 Unsatisfactory	• Shows little or no understanding of the concepts *order of operations, properties of real numbers, absolute value, solving equations and inequalities,* and *measures of central tendency.* • May not use appropriate strategies to solve problems. • Computations are incorrect. • Written explanations are not satisfactory. • Word problem concerning equation is not appropriate or sensible. • Graphs are not accurate or appropriate. • Does not satisfy requirements of problem.

Alternative Assessment

The Alternative Assessment section provides students with the opportunity to assess their own work by thinking critically, working with others, keeping a portfolio, and honestly evaluating their own progress. For more information on alternative forms of assessment, see *Alternative Assessment in the Mathematics Classroom,* one of the titles in the Glencoe Mathematics Professional Series.

Performance Assessment

Performance Assessment tasks for this chapter are included in the *Assessment and Evaluation Masters.* A scoring guide is also provided.

NCTM Standards: 1–8, 10, 12

This Investigation is designed to be completed over several days or weeks. It may be considered optional. You may want to assign the Investigation and the follow-up activities to be completed at the same time.

Objective

Experiment with different sizes of calibration scopes to help determine the actual heights of objects.

Mathematical Overview

This Investigation will use the following mathematical skills and concepts from Chapters 2 and 3.

- determining the slope of a line
- identifying and graphing special functions
- solving systems of equations by substitution and elimination
- solving systems of equations in three variables

Recommended Time		
Part	**Pages**	**Time**
Investigation	60–61	1 class period
Working on the Investigation	100, 108, 140, 159	20 minutes each
Closing the Investigation	174	1 class period

Instructional Resources

Investigations and Projects Masters, pp. 1–4

A recording sheet, teacher notes, and scoring guide are provided for each Investigation in the *Investigations and Projects Masters.*

1 MOTIVATION

This Investigation uses common materials to investigate how different sizes of calibration scopes affect the estimation of the actual height of an object. Ask students if they have seen or heard of this instrument. Discuss the importance of having the proper instruments when estimating heights of objects in a scientific study.

Through the Looking Glass

MATERIALS NEEDED

four cardboard tubes of different sizes

tape measure

grid paper

pens or pencils in two colors

You are a naturalist. You have heard that other naturalists have been using view tubes called *calibration scopes* to estimate the sizes of animals in the wild. You have been told that by using the scopes, along with mathematics, you can determine the actual heights of objects.

In this Investigation, you will experiment with different sizes of calibration scopes. You will answer the following questions.

- How does the size of a particular scope affect the animal's image?
- Is the size of the image you see affected by how far away you are from an object?
- Is there a mathematical relationship between the size of the scope and the distance from the object?

Work in groups of three. You will need four different sizes of cardboard tubes.

A: a tube of any length or diameter
B: a tube longer than Tube A, but of the same diameter
C: a tube the same length as Tube B but wider in diameter
D: a tube that has the same diameter as Tube C and the same length as Tube A

Label each tube as Scope A, B, C, or D.

Cooperative Learning

This Investigation offers an excellent opportunity for using cooperative learning groups. For more information on cooperative learning strategies and group management, see *Cooperative Learning in the Mathematics Classroom,* one of the titles in the Glencoe Mathematics Professional Series.

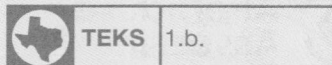

TEKS | 1.b.

SCOPE:	
DIAMETER:	
LENGTH:	
Distance	**Height**

You may want to have a student read the first paragraph of the Investigation to provide background information about calibration scopes. You may then wish to read the rest of the information given on the first page of the Investigation to introduce the activity. Discuss the activity with your students. Then separate the class into groups of three.

3 MANAGEMENT

Each group member should be responsible for a specific task.

Recorder Collects data.
Measurer Measures distances from the wall and marks them with masking tape. Holds measuring tape vertically against the wall.
Observer Views tape measure through the scope from each distance.

At the end of the activity, each member should turn in his or her respective equipment.

Sample Answers

Answers will vary as they are based on distances from the wall.

Investigations and Projects Masters, p. 4

····· **EXPERIMENT—FIRST SCOPE**

1 Begin by copying the chart above onto a sheet of paper.

2 Choose one of the four scopes. Record the label of the tube, its diameter, and its length in your chart.

3 Measure a set distance from the wall. Mark this distance with masking tape and record it in your chart. Move to another distance closer to the wall, mark it with masking tape, and record the distance in your chart. Do the same for two more distances farther than the first distance from the wall.

4 Have one of the group members hold a measuring tape vertically against the wall. Have another group member stand directly behind the first mark and view the tape measure through the scope. Record the height of the image he or she sees through the tube. Repeat this process at each of the other three marks.

····· **EXPERIMENT—SECOND SCOPE**

5 Select another scope. Make another chart like the one you made for the first scope. Repeat the experiment with the new scope using the same distances you marked in the first experiment.

6 Explain any relationship that you notice in the data. Discuss how naturalists might use these scopes to find the actual heights of animals.

You will continue working on this Investigation throughout Chapters 2 and 3.

Be sure to keep your chart and materials in your Investigation Folder.

Through the Looking Glass Investigation

Working on the Investigation
Lesson 2–5, p.100
·················
Working on the Investigation
Lesson 2–6, p.108
·················
Working on the Investigation
Lesson 3–2, p.140
·················
Working on the Investigation
Lesson 3–5, p.159
·················
Closing the Investigation
End of Chapter 3, p.174
·················

2, 3

NAME_____ DATE_____

Investigation, Chapters 2 and 3 Student Edition Pages 60–61, 100, 108, 140, 159, 174

Through the Looking Glass

Work with your group to add to the list of questions to be considered.

· How can calibration scopes be used to find the heights of animals?

· What is the relationship between the distance a viewer is from an image and the height of that image?

· Suppose that you are looking through Tube D and an animal 100 feet away fills your view. If you switch to Tube C, where should you stand so that the animal's image fills your view?

_____

_____

_____

_____

Use this chart to help you plan your explanation on page 174.

Object	How Used
Tape Measure	
Pen	
Calculator	
Piece of Paper	

2

Graphing Linear Relations and Functions

PREVIEWING THE CHAPTER

This chapter begins with students graphing relations and identifying those that are functions. Next, they graph linear equations from a table of ordered pairs, identify the slope and intercepts, and use these to group other linear equations. Graphing technology is applied to graph linear equations and to approximate solutions of equations in one variable. Then students determine if the lines are parallel, perpendicular, or neither. The strategy of identifying and using a pattern is integrated to help students solve problems. Next, students draw scatter plots and find prediction equations to solve problems. They conclude their study by graphing special functions and linear inequalities.

Lesson (Pages)	Lesson Objectives	NCTM Standards	State/Local Objectives
2-1 (64–71)	Graph a relation, state its domain and range, and determine if it is a function. Find values of functions for given elements of the domain.	1–6	1.a., 2.c.
2-2A (72)	Use a graphing calculator to graph linear equations.	1–6	
2-2 (73–78)	Identify equations that are linear and graph them. Write linear equations in standard form. Determine the intercepts of a line and use them to graph an equation.	1–6	1.a., 4.a.
2-2B (79)	Use a graphing calculator to approximate solutions to equations with one variable.	1–6	2.a.
2-3 (80–87)	Determine the slope of a line. Use slope and a point to graph an equation. Determine if two lines are parallel, perpendicular, or neither. Solve problems by identifying and using a pattern.	1–6	4.a., 4.b.
2-4 (88–94)	Write an equation of a line in slope-intercept form given the slope and one or two points. Write an equation of a line that is parallel or perpendicular to the graph of a given equation.	1–6	
2-5 (95–100)	Draw scatter plots. Find and use prediction equations.	1–6	1.b.
2-5B (101–102)	Use a graphing calculator to graph lines of regression.	1–6	1.b.
2-6 (103–108)	Identify and graph special functions.	1–6	1.b., 4.a., 4.b., 10.f.
2-7A (109)	Use a graphing calculator to graph linear inequalities.	1–5	2.a.
2-7 (110–114)	Draw graphs of inequalities in two variables.	1–5	2.a.

A complete, 1-page lesson plan is provided for each lesson in the *Lesson Planning Guide*. Answer keys for each lesson are available in the *Answer Key Masters*.

You may want to refer to the **Course Planning Calendar** on page T12 for detailed information on pacing.
PACING: **Standard**—14 days; **Honors**—13 days; **Block**—7 days

LESSON PLANNING CHART

| Lesson (Pages) | Materials/ Manipulatives | Extra Practice (Student Edition) | BLACKLINE MASTERS | | | | | | | | | Real-World Applications | Interactive Mathematics Tools Software | Teaching Transparencies |
			Study Guide	Practice	Enrichment	Assessment and Evaluation	Modeling Mathematics	Multicultural Activity	Tech Prep Applications	Graphing Calculator	Science and Math Lab Manual			
2-1 (64–71)	graph paper	p. 878	p. 8	p. 8	p. 8									2-1A 2-1B
2-2A (72)	graphing calculator									pp. 19, 20			2-2A	
2-2 (73–78)	graph paper glass	p. 878	p. 9	p. 9	p. 9	p. 44				p. 2		4	2-2	2-2A 2-2B
2-2B (79)	graphing calculator									pp. 21, 22				
2-3 (80–87)	graph paper geoboard* ball board watch graphing calculator	p.879	p. 10	p. 10	p. 10									2-3A 2-3B
2-4 (88–94)	graph paper cellular-phone bill	p. 879	p. 11	p. 11	p. 11	pp. 43, 44			p. 3					2-4A 2-4B
2-5 (95–100)	graph paper SAT scores	p. 879	p. 12	p. 12	p. 12		p. 3		p. 4		pp. 69–74	5	2-5	2-5A 2-5B
2-5B (101–102)	graphing calculator									pp. 23, 24				
2-6 (103–108)	graph paper career charts Indy 500 data	p. 880	p. 13	p. 13	p. 13	p. 45	p. 62		p. 4			6		2-6A 2-6B
2-7A (109)	graphing calculator									pp. 25, 26				
2-7 (110–114)	graph paper	p. 880	p. 14	p. 14	p. 14	p. 45								2-7A 2-7B
Study Guide/ Assessment (115–119)						pp. 29–42, 46–48								

*Included in Glencoe's Student Manipulative Kit and Overhead Manipulative Resources.

ORGANIZING THE CHAPTER

OTHER CHAPTER RESOURCES

Student Edition
Investigation, pp. 60–61
Chapter Opener, pp. 62–63
Mathematics and Society, p. 94
Working on the Investigation,
  pp. 100, 108

Teacher's Classroom Resources
Investigations and Projects Masters,
  pp. 29–32

 Technology
Teacher's Guide for Software
  Resources
Test and Review Software (IBM
  and Macintosh)
CD-ROM Interactions (Windows
  and Macintosh)

 Professional Publications
Block Scheduling Booklet
Glencoe Mathematics Professional
  Series

OUTSIDE RESOURCES

Books/Periodicals
Cartesian Cartoons, Dale Seymour Publications
Coes, L. "The Functions of a Toy Balloon." *The
  Mathematics Teacher*, November 1994
*Using the TI-81 Graphics Calculator to Explore
  Functions*, Dale Seymour Publications

Software
Data Insights, Sunburst
The Function Supposer, Sunburst
Zap-A-Graph, William K. Bradford

Videos/CD-ROMs
Graphing Linear Equations I & II, Math Video
  Company, NASCO
Introduction to the Plane Coordinate System, Math
  Video Company, NASCO

See the *Teacher's Guide for Software Resources* for software addresses.

ASSESSMENT RESOURCES

Student Edition
Math Journal, pp. 76, 84, 91
Mixed Review, pp. 71, 78, 87,
  94, 100, 107, 114
Self Test, p. 87
Chapter Highlights, p. 115
Chapter Study Guide and
  Assessment, pp. 116–118
Alternative Assessment, p. 119
  Portfolio, p. 119

College Entrance Exam Practice,
  pp. 120–121

Teacher's Wraparound Edition
5-Minute Check, pp. 64, 73, 80,
  88, 95, 103, 110
Check for Understanding, pp. 68,
  76, 84, 91, 98, 106, 112
Closing Activity, pp. 71, 78, 87,
  94, 100, 108, 114
Cooperative Learning, pp. 67, 107

Assessment and Evaluation Masters
Multiple-Choice Tests, Forms 1A
  (Honors), 1B (Average), 1C
  (Basic), pp. 29–34
Free-Response Tests, Forms 2A
  (Honors), 2B (Average), 2C
  (Basic), pp. 35–40
Calculator-Based Test, p. 41
Performance Assessment, p. 42
Mid-Chapter Test, p. 43
Quizzes A–D, pp. 44–45
Standardized Test Practice, p. 46
Cumulative Review, pp. 47–48

ENHANCING THE CHAPTER

Examples of some of the materials for enhancing Chapter 2 are shown below.

DIVERSITY

Multicultural Activity Masters, pp. 3, 4

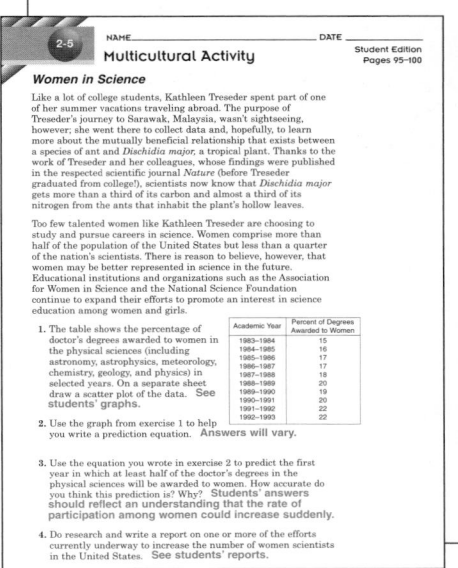

2-5 NAME_____ DATE_____
Multicultural Activity Student Edition Pages 95–100

Women in Science

Like a lot of college students, Kathleen Treseder spent part of one of her summer vacations traveling abroad. The purpose of Treseder's journey to Sarawak, Malaysia, wasn't sightseeing, however; she went there to collect data and, hopefully, to learn more about the mutually beneficial relationship that exists between a species of ant and *Dischidia major*, a tropical plant. Thanks to the work of Treseder and her colleagues, whose findings were published in the respected scientific journal *Nature* (before Treseder graduated from college!), scientists now know that *Dischidia major* gets more than a third of its carbon and almost a third of its nitrogen from the ants that inhabit the plant's hollow leaves.

Too few talented women like Kathleen Treseder are choosing to study and pursue careers in science. Women comprise more than half of the population of the United States but less than a quarter of the nation's scientists. There is reason to believe, however, that women may be better represented in science in the future. Educational institutions and organizations such as the Association for Women in Science and the National Science Foundation continue to expand their efforts to promote an interest in science education among women and girls.

1. The table shows the percentage of doctor's degrees awarded to women in the physical sciences (including astronomy, astrophysics, meteorology, chemistry, geology, and physics) in selected years. On a separate sheet draw a scatter plot of the data. **See students' graphs.**

Academic Year	Percent of Degrees Awarded to Women
1983–1984	15
1984–1985	16
1985–1986	17
1986–1987	17
1987–1988	18
1988–1989	20
1989–1990	19
1990–1991	20
1991–1992	22
1992–1993	22

2. Use the graph from exercise 1 to help you write a prediction equation. **Answers will vary.**

3. Use the equation you wrote in exercise 2 to predict the first year in which at least half of the doctor's degrees in the physical sciences will be awarded to women. How accurate do you think this prediction is? Why? **Students' answers should reflect an understanding that the rate of participation among women could increase suddenly.**

4. Do research and write a report on one or more of the efforts currently underway to increase the number of women scientists in the United States. **See students' reports.**

APPLICATIONS

Real-World Applications, 4, 5, 6

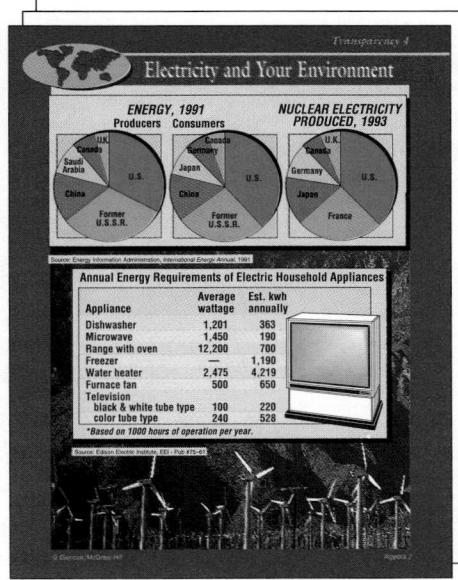

Transparency 4

Electricity and Your Environment

ENERGY, 1991
Producers   Consumers

NUCLEAR ELECTRICITY PRODUCED, 1993

Source: Energy Information Administration, *International Energy Annual, 1991*

Annual Energy Requirements of Electric Household Appliances

Appliance	Average wattage	Est. kwh annually
Dishwasher	1,201	363
Microwave	1,450	190
Range with oven	12,200	700
Freezer		1,190
Water heater	2,475	4,219
Furnace fan	500	650
Television		
black & white tube type	100	220
color tube type	240	528

*Based on 1000 hours of operation per year.

Source: Edison Electric Institute, EEI - Pub #75-61

TECHNOLOGY

Graphing Calculator Masters, p. 2

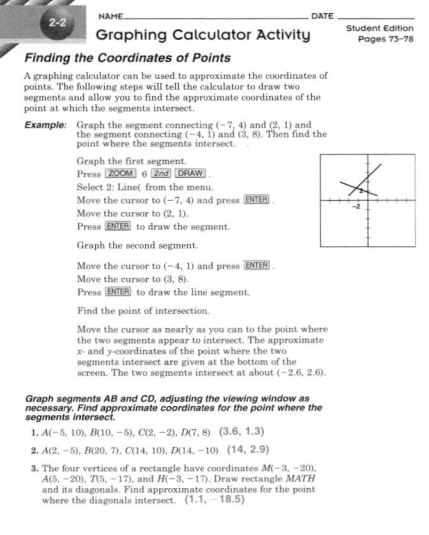

2-2 NAME_____ DATE_____
Graphing Calculator Activity Student Edition Pages 73–78

Finding the Coordinates of Points

A graphing calculator can be used to approximate the coordinates of points. The following steps will tell the calculator to draw two segments and allow you to find the approximate coordinates of the point at which the segments intersect.

Example: Graph the segment connecting $(-7, 4)$ and $(2, 1)$ and the segment connecting $(-4, 1)$ and $(3, 8)$. Then find the point where the segments intersect.

Graph the first segment.
Press ZOOM 6 2nd DRAW.
Select 2: Line(from the menu.
Move the cursor to $(-7, 4)$ and press ENTER.
Move the cursor to $(2, 1)$.
Press ENTER to draw the segment.

Graph the second segment.

Move the cursor to $(-4, 1)$ and press ENTER.
Move the cursor to $(3, 8)$.
Press ENTER to draw the line segment.

Find the point of intersection.

Move the cursor as nearly as you can to the point where the two segments appear to intersect. The approximate x- and y-coordinates of the point where the two segments intersect are given at the bottom of the screen. The two segments intersect at about $(-2.6, 2.6)$.

Graph segments AB and CD, adjusting the viewing window as necessary. Find approximate coordinates for the point where the segments intersect.

1. $A(-5, 10)$, $B(10, -5)$, $C(2, -2)$, $D(7, 8)$ (3.6, 1.3)
2. $A(2, -5)$, $B(20, 7)$, $C(14, 10)$, $D(14, -10)$ (14, 2.9)
3. The four vertices of a rectangle have coordinates $M(-3, -20)$, $A(5, -20)$, $T(5, -17)$, and $H(-3, -17)$. Draw rectangle $MATH$ and its diagonals. Find approximate coordinates for the point where the diagonals intersect. (1.1, -18.5)

TECH PREP

Tech Prep Applications Masters, pp. 3, 4

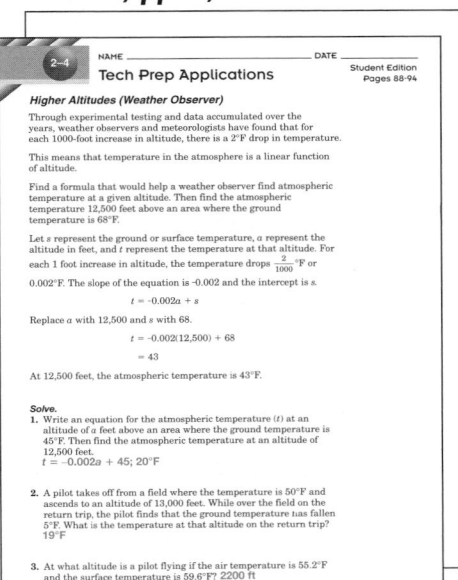

2-4 NAME_____ DATE_____
Tech Prep Applications Student Edition Pages 88–94

Higher Altitudes (Weather Observer)

Through experimental testing and data accumulated over the years, weather observers and meteorologists have found that for each 1000-foot increase in altitude, there is a 2°F drop in temperature.

This means that temperature in the atmosphere is a linear function of altitude.

Find a formula that would help a weather observer find atmospheric temperature at a given altitude. Then find the atmospheric temperature 12,500 feet above an area where the ground temperature is 68°F.

Let s represent the ground or surface temperature, a represent the altitude in feet, and t represent the temperature at that altitude. For each 1 foot increase in altitude, the temperature drops $\frac{2}{1000}$°F or 0.002°F. The slope of the equation is -0.002 and the intercept is s.

$$t = -0.002a + s$$

Replace a with 12,500 and s with 68.

$$t = -0.002(12,500) + 68$$
$$= 43$$

At 12,500 feet, the atmospheric temperature is 43°F.

Solve.
1. Write an equation for the atmospheric temperature (t) at an altitude of a feet above an area where the ground temperature is 45°F. Then find the atmospheric temperature at an altitude of 12,500 feet. $t = -0.002a + 45$; 20°F

2. A pilot takes off from a field where the temperature is 50°F and ascends to an altitude of 13,000 feet. While over the field on the return trip, the pilot finds that the ground temperature has fallen 5°F. What is the temperature at that altitude on the return trip? 19°F

3. At what altitude is a pilot flying if the air temperature is 55.2°F and the surface temperature is 59.6°F? 2200 ft

CONNECTIONS

Science and Math Lab Manual, pp. 69–74

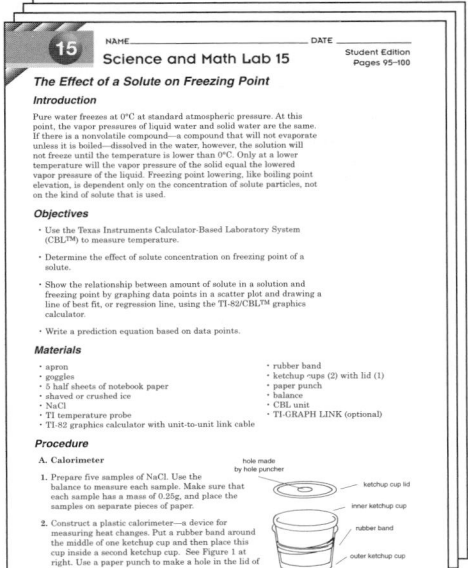

15 NAME_____ DATE_____
Science and Math Lab 15 Student Edition Pages 95–100

The Effect of a Solute on Freezing Point

Introduction

Pure water freezes at 0°C at standard atmospheric pressure. At this point, the vapor pressures of liquid water and solid water are the same. If there is a nonvolatile compound—a compound that will not evaporate unless it is boiled—dissolved in the water, however, the solution will not freeze until the temperature is lower than 0°C. Only at a lower temperature will the vapor pressure of the solid equal the lowered vapor pressure of the liquid. Freezing point lowering, like boiling point elevation, is dependent only on the concentration of solute particles, not on the kind of solute that is used.

Objectives
- Use the Texas Instruments Calculator-Based Laboratory System (CBL™) to measure temperature.
- Determine the effect of solute concentration on freezing point of a solute.
- Show the relationship between amount of solute in a solution and freezing point by graphing data points in a scatter plot and drawing a line of best fit, or regression line, using the TI-82/CBL™ graphics calculator.
- Write a prediction equation based on data points.

Materials
- apron
- goggles
- 5 half sheets of notebook paper
- shaved or crushed ice
- NaCl
- TI temperature probe
- TI-82 graphics calculator with unit-to-unit link cable
- rubber band
- ketchup cups (2) with lid (1)
- paper punch
- balance
- CBL unit
- TI-GRAPH LINK (optional)

Procedure

A. Calorimeter
1. Prepare five samples of NaCl. Use the balance to measure each sample. Make sure that each sample has a mass of 0.25g, and place the samples on separate pieces of paper.
2. Construct a plastic calorimeter—a device for measuring heat changes. Put a rubber band around the middle of one ketchup cup and then place this cup inside a second ketchup cup. See Figure 1 at right. Use a paper punch to make a hole in the lid of a ketchup cup.

hole made by hole puncher
ketchup cup lid
inner ketchup cup
rubber band
outer ketchup cup

PROBLEM SOLVING

Problem of the Week Cards, 4, 5, 6

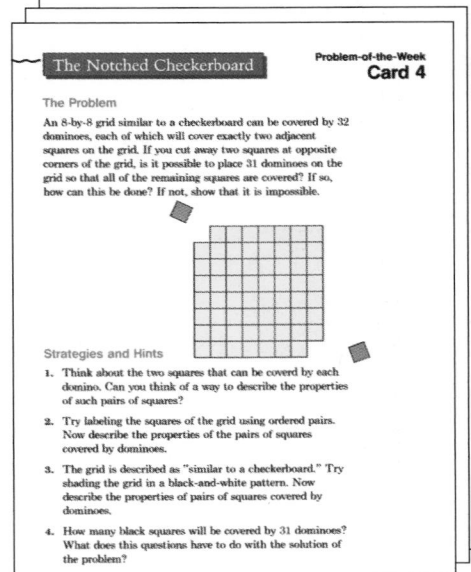

The Notched Checkerboard Problem-of-the-Week Card 4

The Problem

An 8-by-8 grid similar to a checkerboard can be covered by 32 dominoes, each of which will cover exactly two adjacent squares on the grid. If you cut away two squares at opposite corners of the grid, is it possible to place 31 dominoes on the grid so that all of the remaining squares are covered? If so, how can this be done? If not, show that it is impossible.

Strategies and Hints
1. Think about the two squares that can be covered by each domino. Can you think of a way to describe the properties of such pairs of squares?
2. Try labeling the squares of the grid using ordered pairs. Now describe the properties of the pairs of squares covered by dominoes.
3. The grid is described as "similar to a checkerboard." Try shading the grid in a black-and-white pattern. Now describe the properties of pairs of squares covered by dominoes.
4. How many black squares will be covered by 31 dominoes? What does this question have to do with the solution of the problem?

MAKING MATHEMATICS RELEVANT

This two-page introduction to the chapter provides students with an opportunity to explore contemporary topics and their applications to mathematics.

Background Information

The Native American Population
There are 552 federally recognized Native American tribes, with a total population of 1,959,000. There are 250 languages for these tribes. Like most Americans, the members of these tribes live mostly in or near cities. Only 22% live on reservations; the other 78% live in urban areas.

CHAPTER

2

Graphing Linear Relations and Functions

Objectives

In this chapter, you will:

- identify different types of relations and functions,
- graph relations and functions on the coordinate plane,
- look for patterns to solve problems,
- model real-world data using scatter plots, and
- graph inequalities on the coordinate plane.

Tribal Population

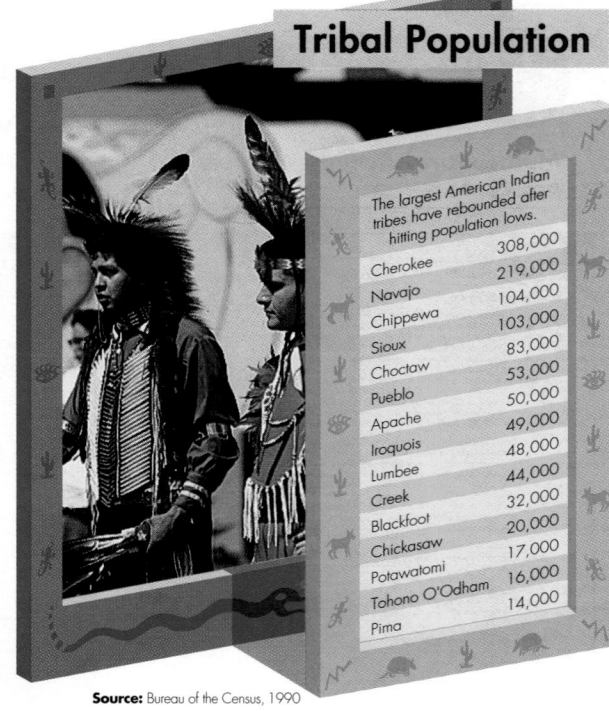

The largest American Indian tribes have rebounded after hitting population lows.

Cherokee	308,000
Navajo	219,000
Chippewa	104,000
Sioux	103,000
Choctaw	83,000
Pueblo	53,000
Apache	50,000
Iroquois	49,000
Lumbee	48,000
Creek	44,000
Blackfoot	32,000
Chickasaw	20,000
Potawatomi	17,000
Tohono O'Odham	16,000
Pima	14,000

Source: Bureau of the Census, 1990

The 1990 U.S. census report indicates that the number of people who call themselves American Indians has tripled since 1960. Are you aware of the rich, Native American diversity that weaves its thread through the history of our continent?

TIME *Line*

260 The Olmecs of Mesoamerica develop their system of numeration, a place-value system based on 20. It is in use during the next 1000 years.

| 39,000 B.C. | 38,000 | 37,000 | 300 B.C. | 200 | 100 | 0 | A.D. 100 | 200 | 300 | 400 | 500 | 600 |

38,000 B.C. The first Americans cross the temporarily dry Bering Straits from Asia and begin to colonize the new continent.

A.D. 680 The first uses of a "goose egg" sign for zero appear in Cambodi and Sumatra.

TIME *Line*

As this time line demonstrates, the earliest numeration systems did not include the "goose egg" symbol for zero. Students might want to investigate the history of the invention of the zero concept and symbol.

*inter*NET
CONNECTION

Read topics on languages, literature, and nations of Earth's indigenous peoples on-line.

World Wide Web
http://web.maxwell.syr.edu/nativeweb/

so much, when school begins, her mother disassembles Cheryl's loom to prevent her from weaving instead of completing her homework.

One of Cheryl's rugs, a type called a chief's blanket, won first prize in the youth division of the arts and crafts contest at the 1991 Intertribal Ceremonial in Gallup. It also took second prize in the young artists' division of the 1992 Navajo Nation Window Rock Fair.

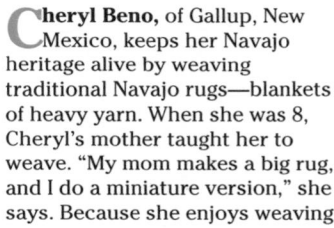

Cheryl Beno, of Gallup, New Mexico, keeps her Navajo heritage alive by weaving traditional Navajo rugs—blankets of heavy yarn. When she was 8, Cheryl's mother taught her to weave. "My mom makes a big rug, and I do a miniature version," she says. Because she enjoys weaving

Chapter Project

Do research to learn about traditional Native American weaving patterns. Draw several designs and describe the patterns in each, paying particular attention to the use of parallel and perpendicular lines in the design. Then try to design a pattern of your own on paper. Be creative in your use of color. Then actually create the design using fabric, construction paper, or any other materials that will best show your design.

While Navajo patterns are the most popular, many other groups of Native Americans produce beautiful fabrics. The Hopi, Tlingit, Kwakiutl, Iroquois, Sioux, Osage, Potawatomi, and Chipewyan tribes all produce these materials.

Chapter Project

Cooperative Learning This chapter introduces linear equations and linear graphs. The Native American weaving patterns in this project are formed from straight-line segments. In principle, these patterns could be superimposed on the coordinate system, and equations could be written to represent the patterns.

Investigations and Projects Masters, p. 29

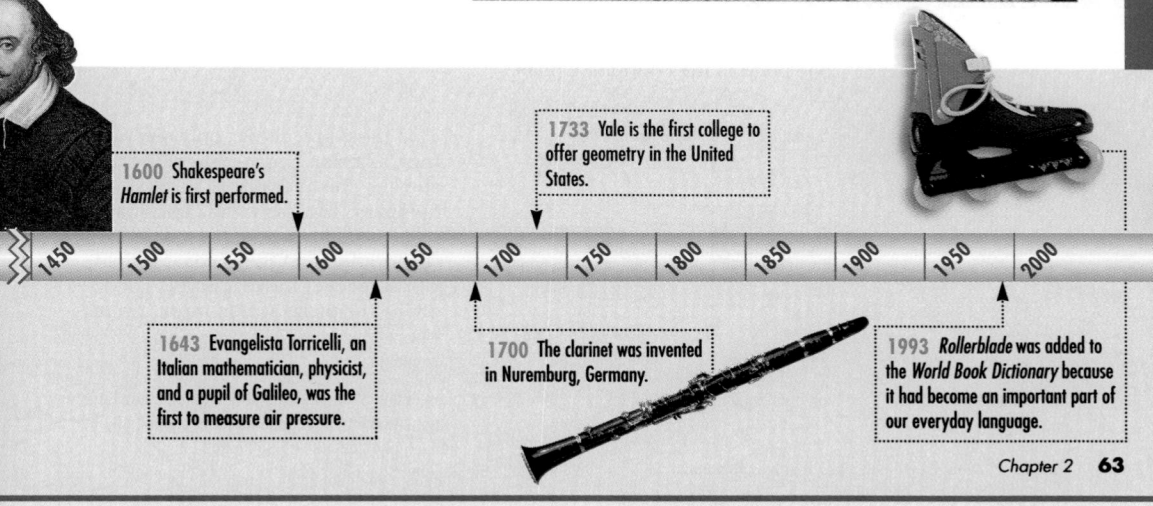

1600 Shakespeare's *Hamlet* is first performed.

1733 Yale is the first college to offer geometry in the United States.

1450 1500 1550 1600 1650 1700 1750 1800 1850 1900 1950 2000

1643 Evangelista Torricelli, an Italian mathematician, physicist, and a pupil of Galileo, was the first to measure air pressure.

1700 The clarinet was invented in Nuremburg, Germany.

1993 *Rollerblade* was added to the *World Book Dictionary* because it had become an important part of our everyday language.

Chapter 2 **63**

NAME_____ DATE_____

2 Chapter 2 Project A
Student Edition Pages 62–1

Native Americans

1. Choose several different groups of Native American peoples that you would like to know more about.

2. Research the groups you selected in exercise 1. A good starting point might be a Native American World Wide Web site; there are a number of them. (If neither you nor your school has access to the Internet, check with your local public library.) Find at least two sets of numerical data that can be shown on a graph.

3. Draw graphs for two of the sets of data you found in exercise 2. If one of the graphs is a scatter plot, find a prediction equation. If the graph of the data is a line, find an equation for the line. Can you make any predictions using your graphs?

4. Write a report about your research. Be sure to include the graphs you drew in exercise 3 and any predictions you made.

Alternative Chapter Projects ▬

Two other chapter projects are included in the *Investigations and Projects Masters*. In Chapter 2 Project A, pp. 29–30, students extend the topic in the chapter opener. In Chapter 2 Project B, pp. 31–32, students explore the work of oceanographers.

NCTM Standards: 1–6

Instructional Resources

- Study Guide Master 2-1
- Practice Master 2-1
- Enrichment Master 2-1

Transparency 2-1A contains the 5-Minute Check for this lesson; **Transparency 2-1B** contains a teaching aid for this lesson.

Recommended Pacing	
Standard Pacing	Day 1 of 14
Honors Pacing	Day 1 of 13
Block Scheduling*	Day 1 of 7

*For more information on pacing and possible lesson plans, refer to the *Block Scheduling Booklet*.

1 FOCUS

5-Minute Check
(over Chapter 1)

1. Evaluate $2(3^2 + 8) + 3 \div \frac{1}{3}$.
  43
2. What property is illustrated?
  a. $b(4 + 1) = b \times 4 + b \times 1$
    distributive
  b. $6 + (2 + 3) = 6 + (3 + 2)$
    commutative

Solve each equation or inequality.

3. $6(x + 2) = 2x + 4$ $x = -2$
4. $|2x + 3| = 5$ $x = 1, -4$
5. $7r + 0.6 \le 0.11$
  $\{r \mid r \le -0.07\}$

Motivating the Lesson
Hands-On Activity Have students use an almanac to complete the following table for their state.

Year	Population
1930	
1940	
1950	
1960	
1970	
1980	
1990	

What YOU'LL LEARN

- To graph a relation, state its domain and range, and determine if it is a function, and
- to find values of functions for given elements of the domain.

Why IT'S IMPORTANT

You can use relations to solve problems involving geography, forestry, and sports.

N. Scott Momaday (1934–)

The first American Indian to win the Pulitzer Prize for Literature was Kiowa Indian N. Scott Momaday. His 1969 novel, *House Made of Dawn*, was based on his experiences growing up in the Southwest.

CONNECTION
Geography

The growth in the population of the state of Arizona over the last several decades can be shown by using a table.

Year	1930	1940	1950	1960	1970	1980	1990
Population (millions)	0.4	0.5	0.7	1.3	1.8	2.7	3.7

Source: U.S. Census

Another way to represent the population growth is to use **ordered pairs**. The ordered pairs for the data above are: (1930, 0.4), (1940, 0.5), (1950, 0.7), (1960, 1.3), (1970, 1.8), (1980, 2.7), and (1990, 3.7). The first number in the ordered pair is the year, and the second number is the population in millions.

You can *graph* these ordered pairs by creating a **coordinate system** with two axes. The horizontal axis represents the year, and the vertical axis represents the population. Each point represents an ordered pair shown in the table above. Remember that each point in the coordinate plane can be named by exactly one ordered pair and that every ordered pair names exactly one point in the coordinate plane.

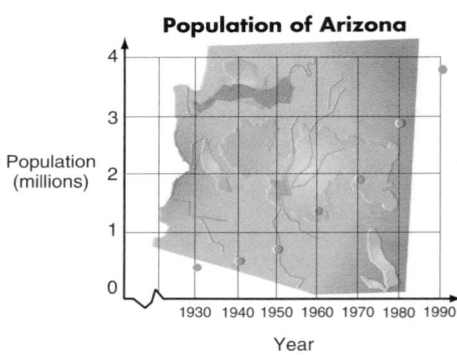

Population of Arizona

(graph: Population (millions) vs. Year 1930 1940 1950 1960 1970 1980 1990)

Quadrant II | Quadrant I
origin | (3, 2)
x-coordinate, y-coordinate
x-axis, y-axis
O
Quadrant III | Quadrant IV

In this book, assume that each square on a graph represents 1 unit unless otherwise labeled.

In the graph above, only one part of the **Cartesian coordinate plane** was shown—the one with all positive numbers. The Cartesian coordinate plane is composed of the *x*-axis (horizontal) and the *y*-axis (vertical), which meet at the **origin** (0, 0) and divide the plane into four **quadrants**. *The points on the two axes do not lie in any quadrant.*

The ordered pairs graphed on this plane can be represented by (*x*, *y*).

fabulous FIRSTS

Momaday's other writings include: *The Way to Rainy Mountain* (1969), *Angle of Geese and Other Poems* (1974), *The Names: A Memoir* (1976), *The Gourd Dancer* (1976), *Ancient Child* (1989), and *In the Presence of the Sun: Stories and Poems* (1993).

TEKS	1.a., 2.c.

A set of ordered pairs, such as the one for the population of Arizona, forms a **relation.** The **domain** of a relation is the set of all first coordinates (*x*-coordinates) from the ordered pairs, and the **range** is the set of all second coordinates (*y*-coordinates) from the ordered pairs.

A **mapping** shows how each member of the domain is paired with each member of the range.

{(4, 5),(−2, 3), (5, 6)}   {(1, 3), (4, −9) (6, 3)}   {(2, 3), (−4, 8), (2, 6), (7, −3)}

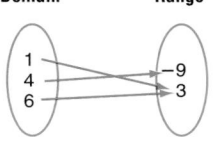 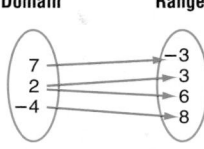

A **function** is a special type of relation in which each element of the domain is paired with *exactly one* element from the range. The first two relations above are functions. The third relation is *not* a function because the 2 in the domain is paired with both 3 and 6 in the range.

Example **1** **State the domain and range of the relation shown in the graph. Is the relation a function?**

The relation is {(−4, 5), (−3, −4), (−2, 0), (1, 1), (2, −4)}.
The domain is {−4, −3, −2, 1, 2}.
The range is {−4, 0, 1, 5}

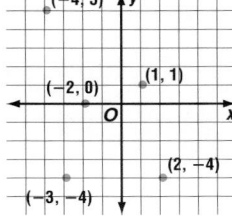

Each member of the domain is paired with exactly one member of the range, so this relation is a function.

Since the domain of the function in Example 1 is a set of individual points, it is called a **discrete function.** Notice that its graph consists of points that are not connected.

You can use the **vertical line test** to determine if a relation is a function. Using the graph in Example 1, place your pencil at the left of the graph to represent a vertical line. Slowly move the pencil to the right across the graph. At each point of the domain, the vertical line intersects the graph of the relation at only one point. Therefore, the relation is a function. If the vertical line intersects the graph at more than one point, the relation is *not* a function.

Is the population growth in Arizona a function? Why or why not?

In-Class Example

For Example 1
State the domain and range of the relation shown in the graph. Is it a function?

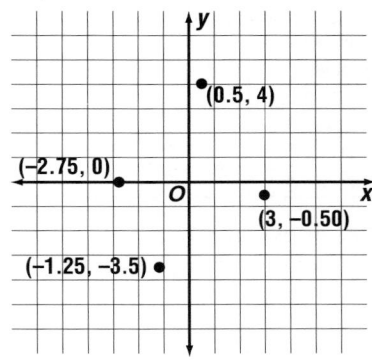

D = {−2.75, −1.25, 0.5, 3}
R = {−3.5, −0.50, 0, 4}; yes

Teaching Tip Every function is a relation, but not every relation is a function. For example, a table of hourly temperatures on a given day is a relation, but not a function.

For Example 2

Mary has five brothers and sisters. She decided to monitor their television viewing for one week and compare the amounts of time with the siblings' ages. Below are the results.

Name	Hours	Age
Mary	10	18
Joe	8	15
Estelle	6	10
Jason	7	9
Alice	3	5
Adam	1	3

Graph this information and determine if it is a function.

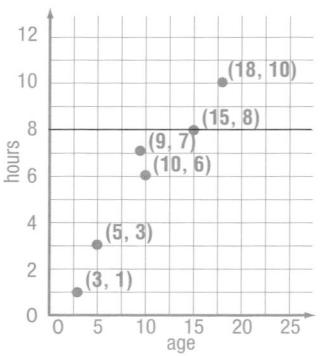

yes, it is

MODELING MATHEMATICS In this modeling exercise, students will create a variety of boxes. Each will have a unique volume, illustrating the fact that volume is a *function* of the length of the side. Have students write an equation for the volume of a box. Then have them graph and determine which value of x gives the greatest volume.

Example  2 The table below shows the number of fires and the number of acres burned over six years on the lands owned by the Bureau of Indian Affairs in the state of Washington. Graph this information and determine if it is a function.

APPLICATION
Forestry

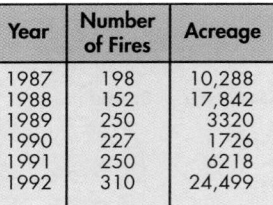

Year	Number of Fires	Acreage
1987	198	10,288
1988	152	17,842
1989	250	3320
1990	227	1726
1991	250	6218
1992	310	24,499

Source: Washington State Department of Natural Resources, 1993

Forest Fires

Using the vertical line test, you can see that 250 in the domain is mapped to two different range values, 3320 and 6218. Therefore, the relation is *not* a function.

Functions and their graphs can help you discover many relationships in mathematics.

MODELING MATHEMATICS   Volume

Materials:  centimeter grid paper   ✂ scissors

In this activity, you will make open boxes from identical square pieces of centimeter paper and investigate their volumes.

Your Turn   b, d–f. See students' work.

a. Cut identical squares from the corners of one square piece of paper and fold along the edges to form an open box.

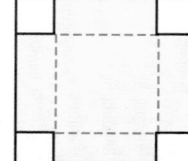

b. Find the volume of the open box.

c. Repeat steps a and b for other cutout squares with whole-number lengths.

d. Organize the data into ordered pairs (length of the side of cutout square, volume of open box). Is this relation a function?   yes

e. Graph the ordered pairs.

f. Which ordered pair results in the greatest volume?

g. Why might some businesses be interested in data like these?   Sample answer: making packages

An equation is another way to represent a relation. The solutions of an equation in x and y are the set of ordered pairs (x, y) that make the equation true. Consider the equation $y = 5x - 4$. Since x can be any real number, the domain has an infinite number of elements. To determine whether an equation represents a function, it is often simpler to look at the graph of the relation.

One way to graph an equation is to make a table of solutions, graph enough ordered pairs to see a pattern, and then connect the points with a line or smooth curve. You can then use the vertical line test to determine whether the equation represents a function.

When the domain of the function has an infinite number of elements and can be graphed with a line or smooth curve, the function is a **continuous function**.

Example **Determine whether each equation represents a function.**

a. $y = 3x - 4$

Prepare a table of values to find ordered pairs that satisfy the equation. Choose values for x and find the corresponding values for y. Then graph the ordered pairs.

x	y
−1	
0	
1	
2	

$\rightarrow$

x	y
−1	−7
0	−4
1	−1
2	2

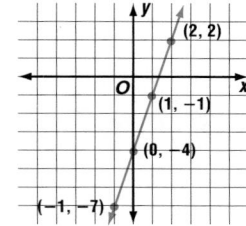

Since x can be any real number, there is an infinite number of ordered pairs that can be graphed. If all of them were graphed, they would form a line. For each x value, there is exactly one y value. Thus, this set of ordered pairs passes the vertical line test and is a function.

b. $x = y^2 + 1$

Complete the table. In this case, it is easier to choose y values and then find the corresponding values for x. Then sketch the graph, connecting the points with a curved line.

x	y
	−2
	−1
	0
	1
	2

$\rightarrow$

x	y
5	−2
2	−1
1	0
2	1
5	2

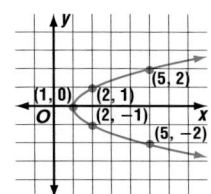

This graph is called a *parabola*. You can see from the table as well as the vertical line test that there are two y values for all but one of the x values. Therefore, this set of ordered pairs is *not* a function.

Letters other than f can be used to represent a function. For example, the equation $y = 4x + 3$ can also be written as $g(x) = 4x + 3$.

Equations that represent functions are often written in *functional notation*. The equation $y = 2x + 3$ can be written as $f(x) = 2x + 3$. The symbol $f(x)$ replaces the y and is read "f of x." The f is just the name of the function, not a variable. Suppose you want to find the value in the range that corresponds to the element 6 in the domain. This is written $f(6)$ and is read "f of 6." The value $f(6)$ is found by substituting 6 for each x in the equation. Therefore, $f(6) = 2(6) + 3$ or 15.

Cooperative Learning

Send-A-Problem Separate students into groups of three. Have one member of each group make up a relation. Another member of the group should make a mapping of some of the relation's elements and determine if it is a function. The third member should list the relation's domain and the range. After each group member has agreed with the answer, have students pass their groups' problems to other groups. For more information on the send-a-problem strategy, see *Cooperative Learning in the Mathematics Classroom*, one of the titles in the Glencoe Mathematics Professional Series, pages 23–24.

In-Class Examples

For Example 4
Given the functions $f(x) = 4x + 10$ and $g(x) = x^2 + 2$, find each value.

a. $f(3)$ **22**
b. $g(-3)$ **11**
c. $g(a - 2)$ $a^2 - 4a + 6$

For Example 5

Use a calculator to find $f\left(\dfrac{4}{9}\right)$ if $f(n) = \dfrac{13}{n^2 - 1}$. **−16.2**

---

3 PRACTICE/APPLY

Check for Understanding

Exercises 1–15 are designed to help you assess your students' understanding through reading, writing, speaking, and modeling. You should work through Exercises 1–6 with your students and then monitor their work on Exercises 7–15.

Error Analysis
Students sometimes interpret $f(3)$ to mean "f times 3" rather than "f of 3." Point out that "f times 3" will conventionally be written as "$3f$" and "$f(3)$" will be reserved for the functional value at $x = 3$.

Additional Answers

1. Sample answer:

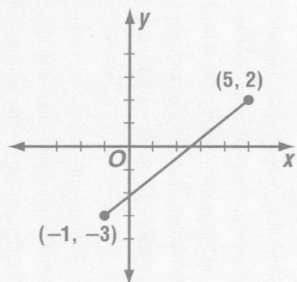

2. See students' work. The graph of a discrete function consists of points that are not connected. A continuous function can be graphed with a straight line or smooth curve.

Example ④ Given the function $g(x) = x^2 - 8$, find each value.
  a. $g(-2)$ **b.** $g(7a)$

$$g(x) = x^2 - 8$$
$$g(-2) = (-2)^2 - 8 \quad \textit{Substitute.}$$
$$= 4 - 8 \text{ or } -4$$

$$g(x) = x^2 - 8$$
$$g(7a) = (7a)^2 - 8 \quad \textit{Substitute.}$$
$$= 49a^2 - 8 \quad (ab)^2 = a^2b^2$$

Example ⑤ Use a calculator to find $f(4.6)$ if $f(x) = 0.5x^2 + 4x - 2.5$.

$$f(4.6) = 0.5(4.6)^2 + 4(4.6) - 2.5$$
Estimate: $0.5(5)^2 + 4(5) - 2.5 = 12.5 + 20 - 2.5$ or 30

Enter: 0.5 $\boxed{\times}$ 4.6 $\boxed{x^2}$ $\boxed{+}$ 4 $\boxed{\times}$ 4.6 $\boxed{-}$ 2.5 $\boxed{=}$ *26.48*

Therefore, $f(4.6) = 26.48.$ *Compare with the estimate.*

CHECK FOR UNDERSTANDING

Communicating Mathematics

Study the lesson. Then complete the following. 1–2. See margin.

1. **Graph** a function that has a domain of $-1 \leq x \leq 5$ and a range of $-3 \leq y \leq 2$. Be sure that your function passes the vertical line test.

2. **Explain** the difference between a discrete function and a continuous function. Give an example of a graph of each type of function.

3. Any vertical line where $x = a$ is not a function.

3. **Find a counterexample** for the statement "Every straight line is a function."

4. **Draw** a Cartesian coordinate plane. Name seven possible locations on the plane where a point might be graphed. Then graph and label a point in each of these locations. **See margin.**

5. **List** four ways to show how the relationship between members of a domain and range can be represented. Give an example of each. **See margin.**

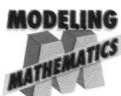
MODELING MATHEMATICS

6. Suppose you are going to construct a graph that shows the relationship between the number of hours worked per week by a student at a fast-food restaurant and the amount of money earned. Identify a reasonable domain and range for the graph. Justify your answer. Then draw a sample graph.
See students' work. Sample answer: D = {0 < x < 20}, R = {0 < y < 105}

Guided Practice

State whether each relation is a function or not.

7.
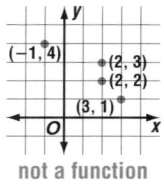
function

8.
x	y
5	−2
10	−2
15	−2
20	−2
function

9.
(−1, 4), (2, 3), (2, 2), (3, 1)
not a function

10–13. See Solutions Manual for graphs.
10. not a function
11. function; discrete
12. function; continuous
13. not a function

State the domain and range of each relation. Then graph the relation and identify whether it is a function or not. For each function, state whether it is discrete or continuous.

10. $\{(7, 8), (7, 5), (7, 2), (7, -1)\}$
11. $\{(6, 2.5), (3, 2.5), (4, 2.5)\}$
12. $y = -2x + 1$
13. $x = y^2$
14. Find $f(5)$ if $f(x) = x^2 - 3x.$ **10**
15. Find $h(-2)$ if $h(x) = x^3 + 1.$ **−7**

Additional Answers

4.
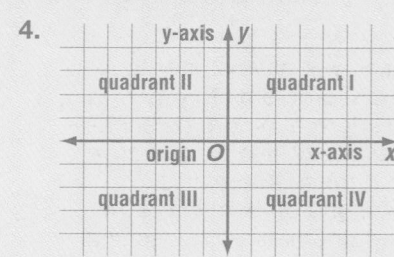

5. The four ways are a mapping, table, graph, and an equation or function. Sample answers:

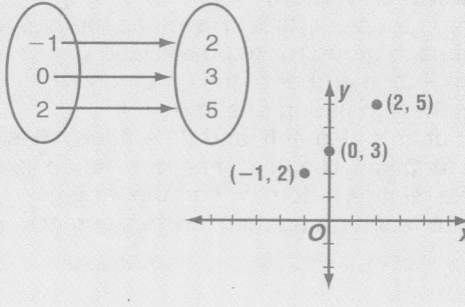

Practice

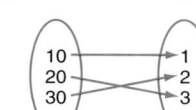

State whether each relation is a function or not.

16. D R 17. D R 18. D R

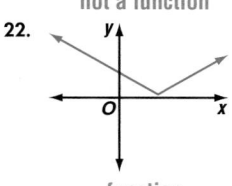   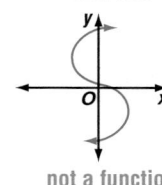 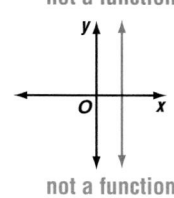

        function   not a function   function

19.

x	y
0.5	-3
2	0.8
0.5	8

not a function

20.

Year	Expenses
1994	$4000
1995	$4300
1996	$4000
1997	$4500

function

21.

x	y
3	5
3	10
3	15
3	20

not a function

22.   23.   24.

      function   not a function   not a function

25–30. See Solutions Manual.

State the domain and range of each relation. Then graph the relation and identify whether it is a function or not. For each function, state whether it is discrete or continuous.

25. $\{(4, 5), (6, 5), (3, 5)\}$ **26.** $\{(-2, 5), (3, 7), (-2, 8)\}$

27. $\{(3, 4), (4, 3), (6, 5), (5, 6)\}$ **28.** $y = 7x - 6$

29. $y = -5x$ **30.** $x = y^2 + 1$

A function h includes the ordered pairs $(-2, 1)$, $(1, 2)$, and $(3.5, -0.3)$. State whether h will still be a function if each ordered pair given below is also included in h.

31. $(-2, 2)$ no   **32.** $(0, 0)$ yes   **33.** $(2, 1)$ yes

Find each value if $f(x) = 3x - 5$ and $g(x) = x^2 - x$.

34. $f(-3)$ -14 **35.** $g(3)$ 6   **36.** $g\left(\frac{1}{3}\right)$ $-\frac{2}{9}$

37. $f\left(\frac{2}{3}\right)$ -3 **38.** $f(a)$ $3a - 5$ **39.** $g(5n)$ $25n^2 - 5n$

Find each value if $h(x) = \dfrac{x^2 + 5x - 6}{x + 3}$.   **42.** $\dfrac{a^2 + 3a - 10}{a + 2}$

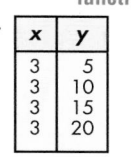

40. $h(3)$ 3   **41.** $h(-2)$ -12 **42.** $h(a - 1)$

43. Sample answer: $f(x) = 2.5x$

43. Write an example of a function that has a value of 5 when $x = 2$.

44. The function $f(x) = 3x$ can be represented by the notation $f : x \rightarrow 3x$, where x "maps" to $3x$. If a function g is defined as $g : x \rightarrow x^2 + x$, find the number that -2 maps to in function g.   2

Lesson 2-1   Relations and Functions   **69**

Reteaching

Using Charts Complete the chart for relations A and B at the right.

		A	**B**
	Relation	2→3 5→6 7→5	$\{(1, 4), (2, 6),$ $(3, 7), (3, 9)\}$
a.	domain	2, 5, 7	1, 2, 3
b.	range	3, 5, 6	4, 6, 7, 9
c.	Is it a function?	yes	no
d.	Why or why not?	Each x is paired with one y.	The x value of 3 is paired with two range elements.

Assignment Guide

Core: 17–53 odd, 55–64
Enriched: 16–48 even, 49–64

For **Extra Practice,** see p. 878.

The red A, B, and C flags, printed only in the Teacher's Wraparound Edition, indicate the level of difficulty of the exercises.

Study Guide Masters, p. 8

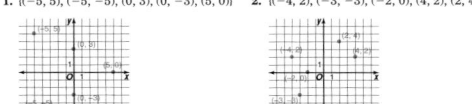

2-1   NAME_____ DATE _____

Study Guide   Student Edition Pages 64–71

Relations and Functions

Points in a plane can be named using ordered pairs of real numbers. The first coordinate indicates how far left or right of the y-axis the point is. The second coordinate indicates how far above or below the x-axis it is.

Example: Graph the set of ordered pairs $\{(1, 5), (3, -2), (-2, 1),$ $(-4, -3), (5, 1)\}$.

Definition of Relation, Domain, and Range	A relation is a set of ordered pairs. The domain is the set of all first coordinates of the ordered pairs. The range is the set of all second coordinates of the ordered pairs.
Definition of Function	A function is a relation in which each element of the domain is paired with exactly one element of the range.

If a function is described by an equation, you can find the y-value of the function for a given x-value by substituting the given value for x in the equation.

Example: Find $f(20)$ if $f(x) = 150 - 4x^2$.
Substitute 20 for x. $f(20) = 150 - 4(20)^2$
$= 150 - 4(400)$
$= -1450$
Therefore, $f(20) = -1450$.

State the domain and range of each relation. Then graph and identify whether it is a function or not. For each function, state whether it is discrete or continuous.

1. $\{(-5, 5), (-5, -5), (0, 3), (0, -3), (5, 0)\}$ **2.** $\{(-4, 2), (-3, -3), (-2, 0), (4, 2), (2, 4)\}$

$D = \{-5, 0, 5\}, R =$ $D = \{-4, -3, -2, 2, 4\}, R =$
$\{-5, -3, 0, 3, 5\}$, not a function $\{-3, 0, 2, 4\}$, function, discrete

Find each value if $f(x) = \frac{6}{x-3}$.
3. $f(12)$ $\frac{2}{3}$ **4.** $f(6)$ 2   **5.** $f(2b)$ $\frac{6}{2b-3}$

Find each value if $g(x) = \frac{x^2 + 1}{4 + x}$.
6. $g(5)$ $\frac{26}{g}$ **7.** $g(-2)$ $\frac{5}{2}$ **8.** $g(7c)$ $\frac{49c^2 + 1}{7c + 4}$

Additional Answers

45–48. Sample answers are given.

45.

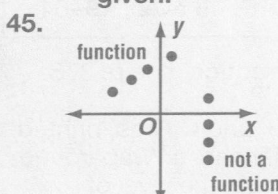

function
not a function

46.

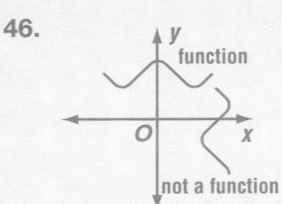

function
not a function

47.

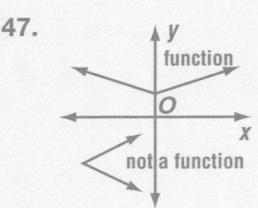

function
not a function

48.

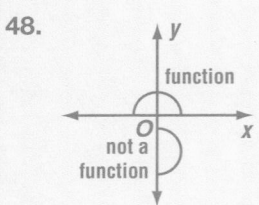

function
not a function

Practice Masters, p. 8

NAME _____ DATE _____

Student Edition
Pages 64–71

Practice

Relations and Functions

State the domain and range of each relation. Then graph and identify whether it is a function or not. For each function, state whether it is discrete or continuous.

1. {(0.75, 0.5), (0.75, −0.5), (−0.75, 0.5)}   2. {(−20, −7), (20, 0), (0, 15), (10, 0)}

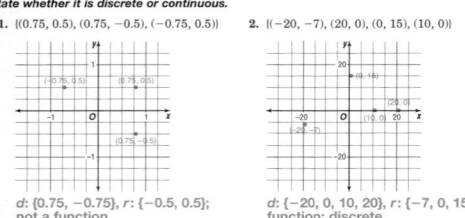

d: {0.75, −0.75}, r: {−0.5, 0.5}; not a function   d: {−20, 0, 10, 20}, r: {−7, 0, 15}; function; discrete

State the domain and range of each relation. Is the relation a function?

3. {(3, 2), (3, 5), (3, 8)} d: {3}, r: {2, 5, 8}; not a function
4. {(2, 6), (6, 2)} d: {2, 6}, r: {2, 6}; function

Use the vertical line test to determine if each relation is a function.

5. function   6. not a function

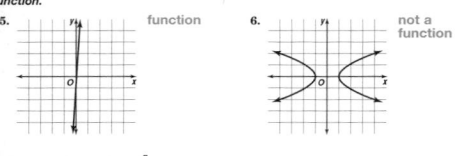

Find each value if $f(x) = \frac{5}{x + 2}$.

7. $f(3)$ 1
8. $f(-4)$ $-\frac{5}{2}$
9. $f(\frac{1}{2})$ 2
10. $f(-2)$ undefined
11. $f(0)$ $\frac{5}{2}$
12. $f(m - 2)$ $\frac{5}{m}$

70 Chapter 2

The graph of each figure described below can be a function or a relation that is *not* a function depending on how it appears on a coordinate plane. Graph each figure as both a function and as a relation that is *not* a function.   45–48. See margin.

45. a set of ordered pairs
46. a wavy line
47. an angle
48. a semicircle

Critical Thinking

49. When a fraction contains a variable in the denominator, there are some values of the variable for which the fraction is undefined. Find the domain of $f(x) = \frac{15}{x^2 - 9}$.   **all real numbers except 3 and −3**

50. If $f(x) = x^2 + 2x + 1$, for what value(s) of x would $f(x) = 0$? On a graph of $f(x)$, describe the graph at which $f(x) = 0$.   **−1; crosses the x-axis**

Applications and Problem Solving

51. **Finance**   On January 1, 1984, the Bell Telephone System gave up its local telephone monopolies and became AT&T. Despite Bell's break-up, the stock price nearly tripled over the next ten years.

Year	'83	'84	'85	'86	'87	'88	'89	'90	'91	'92	'93
Stock Price	19	$20	$25	$25	$28	$29	$45	$30	$39	$50	$55

a. Identify the domain and range.   **51a–d. See margin.**
b. Write the ordered pairs and graph.
c. Is this a function?
d. Would buying AT&T stock in 1983 have been a sound investment? Explain.

52. **Sports**   Sketch a graph of the flight of a baseball, in which the vertical coordinate at each point measures the height of the baseball above the ground and the horizontal coordinate measures the time since the ball was hit. Does the graph represent a function? Explain.   **See margin.**

53. $D = -3 \le x \le 3$, $R = -3 \le y \le 3$; no

53. **Geometry**   Identify the domain and range of the circle shown below. Is this relation a function?

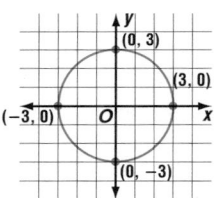

70   Chapter 2   *Graphing Linear Relations and Functions*

Additional Answers

51a. D = {year}, R = {stock price}

51b.

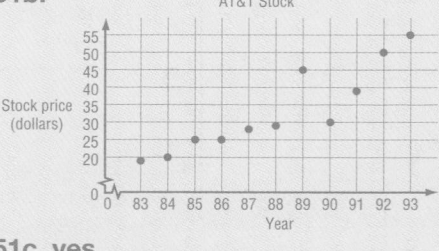

AT&T Stock

51c. yes

51d. Sample answer: Yes; even when it dropped in value, it rose higher still.

52. The graph is a function.

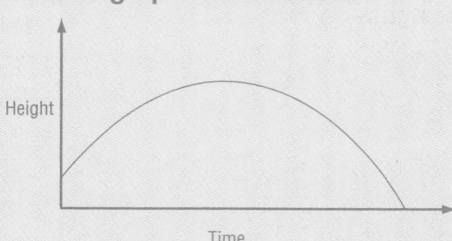

54. Government The table below shows the number of Latino representatives in the U.S. Congress for 1981–1995.

Year	1981	1983	1985	1987	1989	1991	1993	1995
Latino Representatives	6	8	10	11	10	11	17	15

Source: National Association of Latino Elected and Appointed Officials

a. Identify the domain and range. **See margin.**

b. Write the ordered pairs and draw the graph. **See margin.**

c. Is this relation a function? If it is a function, determine whether it is discrete or continuous. **yes; discrete**

d. If the domain and range were switched, would the relation be a function? Explain. **No; 10 and 11 are paired with more than one year.**

Mixed Review

Solve each equation or inequality.

55. $|y + 1| < 7$ (Lesson 1–7)

56. $|5 - m| < 1$ (Lesson 1–7)

57. $x - 5 < 0.1$ (Lesson 1–6)

58. $3|2x - 5| = -\frac{1}{3}$ (Lesson 1–5)

55. $\{y \mid -8 < y < 6\}$
56. $\{m \mid 4 < m < 6\}$
57. $x < 5.1$
58. no solution

59. Consumerism Ryan had $25.04 with him when he went to the mall. His friend, Tim, had $32.67. Ryan wanted to buy a golf shirt for $27.89. (Lesson 1–4)

a. How much money did he have to borrow from Tim in order to buy the shirt? **$2.85**

b. How much money did that leave Tim? **$29.82**

60. substitution (=)

60. State the property used in $9 + (2 + 10) = 9 + 12$. (Lesson 1–4)

61. Write an algebraic expression to represent *seven less than the sum of a number and two times its square*. (Lesson 1–4) $x + 2x^2 - 7$

62. Statistics At a bowling party, the members of the junior class decided to separate into two teams and the team with the lower mean would have to make dinner for the other team. The list at the right shows the two teams and their scores.

Team A	Score	Team B	Score
Ed	281	Laurel	101
Kelley	212	Tammy	236
Paul	72	Smitty	143
Mandi	147	Jeff	154
Maria	110	Renee	111
Bryce	212	Yolanda	88
Ryan	69	Percy	69
Sue	28	Debra	205

62a. 141.38, 128.5, 212; 138.38, 127, none
62b. See margin.

a. What are the mean, median, and mode for Team A? for Team B? (Lesson 1–3)

b. Make a back-to-back stem-and-leaf plot of the data. (Lesson 1–3)

c. Which team had to make dinner? **Team B**

Simplify each expression.

63. $3(5a + 6b) + 8(2a - b)$ (Lesson 1–2) $31a + 10b$

64. $3^2(2^2 - 1^2) + 4^2$ (Lesson 1–1) **43**

Lesson 2–1 Relations and Functions **71**

Extension

Connections The coordinates of three vertices of a parallelogram are (2, 2), (3, −1), and (0, −2). Find the coordinates of the fourth vertex. Can there be more than one point?

$(−1, 1)$, $(5, 3)$, or $(1, −5)$; **yes**

---

4 ASSESS

Closing Activity

Speaking Have students explain the difference between a relation and a function. Then have them give an example of a relation that is not a function.

Additional Answers

54a. D = {year}, R = {Latino members}

54b.
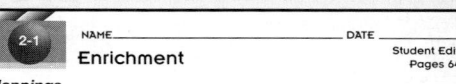

62b.

Team A	Stem	Team B
1 1 8	2	0 3
1 4	1	0 1 4 5
2 6 7	0	6 8

$8|2| = 280$ to 289 $|2|3 = 230$ to 239

Enrichment Masters, p. 8

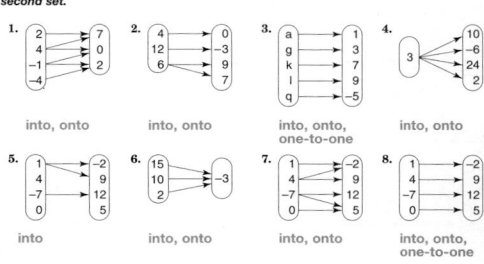

Mappings

There are three special ways in which one set can be mapped to another. A set can be mapped *into* another set, *onto* another set, or can have a *one-to-one correspondence* with another set.

Definition of an into mapping	A mapping from set A to set B is an *into* mapping if every element of A is mapped to one or more elements of set B, but never to an element not in B.
Definition of an onto mapping	A mapping from set A to set B is an *onto* mapping if each element of set B has at least one element of set A mapped to it.
Definition of a one-to-one correspondence	A mapping from set A onto set B is a *one-to-one correspondence* if each element of set A is mapped to exactly one element of set B and different elements of A are never mapped to the same element of B.

State whether each set is mapped into the second set, onto the second set, or has a one-to-one correspondence with the second set.

1. into, onto
2. into, onto
3. into, onto, one-to-one
4. into, onto
5. into
6. into, onto
7. into, onto
8. into, onto, one-to-one

9. Can a set be mapped *onto* a set with fewer elements than it has? **yes**

10. Can a set be mapped *into* a set that has more elements than it has? **yes**

11. If a mapping from set A into set B is a one-to-one correspondence, what can you conclude about the number of elements in A and B? **The sets have the same number of elements.**

Objective
Use a graphing calculator to graph linear equations.

Recommended Time
15 minutes

Instructional Resources
Graphing Calculator Masters, pp. 19 and 20

These masters provide keystroking instruction for this lesson for the TI-81 and Casio graphing calculators.

1 FOCUS

Motivating the Lesson
If you have an overhead graphing calculator or a demonstration computer, use it to draw the graph of $y = 2x + 1$ in the range $[-10, 10]$ by $[-10, 10]$ and then in the range $[-5, 5]$ by $[-10, 10]$. Ask students if the pictures are of the same line. Why or why not? Why do the graphs look different? **They are graphs of the same line. The different scales make them look different.**

2 TEACH

Teaching Tip The more of the viewing window the graph covers, the longer it will take for the TI-82 to graph the function. The calculator must determine more points to cover more of the window. However, the graphic image may not be as clear in a low-resolution window as in a high-resolution window.

3 PRACTICE/APPLY

Assignment Guide
Core: 1–9
Enriched: 1–9

2-2A Graphing Technology
Linear Equations

A Preview of Lesson 2–2

Graphing calculators are powerful tools for studying a wide variety of graphs. The examples below show graphs of linear equations.

Example **Graph each equation in the standard viewing window.**
a. $y - 2x = 3$

First, rewrite the equation so y is isolated on one side. Enter the equation for the line and graph.

Enter: Y= 2 X,T,θ +
3 ZOOM 6

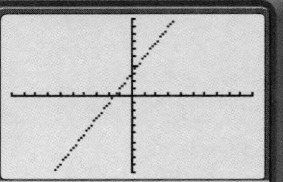

A graph that appears on the graphics screen showing all important characteristics of the graph is called a **complete graph**. The graph of $y = 2x + 3$ is complete because we can see both the x- and y-intercepts.

b. $y = -x + 14$

Enter: Y= (−) X,T,θ +
14 ZOOM 6

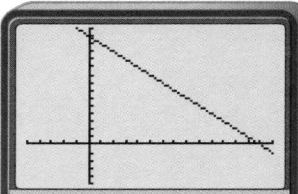

What happened? Only a small portion of the graph is shown in the $[-10, 10]$ by $[-10,10]$ window. This graph is not complete. Adjust the viewing window to include more of the graph. Try $[-5, 15]$ by $[-5, 15]$. This graph is shown at the right.

EXERCISES

Use a graphing calculator to graph each equation. Describe the viewing window that you used to view a complete graph for each equation. 1–9. **See Solutions Manual.**

1. $y = 3x - 3$ **2.** $y = -2x + 5$ **3.** $y = 4 - x$

4. $y = 5x - 35$ **5.** $y = -12x$ **6.** $y = 0.1x - 1$

7. $y = -0.3x + 15$ **8.** $y = 0.01x$ **9.** $y = 100x + 5$

---

4 ASSESS

Observing students working with technology is an excellent method of assessment.

GLENCOE Technology

 Interactive Mathematics Tools Software

This multimedia software provides an interactive lesson by having students find the equation of a line, given the graph of the function. A **Computer Journal** gives students an opportunity to write about what they have learned.

For Windows & Macintosh

Linear Equations

2-2

CONNECTION
Physics

What YOU'LL LEARN
- To identify equations that are linear and graph them,
- to write linear equations in standard form, and
- to determine the intercepts of a line and use them to graph an equation.

Why IT'S IMPORTANT
You can write equations to represent relations in education, physics, and geology.

You might guess that sound would travel fastest through air since air is less dense than other mediums like water, glass, or steel. However, just the opposite is true. Sound travels through air most slowly of all. Through air it travels 1129 feet per second, through water about 4760 feet per second, and through glass and steel about 16,000 feet per second. Distances through air for various numbers of seconds are given in the table below.

Time (seconds)	0	1	2	3	4
Distance (feet)	0	1129	2258	3387	4516

The open sentence that describes this relationship is $y = 1129x$, where x represents the number of seconds, and y represents the distance in feet. Since the value of y *depends* on the value of x, y is called the **dependent variable**, and x is called the **independent variable**.

FYI

In the Old West, people could often tell if a train was coming by "keeping their ears to the ground." They could hear the sound of the train through the tracks before they could hear the train's whistle through the air.

When the relation is graphed on a coordinate plane, the independent variable is graphed on the horizontal axis, and the dependent variable is graphed on the vertical axis. In this case, the points appear to lie on a line. This graph is a function.

Suppose we connect the points with a line. The line would contain an infinite number of points, whose ordered pairs are solutions of the equation $y = 1129x$. An equation whose graph is a line is called a **linear equation**. A linear equation is an equation that can be written in **standard form**, $Ax + By = C$.

Speed of Sound Through Air

Distance (feet): 0, 1000, 2000, 3000, 4000, 5000

Times (seconds): 0, 1, 2, 3, 4, 5

Standard Form of a Linear Equation	The standard form of a linear equation is $$Ax + By = C,$$ where A, B, and C are real numbers and A and B are not both zero.

Usually A, B, and C are given as integers whose greatest common factor is 1.

When variables other than x are used, assume that the letter coming first in the alphabet represents the domain or horizontal coordinate.

Linear equations contain one or two variables, with no variable having an exponent other than 1.

Linear equations	**Not linear equations**
$5x - 3y = 7$	$7a + 4b^2 = -8$
$x = 9$	$y = \sqrt{x + 5}$
$6s = -3t - 15$	$x + xy = 1$

FYI

Sound travels much faster than any train. The speed of sound is 720 mph.

 TEKS | 1.a., 4.a.

NCTM Standards: 1–6

Instructional Resources

- Study Guide Master 2-2
- Practice Master 2-2
- Enrichment Master 2-2
- Assessment and Evaluation Masters, p. 44
- Graphing Calculator Masters, p. 2
- Real-World Applications, 4

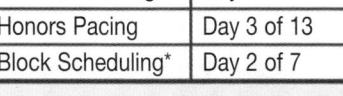 **Transparency 2-2A** contains the 5-Minute Check for this lesson; **Transparency 2-2B** contains a teaching aid for this lesson.

Recommended Pacing	
Standard Pacing	Day 3 of 14
Honors Pacing	Day 3 of 13
Block Scheduling*	Day 2 of 7

*For more information on pacing and possible lesson plans, refer to the *Block Scheduling Booklet*.

1 FOCUS

5-Minute Check
(over Lesson 2-1)

1. State the domain and range of {(4, 4), (1, 1), (3, 3)}. Is it a function? **D = {1, 3, 4}, R = {1, 3, 4}; yes**
2. In which quadrants can the point (a, a) lie? **I and III**
3. Find $f(-3)$ if $f(x) = x^2 + 3x + 2$. **2**
4. Graph {(1970, 80), (1975, 82), (1980, 80), (1985, 90), (1990, 95)}. Is it a function? **yes**

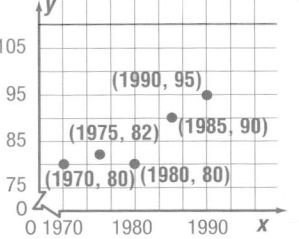

(1990, 95)
(1975, 82) (1985, 90)
(1970, 80) (1980, 80)

Motivating the Lesson

Questioning Discuss hourly wages. Have students who work explain their pay systems. If no one works, use the hourly wage of $5.00. Generate a table of values and graph them. Discuss the type of graph formed.

2 TEACH

Teaching Tip An equation is not linear if it contains variables that have degree greater than 1.

In-Class Examples

For Example 1
Write each equation in standard form where A, B, and C are integers whose greatest common factor is 1. Identify A, B, and C.

a. $y = x + 3$ $-x + y = 3$;
   $A = -1, B = 1, C = 3$
b. $\frac{1}{3}y = 4x + 5$ $12x - y = -15$;
   $A = 12, B = -1, C = -15$
c. $2x + 4y = 10$ $x + 2y = 5$;
   $A = 1, B = 2, C = 5$

For Example 2
State whether each function is a linear function.

a. $f(x) = -3x - 2$ **yes**
b. $g(x) = 2x^2 + 7$ **no**
c. $h(x) = -11 + (-7x)$ **yes**

Example ❶ Write each equation in standard form where A, B, and C are integers whose greatest common factor is 1. Identify A, B, and C.

a. $y = -5x + 6$

$$y = -5x + 6$$
$$5x + y = 6 \qquad \text{Add } 5x \text{ to each side.}$$

So $A = 5$, $B = 1$, and $C = 6$.

b. $\frac{2}{7}x = 2y + 5$

$$\frac{2}{7}x = 2y + 5$$
$$\frac{2}{7}x - 2y = 5 \qquad \text{The equation is in standard form.}$$
$$2x - 14y = 35 \qquad \text{Multiply each side by 7.}$$

So $A = 2$, $B = -14$, and $C = 35$.

c. $5x - 10y = 25$

$$5x - 10y = 25 \qquad \text{The GCF of 5, 10, and 25 is 5.}$$
$$x - 2y = 5 \qquad \text{Divide each side by 5.}$$

So $A = 1$, $B = -2$, and $C = 5$.

Any function whose ordered pairs satisfy a linear equation is called a **linear function**.

Definition of Linear Function	A function is linear if it can be defined by $f(x) = mx + b$, where m and b are real numbers.

In the definition of a linear function, m or b may be zero. If $m = 0$, then $f(x) = b$. The graph is a horizontal line. This function is called a **constant function**. If $f(x) = 0$, the function is called the *zero function*.

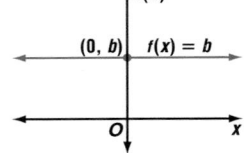

Example ❷ State whether each function is a linear function.

a. $f(x) = 4x + 5$ This is a linear function because it is in the form $f(x) = mx + b$, with $m = 4$ and $b = 5$.

b. $g(x) = x^3 + 2$ This is *not* a linear function because x has an exponent other than 1.

c. $f(x) = 9 - 6x$ This is a linear function because it can be written as $f(x) = -6x + 9$, with $m = -6$ and $b = 9$.

GLENCOE *Technology*

Interactive Mathematics Tools Software

This multimedia software provides an interactive lesson by having students compare and contrast the graphs and equations of linear functions in $y = mx + b$ form. A **Computer Journal** gives students an opportunity to write about what they have learned.

For Windows & Macintosh

In Lesson 2–1, you graphed an equation or function by making a table of values, graphing enough ordered pairs to see a pattern, and connecting the points with a line or smooth curve. However, there are quicker ways to graph a linear equation or function. One way is to find the points at which the graph intersects each axis and connect them with a line. The y-coordinate of the point at which a graph crosses the y-axis is called the **y-intercept.** Likewise, the x-coordinate of the point at which it crosses the x-axis is the **x-intercept.**

Example ③ Graph $5x - 3y = 15$ using the x- and y-intercepts.

The x-intercept is the value of x when $y = 0$.

$5x - 3y = 15$
$5x - 3(0) = 15$ *Substitute 0 for y.*
$x = 3$

The x-intercept is 3. The graph crosses the x-axis at $(3, 0)$.

Likewise, the y-intercept is the value of y when $x = 0$.

$5x - 3y = 15$
$5(0) - 3y = 15$ *Substitute 0 for x.*
$y = -5$

The y-intercept is -5. The graph crosses the y-axis at $(0, -5)$.

Use these ordered pairs to graph the equation.

Linear equations, functions, and their graphs can be used to model situations that occur in real life.

Example ④

APPLICATION
Education

Each year, more than two million high school juniors and seniors across the nation tackle one or more college admission tests. One of them is the SAT (Scholastic Assessment Test), which is divided into two sections, verbal and mathematical. For each section, the possible scores range from 200 to 800. Suppose your counselor advises you that, as one factor for admission, some colleges expect a combined score of 1300. This situation can be represented by the equation $x + y = 1300$, where x is the verbal score and y is the mathematical score.

a. Graph the linear equation.
b. Name an ordered pair that satisfies the equation and explain what it represents.

The total score of 1300 is only an illustration. Different colleges have different entrance requirements.

a. Find the x- and y-intercepts.
$x + y = 1300$
$x + 0 = 1300$ *Substitute 0 for y.*
$x = 1300$

The x-intercept is 1300. Similarly, the y-intercept is 1300.

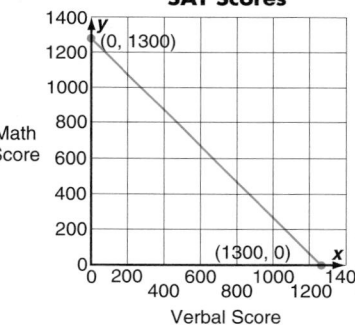

(continued on the next page)

Alternative Learning Styles

Visual Have students make charts of the solutions of $|x + y| = 1300$. Note that a chart of values helps organize the information. Students can use these charts to graph the equations and determine whether they are linear functions.

In-Class Examples

For Example 3
Graph $5x + 2y = 10$ using the x- and y-intercepts.

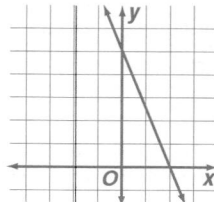

For Example 4
Alan rides his bike to the store. If Alan stops at a red light along the way, it takes him longer to reach the store. The time it takes in minutes for Alan to get to the store can be represented by the equation $y = \left(\frac{1}{2}\right)x + 15$, where x represents the number of stops for red lights. Complete a table and graph the linear equation. How long would it take Alan if he stops at 4 red lights? **17 minutes**

Red lights	Time
0	15
1	15.5
2	16
3	16.5
4	17

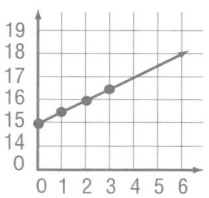

3 PRACTICE/APPLY

Check for Understanding

Exercises 1–17 are designed to help you assess your students' understanding through reading, writing, speaking, and modeling. You should work through Exercises 1–5 with your students and then monitor their work on Exercises 6–17.

Additional Answers

3. To find the *x*-intercept, let $y = 0$ and solve for *x*. To find the *y*-intercept, let $x = 0$ and solve for *y*.

4. Sample answer: Find the *y*-intercept and the *x*-intercept and connect these two points, or graph enough ordered pairs to see a pattern.

5. Sample answer: The equation represented by a horizontal line is a linear equation because its equation is $y = c$, and it is a function because it passes the vertical line test. The equation represented by a vertical line is a linear equation because its equation is $x = c$. It is not a function because it fails the vertical line test.

Study Guide Masters, p. 9

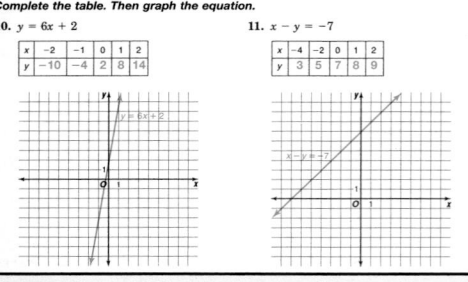

NAME_____ DATE _____

Study Guide

Student Edition
Pages 73–78

2-2

Linear Equations

An equation whose graph is a straight line is called a **linear equation.** Any linear equation can be written in **standard form.**

The standard form of a linear equation is
$Ax + By = C$,
where A, B, and C are real numbers, and A and B are not both zero.

To graph a linear equation, it is helpful to make a table of ordered pairs that satisfy the equation. These ordered pairs can then be graphed and connected with a straight line.

Example: Write the equation $x = \frac{1}{4}y - 9$ in standard form.
$x = \frac{1}{4}y - 9$
$4x = y - 9$ Multiply each side by 4 to eliminate the fraction.
$4x - y = -9$ Add −y to each side.

Write each equation in standard form.

1. $x = \frac{2}{7} + y$
$x - y = \frac{2}{7}$
2. $y = \frac{7}{12}x + 1$
$-7x + 12y = 12$
3. $y = 3x - 5$
$3x - y = 5$
4. $x = 10$
$x + 0y = 10$
5. $y = 5x$
$-5x + y = 0$
6. $5x = 5 + 2x + y$
$3x - y = 5$
7. $y - 6 = 0$
$0x + y = 6$
8. $y = -7x + 2$
$7x + y = 2$
9. $4s + 3r = 12$
in standard form

Complete the table. Then graph the equation.

10. $y = 6x + 2$

x	−2	−1	0	1	2
y	−10	−4	2	8	14

11. $x - y = -7$

x	−4	−2	0	1	2
y	3	5	7	8	9

76 Chapter 2

---

b. There are many ordered pairs that satisfy the equation. However, not all of them are solutions of the problem. Since the scores on each section range from 200 to 800, it is necessary to restrict the domain to $200 \le x \le 800$ and the range to $200 \le y \le 800$.

Therefore, the ordered pairs that are solutions to the problem are shown at the right. One ordered pair is (500, 800). It represents having a verbal score of 500 and a math score of 800 for a total of 1300.

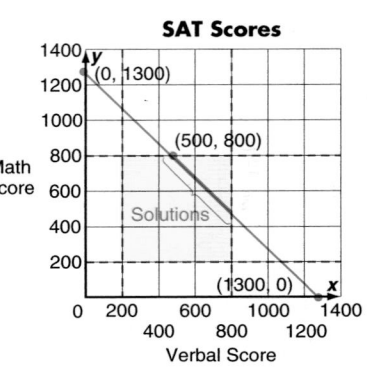

SAT Scores

CHECK FOR UNDERSTANDING

Communicating Mathematics

1. $3x - 4y = -5$, 3, −4, −5

8. $3x - y = 5$; 3, −1, 5
9. $2x - 5y = 3$; 2, −5, 3
10. $2x - 3y = -3$; 2, −3, −3
11. $y : 9, x : \frac{3}{2}$
12. $y : -5, x : -\frac{5}{3}$
13. $y : -2, x : 2$

Study the lesson. Then complete the following.

1. **Write** the equation $4y = 3x + 5$ in standard form. Identify *A*, *B*, and *C*.

2. **Name** the *x*- and *y*-intercepts of the graph shown at the right.   −3, −2

3. **Explain** how to find the *x*- and *y*-intercepts of the graph of $2x + y = 7$.   See margin.

4. **List** at least two ways to graph a linear equation.   See margin.

 MATH JOURNAL

5. **Write** a paragraph explaining why both graphs at the right are graphs of linear equations, but only one is a linear function. Use drawings with your explanation.   See margin.

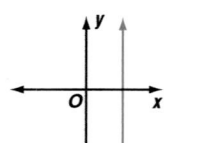 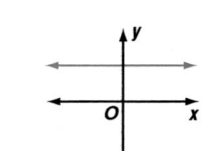

Guided Practice

State whether each equation is linear. Write *yes* or *no* and explain your answer.

6. $x^2 + y^2 = 4$ no

7. $h(x) = 1.1 - 2x$ yes

Write each equation in standard form where *A*, *B*, and *C* are integers whose greatest common factor is 1. Identify *A*, *B*, and *C*.

8. $y = 3x - 5$

9. $4x = 10y + 6$

10. $y = \frac{2}{3}x + 1$

Find the *x*-intercept and the *y*-intercept of the graph of each equation.

11. $6x + y = 9$

12. $y = -3x - 5$

13. $f(x) = x - 2$

Graph each equation.   14–16. See margin.

14. $3x + 2y = 6$

15. $y = -2x$

16. $4x + 8y = 12$

17. **Economics**   On June 20, 1995, the function $f(x) = 0.718x$ was used to convert German marks, *x*, to U.S. dollars, $f(x)$. For that date, find the value in U.S. dollars of 100 German marks. $71.80

76   Chapter 2   *Graphing Linear Relations and Functions*

Reteaching

Writing Equations   Write each linear equation in standard form. Encourage students to discover the general method used in all five problems.

1. $y = 4 - x$ $x + y = 4$
2. $6 - y = -2x$ $2x - y = -6$
3. $5 + 2y = 3x$
   $-3x + 2y = -5$ or $3x - 2y = 5$
4. $8 + 2y = 6x$ $-3x + y = -4$
   or $3x - y = 4$
5. $3y = 12 - x$ $x + 3y = 12$

Practice

22. $3x + y = 4$;
3, 1, 4

23. $12x - y = 0$;
12, −1, 0

24. $x - 4y = -5$;
1, −4, −5

25. $2x - y = 5$; 2, −1, 5

26. $x + y = 12$; 1, 1, 12

27. $y = 40$; 0, 1, 40

28. $y: -6, x: \frac{6}{5}$

30. $y: -2, x$:none

32. $y: -1, x: \frac{1}{4}$

33. $y: 5, x: 3$

49a. same slope,
different y-intercepts,
look parallel

49a–b. See Solutions
Manual for graphs.

Critical Thinking

Applications and Problem Solving

50c. Continuous; there is
an infinite number of
elements in the domain.

State whether each equation is linear. Write *yes* or *no* and explain your answer.

18. $x + y = 5$ yes

19. $\frac{1}{x} + 3y = -5$ no

20. $x + xy = 4$ no

21. $g(x) = 10$ yes

Write each equation in standard form where A, B, and C are integers whose greatest common factor is 1. Identify A, B, and C.

22. $y = -3x + 4$

23. $y = 12x$

24. $x = 4y - 5$

25. $5y = 10x - 25$

26. $\frac{1}{2}x + \frac{1}{2}y = 6$

27. $0.25y = 10$

Find the x-intercept and y-intercept of the graph of each equation.

28. $y + 6 = 5x$

29. $3x = y$ y:0, x:0

30. $y = -2$

31. $x = 8$ y:none, x:8

32. $g(x) = 4x - 1$

33. $5x + 3y = 15$

Graph each equation.   34–48. See Solutions Manual.

34. $y = x$

35. $y = 4x + 2$

36. $x + y = 7$

37. $2x - y = 5$

38. $2x + 5y = 10$

39. $y = 0.5x - 3$

40. $b = 2a - 3$

41. $x - y = 6$

42. $2a + 3b = 6$

43. $3 = 3x$

44. $x + 2y = 7$

45. $4x + 3y = 12$

46. $\frac{1}{3}x + \frac{1}{2}y = 1$

47. $\frac{x}{4} - \frac{y}{3} = 2$

48. $\frac{x}{3} + \frac{y}{2} = \frac{15}{2}$

49. Graph $x + y = 0$, $x + y = 5$, and $x + y = -5$ on the same coordinate plane.
 a. Compare and contrast the graphs.
 b. Write a linear equation whose graph is between the graphs of $x + y = 0$ and $x + y = 5$.   Sample answer: $x + y = 2$

50. **Geology**   Geothermal energy is generated wherever water comes into contact with heated underground rocks. The underground temperature of rocks varies with their depth below the surface. The temperature t in degrees Celsius is estimated by the function $t(d) = 35d + 20$, where d is the depth in kilometers of the rocks.
 a. Graph the linear equation.   See margin.
 b. Find the temperature of the rocks at a depth of 3 kilometers.   125° C
 c. Is this function discrete or continuous? Explain your reasoning.
 d. Find the depth if the temperature of the rocks is 195°C.   5 kilometers.

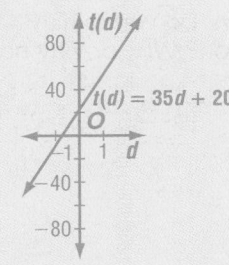

51. **Commercial Fishing**   Fishing boats are usually equipped with sonar—a device used to locate schools of fish by the reflection of sound waves.
 a. Refer to the application at the beginning of the lesson. Write a function that is a model for the relationship between the number of seconds it takes the sound signal to return to the boat and the depth of the school of fish. $d(t) = 2380t$
 b. Suppose the sound signal returned to the boat in 0.05 seconds. Estimate the depth of the school of fish.   119 feet

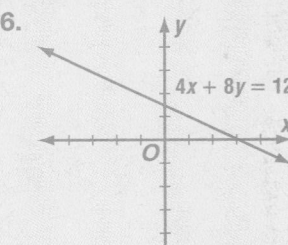

Additional Answers

16.

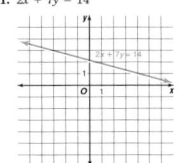
$4x + 8y = 12$

50a.

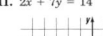
$t(d) = 35d + 20$

Assignment Guide

Core: 19–53 odd, 54–62
Enriched: 18–48 even, 49–62

For **Extra Practice,** see p. 878.

The red A, B, and C flags, printed only in the Teacher's Wraparound Edition, indicate the level of difficulty of the exercises.

Additional Answers

14.

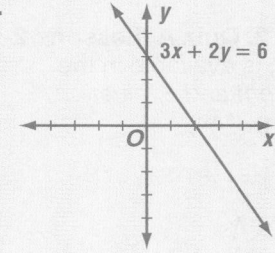
$3x + 2y = 6$

15.

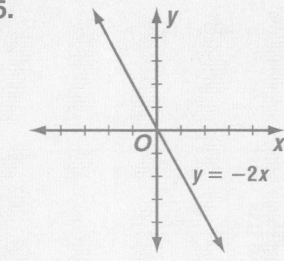
$y = -2x$

Practice Masters, p. 9

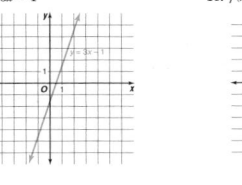

2-2   NAME _____ DATE _____
Practice   Student Edition Pages 73–7

Linear Equations

Write each equation in standard form.
1. $y = 7x - 5$
 $7x - y = 5$
2. $y = \frac{3}{8}x + 5$
 $3x - 8y = -40$
3. $x = -\frac{2}{7}y + \frac{3}{4}$
 $28x + 8y = 21$
4. $3y - 5 = 0$
 $3y = 5$

Find the x-intercept and y-intercept of the graph of each equation.
5. $2x - y = 5$
 x-intercept: $\frac{5}{2}$; y-intercept: −5
6. $3x = 4y - 5$
 x-intercept: $-\frac{5}{3}$; y-intercept: $\frac{5}{4}$
7. $3x - 6 = y$
 x-intercept: 2; y-intercept: −6
8. $5x + 2y = 6$
 x-intercept: $\frac{6}{5}$; y-intercept: 3

Graph each equation.
9. $y = 3x - 1$
10. $f(x) = -2x + 3$

11. $2x + 7y = 14$
12. $\frac{2}{5}x + \frac{y}{4} = 1$

Closing Activity

Modeling Begin by slowly filling a glass with water. The volume of water in the glass is a function of time. Students should notice that at any time, the volume is represented by exactly one number. This ensures that the relation is a function.

Chapter 2, Quiz A (Lessons 2-1 and 2-2), is available in the *Assessment and Evaluation Masters,* p. 44.

Additional Answers

53b.

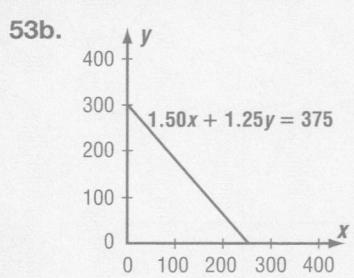

60b.

Stem	Leaf
29	0 1
28	2
27	7 8
26	0 0 0 2 3 4 4 5 6
•	7 7 8
25	8 9 9

$28\,|\,2 = 28{,}200$ to $28{,}299$ feet

Enrichment Masters, p. 9

2-2

NAME_____ DATE _____

Student Edition Pages 73–78

Enrichment

Greatest Common Factor

Suppose we are given a linear equation $ax + by = c$ where a, b, and c are nonzero integers, and we want to know if there exist *integers* x and y that satisfy the equation. We could try guessing a few times, but this process would be time consuming for an equation such as $588x + 432y = 72$. By using the Euclidean Algorithm, we can determine not only if such integers x and y exist, but also find them. The following example shows how this algorithm works.

Example: Find integers x and y that satisfy $588x + 432y = 72$.

Divide the greater of the two coefficients by the lesser to get a quotient and remainder. Then, repeat the process by dividing the divisor by the remainder until you get a remainder of 0. The process can be written as follows.

$588 = 432(1) + 156$ (1)
$432 = 156(2) + 120$ (2)
$156 = 120(1) + 36$ (3)
$120 = 36(3) + 12$ (4)
$36 = 12(3)$

The last nonzero remainder is the GCF of the two coefficients. If the constant term 72 is divisible by the GCF, then integers x and y do exist that satisfy the equation. To find x and y, work backward in the following manner.

$72 = 6 \cdot 12$
$= 6 \cdot [120 - 36(3)]$ substitute for 12 using (4)
$= 6(120) - 18(36)$
$= 6(120) - 18[156 - 120(1)]$ substitute for 36 using (3)
$= -18(156) + 24(120)$
$= -18(156) + 24[432 - 156(2)]$ substitute for 120 using (2)
$= 24(432) - 66(156)$
$= 24(432) - 66[588 - 432(1)]$ substitute for 156 using (1)
$= 588(-66) + 432(90)$

Thus, $x = -66$ and $y = 90$.

Find integers x and y, if they exist, that satisfy the following equation.

1. $27x + 65y = 3$
   $x = -36$ and $y = 15$

2. $45x + 144y = 36$
   $x = -12$ and $y = 4$

3. $90x + 117y = 10$
   no integral solutions exist

4. $123x + 36y = 15$
   $x = 25$ and $y = -85$

5. $1032x + 1001y = 1$
   $x = -226$ and $y = 233$

6. $3125x + 3087y = 1$
   $x = -1381$ and $y = 1398$

---

52. **Entertainment** In the movie *Crimson Tide,* the crew of the submarine *Alabama* tried desperately to restore power to the ship before it sunk to a depth of 1850 feet. Use the function $f(x) = 1.15x$, where x is the depth in miles and $f(x)$ is the pressure in tons per square inch, to estimate the water pressure on the outside of the hull at that depth. **0.403 tons/in²**

53. **Fundraising** The Central High School Band Boosters have a concessions stand for home football games. They sell beverages for \$1.50 and candy for \$1.25.
Their goal is to sell a total of \$375 for each game.
   a. Write an equation that is a model for the different numbers of beverages and candy that can be sold to meet the goal. **$1.50x + 1.25y = 375$**
   b. Graph the equation. **See margin.**
   c. Is this equation also a function? If so, is it discrete or continuous? Explain your reasoning.
   d. If they sell 100 beverages and 200 pieces of candy, will the Band Boosters meet their goal? **yes**

53c. Discrete; it is possible to list the elements of the domain.

Mixed Review

54. Which of the following graphs represent functions? (Lesson 2–1) **a and c**
   a. 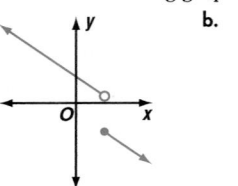   b. 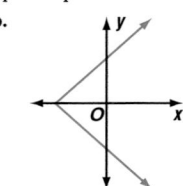   c.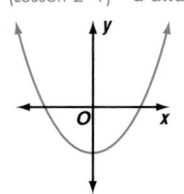

Solve each equation.

55. true for all x

56. $x > \dfrac{9}{2}$

57. $0, -\dfrac{10}{3}$

58. 27.7

55. $|x + 7| > -2$ (Lesson 1–7)
56. $5(2x - 7) > 10$ (Lesson 1–6)
57. $7|3x + 5| = 35$ (Lesson 1–5)
58. $x + 28.3 = 56.0$ (Lesson 1–4)

59. **Statistics** Suppose four tests had been given in your Algebra 2 class this quarter. On the first three, you scored 87, 92, and 81. If you must have at least 350 points to earn an A, what must you score on the fourth test to earn an A? (Lesson 1–6) **90 or higher**

60. The heights in feet of 20 mountains are given below.

26,504	26,041	26,400	26,750	26,810
29,108	26,470	26,360	26,090	26,000
29,064	26,291	25,910	25,895	28,208
25,925	27,890	27,790	26,760	26,660

60a. 26,846.3; 26,487; no mode

   a. Find the mean, median, and mode for the heights. (Lesson 1–3)
   b. Make a stem-and-leaf plot of the heights. (Lesson 1–3) **See margin.**

Simplify each expression.

61. $3s + 14$

61. $(9s - 4) - 3(2s - 6)$ (Lesson 1–2)
62. $[19 - (8 - 1)] \div 3$ (Lesson 1–1) **4**

Extension

Communication Do you think $y = |x|$ is a linear function? Why or why not?
No; the graph isn't a straight line. The equation can't be written in the form $Ax + By = C$.

2–2B Graphing Technology
Using Graphs to Estimate Solutions

An Extension of Lesson 2–2

The graphing features of a graphing calculator allow you to approximate solutions to an equation in one variable from a graph. First set each side of the equation equal to y. Then graph the two equations on the same screen. The solution of the original equation is the x-coordinate of the point of intersection of the two graphs.

Example ⬤ **Solve $5x - 5 = 2x + 1$ graphically.**

Set each side of the equation equal to y.
$y = 5x - 5$
$y = 2x + 1$

Then graph both equations in the standard viewing window.

Enter: Y= 5 X,T,θ — 5 ENTER
2 X,T,θ + 1 ZOOM 6

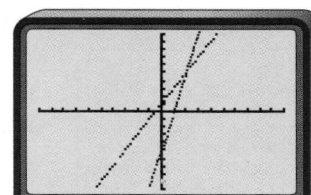

You are interested in the point at which the values of x are equal—namely, the point of intersection. Use TRACE with the left and right arrow keys to approximate the point of intersection. The display gives an approximation for the coordinates of the point. Or press
2nd CALC 5 ENTER ENTER
ENTER and read the x-coordinate at the bottom of the screen.

You can see that the point of intersection occurs when $x = 2$.

Therefore, the solution of $5x - 5 = 2x + 1$ is 2.

Verify the solution by substituting 2 into the original equation.

EXERCISES

Solve each equation graphically to the nearest tenth. Check your solutions algebraically.

1. $2x - 1 = 2$ **1.5**
2. $3x + 9 = 25$ **5.3**
3. $2x + 1 = 16 - x$ **5**
4. $4x + 3 = 5x + 7$ **−4**
5. $7x + 9 = 3(x + 3)$ **0**
6. $5(8 - 2x) = 4x - 2$ **3**
7. $-1.5x = -2x + 5.75$ **11.5**
8. $16x - 3.8 = 12x - 3.8$ **0**
9. $5.2x + 0.7 = 2.8 + 2.2x$ **0.7**
10. $-2(3x - 5) + 3x = 2 - x$ **4**

---

4 ASSESS

Observing students working with technology is an excellent method of assessment.

Using Technology
This lesson offers an excellent opportunity for using technology in your algebra classroom. For more information on using technology, see *Graphing Calculators in the Mathematics Classroom*, one of the titles in the Glencoe Mathematics Professional Series.

2-2B LESSON NOTES

NCTM Standards: 1–6

Objective
Use a graphing calculator to estimate solutions to equations in one variable.

Recommended Time
15 minutes

Instructional Resources
Graphing Calculator Masters, pp. 21 and 22

These masters provide keystroking instruction for this lesson for the TI-81 and Casio graphing calculators.

1 FOCUS

Motivating the Lesson
Discuss with students why we use graphs to solve equations. What do the lines represent? Why are we only interested in the intersection? What advantages are there to solving equations graphically rather than algebraically? Disadvantages?

2 TEACH

Teaching Tip Have students view each side of the equals sign as a separate equation to graph. Therefore, each exercise represents two lines to graph.

3 PRACTICE/APPLY

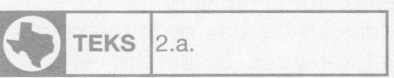

Assignment Guide
Core: 1–10 **Enriched:** 1–10

🌟 TEKS | 2.a.

NCTM Standards: 1–6

Instructional Resources

- Study Guide Master 2-3
- Practice Master 2-3
- Enrichment Master 2-3

 Transparency 2-3A contains the 5-Minute Check for this lesson; **Transparency 2-3B** contains a teaching aid for this lesson.

Recommended Pacing	
Standard Pacing	Day 5 of 14
Honors Pacing	Day 5 of 13
Block Scheduling*	Day 3 of 7 (along with Lesson 2-4)

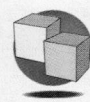 *For more information on pacing and possible lesson plans, refer to the *Block Scheduling Booklet*.

1 FOCUS

 5-Minute Check
(over Lesson 2-2)

1. State whether $x^2 = 9$ is a linear function. **no**

Write each equation in standard form where *A*, *B*, and *C* are integers whose greatest common factor is 1. Identify *A*, *B*, and *C*.

2. $y = 2x - 6$ **$2x - y = 6$; *A* = 2, *B* = −1, *C* = 6**

3. $x = \frac{3}{5} + \frac{y}{4}$ **$20x - 5y = 12$; *A* = 20, *B* = −5, *C* = 12**

4. Solve $3x + 2y = 8$ for *y*. **$y = -\frac{3}{2}x + 4$**

Motivating the Lesson

Hands-On Activity Have students bring in pictures of objects that slant such as ladders, stairs, mountains, and roads. Measure the base and the height of the figures. Divide the vertical distance by the horizontal distance. Discuss the value of the slope.

2-3

Slope

What YOU'LL LEARN

- To determine the slope of a line,
- to use slope and a point to graph an equation,
- to determine if two lines are parallel, perpendicular, or neither, and
- to solve problems by identifying and using a pattern.

Why IT'S IMPORTANT

You can use slope to describe lines and solve problems involving auto racing and entertainment.

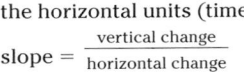 **GLOBAL CONNECTIONS**

Probably the world's best known automobile race, the LeMans 24-hour Grand Prix d'Endurance, has been held yearly with few exceptions since 1923 in LeMans, France. In 1994, the winners traveled 2906.8 miles at an average speed of 121.1 mph.

APPLICATION
Auto Racing

Lady and gentlemen, start your engines! At 11:00 A.M. on May 28, 1995, 32 men and one woman began the Indianapolis 500. Three hours and fifteen minutes later, Canadian racer Jacques Villeneuve crossed the finish line as the winner. Meanwhile, the Diaz family left Indianapolis, Indiana, in the family car, heading for Atlanta, Georgia. They took turns driving, stopped only for gasoline, and completed their 500 mile trip in 9.5 hours. Both of these situations can be modeled graphically.

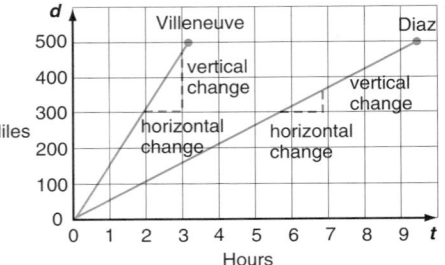

The graph representing Villeneuve's race is much steeper than the graph representing the Diaz family's trip because, on average, Villeneuve traveled a greater distance for each unit of time. The **slope** of each line is the ratio of the change in the vertical units (distance) to the change in the horizontal units (time).

$$\text{slope} = \frac{\text{vertical change}}{\text{horizontal change}}$$

The slope of the line representing Villeneuve's race is $\frac{500}{3.25}$ or about 153.8.

The slope of the line representing the Diaz' trip is $\frac{500}{9.5}$ or about 52.6.

The slope of each line indicates its steepness, and in this case, it also indicates the average speed in miles per hour.

The problem-solving strategy **look for a pattern** is one of the most-used strategies in mathematics. When using this strategy, you will often need to make a table to organize the information.

Example **1**

PROBLEM SOLVING

Look for a Pattern

The symbol used for a cent is a lowercase c with a vertical line through it. The line separates the c into 3 parts, as shown at the right. How many parts would there be if the c had 101 lines through it?

Make a table to show the pattern.

Number of Lines	1	2	3	4	5	x
Number of Parts	3	5	7	9	11	2x + 1

If the c had *x* lines through it, there would be $2x + 1$ parts. Thus, if the c had 101 lines through it, there would be $2(101) + 1$ or 203 parts.

GLOBAL CONNECTIONS

The winning team was Hurley Haywod, Yannick Dulmas, and Mauro Baldi. The winning speeds in the four preceding years were as follows.

1993	132.58 mph
1992	123.89 mph
1991	127.31 mph
1990	126.71 mph

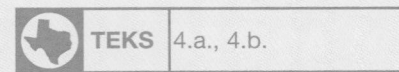 **TEKS** 4.a., 4.b.

You can look for a pattern to help solve many problems involving slope and graphs.

Example ②

APPLICATION

Auto Racing

Ray Harroun winning the Indianapolis 500

The winner of the first Indianapolis 500 was Ray Harroun. In 1911, he completed the race in a Marmon Wasp at an average speed of 74.6 miles per hour. Harroun's race can be modeled by the linear function $d(t) = 74.6t$, where t is the time in hours and $d(t)$ is the distance in miles.
a. Make a table of ordered pairs and graph the linear function.
b. Use the graph to predict the value of t when $d(t) = 500$.
c. The winning speed for the Indianapolis 500 seems to increase each year. Suppose next year's winning speed is 160 mph. Predict where the line representing this race will be graphed.

a. Choose ordered pairs for $1 \le t \le 5$.

Time t (hours)	Distance $d(t)$ (miles)
1	74.6
2	149.2
3	223.8
4	298.4
5	373.0

+1 ⟨ ⟩ +74.6 (between each row)

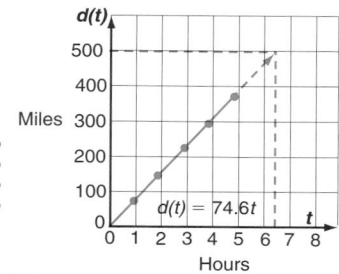

Notice that the ratio of the change in the vertical units to the change in horizontal units is $\frac{74.6}{1}$ or 74.6. Therefore, the slope is 74.6.

b. To predict the value of t when $d(t) = 500$, extend the graph to $d(t) = 500$. The corresponding value of t is between 6 and 7 hours.

c. To predict where the line representing a winning speed of 160 mph will be graphed, look for a pattern in the graphs of Harroun's race and the graphs in the application at the beginning of the lesson. Notice that as the average speed increases, the slope of the line also increases.

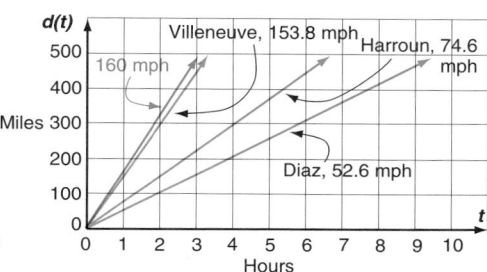

The graph representing a winning speed of 160 mph should have the steepest slope and, following the pattern in the graphs, should be to the left of the graph representing Villeneuve's race.

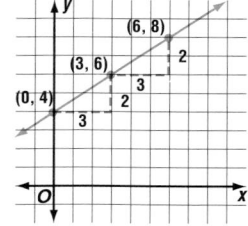

The slopes of linear functions can be defined by looking for a pattern. Consider the equation $y = \frac{2}{3}x + 4$.
In the table of values shown at the right and the graph shown at the left, look for a pattern in the relationship of the change in the y-coordinates to the change in the x-coordinates for the points on the graph.

x	y
0	4
3	6
6	8

+3 ⟨ ⟩ +2

Lesson 2–3 Slope **81**

In-Class Examples

For Example 1
Five people come together for a business meeting. Determine how many total handshakes there would be if each person shook the hand of everyone else. Have the class make a chart that would illustrate the pattern. **10**

For Example 2
In Example 2, suppose instead that the average speed is 82.6 mph.

a. Complete the table and graph the function.

t	f(t)
1	82.6
2	165.2
3	247.8
4	330.4
5	413.0

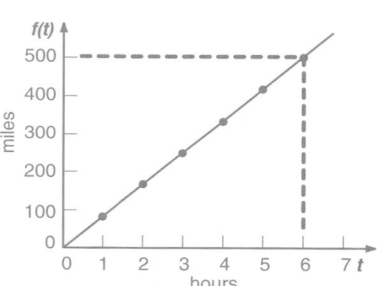

b. Use the graph to predict the value of t when $f(t) = 500$. **6.05**

Classroom Vignette

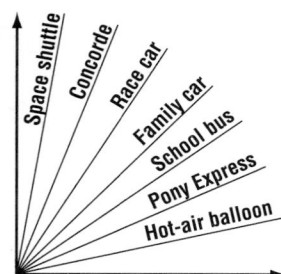

"It might be interesting to compare other methods of transport to the race car in Example 2."

Suzy Ward
Jefferson High School
Louisville, Kentucky

Suzy Ward (signature)

Teaching Tip When discussing the slope formula, emphasize that any two points may be used to compute the slope. It is important to be consistent as to where you put the values from the first point and the values from the second point.

In-Class Examples

For Example 3
Determine the slope of the line passing through each pair of points.

a. $(-2, 3)$ and $(-4, 4)$ $-\dfrac{1}{2}$
b. $(7, 5)$ and $(-3, 5)$ 0
c. $(5, 7)$ and $(5, -3)$ undefined

For Example 4
Graph the line passing through the point $(4, 5)$ with a slope of 3.

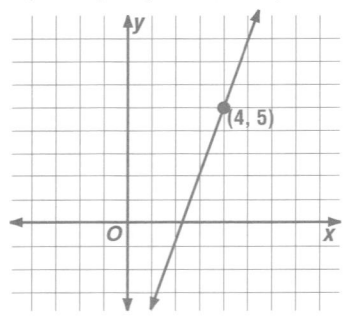

Teaching Tip A vertical line is also said to have no slope. Students sometimes confuse no slope with zero slope, although they do not have the same meaning.

Notice that the y-coordinates increase 2 units for each 3-unit increase in the x-coordinates. Thus, the slope of the line whose equation is $y = \frac{2}{3}x + 4$ is $\frac{2}{3}$.

These examples suggest that the slope of a line can be determined from the coordinates of two points on the line.

Definition of Slope	The slope m of the line passing through points (x_1, y_1) and (x_2, y_2) is given by $m = \dfrac{y_2 - y_1}{x_2 - x_1}$, where $x_1 \neq x_2$.

x_2 is read "x sub 2." The 2 is called a subscript.

Example 3 Determine the slope of the line that passes through the points at $(3, 4)$ and $(6, -8)$. Then graph the line.

$$m = \frac{y_2 - y_1}{x_2 - x_1}$$

$$= \frac{-8 - 4}{6 - 3} \quad (x_1, y_1) = (3, 4), (x_2, y_2) = (6, -8)$$

$$= \frac{-12}{3} \text{ or } -4$$

The slope of the line is -4.

Graph the two ordered pairs and draw the line. Use the slope to check your graph by selecting any point on the line. Then go down 4 units and right 1 unit or go up 4 units and left 1 unit. This point should also be on the line.

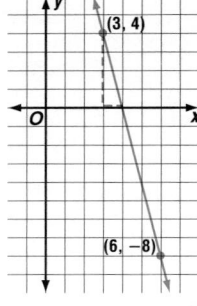

Example 4 Graph the line passing through the point $(-2, -5)$ with a slope of $\frac{3}{5}$.

Graph the ordered pair $(-2, -5)$. Then, using the definition of slope, go up 3 units and 5 units to the right. Plot the point. This new point is $(3, -2)$. *You can also go 5 units right and 3 units up to plot the new point.*

Connect the points to draw the line.

The slope of a line tells the direction in which it rises or falls.

If the line rises to the right, then the slope is positive.

If the line is horizontal, then the slope is zero.

If the line falls to the right, then the slope is negative.

If the line is vertical, then the slope is undefined.

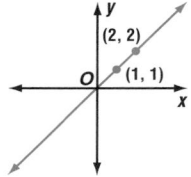
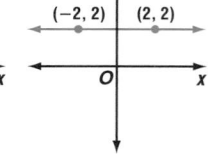
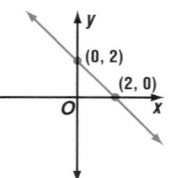
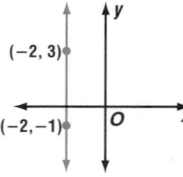

$$m = \frac{2-1}{2-1} \text{ or } 1 \qquad m = \frac{2-2}{2-(-2)} \text{ or } 0 \qquad m = \frac{0-2}{2-0} \text{ or } -1 \qquad m = \frac{3-(-1)}{-2-(-2)} \text{ or } \frac{4}{0}$$

Alternative Learning Styles

Kinesthetic Use a geoboard as a model for the coordinate plane. Let the peg in the lower left-hand corner represent the origin. Have students make as many line segments with different nonnegative slopes as possible. An example of a line segment that has a slope of $\frac{6}{5}$ is shown in the figure.

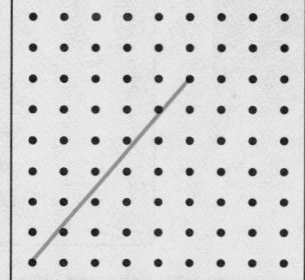

A **family of graphs** is a group of graphs that displays one or more similar characteristics. The **parent graph** is the simplest of the graphs in a family. You can graph families on the same screen and observe their common traits.

Your Turn   **b.** $y = 3x$; parallel lines

a. Graph $y = 3x$, $y = 3x + 2$, $y = 3x - 2$, and $y = 3x - 5$ on the same screen. **See students' work.**

b. Identify the parent function and describe the family of graphs.

c. Find the slope of each line.   **3**

d. Write a function that has the same characteristics as this family of graphs. Check by graphing.   **Sample answer:** $y = 3x - 4$

In the Exploration, you saw that lines that have the same slope are parallel.

Definition of Parallel Lines	**In a plane, nonvertical lines with the same slope are parallel.**

All vertical lines are parallel.

If you know the slope of a line and the coordinates of a point not on the line, you can graph a line through the point that is parallel to the first line.

Example **5**   **Graph the line that goes through the point at $(6, -2)$ and is parallel to the line whose equation is $-4x + y = -2$.**

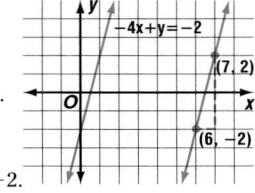

The y-intercept is -2, and the x-intercept is $\frac{1}{2}$.

Use the x- and y-intercepts to graph $-4x + y = -2$. The slope of the line is 4.

Now use the slope and the point at $(6, -2)$ to graph the line parallel to the graph of $-4x + y = -2$.

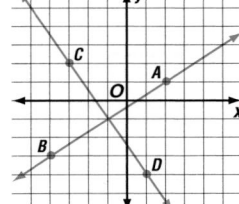

The figure at the left shows the graphs of two lines that are perpendicular. We found that parallel lines have the same slope. Is there a special relationship between the slopes of two perpendicular lines?

slope of line AB   *slope of line CD*

$\dfrac{1 - (-3)}{2 - (-4)} = \dfrac{4}{6}$ or $\dfrac{2}{3}$ $\dfrac{2 - (-4)}{-3 - 1} = \dfrac{6}{-4}$ or $-\dfrac{3}{2}$

The slopes are negative reciprocals of each other. This and other examples suggest that when you multiply the slopes of two perpendicular lines, the product is always -1.

Definition of Perpendicular Lines	**In a plane, two oblique lines are perpendicular if and only if the product of their slopes is -1.**

Lines that are not vertical or horizontal are called <u>oblique</u>.
Any vertical line is perpendicular to any horizontal line.

This activity introduces students to the concept of the vertical shifting of a graph. Point out to students that $3x$ is the base graph and the others are shifts up or shifts down of the base graph.

In-Class Example

For Example 5
Graph the line that goes through the point at $(3, 4)$ and is parallel to the line whose equation is $x + y = 4$.

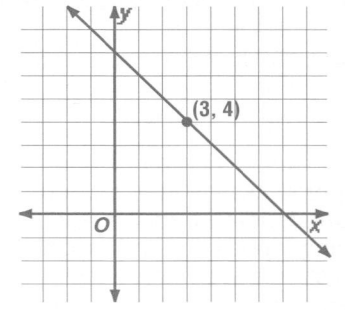

Alternative Teaching Strategies

Student Diversity Have students write hints or shortcuts that they can follow to complete the exercises. Encourage them to write the hints at the top of their paper and use them while doing their homework.

Teaching Tip For Example 6, remind students that the sides of a rectangle are perpendicular and parallel.

In-Class Example

For Example 6
A right triangle has one 90° angle. The endpoints of the base of the triangle are (1, 4) and (5, 1). What is the slope of the adjacent leg?
$-\dfrac{3}{4}$ = slope of base
$\dfrac{4}{3}$ = slope of adjacent leg

3 PRACTICE/APPLY

Check for Understanding
Exercises 1–17 are designed to help you assess your students' understanding through reading, writing, speaking, and modeling. You should work through Exercises 1–5 with your students and then monitor their work on Exercises 6–17.

Error Analysis
Students sometimes divide the difference of the x-coordinates by the difference of the y-coordinates to find the slope. Also, students sometimes subtract the x- and y-coordinates in opposite directions. Remind students the slope is a ratio of the change in y to the change in x.

Additional Answers
1. Find the ratio of the difference of y values to the difference of x values.
$\dfrac{4-3}{-2-(-1)} = \dfrac{1}{-1}$ or -1

2.

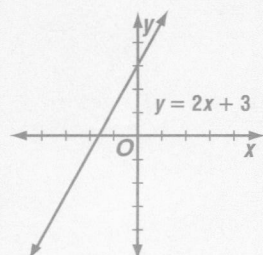

$y = 2x + 3$

You can use the fact that the slopes of perpendicular lines are negative reciprocals of each other to solve problems involving figures with right angles.

Example ⑥

Geometry

The consecutive sides of a rectangle are perpendicular. In rectangle ABCD, the coordinates of point B are (2, 0), and the coordinates of point C are (5, 1). Find the slope of the line containing side $\overline{CD}$ of the rectangle.

In rectangle $ABCD$, $\overline{BC}$ is perpendicular to $\overline{CD}$. First find the slope of side $\overline{BC}$.

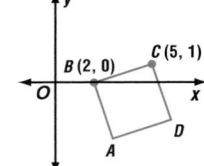

slope of $\overline{BC} = \dfrac{1-0}{5-2}$ or $\dfrac{1}{3}$

Let m represent the slope of $\overline{CD}$. Since the product of the slopes must be -1, you can use this equation.

$$m\left(\dfrac{1}{3}\right) = -1$$

$$m = -1\left(\dfrac{3}{1}\right) \text{ or } -3$$

The slope of the line containing $\overline{CD}$ is -3.

CHECK FOR UNDERSTANDING

Communicating Mathematics

Study the lesson. Then complete the following.

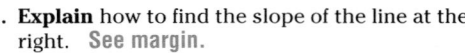

1. **Explain** how to find the slope of the line at the right. **See margin.**

2. **Graph** a line with a slope of 2 and a y-intercept of 3. **See margin.**

3. **Choose** the line that has a negative slope. **C**

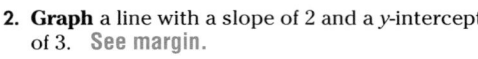

a. 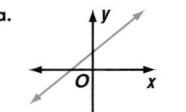   b. 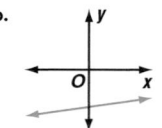   c. 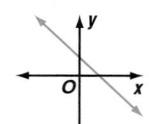   d.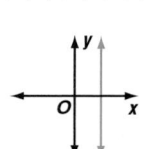

4. **Describe** the relationship between the slopes of two parallel lines. **Their slopes are equal.**

MATH JOURNAL

5. Use a dictionary to find other definitions of slope. **See students' work.**

Guided Practice

State the slope of each line.

6. $-\dfrac{2}{3}$ 7. 1

8. undefined

6.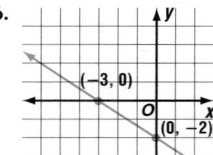

7.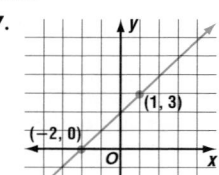

8.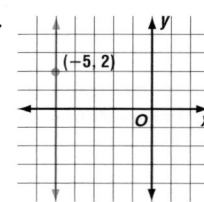

Reteaching

Using Formulas Determine the slope of the line passing through each pair of points. Encourage students to discover the general method used in all three problems.

a. (1, 2) and (3, 8)   3
b. (3, −4) and (−1, −2) $-\dfrac{1}{2}$
c. (2, −2) and (−3, 13)   −3

Find the slope of the line that passes through each pair of points. Then determine whether the line rises to the right, falls to the right, is horizontal, or is vertical.

9. 0; horizontal
10. $-\frac{1}{2}$; falls
11. 1; rises
14. $-\frac{2}{3}$
15. $\frac{3}{4}$; $-\frac{4}{3}$

9. $(1, 1), (3, 1)$ 10. $(-1, 0), (3, -2)$ 11. $(3, 4), (1, 2)$

Find the slope of the graph of each equation.

12. $2x - y = 4$ 2   13. $x + y = 3$ −1   14. $2x + 3y = 6$

15. State the slope of a line parallel to the line passing through $(-1, -1)$ and $(3, 2)$. Then state the slope of a line perpendicular to it.

16. Graph a line that passes through $(0, 0)$ and has a slope of 3.   See margin.

17. Graph the line that passes through $(0, 3)$ and is parallel to the line whose equation is $6y - 10x = 30$.   See margin.

EXERCISES

Practice

Find the slope of the line that passes through each pair of points. Then determine whether the line rises to the right, falls to the right, is horizontal, or is vertical.   19. 13; rises

18. $-\frac{5}{2}$; falls

20. $\frac{3}{5}$; rises

25. undefined

27. $-\frac{2}{3}$ 28. $\frac{3}{4}$

 18. $(6, 1), (8, -4)$ 19. $(6, 8), (5, -5)$ 20. $(-6, -5), (4, 1)$

21. $(7, 8), (1, 8)$ 22. $(2.5, 3), (1, -9)$ 23. $(a, 2), (a, -2)$
   0; horizontal   8; rises   undefined; vertical

Find the slope of the graph of each equation.

24. $x + y = 5$ −1   25. $3x + 9 = 0$ 26. $2x - y = 8$ 2

27. $2x + 3y + 32 = 0$ 28. $3x - 4y = 0$ 29. $y = 5$ 0

Determine the value of r so that a line through the points with the given coordinates has the given slope. Draw a sketch of each situation.

 30. $(r, 2), (4, -6)$; slope $= -\frac{8}{3}$ 1   31. $(5, r), (2, 3)$; slope $= 2$ 9

32. $(r, 6), (8, 4)$; slope $= \frac{1}{2}$ 12   33. $(6, r), (9, 2)$; slope $= \frac{1}{3}$ 1

34–41. See Solutions Manual.

34. Graph a line through $(2, 6)$ that has a slope of $\frac{2}{3}$.

35. Graph a line through $(-2, 2)$ that is parallel to a line whose slope is -1.

36. Graph a line through $(-4, 1)$ that is perpendicular to a line whose slope is $-\frac{3}{2}$.

37. Graph a line through $(3, 3)$ that is perpendicular to the graph of $y = 3$.

 38. Graph a line through the origin that is parallel to the graph of $x + y = 10$.

39. Graph a line through $(-4, -2)$ that has an undefined slope.

40. One line has a slope of 0 and another line has an undefined slope, but they both pass through $(-3, -3)$. Graph the lines.

41. Graph the line perpendicular to the graph of $3x - 2y = 24$ that intersects it at its x-intercept.

42. **Geometry** In the ordered pairs $(3, 0), (4, 2), (5, 5), (6, 9)$, and $(7, \underline{\ ?\ })$, the first coordinate is the number of sides in a polygon, and the second coordinate is the number of diagonals that can be drawn in each polygon. Find the pattern to complete the last ordered pair. 14

Lesson 2–3   Slope **85**

Assignment Guide

Core: 19–49 odd, 51–59
Enriched: 18–44 even, 45–59
All: Self Test, 1–5

For **Extra Practice,** see p. 879.

The red A, B, and C flags, printed only in the Teacher's Wraparound Edition, indicate the level of difficulty of the exercises.

Additional Answers

16.

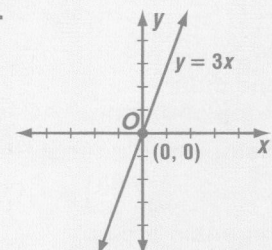

17.

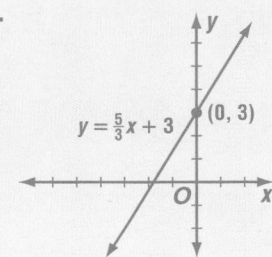

Study Guide Masters, p. 10

NAME_____   DATE _____

2-3   **Study Guide**   Student Edition Pages 80–87

Slope

The slope of a line indicates whether the line is horizontal or whether it rises or falls from left to right.

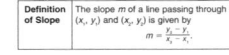

Example: Determine the slope of the line that passes through $(0, -3)$, and $(2, 1)$. Then graph the line.
Let $(x_1, y_1) = (0, -3)$ and $(x_2, y_2) = (2, 1)$.

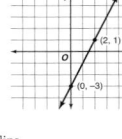

$$m = \frac{y_2 - y_1}{x_2 - x_1}$$
$$= \frac{1 - (-3)}{2 - 0}$$
$$= \frac{4}{2} \text{ or } 2$$

Graph the two ordered pairs and draw the line.

Determine the slope of each line.

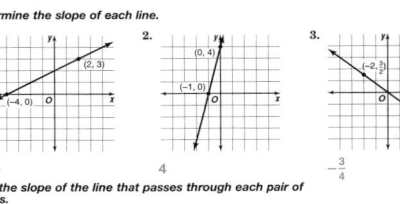

$\frac{1}{2}$ 4 $-\frac{3}{4}$

Find the slope of the line that passes through each pair of points.

4. $(-3, -1), (5, 7)$ 1   5. $(6, 4), (3, 4)$ 0   6. $(5, 1), (7, -3)$ −2

7. $(6, 2), (-3, -8)$ $\frac{10}{9}$ 8. $(6, 1), (-6, -1)$ $\frac{1}{6}$ 9. $(3, 18), (5, 20)$ 1

Determine whether the graph of each equation rises to the right, falls to the right, is horizontal, or is vertical.

10. $x + y = 10$ falls   11. $4x - y = 3$ rises   12. $x = 6$ vertical

Using the Programming
Exercises The program given in Exercise 46 is for use with a TI-82 graphing calculator. For other programmable calculators, have students consult their owner's manual for commands similar to those presented here.

Additional Answers

43. The slope of diagonal $\overline{BD}$ is $\frac{0-(-4)}{9-6} = \frac{4}{3}$; the slope of diagonal $\overline{AC}$ is $\frac{0-(-4)}{5-10} = \frac{-4}{5}$. Since $\left(\frac{4}{3}\right)\left(\frac{-4}{5}\right) \neq -1$, the diagonals are not perpendicular.

44. The slope of diagonal $\overline{AC}$ is $\frac{b}{a}$; the slope of diagonal $\overline{BD}$ is $\frac{-b}{a}$. Since $\left(\frac{b}{a}\right)\left(\frac{-b}{a}\right) \neq -1$, the diagonals are not perpendicular.

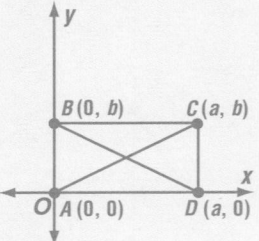

Practice Masters, p. 10

NAME_____ DATE _____

2-3 **Practice**
Student Edition Pages 80–87

Slope

Find the slope of the line that passes through each pair of points.

1. $(3, -8)$ and $(-5, 2)$ $-\frac{5}{4}$
2. $(-10, -3)$ and $(7, 2)$ $\frac{5}{17}$
3. $(-7, -6)$ and $(3, -6)$ 0
4. $(8, 2)$ and $(8, -1)$ undefined

Graph a line that passes through the given point and has the given slope.

5. $(1, -3), m = 3$
6. $(2, 1), m = -\frac{3}{4}$

State whether the graphs of the following equations are parallel, perpendicular, or neither.

7. $2x + 3y = 4$
   $3x + 2y = 6$
   neither
8. $\frac{1}{2}x + 2y = 1$
   $4x - y = 3$
   perpendicular
9. $6x - 9y = 4$
   $\frac{2}{3}x - y = 11$
   parallel
10. $y - 7 = 0$
    $3x = 5$
    perpendicular

11. **Look for a Pattern** A pyramid of aluminum cans is built against a wall so that there are two cans in the top row, four cans in the second row, six cans in the third row, and so on. How many rows are there if the pyramid contains 1190 cans? 34

86 Chapter 2

Geometry

43. See margin.

Graphing Calculator

Programming

46. a, d

Critical Thinking

Applications and Problem Solving

43. Determine whether the diagonals of parallelogram $ABCD$ at the right are perpendicular. Explain your answer.

44. Are the diagonals of a rectangle perpendicular? Use analytic methods to explain your answer. **See margin.**

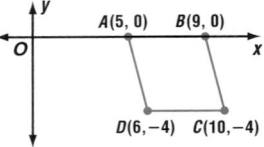

45. Use a graphing calculator to investigate each family of graphs. Explain how changing the slope affects the graph of the line. **a–b. See margin.**
   a. $y = 2x + 3, y = 4x + 3, y = 8x + 3, y = x + 3$
   b. $y = -3x + 1, y = -x + 1, y = -5x + 1, y = -7x + 1$

46. Points that lie on the same line are called *collinear* points. The graphing calculator program at the right will help you determine whether three points are collinear.

Draw $\overline{AB}$ and $\overline{BC}$ for each set of points on a graphing calculator. Then use the program at the right to find the slopes of $\overline{AB}$ and $\overline{BC}$ and determine which points are collinear.
   a. $A(3, 6), B(5, 7), C(7, 8)$
   b. $A(5, 9), B(7, 12), C(11, 17)$
   c. $A(0, 1.5), B(5, 8.2), C(11, 15.4)$
   d. $A(2.2, -2.1), B(0.6, -1.3), C(-3.8, 0.9)$

```
PROGRAM: Slope
: Disp "ENTER X AND Y FOR POINT
  1"
: Input A
: Input B
: Disp "ENTER X AND Y FOR POINT
  2"
: Input C
: Input D
: If (C - A) = 0
: Goto 1
: (D - B)/(C - A) → M
: Disp "THE SLOPE IS  "
: Disp M
: End
: Lbl 1
: Disp "THE SLOPE IS UNDEFINED"
: End
```

47. If the graph of the equation $ax + 2y = 8$ is perpendicular to the graph of the equation $2x + y = -3$, find the value of a. **−1**

48. Ancient Cultures Probably the most famous use of pyramids occurred 4500 years ago as tombs for Egyptian pharaohs and their relatives. But the western hemisphere has also had its share of pyramids. Mayan Indians of Central and South America built pyramids that were used as their temples.
   a. The Pyramid of the Sun in Teotihuacán, Mexico, measures about 700 feet on each side of its square base and is about 210 feet high. Estimate the slope that one of its faces makes with the base. **about 0.6**
   b. The Great Pyramid in Egypt measures 756 feet on each side of its square base and was originally 481 feet high. Estimate the slope that one of its faces makes with the base. **about 1.3**

49. Look for a Pattern Find the next number in each sequence.
   a. $6, 10, 15, 21, 28, \ldots$ **36**
   b. $1, 4, 9, 16, 25, \ldots$ **36**

86 Chapter 2 Graphing Linear Relations and Functions

Tech Prep

Architecture Technologist Students who are interested in ancient structures may wish to investigate more about the information given in Exercise 48 and explore the potential growth of this career. For more information on tech prep, see the *Teacher's Handbook*.

Additional Answers

45a. Graphs have the same *y*-intercept; as slope increases, the lines get steeper.

45b. Graphs have the same *y*-intercept; as the absolute value of the slope increases, the lines get steeper.

**50. tapes: about −5,
CDs: about 110**

50. Entertainment In 1992, CDs passed cassette tapes as the most popular form for pre-recorded music. The graph at the right shows that most of the growth in sales from 1991 to 1994 has been in CDs. If x represents the year and y represents the number of cassettes and CDs sold in millions, find the rate of increase (slope) for both cassette tapes and CDs.

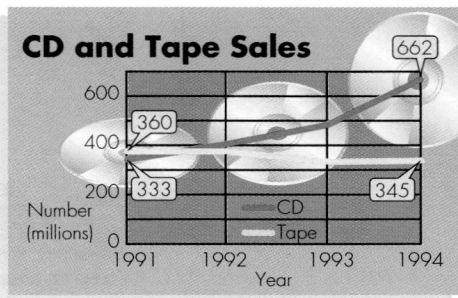

CD and Tape Sales

Source: Recording Industry Association of America

Mixed Review

51. Write $y = -2x + 4$ in standard form. (Lesson 2-2) $2x + y = 4$

52. Aviation The air pressure in the cabin of a fighter jet decreases as the plane ascends. (Lesson 2-1) **b. about 0.5 lb/in²**

Altitude (feet)	10,000	20,000	30,000	40,000	50,000
Air Pressure (lb/in²)	10.2	6.4	4.3	2.7	1.6

  a. Graph the data above. **See margin.**
  b. Predict what you think the air pressure would be at 60,000 feet.

53. Solve $5 < 2x + 7 < 13$. (Lesson 1-7) **$-1 < x < 3$**

54. One number is twice another. Twice the lesser number increased by the greater number is at least 85. Find the least possible value for the lesser number. (Lesson 1-6) **21.25**

55. Solve $|7 + 3a| = 11 - a$. (Lesson 1-5) **1, −9**

56. $-\frac{7}{2}$

56. Solve $0.75(8a + 20) - 2(a - 1) = 3$. (Lesson 1-4)

57. Statistics Find the mean, median, and mode for 100, 45, 105, 98, 97, and 101. (Lesson 1-3) **91; 99; no mode**

58. Simplify $\frac{1}{3}(15a + 9b) - \frac{1}{7}(28b - 84a)$. (Lesson 1-2) **$17a - b$**

59. Simplify $3 + (21 \div 7) \times 8 \div 4$. (Lesson 1-1) **9**

SELF TEST

1. Meteorology When the temperature is 30° F, the speed of the wind makes the temperature feel colder. This is called the windchill factor. The chart below shows how the wind affects your perception of how cold it is when the temperature is 30°. (Lesson 2-1)

  a. State the domain and range of the relation shown in the table below. **See Solutions Manual.**

Wind Speed (mph)	0	5	10	15	20	25	30	35	40
Windchill Factor (°F)	30	27	16	9	4	1	−2	−4	−5

  b. Graph the relation. Is it a function? **Yes; see Solutions Manual for graph.**

2. Find the value of $f(15)$ if $f(x) = 100x - 5x^2$. (Lesson 2-1) **375**

3. Write $y = -6x + 4$ in standard form. (Lesson 2-2) **$6x + y = 4$**

4. Graph $3x + 5y = 30$ using the x- and y-intercepts. (Lesson 2-2) **See Solutions Manual.**

5. Graph the line that goes through $(4, -3)$ and is parallel to the line whose equation is $2x + 3y = 6$. (Lesson 2-3) **See Solutions Manual.**

Extension

Reasoning Find q in terms of a, b, and p if the line that passes through (a, b) and (p, q) has slope $\frac{ap}{b}$.

$$\frac{ap^2 - a^2p + b^2}{b}$$

SELF TEST

The Self Test provides students with a brief review of the concepts and skills in Lessons 2-1 through 2-3. Lesson numbers are given to the right of exercises or instruction lines so students can review concepts not yet mastered.

Closing Activity

Modeling Lean a board against the wall. Roll a ball down the board. Increase the slope of the board and roll the ball again. Measure the time it takes the ball to reach the ground. Find the slope of the line formed by the board in each case. Ask students how the slope and the speed of the ball are related.

Additional Answer

52a.

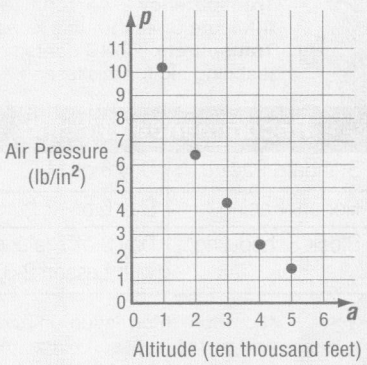

Air Pressure (lb/in²) vs. Altitude (ten thousand feet)

Enrichment Masters, p. 10

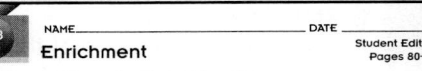

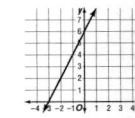

2-3

Enrichment

Two-Intercept Form of a Linear Equation

Any linear equation that can be written in the form $\frac{x}{a} + \frac{y}{b} = 1$ has x-intercept a and y-intercept b.

Example: Draw the graph of $\frac{x}{-3} + \frac{y}{6} = 1$.

The graph crosses the x-axis at -3 and the y-axis at 6. Graph $(-3, 0)$ and $(0, 6)$, then draw a straight line through them.

Example: Write $3x + 4y = 12$ in two-intercept form.

Divide by 12 to obtain 1 on the right side. $\frac{3x}{12} + \frac{4y}{12} = \frac{12}{12}$
Simplify.
The x-intercept is 4; the y-intercept is 3. $\frac{x}{4} + \frac{y}{3} = 1$

Use the given intercepts a and b, to write an equation in two-intercept form. Then draw the graph. See students' graphs.

1. $a = -2, b = -4$ $\frac{x}{-2} + \frac{y}{-4} = 1$ **2.** $a = 1, b = 8$ $\frac{x}{1} + \frac{y}{8} = 1$

3. $a = 3, b = 5$ $\frac{x}{3} + \frac{y}{5} = 1$ **4.** $a = 6, b = 9$ $\frac{x}{6} + \frac{y}{9} = 1$

Write each equation in two-intercept form. Then draw the graph.

5. $3x - 2y = -6$ **6.** $\frac{1}{2}x + \frac{1}{4}y = 1$ **7.** $5x + 2y = -10$

$\frac{x}{-2} + \frac{y}{3} = 1$ $\frac{x}{2} + \frac{y}{4} = 1$ $\frac{x}{-2} + \frac{y}{-5} = 1$

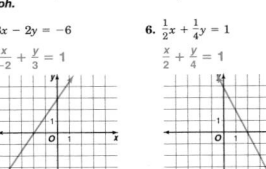
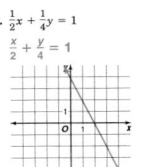
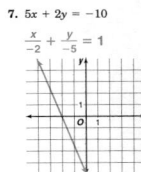

Instructional Resources

- Study Guide Master 2-4
- Practice Master 2-4
- Enrichment Master 2-4
- Assessment and Evaluation Masters, pp. 43–44
- Tech Prep Applications Masters, p. 3

 Transparency 2-4A contains the 5-Minute Check for this lesson; **Transparency 2-4B** contains a teaching aid for this lesson.

Recommended Pacing	
Standard Pacing	Day 6 of 14
Honors Pacing	Day 6 of 13
Block Scheduling*	Day 3 of 7 (along with Lesson 2-3)

 *For more information on pacing and possible lesson plans, refer to the *Block Scheduling Booklet*.

1 FOCUS

 ### 5-Minute Check
(over Lesson 2-3)

1. State the *y*-intercept, *x*-intercept, and slope of the line in the graph below.

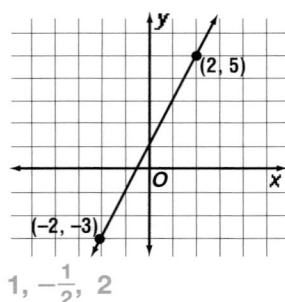

$1, -\frac{1}{2}, 2$

2. Find the slope of the line that passes through (2.3, 9.5) and (3.8, 20). 7

3. Describe the slope of the graph of the equation $y - 3x = 2$. rises to right

---

Writing Linear Equations

 **2-4**

What YOU'LL LEARN

- To write an equation of a line in slope-intercept form given the slope and one or two points, and
- to write an equation of a line that is parallel or perpendicular to the graph of a given equation.

Why IT'S IMPORTANT

You can use equations to explore relations in telecommunications and business.

APPLICATION
Telecommunications

Did you ever wonder why there are so many advertisements for long-distance telephone companies on television? Well, the long-distance market is huge! In 1989, there were 4.6 *billion* hours of long-distance calls made in the United States. Since 1989, the number of hours has increased by about 0.4 billion each year.

The equation $y = 0.4x + 4.6$ can be used to find *y*, the number of hours of long-distance calls (in billions) for any number of years, *x*, after 1989. This equation is graphed at the right. The *y*-intercept, 4.6, represents the number of billions of hours in 1989. The slope, 0.4, represents the yearly increase.

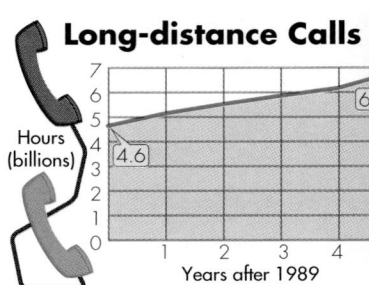

Long-distance Calls

Hours (billions)

Years after 1989

Source: Commonwealth Associates

In Lesson 2–2, you learned if a function can be written in the form $y = mx + b$, then it is a linear function. In the example above, *m* is 0.4, which is the slope, and *b* is 4.6, which is the *y*-intercept. Is it always true that *m* is the slope and *b* is the *y*-intercept?

Consider the graph below. The line passes through points $A(0, b)$ and $C(x, y)$. Notice that *b* is the *y*-intercept of $\overline{AC}$. Suppose you need to find the slope of $\overline{AC}$. Substitute the coordinates of points *A* and *C* into the slope equation.

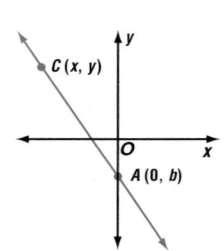

$$m = \frac{y_2 - y_1}{x_2 - x_1}$$

$$m = \frac{y - b}{x - 0} \quad \text{Substitute } (0, b) \text{ for } (x_1, y_1) \text{ and } (x, y) \text{ for } (x_2, y_2).$$

$$m = \frac{y - b}{x}$$

Now solve the equation for *y*.

$mx = y - b$ *Multiply each side by x.*

$mx + b = y$ *Add b to each side.*

$y = mx + b$ *Symmetric property of equality*

When an equation is written in this form, it is in **slope-intercept form**.

Slope-Intercept Form of a Linear Equation	The slope-intercept form of the equation of a line is $y = mx + b$, where *m* is the slope and *b* is the *y*-intercept.

If you are given the slope and the *y*-intercept of a line, you can find an equation of the line by substituting the values of *m* and *b* into the slope-intercept form. For example, if you know that the slope of a line is -4 and the *y*-intercept is 5, the equation of the line is $y = -4x + 5$, or, in standard form, $4x + y = 5$.

You can also use the slope-intercept form to find an equation of a line if you know the slope and the coordinates of a point on the line.

Example 1 Find the slope-intercept form of an equation of the line that has a slope of $-\frac{2}{3}$ and passes through $(-6, 1)$.

TECHNOLOGY
Tips
You also use the slope-intercept form when entering an equation into a graphing calculator.

You know the slope and the x and y values of one point on the graph. Substitute for m, x, and y in the slope-intercept form.

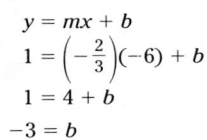

$$y = mx + b$$
$$1 = \left(-\frac{2}{3}\right)(-6) + b$$
$$1 = 4 + b$$
$$-3 = b$$

The y-intercept is -3. So, the equation in slope-intercept form is $y = -\frac{2}{3}x - 3$.

If you are given the coordinates of two points on a line, you can use the **point-slope form** to find the equation of the line that passes through them.

Point-Slope Form of a Linear Equation	The point-slope form of the equation of a line is $y - y_1 = m(x - x_1)$, where (x_1, y_1) are the coordinates of a point on the line and m is the slope of the line.

Example 2 Find an equation of the line that passes through $(3, 2)$ and $(5, 3)$.

First, use the two points given to find the slope of the line.

$$m = \frac{3 - 2}{5 - 3} \text{ or } \frac{1}{2}$$

Then use the point-slope form to write the linear equation.

$$y - y_1 = m(x - x_1)$$
$$y - 2 = \frac{1}{2}(x - 3) \quad \text{\textit{Replace } m \text{ with } \frac{1}{2} \text{ and } (x_1, y_1) \text{ with the}}$$
$$y - 2 = \frac{1}{2}x - \frac{3}{2} \quad \text{\textit{coordinates of either point. We chose } (3, 2).}$$
$$y = \frac{1}{2}x + \frac{1}{2}$$

The slope-intercept form of the equation of the line is $y = \frac{1}{2}x + \frac{1}{2}$.

In standard form, the equation is $x - 2y = -1$.

Lesson 2–4 *Writing Linear Equations* **89**

Motivating the Lesson
Questioning Have students find the distance traveled for a person bicycling at a rate of 10 miles per hour. Write an equation that represents the distance traveled compared to the time traveled. Is this a linear function? Find the slope.

2 TEACH

In-Class Examples

For Example 1
Find the slope-intercept form of an equation of the line that has a slope of 2 and passes through $(-1, 3)$. $y = 2x + 5$

For Example 2
Find an equation of the line that passes through $(2, 3)$ and $(1, 5)$. $y = -2x + 7$

Alternative Learning Styles

Auditory Read the following equations to students. For each equation, instruct students to plot the y-intercept on the y-axis first, then use the slope to go to the right and up the appropriate number of units to plot a second point, and then draw the line.

a. $y = 2x + 3$
b. $y = \frac{1}{2}x - 2$
c. $y = \frac{-3}{2}x + 1$

In-Class Example

For Example 3
Rachel Lewis sells cars. She makes a base salary of $1000 per month plus a commission of 1% of the selling price of each car. For six months Ms. Lewis has tabulated the number of cars she has sold each month and the amount of money she has made. Is there a relationship between the numbers so she can estimate her monthly salary? Use the chart to write an equation in slope-intercept form that approximates the relationship. If Ms. Lewis sells five cars, how much money will she make for the month?

Number of Cars Sold	Money Made
18	3544
22	4108
10	2413
11	2554
14	2978
17	3401

$m = \dfrac{4108 - 243}{22 - 10}$ or 141

$y = 141x + 1000$

If Ms. Lewis sells 5 cars, she will make approximately $1705 for the month.

What factors contribute to the fact that the U.S. has fewer telephones per 100 people than Sweden? One factor may be the number of people per household.

When changes in real-life situations occur at a linear rate, a linear equation can be used as a model for describing the situation.

Example ③

Business

With a certain long-distance company, the price of a 4-minute long-distance call is $1.70. An 11-minute call with the same company costs $4.15.

a. Write a linear equation that describes the cost of these telephone calls. Assume that the changes increase linearly.

b. How much would a 20-minute telephone call cost?

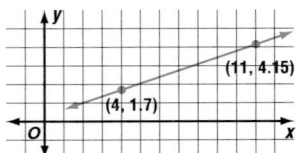

Countries with the most telephones per 100 people
1. Sweden, 68.4
2. Switzerland, 60.8
3. Canada, 59.2
4. Denmark, 58.3
5. United States, 56.1

a. The line passes through the points (4, 1.7) and (11, 4.15). Find the slope of the line. *Use $(x_1, y_1) = (4, 1.7)$ and $(x_2, y_2) = (11, 4.15)$.*

$$m = \frac{y_2 - y_1}{x_2 - x_1}$$
$$= \frac{4.15 - 1.7}{11 - 4}$$
$$= \frac{2.45}{7} \text{ or } 0.35$$

Now use the point-slope form to write the linear equation.

$y - y_1 = m(x - x_1)$
$y - 1.7 = 0.35(x - 4)$ *Replace m with 0.35 and (x_1, y_1) with (4, 1.7).*
$y - 1.7 = 0.35x - 1.4$
$\quad\quad y = 0.35x + 0.3$

The slope-intercept form of the equation of the line is $y = 0.35x + 0.3$.

b. Use the equation to find the cost of a 20-minute call.

$y = 0.35x + 0.3$
$y = 0.35(20) + 0.3$ *Replace x with 20.*
$y = 7 + 0.3 \text{ or } 7.3$

A 20-minute call would cost $7.30.

Check this by estimating the cost from the graph.

The slope-intercept form can also be used to find equations of lines that are parallel or perpendicular.

Alternative Teaching Strategies

Reading Algebra Have students research the nonmathematical meanings of the terms *slope* and *linear*. They can think of slope in terms of driving up a hill. The steeper the hill, the steeper the slope. Remind them that the word *linear* contains the word *line*. They should think of a straight line.

Example ④

INTEGRATION

Geometry

Write an equation of the line that passes through $(-9, 5)$ and is perpendicular to the line whose equation is $y = -3x + 2$.

The slope of the given line is -3. Since the product of this slope and the slope of the perpendicular line is -1, the slope of the perpendicular line is $\frac{1}{3}$.

Use the slope-intercept form and the ordered pair $(-9, 5)$ to write the equation.

$y = mx + b$

$5 = \left(\frac{1}{3}\right)(-9) + b$ *Replace m with $\frac{1}{3}$ and (x, y) with $(-9, 5)$.*

$5 = -3 + b$

$8 = b$

An equation of the line is $y = \frac{1}{3}x + 8$.

Use a graphing calculator to verify that the equation is correct.

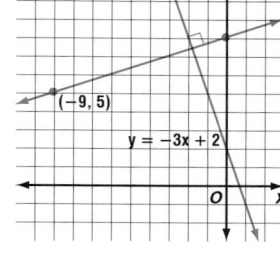

Teaching Tip For Example 4, remind students of the relationships of the slopes of parallel lines and perpendicular lines.

In-Class Example

For Example 4
Write an equation of the line that passes through (3, 2) and is perpendicular to the line whose equation is $y = 2x + 5$.
$y = -\frac{1}{2}x + \frac{7}{2}$

3 PRACTICE/APPLY

CHECK FOR UNDERSTANDING

Communicating Mathematics

1. Solve the equation for y; $m = $ slope, $b = y$-intercept.

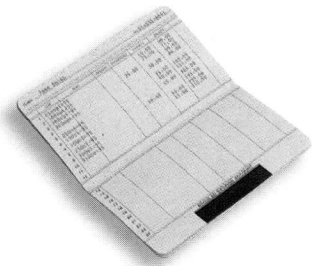

MATH JOURNAL

9. $y = -\frac{1}{3}x + 4$

Guided Practice

10. $m = 2$; b, -5

11. $m = 2$; b, 3

12. $m = -\frac{3}{2}$; b, 5

Study the lesson. Then complete the following.   2. $y = 5x - 4$

1. **Explain** how to write an equation in slope-intercept form and tell what each variable represents.

2. **Write** an equation of a line with slope of 5 and y-intercept of -4.

3. **Explain** how to write the equation of a line if you know the ordered pairs for two points on the line.   See margin.

4. **Choose** the graph that shows $y = mx + b$, $m < 0$, $b > 0$.   b

   a. 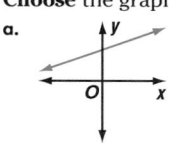   b. 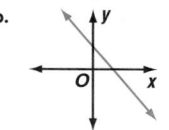   c. 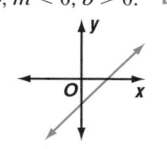   d.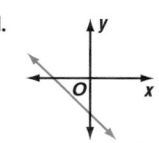

5. **You Decide**   Maribela thinks that the graphs of $y = 4x + 2$ and $4x - y = -2$ are different lines. Karen thinks that they are the same. Who is correct? Explain your reasoning.   See margin.

6. **Assess Yourself**   Suppose you have $250 in a savings account and decide to save an additional $10 each month. Write an equation to find the total amount, y, in your savings account after x months. Graph the equation. Then explain what the slope and y-intercept represent. $y = 10x + 250$; $m = 10$; y-intercept $= 250$

The slope and y-intercept of a line are given. Write the slope-intercept form of the equation for each line described.

7. $m = 7$, $b = -3$ 8. $m = 1.5$, $b = 0$ 9. $m = -\frac{1}{3}$, $b = 4$
   $y = 7x - 3$ $y = 1.5x$

State the slope and y-intercept of the graph of each equation.

10. $y = 2x - 5$ 11. $2y = 4x + 6$ 12. $3x + 2y = 10$

Lesson 2–4 Writing Linear Equations   **91**

Check for Understanding
Exercises 1–20 are designed to help you assess your students' understanding through reading, writing, speaking, and modeling. You should work through Exercises 1–6 with your students and then monitor their work on Exercises 7–20.

Error Analysis
Students sometimes confuse zero slope with undefined slope. Zero is between negative and positive. A line with a slope of 0 is a horizontal line. It neither rises nor falls from left to right, and thus its slope is between negative and positive. A vertical line does not go from left to right, so its slope is not positive, negative, or zero. The slope of a vertical line is undefined.

Additional Answers

3. First find the slope of the line. To find the y-intercept, substitute the coordinates of one of the points into the point-slope form or slope-intercept form of the equation and solve for b. Write the equation in slope-intercept form.

5. Karen is correct because even though one line is written in slope-intercept form, they are the same line.

Reteaching

Using Discussion Have students describe the general method for changing a point-slope equation into a slope-intercept equation. Then do the reverse.

Assignment Guide

Core: 21–49 odd, 50, 51, 53, 55–65
Enriched: 22–48 even, 50–65

For **Extra Practice,** see p. 879.

The red A, B, and C flags, printed only in the Teacher's Wraparound Edition, indicate the level of difficulty of the exercises.

13. $y = \frac{5}{4}x + 7$

14. $y = \frac{7}{2}x - 5$

15. $y = \frac{1}{3}x - 2$

16. $y = 0.5x + 1$

17. $y = -\frac{5}{2}x + 16$

18. $y = 4x + 5$

Write an equation in slope-intercept form for each graph.

13.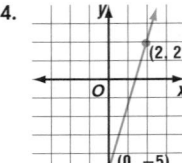

14.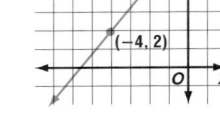

15.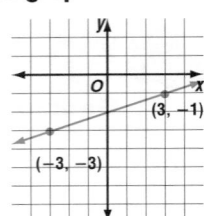

Write an equation in slope-intercept form that satisfies each condition.

16. slope = 0.5, passes through (6, 4)

17. passes through (6, 1) and (8, −4)

18. passes through (0, 5) and is parallel to the graph of $y = 4x + 12$

19. passes through (0, −2) and is perpendicular to the graph of $y = x - 2$ $y = -x - 2$

20. **Ecology**   A nature-preserve worker estimates there are 6000 deer in Sharon Woods Park. She also estimates that the population will increase by 75 deer each year thereafter. Write an equation that represents how many deer will be in the park in x years. $y = 75x + 6000$

EXERCISES

Practice

21. $m = -\frac{2}{3}$; b, −4

22. $m = \frac{3}{4}$; b, 0

23. $m = -0.3$; b, −6

24. $m = \frac{1}{2}$; b, $-\frac{5}{2}$

25. $m = -\frac{3}{5}$; b, 6

26. $m = c$; $b = d$

27. $y = \frac{4}{5}x$

28. $y = -4$

29. $y = -\frac{5}{3}x + \frac{29}{3}$

33. $y = -\frac{4}{5}x + \frac{17}{5}$

35. $y = \frac{3}{2}x$

State the slope and y-intercept of the graph of each equation.

21. $y = -\frac{2}{3}x - 4$

22. $y = \frac{3}{4}x$

23. $-y = 0.3x + 6$

24. $4y = 2x - 10$

25. $-5y = 3x - 30$

26. $y = cx + d$

Write an equation in slope-intercept form for each graph.

27.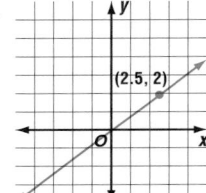

28.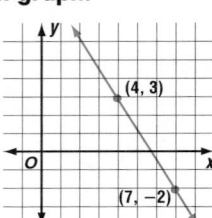

29.

Write an equation in slope-intercept form that satisfies each condition.

B

30. slope = 0.25, passes through (0, 4) $y = 0.25x + 4$

31. slope = −0.5, passes through (2, −3) $y = -0.5x - 2$

32. slope = 4, passes through the origin $y = 4x$

33. passes through (−2, 5) and (3, 1)

34. passes through (7, 1) and (7, 8)   no slope-intercept form, $x = 7$

35. passes through (−2, −3) and (0, 0)

36. x-intercept = −4, y-intercept = 4 $y = x + 4$

92   *Chapter 2   Graphing Linear Relations and Functions*

Study Guide Masters, p. 11

NAME_____ DATE _____

Study Guide

Student Edition
Pages 88–94

Writing Linear Equations

Given the slope and y-intercept of a line, you can find an equation of the line by substituting these values into the *slope-intercept form* of the equation. The slope-intercept form of the equation of the line is $y = mx + b$, where m is the slope and b is the y-intercept.

Example: Find the slope-intercept form of the equation of the line that has a slope of $\frac{1}{2}$ and that passes through (3, 6).

First, substitute the slope and coordinates of the point into the slope-intercept form and solve for b.

$y = mx + b$

$6 = \frac{1}{2}(3) + b$ Substitute 6 for y, $\frac{1}{2}$ for m, and 3 for x.

$6 = \frac{3}{2} + b$

$4\frac{1}{2} = b$

Write the equation in slope-intercept form.

$y = \frac{1}{2}x + 4\frac{1}{2}$ Substitute $\frac{1}{2}$ for m, and $4\frac{1}{2}$ for b.

State the slope and y-intercept of the graph of each equation.

1. $y = 7x - 14$

$m = 7$,
y-intercept = −14

2. $4y = 2x - 10$

$m = \frac{1}{2}$,
y-intercept = $-\frac{5}{2}$

3. $-y = \frac{2}{3}x + 3$

$m = -\frac{2}{3}$,
y-intercept = −3

Write an equation in slope-intercept form that satisfies each condition.

4. slope = −2, passes through (−4, 6)

$y = -2x - 2$

5. slope = $-\frac{13}{5}$, passes through (5, −7)

$y = -\frac{13}{5}x + 6$

6. slope = 1, passes through (2, 5)

$y = x + 3$

7. no x-intercept, y-intercept = −4

$y = 0x - 4$

8. passes through (−2, −2) and (3, 3)

$x - y = 0$

9. x-intercept = −3, and y-intercept = 2

$-2x + 3y = 6$

10. slope = $-\frac{3}{2}$, passes through (3, −2)

$3x + 2y = 5$

11. slope = $-\frac{5}{2}$, passes through (8, −4)

$5x + 2y = 32$

92   *Chapter 2*

37. x-intercept $= \frac{1}{3}$, y-intercept $= -\frac{1}{4}$ $y = \frac{3}{4}x - \frac{1}{4}$

38. x-intercept $= 0$, y-intercept $= 4$ no slope-intercept form, $x = 0$

39. passes through (4, 6), parallel to the graph of $y = \frac{2}{3}x + 5$ $y = \frac{2}{3}x + \frac{10}{3}$

40. $y = \frac{1}{3}x + \frac{2}{3}$    **40.** passes through $(-2, 0)$, perpendicular to the graph of $y = -3x + 7$

41. passes through $(-3, -1)$, parallel to the line that passes through (3, 3) and (0, 6) $y = -x - 4$

42. passes through $(6, -5)$, perpendicular to the line whose equation is $3x - \frac{1}{5}y = 3$ $y = -\frac{1}{15}x - \frac{23}{5}$

Find the value of k in each equation if the given ordered pair is a solution of the equation.

46. $\frac{5}{7}$

43. $5x + ky = 8$, $(3, -1)$ 7

44. $4x - ky = 7$, $(4, 3)$ 3

45. $3x + 8y = k$, $(0, 0.5)$ 4

46. $kx + 3y = 11$, $(7, 2)$

Graphing Calculator

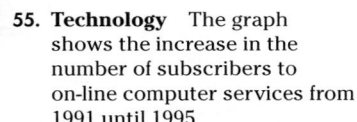

Compare and contrast the graphs of each pair of equations. Use a graphing calculator to check your answers.   47–49. See margin.

47. $2y = 6x + 14$
   $3x - y = 6$

48. $2y - 4 = x$
   $y = -2x + 2$

49. $3x + 5y = 15$
   $y = -\frac{3}{5}x + 3$

Critical Thinking

50. Geometry   Given $\triangle ABC$ with $A(-6, -8)$, $B(6, 4)$, and $C(-6, 10)$, write the equation of the line containing the altitude from A. Remember that the altitude from A is perpendicular to $\overline{BC}$. $y = 2x + 4$

Applications and Problem Solving

51. Telecommunications   Refer to the application at the beginning of the lesson. Estimate the number of hours of long-distance calls that will be made in 1999.   8.6 billion hours

52. Geometry   The equation $d = 180(c - 2)$ can be used to find the number of degrees, d, in any convex polygon with c sides.
   a. Write this equation in slope-intercept form. $d = 180c - 360$
   b. Identify the slope and y-intercept. $m = 180$; b, -360
   c. Find the number of degrees in a pentagon.   540°

53. Science   At 20°F, 1 gallon of water weighs approximately 8.33 pounds. Write a linear equation to represent this situation. $y = 8.33x$

54. Business   Benny's Floral Shop charges $3 per mile for delivery of a $20 floral arrangement. Carmelita's Floral Shop charges $2 per mile for delivery of a $30 arrangement. When is it less expensive to buy from Carmelita?

54. when the number of miles is greater than 10

55a. $y = 1.45x + 3.2$

55b. 16.25 million

55c. The slope is the average increase in subscribers; the y-intercept is the number of subscribers in 1990.

55. Technology   The graph shows the increase in the number of subscribers to on-line computer services from 1991 until 1995.
   a. Assuming that the increase is linear, write an equation to represent this situation.
   b. Predict the number of subscribers in the year 2000.
   c. What is the meaning of the slope and y-intercept?

On-Line Services

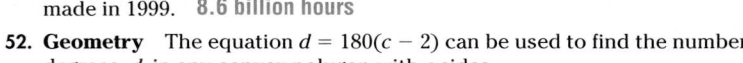

Customers (millions)

9 million

3.2 million

Years after 1991

Source: Information and Interactive Services Report, Dataquest

Lesson 2–4   Writing Linear Equations   **93**

Extension

Problem Solving   Give the equation $k = \frac{1}{4}m + 10$ to students.

Have them write a problem to fit the equation. State the slope, x-intercept, and y-intercept.

$\frac{1}{4}$, -40, 10

Additional Answers

47. The lines are parallel with different y-intercepts.

48. The lines are perpendicular and intersect at their y-intercepts.

49. The lines are the same.

Practice Masters, p. 11

2-4   NAME_____   DATE_____
Practice   Student Edition Pages 88–9...

Writing Linear Equations

State the slope and y-intercept of the graph of each equation.

1. $5x - 4y = 8$ $m = \frac{5}{4}$, $b = -2$

2. $3x - y = -11$ $m = 3$, $b = 11$

3. $\frac{2}{3}x + \frac{4}{7}y = 1$ $m = -\frac{7}{6}$, $b = \frac{7}{4}$

4. $3y = 7$ $m = 0$, $b = \frac{7}{3}$

Write each equation in slope-intercept form.

5. $3x - 5y = 15$ $y = \frac{3}{5}x - 3$

6. $4x + 7y = 12$ $y = -\frac{4}{7}x + \frac{12}{7}$

7. $7y = -15$ $y = -\frac{15}{7}$

8. $2x = -8$ no slope-intercept form

Write an equation in slope-intercept form that satisfies each given condition.

9. slope $= -5$, passes through $(-3, -8)$ $y = -5x - 23$

10. slope $= \frac{4}{5}$, passes through $(10, -3)$ $y = \frac{4}{5}x - 11$

11. passes through (4, 3) and (7, -2) $y = -\frac{5}{3}x + \frac{29}{3}$

12. passes through $(-6, -3)$ and $(-8, 4)$ $y = -\frac{7}{2}x - 24$

13. passes through (3, 11) and $(-6, 5)$ $y = \frac{2}{3}x + 9$

14. passes through (7, 2) and $(3, -5)$ $y = \frac{7}{4}x - \frac{41}{4}$

15. x-intercept $= 3$, y-intercept $= 2$ $y = -\frac{2}{3}x + 2$

16. x-intercept $= -5$, y-intercept $= 7$ $y = \frac{7}{5}x + 7$

17. x-intercept $= -5$, y-intercept $= -5$ $y = -x - 5$

18. x-intercept $= \frac{1}{2}$, y-intercept $= 4$ $y = -8x + 4$

Closing Activity

Writing Separate the class into groups of four. Have each group research an application of linear equations and write a problem. Have groups exchange problems with other groups and solve them, making sure they state the equation of the line and its slope.

Chapter 2, Quiz B (Lessons 2-3 and 2-4), is available in the *Assessment and Evaluation Masters,* p. 44.

Mid-Chapter Test (Lessons 2-1 through 2-4) is available in the *Assessment and Evaluation Masters,* p. 43.

Enrichment Masters, p. 11

2-4

NAME_____ DATE _____

Enrichment

Student Edition
Pages 88–94

Finding Equations for Non-Linear Functions

You can often find an equation for a non-linear function by looking for a pattern in a chart that shows values of the variables.

Example: Write an equation describing the relationship between the variables in the chart.

+1 +1 +1 +1 +1 +1

x	−3	−2	−1	0	1	2	3
y	2	1	0	1	2	3	4

−1 −1 +1 +1 +1 +1

Notice that the function is not linear. The values of the y are positive. As x goes from −3 to 3, the values of y decrease steadily then increase steadily. This suggests a function similar to $y = |x|$. Clearly $y = |x|$ does not quite work, but a little adjustment shows that $y = |x + 1|$ does. Why is the equation not $y = |x| + 1$?
The y values would be 4, 3, 2, 1, 2, 3, 4.

Write an equation describing the relationship between variables in each table.

1.
x	−3	−2	−1	0	1	2	3
y	4	3	2	1	0	1	2
$y = |x - 1|$

2.
x	−3	−2	−1	0	1	2	3
y	6	4	2	0	2	4	6
$y = |2x|$

3.
x	−3	−2	−1	0	1	2	3
y	8	5	2	1	4	7	10
$y = |3x + 1|$

Solve each of the following.

4. Rob's charges for mowing a lawn are directly proportional to the number of hours he works. He charged Mr. Wilson $13.75 for 2.5 hours work. Write an equation for Rob's charges C as a function of the number of hours h that he works.
$C = 5.5h$

5. A cube-shaped box with no top has a surface area of S square units. Write an equation for the length E of an edge as a function of S.
$E = \sqrt{\dfrac{S}{5}}$

56. **Zoology** According to the *World Almanac*, a zebra can run at speeds up to 40 mph. Suppose a zebra could run at 40 mph for a long period of time. If at 1:30 P.M, a zebra had already traveled 32 miles, use the definition of slope to find how many miles the zebra could have traveled by 3:00 P.M. if it was running at top speed. (Lesson 2–3) **92 miles**

57. Determine if $g(x) = x(2 - x)$ is a linear function. (Lesson 2–2) **no**

58. Find the value of $h(a + 1)$ if $h(x) = 3x - 1$ and $a = 4$. (Lesson 2–1) **14**

Solve each inequality.   59. **no solution**   60. **{r | r ≥ 6}**

59. $|x - 2| \le -99$ (Lesson 1–7)   60. $2(r - 4) + 5 \ge 9$ (Lesson 1–6)

61. Solve $|x - 3| = 2x$. (Lesson 1–5) **1**

62. $\frac{1}{5}(4 + n)$

62. Write an algebraic expression to represent *one-fifth the sum of four and a number.* (Lesson 1–4)

63. **Statistics** Find the mean, median, and mode of the hourly wages of 200 employees. One hundred earn $5.00 per hour, ten earn $6.25 per hour, ten earn $7.75 per hour, twenty earn $4.50 per hour, and sixty earn $5.90 per hour. (Lesson 1–3) **$5.42; $5.00; $5.00**

64. Name the property illustrated by $11 + a = a + 11$. (Lesson 1–2) **commutative (+)**

65. Evaluate $(5a + 3d)^2 - e^2$ if $a = 3$, $d = 0.5$, and $e = 0.3$. (Lesson 1–1) **272.16**

Mathematics and SOCIETY

Honeybee Counting

The excerpts below appeared in an article in *New Scientist* on March 4, 1995.

HONEYBEES CAN COUNT, ACCORDING TO two researchers in Germany. Lars Chittka and Karl Geiger of the Free University of Berlin say that bees measure the distance from their hive to a food source by counting landmarks as they fly past them . . . Chittka and Geiger trained bees to collect sugar solutions from a feeder more than 250 metres from their hive, which was in the centre of a large featureless meadow. Then they placed a series of obvious landmarks—tents about 3.5 metres high—along the bees' line of flight from the hive to the feeding station. To start with, there were four tents, spaced 75 metres apart, so the feeder was between the third and fourth landmarks. Even if sugar was also available between the second and third tents, most of the bees flew to the original feeder. The researchers then changed the number or position of the landmarks . . . Many of the bees simply stopped at the first feeder they encountered after the third landmark, even though this meant that they were nowhere near the feeder on which they had been trained . . . Chittka and Geiger say that bees clearly react to the number of landmarks they have passed, rather than to the distance they have flown, which means they must have the beginnings of an ability to count. ■

2. Sample answer: People also count landmarks when traveling.

3. Sample answer: The landmarks on graphs are units used to provide numerical scales.

1. Sample answer: shrubs, trees, fences, and so on
1. Under natural conditions, what types of landmarks might bees use to find their way to food sources?

2. If bees do in fact count landmarks, compare their behavior with the methods you use to find your way when traveling.

3. How is the bees' behavior similar to your use of graphs or measuring lines when illustrating or solving problems?

94 Chapter 2 *Graphing Linear Relations and Functions*

Mathematics and SOCIETY

Scientists often have to reason like mathematicians—deductively. For example, assume there are two hypotheses: (1) the bees can count, and (2) the bees cannot count. If (2) is true, the bees would stop at the first feeder instead of continuing to the feeder after the third landmark. Therefore, (2) is false, so (1) must be true.

Integration: Statistics
Modeling Real-World Data Using Scatter Plots

CONNECTION
Science

What YOU'LL LEARN

- To draw scatter plots, and
- to find and use prediction equations.

Why IT'S IMPORTANT

You can use scatter plots to display data, examine trends, and make predictions.

When you ride the express elevator to the top floor of a skyscraper, you experience the effects of changing air pressure. Because of the rapid increase in altitude, the air pressure outside your eardrum is lower than the air pressure inside your eardrum. This difference in air pressure causes your eardrums to push out until some air finally forces its way out of your ears and goes pop!

The weight of the air pressing down around us produces air pressure. Generally, air pressure is greatest near Earth's surface, where it averages 14.7 pounds per square inch (psi). It decreases as you move out toward space, simply because there is less air pressing down. The chart at the right shows average air pressure measured at different altitudes.

Altitude (thousand feet)	Air Pressure (psi)
0	14.7
5	12.3
10	10.2
15	7.0
20	6.4
25	5.2
30	4.3
35	3.5
40	2.7
45	2.0
50	1.6

Air Pressure

Altitude (thousand feet)

To determine the relationship between altitude and air pressure, graph the data points in a **scatter plot.** When real-life data is collected, the points graphed usually do not form a straight line, but may *approximate* a linear relationship. When this is the case, a **best-fit line** can be drawn, as shown at the left.

A **prediction equation** can be determined by employing a process similar to that used to determine an equation of a line when you know two points. You can use the prediction equation to estimate, or predict, one of the variables given the other.

Use two points from the line, (45, 2.0) and (25, 5.2), to find the slope.

$$m = \frac{2.0 - 5.2}{45 - 25} \text{ or } -0.16$$

Let x represent the altitude, and let y represent the air pressure. Use the slope and one of the points in the slope-intercept form to find a prediction equation.

$y - y_1 = m(x - x_1)$ *Use point-slope form.*

$y - 2 = -0.16(x - 45)$ *Let $(x_1, y_1) = (45, 2)$.*

$y = -0.16x + 9.2$

A prediction equation is $y = -0.16x + 9.2$.

GLENCOE Technology

 CD-ROM Interaction

A multimedia simulation ties data analysis, line fitting, and writing equations with car racing. A blackline master activity with teacher's notes provides a follow-up to the CD-ROM simulation.

For Windows & Macintosh

NCTM Standards: 1–6

Instructional Resources

- Study Guide Master 2-5
- Practice Master 2-5
- Enrichment Master 2-5
- Multicultural Activity Masters, p. 3
- Real-World Applications, 5
- Science and Math Lab Manual, pp. 69–74
- Tech Prep Applications Masters, p. 4

 Transparency 2-5A contains the 5-Minute Check for this lesson; **Transparency 2-5B** contains a teaching aid for this lesson.

Recommended Pacing	
Standard Pacing	Day 7 of 14
Honors Pacing	Day 7 of 13
Block Scheduling*	Day 4 of 7

 *For more information on pacing and possible lesson plans, refer to the *Block Scheduling Booklet.*

1 FOCUS

5-Minute Check
(over Lesson 2-4)

1. State the slope and y-intercept of the graph of the equation.
$y = \frac{2}{5}x + 1$ $\frac{2}{5}x; 1$

2. Find the slope-intercept form of the equation $4x + 8y = 11$.
$y = -\frac{1}{2}x + \frac{11}{8}$

3. Find the slope-intercept form of the equation of the line that has a slope of $\frac{2}{3}$ and passes through (6, −2).
$y = \frac{2}{3}x - 6$

 TEKS   1.b.

Motivating the Lesson

Situational Problem Have students give their height in inches and their shoe size. Record these on a chart. Then graph them, using height as the independent variable and shoe size as a dependent variable. Is the relationship between height and shoe size a linear function? Can you predict anything from the graph?

2 TEACH

 This activity allows students to get hands-on experience in collecting real-world data, making a conjecture about the mathematical relationship between two measurable features, and using this relationship to predict future observations.

Teaching Tip When drawing the line in Example 1, try to center it within the points.

In-Class Example

For Example 1
The population of the city of Jackson for the past ten years is listed in the chart below.

Age of Jackson	Population
34	22,000
36	23,090
38	23,990
40	25,032
42	25,983
44	27,095

Draw a scatter plot and find a prediction equation to show the relationship between the age of the city and its population.
$y = 500.6x + 5068.6$

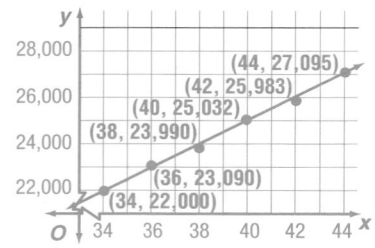

 **MODELING MATHEMATICS**

Head Versus Height

Materials:  tape measure 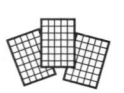 grid paper

In this activity, you will collect data to determine whether there is a relationship between the circumference of a person's head and his or her height.

Your Turn   a. See students' work.

a. Collect data from several of your classmates. Measure the circumference of each person's head and his or her height. Record the data as ordered pairs (circumference, height).

b. See students' work.
b. Graph the data in a scatter plot.

c. Choose two ordered pairs and write a prediction equation.   Sample answer: $y = 3x$

d. Explain the meaning of the slope in the prediction equation.   See margin.

e. Predict the head size of a person who is 66 inches tall.   Sample answer: 22 inches

f. Predict the height of an individual whose head size is 18 inches.   Sample answer: 54 inches

---

Example 1  **APPLICATION Keyboarding**

Draw a scatter plot and find two prediction equations to show how keyboarding speed and experience are related. Predict the keyboarding speed in words per minute (wpm) of a student who has 11 weeks of experience.

Experience (weeks)	4	7	8	1	6	3	5	2	9	6	7	10
Speed (wpm)	33	45	49	20	40	30	38	22	52	44	42	55

Explore   The problem asks for two prediction equations.

Plan   Make a scatter plot to determine the relationship between experience and speed. Since keyboarding speed is dependent on experience, the independent variable is the number of weeks of experience.

The best-fit line does not necessarily contain any points from the data.

Solve   The pattern of points suggests a possible line that passes through (5, 36) and (8, 49).

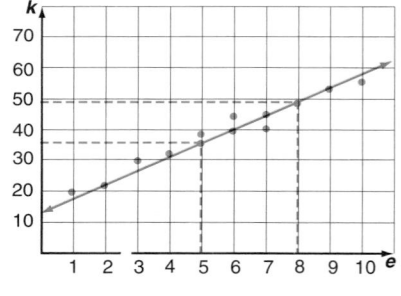

$m = \frac{49 - 36}{8 - 5}$

$= \frac{13}{3}$ or about 4.3

Let e stand for experience in weeks. Let k stand for keyboarding speed in words per minute.

$y = mx + b$
$k = 4.3e + b$
$36 = 4.3(5) + b$
$14.5 = b$

One prediction equation is $k = 4.3e + 14.5$.

Classroom Vignette

"Have students take a piece of uncooked spaghetti and place it on a grid so that there are about the same number of points on either side. Then write the equation!"

Eva Gates
Independent Mathematics Consultant
Pearland, Texas

Rita Moreno
(1931–)

Rita Moreno, a Hispanic-American actress, singer, and dancer, was the first and only artist to win an Oscar®, a Tony, an Emmy, and a Grammy award.

Another line can be suggested by using (2, 22) and (9, 52). Using these points results in a prediction equation of $t = 4.3e + 13.4$.

If a student had 11 weeks of experience, the first equation would predict that the student could type approximately 62 words per minute.

Examine Locate the ordered pair (11, 62) on the scatter plot. The point lies close to the graph of the prediction equation. Therefore, the solution is reasonable.

The procedure for determining a prediction equation is dependent upon your judgment. You decide where to draw the best-fit line. You decide which two points on the line are used to find the slope and intercept. Your prediction equation may be different from someone else's. The prediction equation is used when a rough estimate is sufficient.

Example ②

APPLICATION
Entertainment

Each year, the entertainment industry publishes a list of the top earners. The table at the right shows the top ten earners for 1993–1994.

a. Draw a scatter plot for the data.

b. Predict the earnings of the fifteenth person on the list.

Rank	Person or Group	Earnings (millions)
1	Steven Spielberg	$335
2	Oprah Winfrey	105
3	Barney	84
4	Pink Floyd	62
5	Bill Cosby	60
6	Barbra Streisand	57
7	Eagles	56
8	David Copperfield	55
9	Rolling Stones	53
10	Harrison Ford	44

a.

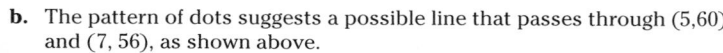

b. The pattern of dots suggests a possible line that passes through (5, 60) and (7, 56), as shown above.

Find the slope.

$$m = \frac{56 - 60}{7 - 5}$$

$$= \frac{-4}{2} \text{ or } -2$$

Then find a prediction equation.

$$y = mx + b$$

$$60 = -2(5) + b$$

$$70 = b$$

A prediction equation is $y = -2x + 70$. If an entertainer was fifteenth on the list, the equation would predict earnings of $-2(15) + 70$ or $40 million. *Do you think a line is a good predictor in this case?*

GLENCOE *Technology*

Interactive Mathematics Tools Software

This multimedia software provides an interactive lesson by helping students observe positive and negative relationships of points on a scatter plot. A **Computer Journal** gives students an opportunity to write about what they have learned.

For Windows & Macintosh

Teaching Tip Have students draw three best-fit lines for Example 2. Have them make a prediction based on their lines.

In-Class Example

For Example 2
Each of seven executives oversees a varied number of salespersons. Below is a chart with the number of salespersons and total sales for one month for each executive.

Number of Salespersons		Sales
(1)	12	$250
(2)	33	699
(3)	17	350
(4)	22	460
(5)	24	501
(6)	8	162
(7)	19	

Find the prediction equation for this relationship. Predict the total sales for the seventh executive.

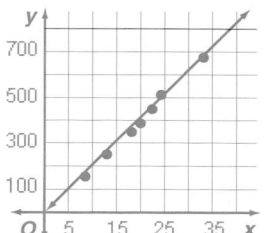

$y = 21.3x - 5.6$; $398

fabulous
FIRSTS

Rita Moreno's awards include the following: Tony Award in 1975 for *The Ritz*, Emmy Award in 1977 for *The Muppet Show*, Emmy Award in 1978 for *The Rockford Files*, Grammy Award in 1972 for *The Electric Company*, Academy Award in 1961 for *West Side Story*.

Check for Understanding

Exercises 1–9 are designed to help you assess your students' understanding through reading, writing, speaking, and modeling. You should work through Exercises 1–5 with your students and then monitor their work on Exercises 6–9.

Additional Answer

9a.

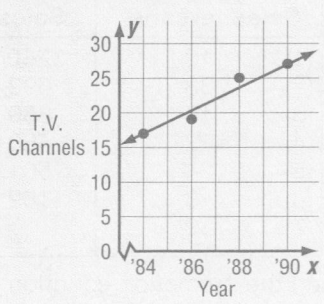

Study Guide Masters, p. 12

NAME_____ DATE_____

2-5

Study Guide

Student Edition
Pages 95–100

Integration: Statistics
Modeling Real-World Data Using Scatter Plots

One method for analyzing data is the **scatter plot.** A scatter plot visually shows the nature of a relationship, both its shape and dispersion. A line may be drawn to show the approximate relationship formed by the plotted points. By choosing several points on the lines, you can find the equation of the line. This equation is called the **prediction equation** of the relationship.

1. According to a certain prediction equation, the cost of 200 square feet of storage space is $60. The cost of 325 square feet of storage space is $160. Let x stand for the amount of storage space in square feet and y stand for the cost in dollars.
   a. What is the independent variable?
      x, the amount of storage space
   b. What is the dependent variable?
      y, the cost in dollars
   c. Find the prediction equation.
      y = 0.8x − 100
   d. Find the slope of the prediction equation.
      0.8
   e. Predict the number of square feet for storage space costing $44.
      180 square feet

2. The table below shows the years of experience for eight technicians at Lewis Techomatic and the hourly rate of pay each technician earns.

Experience (years)	9	4	3	1	10	6	12	8
Hourly Rate of Pay	$17	$10	$10	$7	$19	$12	$20	$15

   a. Draw a scatter plot to show how experience and hourly rate of pay are related. Draw a line along which the points seem to cluster.

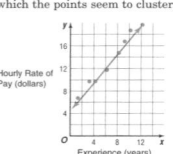

   b. Write a prediction equation to show how hourly rate of pay (y) and years of experience (x) are related.
      Equations may vary.
      Possible equation:
      y = 5.5 + 1.2x
   c. Predict the hourly rate of pay for a person who has 7 years of experience.
      Answers may vary.
      Possible answer: $13.90
   d. Predict the years of experience for a technician who makes $16 an hour.
      about 8.75 years

Lines may vary.

Communicating Mathematics

1. Sample answer: Best-fit lines help to make predictions.

4. Sample answer: Juanita is probably correct because typing speed will eventually level off.

Study the lesson. Then complete the following. 2. See students' work.

1. **Explain** why best-fit lines are helpful.

2. **Make** a scatter plot that shows the relationship between your test scores and the number of hours you do homework for each class you take.

3. **Choose** the scatter plot that has a prediction equation with a positive slope. **c**

a. 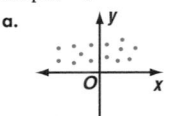 b. 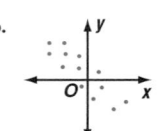 c. 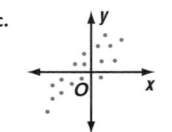 d.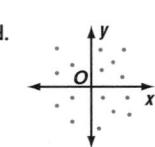

4. **You Decide** Refer to Example 1. Yoki thinks a prediction equation is accurate for values of *e* greater than 25. Juanita thinks a prediction equation probably won't be accurate at those values. Who is correct? Explain your reasoning.

MODELING MATHEMATICS

5. Collect data to determine whether there is any relationship between the circumference of a person's wrist and neck. If so, write a prediction equation for the relationship. **See students' work.**

Guided Practice

In a study of the relationship between the height (*h*), in inches, and the ideal weight (*w*), in pounds, of adult men, a prediction equation is *w* = 5*h* − 187. Predict the ideal weight for each height.

6. 66 inches   **143 lb**   7. 72 inches   **173 lb**   8. 78 inches   **203 lb**

9a. See margin.

9b. $m = \frac{5}{3}$; y-intercept, 17

T.V. Channels

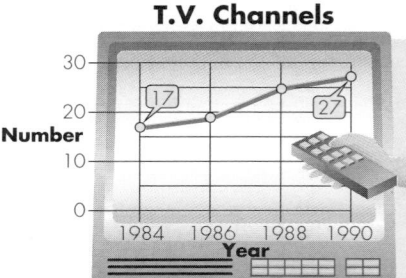

Number

1984   1986   1988   1990
Year

Source: Nielsen Media Research

9. **Television** The graph at the left shows the average number of television stations that were received in U.S. households from 1984 until 1990.
   a. Copy the graph and draw a best-fit line.
   b. Find the slope and y-intercept of a prediction equation.
   c. Predict the average number of television stations that a household will receive in 1999.
      about 42

Applications and Problem Solving

10. **Safety** The graph at the right shows how the percentage of traffic fatalities that were in alcohol-related crashes has decreased from 1982 through 1994. Predict the percentage of fatalities for the year 2000 if this trend continues. **35%**

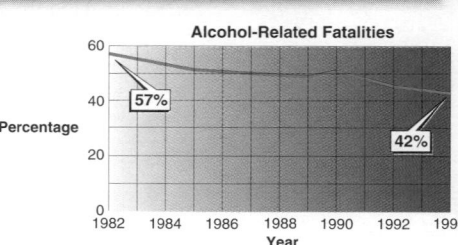

Alcohol-Related Fatalities

Percentage

1982   1984   1986   1988   1990   1992   1994
Year

Source: National Highway Traffic Safety Administration

Reteaching

Using Cooperative Learning Have students work in groups of three. Use the average SAT math and verbal scores in a recent year for seniors in each of the 50 states.

1. Make a scatter plot of average SAT math score (*y*) versus the average SAT verbal score (*x*).

2. Draw a line suggested by the data.
3. Pick two points on the line and find the slope.
4. Find the y-intercept.
5. Write a prediction equation.
6. Predict the math score in any state given its verbal score.

11. Health The table below shows the age and systolic blood pressure for a group of people who recently donated blood.

Age	35	24	48	50	34	55	30	26	41	37
Blood Pressure	128	108	140	135	119	146	132	104	132	121

11b. Sample answer:
$y = \frac{4}{3}x + 76$

11c. Sample answer:
based on the equation for 10b, 148

B

a. Draw a scatter plot to show how age x and systolic blood pressure y are related. **See margin.**
b. Write a prediction equation that relates a person's age to their approximate systolic blood pressure.
c. Find the approximate systolic blood pressure of a person 54 years old.

12. Geography The table below shows elevation and average precipitation for selected cities.

City	Elevation (feet)	Average Precipitation (inches)
Beirut, Lebanon	111	35
London, England	149	23
Paris, France	164	22
Montreal, Canada	187	41
Algiers, Algeria	194	30
Bucharest, Romania	269	23
Warsaw, Poland	294	22
Oslo, Norway	308	27
Rome, Italy	377	30
Toronto, Canada	379	32
Budapest, Hungary	394	24
Moscow, Russia	505	25

13a. Sample answer:
$y = -50x + 226$; see margin for graph.

13c. $4.01

a. Draw a scatter plot to show how elevation e and precipitation p are related. **See margin.**
b. Write a prediction equation. **Sample answer:** $p = -0.04e + 39.44$
c. Check your equation by using the elevation of Dublin, Ireland, which is 155 feet with an average precipitation of 30 inches. **See students' work.**

C

13. Agriculture Farmers will sometimes hold their crops from market until the price goes up to a level they think is satisfactory. The table below records the price per bushel and how many thousand bushels of wheat were sold at that price during a 10-day selling period in Iowa.

Price ($ / bushel)	3.84	3.66	3.87	3.96	3.60	4.05	3.63	3.60	3.72	3.87
Bushels Sold (thousands)	50	47	38	28	49	23	47	46	39	42

a. Draw a scatter plot and find a prediction equation for the data.
b. If the market price of wheat is $3.90/bushel next week, how many bushels of wheat can you predict will be sold? **31,000 bushels**
c. Estimate what the price of wheat was when 25,500 bushels were sold.

Lesson 2–5 *Statistics Modeling Real-World Data Using Scatter Plots* **99**

Extension

Connections Draw six different rectangles. Measure each height and width. Find each perimeter. Plot the perimeter versus the height. Is there a relationship between these numbers?

Additional Answer

13a.

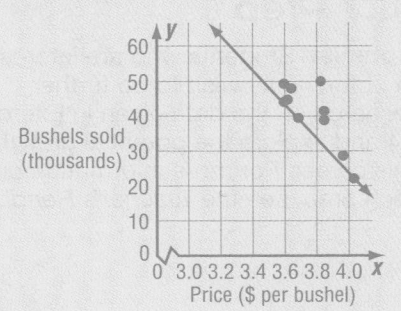

Assignment Guide

Core: 10–19
Enriched: 10–19

For **Extra Practice,** see p. 879.

The red A, B, and C flags, printed only in the Teacher's Wraparound Edition, indicate the level of difficulty of the exercises.

Additional Answers

11a.

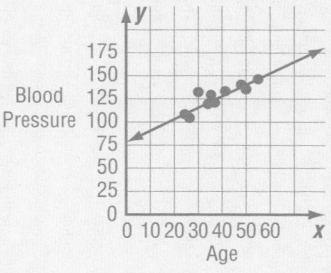

12a.

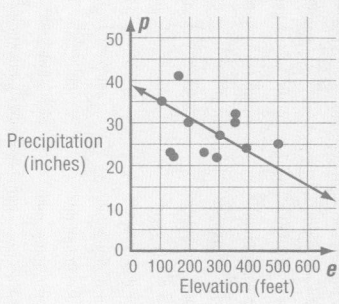

Practice Masters, p. 12

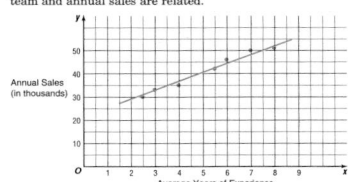

2-5 NAME_____ DATE_____
Practice Student Edition Pages 95–100

Integration: Statistics
Modeling Real-World Data Using Scatter Plots

According to a certain linear prediction equation, a person 25 years old needs 2400 calories of food intake a day. A person 30 years old needs 2300 calories. Let x stand for age in years and y stand for calories.

1. Find the slope of the prediction equation. −20

2. Find the y-intercept of the prediction equation. What does it measure? 2900; the calories needed by a newborn

3. Write the prediction equation. $y = -20x + 2900$

4. Predict the caloric needs of a person who is 34 years old. 2220 calories

The Cody Company ran a study on its sales force and learned that the average number of years of experience for each sales team was in direct relation to annual sales volume. Use the data below to answer the following.

Annual Sales (in thousands)	46	35	51	42	33	50	30
Average Years of Experience	6	4	8	5.5	3	7	2.5

5. Draw a scatter plot to show how years of experience per sales team and annual sales are related.

6. Find a prediction equation to show how years of experience and annual sales are related. Typical answer: $y = 3.6x + 22.2$

Closing Activity

Writing Have students write an explanation as to why best-fit lines are helpful and why they may not be reliable.

Additional Answer

14. One best-fit line may not be accurate enough because the graph "flattens out" at the top and doesn't follow the same pattern as the first part of the graph.

Critical Thinking

14. **Botany** The graph at the right shows the germination rate of batches of bristlecone pine seeds that have been exposed to cold temperatures. Explain why one best-fit line may not be the best solution to finding a prediction equation. **See margin.**

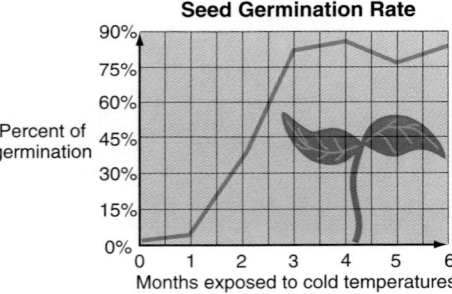

Seed Germination Rate

Percent of germination (y-axis: 0%, 15%, 30%, 45%, 60%, 75%, 90%)

Months exposed to cold temperatures (x-axis: 0 1 2 3 4 5 6)

15. $y = -\frac{1}{3}x + 4$,
$y = 3x - 6,\ y = 3$

Mixed Review

15. Suppose there are three lines in a plane. Line a passes through Quadrants I, II, and IV. Line b passes through Quadrants I, III, and IV. Line c only passes through Quadrants I and II. Line a is perpendicular to Line b. All three lines pass through $(3, 3)$. Given that the slope of Line b is 3, write the equations of the three lines in slope-intercept form. (Lesson 2–4)

16. Find $g(3)$ if $g(x) = -\frac{4x}{2} + 7$. (Lesson 2–1) **1**

17. Solve $|x + 4| > 3$. (Lesson 1–7) $\{x \mid x < -7 \text{ or } x > -1\}$

18. Write an algebraic expression to represent *the sum of a number and its square*. (Lesson 1–4) $x + x^2$

19. Simplify $3(2x + 2) - 2(x - 1)$. (Lesson 1–2) $4x + 8$

WORKING ON THE In·ves·ti·ga·tion

Refer to the Investigation on pages 60–61.

Through the Looking Glass

To determine if their data are characteristic of a species or just random observations, naturalists often plots their observances on a graph such as a scatter plot. Then they look for patterns and draw conclusions from the patterns they observe.

1 Graph the data in your two charts in a single scatter plot. Use different colors for the data from each chart. Let one axis represent the height of the image and let the other axis represent the distance the viewer stood from the wall. Look for a pattern or relationship in the number pairs. How does the distance from the wall compare to the height of the image? Find a mathematical relationship between those two measures. Then explain your findings.

2 Write a function for each scope you used that relates distance from an image and its height. Explain the similarities and differences between the functions. Include a description of a reasonable domain and range in your discussion.

3 How does the size of the scope compare with the other data? Find a ratio between the width and the length of each scope. Explain how the equations relate to the sizes of the scopes.

4 Find two best-fit lines for the points on the scatter plot. How does the ratio for the size of the scope compare to the slope of the corresponding best-fit line? Explain the relationships that exist.

Add the results of your work to your Investigation Folder.

Tech Prep

Botanist Students who are interested in botany may wish to do further research on the data given in Exercise 14 and explore the potential growth of this career. For more information on tech prep, see the *Teacher's Handbook*.

In·ves·ti·ga·tion

Working on the Investigation

The Investigation on pages 60–61 is designed to be a long-term project that is completed over several days or weeks. Encourage students to keep their materials in their Investigation Folder as they work on the Investigation.

Enrichment Masters, p. 12

2-5

NAME _____ DATE _____

Student Edition Pages 95–100

Enrichment

Reading Mathematics

The following paragraph states a result you might be asked to prove in a mathematics course. Parts of the paragraph are numbered.

01 Let n be a positive integer.

02 Also, let $n_1 = s(n_1)$ be the sum of the squares of the digits in n.

03 Then $n_2 = s(n_1)$ is the sum of the squares of the digits of n_1, and $n_3 = s(n_2)$ is the sum of the squares of the digits of n_2.

04 In general, $n_k = s(n_{k-1})$ is the sum of the squares of the digits of n_{k-1}.

05 Consider the sequence: $n, n_1, n_2, n_3, \cdots, n_k, \cdots$.

06 In this sequence either all the terms from some k on have the value 1,

07 or some term, say n_j, has the value 4, so that the eight terms 4, 16, 37, 58, 89, 145, 42, and 20 keep repeating from that point on.

Use the paragraph to answer these questions.

1. Use the sentence in line 01. List the first five values of n.
   1, 2, 3, 4, 5

2. Use 9246 for n and give an example to show the meaning of line 02.
   $n_1 = s(9246) = 137$, because $137 = 81 + 4 + 16 + 36$

3. In line 02, which symbol shows a function? Explain the function in a sentence. $s(n)$; the sum of the squares of the digits of a number is a function of the number

4. For $n = 9246$, find n_2 and n_3 as described in sentence 03.
   $n_2 = 59, n_3 = 106$

5. How do the first four sentences relate to sentence 05?
   They explain how to compute the terms of the sequence.

6. Use $n = 31$ and find the first four terms of the sequence.
   31, 10, 1, 1

7. Which sentence of the paragraph is illustrated by $n = 31$?
   sentence 06

8. Use $n = 61$ and find the first ten terms.
   61, 37, 58, 89, 145, 42, 20, 4, 16, 37

9. Which sentence is illustrated by $n = 61$?
   sentence 07

2–5B Graphing Technology
Lines of Regression

An Extension of Lesson 2–5

You can use a graphing calculator to draw scatter plots and a line that best fits the points in the scatter plot. This line is called a **regression line**. Once you have drawn the regression line, you can use the TRACE feature on the graphing calculator to make predictions about the data.

Example ● **Some scientists believe that global warming is a result of carbon dioxide emissions from fuel consumption. The table below shows world carbon dioxide emissions for 1950–1989. Draw a scatter plot and regression line to show how the year is related to the level of carbon dioxide emissions.**

Year	Emissions (millions of metric tons)
1950	6002
1955	7511
1960	9475
1965	11,556
1970	14,989
1975	16,961
1980	19,287
1985	19,672
1990	22,588

Source: Carbon Dioxide Information Analysis Center, 1992

Let the independent variable be the years since 1940, and let the dependent variable be the emissions. First, set the window parameters. The values of the data suggest a viewing window of [0, 55] by [5000, 25000] with Xscl = 5 and Yscl = 1000.

Next, enter the data. Press $\boxed{\text{STAT}}$ 1 to display lists for storing data.

If old data has previously been stored, enter $\boxed{\text{STAT}}$ 1 $\boxed{\blacktriangle}$ $\boxed{\text{CLEAR}}$ $\boxed{\text{ENTER}}$ $\boxed{\blacktriangleright}$ $\boxed{\blacktriangle}$ $\boxed{\text{CLEAR}}$ $\boxed{\text{ENTER}}$ to clear the lists. The years will be entered into column L1.

Enter: 10 $\boxed{\text{ENTER}}$ 15 $\boxed{\text{ENTER}}$ 20 $\boxed{\text{ENTER}}$ ... 50 $\boxed{\text{ENTER}}$

Use $\boxed{\blacktriangleright}$ to move the cursor to column L2 to enter carbon dioxide emissions.

Enter: 6002 $\boxed{\text{ENTER}}$ 7511 $\boxed{\text{ENTER}}$ 9475 $\boxed{\text{ENTER}}$ ... 22588 $\boxed{\text{ENTER}}$

We are now ready to draw the scatter plot.

Enter: $\boxed{\text{2nd}}$ $\boxed{\substack{\text{STAT}\\\text{PLOT}}}$ 1 $\boxed{\text{ENTER}}$ $\boxed{\blacktriangledown}$ $\boxed{\text{ENTER}}$ $\boxed{\blacktriangledown}$ $\boxed{\text{ENTER}}$ $\boxed{\blacktriangledown}$ $\boxed{\blacktriangleright}$ $\boxed{\text{ENTER}}$ $\boxed{\blacktriangledown}$ $\boxed{\text{ENTER}}$ $\boxed{\text{GRAPH}}$

(continued on the next page)

2-5B LESSON NOTES

NCTM Standards: 1–6

Objective
Use a graphing calculator to graph lines of regression.

Recommended Time
25 minutes

Instructional Resources
Graphing Calculator Masters, pp. 23 and 24

These masters provide keystroking instruction for this lesson for the TI-81 and Casio graphing calculators.

1 FOCUS

Motivating the Lesson
Plot the values in the chart on page 101 by hand. Then ask students what the best possible line is that would represent those points. Have some of the students draw an estimate. Then keep this and compare it to the one the calculator draws.

2 TEACH

Teaching Tip Point out to students that the regression line is an approximation of the data.

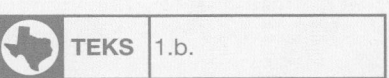

TEKS | 1.b.

Assignment Guide

Core: 1–3
Enriched: 1–3

Additional Answers

1.
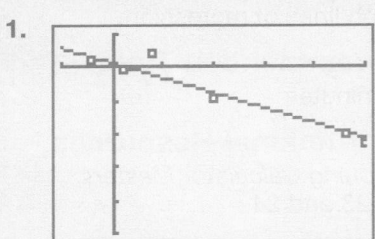

2.
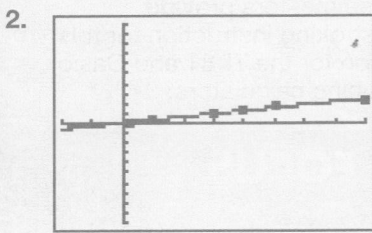

3a.
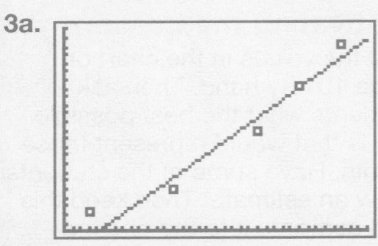

3b.
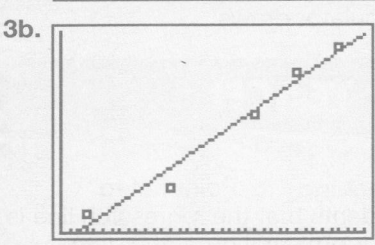

3c. The women's average income since 1950 has increased at a greater rate than the men's; however, the men's average income was greater than the women's in 1950 and remained greater in 1990.

Observing students working with technology is an excellent method of assessment.

Next, graph the equation for the regression line.

Enter: STAT ▶ 5 2nd L1
, 2nd L2 ENTER Y=
VARS 5 ▶ ▶ 7
GRAPH

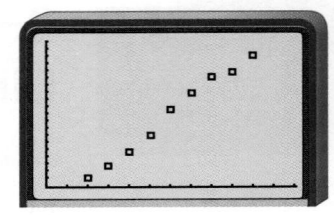

The TRACE feature allows you to move a cursor along the graph or scatter plot and read the coordinates of the points. Press TRACE and any of the arrow keys to observe what happens. Approximately what would you expect the carbon dioxide emissions to have been in 1971?

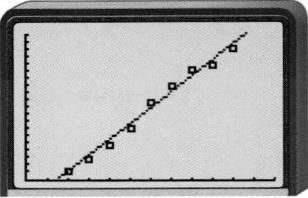

EXERCISES

Use a graphing calculator to draw a scatter plot and a regression line for the data in each table. 1–2. See margin.

1.

x	−2	1	4	10	23	25
y	1	−0.5	2	−4.5	−10	−11.5

2.

x	0.2	1	3	4	5	8
y	0.11	0.31	0.9	1.25	1.75	2.3

3. **Employment** The table below shows the average yearly incomes (in dollars) of men and women in the United States. a–c. See margin.

Year	1960	1970	1980	1985	1990
Women	3257	5323	11,197	15,624	19,822
Men	5368	8966	18,612	24,195	27,678

Source: *The 1993 Information Please Almanac*

a. Use a graphing calculator to draw a scatter plot and regression line to show how the year is related to women's salaries for 1960 to 1990. Let the independent variable be the years since 1950, and let the dependent variables be the incomes. Predict the average salary for women in the year 2000.
b. Repeat part a with the men's salaries.
c. Compare and contrast the data in the two scatter plots.

102 Chapter 2 Graphing Linear Relations and Functions

Using Technology

This lesson offers an excellent opportunity for using technology in your algebra classroom. For more information on using technology, see *Graphing Calculators in the Mathematics Classroom*, one of the titles in the Glencoe Mathematics Professional Series.

Special Functions

2-6

What YOU'LL LEARN

- To identify and graph special functions.

Why IT'S IMPORTANT

You can use functions to explore relations in technology and finance.

Of course, you know that the formula $C = \pi d$ describes the relationship between the diameter and circumference of a circle. Notice that the slope, 3.32, is close to π.

INTEGRATION
Geometry

Rebeca's little brother, Jorge, was doing a project for his mathematics class in which he measured the diameter and circumference of several circular objects. The data are shown below.

Diameter (centimeters)	4.8	10.5	17.3	23.8	25.0
Circumference (centimeters)	15.4	31.5	54.1	75.2	79.1

Rebeca helped Jorge graph the data, and it appeared to be a linear function. Using the points (10.5, 31.5) and (17.3, 54.1), the slope of the prediction equation is about 3.32. It appears that the *y*-intercept is the origin.

Whenever a linear function in the form $y = mx + b$ has $b = 0$ and $m \neq 0$, the function is called a **direct variation.** In this situation, the circumference varies directly as the diameter. In other words, as the diameter gets larger, the circumference also gets larger.

There are other special cases of linear functions. Two of these, the **constant function** and the **identity function** are shown below.

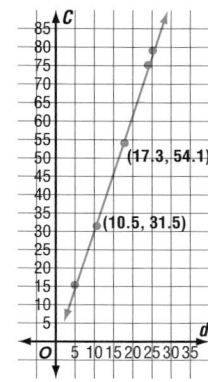

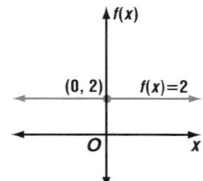

constant function
$m = 0$

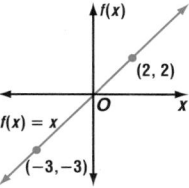

identity function
$m = 1, b = 0$

Step functions like the ones shown below are also related to linear functions. The open circle means that the point is *not* included in the graph.

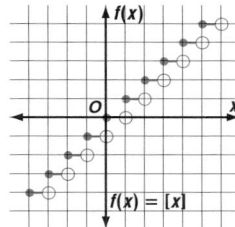

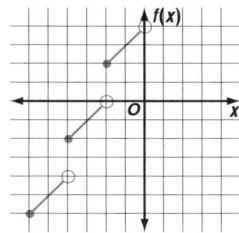

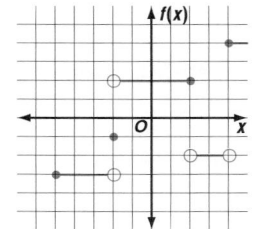

Lesson 2–6 Special Functions **103**

CAREER CHOICES

A **financial planner** helps clients plan how to make the most from their money. In their careers, they frequently translate data into various graphical forms.

For more information, contact:

American Economics Association
1313 21st Ave.
Nashville, TN 37212

CAREER CHOICES

Circle graphs are often used to represent the percentage of a budget that is spent on each item in the budget. Bar graphs are often used to represent number of items sold each month of a given year.

2-6 LESSON NOTES

NCTM Standards: 1–6

Instructional Resources

- Study Guide Master 2-6
- Practice Master 2-6
- Enrichment Master 2-6
- Assessment and Evaluation Masters, p. 45
- Modeling Mathematics Masters, p. 62
- Multicultural Activity Masters, p. 4
- Real-World Applications, 6

Transparency 2-6A contains the 5-Minute Check for this lesson; **Transparency 2-6B** contains a teaching aid for this lesson.

Recommended Pacing	
Standard Pacing	Days 9 & 10 of 14
Honors Pacing	Day 9 of 13
Block Scheduling*	Day 5 of 7

*For more information on pacing and possible lesson plans, refer to the Block Scheduling Booklet.

1 FOCUS

5-Minute Check
(over Lesson 2-5)

A certain prediction equation says that if the average temperature outside is 22°F, then the cost of fuel for a household is $50 for a month. If the temperature averages 15°F, then the average cost for fuel is $64 per month.

1. Find the slope of the prediction equation. -2
2. Find the *y*-intercept of the prediction equation. 94
3. Find the prediction equation. $f(t) = -2t + 94$
4. Predict the cost for fuel if the temperature averages 11°F for the month. $72

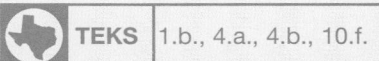

TEKS | 1.b., 4.a., 4.b., 10.f.

Situational Problem Have students find the speeds for the last 10 winners of the Indianapolis 500. Have students determine the time it took to drive the race (excluding time for pit stops). Discuss the relationship between rate, time, and distance.

2 TEACH

Teaching Tip For Example 1, have students look for a pattern in the graph of the greatest integer function. Emphasize that students need to use elements of the domain that are not integers when sketching the graph.

In-Class Example

For Example 1
The price of aluminum given by a recycling center is based on weight. If the aluminum weighs more than 0 pounds but less than or equal to 1 pound, there is no payment. If the aluminum weighs more than 1 pound but less than or equal to 2 pounds, the price is $2.00. For each additional pound, the price of aluminum increases $1.00. Graph the function that describes this relationship.

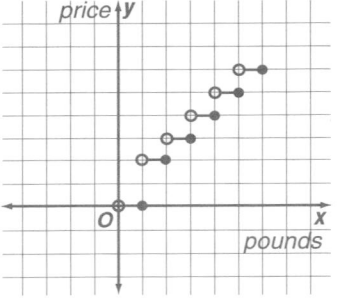

One type of step function is the **greatest integer function.** The symbol [x] means *the greatest integer not greater than x*. For example, [7.3] = 7 and [−1.5] = −2 because −1 > −1.5. The greatest integer function is given by f(x) = [x]. Its graph is the first step function graph shown on the previous page.

The graphs of step functions are often used to model real-world problems.

Example 1

APPLICATION
Postal Service

When you go to the post office to mail a first-class letter, you may need to ask the clerk how much it will cost to mail it—that is, how much postage is required. In 1995, first-class mail cost 32¢ for the first ounce and 23¢ for each additional ounce. So if your letter weighed one ounce or less, it cost you 32¢ to mail. A letter weighing 1.1 ounces cost 32 + 23 or 55¢ to mail. Graph the function that describes the relationship between the number of ounces and the cost of postage.

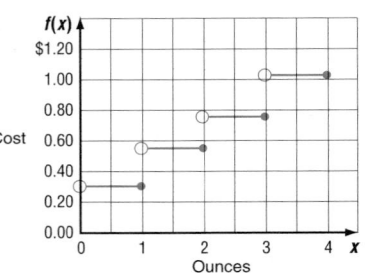

The equation that describes this function is $f(x) = 0.32 + 0.23[x - 0.1]$, where x is the number of ounces.

Make a table of values to help you draw the graph.

x	0.32 + 0.23[x − 0.1]	f(x)
0.1	0.32 + 0	0.32
0.7	0.32 + 0	0.32
1.0	0.32 + 0	0.32
1.5	0.32 + 0.23(1)	0.55
1.9	0.32 + 0.23(1)	0.55
2.0	0.32 + 0.23(1)	0.55
2.3	0.32 + 0.23(2)	0.78
2.8	0.32 + 0.23(2)	0.78
3.0	0.32 + 0.23(2)	0.78
3.2	0.32 + 0.23(3)	1.01

Another function that is closely related to linear functions is the **absolute value function.** Consider $f(x) = |x|$ or $y = |x|$. Look for a pattern when studying the values in the chart.

LOOK BACK

You can refer to Lesson 1-5 for information about absolute value equations.

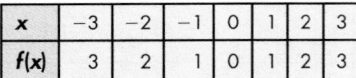

x	−3	−2	−1	0	1	2	3
f(x)	3	2	1	0	1	2	3

You can see that when x is positive or zero, the absolute value function looks like the graph of y = x. When x is negative, the absolute value function looks like the graph of y = −x.

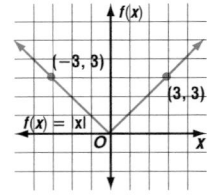

Classroom Vignette

"Students can use a TI-82 graphing calculator to graph absolute value functions and step functions. To graph the greatest integer function, press [MODE], select DOT, press [Y=], press [MATH], select NUM, press 4, enter the function, and press [GRAPH]."

Martha Britton

Martha Britton
Cabell Midland High School
Ona, West Virginia

Example **2** Graph $f(x) = |x| + 2$ and $g(x) = 3|x| + 2$ on the same coordinate plane. Determine the similarities and differences in the two graphs.

Find several ordered pairs for each function.

x	$|x| + 2$
−2	4
−1	3
0	2
1	3
2	4

→

x	$3|x| + 2$
−2	8
−1	5
0	2
1	5
2	8

Graph the points and connect them. Both graphs have the same *y*-intercept. The graph of $g(x) = 3|x| + 2$ is narrower than the graph of $f(x) = |x| + 2$.

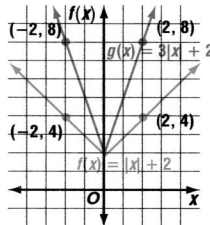

Recall that families of graphs are groups of graphs that display one or more similar characteristics. Graphs of absolute value functions may also display similar characteristics.

EXPLORATION   GRAPHING CALCULATORS

When a linear equation is written in the form $y = mx + b$, m is the slope, and b is the *y*-intercept. In this Exploration, you will use a graphing calculator to investigate absolute value functions of the form $y = a|x|$.
The parent graph of most families of absolute value functions is the graph of $y = |x|$.

Your Turn

a. Graph $y = |x|$, $y = 2|x|$, $y = 3|x|$, and $y = 5|x|$ on the same screen.

b. Describe this family of graphs. What pattern do you see?

c. In $y = mx + b$, as m increases, the slope of the line also increases. Describe how the graph of $y = a|x|$ changes as a increases.

d. Write an absolute value function whose graph is between the graphs of $y = 2|x|$ and $y = 3|x|$.

e. Graph $y = |x|$ and $y = -|x|$ on the same screen. Then graph $y = 2|x|$ and $y = -2|x|$ on the same screen.

f. Describe this family of graphs. What pattern do you see?

g. In a linear equation $y = mx + b$ with $m < 0$, the line falls to the right. Describe how the graph of $y = a|x|$ changes when $a < 0$.

h. Write an absolute value function whose graph opens down.

b. The graphs go through the origin; the graphs become narrower.

c. The graph becomes narrower.

f. The graphs reflect over the *x*-axis.

g. If $a < 0$, the graph opens down.

h. Sample answer: $y = -4|x|$

In-Class Example

For Example 2
Graph $f(x) = |x + 2|$ and $f(x) = |x| + 2$ on the same plane.

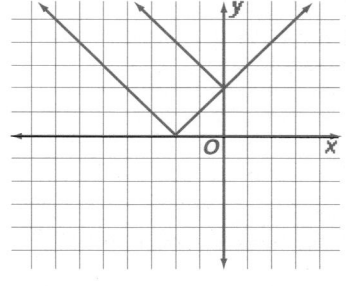

EXPLORATION

Students might mistakenly assume that the ranges of these functions comprise only positive values. However, since *a* and *b* can be negative, this is not the case.

Classroom Vignette

"I like to take the students to our computer lab to use DERIVE software. For this lesson, students can graph and compare various equations, such as $y = |x|$, $y = 2|x|$, $y = |x - 2|$, $y = |x| - 1$, $y = \dfrac{|x|}{2}$, and $y = |3x|$."

Charlotte P. Duis

Charlotte Duis
Brookville High School
Lynchburg, Virginia

Check for Understanding

Exercises 1–12 are designed to help you assess your students' understanding through reading, writing, speaking, and modeling. You should work through Exercises 1–5 with your students and then monitor their work on Exercises 6–12.

Assignment Guide

Core: 13–45 odd, 47–54
Enriched: 14–42 even, 43–54

For **Extra Practice,** see p. 880.

The red A, B, and C flags, printed only in the Teacher's Wraparound Edition, indicate the level of difficulty of the exercises.

Additional Answer

5. The graphs have the same shape but different y-intercepts. The graph of $f(x) = |x|$ has its vertex at the origin; the graph of $f(x) = |x| - 2$ has its vertex at $(0, -2)$.

Study Guide Masters, p. 13

2-6

NAME_____ DATE_____

Student Edition
Pages 103–108

Study Guide

Special Functions

Some linear functions have special names and special graphs.

Function	Written as	Graph
constant	$y = b$ or $f(x) = b$	horizontal line
direct variation	$y = mx$ or $f(x) = mx$ where $m \neq 0$	passes through origin
absolute value	$y = |x|$ or $f(x) = |x|$	mirror image
greatest integer	$f(x) = [x]$	one-unit horizontal segments (right endpoints missing) arranged like steps

Identify each function as constant, direct variation, absolute value, or greatest integer function. Then graph each function.

1. $f(x) = 2[x]$

2. $f(x) = 2$

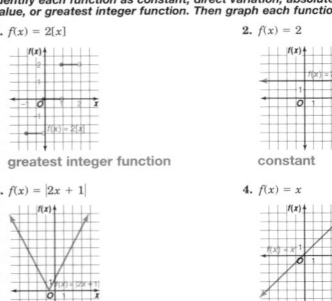

greatest integer function

constant

3. $f(x) = |2x + 1|$

4. $f(x) = x$

absolute value

direct variation

5. $r(x) = |2x|$

6. $f(x) = [x - \frac{1}{2}]$

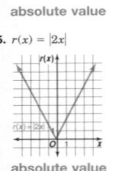

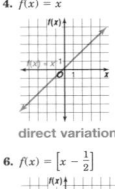

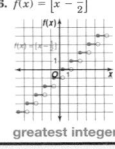

absolute value

greatest integer

CHECK FOR UNDERSTANDING

Communicating Mathematics

1. 3.32 is close to π due to measurement error and rounding.

3. $[-4.1] = -5$ instead of -4 because $-4 > -4.1$.

4. One part of the graph is a reflection of the other.

Study the lesson. Then complete the following.

1. **Explain** why the slope was not 3.14 in the application at the beginning of the lesson.

2. **Choose** which function is a direct variation. **d**
   a. $f(x) = 4$ b. $y = -3$ c. $y = |x| + 2$ d. $f(x) = 5x$

3. **Explain** why the value of $[4.3]$ is 4, but the value of $[-4.3]$ is -5.

4. **Describe** the pattern for graphing an absolute value function.

5. **Compare and contrast** the graphs of $f(x) = |x|$ and $f(x) = |x| - 2$. See margin.

Guided Practice

Identify each function as C for constant, D for direct variation, A for absolute value, or G for greatest integer function. Then graph each function. 6–9. See Solutions Manual for graphs.

6. $f(x) = |3x - 2|$ **A**

7. $g(x) = -[x]$ **G**

8. $f(x) = 2x$ **D**

9. $h(x) = 0.5$ **C**

10. If $g(x) = |x - 5|$, find $g(4)$. **1**

11. If $f(x) = 2[x - 1]$, find $f(6.9)$. **10**

12. **Business** The Fix-It Auto Repair Shop has a sign in the Service Department that states that the labor costs are $35 per hour or any fraction thereof. What type of function does this relationship represent? **step function**

EXERCISES

Practice

If $h(x) = [2x + 3]$, find each value.

13. $h(2)$ **7**

14. $h(-2)$ **−1**

15. $h(-2.3)$ **−2**

16. $h\left(\frac{1}{4}\right)$ **3**

Identify each function as C for constant, D for direct variation, A for absolute value, or G for greatest integer function. Then graph each function. 17–28. See Solutions Manual for graphs.

17. $h(x) = x$ **D**

18. $f(x) = |2x|$ **A**

19. $g(x) = -3$ **C**

20. $f(x) = [2x + 1]$ **G**

21. $f(x) = \left|x - \frac{1}{4}\right|$ **A**

22. $f(x) = -\frac{2}{3}x$ **D**

23. $f(x) = x + 3$ **D**

24. $f(x) = |x + 3|$ **A**

25. $f(x) = [x + 3]$ **G**

26. $g(x) = |x| + 3$ **A**

27. $g(x) = [x] + 3$ **G**

28. $g(x) = 3|x|$ **A**

Graph each pair of equations on the same coordinate plane. Discuss the similarities and differences in the two graphs.

29–36. See Solutions Manual.

29. $y = |x + 2|, y = |x - 2|$

30. $y = |x| + 4, y = |x| - 4$

31. $y = |x + 2|, y = |x + 2| - 1$

32. $y = 2[x], y = [2x]$

33. $y = [x + 5], y = [x] + 5$

34. $y = |2x|, y = 2|x|$

35. $y = -2|4x|, y = 4|-2x|$

36. $y = -3[x], y = [-3x]$

Reteaching

Decision Making Identify each function as C for constant, D for direct variation, A for absolute value, G for greatest integer, or I for identity. Then graph each function.

1. $f(x) = 0.5x - 1$ **D**
2. $g(x) = -3$ **C**
3. $h(x) = x$ **I**
4. $j(x) = [x + 2]$ **G**
5. $k(x) = 1 - |x - 2|$ **A**

1–3.

4.

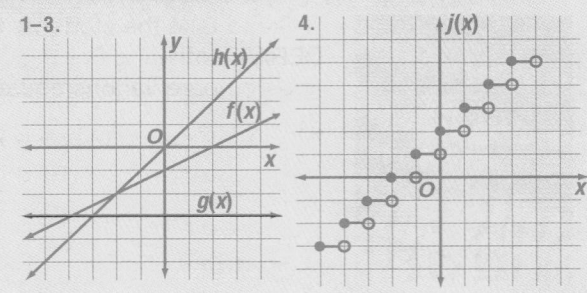

Graph each equation.   37–40. See Solutions Manual.

37. $y = [|x|]$ **38.** $y = |[x]|$ **39.** $y = x - [x]$ **40.** $y = x + |x|$

41–42. See margin for graphs.

Graphing Calculator   Use a graphing calculator to solve each equation graphically.

41. $|2x - 4| = 6$ $x = -1$ or 5 **42.** $|x + 2| = 4$ $x = 2$ or -6

Critical Thinking   **43.** Compare and contrast the graphs of $y = |x|$ and $|y| = x$. Identify the domain and range of each.   See margin.

Applications and Problem Solving

44. Technology   The graph at the right shows the number of CD-ROM multimedia software packages shipped since 1991.

CD-Rom Software Packages

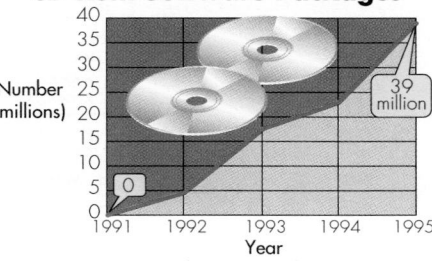

Source: Information and Interactive Services Report, Dataquest

  a. Write an equation to represent a best-fit line for this graph.
  b. What type of function does this relationship represent?   **direct variation**
  c. Predict the number of software packages that will be shipped in 1999.   **78 million**

45. Transportation   When the Westerville North boy's basketball team went to the Ohio state tournament, the school chartered buses so that the student body could attend the games. Each bus held a maximum of 60 students.
  a. Make a graph that shows the relationship between the number of students that went to the game by bus x and the number of buses that were needed y.   **See margin.**
  b. What type of function does this relationship represent?   **step function**

46. Finance   Lupe earns $5.25 per hour working at a video store after school. About 25% of her earnings are taken out for taxes and other deductions.
  a. Write an equation that shows the relationship between the number of hours worked per week and Lupe's take-home pay. $y = 3.94x$
  b. About how many hours will Lupe need to work to take home $100?
  c. What type of function does this relationship represent?   **direct variation**

44a. Sample answer:
$y = 9.75x$
46b. about 25 hours

Mixed Review

47a. See Solutions Manual.

47. Smoking   The chart at the right shows the percent of people ages 20 to 24 who smoked for selected years.   (Lesson 2–5)
  a. Draw a scatter plot and find a prediction equation for the data.
  b. Estimate what percent of the population in this age group will be smoking by the year 2000, if current trends continue.   **20%**

Year	People Ages 20–24 Who Smoke
1965	47.8%
1970	41.5
1974	39.6
1976	39.6
1978	35.3
1979	35.9
1980	36.1
1983	36.9
1985	31.8
1987	29.5
1988	27.6
1993	25.0

Lesson 2–6   Special Functions   **107**

Additional Answers

41.

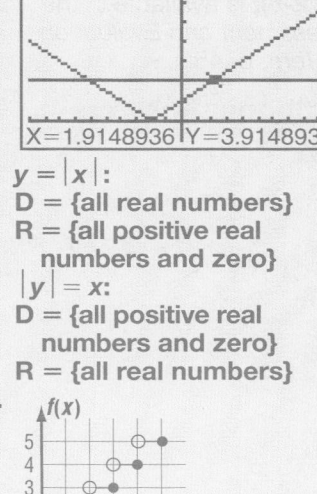

X=5.0212766 Y=6.0425532

42.

X=1.9148936 Y=3.9148936

43. $y = |x|$:
D = {all real numbers}
R = {all positive real numbers and zero}
$|y| = x$:
D = {all positive real numbers and zero}
R = {all real numbers}

45a.

Practice Masters, p. 13

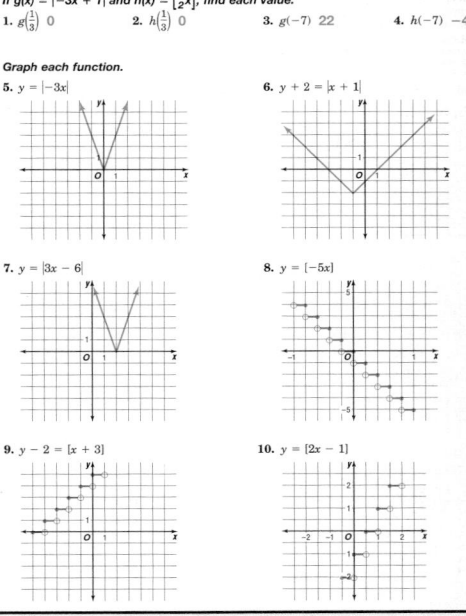

2-6 **Practice**

NAME_____ DATE_____

Student Edition
Pages 103–10

Special Functions

If $g(x) = |-3x + 1|$ and $h(x) = \left[\frac{1}{2}x\right]$, find each value.

1. $g\left(\frac{1}{3}\right)$ 0   **2.** $h\left(\frac{1}{3}\right)$ 0   **3.** $g(-7)$ 22   **4.** $h(-7)$ -4

Graph each function.

5. $y = |-3x|$ **6.** $y + 2 = |x + 1|$

7. $y = |3x - 6|$ **8.** $y = [-5x]$

9. $y - 2 = [x + 3]$ **10.** $y = [2x - 1]$

Reteaching (cont.)

5.

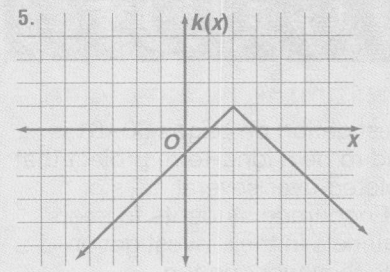

Cooperative Learning

Group Discussion   Separate students into groups of four. Each group is to find five examples of step functions in the real world. For more information on the group discussion strategy, see *Cooperative Learning in the Mathematics Classroom*, one of the titles in the Glencoe Mathematics Professional Series, page 31.

Chapter 2   **107**

Closing Activity

Speaking Have students explain the absolute value function. How can it translate up and down on the *y*-axis? How can it translate left and right on the *x*-axis?

Chapter 2, Quiz C (Lessons 2-5 and 2-6), is available in the *Assessment and Evaluation Masters*, p. 45.

Additional Answers

49.

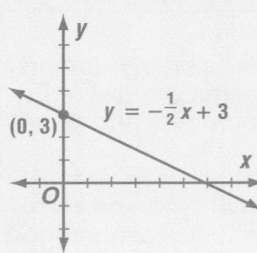

$y = -\frac{1}{2}x + 3$

(0, 3)

50.

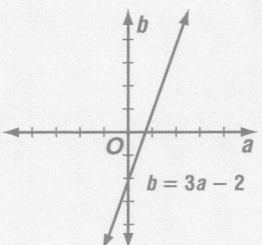

$b = 3a - 2$

Enrichment Masters, p. 13

Enrichment 2-6

NAME_____ DATE_____

Student Edition Pages 103–108

Graphs of Functions that Use [x]

You may find it interesting to explore some of the unusual graphs that result by making use of the greatest integer function. When you graph these functions, use a colored pen or pencil. You will probably find it helpful to make a chart of values for each function.

Graph each function.

1. $y = 2x - [x]$

2. $y = \frac{[x]}{[x]}$

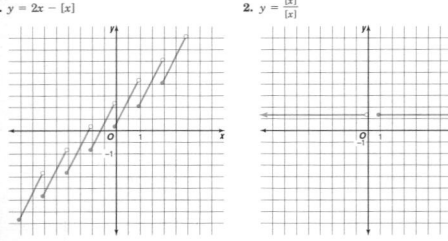

3. $y = \frac{[0.5x + 1]}{[0.5x + 1]}$

4. $y = \frac{x}{[x]}$

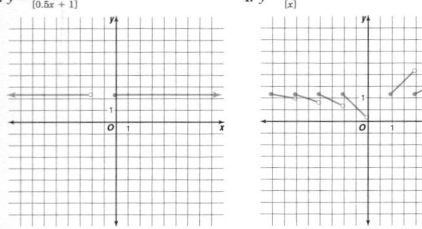

48. $y = \frac{2}{3}x - 9$

52. $\left\{ y \mid y > \frac{5}{6} \right\}$

48. Write an equation in slope-intercept form for the line with slope $\frac{2}{3}$ that passes through $(6, -5)$. (Lesson 2–4)

49. Graph a line that passes through $(0, 3)$ and is perpendicular to the line $y - 2x = 4$. (Lesson 2–3) **See margin.**

50. Graph $b = 3a - 2$. (Lesson 2–2) **See margin.**

51. Find $h(-1)$ if $h(x) = \frac{x^2 + 2x - 5}{x^2 - 2}$. (Lesson 2–1) **6**

52. Solve $28 - 6y < 23$. (Lesson 1–6)

53. Statistics Use the line plot below to answer each question. (Lesson 1–3)

Number of Morning Newspapers (States and D.C.)

a. What is the greatest number of newspapers in one state? **51**
b. What is the least number of newspapers in one state? **1**
c. How many states have 10 to 20 newspapers? **16**
d. How many newspapers do most states have? **5 or 11**

54. Simplify $3 + \{8 \div [9 - 2(4)]\}$. (Lesson 1–1) **11**

WORKING ON THE

In·ves·ti·ga·tion

Refer to the Investigation on pages 60–61.

Through the Looking Glass

Many species react when an invader to their territory comes too close. They often become defensive and may attack. So, it is often handy for naturalists to have equipment, such as a scope, to observe animals from a distance without creating a threat to the animal or to the naturalist's safety.

1 Select one of the scopes that you used in your experiment. Suppose you were 60 feet from a giraffe and the animal's image exactly filled the viewer. How tall would the giraffe be?

2 Using a second scope that was a different size than your first scope, how would the image of the giraffe change when looking through the second tube? Where would you need to stand to see the entire image of the giraffe fill the view of the second scope? Can you see the same image if you are standing in the same location and looking through two view tubes of different sizes?

3 Explain the methods you discovered for determining heights using the view tubes. Analyze those methods and discuss your findings in writing.

Add the results of your work to your Investigation Folder.

Extension

Reasoning Use the greatest integer function to write a function that rounds any number to the nearest integer.
$f(x) = [x + 0.5]$

In·ves·ti·ga·tion

Working on the Investigation

The Investigation on pages 60–61 is designed to be a long-term project that is completed over several days or weeks. Encourage students to keep their materials in their Investigation Folder as they work on the Investigation.

2–7A Graphing Technology
Linear Inequalities

A Preview of Lesson 2–7

You can graph inequalities with a graphing calculator by using the Shade(command located in the DRAW menu. You must enter *two* functions to activate the shading. The first function defines the lower boundary of the region to be shaded. The second function defines the upper boundary of the region. The calculator will graph both functions and shade between the two. If the inequality is "$y \leq$", you can use the Ymin window value as the lower boundary since the points that satisfy the inequality are below the graph of the related equation. If the inequality is "$y \geq$", you can use the Ymax window value as the upper boundary since the points that satisfy the inequality are above the graph of the related function.

Before using the Shade(option, be sure to clear equations stored in the Y = list.

Example

Graph $y \geq 3x - 2$ in the standard viewing window.

The inequality asks for points where y is greater than or equal to $3x - 2$, so we will use Ymax, or 10, as the upper boundary and $3x - 2$ as the lower boundary. This will shade all points on the graphics screen between $y = 3x - 2$ and $y = 10$.

Enter:  ZOOM 6 2nd DRAW 7
3 X,T,θ − 2 , 10
) ENTER

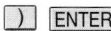

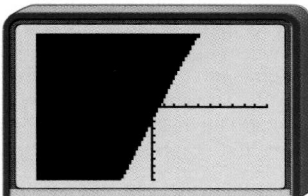

Since both the *x*- and *y*-intercepts of the line $y = 3x - 2$ are within the current viewing window, the graph of the inequality is complete.

EXERCISES

Use a graphing calculator to graph each inequality. Then sketch your graph on a sheet of paper. 1–9. See Solutions Manual.

1. $y \geq 3$
2. $y \geq x + 2$
3. $y \leq -2x - 4$
4. $y > \frac{1}{3}x + 7$
5. $y \geq \frac{1}{2}x - 3$
6. $x - 7 \leq y$
7. $y + 1 \leq 0.5x$
8. $y - 3 > -2x$
9. $2 \geq x - 2y$

Lesson 2–7A Graphing Technology: Linear Inequalities **109**

Using Technology
This lesson offers an excellent opportunity for using technology in your algebra classroom. For more information on using technology, see *Graphing Calculators in the Mathematics Classroom*, one of the titles in the Glencoe Mathematics Professional Series.

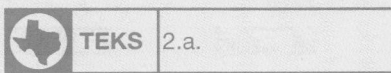 TEKS 2.a.

2-7A LESSON NOTES

NCTM Standards: 1–5

Objective
Use a graphing calculator to graph linear inequalities.

Recommended Time
15 minutes

Instructional Resources
Graphing Calculator Masters, pp. 25 and 26

These masters provide keystroking instruction for this lesson for the TI-81 and Casio graphing calculators.

1 FOCUS

Motivating the Lesson
Remind students that if one point above the graph of the line $y = 3x - 2$ satisfies the inequality $y > 3x - 2$, then all points above the line satisfy it.

2 TEACH

Teaching Tip Remind students that a graphing calculator cannot graph vertical lines that are of the form $x = a$ because this cannot be written in slope-intercept form.

3 PRACTICE/APPLY

Assignment Guide
Core: 1–9
Enriched: 1–9

4 ASSESS

Observing students working with technology is an excellent method of assessment.

NCTM Standards: 1–5

Instructional Resources

- Study Guide Master 2-7
- Practice Master 2-7
- Enrichment Master 2-7
- Assessment and Evaluation Masters, p. 45

 Transparency 2-7A contains the 5-Minute Check for this lesson; **Transparency 2-7B** contains a teaching aid for this lesson.

Recommended Pacing	
Standard Pacing	Day 12 of 14
Honors Pacing	Day 11 of 13
Block Scheduling*	Day 6 of 7

 *For more information on pacing and possible lesson plans, refer to the *Block Scheduling Booklet*.

1 FOCUS

 5-Minute Check
(over Lesson 2-6)

Identify each type of function.

1. $y = |2x|$ absolute value
2. $g(x) = [2x]$ greatest integer
3. $f(x) = 2x$ direct variation
4. Graph $f(x) = |x - 1|$.

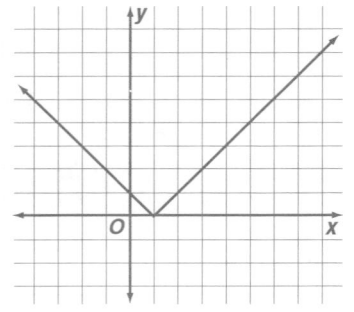

Motivating the Lesson

Questioning Have students graph an equation such as $y = -2x + 4$. Select a point above the line. How does this point relate to the points on the line?

Linear Inequalities

 **YOU'LL LEARN**

- To draw graphs of inequalities in two variables.

Why IT'S IMPORTANT

You can use inequalities to solve problems involving manufacturing and shopping.

In 1994, over 600 million CDs and 345 million cassettes were sold!

APPLICATION
Shopping

In 1978, the Sony Corporation revolutionized the music industry when it introduced its portable cassette player, the Walkman. In effect, this marked the end of records as a means to enjoy music. Today, CDs are the most popular format for recorded music.

Suppose you have $35 to spend and want to purchase some cassettes that cost $7 and some CDs that cost $14. If c represents the number of cassettes, and d represents the number of CDs, the equation $7c + 14d = 35$ describes the different ways for you to spend *exactly* $35. The graph at the right shows all of the ordered pairs that are solutions of the equation $7c + 14d = 35$. One solution is (3, 1).

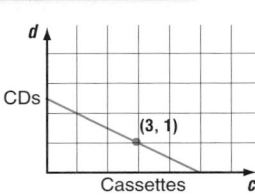

However, when you're shopping, it's not necessary to spend exactly $35. You want to spend *at most* $35. You know that if you spend *more than* $35, you won't have enough money left to go out with your friends. These situations can be represented by the linear inequalities $7c + 14d \le 35$ and $7c + 14d > 35$, respectively. The graph of $7c + 14d = 35$ separates the coordinate plane into two regions. The line is called the *boundary* of the regions. To graph an inequality, first graph the boundary and then determine which region to shade.

The graph of $7c + 14d \le 35$ contains points for which the cost of the cassettes and CDs is less than or equal to 35. For example, the ordered pair (2, 1) is in the shaded region and therefore, is one of the solutions. Note that the boundary is a solid line. If the inequality uses the symbols $\le$ or $\ge$, the boundary is solid to show that it is included.

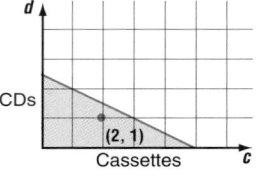

The graph of $7c + 14d > 35$ contains points for which the cost of the cassettes and CDs is greater than $35. For example, the ordered pair (3, 2) is in the shaded region and therefore, is one of the solutions. Note that the boundary is a dashed line. If the inequality uses the symbols $<$ or $>$, the boundary is dashed to show that it is *not* included.

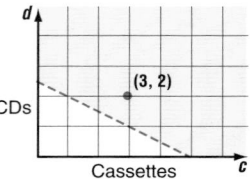

110   *Chapter 7   Graphing Linear Relations and Functions*

With the advancements in technology and better sound quality, CDs are quickly replacing cassettes, which in turn replaced the records before them.

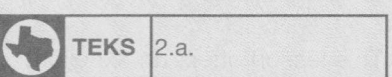 **TEKS** 2.a.

You can graph an inequality by following these steps.

1. Graph the boundary. Determine whether it should be solid or dashed.
2. Test a point in each region.
3. Shade the region whose ordered pair results in a true inequality.

Example **Graph $2y - 3x \leq 6$.**

The boundary will be the graph of $2y - 3x = 6$. Let's use intercepts to graph the boundary more easily.

x-intercept	*y-intercept*
$2(0) - 3x = 6$	$2y - 3(0) = 6$
$-3x = 6$	$2y = 6$
$x = -2$	$y = 3$

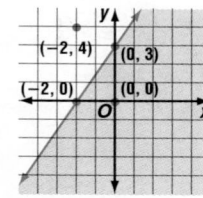

Since the inequality is "less than or equal to," draw a solid line connecting the two intercepts. This is the boundary.

Try to test the origin because it is easy to substitute 0 for x and y.

Now test a point in each region.

Try $(0, 0)$.   Try $(-2, 4)$.

$2(0) - 3(0) \leq 6$ $2(4) - 3(-2) \leq 6$

     $0 \leq 6$ true $8 - (-6) \leq 6$

                              $14 \leq 6$ false

The region that contains $(0, 0)$ should be shaded.

Sometimes inequalities contain absolute value. When this occurs, you must consider that the expression within the absolute value bars may be positive *or* negative.

Example **Graph $y > |x| - 2$.**

This absolute value function has two conditions to consider.

when $x < 0$	*when $x \geq 0$*
$y > -x - 2$	and $y > x - 2$

Graph each inequality for the specified values of x. The lines will be dashed.

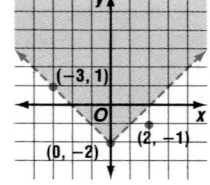

When one ordered pair results in a true inequality, it is not necessary to test a point in the other region.

Test $(0, 0)$.

$y > |x| - 2$

$0 > |0| - 2$ *Note that the boundary is <u>not</u> included.*

$0 > -2$ true

The shaded region should include $(0, 0)$.

Teaching Tip You may want students to test two points in Example 1, one on each side of the boundary, when determining which region should be shaded.

In-Class Examples

For Example 1
Graph $y < 3$.

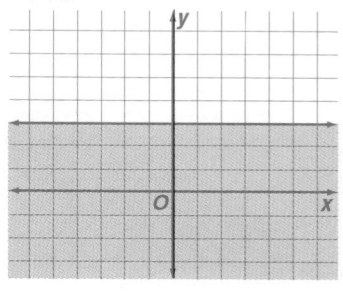

For Example 2
Graph $y \leq |x|$.

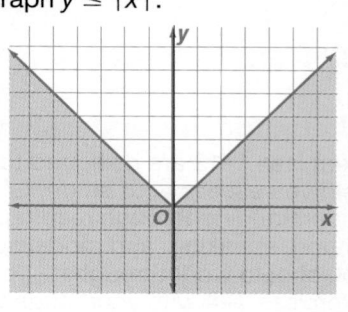

Teaching Tip For Example 2, remind students what happens to absolute value graphs when a quantity is subtracted.

In-Class Example

For Example 3

Ben plans to use a cellular phone for about 50 minutes a month. Club Cellular advertises that its monthly rate is $14 plus 60¢ per minute. Cellular I charges $27 a month with 50 free minutes. Which company should Ben go with?
The point at (50, 27) represents Cellular I's cost. Ben should go with Cellular I.

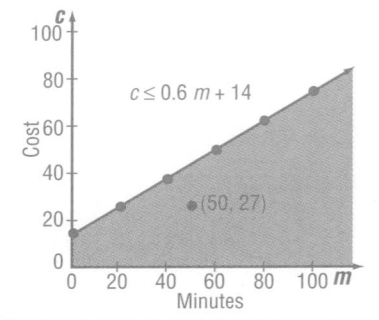

$c \leq 0.6\,m + 14$

(50, 27)

3 PRACTICE/APPLY

Check for Understanding

Exercises 1–12 are designed to help you assess your students' understanding through reading, writing, speaking, and modeling. You should work through Exercises 1–4 with your students and then monitor their work on Exercises 5–12.

Study Guide Masters, p. 14

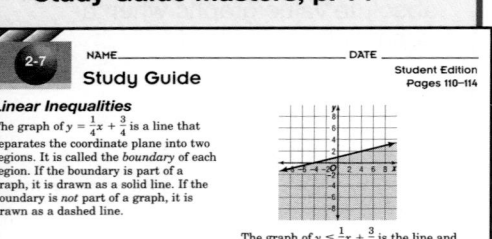

2-7
NAME_____ DATE_____
Student Edition
Pages 110–114

Study Guide

Linear Inequalities

The graph of $y = \frac{1}{4}x + \frac{3}{4}$ is a line that separates the coordinate plane into two regions. It is called the *boundary* of each region. If the boundary is part of a graph, it is drawn as a solid line. If the boundary is *not* part of a graph, it is drawn as a dashed line.

The graph of $y \leq \frac{1}{4}x + \frac{3}{4}$ is the line and the region *below* the line.

Graph each inequality.

1. $y < 3x + 1$

2. $y \geq |x| + 1$

3. $3x \geq 4y$

4. $y \geq x - 5$

5. $|x| + y \geq 4$

6. $3x - y < 6$

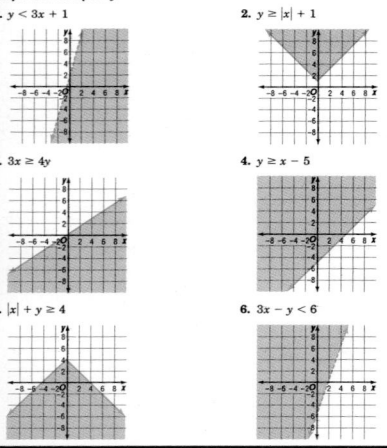

Inequalities can sometimes be used to analyze a situation and determine the trends in business and profitability.

Example ③

APPLICATION
Business

Amanda Harris wants to rent a car for a business trip of about 100 miles. Reasonable Car Rental advertises that their daily rental rate is $30 plus $0.25 a mile. She knows that Executive Car Rental charges $70 for a car rental with 100 free miles. Which company has the better rate?

Explore   One way to solve the problem is to make a graph for one company that shows the relationship between the number of miles driven d and the total cost of the rental r.

Plan   The initial cost of a car from Reasonable Car Rental is $30. Since this is the point at which no miles are driven, it is the y-intercept of the graph. The slope would be the rate of change in the total cost. In this case, the rate is $0.25 per mile. Thus, the slope is 0.25, and an equation of the line is $r = 0.25d + 30$.

Solve   Graph the equation $r = 0.25d + 30$. Then graph the point (100, 70), which represents Executive Car Rental's charge of $70 for a rental of 100 miles.

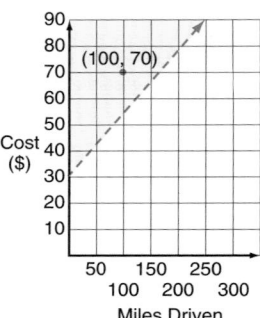
(100, 70)
Cost ($)
50 150 250
100 200 300
Miles Driven

Since the point (100, 70) lies above the boundary, it is in the graph of $r > 0.25d + 30$. For all points in this region, the cost of renting a car is greater than the cost of renting from Reasonable Car Rental. Thus, Reasonable Car Rental has a better rate than Executive Car Rental for a car rental of 100 miles.

Examine   For a rental of 100 miles, Reasonable Car Rental charges $0.25(100) + 30$ or $55. This is a better rate than $70. Thus, the solution seems reasonable.

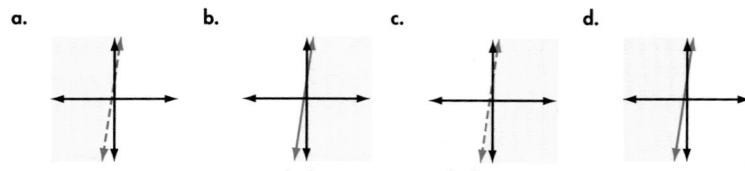

CHECK FOR UNDERSTANDING

Communicating Mathematics

Study the lesson. Then complete the following.   1–2. See margin.

1. **Explain** how you decide if the boundary of an inequality should be solid or dashed.

2. **Explain** why (0, 2) is a solution of $y \geq -8x + 2$.

3. **Choose** the graph of $y < 3x + 2$.   c

   a.   b.   c.   d.

4. **Compare** the graphs of $y = |x| + 1$ and $y < |x| + 1$.   See Solutions Manual.

Reteaching

Analyzing Graphs   Have students graph the equation $x = y$. Then have them identify which part of the graph represents each of the following.

a. $x < y$ points above the line
b. $x = y$ the line itself
c. $x \geq y$ points below the line and the line

Additional Answers

1. The boundary is a dashed line if the inequality is $<$ or $>$. The boundary is a solid line if the inequality is $\geq$ or $\leq$.

2. When you substitute the value (0, 2) into $y \geq -8x + 2$, you get a true statement $2 \geq 2$.

State which points, (0, 0), (3, −4), or (−1, 3), satisfy each inequality.

5. $x + 2y < 5$
(0, 0), (3, −4)

6. $4x + 3y \le 0$
(0, 0), (3, −4)

7. $5x − y \ge 6$
(3, −4)

Graph each inequality. 8–10. See Solutions Manual.

8. $y > 2$

9. $x − y \ge 0$

10. $y > 2x$

11. Graph $y > |2x|$. See margin.

12. Graph all the points on the coordinate plane to the right of $x = 4$. Write an inequality to describe these points. See margin for graph; $x > 4$.

EXERCISES

Graph each inequality. 13–24. See Solutions Manual.

13. $x + y > −5$

14. $y + 1 < 4$

15. $y > 6x − 2$

16. $x − 5 \le y$

17. $y \ge −4x + 3$

18. $y − 2 < 3x$

19. $y > \frac{1}{3}x + 5$

20. $y \ge \frac{1}{2}x − 5$

21. $3 \ge x − 3y$

25–28. See Solutions Manual for graphs.

22. $y \le |x|$

23. $y + |x| < 3$

24. $y > |4x|$

25. Graph all the points on the coordinate plane to the left of $x = −2$. Write an inequality to describe these points. $x < −2$

26. Graph all the points in the first quadrant bounded by the two axes and the line $x + 2y = 5$.

27. Graph all second quadrant points bounded by the lines $x = −3$, $x = −6$, and $y = 4$.

28. Graph all points in the fourth quadrant bounded by the two axes and the lines $3x − y = 4$ and $x − y = 5$.

Graph each inequality. 29–32. See Solutions Manual.

29. $|x| \le |y|$

30. $|x| − |y| = 1$

31. $|x| + |y| \ge 1$

32. $|x + y| > 1$

Critical Thinking

33. Describe the graph of $|y| < x$. See Solutions Manual.

Applications and Problem Solving

34. **Business** The No-Drip Sponge Company must produce a certain number of sponges each day to keep the assembly-line staff busy. If production falls, then layoffs may be necessary. The equation that describes this relationship is $s > 50e + 25$, where e is the number of employees and s is the number of sponges. Graph this inequality. See margin.

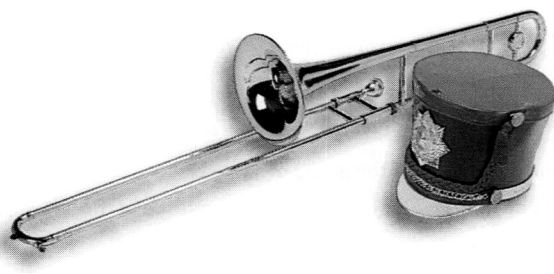

35. **Drama** Tickets for the Kingwood High School Drama Club's production of *The Music Man* cost $5 for adults and $4 for students. In order to cover expenses, at least $2500 worth of tickets must be sold.

a. Write an inequality that describes this situation. $5x + 4y \ge 2500$

b. Graph the inequality. See margin.

c. If 175 adult and 435 student tickets are sold, will the Drama Club cover its expenses? yes

Assignment Guide

Core: 13–37 odd, 38–43
Enriched: 14–32 even, 33–43

For **Extra Practice,** see p. 880.

The red A, B, and C flags, printed only in the Teacher's Wraparound Edition, indicate the level of difficulty of the exercises.

Additional Answers

11.

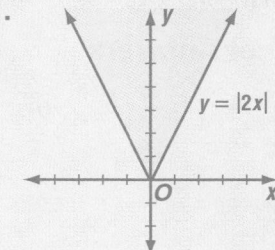

$y = |2x|$

12.

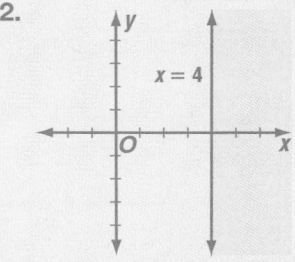

$x = 4$

Practice Masters, p. 14

2-7   NAME_____ DATE_____
Practice   Student Edition
Pages 110–114

Linear Inequalities
Graph each inequality.

1. $3 − x > 0$

2. $y < −4x − 2$

3. $y \ge 2x + 5$

4. $x − 3y \le 6$

5. $y > |x| − 1$

6. $y > −3|x + 1| − 2$

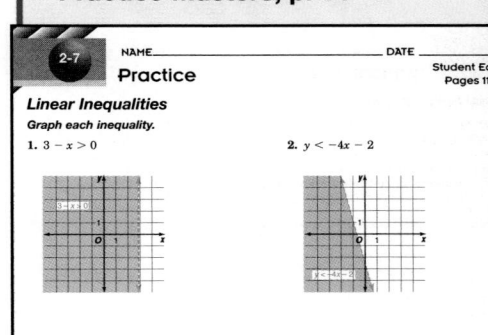

Additional Answers

34.

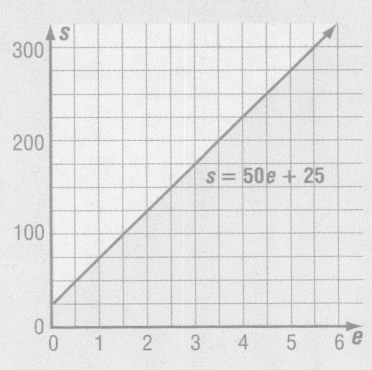

$s = 50e + 25$

35b.

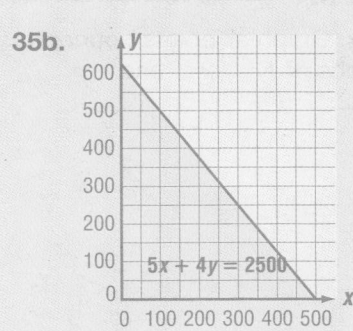

$5x + 4y = 2500$

4 ASSESS

Closing Activity

Writing Have students write the steps that are needed to graph a linear inequality. Then have students think of one example for using linear inequalities.

Chapter 2, Quiz D (Lesson 1-7), is available in the *Assessment and Evaluation Masters*, p. 45.

Additional Answers

36a.

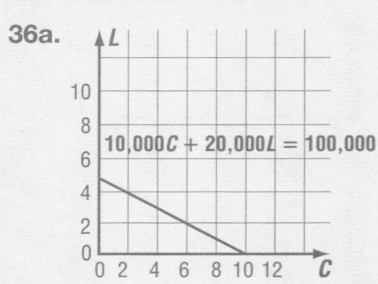

10,000C + 20,000L = 100,000

37b.

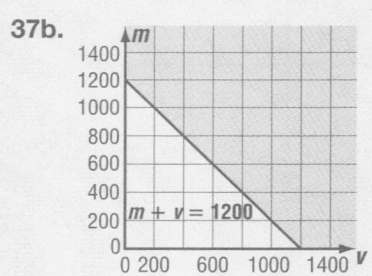

m + v = 1200

Enrichment Masters, p. 14

2-7
Enrichment

NAME _____ DATE _____
Student Edition
Pages 110–114

Aerial Surveyors and Area

Many land regions have irregular shapes. Aerial surveyors often use coordinates when finding areas of such regions.

Step 1 List the ordered pairs for the vertices in counterclockwise order, repeating the first ordered pair at the bottom of the list.

Step 2 Find D, the sum of the downward diagonal products (from left to right).
$D = (5 \cdot 5) + (2 \cdot 1) + (2 \cdot 3) + (6 \cdot 7)$
$= 25 + 2 + 6 + 42$ or 75

Step 3 Find U, the sum of the upward diagonal products (from left to right).
$U = (2 \cdot 7) + (2 \cdot 5) + (6 \cdot 1) + (5 \cdot 3)$
$= 14 + 10 + 6 + 15$ or 45

Step 4 Use the formula $A = \frac{1}{2}(D - U)$ to find the area.
$A = \frac{1}{2}(75 - 45)$
$= \frac{1}{2}(30)$ or 15

The area is 15 square units. Count the number of square units enclosed by the polygon. Does this result seem reasonable?

Use the coordinate method to find the area of each region in square units.

1.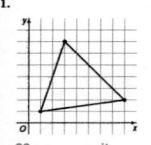
20 square units

2.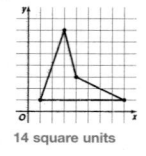
14 square units

3.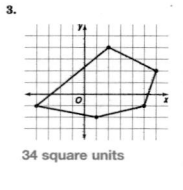
34 square units

114 Chapter 2

---

36. **Manufacturing** The Lone Star Auto Company has a daily production quota of $100,000 worth of cars. They produce two types of cars. Their compact model C is valued at $10,000 and their luxury car L is valued at $20,000. The equation $10,000C + 20,000L = 100,000$ describes the production quota.

   a. Make a graph of the quota equation.   **See margin.**

36b. below; 10,000C + 20,000L < 100,000

   b. On December 17, the factory produced 5 compacts and 2 luxury cars. Was the company above, below, or on target with their quota? Write the equation or inequality that contains this point.

36c. 10,000C + 20,000L = 100,000
36d. 10,000C + 20,000L > 100,000

   c. On February 24, the factory produced 6 compacts and 2 luxury cars. Write the equation or inequality that contains this point.

   d. On March 5, the factory produced 9 compacts and 2 luxury cars. Write the equation or inequality that contains this point.

37. **Education** Your school counselor advises you that to be admitted to the college of your choice, you need to score at least 1200 for the combined verbal and mathematics parts of the SAT.

   a. Write an inequality that describes this situation. $m + v \geq 1200$

   b. Graph the inequality.   **See margin.**

   c. What restrictions, if any, are necessary to impose on the domain and range? $D = \{200 \leq m \leq 800\}, R = \{200 \leq v \leq 800\}$

Mixed Review

38. Graph $y = [x] - 4$.   (Lesson 2–6)   **See margin.**

39. **Statistics** The table below shows the years of experience for eight encyclopedia sales representatives and the amount of sales during a given period of time.   (Lesson 2–5)

Sales	$9000	$6000	$4000	$3000	$3000	$5000	$8000	$2000
Years	6	5	3	1	4	3	6	2

   a. Draw a scatter plot to show how the years of experience and the amount of sales are related.   **See Solutions Manual.**

   b. Write a prediction equation from these data. $y = 1333x$

   c. Predict the amount of sales for a representative with 8 years of experience.   **$10,664**

40. $y = \frac{2}{3}x - 9$

40. Write an equation in slope-intercept form for the line with slope $\frac{2}{3}$ that passes through the point at $(6, -5)$.   (Lesson 2–4)

41. Graph a line that passes through the point at $(-2, 7)$ and is perpendicular to the graph of $x - 2y = 3$.   (Lesson 2–3)   **See Solutions Manual.**

42. $y, 2; x, 2.5$

42. Find the x-intercept and y-intercept of the graph of $4x + 5y = 10$.   (Lesson 2–2)

43. **Geometry** The points at $(-2, 2)$, $(7, 1)$, and $(-2, 1)$ form three of the vertices of a rectangle. Find the coordinates of the fourth vertex.   (Lesson 2–1)   **(7, 2)**

114   Chapter 2   Graphing Linear Relations and Functions

Extension

Reasoning Graph all points bounded by the graphs of $y = |2x|$ and $|y| = x + 2$.

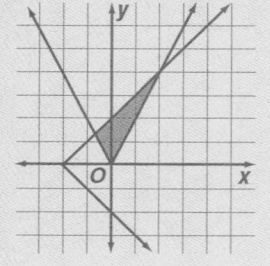

Additional Answer

38.

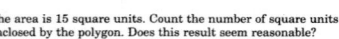

$y = [x] - 4$

CHAPTER 2 HIGHLIGHTS

VOCABULARY

After completing this chapter, you should be able to define each term, property, or phrase and give an example or two of each.

Algebra

absolute value function (p. 104)
Cartesian coordinate plane (p. 64)
coordinate system (p. 64)
constant function (pp. 74, 103)
continuous function (p. 67)
dependent variable (p. 73)
direct variation (p. 103)
domain (p. 65)
family of graphs (p. 83)
function (p. 65)
greatest integer function (p. 104)
identity function (p. 103)
independent variable (p. 73)
linear equation (p. 73)
linear function (p. 74)
mapping (p. 65)
ordered pairs (p. 64)
origin (p. 64)
parent graph (p. 83)
point-slope form (p. 89)
quadrants (p. 64)
range (p. 65)
relation (p. 65)
slope (p. 80)
slope-intercept form (p. 88)
standard form (p. 73)
step functions (p. 103)
vertical line test (p. 65)
x-axis (p. 64)
x-intercept (p. 75)
y-axis (p. 64)
y-intercept (p. 75)

Discrete Mathematics

discrete function (p. 65)

Geometry

parallel lines (p. 83)
perpendicular lines (p. 83)

Problem Solving

look for a pattern (p. 80)

Statistics

best-fit line (p. 95)
prediction equation (p. 95)
regression line (p. 101)
scatter plot (p. 95)

UNDERSTANDING AND USING THE VOCABULARY

Choose the term from the list above that best completes each statement or phrase.

1. The equation of the line suggested by the points on a scatter plot is a prediction equation.
2. An identity function is a linear function described by $f(x) = x$.
3. A constant function is a function of the form $f(x) = b$, and the slope of the function is zero.
4. A linear function described by $f(x) = mx$, where $m \neq 0$, is known as a direct variation.
5. An absolute value function is closely related to a linear function, except that the graph of this function always forms a V-shape and is described by $f(x) = |x|$.
6. The standard form of a linear function is $Ax + By = C$, where A, B, and C are real numbers and A and B are not both zero.
7. Two or more lines in the same plane having the same slope are parallel lines.
8. The domain is the set of all x-coordinates of the ordered pairs of a relation.
9. Two lines with slopes that are negative reciprocals of each other form right angles and therefore are perpendicular lines.
10. The set of all y-coordinates of the ordered pairs of a relation are known as the range.
11. The slope of a line may be described in two ways, the first as the vertical change divided by the horizontal change and the second as $(y_2 - y_1)$ divided by $(x_2 - x_1)$.

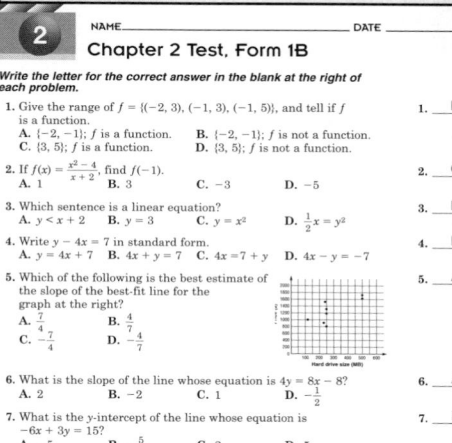

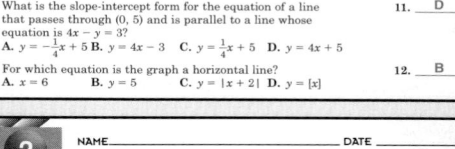

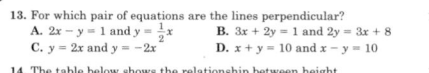

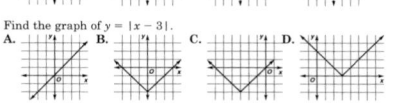

Instructional Resources

Three multiple-choice tests and three free-response tests are provided in the *Assessment and Evaluation Masters*. Forms 1A and 2A are for honors pacing, and Forms 1B, 1C, 2B, and 2C are for average pacing. Chapter 2 Test, Form 1B is shown at the right. Chapter 2 Test, Form 2B is shown on the next page.

Using the CHAPTER HIGHLIGHTS

The Chapter Highlights begins with a listing of the new terms, properties, and phrases that were introduced in this chapter. Have students define each term and provide an example or two of it, if appropriate.

Assessment and Evaluation Masters, pp. 31–32

2 NAME ______ DATE ______

Chapter 2 Test, Form 1B

Write the letter for the correct answer in the blank at the right of each problem.

1. Give the range of $f = \{(-2, 3), (-1, 3), (-1, 5)\}$, and tell if f is a function. — 1. D
   A. $\{-2, -1\}$; f is a function. B. $\{-2, -1\}$; f is not a function.
   C. $\{3, 5\}$; f is a function. D. $\{3, 5\}$; f is not a function.
2. If $f(x) = \frac{x^2 - 4}{x + 2}$, find $f(-1)$. — 2. C
   A. 1 B. 3 C. -3 D. -5
3. Which sentence is a linear equation? — 3. B
   A. $y < x + 2$ B. $y = 3$ C. $y = x^2$ D. $\frac{1}{2}x = y^2$
4. Write $y - 4x = 7$ in standard form. — 4. D
   A. $y = 4x + 7$ B. $4x + y = 7$ C. $4x = 7 + y$ D. $4x - y = -7$
5. Which of the following is the best estimate of the slope of the best-fit line for the graph at the right? — 5. A
   A. $\frac{7}{4}$ B. $\frac{4}{7}$ C. $-\frac{7}{4}$ D. $-\frac{4}{7}$

6. What is the slope of the line whose equation is $4y = 8x - 8$? — 6. A
   A. 2 B. -2 C. 1 D. $-\frac{1}{2}$
7. What is the y-intercept of the line whose equation is $-6x + 3y = 15$? — 7. D
   A. -5 B. $-\frac{5}{2}$ C. 2 D. 5
8. What is the x-intercept of the line whose equation is $y = \frac{2}{3}x - 12$? — 8. C
   A. $\frac{2}{3}$ B. -12 C. 18 D. 12
9. What is the slope of the line passing through (2, 6) and (−7, 8)? — 9. A
   A. $-\frac{2}{9}$ B. $-\frac{9}{2}$ C. $-\frac{2}{5}$ D. $-\frac{5}{2}$
10. What is the standard form of the equation for a line that passes through (1, 2) and that has a slope of −4? — 10. C
    A. $y = -4x + 2$ B. $2x + y = 4$ C. $4x + y = 6$ D. $y = -4x + 9$
11. What is the slope-intercept form for the equation of a line that passes through (0, 5) and is parallel to a line whose equation is $4x - y = 3$? — 11. D
    A. $y = -\frac{1}{4}x + 5$ B. $y = 4x - 3$ C. $y = \frac{1}{4}x + 5$ D. $y = 4x + 5$
12. For which equation is the graph a horizontal line? — 12. B
    A. $x = 6$ B. $y = 5$ C. $y = |x + 2|$ D. $y = [x]$

2 NAME ______ DATE ______

Chapter 2 Test, Form 1B (continued)

13. For which pair of equations are the lines perpendicular? — 13. D
    A. $2x - y = 1$ and $y = \frac{1}{2}x$ B. $3x + 2y = 1$ and $2y = 3x + 8$
    C. $y = 2x$ and $y = -2x$ D. $x + y = 10$ and $x - y = 10$
14. The table below shows the relationship between height and growing times for 6 plants of the same type. Which equation best predicts the height of a plant that has been growing 30 weeks? — 14. A

Height in inches (h)	15	17	18	19	20	21
Growing time in weeks (w)	11	14	15	16	17	18

    A. $h = w + 3$ B. $h = w - 3$ C. $h + w = 26$ D. $w = h + 3$

Find the slope-intercept form for each graph described.

15. slope $= \frac{2}{3}$, passes through (−5, 2) — 15. A
    A. $y = \frac{2}{3}x + \frac{16}{3}$ B. $y = \frac{2}{3}x - \frac{19}{3}$ C. $y = \frac{2}{3}x - \frac{16}{3}$ D. $y = \frac{2}{3}x + \frac{19}{3}$
16. passes through (1, −2) and (3, 7) — 16. A
    A. $y = \frac{9}{2}x - \frac{13}{2}$ B. $y = \frac{9}{2}x - \frac{57}{2}$ C. $y = \frac{2}{9}x + \frac{19}{3}$ D. $y = \frac{2}{9}x + \frac{13}{9}$
17. Find the graph of $-5x + 10y = 20$. — 17. D

18. Find the graph of $y = |x - 3|$. — 18. D

19. Which inequality is graphed at the right? — 19. C
    A. $y \geq -\frac{2}{3}x + 2$ B. $y \leq \frac{2}{3}x + 2$
    C. $y \leq -\frac{2}{3}x + 2$ D. $y > -\frac{2}{3}x + 2$

20. For the step function $f(x) = [x + 3]$, find $f(1.75)$. — 20. D
    A. 4.75 B. 5 C. 0.75 D. 4

Bonus

Find the value of k for which the graph of $7x + ky = 10$ is perpendicular to the graph of $3y + 6x = 18$. — Bonus D
A. $\frac{7}{2}$ B. $-\frac{7}{2}$ C. 14 D. -14

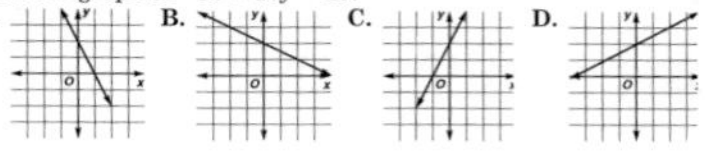

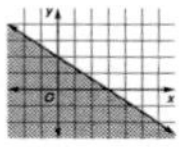

Skills and Concepts Encourage students to refer to the objectives and examples on the left as they complete the review exercises on the right.

Assessment and Evaluation Masters, pp. 37–38

NAME_____ DATE _____

2 Chapter 2 Test, Form 2B

1. Graph the following relation on a separate sheet. State the domain and the range. Is the relation a function?
$\{(-3, 2), (-2, 1), (-1, 0), (-1, 1), (0, 1)\}$

1. See students' graphs. domain $\{-3, -2, -1, 0\}$; range $\{0, 1, 2\}$; not a function

Use the vertical line test to determine if each relation is a function.

2. 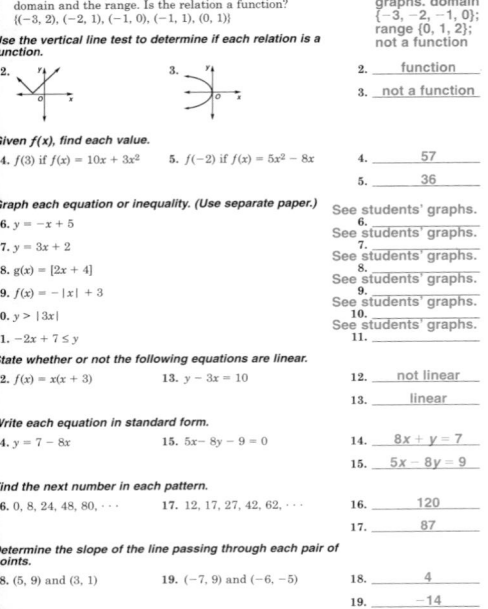   3.

2. ___function___
3. ___not a function___

Given f(x), find each value.

4. $f(3)$ if $f(x) = 10x + 3x^2$ 5. $f(-2)$ if $f(x) = 5x^2 - 8x$

4. ___57___
5. ___36___

Graph each equation or inequality. (Use separate paper.)

6. $y = -x + 5$
7. $y = 3x + 2$
8. $g(x) = [2x + 4]$
9. $f(x) = -|x| + 3$
10. $y > |3x|$
11. $-2x + 7 \le y$

See students' graphs.
6. See students' graphs.
7. See students' graphs.
8. See students' graphs.
9. See students' graphs.
10. See students' graphs.
11. _____

State whether or not the following equations are linear.

12. $f(x) = x(x + 3)$ 13. $y - 3x = 10$

12. ___not linear___
13. ___linear___

Write each equation in standard form.

14. $y = 7 - 8x$ 15. $5x - 8y - 9 = 0$

14. ___$8x + y = 7$___
15. ___$5x - 8y = 9$___

Find the next number in each pattern.

16. 0, 8, 24, 48, 80, ···   17. 12, 17, 27, 42, 62, ···

16. ___120___
17. ___87___

Determine the slope of the line passing through each pair of points.

18. (5, 9) and (3, 1)   19. (−7, 9) and (−6, −5)

18. ___4___
19. ___−14___

NAME_____ DATE _____

2 Chapter 2 Test, Form 2B (continued)

Find the x-intercept and y-intercept of the line described by each equation.

20. $-2x = 20 + 5y$ 21. $y = -4x + 5$

20. ___x: −10; y: −4___
21. ___x: 5/4; y: 5___

Find the slope-intercept form of an equation for each graph described.

22. slope = 2, passes through (1, 5)
23. passes through (−1, −5) and (3, 2)
24. passes through (0, 3) and is perpendicular to a line whose equation is $y - 7x = 4$

22. ___$y = 2x + 3$___
23. ___$y = \frac{7}{4}x - \frac{13}{4}$___
24. ___$y = -\frac{1}{7}x + 3$___

Find the standard form of an equation for each graph described.

25. x-intercept = $-\frac{8}{3}$, y-intercept = 6
26. slope = 5, x-intercept = −4
27. passes through (5, 0) and is parallel to the line whose equation is $x + 5y = 15$

25. ___$-9x - 4y = -24$___
26. ___$5x - yz = 20$___
27. ___$x + 5y = 5$___

For each pair of equations, determine if the lines are parallel, perpendicular, or neither.

28. $x + 4y = 20$ and $y - x = 10$
29. $y = \frac{3}{5}x$ and $y - 8 = -\frac{5}{3}x$
30. $4x - 6y = 18$ and $2x = 3y + 5$

28. ___neither___
29. ___perpendicular___
30. ___parallel___

Use the information in the table to solve the following problems.

The table shows the relationship between the field goals attempted and points scored by one basketball player over a 6-game period.

| field goals attempted (b) | 8 | 6 | 10 | 9 | 7 | 10 |
| points scored (p) | 12 | 9 | 14 | 14 | 11 | 15 |

31. On a separate sheet, draw a scatter plot to show how the field goals attempted and points scored are related.
32. Find a prediction equation to show how the points scored are related to the field goals attempted.
33. Predict the points scored if 20 field goals are attempted.

31. ___See students' graphs.___
32. ___$p = \frac{3}{2}b$___
33. ___30 points___

Bonus Graph $y = 1[x]$. Use separate paper.
Bonus ___See students' graphs.___

116 Chapter 2

OBJECTIVES AND EXAMPLES

Upon completing this chapter, you should be able to:

- graph a relation, state its domain and range, and determine if it is a function   (Lesson 2–1)

$\{(-5, 6), (-3, -4), (-1, -6), (2, 6)\}$

The domain is $\{-5, -3, -1, 2\}$.

The range is $\{6, -4, -6\}$.

It is a function because each element of the domain is paired with exactly one element of the range. 12–15. See margin for graphs.

- find values of functions for given elements of the domain   (Lesson 2–1)

If $f(x) = x^3 - 5$, find $f(-3)$.

$f(-3) = (-3)^3 - 5$
$= -27 - 5$ or -32

- identify equations that are linear and graph them   (Lesson 2–2)

$4x + y = -3$ is a linear equation.

$4x + y^2 = -3$ is *not* a linear equation.

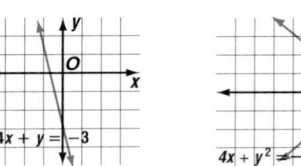

- write linear equations in standard form   (Lesson 2–2)

Write $2x - 6 = y + 8$ in standard form where A, B, and C are integers whose greatest common factor is 1.

$2x - 6 = y + 8$

$2x - y - 6 = 8$ *Subtract y from each side.*

$2x - y = 14$ *Add 6 to each side.*

REVIEW EXERCISES

Use these exercises to review and prepare for the chapter test.

State the domain and range of each relation. Then graph the relation and identify whether it is a function or not.

12. $\{(4, -7), (-4, -7), (-4, 7), (4, 7)\}$
13. $\{(9, 1), (7, 2), (5, 3), (3, 4), (1, 5)\}$
14. $3x - 4y = -7$ D, R = {all reals}; yes
15. $-2y + 4 = 1 - 5x$ D, R = {all reals}; yes
12. D = {−4, 4}, R = {−7, 7}; no
13. D = {1, 3, 5, 7, 9}, R = {1, 2, 3, 4, 5}; yes

Find each value if $f(x) = 4x^2 + 5x - 9$.

16. $f(6)$ 165
17. $f(-2)$ −3
18. $f(3y)$ $36y^2 + 15y - 9$
19. $f(-2v)$ $16v^2 - 10v - 9$

State whether each equation is linear. Write yes or no. If it is a linear equation, graph it.

20. $3x^2 - y = 6$ no
21. $2x + y = 11$ yes
22. $y = -7$ yes
23. $x^2 + y^2 = 25$ no

21–22. See margin for graphs.

Write each equation in standard form where A, B, and C are integers whose greatest common factor is 1.

24. $y = 7x + 15$ $7x - y = -15$
25. $0.5x = -0.2y - 0.4$ $5x + 2y = -4$
26. $\frac{2}{3}x - \frac{3}{4}y = 6$ $8x - 9y = 72$
27. $-\frac{1}{5}y = x + 4$ $5x + y = -20$
28. $6x = -12y + 48$ $x + 2y = 8$
29. $y - x = -9$ $x - y = 9$

116   Chapter 2   Study Guide and Assessment

GLENCOE Technology

Test and Review Software

You may use this software, a combination of an item generator and item bank, to create your own tests or worksheets. Types of items include free response, multiple choice, short answer, and open ended.

For IBM & Macintosh

OBJECTIVES AND EXAMPLES

- determine the slope of a line   (Lesson 2–3)

Determine the slope of the line that passes through $(-5, 3)$ and $(7, 9)$.

$$m = \frac{9 - 3}{7 - (-5)}$$

$$= \frac{6}{12} \text{ or } \frac{1}{2}$$

- write an equation of a line in slope-intercept form given the slope and one or two points (Lesson 2–4)

The slope-intercept form of the line that has a slope of $\frac{2}{3}$ and a y-intercept of 3 is $y = \frac{2}{3}x + 3$.

The standard form of this equation is $-2x + 3y = 9$.

- write an equation of a line that is parallel or perpendicular to the graph of a given equation (Lesson 2–4)

The equation of a line parallel to $y = 2x - 2$ is $y = 2x + 1$.

The equation of a line perpendicular to $y = 2x - 2$ is $y = -\frac{1}{2}x + 1$.

38. $y = \frac{1}{3}x + \frac{7}{3}$ **39.** $y = -\frac{3}{4}x + \frac{17}{4}$

- draw a scatter plot and find a prediction equation   (Lesson 2–5)

Construct a scatter plot for the given data. Then sketch the line that appears to best fit the points and find an equation of the line that best fits the data.

x	−1	0	0.5	1	2	3.5	4
y	3	3.5	1.5	2	0	−3.5	−2

The slope-intercept form of the equation of the best-fit line is $y = -\frac{5}{4}x + \frac{17}{8}$.

REVIEW EXERCISES

Determine the slope of the line that passes through each pair of points.

30. $(-6, -3)$ and $(6, 7)$ $\frac{5}{6}$

31. $(5.5, -5.5)$ and $(11, -7)$ $-\frac{3}{11}$

32. $(-3, 24)$ and $(10, -41)$ -5

Write an equation in slope-intercept form that satisfies each condition.

33. slope $= \frac{3}{4}$, passes through $(-6, 9)$

34. slope $= 2$, x-intercept $\frac{3}{2}$ $y = 2x - 3$

35. passes through $(3, -8)$ and $(-3, 2)$

36. passes through $(0.35, 0.7)$ and $(0.7, 0.35)$

33. $y = \frac{3}{4}x + \frac{27}{2}$ **35.** $y = -\frac{5}{3}x - 3$ **36.** $y = -x + 1.05$

Write an equation in slope-intercept form for each given situation.

37. passes through $(1, 2)$ and is parallel to the graph of $y = -3x + 7$ $y = -3x + 5$

38. passes through $(-1, 2)$ and is parallel to the graph of $x - 3y = 14$

39. passes through $(3, 2)$ and is perpendicular to the graph of $4x - 3y = 12$

40. passes through $(1, 3)$ and is perpendicular to the graph of $y = -\frac{2}{3}x + \frac{11}{3}$ $y = \frac{3}{2}x + \frac{3}{2}$

41. On average, a person that is 70 inches tall (5′10″) weighs about 167 pounds. A person who is 62 inches tall (5′2″) weighs about 125 pounds. Let h represent the height, and let w represent the weight.   b. $w = 5.25h - 200.5$
   a. Draw a scatter plot to show how height and weight are related.   **See margin.**
   b. Find a prediction equation for the data.
   c. Predict the weight of a person who is 77 inches tall.   **203.75 pounds**
   d. Predict the height of a person who weighs 155 pounds.   **about 67.75 inches tall**

41a.

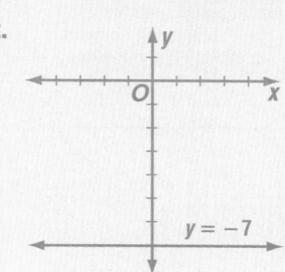

Additional Answers

12.

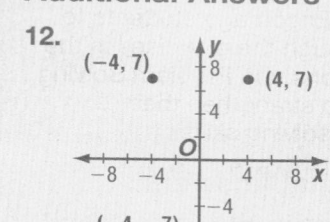

13.

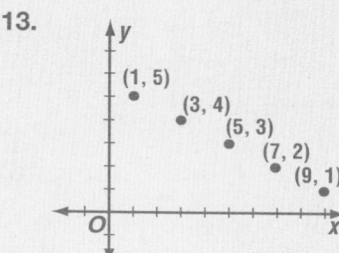

14.

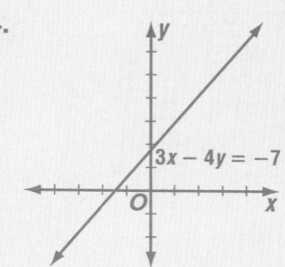

15.

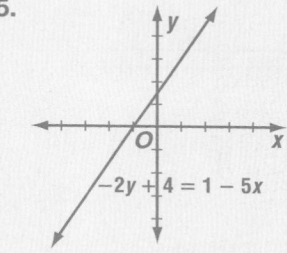

21.

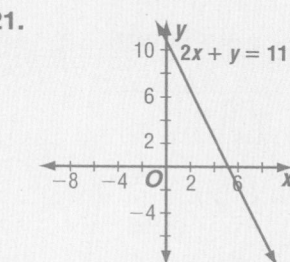

22.

Applications and Problem Solving Encourage students to work through the exercises in the Applications and Problem Solving section to strengthen their problem-solving skills.

Additional Answers

42.
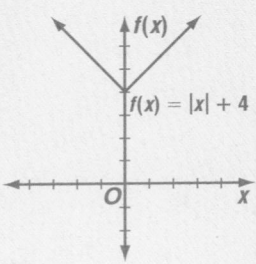

43.
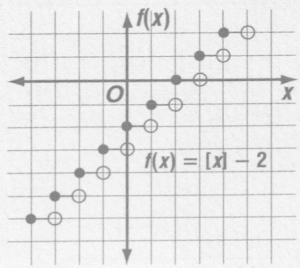

44.
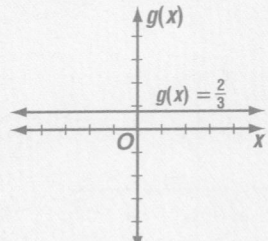

45.
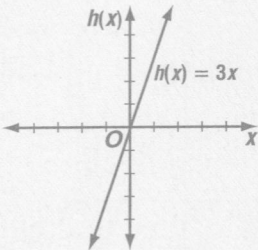

46.
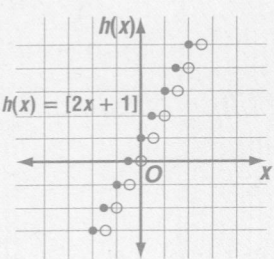

OBJECTIVES AND EXAMPLES

• identify and graph special functions
(Lesson 2–6)

$y = [0.3x] + 5$ is a greatest integer function.

$y = |0.5x + 9| - 21$ is an absolute value function.

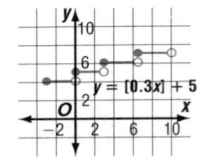

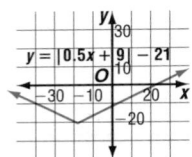

REVIEW EXERCISES

Identify each function as C for constant, D for direct variation, A for absolute value, or G for greatest integer function. Then graph each function. 42–47. See margin for graphs.

42. $f(x) = |x| + 4$ **A**

43. $f(x) = [x] - 2$ **G**

44. $g(x) = \frac{2}{3}$ **C**

45. $h(x) = 3x$ **D**

46. $h(x) = [2x + 1]$ **G**

47. $g(x) = |x - 1| + 7$ **A**

• draw graphs of inequalities in two variables
(Lesson 2–7)

Replace the inequality symbol with an equal sign to find the equation for the boundary line. Graph the boundary line, using a solid line for $\le$ or $\ge$, or a dashed line for $<$ or $>$. Test a point to determine which region to shade.

Graph each inequality.

48. $y \le 3x - 5$

49. $x > y - 1$

50. $y \ge |x| + 2$

51. $y + 0.5x < 4$

48–51. See Solutions Manual.

APPLICATIONS AND PROBLEM SOLVING

52. **Employment** Ley works at a clothing store for men. He earns $7.00 an hour plus 50¢ for every item over 25 items that he sells. He works 40 hours a week. How much money will he make if he sells x items? (Lesson 2–6) $p = 280 + 0.50(x - 25)$ if $x > 25$; $p = 280$ if $x < 25$

53. **Consumer Awareness** Monique's Fine Fashions allows its customers to charge their purchases on a delayed payment plan. When the customer receives a bill from Monique's,

there is a $5 charge for using the delayed payment plan, plus 2% interest on the purchase. Calculate the bill for a purchase of $110. (Lesson 2–2) **$117.20**

54. **Geometry** What are the equations of the five lines that make up the sides of the star shown below? (Lesson 2–4)

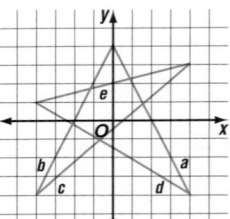

a. $y = -2x + 4$, b. $2x + 4$, c. $y = 0.875x - 0.5$, d. $y = -0.625x - 1.5$, e. $y = 0.25x + 2$
A practice test for Chapter 2 is provided on page 913.

47.
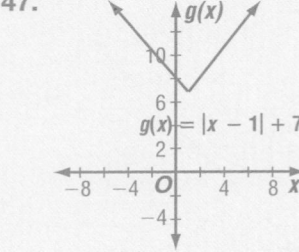

ALTERNATIVE ASSESSMENT

COOPERATIVE LEARNING PROJECT

Predicting the Future   The better we understand nature, the more accurately we are able to predict its behavior.

Ancient peoples had no understanding of the movements of the sun, the moon, or the stars. Predicting such events with accuracy was impossible. As a result, eclipses were believed to be a sign that the gods were angry. When astronomers discovered the cause of an eclipse and calculated the orbits of the sun and the other planets in our solar system, they were able to predict the timing of an eclipse with great accuracy.

In an effort to make predictions about natural occurrences that are not fully understood, scientists search for predictors or events which, for no apparent reason, seem to correlate with the occurrences. For example, geologist Ruth Simon discovered that cockroaches become more active a few hours preceding a major earthquake. Political analysts have noted that the candidate with the longer name wins nearly 75% of the presidential elections.

In this project, you will attempt to find a predictor that can be used to predict the behavior of some natural phenomenon. You will analyze several possible predictors to find the one with the best promise. Then you will use that one to make a prediction about the future.

Follow these steps to carry out your project.

- Choose a phenomenon that interests your group, whose behavior cannot be predicted with complete accuracy. Be sure there is plenty of data available on the phenomenon you choose and that the phenomenon is not completely arbitrary in its behavior.

- Collect data on the phenomenon. Study it, looking for patterns, and discuss your findings with the rest of your group.

- Brainstorm with your fellow group members to find at least three possible predictors of the phenomenon you chose.

- Collect data on your predictors.

- Analyze your predictors. You may wish to draw scatter plots and find a prediction equation. You can use a graphing calculator to help you draw lines of regression. After you complete your analysis, choose the predictor that shows the best promise.

- Write a report summarizing your work as a group. Explain how you chose your predictors and how they were analyzed. Describe the results of your prediction. List any discrepancies found between predicted and actual results.

THINKING CRITICALLY

You have learned several ways to find the slope of a line: by using the vertical change divided by the horizontal change, by using the formula $m = \dfrac{y_2 - y_1}{x_2 - x_1}$, and by simply viewing the graph of a line. Is one way better than another? Write a one-page paper on the method you prefer, citing examples, and explaining why you prefer it.

PORTFOLIO

Select one of the assignments from this chapter that you found especially challenging and place it in your portfolio.

SELF EVALUATION

In this chapter, you examined many types of graphs. They show how quantities relate to each other. Some graphs are used to show change. Jonathan Swift said, "There is nothing in this world constant, but inconstancy."

Assess yourself. Do you like change? How do you react when your plans get changed at the last minute? At school, home or the workplace, having the flexibility to change and adapt is necessary to solve problems and to work together.

 **Alternative Assessment**

The Alternative Assessment section provides students with the opportunity to assess their own work by thinking critically, working with others, keeping a portfolio, and honestly evaluating their own progress. For more information on alternative forms of assessment, see *Alternative Assessment in the Mathematics Classroom,* one of the titles in the Glencoe Mathematics Professional Series.

 **Performance Assessment**

Performance Assessment tasks for this chapter are included in the *Assessment and Evaluation Masters.* A scoring guide is also provided.

Assessment and Evaluation Masters, pp. 42, 53

2   NAME_____   DATE_____

Chapter 2 Performance Assessment

Instructions: *Demonstrate your knowledge by giving a clear, concise solution to each problem. Be sure to include all relevant drawings and justify your answers. You may show your solution in more than one way or investigate beyond the requirements of the problem.*

1. Bailey is vacationing at Myrtle Beach, South Carolina, this July. She likes to swim at low tide when the beach is wide and the waves are calm. She consults a tide chart to find the best time to swim.

July	2	3	4	5	6	7
Low tide	1:20	2:10	2:50	3:40	4:20	5:10

   a. Draw a scatter plot and write a prediction equation for the data.

   b. Predict when low tide will be on July 8. Explain how you determined your prediction.

   c. About what time was low tide on July 1?

   d. How do you think the prediction equation would change if each low tide was 15 minutes later than the day before?

   e. How do you think the prediction equation would change if low tides were about 15 minutes earlier than the day before?

2. a. Name two ways you can tell whether a relation is a function.

   b. Draw a mapping from the domain to the range that is a function.

   c. List a set of ordered pairs for a relation that is not a function. Explain why it is not a function.

   d. Graph $y \le 3x + 5$. Is the relation a function? Why or why not?

Scoring Guide
Chapter 2
Performance Assessment

Level	Specific Criteria
3 Superior	• Shows thorough understanding of the concepts *scatter plot, prediction equation, relation, function, domain,* and *range.* • Uses appropriate strategies to solve problems. • Computations are correct. • Written explanations are exemplary. • Graphs, diagram, and table are accurate and appropriate. • Goes beyond requirements of problems.
2 Satisfactory, with Minor Flaws	• Shows understanding of the concepts *scatter plot, prediction equation, relation, function, domain,* and *range.* • Uses appropriate strategies to solve problems. • Computations are mostly correct. • Written explanations are effective. • Graphs, diagram, and table are mostly accurate and appropriate. • Satisfies all requirements of problems.
1 Nearly Satisfactory, with Serious Flaws	• Shows understanding of most of the concepts *scatter plot, prediction equation, relation, function, domain,* and *range.* • May not use appropriate strategies to solve problems. • Computations are mostly correct. • Written explanations are satisfactory. • Graphs, diagram, and table are mostly accurate and appropriate. • Satisfies most requirements of problems.
0 Unsatisfactory	• Shows little or no understanding of the concepts *scatter plot, prediction equation, relation, function, domain,* and *range.* • May not use appropriate strategies to solve problems. • Computations are incorrect or inappropriate. • Graphs, diagram, and table are not accurate or appropriate. • Does not satisfy requirements of problems.

These two pages review the skills and concepts presented in Chapters 1–2. This review is formatted to reflect new trends in college entrance testing.

A more traditional cumulative review, shown below, is provided in the *Assessment and Evaluation Masters,* pp. 47–48.

Assessment and Evaluation Masters, pp. 47–48

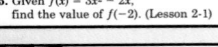

NAME_____ DATE _____

Chapter 2 Cumulative Review

Find the value of each expression. (Lesson 1-1)

1. $2(6 - 2) + 4^2$ — 1. _____24_____

2. $5(11 - 3) + (-3)^2$ — 2. _____49_____

3. Evaluate $\frac{7a - 2c}{a^2 + b}$ if $a = 3, b = 2,$ and $c = 5.$ — 3. _____1_____

4. Name the set(s) of numbers to which -42.1 belongs. Use R for reals, I for irrationals, W for wholes, Q for rationals, Z for integers, and N for naturals. (Lesson 1-2) — 4. _____Q, R_____

State the property illustrated in each equation. (Lesson 1-2)

5. $-4 + 0 = -4$ — 5. _additive identity_

6. $\left(\frac{5}{3}\right)\frac{3}{5}x = x$ — 6. _multiplicative inverse_

Solve. (Lessons 1-4 and 1-5)

7. $2(5x + 3) = 5(x + 5)$ — 7. _____$\frac{19}{5}$_____

8. $3|7 - a| = 12$ — 8. _____3, 11_____

Solve each inequality. Graph the solution set. (Lessons 1-6 and 1-7)

9. $2(3x - 1) \le 5x - 3$ — 9. See students' graphs; $x \le -1$.

10. $6 \le 2(y - 1) \le 10$ — 10. See students' graphs; $4 \le y \le 6$.

11. $|3 + 2x| < 7$ — 11. See students' graphs; $-5 < x < 2$.

State the domain and range of each relation. Then state if it is a function. (Lesson 2-1)

12. $\{(4, -7), (7, -3), (-2, -6), (3, -16)\}$ — 12. D: $\{4, 7, -2, 3\}$; R: $\{-7, -3, -6, -16\}$; function

13. $\{(4, 6), (4, 7), (4, 8), (4, 9)\}$ — 13. D: $\{43\}$; R: $\{6, 7, 8, 9\}$; not a function

14. Use the vertical line test to determine if the relation is a function. (Lesson 2-1) — 14. not a function

15. Given $f(x) = 3x^2 - 2x,$ find the value of $f(-2).$ (Lesson 2-1) — 15. _____16_____

NAME_____ DATE _____

Chapter 2 Cumulative Review (continued)

Find the slope, x-intercept, and y-intercept of each line whose equation is given below. (Lesson 2-2)

16. $3x - y = 6$ — 16. $3; 2; -6$

17. $2x + 4y = 7$ — 17. $-\frac{1}{2}, \frac{7}{2}, \frac{7}{4}$

18. Find the slope-intercept form of the equation of the line passing through the point $(3, -5)$ with a slope of $-4.$ (Lesson 2-4) — 18. $y = -4x + 7$

19. Find the standard form of the equation of the line whose x-intercept is 4 and whose y-intercept is 2. (Lesson 2-4) — 19. $x + 2y = 4$

20. Find the standard form of the equation of the line that passes through $(0, 5)$ and is parallel to the line whose equation is $y = -\frac{1}{2}x + 6.$ (Lesson 2-3) — 20. $x + 2y = 10$

Graph each equation or inequality. Use a separate sheet. (Lessons 2-1, 2-3, 2-6, and 2-7)

21. $y = 2x + 1$ — 21. See students' graphs.

22. $y = |x + 2|$ — 22. See students' graphs.

23. $x = -5$ — 23. See students' graphs.

24. $2x + y < 4$ — 24. See students' graphs.

25. $y \ge |x + 1|$ — 25. See students' graphs.

COLLEGE ENTRANCE EXAM PRACTICE

CHAPTERS 1–2

SECTION ONE: MULTIPLE CHOICE

There are eight multiple-choice questions in this section. After working each problem, write the letter of the correct answer on your paper.

1. Determine which graph represents a function. **C**

   A. 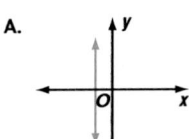   **B.**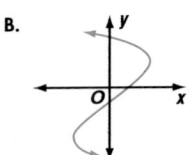

   C. 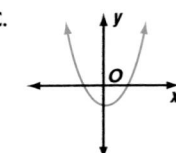   **D.**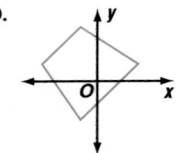

2. Choose the equation that is equivalent to $3(a + 2b) - c = 0.$ **B**

   A. $a + 2b = c$

   B. $b = \frac{c - 3a}{6}$

   C. $a = \frac{2b - c}{3}$

   D. $3a + 6b - 3c = 0$

3. What is the mean age of those in attendance at the Cruz family reunion if their ages are represented in the stem-and-leaf plot below? **A**

Stem	Leaf
0	3 7
1	2 2 5 8 8
2	3 5 5 6 7
3	6
4	0 3 3 3
5	0 3
6	2 6 8 4	3 = 43 years

   A. 32.5 years

   B. 26.5 years

   C. 43 years

   D. 102 years

4. Evaluate the expression $\left(\frac{a}{x} + b\right)^2 - gh$ if $a = 9, b = 2, g = 4, h = 6,$ and $x = 3.$ **D**

   A. 19   **B.** -11

   C. -3 **D.** 1

5. Determine which description of the graph of the equation $2x - 4y = 8$ is true. **C**

   A. It is parallel to the graph of the equation $2x - y = 8.$

   B. Its slope is 2.

   C. The point $(6, 1)$ lies on it.

   D. It is perpendicular to the equation $4x - 8y = 16.$

6. Choose the statement that is false for all real numbers $a, b,$ and $c.$ **B**

   A. If $a = b,$ then $a + c = b + c$ and $a - c = b - c.$

   B. $a \cdot \frac{1}{a} = 1 \cdot a$

   C. If $a = b$ and $b = c,$ then $a = c.$

   D. $(a + b) + c = a + (b + c)$

7. Choose the inequality that describes the graph below. **A**

   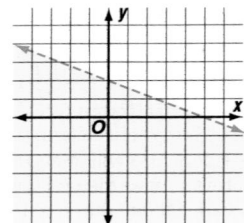

   A. $2x + 5y < 10$

   B. $y > 2 - \frac{2}{5}x$

   C. $y \ge -2x - 5$

   D. $5x + 2y \le 10$

8. Choose the type of function that represents the following relationship. For every yard Melissa mows, she earns \$7.00. **D**

   A. absolute value

   B. step

   C. greatest integer

   D. direct variation

Standardized Test Practice Questions are also provided in the *Assessment and Evaluation Masters,* p. 46.

SECTION TWO: SHORT ANSWER

This section contains seven questions for which you will provide short answers. Write your answer on your paper.

9. Solve $8|2b - 3| = 64$. $-2.5, 5.5$

10. The width of a rectangular rug is four feet more than one third its length. The perimeter is 64 feet. What are the length and width of the rug?   **length — 21 ft, width — 11 ft**

11. Intercity Car Rental offers a mid-size car that costs 20¢ per mile plus an initial fee of $20. To rent the same car from Big Wheels Car Rental, each mile costs 23¢ with an initial fee of $10. Barry plans to drive about 875 miles. Which company provides the cheaper offer, and how much will Barry save with this offer?   **Intercity Car Rental; $16.25**

12. Solve $\left\{\dfrac{x+8}{4} - 1 > \dfrac{x}{3} \text{ and } 7 < 2x - 11\right\}$. Then graph the solution set. $\{x \mid 9 < x < 12\}$

13. Determine the slope of a line perpendicular to the line that passes through $(-3, -1)$ and $(4, -7)$. $\dfrac{7}{6}$

14. The marching band at Scoring High School is raising money for new uniforms by selling candy. They need to earn at least $1025 to receive a 10% discount on the price of uniforms. During the first week of the sale, the amounts turned in by each music class were $125, $86, $98, $72, $63, and $135. What is the minimum amount the band must raise to receive the 10% discount?   **$446**

15. Describe the steps you would take to graph the equation $3y - 2x = 15$.   **See students' work.**

SECTION THREE: COMPARISON

This section contains five comparison problems that involve comparing two quantities, one in column A and one in column B. In certain questions, information related to one or both quantities is centered above them. All variables used represent real numbers.

Compare quantities A and B below.

- Write A if quantity A is greater.
- Write B if quantity B is greater.
- Write C if the two quantities are equal.
- Write D if there is not enough information to determine the relationship.

16. C   17. A   18. D   19. B   20. C

Column A	Column B
16. the slope of a line perpendicular to the line that passes through $(-3, 2)$ and $(5, -1)$	$\dfrac{8}{3}$

$$g = 3, k = -2, m = 5, p = 4$$

Column A	Column B
17. $g^2 + (k - p) \div g$	$\left(\dfrac{p}{k} + m\right)^2 \div g + k$

Column A	Column B
18. $y - 3 \geq 4x$	$3x + 5 < 10$

Column A	Column B
19. the median of $\{41, 33, 12, 38, 27, 19\}$	the mean of $\{14, 23, 35, 18, 32, 27, 39\}$

$$a > b, b = c$$

Column A	Column B
20. $(b + a) - d$	$-d + a + c$

Solving Systems of Linear Equations and Inequalities

PREVIEWING THE CHAPTER

This chapter reviews and extends students' understanding of linear equations and inequalities developed in Chapter 2 by examining and solving systems of linear equations and inequalities. Students use graphing techniques, graphing technology, and algebraic methods to solve systems of linear equations and inequalities. Then determinants are introduced and systems are solved by using Cramer's rule. Linear programming techniques and the strategy of solving a similar problem are integrated for the purpose of finding maximum and minimum values of a function over a region. The chapter concludes with students solving and modeling systems of three equations in three variables.

Lesson (Pages)	Lesson Objectives	NCTM Standards	State/Local Objectives
3-1A (124–125)	Use a graphing calculator to graph and solve systems of linear equations.	1–5, 8	3.b.
3-1 (126–132)	Solve systems of equations by graphing.	1–5, 8	3.a., 3.b., 3.c.
3-2 (133–140)	Use the substitution and elimination methods to solve systems of equations.	1–5	3.a., 3.b., 3.c.
3-3 (141–146)	Find the values of second-order determinations. Solve systems of equations by using Cramer's rule.	1–5	3.a., 3.b., 3.c.
3-4A (147)	Use a graphing calculator to graph and solve systems of linear inequalities.	1–5	
3-4 (148–152)	Solve systems of inequalities by graphing.	1–5, 8	3.a., 3.b.
3-5 (153–159)	Find the maximum and minimum values of a function over a region using linear programming techniques. Solve problems by solving a simpler problem.	1–6	3.a., 3.b.
3-6 (160–164)	Solve problems involving maximum and minimum values by using linear programming techniques.	1–6	3.a., 3.b.
3-7 (165–171)	Solve a system of three equations in three variables.	1–5	3.a., 3.b., 3.c.
3-7B (172–173)	Determine the octant in which a point in space is located. Graph linear equations in space and determine the intercepts.	1–5, 8	

A complete, 1-page lesson plan is provided for each lesson in the *Lesson Planning Guide*. Answer keys for each lesson are available in the *Answer Key Masters*.

ORGANIZING THE CHAPTER

You may want to refer to the **Course Planning Calendar** on page T12 for detailed information on pacing.
PACING: Standard—14 days; **Honors**—12 days; **Block**—6 days

LESSON PLANNING CHART

| Lesson (Pages) | Materials/ Manipulatives | Extra Practice (Student Edition) | BLACKLINE MASTERS | | | | | | | | | Real-World Applications | Interactive Mathematics Tools Software | Teaching Transparencies |
			Study Guide	Practice	Enrichment	Assessment and Evaluation	Modeling Mathematics	Multicultural Activity	Tech Prep Applications	Graphing Calculator	Science and Math Lab Manual			
3-1A (124–125)	graphing calculator									pp. 27, 28				
3-1 (126–132)	graphing calculator	p. 880	p. 15	p. 15	p. 15					p. 3			3-1	3-1A 3-1B
3-2 (133–140)		p. 881	p. 16	p. 16	p. 16	p. 72	p. 63		p. 5		pp. 35–38			3-2A 3-2B
3-3 (141–146)		p. 881	p. 17	p. 17	p. 17								3-3	3-3A 3-3B
3-4A (147)	graphing calculator									pp. 29, 30				
3-4 (148–152)		p. 881	p. 18	p. 18	p. 18	pp. 71, 72	pp. 28–30			p. 6				3-4A 3-4B
3-5 (153–159)		p. 882	p. 19	p. 19	p. 19				p. 5			7		3-5A 3-5B
3-6 (160–164)		p. 882	p. 20	p. 20	p. 20	p. 73			p. 6					3-6A 3-6B
3-7 (165–171)		p. 882	p. 21	p. 21	p. 21	p. 73	pp. 31–33					8		3-7A 3-7B
3-7B (172–173)	isometric dot paper							p. 21						
Study Guide/ Assessment (175–179)						pp. 57–70, 74–76								

ORGANIZING THE CHAPTER

OTHER CHAPTER RESOURCES

Student Edition
Chapter Opener, pp. 122–123
Mathematics and Society, p. 146
Working on the Investigation,
    pp. 140, 159
Closing the Investigation, p. 174

Teacher's Classroom Resources
Investigations and Projects Masters,
    pp. 33–36

Technology
Teacher's Guide for Software
    Resources
Test and Review Software (IBM
    and Macintosh)
CD-ROM Interactions (Windows
    and Macintosh)

Professional Publications
Block Scheduling Booklet
Glencoe Mathematics Professional
    Series

OUTSIDE RESOURCES

Books/Periodicals
Dalton, LeRoy, *Algebra in the Real World*, Dale
    Seymour Publications
Heid, M. Kathleen, Jonathan Choate, Charlene
    Sheets, and Rose Mary Zbiek, *Algebra in a
    Technological World: Addenda Series*, NCTM

Software
PC 81 Emulation Software, Dale Seymour
    Publications

Videos/CD-ROMs
Algebra for Everyone, NCTM
Using Calculators in Mathematics Education, Dale
    Seymour Publications

See the *Teacher's Guide for Software Resources* for software addresses.

ASSESSMENT RESOURCES

Student Edition
Math Journal, pp. 129, 150, 162
Mixed Review, pp. 132, 140,
    146, 152, 159, 164, 171
Self Test, p. 152
Chapter Highlights, p. 175
Chapter Study Guide and
    Assessment, pp. 176–178
Alternative Assessment, p. 179
Portfolio, p. 179

Teacher's Wraparound Edition
5-Minute Check, pp. 126, 133,
    141, 148, 153, 160, 165
Check for Understanding, pp. 129,
    137, 144, 150, 156, 162, 169
Closing Activity, pp. 132, 139,
    146, 152, 159, 164, 170
Cooperative Learning, pp. 142,
    155

Assessment and Evaluation Masters
Multiple-Choice Tests, Forms 1A
    (Honors), 1B (Average), 1C
    (Basic), pp. 57–62
Free-Response Tests, Forms 2A
    (Honors), 2B (Average), 2C
    (Basic), pp. 63–68
Calculator-Based Test, p. 69
Performance Assessment, p. 70
Mid-Chapter Test, p. 71
Quizzes A–D, pp. 72–73
Standardized Test Practice, p. 74
Cumulative Review, pp. 75–76

ENHANCING THE CHAPTER

Examples of some of the materials for enhancing Chapter 3 are shown below.

DIVERSITY

Multicultural Activity Masters, pp. 5, 6

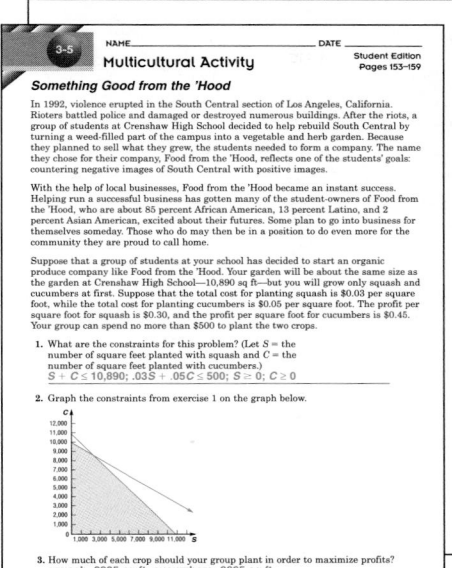

3-5
Multicultural Activity
Student Edition
Pages 153–159

Something Good from the 'Hood

In 1992, violence erupted in the South Central section of Los Angeles, California. Rioters battled police and damaged or destroyed numerous buildings. After the riots, a group of students at Crenshaw High School decided to help rebuild South Central by turning a weed-filled part of the campus into a vegetable and herb garden. Because they planned to sell what they grew, the students needed to form a company. The name they chose for their company, Food from the 'Hood, reflects one of the students' goals: countering negative images of South Central with positive images.

With the help of local businesses, Food from the 'Hood became an instant success. Helping run a successful business has gotten many of the student-owners of Food from the 'Hood, who are about 85 percent African American, 13 percent Latino, and 2 percent Asian American, excited about their futures. Some plan to go into business for themselves someday. Those who may then be in a position to do even more for the community they are proud to call home.

Suppose that a group of students at your school has decided to start an organic produce company like Food from the 'Hood. Your garden will be about the same size as the garden at Crenshaw High School—10,890 sq ft—but you will grow only squash and cucumbers at first. Suppose that the total cost for planting squash is $0.03 per square foot, while the total cost for planting cucumbers is $0.05 per square foot. The profit per square foot for squash is $0.30, and the profit per square foot for cucumbers is $0.45. Your group can spend no more than $500 to plant the two crops.

1. What are the constraints for this problem? (Let S = the number of square feet planted with squash and C = the number of square feet planted with cucumbers.)
$S + C \le 10,890; .03S + .05C \le 500; S \ge 0; C \ge 0$

2. Graph the constraints from exercise 1 on the graph below.

3. How much of each crop should your group plant in order to maximize profits?
squash: 2225 sq ft; cucumbers: 8665 sq ft

APPLICATIONS

Real-World Applications, 7, 8

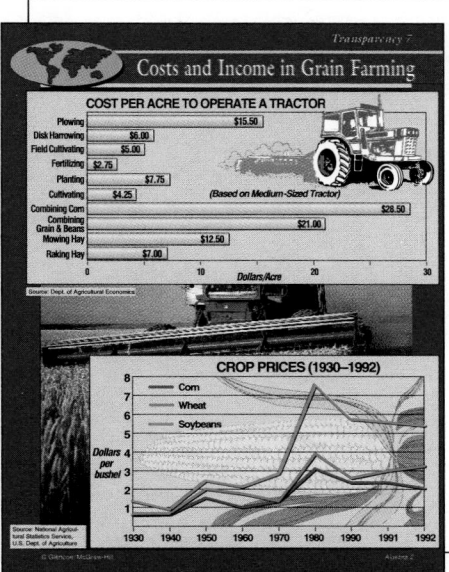

Transparency 7
Costs and Income in Grain Farming

COST PER ACRE TO OPERATE A TRACTOR

Plowing	$15.50
Disk Harrowing	$6.00
Field Cultivating	$5.00
Fertilizing	$2.75
Planting	$7.75
Cultivating	$4.25
Combining Corn	$28.50
Combining Grain & Beans	$21.00
Mowing Hay	$12.50
Raking Hay	$7.00

(Based on Medium-Sized Tractor)
Dollars/Acre
Source: Dept. of Agricultural Economics

CROP PRICES (1930–1992)
Corn
Wheat
Soybeans
Dollars per bushel

Source: National Agricultural Statistics Service, U.S. Dept. of Agriculture

TECHNOLOGY

Graphing Calculator Masters, p. 3

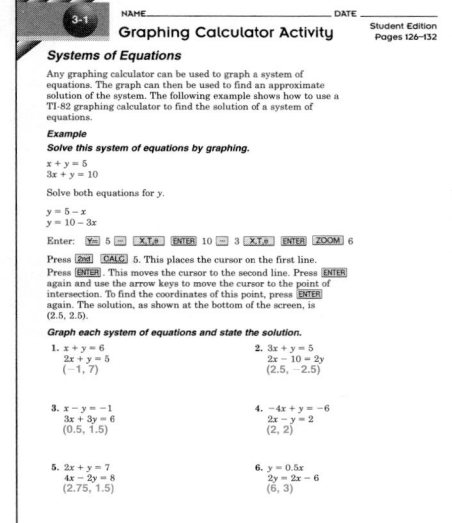

3-1
Graphing Calculator Activity
Student Edition
Pages 126–132

Systems of Equations

Any graphing calculator can be used to graph a system of equations. The graph can then be used to find an approximate solution of the system. The following example shows how to use a TI-82 graphing calculator to find the solution of a system of equations.

Example
Solve this system of equations by graphing.
$x + y = 5$
$3x + y = 10$

Solve both equations for y.

$y = 5 - x$
$y = 10 - 3x$

Enter: Y= 5 − X,T,θ ENTER 10 − 3 X,T,θ ENTER ZOOM 6

Press 2nd CALC 5. This places the cursor on the first line. Press ENTER. This moves the cursor to the second line. Press ENTER again and use the arrow keys to move the cursor to the point of intersection. To find the coordinates of this point, press ENTER again. The solution, as shown at the bottom of the screen, is (2.5, 2.5).

Graph each system of equations and state the solution.

1. $x + y = 6$
$2x + y = 5$
$(-1, 7)$

2. $3x + y = 5$
$2x - 10 = 2y$
$(2.5, -2.5)$

3. $x - y = -1$
$3x + 3y = 6$
$(0.5, 1.5)$

4. $-4x + y = -6$
$2x - y = 2$
$(2, 2)$

5. $2x + y = 7$
$4x - 2y = 8$
$(2.75, 1.5)$

6. $y = 0.5x$
$2y = 2x - 6$
$(6, 3)$

TECH PREP

Tech Prep Applications Masters, pp. 5, 6

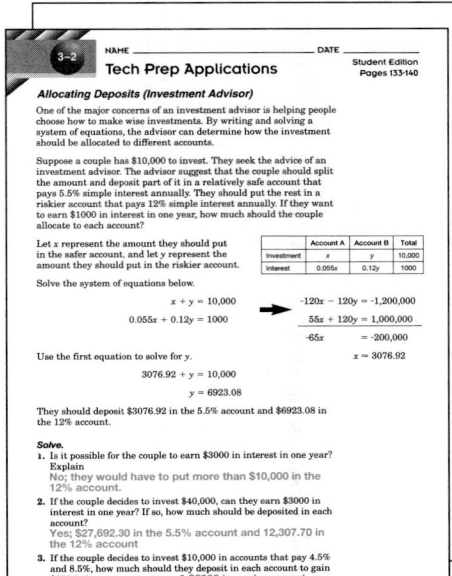

3-2
Tech Prep Applications
Student Edition
Pages 133–140

Allocating Deposits (Investment Advisor)

One of the major concerns of an investment advisor is helping people choose how to make wise investments. By writing and solving a system of equations, the advisor can determine how the investment should be allocated to different accounts.

Suppose a couple has $10,000 to invest. They seek the advice of an investment advisor. The advisor suggest that the couple should split the amount and deposit part of it in a relatively safe account that pays 5.5% simple interest annually. They should put the rest in a riskier account that pays 12% simple interest annually. If they want to earn $1000 in interest in one year, how much should the couple allocate to each account?

Let x represent the amount they should put in the safer account, and let y represent the amount they should put in the riskier account.

	Account A	Account B	Total
Investment	x	y	10,000
Interest	0.055x	0.12y	1000

Solve the system of equations below.

$x + y = 10,000$
$0.055x + 0.12y = 1000$

$-120x - 120y = -1,200,000$
$55x + 120y = 1,000,000$
$-65x = -200,000$
$x \approx 3076.92$

Use the first equation to solve for y.

$3076.92 + y = 10,000$
$y = 6923.08$

They should deposit $3076.92 in the 5.5% account and $6923.08 in the 12% account.

Solve.

1. Is it possible for the couple to earn $3000 in interest in one year? Explain
No; they would have to put more than $10,000 in the 12% account.

2. If the couple decides to invest $40,000, can they earn $3000 in interest in one year? If so, how much should be deposited in each account?
Yes; $27,692.30 in the 5.5% account and 12,307.70 in the 12% account

3. If the couple decides to invest $10,000 in accounts that pay 4.5% and 8.5%, how much should they deposit in each account to gain $650 in interest over one year? $5000 in each account

CONNECTIONS

Science and Math Lab Manual, pp. 35–38

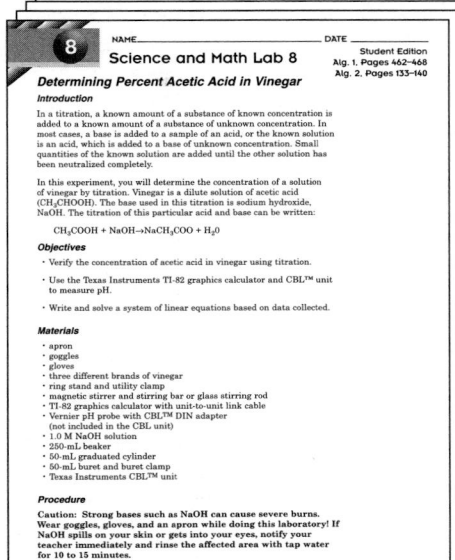

8
Science and Math Lab 8
Student Edition
Alg. 1. Pages 462–468
Alg. 2. Pages 133–140

Determining Percent Acetic Acid in Vinegar

Introduction

In a titration, a known amount of a substance of known concentration is added to a known amount of a substance of unknown concentration. In most cases, a base is added to a sample of an acid, or the known solution is an acid, which is added to a base of unknown concentration. Small quantities of the known solution are added until the other solution has been neutralized completely.

In this experiment, you will determine the concentration of a solution of vinegar by titration. Vinegar is a dilute solution of acetic acid (CH_3COOH). The base used in this titration is sodium hydroxide, NaOH. The titration of this particular acid and base can be written:

$$CH_3COOH + NaOH \rightarrow NaCH_3COO + H_2O$$

Objectives

· Verify the concentration of acetic acid in vinegar using titration.

· Use the Texas Instruments TI-82 graphics calculator and CBL™ unit to measure pH.

· Write and solve a system of linear equations based on data collected.

Materials

· apron
· goggles
· gloves
· three different brands of vinegar
· ring stand and utility clamp
· magnetic stirrer and stirring bar or glass stirring rod
· TI-82 graphics calculator with unit-to-unit link cable
· Vernier pH probe with CBL™ DIN adapter (not included in the CBL unit)
· 1.0 M NaOH solution
· 250-mL beaker
· 50-mL graduated cylinder
· 50-mL buret and buret clamp
· Texas Instruments CBL™ unit

Procedure

Caution: Strong bases such as NaOH can cause severe burns. Wear goggles, gloves, and an apron while doing this laboratory! If NaOH spills on your skin or gets into your eyes, notify your teacher immediately and rinse the affected area with tap water for 10 to 15 minutes.

PROBLEM SOLVING

Problem of the Week Cards, 7, 8, 9

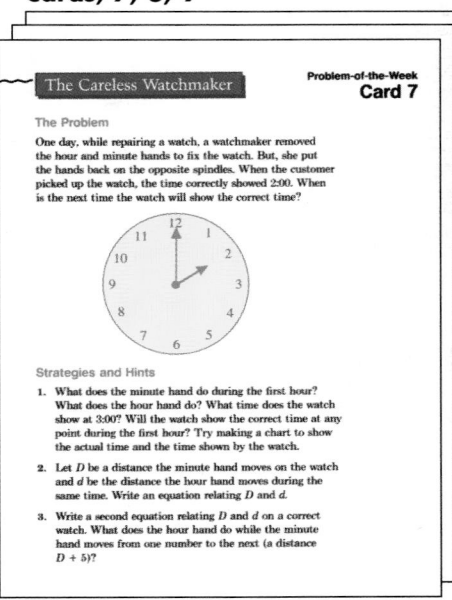

The Careless Watchmaker
Problem-of-the-Week
Card 7

The Problem

One day, while repairing a watch, a watchmaker removed the hour and minute hands to fix the watch. But, she put the hands back on the opposite spindles. When the customer picked up the watch, the time correctly showed 2:00. When is the next time the watch will show the correct time?

Strategies and Hints

1. What does the minute hand do during the first hour? What does the hour hand do? What time does the watch show at 3:00? Will the watch show the correct time at any point during the first hour? Try making a chart to show the actual time and the time shown by the watch.

2. Let D be a distance the minute hand moves on the watch and d be the distance the hour hand moves during the same time. Write an equation relating D and d.

3. Write a second equation relating D and d on a correct watch. What does the hour hand do while the minute hand moves from one number to the next (a distance $D + 5$)?

MAKING MATHEMATICS RELEVANT

This two-page introduction to the chapter provides students with an opportunity to explore contemporary topics and their applications to mathematics.

Background Information

What Will You Do for a Living?
The table provided shows those occupations that are expected to grow the fastest in the next decade. Two areas near the top of the list, computer engineers and scientists and systems analysts, require advanced training in mathematics. Many other occupations listed use computer technology heavily. Encourage students to discuss how each occupation listed would use computers and how mathematics might be used.

Solving Systems of Linear Equations and Inequalities

Objectives

In this chapter, you will:

- solve systems of equations in two or three variables,
- solve systems of inequalities,
- use linear programming to find maximum and minimum values of functions, and
- solve problems by solving a simpler problem.

What Will You Do for a Living?

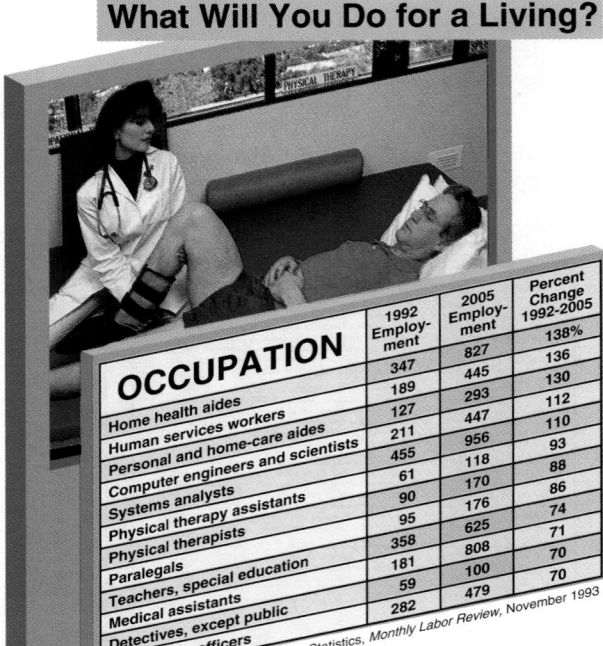

OCCUPATION	1992 Employment	2005 Employment	Percent Change 1992-2005
Home health aides	347	827	138%
Human services workers	189	445	136
Personal and home-care aides	127	293	130
Computer engineers and scientists	211	447	112
Systems analysts	455	956	110
Physical therapy assistants	61	118	93
Physical therapists	90	170	88
Paralegals	95	176	86
Teachers, special education	358	625	74
Medical assistants	181	808	71
Detectives, except public	59	100	70
Corrections officers	282	479	70

Source: Bureau of Labor Statistics, *Monthly Labor Review*, November 1993

The 21st century will truly be the age of science and technology, the age of information. How will the age of information affect the job market of the future? The table above lists the occupations that will be most in demand in 2005.

TIME Line

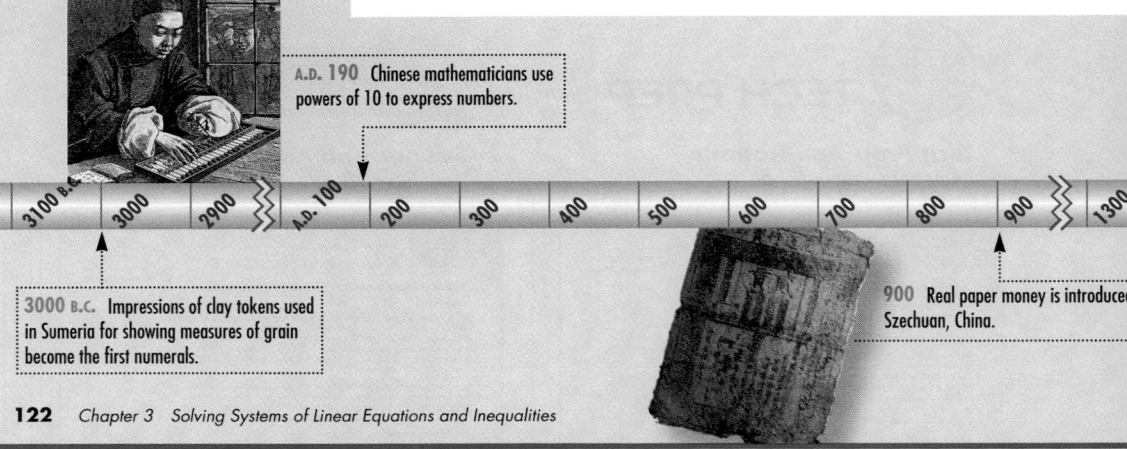

A.D. 190 Chinese mathematicians use powers of 10 to express numbers.

3100 B.C.   3000   2900   A.D. 100   200   300   400   500   600   700   800   900   1300

3000 B.C. Impressions of clay tokens used in Sumeria for showing measures of grain become the first numerals.

900 Real paper money is introduced Szechuan, China.

TIME Line

Students often assume that our numeral system is the natural numeral system. Have them write a report on different numeral systems, beginning with the Sumerian system developed 5000 years ago.

interNET CONNECTION

Browse job openings through one of the top 25 electronic recruiting websites. Investigate requirements for technology-related jobs.

World Wide Web
http://www.interbiznet.com/top2 5.html

Chapter Project

Choose five stocks on the New York Stock Exchange that sell for about the same amount of money. Suppose you purchase 100 shares of each of these stocks.

- Create a graph to track your stock purchases showing their ups and downs over the course of a few weeks.

- Use your graph to compare the values of the stocks. Are there times when two or more of the stocks are worth the same amount of money? Which stock was worth the most at the beginning of the project? Which stock was worth the most at the end of the project?

- Determine the percent of gain or loss on your original capital investment.

Matt Seto, a 17-year-old from Troy, Michigan, is a teen financial wizard who earns respect as he outperforms professional money managers. In 1994, Matt invested in 300 of Best Buy's shares at $21 each and then unloaded all of them for $41 a share. The transaction brought in a $6000 profit, which grew to an incredible $40,700 by the end of 1994 because of his additional investments. Compare that with his $27,900 balance at the beginning of 1994. "It was the best year of my life, definitely," Matt says. "It was the year when everyone started to respect me."

Matt's ambition is balanced by two adults in his life. His economics teacher, David Fillmore, challenges Matt to think critically about his analyses in class. And Matt's father, Chick, inspired by Confucian ideals from his native China, is always looking out for Matt's moral development. "I tell Matt I wish he could be successful in the financial world but still be a good human being." He worries that Matt may become too successful too soon and sacrifice his youth, or worse still, fail and become disillusioned.

Chapter Project

Cooperative Learning You may choose to have students work in groups of four or five to discuss where they should invest their money. They may want to graph the performance of possible stocks over the previous months.

Investigations and Projects Masters, p. 33

| 1602 | Shares of the Dutch East India Company are traded in Amsterdam, claimed to be the first true stock exchange. |

| 1929 | Stock market crash starts the Great Depression. |

VARIETY
WALL ST. LAYS AN EGG

| 1450 | 1500 | 1550 | 1600 | 1650 | 1700 | 1750 | 1800 | 1850 | 1900 | 1950 | 2000 |

1556 First mathematics book in the New World is published by Juan Diez Freyle in Mexico City.

1884 First roller coaster, the Switchback, is built by L. N. Thompson at Luna Park, Coney Island, New York.

Chapter 3 **123**

3 NAME _____ DATE _____
Chapter 3 Project A   Student Edition Pages 124–174

What Will You Do for a Living?

1. Do you know how you want to earn your living? You're probably trying to decide among several careers. List the ones you're considering.

2. Do research to find out more about the careers you listed. A good place to start is the *Occupational Outlook Handbook*, published by the United States Department of Labor. In addition to job descriptions, the handbook contains educational and training requirements and information about whether the number of jobs in various industries will be growing or declining in the future.

3. Select one of the careers on your list. Then interview someone who has chosen a similar career. Find out how the person made his or her career decision, what steps the person took in order to get the position he or she currently holds, and what the person likes or does not like about the work he or she does. Be sure to ask how mathematics, science, and technology are used on the job.

4. Work with several other students to compile your own handbook of careers. Information from the interviews conducted by group members should be included as special features. Wherever possible, use graphs or tables to present your findings.

Alternative Chapter Projects ▬▬▬

Two other chapter projects are included in the *Investigations and Projects Masters*. In Chapter 3 Project A, pp. 33–34, students extend the topic in the chapter opener. In Chapter 3 Project B, pp. 35–36, students study the feasibility of starting a business.

Objective

Use a graphing calculator to graph and solve systems of linear equations.

Recommended Time

25 minutes

Instructional Resources

Graphing Calculator Masters,
pp. 27 and 28

These masters provide keystroking instruction for this lesson for the TI-81 and Casio graphing calculators.

1 FOCUS

Motivating the Lesson

Ask students what is meant by *systems of equations.* Have several students try to define what they think a system of equations is, even if they do not know. How many equations does a system have? After you have explained what a system of equations is, have each student write a system of equations.

2 TEACH

Teaching Tip Point out in paragraph 1 that a system can have none, one, or an infinite number of solutions.

Teaching Tip Point out in Example 1 that if there are other equations entered in your calculator, clear them or turn them off. If the "=" is highlighted, use the arrow keys to move to the "=" and press (ENTER) .

 TEKS 3.b.

3–1A Graphing Technology
Systems of Equations

A Preview of Lesson 3–1

You can use a graphing calculator to graph systems of equations because several equations can be graphed on the screen at the same time. If a system of equations has a solution, it is located where the graphs intersect. The coordinates of the intersection point, (x, y), can be determined by using the TRACE function.

Example Solve the system of equations to the nearest hundredth.

$$y = -x + 4.35$$
$$y = 3x - 3.25$$

Begin by graphing both equations in the standard viewing window.

Enter:  Y=   (-)   X,T,θ   +
4.35   ENTER   3   X,T,θ
—   3.25   ZOOM   6

Use the TRACE function to determine the coordinates of the point of intersection. Press TRACE and use the arrow keys to place the cursor on the intersection point. Observe the coordinates at the bottom of the screen. Then ZOOM IN to determine the coordinates of the intersection point with greater accuracy.

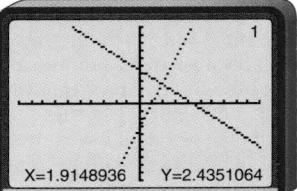

X=1.9148936   Y=2.4351064

Enter: ZOOM   2   ENTER

Use TRACE to position the cursor at the point of intersection and ZOOM IN again. Observe the coordinates. Now move the cursor one time to the left or right. Any digits that remain unchanged as you move are accurate.

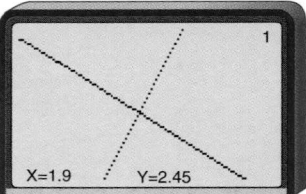

X=1.9   Y=2.45

Repeat the process of zooming and checking digits until you have the number of accurate digits that you desire.

The solution is approximately (1.90, 2.45).   *Verify this result.*

The graphing calculator also has an INTERSECT feature that automatically finds the coordinates of the point of intersection.

Enter: `2nd` `CALC` 5 `ENTER` `ENTER` `ENTER`

You can use the TABLE function on the TI-82 to solve systems of equations.

Example ❷ Solve the system of equations to the nearest hundredth.
$x + y = 4$
$2x + 3y = 9$

First solve each equation for y. $y = -x + 4$
$$y = -\frac{2}{3}x + 3$$

It is not necessary to graph the equations first.

Graph both equations in the standard viewing window.

Enter: `Y=` `(−)` `X,T,θ` `+` 4
`ENTER` `(` `(−)` 2 `÷` 3
`)` `X,T,θ` `+` 3 `ZOOM` 6

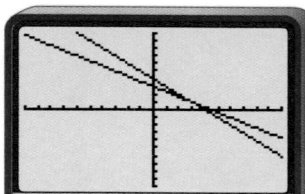

Then press `2nd` `TABLE` . On the screen, you will see the coordinates of points on both lines. Use the arrow keys to scroll up or down and watch the trend of the coordinates. When you find a row at which Y1 = Y2, you have found the solution.

X	Y₁	Y₂
0	4	3
1	3	2.3333
2	2	1.6667
3	1	1
4	0	.33333
5	-1	-.3333
6	-2	-1

X=3

The solution is (3, 1).   *Verify this result.*

EXERCISES

Use a graphing calculator to solve each system of equations to the nearest hundredth.

1. $y = 3x - 2$
$y = -0.5x + 5$ (2, 4)

2. $y = \frac{1}{4}x + 3$
$y = -2x + 21$ (8, 5)

3. $2x + 3y = 8$
$3x - 8y = -13$ (1, 2)

4. $y = -x + 7$
$8 = 2x - y$ (5, 2)

5. $y = 0.125x - 3.005$
$y = -2.58$ (3.40, −2.58)

6. $\frac{1}{2}x + \frac{1}{3}y = 1$
$3x + 2y = 6$ infinitely many

7. (−0.03, 1.03)

8. no solution

7. $3.14x + 2.03y = 1.99$
$9.32x - 3.77y = -4.21$

8. $12y = 4x - 16$
$9y - 3x = 3$

Teaching Tip In Example 1, point out that the `▼` and `▲` keys on the TI-82 will let you alternate between functions. The `►` and `◄` keys will move you along a function.

Teaching Tip To TRACE on the TI-82, as in Example 2, you can move the blinking dot in the center of the screen to the intersection point and press `ZOOM` 2 `ENTER` (in which case you will need to use all four arrow keys) or you can press `TRACE` again and trace along a function (in which case you will only need to use the left and right arrow keys).

Teaching Tip In Example 2, the standard viewing window of [−10, 10] by [−10, 10] is easily accessed on the TI-82 by pressing `ZOOM` 6.

3 PRACTICE/APPLY

Assignment Guide

Core: 1–8
Enriched: 1–8

4 ASSESS

Observing students working with technology is an excellent method of assessment.

Using Technology

This lesson offers an excellent opportunity for using technology in your algebra classroom. For more information on using technology, see *Graphing Calculators in the Mathematics Classroom,* one of the titles in the Glencoe Mathematics Professional Series.

Instructional Resources

- Study Guide Master 3-1
- Practice Master 3-1
- Enrichment Master 3-1
- Graphing Calculator Masters, p. 3

Transparency 3-1A contains the 5-Minute Check for this lesson; **Transparency 3-1B** contains a teaching aid for this lesson.

Recommended Pacing	
Standard Pacing	Day 2 of 14
Honors Pacing	Day 2 of 12
Block Scheduling*	Day 1 of 6

*For more information on pacing and possible lesson plans, refer to the *Block Scheduling Booklet.*

1 FOCUS

5-Minute Check
(over Chapter 2)

1. State the domain and range of {(3, 1),(4, 2),(3, 8),(2, −4)}. Is it a function? **D = {2, 3, 4}, R = {−4, 1, 2, 8}; no**
2. Name the slope, y-intercept, and x-intercept of the graph of $2x − 4y = 10$.
   slope = $\frac{1}{2}$
   y-intercept = $−\frac{5}{2}$
   x-intercept = 5
3. Find the slope-intercept form and the standard form of the equation of the line that has a slope of 4 and passes through the point (4, 1). **$4x − y = 15$ $y = 4x − 15$**

Motivating the Lesson

Hands-On Activity Using a graphing calculator, graph $x + y = 4$ and $x + y = −10$ on the same screen. Do these graphs intersect? **no** Graph $x + y = 2$ and $3x + 4y = 7$ on the same screen. Do these graphs intersect? **yes**

What YOU'LL LEARN

- To solve systems of equations by graphing.

Why IT'S IMPORTANT

You can graph systems of equations to solve problems involving business and nutrition.

APPLICATION
Business

Terri Shackelford is the chief executive officer (CEO) of a commuter airline company. One day, the business section of a newspaper reported that a competing airline had purchased eight new aircraft. They purchased two different sizes of planes for a total of $13.5 million. Ms. Shackelford calls the manufacturer of the planes and learns that the smaller planes cost $1.5 million and the larger planes cost $2 million. She would like to know how many of each size plane her competitor purchased.

She could find the answer by guess and check, but she did not become a CEO by guessing. She decides that using equations might be more straightforward. Let a represent the number of smaller planes purchased, and let b represent the number of larger planes purchased. We can then write the following equations.

$a + b = 8$ *A total of 8 planes was purchased.*

$1.5a + 2b = 13.5$ *The total cost of the planes was $13.5 million.*

By graphing these two equations, we can find the number of each type of plane. Each point of each line has coordinates that satisfy the equation of that line. The one point that satisfies both equations is the point at which the two lines intersect, namely, (5, 3).

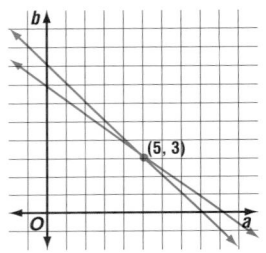

Therefore, the competing company purchased 5 of the smaller planes and 3 of the larger planes.

Together the equations $a + b = 8$ and $1.5a + 2b = 13.5$ are called a **system of equations.** The *solution* of this system is (5, 3). To check this solution, replace a with 5 and b with 3 in each equation.

$$a + b = 8 \qquad\qquad 1.5a + 2b = 13.5$$
$$5 + 3 \overset{?}{=} 8 \qquad\qquad 1.5(5) + 2(3) \overset{?}{=} 13.5$$
$$8 = 8 \checkmark \qquad\qquad 7.5 + 6 \overset{?}{=} 13.5$$
$$13.5 = 13.5 \checkmark$$

The solution (5, 3) is correct.

GLENCOE Technology

CD-ROM Interaction

A multimedia simulation allows students to use systems of equations to determine cost effectiveness of renting a delivery truck. A blackline master activity with teacher's notes provides a follow-up to the CD-ROM simulation.

For Windows & Macintosh

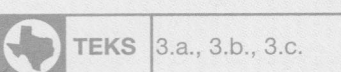
TEKS | 3.a., 3.b., 3.c.

Use a graphing calculator to graph each system of equations. You must first solve each equation for y.

1. $\frac{1}{2}x + \frac{1}{3}y = 2$ **2.** $2x + 3y = 5$ **3.** $y = \frac{x}{2}$

    $x - y = -1$ $-6x - 9y = -15$ $2y = x + 4$

a. Describe the graphs of each system of equations.   a–c. See margin.

b. How are the graphs of the systems of equations similar?

c. How are the graphs of the systems of equations different?

When two lines have different slopes, the graphs of the equations are intersecting lines.

Example 1 **Solve the system of equations by graphing.**
$x + y = 6$
$3x - 4y = 4$

The slope-intercept form of $x + y = 6$ is $y = -x + 6$.

The slope-intercept form of $3x - 4y = 4$ is $y = \frac{3}{4}x - 1$.

In this case, the lines have different slopes and intersect at $(4, 2)$. The solution of the system is $(4, 2)$.

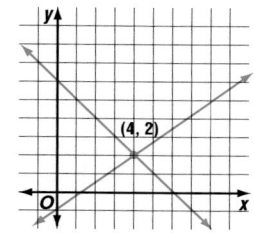

Check: $x + y = 6$ $3x - 4y = 4$

         $4 + 2 \overset{?}{=} 6$ $3(4) - 4(2) \overset{?}{=} 4$

            $6 = 6$ ✓ $12 - 8 \overset{?}{=} 4$

                           $4 = 4$ ✓

A system of equations that has at least one solution is called a **consistent system** of equations. If a system has exactly one solution, it is an **independent system.** So, the system in Example 1 is consistent and independent.

Example 2 **Solve the system of equations by graphing.**
$12x - 9y = 27$
$8x - 6y = 18$

The slope-intercept form of $12x - 9y = 27$ is $y = \frac{4}{3}x - 3$.

The slope-intercept form of $8x - 6y = 18$ is $y = \frac{4}{3}x - 3$.

Since the equations are equivalent, their graphs are the same line. Any ordered pair representing a point on that line will satisfy both equations. So, there are *infinitely many* solutions to this system.

Lesson 3–1 Graphing Systems of Equations **127**

Answers for the Exploration

a. 1. two intersecting lines
    2. one straight line
    3. two parallel lines
b. All are straight lines.
c. The graph of the first system of equations is two intersecting lines. The graph of the second system of equations is just one line. The graph of the third system of equations is a set of parallel lines.

---

2 TEACH

Point out that, in the second pair of equations, the second equation is obtained from the first by multiplying by -3. In the third pair of equations, multiplying the first one by 2 yields $2y = x$, which differs from the second only by adding $+4$.

In-Class Examples

For Example 1
Solve the system of equations by graphing.
$x + y = 5$
$3x - 2y = 20$

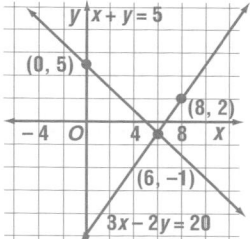

The solution is $(6, -1)$.

For Example 2
Solve the system of equations by graphing.
$y = -3x + 5$
$9x + 3y = 15$

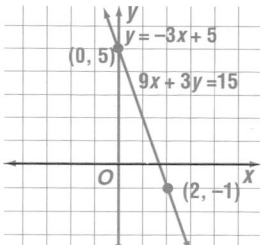

The solution set is $\{(x, y) \mid y = -3x + 5\}$.

Teaching Tip Point out in Example 2 that when the graphs of two equations are the same line, we say the lines *coincide.*

Teaching Tip After studying Example 2, point out that a solution of a system of equations with two variables will be one ordered pair or an infinite number of ordered pairs (lines that coincide), if it exists.

Chapter 3 **127**

Teaching Tip After studying
Example 3, point out that a
system that is consistent has lines
that are not parallel.

In-Class Examples

For Example 3
**Solve the system of equations
by graphing.**
$8x - 4y = 10$
$12x - 6y = 10$
**The solution set is the empty
set $\emptyset$.**

For Example 4
Suppose Frank Jones wants to
start a business similar to Lina
Sanchez, but does not have as
much investment capital. He
finds a less expensive way to
begin. Startup costs are only
$200; each shirt costs only $9
to produce. He can sell his
product for $18. How many
shirts must Frank sell before he
starts to make a profit?
23 shirts

A system is **dependent** if it has an infinite number of solutions. So, the system in Example 2 is consistent and dependent.

Example **Solve the system of equations by graphing.**
$4x + 6y = 18$
$6x + 9y = 18$

The slope-intercept form of $4x + 6y = 18$ is
$y = -\frac{2}{3}x + 3$.

The slope-intercept form of $6x + 9y = 18$ is
$y = -\frac{2}{3}x + 2$.

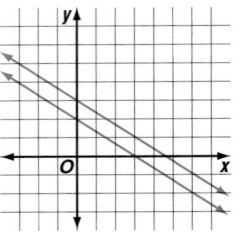

The empty set is also called the null set. The empty or null set can be represented as $\emptyset$ or $\{\}$.

The lines have the same slope, but different y-intercepts. Their graphs are parallel lines. Since they never intersect, there are no solutions to this system. *The solution set is the empty set, $\emptyset$.*

A system with no solutions, like the one in Example 3, is called an **inconsistent system.**

The chart below summarizes the possibilities for the graphs and solutions of two linear equations in two variables, which are illustrated in Examples 1–3.

Example	Graphs of Equations	Slopes and Intercepts	Name of System of Equations	Number of Solutions
1	lines intersect	different slopes	consistent, independent	one
2	lines coincide	same slope, same intercepts	consistent, dependent	infinite
3	lines parallel	same slope, different intercepts	inconsistent	zero

A business can use equations to represent both its costs and its income. A graph of the resulting system of equations clearly illustrates when the business is making a profit and when it is not.

Example  **Lina Sanchez is starting a business in Vail, Colorado. She plans to make souvenir sweatshirts to sell to skiers. She has initial start-up costs of $900. Each sweatshirt costs $18 to produce, and she plans to sell the sweatshirts for $30. How many sweatshirts must Lina sell before she starts to make a profit?**

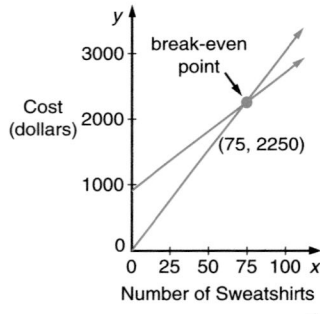

The cost of making x sweatshirts is represented by $y = 900 + 18x$.

The income from x sweatshirts is represented by $y = 30x$.

Graph this system of equations. The graphs of these two equations intersect at $(75, 2250)$. This point is called the *break-even point*. If Lina sells fewer than 75 sweatshirts, she loses money. If she sells more than 75 sweatshirts, she makes a profit.

 ## Alternative Learning Styles

Visual Have students graph a linear equation on graph paper. They should compute two points by hand, plot these, and then draw a straight line through the two points.

 ## Alternative Teaching Strategies

Reading Algebra Knowing the non-mathematical meaning can help students remember the meaning of mathematical terms. Explore the dictionary definitions of *consistent, inconsistent, dependent,* and *independent* and relate these definitions to their meaning in systems of linear equations.

Communicating Mathematics

1a. inconsistent, because lines are parallel

1b. same slope, different intercepts

4. Sample answer: $x + y = 5$ and $x - y = 5$

5a. profit; about $300

MATH JOURNAL

9. $y = 5x - 3$; consistent, dependent

10. $(3.5, 0)$; consistent, independent

11. no solution; inconsistent

12. $(-4, -2)$; consistent, independent

Study the lesson. Then complete the following.

1. Refer to the graph at the right.
   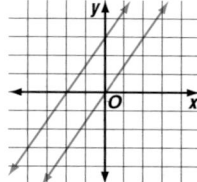
   a. **Explain** whether the graph represents a system of equations that is *consistent and independent, consistent and dependent,* or *inconsistent.*
   b. **Describe** the slope and *y*-intercepts of the graphs.

2. **Sketch** and describe the graphs of $y = -2$ and $x = 4$. What is the solution to this system of linear equations?   See margin.

3. **Explain** why a system of linear equations cannot have exactly two solutions.   Two straight lines cannot intersect in exactly two points.

4. **Write** a system of equations that is consistent.

5. Refer to the graph in Example 4.
   a. Determine if Lina Sanchez would have a profit or a loss if she sold 100 sweatshirts. Estimate the amount of the profit or loss.
   b. How many sweatshirts must Lina sell in order to make a profit of $600?
      125 sweatshirts

6. **Write** a paragraph explaining how to identify whether the graph of a system of linear equations would be two intersecting lines, two distinct parallel lines, or two coincident lines.   See Solutions Manual.

Guided Practice

State the number of solutions to each system of equations. State whether the system is *consistent and independent, consistent and dependent,* or *inconsistent*. If the system is consistent and independent, estimate the solution.

7.
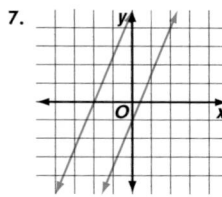
0; inconsistent

8.
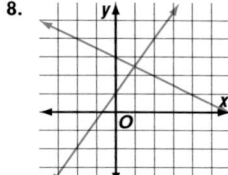
1; consistent, independent; (1, 2.5)

Graph each system of equations and state its solution. Also, state whether the system is *consistent and independent, consistent and dependent,* or *inconsistent*.   9–12. See margin for graphs.

9. $5x - y = 3$
   $y = 5x - 3$

10. $2x - 3y = 7$
    $2x + 3y = 7$

11. $x + y = 6$
    $3x + 3y = 3$

12. $\frac{1}{2}x - y = 0$
    $\frac{1}{4}x + \frac{1}{2}y = -2$

Lesson 3-1 Graphing Systems of Equations   **129**

GLENCOE *Technology*

 Interactive Mathematics Tools Software

This multimedia software provides an interactive lesson by having students compare graphs and equations of linear functions in real-life situations to determine the best deal. A **Computer Journal** gives students an opportunity to write about what they have learned.

For Windows & Macintosh

Reteaching

Using Reasoning The table on page 128 can be developed through reasoning. If two lines have different slopes, they must intersect at exactly one point. If they do not have different slopes, they are either the same line with infinitely many points in common, or distinct parallel lines with no points in common.

Check for Understanding

Exercises 1–13 are designed to help you assess your students' understanding through reading, writing, speaking, and modeling. You should work through Exercises 1–6 with your students and then monitor their work on Exercises 7–13.

Additional Answers

2. a horizontal line and a vertical line intersecting at $(4, -2)$
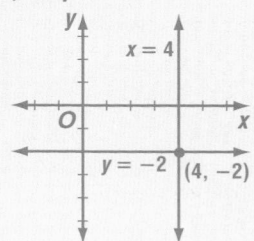

9.
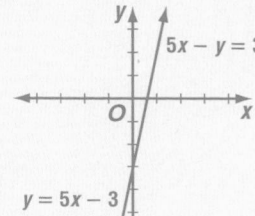

10.
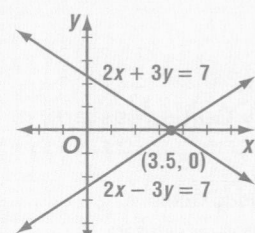

11.
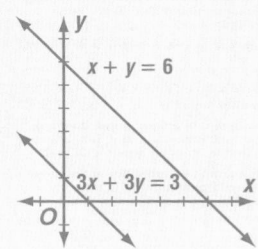

12.
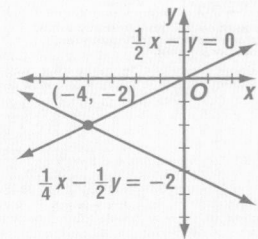

Assignment Guide

Core: 15–47 odd, 49–56
Enriched: 14–42 even, 43–56

For **Extra Practice,** see p. 880.

The red A, B, and C flags, printed only in the Teacher's Wraparound Edition, indicate the level of difficulty of the exercises.

13. Which graph illustrates the solution to the system of equations $x + y = 4$ and $y = x - 2$? **a**

a.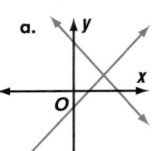
b.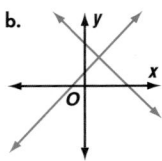
c.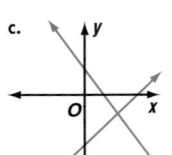
d.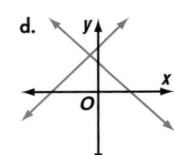

EXERCISES

Practice

State the number of solutions to each system of equations. State whether the system is *consistent and independent, consistent and dependent,* or *inconsistent.* If the system is consistent and independent, estimate the solution.

18. (3, 2); consistent, independent

19. (0, −8); consistent, independent

20. no solution; inconsistent

21. (4, 1); consistent, independent

22. no solutions; inconsistent

23. $x + 2y = 4$; consistent, dependent

24. no solutions; inconsistent

25. (5, 3); consistent, independent

26. $9x + 2y = 8$; consistent, dependent

27. (−9, 3); consistent, independent

28. (3, −5); consistent, independent

29. no solution; inconsistent

30. $3x + 4y = 7$; consistent, dependent

31. (−5,4); consistent, independent

32. no solution; inconsistent

A

14.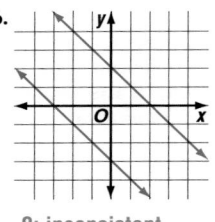

1; consistent, independent; (−1, 4)

15.

1; consistent, independent; (−3, 0)

16.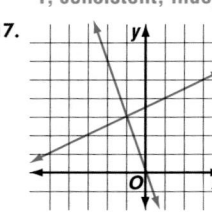

0; inconsistent

17.

1; consistent, independent; (−1, 3)

Graph each system of equations and state its solution. Also, state whether the system is *consistent and independent, consistent and dependent,* or *inconsistent.*   18–32. See Solutions Manual for graphs.

18. $2x + 3y = 12$
$\quad 2x - y = 4$

19. $3x - y = 8$
$\quad x - y = 8$

20. $4x - 6y = 5$
$\quad 2x - 3y = 5$

21. $x + 2y = 6$
$\quad 2x + y = 9$

22. $x + 1 = y$
$\quad 2x - 2y = 8$

23. $2x + 4y = 8$
$\quad x + 2y = 4$

B

24. $3x - 8y = 4$
$\quad 6x - 42 = 16y$

25. $3x + 6 = 7y$
$\quad x + 2y = 11$

26. $\frac{3}{4}x + \frac{1}{6}y = \frac{2}{3}$
$\quad 9x + 2y = 8$

27. $\frac{2}{3}x + y = -3$
$\quad y - \frac{1}{3}x = 6$

28. $\frac{4}{3}x + \frac{1}{5}y = 3$
$\quad \frac{2}{3}x - \frac{3}{5}y = 5$

29. $9x + 8y = 8$
$\quad \frac{3}{4}x + \frac{2}{3}y = 8$

30. $3x + 4y = 7$
$\quad 1.5x + 2y = 3.5$

31. $1.2x + 2.5y = 4$
$\quad 0.8x - 1.5y = -10$

32. $5x - 7y = 70$
$\quad -10x + 14y = 120$

Study Guide Masters, p. 15

NAME _____   DATE _____

Study Guide   Student Edition Pages 126–132

Graphing Systems of Equations

You can solve a system of equations (two equations) by graphing the slope-intercept form of an equation. The *solution* is the intersection point of the two graphs.

Example: Graph this system of equations and state its solution.
$x + y = 6$
$3x + 4y = 12$
The slope-intercept form of $x + y = 6$ is $y = -x + 6$.
The slope-intercept form of $3x + 4y = 12$ is $y = -\frac{3}{4}x + 3$.
Since the two lines have different slopes, the graphs of the equations are intersecting lines. They intersect at (12, −6). The solution of the system is (12, −6).

The following chart summarizes the possibilities for the graphs of two linear equations in two variables.

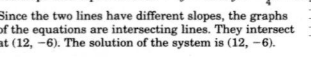

Graphs of Equations	Slopes of Lines	Name of System of Equations	Number of Solutions
lines intersect	different slopes	consistent and independent	one
lines coincide	same slope, same intercepts	consistent and dependent	infinite
lines parallel	same slope, different intercepts	inconsistent	none

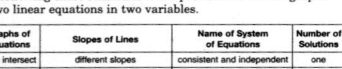

Graph each system of equations and state its solution. Also, state whether the system is consistent and independent, consistent and dependent, or inconsistent.

1. $3x - y = 0$ consistent,
   $x - y = -2$ independent, (1, 3)

2. $3x + y = -2$ inconsistent,
   $6x + 2y = 10$ ∅

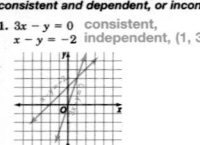
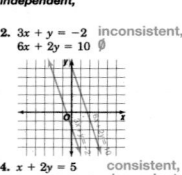

3. $4x + 2y = 8$ consistent,
   $12x + 6y = 24$ dependent, {(x, y)| $4x + 2y = 8$}

4. $x + 2y = 5$ consistent,
   $3x - 15 = -6y$ dependent, {(x, y)| $x + 2y = 4$}

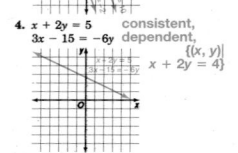

33. $m = \frac{5}{2}$, $n = -\frac{3}{2}$

34. $m \neq \frac{4}{5}$,

$n =$ any real number

35. $m = \frac{3}{2}$, $n \neq 4$

36. $m = \frac{7}{2}$, $n = \frac{5}{2}$

Find values of m and n that satisfy the condition given for each system.

33. $5x - 3y = 8$
    $mx + ny = 4$
    consistent and dependent

34. $4x - 5y = 10$
    $mx - y = n$
    consistent and independent

35. $3x + 4y = 8$
    $mx + 2y = n$
    inconsistent

36. $2x + 7y = 5$
    $x + my = n$
    consistent and dependent

37. **Geometry**   The sides of an angle are parts of two lines whose equations are $y = -\frac{3}{2}x - 6$ and $y = \frac{2}{3}x + 7$. Find the coordinates of the vertex of the angle. $(-6, 3)$

38. **Geometry**   The length of the base of an isosceles triangle is 2 centimeters shorter than the length of either of the other sides. If the perimeter of the triangle is 16 centimeters, find the length of each side of the triangle.
    6 cm, 6 cm, 4 cm

Graphing Calculator

Use a graphing calculator to solve each system of equations to the nearest hundredth.

39. $3.6x + 4.8y = -7.2$
    $5.8x - 7.1y = 32.9$ $(2, -3)$

40. $-14x + 18y = 75$
    $9.1x - 11.7y = 36$ no solution

41. $3.6x - 2y = 4$
    $-2.7x + y = 3$ $(-5.56, -12.00)$

42. $7x + 13.5y = 31$
    $9.8x + 18.9y = 43.4$ $7x + 13.5y = 31$

Critical Thinking

43. State the conditions for which the system below is: (a) consistent and dependent, (b) consistent and independent, and (c) inconsistent.

$ax + by = c$ (a) $\frac{a}{d} = \frac{b}{e} = \frac{c}{f}$; (b) $\frac{a}{d} \neq \frac{b}{e}$; (c) $\frac{a}{d} = \frac{b}{e} \neq \frac{c}{f}$
$dx + ey = f$

Applications and Problem Solving

44. **Consumer Awareness**   During the week of February 27 to March 5, 1995, the Kroger and Meijer grocery stores in Columbus, Ohio, had sales on General Mills cereals. At Kroger, all General Mills cereals were $33\frac{1}{3}\%$ off, while at Meijer, the cereals were $1 off. Assume that the regular prices of the cereals were the same at each store.   **a–d. See margin.**

    a. Graph a system of equations representing the sales at the two stores.
    b. What does the point of intersection represent?
    c. For what regular prices would Kroger's sale be a better deal?
    d. For what regular prices would Meijer's sale be a better deal?

45. 3 field goals and
4 points after

45. **Football**   Mani Peters is the kicker for the Winston College football team. In one game, Mani kicked the ball 9 times for a total of 13 points. If 2 of the 9 kicks were no good, how many field goals (worth 3 points each) and how many points after touchdowns (worth 1 point each) did Mani make?

46. **Consumer Awareness**   The Photo Shop charges $1.60 to develop a roll of film plus 11¢ for each print, while Photos R Us charges $1.20 to develop a roll plus 11¢ a print. Under what conditions is it best to use the Photo Shop and when is it best to use Photos R Us?   **Photos R Us is always cheaper.**

Additional Answers

44a. Let c = regular price, and let d = discount price.
    Graph $d = \frac{2}{3}c$
    and $d = c - 1$.

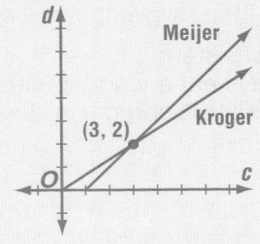

44b. the regular price where the discount prices would be the same
44c. For cereals that cost more than $3, Kroger had the better deal.
44d. For cereals that cost less than $3, Meijer had the better deal.

Practice Masters, p. 15

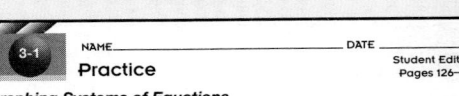

Graphing Systems of Equations

Graph each system of equations and state its solution. Also, state whether the system is consistent and independent, consistent and dependent, or inconsistent.

1. $2x + y = 4$ (2, 0); consistent
   $x - y = 2$ and independent

2. $x + y = 2$ no solutions;
   $x + y = 6$ inconsistent

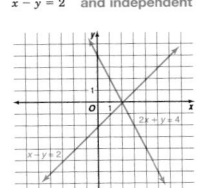
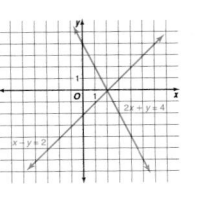

3. $2y - 8 = x$ all points on the
   $y = \frac{1}{2}x + 4$ line; consistent and dependent

4. $x - 2y = 0$ (2, 1); consistent
   $y = 2x - 3$ and independent

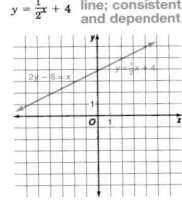
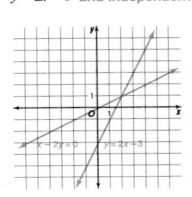

Closing Activity

Modeling Have students sketch each of the following three cases:

1. inconsistent
2. consistent and independent
3. consistent and dependent

Additional Answers

47c. Yes, the consumption of margarine has decreased in recent years.

49.

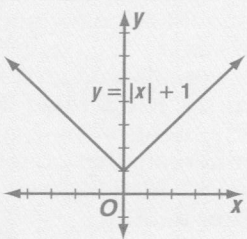

$y = |x| + 1$

53.

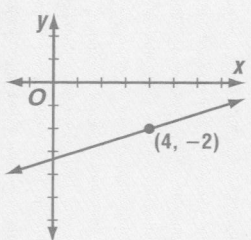

$(4, -2)$

Enrichment Masters, p. 15

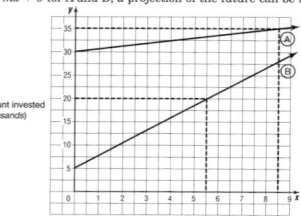

47. Nutrition The graph at the right shows how the consumption of butter and margarine has changed over the years.

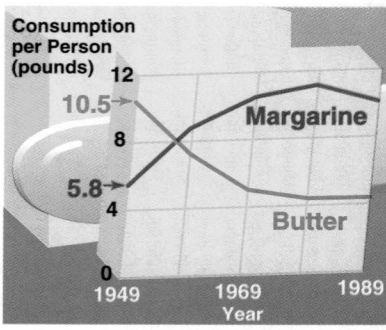

a. During the early 1950s, which was more popular, butter or margarine?   **butter**

b. Estimate the year that the consumption of butter and margarine was equal.   **about 1957**

c. A recent study has shown that the consumption of margarine raises cholesterol levels. Do you think that this information has changed the consumption of margarine? Explain.   **See margin.**

d. Do you think that the consumption of butter and margarine will be the same again sometime in the future? Explain.   **See students' work.**

48. Guess and Check Mr. and Mrs. Leshin have fewer than ten children. The sum of the squares of the number of boys and the number of girls in the family equals 25. How many children do Mr. and Mrs. Leshin have?   **7 children**

50. $d = 12.79t$; direct variation

Mixed Review

49. Graph $y = |x| + 1$. (Lesson 2–6)   **See margin.**

50. Speed Skating In the 1988 Winter Olympics, Bonnie Blair set a world record for women's speed skating by skating approximately 12.79 meters per second in the 500-meter race. Suppose she could maintain that speed. Write an equation that represents how far she could travel in t seconds. What type of function does the equation represent? (Lesson 2–6)

51. Economics A developer surveyed families in a suburb of Raleigh, North Carolina, to determine their monthly household income and the percent of their income spent on housing. The table below shows the data from eight families. (Lesson 2–5)

Monthly Income ($)	870	1430	1920	2460	2850	3240	3790	4510
Percent Spent on Housing	44	39	40	35	43	38	37	33

51a. Sample answer: $y = -0.003x + 47$

a. Write a prediction equation for this relationship.

b. Predict the percent of income spent on housing by a family with a monthly income of $3000.   **about 38%**

52. $y = -\frac{1}{8}x + 5$

52. Write an equation of the line that passes through $(-16, 7)$ and is perpendicular to the line whose equation is $y = 8x - 4$. (Lesson 2–4)

53. Graph a line that passes through $(4, -2)$ and is perpendicular to a line whose slope is -3. (Lesson 2–3)   **See margin.**

54. Find the slope of a line passing through $(5, 4)$ and $(2, 2)$. (Lesson 2–3) $\frac{2}{3}$

55. Write $x = \frac{1}{3}y + 3$ in standard form. (Lesson 2–2) $3x - y = 9$

56. Evaluate $[25 - (5 - 2)^2 + 5] \div 7$. (Lesson 1–1)   **3**

132 Chapter 3 Solving Systems of Linear Equations and Inequalities

Extension

Reasoning When are graphs of two equations:

a. the same line?

b. intersecting lines?

c. parallel lines?

a. When the system of equations is consistent and dependent.

b. When the system of equations is consistent and independent.

c. When the system of equations is inconsistent.

Solving Systems of Equations Algebraically

What YOU'LL LEARN

- To use the substitution and elimination methods to solve systems of equations.

Why IT'S IMPORTANT

You can use systems of equations to solve problems involving literature and population growth.

APPLICATION
Consumerism

Austin is moving to a new condominium. He is sure that he can complete the move in one day, but he does not know how many trips he will need to make between his old and new residences. He plans to rent a 16-foot moving van for a day. When he checks the cost, he finds the following.

Rent-A-Truck: $59.95 a day plus 49¢ per mile
Sam's U-Drive: $81 per day plus 38¢ per mile

Austin needs to determine the mileage at which it is better to rent from Rent-A-Truck and the mileage at which it is better to rent from Sam's U-Drive.

To solve the problem, let m represent the miles driven and let c represent the total cost. Then we can write and graph the following equations.

$c = 59.95 + 0.49m$ *Cost for Rent-A-Truck*
$c = 81 + 0.38m$ *Cost for Sam's U-Drive*

It is very difficult to determine an exact solution from the graph. However, we can use the graph to estimate the solution. An estimate of the solution of this system of equations is (190, 150).

The cost will be the same if the mileage is somewhere around 190 miles. For lesser distances, Rent-A-Truck is cheaper, and for greater distances, Sam's U-Drive is cheaper.

For systems of equations like this one, it may be easier to solve the system by using algebraic methods rather than by graphing. Two algebraic methods are the **substitution method** and the **elimination method.** *This system of equations will be solved algebraically in Example 1.*

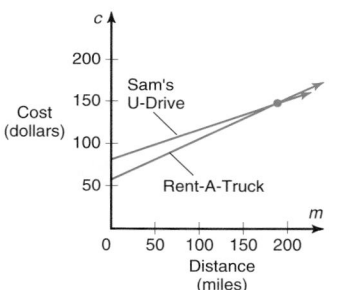

Lesson 3–2 Solving Systems of Equations Algebraically **133**

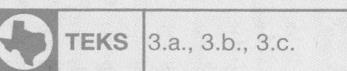
TEKS   3.a., 3.b., 3.c.

3-2 LESSON NOTES

NCTM Standards: 1–5

Instructional Resources

- Study Guide Master 3-2
- Practice Master 3-2
- Enrichment Master 3-2
- Assessment and Evaluation Masters, p. 72
- Modeling Mathematics Masters, p. 63
- Science and Math Lab Manual, pp. 35–38
- Tech Prep Applications Masters, p. 5

 Transparency 3-2A contains the 5-Minute Check for this lesson; **Transparency 3-2B** contains a teaching aid for this lesson.

Recommended Pacing	
Standard Pacing	Day 3 of 14
Honors Pacing	Day 3 of 12
Block Scheduling*	Day 2 of 6 (along with Lesson 3-3)

 *For more information on pacing and possible lesson plans, refer to the *Block Scheduling Booklet.*

1 FOCUS

 5-Minute Check
(over Lesson 3-1)

Solve the system of equations by graphing. State whether the system is consistent and independent, consistent and dependent, or inconsistent.

$2x + 3y = 5$
$3x - 4y = -1$
consistent and independent

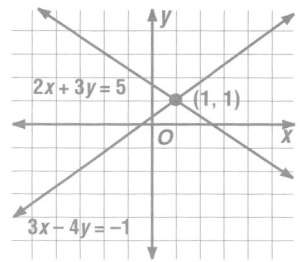

Motivating the Lesson

Situational Problem Have students solve the system of equations by graphing.

$x - y = 10$
$x + y = 13.6$
(11.8, 1.8)

What happens when you try to determine the solution? How could you handle the difficulty?

2 TEACH

MODELING MATHEMATICS Remind students that the same number of counters (either positive or negative) can be added to or removed from each side without changing the value of the equation.

In-Class Example

For Example 1
Suppose Rent-A-Truck's rates are $50 a day plus 50¢ per mile and Sam's U-Drive's are $70 a day plus 45¢ per mile.

a. Find the mileage at which the cost for the two would be the same. **400 miles**
b. What is the cost? **$250**
c. Under what conditions should one rent from Rent-A-Truck?
Under 400 miles; it is better to rent Sam's when planning to drive more than 400 miles.

Teaching Tip In Example 1, make sure students understand that the substitution method is chosen when one of the equations can be easily solved for one of the variables.

MODELING MATHEMATICS

Systems of Equations

Materials: equation mat   cups and counters

Use modeling to solve the system of equations.

$3x + 2y = 9$
$y = x + 2$

Your Turn

a. Let one cup represent x. If $y = x + 2$, how can you represent y? **a cup and 2 positive counters**
b. Represent $3x + 2y = 9$ on the equation mat. On one side of the mat, place three cups to represent $3x$ and two representations of y from step a. On the other side of the mat, place nine positive counters.

c. Use what you know about equation mats and zero pairs to solve the equation. What value of x solves the system of equations? **1**
d. Use the value of x from step c and the equation $y = x + 2$ to find the value of y. **3**
e. What is the solution of the system of equations? **(1, 3)**

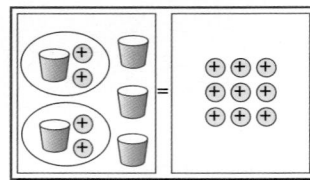

In the substitution method, one equation is solved for one variable in terms of the other. Then, this expression for the variable is substituted in the other equation.

Example ❶ Refer to the application at the beginning of the lesson.

APPLICATION
Consumerism

a. Determine the mileage for which the cost for Rent-A-Truck and Sam's U-Drive would be the same. Find the cost.
b. Under what conditions should Austin rent from Rent-A-Truck and under what conditions should Austin rent from Sam's U-Drive?

a. The two equations are $c = 59.95 + 0.49m$ and $c = 81 + 0.38m$. To solve this system of equations, use the substitution method.

$$c = 59.95 + 0.49m$$
$$81 + 0.38m = 59.95 + 0.49m \quad \textit{Substitute (81 + 0.38m) for c.}$$
$$8100 + 38m = 5995 + 49m \quad \textit{Multiply by 100. Why?}$$
$$2105 = 11m$$
$$191.36 \approx m \quad \textit{Solve for m.}$$

Alternative Learning Styles

Auditory Read the problem in Example 1 aloud in class. At key points, summarize what is known at that point. Have students relate how they would solve the problem.

Substitute 191.36 for m in $c = 59.95 + 0.49m$.

$c = 59.95 + 0.49m$
$c \approx 59.95 + 0.49(191.36)$ *Substitute 191.36 for m.*
$c \approx 153.72$ *Solve for c.*

The solution is about (191.36, 153.72). Therefore, at about 191.36 miles, the cost of $153.72 is equal for both Rent-A-Truck and Sam's U-Drive. *Compare this result to the estimate we obtained from the graph.*

b. Austin will need to decide how many trips he thinks he will need to make. If he thinks he will be driving fewer than 191.36 miles, he should rent from Rent-A-Truck. If he thinks he will be driving more than 191.36 miles, he should rent from Sam's U-Drive.

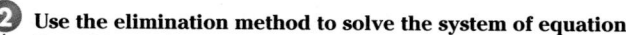

The second algebraic method is the elimination method. To use the elimination method effectively, first compare the coefficients of the variables.

Example **2** Use the elimination method to solve the system of equations.
$3a - 2b = -3$
$3a + b = 3$

In each equation, the coefficient of a is 3. If one equation is subtracted from the other, the variable a will be eliminated.

$$
\begin{array}{rl}
3a - 2b = -3 & \\
(-)\ 3a + b = 3 & \text{\textit{Subtract.}} \\
\hline
-3b = -6 & \text{\textit{The variable a is eliminated.}} \\
b = 2 & \text{\textit{Solve for b.}}
\end{array}
$$

Now, find a by substituting 2 for b in either original equation.

First Equation   or   **Second Equation**

$3a - 2b = -3$ $3a + b = 3$
$3a - 2(2) = -3$ *Substitute 2 for b.* $3a + 2 = 3$
$3a - 4 = -3$ $3a = 1$
$3a = 1$ $a = \dfrac{1}{3}$
$a = \dfrac{1}{3}$

The solution is $\left(\dfrac{1}{3}, 2\right)$.

Check by replacing (a, b) with $\left(\dfrac{1}{3}, 2\right)$ in each equation.

First Equation: $3\left(\dfrac{1}{3}\right) - 2(2) \overset{?}{=} -3$ *Second Equation:* $3\left(\dfrac{1}{3}\right) + 2 \overset{?}{=} 3$
$-3 = -3$ ✓ $3 = 3$ ✓

In-Class Example

For Example 2
Use the elimination method to solve the system of equations.
$7x - 4y = 17$
$3x + 5y = 14$
(3, 1)

In-Class Example

For Example 3
**Use the elimination method
to solve the system of
equations.**
$2x - y = 6$
$3x + 5y = 22$
(4, 2)

In the following example, adding or subtracting the two equations will not eliminate either variable.

Example Use the elimination method to solve the system of equations.
$3x + 5y = -4$
$2x - 3y = 29$

To use the elimination method we must write equivalent equations containing the same coefficient for either x or y.

Method 1
Multiply the first equation by 3 and the second by 5. Then the variable y can be eliminated by addition.

$3x + 5y = -4$ Multiply by 3. ➔ $9x + 15y = -12$

$2x - 3y = 29$ Multiply by 5. ➔ $10x - 15y = 145$

Now, add to eliminate y.

$$
\begin{array}{rl}
9x + 15y = -12 & \\
(+)\ 10x - 15y = 145 & \text{Add.} \\
\hline
19x \quad\quad\ = 133 & \text{The variable } x \text{ is eliminated.} \\
x = 7 &
\end{array}
$$

Find y by substituting 7 for x in $3x + 5y = -4$.

$$
\begin{array}{rl}
3(7) + 5y = -4 & \text{Substitute 7 for x.} \\
21 + 5y = -4 & \\
5y = -25 & \\
y = -5 & \text{Solve for y.}
\end{array}
$$

The solution is $(7, -5)$. *Check this solution.*

Method 2
We could also solve the system by eliminating x first. Multiply the first equation by 2 and the second by -3. Then add.

$3x + 5y = -4$ Multiply by 2. ➔ $6x + 10y = -8$

$2x - 3y = 29$ Multiply by -3. ➔

$$
\begin{array}{r}
(+)\ -6x + 9y = -87 \\
\hline
19y = -95 \\
y = -5
\end{array}
$$

Finally, solve for x.

$$
\begin{array}{rl}
3x + 5(-5) = -4 & \text{Substitute } -5 \text{ for y.} \\
3x - 25 = -4 & \\
3x = 21 & \\
x = 7 & \text{Solve for x.}
\end{array}
$$

The solution is $(7, -5)$.

Communicating Mathematics

Study the lesson. Then complete the following. 1–2. See margin.

1. **Describe** how we could have solved Example 1 by using elimination.

2. **Explain** when you might use substitution rather than elimination.

3. Consider the system of equations $y = 4x + 3$ and $y = 2x - 5$.
   a. Use the symmetric and transitive properties of equality to write a statement about $4x + 3$ and $2x - 5$. $4x + 3 = 2x - 5$

3b. See margin.
3c. $(-4, -13)$

   b. Explain how you could solve the system of equations now.
   c. If you graph the system of equations, where would the lines intersect?

4. **You Decide** When Helen solves the system of equations $4y - 8x = 28$ and $y = 2x - 5$, the result is $-20 = 28$. Helen decides that the graphs of the equations are the same line. Juanita says that the graphs of the equations are parallel lines. Who is correct, and why? See margin.

MODELING MATHEMATICS

5. Use cups and counters to model and solve the system of equations.
   $x + 2y = -5$ $(-3, -1)$
   $y = x + 2$

Guided Practice

Solve each system of equations by using substitution.

6. $x - 2y = 1$
   $x + y = 4$ (3, 1)

7. $2p + 3q = 2$
   $p - 3q = -17$ $(-5, 4)$

Solve each system of equations by using elimination.

8. $m + n = 6$
   $m - n = 5$ (5.5, 0.5)

9. $5x + 3y = 0$
   $4x + 5y = 13$ $(-3, 5)$

Solve each system of equations. Use either algebraic method.

10. $4a - b = 26$
    $8a - b = 54$ (7, 2)

11. $6x + 9y = -45$
    $2x + 3y = -15$ $2x + 3y = -15$

12. $3s - 2t = 10$
    $4s + t = 6$ (2, −2)

13. $\frac{1}{4}x + y = \frac{7}{2}$
    $2x - y = 4$ $\left(\frac{10}{3}, \frac{8}{3}\right)$

14. 69°, 111°

14. **Geometry** If the measure of one angle is five less than two-thirds of the measure of its supplementary angle, find the measure of the angles.

Practice

A

Solve each system of equations by using substitution. 16. $(-5, 6)$

15. $4x - 3y = 18$
    $3x + y = 7$ (3, −2)

16. $x + 3y = 13$
    $-3x + 2y = 27$

17. $3r + 9s = 36$
    $r = 8s - 10$ (6, 2)

19. $\left(-3, \frac{1}{2}\right)$

20. $\left(\frac{1}{2}, \frac{2}{3}\right)$

18. $n = 3m + 7$
    $4m + 9n = 1$ $(-2, 1)$

19. $4x + 6y = -9$
    $2x - 10y = -11$

20. $4x + 3y = 4$
    $6x - 6y = -1$

Solve each system of equations by using elimination. 23. $(8, -5)$

21. $x - 3y = -12$
    $2x + 11y = -7$ $(-9, 1)$

22. $3x - 4y = 1$
    $5x + 2y = 45$ (7, 5)

23. $4p + 5q = 7$
    $3p - 2q = 34$

26. $(5, -8)$

B

24. $5c - 6d = -27$
    $7c + 3d = -15$ $(-3, 2)$

25. $\frac{1}{3}x + \frac{1}{2}y = 7$
    $\frac{2}{3}x - y = -2$ (9, 8)

26. $\frac{2}{5}x - \frac{1}{2}y = 6$
    $\frac{4}{5}x + \frac{3}{2}y = -8$

Check for Understanding

Exercises 1–14 are designed to help you assess your students' understanding through reading, writing, speaking, and modeling. You should work through Exercises 1–5 with your students and then monitor their work on Exercises 6–14.

Error Analysis
Students might solve one of the equations for one variable and then substitute that expression into the same equation. When they do this, they will arrive at $0 = 0$ and incorrectly conclude that the solution set is infinite.

Additional Answers
1. By subtracting the equations, the variable c would disappear.
2. One of the equations is already solved for a variable, one of the variables has a coefficient of 1, or equations are in slope-intercept form.
3b. Solve $4x + 3 = 2x - 5$ for x, and then use one equation to solve for y.
4. Juanita; $-20 = 28$ is an incorrect statement; therefore, there are no solutions, and the graph is parallel lines.

Reteaching

Using Substeps List the steps you would take to solve each system of equations by elimination or substitution. Then solve.

1. $x - 2y = 1$
   $3x + 2y = 19$
   (5, 2)

2. $3x - y = 10$
   $x - 5y = -6$
   (4, 2)

3. $y = 5 - 2x$
   $3x - 2y = 11$
   (3, −1)

4. $2x - 3y = 13$
   $x - y = 5$
   (2, −3)

Assignment Guide

Core: 15–41 odd, 42, 43, 45, 47–55
Enriched: 16–40 even, 41–55

For **Extra Practice,** see p. 881.

The red A, B, and C flags, printed only in the Teacher's Wraparound Edition, indicate the level of difficulty of the exercises.

Teaching Tip In Exercises 27–38, encourage students to decide which method, substitution or elimination, is easier to use for solving a given system.

Using the Programming Exercises The program given in Exercise 41 is for use with a TI–82 graphing calculator. For other programmable calculators, have students consult their owner's manual for commands similar to those presented here.

Study Guide Masters, p. 16

NAME_____ DATE _____
3-2
Study Guide
Student Edition
Pages 133–140

Solving Systems of Equations Algebraically

sually a system of equations is easier to solve by algebraic
ethods than by graphing. Two algebraic methods are the
ubstitution method and the elimination method.

xample: $4x - y = 11$
$2x + 2y = 18$

Substitution Method
1. Solve the first equation for y: $y = 4x - 11$.
2. Substitute $4x - 11$ for y in the second equation.
3. Solve for x: $x = 4$.
4. Find y by substituting 4 for x in $4x - y = 11$. The solution is (4, 5).

xample: $5x + 3y = -1$
$4x - 3y = -17$

Elimination Method
1. Add the two equations: $9x = -18$
2. Solve for x: $x = -2$
3. Find y by substituting -2 for x in $4x - 3y = -17$. The solution is $(-2, 3)$.

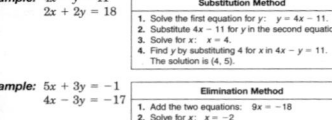

lve each system of equations by using substitution.

. $x = 4$ 2. $3x + y = 7$
$2x - 3y = -19$ $4x + 2y = 16$
(4, 9)   (−1, 10)

$2x + y = 5$ 4. $2x + 2y = 4$
$3x - 3y = 3$ $x - 2y = 0$
(2, 1) $\left(\frac{4}{3}, \frac{2}{3}\right)$

lve each system of equations by using elimination.

. $-4x + y = -12$ 6. $5x + 2y = 12$
$4x + 2y = 6$ $-6x - 2y = -14$
$\left(\frac{5}{2}, -2\right)$ (2, 1)

. $5x + 4y = 12$ 8. $5m + 2n = -8$
$7x - 6y = 40$ $4m + 3n = 2$
(4, −2)   (−4, 6)

27. $\left(\frac{1}{2}, -\frac{1}{2}\right)$

34. $2.5m -$
$1.3m = 0.9$

37. $(-5, 4)$

38. $\left(-\frac{3}{4}, \frac{2}{3}\right)$

40. $(-5, -2)$, $(4, 4)$,
$(-2, -8)$, $(1, 10)$

Solve each system of equations. Use either substitution or elimination. 29. no solution

27. $3x - 7y = 5$
$x + 3y = -1$

28. $2p - 5q = -53$
$6p + 7q = 39$ $(-4, 9)$

29. $2a - b = 8$
$6a - 3b = -9$

30. $3u + 5v = -12$
$2u - 3v = -8$ $(-4, 0)$

31. $y = 5x + 37$
$2x - 3y = -20$ $(-7, 2)$

32. $5s - t = 2$
$t = 4s + 3$ $(5, 23)$

33. $y = 3x - 27$
$y = \frac{1}{2}x - 7$ $(8, -3)$

34. $2.5m - 1.3n = 0.9$
$10m - 5.2n = 3.6$

35. $\frac{1}{4}x + \frac{3}{5}y = -3$
$\frac{3}{4}x - \frac{2}{5}y = 13$
$(12, -10)$

36. $\frac{3}{5}s - \frac{1}{6}t = 1$
$\frac{1}{5}s + \frac{5}{6}t = 11$ $(5, 12)$

37. $1.5a - 0.2b = -8.3$
$0.4a + 0.4b = -0.4$

38. $4m + 9n = 3$
$8m - 3n = -8$

39. **Geometry** Find the coordinates of the vertices of the triangle whose sides are contained in the lines whose equations are $5x - 3y = -7$, $x + 2y = 9$, and $3x - 7y = 1$. $(1, 4), (-2, -1), (5, 2)$

40. **Geometry** Find the coordinates of the vertices of the parallelogram whose sides are contained in the lines whose equations are $2x + y = -12$, $2x - y = -8$, $2x - y - 4 = 0$, and $4x + 2y = 24$.

Programming

41. The graphing calculator program at the right will help you solve systems of equations of the form $Ax + By = C$ and $Dx + Ey = F$.

Run the program to find the solution for each system of equations.

a. $x - 3y = 6$
$2x + 6y = 24$ $(9, 1)$

b. $x + 4y = 2$
$-x + y = -7$ $(6, -1)$

c. $2x - y = 36$
$3x - 0.5y = 26$ $(4, -28)$

d. $2x + y = 45$
$3x - y = 5$ $(10, 25)$

```
PROGRAM:SLVSYSTM
: Disp "ENTER COEFFICIENTS"
: Prompt A,B,C,D,E,F
: If AE-BD=0
: Then
: Goto 1
: End
: (CE-BF)/(AE-BD) → X
: (AF-CD)/(AE-BD) → Y
: Disp "THE SOLUTION IS"
: Disp "X=", X
: Disp "Y=", Y
: Stop
: Lbl 1
: If CE-BF=0 or AF-CD=0
: Then
: Disp "INFINITE", "SOLUTIONS"
: Else
: Disp "NO SOLUTION"
```

Critical Thinking

42. Solve the system of equations. (*Hint:* Let $n = \frac{1}{x}$ and $m = \frac{1}{y}$.)
$\frac{1}{x} + \frac{3}{y} = \frac{3}{4}$
$\frac{3}{x} - \frac{2}{y} = \frac{5}{12}$ $(4, 6)$

Applications and Problem Solving

43. 210 cups of hot chocolate, 85 cups of coffee

43. **Sales** The drama club at Lincoln High School sells hot chocolate and coffee at the school's football games to make money for a special trip. At one game, they sold $200 worth of hot drinks. They need to report how many of each type of drink they sold for their club records. Macha knows that they used 295 cups that night. If hot chocolate sells for 75¢ and coffee sells for 50¢, how many of each type of hot drinks did they sell?

44. Literature Lewis Carroll was a mathematician and an author. He used mathematical logic when writing his stories. In his book, *Through the Looking Glass,* there is a conversation between Tweedledum and Tweedledee. Tweedledum says, "The sum of your weight and twice mine is 361 pounds." Tweedledee answers, "Contrariwise, the sum of your weight and twice mine is 362 pounds." What are the weights of Tweedledum and Tweedledee?
44. 120 lb, 121 lb

45. Population Growth The chart below shows the states with the greatest percentage of population growth during the 1980s. In 1990, the population of New York was 17.99 million, which represented a growth of 0.43 million over its 1980 population. Assume that each state continues to gain the same number of residents every ten years.

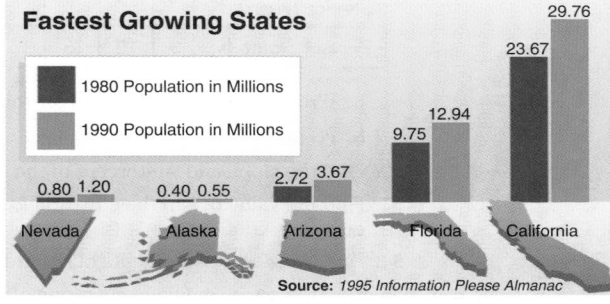

Fastest Growing States

- 1980 Population in Millions
- 1990 Population in Millions

Nevada 0.80 1.20 · Alaska 0.40 0.55 · Arizona 2.72 3.67 · Florida 9.75 12.94 · California 23.67 29.76

Source: *1995 Information Please Almanac*

a. Write an equation that represents the population of New York *d* decades after 1990. $p = 17.99 + 0.43d$

b. Write an equation that represents the population of Arizona *d* decades after 1990. $p = 3.67 + 0.95d$

c. When will the populations of Arizona and New York be equal? during the year 2265

Longest Subway Networks
1. Washington, D.C., 612 km
2. London, 430 km
3. New York, 370 km
4. Paris, 301 km
5. Moscow, 225 km

46. $\left(\dfrac{5}{7}, \dfrac{5}{7}\right)$

47. Sample answer: 20¢ a mile or $15 plus 10¢ a mile

46. City Planning A portion of the subway in Washington, D.C., heads out of the main part of town in a northwesterly direction. It goes under New Hampshire Avenue as shown at the right. If distances are measured in kilometers, the path of the subway can be represented by the equation $y = -2.5x + 2.5$, and the path of New Hampshire Avenue can be represented by the equation $y = x$. What are the coordinates of the point at which the subway goes under New Hampshire Avenue?

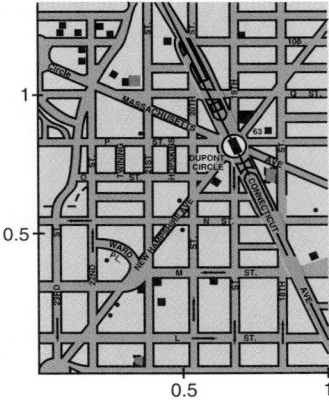

47. Consumer Awareness A new car rental company wants to offer two rental options similar to the truck rental plans offered in the application at the beginning of the lesson. Design two rate structure options that will offer different rates per mile, but will be equal for customers driving 150 miles.

Lesson 3–2 Solving Systems of Equations Algebraically **139**

Extension

Reasoning Solve the system of equations.

$$\frac{1}{x} - \frac{1}{y} = \frac{5}{8}$$

$$\frac{3}{x} + \frac{2}{y} = \frac{5}{8}$$

You may want to give the hint to substitute *m* for $\frac{1}{x}$ and *n* for $\frac{1}{y}$.

$\left(2\frac{2}{3}, -4\right)$

4 ASSESS

Closing Activity

Speaking Separate the class into groups of three. Give them a system of equations such as $2x + 3y - 8 = 0$ or $3x + 2y - 17 = 0$. Have each group solve the equation by the three methods studied so far. Discuss which method is best and why.

Chapter 3, Quiz A (Lessons 3-1 and 3-2), is available in the *Assessment and Evaluation Masters,* p. 72.

The first subway system, in London, England, began construction in 1860 and opened in 1863.

Practice Masters, p. 16

3-2 NAME_____ DATE_____

Practice Student Edit Pages 133–

Solving Systems of Equations Algebraically

Solve each system of equations by using substitution.

1. $2x + y = 4$
   $3x + 2y = 1$ (7, −10)

2. $x - 9 = 3y$
   $x + 2y = -1$ (3, −2)

3. $x + 3y = 8$
   $\frac{1}{3}x + y = 9$ no solutions

4. $2x - 3y = 6$
   $-\frac{2}{3}x + y = -2$
   $\{(x, y)|2x - 3y = 6\}$

Solve each system of equations by using elimination.

5. $2x + y = 1$
   $3x - y = 14$ (3, −5)

6. $2x - y = -1$
   $3x + 2y = 30$ (4, 9)

7. $6x + 3y = 6$
   $8x + 5y = 12$ (−1, 4)

8. $\frac{3x - y}{2} = 5$
   $\frac{4x - y}{4} = 4$ (6, 8)

Solve each system of equations. Use either substitution or elimination.

9. $8x + 3y + 5 = 0$
   $10x + 6y + 13 = 0$ $\left(\frac{1}{2}, -3\right)$

10. $\frac{2x}{5} - \frac{3y}{4} = -2$
    $\frac{x}{2} + \frac{y}{4} = 7$ (10, 8)

11. $\frac{x}{4} - \frac{y}{3} = 1$
    $\frac{1}{3}x - \frac{4y}{9} = \frac{4}{3}$ $\left\{(x, y)|\frac{x}{4} - \frac{y}{3} = 1\right\}$

12. $4x - 2y = 5$
    $2x = y - 1$ no solutions

48. Which graph illustrates the solution to the system of equations $y = 2x - 5$ and $x + y = -3$? (Lesson 3–1) **b**

a. 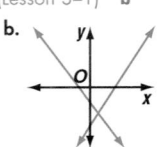 b. 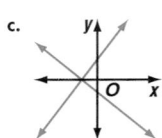 c. 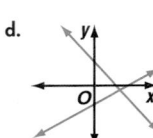 d.

49. Business The Fix-It Auto Repair Shop has a sign that states that the labor costs are $40 per hour or any fraction thereof. What type of function does this relationship represent? (Lesson 2–6) **step function**

50. If $g(x) = |4x + 17|$, find the value of $g(-2)$. (Lesson 2–6) **9**

51. Postal Service The table shows the price for first-class stamps since the U.S. Postal Service was created on July 1, 1971. (Lesson 2–5)

Age of U.S. Postal Service (years)	0	3	4	7	10	10	14	17	20	25
Price of Stamp (¢)	8	10	13	15	18	20	22	25	29	32

51a. Sample answer:
$y = \frac{7}{8}x + 8$

51b. about 42¢

52. $\frac{5}{2}$; 3

54. 9; none

a. Write a prediction equation for this relationship.

b. Predict the price for a first-class stamp issued in the year 2010.

52. Find the slope and y-intercept of the graph of $-5x = 6 - 2y$. (Lesson 2–4)

53. Find the value of k in the equation $kx - 3y = 12$ if $(2, 2)$ is a solution of the equation. (Lesson 2–4) **9**

54. Find the x- and y-intercepts of the graph of $x = 9$. (Lesson 2–3)

55. Find the mean, median, and mode of the prime numbers between 0 and 35. (Lesson 1–3) **14.55; 13; no mode**

WORKING ON THE **In·ves·ti·ga·tion** **Refer to the Investigation on pages 60–61.**

Through the Looking Glass

By making observations with different instruments and comparing the results, naturalists can make more reliable conclusions than by using just one instrument.

1 You have four different sizes of calibration scopes. Record the dimensions of each of the four tubes.

2 Suppose you were standing 50 feet from an animal. Looking through Tube A, the animal's

image fills your view exactly. Explain what you need to do to be able to look through Tube B so that the animal's image fills your view exactly. Explain what you need to do to be able to look through Tube D so that the animal's image fills your view exactly.

3 Suppose you had a Tube E that was 3 times as long and twice as wide as Tube A. Exactly where would you need to stand so that the animal's image fills your view exactly?

Add the results of your work to your Investigation Folder.

Enrichment Masters, p. 16

3-2 NAME_____ DATE _____

Enrichment Student Edition Pages 133–140

_sing Coordinates

_rom one observation point, the line of sight to a downed plane _given by $y = x - 1$. From another observation point, the line _sight is given by $x + 3y = 21$. What are the coordinates of the _int at which the crash occurred?

_lve the system of equations $\begin{cases} y = x - 1 \\ x + 3y = 21 \end{cases}$

$x + 3y = 21$
$x + 3(x - 1) = 21$ Substitute $x - 1$ for y.
$x + 3x - 3 = 21$
$4x = 24$
$x = 6$

$x + 3y = 21$
$6 + 3y = 21$ Substitute 6 for x.
$3y = 15$
$y = 5$

_e coordinates of the crash are (6, 5).

_lve the following.

The lines of sight to a forest fire are as follows.

From Ranger Station A: $3x + y = 9$
From Ranger Station B: $2x + 3y = 13$
Find the coordinates of the fire.
(2, 3)

A Delta flight is traveling along the line $x - y = -1$
A TWA flight is traveling along the line $5x + 3y = 19$.
If they continue along the same lines, at what point will the flight paths cross?
(2, 3)

Two mine shafts are dug along the paths of the following equations.
$x - y = 1400$
$2x + y = 1300$
If the shafts meet at a depth of 200 feet, what are the coordinates of the point at which they meet?
(900, −500)

In·ves·ti·ga·tion

Working on the Investigation

The Investigation on pages 60–61 is designed to be a long-term project that is completed over several days or weeks. Encourage students to keep their materials in their Investigation Folder as they work on the Investigation.

Cramer's Rule

What YOU'LL LEARN

- To find the values of second-order determinants, and
- to solve systems of equations by using Cramer's rule.

Why IT'S IMPORTANT

You can use Cramer's rule to solve problems involving sports and politics.

INTEGRATION
Geometry

Two sides of a parallelogram are contained in the lines whose equations are $2.3x + 1.2y = 2.1$ and $4.1x - 0.5y = 14.3$. To find the coordinates of a vertex of the parallelogram, we must solve the system of equations. However, solving this system by using substitution or elimination would require many calculations. *This problem will be solved in Example 3.*

Another method for solving systems of equations is **Cramer's rule.** The rule gives us a quick way to find the solution to a system of two equations with two variables. It is especially useful when the coefficients are large or involve fractions or decimals. Cramer's rule makes use of **determinants**. A determinant is a square array of numbers or variables enclosed between two parallel vertical bars. The numbers or variables written within a determinant are called **elements**. The determinant below has two rows and two columns and is called a **second-order determinant.**

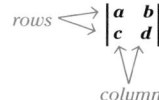

$$rows \Rightarrow \begin{vmatrix} a & b \\ c & d \end{vmatrix}$$
$$columns$$

A second-order determinant is evaluated as follows.

Value of a Second-Order Determinant	$\begin{vmatrix} a & b \\ c & d \end{vmatrix} = ad - bc$

F Y I

The theory of determinants is attributed to German mathematician Gottfried Wilhelm Leibnitz. His work expanded upon the earlier work of a Japanese mathematician, Seki Kowa.

Notice that the value of the determinant is found by calculating the difference of the products of the two diagonals.

$$\begin{vmatrix} a & b \\ c & d \end{vmatrix} \begin{matrix} bc \\ ad \end{matrix} \longrightarrow ad - bc$$

Example Find the value of each determinant.

a. $\begin{vmatrix} 3 & 5 \\ 2 & 6 \end{vmatrix}$ b. $\begin{vmatrix} -2 & 7 \\ 5 & 8 \end{vmatrix}$

$\begin{vmatrix} 3 & 5 \\ 2 & 6 \end{vmatrix} = 3(6) - 5(2)$ $\begin{vmatrix} -2 & 7 \\ 5 & 8 \end{vmatrix} = -2(8) - 7(5)$

$= 8$ $= -51$

F Y I

Leibniz was not only one of the great mathematicians of the seventeenth century, but also a great philosopher. It was Leibniz who described this world as the best of all possible worlds, a claim he attempted to prove with mathematical precision.

NCTM Standards: 1–5

Instructional Resources

- Study Guide Master 3-3
- Practice Master 3-3
- Enrichment Master 3-3

 Transparency 3-3A contains the 5-Minute Check for this lesson; **Transparency 3-3B** contains a teaching aid for this lesson.

Recommended Pacing	
Standard Pacing	Day 4 of 14
Honors Pacing	Day 4 of 12
Block Scheduling*	Day 2 of 6 (along with Lesson 3-2)

*For more information on pacing and possible lesson plans, refer to the *Block Scheduling Booklet.*

1 FOCUS

 5-Minute Check
(over Lesson 3-2)

Solve each system of equations by substitution.

1. $x - 4y = -12$
   $3x + 2y = 20$ (4, 4)
2. $x + 2y = 6$
   $2x + 4y = 15$ no solution

Solve each system of equations by elimination.

3. $2x + 5y = 9$
   $-2x + 8y = 4$ (2, 1)
4. $x + 2y = 7$
   $14 - 4y = 2x$
   $x + 2y = 7$

Solve the system of equations by using either substitution or elimination.

5. $3x - 5y = 17$
   $4x + 5y = 46$ (9, 2)

 TEKS 3.a., 3.b., 3.c.

Motivating the Lesson

Questioning Solve the system of equations $6x + 2y = 4$ and $3x + y = 5$. The lines are parallel, so the system has no solution. Now multiply the coefficient of x in the first equation and the coefficient of y in the second equation and call this value m. Then multiply the coefficient of y in the first equation and the coefficient of x in the second equation and call this value n. Subtract n from m. What is this value? **0**

2 TEACH

In-Class Examples

For Example 1
Find the value of the determinant.

$\begin{vmatrix} 3 & 4 \\ 2 & 5 \end{vmatrix}$

7

For Example 2
Use Cramer's rule to solve the system of equations.
$6x + 7y = -9$
$x - y = 5$ **(2, −3)**

Teaching Tip Emphasize that in order to use Cramer's rule, equations must be in standard form. Discuss why the condition $\begin{vmatrix} a & b \\ d & e \end{vmatrix} = 0$ is necessary. If two lines do not intersect, then their slopes are equal.

$ax + by = c$ has slope $-\dfrac{a}{b}$.

$dx + ey = f$ has slope $-\dfrac{d}{e}$.

So, if $-\dfrac{a}{b} = -\dfrac{d}{e}$, the lines have the same slope, and therefore there is no unique solution.

$$-\frac{a}{b} = -\frac{d}{e}$$
$$ae = bd$$

$ae - bd = 0$ or $\begin{vmatrix} a & b \\ d & e \end{vmatrix} = 0$

F Y I

It is quite common that two people come up with the same idea independently. Both Leibniz and Newton developed the idea of the calculus at the same time.

F Y I

Swiss mathematician Gabriel Cramer (1704–52) published the method of solving systems of equations using determinants in 1750. However, in 1748, this method appeared in a publication by Scottish mathematician Colin Maclaurin (1698–1746), two years after his death.

To discover how Cramer's rule uses determinants to solve a system of linear equations, consider the following system.

$ax + by = e$ $a, b, c, d, e,$ and f represent constants, <u>not</u> variables.
$cx + dy = f$

Solve for x by using elimination.

$\begin{array}{ll} adx + bdy = de & \text{Multiply the first equation by } d. \\ (-)\ bcx + bdy = bf & \text{Multiply the second equation by } b. \\ \hline adx - bcx = de - bf & \text{Subtract.} \\ (ad - bc)x = de - bf & \text{Factor.} \\ \quad x = \dfrac{de - bf}{ad - bc} & \text{Notice that } ad - bc \text{ must not be zero.} \end{array}$

Solving for y in the same way produces the following expression.

$y = \dfrac{af - ce}{ad - bc}$

So, the solution to the system of equations $\begin{cases} ax + by = e \\ cx + dy = f \end{cases}$ is $\left(\dfrac{de - bf}{ad - bc}, \dfrac{af - ce}{ad - bc} \right)$.

Notice that the two fractions have the same denominator. It can be written as a determinant. The numerators can also be written as determinants.

$ad - bc = \begin{vmatrix} a & b \\ c & d \end{vmatrix}$ $de - bf = \begin{vmatrix} e & b \\ f & d \end{vmatrix}$ $af - ce = \begin{vmatrix} a & e \\ c & f \end{vmatrix}$

So, now we can find the solution to a system of two linear equations in two variables by using determinants. This method is called Cramer's rule.

Cramer's Rule

The solution to the system $\begin{cases} ax + by = e \\ cx + dy = f \end{cases}$ is (x, y),

where $x = \dfrac{\begin{vmatrix} e & b \\ f & d \end{vmatrix}}{\begin{vmatrix} a & b \\ c & d \end{vmatrix}}$, $y = \dfrac{\begin{vmatrix} a & e \\ c & f \end{vmatrix}}{\begin{vmatrix} a & b \\ c & d \end{vmatrix}}$, and $\begin{vmatrix} a & b \\ c & d \end{vmatrix} \neq 0$.

Example Use Cramer's rule to solve the system of equations.

$2x - 3y = 9$
$x + 5y = -2$

$x = \dfrac{\begin{vmatrix} 9 & -3 \\ -2 & 5 \end{vmatrix}}{\begin{vmatrix} 2 & -3 \\ 1 & 5 \end{vmatrix}}$ $y = \dfrac{\begin{vmatrix} 2 & 9 \\ 1 & -2 \end{vmatrix}}{\begin{vmatrix} 2 & -3 \\ 1 & 5 \end{vmatrix}}$

$\quad = \dfrac{9(5) - (-3)(-2)}{2(5) - (-3)(1)}$ $\quad = \dfrac{2(-2) - 9(1)}{2(5) - (-3)(1)}$

$\quad = \dfrac{39}{13}$ $\quad = \dfrac{-13}{13}$

$\quad = 3$ $\quad = -1$

The solution is $(3, -1)$.

Check by graphing.

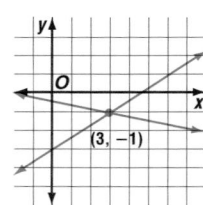

(3, −1)

 ## Cooperative Learning

Co-op Co-op Have students separate into groups of four. Then, have them evaluate a second-order determinant with one row or column composed of zeros. Give an example of a second-order determinant that has a value of zero. What can you say about the relationship between the elements when the determinant has a value of zero? For more information on the co-op co-op strategy, see *Cooperative Learning in the Mathematics Classroom*, one of the titles in the Glencoe Mathematics Professional Series, pages 32–33.

Example **3**

INTEGRATION

Geometry

Refer to the application at the beginning of the lesson. Find the coordinates of a vertex of the parallelogram.

To find the coordinates of a vertex, you need to solve the system of equations.

$2.3x + 1.2y = 2.1$
$4.1x - 0.5y = 14.3$

Since the numbers in the equations would make solving the system by substitution or elimination difficult, use Cramer's rule.

$$x = \frac{\begin{vmatrix} 2.1 & 1.2 \\ 14.3 & -0.5 \end{vmatrix}}{\begin{vmatrix} 2.3 & 1.2 \\ 4.1 & -0.5 \end{vmatrix}} \qquad\qquad y = \frac{\begin{vmatrix} 2.3 & 2.1 \\ 4.1 & 14.3 \end{vmatrix}}{\begin{vmatrix} 2.3 & 1.2 \\ 4.1 & -0.5 \end{vmatrix}}$$

$$= \frac{2.1(-0.5) - 14.3(1.2)}{2.3(-0.5) - 4.1(1.2)} \qquad\qquad = \frac{2.3(14.3) - 4.1(2.1)}{2.3(-0.5) - (4.1)(1.2)}$$

$$= \frac{-18.21}{-6.07} \qquad\qquad\qquad = \frac{24.28}{-6.07}$$

$$= 3 \qquad\qquad\qquad\qquad = -4$$

The coordinates of a vertex of the parallelogram are $(3, -4)$.

Check by using substitution.

First Equation: $2.3(3) + 1.2(-4) = 2.1$ ✓
Second Equation: $4.1(3) - 0.5(-4) = 14.3$ ✓

Systems of equations can also be solved by using a BASIC program.

EXPLORATION

BASIC

The BASIC program below finds the solution of the system of equations of the form $ax + by = c$ and $dx + ey = f$.

```
10   PRINT "ENTER THE COEFFICIENTS."
20   INPUT A, B, C, D, E, F
30   IF A*E-B*D = 0 THEN 80
40   LET X = (C*E-B*F)/(A*E-B*D)
50   LET Y= (A*F-C*D)/(A*E-B*D)
60   PRINT "(";X;",";Y;") IS A SOLUTION"
70   GOTO 10
80   IF C*E-B*F = 0 OR A*F-C*D=0 THEN 110
90   PRINT "NO SOLUTION."
100  GOTO 10
110  PRINT "INFINITE NUMBER OF SOLUTIONS."
120  GOTO 10
130  END
```

Your Turn   a. $(3, -1)$ b. $(3, -4)$ c. Steps 40 and 50 are Cramer's rule.

a. Use the program to solve the system of equations in Example 2.

b. Use the program to solve the system of equations in Example 3.

c. Study Steps 40 and 50. How does this program relate to Cramer's rule?

In-Class Example

For Example 3
Two sides of a parallelogram are contained in the lines whose equations are $3x - 2y = -24$ and $5x + y = -14$. Find the coordinates of a vertex of the parallelogram.
$(-4, 6)$

EXPLORATION

Step 30 is the value of the determinant $\begin{vmatrix} a & b \\ d & e \end{vmatrix}$, which must be nonzero in order to apply Cramer's rule. If it is zero, the quotients in steps 40 and 50 cannot be computed.

GLENCOE *Technology*

Interactive Mathematics Tools Software

This multimedia software provides an interactive lesson by helping students find the second-order determinant of a matrix. A **Computer Journal** gives students an opportunity to write about what they have learned.

For Windows & Macintosh

Check for Understanding

Exercises 1–12 are designed to help you assess your students' understanding through reading, writing, speaking, and modeling. You should work through Exercises 1–4 with your students and then monitor their work on Exercises 5–12.

CHECK FOR UNDERSTANDING

Communicating Mathematics

Study the lesson. Then complete the following.

1. **Evaluate** a determinant if both elements of a row or column are 0.   0

2. **Describe** the elements of a determinant when the value of the determinant is 0 and none of the elements is 0. $ad = bc$

3. In Cramer's rule, if the value of the determinant in the denominator is 0, what must be true of the graph of the system of equations represented by the determinant?   **The lines are parallel or coincident.**

4. Carmen used Cramer's rule and solved for x as follows.

$$x = \frac{\begin{vmatrix} 18 & -5 \\ -4 & 8 \end{vmatrix}}{\begin{vmatrix} 2 & -5 \\ 3 & 8 \end{vmatrix}}$$

Write the system of equations that she was solving.
$2x - 5y = 18,\ 3x + 8y = -4$

Guided Practice

Find the value of each determinant.

5. $\begin{vmatrix} 5 & 2 \\ 4 & 1 \end{vmatrix}$ -3

6. $\begin{vmatrix} 6 & -2 \\ 7 & 3 \end{vmatrix}$ 32

7. $\begin{vmatrix} \frac{2}{5} & 6 \\ \frac{1}{3} & 2 \end{vmatrix}$ $-\frac{6}{5}$

Use Cramer's rule to solve each system of equations.

8. $2x - y = 1$
   $3x + 2y = 19$ $(3, 5)$

9. $5x + 2y = 8$
   $2x - 3y = 7$ $(2, -1)$

10. $\frac{1}{6}x - \frac{1}{9}y = 0$
    $x + y = 15$ $(6, 9)$

11. $2m - 5n = 2$
    $3m + 4n = -5$ $\left(-\frac{17}{23}, -\frac{16}{23}\right)$

12. **Geometry**   The two sides of an angle are contained in lines whose equations are $4x + y = -4$ and $2x - 3y = -9$. Find the coordinates of the vertex of the angle. $\left(-\frac{3}{2}, 2\right)$

EXERCISES

Find the value of each determinant.

13. $\begin{vmatrix} 8 & 5 \\ 6 & -2 \end{vmatrix}$ -46

14. $\begin{vmatrix} -2 & 4 \\ 8 & -7 \end{vmatrix}$ -18

15. $\begin{vmatrix} -8 & 3 \\ -9 & 7 \end{vmatrix}$ -29

16. $\begin{vmatrix} -6 & -2 \\ 8 & 5 \end{vmatrix}$ -14

17. $\begin{vmatrix} 2 & -7 \\ -5 & 3 \end{vmatrix}$ -29

18. $\begin{vmatrix} 21 & 43 \\ 17 & -29 \end{vmatrix}$ -1340

19. $\begin{vmatrix} -54 & 39 \\ 18 & -13 \end{vmatrix}$ 0

20. $\begin{vmatrix} -3.2 & -5.8 \\ 4.1 & 3.9 \end{vmatrix}$ 11.3

21. $\begin{vmatrix} 7 & -5.2 \\ 1.3 & 2.29 \end{vmatrix}$ 22.79

Use Cramer's rule to solve each system of equations.   27. $\left(-\frac{3}{4}, 3\right)$

24. $(-12, 4)$

25. $\left(\frac{2}{3}, -1\right)$

26. $(-2, 5)$

22. $5x + 7y = 13$
    $2x - 5y = 13$ $(4, -1)$

23. $3a + 5b = 33$
    $5a + 7b = 51$ $(6, 3)$

24. $2m + 7n = 4$
    $m - 2n = -20$

25. $3x - 2y = 4$
    $\frac{1}{2}x - \frac{2}{3}y = 1$

26. $1.5x + 0.7y = 0.5$
    $2.2x - 0.6y = -7.4$

27. $4u + 3v = 6$
    $8u - v = -9$

Study Guide Masters, p. 17

3-3   NAME_____ DATE_____
Student Edition
Pages 141–146

Study Guide

Cramer's Rule

A **determinant** is a square arrangement of numbers or variables enclosed between vertical lines.

To find the value of the determinant use the following:

$$\begin{vmatrix} a & b \\ c & d \end{vmatrix} = ad - bc$$

The solution to a system of two linear equations in two variables can be found using determinants. This method is known as **Cramer's Rule:**

If $\begin{vmatrix} a & b \\ d & e \end{vmatrix} \neq 0$, then the solution of $\begin{matrix} ax + by = c \\ dx + ey = f \end{matrix}$ is $x = \dfrac{\begin{vmatrix} c & b \\ f & e \end{vmatrix}}{\begin{vmatrix} a & b \\ d & e \end{vmatrix}}, y = \dfrac{\begin{vmatrix} a & c \\ d & f \end{vmatrix}}{\begin{vmatrix} a & b \\ d & e \end{vmatrix}}$.

Use Cramer's Rule to solve each system of equations.

1. $7x - 2y = 4$
   $3x + y = -6$ $\left(-\frac{8}{13}, -\frac{54}{13}\right)$

2. $2x - 5y = 18$
   $-x + 3y = -10$ $(4, -2)$

3. $3x - 2y = 15$
   $4x + y = 9$ $(3, -3)$

4. $5x + 4y = -4$
   $2x - y = 10$ $(3, -4)$

5. $-7x + 5y = 1$
   $x - 2y = 9$ $\left(-\frac{47}{9}, -\frac{64}{9}\right)$

6. $6x - 4y = 1$
   $-3x + 3y = 2$ $\left(\frac{11}{6}, \frac{5}{2}\right)$

7. $\frac{1}{2}x - \frac{7}{5}y = 8$
   $\frac{1}{3}x - y = 1$ $(198, 65)$

8. $5x + 6y = 7$
   $4x + 5y = -9$ $(89, -73)$

Reteaching

Using Alternative Methods   Point out to students that Cramer's rule can be applied without writing it in determinant form. Cover the constant terms in the system $ax + by = c$ and $dx + ey = f$, and take the determinant of the remaining coefficients. Cover the x-terms to find the numerator of the x solution. Cover the y-terms to find the numerator of the y solution.

30. $\left(-\frac{3}{4}, \frac{5}{8}\right)$

31. $\left(\frac{2}{3}, \frac{5}{6}\right)$

32. (0.75, 0.5)
33. (2, −3)

C

28. $\frac{1}{2}r + \frac{3}{4}s = -4$

$\frac{3}{4}r - \frac{7}{8}s = 10$ **(4, −8)**

29. $\frac{1}{3}x + \frac{2}{5}y = 5$

$\frac{2}{3}x - \frac{1}{2}y = -3$ **(3, 10)**

30. $\frac{1}{2}x - y = -1$

$\frac{3}{4}x + \frac{1}{2}y = -\frac{1}{4}$

31. $\frac{3}{4}a + \frac{1}{2}b = \frac{11}{12}$

$\frac{1}{2}a - \frac{1}{4}b = \frac{1}{8}$

32. $0.2a = 0.3b$

$0.4a - 0.2b = 0.2$

33. $3.5x + 4y = -5$

$2(x - y) = 10$

34. **Geometry**   The sides of a triangle are contained in the lines represented by $x - 4y = -6$, $5x + y = 33$, and $2x - y = 2$. Find the coordinates of the vertices of the triangle.   **(6, 3), (5, 8), (2, 2)**

Critical Thinking

35. When using Cramer's rule, how can you tell whether there is no solution or an infinite number of solutions?   **See margin.**

Applications and Problem Solving

36. **Sports**   The winning times for various speed-skating events in the 1994 Winter Olympics are given in the chart below. Suppose the men and women continue to decrease their times for the 1000-meter event by the same amount each Winter Olympics. In what Olympics will the women's times be faster than the men's in this event?   **2030 Winter Olympics**

GLOBAL CONNECTIONS

Malaysian foot tennis is a very popular sport in Malaysia and other countries in the Far East. It is played by teams of two using a ball woven from rattan must be kept in the air using only feet, knees, or thighs.

Winning Times for Speed Skaters in the 1994 Winter Olympics				
Event	Men's Time	Change from 1992 Winner	Women's Time	Change from 1992 Winner
500 m	36.33 s	−0.81 s	39.25 s	−1.08 s
1000 m	72.43 s	−2.42 s	78.74 s	−3.16 s
1500 m	111.29 s	−3.52 s	122.19 s	−3.68 s

Source: The World Almanac and Book of Facts 1995

37. **Exercise**   Rosa rides the bus to work. Usually she rides 35 minutes and then walks 6 minutes to get to her place of employment. Since the bus travels 30 miles per hour and her walking speed is 5 miles per hour, she can easily determine that the total distance is 18 miles. One day when the weather is nice, she decides to get off the bus earlier and walk the rest of the way for exercise. She only has a total of 75 minutes to get to work, so she can't afford to get off the bus too early. How much time should she spend on the bus before getting off to walk?   **28.2 min**

38. about 7,100,000 people; about 5,800,000 people

38. **Politics**   The three states with the most electoral votes are California (54), New York (33), and Texas (32). The graph at the right shows the results of the popular votes in the 1992 presidential election. Bill Clinton received about 5,700,000 popular votes from the voters in New York and Texas, and George Bush received about 4,800,000 from the same voters. About how many people voted in the 1992 presidential election in New York? in Texas?

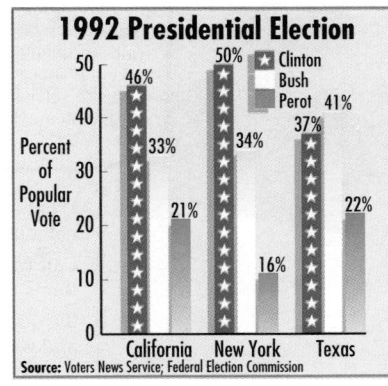

Extension

Reasoning   Solve for x.

$$\begin{vmatrix} x^2 & 5 \\ x & 1 \end{vmatrix} = 36$$

$x = -4$ or 9

Assignment Guide

Core: 13–37 odd, 39–45
Enriched: 14–34 even, 35–45

For **Extra Practice,** see p. 881.

The red A, B, and C flags, printed only in the Teacher's Wraparound Edition, indicate the level of difficulty of the exercises.

GLOBAL CONNECTIONS

In Malaysian foot tennis, a point is scored each time the ball touches the ground on the opponent's side of the net. One team is also awarded a point if the opposing team kicks the ball into the net.

Additional Answer

35. In both cases, the denominator is 0. If the numerator is also 0, there is an infinite number of solutions. If the numerator is not 0, there are no solutions.

Practice Masters, p. 17

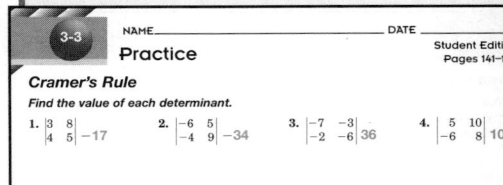

3-3 Practice   **Cramer's Rule**

Find the value of each determinant.

1. $\begin{vmatrix} 3 & 8 \\ 4 & 5 \end{vmatrix}$ −17
2. $\begin{vmatrix} -6 & 5 \\ -4 & 9 \end{vmatrix}$ −34
3. $\begin{vmatrix} -7 & -3 \\ -2 & -6 \end{vmatrix}$ 36
4. $\begin{vmatrix} 5 & 10 \\ -6 & 8 \end{vmatrix}$ 100

Use Cramer's rule to solve each system of equations.

5. $4x - 3y = -6$
   $x + 2y = -7$ (−3, −2)

6. $5s + 6u = 1$
   $-2s - u = -6$ (5, −4)

7. $2w - 5z = 13$
   $6w + 3z = 10$ $\left(\frac{89}{36}, -\frac{29}{18}\right)$

8. $m + 3p = -6$
   $2m - 5p = 7$ $\left(-\frac{9}{11}, -\frac{19}{11}\right)$

9. $2x - 4y = 1$
   $-x + 2y = 5$ no solutions

10. $3c + 9d = 2$
    $c + 3d = \frac{2}{3}$ $\{(c, d)|3c + 9d = 2\}$

Closing Activity

Modeling Draw a flowchart detailing the steps necessary to solve the following system by substitution.

$ax + by = c$

$dx + ey = f$

Mathematics and SOCIETY

Lead a discussion with the following question. Do you see anything contradictory about a particle following more than one path at the same time? **This implies that one particle can be in two places at the same time.**

Additional Answer

41.

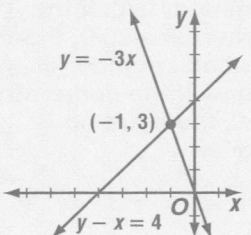

$(-1, 3)$; consistent, independent

Enrichment Masters, p. 17

3-3   NAME_____ DATE_____

Enrichment   Student Edition Pages 141–146

Properties of Determinants

The following properties often help when evaluating determinants.

1) If all the elements of a row (or column) are zero, the value of the determinant is zero.

$$\begin{vmatrix} a & b \\ 0 & 0 \end{vmatrix} = 0 \quad (a \cdot 0) - (0 \cdot b) = 0$$

2) Multiplying all the elements of a row (or column) by a constant is equivalent to multiplying the value of the determinant by the constant.

$$3\begin{vmatrix} 4 & -1 \\ 5 & 3 \end{vmatrix} = \begin{vmatrix} 12 & -3 \\ 5 & 3 \end{vmatrix} \quad \begin{matrix} 3[4(3) - 5(-1)] = \\ 3[12 + 5] = 51 \\ 12(3) - 5(-3) = 51 \end{matrix}$$

3) If two rows (or columns) have equal corresponding elements, the value of the determinant is zero.

$$\begin{vmatrix} 5 & 5 \\ -3 & -3 \end{vmatrix} = 0 \quad 5(-3) - (-3)(5) = 0$$

4) The value of a determinant is unchanged if any multiple of a row (or column) is added to corresponding elements of another row (or column).

(Row 2 is added to row 1.) $\begin{vmatrix} 4 & -3 \\ 2 & 5 \end{vmatrix} = \begin{vmatrix} 6 & 2 \\ 2 & 5 \end{vmatrix}$

$\begin{matrix} 4(5) - 2(-3) = \\ 20 + 6 = 26 \end{matrix}$ $\begin{matrix} 6(5) - 2(2) = \\ 30 - 4 = 26 \end{matrix}$

5) If two rows (or columns) are interchanged, the sign of the determinant is changed.

$\begin{vmatrix} 4 & 5 \\ -3 & 8 \end{vmatrix} = -\begin{vmatrix} -3 & 8 \\ 4 & 5 \end{vmatrix}$ $\begin{matrix} 4(8) - (-3)(5) = \\ 32 + 15 = 47 \end{matrix}$ $\begin{matrix} -[(-3)(5) - 4(8)] = \\ -[-15 - 32] = 47 \end{matrix}$

6) The value of the determinant is unchanged if row 1 is interchanged with column 1, and row 2 is interchanged with column 2. The result is called the transpose.

$\begin{vmatrix} 5 & -7 \\ 3 & 4 \end{vmatrix} = \begin{vmatrix} 5 & 3 \\ -7 & 4 \end{vmatrix}$ $\begin{matrix} 5(4) - 3(-7) = \\ 20 + 21 = 41 \end{matrix}$ $\begin{matrix} 5(4) - (-7)(3) = \\ 20 + 21 = 41 \end{matrix}$

Exercises 1–6

Verify each property above by evaluating the given determinants and give another example of the property. Examples will vary.

---

39. Solve the system of equations $2x + y = 0$ and $5x + 3y = 1$ by using either substitution or elimination. (Lesson 3–2) $(-1, 2)$

40. Consumer Awareness Mrs. Katz is planning a family vacation. She bought 8 rolls of film and 2 camera batteries for $23.00. The next day, her daughter went back and bought 6 more rolls of film and 2 batteries for her camera. This bill was $18.00. What is the price of a roll of film and a camera battery? (Lesson 3–2)   **$2.50; $1.50**

41. Graph the system of equations $y = -3x$ and $y - x = 4$. State the solution. Is the system of equations consistent and independent, consistent and dependent, or inconsistent? (Lesson 3–1)   **See margin.**

42. If $f(x) = [5x - 3]$, find $f\left(-\frac{1}{2}\right)$. (Lesson 2–6)   **−6**

43. Write a prediction equation for the data in the following table. (Lesson 2–5)

Sample answer: $y = -x + 3$

x	−3	0	4	6	8
y	5	3	0	−3	−5

44. Solve $\frac{w - 6}{3} \le 6 - w$. (Lesson 1–6) $6 \ge w$

45. Geometry The formula for the area of a trapezoid is $A = \frac{1}{2}h(b_1 + b_2)$, where h is the height of the trapezoid and b_1 and b_2 are the lengths of the bases. Find the area of the trapezoid at the right. (Lesson 1–1)   **120 units²**

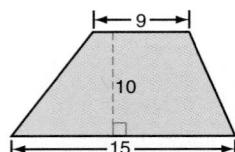

Mathematics and SOCIETY

Quantum Computing

The article below appeared in *Science News* on May 14, 1994.

IN THE QUANTUM WORLD, A PARTICLE—undisturbed by any attempt to observe it—can be in myriad places at the same time. Thus, a single photon traveling through a crystal simultaneously follows all possible optical paths through the material. . . . Computer scientists have speculated that computers operating according to the rules of quantum mechanics can potentially take advantage of a similar multiplicity of paths to solve certain types of mathematical problems much more quickly than conventional computers can. Now, mathematician Peter W. Shor . . . has proved that, in principle, quantum computation can provide the shortcut needed to convert the factoring of large numbers from a time-consuming chore into an amazingly quick operation. . . . Quantum computers don't exist yet, and building them involves surmounting significant technological barriers. Nonetheless, some researchers are starting to produce designs . . . that may lead eventually to working models. ■

1. What are some advantages of greatly speeding up some computer calculations?   **1–3. See margin.**

2. Can you think of an example in everyday life where moving numerous items along many paths is faster than using only one path?

3. If a quantum computer is built, we will learn a lot if it works successfully, and we will learn a lot if it doesn't work successfully. Explain.

Answers for Mathematics and Society

1. ability to perform more work in less time, ability to solve complex and newer problems that previously could not be solved, and less need to buy and maintain as many computers

2. Answers will vary. Sample answer: people passing through many gates instead of just one to enter a stadium

3. If it works, we will have a powerful new tool to use and new applications to be developed. We will find solutions to problems that were previously too large to solve. If it doesn't work, we will learn that our knowledge of quantum mechanics is incomplete and/or incorrect. We may need to try a new way to build quantum computers, or perhaps we'll learn that they can't be built at all.

3-4A Graphing Technology
Systems of Linear Inequalities

A Preview of Lesson 3–4

You can graph systems of linear inequalities with a graphing calculator by using the SHADE feature described in Lesson 2–7A. It shades above the first function entered and below the second function entered. Be sure to clear any equations currently stored in the Y= list of the calculator before you begin.

Example **Graph the system of inequalities in the standard viewing window.**

$y \geq x + 2$
$y \leq -2x + 5$

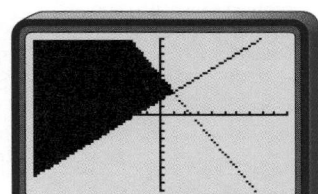

The greater than or equal to symbol in $y \geq x + 2$ indicates the values on or above the line $y = x + 2$. Similarly, the less than or equal to symbol in $y \leq -2x + 5$ indicates values on or below the line $y = -2x + 5$. Therefore, the function $y = x + 2$ will be entered first, and $y = -2x + 5$ will be entered second.

Enter: `ZOOM` 6 `2nd` `DRAW` 7 `X,T,θ` `+` 2 `,` `(−)`

 2 `X,T,θ` `+` 5 `)` `ENTER`

The shaded area indicated points that satisfy the system of inequalities $y \geq x + 2$ and $y \geq -2x + 5$.

Before graphing again, you must clear the graphics screen.

Enter: `2nd` `DRAW` 1 `ENTER`

EXERCISES

Use a graphing calculator to solve each system of inequalities. Sketch each graph on a sheet of paper. 1–9. See Solutions Manual.

1. $y \geq x$
$y \leq 5$

2. $y \geq -2x + 4$
$y \leq x - 1$

3. $y \leq 6x - 3$
$y \geq 0.5x$

4. $y \leq 0.1x + 1$
$y \geq -0.5x - 3$

5. $3x - 4y \leq 12$
$2x + y \leq 10$

6. $y - 2 \leq x$
$y \geq -3x + 5$

7. $y \geq 0$
$y \leq -2x + 12$

8. $y \leq \frac{2}{3}x - 1$
$y \geq -\frac{1}{5}x + 3$

9. $-5y \leq -2x$
$2y \leq 3x - 8$

Using Technology

This lesson offers an excellent opportunity for using technology in your algebra classroom. For more information on using technology, see *Graphing Calculators in the Mathematics Classroom,* one of the titles in the Glencoe Mathematics Professional Series.

3-4A LESSON NOTES

NCTM Standards: 1–5

Objective
Use a graphing calculator to graph and solve systems of linear inequalities.

Recommended Time
15 minutes

Instructional Resources
Graphing Calculator Masters, pp. 29 and 30

1 FOCUS

Motivating the Lesson
Select any linear inequality. Graph the corresponding linear equation. Pick one point above the line and one point below the line. Substitute the values into the equation. Students will see that one point satisfies the inequality while the other does not.

2 TEACH

Teaching Tip Point out to students that an inequality of the form $y \geq ax + b$ is entered first and an inequality of the form $y \leq cx + d$ is entered second.

3 PRACTICE/APPLY

Assignment Guide

Core: 1–9
Enriched: 1–9

4 ASSESS

Observing students working in cooperative groups is an excellent method of assessment.

NCTM Standards: 1–5, 8

Instructional Resources

- Study Guide Master 3-4
- Practice Master 3-4
- Enrichment Master 3-4
- Assessment and Evaluation Masters, pp. 71–72
- Modeling Mathematics Masters, pp. 28–30
- Tech Prep Applications Masters, p. 6

Transparency 3-4A contains the 5-Minute Check for this lesson; **Transparency 3-4B** contains a teaching aid for this lesson.

Recommended Pacing	
Standard Pacing	Days 6 & 7 of 14
Honors Pacing	Day 6 of 12
Block Scheduling*	Day 3 of 6

*For more information on pacing and possible lesson plans, refer to the *Block Scheduling Booklet*.

1 FOCUS

5-Minute Check
(over Chapter 3-3)

Find the value of each second-order determinant.

1. $\begin{vmatrix} 3 & 4 \\ -2 & 9 \end{vmatrix}$

35

2. $\begin{vmatrix} 5 & 2 \\ -2 & 5 \end{vmatrix}$

29

Solve each system using Cramer's rule.

3. $-3x + 5y = 4$
$-2x - 4y = -8$
$\left(\dfrac{12}{11}, \dfrac{16}{11}\right)$

4. $y = 3x + 5$
$-6x + 2y = 6$
no solution

What YOU'LL LEARN

- To solve systems of inequalities by graphing.

Why IT'S IMPORTANT

You can use systems of inequalities to solve problems involving space science and higher education.

fabulous
FIRSTS

Mae Carol Jemison (1956–)

Mae Carol Jemison was the first African-American woman astronaut. She was the computer engineer and physician aboard the space shuttle Endeavor, launched September 12, 1992.

Graphing Systems of Inequalities

APPLICATION
Space Science

When the National Aeronautics and Space Administration (NASA) chose the first astronauts in 1959, size was important since the space available in the Mercury capsule was very limited. NASA called for men who were between 5 feet 4 inches and 5 feet 11 inches tall, inclusively, and who were between 21 and 40 years of age.

This information can be represented by a **system of inequalities**. To solve such a system of inequalities, we need to find the ordered pairs that satisfy all the inequalities involved. One way to do this is to graph the inequalities on the same coordinate plane. The solution set is then represented by the intersection, or overlap, of the graphs.

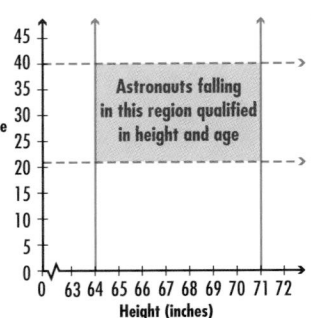

Since the heights of the astronauts are between 5 feet 4 inches (or 64 inches) and 5 feet 11 inches (or 71 inches), inclusively, we can write this information as the following two inequalities using h as the height in inches.

$$h \geq 64 \text{ and } h \leq 71$$

This could also be expressed as $64 \leq h \leq 71$.

The acceptable ages, a, can be expressed as the following inequalities.

$$a > 21 \text{ and } a < 40$$

The broken lines indicate that the boundaries are not part of the graphs.

This could also be expressed as $21 < a < 40$.

Graph both inequalities. Any point in the intersection of the two graphs is a solution to the system.

Example **Solve the system of inequalities by graphing.**

$$x - 2y \geq -2$$
$$x + y \leq -1$$

$x - 2y \geq -2$ represents Regions 2 and 3.
$x + y \leq -1$ represents Regions 1 and 2.

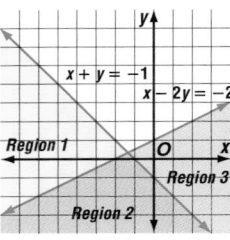

The intersection of these regions is Region 2, which is the solution of the system of inequalities.

---

fabulous
FIRSTS

Ms. Jemison, from Decatur, Georgia, was selected by NASA in 1987 for the space program, became mission specialist for the *Discovery* flight Spacelab-5 in June of 1991, and then traveled as a science mission specialist on the *Endeavor* flight the following year.

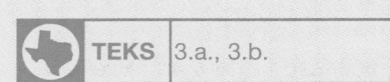
TEKS 3.a., 3.b.

It is possible that two regions do *not* intersect. In such cases, we say the solution is the empty set, shown as ∅, and no solution exists.

Example **2** Solve the system of inequalities by graphing.

$$y > \frac{2}{3}x + 2$$

$$y < \frac{2}{3}x - 1$$

The two solutions have no points in common. The solution set is ∅.

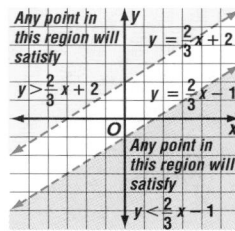

As you recall, an absolute value inequality can be restated as two inequalities using an *and* or an *or*. So, an absolute value inequality can be graphed like a system of inequalities.

Example **3** Solve the system of inequalities by graphing.
$$|x| < 3$$
$$y \geq x - 2$$
$$y \leq -\frac{1}{2}x + 4$$

The inequality $|x| < 3$ can be rewritten as $x > -3$ and $x < 3$.

Graph all of the inequalities on the same grid and look for the region or regions that are common to all.

Check to be sure the proper region is shaded.

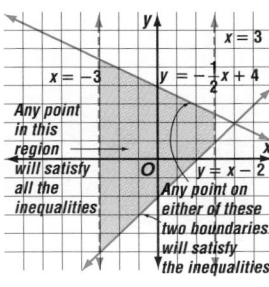

Example **4** The system of inequalities $x - y \leq 7$, $3x - 11y \geq -11$, and $x + y + 1 \geq 0$ form a triangle and its interior.

INTEGRATION
Geometry

a. **Graph the system and describe the triangle.**
b. **Name the coordinates of the vertices of the triangle.**

a. The lines are graphed at the right. The triangle is a right triangle.

b. The coordinates (11, 4) and (3, −4) can be determined from the graph. To find the coordinates of the third vertex, solve the system of equations $3x - 11y = -11$ and $x + y + 1 = 0$.

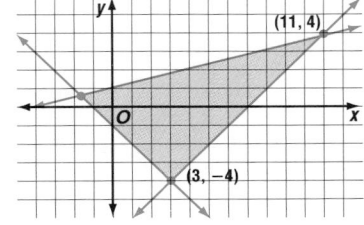

$$x + y + 1 = 0 \qquad \textit{Solve for x.}$$
$$x = -y - 1$$

(continued on the next page)

Classroom Vignette

"When we study graphing systems of inequalities, I like to use the overhead projector and different color pens to shade in the solutions in a checkerboard design made of the colors of the overlapping regions."

Linda Matthews
Egg Harbor Township High School
Pleasantville, New Jersey

Linda E. Matthews

Motivating the Lesson
Situational Problem Read the following to the class.
In order to ride a roller coaster you must be at least 50 inches tall and at least six years of age. Explain how you would find all solutions to the situation. Graph each inequality on different graphs. Does this help in solving the situation?

2 TEACH

In-Class Examples

For Example 1
Solve the system of inequalities by graphing.

$$x \geq 5$$
$$x + y \leq 3$$

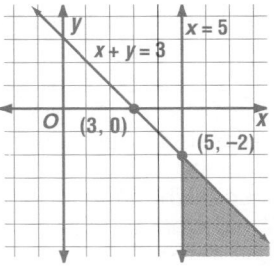

For Example 2
Solve the system of inequalities by graphing.

$$y > -\frac{4x}{5} - 4$$

$$y > -\frac{4x}{5} + 2$$

The solution set is ∅.

For Example 3
Solve the system of inequalities by graphing.

$$|y| \leq 3$$
$$0 \leq x \leq 5$$
$$x > -y$$

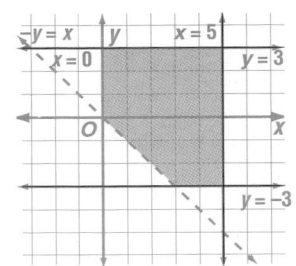

In-Class Examples

For Example 4
The system of inequalities
$x - y \le 6$, $-2x - 3y \ge -22$,
and $-4x - y \le -14$ form a
triangle and its interior.
a. Graph the system.

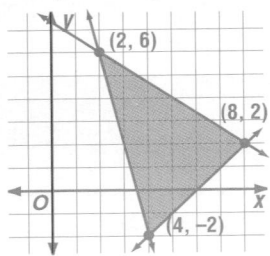

b. Name the coordinates of the vertices of the triangle.
(2, 6), (8, 2), and (4, 22)

3 PRACTICE/APPLY

Check for Understanding
Exercises 1–12 are designed to help you assess your students' understanding through reading, writing, speaking, and modeling. You should work through Exercises 1–6 with your students and then monitor their work on Exercises 7–12.

Study Guide Masters, p. 18

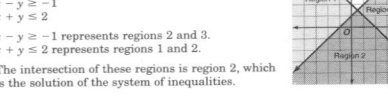

Study Guide

Student Edition
Pages 148–152

Graphing Systems of Inequalities
To solve a system of inequalities, we need to find the ordered pairs that satisfy all the inequalities involved. One way to do this is to graph the inequalities on the same coordinate plane. The solution set is then represented by the intersection, or overlap, of the graphs.

Example 1: Solve the system of inequalities by graphing.
$x - y \ge -1$
$x + y \le 2$

$x - y \ge -1$ represents regions 2 and 3.
$x + y \le 2$ represents regions 1 and 2.

The intersection of these regions is region 2, which is the solution of the system of inequalities.

It is possible that two regions *do* not intersect. In such cases, we say the solution is the empty set, ∅, and no solution exists.

Example 2: Solve the system of inequalities by graphing.
$y < x + 1$
$y > x + 2$

The two solutions have no points in common. The solution set is ∅.

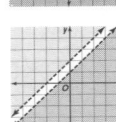

Solve each system of inequalities by graphing.

1. $x < 3$
   $y \ge -1$

2. $x - y \le 2$
   $x + 2y \ge 1$

3. $|y| \le 1$
   $x > 2$

4. $3x - 2y \le -1$
   $x + 4y \ge -12$

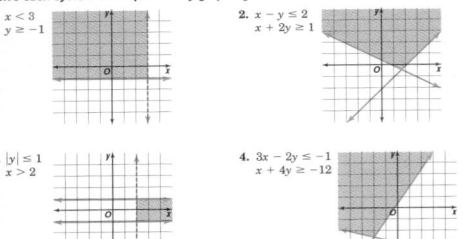

150 Chapter 3

Substitute $-y - 1$ for x.

$$3x - 11y = -11$$
$$3(-y - 1) - 11y = -11$$
$$-3y - 3 - 11y = -11$$
$$-14y = -8$$
$$y = \frac{8}{14} \text{ or } \frac{4}{7}$$

Evaluate when $y = \frac{4}{7}$.
$$x = -y - 1$$
$$= -\left(\frac{4}{7}\right) - 1$$
$$= -\frac{11}{7}$$

The coordinates of the vertices of the triangle are $(11, 4)$, $(3, -4)$, and $\left(-\frac{11}{7}, \frac{4}{7}\right)$.

CHECK FOR UNDERSTANDING

Communicating Mathematics

Mᴀᴛʜ Jᴏᴜʀɴᴀʟ

Study the lesson. Then complete the following.

1. How do you determine whether a point is a solution to a system of inequalities? **See Solutions Manual.**

2. **Describe** the difference between the graphs of the following two systems of inequalities. **a. two separate regions   b. no overlapping regions, no solution**
   a. $2x + 3y > 6$ or $2x + 3y < 3$ **b.** $2x + 3y > 6$ and $2x + 3y < 3$

3. **Describe** how the graphs of $|x| \ge 2$ and $|x| \le 2$ differ.

4. **Research** the names, ages, and heights of the original seven astronauts. Graph this information on a graph similar to the one on page 148. Describe your results in a paragraph.   **3–4. See Solutions Manual.**

5. **Write** a system of two inequalities that will have no intersection. **Sample answer: $x < 5$ and $x > 7$**

6. **Assess Yourself**   Write a paragraph describing what you like and/or dislike about graphing systems of inequalities.   **See students' work.**

Guided Practice

7. Which graph illustrates the solution to the system of inequalities $x + y \ge 1$ and $x - y \le 0$.   **c**

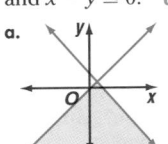
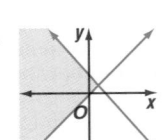
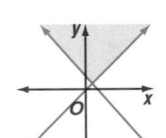

a.   b.   c.   d.

Solve each system of inequalities by graphing.

8–11. See Solutions Manual.

8. $x \le 1$
   $y > 3$

9. $y \ge 2x - 2$
   $y \le -x + 2$

10. $x - 3y \le -3$
    $2x + 3y < 12$

11. $x - 3y \ge -9$
    $4x - y \le 4$
    $x + 2y \ge -2$

12. 18 square units;
See margin for graph.

12. **Geometry**   Graph the system of inequalities $x \ge 0$, $y \ge 0$, and $x + y \le 6$. Find the area of the region defined by the system of inequalities.

150   Chapter 3   Solving Systems of Linear Equations and Inequalities

Reteaching

Using Substeps   List the steps that you would use to solve the system of inequalities by graphing. Then solve.
$y > 3x - 2$
$x + y < 6$

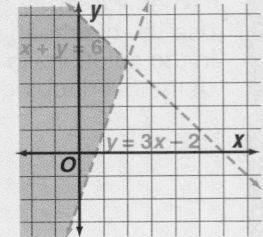

Practice

A

13–27. See Solutions Manual.

B

C

Solve each system of inequalities by graphing.

13. $x < 2$
    $y \geq 1$

14. $x - y \leq 3$
    $x + y \geq 2$

15. $x + y > 2$
    $y > 3$

16. $y - x \leq 3$
    $y \geq x + 2$

17. $y \geq x - 3$
    $y \geq -x + 1$

18. $y < -x - 3$
    $x > y - 2$

19. $y \leq 2x - 3$
    $y \leq \frac{1}{2}x + 1$

20. $y > \frac{2}{3}x - 1$
    $y \leq -\frac{3}{4}x + 2$

21. $|x| < 3$
    $|y| > 2$

22. $|x + 1| \leq 2$
    $x - 2y \geq 1$

23. $3x + 2y \leq 6$
    $4x - y < 2$

24. $4x - 3y \geq 7$
    $y < 2$

25. $x - 3y > 2$
    $2x - y < 4$
    $3x + 4y > 0$

26. $5x - y < 0$
    $4x + 3y > 6$
    $x - 3y > 3$

27. $y < 2x + 1$
    $y > 2x - 2$
    $3x + y > 8$

28a. $x + y \leq 3$, $4x - 3y \geq -9$, $y \geq -1$

28. **Geometry** Study the graph at the right.
    a. Write the system of inequalities whose solution forms the triangular region shown in the graph.
    b. Replace $y \geq -1$ with an inequality that would result in a triangular region with four times the area of the first region. $y \geq -5$

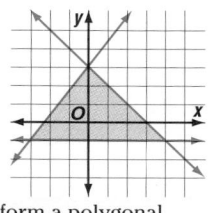

29. Sample answer:
    $x + y \leq 4$,
    $x - y \leq 4$, $x \geq -1$

30b. $x + 3y \geq -10$,
    $x - y \leq 2$,
    $x + 3y \leq 14$,
    $y - x \leq 2$

29. **Geometry** Write a system of inequalities that would form a polygonal region having at least three sides.

30. **Geometry** Study the region at the right. **a. parallelogram**
    a. What is the most descriptive name for the quadrilateral?
    b. Write the system of inequalities whose solution forms the region.
    c. Find the area of the region. **24 square units**

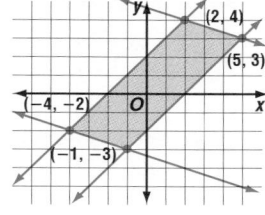

(2, 4)
(5, 3)
(−4, −2)
(−1, −3)

Critical Thinking

31. **Geometry** Find the area of the region defined by $|x| + |y| \leq 5$ and $|x| + |y| \geq 2$. **42 square units**

Applications and Problem Solving

University of Notre Dame

32. **Higher Education** According to *Lovejoy's College Guide,* the middle 50% of the freshmen entering the University of Notre Dame have a score between 540 and 650, inclusively, on the verbal portion of the SAT. The middle 50% of these same freshmen have between 620 and 720, inclusively, on the math portion of the SAT. Write a system of inequalities that describes the SAT scores of the middle 50% of Notre Dame freshmen. Then, graph the system of inequalities. **See margin.**

33. **Time Management** Paloma attends Jones High School. Each school day, she spends 7 hours in school and usually some time after school studying and doing homework. She tries to sleep exactly 8 hours out of every 24-hour period. Let s represent the time Paloma spends on school and studying, and let a represent the time she spends on activities other than school, studying, and sleep. Write a system of inequalities that describes the way Paloma manages her time during a typical school day. Then graph the system of inequalities. **$s \geq 7$ and $s + a \leq 16$; See margin for graph.**

Extension

Reasoning Graph the inequality $|x| + |y| \leq 2$. How many cases do you have to consider? What are the cases?

Core: 13–33 odd, 34–39
Enriched: 14–30 even, 31–39
All: Self Test, 1–10

For **Extra Practice,** see p. 881.

The red A, B, and C flags, printed only in the Teacher's Wraparound Edition, indicate the level of difficulty of the exercises.

Additional Answers

32.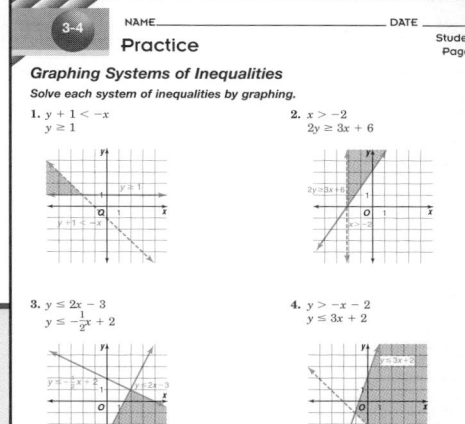

33.

Practice Masters, p. 18

4 ASSESS

Closing Activity
Writing Have students write a step-by-step explanation for solving a system of inequalities.

Chapter 3, Quiz B (Lessons 3-3 and 3-4), is available in the *Assessment and Evaluation Masters*, p. 72.

Mid-Chapter Test (Lessons 3-1 through 3-4) is available in the *Assessment and Evaluation Masters*, p. 71.

Answers for the Self Test

9.
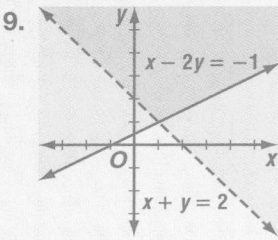

10.
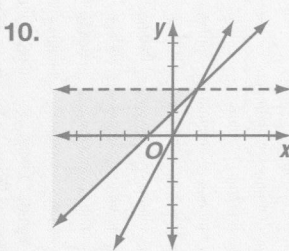

Enrichment Masters, p. 18

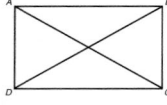
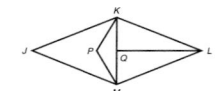

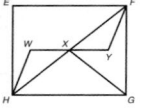
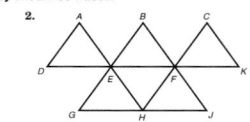

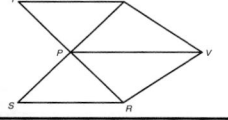

Mixed Review

34. Use Cramer's rule to solve the system of equations $x - 4y = 1$ and $2x + 3y = 13$. (Lesson 3–3) **(5, 1)**

Solve each system of equations. Use either substitution or elimination. (Lesson 3–2)

35. $4a - 3b = -4$
$3a - 2b = -4$ **(−4, −4)**

36. $2r + s = 1$
$r - s = 8$ **(3, −5)**

37. Graph the system of equations $x + 5y = 10$ and $x + 5y = 15$. State its solution. (Lesson 3–1) **No solution; see margin for graph.**

38. Which equation is represented by the graph at the right? (Lesson 2–6) **d**

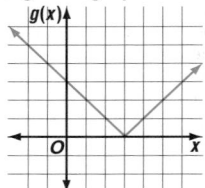

a. $g(x) = |x| + 3$
b. $g(x) = |x + 3|$
c. $g(x) = |x| - 3$
d. $g(x) = |x - 3|$

39. Salina earned $8 more than Tyler selling newspaper subscriptions. At the end of the day, Salina was given $1 as a sales bonus, and Tyler spent $3 on snacks. When they returned home, they had a total of $12. How much money did Tyler earn selling newspaper subscriptions? (Lesson 1–4) **$3**

SELF TEST

Solve the system of equations by graphing. (Lesson 3–1)

1. $2x - 5y = 14$
$x - y = 1$ **(−3, −4)**

2. $4x - 3y = -9$
$x + 2y = -5$ **(−3, −1)**

Solve each system of equations by using substitution or elimination. (Lesson 3–2)

3. $y = 3x$
$x + 21 = -2y$ **(−3, −9)**

4. $4a + 3b = -2$
$5a + 7b = 17$ **(−5, 6)**

5. Find the value of the determinant $\begin{vmatrix} -5 & -2 \\ -3 & 11 \end{vmatrix}$. (Lesson 3–3) **−61**

Use Cramer's rule to solve each system of equations. (Lesson 3–3)

6. $3x - 7y = 2$
$6x - 13y = 4$ $\left(\frac{2}{3}, 0\right)$

7. $6x + 5y = -7$
$2x - 3y = 7$ $\left(\frac{1}{2}, -2\right)$

8. Travel A hotel at the Downhill Ski Resort advertises two package deals. One package offers three nights at the hotel and a two-day lift ticket for $245. The other offers five nights at the hotel and a three-day lift ticket for $400. For these specials, what is the cost of staying at the hotel one night and what is the cost of a one-day lift ticket? (Lesson 3–3) **hotel, $65; lift ticket, $25**

Solve each system of inequalities by graphing. (Lesson 3–4) **9–10. See margin.**

9. $x + y > 2$
$x - 2y \leq -1$

10. $y < 2$
$y \geq 2x$
$y \geq x + 1$

SELF TEST

The Self Test provides students with a brief review of the concepts and skills in Lessons 3-1 through 3-4. Lesson numbers are given to the right of exercises or instruction lines so students can review concepts not yet mastered.

Additional Answer

37.
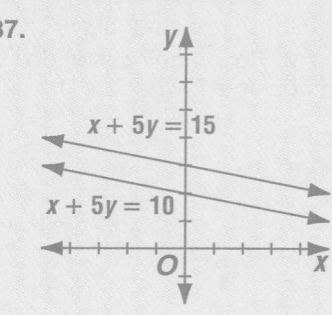

Linear Programming

APPLICATION
Agriculture

Harris Grunden has 20 days in which to plant corn and soybeans. The corn can be planted at a rate of 60 acres per day and the soybeans at a rate of 70 acres per day. He has 1300 acres available for planting these two crops. Write inequalities to show the possible ways he can plant the available acres.

What YOU'LL LEARN

- To find the maximum and minimum values of a function over a region by using linear programming techniques, and
- to solve problems by solving a simpler problem.

Why IT'S IMPORTANT

You can use linear programming to solve problems involving agriculture and manufacturing.

Let c represent the acres planted in corn and let s represent the acres planted in soybeans. Since Harris cannot plant negative acres of corn or soybeans, c and s must be nonnegative numbers.

$$c \geq 0 \text{ and } s \geq 0$$

Since corn can be planted at a rate of 60 acres per day, Harris can plant no more than 20×60 or 1200 acres of corn.

$$c \leq 1200 \quad \textit{Thus, } 0 \leq c \leq 1200.$$

Since soybeans can be planted at a rate of 70 acres per day, Harris can plant no more than 20×70 or 1400 acres of soybeans.

$$s \leq 1400 \quad \textit{Thus, } 0 \leq s \leq 1400.$$

Harris cannot plant more than 1300 acres of corn and soybeans.

$$c + s \leq 1300$$

Since Harris has 20 days to plant the corn and soybeans, the number of days spent planting these crops must be less than or equal to 20.

$$\frac{c}{60} + \frac{s}{70} \leq 20 \quad \begin{array}{l} \frac{c}{60} \textit{ represents the time needed to plant the corn.} \\ \frac{s}{70} \textit{ represents the time needed to plant the soybeans.} \end{array}$$

$$7c + 6s \leq 8400 \quad \textit{Multiply each side by 420 to eliminate fractions.}$$

If we graph these inequalities, all of the points in their intersection are possible ways Harris can plant the available acres. The inequalities are called the **constraints**. The area of intersection of the graphs, in which every constraint is met, is called the **feasible region** of the planting.

Lesson 3–5 Linear Programming **153**

TEKS 3.a., 3.b.

NCTM Standards: 1–6

Instructional Resources

- Study Guide Master 3-5
- Practice Master 3-5
- Enrichment Master 3-5
- Multicultural Activity Masters, p. 5
- Real-World Applications, 7

 Transparency 3-5A contains the 5-Minute Check for this lesson; **Transparency 3-5B** contains a teaching aid for this lesson.

Recommended Pacing	
Standard Pacing	Day 8 of 14
Honors Pacing	Day 7 of 12
Block Scheduling*	Day 4 of 6 (along with Lesson 3-6)

 *For more information on pacing and possible lesson plans, refer to the *Block Scheduling Booklet*.

1 FOCUS

 5-Minute Check
(over Lesson 3-4)

1. Does the point (2, 1) satisfy this system of inequalities? $y < 2x + 1$; $y > 2x - 1$ **no**

Determine which, if any, of the ordered pairs (1, 1), (2, 2), (−1, −1), and (0, 0) satisfy each system.

2. $x > 1$; $y < 3$ **(2, 2)**
3. $y \leq x + 4$; $y \geq 2x - 3$ **(1, 1), (2, 2), (−1, −1), (0, 0)**
4. Solve the system of inequalities by graphing. $y \leq 3x + 2$; $y > -5x - 7$

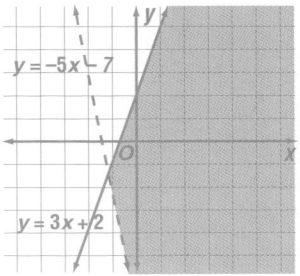

Motivating the Lesson

Situational Problem Given a rectangle with vertices at (1, 2), (1, 6), (4, 6), and (4, 2), find a system of inequalities that would result in the shading of the interior of the figure.

$x > 1$ and $x < 4$
$y > 2$ and $y < 6$

Technology Tip
Point out to students that this method may give only approximate solutions.

Let's graph the constraints.

$0 \leq c \leq 1200$
$0 \leq s \leq 1400$
$c + s \leq 1300$
$7c + 6s \leq 8400$

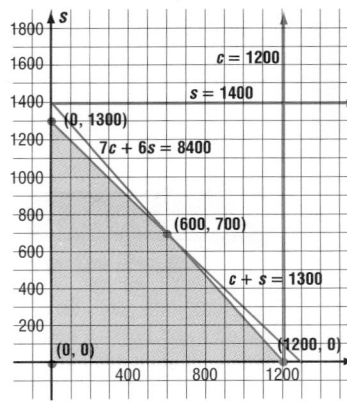

The first two constraints indicate that the graph is in the first quadrant.

The feasible region contains all possible solutions. If we choose any point within the region, its ordered pair should be a solution to each inequality. Let's try (600, 400).

Check:
$0 \leq 600 \leq 1200$
$0 \leq 400 \leq 1400$
$600 + 400 \leq 1400$
$7 \cdot 600 + 6 \cdot 400 \leq 8400$ *All are true.*

Choose a point outside the region and test it in each inequality. Is its ordered pair a solution to all of the inequalities?

Harris needs to decide how many acres of each crop to plant. There are many options, as we have seen by graphing the constraints. Of course Harris would like to make as much of a profit as possible. If the profit on corn is $30 per acre and the profit on soybeans is $26 per acre, how much of each should he plant to maximize his profit? Harris uses a spreadsheet to organize his results.

The notation $f(c, s)$ is used to represent a function with two variables c and s.

The profit can be defined by the function $f(c, s) = 30c + 26s$. Mathematicians have shown that the maximum and minimum values of a function, $f(c, s)$, occur at the vertices of the feasible region. The coordinates of the vertices of a feasible region can be found by reading a graph or by solving systems of equations. The points we need to try have coordinates (0, 1300), (600, 700), (1200, 0), and (0, 0).

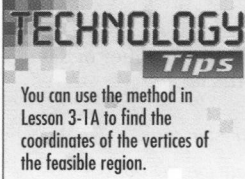

TECHNOLOGY Tips
You can use the method in Lesson 3-1A to find the coordinates of the vertices of the feasible region.

(c, s)	$30c + 26s$	Profit $f(c, s)$
(0, 1300)	30(0) + 26(1300)	$33,800
(600, 700)	30(600) + 26(700)	36,200
(1200, 0)	30(1200) + 26(0)	36,000
(0, 0)	30(0) + 26(0)	0

Check some other values within the feasible region to convince yourself that we have found the maximum profit for the 1300 acres. According to our results, Harris should plant 600 acres of corn and 700 acres of soybeans for a profit of $36,200.

The process we have just used is called **linear programming**. This procedure is used to find the maximum or minimum value of a linear function subject to given conditions on the variables, called constraints. When a system of inequalities produces a convex polygonal region as a solution, the maximum or minimum value of a related function will occur at a vertex of the region.

Example Find the maximum and minimum values of $f(x, y) = 2x - 3y$ for the polygonal region determined by the system of inequalities.
$x \geq 1$
$y \geq 2$
$x + 2y \leq 9$

First we must find the vertices of the feasible region. Graph the inequalities.

The polygon formed is a triangle with vertices at $(1, 2)$, $(5, 2)$, and $(1, 4)$.

Use a chart to find the maximum and minimum values of the function.

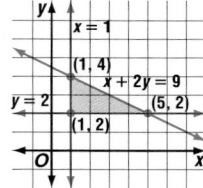

(x, y)	2x − 3y	f(x, y)
(1, 2)	2(1) − 3(2)	−4
(5, 2)	2(5) − 3(2)	4
(1, 4)	2(1) − 3(4)	−10

The maximum value is 4 at $(5, 2)$. The minimum value is -10 at $(1, 4)$.

Sometimes a polygonal region is not formed. In this case, the function is said to be **unbounded**.

Example Graph the following constraints. Then find the maximum and minimum values of the function $f(x, y) = 5x + 2y$.
$x - 3y \leq 0$
$x - 3y \geq -15$
$4x + 3y \geq 15$

Graph the system of inequalities. There are only two points of intersection, $(0, 5)$ and $(3, 1)$.

(x, y)	5x + 2y	f(x, y)
(0, 5)	5(0) + 2(5)	10
(3, 1)	5(3) + 2(1)	17

The minimum is 10 at $(0, 5)$.

Although $f(3, 1)$ is 17, it is not the maximum value since there are other points in the feasible region that produce greater values. For example, $f(4, 2) = 24$ and $f(300, 101) = 1702$. It appears that $f(x, y) = 5x + 2y$ has no maximum value when using the given constraints. Thus, the region is unbounded.

In-Class Examples

For Example 1
Find the maximum and minimum values of $f(x, y) = 0.5x + y$ for the polygonal region determined by the system of inequalities.
$x \geq 2$
$3y \leq 15$
$0.5x + 2y \geq 6$
$2x - 5y \leq 12$
max: $(18.5, 5) = 14.25$
min: $(2, 2.5) = 3.5$

For Example 2
Graph the following constraints. Then find the maximum and minimum values of the function $f(x, y) = 8x + 3y$.
$x - 2y \leq 0$
$x - 2y \geq -10$
$6x + 3y \geq 10$
The minimum is -4 at $(-2, 4)$. Since $f(0, 4) = 12$ and $f(0, 0) = 0$, $(0, 0)$ is not the maximum. Therefore, there is no maximum.

Teaching Tip Sometimes you do not need to check all the vertices of the maximum and minimum points.

Cooperative Learning

Group Discussion Have students work in groups of three to solve the following problem. Suggest they make a model and act out the tournament's wins and losses and share their findings with the class.
In a double-elimination tournament, a team is out if it loses two games. The team left is the champion. If there are 30 teams playing in the tournament, how many games will need to be played to determine a champion? Explain your answer. 58 or 59
For more information on the group discussion strategy, see *Cooperative Learning in the Mathematics Classroom*, one of the titles in the Glencoe Mathematics Professional Series, page 31.

3 PRACTICE/APPLY

Check for Understanding
Exercises 1–9 are designed to help you assess your students' understanding through reading, writing, speaking, and modeling. You should work through Exercises 1–3 with your students and then monitor their work on Exercises 4–9.

Error Analysis
Sometimes there is no maximum or minimum on the feasible region. Finding one point in the region with a value between the values at the vertices does not prove that the maximum and minimum are at the vertices. To confirm this, students must check several points.

Additional Answer

2. the process of finding a maximum or a minimum value of a function by using the coordinates of the vertices of the polygon formed by the graphs of the constraints

When using linear programming, we do not check every ordered pair in the feasible region to find the maximum and minimum values of the function. Instead we solve a simpler problem by checking only the values at the vertices. **Solve a simpler problem** is one of many problem-solving strategies that you can use to solve problems.

Example Find the sum of the whole numbers 1 to 1000, inclusive.

PROBLEM SOLVING
Solve a Simpler Problem

We could add all of the numbers directly, but even with a calculator that would be time-consuming and tedious. Let's look at the sum of the whole numbers 1 to 10 to see if we can find a faster way.

$$
\begin{aligned}
S &= 1 + 2 + 3 + \ldots + 10 \\
(+)\, S &= 10 + 9 + 8 + \ldots + 1 \\
\hline
2S &= 11 + 11 + 11 + \ldots + 11 \\
2S &= 10 \cdot 11 \\
2S &= 110 \\
S &= 55
\end{aligned}
$$

S represents the sum of the whole numbers.

Now, extend this concept to the original problem.

$$
\begin{aligned}
S &= 1 + 2 + 3 + \ldots + 1000 \\
(+)\, S &= 1000 + 999 + 998 + \ldots + 1 \\
\hline
2S &= 1001 + 1001 + 1001 + \ldots + 1001 \\
2S &= 1000 \cdot 1001 \\
2S &= 1,001,000 \\
S &= 500,500
\end{aligned}
$$

The sum of the numbers of the right side of the equals sign has 1000 addends of 1001.

Therefore, the product of 1000 and 1001 equals twice the sum.

The sum of the whole numbers from 1 to 1000 is 500,500.

CHECK FOR UNDERSTANDING

Communicating Mathematics

Study the lesson. Then complete the following.

1a. (−1, 3), (3, 5), (5, −1), (−2, −2)

1. A feasible region is defined by the graph at the right.
   a. **Name** the points at which a maximum or minimum value of a function could occur for the feasible region.
   b. **Find** the maximum and minimum value of the function $f(x, y) = 2x + 3y$.   21; −10

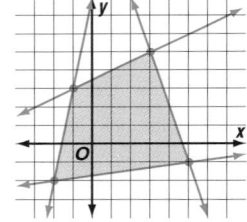

3. Sample answer: a difficult problem with a solution that is not obvious

2. **Define** linear programming in your own words.   See margin.

3. **Describe** a problem that might be solved by the strategy of solving a simpler problem.

Reteaching

Using Discussion Have students talk through their method of solving the exercise. Then solve.
A convex polygon has vertices $A(0, 2)$, $B(4, −1)$, $C(5, 1)$, and $D(3, 5)$. Find the maximum and minimum values of each function for the region determined by the polygon.

1. $f(x, y) = 2x + 5y$
   min is 3 at B; max is 31 at D
2. $g(x, y) = 3x + y$
   min is −14 at C; max is 2 at A

Guided Practice

4. max: $f(2, 6) = 14$
min: $f(1, -2) = -3$
5. max: $f(4, 1) = 15$
min: $f(-3, 2) = -14$

6–8. See Solutions Manual.

A feasible region has vertices at $(-3, 2)$, $(4, 1)$, $(2, 6)$, and $(1, -2)$. Find the maximum and minimum values of each function.

4. $f(x, y) = x + 2y$

5. $f(x, y) = 4x - y$

Graph each system of inequalities. Name the coordinates of the vertices of the feasible region. Find the maximum and minimum values of the given function for this region.

6. $y \geq 1$
$x \leq 6$
$y \leq 2x + 1$
$f(x, y) = x + y$

7. $4y \leq x + 8$
$x + y \geq 2$
$y \geq 2x - 5$
$f(x, y) = 4x + 3y$

8. $y \geq 2$
$1 \leq x \leq 5$
$y \leq x + 3$
$f(x, y) = 3x - 2y$

9. Solve a Simpler Problem Carl Friedrich Gauss (1777–1855) of Germany was the greatest mathematician of his time. When he was in elementary school, his teacher wanted to keep the students busy by asking them to add the numbers from 1 to 100, inclusive. Within seconds, Gauss declared that the answer was 5050.

   a. How did Gauss add the numbers so quickly? **See margin.**

   b. What is the sum of the whole numbers from 1 to 2000, inclusive? **2,001,000**

EXERCISES

Practice

10. max:
$f(4, -1) = 5$
min: $f(-1, 3) = -4$
11. max: $f(3, 5) = 19$
min: $f(-1, -2) = -7$
12. max: $f(3, 5) = 12$
min: $f(4, -1) = -7$
13. max:
$f(-1, -2) = 4$
min: $f(3, 5) = -11$

14–22. See Solutions Manual.

A feasible region has vertices at $(-1, 3)$, $(3, 5)$, $(4, -1)$, and $(-1, -2)$. Find the maximum and minimum values of each function.

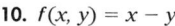

10. $f(x, y) = x - y$

11. $f(x, y) = 3x + 2y$

12. $f(x, y) = 3y - x$

13. $f(x, y) = -2x - y$

Graph each system of inequalities. Name the coordinates of the vertices of the feasible region. Find the maximum and minimum values of the given function for this region.

14. $2x + 3y \geq 6$
$3x - 2y \geq -4$
$5x + y \leq 15$
$f(x, y) = x + 3y$

15. $x \geq 1$
$y \geq 0$
$2x + y \leq 6$
$f(x, y) = 3x + y$

16. $x + y \geq 4$
$3x - 2y \leq 12$
$x - 4y \geq -16$
$f(x, y) = x - 2y$

17. $y \leq 2x + 1$
$1 \leq y \leq 3$
$y \leq -0.5x + 6$
$f(x, y) = 3x + y$

18. $y \leq x + 6$
$y + 2x \geq 6$
$2 \leq x \leq 6$
$f(x, y) = -x + 3y$

19. $x + y \geq 2$
$2y \geq 3x - 6$
$4y \leq x + 8$
$f(x, y) = 3y + x$

20. $x - 3y \geq -7$
$5x + y \leq 13$
$x + 6y \geq -9$
$3x - 2y \geq -7$
$f(x, y) = x - y$

21. $x \geq 2$
$x \leq 4$
$y \geq 1$
$x - 2y \geq -4$
$f(x, y) = x - 3y$

22. $x \geq 0$
$y \geq 0$
$x + 2y \leq 6$
$2y - x \leq 2$
$x + y \leq 5$
$f(x, y) = 3x - 5y$

Alternative Teaching Strategies

Student Diversity Review the terms *constraint, feasible region,* and *unbounded* with the class. Then separate students into groups, equally distributing students with diverse backgrounds and mathematical skills. Have each group prepare graphs that demonstrate the meanings of these terms.

Assignment Guide

Core: 11–25 odd, 26, 27, 29, 31–37
Enriched: 10–26 even, 27–37

For **Extra Practice,** see p. 882.

The red A, B, and C flags, printed only in the Teacher's Wraparound Edition, indicate the level of difficulty of the exercises.

Additional Answer

9a. Gauss used the strategy of solving a simpler problem as in Example 3.

Study Guide Masters, p. 19

3-5   NAME_____   DATE_____
Study Guide   Student Edition
Pages 153–159

Linear Programming

Practical problems can be solved by **linear programming.** Linear programming is a procedure for finding the maximum or minimum value of a function in two variables, subject to given conditions on the variables called **constraints.**

Example: Find the maximum or minimum value for the function $f(x, y) = 6x - 2y$.

The values of x and y have the following constraints.
$x \geq 0$ $0 \leq y \leq 4$ $x + y < 5$ $2y \geq x - 2$

Graph each inequality.

The maximum and the minimum occur at vertices of the region for the solution set. The minimum value of $f(x, y)$ is $f(0, 4) = -8$. The maximum is $f(4, 1) = 22$.

Graph each system of inequalities. Name the coordinates of the vertices of the feasible region. Find the maximum and minimum value of the given function for this region.

1. $y \geq 2$ vertices: (1, 2),
$1 \leq x \leq 5$ (1, 4), (5, 8), (5, 2);
$y \leq x + 3$ max: 11; min: -5
$f(x, y) = 3x - 2y$

2. $x + y \geq 2$ vertices: (0, 2),
$4y \leq x + 8$ (4, 3), $\left(\frac{7}{3}, -\frac{1}{3}\right)$;
$y \geq 2x - 5$ max: 25; min: 6
$f(x, y) = 4x + 3y$

3. $x + y \geq 2$ vertices: (0, 2),
$4y \leq x + 8$ (4, 3), (2, 0);
$2y \geq 3x - 6$ max: 13; min: 2
$f(x, y) = 3y + x$

4. $y \leq x + 5$ vertices: (-3, -3),
$y \geq x$ (-3, 2), (0, 5),
$x \geq -3$ $\left(\frac{5}{3}, \frac{5}{3}\right)$;
$y + 2x \leq 5$ max: 3; min: -10
$f(x, y) = x - 2y$

Additional Answers

23. vertices: (5, 0), (0, 0), (0, 2), (2, 4), (5, 1)
    max: $f(5, 0) = 25$
    min: $f(0, 2) = -6$
24. vertices: (0, 1), (1, 0), (3, 0), (3, 5), (0, 5)
    max: $f(3, 5) = 56$
    min: $f(1, 0) = 12$
25. vertices: (−4.08, −2), (−1.58, 1), (−0.4, 1), (−0.4, −2)
    max: $f(−0.4, 1) = 0.4$
    min: $f(−4.08, −2) = −20.32$
28. 120 units of notebook paper and 80 units of newsprint
29. Sample answer: No, he could only increase his income by $100.

Graphing Calculator

Use a graphing calculator to find the coordinates of the vertices of the feasible region. Find the maximum and minimum values of the given function for this region.   23–25. See margin.

23. $0 \le x \le 5$
    $y \ge 0$
    $-x + y \le 2$
    $x + y \le 6$
    $f(x, y) = 5x - 3y$

24. $x \le 3$
    $y \le 5$
    $x + y \ge 1$
    $x \ge 0$
    $y \ge 0$
    $f(x, y) = 2x + 8y + 10$

25. $y \le 1$
    $y \ge -2$
    $5x \le -2$
    $1.2x - y \ge -2.9$
    $f(x, y) = 4x + 2y$

Critical Thinking

26. The vertices of a feasible region are $A(1, 2)$, $B(5, 2)$, and $C(1, 4)$. Write a function that satisfies each condition.   **Sample answers are given.**
    a. A is the maximum and B is the minimum. $f(x, y) = -2x - y$
    b. C is the maximum and B is the minimum. $f(x, y) = 3y - 2x$
    c. B is the maximum and A is the minimum. $f(x, y) = x + y$
    d. A is the maximum and C is the minimum. $f(x, y) = -x - 3y$
    e. A is the minimum and both B and C are maximums. $f(x, y) = x + 2y$

Applications and Problem Solving

27. **Employment**   Rosalyn works no more than 20 hours a week during the school year. She is paid $10 an hour for tutoring geometry students and $7 an hour for delivering pizzas for Pizza King. She wants to spend at least 3 hours but no more than 8 hours a week tutoring. Find Rosalyn's maximum earnings. $164

28. **Manufacturing**   The Northern Wisconsin Paper Mill can convert wood pulp to either notebook paper or newsprint. The mill can produce at most 200 units of paper a day. At least 10 units of notebook paper and 80 units of newspaper are required daily by regular customers. If the profit on a unit of notebook paper is $500 and the profit on a unit of newsprint is $350, how many units of each type of paper should the manager have the mill produce each day to maximize profits?
    See margin.

29. **Agriculture**   Refer to the application at the beginning of the lesson. Suppose Harris has an opportunity to plant 50 acres of his father's land in corn and soybeans. Do you think Harris should farm the land? Explain.
    See margin.

30. **Solve a Simpler Problem**   A team is eliminated from the Central Indiana Women's Basketball Tournament when it loses a game. If there are 30 teams playing in the tournament, how many games will need to be played to determine a champion?   **29 games**

Practice Masters, p. 19

NAME_____ DATE_____
3-5   Practice   Student Edition
                                               Pages 153–159

Linear Programming

Graph each system of inequalities. Name the coordinates of the vertices of the feasible region. Find the maximum and minimum values of the given function for this region.

1. $2x - 4 \le y$ vertices: (3, 2),
   $-2x - 4 \le y$ (−3, 2), (0, −4);
   $2 \ge y$ max = 8,
   $f(x, y) = -2x + y$ min = −4

2. $3x - y \le 7$ vertices: (4, 5),
   $2x - y \ge 3$ (2, −1), (0, −3);
   $y \ge x - 3$ max = 12,
   $f(x, y) = x - 4y$ min = −16

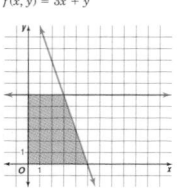
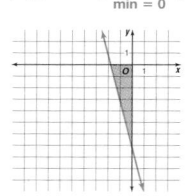

3. $x \ge 0$ vertices: (0, 0),
   $y \ge 0$ (5, 0), (3, 6), (0, 6);
   $3x + y \le 15$ max = 15,
   $y \le 6$ min = 0
   $f(x, y) = 3x + y$

4. $x \le 0$ vertices: (0, 0),
   $y \le 0$ (0, −7), (−$\frac{7}{4}$, 0);
   $4x + y \ge -7$ max = 28,
   $f(x, y) = -x - 4y$ min = 0

5. **Solve a simpler problem.**   A snail is at the bottom of a well that is 24 feet deep. The snail can climb 2 inches each hour, but then falls back 1 inch. How many hours will it take the snail to crawl out of the well?   287 hours

Tech Prep

Agriculturist   Students who are interested in agriculture or agronomy may wish to do further research on the information given in Exercise 29 and in the chapter-opening application and explore the potential growth of this career. For more information on tech prep, see the *Teacher's Handbook*.

31. **Solve a Simpler Problem**   Opa Azul is a marketing research executive for a soft drink company. The research team has arranged to perform a survey in 16 different local shopping malls. To ensure that competing soft drink companies will not learn of the survey results, Opa has arranged for telephone lines to be set up so that each survey station has a direct line to each of the other stations. How many telephone lines does Opa need to have installed?   **120 telephone lines**

Mixed Review

32. **Geometry**   Consider the system of inequalities $x - 2y \leq -1$, $5x - 2y \geq -21$, $x - 2y \geq -9$, and $3x + 2y \leq 13$.   (Lesson 3–4)
   a. What is the most descriptive name for the region formed by this system?   **trapezoid**
   b. Name the coordinates of the vertices.

32b. $(-5, -2)$, $(3, 2)$, $(-3, 3)$, $(1, 5)$

33. Use Cramer's rule to solve the system of equations.   (Lesson 3–3) $(5, -3)$
   $3x + 2y = 9$
   $2x - 3y = 19$

34. Write an equation for the line that passes through $(-7, 9)$ and is perpendicular to the y-axis.   (Lesson 2–4) $y = 9$

35. no

35. Is the relation at the right a function?   (Lesson 2–1)

36. $513\frac{2}{3}$ miles

36. **Business**   Reliable Rentals rents cars for $12.95 per day plus 15¢ per mile. Luis Romero works for a company that limits expenses for car rentals to $90 per day. What is the maximum number of miles that Mr. Romero can drive each day?   (Lesson 1–6)

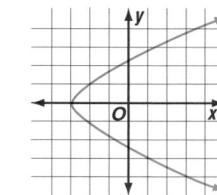

37. $54 - 32b$

37. Simplify $4(12 - 5b) - 3(4b - 2)$.   (Lesson 1–2)

WORKING ON THE

Refer to the Investigation on pages 60–61.

Through the Looking Glass

A proportion is an equality in which $\frac{a}{b} = \frac{c}{d}$. A proportion exists that relates the dimensions of the scope, the height of the animal's image through the tube, and the distance you are from the animal.

1   Look for this relationship and compare your results from the different scopes as worked on the Investigation in Lesson 3–2.

2   Use your data to write a proportion for each scope.

3   Graph these equations on the same coordinate plane. Write any observations you make about these graphs.

Add the results of your work to your Investigation Folder.

Extension

Reasoning Is it possible to have more than one value that produces a maximum or minimum for a given function?

Yes; if the function represents a line that is a boundary of the polygonal region, the coordinates of any point on that side of the polygon would produce the same maximum or minimum value.

Working on the Investigation

The Investigation on pages 60–61 is designed to be a long-term project that is completed over several days or weeks. Encourage students to keep their materials in their Investigation Folder as they work on the Investigation.

---

4 ASSESS

Closing Activity

Speaking Have students explain when a function will attain both a maximum and a minimum value for a given set of constraints. The solution is the interior and boundary of a polygonal region.

Enrichment Masters, p. 19

3-5   NAME_____   DATE _____
Enrichment   Student Edition
Pages 153–159

Truth Tables

In mathematics, the basic operations are addition, subtraction, multiplication, division, finding a root, and raising to a power. In logic, the basic operations are the following: *not* ($\sim$), *and* ($\wedge$), *or* ($\vee$), and *implies* ($\rightarrow$).

If P and Q are statements, then $\sim P$ means not P; $\sim Q$ means not Q; $P \wedge Q$ means P and Q; $P \vee Q$ means P or Q; and $P \rightarrow Q$ means P implies Q. The operations are defined by truth tables. On the left below is the truth table for the statement $\sim P$. Notice that there are two possible conditions for P, true (T) or false (F). If P is true, $\sim P$ is false; if P is false, $\sim P$ is true. Also shown are the truth tables for $P \wedge Q$, $P \vee Q$, and $P \rightarrow Q$.

P	$\sim P$		P	Q	$P \wedge Q$		P	Q	$P \vee Q$		P	Q	$P \rightarrow Q$
T	F		T	T	T		T	T	T		T	T	T
F	T		T	F	F		T	F	T		T	F	F
			F	T	F		F	T	T		F	T	T
			F	F	F		F	F	F		F	F	T

You can use this information to find out under what conditions a complex statement is true.

Example: Under what conditions is $\sim P \vee Q$ true?

Create the truth table for the statement. Use the information from the truth table above for $P \vee Q$ to complete the last column.

P	Q	$\sim P$	$\sim P \vee Q$	
T	T	F	T	When one statement is
T	F	F	F	true and one is false,
F	T	T	T	the conjunction is true.
F	F	T	T	

The truth table indicates that $\sim P \vee Q$ is true in all cases except where P is true and Q is false.

Use truth tables to determine the conditions under which each statement is true.

1. $\sim P \vee \sim Q$ all except where both P and Q are true
2. $\sim P \rightarrow (P \rightarrow Q)$ all
3. $(P \vee Q) \vee (\sim P \wedge \sim Q)$ all
4. $(P \rightarrow Q) \vee (Q \rightarrow P)$ all
5. $(P \rightarrow Q) \wedge (Q \rightarrow P)$ both P and Q are true; both P and Q are false
6. $(\sim P \wedge \sim Q) \rightarrow \sim (P \vee Q)$ all

Instructional Resources

- Study Guide Master 3-6
- Practice Master 3-6
- Enrichment Master 3-6
- Assessment and Evaluation Masters, p. 73
- Multicultural Activity Masters, p. 6

Transparency 3-6A contains the 5-Minute Check for this lesson; **Transparency 3-6B** contains a teaching aid for this lesson.

Recommended Pacing	
Standard Pacing	Day 9 of 14
Honors Pacing	Day 8 of 12
Block Scheduling*	Day 4 of 6 (along with Lesson 3-5)

*For more information on pacing and possible lesson plans, refer to the *Block Scheduling Booklet*.

1 FOCUS

5-Minute Check
(over Lesson 3-5)

Graph the system of inequalities. Find the maximum and minimum values of the given function.

$x \geq 0$ max: $f(5, 0) = 10$;
$y \geq 0$ min: $f(0, 6) = -6$
$x \leq 5$
$y \leq 6$
$x + y \leq 6$
$f(x, y) = 2x - y$

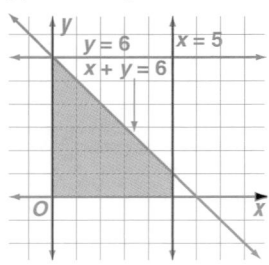

3-6

Applications of Linear Programming

What YOU'LL LEARN

- To solve problems involving maximum and minimum values by using linear programming techniques.

Why IT'S IMPORTANT

You can use linear programming to solve problems involving manufacturing and business.

APPLICATION
Business

Mrs. Fernandez's Cookie Factory makes different-sized packages of cookies that contain a combination of chocolate chip and peanut butter cookies. Mrs. Fernandez places at least three of each type of cookie in each of the combination packages. The largest package, the "Baker's Dozen," contains thirteen cookies. It costs Mrs. Fernandez 19¢ to make a chocolate chip cookie and 13¢ to make a peanut butter cookie. She sells them for 44¢ and 39¢, respectively. How should Mrs. Fernandez package the cookies to maximize profit? Which packaging will yield the least profit?

Linear programming can be used to solve many types of problems like the one above. These problems have certain restrictions placed on the variables, and some function of the variables must be maximized or minimized. The steps used to solve a problem using linear programming are listed below.

Linear Programming Procedure	1. **Define the variables.** 2. **Write a system of inequalities.** 3. **Graph the system of inequalities.** 4. **Find the coordinates of the vertices of the feasible region.** 5. **Write an expression to be maximized or minimized.** 6. **Substitute the coordinates of the vertices into the expression.** 7. **Select the greatest or least result. Answer the problem.**

Use this procedure to solve the problem given above.

F Y I

The largest cookie ever made was a chocolate chip cookie made in Arcadia, California, on October 15, 1993. It was a rectangle 35 feet by 28 feet 7 inches, and it contained more than 3 million chocolate chips.

Let c represent the number of chocolate chip cookies, and let p represent the number of peanut butter cookies in a package. Write the system of inequalities and graph.

$c \geq 3$
$p \geq 3$
$c + p \leq 13$

The vertices of the feasible region are at $(3, 3)$, $(3, 10)$, and $(10, 3)$.

Then write an equation for the profit.

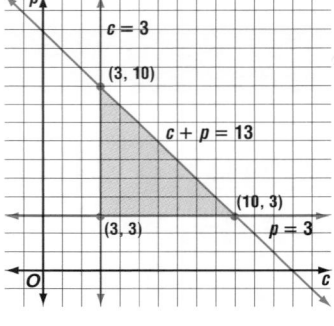

	Selling Price		Baking Cost		Profit
Chocolate Chip:	44¢	−	19¢	=	25¢
Peanut Butter:	39¢	−	13¢	=	26¢

The profit function is $f(c, p) = 25c + 26p$.

F Y I

A simple calculation shows that this cookie has about 1100 chips per square foot.

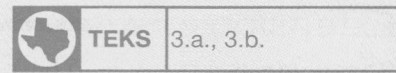

TEKS 3.a., 3.b.

Make a chart to find the maximum and minimum profit.

(c, p)	25c + 26p	f(c, p)
(3, 3)	25(3) + 26(3)	153
(3, 10)	25(3) + 26(10)	335
(10, 3)	25(10) + 26(3)	328

Using the chart, we can see that packaging 3 chocolate chip cookies with 10 peanut butter cookies yields a maximum profit, $3.35. Packaging 3 chocolate chip cookies with 3 peanut butter cookies yields a minimum profit, $1.53.

Students who use test-taking strategies can improve their scores. Making the best use of the time available is one important strategy.

Example

APPLICATION

Education

Dolores Acosta arrives at school late because her car broke down, and therefore, has only 45 minutes to complete a history exam. The exam has 2 open-ended questions and 30 multiple-choice questions. Each correct open-ended question is worth 20 points, and each multiple-choice question is worth 2 points. She knows that it usually takes her 15 minutes to answer an open-ended question and only one minute to answer a multiple-choice question. Assume that for each question Dolores answers, she receives full credit. How many of each type of question should she answer to receive the maximum possible points?

Let e represent the number of open-ended questions answered, and let m represent the number of multiple-choice questions answered.

The number of open-ended questions must be between 0 and 2, inclusive.

$0 \le e \le 2$

The number of multiple-choice questions must be between 0 and 30, inclusive.

$0 \le m \le 30$

The total time spent on the test must be less than or equal to 45 minutes.

$15e + 1m \le 45$

Graph the system. The vertices of the feasible region are at (0, 0), (2, 0), (2, 15), (1, 30), and (0, 30).

The function that describes the number of points earned is $f(e, m) = 20e + 2m$.

(e, m)	20e + 2m	f(e, m)
(0, 0)	20(0) + 2(0)	0
(2, 0)	20(2) + 2(0)	40
(2, 15)	20(2) + 2(15)	70
(1, 30)	20(1) + 2(30)	80
(0, 30)	20(0) + 2(30)	60

Dolores should answer 1 open-ended question and 30 multiple-choice questions to get a maximum score of 80.

Questioning Individual performance in basketball depends on many factors, such as height and speed. However, there are limits on each of these factors. Ask students to list other factors and the limits on each.

2 TEACH

In-Class Example

For the Example
A farmer has 25 days to plant cotton and soybeans. The cotton can be planted at a rate of 9 acres per day, and the soybeans at a rate of 12 acres per day. The farm has 275 acres available. If the profit for cotton is $25 per acre and the profit for soybeans is $18 per acre, how many of each should be planted to maximize profit?
c = number of acres of cotton
t = number of acres of soybeans
$f(c, t) = 25c + 18t$
$c \ge 0$
$t \ge 0$
$c + t \le 275$
$\frac{c}{9} + \frac{t}{12} \le 25$

Teaching Tip In the example, only integer values are considered.

Check for Understanding

Exercises 1–4 are designed to help you assess your students' understanding through reading, writing, speaking, and modeling. You should work through Exercises 1–3 with your students and then monitor their work on Exercise 4.

Assignment Guide

Core: 5–11 odd, 12–17
Enriched: 6–12 even, 13–17

For **Extra Practice,** see p. 882.

The red A, B, and C flags, printed only in the Teacher's Wraparound Edition, indicate the level of difficulty of the exercises.

Additional Answers

1. Lula; if the region is not bounded, there may be no minimum.
2. The vertices represent the extreme possibilities and therefore must produce the maximum and minimum.

Study Guide Masters, p. 20

NAME _____ DATE _____
3-6
Study Guide
Student Edition
Pages 160–164

Applications of Linear Programming

When solving linear programming problems, use the following procedure.

Linear Programming Procedure
1. Define variables.
2. Write a system of inequalities.
3. Graph the system of inequalities.
4. Find the coordinates of the vertices of the feasible region.
5. Write an expression to be maximized or minimized.
6. Substitute values for the vertices in the expression.
7. Select the greatest or least result. Answer the problem.

Solve.

1. A painter has exactly 32 units of yellow dye and 54 units of green dye. He plans to mix as many gallons as possible of color A and color B. Each gallon of color A requires 4 units of yellow dye and 1 unit of green dye. Each gallon of color B requires 1 unit of yellow dye and 6 units of green dye.

   a. Let x be the number of gallons of color A and let y be the number of gallons of color B. Write the inequalities.
   $x \geq 0, y \geq 0, 4x + y \leq 32, x + 6y \leq 54$

   b. Graph the system of inequalities and name the vertices of the polygon formed.
   (0, 9), (8, 0), (6, 8), (0, 0)

   c. Find the maximum number of gallons, $x + y$, possible.
   14 gallons (6A, 8B)

2. A delicatessen has 10 pounds of garlic-flavored sausage and 10 pounds of plain sausage. The deli wants to make as many pounds of bratwurst as possible. Each pound of bratwurst requires $\frac{1}{2}$ pound of plain sausage and $\frac{1}{2}$ pound of garlic-flavored sausage. Find the maximum number of pounds of bratwurst, $x + y$, that can be made.
   20 pounds

3. Machine A can produce 30 steering wheels per hour at a cost of $16 per hour. Machine B can produce 40 steering wheels per hour at a cost of $22 per hour. At least 360 steering wheels must be made in each 8-hour shift. What is the least cost involved in making 360 steering wheels, if maintenance of the machines limits their use to no more than 8 consecutive hours? $194

Communicating Mathematics

Study the lesson. Then complete the following.   1–3. See margin.

1. **You Decide**   Pan says that a function always has a minimum value for a given region. Lula says that sometimes a function does not have a minimum value. Who is correct and why?

2. **Explain** why coordinates of the vertices of the feasible region produce the maximum and minimum values in a linear programming situation.

3. **Write** a paragraph explaining in your own words how to solve a linear programming problem.

Guided Practice

4. NaKisha Heyman has just finished writing a research paper. She has hired a typist who will type the paper using a word processor. The typist charges $3.50 per page if no charts or graphs are used and $8.00 per page if a chart or graph appears on the page. NaKisha knows there will be at most 40 pages having no charts or graphs. There will be no more than 16 pages with charts or graphs, and the paper will be 50 pages or less.

   4a. If p = plain pages, then $0 \leq p \leq 40$.

   a. Write inequalities that limit the number of plain pages to be typed.

   b. Write inequalities that limit the number of pages with charts or graphs to be typed.   If c = pages with charts or graphs, then $0 \leq c \leq 16$.

   c. Write an equality that expresses the total number of pages to be prepared. $c + p \leq 50$

   d. Draw the graph showing the feasible region.   See margin.

   4e. (0, 0), (0, 40), (10, 40), (16, 34), (16, 0)

   e. List the coordinates of all the vertices of the feasible region.

   f. Write an expression for the cost to have the paper typed.

   4f. $f(c, p) = 8.00c + 3.50p$

   g. Which vertex produces the greatest cost?   (16, 34)

   h. What is the greatest possible cost to have the paper typed? $247

Applications and Problem Solving

A

5. **Manufacturing**   Superbats, Inc., manufactures two different quality wood baseball bats, the Wallbanger and the Dingbat. The Wallbanger takes 8 hours to trim and turn on a lathe and 2 hours to finish it. It has a profit of $17. The Dingbat takes 5 hours to trim and turn on a lathe and 5 hours to finish, but its profit is $29. The total time per day available for trimming and lathing is 80 hours and for finishing is 50 hours.

   5a. $w \geq 0, d \geq 0,$
   $8w + 5d \leq 80,$
   $2w + 5d \leq 50$

   a. If w represents the number of Wallbangers produced per day and d represents the number of Dingbats produced per day, write a system of inequalities to represent the number of Wallbanger and Dingbats that can be produced per day.

   b. Draw the graph showing the feasible region.   See margin.

   c. Write an expression for the profit per day. $f(w, d) = 17w + 29d$

   5d. 5 Wallbangers and 8 Dingbats; $317

   d. How many of each type of bat should be produced to have the maximum profit? What is the maximum profit?

Reteaching

Logical Thinking   Have students think through the problem and make notes to guide their thought process. Then solve. A tailor has 16 yd^2 of cotton fabric, 11 yd^2 of silk, and 15 yd^2 of wool. A suit requires 2 yd^2 cotton, 2 yd^2 silk, and 1 yd^2 wool. A gown requires 1 yd^2 cotton, 2 yd^2 silk, and 3 yd^2 wool. A suit sells for $30 and a gown sells for $50. Let x = the number of suits and y = the number of gowns.

a. Find $f(x, y)$ to find total sales.
b. Express constraints in a system of inequalities.
c. Graph the feasible region.
d. Check values of $f(x, y)$ at the vertices of the region.
e. How many of each garment should the tailor make to maximize his income?
   7 suits, 2 gowns; $310

6. Business The available parking area of a parking lot is 600 square meters. A car requires 6 square meters of space, and a bus requires 30 square meters of space. The attendant can handle no more than 60 vehicles.

6a. $c \geq 0$, $b \geq 0$, $6c + 30b \leq 600$, $c + b \leq 60$

a. Let c represent the number of cars, and let b represent the number of buses. Write a system of inequalities to represent the number of cars and buses that can be parked on the lot.

b. If the parking fees are $2.50 for cars and $7.50 for buses, how many of each type of vehicle should the attendant accept to maximize income? What is the maximum income?   **50 cars and 10 buses; $200.**

6c. 50 cars and 10 buses; $280

c. The parking fees for special events are $4.00 for cars and $8.00 for buses. How many of each vehicle should the attendant accept during a special event to maximize income? What is the maximum income?

7. Veterinary Medicine The table below shows the amounts of nutrient A and nutrient B in two types of dog food, X and Y.

Food Type	Amount of Ingredient A	Amount of Ingredient B
X	1 unit per pound	$\frac{1}{2}$ unit per pound
Y	$\frac{1}{3}$ unit per pound	1 unit per pound

The dogs in Kay's K-9 Kennel must get at least 40 pounds of food per day. The food may be a mixture of foods X and Y. The daily diet must include at least 20 units of nutrient A and at least 30 units of nutrient B. The dogs must not get more than 100 pounds of food per day.

a. Food X costs $0.80 per pound and food Y costs $0.40 per pound. What is the least possible cost per day for feeding the dogs?   **$20**

b. If the price of food X is raised to $1.00 per pound, and the price of food Y stays the same, should Kay change the combination of foods she is using? Explain why or why not.   **See margin.**

8. Manufacturing One of the dolls that Dolls R Us manufactures is Talking Tommy. Another doll without the talking mechanism is called Silent Sally. In one hour, the company can produce 8 Talking Tommy dolls or 20 Silent Sally dolls. Because of the demand, the company knows that it must produce at least twice as many Talking Tommy dolls as Silent Sally dolls. The company spends no more than 48 hours per week making these two dolls. The profit on each Talking Tommy is $3.00, and the profit on each Silent Sally is $7.50.

a. How many of each doll should be produced to maximize profit each week?   **160 Sally dolls and 320 Tommy dolls**

b. What is the profit?   **$2160**

9. Retail A sales associate at a paint store plans to mix color A and color B. The sales associate has exactly 32 units of blue dye and 54 units of red dye. Each gallon of color A requires 4 units of blue dye and one unit of red dye. Each gallon of color B requires one unit of blue dye and 6 units of red dye.

9a. $a \geq 0$, $b \geq 0$, $4a + b \leq 32$, $a + 6b \leq 54$

a. Let a represent the number of gallons of color A, and let b represent the number of gallons of color B. Write the inequalities that represent the number of gallons of paint that can be mixed.

b. Find the maximum number of gallons, $a + b$, that can be mixed.   **14 gal**

Tech Prep

Veterinary Technician Students who are interested in veterinary medicine may wish to do further research on the information given in Exercise 7 and explore the potential growth of this career. For more information on tech prep, see the *Teacher's Handbook*.

Additional Answers

3. Write the restrictions as inequalities, graph the inequalities, identify the vertices of the polygon formed, and substitute the coordinates of the vertices in the expression to be maximized or minimized.

4d.
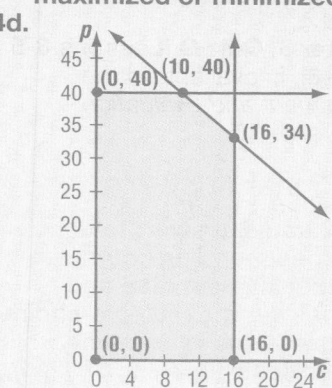

5b.
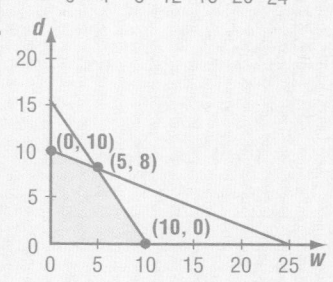

7b. No; the vertex at (10, 30) still produces the least cost ($22).

Practice Masters, p. 20

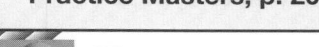

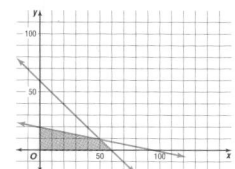

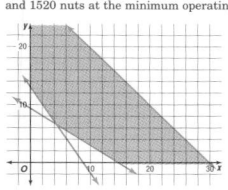

Closing Activity

Writing Have students write a detailed explanation of how to solve one of the problems in the exercises.

Chapter 3, Quiz C (Lessons 3-5 and 3-6), is available in the *Assessment and Evaluation Masters,* p. 73.

Additional Answers

11b. Sample answer: Take a speed reading course so that she can read and answer the multiple-choice questions in less time.

13. vertices: (0, 3), (0, 6), (2, 5), (1, 3)
max: $f(1, 3) = -3$
min: $f(0, 6) = -12$

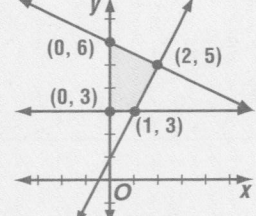

Enrichment Masters, p. 20

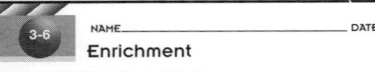

Computer Circuits and Logic

Computers operate according to the laws of logic. The circuits of a computer can be described using logic.

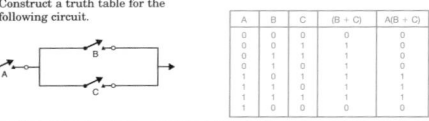

---

10. Manufacturing TeeVee Electronics, Inc., makes console and wide-screen televisions. The equipment in the factory allows for making at most 450 console televisions and 200 wide-screen televisions in one month. The chart below shows the cost of making each type of television, as well as the profit for each type.

Television	Cost per Unit	Profit per Unit
Console	$600	$125
Wide Screen	$900	$200

During the month of November, the company can spend $360,000 to make these televisions. To maximize profits, how many of each type should they make? **300 consoles and 200 wide screens for a profit of $77,500**

11. Education Carol Sommers has 50 minutes to take an English test that has 20 multiple-choice questions and 20 short-answer questions. She knows she can answer a multiple-choice question in $1\frac{1}{2}$ minutes and a short-answer question in 2 minutes. Each correct multiple-choice answer receives 2 points, and each correct short-answer receives 3 points. Assume that any question Carol answers, she gets correct.
  a. What is the maximum possible score she can receive? **72**
  b. What advice might you give Carol to improve her score? **See margin.**

Critical Thinking

12. Consider the feasible region defined by the system of inequalities below.

$$0 \le x \le 5$$
$$0 \le y \le 6$$
$$x + 2y \le 13$$
$$2x + y \le 11$$

  a. Suppose the profit function for the feasible region is $f(x, y) = 3x + 4y$. Graph the feasible region. On the same coordinate plane, graph the profit function for $f(x, y) = 32, 28, 24, 20,$ and 16. What does the graph tell you about the maximum point? **See Solutions Manual.**
  b. Suppose the profit function for the feasible region is $g(x, y) = 3x + 6y$. Graph the feasible region on another coordinate plane. Then add the graph of the profit function for $g(x, y) = 42, 36, 30,$ and 24. What does the graph tell you about the maximum point? **See Solutions Manual.**

Mixed Review

13. Graph the system of inequalities $x \ge 0, y \ge 3, y \ge 2x + 1$ and $y \le -0.5x + 6$. Name the coordinates of the vertices of the feasible region. Find the maximum and minimum values of the function $f(x, y) = 3x - 2y$ for this region. (Lesson 3–5) **See margin.**

14. Sample answer: $x \ge 0, y \ge 0, x + y \le 6$

14. Geometry Write a system of inequalities that will form a region shaped like an isosceles right triangle. (Lesson 3–4)

15. At 10:00 A.M., Monsa had traveled 195 miles across the plains states on his way to California. At 2:00 P.M., he had traveled 415 miles. Use slope to calculate his rate of travel. (Lesson 2–3) **55 mph**

16. Graph $5y - 25x = -10$. (Lesson 2–2) **See margin.**

17. $|x| < 4$

17. State an absolute value inequality for the graph at the right. (Lesson 1–7)

Extension

Problem Solving Corporation A has a fixed cost of $4000 per week. It costs $10,000 to produce 500 units. The units are sold for $40 each. Write the equations for the cost and the sales. Find the break-even point at which the cost and sales are equal.
$4000 + 20x = c, 40x = s$; **200 units**

Additional Answer

16.

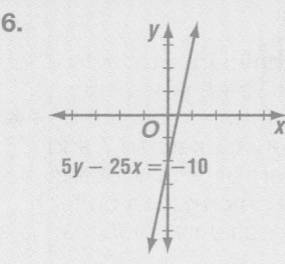

Solving Systems of Equations in Three Variables

What YOU'LL LEARN

- To solve a system of three equations in three variables.

Why IT'S IMPORTANT

You can use systems of equations to solve problems involving banking and consumer awareness.

APPLICATION

Business

The Nutty Food Company sells trail mixes and other snacks by the pound. A clerk is filling a barrel with peanuts, raisins, and carob-coated pretzels. The manager wants the associate to make 80 pounds of this mixture and to sell it for $3.35 per pound. The peanuts sell for $3.20 per pound, the raisins sell for $2.40 per pound, and the carob-coated pretzels sell for $4.00 per pound. If the mixture has twice as many pounds of carob-coated pretzels as raisins, how many pounds of each ingredient should the clerk use?

Problems like this can be expressed using a system of equations in three variables. Let p represent the number of pounds of peanuts, let r represent the number of pounds of raisins, and let c represent the number of pounds of carob-coated pretzels. Then write a system of equations using the information given.

$$p + r + c = 80 \qquad \textit{The clerk makes 80 pounds of the mixture.}$$
$$3.20p + 2.40r + 4.00c = 268 \qquad \textit{The total selling price is 80 × \$3.35, or \$268.}$$
$$c = 2r \qquad \textit{There are twice as many pounds of carob-coated pretzels as raisins.}$$

Solving systems such as this one is similar to solving systems of equations in two variables.

Since $c = 2r$, substitute $2r$ for c in each of the first two equations.

$$p + r + (2r) = 80 \quad \rightarrow \quad p + 3r = 80$$
$$3.20p + 2.40r + 4.00(2r) = 268 \quad \rightarrow \quad 3.20p + 10.40r = 268$$

The result is two equations with the same two variables. Use elimination to solve for r.

$$\begin{array}{l} p + 3r = 80 \\ 3.20p + 10.40r = 268 \end{array} \quad \boxed{\text{Multiply by 3.20.}} \quad \begin{array}{r} 3.20p + 9.60r = 256 \\ (-) \ 3.20p + 10.40r = 268 \\ \hline \textit{Subtract to eliminate } p. \quad -0.8r = -12 \\ \textit{Solve for } r. \qquad r = 15 \end{array}$$

Since $r = 15$, substitute 15 for r in the equation $p + 3r = 80$.

$$p + 3(15) = 80$$
$$p + 45 = 80$$
$$p = 35 \quad \textit{Solve for p.}$$

Finally, substitute 15 for r in the original equation $c = 2r$.

$$c = 2(15)$$
$$= 30$$

The associate should use 35 pounds of peanuts, 15 pounds of raisins, and 30 pounds of carob-coated pretzels.

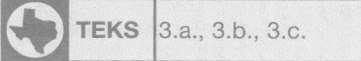 **TEKS** 3.a., 3.b., 3.c.

NCTM Standards: 1–5

Instructional Resources

- Study Guide Master 3-7
- Practice Master 3-7
- Enrichment Master 3-7
- Assessment and Evaluation Masters, p. 73
- Modeling Mathematics Masters, pp. 31–33
- Real-World Applications, 8

 Transparency 3-7A contains the 5-Minute Check for this lesson; **Transparency 3-7B** contains a teaching aid for this lesson.

Recommended Pacing	
Standard Pacing	Days 10 & 11 of 14
Honors Pacing	Day 9 of 12
Block Scheduling*	Day 5 of 6

 *For more information on pacing and possible lesson plans, refer to the *Block Scheduling Booklet*.

1 FOCUS

 5-Minute Check
(over Lesson 3-6)

The cost to run Machine A for an hour is $2.00. During that hour, Machine A produces 240 bolts and 100 nuts. The cost to run Machine B for an hour is $2.40. During that hour, Machine B produces 160 bolts and 160 nuts. Machine A and Machine B combined can run no longer than 30 hours. How long should each machine run to produce an order of at least 2080 bolts and 1520 nuts at the minimum operating costs?
$A \geq 0$
$B \geq 0$
$A + B \leq 30$
$240A + 160B \geq 2080$
$100A + 160B \geq 1520$
$f(x, y) = 2.4x + 2y$
Machine A $= y + 4$ hours
Machine B $= x + 7$ hours

Motivating the Lesson

Questioning Discuss with students how they locate points on a plane. Ask them how they think points in space could be located. Have them use the classroom to explain their location theory. Ask students what occupations might require their employees to locate points in space on a graph.

2 TEACH

In-Class Example

For Example 1
Solve the system of equations.
$x + 2y + z = 4$
$4y - 3z = 1$
$y + 5z = 6$
The solution is (1, 1, 1).

Teaching Tip Stress that students should check their solutions in all three original equations.

Teaching Tip Remind students that drawing a figure and labeling it often helps to solve a problem.

The solution of a system of equations in three variables x, y, and z, is called an **ordered triple** (x, y, z).

Example **Solve the system of equations.**
$x + 2y - 3z = 50$
$2x + y + 2z = 3$
$2x - 5y + 4z = -79$

Use elimination to make a system of two equations in two variables.

$x + 2y - 3z = 50$ **Multiply by 2.** $2x + 4y - 6z = 100$

$2x + y + 2z = 3$ **Multiply by -1.** $\dfrac{(+) -2x - y - 2z = -3}{\text{Add to eliminate } x. \quad 3y - 8z = 97}$

$2x + y + 2z = 3$
$2x - 5y + 4z = -79$ **Multiply by -1.** $\dfrac{2x + y + 2z = 3}{(+) -2x + 5y - 4z = 79}$
$\text{Add to eliminate } x. \quad 6y - 2z = 82$

The result is two equations with the same two variables. Use elimination to solve for z.

$3y - 8z = 97$
$6y - 2z = 82$ **Multiply by -2.** $-6y + 16z = -194$
$\dfrac{(+) 6y - 2z = 82}{\text{Add to eliminate } y. \quad 14z = -112}$
$\text{Solve for } z. \quad z = -8$

Substitute -8 for z in the equation $3y - 8z = 97$.

$3y - 8(-8) = 97$
$3y + 64 = 97$
$3y = 33$
$y = 11$ *Solve for y.*

Substitute 11 for y and -8 for z in the original equation $x + 2y - 3z = 50$.

$x + 2(11) - 3(-8) = 50$
$x + 22 + 24 = 50$
$x + 46 = 50$
$x = 4$ *Solve for x.*

The solution is $(4, 11, -8)$.

LOOK BACK
You can refer to Lesson 3-1 for information on the number of solutions for systems of two linear equations in two variables.

You know that a system of two linear equations in two variables does not always have a unique solution that is an ordered pair. Similarly, a system of three linear equations in three variables does not always have a unique solution that is an ordered triple. The graph of each equation in a system of three linear equations in three variables is a plane. The three planes can appear in various configurations.

Alternative Learning Styles

Kinesthetic Use three rulers placed in the corner of the room to simulate the first octant. Place a box in the corner and find the coordinates of each vertex of the box. Set the box on its side and find the coordinates of each vertex. Did the coordinates change from the first time? If so, why?

The three planes intersect at one point, so the system has a unique solution, an ordered triple (x, y, z).

The three planes intersect in a line. There is an infinite number of solutions to the system.

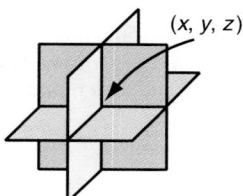

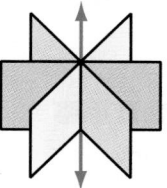

Each of the figures below shows three planes that have *no* points in common. These systems of equations have *no* solutions.

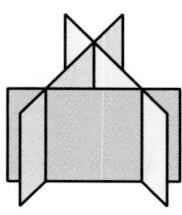 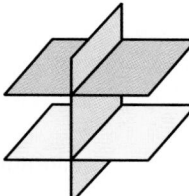 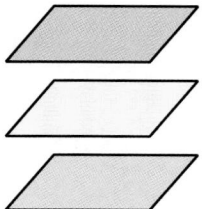

If all three planes coincide, there are infinite number of solutions. Also if two planes coincide and intersect the third plane in a line, there are infinite number of solutions.

When graphing two equations in two variables, it is obvious when the system is inconsistent or dependent. However, it is usually *not* obvious when solving a system of three equations algebraically whether there is a unique solution, no solutions, or many solutions.

Example ❷ **Solve the system of equations.**
$$3x - 6y + 3z = 33$$
$$2x - 4y + 2z = 22$$
$$4x + 2y - z = -6$$

Eliminate x in the first two equations.

$3x - 6y + 3z = 33$ **Multiply by 2.** $6x - 12y + 6z = 66$

$2x - 4y + 2z = 22$ **Multiply by −3.** $\underline{(+) -6x + 12y - 6z = -66}$

$$0 = 0$$

The equation $0 = 0$ is always true. This indicates that there are infinite number of solutions. In this case, the first two equations represent the same plane. This plane intersects the plane represented by the third equation. The coordinates of any point on the line of intersection are a solution to the system of equations.

In-Class Example

For Example 2
Solve the system of equations.
$x + 2y + z = 9$
$3y - z = -1$
$3z = 12$
(3, 1, 4)

168 *Chapter 3*

In-Class Example

For Example 3

Luisa, Yoko, and Amy all went to the matinee. Luisa took her two children and her mother, who is a senior citizen. She paid $12. Yoko took her two children and her mother, who is not a senior citizen. She paid $13. Amy took her son, her husband, and her mother and father, both of whom are senior citizens. She paid $16.50. What are the matinee ticket prices for adults, children, and senior citizens?

x = adult
y = senior
z = child

$x + y + 2z = 12$
$2x + 2z = 13$
$2x + 2y + z = \$16.50$

$x = \$4$
$y = \$3$
$z = \$2.50$

What are the sources of a university's endowment? The alumni contribute money, but the largest amount comes from corporate donors.

Example ③

APPLICATION
Education

The three American universities with the greatest endowments are Harvard, Yale, and Princeton. Their combined endowments are $12.09 billion. Together Yale and Princeton have $0.53 billion more in endowments than Harvard. Princeton's endowments trail Harvard's by $2.70 billion. What are the endowments of each of these universities?

F Y I

Funds held by a university, hospital, or other institution are called *endowments.* Usually these funds are invested, and only the income from these investments is spent. In this way, the endowment can last forever.

Explore   Read the problem and define the variables.
Let h represent Harvard's endowments, let y represent Yale's endowments, and let p represent Princeton's endowments.

Plan   Write three equations.

$h + y + p = 12.09$ *The combined endowments are $12.09 billion.*
$y + p = h + 0.53$ *Together Yale and Princeton have $0.53 billion more than Harvard.*
$p = h - 2.70$ *Princeton's endowments trail Harvard's by $2.70 billion.*

Solve   Use the elimination method to solve for h.

$h + y + p = 12.09$ → $h + y + p = 12.09$
$y + p = h + 0.53$ → $(-)\ -h + y + p = 0.53$
$$2h = 11.56$$
$$h = 5.78$$

Substitute 5.78 for h in the equation $p = h - 2.70$.

$p = 5.78 - 2.70$
   $= 3.08$

Substitute 5.78 for h and 3.08 for p in the equation $h + y + p = 12.09$.

$5.78 + y + 3.08 = 12.09$
$y + 8.86 = 12.09$
$y = 3.23$ *Solve for y.*

Harvard has $5.78 billion, Yale has $3.23 billion, and Princeton has $3.08 billion.

Examine   Check to see if all of the criteria are met.

The combined endowments are $12.09 billion.
   $5.78 + 3.23 + 3.08 = 12.09$ ✓

Yale and Princeton have $0.53 billion more than Harvard.
   $3.23 + 3.08 = 5.78 + 0.53$ ✓

Princeton's endowments trail Harvard's by $2.70 billion.
   $3.08 = 5.78 - 2.70$ ✓

CHECK FOR UNDERSTANDING

Communicating Mathematics

Study the lesson. Then complete the following. 1–2. See margin.

1. Refer to the application at the beginning of the lesson. Explain why substitution is the best first step in solving the system of equations.

2. **Describe** a situation that might occur when you solve a system of three equations in three variables that has each of the following number of solutions.
   a. none
   b. an infinite number

Guided Practice

For each system of equations, an ordered triple is given. Determine whether it is a solution of the system.

3. $3x - 7y + 2z = 43$
   $5x + 2y - 3z = -1$ **yes**
   $2x + 5y - z = -12; \ (4, -3, 5)$

4. $5a - 3b + c = -3$
   $7a + 2b - 3c = -35$ **no**
   $a - 6b + 7c = 51; \ (-2, 0, 7)$

Solve each system of equations.

5. $4x - 3y + 5z = 43$
   $2x + y = 9$ **(4, 1, 6)**
   $3y - 2z = -9$

6. $6a - 2b = 18$
   $3b + 5c = -34$ **(2, -3, -5)**
   $a + 6c = -28$

7. $4x + 3y + 2z = 34$
   $2x + 4y + 3z = 45$ **(1, 4, 9)**
   $3x + 2y + 4z = 47$

8. $x + y + z = -1$
   $3x - 2y - 4z = 16$ **(4, -8, 3)**
   $2x - y + z = 19$

9. **Sample answer:**
   $x + y + z = -9,$
   $x + y - z = 1,$
   $x - y + z = -13$

9. Write a system of three equations in three variables that has $(-6, 2, -5)$ as a solution.

10. Write a system of three equations in three variables in which $(-2, -3, 6)$ satisfies only two of the three equations. **Sample answer:** $x + y + z = 1,$
    $x + y - z = -11, x - y + z = 7$

EXERCISES

Practice

For each system of equations, an ordered triple is given. Determine whether it is a solution of the system.

11. $3a + 7b - 4c = -17$
    $2a - 8b - c = 8$
    $6a - b + 3c = 23; \ (2, -1, 4)$ **no**

12. $x + 3z = -5$
    $5x - 2y = -22$
    $5y - 6z = 36; \ (-2, 6, -1)$ **yes**

Solve each system of equations.

13. $5r + 2s = 0$
    $-3t = 12$ **(-2, 5, -4)**
    $6s + 5t = 10$

14. $2b - c = -13$
    $2a = 12$ **(6, -5, 3)**
    $3a + b = 13$

15. $x + y - z = -1$
    $x + y + z = 3$ **(0, 1, 2)**
    $3x - 2y - z = -4$

16. $b + c = 4$
    $2a + 4b - c = -3$ **(3, -1, 5)**
    $3b = -3$

17. $5x + 7y = -1$
    $-2y + 3z = 9$ **(4, -3, 1)**
    $7x - z = 27$

18. $r - s + 3t = -8$
    $2s - t = 15$ **(-3, 8, 1)**
    $3r + 2t = -7$

19. $5a - b + 3c = 5$
    $2a + 7b - 2c = 5$ **(-2, 3, 6)**
    $4a - 5b - 7c = -65$

20. $6x + 2y - 3z = -17$
    $7x - 5y + z = 72$ **(4, -7, 9)**
    $2x + 8y + 3z = -21$

Lesson 3-7 Solving Systems of Equations in Three Variables **169**

Reteaching

Using Substeps List the steps you would take to solve each system of equations. Then solve.

1. $2x - y + z = 3$
   $x + 3y - 2z = 11$
   $3x - 2y + 4z = 1$
   $(3, 2, -1)$

2. $2x - y + 2z = -8$
   $x + 2y - 3z = 9$
   $3x - y - 4z = 3$
   $(-1, 2, -2)$

---

3 PRACTICE/APPLY

Check for Understanding

Exercises 1–10 are designed to help you assess your students' understanding through reading, writing, speaking, and modeling. You should work through Exercises 1–2 with your students and then monitor their work on Exercises 3–10.

Assignment Guide

Core: 11–27 odd, 28, 29, 31–37
Enriched: 12–28 even, 29–37

For **Extra Practice**, see p. 882.

The red A, B, and C flags, printed only in the Teacher's Wraparound Edition, indicate the level of difficulty of the exercises.

Additional Answers

1. The third equation tells us that $c = 2r$.
2a. Sample answer: The system may produce an obvious error, such as $0 = 5$.
2b. Sample answer: The system may produce two equations in three unknowns.

Study Guide Masters, p. 21

3-7   NAME_____ DATE_____
Study Guide   Student Edition Pages 165–171

Solving Systems of Equations in Three Variables

Systems of equations in three variables are solved using the same methods as those for equations in two variables.

Example: Solve this system of equations.
$$x + y + 3z = 7$$
$$2x - z = 6$$
$$z = 4$$

The third equation is already solved.
$$z = 4$$

Substitute 4 for z in the second equation, $2x - z = 6$, to find x.
$$2x - 4 = 6$$
$$2x = 10$$
$$x = 5$$

Substitute 4 for z and 5 for x in the first equation, $x + y + 3z = 7$, to find y.
$$5 + y + 3(4) = 7$$
$$5 + y + 12 = 7$$
$$y = -10$$

The solution is $(5, -10, 4)$.

Check: First equation: $5 - 10 + 12 = 7$
Second equation: $10 - 4 = 6$
Third equation: $4 = 4$ ✔

Solve each system of equations.

1. $x + 2z = 5$
   $-4x + 6y = 0$
   $x - 2z = 9$
   $\left(7, \frac{14}{3}, -1\right)$

2. $4x + 6y + 4z = 5$
   $2x - 9y + 8z = 0$
   $6x + 15y - 4z = 5$
   $\left(0, \frac{10}{21}, \frac{15}{28}\right)$

3. The Laredo Sports Shop sold 10 balls, 3 bats, and 2 bases for $99 on Monday; 4 balls, 8 bats, and 2 bases for $78 on Tuesday; and 2 balls, 3 bats, and 1 base for $33.60 on Wednesday. What are the prices of 1 ball, 1 bat, and 1 base?
   ball = $8.00; bat = $5.40;
   base = $1.40

4. The sum of three numbers is 110. The second number is twice the first. The third number is equal to three times the first minus one-half the first. Find the numbers.
   $x = 20; y = 40; z = 50$

Closing Activity

Writing Have students write a paragraph explaining how to use the elimination method to solve equations in three variables.

Chapter 3, Quiz D (Lesson 3-7), is available in the *Assessment and Evaluation Masters,* p. 73.

Solve each system of equations.

21. $3x + 4y - 3z = 5$
$x + 6y + 2z = 3$ $\left(\frac{2}{3}, \frac{1}{2}, -\frac{1}{3}\right)$
$6x + 2y + 3z = 4$

22. $4x + 7y - z = -10$
$6x - 3y + 6z = 3$ $\left(-\frac{5}{4}, -\frac{1}{2}, \frac{3}{2}\right)$
$2x + y + 8z = 9$

23. $2r + 3s + 4t = 3$
$5r - 9s + 6t = 1$ $\left(\frac{1}{2}, \frac{1}{3}, \frac{1}{4}\right)$
$\frac{1}{3}r - \frac{1}{2}s + \frac{1}{3}t = \frac{1}{12}$

24. $2x + y + z = 7$
$12x - 2y - 2z = 2$ $(1, 2, 3)$
$\frac{2x}{3} - y + \frac{z}{3} = -\frac{1}{3}$

25. The sum of three numbers is 12. The first is five times the second and the sum of the first and third is 9. Find the numbers. $15, 3, -6$

26. $10, -20, 30$

26. The sum of three numbers is 20. The first number is the sum of the second and the third. The third number is three times the first. Find the numbers.

27. The sum of three numbers is 18. The first is eight times the sum of the second and third. The sum of the first number and the last number is 11. Find the numbers. $16, 7, -5$

Critical Thinking

28. Now that you know how to solve a system of three equations in three variables, use what you know to solve the system of equations below.

$w + x + y + z = 2$
$2w - x - y + 2z = 7$ $(1, 0, -1, 2)$
$2w + 3x + 2y - z = -2$
$3w - 2x - y - 3z = -2$

Applications and Problem Solving

CAREER CHOICES

A **stockbroker** provides financial advice about buying or selling stocks, bonds, or other financial products.

A bachelor's degree in business administration, economics, or finance is expected.

For more information, contact:

Securities Industry Association
120 Broadway
New York, NY 10271

30. Hamburger, $0.85; Double Cheeseburger, $1.79; Jumbo Jack, $2.29

29. Banking Maria Hernandez has $15,000 that she would like to invest in certificates of deposit. The bank has the following rates.

Number of Years	1	2	3
Rate	3.4%	5.0%	6.0%

She does not want to have all her money committed for more than one year, so she plans to invest some money at each rate. She wants her total interest for one year to be $800, so she will not be in a higher tax bracket. She decides to put $1000 more in a 2-year certificate than in a 1-year certificate and invest the rest in a 3-year certificate. How much should she invest in each type of certificate?
1-year, $2500; 2-year, $3500; 3-year, $9000

30. Consumer Awareness Jack-in-the-Box offers three different types of hamburgers at three different prices. The types are the Hamburger, the Double Cheeseburger, and the Jumbo Jack. The decathlon team at Kennedy High School went to the local Jack-in-the-Box on three different occasions and ordered different burgers. The first time, they ordered 3 Hamburgers, 5 Double Cheeseburgers, and 6 Jumbo Jacks and paid $25.24. The second time, they ordered 2 Hamburgers, 7 Double Cheeseburgers, and 5 Jumbo Jacks and paid $25.68. The last time, they ordered 4 Hamburgers, 4 Double Cheeseburgers, and 7 Jumbo Jacks and paid $26.59. The coach, who did not go along on the burger-buying trips, needs to know the price of each type of burger. What is the price of each kind of burger?

Practice Masters, p. 21

3-7 NAME_____ DATE _____
Practice Student Edition
Pages 165–171

Solving Systems of Equations in Three Variables
Solve each system of equations.

1. $2x - y + 2z = 15$
$-x + y + z = 3$
$3x - y + 2z = 18$ $(3, 1, 5)$

2. $x - 4y + 3z = -27$
$2x + 2y - 3z = 22$
$4z = -16$ $(1, 4, -4)$

3. $a + b = 3$
$-b + c = 3$
$a + 2c = 10$ $(2, 1, 4)$

4. $3x - 2y + 4z = 15$
$x - y + z = 3$
$x + 4y - 5z = 0$ $(3, 3, 3)$

5. $2x + 3y + 4z = 2$
$5x - 2y + 3z = 0$
$x - 5y - 2z = -4$ $(2, 2, -2)$

6. $2x + y - z = -8$
$4x - y + 2z = -3$
$-3x + y + 2z = 5$ $(-2, -3, 1)$

7. $2x - 5y + z = 5$
$3x + 2y - z = 17$
$4x - 3y + 2z = 17$ $(5, 1, 0)$

8. $p + 4r = -7$
$p - 3q = -8$
$q + r = 1$ $(1, 3, -2)$

9. The sum of three numbers is 6. The third number is the sum of the first and second number. The first number is one more than the third number. Find the numbers.
first = 4, second = -1, third = 3

10. The sum of three numbers is -4. The second number decreased by the third is equal to the first. The sum of the first and second number is -5. Find the numbers.
first = -3, second = -2, third = 1

CAREER CHOICES

The outlook for this occupation is excellent. It is expected to grow faster than the average for all occupations. The median annual salary in 1992 was $40,300, and 10% earned more than $70,000.

31. 3-pointers, 4;
2-pointers, 9;
free throws, 5

31. Basketball One night Glen Rice of the NBA's Miami Heat scored a total of 35 points against the Los Angeles Clippers. In basketball, it is possible to make a 3-point field goal, a 2-point field goal, or a 1-point free throw. He made as many 2-pointers as 3-pointers and free throws combined. He scored one point more with 2-pointers than he did with 3-pointers and free throws combined. How many of each did he score?

Mixed Review

32. Manufacturing Stitches Inc. can make at most 30 jean jackets and 20 leather jackets in a week. It takes a worker 10 hours to make a jean jacket and 20 hours to make a leather jacket. The total number of hours by all of the employees can be no more than 500 hours per week. (Lesson 3–6)

32a. 30 jean jackets, 10 leather jackets

32b. 10 jean jackets, 20 leather jackets

   a. If the profit on a jean jacket is the same as the profit on a leather jacket, how many of each should be made to maximize profit?

   b. How many of each should be made if the profit on a leather jacket is three times the profit on a jean jacket?

33. Which system of inequalities is represented by the graph at the right? (Lesson 3–4) **a**

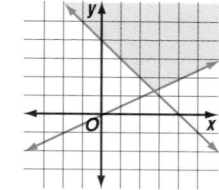

   a. $x + y \geq 4$ and $x \leq 2y$
   b. $x + y \geq 4$ and $x \geq 2y$
   c. $x + y \leq 4$ and $x \leq 2y$
   d. $x + y \leq 4$ and $x \geq 2y$

34. Telecommunications The formula relating the cost of a long-distance phone call in which the initial cost for the call is \$0.50 for the first minute and each additional minute costs \$0.95 is $c = 0.95(t - 1) + 0.50$, where t is the length of the call in minutes. The length of a call is always rounded up to the next minute if it includes part of a minute. For example, a 2.3 minute call is charged at a rate of 3 minutes. (Lesson 2–6)

34a. \$1.45, \$2.40, \$2.40, \$2.40, \$3.35, \$3.35

   a. Determine the cost of calls lasting 2 minutes, 2.25 minutes, 2.5 minutes, 3 minutes, 3.75 minutes, and 4 minutes.

   b. Write the minute amounts and charges as ordered pairs and graph the function. **See margin.**

   c. Use your graph to predict the cost of a call lasting 8 minutes. **\$7.15**

   d. Describe how the complete graph of the formula for calculating the cost of phone calls would look. What type of function is this? **See margin.**

35. Economics The Serves-You-Best Rental Car Company has two rental offers. The first offer charges the customer \$20 plus 25¢ a mile for a compact car. The second offer charges the customer \$35 plus 25¢ a mile for a luxury car. (Lesson 2–4) **35a.** $y = 0.25x + 20$; $y = 0.25x + 35$

   a. Write an equation to represent each offer, if the cars are rented for one day.

   b. What is the relationship between the graphs of these offers? **parallel**

   c. If both cars are driven 750 miles, what is the cost difference between renting the compact car and the luxury car? **\$15**

36. If $f(x) = x^2 + 3x$, find $f(5)$. (Lesson 2–1) **40**

37. Solve $2\left|-x - 6\right| = -3x$. (Lesson 1–5) $-\dfrac{12}{5}$

Extension

Problem Solving The sum of four numbers is 22. The first number is twice the difference of the second and the fourth. The second number is 5 times the difference of the third and the fourth. The third number is twice the difference of the first and the fourth. What are the four numbers? **4, 5, 6, 7**

Additional Answers

34b. (2, 1.45), (2.25, 2.40), (2.5, 2.40), (3, 2.40), (3.75, 3.35), (4, 3.35)

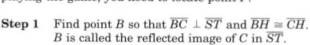
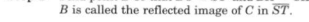

34d. It is a series of steps with open circles on the left and closed circles on the right; a step function.

Enrichment Masters, p. 21

3-7   NAME_____   DATE _____

Enrichment   Student Edition Pages 165–171

Billiards

The figure at the right shows a billiard table. The object is to use a cue stick to strike the ball at point C so that the ball will hit the sides (or cushions) of the table at least once before hitting the ball located at point A. In playing the game, you need to locate point P.

Step 1 Find point B so that $\overline{BC} \perp \overline{ST}$ and $\overline{BH} \cong \overline{CH}$. B is called the reflected image of C in $\overline{ST}$.

Step 2 Draw $\overline{AB}$.

Step 3 $\overline{AB}$ intersects $\overline{ST}$ at the desired point P.

For each billiards problem, the cue ball at point C must strike the indicated cushion(s) and then strike the ball at point A. Draw and label the correct path for the cue ball using the process described above.

1. cushion $\overline{KR}$
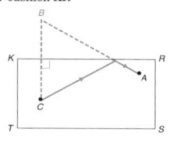

2. cushion $\overline{RS}$
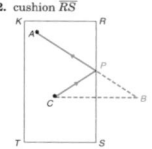

3. cushion $\overline{TS}$, then cushion $\overline{RS}$
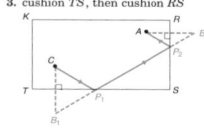

4. cushion $\overline{KT}$, then cushion $\overline{RS}$
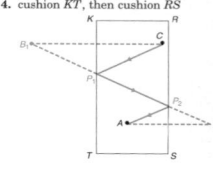

Objective

Determine the octant in which a point in space is located. Graph linear equations in space and determine the intercepts.

Recommended Time

Demonstration and discussion: 30 minutes; Exercises: 30 minutes

Instructional Resources

For each student or group of students
Modeling Mathematics Masters
• p. 17 (isometric dot paper)
• p. 21 (worksheet)
For teacher demonstration
Algebra and Geometry Overhead Manipulative Resources

1 FOCUS

Motivating the Lesson

Discuss with students how they locate points on a plane. Ask them how they think points in space could be located. Have them use the classroom to explain their ideas. Ask students what occupations might require their employees to locate points in space on a graph.

2 TEACH

Teaching Tip To help plot points in each activity, students can think of moving to the front or back along the x-axis, right or left along the y-axis, and up and down along the z-axis. Front, right, and up are all positive; back, left, and down are all negative.

Teaching Tip A *trace* is the intersection of a plane with one of the coordinate planes. The xy-trace is the line formed by the intersection of a plane with the xy-plane. All points in the xy-trace have a z-coordinate of 0.

3–7B Graphing Equations in Three Variables

Materials: isometric dot paper

An Extension of Lesson 3–7

To draw the graph of an equation in three variables, it is necessary to add a third dimension to our coordinate system. The graph of an equation of the form $Ax + By + Cz = D$, where either A, B, C, or D can be equal to zero, is a plane.

When graphing in space (three dimensions), space is separated into eight regions, called **octants.** Think of three coordinate planes intersecting at right angles as shown at the right. Any point lying on a coordinate plane is not in an octant.

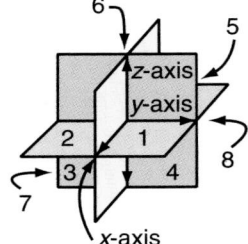

The octants are numbered as shown.

Activity 1 Use isometric dot paper to draw and label a three-dimensional axis system. Then graph the ordered triple (3, 6, 1).

Step 1 Draw the x-, y-, and z-axes as shown below.

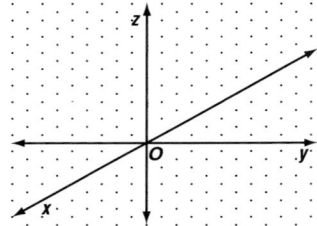

Step 2 Locate 3 on the positive x-axis, 6 on the positive y-axis, and 1 on the positive z-axis. Complete a "box" by drawing lines parallel to the axes through each intercept. Draw the graph, which is a point, at (3, 6, 1).

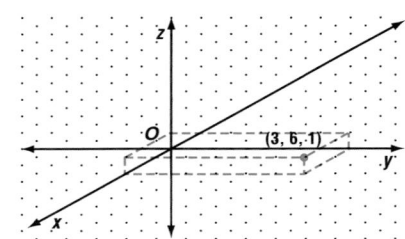

This point is in octant 1, which is also called the <u>first octant</u>.

It is not necessary to show the entire "box" when you graph an ordered triple. The desired point will always be the corner farthest from the point of origin.

To graph a linear equation in three variables, first find the intercepts of the graph. Connect the intercepts on each axis. This forms a portion of a plane that lies in a single octant.

Activity 2 Graph $2x + 4y + 3z = 12$.

To find the x-intercept, let $y = 0$ and $z = 0$.
$$2x = 12$$
$$x = 6$$
To find the y-intercept, let $x = 0$ and $z = 0$.
$$4y = 12$$
$$y = 3$$
To find the z-intercept, let $x = 0$ and $y = 0$.
$$3z = 12$$
$$z = 4$$
To indicate the plane, graph the intercepts, which have coordinates (6, 0, 0), (0, 3, 0), and (0, 0, 4), respectively, and then connect the points. Remember that the plane extends indefinitely.

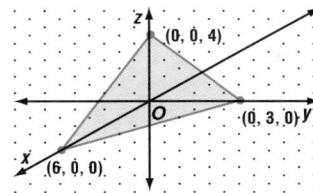

Draw Graph each ordered triple using isometric dot paper. Name the octant in which each point lies.   1–4. See margin for graphs.

   1. (5, 2, 3)   1   **2.** (7, 5, −6)   4   **3.** (3, 0, 1)   none   **4.** (3, −7, 2)   2

Graph each equation using isometric dot paper. Name the coordinates for the x-, y-, and z-intercepts.   5–10. See Solutions Manual for graphs.

   5. $4x + y + 2z = 4$
     (1, 0, 0), (0, 4, 0), (0, 0, 2)
   6. $3x − 2y + 2z = 6$
     (2, 0, 0), (0, −3, 0), (0, 0, 3)
   7. $3x − y + 6z = 3$
     (1, 0, 0), (0, −3, 0), $\left(0, 0, \frac{1}{2}\right)$
   8. $4x + 5y − 10z = 20$
     (5, 0, 0), (0, 4, 0), (0, 0, −2)
   9. $3z − 2x = 6$
     (−3, 0, 0), none, (0, 0, 2)
   10. $3x − 4y = −12$
     (−4, 0, 0), (0, 3, 0), none

Write Write an equation of the plane given its x-, y-, and z-intercepts, respectively.

   11. 2, −2, 5 $5x − 5y + 2z = 10$ **12.** $\frac{1}{2}$, 3, −2 $12x + 2y − 3z = 6$
11–12. Sample answers are given.

   13. Describe the relationship between quadrants and octants.   See margin.

   14. Consider the graph of $x = 2$ in one, two, and three dimensions.

     a. Describe the graph on a number line.   a point at 2
     b. Describe the graph on a coordinate plane.   a line perpendicular to the x-axis at $x = 2$
     c. Describe the graph in a three-dimensional coordinate axis.   See margin.
     d. Compare the graphs in parts a, b, and c.   See margin.

Using Manipulatives

The inclusion of manipulative activities in the algebra classroom offers students the opportunity to use models to bridge the gap from the concrete to the abstract. For more information on using manipulatives, see *Manipulatives in the Mathematics Classroom*, one of the titles in the Glencoe Mathematics Professional Series.

Additional Answers

13. Two-dimensional graphs are divided into quadrants, and three-dimensional graphs are divided into octants.

14c. a plane perpendicular to the x-axis at $x = 2$

14d. One is a point (one-dimensional), one is a line (two-dimensional), and one is a plane (three-dimensional).

---

3 PRACTICE/APPLY

Assignment Guide

Core: 1–14
Enriched: 1–14

Additional Answers

1.
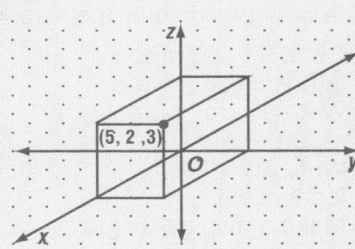

2.
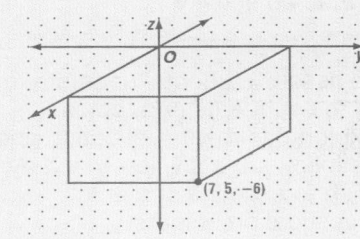

3.
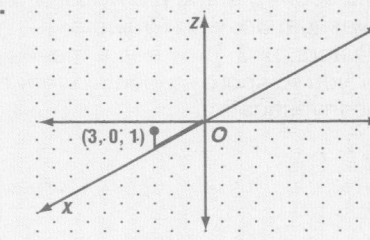

4.
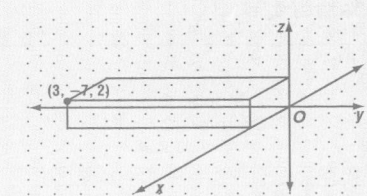

4 ASSESS

Observing students working in cooperative groups is an excellent method of assessment.

In·ves·ti·ga·tion
TEACHER NOTES

Closing the Investigation

This activity provides students an opportunity to bring their work on the Investigation to a close. For each Investigation, students should present their findings to the class. Here are some ways students can display their work.

- Conduct and report on an interview or survey.
- Write a letter, proposal, or report.
- Write an article for the school or local paper.
- Make a display, including graphs and/or charts.
- Plan an activity.

Assessment

To assess students' understanding of the concepts and topics explored in the Investigation and its follow-up activities, you may wish to examine students' Investigation Folders.

The scoring guide provided in the *Investigations and Projects Masters*, p. 3, provides a means for you to score students' work on the Investigation.

Investigations and Projects Masters, p. 3

Scoring Guide
Chapters 2 and 3
Investigation

Level	Specific Criteria
3 Superior	• Shows thorough understanding of the concepts of *calibration scope, scatter plot, equation, best fit line,* and *proportion.* • Uses appropriate strategies to solve problems. • Computations are correct. • Written explanations are exemplary. • Charts, graphs, and explanations are appropriate and sensible. • Goes beyond the requirements of some or all problems.
2 Satisfactory, with Minor Flaws	• Shows understanding of the concepts of *calibration scope, scatter plot, equation, best fit line,* and *proportion.* • Uses appropriate strategies to solve problems. • Computations are mostly correct. • Written explanations are effective. • Charts, graphs, and explanations are appropriate and sensible. • Satisfies the requirements of problems.
1 Nearly Satisfactory, with Obvious Flaws	• Shows understanding of most of the concepts of *calibration scope, scatter plot, equation, best fit line,* and *proportion.* • May not use appropriate strategies to solve problems. • Computations are mostly correct. • Written explanations are satisfactory. • Charts, graphs, and explanations are appropriate and sensible. • Satisfies the requirements of problems.
0 Unsatisfactory	• Shows little or no understanding of the concepts of *calibration scope, scatter plot, equation, best fit line,* and *proportion.* • May not use appropriate strategies to solve problems. • Computations are incorrect. • Written explanations are not satisfactory. • Charts, graphs, and explanations are not appropriate or sensible. • Does not satisfy the requirements of problems.

In·ves·ti·ga·tion

Through the Looking Glass

Refer to the Investigation on pages 60–61.

Through observations of species in their habitat, naturalists have been able to identify characteristics of the species, their migratory and breeding patterns, and the size of their population in any given area. These efforts have helped in preventing extinction of some species and better control for those species that are over-populating some areas of Earth. Continued observations with more advanced equipment will make the naturalist's job easier in the future and offer an abundance of information that cannot be acquired from other long-distance observations.

Analyze

You have conducted experiments and organized your data in various ways. It is now time to analyze your findings and state your conclusions.

> **PORTFOLIO ASSESSMENT**
>
> You may want to keep your work on this Investigation in your portfolio.

1 Write an expression that relates the size of the image through your scope with the distance you are from the image for each scope. How does this relate to the dimensions of each scope?

2 Study the various graphs you made for each of the scopes. Write an explanation of how the scope can help you determine the actual size of an animal you are observing.

174 *Investigation: Through the Looking Glass*

3 If you were trying to observe an object from 100 yards away, describe the tube that would enable you to see the entire object in your view.

4 Make a general statement about the dimensions of the tube in relation to the distance you are from an object when trying to view it in its entirety.

Write

Imagine that you are a tourist on safari on an African plain. There is an elephant standing a distance away across the river. The current of the river is swift and you cannot cross it. You have in your possession a tape measure, a pen, a calculator, and a piece of paper that can be rolled into various sizes of view tubes.

5 You would like to determine the height of the elephant. Write how you would explain to another tourist how you could accurately determine the elephant's height.

CHAPTER 3 HIGHLIGHTS

VOCABULARY

After completing this chapter, you should be able to define each term, property, or phrase and give an example or two of each.

Algebra

consistent system (p. 127)
constraints (p. 153)
Cramer's rule (p. 141)
dependent system (p. 128)
determinant (p. 141)
element (p. 141)
elimination method (p. 133)
inconsistent system (p. 128)
independent system (p. 127)
linear programming (p. 155)
octants (p. 172)
ordered triple (p. 166)
second-order determinant (p. 141)
substitution method (p. 133)
system of equations (p. 126)
system of inequalities (p. 148)
unbounded (p. 155)

Problem Solving

solve a simpler problem (p. 156)

UNDERSTANDING AND USING THE VOCABULARY

Choose the letter of the term that best matches each phrase.

1. a square array of numbers or variables having a numerical value c
2. a system of equations that has an infinite number of solutions b
3. the region of intersection of graphs of inequalities, where every constraint is met f
4. a method of solving equations in which one equation is solved for one variable in terms of the other variable j
5. a system of equations that has at least one solution a
6. a method of solving equations in which one variable is eliminated when the two equations are combined e
7. the solution of a system of equations in three variables (x, y, z) i
8. a method for finding the maximum or the minimum value of a function with two variables. h
9. the numbers or variables written within a determinant d
10. a system of equations that has exactly one solution g
11. a function in which no maximum value exists k

a. consistent system
b. dependent system
c. determinant
d. elements
e. elimination method
f. feasible region
g. independent system
h. linear programming
i. ordered triple
j. substitution method
k. unbounded

Instructional Resources

Three multiple-choice tests and three free-response tests are provided in the *Assessment and Evaluation Masters.* Forms 1A and 2A are for honors pacing, and Forms 1B, 1C, 2B, and 2C are for average pacing. Chapter 3 Test, Form 1B is shown at the right. Chapter 3 Test, Form 2B is shown on the next page.

Using the CHAPTER HIGHLIGHTS

The Chapter Highlights begins with a listing of the new terms, properties, and phrases that were introduced in this chapter. Have students define each term and provide an example or two of it, if appropriate.

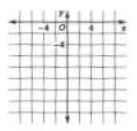

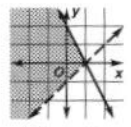

Assessment and Evaluation Masters, pp. 59–60

3 NAME________________ DATE ________

Chapter 3 Test, Form 1B

Write the letter for the correct answer in the blank at the right of each problem.

1. What kind of system of equations is $\begin{array}{l}2x - 3y = 5\\ 9y = 6x - 15\end{array}$? 1. B
   A. consistent and independent B. consistent and dependent
   C. inconsistent D. inconsistent and dependent
2. Which of the following systems is shown in the graph at the right? 2. A
   A. $y - x = 5$, $y = -2x$ B. $y + x = -5$, $y + 2x = 0$
   C. $-y = 5 + x$, $y - 2x = 0$ D. $y = x + 5$, $y = 2x$
3. Which expression can be substituted for y in the top equation of the system $\begin{array}{l}5x + 3y = 9\\ 4x + y = 8\end{array}$ to solve the system by substitution? 3. D
   A. $12x - 3y$ B. $-\frac{3}{5}x + 3$ C. $4x - 8$ D. $8 - 4x$
4. You want to eliminate y by addition in the system $\begin{array}{l}6x + 8y = 5\\ 9x - 6y = 1\end{array}$. 4. D
   If you multiply each side of the top equation by 3, by which number would you multiply each side of the bottom equation?
   A. -2 B. 2 C. -4 D. 4
5. What does x equal in the solution of the system at the right? $\begin{array}{l}4x - y = 4\\ 6x - 5y = -1\end{array}$ 5. A
   A. $\frac{3}{2}$ B. 2 C. $\frac{1}{2}$ D. $\frac{19}{4}$
6. For which system is there no solution? 6. B
   A. $2x + y = 1$, $4x + 2y = 2$ B. $2x + y = 1$, $4x + 2y = 5$ C. $2x + y = 4$, $4x - y = 8$ D. $x - y = 8$, $x + y = 16$
7. What does y equal in the solution of the system at the right? $\begin{array}{l}\frac{x}{2} + \frac{y}{3} = 1\\ \frac{x}{5} + \frac{y}{2} = 1\end{array}$ 7. C
   A. $\frac{2}{11}$ B. $\frac{42}{19}$ C. $\frac{18}{11}$ D. $\frac{2}{19}$
8. On certain calls company A charges $1.25 for the first minute and $0.35 for each additional minute. Company B charges $1.75 for the first minute and $0.30 for each additional minute. Both companies charge the same amount for calls that last 8. B
   A. 4.75 minutes. B. 10 minutes. C. 60 minutes. D. 100 minutes.
9. In 1988, each person in the United States threw out, on average, 1.92 pounds of paper and plastic every day. By weight, the amount of paper thrown away was 5 times greater than the amount of plastic. How many pounds of paper was this? 9. C
   A. 1.44 B. 0.32 C. 1.60 D. 9.60
10. What is the value of $\begin{vmatrix}11 & 8\\ -12 & 6\end{vmatrix}$? 10. A
   A. 162 B. -30 C. 30 D. -162

3 NAME________________ DATE ________

Chapter 3 Test, Form 1B (continued)

11. Which expression represents x in the system at the right? $\begin{array}{l}3x - 7 = 2y\\ 4x + 5y = 8\end{array}$ 11. B
   A. $\dfrac{\begin{vmatrix}3 & 2\\ 4 & 8\end{vmatrix}}{\begin{vmatrix}3 & -7\\ 4 & 5\end{vmatrix}}$ B. $\dfrac{\begin{vmatrix}7 & -2\\ 8 & 5\end{vmatrix}}{\begin{vmatrix}3 & -2\\ 4 & 5\end{vmatrix}}$ C. $\dfrac{\begin{vmatrix}2 & -7\\ 8 & 5\end{vmatrix}}{\begin{vmatrix}3 & -7\\ 4 & 5\end{vmatrix}}$ D. $\dfrac{\begin{vmatrix}3 & 7\\ 4 & 8\end{vmatrix}}{\begin{vmatrix}3 & -2\\ 4 & 5\end{vmatrix}}$
12. Find the value of w that makes the sentence at the right true. $\begin{vmatrix}8 & w\\ 6 & -2\end{vmatrix} = 2w - 4$ 12. D
   A. 5 B. -5 C. 3 D. $-\frac{3}{2}$

Use the graph at the right for questions 13 and 14.

13. Which system of inequalities is graphed? 13. B
   A. $y < x - 1$, $y \geq -2x + 2$ B. $y > x - 1$, $y \leq -2x + 2$ C. $y < x - 1$, $y \leq -2x + 2$ D. $y > x - 1$, $y \geq -2x + 2$
14. Which point is a solution to the system in the graph? 14. D
   A. (1, 1) B. (1, 0) C. (1, -1) D. none of these
15. Given $0 \leq 2x - y + 2$, $x \geq 0$, $y \leq 4$, and $3y \geq 8x - 24$, find the maximum value of $f(x, y) = 2x - y$. 15. B
   A. 8 B. 6 C. -2 D. 10
16. A person is buying x units of vegetables and y units of meat. The minimum daily requirements are 6 units of protein and 10 units of vitamins. Use the table to determine which inequalities describe how to obtain the minimum daily requirements. 16. C

	Protein	Vitamins
1 unit of vegetables	2 units	5 units
1 unit of meat	4 units	3 units

   A. $2x + 5y \geq 6$, $4x + 3y \geq 10$, $x \geq 0$, $y \geq 0$
   B. $2x + 5y \leq 6$, $4x + 3y \leq 10$, $x \geq 0$, $y \geq 0$
   C. $2x + 4y \geq 6$, $5x + 3y \geq 10$, $x \geq 0$, $y \geq 0$
   D. $2x + 4y \leq 6$, $5x + 3y \leq 10$, $x \geq 0$, $y \geq 0$
17. How many multiples of 2 or 5 (or both) are there from 1–1000? 17. D
   A. 200 B. 500 C. 700 D. 600
18. A feasible region has vertices at $(-2, -3)$, (0, 4), (3, 1), and $(1, -1)$. The maximum value of the function $f(x, y) = 3x - y$ for this region is 8 at 18. C
   A. $(-2, -3)$. B. (0, 4). C. (3, 1). D. $(1, -1)$.
19. Which ordered triple is a solution of the system shown at the right? $\begin{array}{l}8x + 2y - 3z = 20\\ x - 5y + 4z = -22\\ -2x + y + z = 3\end{array}$ 19. D
   A. $(0, 7, -2)$ B. $(-2, -4, 0)$ C. $(1, 6, -1)$ D. $(1, 3, -2)$
20. What does y equal in the solution of the system at the right? $\begin{array}{l}2x + 3y + z = 9\\ x - 2y - z = 4\\ x - 3y + 2z = -3\end{array}$ 20. D
   A. $-\frac{9}{4}$ B. 2 C. 7 D. 1

Bonus What does x equal in the system at the right? $\begin{array}{l}\frac{1}{x} + \frac{1}{y} = \frac{3}{4}\\ \frac{3}{x} + \frac{2}{y} = 2\end{array}$ Bonus B
   A. 4 B. 2 C. $\frac{1}{2}$ D. $\frac{1}{4}$

Skills and Concepts Encourage students to refer to the objectives and examples on the left as they complete the review exercises on the right.

Assessment and Evaluation Masters, pp. 65–66

NAME_____ DATE_____

Chapter 3 Test, Form 2B

1. Classify the system as consistent and independent, consistent and dependent, or inconsistent.
$y = 3x + 5$
$y = 3x - 9$
1. ___inconsistent___

2. Solve this system of equations by graphing, and state the solution.
$y = 7x - 8$
$y = 3x - 12$
2. ___(−1, −15)___

3. Solve this system of equations using the substitution method.
$6x + 7y = 19$
$x + y = 5$
3. ___(16, −11)___

4. Solve this system of equations using the elimination method.
$3x - 2y = 4$
$2x + y = 12$
4. ___(4, 4)___

Solve each system of equations.
5. $3x - 6y = -3$
$6x + 3y = 9$
6. $x + 4y = 3$
$4x + 3y = 7$
7. $x = \frac{1}{2}y + 4$
$2y + 3x = 12$
5. ___(1, 1)___
6. ___(19/13, 5/13)___
7. ___(4, 0)___

Find the value of each determinant.
8. $\begin{vmatrix} 6 & 3 \\ 4 & 5 \end{vmatrix}$
9. $\begin{vmatrix} -5 & 0 \\ \frac{1}{2} & -6 \end{vmatrix}$
8. ___18___
9. ___30___

10. Solve this system using Cramer's rule.
$4x - 2y = 15$
$5x + 3y = 7$
10. ___(59/22, −47/22)___

Solve each system of inequalities by graphing.
11. $y \le 5$
$x > 4$
11. ___See students' graphs.___

12. $2x + 3y > 4$
$5x - 3y < 10$
12. ___See students' graphs.___

NAME_____ DATE_____

Chapter 3 Test, Form 2B (continued)

13. Write a system of inequalities that could be added to the system of inequalities at the right to form a polygonal region of at least three sides.
$y \ge 2$
$y \le -2x + 6$
Answers will vary. Sample:
13. $y \le x + 8$

Graph each system of inequalities. Name the coordinates of the vertices of the feasible region. Find the maximum and minimum values of $f(x) = 4x + 3y$.

14. $y \ge 1$
$x \le 3$
$y \le 2x + 1$
15. $y \le 3$
$5 \le x \le 9$
$y \ge 0$

14. vertices: (3, 1), (0, 1), (3, 7); maximum is 33, minimum is 3
15. vertices: (5, 3), (5, 0), (9, 3), (9, 0); maximum is 45, minimum is 20

16. How many multiples of 5 or 8 (or both) are there from 1 through 1000?
16. ___300___

17. The area of a parking lot is 600 square meters. A car requires 6 square meters and a bus requires 30 square meters of space. The attendant can handle only 60 vehicles. If a car is charged $3.00 and a bus is charged $8.00, find how many of each type of vehicle should be accepted to maximize income.
17. ___50 cars and 10 buses___

18. You need to make at least 10,000 copies of an advertising flier. Copy shop A charges $0.06 per copy. Copy shop B charges $0.04 per copy. Because you know the owners, you want to give both copy shops at least $50 of business. What is the least amount you could pay to have your copies made?
18. ___$416.68___

Solve each system of equations.
19. $x + 2y - 3z = 5$
$x - y + 2z = -3$
$x + y - z = 2$
20. $3x + y + 2z = 1$
$2x - y + z = -3$
$x + y - 4z = -3$
19. ___(0, 1, −1)___
20. ___(−1, 2, 1)___

Bonus Solve the system at the right.
$a + b = 6$
$b + c = 5$
$c + d = 4$
$d + e = 3$
$e + a = 2$
Bonus ___2, 4, 1, 3, 0___

CHAPTER 3   STUDY GUIDE AND ASSESSMENT

OBJECTIVES AND EXAMPLES

Upon completing this chapter, you should be able to:

- solve systems of equations by graphing (Lesson 3–1)

Solve the system of equations.
$y + x = 3$
$3x - y = 1$

Graph each equation. The intersection of the graphs is the solution.

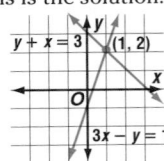

The solution is (1, 2).

- use the substitution and elimination methods to solve systems of equations (Lesson 3–2)

Solve the system of equations.
$x = 4y + 7$
$x = -y - 3$

$-y - 3 = 4y + 7$
$-10 = 5y$
$-2 = y$

$x = 4(-2) + 7$
$= -8 + 7$
$= -1$

The solution is (−1, −2).

- solve systems of equations by using Cramer's rule (Lesson 3–3)

Solve the system of equations.
$4x + 7y = -1$
$2x + y = 7$

$x = \dfrac{\begin{vmatrix} -1 & 7 \\ 7 & 1 \end{vmatrix}}{\begin{vmatrix} 4 & 7 \\ 2 & 1 \end{vmatrix}} = \dfrac{-1(1) - 7(7)}{4(1) - 7(2)}$ or 5

$y = \dfrac{\begin{vmatrix} 4 & -1 \\ 2 & 7 \end{vmatrix}}{\begin{vmatrix} 4 & 7 \\ 2 & 1 \end{vmatrix}} = \dfrac{4(7) - (-1)(2)}{4(1) - 7(2)}$ or −3

The solution is (5, −3).

REVIEW EXERCISES

Use these exercises to review and prepare for the chapter test.

Graph each system of equations and state its solution. Also, state whether the system is consistent and independent, consistent and dependent, or inconsistent.

12. $3x + 2y = 12$
$x - 2y = 4$
13. $8x - 10y = 7$
$4x - 5y = 7$
14. $y - 2x = 8$
$y = \frac{1}{2}x - 4$
15. $20y + 13x = 10$
$0.65x + y = 0.5$

12. (4, 0); cons, indep. 13. no sol.; inconsistent
14. (−8, −8); cons, indep.
15. $20y - 13x = 10$; con, dep.
12–15. See Solutions Manual for graphs.

Solve each system of equations. Use either substitution or elimination.

16. $x + y = 4$
$x - y = 8.5$
17. $2x + 3y = -6$
$3x + 2y = 25$
18. $7y - 2x = 10$
$-3y + x = -3$
19. $-6y - 2x = 0$
$11y + 3x = 4$
20. $3x - 5y = -13$
$4x + 2y = 0$
21. $c + d = 5$
$2c - d = 4$

16. (6.25, −2.25) 17. (17.4, −13.6) 18. (9, 4)
19. (−6, 2)   20. (−1, 2)   21. (3, 2)

Use Cramer's rule to solve each system of equations.

22. $2x - 3y = 4$
$x + 5y = 2$
23. $7x + 3y = 5$
$2x + 4y = 3$
24. $2x - y = 7$
$x + 3y = 7$
25. $u + 11 = 8v$
$8(u - v) = 3$
26. $f - 2g = -1$
$2f + 3g = -16$
27. $m - n = 0$
$4m + 10n = -6$

22. (2, 0)   23. $\left(\frac{1}{2}, \frac{1}{2}\right)$ 24. (4, 1)
25. $\left(2, \frac{13}{8}\right)$ 26. (−5, −2)   27. $\left(-\frac{3}{7}, -\frac{3}{7}\right)$

GLENCOE Technology

Test and Review Software

You may use this software, a combination of an item generator and item bank, to create your own tests or worksheets. Types of items include free response, multiple choice, short answer, and open ended.

For IBM & Macintosh

Additional Answers

28.
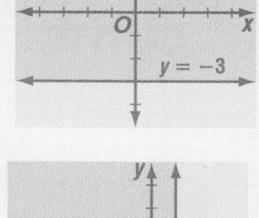

OBJECTIVES AND EXAMPLES

• solve systems of inequalities by graphing
(Lesson 3–4)

Solve the system of inequalities by graphing.
$y - x \le 2$
$0.5x + y \ge -4$

$y - x \le 2$ represents Regions 1 and 2.
$0.5x + y \ge -4$ represents Regions 2 and 3.

The intersection is Region 2, which is the solution of this system of inequalities.

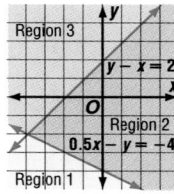

REVIEW EXERCISES

Solve each system of inequalities by graphing.   28–33. See margin.

28. $y \le 4$
$y > -3$

29. $y > 3$
$x \le 1$

30. $y < x + 1$
$x > 5$

31. $x + y \ge 3$
$x \le 0$

32. $y \le x + 4$
$2y \ge x - 3$

33. $y < 2$
$y \ge -7$
$y \ge 2x$
$y \le x + 1$

29.
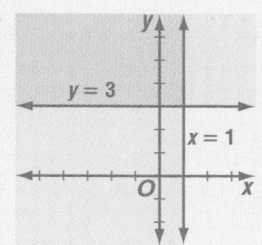

30.
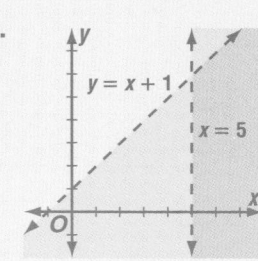

• find the maximum and minimum values of a function over a region using linear programming techniques   (Lesson 3–5)

$x \ge 0$
$y \ge 0$
$3x + y \le 15$
$y \le 6$
$f(x, y) = 3x + y$

vertices: (0, 0), (5, 0),
(3, 6), (0, 6)

(x, y)	3x + y	f(x, y)
(0, 0)	3(0) + 0	0
(5, 0)	3(5) + 0	15
(3, 6)	3(3) + 6	15
(0, 6)	3(0) + 6	6

maximum value = 15, minimum value = 0

Graph each system of inequalities. Name the coordinates of the vertices of the feasible region. Find the maximum and minimum values of the given function.

34. $f(x, y) = -2x + y$
$x \ge -5$
$x \le 4$
$y \ge -1$
$y \le 3$

35. $f(x, y) = 3x + 2y$
$x \ge 0$
$y \ge 0$
$x + 3y \le 15$
$4x + y \le 16$

vertices: (4, 3), (−5, 3),
(−5, −1), (4, −1)
max: $f(-5, 3) = 13$
min: $f(4, -1) = -9$

vertices: (0, 5), (3, 4),
(4, 0), (0, 0)
max: $f(3, 4) = 17$
min: $f(0, 0) = 0$

34–35. See margin for graphs.

31.
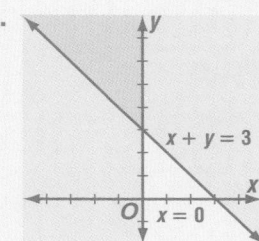

• solve problems involving maximum and minimum values by using linear programming techniques. (Lesson 3–6)

The available parking area of a parking lot is 600 m². A car requires 6 m² of space, and a bus requires 30 m² of space. The attendant can handle no more than 60 vehicles. If a car is charged $3.00 to park and a bus is charged $8.00, how many of each should the attendant accept to maximize income?   50 cars, 10 buses

36. Community Service   A theater at which a drug abuse program is being presented seats 150 people. The proceeds will be donated to a local drug information center. Admission is $2 for adults and $1 for students. Every two adults must bring at least one student. How many adults and students should attend in order to raise the maximum amount of money?
100 adults and 50 students

32.
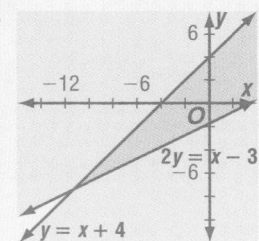

33.
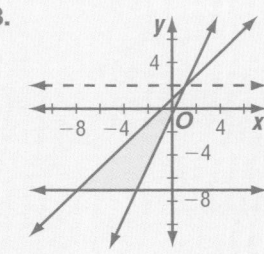

Additional Answers

34.
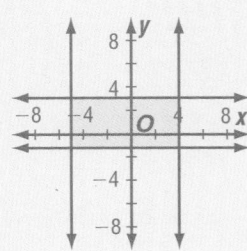

35.
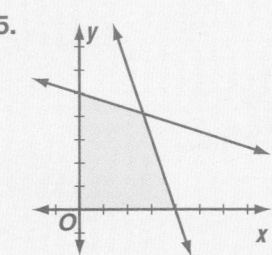

Applications and Problem Solving Encourage students to work through the exercises in the Applications and Problem Solving section to strengthen their problem-solving skills.

OBJECTIVES AND EXAMPLES

solve a system of three equations in three variables (Lesson 3–7)

Solve the system of equations.
$2x + y - z = 2$
$x + 3y + 2z = 1$
$x + y + z = 2$

$$
\begin{array}{rl}
-2x - y + z = -2 & \quad 2(2) + (-z) - z = 2 \\
\underline{(+)\ 2x + 6y + 4z = 2} & \quad 4 - 2z = 2 \\
5y + 5z = 0 & \quad -2z = -2 \\
y + z = 0 & \quad z = 1 \\
y = -z & \\
\end{array}
$$

$$
\begin{array}{rl}
x + (-z) + z = 2 & \quad 2 + y + 1 = 2 \\
x = 2 & \quad y = -1 \\
\end{array}
$$

The solution is $(2, -1, 1)$.

REVIEW EXERCISES

Solve each system of equations.

37. $x + 4y - z = 6$
$3x + 2y + 3z = 16$
$2x - y + z = 3$ $(1, 2, 3)$

38. $2a + b - c = 5$
$a - b + 3c = 9$
$3a - 6c = 6$ $(4, -2, 1)$

39. $e + f = 4$
$2d + 4e - f = -3$
$3e = -3$ $(3, -1, 5)$

APPLICATIONS AND PROBLEM SOLVING

40. **Donkey Basketball** Your school has contracted with a professional animal trainer to host a donkey basketball game at the school. The school has guaranteed an attendance of at least 1000 people and $4800 in total ticket sales. The tickets are $4 for students $6 for nonstudents, of which the animal trainer receives $3 from students and $4 from nonstudents. What is the minimum amount of money the animal trainer could receive? What is the maximum amount of money the animal trainer could receive? (Lesson 3–6)
$3400; unbounded

41. **Lunch Costs** Melissa, Wes, and Daryl went to Fred's Burgers to get food for their friends at school. Melissa spent $6.35 on two burgers, one order of french fries, and two colas. Wes ordered 1 burger, 2 orders of french fries, and 2 colas. His bill was $5.45. Daryl's order of 3 burgers, 3 orders of french fries, and 3 colas totaled $11.01. Find the price of each item. (Lesson 3–7)

burger, $1.89; fries, $0.99; cola, $0.79

42. **State Fair** A dairy makes three types of cheese—cheddar, Monterey Jack and Swiss— and sells the cheese in three booths at the state fair. At the beginning of one day, the first booth received x pounds of each type of cheese. The second booth received y pounds of each type of cheese, and the third booth received z pounds of each type of cheese. By the end of the day, the dairy had sold 131 pounds of cheddar, 291 pounds of Monterey Jack, and 232 pounds of Swiss. The table below shows the percent of the cheese delivered in the morning that was sold at each booth. How many pounds of cheddar cheese did each booth receive in the morning? (Lesson 3–7)

Type	Booth 1	Booth 2	Booth 3
Cheddar	40%	30%	10%
Monterey Jack	40%	90%	80%
Swiss	30%	70%	70%

Booth 1, 190 lb; Booth 2, 150 lb; Booth 3, 100 lb

A practice test for Chapter 3 is provided on page 914.

ALTERNATIVE ASSESSMENT

COOPERATIVE LEARNING PROJECT

You have just been promoted to the position of national purchasing agent for a large rental car company. Having worked as a manager for several years in one of their local offices, you have become familiar with many different makes and models of automobiles. The executive officers of the company have narrowed the field to two models having the following characteristics.

Characteristics	Model A	Model B
Purchase price per unit	$10,000	$15,000
Number of units needed	5000	5000
Total cash outlay	$50,000,000	$75,000,000
Projected revenue per year	$36,500,000	$36,500,000
Projected expense per year	$21,900,000	$18,250,000
Projected utilization	85%	85%
Useful life per unit	3 years	4 years
Resale value per unit	$1,500	$2,000

The executive officers have asked you to create a graph of the information on the chart and make a recommendation. Here are some things you might want to show on your graph.

- total cash outlay
- purchase price of each unit
- profit line
- when each model has paid for itself
- when the two models generate the same profit

You have three recommendations to choose from: Model A, Model B or a combination of the two. Tell which recommendation you would choose and why.

What other factors might influence your decision?

THINKING CRITICALLY

- Write a system of equations in three variables that has one unique solution. Explain why there is only one solution.
- Write a system of equations in three variables that has no solution. Explain why there is no solution.
- Write a system of equations in three variables that has an infinite number of solutions. Explain why this is the case.

PORTFOLIO SUGGESTIONS

Select an item from this chapter that you feel shows your best work and place it in your portfolio. Explain why you selected it.

SELF EVALUATION

Systems of linear equations and linear inequalities occur often as models of real-life situations. As you grow older, these real-life situations will become more evident in your own life. How will you solve these problems?

Assess yourself. How well am I able to solve the problems I encounter? Write a paragraph that describes what you know about systems of equations and inequalities. Describe the kinds of problems you have solved using systems of equations. Write down parts that are difficult for you to understand and parts that are easy. This will help you to identify sections that need further study to better understand these topics.

Assessment and Evaluation Masters, pp. 70, 81

3   NAME _____ DATE _____

Chapter 3 Performance Assessment

Instructions: Demonstrate your knowledge by giving a clear, concise solution to each problem. Be sure to include all relevant drawings and justify your answers. You may show your solution in more than one way or investigate beyond the requirements of the problem.

1. a. Write a system of two equations in two variables that has no solutions. Describe how to write such a system.

   b. Write a system of two equations in two variables that has an infinite set of solutions. Describe how to write such a system. Give two solutions.

   c. Write a system of two equations in two variables that has a single solution.

   d. Solve the system in part c in at least two ways. Which method do you like best? Why?

   e. Try solving the system of equations below.
   $$3x - y + z = 5$$
   $$-6x + 2y - 2z = 1$$
   $$x - 4y - 3z = -5$$

   How many solutions do you think the system has? Why?

2. The square of Janet's age is 400 more than the square of the sum of Kim's and Sue's ages. Kim's and Sue's ages total 10 less than Janet's age. Find the square of the sum of the ages of Janet, Kim, and Sue. Explain your reasoning.

3. a. Mrs. Feldman sells artificial flower arrangements. She can make no more than 10 arrangements a week. Small arrangements sell for $10 and large arrangements for $50. If she prefers to make no more than 6 large arrangements a week, how many of each size should she make to maximize her weekly sales?

   b. Explain why the answer makes sense.

   c. If she decided that she should make 12 arrangements a week and could make as many as 8 large arrangements a week, how do you think this would affect the number of each size arrangement she should make to maximize income? Why?

Scoring Guide
Chapter 3
Performance Assessment

Level	Specific Criteria
3 Superior	• Shows thorough understanding of the concepts of *solving systems of linear equations and inequalities*. • Attempt at solving system in three variables is well-organized and correct. • Uses appropriate strategies to solve problems. • Computations are correct. • Written explanations are exemplary. • Graphs are accurate and appropriate. • Goes beyond requirements of problem.
2 Satisfactory, with Minor Flaws	• Shows understanding of the concepts of *solving systems of linear equations and inequalities*. • Attempt at solving system in three variables is well-organized and mostly correct. • Uses appropriate strategies to solve problems. • Computations are mostly correct. • Written explanations are effective. • Graphs are mostly accurate and appropriate. • Satisfies all requirements of problem.
1 Nearly Satisfactory, with Serious Flaws	• Shows understanding of most of the concepts of *solving systems of linear equations and inequalities*. • Attempt at solving system in three variables is well-organized, but not correct. • May not use appropriate strategies to solve problems. • Computations are mostly correct. • Written explanations are satisfactory. • Graphs are mostly accurate and appropriate. • Satisfies most requirements of problem.
0 Unsatisfactory	• Shows little or no understanding of the concepts of *solving systems of linear equations and inequalities*. • Attempt at solving system in three variables is not well-organized or correct. • May not use appropriate strategies to solve problems. • Computations are incorrect. • Written explanations are not satisfactory. • Graphs are not accurate or appropriate. • Does not satisfy requirements of problem.

Alternative Assessment

The Alternative Assessment section provides students with the opportunity to assess their own work by thinking critically, working with others, keeping a portfolio, and honestly evaluating their own progress. For more information on alternative forms of assessment, see *Alternative Assessment in the Mathematics Classroom,* one of the titles in the Glencoe Mathematics Professional Series.

Performance Assessment

Performance Assessment tasks for this chapter are included in the *Assessment and Evaluation Masters.* A scoring guide is also provided.

NCTM Standards: 1–5, 7–8, 10, 12

This Investigation is designed to be completed over several days or weeks. It may be considered optional. You may want to assign the Investigation and the follow-up activities to be completed at the same time.

Objective
Design, build, and test a launch system.

Mathematical Overview
This Investigation will use the following mathematical skills and concepts from Chapters 4 and 5.

- solving matrices for variables
- solving systems of linear equations
- dividing polynomials
- evaluating expressions in exponential or radical form

Recommended Time		
Part	Pages	Time
Investigation	180–181	1 class period
Working on the Investigation	193, 231, 273, 302	20 minutes each
Closing the Investigation	322	1 class period

Instructional Resources
Investigations and Projects Masters, pp. 5–8

A recording sheet, teacher notes, and scoring guide are provided for each investigation in the *Investigations and Projects Masters.*

1 MOTIVATION

This Investigation uses simple materials to design, build, and test a model for a launch system and run a series of tests to calibrate the launcher. Ask students if they have seen a launch system. Discuss the importance of calibrating the launcher to hit a designated target.

3-2-1-Blast-Off!

MATERIALS NEEDED

- shoe box
- paper cups
- wooden craft sticks
- ruler with groove down the middle
- Ping-Pong™ ball
- plastic spoon
- golf tee
- masking tape
- string
- rubber bands (various sizes)
- paper clips
- measuring tape

You work for a scientific research company that has just received a government contract. This contract involves designing, building, and testing a prototype launching system. Currently, the government is using inefficient designs supplied by previous companies. The government has requested rush status for this operation and is requiring a shoot-off to demonstrate the accuracy and features of the system.

Your research company must design, build, and test the launch system. It must be calibrated by shooting a number of test shots. To calibrate the launcher, shoot several test shots, mark the results, and adjust the launcher until it will hit a designated target. The test data will show the accuracy of the system. Then a detailed individual report must be written.

The government has furnished the following raw materials to be used to construct the launching system.

- launcher component kit (shoe box, paper cups, and craft sticks)
- linear scale (ruler with groove down the middle)
- projectile (Ping-Pong™ ball)
- cradles (plastic spoon and golf tee)
- adhesive lamination (masking tape)
- rope (string)
- power supply (rubber bands of various size)
- bars (paper clips)
- test range calibration device (measuring tape)

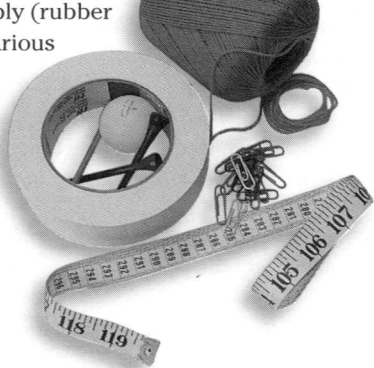

Cooperative Learning

This Investigation offers an excellent opportunity for using cooperative learning groups. For more information on cooperative learning strategies and group management, see *Cooperative Learning in the Mathematics Classroom,* one of the titles in the Glencoe Mathematics Professional Series.

 TEKS | 1.b., 2.a.

Your team of four researchers must design and build a launcher out of the raw materials provided. The launcher must be capable of hitting the government's specified target at a distance somewhere between 50 cm and 250 cm from the launcher. Since you will need to calibrate your launcher to hit a specified target at a given distance within that range, you will need to conduct several tests to perfect your design.

In this Investigation, you will examine ways in which the launcher can be designed. Once the design has been determined, the launcher will need to be built and then tested for accuracy.

Make an Investigation Folder in which you can store all of your work on this Investigation for future use.

PLAN THE DESIGN

1 Think about several different launcher designs. Look in books, magazines, and science literature to find pictures of various launchers.
2 Discuss these designs with your teammates. Narrow the list of options down to one launcher design on which you all agree.
3 Write a design proposal in which you include a blueprint of your design and launching instructions.

BUILD THE LAUNCHER

4 Use the materials that the government has furnished to build the launcher.
5 Be sure that the blueprint in your proposal matches the actual model that you built. Modify the blueprint as necessary to match your model.

6 Review the launching instructions that you wrote in your proposal for clarity and understandability. Revise your proposal as necessary.

You will continue working on this Investigation throughout Chapters 4 and 5.

Be sure to keep your chart and materials in your Investigation Folder.

3-2-1-Blast-Off! Investigation

Working on the Investigation
Lesson 4-1, p. 193
....
Working on the Investigation
Lesson 4-7, p. 231
....
Working on the Investigation
Lesson 5-3, p. 273
....
Working on the Investigation
Lesson 5-7, p. 302
....
Closing the Investigation
End of Chapter 5, p. 322
....

Investigation: 3–2–1–Blast-Off! **181**

2 SETUP

You may wish to have a student read the first three paragraphs of the Investigation to provide background information about designing and creating a model for a launch system. You may wish to read the next two paragraphs, which introduce the activity. Discuss the activity with your students. Then separate the class into groups of four.

3 MANAGEMENT

Each group member should be responsible for a specific task.

Recorder Collects data.
Measurer Sets measurements of different parts needed to create the launch system.
Builder Builds the design.
Writer Writes the proposal.

At the end of the activity, each member should turn in his or her respective equipment.

Sample Answers

Answers will vary as they are based on the type of design created by each team.

Investigations and Projects Masters, p. 8

NAME _____ DATE _____
Investigation, Chapters 4 and 5 Student Edition Pages 180–1 193, 231, 273, 302, 3

3-2-1 Blast Off!

Use the following chart to record your data from Working on the Investigation in section 5-3.

Launcher	Error Range	Tolerance	Relative Error	Average Error

	Error Range	Tolerance	Relative Error	Average Error
What each measure represents when analyzing the data				

Which launcher would you consider to be the most accurate?
_____

Why?
_____
_____
_____

Using Matrices

PREVIEWING THE CHAPTER

This chapter introduces students to matrices through the concept of matrix logic. Students organize known data into a table that enables them to eliminate possibilities and arrive at the only possible solution. Students learn to create a matrix, perform scalar multiplication on it, and then add matrices. Determinants are related to matrices, and students connect the content to a number of real-world applications, as well as to other areas of mathematics, such as transformational geometry. Students also solve systems of equations by using inverse and augmented matrices. Finally, students examine the statistical tool known as a box-and-whisker plot.

Lesson (Pages)	Lesson Objectives	NCTM Standards	State/Local Objectives
4-1A (184–185)	Use a graphing calculator to perform operations with matrices and find determinants and inverses.	1–5, 12	
4-1 (186–193)	Perform scalar multiplication on a matrix. Solve matrices for variables. Solve problems using matrix logic.	1–5, 8, 12	2.a.
4-2 (194–198)	Add and subtract matrices.	1–5, 8, 12	2.a.
4-3 (199–204)	Multiply matrices.	1–5, 8, 12	2.a.
4-4 (205–211)	Evaluate the determinant of a 3×3 matrix. Find the area of a triangle, given the coordinates of its vertices.	1–5, 8, 12	2.a.
4-5 (212–218)	Write the identity matrix for any square matrix. Find the inverse of a 2×2 matrix.	1–5, 12	2.a.
4-6 (219–225)	Solve systems of linear equations by using inverse matrices.	1–5, 12	2.a., 3.b., 3.c.
4-7 (226–231)	Solve systems of linear equations by using augmented matrices.	1–5, 12	2.a., 3.b., 3.c.
4-7B (232–234)	Use a graphing calculator to solve systems of linear equations.	1–5, 12	
4-8 (235–244)	Find the range, quartiles, and interquartile range for a set of data. Determine if any values in a set of data are outliers. Represent data using box-and-whisker plots.	1–4, 10	

A complete, 1-page lesson plan is provided for each lesson in the *Lesson Planning Guide*. Answer keys for each lesson are available in the *Answer Key Masters*.

You may want to refer to the **Course Planning Calendar** on page T12 for detailed information on pacing.
PACING: Standard—14 days; **Honors**—12 days; **Block**—7 days

LESSON PLANNING CHART

Lesson (Pages)	Materials/ Manipulatives	Extra Practice (Student Edition)	BLACKLINE MASTERS									Real-World Applications	Interactive Mathematics Tools Software	Teaching Transparencies
			Study Guide	Practice	Enrichment	Assessment and Evaluation	Modeling Mathematics	Multicultural Activity	Tech Prep Applications	Graphing Calculator	Science and Math Lab Manual			
4-1A (184–185)	graphing calculator									pp. 31, 32				
4-1 (186–193)		p. 883	p. 22	p. 22	p. 22		pp. 34–36					4-1		4-1A 4-1B
4-2 (194–198)		p. 883	p. 23	p. 23	p. 23	p. 100								4-2A 4-2B
4-3 (199–204)	grid paper tracing paper protractor*	p. 883	p. 24	p. 24	p. 24			p. 7	p. 7			4-3		4-3A 4-3B
4-4 (205–211)	graphing calculator	p. 884	p. 25	p. 25	p. 25	pp. 99, 100	p. 64	p. 8		p. 4		9		4-4A 4-4B
4-5 (212–218)	graphing calculator	p. 884	p. 26	p. 26	p. 26							10		4-5A 4-5B
4-6 (219–225)	graphing calculator	p. 884	p. 27	p. 27	p. 27	p. 101			p. 8					4-6A 4-6B
4-7 (226–231)		p. 885	p. 28	p. 28	p. 28									4-7A 4-7B
4-7B (232–234)	graphing calculator									pp. 33, 34	•			
4-8 (235–244)	graphing calculator	p. 885	p. 29	p. 29	p. 29	p. 101					pp. 75–80	11		4-8A 4-8B
Study Guide/ Assessment (245–249)						pp. 85–98, 102–104								

*Included in Glencoe's Student Manipulative Kit and Overhead Manipulative Resources.

ORGANIZING THE CHAPTER

OTHER CHAPTER RESOURCES

Student Edition
Investigation, pp. 180–181
Chapter Opener, pp. 182–183
Mathematics and Society, p. 218
Working on the Investigation,
   pp. 193, 231

Teacher's Classroom Resources
Investigations and Projects Masters,
   pp. 37–40

Technology
Teacher's Guide for Software
   Resources
Test and Review Software (IBM
   and Macintosh)
CD-ROM Interactions (Windows
   and Macintosh)

Professional Publications
Block Scheduling Booklet
Glencoe Mathematics Professional
   Series

OUTSIDE RESOURCES

Books/Periodicals
Connecting Mathematics: Addenda Series,
   Grades 9–12, NCTM
Matrices, NCTM

Software
Math Connections: Algebra II, Sunburst
Matrices, NCTM

Videos/CD-ROMs
Mastering Algebra, Merit Audio Visual

See the *Teacher's Guide for Software Resources* for software addresses.

ASSESSMENT RESOURCES

Student Edition
Math Journal, pp. 190, 196, 229
Mixed Review, pp. 193, 198,
   204, 211, 218, 225, 231,
   244
Self Test, p. 211
Chapter Highlights, p. 245
Chapter Study Guide and
   Assessment, pp. 246–248
Alternative Assessment, p. 249
    Portfolio, p. 249

College Entrance Exam Practice,
   pp. 250–251

Teacher's Wraparound Edition
5-Minute Check, pp. 186, 194,
   199, 205, 212, 219, 226, 235
Check for Understanding, pp. 190,
   196, 202, 208, 216, 223, 229,
   240
Closing Activity, pp. 192, 198,
   204, 211, 218, 225, 231, 244
Cooperative Learning, pp. 197,
   201

Assessment and Evaluation Masters
Multiple-Choice Tests, Forms 1A
   (Honors), 1B (Average), 1C
   (Basic), pp. 85–90
Free-Response Tests, Forms 2A
   (Honors), 2B (Average), 2C
   (Basic), pp. 91–96
Calculator-Based Test, p. 97
Performance Assessment, p. 98
Mid-Chapter Test, p. 99
Quizzes A–D, pp. 100–101
Standardized Test Practice, p. 102
Cumulative Review, pp. 103–104

ENHANCING THE CHAPTER

Examples of some of the materials for enhancing Chapter 4 are shown below.

 **DIVERSITY**

Multicultural Activity Masters, pp. 7, 8

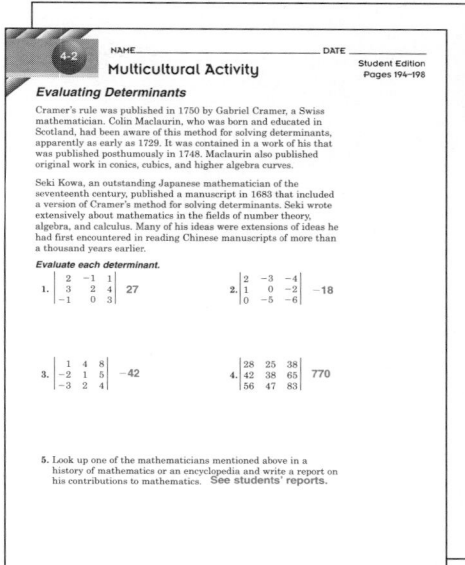

4-2 NAME _____ DATE _____ Student Edition Pages 194–198

Multicultural Activity

Evaluating Determinants

Cramer's rule was published in 1750 by Gabriel Cramer, a Swiss mathematician. Colin Maclaurin, who was born and educated in Scotland, had been aware of this method for solving determinants, apparently as early as 1729. It was contained in a work of his that was published posthumously in 1748. Maclaurin also published original work in conics, cubics, and higher algebra curves.

Seki Kowa, an outstanding Japanese mathematician of the seventeenth century, published a manuscript in 1683 that included a version of Cramer's method for solving determinants. Seki wrote extensively about mathematics in the fields of number theory, algebra, and calculus. Many of his ideas were extensions of ideas he had first encountered in reading Chinese manuscripts of more than a thousand years earlier.

Evaluate each determinant.

1. $\begin{vmatrix} 2 & -1 & 1 \\ 3 & 2 & 4 \\ -1 & 0 & 3 \end{vmatrix}$ 27

2. $\begin{vmatrix} 2 & -3 & -4 \\ 1 & 0 & -2 \\ 0 & -5 & -6 \end{vmatrix}$ −18

3. $\begin{vmatrix} 1 & 4 & 8 \\ -2 & 1 & 5 \\ -3 & 2 & 4 \end{vmatrix}$ −42

4. $\begin{vmatrix} 28 & 25 & 38 \\ 42 & 38 & 65 \\ 56 & 47 & 83 \end{vmatrix}$ 770

5. Look up one of the mathematicians mentioned above in a history of mathematics or an encyclopedia and write a report on his contributions to mathematics. **See students' reports.**

 **APPLICATIONS**

Real-World Applications, 9, 10, 11

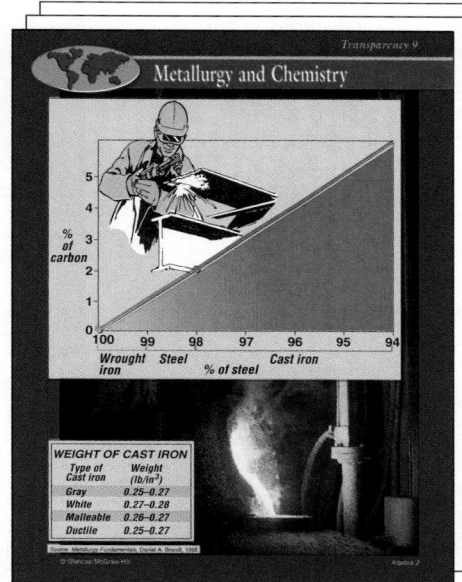

Transparency 9

Metallurgy and Chemistry

WEIGHT OF CAST IRON

Type of Cast Iron	Weight (lb/in³)
Gray	0.25–0.27
White	0.27–0.28
Malleable	0.26–0.27
Ductile	0.25–0.27

 **TECHNOLOGY**

Graphing Calculator Masters, p. 4

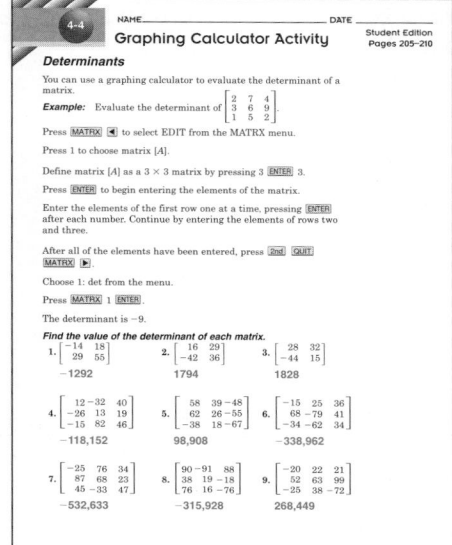

4-4 NAME _____ DATE _____ Student Edition Pages 205–210

Graphing Calculator Activity

Determinants

You can use a graphing calculator to evaluate the determinant of a matrix.

Example: Evaluate the determinant of $\begin{bmatrix} 2 & 7 & 4 \\ 3 & 6 & 9 \\ 1 & 5 & 2 \end{bmatrix}$.

Press MATRX ◄ to select EDIT from the MATRX menu.

Press 1 to choose matrix [A].

Define matrix [A] as a 3 × 3 matrix by pressing 3 ENTER 3.

Press ENTER to begin entering the elements of the matrix.

Enter the elements of the first row one at a time, pressing ENTER after each number. Continue by entering the elements of rows two and three.

After all of the elements have been entered, press 2nd QUIT MATRX ►.

Choose 1: det from the menu.

Press MATRX 1 ENTER

The determinant is −9.

Find the value of the determinant of each matrix.

1. $\begin{bmatrix} -14 & 18 \\ 29 & 55 \end{bmatrix}$ −1292

2. $\begin{bmatrix} 16 & 29 \\ -42 & 36 \end{bmatrix}$ 1794

3. $\begin{bmatrix} 28 & 32 \\ -44 & 15 \end{bmatrix}$ 1828

4. $\begin{bmatrix} 12 & -32 & 40 \\ -26 & 13 & 19 \\ -15 & 82 & 46 \end{bmatrix}$ −118,152

5. $\begin{bmatrix} 58 & 39 & -48 \\ 62 & 26 & -55 \\ -38 & 18 & -67 \end{bmatrix}$ 98,908

6. $\begin{bmatrix} -15 & 25 & 36 \\ 68 & -79 & 41 \\ -34 & -62 & 34 \end{bmatrix}$ −338,962

7. $\begin{bmatrix} -25 & 76 & 34 \\ 87 & 68 & 23 \\ 45 & -33 & 47 \end{bmatrix}$ −532,633

8. $\begin{bmatrix} 90 & -91 & 88 \\ 38 & 19 & -18 \\ 76 & 16 & -76 \end{bmatrix}$ −315,928

9. $\begin{bmatrix} -20 & 22 & 21 \\ 52 & 63 & 99 \\ -25 & 38 & -72 \end{bmatrix}$ 268,449

 **TECH PREP**

Tech Prep Applications Masters, pp. 7, 8

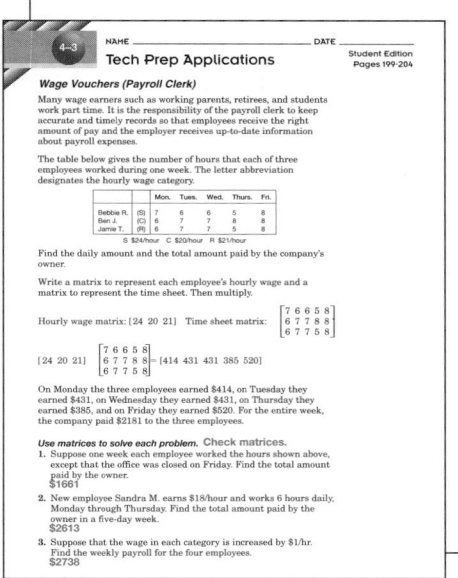

4-3 NAME _____ DATE _____ Student Edition Pages 199-204

Tech Prep Applications

Wage Vouchers (Payroll Clerk)

Many wage earners such as working parents, retirees, and students work part time. It is the responsibility of the payroll clerk to keep accurate and timely records so that employees receive the right amount of pay and the employer receives up-to-date information about payroll expenses.

The table below gives the number of hours that each of three employees worked during one week. The letter abbreviation designates the hourly wage category.

		Mon.	Tues.	Wed.	Thurs.	Fri.
Bebbie R.	(S)	7	6	6	5	8
Ben J.	(C)	6	7	7	8	8
Jamie T.	(R)	6	7	7	5	8

S $24/hour   C $20/hour   R $21/hour

Find the daily amount and the total amount paid by the company's owner.

Write a matrix to represent each employee's hourly wage and a matrix to represent the time sheet. Then multiply.

Hourly wage matrix: [24 20 21]   Time sheet matrix: $\begin{bmatrix} 7 & 6 & 6 & 5 & 8 \\ 6 & 7 & 7 & 8 & 8 \\ 6 & 7 & 7 & 5 & 8 \end{bmatrix}$

$[24 \ 20 \ 21] \begin{bmatrix} 7 & 6 & 6 & 5 & 8 \\ 6 & 7 & 7 & 8 & 8 \\ 6 & 7 & 7 & 5 & 8 \end{bmatrix} = [414 \ 431 \ 431 \ 385 \ 520]$

On Monday the three employees earned $414, on Tuesday they earned $431, on Wednesday they earned $431, on Thursday they earned $385, and on Friday they earned $520. For the entire week, the company paid $2181 to the three employees.

Use matrices to solve each problem. Check matrices.

1. Suppose one week each employee worked the hours shown above, except that the office was closed on Friday. Find the total amount paid by the owner.
$1661

2. New employee Sandra M. earns $18/hour and works 6 hours daily, Monday through Thursday. Find the total amount paid by the owner in a five-day week.
$2613

3. Suppose that the wage in each category is increased by $1/hr. Find the weekly payroll for the four employees.
$2738

 **CONNECTIONS**

Science and Math Lab Manual, pp. 75–80

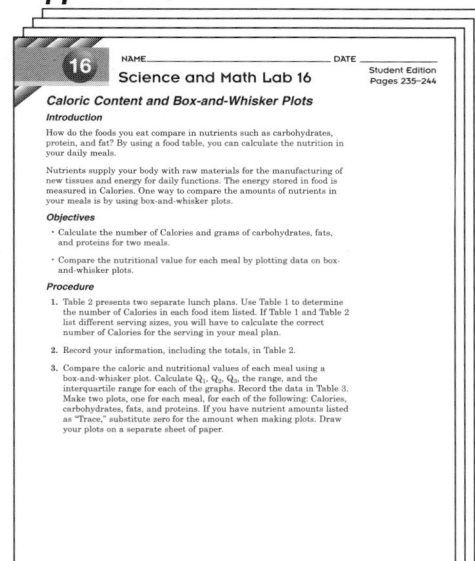

16 NAME _____ DATE _____ Student Edition Pages 235-244

Science and Math Lab 16

Caloric Content and Box-and-Whisker Plots

Introduction

How do the foods you eat compare in nutrients such as carbohydrates, protein, and fat? By using a food table, you can calculate the nutrition in your daily meals.

Nutrients supply your body with raw materials for the manufacturing of new tissues and energy for daily functions. The energy stored in food is measured in Calories. One way to compare the amounts of nutrients in your meals is by using box-and-whisker plots.

Objectives

· Calculate the number of Calories and grams of carbohydrates, fats, and proteins for two meals.

· Compare the nutritional value for each meal by plotting data on box-and-whisker plots.

Procedure

1. Table 2 presents two separate lunch plans. Use Table 1 to determine the number of Calories in each food item listed. If Table 1 and Table 2 list different serving sizes, you will have to calculate the correct number of Calories for the serving in your meal plan.

2. Record your information, including the totals, in Table 2.

3. Compare the caloric and nutritional values of each meal using a box-and-whisker plot. Calculate Q_1, Q_2, Q_3, the range, and the interquartile range for each of the graphs. Record the data in Table 3. Make two plots, one for each meal, for each of the following: Calories, carbohydrates, fats, and proteins. If you have nutrient amounts listed as "Trace," substitute zero for the amount when making plots. Draw your plots on a separate sheet of paper.

 **PROBLEM SOLVING**

Problem of the Week Cards, 10, 11, 12

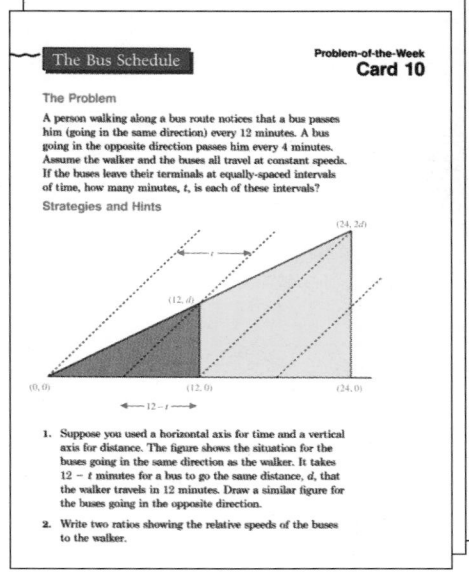

The Bus Schedule   Problem-of-the-Week Card 10

The Problem

A person walking along a bus route notices that a bus passes him (going in the same direction) every 12 minutes. A bus going in the opposite direction passes him every 4 minutes. Assume the walker and the buses all travel at constant speeds. If the buses leave their terminals at equally-spaced intervals of time, how many minutes, t, is each of these intervals?

Strategies and Hints

1. Suppose you used a horizontal axis for time and a vertical axis for distance. The figure shows the situation for the buses going in the same direction as the walker. It takes $12 - t$ minutes for a bus to go the same distance, d, that the walker travels in 12 minutes. Draw a similar figure for the buses going in the opposite direction.

2. Write two ratios showing the relative speeds of the buses to the walker.

MAKING MATHEMATICS RELEVANT

This two-page introduction to the chapter provides students with an opportunity to explore contemporary topics and their applications to mathematics.

Background Information

Get Involved! Almost half of all American adults perform volunteer activities. Most of these activities are conducted through religious institutions. The average volunteer provides about 4.2 hours of service a week. Almost a third of all volunteers work with more than one organization.

CHAPTER

4

Using Matrices

Objectives

In this chapter, you will:

- create matrices and box-and-whisker plots to represent data,
- solve problems by using matrix logic,
- perform operations with matrices,
- use matrices to achieve transformations of geometric figures, and
- use matrices to solve systems of equations.

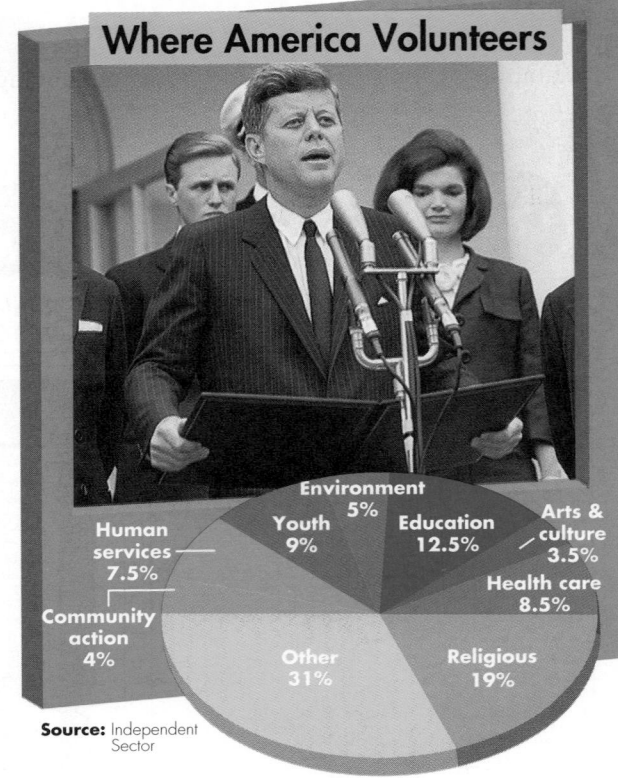

Where America Volunteers

Environment 5%
Youth 9%
Education 12.5%
Arts & culture 3.5%
Human services 7.5%
Health care 8.5%
Community action 4%
Other 31%
Religious 19%

Source: Independent Sector

"**A**sk not what your country can do for you—ask what you can do for your country." These famous words from President John Kennedy's 1961 inaugural address are meaningful and significant today. It may seem that the actions of one individual high school student can't make a major difference in the course of America's history. However, energy put into volunteering in your local community is an excellent way to make a difference.

TIME Line

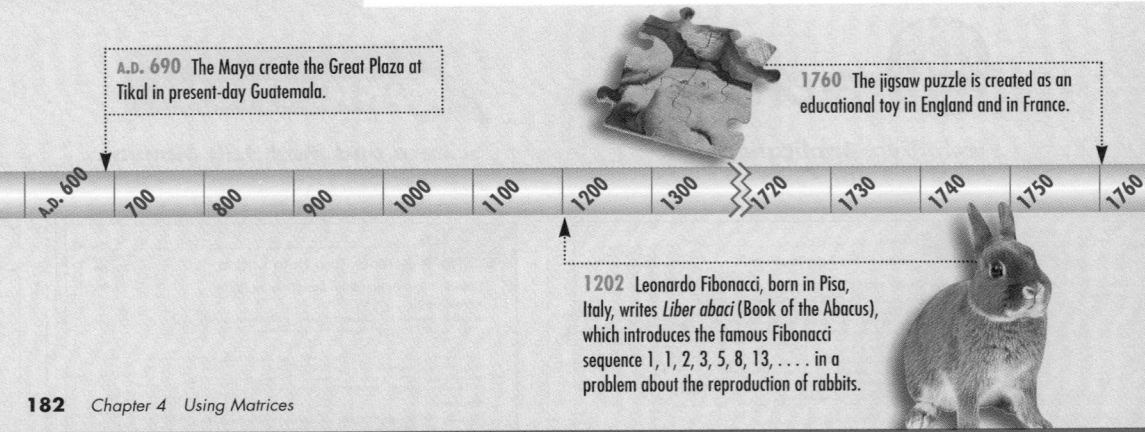

A.D. 690 The Maya create the Great Plaza at Tikal in present-day Guatemala.

1760 The jigsaw puzzle is created as an educational toy in England and in France.

A.D. 600 | 700 | 800 | 900 | 1000 | 1100 | 1200 | 1300 | 1720 | 1730 | 1740 | 1750 | 1760

1202 Leonardo Fibonacci, born in Pisa, Italy, writes *Liber abaci* (Book of the Abacus), which introduces the famous Fibonacci sequence 1, 1, 2, 3, 5, 8, 13, ... in a problem about the reproduction of rabbits.

TIME Line

Students interested in the biological sciences might want to learn more about Fibonacci and the many applications of Fibonacci sequences within that area of science.

inter**NET** CONNECTION

Investigate volunteer work by reading suggestions for volunteers such as family and youth services, the arts, and poverty and homelessness.

World Wide Web
http://www.terrymax.org/volunteer/

Chapter Project

Investigate volunteering in your community. Find some of the interesting ways you can help your city and country in your spare time. Do research by contacting as many organizations as possible who use volunteers. Also, conduct a survey of your classmates to find the number of hours per week they volunteer in the community.

Report to the class on the different opportunities for volunteering, especially groups that can use teen volunteers. In your report, organize your data into graphs and box-and-whisker plots. Explain the advantages and disadvantages of each method of data presentation.

Amy Banna, a Rochester Hills, Michigan, teenager who likes to help others, won an award for her volunteer efforts. She was one of only five students in southeastern Michigan who received a Young Metro Volunteer Award in 1995, recognizing her service to the community, her leadership, commitment, and character. Amy tutors elementary students after school, packs and delivers food monthly to a Detroit housing project, helps with child care at a shelter for mothers and their children, and is a teacher's aide for a Head Start program.

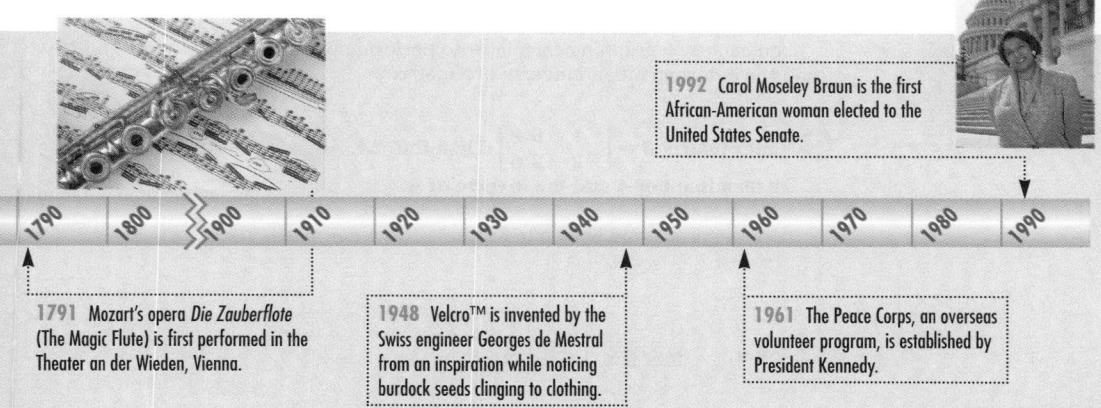

1790 — 1800 — 1900 — 1910 — 1920 — 1930 — 1940 — 1950 — 1960 — 1970 — 1980 — 1990

1791 Mozart's opera *Die Zauberflöte* (The Magic Flute) is first performed in the Theater an der Wieden, Vienna.

1948 Velcro™ is invented by the Swiss engineer Georges de Mestral from an inspiration while noticing burdock seeds clinging to clothing.

1961 The Peace Corps, an overseas volunteer program, is established by President Kennedy.

1992 Carol Moseley Braun is the first African-American woman elected to the United States Senate.

Amy finds that her volunteer work helps her to organize herself. She tutors every day after school until 6 P.M. and then finds time to do her homework and some of the activities she considers fun, like sweatshirt painting, baby-sitting, and "hanging out." Amy keeps her grades up, too, as indicated by her membership in the National Honor Society and her school academic honors.

Chapter Project

Cooperative Learning You may choose to have students work in cooperative groups as they research volunteering in the community. Group members may split up the responsibilities for contacting organizations and conducting surveys, but they should work together closely when organizing their data and preparing their report. This activity allows students to closely examine the processes involved in collecting and presenting data.

Investigations and Projects Masters, p. 37

Alternative Chapter Projects

Two other chapter projects are included in the *Investigations and Projects Masters*. In Chapter 4 Project A, pp. 37–38, students extend the topic in the chapter opener. In Chapter 4 Project B, pp. 39–40, students design a new product.

4

NAME_____ DATE_____

Chapter 4 Project A

Student Edition
Pages 184–244

How Can I Help?

1. How can you help your community? Find out about a local organization that does the type of community service in which you are interested. Look into how you can get involved with the organization.

2. Interview a person who is part of the organization you chose in exercise 1. Some questions you may want to ask during the interview are given below.
   • Why did you decide to become involved with this organization?
   • How much time do you spend each week doing volunteer work for this organization?
   • What is your role in this organization?

3. If possible, spend at least one day working with the person you interviewed in exercise 2. Keep a log of the types of activities in which you participate.

4. Find out about the finances involved in running the organization. If possible, obtain a financial statement.

5. Review the information you obtained in exercises 2, 3, and 4. Find a way to use matrices and graphs to help communicate and organize this information.

6. Use the information you have gathered to make a poster describing your organization. Be sure to include your matrices and graphs from exercise 5. Share your poster with your class.

Objective

Use a graphing calculator to perform operations with matrices and find determinants and inverses.

Recommended Time

25 minutes

Instructional Resources

Graphing Calculator Masters, pp. 31 and 32

These masters provide keystroking instruction for this lesson for the TI-81 and Casio graphing calculators.

1 FOCUS

Motivating the Lesson

Begin the lesson by writing the equations $3x - y = 0$ and $4x + 2y = 0$ on the chalkboard or overhead. Ask students how they might solve these equations. Students may suggest solving them graphically or algebraically. Note that there are a number of ways to solve the equations algebraically, and one of them is by using matrices.

2 TEACH

Teaching Tip The concepts presented in this lesson make the arithmetic manipulations in the following lessons unnecessary. You may wish to present the use of the graphing calculator after you have presented the lessons containing these concepts.

Teaching Tip Point out to students that the elements of the matrix are entered row by row, beginning with the left-most entry.

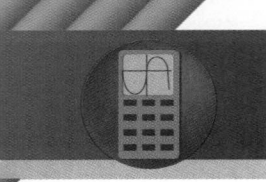

4–1A Graphing Technology
Matrices

A Preview of Lesson 4–1

Most graphing calculators can perform operations with matrices, as well as find determinants and inverse matrices. On a TI-82, the [MATRX] key accesses the matrix operation menus. The EDIT menu allows you to define matrices. When the EDIT menu is accessed, the dimensions of matrices $A–E$ are listed. A matrix dimension of 2×3 indicates a matrix has 2 rows and 3 columns.

To enter a matrix into the calculator, choose the EDIT menu and select matrix A. Then enter the dimensions and elements of the matrix.

Example ❶ Define matrix $A = \begin{bmatrix} 6 & 7 \\ 1 & 2 \end{bmatrix}$ with a graphing calculator.

This is a 2×2 matrix. Enter the matrix dimensions. Then enter the matrix elements.

Enter: [MATRX] [▶] [▶] [ENTER] 2 [ENTER] 2 [ENTER]

 6 [ENTER] 7 [ENTER] 1 [ENTER] 2 [ENTER]

The [ENTER] *key fills the row, not the column.*

You can display the matrix by quitting the matrix menus and then requesting matrix A by name.

Enter: [2nd] [QUIT] [MATRX] 1 [ENTER]

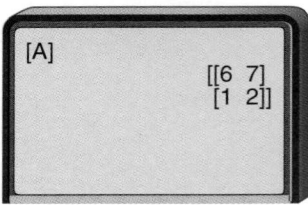

You can use a graphing calculator to perform operations on matrices and to find the determinant and inverse of a matrix.

Example ❷ Enter matrix $B = \begin{bmatrix} 1 & 0 & 8 \\ -2 & -3 & 6 \end{bmatrix}$. Then find $2A$, AB, A^2, $B + AB$, the determinant of A and the inverse of A.

Use the procedure shown in Example 1 to enter matrix B.
This is a 2×3 matrix.

Find $2A$.

Enter: 2 [MATRX] 1 [ENTER]   [[12 14]
                                              [2 4]]

Find AB.

Enter: [MATRX] 1 [MATRX] 2 [ENTER] $[[-8 \ -21 \ 90]$
                                              $[-3 \ -6 \ 20]]$

Find A^2.

Enter: [MATRX] 1 [x^2] [ENTER] $[[43 \ 56]$
                                          $[8 \ 11]]$

Find $B + AB$.

Enter: [MATRX] 2 [+] [MATRX] 1 [MATRX] 2 [ENTER] $[[-7 \ -21 \ 98]$
                                                         $[-5 \ -9 \ 26]]$

Find the determinant of A.   *The determinant of A is denoted det A.*

Enter: [MATRX] [▶] 1 [MATRX] 1 [ENTER] 5

Find the inverse of A.   *The inverse of A is denoted A^{-1}.*

Enter: [MATRX] 1 [x^{-1}] [ENTER] $[[.4 \ -1.4]$
                                             $[-.2 \ 1.2]]$

EXERCISES

Enter the matrices below into a graphing calculator. Then find each of the following.   1–18. See margin.

$$A = \begin{bmatrix} 2 & 1 & 4 \\ 0 & 1 & -1 \\ 4 & 2 & 3 \end{bmatrix} \qquad B = \begin{bmatrix} 6 & -2 & 5 \\ 0 & 7 & -1 \end{bmatrix} \qquad C = \begin{bmatrix} 1 & 4 \\ -3 & 6 \\ 7 & -2 \end{bmatrix}$$

1. $-C$ 2. $4B$ 3. $\det A$ -10

4. $-2A$ 5. A^{-1} 6. CB

7. BC 8. $\det BC$ 2124   9. BA

10. $CB - A$ 11. $\det CB$ 0   12. $A + CB$

13. $(BC)^{-1}$ 14. A^2 15. $(BC)^2$

16. $B + BA$ 17. BAC 18. CBA

Lesson 4–1A Graphing Technology: Matrices   **185**

Using Technology

This lesson offers an excellent opportunity for using technology in your algebra classroom. For more information on using technology, see *Graphing Calculators in the Mathematics Classroom*, one of the titles in the Glencoe Mathematics Professional Series.

Additional Answers

16. $\begin{bmatrix} 38 & 12 & 46 \\ -4 & 12 & -11 \end{bmatrix}$

17. $\begin{bmatrix} 277 & 130 \\ -89 & 34 \end{bmatrix}$

18. $\begin{bmatrix} 16 & 34 & 1 \\ -120 & -12 & -183 \\ 232 & 88 & 307 \end{bmatrix}$

3 PRACTICE/APPLY

Assignment Guide

Core: 1–18
Enriched: 1–18

4 ASSESS

Observing students working with technology is an excellent method of assessment.

Additional Answers

1. $\begin{bmatrix} -1 & -4 \\ 3 & -6 \\ -7 & 2 \end{bmatrix}$

2. $\begin{bmatrix} 24 & -8 & 20 \\ 0 & 28 & -4 \end{bmatrix}$

4. $\begin{bmatrix} -4 & -2 & -8 \\ 0 & -2 & 2 \\ -8 & -4 & -6 \end{bmatrix}$

5. $\begin{bmatrix} -0.5 & -0.5 & 0.5 \\ 0.4 & 1 & -0.2 \\ 0.4 & 0 & -0.2 \end{bmatrix}$

6. $\begin{bmatrix} 6 & 26 & 1 \\ -18 & 48 & -21 \\ 42 & -28 & 37 \end{bmatrix}$

7. $\begin{bmatrix} 47 & 2 \\ -28 & 44 \end{bmatrix}$

9. $\begin{bmatrix} 32 & 14 & 41 \\ -4 & 5 & -10 \end{bmatrix}$

10. $\begin{bmatrix} 4 & 25 & -3 \\ -18 & 47 & -20 \\ 38 & -30 & 34 \end{bmatrix}$

12. $\begin{bmatrix} 8 & 27 & 5 \\ -18 & 49 & -22 \\ 46 & -26 & 40 \end{bmatrix}$

13. $\begin{bmatrix} 0.0207156309 & -9.416195857E-4 \\ 0.0131826742 & 0.0221280603 \end{bmatrix}$

14. $\begin{bmatrix} 20 & 11 & 19 \\ -4 & -1 & -4 \\ -20 & 12 & 23 \end{bmatrix}$

15. $\begin{bmatrix} 2153 & 182 \\ -2548 & 1880 \end{bmatrix}$

Instructional Resources

- Study Guide Master 4-1
- Practice Master 4-1
- Enrichment Master 4-1
- Modeling Mathematics Masters, pp. 34–36

 Transparency 4-1A contains the 5-Minute Check for this lesson; **Transparency 4-1B** contains a teaching aid for this lesson.

Recommended Pacing	
Standard Pacing	Day 2 of 14
Honors Pacing	Day 2 of 12
Block Scheduling*	Day 1 of 7

 *For more information on pacing and possible lesson plans, refer to the *Block Scheduling Booklet*.

1 FOCUS

 5-Minute Check
(over Chapter 3)

Solve each system of equations.

1. $4a + b = 4$
$8a = 16$
$a + b + c = -2$
(2, −4, 0)

2. $x + y - z = -1$
$x + y + z = 7$
$3x - 2y - z = -10$
(0, 3, 4)

Use Cramer's rule to solve each system of equations.

3. $3a - 6b = 9$
$2a + b = 16$
(7, 2)

4. $2a + b = 10$
$-4a - 3b = -18$
(6, −2)

 TEKS | 2.a.

4-1

An Introduction to Matrices

- To perform scalar multiplication on a matrix,
- to solve matrices for variables, and
- to solve problems using matrix logic.

Why IT'S IMPORTANT

You can use matrices to make decisions and solve many types of problems.

The plural of matrix is matrices.

 **APPLICATION**
Decision Making

Emilio has been accepted at three colleges in Ohio: Denison University, Marietta College, and Muskingum College. He and his parents are trying to make a final decision based on cost, distance from home, campus life, and educational quality. Emilio rates each criteria on a scale from 1 (least favorable) to 10 (most favorable) and organizes the information in a **matrix** like the one shown below. A matrix is a rectangular array of variables or constants in horizontal rows and vertical columns, usually enclosed in brackets.

Matrices are often used as problem-solving tools.

GLOBAL CONNECTIONS

The term *matrix* was first used by the British-born mathematician James Joseph Sylvester in 1850 to designate a rectangular array of numbers from which determinants may be formed.

$$\begin{array}{c} \\ \text{Denison} \\ \text{Marietta} \\ \text{Muskingum} \end{array} \begin{array}{cccc} \text{cost} & \text{distance} & \text{campus} & \text{quality} \\ \begin{bmatrix} 5 & 6 & 6 & 8 \\ 6 & 6 & 8 & 9 \\ 5 & 6 & 7 & 7 \end{bmatrix} \end{array}$$

When the information is shown in a matrix, it is easy to see that distances from home are not a useful criteria, because each college received the same score. You can also see that all of the entries in the second row are greater than the entries in either the first or third row. Based on these criteria, Emilio should attend Marietta College.

In a matrix, numbers or data are organized so that each position in the matrix has a purpose. Each value in the matrix is called an **element**.

$$C = \begin{bmatrix} 5 & 6 & 6 & 8 \\ 6 & 6 & 8 & 9 \\ 5 & 6 & 7 & 7 \end{bmatrix} \Big\} \text{3 rows}$$

The element 9 is in row 2, column 4.

4 columns

GLOBAL CONNECTIONS

Borrowed from a Latin term meaning *womb*, the word *matrix* first appeared in English usage in the early 1400s. In its more general English usage, it refers to that which gives origin or form to something enclosed within it. In 1878, while teaching at Johns Hopkins University, James Sylvester founded the *American Journal of Mathematics*.

A matrix that has only one row is called a <u>row matrix</u>. A matrix that has only one column is called a <u>column matrix</u>.

A matrix is usually named using an uppercase letter, as in matrix *C* on the previous page. A matrix can also be named by using the matrix **dimensions** with the letter name. The dimensions tell how many rows and columns, in that order, are in the matrix. The matrix above would be named $C_{3\times4}$ since it has 3 rows and 4 columns.

Many problems can be solved using a method sometimes referred to as **matrix logic**. When you use matrix logic, you create a matrix that helps you organize all the information in the problem. By using the matrix, you can eliminate one possibility after another until you eventually arrive at a solution.

Example **1**

PROBLEM SOLVING
Use Matrix Logic

Miko, Amanda, Latisha, and Tara are friends, and each has one of these pets: dog, cat, parrot, and gerbil. Use these clues to match each girl with her pet.

- Latisha likes to visit the friend with the gerbil.
- Tara and Amanda frequently help their friend walk her dog.
- Miko cannot have a dog or a cat because she is allergic to them.
- Tara plans to teach her pet how to talk.

Explore   There are 4 girls and 4 pets. You must match each girl with her pet by using the information from the statements above.

A matrix that has the same number of rows and columns is called a <u>square matrix</u>.

Plan   Make a 4 × 4 matrix to organize the information. Through the process of elimination, each girl can be matched with her pet.

Solve   Put an × in the first row under gerbil to show that Latisha does not have the gerbil. Put two ×s to show that Tara and Amanda do not own the dog. Put two ×s to show that Miko cannot have a cat or dog. By the process of elimination, Latisha owns the dog. Put a circle in this box. Since only one girl owns the dog, put ×s in the rest of the boxes in that row. Continue to eliminate possibilities in this manner.

	dog	cat	parrot	gerbil
Latisha	O	×	×	×
Tara	×	×	O	×
Amanda	×	O	×	×
Miko	×	×	×	O

Miko has the gerbil, Amanda has the cat, Latisha has the dog, and Tara has the parrot.

Examine   Check the result against the statements. The first statement says that Latisha likes to visit the girl with the gerbil, and the answer says that Miko has the gerbil. There is no conflict here. Using the same method for each sentence, you can see that there are no conflicts.

Motivating the Lesson
Hands-On Activity Have students make a table for the following situation. Cole, Juanita, and Jamaal played each other in several games of tic-tac-toe. Cole played Juanita and won 4 of 7 games. He played Jamaal and won 6 of 9 games. Jamaal played Juanita and lost 5 of 8 games. Show the win-loss records.

2 TEACH

Teaching Tip Emphasize that a matrix named $B_{3\times4}$ does not have the same dimensions as $B_{4\times3}$.

In-Class Example

For Example 1
Jim, Mario, and Mike are married to Shana, Kelly, and Lisa. Use these clues to find out who is married to whom.

1. Mario is Kelly's brother and lives in Florida with his wife.
2. Mike is shorter than Lisa's husband.
3. Mike works at a bank.
4. Shana and her husband live in Kentucky.
5. Kelly and her husband work in their candy store.
   Jim and Kelly, Mario and Lisa, Mike and Shana

In-Class Example

For Example 2
Write a matrix that shows the store's sales goals representing a 10% increase.

$$\begin{bmatrix} 41.80 & 31.90 & 19.80 & 47.30 \\ 46.20 & 27.50 & 17.60 & 56.10 \end{bmatrix}$$

LOOK BACK

You can refer to Lesson 2-1 for information on the graphs of continuous and discrete functions.

Although matrices are sometimes used as a problem-solving tool, their importance extends to another branch of mathematics called **discrete mathematics**. Discrete mathematics deals with finite or discontinuous quantities. The distinction between continuous and discrete quantities is one that you have encountered before. Think of a staircase. You can slide your hand up the banister, but you have to climb the steps one by one. The banister represents a continuous quantity, like a linear function. However, each step represents a discrete quantity, like a point on a scatter plot or an element of a matrix.

Just as algebraic rules exist for functions, matrices have special algebraic rules. For example, you can multiply any matrix by a constant called a **scalar**. This is called **scalar multiplication**. When scalar multiplication is performed, each element is multiplied by that constant, and a new matrix is formed.

Scalar Multiplication of a Matrix	$k\begin{bmatrix} a & b & c \\ d & e & f \end{bmatrix} = \begin{bmatrix} ka & kb & kc \\ kd & ke & kf \end{bmatrix}$

Example ❷

APPLICATION
Business

The manager of Just Sports keeps track of monthly sales on a spreadsheet. The spreadsheet below shows the number of baseball and softball bats, balls, shoes, and gloves sold last May. This May, the store is going to have a promotion and hopes to increase sales by 8%. Write a matrix that shows the store's sales goals for this May.

	A	B	C	D	E
1		bats	balls	shoes	gloves
2	baseball	38	29	18	43
3	softball	42	25	16	51

First, write the matrix for last May.

$$\begin{bmatrix} 38 & 29 & 18 & 43 \\ 42 & 25 & 16 & 51 \end{bmatrix}$$

Multiply the matrix by 1.08 to show an increase of 8% for this May.

$$1.08 \begin{bmatrix} 38 & 29 & 18 & 43 \\ 42 & 25 & 16 & 51 \end{bmatrix} = \begin{bmatrix} 41.04 & 31.32 & 19.44 & 46.44 \\ 45.36 & 27.00 & 17.28 & 55.08 \end{bmatrix}$$

TECHNOLOGY
Tips

If you are using a graphing calculator, enter the sales matrix into matrix A. Then find 1.08A. You may need to use the arrow keys to see the entire matrix.

Two matrices are considered to be *equal* if they have the same dimensions and if each element of one matrix is equal to the corresponding element of the other matrix.

$$\begin{bmatrix} 2 & 5 & 4 \\ 8 & 6 & 1 \end{bmatrix} \neq \begin{bmatrix} 2 & 8 \\ 5 & 6 \\ 4 & 1 \end{bmatrix} \qquad \begin{bmatrix} 4 & 16 \\ 5 & 3 \end{bmatrix} \neq \begin{bmatrix} 4 & 16 \\ 5 & 3 \\ 0 & 0 \end{bmatrix}$$

$$\begin{bmatrix} 8 & 3 \\ 9 & 1 \end{bmatrix} \neq \begin{bmatrix} 8 & 9 \\ 3 & 1 \end{bmatrix} \qquad \begin{bmatrix} 3 & 12 \\ 20 & 8 \end{bmatrix} = \begin{bmatrix} 3 & 12 \\ 20 & 8 \end{bmatrix}$$

 Alternative Learning Styles

Kinesthetic Students can use a checkerboard and checkers to model a problem involving matrix logic. Example 1 and Exercise 32 can be approached in this way.

GLENCOE Technology

Interactive Mathematics Tools Software

This multimedia software provides an interactive lesson of scalar multiplication by studying a coordinate matrix. A **Computer Journal** gives students an opportunity to write about what they have learned.

For Windows & Macintosh

The definition of equal matrices can be used to find values when elements of the matrices are algebraic expressions.

Example ③ Solve $\begin{bmatrix} 2x \\ 2x + 3y \end{bmatrix} = \begin{bmatrix} y \\ 12 \end{bmatrix}$ for *x* and *y*.

Since the matrices are equal, the corresponding elements are equal. When you write the sentences that show this equality, two linear equations are formed.

$$2x = y$$
$$2x + 3y = 12$$

The first equation gives you a value for *y* that can be substituted into the second equation. Then you can find a value for *x*.

$$2x + 3y = 12$$
$$2x + 3(2x) = 12 \quad \text{Replace y with 2x.}$$
$$2x + 6x = 12 \quad \text{Simplify.}$$
$$8x = 12 \quad \text{Combine like terms.}$$
$$x = 1.5 \quad \text{Divide each side by 8.}$$

To find a value for *y*, you can substitute 1.5 into either equation.

$$2x = y$$
$$2(1.5) = y \quad \text{Replace x with 1.5.}$$
$$3 = y$$

The solution is (1.5, 3).

LOOK BACK

You can refer to Lesson 3-2 for information on using substitution to solve systems of equations.

Check your solution by substituting the values into the equation you did *not* use to find *y*.

$$2x + 3y = 12$$
$$2(1.5) + 3(3) \stackrel{?}{=} 12 \quad \text{Replace x with 1.5 and y with 3.}$$
$$12 = 12 \quad \checkmark$$

A matrix containing coordinates of a geometric figure is often called a coordinate matrix.

Matrices are an important tool for integrating algebra and geometry because points and polygons can be represented by matrices. The ordered pair (x, y) is usually represented by the column matrix $\begin{bmatrix} x \\ y \end{bmatrix}$, where the *x*-coordinate is in row 1, and the *y*-coordinate is in row 2. Similarly, polygons can be represented by grouping all of the column matrices of the coordinates of the vertices into one matrix.

coordinates of vertices

$$\triangle ABC = \begin{bmatrix} 3 & -2 & 1 \\ 2 & 1 & -4 \end{bmatrix} \begin{matrix} \leftarrow \textit{x-coordinate} \\ \leftarrow \textit{y-coordinate} \end{matrix}$$

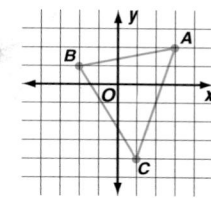

Teaching Tip For Example 3, the matrices can be written by making the first element of the first matrix equal to the first element of the second matrix and by making the second element of the first matrix equal to the second element of the second matrix.

In-Class Example

For Example 3
Solve for *x* and *y*.

a. $\begin{bmatrix} 2x + y \\ x - 3y \end{bmatrix} = \begin{bmatrix} 6 \\ 31 \end{bmatrix}$
   (7, −8)

b. $\begin{bmatrix} 3x + y \\ x - 2y \end{bmatrix} = \begin{bmatrix} x + 3 \\ y - 2 \end{bmatrix}$
   (1, 1)

In-Class Example

For Example 4
Enlarge $\triangle ABC$, with vertices $A(-1, 2)$, $B(-4, -2)$, and $C(3, -1)$, so that its perimeter is twice as large as the original figure.

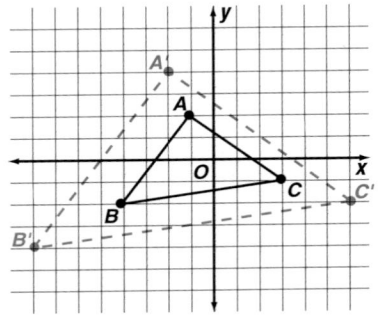

3 PRACTICE/APPLY

Check for Understanding
Exercises 1–12 are designed to help you assess your students' understanding through reading, writing, speaking, and modeling. You should work through Exercises 1–6 with your students and then monitor their work on Exercises 7–12.

Error Analysis
In matrices, rows run horizontally and columns vertically. Yet teachers commonly refer to a row of desks as those desks in a vertical line (i.e., a line perpendicular to the front of the classroom). In theaters and stadiums, rows run horizontally. For consistency and transfer, teachers could refer to a line of desks parallel to the sides of a room as a column.

Additional Answer

6. **Sample answer:** When the matrix is multiplied by a number greater than 1, the figure is enlarged; when the matrix is multiplied by a number between 0 and 1, the figure is reduced. See students' work for drawings.

One of the ways that matrices help connect algebra and geometry is through **transformations.** Transformations are functions that map points of a shape onto its image. When a geometric figure is enlarged or reduced, this transformation is called a **dilation.** When the size of a figure changes, all linear measures of its image change in the same ratio. For example, if the perimeter of a figure triples, the length of each side of the figure also triples.

Example  ④ $\triangle ABC$ has vertices $A(1, -4)$, $B(2, 3)$, and $C(-2, -1)$. Enlarge $\triangle ABC$ so that its perimeter is twice the original perimeter. What are the coordinates of the vertices of $\triangle A'B'C'$?

INTEGRATION
Geometry

Graph $\triangle ABC$. Since perimeter is a linear measurement, multiply the coordinate matrix by the scalar 2.

$$2\begin{bmatrix} 1 & 2 & -2 \\ -4 & 3 & -1 \end{bmatrix} = \begin{bmatrix} 2 & 4 & -4 \\ -8 & 6 & -2 \end{bmatrix}$$

The coordinates of the vertices of $\triangle A'B'C'$ are $A'(2, -8)$, $B'(4, 6)$, and $C'(-4, -2)$. Graph $\triangle A'B'C'$.

You can measure to verify that the perimeter of $\triangle A'B'C'$ is twice the original perimeter.

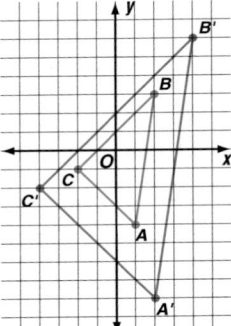

CHECK FOR UNDERSTANDING

Communicating Mathematics

Study the lesson. Then complete the following.   2. See students' work.

1. **Define** a matrix in your own words.

2. **Find** an example of a matrix in a newspaper and name it using its dimensions.

1. Sample answer: a rectangular array of numbers in rows and columns

3. **Choose** the matrix that represents the ordered pair $(-1, 3)$.   b

    a. $[-1, 3]$ **b.** $\begin{bmatrix} -1 \\ 3 \end{bmatrix}$

    c. $[3, -1]$ **d.** $\begin{bmatrix} 3 \\ -1 \end{bmatrix}$

4. $\begin{bmatrix} 1 & 2 & -4 \\ 4 & -3 & -4 \end{bmatrix}$

4. **Write** a coordinate matrix for the triangle shown at the right.

5. **Explain** the meaning of *dilation.*

    Sample answer: an enlargement or reduction

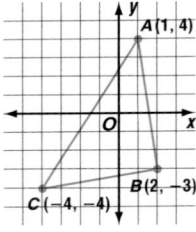

 M*ATH* J*OURNAL*

6. **Draw** a figure on a coordinate plane and write a coordinate matrix for its vertices. Explain what happens to the figure when the matrix is multiplied by a number greater than 1. Explain what happens when the matrix is multiplied by a number between 0 and 1. Use drawings to justify your answers.   See margin.

Reteaching

Using Models Use the class seating arrangement to form matrices, with each student's desk as an element or cell. Make large cards to denote values of elements of several matrices. Some cards for matrix $A_{4\times3}$ might be $A_{2,3} = 7$ or $B_{3,1} = -4$. Form two matrices $A_{4\times3}$ and $B_{4\times3}$ using two arrangements of seats with 4 rows and 3 columns. Have

students deliver cards to each member (student) of the matrix. Here are some problems to consider.

1. Does $A = B$?
2. Find $A + B$.
3. Find $3A$.
4. If $B_{3,2} = 4x - 6$, find x.

Try different size matrices.

Guided Practice

Perform the indicated operation.

7. $-2[7 \; 3 \; -1]$ $[-14 \; -6 \; 2]$

8. $4\begin{bmatrix} -1 & 0 \\ 3 & -2 \end{bmatrix}$ $\begin{bmatrix} -4 & 0 \\ 12 & -8 \end{bmatrix}$

Solve for the variables.

9. $x = 2.5, y = 1, z = 3$

10. $x = 5, y = -4$

9. $[2x \; 3 \; 3z] = [5 \; 3y \; 9]$

10. $\begin{bmatrix} 6x \\ y \end{bmatrix} = \begin{bmatrix} 62 + 8y \\ 6 - 2x \end{bmatrix}$

11. **Business** On Monday, the Main Street Deli sold the following number of sandwiches: 15 turkey, 12 turkey and cheese, 8 ham, 10 ham and cheese, 8 roast beef, 11 roast beef and cheese. Organize the information into a 3×2 matrix.   **See margin.**

12. **Geometry** Triangle ABC with $A(4, 5)$, $B(-3, -2)$, and $C(1, -4)$ is reduced so that its perimeter is one-half the original perimeter.

12a. $\begin{bmatrix} 4 & -3 & 1 \\ 5 & -2 & -4 \end{bmatrix}$

    a. Write the coordinate matrix for $\triangle ABC$.

    b. Write the coordinates of $\triangle A'B'C'$ in matrix form.

12b. $\begin{bmatrix} 2 & -1.5 & 0.5 \\ 2.5 & -1 & -2 \end{bmatrix}$

    c. Graph this situation.   **See margin.**

EXERCISES

Practice

Perform the indicated operation.   18. $[-2.685 \; -2.25]$

13. $\begin{bmatrix} 15 & -6 & 21 \\ -9 & 24 & 12 \end{bmatrix}$

A   13. $3\begin{bmatrix} 5 & -2 & 7 \\ -3 & 8 & 4 \end{bmatrix}$

14. $-2\begin{bmatrix} 6 & -4 \\ -2 & 4 \end{bmatrix}$

15. $\frac{1}{3}[6 \; -5]$ $\begin{bmatrix} 2 & -\frac{5}{3} \end{bmatrix}$

14. $\begin{bmatrix} -12 & 8 \\ 4 & -8 \end{bmatrix}$

16. $0.2\begin{bmatrix} 10.50 \\ 8.75 \end{bmatrix}$ $\begin{bmatrix} 2.1 \\ 1.75 \end{bmatrix}$

17. $-5\begin{bmatrix} 1.3 & 0 & 5.1 \\ 0.4 & 1.0 & 2.5 \end{bmatrix}$

18. $-0.3[8.95 \; 7.50]$

17. $\begin{bmatrix} -6.5 & 0 & -25.5 \\ -2 & -5 & -12.5 \end{bmatrix}$

Solve for the variables.   21. $x = 3, y = -5, z = 6$ 22. $x = 5, y = 3, z = 2$

19. $x = 3, \; y = -\frac{1}{3}$

19. $[4x \; 3y] = [12 \; -1]$

20. $\begin{bmatrix} 2x + y \\ x - 3y \end{bmatrix} = \begin{bmatrix} 5 \\ 13 \end{bmatrix}$ $x = 4, y = -3$

21. $x\begin{bmatrix} 4 & y \\ 7 & 2 \end{bmatrix} = \begin{bmatrix} 12 & -15 \\ 21 & z \end{bmatrix}$

22. $4\begin{bmatrix} x & y - 1 \\ 3 & z \end{bmatrix} = \begin{bmatrix} 20 & 8 \\ 6z & x + y \end{bmatrix}$

B   23. $\begin{bmatrix} x^2 & 7 & 9 \\ 5 & 12 & 6 \end{bmatrix} = \begin{bmatrix} 25 & 7 & y \\ 5 & 2z & 6 \end{bmatrix}$

24. $\begin{bmatrix} x + 3y \\ 3x + y \end{bmatrix} = \begin{bmatrix} -13 \\ 1 \end{bmatrix}$

    $x = \pm 5, y = 9, z = 6$ $x = 2, y = -5$

25. **Geometry** The vertex of the right angle of a right triangle is located at the origin with its other vertices at $(0, 12)$ and $(5, 0)$. Find the coordinates of the vertices of a similar triangle whose perimeter is one-fourth that of the original triangle. $(0, 0), (0, 3), (1.25, 0)$

26. **Geometry** Enlarge $\triangle ABC$ shown at the right so that the resulting perimeter is three times the original perimeter.

26a. See margin.

    a. Graph $\triangle ABC$ and $\triangle A'B'C'$.

26b. $\begin{bmatrix} 0 & 4.5 & -7.5 \\ 6 & -4.5 & 0 \end{bmatrix}$

    b. Write the coordinates of $\triangle A'B'C'$ in matrix form.

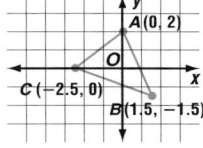

Lesson 4–1   An Introduction to Matrices   **191**

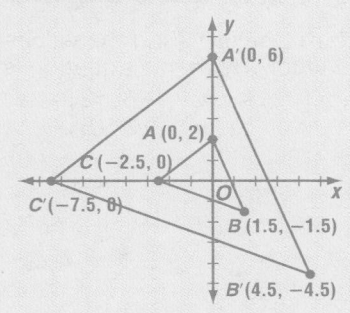

Additional Answer
26a.

Assignment Guide

Core: 13–33 odd, 34–39
Enriched: 14–30 even, 31–39

For **Extra Practice,** see p. 883.

The red A, B, and C flags, printed only in the Teacher's Wraparound Edition, indicate the level of difficulty of the exercises.

Additional Answers

11.

	plain	cheese
turkey	15	12
$S = $ ham	8	10
roast beef	8	11

12c.

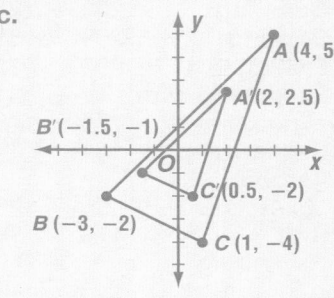

Study Guide Masters, p. 22

NAME _____ DATE _____

4-1   **Study Guide**   Student Edition Pages 186–193

An Introduction to Matrices

A **matrix** is a system of rows and columns that is often used as a problem-solving tool. Each value in the matrix is called an **element.**

Matrices are usually named by an uppercase letter. Matrices can also be named by using the matrix **dimensions** with the letter name. The dimensions tell how many rows and columns, in that order, are in the matrix. The matrix at the right would be named $A_{2 \times 3}$, since it has 2 rows and 3 columns.

$A = \begin{bmatrix} 2 & 1 & 3 \\ 0 & 5 & 6 \end{bmatrix}$ 2 rows   3 columns   The element 6 is in row 2, column 3.

Matrices have special algebraic rules. For example, you can multiply any matrix by a constant. This is called **scalar multiplication.**

Scalar Multiplication of a Matrix $k\begin{bmatrix} a & b & c \\ d & e & f \end{bmatrix} = \begin{bmatrix} ka & kb & kc \\ kd & ke & kf \end{bmatrix}$

Two matrices are considered equal if they have the same dimensions and each element of one matrix is equal to the corresponding element of the other.

Example: Solve $\begin{bmatrix} 5x \\ 5x + 4y \end{bmatrix} = \begin{bmatrix} y \\ 10 \end{bmatrix}$ for x and y.

Since the matrices are equal, the corresponding elements are equal.
$5x = y$
$5x + 4y = 10$

The first equation gives a value for y that can be substituted into the second equation to find a value for x.
$5x + 4y = 10$
$5x + 4(5x) = 10$ Substitute 5x for y.
$5x + 20x = 10$ Simplify.
$25x = 10$ Combine like terms.
$x = \frac{2}{5}$ Divide each side by 25 and simplify.

To find a value for y, substitute $\frac{2}{5}$ into either equation.
$5x = y$
$5\left(\frac{2}{5}\right) = y$ Substitute $\frac{2}{5}$ for x.
$2 = y$

The solution is $\left(\frac{2}{5}, 2\right)$.

Perform the indicated operation.
1. $-3[6 \; 8 \; 10]$ $[-18 \; -24 \; -30]$
2. $5\begin{bmatrix} 0 & -6 & 4 \\ 1 & -8 & 7 \end{bmatrix}$ $\begin{bmatrix} 0 & -30 & 20 \\ 5 & -40 & 35 \end{bmatrix}$

Solve for the variables.
3. $[6x \; 2y] = [3 \; 2]$ $x = \frac{1}{2}; y = 1$
4. $\begin{bmatrix} 2x \\ y \end{bmatrix} = \begin{bmatrix} 40 + 2y \\ 5 - 4x \end{bmatrix}$ $x = 5; y = -15$
5. $\begin{bmatrix} 3x \\ y \end{bmatrix} = \begin{bmatrix} 28 + 4y \\ -3x - 2 \end{bmatrix}$ $x = 1\frac{1}{3}; y = -6$

Chapter 4   **191**

Closing Activity

Speaking Have students explain how to use scalar multiplication.

Additional Answers

27. The perimeter is one-half the original perimeter; the triangle is rotated 180°.

33.

Exercise	Male	Female
Walking	21%	38%
Swimming	27%	28%
Bicycle Riding	25%	22%
Camping	23%	18%
Bowling	20%	18%
Fishing	25%	11%
Exercising with Equipment	17%	17%
Basketball	18%	6%
Aerobic Exercise	5%	19%
Golf	17%	5%

Practice Masters, p. 22

4-1

NAME_____ DATE _____

Practice

Student Edition
Pages 186–193

An Introduction to Matrices

Perform the indicated operation.

1. $4\begin{bmatrix} 1 & 5 & 9 \\ 3 & 6 & 3 \\ 0 & 7 & 2 \end{bmatrix}$ $\begin{bmatrix} 4 & 20 & 36 \\ 12 & 24 & 12 \\ 0 & 28 & 8 \end{bmatrix}$

2. $-1\begin{bmatrix} 6 & -4 \\ 3 & -2 \\ 5 & -5 \end{bmatrix}$ $\begin{bmatrix} -6 & 4 \\ -3 & 2 \\ -5 & 5 \end{bmatrix}$

3. $\frac{1}{2}\begin{bmatrix} -8 & 0 \\ 2 & -12 \\ 6 & -14 \end{bmatrix}$ $\begin{bmatrix} -4 & 0 \\ 1 & -6 \\ 3 & -7 \end{bmatrix}$

4. $-1.1\begin{bmatrix} 0.75 & 0.1 \\ 0.99 & 0.7 \end{bmatrix}$ $\begin{bmatrix} -0.825 & -0.11 \\ -1.089 & -0.77 \end{bmatrix}$

Solve for the variables.

5. $\begin{bmatrix} 3x & 4y \\ -48 & 49 \end{bmatrix} = \begin{bmatrix} 27 & -16 \\ -3w & 7z \end{bmatrix}$
$x = 9, y = -4, w = 16, z = 7$

6. $\begin{bmatrix} 3x \\ y+4 \end{bmatrix} = \begin{bmatrix} y+8 \\ 17 \end{bmatrix}$
$x = 7, y = 13$

7. $x\begin{bmatrix} 2 & -5 \\ 7 & y \end{bmatrix} = \begin{bmatrix} 8 & -20 \\ z & 24 \end{bmatrix}$
$x = 4, y = 6, z = 28$

8. $5\begin{bmatrix} x & y+2 \\ 6 & z \end{bmatrix} = \begin{bmatrix} 10 & 25 \\ 2z & 30x+5y \end{bmatrix}$
$x = 2, y = 3, z = 15$

9. Use Matrix Logic. The Peterson children are 13, 14, and 15 years old. One collects stamps, one collects coins, and one collects shells. From the clues, find each child's age and what he or she collects.

• The oldest collects stamps.
• Bart collects coins.
• Annette is older than Cassie.
• The 14-year-old does not collect coins.

	13	14	15	stamps	coins	shells
Annette		✓	✓	✓		
Bart	✓				✓	
Cassie		✓				✓

---

27. Geometry The coordinate matrix for $\triangle XYZ$ is $\begin{bmatrix} -2 & 4 & -1 \\ -1 & 2 & 3 \end{bmatrix}$. Explain what happens to the triangle when the matrix is multiplied by -0.5. Make a drawing to justify your answer. **See margin.**

Solve for the variables.

28. $\begin{bmatrix} r^2 - 24 & 17 \\ 7 & t^3 \end{bmatrix} = \begin{bmatrix} 1 & 2y+3 \\ z^2-12 & 27 \end{bmatrix}$ $r = \pm5, y = 7, t = 3, z = \pm\sqrt{19}$

29. $\begin{bmatrix} 5x-7 & 11 \\ 5 & 23 \end{bmatrix} = \begin{bmatrix} 8 & 21-m \\ r^3-3 & 4y+x \end{bmatrix}$ $x = 3, y = 5, m = 10, r = 2$

30. $\begin{bmatrix} 13-7y & a \\ 1 & 2b-38 \end{bmatrix} = \begin{bmatrix} 5x & 2-6b \\ 2x+3y & 5a \end{bmatrix}$ $x = 32, y = -21, a = -7, b = 1.5$

Critical Thinking

31. When the size of a figure changes, all linear measures of its image, such as the perimeter, change in the same ratio. Is it also true that the area of the figure changes in the same ratio? Justify your answer with matrices and a graph. **No; see students' work for graph.**

Applications and Problem Solving

32. Use Matrix Logic Fred, Ted, and Ed are taking Mary, Carrie, and Terri to the homecoming dance. Use these clues to find which couples will be attending the dance. **Ed-Carrie, Ted-Mary, Fred-Terri**

Mary is Ed's sister and lives on Fifth Avenue.

Ted drives a car to school each day.

Ed is taller than Terri's date.

Carrie and her date ride their bicycles to school every day.

Fred's date lives on State Street.

33. Sports The graph below shows the percent of the U.S. population that participates in the ten most popular sporting activities. Estimate the percents from the graph and organize the information in a matrix. **See margin.**

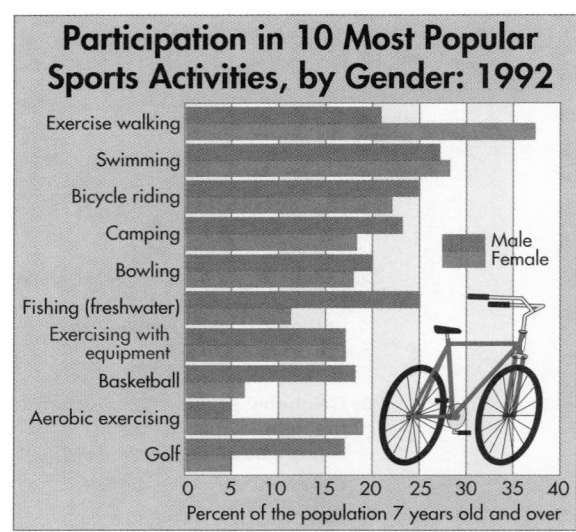

Participation in 10 Most Popular Sports Activities, by Gender: 1992

Source: National Sporting Goods Association

192 Chapter 4 Using Matrices

Extension

Problem Solving Find the values x, y, z, and w for which this equation is true.

$$3\begin{bmatrix} x & y \\ z & w \end{bmatrix} = \begin{bmatrix} 6 & 12 \\ 3 & 15 \end{bmatrix}$$

$x = 2, y = 4$
$z = 1, w = 5$

Mixed Review

34. 8; 4; −3

35. 100 A, 50 S

38. $\left\{ t \mid t < \frac{4}{3} \text{ or } t > \frac{14}{3} \right\}$

39a. 30; 26; about $30.\overline{4}$
39b. They are all located in the southwestern U.S.

34. Find the *x*-, *y*-, and *z*-intercepts for $3x + 6y - 8z = 24$. (Lesson 3–7)

35. **Theater** The Woodward Park High School auditorium seats 150 people. Admission to the spring play is \$2.00 for adults and \$1.00 for students. The Drama Club has already sold fifty student tickets and the rest are to be sold at the door. How many of each type of ticket should be sold for the Drama Club to earn the maximum amount of money? (Lesson 3–6)

36. Solve the system of inequalities by graphing. (Lesson 3–4)

    $x + y < 8$
    $x + y > 5$ **See margin.**

37. Find the value of $f(-2)$, if $f(x) = x^2 - 4$. (Lesson 2–1) **0**

38. Solve $|9 - 3t| > 5$. (Lesson 1–7)

39. **Statistics** The table at the right lists the nine cities in the United States with the fewest average rainy days per year. (Lesson 1–3)

    a. Find the median, mode, and mean of the average number of rainy days.

    b. What do you notice about the locations of these cities?

City	Days
San Diego, CA	42
Bakersfield, CA	37
Los Angeles, CA	35
Long Beach, CA	32
Santa Barbara, CA	30
Bishop, CA	29
Las Vegas, NV	26
Phoenix, AZ	26
Yuma, AZ	17

Additional Answer

36.

WORKING ON THE In·ves·ti·ga·tion

Refer to the Investigation on pages 180–181.

3–2–1–Blast-Off!

Using the design of your launcher, conduct tests by shooting the Ping-Pong™ ball various distances. During these tests, the launcher should be operated by one to four people in the group, the launcher should be shot from the floor, and the distance should be measured from the launcher's location to the spot where the Ping-Pong ball hits the floor.

Also, use this testing time to calibrate your launcher to hit different distances in your firing range. In other words, determine the launch settings for several distances.

1 List your test results.
2 Describe your calibration system.
3 What is the process you used to hit a target at 50 cm, 100 cm, 150 cm, 200 cm, or 250 cm?
4 How accurate have your tests been? Explain.
5 List your launch settings for at least six target distances between 50 cm and 250 cm.
6 Create a table of launch settings and target distances. How can this data be put into a matrix? What would be the dimensions of the matrix? Create this matrix.
7 Draw a scatter plot of the relationship between the launch settings and the target distances. Describe the graph.
8 Determine a mathematical relationship between the two values.

Add the results of your work to your Investigation Folder.

In·ves·ti·ga·tion

Working on the Investigation

The Investigation on pages 180–181 is designed to be a long-term project that is completed over several days or weeks. Encourage students to keep their materials in their Investigation Folder as they work on the Investigation.

Enrichment Masters, p. 22

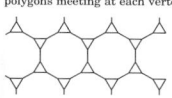

4-1 **Enrichment**

NAME_____ DATE_____

Student Edition Pages 186–193

Tessellations

A tessellation is an arrangement of polygons covering a plane without any gaps or overlapping. One example of a tessellation is a honeycomb. Three congruent regular hexagons meet at each vertex, and there is no wasted space between cells. This tessellation is called a regular tessellation since it is formed by congruent regular polygons.

A **semi-regular tessellation** is a tessellation formed by two or more regular polygons such that the number of sides of the polygons meeting at each vertex is the same.

For example, the tessellation at the left has two regular dodecagons and one equilateral triangle meeting at each vertex. We can name this tessellation a 3-12-12 for the number of sides of each polygon that meet at one vertex.

Name each semi-regular tessellation shown according to the number of sides of the polygons that meet at each vertex.

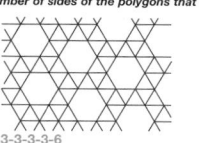

1. 3-3-3-3-6
2. 4-6-12

An equilateral triangle, two squares, and a regular hexagon can be used to surround a point in two different orders. Continue each pattern to see which is a semi-regular tessellation.

3. 3-4-4-6
not semi-regular

4. 3-4-6-4
semi-regular

On another sheet of paper, draw part of each design. Then determine if it is a semi-regular tessellation.

5. 3-3-4-12   6. 3-4-3-12   7. 4-8-8   8. 3-3-3-4-4
not semi-regular not semi-regular semi-regular semi-regular

Instructional Resources

- Study Guide Master 4-2
- Practice Master 4-2
- Enrichment Master 4-2
- Assessment and Evaluation Masters, p. 100

Transparency 4-2A contains the 5-Minute Check for this lesson; **Transparency 4-2B** contains a teaching aid for this lesson.

Recommended Pacing	
Standard Pacing	Day 3 of 14
Honors Pacing	Day 3 of 12
Block Scheduling*	Day 2 of 7 (along with Lesson 4-3)

*For more information on pacing and possible lesson plans, refer to the *Block Scheduling Booklet*.

1 FOCUS

5-Minute Check
(over Lesson 4-1)

Name the matrix using the dimensions.

1. $M = \begin{bmatrix} 8 & 0 & 2 \\ 6 & 3 & -1 \end{bmatrix}$

$M_{2\times3}$

2. $N = \begin{bmatrix} 6 & -3 & 4 \end{bmatrix}$

$N_{1\times3}$

Solve for the variables.

3. $\begin{bmatrix} 1 & 3a \end{bmatrix} = \begin{bmatrix} 4b & 21 \end{bmatrix}$

$a = 7, b = \frac{1}{4}$

4. $\begin{bmatrix} 5a & - & 2b \\ a & + & 6b \end{bmatrix} = \begin{bmatrix} 18 \\ 10 \end{bmatrix}$

$a = 4, b = 1$

Perform the indicated operation.

5. $3\begin{bmatrix} 2 & 7 & -2 \\ 1 & -3 & 5 \end{bmatrix}$

$\begin{bmatrix} 6 & 21 & -6 \\ 3 & -9 & 15 \end{bmatrix}$

4-2

Adding and Subtracting Matrices

What YOU'LL LEARN

- To add and subtract matrices.

Why IT'S IMPORTANT

You can use matrices to solve problems involving meteorology, geography, and recreation.

F Y I

About 60% of flood victims die in their cars, trying to drive through water flowing across a road.

APPLICATION
Meteorology

At the turn of the century, weather forecasters were unable to give residents of coastal areas much warning of an approaching hurricane. On September 8, 1900, Isaac Cline, the head of the Galveston Weather Bureau in Texas, rode a horse along the beach front, urging people to evacuate as an unnamed hurricane approached. Even so, nearly 6000 people lost their lives later that day due to the flooding caused by the storm surge. In contrast, when hurricane Andrew hit the Florida and Louisiana coasts in 1992, only 23 deaths were attributed to it—most likely because of better forecasting and evacuation planning than in 1900.

Other types of severe weather give little notice. Between 1940 and 1990, 21,447 people have died in the United States due to lightning, tornadoes, floods, and hurricanes. The data for each decade since the 1940s are shown in the spreadsheet below.

	A	B	C	D	E
1		lightning	tornadoes	floods	hurricanes
2	1940s	3293	1788	619	216
3	1950s	1841	1409	791	877
4	1960s	1332	935	1297	587
5	1970s	978	986	1819	217
6	1980s	726	521	1097	118

Source: National Weather Service

The information in the spreadsheet can also be represented by column matrices, with one for each type of severe weather. To find the total number of deaths due to severe weather, add the corresponding elements.

$$\begin{bmatrix} 3293 \\ 1841 \\ 1332 \\ 978 \\ 726 \end{bmatrix} + \begin{bmatrix} 1788 \\ 1409 \\ 935 \\ 986 \\ 521 \end{bmatrix} + \begin{bmatrix} 619 \\ 791 \\ 1297 \\ 1819 \\ 1097 \end{bmatrix} + \begin{bmatrix} 216 \\ 877 \\ 587 \\ 217 \\ 118 \end{bmatrix} = \begin{bmatrix} 5916 \\ 4918 \\ 4151 \\ 4000 \\ 2462 \end{bmatrix} \begin{matrix} \leftarrow 1940s \\ \leftarrow 1950s \\ \leftarrow 1960s \\ \leftarrow 1970s \\ \leftarrow 1980s \end{matrix}$$

Since 1940, the following number of deaths occurred due to lightning, tornadoes, floods, or hurricanes: 1940s, 5916; 1950s, 4918; 1960s, 4151; 1970s, 4000; 1980s, 2462.

F Y I

Listed below are the number of lives lost to floods in the United States during certain years. They are listed in descending order. Surprisingly, the great flood of 1993 that devastated the midwestern United States took only 50 lives.

Year	Deaths
1985	304
1983	200
1982	155
1984	126
1980	97

TEKS 2.a.

This example illustrates that in order to add matrices, they must have the same dimensions.

Addition of Matrices

> If **A** and **B** are two $m \times n$ matrices, then **A + B** is an $m \times n$ matrix in which each element is the sum of the corresponding elements of **A** and **B**.
>
> $$\begin{bmatrix} a & b & c \\ d & e & f \\ g & h & i \end{bmatrix} + \begin{bmatrix} j & k & l \\ m & n & o \\ p & q & r \end{bmatrix} = \begin{bmatrix} a+j & b+k & c+l \\ d+m & e+n & f+o \\ g+p & h+q & i+r \end{bmatrix}$$

Similarly, it is possible to subtract matrices.

Example 1

APPLICATION

Recreation

The matrices below show sporting goods sales in the United States in millions of dollars for 1992 and 1993. By how many dollars did each category change from 1992 to 1993?

$$A = \begin{array}{l} \textit{athletic clothing} \\ \textit{athletic shoes} \\ \textit{athletic equipment} \\ \textit{recreational vehicles} \end{array} \overset{\textbf{1992}}{\begin{bmatrix} 12{,}057 \\ 6{,}300 \\ 12{,}063 \\ 12{,}524 \end{bmatrix}} \qquad B = \begin{array}{l} \textit{athletic clothing} \\ \textit{athletic shoes} \\ \textit{athletic equipment} \\ \textit{recreational vehicles} \end{array} \overset{\textbf{1993}}{\begin{bmatrix} 10{,}101 \\ 6{,}242 \\ 12{,}816 \\ 13{,}275 \end{bmatrix}}$$

To determine the change in each category, find $B - A$.

$$B - A = \begin{bmatrix} 10{,}101 \\ 6{,}242 \\ 12{,}816 \\ 13{,}275 \end{bmatrix} - \begin{bmatrix} 12{,}057 \\ 6{,}300 \\ 12{,}063 \\ 12{,}524 \end{bmatrix} \text{ or } \begin{bmatrix} -1956 \\ -58 \\ 753 \\ 751 \end{bmatrix}$$

From 1992 until 1993, sales of athletic clothing decreased $1956 million, athletic shoes decreased $58 million, athletic equipment increased $753 million, and recreational vehicles increased $751 million.

Top Five List

Sports activities with greatest participation, in millions

1. walking, 67.8
2. swimming, 63.1
3. bicycle riding, 54.6
4. camping, 47.3
5. bowling, 42.4

In Lesson 4–1, you used matrices to represent polygons and their dilation images. Another type of transformation is a **translation**. A translation occurs when a figure is moved from one location to another on the coordinate plane without changing its size, shape, or orientation. You can use matrix addition to find the coordinates of translated figures.

Lesson 4–2 Adding and Subtracting Matrices **195**

Top Five List

Among the other top sports Americans participate in are fishing, billiards, hiking, golf, and volleyball.

Motivating the Lesson

Hands-On Activity Have students plot (2, 3) and (4, 1) on a coordinate plane and draw lines from the origin to each point. Then have students plot the point (2 + 4, 3 + 1) or (6, 4) and draw a line from the origin to that point. Explain that the line to (6, 4) represents the sum of the other two lines. The operation they have just carried out is a simple case of matrix addition represented geometrically.

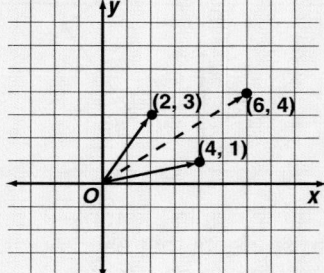

2 TEACH

In-Class Example

For Example 1
Add matrices *A* and *B*.

$$A = \begin{bmatrix} 12 \\ -23 \\ 81 \end{bmatrix} \quad B = \begin{bmatrix} -7 \\ 18 \\ 12 \end{bmatrix}$$

$$\begin{bmatrix} 5 \\ -5 \\ 93 \end{bmatrix}$$

Teaching Tip Emphasize that to add matrices, the matrices must have the same number of rows and columns and that the answer will also have the same dimensions.

For Example 2
Find the coordinates of the vertices of quadrilateral *QRST* if the figure is moved 3 units to the left and 5 units up.

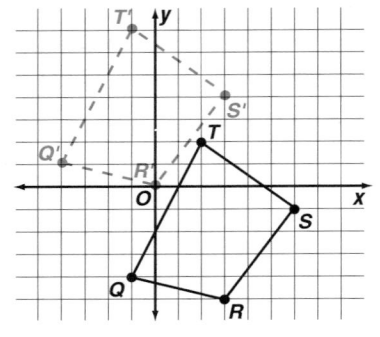

Teaching Tip In Example 2, point out to students that each point can be viewed as a matrix.

3 PRACTICE/APPLY

Check for Understanding

Exercises 1–9 are designed to help you assess your students' understanding through reading, writing, speaking, and modeling. You should work through Exercises 1–4 with your students and then monitor their work on Exercises 5–9.

Study Guide Masters, p. 23

NAME_____ DATE _____
4-2
Study Guide   Student Edition
                                    Pages 194–198

Adding and Subtracting Matrices
In order to add or subtract matrices, the matrices must have the same dimensions.

Addition of Matrices	If A and B are two $m \times n$ matrices, then $A + B$ is an $m \times n$ matrix where each element is the sum of the corresponding elements of A and B. $\begin{bmatrix} a & b \\ c & d \end{bmatrix} + \begin{bmatrix} e & f \\ g & h \end{bmatrix} = \begin{bmatrix} a+e & b+f \\ c+g & d+h \end{bmatrix}$
Subtraction of Matrices	If A and B are two $m \times n$ matrices, then $A - B$ is an $m \times n$ matrix where each element is the difference of the corresponding elements of A and B. $\begin{bmatrix} a & b \\ c & d \end{bmatrix} - \begin{bmatrix} e & f \\ g & h \end{bmatrix} = \begin{bmatrix} a-e & b-f \\ c-g & d-h \end{bmatrix}$

Examples: Perform the indicated operations.

1. $\begin{bmatrix} 8 & -2 \\ 7 & 3 \end{bmatrix} + \begin{bmatrix} 4 & 1 \\ 6 & 5 \end{bmatrix} = \begin{bmatrix} 12 & -1 \\ 13 & 8 \end{bmatrix}$

2. $\begin{bmatrix} 15 & 0 \\ 12 & -9 \end{bmatrix} - \begin{bmatrix} -3 & 2 \\ 6 & -4 \end{bmatrix} = \begin{bmatrix} 18 & -2 \\ 6 & -5 \end{bmatrix}$

Perform the indicated operations.

1. $\begin{bmatrix} 10 & -3 \\ 5 & 8 \end{bmatrix} + \begin{bmatrix} -2 & -12 \\ 20 & 22 \end{bmatrix}$ 2. $\begin{bmatrix} 3 & -2 \\ 1 & 2 \end{bmatrix} - \begin{bmatrix} 1 & 1 \\ -5 & -6 \end{bmatrix}$

$\begin{bmatrix} 8 & -15 \\ 25 & 30 \end{bmatrix}$ $\begin{bmatrix} 2 & -3 \\ 6 & 8 \end{bmatrix}$

3. $\begin{bmatrix} 5 & -4 & 35 \\ 2 & -2 & 16 \end{bmatrix} - \begin{bmatrix} 1 & 4 & -35 \\ -2 & 2 & 0 \end{bmatrix}$ $\begin{bmatrix} 4 & -8 & 70 \\ 4 & -4 & 16 \end{bmatrix}$

4. $3\begin{bmatrix} 1 & 3 \\ -2 & 1 \end{bmatrix} - 2\begin{bmatrix} 1 & 1 \\ -5 & -6 \end{bmatrix} \begin{bmatrix} -2 & 5 \\ -3 & -1 \end{bmatrix}$

5. $\frac{1}{4}\left(\begin{bmatrix} 9 & 1 \\ -7 & 0 \end{bmatrix} + \begin{bmatrix} 3 & -5 \\ 1 & 7 \end{bmatrix}\right) \begin{bmatrix} 3 & -1 \\ -\frac{3}{2} & \frac{3}{4} \end{bmatrix}$

Example ② Find the coordinates of the vertices of quadrilateral *QUAD* with *Q*(-2, -3), *U*(-1, 2), *A*(3, 4), and *D*(1, -2) if it is moved 3 units to the right and 1 unit down.

INTEGRATION
Geometry

Write the coordinates of quadrilateral *QUAD* as a coordinate matrix.

$$\begin{bmatrix} -2 & -1 & 3 & 1 \\ -3 & 2 & 4 & -2 \end{bmatrix}$$

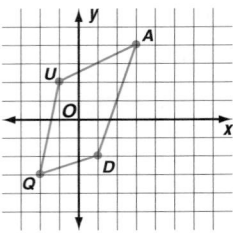

To translate the quadrilateral 3 units to the right means that each *x*-coordinate increases by 3. Translating 1 unit down means that each *y*-coordinate decreases by 1.

The matrix, called the *translation matrix*, that will increase each *x*-coordinate by 3 and decrease each *y*-coordinate by 1 is
$\begin{bmatrix} 3 & 3 & 3 & 3 \\ -1 & -1 & -1 & -1 \end{bmatrix}$.

To find the coordinates of the vertices of the translated quadrilateral *Q'U'A'D'*, add the translation matrix to the coordinate matrix of *QUAD*.

$$\begin{bmatrix} -2 & -1 & 3 & 1 \\ -3 & 2 & 4 & -2 \end{bmatrix} + \begin{bmatrix} 3 & 3 & 3 & 3 \\ -1 & -1 & -1 & -1 \end{bmatrix} = \begin{bmatrix} 1 & 2 & 6 & 4 \\ -4 & 1 & 3 & -3 \end{bmatrix}$$

The coordinates of the vertices of *Q'U'A'D'* are *Q'*(1, -4), *U'*(2,1), *A'*(6, 3), and *D'*(4, -3).

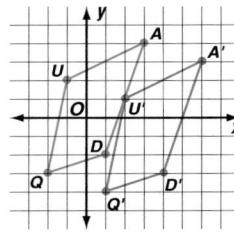

Graph the coordinates of *Q'U'A'D'* to check the accuracy of your coordinates. The two quadrilaterals have the same size and shape. *Q'U'A'D'* has moved to the right 3 units and 1 unit down from *QUAD*.

CHECK FOR UNDERSTANDING

Communicating Mathematics

Study the lesson. Then complete the following. 2, 4. See margin.

1. **Explain** the conditions under which matrices can be added.   They must have the same dimensions.

2. **Illustrate** the difference between a dilation and a translation.

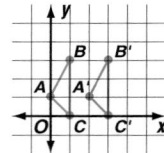

3. $\begin{bmatrix} 2 & 2 & 2 \\ 0 & 0 & 0 \end{bmatrix}$

3. **Write** the translation matrix for $\triangle ABC$ and its image $\triangle A'B'C'$ shown at the right.

MATH JOURNAL

4. **Write** a convincing argument for the statement *Matrix addition is commutative and associative*. If the statement is not true, find a counterexample.

Reteaching ▬▬▬

Using Properties Demonstrate that for

the matrix $\begin{bmatrix} 0 & 0 \\ 0 & 0 \end{bmatrix}$, $\begin{bmatrix} a & b \\ c & d \end{bmatrix} + \begin{bmatrix} 0 & 0 \\ 0 & 0 \end{bmatrix} = \begin{bmatrix} a & b \\ c & d \end{bmatrix}$,

and that for $\begin{bmatrix} -a & -b \\ -c & -d \end{bmatrix}$,

$\begin{bmatrix} a & b \\ c & d \end{bmatrix} + \begin{bmatrix} -a & -b \\ -c & -d \end{bmatrix} = \begin{bmatrix} 0 & 0 \\ 0 & 0 \end{bmatrix}$.

Show that addition of matrices is commutative and associative.

Additional Answers

2. A dilation changes the size but not the shape of a figure. A translation moves a figure, but does not change its orientation, size, or shape.

4. The statement is true because you are adding pairs of real numbers. Since addition of real numbers is commutative and associative, so is matrix addition.

Guided Practice

Perform the indicated operations.

5. $\begin{bmatrix} 1 & 10 \\ -7 & 5 \end{bmatrix}$

6. $\begin{bmatrix} 10 \\ -4 \\ 5 \end{bmatrix}$

8. $\begin{bmatrix} 3077 \\ 964 \\ 745 \\ 761 \\ 608 \end{bmatrix}$

9b. $\begin{bmatrix} 3 & 3 & 3 \\ -7 & -7 & -7 \end{bmatrix}$

9c. $\begin{bmatrix} 1 & 6 & 8 \\ -5 & -2 & -9 \end{bmatrix}$

5. $\begin{bmatrix} 3 & 7 \\ -2 & 1 \end{bmatrix} - \begin{bmatrix} 2 & -3 \\ 5 & -4 \end{bmatrix}$ 6. $\begin{bmatrix} 4 \\ 1 \\ -3 \end{bmatrix} + \begin{bmatrix} 6 \\ -5 \\ 8 \end{bmatrix}$

7. $2[3 \ -1] + 3[5 \ 0]$ $[21 \ -2]$

8. **Meteorology**   Refer to the application at the beginning of the lesson. For each decade since 1940, how many more people died as a result of lightning than hurricanes?

9. **Geometry**   Triangle ABC with vertices $A(-2, 2)$, $B(3, 5)$, and $C(5, -2)$ is translated so that A' is at $(1, -5)$.   **a. See margin.**
   a. Draw a graph of this situation.
   b. Find the translation matrix.
   c. Write the coordinates of $A'B'C'$ in matrix form.

EXERCISES

Practice

11. $[4 \ 20 \ 1]$

12. $\begin{bmatrix} -22 & 8 \\ 3 & 24 \end{bmatrix}$

13. $\begin{bmatrix} -4 & -15 \\ 1.5 & -2 \end{bmatrix}$

17a. $\begin{bmatrix} 4 & 4 & 4 & 4 \\ -2 & -2 & -2 & -2 \end{bmatrix}$

17b. $B'(10, -1)$, $T'(1, -7)$, $U'(7, 3)$

18. $Y'(4, 5)$, $Z'(7, -1.5)$

Perform the indicated operations.

A 10. $\begin{bmatrix} 3 & -9 \\ 4 & 2 \end{bmatrix} + \begin{bmatrix} -8 & -4 \\ 3 & 10 \end{bmatrix}$ $\begin{bmatrix} -5 & -13 \\ 7 & 12 \end{bmatrix}$ 11. $[5 \ 8 \ -4] + [-1 \ 12 \ 5]$

12. $4\begin{bmatrix} 2 & 7 \\ -3 & 6 \end{bmatrix} + 5\begin{bmatrix} -6 & -4 \\ 3 & 0 \end{bmatrix}$ 13. $\frac{1}{2}\begin{bmatrix} 4 & 6 \\ 3 & 0 \end{bmatrix} - \frac{2}{3}\begin{bmatrix} 9 & 27 \\ 0 & 3 \end{bmatrix}$

B 14. $5\begin{bmatrix} 1 \\ -1 \\ -3 \end{bmatrix} + 6\begin{bmatrix} -4 \\ 3 \\ 5 \end{bmatrix} - 2\begin{bmatrix} -3 \\ 8 \\ -4 \end{bmatrix}$ $\begin{bmatrix} -13 \\ -3 \\ 23 \end{bmatrix}$

15. $2\begin{bmatrix} -2 & 4 \\ 1 & -1 \\ 3 & 0 \end{bmatrix} - 3\begin{bmatrix} 5 & 3 \\ -3 & 2 \\ 8 & -9 \end{bmatrix} + \begin{bmatrix} 0 & -5 \\ 9 & -3 \\ -2 & 7 \end{bmatrix}$ $\begin{bmatrix} -19 & -6 \\ 20 & -11 \\ -20 & 34 \end{bmatrix}$

INTEGRATION
Geometry

16. Translate $\triangle ABC$ shown at the right so that A' is at $(3, 4)$.
   a. Graph $\triangle ABC$ and $\triangle A'B'C'$.   **See margin.**
   b. Write the coordinates of $\triangle A'B'C'$ in matrix form.
   $\begin{bmatrix} 3 & 6 & -5 \\ 4 & 10 & 5 \end{bmatrix}$

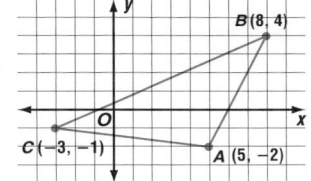

17. Quadrilateral $BURT$ has vertices $B(6, 1)$, $U(3, 5)$, $R(-1, 4)$, and $T(-3, -5)$.
   a. What translation matrix would you need to use to translate $BURT$ so that R' has coordinates $(3, 2)$?
   b. Use your translation matrix to find the coordinates of B', T', and U'.

18. Dilate and then translate $\triangle XYZ$ with vertices $X(-6, 2)$, $Y(-2, 8)$, and $Z(4, -5)$ so that X' has coordinates $(2, 2)$ and the perimeter of $\triangle X'Y'Z'$ is one-half the perimeter of $\triangle XYZ$. State the coordinates of Y' and Z'.

19. Solve for the variables.
   $\begin{bmatrix} x \\ 7z \\ 2y \end{bmatrix} - \begin{bmatrix} 4z \\ -3y \\ 3x \end{bmatrix} + \begin{bmatrix} -2y \\ 2x \\ -5z \end{bmatrix} = \begin{bmatrix} -4 \\ 11 \\ 18 \end{bmatrix}$ $x = 2$, $y = 7$, $z = -2$

Lesson 4-2 Adding and Subtracting Matrices   **197**

Cooperative Learning

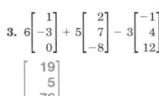

Trade-A-Problem Have students work in pairs. One student draws a triangle on graph paper. The other student finds the vertices and draws a second triangle that is either a dilation or a translation and gives the paper back to the first student. The first student then determines whether the triangle is a dilation or translation. For more information on the trade-a-problem strategy, see *Cooperative Learning in the Mathematics Classroom,* one of the titles in the Glencoe Mathematics Professional Series, pages 25–26.

Assignment Guide

Core: 11–19 odd, 20, 21, 23–27
Enriched: 10–18 even, 20–27

For **Extra Practice,** see p. 883.

The red A, B, and C flags, printed only in the Teacher's Wraparound Edition, indicate the level of difficulty of the exercises.

Additional Answers

9a.

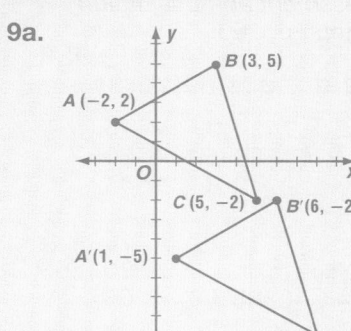

16a.

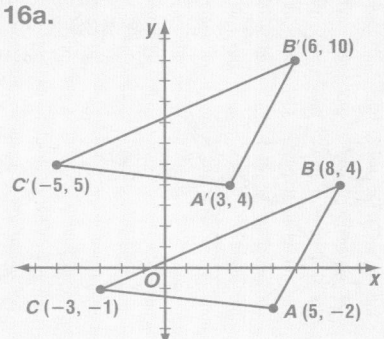

Practice Masters, p. 23

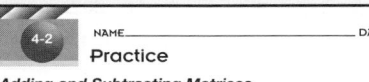

Closing Activity

Writing Write in general terms a definition for adding $m \times n$ matrices where m and n are not known.

Chapter 4, Quiz A (Lessons 4-1 and 4-2), is available in the *Assessment and Evaluation Masters*, p. 100.

Additional Answers

22a.

$$F = \begin{bmatrix} 120 & 97 & 64 & 75 \\ 80 & 59 & 36 & 60 \\ 72 & 84 & 29 & 48 \end{bmatrix}$$

$$S = \begin{bmatrix} 112 & 87 & 56 & 74 \\ 84 & 65 & 39 & 70 \\ 88 & 98 & 43 & 60 \end{bmatrix}$$

$$T = \begin{bmatrix} 232 & 184 & 120 & 149 \\ 164 & 124 & 75 & 130 \\ 160 & 182 & 72 & 108 \end{bmatrix}$$

25.

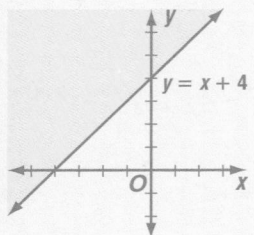

$y = x + 4$

Enrichment Masters, p. 23

4-2

NAME_____ DATE _____

Student Edition
Pages 194–198

Enrichment

Sundaram's Sieve

The properties and patterns of prime numbers have fascinated many mathematicians. In 1934, a young East Indian student named Sundaram constructed the following matrix.

4	7	10	13	16	19	22	25	. . .
7	12	17	22	27	32	37	42	. . .
10	17	24	31	38	45	52	59	. . .
13	22	31	40	49	58	67	76	. . .
16	27	38	49	60	71	82	93	. . .
.	.	.	.	.	.	.	.	

A surprising property of this matrix is that it can be used to determine whether or not some numbers are prime.

Complete these problems to discover this property.

1. The first row and the first column are created by using an arithmetic sequence. What is the common difference used in the sequence?
3

2. Find the next four numbers in the first row.
28, 31, 34, 37

3. What are the common differences used to create the sequences in rows 2, 3, 4, and 5?
5, 7, 9, 11

4. Write the next two rows of the matrix. Include eight numbers in each row. row 6: 19, 32, 45, 58, 71, 84, 97, 110
row 7: 22, 37, 52, 67, 82, 97, 112, 127

5. Choose any five numbers from the matrix. For each number n, that you chose from the matrix, find $2n + 1$.
Answers will vary.

6. Write the factorization of each value of $2n + 1$ that you found in problem 5. Answers will vary, but all numbers are composite.

7. Use your results from problems 5 and 6 to complete this statement: If n occurs in the matrix, then $2n + 1$ _is not_ (is/is not) a prime number.

8. Choose any five numbers that are not in the matrix. Find $2n + 1$ for each of these numbers. Show that each result is a prime number.
Answers will vary, but all numbers are prime.

9. Complete this statement: If n does not occur in the matrix, then $2n + 1$ is _a prime number_ .

---

20. Geometry Find the coordinates of the vertices of quadrilateral *MNPQ* that is a translation of quadrilateral *XYZW* whose vertices are $X(5, -3)$, $Y(2, 7)$, $Z(-3, 3)$, and $W(-5, 1)$, if *M* is located at the origin. $M(0, 0)$, $N(-3, 10)$, $P(-8, 6)$, $Q(-10, 4)$

Applications and Problem Solving

21. Geography The matrices below represent the number of births and deaths in seven Atlantic seaboard states in 1992.

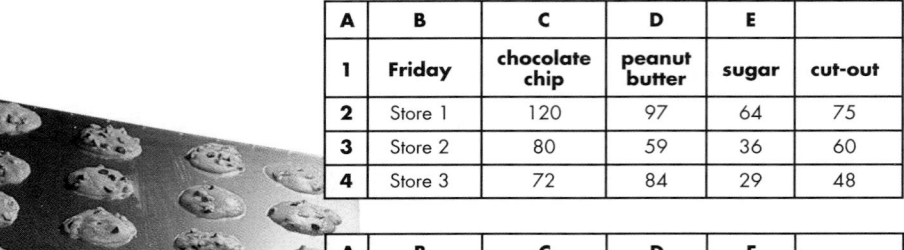

	Births			**Deaths**
Delaware	10,902		Delaware	5937
Maryland	76,173		Maryland	37,806
Virginia	97,600		Virginia	49,541
$B =$ North Carolina	103,047	$D =$	North Carolina	59,478
South Carolina	56,635		South Carolina	30,609
Georgia	111,397		Georgia	53,288
Florida	192,291		Florida	140,401

21a. Sample answer: No; births and deaths are opposite occurrences.

21b. Yes; $B - D$ represents the population increase for 1992.

21c. Find $0.99D$.

a. Does it make sense to find the sum of the matrices? Why or why not? If so, explain the meaning of the sum.

b. Does it make sense to find the difference of the matrices? Why or why not? If so, explain the meaning of the difference.

c. Suppose the Census Bureau predicts a 1% decrease in the number of deaths for this region. How would you show this in a matrix?

22. Business The Cookie Cutter Bakery keeps a log of each type of cookie sold in a spreadsheet at three of their branch stores so that they can monitor their purchases of supplies. Two days of sales are shown below.

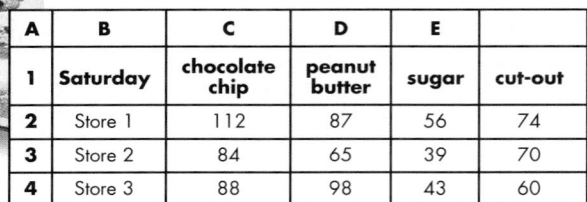

A	B	C	D	E	
1	**Friday**	chocolate chip	peanut butter	sugar	cut-out
2	Store 1	120	97	64	75
3	Store 2	80	59	36	60
4	Store 3	72	84	29	48

A	B	C	D	E	
1	**Saturday**	chocolate chip	peanut butter	sugar	cut-out
2	Store 1	112	87	56	74
3	Store 2	84	65	39	70
4	Store 3	88	98	43	60

a. Write a matrix for each day's sales. Then find the sum of the two days' sales expressed as a matrix.   **See margin.**

b. Each cookie takes approximately one-fourth cup of flour. If there are four cups of flour in one pound, how many pounds of flour were needed for these two days of baking?   **106.25 pounds**

Mixed Review

23. Find $4 \begin{bmatrix} -7 & 5 & -11 \\ 2 & -4 & 9 \end{bmatrix}$. (Lesson 4–1) $\begin{bmatrix} -28 & 20 & -44 \\ 8 & -16 & 36 \end{bmatrix}$

24. Geometry In which octant does the point $(5, -1, 9)$ lie? (Lesson 3–7)   **2**

25. Graph $y > x + 4$. (Lesson 2–7)   **See margin.**

26. State whether $y = x^2 - 4$ is a linear equation. (Lesson 2–2)   **no**

27. Solve $\frac{3}{4}t + 1 = 10$. (Lesson 1–4)   **12**

Extension

Connections Graph the function $f(x) = x^2$. Then graph the function $g(x) = x^2 + 2$. The function $f(x)$ can be viewed as an infinite matrix.

$$\begin{bmatrix} 0 & 1 & 2 & 2.1... \\ 0 & 1 & 4 & 4.41... \end{bmatrix}$$

The function $g(x)$ is also an infinite matrix with 2 added to each entry in the bottom row.

Multiplying Matrices

What YOU'LL LEARN

- To multiply matrices.

Why IT'S IMPORTANT

You can use matrices to solve problems involving probability and track and field.

APPLICATION
Sales

The manager of DK's Donuts makes a daily report to the owner that summarizes the cost of each kind of donut and the number of donuts sold for that day. The sales for one day are summarized in the cost matrix C and sales matrix S shown below.

$$\overset{\textbf{cost (\$)}}{\underset{\begin{matrix} plain & jelly & glazed & specialty \end{matrix}}{C = [0.45 \quad 0.55 \quad 0.50 \quad 0.85]}}$$

$$\overset{\textbf{number}}{S = \begin{matrix} plain \\ jelly \\ glazed \\ specialty \end{matrix} \begin{bmatrix} 191 \\ 122 \\ 98 \\ 69 \end{bmatrix}}$$

You can use matrix multiplication to find the income for the day. In this case, multiply each element in the cost matrix by its corresponding element in the sales matrix and find the total.

Notice that each element in the <u>row</u> matrix is multiplied by an element in the <u>column</u> matrix.

$$CS = [0.45 \quad 0.55 \quad 0.50 \quad 0.85] \cdot \begin{bmatrix} 191 \\ 122 \\ 98 \\ 69 \end{bmatrix}$$

$$= [0.45(191) + 0.55(122) + 0.50(98) + 0.85(69)]$$

$$= [85.95 + 67.10 + 49.00 + 58.65]$$

$$= [260.70]$$

The income for the day was $260.70.

In general, the product of the two matrices is found by multiplying rows and columns.

Multiplying Matrices	The product of $A_{m \times n}$ and $B_{n \times r}$ is $(AB)_{m \times r}$. The element in the ith row and the jth column of AB is the sum of the products of the corresponding elements in the ith row of A and the jth column of B.

Notice that you can multiply two matrices only if the number of columns in the first matrix is equal to the number of rows in the second matrix.

$$\underset{2 \times 2}{\begin{bmatrix} 2 & -1 \\ 3 & 4 \end{bmatrix}} \cdot \underset{2 \times 3}{\begin{bmatrix} 3 & -9 & 2 \\ 5 & 7 & -6 \end{bmatrix}} \qquad \underset{2 \times 3}{\begin{bmatrix} 3 & -9 & 2 \\ 5 & 7 & -6 \end{bmatrix}} \cdot \underset{2 \times 2}{\begin{bmatrix} 2 & -1 \\ 3 & 4 \end{bmatrix}}$$

$$\underset{\text{possible}}{\uparrow \qquad \uparrow} \qquad \qquad \underset{\underset{\text{possible}}{\text{not}}}{\uparrow \qquad \uparrow}$$

The product on the left is defined, but the product on the right is not.

4-3 LESSON NOTES

NCTM Standards: 1–5, 8, 12

Instructional Resources

- Study Guide Master 4-3
- Practice Master 4-3
- Enrichment Master 4-3
- Multicultural Activity Masters, p. 7
- Tech Prep Applications Masters, p. 7

Transparency 4-3A contains the 5-Minute Check for this lesson; **Transparency 4-3B** contains a teaching aid for this lesson.

Recommended Pacing	
Standard Pacing	Day 4 of 14
Honors Pacing	Day 4 of 12
Block Scheduling*	Day 2 of 7 (along with Lesson 4-2)

*For more information on pacing and possible lesson plans, refer to the *Block Scheduling Booklet.*

1 FOCUS

5-Minute Check
(over Lesson 4-2)

Perform the indicated operations.

1. $\begin{bmatrix} 3 & -2 & 5 \\ 2 & 7 & -5 \end{bmatrix} + \begin{bmatrix} -1 & 3 & 4 \\ 2 & -3 & 0 \end{bmatrix}$

$\begin{bmatrix} 2 & 1 & 9 \\ 4 & 4 & -5 \end{bmatrix}$

2. $2\begin{bmatrix} 3 \\ -2 \\ 6 \end{bmatrix} - 5\begin{bmatrix} 2 \\ -3 \\ 6 \end{bmatrix}$ $\begin{bmatrix} -4 \\ 11 \\ -18 \end{bmatrix}$

3. Find the coordinates of the vertices of triangle STU with $S(3, 1)$, $T(5, 3)$, and $U(0, 5)$ if it is moved 1 unit to the left and 4 units up.
$S(2, 5)$, $T(4, 7)$, $U(-1, 9)$

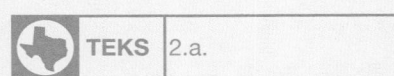

TEKS 2.a.

Situational Problem Two grocery stores have two kinds of fruits—apples and oranges. Saver's Mart has 45 apples and 55 oranges. Sam's Shoppe has 15 apples and 80 oranges. Make a matrix to show the relationship.

2 TEACH

In-Class Examples

For Example 1

If $A = \begin{bmatrix} 3 & 2 \\ -1 & -2 \end{bmatrix}$

and $B = \begin{bmatrix} 5 & 1 & 2 \\ 5 & 3 & -1 \end{bmatrix}$,

find AB.

$\begin{bmatrix} 25 & 9 & 4 \\ -15 & -7 & 0 \end{bmatrix}$

For Example 2

In Example 2, suppose 80% of the mice went right on the first trial. Make a prediction for the second trial. **68% should go right, 32% should go left.**

Example 1 If $A = \begin{bmatrix} 3 & -5 \\ 2 & 7 \end{bmatrix}$ and $B = \begin{bmatrix} 5 & 1 & -3 \\ 8 & -4 & 9 \end{bmatrix}$, find AB.

$$AB = \begin{bmatrix} 3(5) + (-5)(8) & 3(1) + (-5)(-4) & 3(-3) + (-5)(9) \\ 2(5) + 7(8) & 2(1) + 7(-4) & 2(-3) + 7(9) \end{bmatrix}$$

$$= \begin{bmatrix} 15 - 40 & 3 + 20 & -9 - 45 \\ 10 + 56 & 2 - 28 & -6 + 63 \end{bmatrix} \quad \text{Note that } A_{2 \times 2} \cdot B_{2 \times 3} = (AB)_{2 \times 3}.$$

$$= \begin{bmatrix} -25 & 23 & -54 \\ 66 & -26 & 57 \end{bmatrix}$$

In many situations involving chance, matrices can be used to represent probabilities. Matrix multiplication can be used to predict future events.

Example 2

INTEGRATION

Probability

A transition matrix contains information about the transition from one event to another.

A psychologist notes the behavior of mice at a certain point in a maze. For any particular trial, 70% of the mice that went right on the previous trial will go right on this trial, and 60% of those that went left on the previous trial will go right on this trial. This information can be represented by the following *transition matrix*.

$$T = \begin{array}{c} R \\ L \end{array} \begin{array}{cc} R & L \\ \begin{bmatrix} 0.7 & 0.3 \\ 0.6 & 0.4 \end{bmatrix} \end{array}$$

first trial ⟶   second trial ⟵

Suppose 50% of the mice went right on the first trial. This is represented by the following *probability matrix*.

$$P = \begin{array}{cc} R & L \\ [0.5 & 0.5] \end{array}$$

a. Make a prediction for the second trial.

b. Make a prediction for the third trial.

a. To make a prediction about what will happen on the second trial, find PT.

$$PT = [0.5 \ 0.5] \cdot \begin{bmatrix} 0.7 & 0.3 \\ 0.6 & 0.4 \end{bmatrix} \text{ or } [0.65 \ 0.35]$$

On the second trial, 65% of the mice should go right, and 35% should go left.

b. For the third trial, the new probability matrix is $P = [0.65 \ 0.35]$. Find PT.

$$PT = [0.65 \ 0.35] \cdot \begin{bmatrix} 0.7 & 0.3 \\ 0.6 & 0.4 \end{bmatrix} \text{ or } [0.665 \ 0.335]$$

On the third trial, 66.5% of the mice should go right, and 33.5% should go left.

GLENCOE Technology

Interactive Mathematics Tools Software

This multimedia software provides an interactive lesson that uses matrix multiplication in real-world application of airplane flights to different cities. A **Computer Journal** gives students an opportunity to write about what they have learned.

For Windows & Macintosh

Alternative Teaching Strategies

Student Diversity Review with students the geometry-related vocabulary found in the chapter: *transformations, dilation, translation,* and *rotation*. Sketch a number of transformations on the board and have students identify the transformations illustrated. You might also wish to show an example of the operation used on the matrix to achieve each transformation.

Another use of matrix multiplication is in transformational geometry. You have already learned how to translate a geometric figure and change its size by using matrices. Another type of transformation is a **rotation**. A rotation occurs when a figure is moved around a center point. To move a figure by rotation, you can use a rotation matrix.

MODELING MATHEMATICS

Rotations

Materials: grid paper  tracing paper protractor

The matrix $\begin{bmatrix} 0 & -1 \\ 1 & 0 \end{bmatrix}$ will rotate a figure on the coordinate plane about the origin. In this activity, you will determine the direction and degrees of rotation.

Your Turn

a. Draw a triangle on a coordinate plane and label it $\triangle ABC$. Write the coordinates of the vertices as a coordinate matrix. **See students' work.**

b. Multiply the rotation matrix shown above by your coordinate matrix. Graph the resulting triangle on the same coordinate plane and label it $\triangle A'B'C'$. *Note that the rotation matrix should be on the left when multiplying.* **See students' work.**

c. Place a piece of tracing paper over $\triangle ABC$ and trace it. With your pencil at the origin as a pivot point, slowly turn the tracing paper until the drawing of $\triangle ABC$ matches $\triangle A'B'C'$. Describe the motion of the triangle. **See students' work.**

d. On the coordinate plane, draw $\overline{OA}$ and $\overline{OA'}$. Find the measure of $\angle A'OA$. Repeat for the remaining vertices. **90°**

e. Write a sentence that describes the effect of multiplying a coordinate matrix by the rotation matrix $\begin{bmatrix} 0 & -1 \\ 1 & 0 \end{bmatrix}$. **It rotates a figure 90° counterclockwise about the origin.**

Example ③

Geometry

Line AB passes through points $A(4, -2)$ and $B(-3, 5)$. Find the coordinates of two points on line $A'B'$ that has been rotated 90° counterclockwise about the origin. Draw its graph and describe the relationship between lines AB and $A'B'$.

Write the ordered pairs in a coordinate matrix. Then multiply the coordinate matrix by the rotation matrix.

$$\begin{bmatrix} 0 & -1 \\ 1 & 0 \end{bmatrix} \cdot \begin{bmatrix} 4 & -3 \\ -2 & 5 \end{bmatrix} = \begin{bmatrix} 2 & -5 \\ 4 & -3 \end{bmatrix}$$

Coordinates of two points on the line are $A'(2, 4)$ and $B'(-5, -3)$. The two lines appear to be perpendicular.

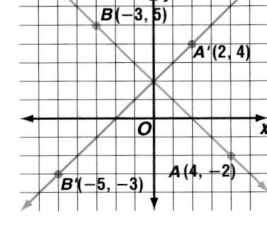

You can check that the lines are perpendicular by finding the slope of each line.

 ## Cooperative Learning

Numbered Heads Together Separate the class into groups. Have each group make three triangles and place them on a grid. Then have them rotate the figures clockwise 90°. Determine the matrix that would give the new coordinates for the rotation. Prove the matrix works by multiplying each triangle's coordinate with the new matrix.

$$\begin{bmatrix} 0 & 1 \\ -1 & 0 \end{bmatrix}$$

For more information on the numbered heads together strategy, see *Cooperative Learning in the Mathematics Classroom*, one of the titles in the Glencoe Mathematics Professional Series, pages 9–12.

 MODELING MATHEMATICS It might be helpful at this point to extend the activity by looking at Exercises 31–34. It is worth noting that for each rotation matrix, there is another rotation matrix that does just the opposite.

In-Class Example

For Example 3
Quadrilateral *ABCD* has vertices *A*(−3, 8), *B*(−2, −1), *C*(5, −4), and *D*(3, 6). Find the coordinates of the vertices of this quadrilateral after it is rotated counterclockwise 90° about the origin.
A′(−8, −3), *B′*(1, −2), *C′*(4, 5), *D′*(−6, 3)

Teaching Tip Have students find the matrix that can rotate a figure about the origin 180°.
$$\begin{bmatrix} -1 & 0 \\ 0 & -1 \end{bmatrix}$$

3 PRACTICE/APPLY

Check for Understanding

Exercises 1–11 are designed to help you assess your students' understanding through reading, writing, speaking, and modeling. You should work through Exercises 1–6 with your students and then monitor their work on Exercises 7–11.

Additional Answers

1. The first matrix has the same number of columns as the second matrix has rows.
3. The statement is false. Sample answer: $A_{2\times3} \cdot B_{3\times3} = (AB)_{2\times3}$ but BA is not defined.
5. Dolores; Sample answer: $A_{2\times3}$ and $B_{2\times3}$ can be added, but not multiplied.

11.

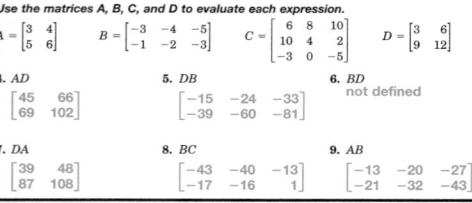

Study Guide Masters, p. 24

NAME_____ DATE_____
Study Guide
Student Edition
Pages 199–204

Multiplying Matrices

The product AB of two matrices is defined if and only if the number of columns in A equals the number of rows in B. For the product AB, the element in row i column j is found as follows: Use the ith row of A and the jth row of B. Multiply the corresponding elements and add the products.

Example:

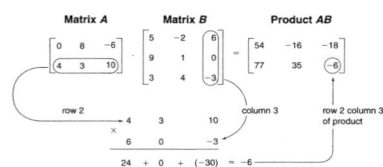

Perform the indicated operations, if possible.

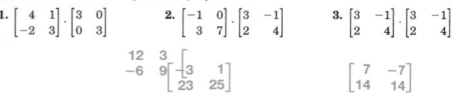

Use the matrices A, B, C, and D to evaluate each expression.

$A = \begin{bmatrix} 3 & 4 \\ 5 & 6 \end{bmatrix}$ $B = \begin{bmatrix} -3 & -4 & -5 \\ -1 & -2 & -3 \end{bmatrix}$ $C = \begin{bmatrix} 6 & 8 & 10 \\ 10 & 4 & 2 \\ -3 & 0 & -5 \end{bmatrix}$ $D = \begin{bmatrix} 3 & 6 \\ 9 & 12 \end{bmatrix}$

4. AD
$\begin{bmatrix} 45 & 66 \\ 69 & 102 \end{bmatrix}$

5. DB
$\begin{bmatrix} -15 & -24 & -33 \\ -39 & -60 & -81 \end{bmatrix}$

6. BD
not defined

7. DA
$\begin{bmatrix} 39 & 48 \\ 87 & 108 \end{bmatrix}$

8. BC
$\begin{bmatrix} -43 & -40 & -13 \\ -17 & -16 & 1 \end{bmatrix}$

9. AB
$\begin{bmatrix} -13 & -20 & -27 \\ -21 & -32 & -43 \end{bmatrix}$

CHECK FOR UNDERSTANDING

Communicating Mathematics

Study the lesson. Then complete the following. 1, 3. See margin.

1. **Name** the conditions under which two matrices can be multiplied.

2. **Find** the dimensions of matrix M if $M = A_{3\times2} \cdot B_{2\times4}$. 3×4

3. **Write** a convincing argument for the statement *Matrix multiplication is commutative*. If the statement is not true, find a counterexample.

4. **Give an example** of two matrices M and N for which the products MN and NM are both defined. Sample answer: $M_{2\times3}$ and $N_{3\times2}$

5. **You Decide** Brandon thinks two matrices can always be multiplied if they can be added. Dolores thinks that isn't necessarily true. Who is correct? Explain your reasoning. See margin.

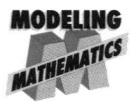 MODELING MATHEMATICS

6. Apply a 90° counterclockwise rotation about the origin twice to a triangle on the coordinate plane. Compare the new coordinates to the original ones. Make a conjecture about what effect this rotation has on any figure. It rotates the figure 180°.

Guided Practice

Find the dimensions of each matrix product.

7. $A_{3\times5} \cdot B_{5\times2}$ 3×2

8. $P_{2\times2} \cdot Q_{2\times4}$ 2×4

Perform the indicated operations, if possible.

10. not possible to evaluate

9. $\begin{bmatrix} 4 & -2 & -7 \\ 6 & 3 & 5 \end{bmatrix} \cdot \begin{bmatrix} -2 \\ 5 \\ 3 \end{bmatrix}$ $\begin{bmatrix} -39 \\ 18 \end{bmatrix}$

10. $\begin{bmatrix} 4 & -1 & 6 \\ 1 & 5 & -8 \end{bmatrix} \cdot \begin{bmatrix} 1 & 3 \\ 9 & -6 \end{bmatrix}$

11. **Geometry** Find the new coordinates of the vertices of triangle ABC with vertices $A(-5, 2)$, $B(3, 4)$, and $C(1, -4)$, when the triangle is rotated 90° counterclockwise about the origin. Graph the original triangle and its rotation $A'B'C'$. $A'(-2, -5)$, $B'(-4, 3)$, $C'(4, 1)$; See margin for graph.

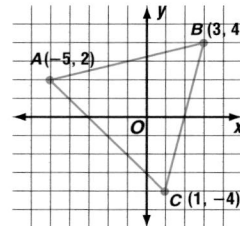

EXERCISES

Practice
A

Find the dimensions of each matrix product.

12. $A_{5\times2} \cdot B_{2\times5}$ 5×5

13. $M_{4\times2} \cdot N_{1\times3}$ not defined

14. $R_{2\times3} \cdot S_{3\times4}$ 2×4

15. $X_{3\times4} \cdot Y_{4\times1}$ 3×1

16. $P_{1\times5} \cdot Q_{5\times1}$ 1×1

17. $A_{3\times2} \cdot B_{3\times2}$ not defined

Perform the indicated operations, if possible.

19. $\begin{bmatrix} 1 & -25 & 2 \\ 29 & 1 & -30 \end{bmatrix}$

18. $[2 \ -1] \cdot \begin{bmatrix} 5 \\ 3 \end{bmatrix}$ $[7]$

19. $\begin{bmatrix} 2 & -1 \\ 3 & 4 \end{bmatrix} \cdot \begin{bmatrix} 3 & -9 & -2 \\ 5 & 7 & -6 \end{bmatrix}$

21. not possible to evaluate

20. $\begin{bmatrix} 4 & -1 \\ 3 & 5 \end{bmatrix} \cdot \begin{bmatrix} 7 \\ 4 \end{bmatrix}$ $\begin{bmatrix} 24 \\ 41 \end{bmatrix}$

21. $\begin{bmatrix} 5 & -2 & -1 \\ 8 & 0 & 3 \end{bmatrix} \cdot \begin{bmatrix} -4 & 2 \\ 1 & 0 \end{bmatrix}$

Reteaching

Using Models As in the Reteaching Activity for Lesson 4-1, use the class seating arrangement to form matrices with each student's desk as a cell. Fill two matrices $A_{2\times3}$ and $B_{3\times2}$ with values. For $AB = C$, write a blank 2×2 matrix on the chalkboard. For each element of C (say $C_{i,j}$), have students "walk out" the products of

corresponding elements of $A_{i,x}$ and $B_{x,j}$ (x represents corresponding position number) to get the addends for $C_{i,j}$.

Write these values on the board. Point out how the elements "zipper together." Try matrices of different sizes.

Perform the indicated operations, if possible.

$$23.\begin{bmatrix} 0 & 64 & -40 \\ 9 & 11 & -11 \\ -3 & 39 & -23 \end{bmatrix}$$

24. $A'(-4, 3)$, $B'(-5, 6)$, $C'(0, 0)$

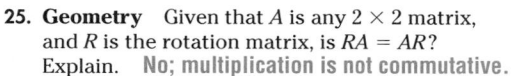

22. $3\begin{bmatrix} 5 & 7 \\ 1 & -2 \end{bmatrix} + 2\begin{bmatrix} -3 & 0 \\ -4 & 2 \end{bmatrix}$ $\begin{bmatrix} 9 & 21 \\ -5 & -2 \end{bmatrix}$ **23.** $\begin{bmatrix} 0 & 8 \\ 3 & 1 \\ -1 & 5 \end{bmatrix} \cdot \begin{bmatrix} 3 & 1 & -2 \\ 0 & 8 & -5 \end{bmatrix}$

24. Geometry Find the new coordinates of the vertices of $\triangle ABC$ shown at the right after it has been rotated 90° counterclockwise about the origin.

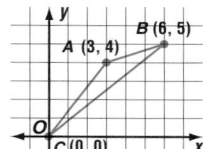

25. Geometry Given that A is any 2×2 matrix, and R is the rotation matrix, is $RA = AR$? Explain. **No; multiplication is not commutative.**

Use the matrices A, B, C, and D to evaluate each expression.

$$26.\begin{bmatrix} 9 & 5 & -21 \\ 43 & -25 & 39 \end{bmatrix}$$

27. not defined
28. not defined

$$29.\begin{bmatrix} -39 & 9 \\ 5 & 16 \end{bmatrix}$$

$A = \begin{bmatrix} 3 & -1 \\ 2 & 4 \end{bmatrix}$ $B = \begin{bmatrix} 4 & 0 & -3 \\ 7 & -5 & 9 \end{bmatrix}$ $C = \begin{bmatrix} -6 & 4 \\ -2 & 8 \\ 3 & 0 \end{bmatrix}$ $D = \begin{bmatrix} -1 & 0 \\ 3 & 7 \end{bmatrix}$

26. $AB + B$ **27.** $CB + B$ **28.** $AD + CB$ **29.** $AD + BC$

30. Geometry After a triangle was rotated 90° counterclockwise about the origin, the coordinates of the vertices are $(-3, -5)$, $(-2, 7)$, and $(1, 4)$. What were the coordinates of the vertices of the triangle in its original position? $(-5, 3)$, $(7, 2)$, $(4, -1)$

Graphing Calculator

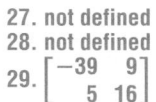

31. rotates 180°
32. reflects over x-axis
33. reflects over y-axis
34. reflects over $y = x$

Use a graphing calculator to determine the effect of multiplying the unit square matrix,

$S = \begin{bmatrix} 0 & 1 & 1 & 0 \\ 0 & 0 & 1 & 1 \end{bmatrix}$, **illustrated in the graph at the right, by each matrix below.**

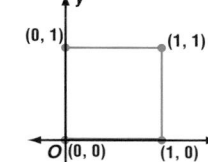

31. $A = \begin{bmatrix} -1 & 0 \\ 0 & -1 \end{bmatrix}$ **32.** $B = \begin{bmatrix} 1 & 0 \\ 0 & -1 \end{bmatrix}$

33. $C = \begin{bmatrix} -1 & 0 \\ 0 & 1 \end{bmatrix}$ **34.** $D = \begin{bmatrix} 0 & 1 \\ 1 & 0 \end{bmatrix}$

Critical Thinking

35. $w = 1$, $x = 0$, $y = 0$, $z = 1$; the original matrix

35. Find the values of w, x, y, and z to make the statement $\begin{bmatrix} 1 & 2 \\ 3 & 4 \end{bmatrix} \cdot \begin{bmatrix} w & x \\ y & z \end{bmatrix} = \begin{bmatrix} 1 & 2 \\ 3 & 4 \end{bmatrix}$ true. If the matrix containing w, x, y, and z were multiplied by any other matrix containing two columns, what do you think the result would be?

Applications and Problem Solving

36. Blendon: 56, Walnut Springs: 62, Heritage: 53

36. Track and Field In a three-team track meet, the following numbers of first-, second-, and third-place finishes were recorded.

School	First Place	Second Place	Third Place
Blendon	4	10	6
Walnut Springs	7	6	9
Heritage	8	3	4

If 5 points are awarded for first, 3 for second, and 1 for third, use matrix multiplication to find the final scores for each school.

Assignment Guide

Core: 13–39 odd, 40–46
Enriched: 12–34 even, 35–46

For **Extra Practice**, see p. 883.

The red A, B, and C flags, printed only in the Teacher's Wraparound Edition, indicate the level of difficulty of the exercises.

Practice Masters, p. 24

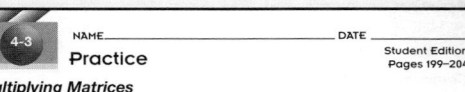

4-3   NAME_____ DATE_____
Practice   Student Edition Pages 199–204

Multiplying Matrices
Find the dimensions of each matrix M.

1. $A_{7 \times 4} \cdot B_{4 \times 3} = M$ 2. $A_{3 \times 3} \cdot M = B_{3 \times 8}$ 3. $M \cdot A_{1 \times 6} = B_{2 \times 6}$
   7×3 5×8 2×1

Perform the indicated operations, if possible.

4. $2\begin{bmatrix} 2 & 4 \\ 3 & -1 \end{bmatrix} + 3\begin{bmatrix} -3 & 0 \\ 2 & 5 \end{bmatrix}$ 5. $\begin{bmatrix} 2 & 4 \\ 3 & -1 \end{bmatrix} \cdot \begin{bmatrix} 3 & -2 & 7 \\ 6 & 0 & -5 \end{bmatrix}$
   $\begin{bmatrix} -5 & 8 \\ 12 & 13 \end{bmatrix}$ $\begin{bmatrix} 30 & -4 & -6 \\ 3 & -6 & 26 \end{bmatrix}$

6. $\begin{bmatrix} 2 & 4 \\ 3 & -1 \end{bmatrix} \cdot \begin{bmatrix} -3 & 0 \\ 2 & 5 \end{bmatrix} + 2\begin{bmatrix} -3 & 0 \\ 2 & 5 \end{bmatrix}$ 7. $\begin{bmatrix} 3 & -2 & 7 \\ 6 & 0 & -5 \end{bmatrix} \cdot \begin{bmatrix} 3 & -2 & 7 \\ 6 & 0 & -5 \end{bmatrix}$
   $\begin{bmatrix} -4 & 20 \\ -7 & 5 \end{bmatrix}$ not possible to evaluate

8. $\begin{bmatrix} 2 & 4 \\ 7 & -1 \end{bmatrix} \cdot \begin{bmatrix} -3 & 0 \\ 2 & 5 \end{bmatrix}$ 9. $\begin{bmatrix} -3 & 0 \\ 2 & 5 \end{bmatrix} \cdot \begin{bmatrix} 2 & 4 \\ 7 & -1 \end{bmatrix}$
   $\begin{bmatrix} 2 & 20 \\ -23 & -5 \end{bmatrix}$ $\begin{bmatrix} -6 & -12 \\ 39 & 3 \end{bmatrix}$

Find the new coordinates of the vertices of each polygon after the polygon is rotated 90° counterclockwise about the origin.

10. triangle ABC with vertices $A(2, 5)$, $B(5, 8)$, $C(3, 15)$
    $(-5, 2)$, $(-8, 5)$, $(-15, 3)$

11. square $DEFG$ with vertices $D(-1, 2)$, $E(-1, -2)$, $F(3, -2)$, $G(3, 2)$
    $(-2, -1)$, $(2, -1)$, $(2, 3)$, $(-2, 3)$

12. rectangle $HIJK$ with vertices $H(-1, 1)$, $I(1, -1)$, $J(7, 5)$, $K(5, 7)$
    $(-1, -1)$, $(1, 1)$, $(-5, 7)$, $(-7, 5)$

Closing Activity

Writing Have students write a paragraph explaining why multiplication of matrices is not commutative.

Additional Answers

39a.

$$[150 \ 100 \ 200] \cdot \begin{bmatrix} 54 \\ 60 \\ 43.50 \end{bmatrix} =$$

$$[22,800]$$

39b.

$$[150 \ 100 \ 200] \cdot \begin{bmatrix} 1.25 \\ 1.00 \\ -1.75 \end{bmatrix} =$$

$$[-62.50]$$

38a. $\begin{bmatrix} 0.7 & 0.3 \\ 0.5 & 0.5 \end{bmatrix}$

Enrichment Masters, p. 24

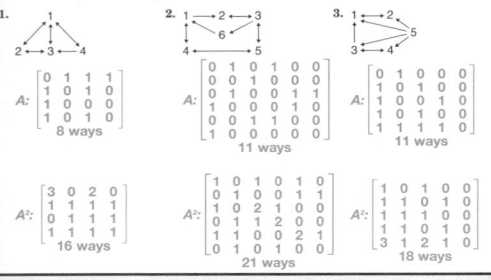

4-3
NAME_____ DATE _____
Enrichment
Student Edition Pages 199–204

Communications Networks

The diagram at the right represents a communications network linking five computer remote stations. The arrows indicate the direction in which signals can be transmitted and received by each computer. We can generate a matrix to describe this network.

$$A = \begin{bmatrix} 0 & 1 & 0 & 1 & 0 \\ 0 & 0 & 0 & 1 & 1 \\ 1 & 0 & 0 & 1 & 0 \\ 1 & 1 & 1 & 0 & 1 \\ 0 & 1 & 0 & 1 & 0 \end{bmatrix}$$

The entry in position a_{ij} represents the number of ways to send a message from computer i to computer j directly. Compare the entries of matrix A to the diagram to verify the entries.

Matrix A is a communications network for direct communication. Suppose you want to send a message from one computer to another using exactly one other computer as a relay point. It can be shown that the entries of matrix A^2 represent the number of ways to send a message from one point to another using exactly one relay point.

$$A^2 = \begin{bmatrix} 1 & 1 & 1 & 1 & 2 \\ 1 & 2 & 1 & 1 & 1 \\ 1 & 2 & 1 & 1 & 1 \\ 1 & 2 & 0 & 4 & 1 \\ 1 & 1 & 1 & 1 & 2 \end{bmatrix}$$

Again, compare the entries of matrix A^2 to the communications diagram to verify that the entries are correct. Matrix A^2 represents using exactly one relay.

For each network, find the matrices A and A². Then write the number of ways the messages can be sent for each matrix.

1.

$$A: \begin{bmatrix} 0 & 1 & 1 & 1 \\ 1 & 0 & 1 & 0 \\ 1 & 1 & 0 & 0 \\ 1 & 0 & 1 & 0 \end{bmatrix}$$
8 ways

$$A^2: \begin{bmatrix} 3 & 0 & 2 & 0 \\ 1 & 1 & 1 & 1 \\ 0 & 1 & 1 & 1 \\ 1 & 1 & 1 & 1 \end{bmatrix}$$
16 ways

2.

$$A: \begin{bmatrix} 0 & 1 & 0 & 1 & 0 & 0 \\ 0 & 0 & 1 & 0 & 0 & 0 \\ 0 & 1 & 0 & 0 & 1 & 1 \\ 1 & 0 & 0 & 0 & 1 & 0 \\ 0 & 0 & 1 & 1 & 0 & 0 \\ 1 & 0 & 0 & 0 & 0 & 0 \end{bmatrix}$$
11 ways

$$A^2: \begin{bmatrix} 1 & 0 & 1 & 0 & 1 & 0 \\ 0 & 1 & 0 & 0 & 1 & 1 \\ 1 & 0 & 2 & 1 & 0 & 0 \\ 0 & 1 & 1 & 2 & 0 & 0 \\ 1 & 1 & 0 & 0 & 2 & 1 \\ 0 & 1 & 0 & 1 & 0 & 0 \end{bmatrix}$$
21 ways

3.

$$A: \begin{bmatrix} 0 & 1 & 0 & 0 & 0 \\ 1 & 0 & 1 & 0 & 0 \\ 1 & 0 & 0 & 1 & 0 \\ 1 & 0 & 1 & 0 & 0 \\ 1 & 1 & 1 & 1 & 0 \end{bmatrix}$$
11 ways

$$A^2: \begin{bmatrix} 1 & 0 & 1 & 0 & 0 \\ 1 & 1 & 0 & 1 & 0 \\ 1 & 1 & 1 & 0 & 0 \\ 1 & 1 & 0 & 1 & 0 \\ 3 & 1 & 2 & 1 & 0 \end{bmatrix}$$
18 ways

---

37. Probability A weather station in a certain area gathers data about the chance of precipitation. It predicts that, if it rains on a given day, 50% of the time it will rain on the next day. If it is not raining, it will rain on the next day only 30% of the time. The weather forecast for Monday predicts the chance of rain is 80%. Find the chance of rain on Wednesday using this pattern. **about 39%**

38. Health Due to a flu epidemic, the school nurse estimates that 30% of the students who are well today will be sick tomorrow and 50% of the students who are sick today will be well tomorrow.
  a. Write a transition matrix to show this situation.
  b. If 80% of the student population is well today, predict what percent will be sick tomorrow. **34%**

39. Finance Isabel "bought" shares of stock in three U.S. companies for a project in her economics class. She bought 150 shares of General Electric, 100 shares of General Mills, and 200 shares of General Motors. At the time she purchased the stocks, General Electric was $54 per share, General Mills was $60 per share, and General Motors was $43.50 per share.
  a. Organize the data into two matrices and use matrix multiplication to find the total amount she spent for the shares of stock. **$22,800**
  b. At the end of the project, she "sold" all of her stock. General Electric was $55.25 per share, General Mills was $61 per share, and General Motors was $41.75 per share. Use matrix operations to determine how much money Isabel "made" or "lost" in her project.
  sold, $22,735.50; lost, $62.50

Mixed Review

40. Find $[4 \ 1 \ -3] + [6 \ -5 \ 8]$. (Lesson 4–2) **$[10 \ -4 \ 5]$**

41. Find $-6 \begin{bmatrix} 2 & -1 \\ -5 & 7 \end{bmatrix}$. (Lesson 4–1) $\begin{bmatrix} -12 & 6 \\ 30 & -42 \end{bmatrix}$

42. School Your semester test in English consists of short answers and essay questions. Each short answer question is worth 5 points, and each essay question is worth 15 points. You may choose up to 20 questions of any type to answer. It takes 2 minutes to answer each short answer question and 12 minutes to answer each essay question. If you have one hour to complete the test, and assuming you answer all of the questions that you attempt correctly, how many of each type of question should you answer to earn the highest score? (Lesson 3–6)
18 short answer and 2 essay, for a score of 120

43. Solve the system of equations by using the elimination method. (Lesson 3–2)
$$3x - 6y = 15$$
$$-3x + 5y = -8 \quad (-9, -7)$$

44. Write the slope-intercept form of the equation of the line with slope of -2 that passes through the point $(3, 1)$. (Lesson 2–4) $y = -2x + 7$

45. State the x- and y-intercepts of the graph of the line with equation $3x - 12y = 24$. (Lesson 2–2) **(8, 0) and (0, -2)**

46. Telecommunications A call to a sports hotline costs $3.38 for the first three minutes and $0.96 for each minute thereafter. What is the cost of a 12-minute phone call? (Lesson 1–4) **$12.02**

Extension ▬▬▬▬

Problem Solving Apply the rotation matrix twice on the triangle with vertices $(-2, 5)$, $(1, -3)$, and $(4, 6)$. Discuss what effect it has on the original vertices. Could you have done this "double rotation" using one rotation? The double rotation has the same effect as multiplying each coordinate by -1.

Tech Prep

Nurse Students who are interested in nursing may wish to do further research into the use of mathematics in that occupation, as mentioned in Exercise 38. For more information on tech prep, see the *Teacher's Handbook*.

Matrices and Determinants

What YOU'LL LEARN

- To evaluate the determinant of a 3 × 3 matrix, and
- to find the area of a triangle, given the coordinates of its vertices.

Why IT'S IMPORTANT

You can use matrices and determinants to solve problems involving geometry and geography.

CONNECTION
Math History

Although matrices are a relatively new notation in mathematics, the *idea* of matrices can be traced back to the Chinese book *Nine Chapters on the Mathematical Art*, which was published about 250 B.C. This book contained many problems that are solved by using matrices. The Chinese matrix was a large counting board resembling a checkerboard, and bamboo rods were placed on the squares to represent equations.

When the Japanese mathematician Seki Kowa (1683) investigated the Chinese system of solving systems of equations, his calculations were similar to those used today to simplify a **determinant**.

Every square matrix has a number associated with it, called its determinant. The notation for the determinant of $\begin{bmatrix} -5 & -7 \\ 11 & 8 \end{bmatrix}$ is $\begin{vmatrix} -5 & -7 \\ 11 & 8 \end{vmatrix}$. To evaluate the determinant, use the rule for second-order determinants.

$$\begin{vmatrix} -5 & -7 \\ 11 & 8 \end{vmatrix} = -5(8) - (-7)(11) \quad \textit{Recall that } \begin{vmatrix} a & b \\ c & d \end{vmatrix} = ad - bc.$$
$$= -40 + 77$$
$$= 37$$

LOOK BACK

You can refer to Lesson 3-3 for information about second-order determinants.

Determinants of 3 × 3 matrices are called **third-order determinants**. One method of evaluating third-order determinants is called **expansion by minors**. The **minor** of an element is the determinant formed when the row and column containing that element are deleted. For the determinant $\begin{vmatrix} -2 & 3 & 8 \\ 6 & 7 & -1 \\ -4 & 5 & 9 \end{vmatrix}$, the minor of 5 is $\begin{vmatrix} -2 & 3 & 8 \\ 6 & 7 & -1 \\ -4 & ⑤ & 9 \end{vmatrix}$ or $\begin{vmatrix} -2 & 8 \\ 6 & -1 \end{vmatrix}$.

To use expansion by minors with third-order determinants, each member of one row is multiplied by its minor. The signs of the products alternate, beginning with a positive sign in the first and third row and a negative sign in the second row. The following definition shows an expansion using the elements in the first row of the determinant. However, any row can be used.

TEKS 2.a.

NCTM Standards: 1–5, 8, 12

Instructional Resources

- Study Guide Master 4-4
- Practice Master 4-4
- Enrichment Master 4-4
- Assessment and Evaluation Masters, pp. 99–100
- Graphing Calculator Masters, p. 4
- Modeling Mathematics Masters, p. 64
- Multicultural Activity Masters, p. 8
- Real-World Applications, 9

 Transparency 4-4A contains the 5-Minute Check for this lesson; **Transparency 4-4B** contains a teaching aid for this lesson.

Recommended Pacing	
Standard Pacing	Days 5 & 6 of 14
Honors Pacing	Day 5 of 12
Block Scheduling*	Day 3 of 7 (along with Lesson 4-5)

 *For more information on pacing and possible lesson plans, refer to the *Block Scheduling Booklet*.

1 FOCUS

 5-Minute Check
(*over Lesson 4-3*)

Find each matrix *N*.

1. $N = \begin{bmatrix} 3 & 2 \\ -1 & 5 \end{bmatrix} \cdot \begin{bmatrix} 3 & -2 \\ 0 & 4 \end{bmatrix}$

   $\begin{bmatrix} 9 & 2 \\ -3 & 22 \end{bmatrix}$

2. $N = \begin{bmatrix} 4 & 2 & -3 \end{bmatrix} \cdot \begin{bmatrix} 2 & -3 \\ 5 & 0 \\ -6 & 2 \end{bmatrix}$

   $\begin{bmatrix} 36 & -18 \end{bmatrix}$

3. Triangle *ABC* has vertices with coordinates *A*(−8, 0), *B*(2, −3), and *C*(5, 6). Find the coordinates of the vertices of the triangle after it is rotated counterclockwise 90° about the origin.
   A′(0, −8), *B*′(3, 2), *C*′(−6, 5)

$$\begin{vmatrix} a & b & c \\ d & e & f \\ g & h & i \end{vmatrix} = a\begin{vmatrix} e & f \\ h & i \end{vmatrix} - b\begin{vmatrix} d & f \\ g & i \end{vmatrix} + c\begin{vmatrix} d & e \\ g & h \end{vmatrix}$$

Motivating the Lesson

Questioning Have students name some necessary conditions for $\begin{vmatrix} a & b \\ c & d \end{vmatrix} = 0$ to be true. Remind them about determinants from Cramer's rule.

2 TEACH

Teaching Tip In expansion by minors, you can also multiply each member of one column by its minor.

In-Class Example

For Example 1
Evaluate
$$\begin{vmatrix} 5 & -1 & 2 \\ 2 & -3 & 5 \\ 3 & 2 & -3 \end{vmatrix}$$
using expansion by minors. **0**

Teaching Tip The determinant of an $n \times n$ matrix is called an nth order determinant.

Teaching Tip The diagonal method does not work for fourth- or higher-order determinants.

Example **Evaluate** $\begin{vmatrix} 2 & 3 & 4 \\ 6 & 5 & 7 \\ -1 & 9 & 8 \end{vmatrix}$ **using expansion by minors.**

Decide which row of elements you will use for the expansion. Let's use the first row.

$$\begin{vmatrix} 2 & 3 & 4 \\ 6 & 5 & 7 \\ -1 & 9 & 8 \end{vmatrix} = 2\begin{vmatrix} 5 & 7 \\ 9 & 8 \end{vmatrix} - 3\begin{vmatrix} 6 & 7 \\ -1 & 8 \end{vmatrix} + 4\begin{vmatrix} 6 & 5 \\ -1 & 9 \end{vmatrix}$$
$$= 2(40 - 63) - 3(48 + 7) + 4(54 + 5)$$
$$= -46 - 165 + 236$$
$$= 25$$

You can check your work by evaluating the determinant again using a different row of elements.

Another method for evaluating a third-order determinant is using diagonals. In this method, you begin by writing the first two columns on the right side of the determinant.

$$\begin{vmatrix} a & b & c \\ d & e & f \\ g & h & i \end{vmatrix} \rightarrow \begin{array}{|ccc|cc} a & b & c & a & b \\ d & e & f & d & e \\ g & h & i & g & h \end{array}$$

Next, draw diagonals from each element of the top row of the determinant downward to the right. Find the product of the elements on each diagonal.

$$\begin{vmatrix} a & b & c \\ d & e & f \\ g & h & i \end{vmatrix} \rightarrow \begin{array}{|ccc|cc} a & b & c & a & b \\ d & e & f & d & e \\ g & h & i & g & h \end{array}$$
$$aei \quad bfg \quad cdh$$

Then, draw diagonals from the elements in the third row of the determinant upward to the right. Find the product of the elements on each diagonal.

$$gec \quad hfa \quad idb$$
$$\begin{vmatrix} a & b & c \\ d & e & f \\ g & h & i \end{vmatrix} \rightarrow \begin{array}{|ccc|cc} a & b & c & a & b \\ d & e & f & d & e \\ g & h & i & g & h \end{array}$$

To find the value of the determinant, add the products of the first set of diagonals and then subtract the products of the second set of diagonals. The value is $aei + bfg + cdh - gec - hfa - idb$.

Example ② Evaluate $\begin{vmatrix} -1 & 0 & 8 \\ 7 & 3 & 4 \\ 2 & 2 & 5 \end{vmatrix}$ using diagonals.

TECHNOLOGY
Tips

If you are using a graphing calculator, press MATRX and use the arrow keys to highlight the MATH menu. Item 1:det is used to calculate the determinant.

First, rewrite the first two columns to the right of the determinant.

$$\begin{vmatrix} -1 & 0 & 8 \\ 7 & 3 & 4 \\ 2 & 2 & 5 \end{vmatrix} \begin{matrix} -1 & 0 \\ 7 & 3 \\ 2 & 2 \end{matrix}$$

Next, find the products of the elements of the diagonals.

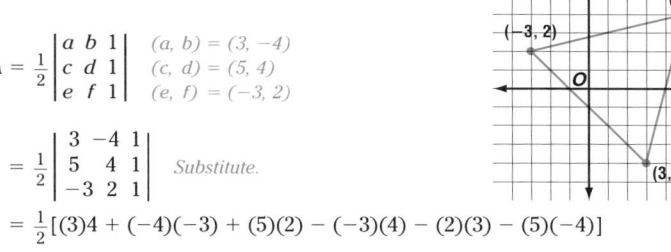

Then, add the bottom products and subtract the top products.

$$-15 + 0 + 112 - 48 - (-8) - 0 = 57$$

The value of the determinant is 57.

One very powerful application of determinants is finding the areas of polygons. The formula below shows how determinants serve as a mathematical tool to find the area of a triangle when the coordinates of the three vertices are given.

Area of Triangles

> The area of a triangle having vertices at (a, b), (c, d), and (e, f) is $|A|$, where
> $$A = \frac{1}{2}\begin{vmatrix} a & b & 1 \\ c & d & 1 \\ e & f & 1 \end{vmatrix}.$$

Notice that it is necessary to use the absolute value of A to guarantee a nonnegative value for area.

Example ③

INTEGRATION
Geometry

Find the area of the triangle whose vertices are located at $(3, -4)$, $(5, 4)$, and $(-3, 2)$.

Assign values to $a, b, c, d, e,$ and f and substitute them into the area formula and evaluate.

$$A = \frac{1}{2}\begin{vmatrix} a & b & 1 \\ c & d & 1 \\ e & f & 1 \end{vmatrix} \quad \begin{array}{l}(a, b) = (3, -4) \\ (c, d) = (5, 4) \\ (e, f) = (-3, 2)\end{array}$$

$$= \frac{1}{2}\begin{vmatrix} 3 & -4 & 1 \\ 5 & 4 & 1 \\ -3 & 2 & 1 \end{vmatrix} \quad \textit{Substitute.}$$

$$= \frac{1}{2}[(3)4 + (-4)(-3) + (5)(2) - (-3)(4) - (2)(3) - (5)(-4)]$$

$$= \frac{1}{2}[12 + 12 + 10 - (-12) - 6 - (-20)]$$

$$= \frac{1}{2}(60) \text{ or } 30$$

The area of the triangle is 30 square units.

In-Class Examples

For Example 2
Evaluate
$$\begin{vmatrix} 1 & 2 & -3 \\ 3 & -5 & -1 \\ 4 & 4 & 1 \end{vmatrix}$$
using diagonals. **−111**

For Example 3
Find the area of the triangle whose vertices are located at $(1, -1)$, $(4, 3)$, and $(0, 5)$. **11**

Teaching Tip This is another method of finding area. For a pentagon with coordinates $(-2, -2)$, $(2, -1)$, $(6, -4)$, $(5, 7)$, $(-4, 5)$, repeat the first ordered pair and make a 6×2 matrix. Then find the product of the numbers on each diagonal as shown below.

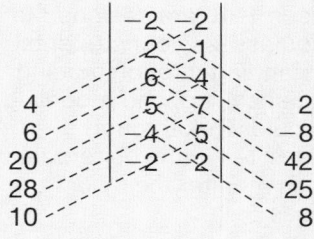

The area is the absolute value of one-half the sum of the products.

$$A = \left|\left(\frac{1}{2}\right)(4 + 6 + 20 + 28 + 10 + 2 - 8 + 42 + 25 + 8)\right|$$

$$= \left|\left(\frac{1}{2}\right)(137)\right|$$

$$= |68.5|$$

$A = 68.5$ square units

Classroom Vignette

"Students familiar with Hero's formula might want to use the scale to estimate the lengths of the three sides of the triangle and calculate the area."

Joan Gell
Palos Verdes High School
Palos Verdes Estates, California

In-Class Example

For Example 4
Find the area of the geometric figure in the diagram shown.

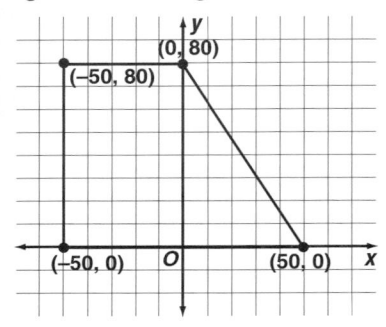

Area = 6000 square units

3 PRACTICE/APPLY

Check for Understanding

Exercises 1–10 are designed to help you assess your students' understanding through reading, writing, speaking, and modeling. You should work through Exercises 1–4 with your students and then monitor their work on Exercises 5–10.

Error Analysis

Students sometimes miss the signs of the terms when expanding by minors. Common mistakes are starting with the wrong sign for the first term and not alternating the signs. An easy rule to determine the sign of each term uses the sum of the indices (row number and column number). The sign of a term is positive if the sum of the indices is even, and the sign of the term is negative if the sum of the indices is odd. For example, $A_{3,4}$ uses a negative sign while $A_{1,3}$ uses a positive sign.

Additional Answers

1. $\begin{vmatrix} 7 & 8 \\ 3 & -2 \end{vmatrix}$ is a real number;

$\begin{bmatrix} 7 & 8 \\ 3 & -2 \end{bmatrix}$ is a matrix.

2. Cross out the row containing 8. Cross out the column containing 8. The four remaining elements are the minor of 8.

Maps usually have grids, similar to a coordinate system, that make it easier for you to locate cities, states, or landmarks. A coordinate system can also be used to find the area of large regions.

Example 4

APPLICATION
Cartography

The figure at the right shows a map of the state of Nevada that has been placed on a coordinate plane in which 1 unit = 1 mile. Estimate the area of Nevada from the coordinates of the vertices.

The x-axis separates the map into a triangular region and a rectangular region. Find the area of the rectangular region.

$A = \ell w$
$\quad = 318 \cdot 220$ or 69,960

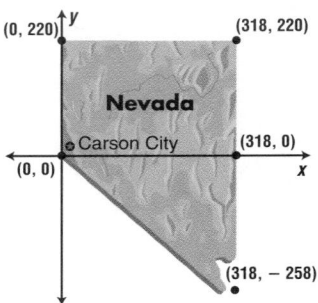

Now find the area of the triangular region using the coordinates (0, 0), (318, 0), and (318, −258). Use expansion by minors.

$$A = \frac{1}{2} \begin{vmatrix} a & b & 1 \\ c & d & 1 \\ e & f & 1 \end{vmatrix} \quad \begin{array}{l}(a, b) = (0, 0) \\ (c, d) = (318, 0) \\ (e, f) = (318, -258)\end{array}$$

$$= \frac{1}{2} \begin{vmatrix} 0 & 0 & 1 \\ 318 & 0 & 1 \\ 318 & -258 & 1 \end{vmatrix} = \frac{1}{2} \cdot 1 \begin{vmatrix} 318 & 0 \\ 318 & -258 \end{vmatrix} \text{ or } -41,022$$

Finally, add the areas of the two regions. The area of Nevada is 69,960 + 41,022 or about 111,000 square miles. *Compare this to the actual area.*

CHECK FOR UNDERSTANDING

Communicating Mathematics

Study the lesson. Then complete the following.

1. **Explain** how $\begin{bmatrix} 7 & 8 \\ 3 & -2 \end{bmatrix}$ and $\begin{vmatrix} 7 & 8 \\ 3 & -2 \end{vmatrix}$ are different. **See margin.**

2. **Describe** how to find the minor of 8 in $\begin{bmatrix} 1 & 2 & 3 \\ 4 & 5 & 6 \\ 7 & 8 & 9 \end{bmatrix}$. **See margin.**

3. **State** the condition(s) under which a matrix has a determinant. **square matrix**

4. **Write** a matrix that will help you use a determinant to find the area of the triangle shown at the right.

4. $\frac{1}{2} \begin{vmatrix} -2 & 3 & 1 \\ 1 & 2 & 1 \\ 4 & 4 & 1 \end{vmatrix}$

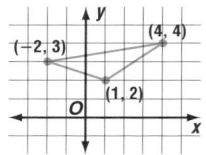

Guided Practice

Determine whether each matrix has a determinant. Write *yes* or *no*. If *yes*, find the value of the determinant.

5. $\begin{bmatrix} 6 \\ 2 \end{bmatrix}$ **no**

6. $\begin{bmatrix} -8 & 0 \\ 5 & -4 \end{bmatrix}$ **yes, 32**

7. $\begin{bmatrix} 1 & 0 & 0 \\ 0 & 1 & 0 \\ 0 & 0 & 1 \end{bmatrix}$ **yes, 1**

Reteaching

Using Discussion Discuss which of the following matrices have determinants and which of the determinants equal zero. Have students explain their reasoning.

a. $\begin{bmatrix} 3 & 5 \\ -1 & 4 \end{bmatrix}$

b. $\begin{bmatrix} 4 \\ 3 \end{bmatrix}$

c. $\begin{bmatrix} 4 & 2 \\ 6 & 3 \end{bmatrix}$

d. $\begin{bmatrix} 0 & -2 \\ -1 & 2 \end{bmatrix}$

Only square matrices have determinants. The determinant is zero if the two diagonals are equal.

8. Evaluate $\begin{vmatrix} 2 & 3 & 4 \\ 6 & 5 & 7 \\ 1 & 2 & 8 \end{vmatrix}$ using expansion by minors. -43

9. Evaluate $\begin{vmatrix} -1 & 4 & 0 \\ 3 & -2 & -5 \\ -3 & -1 & 2 \end{vmatrix}$ using diagonals. 45

10. **Geometry** Use a determinant to find the area of the triangle whose vertices have coordinates $(-2, 3)$, $(5, 8)$, and $(1, 2)$. 11 units^2

EXERCISES

Practice **Determine whether each matrix has a determinant. Write *yes* or *no*. If *yes*, find the value of the determinant.**

 11. $\begin{bmatrix} -3 & 5 \\ 6 & -10 \end{bmatrix}$ yes, 0 12. $\begin{bmatrix} 3 \\ -2 \\ 6 \end{bmatrix}$ no 13. $\begin{vmatrix} 4 & 3 \\ 8 & -1 \\ 7 & 2 \end{vmatrix}$ no

15. yes, -13
16. yes, 89

14. $\begin{bmatrix} -5 & 8 \\ 3 & 0 \end{bmatrix}$ yes, -24 15. $\begin{bmatrix} -2 & 0 & 1 \\ 1 & 2 & 0 \\ 4 & -1 & 1 \end{bmatrix}$ 16. $\begin{bmatrix} 5 & 7 & -2 \\ 3 & -2 & 6 \\ 1 & -4 & 3 \end{bmatrix}$

17. **Geometry** Use a determinant to find the area of $\triangle ABC$ shown at the right. Check your answer by using the formula $A = \frac{1}{2}bh$. 16 units^2

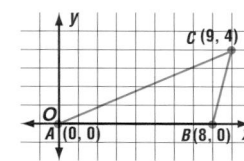

Evaluate each determinant using expansion by minors.

 18. $\begin{vmatrix} -3 & 0 & 6 \\ 6 & 5 & -2 \\ 1 & 4 & 2 \end{vmatrix}$ 60 19. $\begin{vmatrix} 0 & -4 & 0 \\ 3 & -2 & 5 \\ 2 & -1 & 1 \end{vmatrix}$ -28 20. $\begin{vmatrix} -2 & 7 & -2 \\ 4 & 6 & 2 \\ 1 & 0 & -1 \end{vmatrix}$ 66

Evaluate each determinant using diagonals.

21. $\begin{vmatrix} 1 & 6 & 4 \\ -2 & 3 & 1 \\ 1 & 6 & 4 \end{vmatrix}$ 0 22. $\begin{vmatrix} 1 & -1 & 1 \\ 3 & 3 & 1 \\ 0 & 5 & 2 \end{vmatrix}$ 22 23. $\begin{vmatrix} 2 & -3 & 4 \\ -2 & 1 & 5 \\ 5 & 3 & -2 \end{vmatrix}$ -141

Use a determinant to find the area of each triangle below.

24.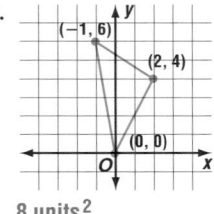
8 units^2

25.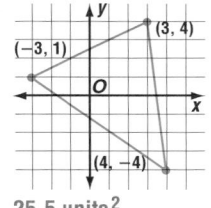
11 units^2

26.
25.5 units^2

Solve for the variable.

 27. $\begin{vmatrix} 2 & x \\ 5 & -3 \end{vmatrix} = 24$ $x = -6$ 28. $\begin{vmatrix} 4 & x & -2 \\ -x & -3 & 1 \\ -6 & 2 & 3 \end{vmatrix} = -3$ $x = \frac{5}{3}$ or -1

Assignment Guide

Core: 11–35 odd, 36–42
Enriched: 12–32 even, 33–42
All: Self Test, 1–10

For **Extra Practice**, see p. 884.

The red A, B, and C flags, printed only in the Teacher's Wraparound Edition, indicate the level of difficulty of the exercises.

Study Guide Masters, p. 25

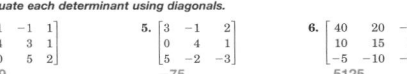

Additional Answers

32. Sample answer:

$$\begin{bmatrix} 1 & 1 & 0 \\ 1 & 0 & 1 \\ 1 & 1 & 1 \end{bmatrix}$$

and

$$\begin{bmatrix} 1 & 1 & -1 \\ 1 & 0 & -1 \\ 1 & 1 & 0 \end{bmatrix}$$

33. Sample answer: $\begin{bmatrix} 1 & 1 & 1 \\ 1 & 1 & 1 \\ 1 & 1 & 1 \end{bmatrix}$

34. Sample answer: Place a coordinate grid over the map so that Midway is on the y-axis and Easter Island is on the x-axis. Then use the scale to estimate the coordinates of the vertices. Finally, use a determinant to estimate the area.

Practice Masters, p. 25

4-4

NAME _____ DATE _____

Practice

Student Edition
Pages 205–211

Matrices and Determinants

Determine the value of the determinant of each matrix.

1. $\begin{bmatrix} -5 & 2 \\ -8 & -7 \end{bmatrix}$ 51

2. $\begin{bmatrix} -2 & 3 & 1 \\ 0 & 4 & -3 \\ 2 & 5 & -1 \end{bmatrix}$ −48

3. $\begin{bmatrix} 0 & -4 & 0 \\ 2 & -1 & 1 \\ 3 & -2 & 5 \end{bmatrix}$ 28

4. $\begin{bmatrix} 2 & -4 & 1 \\ 3 & 0 & 9 \\ -1 & 5 & 7 \end{bmatrix}$ 45

5. $\begin{bmatrix} 3 & -4 \\ 7 & 9 \end{bmatrix}$ 55

6. $\begin{bmatrix} 2 & 7 & -6 \\ 8 & 4 & 0 \\ 1 & -1 & 3 \end{bmatrix}$ −72

Solve for the variable.

7. $\begin{vmatrix} 3 & -4 \\ 2x & 5 \end{vmatrix} = 30$ $x = \frac{15}{8}$

8. $\begin{vmatrix} 2 & -1 \\ 3 & 4m \end{vmatrix} = -16$ $m = -\frac{19}{8}$

9. $\begin{vmatrix} x & 3 & -1 \\ 2 & 1 & -2 \\ 4 & 1 & x \end{vmatrix} = 10$ $x = 8$ or $x = -4$

10. $\begin{vmatrix} 2x & 0 & 3 \\ 7 & 5 & -1 \\ 4 & 2 & x \end{vmatrix} = 8x^2 - 3x + 12$

$x = \frac{5}{2}$ or $x = -6$

11. Find the area of a triangle whose vertices have coordinates (3, 5), (6, −5), and (−4, 10).
27.5 units²

12. Find the area of a triangle whose vertices have coordinates (−8, 10), (6, 17), and (2, −4).
133 units²

210 *Chapter 4*

Geometry

Use determinants to find the area of each polygon below.

29.
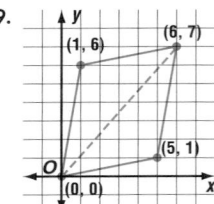

30.
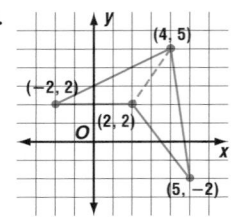

29. 29 sq units

30. 14.5 sq units

31. Find the value of x such that the area of a triangle whose vertices have coordinates (6, 5), (8, 2), and (x, 11) is 30. **x = 22**

Graphing Calculator

32. Use a graphing calculator to find two third-order matrices that are not equal, but have equal determinants. **See margin.**

Critical Thinking

33. Find a third-order matrix in which no element is 0, but for which the determinant is 0. **See margin.**

Applications and Problem Solving

34. **World Cultures** Easter Island is the easternmost island of Polynesia, which is a triangular area containing thousands of islands in the South Pacific. Its northern vertex is Midway Island and the southern boundary runs from New Zealand to Easter Island. A map of Polynesia is shown below. Explain how to use a coordinate grid to estimate the area of Polynesia. **See margin.**

GLOBAL CONNECTIONS

Easter Island is famous for its enormous statues, called *moai*, which were carved hundreds of years ago. Today, more than 600 statues, some as tall as 40 feet, are scattered over the island.

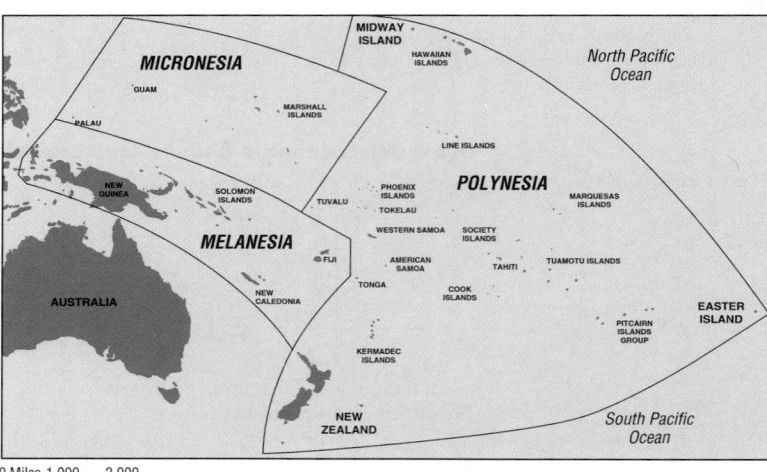

210 Chapter 4 Using Matrices

GLOBAL CONNECTIONS

Some of the statues had large stone cylinders balanced on their heads, like hats. Scientists are uncertain how a people with primitive technology accomplished such a difficult feat of engineering.

Extension

Reasoning Find x if (−1, 8), (2, 5), and (x, 3) are collinear. **4**

35. Geography The region in North Carolina bounded by Chapel Hill, Durham, and Raleigh is known as the Research Triangle Park. If a coordinate grid in which 1 unit = 1 mile is placed over the map of North Carolina with Chapel Hill at the origin, the coordinates of these three cities are $(0, 0)$, $(6, 3.5)$ and $(21, -10.5)$. Estimate the area of Research Triangle Park. **about 68 mi²**

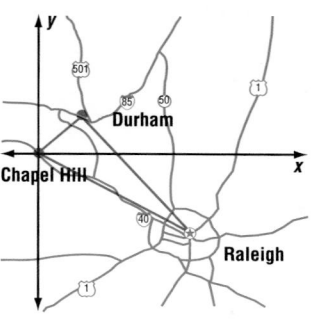

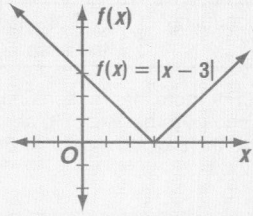

Mixed Review

36. Find $\begin{bmatrix} 4 & 0 & -8 \\ 7 & -2 & 10 \end{bmatrix} \cdot \begin{bmatrix} -1 & 3 \\ 6 & 0 \end{bmatrix}$. (Lesson 4–3) **not possible**

37. Solve $\begin{bmatrix} 2 & x \\ y & 5 \end{bmatrix} = \begin{bmatrix} 2 & 1 \\ 3 & z \end{bmatrix}$ for the variables. (Lesson 4–1) $x = 1$, $y = 3$, $z = 5$

38. Given $f(x, y) = 12x - 8y$, find the value of $f(-2, -4)$. (Lesson 3–5) **8**

39. Use Cramer's rule to solve the system of equations. (Lesson 3–3) **(4, 1)**
$$2x - y = 7$$
$$x + 3y = 7$$

40. Graph $f(x) = |x - 3|$. (Lesson 2–6) **See margin.**

41. Ecology If you recycle a $3\frac{1}{2}$-foot stack of newspapers, you can save one 20-foot loblolly pine tree. Use the formula $f(x) = \frac{x}{3.5}$, where x is the height of the newspaper in feet, to determine how many 20-foot loblolly pine trees you can save when you recycle a pile of newspapers 20 feet tall. (Lesson 2–1) **about 5.7**

42. Name the property illustrated by $x(a + b) = xa + xb$. (Lesson 1–2) **distributive**

State Capitol, Raleigh, North Carolina

SELF TEST

1. Use Matrix Logic Three women and their husbands invested a total of $5400 in a sandwich shop. The women invested $2400 in all; Sue invested $200 more than Tamara, and Elisa invested $200 more than Sue. Lou invested half as much as his wife, Bob invested the same as his wife, and Mateo invested twice as much as his wife. Who is married to whom? (Lesson 4–1) **Sue - Lou; Elisa - Mateo; Tamara - Bob**

2. Find the dimensions of the matrix product $A_{3\times4} \cdot B_{4\times3}$. (Lesson 4–3) **3 × 3**

Perform the indicated operations, if possible. (Lessons 4–1, 4–2, and 4–3) **3, 5. See margin.**

3. $\begin{bmatrix} -2 & 1.5 \\ 3 & -0.25 \end{bmatrix} - \begin{bmatrix} -6 & 2 \\ 3 & 1.25 \end{bmatrix}$

4. $\begin{bmatrix} 5.3 & -1.2 \\ 1.6 & 2 \end{bmatrix} + \begin{bmatrix} 0.3 \\ 0.2 \end{bmatrix}$ **not possible**

5. $2\begin{bmatrix} 5 & 4 \\ -1 & 6 \end{bmatrix} - 3\begin{bmatrix} -3 & 0 \\ -2 & 0 \end{bmatrix}$

6. $-4\begin{bmatrix} -1 & -0.25 \\ 0 & 2 \\ 0.5 & 4 \end{bmatrix}$ $\begin{bmatrix} 4 & 1 \\ 0 & -8 \\ -2 & -16 \end{bmatrix}$

7. $\begin{bmatrix} -2 & 3 \\ 1 & 10 \\ 0 & -6 \end{bmatrix} \cdot \begin{bmatrix} 9 & 3 \\ 1 & 4 \end{bmatrix}$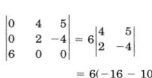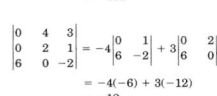

8. $\begin{bmatrix} 1 & 0 & 2 \\ 0 & 4 & 2 \\ 3 & 5 & 0 \end{bmatrix} \cdot \begin{bmatrix} 1 & 0 \\ 0 & 1 \end{bmatrix}$ **not possible**

9. Evaluate the determinant of $\begin{bmatrix} -1 & 3 & 4 \\ 0 & 5 & 1 \\ 6 & -2 & 3 \end{bmatrix}$. (Lesson 4–4) **−119**

10. Geometry Use determinants to find the area of a triangle with vertices having coordinates $(-1, -2)$, $(5, 3)$, and $(2, 6)$. (Lesson 4–4) **16.5 units²**

Lesson 4–4 Matrices and Determinants **211**

SELF TEST

The Self Test provides students with a brief review of the concepts and skills in Lessons 4-1 through 4-4. Lesson numbers are given to the right of exercises or instruction lines so students can review concepts not yet mastered.

Answers for the Self Test

3. $\begin{bmatrix} 4 & -0.5 \\ 0 & -1.5 \end{bmatrix}$

5. $\begin{bmatrix} 19 & 8 \\ 4 & 12 \end{bmatrix}$

---

4 ASSESS

Closing Activity
Writing Have students write a description of the step-by-step method for computing a 2×2 determinant and a 3×3 determinant.

Chapter 4, Quiz B (Lessons 4-3 and 4-4), is available in the *Assessment and Evaluation Masters*, p. 100.

Mid-Chapter Test (Lessons 4-1 through 4-4) is available in the *Assessment and Evaluation Masters*, p. 99.

Additional Answer

40.

Enrichment Masters, p. 25

4-4 NAME _____ DATE _____
Enrichment Student Edition Pages 205–211

Fourth-Order Determinants

Expansion by minors may be used to find the value of a 4 × 4 determinant, as shown below.

First write the expansion. Use the first row of the determinant. Remember that the signs of the terms alternate.

$$\begin{vmatrix} 6 & -3 & 2 & 7 \\ 0 & 4 & 3 & 5 \\ 0 & 2 & 1 & -4 \\ 6 & 0 & -2 & 0 \end{vmatrix} = 6\begin{vmatrix} 4 & 3 & 5 \\ 2 & 1 & -4 \\ 0 & -2 & 0 \end{vmatrix} - (-3)\begin{vmatrix} 0 & 3 & 5 \\ 0 & 1 & -4 \\ 6 & -2 & 0 \end{vmatrix} + 2\begin{vmatrix} 0 & 4 & 5 \\ 2 & -4 \\ 6 & 0 & 0 \end{vmatrix} - 7\begin{vmatrix} 0 & 4 & 3 \\ 2 & 1 \\ 6 & 0 & -2 \end{vmatrix}$$

Then evaluate each 3 × 3 determinant. Use any row.

$$\begin{vmatrix} 4 & 3 & 5 \\ 2 & 1 & -4 \\ 0 & -2 & 0 \end{vmatrix} = -(-2)\begin{vmatrix} 4 & 5 \\ 2 & -4 \end{vmatrix}$$
$$= 2(-16 - 10)$$
$$= -52$$

$$\begin{vmatrix} 0 & 3 & 5 \\ 0 & 1 & -4 \\ 6 & -2 & 0 \end{vmatrix} = -3\begin{vmatrix} 0 & -4 \\ 6 & 0 \end{vmatrix} + 5\begin{vmatrix} 0 & 1 \\ 6 & -2 \end{vmatrix}$$
$$= -3(24) + 5(-6)$$
$$= -102$$

$$\begin{vmatrix} 0 & 4 & 5 \\ 0 & 2 & -4 \\ 6 & 0 & 0 \end{vmatrix} = 6\begin{vmatrix} 4 & 5 \\ 2 & -4 \end{vmatrix}$$
$$= 6(-16 - 10)$$
$$= -156$$

$$\begin{vmatrix} 0 & 4 & 3 \\ 0 & 2 & 1 \\ 6 & 0 & -2 \end{vmatrix} = -4\begin{vmatrix} 0 & 1 \\ 6 & -2 \end{vmatrix} + 3\begin{vmatrix} 0 & 2 \\ 6 & 0 \end{vmatrix}$$
$$= -4(-6) + 3(-12)$$
$$= -12$$

Finally, evaluate the original 4 × 4 determinant.

$$\begin{vmatrix} 6 & -3 & 2 & 7 \\ 0 & 4 & 3 & 5 \\ 0 & 2 & 1 & -4 \\ 6 & 0 & -2 & 0 \end{vmatrix} = 6(-52) + 3(-102) + 2(-156) - 7(-12) = -846$$

Evaluate each determinant.

1. $\begin{vmatrix} 1 & 2 & 3 & 1 \\ 4 & 3 & -1 & 0 \\ 2 & -5 & 4 & 4 \\ 1 & -2 & 0 & 2 \end{vmatrix}$ −109

2. $\begin{vmatrix} 3 & 3 & 3 & 3 \\ 2 & 1 & 2 & 1 \\ 4 & 3 & -1 & 5 \\ 2 & 5 & 0 & 1 \end{vmatrix}$ −72

3. $\begin{vmatrix} 1 & 4 & 3 & 0 \\ -2 & -3 & 6 & 4 \\ 5 & 1 & 1 & 2 \\ 4 & 2 & 5 & -1 \end{vmatrix}$ −676

4-5 Identity and Inverse Matrices

Instructional Resources

- Study Guide Master 4-5
- Practice Master 4-5
- Enrichment Master 4-5
- Real-World Applications, 10

 Transparency 4-5A contains the 5-Minute Check for this lesson; **Transparency 4-5B** contains a teaching aid for this lesson.

Recommended Pacing

Standard Pacing	Day 7 of 14
Honors Pacing	Day 6 of 12
Block Scheduling*	Day 3 of 7 (along with Lesson 4-4)

 *For more information on pacing and possible lesson plans, refer to the *Block Scheduling Booklet*.

1 FOCUS

 ### 5-Minute Check
(over Lesson 4-4)

1. Determine whether the matrix has a determinant. If it does, find the value of the determinant.
$$\begin{bmatrix} 2 & 7 & -1 \\ 4 & 5 & 10 \end{bmatrix}$$ **no determinant**

2. Evaluate $\begin{vmatrix} 1 & 3 & -2 \\ 2 & -1 & 4 \\ 4 & 3 & 5 \end{vmatrix}$ using expansion by minors. **−19**

3. Evaluate $\begin{vmatrix} -1 & 1 & 2 \\ 2 & 1 & 0 \\ 3 & 6 & -2 \end{vmatrix}$ using diagonals. **24**

4. Find the area of the triangle whose vertices are $A(6, 4)$, $B(-2, 3)$, and $C(2, -3)$. **26**

5. Solve for x if $\begin{bmatrix} 1 & -2 & -3 \\ 7 & 5 & 0 \\ x & 2x & 1 \end{bmatrix} = -35$. **2**

What YOU'LL LEARN

- To write the identity matrix for any square matrix, and
- to find the inverse of a 2×2 matrix.

Why IT'S IMPORTANT

You can use matrices to solve problems involving cryptology and geometry.

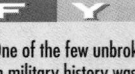

F Y I

One of the few unbroken codes in military history was constructed by a group of American Indians called the Navaho Code Talkers. During World War II, the entire military operation at Iwo Jima was directed through orders communicated by the Code Talkers. The Japanese were never able to break the code.

Two U.S. Marines use their Navajo code during battle, 1943

APPLICATION
Cryptology

You're sitting in math class reading a note that has been passed to you by your friend. Suddenly, the silence is broken by the teacher's voice saying, "If that note is so interesting, why don't you read it to the whole class?" As you slowly walk to the front of the room you think, "If I had written this note in code, I wouldn't be so embarrassed to read it!"

Cryptology deals with coding messages so that only people with the key can decipher them. In ancient Greece, Spartans wound a belt in a spiral around a stick and wrote messages along the length of the stick. When they unwound the belt, only those people who had a stick exactly the same size as the first could read the message. Since then, cryptology has been important in military communications, particularly in time of war. Today, programmers use cryptology to protect secret data stored in computers.

An important advancement in cryptology occurred in the 1930s when American mathematician Lester Hill used matrices to encode messages. Here's a simplified version of how it works.

Step 1

Suppose the first word in a message is MEET. Assign each letter a number based on its position in the alphabet (A = 1, B = 2, ..., Y = 25, Z = 26). Thus, M = 13, E = 5, and T = 20. Write the numbers in a matrix.

$$\begin{bmatrix} M & E \\ E & T \end{bmatrix} = \begin{bmatrix} 13 & 5 \\ 5 & 20 \end{bmatrix}$$

Step 2

Multiply the matrix by a *coding matrix*. Let's use $\begin{bmatrix} 0 & 1 \\ 1 & 1 \end{bmatrix}$.

$$\begin{bmatrix} 0 & 1 \\ 1 & 1 \end{bmatrix} \cdot \begin{bmatrix} 13 & 5 \\ 5 & 20 \end{bmatrix} = \begin{bmatrix} 5 & 20 \\ 18 & 25 \end{bmatrix}$$

Step 3

Assign a letter to each number of the matrix based on Step 1.

$$\begin{bmatrix} 5 & 20 \\ 18 & 25 \end{bmatrix} = \begin{bmatrix} E & T \\ R & Y \end{bmatrix}$$

Therefore, MEET would encode as ETRY. *Notice that each E in the uncoded message is assigned to a different letter in the coded message.*

F Y I

Early in World War II, the British obtained a machine the German military used to encode messages. With great effort, British mathematicians and codebreakers cracked the German code, giving the British military a great advantage. Known as the "ultra" secret by the British, the Germans never realized that their code had been broken.

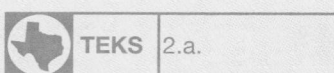 **TEKS** 2.a.

When the person receives the message, he or she needs to decipher it by *undoing* the multiplication to get back to the original matrix. Mathematically, this means finding the **inverse** of the coding matrix. *You will use this code in Example 4.*

Recall from your work with real numbers that the inverse and identity of a number are related. In real numbers, 1 is the identity for multiplication because $a \cdot 1 = 1 \cdot a = a$. Similarly, the inverse of a matrix is related to the **identity matrix**. The identity matrix is a square matrix that, when multiplied by another matrix, equals that same matrix.

With 2×2 matrices, $\begin{bmatrix} 1 & 0 \\ 0 & 1 \end{bmatrix}$ is the identity matrix because $\begin{bmatrix} a & b \\ c & d \end{bmatrix} \cdot \begin{bmatrix} 1 & 0 \\ 0 & 1 \end{bmatrix} = \begin{bmatrix} a & b \\ c & d \end{bmatrix}$ and $\begin{bmatrix} 1 & 0 \\ 0 & 1 \end{bmatrix} \cdot \begin{bmatrix} a & b \\ c & d \end{bmatrix} = \begin{bmatrix} a & b \\ c & d \end{bmatrix}$. The identity matrix is symbolized by I.

Since one of the properties of the identity matrix is that it is commutative, only a square matrix can have an identity. In an identity matrix, the principal diagonal goes from upper left to lower right and consists only of ones.

Identity Matrix for Multiplication	The identity matrix for multiplication, *I*, is a square matrix with 1 for every element of the principal diagonal and 0 in all other positions. For any square matrix *A* of the same order as *I*, **A · I = I · A = A.**

Example ❶ If $N = \begin{bmatrix} -2 & 4 & 7 \\ 5 & -3 & 6 \\ -8 & 2 & -1 \end{bmatrix}$, find I so that $N \cdot I = N$.

The dimensions of N are 3×3. So, I must also be 3×3. The principal diagonal contains only 1s. Complete the matrix with 0s.

$$\begin{bmatrix} 1 & & \\ & 1 & \\ & & 1 \end{bmatrix} \rightarrow \begin{bmatrix} 1 & 0 & 0 \\ 0 & 1 & 0 \\ 0 & 0 & 1 \end{bmatrix} \text{ The } 3 \times 3 \text{ identity matrix is } \begin{bmatrix} 1 & 0 & 0 \\ 0 & 1 & 0 \\ 0 & 0 & 1 \end{bmatrix}.$$

$$\begin{bmatrix} -2 & 4 & 7 \\ 5 & -3 & 6 \\ -8 & 2 & -1 \end{bmatrix} \cdot \begin{bmatrix} 1 & 0 & 0 \\ 0 & 1 & 0 \\ 0 & 0 & 1 \end{bmatrix} = \begin{bmatrix} -2 & 4 & 7 \\ 5 & -3 & 6 \\ -8 & 2 & -1 \end{bmatrix}$$

Therefore, $N \cdot I = N$.

Another property of real numbers is that every real number, except 0, has a multiplicative inverse. That is, $\frac{1}{a}$ is the multiplicative inverse of a because

When we refer to the inverse of a matrix, it implies the multiplicative inverse unless otherwise stated.

$a \cdot \frac{1}{a} = \frac{1}{a} \cdot a = 1$. Likewise, if matrix A has an inverse named A^{-1}, then $A \cdot A^{-1} = A^{-1} \cdot A = I$. The following example shows how the inverse of a 2×2 matrix can be found.

Alternative Learning Styles

Auditory Have students discuss the inverses of real numbers. Why does zero not have an inverse? What restrictions must be made on matrices for inverses? Why do these restrictions have to be made?

Motivating the Lesson
Hands-On Activity Have students examine the concept of inverses by looking at some real-world examples. You might have students pour a certain quantity of water from one container to another and then back again. Or you could have students walk from one point to another in the classroom, then return.

2 TEACH

In-Class Example

For Example 1

If $N = \begin{bmatrix} 5 & 1 & 2 \\ 4 & 3 & -1 \end{bmatrix}$, find I so that $N \cdot I = N$.

$\begin{bmatrix} 1 & 0 & 0 \\ 0 & 1 & 0 \\ 0 & 0 & 1 \end{bmatrix}$

Teaching Tip Emphasize that an inverse matrix for matrix A is the multiplicative inverse of matrix A, not the additive inverse.

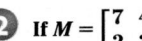

In-Class Example

For Example 2

If $A = \begin{bmatrix} 5 & 3 \\ 2 & 1 \end{bmatrix}$, find A^{-1}.

$\begin{bmatrix} -1 & 3 \\ 2 & -5 \end{bmatrix}$

Example ❷ If $M = \begin{bmatrix} 7 & 4 \\ 2 & 3 \end{bmatrix}$, find M^{-1}. **Check your result.**

Let M^{-1} be $\begin{bmatrix} w & x \\ y & z \end{bmatrix}$. By the definition of an inverse, $M \cdot M^{-1} = I$.

$$\begin{bmatrix} 7 & 4 \\ 2 & 3 \end{bmatrix} \cdot \begin{bmatrix} w & x \\ y & z \end{bmatrix} = \begin{bmatrix} 1 & 0 \\ 0 & 1 \end{bmatrix}$$

$$\begin{bmatrix} 7w + 4y & 7x + 4z \\ 2w + 3y & 2x + 3z \end{bmatrix} = \begin{bmatrix} 1 & 0 \\ 0 & 1 \end{bmatrix} \quad \text{Multiply.}$$

TECHNOLOGY *Tips*

The x^{-1} key on a graphing calculator is used to find the inverse of a matrix.

When two matrices are equal, their corresponding elements are equal. So the following equations can be generated from the two equal matrices.

(1) $7w + 4y = 1$ (2) $7x + 4z = 0$ (3) $2w + 3y = 0$ (4) $2x + 3z = 1$

Use equations (1) and (3) to find values for w and y.

First solve for w. Then substitute the w value into one of the equations to find y.

$$
\begin{array}{l}
7w + 4y = 1 \\
2w + 3y = 0
\end{array}
\rightarrow
\begin{array}{l}
21w + 12y = 3 \\
(-)\ 8w + 12y = 0 \\
\hline
13w \qquad = 3 \\
\qquad w = \frac{3}{13}
\end{array}
\longrightarrow
\begin{array}{l}
7w + 4y = 1 \\
7\left(\frac{3}{13}\right) + 4y = 1 \\
4y = -\frac{8}{13} \\
y = -\frac{2}{13}
\end{array}
$$

Use equations (2) and (4) to find values for x and z.

First solve for z. Then substitute the z value into one of the equations to find x.

$$
\begin{array}{l}
7x + 4z = 0 \\
2x + 3z = 1
\end{array}
\rightarrow
\begin{array}{l}
14x + 8z = 0 \\
(-)\ 14x + 21z = 7 \\
\hline
-13z = -7 \\
z = \frac{7}{13}
\end{array}
\longrightarrow
\begin{array}{l}
7x + 4z = 0 \\
7x + 4\left(\frac{7}{13}\right) = 0 \\
7x = -\frac{28}{13} \\
x = -\frac{4}{13}
\end{array}
$$

Therefore, $M^{-1} = \begin{bmatrix} \frac{3}{13} & -\frac{4}{13} \\ -\frac{2}{13} & \frac{7}{13} \end{bmatrix}$.

Check: $\begin{bmatrix} 7 & 4 \\ 2 & 3 \end{bmatrix} \cdot \begin{bmatrix} \frac{3}{13} & -\frac{4}{13} \\ -\frac{2}{13} & \frac{7}{13} \end{bmatrix} = \begin{bmatrix} \frac{21}{13} - \frac{8}{13} & -\frac{28}{13} + \frac{28}{13} \\ \frac{6}{13} - \frac{6}{13} & -\frac{8}{13} + \frac{21}{13} \end{bmatrix}$ or $\begin{bmatrix} 1 & 0 \\ 0 & 1 \end{bmatrix}$ ✓

You should also check to be sure that $M^{-1} \cdot M = I$.

214 *Chapter 4 Using Matrices*

Alternative Teaching Strategies

Reading Algebra *Identity* is usually defined as the quality of being the same as. *Inverse* is often thought of as that which undoes the effect of the original operation or element.

The same method used in Example 2 can be used to develop the general form of the inverse of a 2×2 matrix.

The inverse of $\begin{bmatrix} a & b \\ c & d \end{bmatrix}$ is $\begin{bmatrix} \dfrac{d}{ad-bc} & \dfrac{-b}{ad-bc} \\ \dfrac{-c}{ad-bc} & \dfrac{a}{ad-bc} \end{bmatrix}$ or $\dfrac{1}{ad-bc}\begin{bmatrix} d & -b \\ -c & a \end{bmatrix}$.

Notice that $ad - bc$ is the value of the determinant of the matrix. Remember that $\dfrac{1}{ad-bc}$ is not defined when $ad - bc = 0$. Therefore, if the value of the determinant of a matrix is 0, the matrix cannot have an inverse.

Inverse of a 2×2 Matrix	Any matrix $M = \begin{bmatrix} a & b \\ c & d \end{bmatrix}$ will have an inverse M^{-1} if and only if $\begin{vmatrix} a & b \\ c & d \end{vmatrix} \neq 0$. Then $M^{-1} = \dfrac{1}{ad-bc}\begin{bmatrix} d & -b \\ -c & a \end{bmatrix}$.

Example ③ If $Q = \begin{bmatrix} 2 & -1 \\ 1 & -3 \end{bmatrix}$, find Q^{-1}. Check your result.

Find the value of the determinant.

$$\begin{vmatrix} 2 & -1 \\ 1 & -3 \end{vmatrix} = -6 - (-1) \text{ or } -5$$

Since the determinant does not equal 0, Q^{-1} exists.

$$Q^{-1} = \frac{1}{ad-bc}\begin{bmatrix} d & -b \\ -c & a \end{bmatrix}$$

$$= -\frac{1}{5}\begin{bmatrix} -3 & 1 \\ -1 & 2 \end{bmatrix}$$

Check: $-\dfrac{1}{5}\begin{bmatrix} -3 & 1 \\ -1 & 2 \end{bmatrix} \cdot \begin{bmatrix} 2 & -1 \\ 1 & -3 \end{bmatrix} = -\dfrac{1}{5}\begin{bmatrix} -6+1 & 3-3 \\ -2+2 & 1-6 \end{bmatrix} = \begin{bmatrix} 1 & 0 \\ 0 & 1 \end{bmatrix}$ ✓

TECHNOLOGY Tips

If you get a SINGULAR MATRIX error on a graphing calculator when trying to find an inverse, it means that the matrix has no inverse.

In the application at the beginning of the lesson, the coding matrix $\begin{bmatrix} 0 & 1 \\ 1 & 1 \end{bmatrix}$ was used to encode the word MEET as ETRY. In the following Example, you will *decode* part of the message by finding the inverse of the coding matrix.

Example ④

APPLICATION
Cryptology

Suppose a person receives the message ETRYATNYEMYULAMMIXCQ that has been encoded using the matrix $C = \begin{bmatrix} 0 & 1 \\ 1 & 1 \end{bmatrix}$. You already know that the first four letters, ETRY, correspond to MEET. Decode the next four letters in the message.

First, write the letters in a 2×2 matrix and assign each letter a number based on its position in the alphabet.

$$\begin{bmatrix} A & T \\ N & Y \end{bmatrix} = \begin{bmatrix} 1 & 20 \\ 14 & 25 \end{bmatrix}$$

(continued on the next page)

Lesson 4–5   Identity and Inverse Matrices   **215**

In-Class Examples

For Example 3
If $P = \begin{bmatrix} 2 & -5 \\ 0 & 7 \end{bmatrix}$, find P^{-1}.
$\dfrac{1}{14}\begin{bmatrix} 7 & 5 \\ 0 & 2 \end{bmatrix}$

For Example 4
Suppose the same message were encoded with coding matrix $\begin{bmatrix} 1 & 0 \\ 1 & 0 \end{bmatrix}$.

Explain why this would not work. **Two out of every four letters in the message are lost in the encoding.**

Teaching Tip Emphasize that b and c each change signs; they do not exchange signs.

fabulous
FIRSTS
Women began attending West Point in 1976. By 1995 West Point graduated a total of 1400 women.

3 PRACTICE/APPLY

Check for Understanding

Exercises 1–10 are designed to help you assess your students' understanding through reading, writing, speaking, and modeling. You should work through Exercises 1–5 with your students and then monitor their work on Exercises 6–10.

Error Analysis
Students sometimes give the inverse of a matrix A as

$$\begin{bmatrix} \frac{1}{a_{11}} & \frac{1}{a_{12}} \cdots \\ \frac{1}{a_{21}} \\ \vdots \end{bmatrix}.$$

To dispel this notion, have students verify that

$$\begin{bmatrix} a & b \\ c & d \end{bmatrix} \begin{bmatrix} \frac{1}{a} & \frac{1}{b} \\ \frac{1}{c} & \frac{1}{d} \end{bmatrix} \neq 1.$$

Study Guide Masters, p. 26

4-5
NAME_____ DATE_____
Study Guide
Student Edition
Pages 212–218

Identity and Inverse Matrices
Apply the following definitions for identities and inverses of matrices.

Identity Matrix for Multiplication

Definition	Example
The identity matrix for multiplication, I, is a square matrix with 1 for every element of the principal diagonal and 0 for all other positions. The principal diagonal extends from upper left to lower right.	For 2×2 matrices, $\begin{bmatrix} 1 & 0 \\ 0 & 1 \end{bmatrix}$ is the identity matrix because $\begin{bmatrix} a & b \\ c & d \end{bmatrix}\begin{bmatrix} 1 & 0 \\ 0 & 1 \end{bmatrix} = \begin{bmatrix} a & b \\ c & d \end{bmatrix}$ and $\begin{bmatrix} 1 & 0 \\ 0 & 1 \end{bmatrix}\begin{bmatrix} a & b \\ c & d \end{bmatrix} = \begin{bmatrix} a & b \\ c & d \end{bmatrix}$

Inverse of a 2 × 2 Matrix

Definition	Example
Any matrix $M = \begin{bmatrix} a & b \\ c & d \end{bmatrix}$ will have an inverse M^{-1} if and only if $\begin{vmatrix} a & b \\ c & d \end{vmatrix} \neq 0$. Then $M^{-1} = \frac{1}{ad-bc}\begin{bmatrix} d & -b \\ -c & a \end{bmatrix}$.	Find the inverse of $A = \begin{bmatrix} 4 & 3 \\ -2 & 8 \end{bmatrix}$ if it exists. 1. Compute the value of the determinant to make sure that the inverse exists. $\begin{vmatrix} 4 & 3 \\ -2 & 8 \end{vmatrix} = 32 - (-6) = 38$ 2. Since the determinant does not equal 0, A^{-1} exists and $A^{-1} = \frac{1}{38}\begin{bmatrix} 8 & -3 \\ 2 & 4 \end{bmatrix}$.

Find the inverse of each matrix, if it exists.

1. $\begin{bmatrix} 24 & 12 \\ 8 & 4 \end{bmatrix}$ no inverse exists

2. $\begin{bmatrix} 26 & -8 \\ 4 & -9 \end{bmatrix}$ $\frac{1}{202}\begin{bmatrix} -9 & 8 \\ -4 & 26 \end{bmatrix}$

3. $\begin{bmatrix} 40 & -10 \\ -20 & 30 \end{bmatrix}$ $\frac{1}{1000}\begin{bmatrix} 30 & 10 \\ 20 & 40 \end{bmatrix}$

4. $\begin{bmatrix} -5 & -4 \\ 0 & 3 \end{bmatrix}$ $\frac{1}{15}\begin{bmatrix} 3 & 4 \\ 0 & -5 \end{bmatrix}$

5. $\begin{bmatrix} 18 & 9 \\ 3 & 6 \end{bmatrix}$ $\frac{1}{81}\begin{bmatrix} 6 & -9 \\ -3 & 18 \end{bmatrix}$

6. $\begin{bmatrix} 3 & 6 \\ 4 & 8 \end{bmatrix}$ no inverse exists

7. $\begin{bmatrix} 1 & 0 \\ 0 & 1 \end{bmatrix}\begin{bmatrix} 1 & 0 \\ 0 & 1 \end{bmatrix}$

8. $\begin{bmatrix} -2 & 0 \\ 0 & -2 \end{bmatrix}\begin{bmatrix} -\frac{1}{2} & 0 \\ 0 & -\frac{1}{2} \end{bmatrix}$

9. $\begin{bmatrix} 1 & 1 \\ 0 & 1 \end{bmatrix}\begin{bmatrix} 1 & -1 \\ 0 & 1 \end{bmatrix}$

fabulous
FIRSTS

Rebecca Marier (1974–)

For the first time in the U.S. Military Academy's 193-year history, a woman—Rebecca Marier—graduated first in her class among 987 other senior cadets on June 3, 1995, at West Point, New York.

Now, find the inverse of the coding matrix $C = \begin{bmatrix} 0 & 1 \\ 1 & 1 \end{bmatrix}$. The determinant is $0 - 1$ or -1.

$$C^{-1} = \frac{1}{-1}\begin{bmatrix} 1 & -1 \\ -1 & 0 \end{bmatrix} \text{ or } \begin{bmatrix} -1 & 1 \\ 1 & 0 \end{bmatrix}$$

Finally, multiply the inverse matrix by the first matrix and assign letters to the elements in the product.

$$\begin{bmatrix} -1 & 1 \\ 1 & 0 \end{bmatrix} \cdot \begin{bmatrix} 1 & 20 \\ 14 & 25 \end{bmatrix} = \begin{bmatrix} 13 & 5 \\ 1 & 20 \end{bmatrix} \text{ or } \begin{bmatrix} M & E \\ A & T \end{bmatrix}$$

Therefore, the next four letters of the message are MEAT.

The first eight letters of the message are MEETMEAT. You will decode the rest of the message in Exercises 10 and 33.

CHECK FOR UNDERSTANDING

Communicating Mathematics

2. $\begin{bmatrix} 1 & 0 & 0 & 0 \\ 0 & 1 & 0 & 0 \\ 0 & 0 & 1 & 0 \\ 0 & 0 & 0 & 1 \end{bmatrix}$

4. Sample answer:
$\begin{bmatrix} 1 & 2 \\ 3 & 6 \end{bmatrix}$

Study the lesson. Then complete the following.

1. **Explain** how the multiplicative inverse and identity for real numbers are similar to the matrix inverse and identity. **See margin.**

2. **Write** the 4×4 identity matrix.

3. **Choose** the inverse of $\begin{bmatrix} 2 & 2 \\ 3 & 4 \end{bmatrix}$. **c**

   a. $\begin{bmatrix} \frac{1}{2} & \frac{1}{2} \\ \frac{1}{3} & \frac{1}{4} \end{bmatrix}$
   b. $\begin{bmatrix} 1 & 0 \\ 0 & 1 \end{bmatrix}$
   c. $\begin{bmatrix} 2 & -1 \\ -\frac{3}{2} & 1 \end{bmatrix}$
   d. $\begin{bmatrix} 4 & -2 \\ -3 & 2 \end{bmatrix}$

4. **Create** a square matrix that does not have an inverse.

5. **You Decide** Miyoki says that the matrix $\begin{bmatrix} 1 \\ 4 \end{bmatrix}$ does not have a multiplicative identity. Hector says the identity is $\begin{bmatrix} 1 & 0 \\ 0 & 1 \end{bmatrix}$ because $\begin{bmatrix} 1 & 0 \\ 0 & 1 \end{bmatrix} \cdot \begin{bmatrix} 1 \\ 4 \end{bmatrix} = \begin{bmatrix} 1 \\ 4 \end{bmatrix}$. Who is correct? Explain your reasoning. **See margin.**

Guided Practice

6. $\begin{bmatrix} 2 & -1 \\ -5 & 3 \end{bmatrix}$

9. $-\frac{1}{27}\begin{bmatrix} 4 & -1 \\ -7 & -5 \end{bmatrix}$

Find the inverse of each matrix, if it exists. If it does not exist, explain why not. 7. not square 8. det = 0

6. $\begin{bmatrix} 3 & 1 \\ 5 & 2 \end{bmatrix}$
7. $\begin{bmatrix} 1 \\ 2 \end{bmatrix}$
8. $\begin{bmatrix} 6 & 3 \\ 8 & 4 \end{bmatrix}$
9. $\begin{bmatrix} -5 & 1 \\ 7 & 4 \end{bmatrix}$

10. **Cryptology** Decode the next four letters, EMYU, of the message in Example 4. **THEM**

216 Chapter 4 Using Matrices

Reteaching

Using Substeps For the 2×2 matrix $\begin{bmatrix} 3 & 2 \\ 4 & 3 \end{bmatrix}$, have students find the multiplicative inverse $\begin{bmatrix} 3 & -2 \\ -4 & 3 \end{bmatrix}$ and the additive inverse $\begin{bmatrix} -3 & -2 \\ -4 & -3 \end{bmatrix}$.

Then have them show that
$$\begin{bmatrix} 1 & 0 \\ 0 & 1 \end{bmatrix} \cdot \begin{bmatrix} 3 & 2 \\ 4 & 3 \end{bmatrix} = \begin{bmatrix} 3 & 2 \\ 4 & 3 \end{bmatrix}.$$

Additional Answers

1. With real numbers, the product of any number, except 0, and its inverse is the identity. With matrices, the product of any square matrix, except one with a determinant of 0, and its inverse is the identity matrix.

5. Miyoki; multiplication with the identity matrix is commutative and $\begin{bmatrix} 1 \\ 4 \end{bmatrix} \cdot \begin{bmatrix} 1 & 0 \\ 0 & 1 \end{bmatrix}$ is not defined.

Practice

Find the inverse of each matrix, if it exists. If it does not exist, explain why not.

11. $\begin{bmatrix} 5 & 0 \\ 0 & 1 \end{bmatrix}$ $\frac{1}{5}\begin{bmatrix} 1 & 0 \\ 0 & 5 \end{bmatrix}$ **12.** $\begin{bmatrix} 8 & -5 \\ -3 & 2 \end{bmatrix}$ $\begin{bmatrix} 2 & 5 \\ 3 & 8 \end{bmatrix}$ **13.** $\begin{bmatrix} 4 & -8 \\ -1 & 2 \end{bmatrix}$ det = 0

14. $\begin{bmatrix} 6 \\ 4 \end{bmatrix}$ not square   **15.** $\begin{bmatrix} 4 & -3 \\ 2 & 7 \end{bmatrix}$ $\frac{1}{34}\begin{bmatrix} 7 & 3 \\ -2 & 4 \end{bmatrix}$ **16.** $\begin{bmatrix} -1 & 5 & -2 \\ 4 & 2 & -3 \end{bmatrix}$ not square

17. $\begin{bmatrix} 2 & -5 \\ 6 & 1 \end{bmatrix}$ $\frac{1}{32}\begin{bmatrix} 1 & 5 \\ -6 & 2 \end{bmatrix}$ **18.** $\begin{bmatrix} 4 & 4 \\ 4 & 4 \end{bmatrix}$ det = 0   **19.** $\begin{bmatrix} -2 & 0 \\ 5 & 6 \end{bmatrix}$ $-\frac{1}{12}\begin{bmatrix} 6 & 0 \\ -5 & -2 \end{bmatrix}$

Determine whether each statement is _true_ or _false_.

20. $\begin{bmatrix} 0 & 1 \\ 1 & 1 \end{bmatrix} \cdot \begin{bmatrix} -1 & 1 \\ 1 & 0 \end{bmatrix} = I$ true   **21.** $\begin{bmatrix} 2 & 1 & -4 \\ -3 & 6 & 5 \\ 1 & 2 & -2 \end{bmatrix} \cdot I = \begin{bmatrix} 2 & 1 & -4 \\ -3 & 6 & 5 \\ 1 & 2 & -2 \end{bmatrix}$ true

22. $\begin{bmatrix} \frac{1}{3} & -\frac{2}{3} \\ \frac{2}{3} & -\frac{1}{3} \end{bmatrix} \cdot \begin{bmatrix} 1 & 2 \\ 2 & 1 \end{bmatrix} = I$ false   **23.** $\begin{bmatrix} 1 & 5 \\ 1 & -2 \end{bmatrix} \cdot \begin{bmatrix} \frac{2}{7} & \frac{5}{7} \\ \frac{1}{7} & -\frac{1}{7} \end{bmatrix} = I$ true

24. The inverse of $\begin{bmatrix} 3 & 1 & 2 \\ -2 & 0 & 4 \\ 3 & 5 & 2 \end{bmatrix}$ is $-\frac{1}{64}\begin{bmatrix} -20 & 8 & 4 \\ 16 & 0 & -16 \\ -10 & -12 & 2 \end{bmatrix}$.   true

25. All square matrices have multiplicative identities.   true

26. Only square matrices have multiplicative inverses.   true

27. Some square matrices do not have multiplicative inverses.   true

28. Some square matrices do not have multiplicative identities.   false

29. All multiplicative identities are square matrices.   true

Graphing Calculator

30. When Mike used a graphing calculator to find the inverse of $\begin{bmatrix} -3 & -2 \\ 6 & 4 \end{bmatrix}$, there was an ERROR statement. Explain why.
The determinant is 0, so the matrix has no inverse.

Critical Thinking

31. Prove that $A \cdot I = I \cdot A = A$ for all second-order matrices.
See margin.

Applications and Problem Solving

32a. $\begin{bmatrix} 0 & 1 \\ -1 & 0 \end{bmatrix}$

32b. Sample answer: rotate figure 90° clockwise.

32. Geometry Recall that the matrix $\begin{bmatrix} 0 & -1 \\ 1 & 0 \end{bmatrix}$ will rotate a figure on a coordinate plane 90° counterclockwise about the origin.
  a. Find the inverse of this rotation matrix.
  b. Make a conjecture about what movement the inverse describes on a coordinate plane.
  c. Test your conjecture on the triangle shown at the right. Make a drawing to verify your conjecture.   See margin.

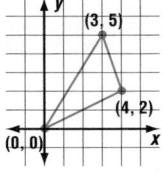

Lesson 4–5 Identity and Inverse Matrices **217**

Assignment Guide

Core: 11–33 odd, 34–39
Enriched: 12–30 even, 31–39

For **Extra Practice,** see p. 884.

The red A, B, and C flags, printed only in the Teacher's Wraparound Edition, indicate the level of difficulty of the exercises.

Additional Answers

31. Let $\begin{bmatrix} a & b \\ c & d \end{bmatrix}$ represent A and let $\begin{bmatrix} 1 & 0 \\ 0 & 1 \end{bmatrix}$ represent I.

$\begin{bmatrix} a & b \\ c & d \end{bmatrix} \cdot \begin{bmatrix} 1 & 0 \\ 0 & 1 \end{bmatrix} = \begin{bmatrix} a & b \\ c & d \end{bmatrix}$

$\begin{bmatrix} 1 & 0 \\ 0 & 1 \end{bmatrix} \cdot \begin{bmatrix} a & b \\ c & d \end{bmatrix} = \begin{bmatrix} a & b \\ c & d \end{bmatrix}$

Therefore, $A \cdot I = I \cdot A = A$.

32c.

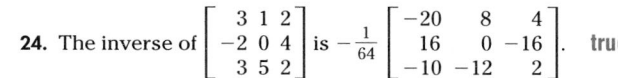

(3, 5)
(4, 2)
(0, 0)
(5, −3)
(2, −4)

Practice Masters, p. 26

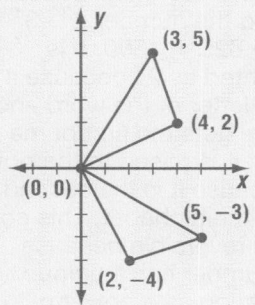

4-5   NAME _____ DATE _____
Student Edition Pages 212–218
Practice

Identity and Inverse Matrices

Find the inverse of each matrix, if it exists.

1. $\begin{bmatrix} 3 & 1 \\ -4 & 2 \end{bmatrix}$ **2.** $\begin{bmatrix} 4 & 5 \\ -4 & -3 \end{bmatrix}$

$\begin{bmatrix} \frac{1}{5} & -\frac{1}{10} \\ \frac{2}{5} & \frac{3}{10} \end{bmatrix}$ $\begin{bmatrix} -\frac{3}{8} & -\frac{5}{8} \\ \frac{1}{2} & \frac{1}{2} \end{bmatrix}$

3. $\begin{bmatrix} 4 & 6 \\ 6 & 9 \end{bmatrix}$ **4.** $\begin{bmatrix} 2 & 5 \\ -1 & 3 \end{bmatrix}$

does not exist $\begin{bmatrix} \frac{3}{11} & -\frac{5}{11} \\ \frac{1}{11} & \frac{2}{11} \end{bmatrix}$

5. $\begin{bmatrix} -4 & 7 \\ 8 & 1 \end{bmatrix}$ **6.** $\begin{bmatrix} 2 & 0 \\ 3 & 5 \end{bmatrix}$

$\begin{bmatrix} -\frac{1}{60} & \frac{7}{60} \\ \frac{2}{15} & \frac{1}{15} \end{bmatrix}$ $\begin{bmatrix} \frac{1}{2} & 0 \\ -\frac{3}{10} & \frac{1}{5} \end{bmatrix}$

7. $\begin{bmatrix} 2 & -5 \\ 3 & 1 \end{bmatrix}$ **8.** $\begin{bmatrix} -1 & 3 \\ 4 & -7 \end{bmatrix}$

$\begin{bmatrix} \frac{1}{17} & \frac{5}{17} \\ -\frac{3}{17} & \frac{2}{17} \end{bmatrix}$ $\begin{bmatrix} \frac{7}{5} & \frac{3}{5} \\ \frac{4}{5} & \frac{1}{5} \end{bmatrix}$

Closing Activity

Modeling Have students cut an equilateral triangle from a piece of paper. They should explore all rotations that would leave the triangle appearing the same: 120° (one-third rotation), 240° (two-thirds rotation), 360° (full rotation). Have them identify the inverse (in degrees) and the identity for each.

Mathematics and SOCIETY

Students might like to work with a few simple codes. A clever one developed by Kurt Gödel in the early 1900s uses prime numbers. A word like *bad* is assigned the number $2^2 \cdot 3^1 \cdot 5^4 = 4 \cdot 3 \cdot 625 = 7500$. *b* is represented as 2^2 because it is the first letter of the word and therefore gets the first prime number; it is raised to the power of 2 because it is the second letter in the alphabet. This code is easily reversible because every number has a unique factorization as a power of primes.

Enrichment Masters, p. 26

4-5

NAME _____ DATE _____

Student Edition
Pages 212–218

Enrichment

Permutation Matrices

A permutation matrix is a square matrix in which each row and each column has one entry that is 1. All the other entries are 0. It is easy to find the inverse of a permutation matrix. You just interchange the rows and columns.

$$P = \begin{bmatrix} 0 & 0 & 1 & 0 \\ 0 & 1 & 0 & 0 \\ 0 & 0 & 0 & 1 \\ 1 & 0 & 0 & 0 \end{bmatrix} \quad P^{-1} = \begin{bmatrix} 0 & 0 & 0 & 1 \\ 0 & 1 & 0 & 0 \\ 1 & 0 & 0 & 0 \\ 0 & 0 & 1 & 0 \end{bmatrix}$$

P is a 4×4 permutation matrix. P^{-1} is the inverse of P.

Solve each problem.

1. There is just one 2×2 permutation matrix that is not also an identity matrix. Write this matrix.
$$\begin{bmatrix} 0 & 1 \\ 1 & 0 \end{bmatrix}$$

2. Find the inverse of the matrix you wrote in problem 1. What do you notice?
$$\begin{bmatrix} 0 & 1 \\ 1 & 0 \end{bmatrix}$$ The two matrices are the same.

3. Show that the two matrices in problems 1 and 2 are inverses.
$$\begin{bmatrix} 0 \cdot 1 + 1 \cdot 1 & 0 \cdot 1 + 1 \cdot 0 \\ 1 \cdot 0 + 0 \cdot 1 & 1 \cdot 1 + 0 \cdot 0 \end{bmatrix} = \begin{bmatrix} 1 & 0 \\ 0 & 1 \end{bmatrix}$$

4. Write the inverse of this matrix. $B = \begin{bmatrix} 0 & 0 & 1 \\ 1 & 0 & 0 \\ 0 & 1 & 0 \end{bmatrix}$
$$B^{-1} = \begin{bmatrix} 0 & 1 & 0 \\ 0 & 0 & 1 \\ 1 & 0 & 0 \end{bmatrix}$$

5. Use B^{-1} from problem 4. Verify that B and B^{-1} are inverses.
$$\begin{bmatrix} 0 \cdot 0 + 0 \cdot 0 + 1 \cdot 1 & 0 \cdot 1 + 0 \cdot 0 + 1 \cdot 0 & 0 \cdot 0 + 0 \cdot 1 + 1 \cdot 0 \\ 1 \cdot 0 + 0 \cdot 0 + 0 \cdot 1 & 1 \cdot 1 + 0 \cdot 0 + 0 \cdot 0 & 1 \cdot 0 + 0 \cdot 1 + 0 \cdot 0 \\ 0 \cdot 0 + 1 \cdot 0 + 0 \cdot 1 & 0 \cdot 1 + 1 \cdot 0 + 0 \cdot 0 & 0 \cdot 0 + 1 \cdot 1 + 0 \cdot 0 \end{bmatrix} = \begin{bmatrix} 1 & 0 & 0 \\ 0 & 1 & 0 \\ 0 & 0 & 1 \end{bmatrix}$$

6. Permutation matrices can be used to write and decipher codes. To see how this is done, use the message matrix M and matrix B from problem 4. Find matrix C so that C equals the product MB. Use the rules below.

0 times a letter = 0
1 times a letter = the same letter
0 plus a letter = the same letter

$$M = \begin{bmatrix} S & H & E \\ S & A & W \\ H & I & M \end{bmatrix} \quad C = \begin{bmatrix} H & E & S \\ A & W & S \\ I & M & H \end{bmatrix}$$

7. Now find the product CB^{-1}. What do you notice?
$$\begin{bmatrix} H & E & S \\ A & W & S \\ I & M & H \end{bmatrix} \cdot \begin{bmatrix} 0 & 1 & 0 \\ 0 & 0 & 1 \\ 1 & 0 & 0 \end{bmatrix} = \begin{bmatrix} S & H & E \\ S & A & W \\ H & I & M \end{bmatrix}$$

Multiplying M by B encodes the message. To decipher, multiply by B^{-1}.

33a. ALLATSIX

33b. MEET ME AT THE MALL AT SIX

33c. See students' work.

36. $\left(\frac{1}{3}, 2\right)$

33. **Cryptology** Refer to Example 4 and Exercise 10.
   a. Decode the last eight letters, LAMMIXCQ, of the coded message. (*Hint:* Negative integers and zero are assigned letters as follows: $0 = Z$, $-1 = Y$, $-2 = X$, $-3 = W$, and so on.)
   b. Write the entire decoded message from Example 4.
   c. Write a message and code it using your own coding matrix. (*Hint:* Use a coding matrix whose determinant is 1 or -1.) Trade messages with a partner and decode the messages.

Mixed Review

34. Solve $\begin{vmatrix} 4 & -a \\ 7 & 3a \end{vmatrix} = 57$. (Lesson 4–4)   **3**

35. **Geometry** The perimeter of a right triangle is 24 centimeters. Three times the length of the longer leg minus two times the length of the shorter leg exceeds the hypotenuse by 2 centimeters. The length of the shorter leg is one centimeter more than half the hypotenuse. What are the lengths of all three sides? (Lesson 3–7)   **6, 8, 10 cm**

36. Solve the system of equations by using substitution. (Lesson 3–2)
   $3x - 2y = -3$
   $3x + y = 3$

37. Find the value of $g(12)$ when $g(x) = \frac{26 - x}{2}$. (Lesson 2–1)   **7**

38. Solve $5 < 2x - 9 < 11$. (Lesson 1–6) $\{x \mid 7 < x < 10\}$

39. Solve $|a + 5| + 5 = 3$. (Lesson 1–5)   **no solution**

Mathematics and SOCIETY

DSS Code

The excerpt below appeared in an article in *Popular Science* in December, 1994.

THE GROWING AMOUNT OF BUSINESS being conducted electronically these days raises thorny questions: How does your broker, lawyer, or accountant know that your e-mail message really came from you? And just how valid is a computerized contract when there are no signatures on the bottom line? These are among the questions being addressed by the National Institute of Standards and Technology, which has proposed a solution called the Digital Signal Standard (DSS). Essentially, the DSS is a method for creating a mathematical "signature" on your documents . . . . The DSS relies on a well-known cryptology concept called public and private keys. You use a private key—a long number you keep to yourself—to generate an encoded, "signed" version of your message. A recipient verifies this signature using your public key, another long number. The public key is tied to the private key by a mathematical equation that makes it easy to compute the public key from the private key, but nearly impossible to perform the reverse calculation. If the math indicates a match, your signature has been verified. ∎

1–3. See Solutions Manual.

1. You could call the DSS code a "one-way" function because it is relatively easy to do in one direction, but much more difficult to do in the reverse direction. Can you think of another example of a one-way function?

2. If the federal government used the DSS, who might want to keep a "master key" so they could decode all messages flowing through the government's systems?

3. List some of the advantages and disadvantages of having a "master key."

Extension

Reasoning Find a 2×2 matrix, other than the identity matrix, that is its own inverse.

$\begin{bmatrix} 0 & 1 \\ 1 & 0 \end{bmatrix}$ and $\begin{bmatrix} -2 & 1 \\ -3 & 2 \end{bmatrix}$ are typical answers.

Using Matrices to Solve Systems of Equations

What YOU'LL LEARN

- To solve systems of linear equations by using inverse matrices.

Why IT'S IMPORTANT

You can use matrices and systems of equations to solve problems involving chemistry and business.

APPLICATION

Business

Katie earns extra money by making stuffed teddy bears and rabbits and then selling them to a local craft store. She has arranged to sell a total of 15 stuffed animals to the owner of the craft store each week. Her profit on each rabbit is $5 and each bear is $9. Her goal is to earn at least $120 each week. Of course, Katie could make 15 bears and easily meet her goals. But it takes her longer to make a bear than a rabbit, and she doesn't have time to make 15 bears. Katie wants to know what combination of stuffed animals she should make each week to guarantee a profit of $120. *This problem will be solved in Example 3.*

Remember, two matrices are equal if their corresponding elements are equal.

The problem above can be solved by using a system of equations. You have already learned several methods for solving a system of equations, including graphing, substitution, addition and subtraction, and Cramer's rule. Matrices can also be used to solve systems of equations. In this lesson, you will be using inverses of matrices.

Consider the system of equations below. You can write this system with matrices by using the left and right sides of the equations.

$$\begin{array}{r} 7x + 5y = 3 \\ 3x - 2y = 22 \end{array} \quad \rightarrow \quad \begin{bmatrix} 7x + 5y \\ 3x - 2y \end{bmatrix} = \begin{bmatrix} 3 \\ 22 \end{bmatrix}$$

LOOK BACK

You can refer to Lessons 3-1, 3-2, and 3-3 for information about solving systems of equations.

Write the matrix on the left as the product of the coefficients and variables.

$$\begin{bmatrix} 7 & 5 \\ 3 & -2 \end{bmatrix} \cdot \begin{bmatrix} x \\ y \end{bmatrix} = \begin{bmatrix} 3 \\ 22 \end{bmatrix}$$

coefficient   variable   constant
matrix   matrix   matrix

The system of equations is now expressed as a **matrix equation**. *This system will be solved in Example 2.*

Example **1** Write each system of equations as a matrix equation.

a. $3x - 2y = 7$
$4x + y = 8$

b. $3a - 5b + 2c = 9$
$4a + 7b + c = 3$
$2a - c = 12$

The matrix equation is

$$\begin{bmatrix} 3 & -2 \\ 4 & 1 \end{bmatrix} \cdot \begin{bmatrix} x \\ y \end{bmatrix} = \begin{bmatrix} 7 \\ 8 \end{bmatrix}.$$

The matrix equation is

$$\begin{bmatrix} 3 & -5 & 2 \\ 4 & 7 & 1 \\ 2 & 0 & -1 \end{bmatrix} \cdot \begin{bmatrix} a \\ b \\ c \end{bmatrix} = \begin{bmatrix} 9 \\ 3 \\ 12 \end{bmatrix}.$$

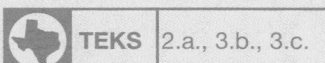

TEKS | 2.a., 3.b., 3.c.

NCTM Standards: 1–5, 12

Instructional Resources

- Study Guide Master 4-6
- Practice Master 4-6
- Enrichment Master 4-6
- Assessment and Evaluation Masters, p. 101
- Tech Prep Applications Masters, p. 8

 Transparency 4-6A contains the 5-Minute Check for this lesson; **Transparency 4-6B** contains a teaching aid for this lesson.

Recommended Pacing	
Standard Pacing	Days 8 & 9 of 14
Honors Pacing	Day 7 of 12
Block Scheduling*	Day 4 of 7

*For more information on pacing and possible lesson plans, refer to the *Block Scheduling Booklet*.

1 FOCUS

5-Minute Check
(over Lesson 4-5)

Find the identity matrix for each matrix.

1. $[4 \ \ -7 \ \ 12]$

$$\begin{bmatrix} 1 & 0 & 0 \\ 0 & 1 & 0 \\ 0 & 0 & 1 \end{bmatrix}$$

2. $\begin{bmatrix} 6 & 9 & 7 \\ 4 & 2 & -2 \\ -3 & 5 & 1 \end{bmatrix}$ $\begin{bmatrix} 1 & 0 & 0 \\ 0 & 1 & 0 \\ 0 & 0 & 1 \end{bmatrix}$

3. If $A = \begin{bmatrix} 43 & 12 \\ -7 & -2 \end{bmatrix}$, find A^{-1}.

$$-\frac{1}{2}\begin{bmatrix} -2 & -12 \\ 7 & 43 \end{bmatrix}$$

4. If $A = \begin{bmatrix} 2 & -1 \\ 3 & -2 \end{bmatrix}$, find A^{-1}.

$$-1\begin{bmatrix} -2 & 1 \\ -3 & 2 \end{bmatrix}$$

5. If $A = \begin{bmatrix} 1 & 1 \\ 0 & 1 \end{bmatrix}$, find A^{-1}.

$$\begin{bmatrix} 1 & -1 \\ 0 & 1 \end{bmatrix}$$

2 TEACH

In-Class Examples

For Example 1
Write each system of equations as a matrix equation.

a. $4a - 12b = 7$
$a + 6b = 9$

$$\begin{bmatrix} 4 & -12 \\ 1 & 6 \end{bmatrix} \cdot \begin{bmatrix} a \\ b \end{bmatrix} = \begin{bmatrix} 7 \\ 9 \end{bmatrix}$$

b. $m - 2n + p = 14$
$-3m - 3n + 5p = -22$
$11m + 4n - 7p = 35$

$$\begin{bmatrix} 1 & -2 & 1 \\ -3 & -3 & 5 \\ 11 & 4 & -7 \end{bmatrix} \cdot \begin{bmatrix} m \\ n \\ p \end{bmatrix} = \begin{bmatrix} 14 \\ -22 \\ 35 \end{bmatrix}$$

For Example 2
Use a matrix equation to solve the system of equations.
$7x - 11y = 10$
$3x + 2y = 58$
(14, 8)

Teaching Tip Remind students that positioning of the matrices is important since multiplication of matrices is not commutative.

A linear equation in the form $ax = b$ and a matrix equation in the form $AX = B$, where A is the coefficient matrix, X is the variable matrix, and B is the constant matrix, can be solved in a similar manner.

Since matrix multiplication is not commutative, the inverse matrix should be at the left on each side of the matrix equation.

$$ax = b \qquad\qquad\qquad\qquad AX = B$$
$$\left(\tfrac{1}{a}\right)ax = \left(\tfrac{1}{a}\right)b \quad \textit{Multiply by the inverse if it exists.} \quad A^{-1}AX = A^{-1}B$$
$$1x = \left(\tfrac{1}{a}\right)b \quad \textit{1 and I are identities.} \qquad\qquad IX = A^{-1}B$$
$$x = \left(\tfrac{1}{a}\right)b \qquad\qquad\qquad\qquad\qquad X = A^{-1}B$$

The solution of the linear equation is the product of the inverse of the coefficient and the constant term. In the matrix equation, the solution is the product of the inverse of the coefficient matrix and the constant matrix.

Example ② Use a matrix equation to solve the system of equations.
$7x + 5y = 3$
$3x - 2y = 22$

The matrix equation is $\begin{bmatrix} 7 & 5 \\ 3 & -2 \end{bmatrix} \cdot \begin{bmatrix} x \\ y \end{bmatrix} = \begin{bmatrix} 3 \\ 22 \end{bmatrix}$.

First, find the inverse of the coefficient matrix. The inverse of $\begin{bmatrix} 7 & 5 \\ 3 & -2 \end{bmatrix}$ is

$$\frac{1}{-14-(15)}\begin{bmatrix} -2 & -5 \\ -3 & 7 \end{bmatrix} \text{ or } -\frac{1}{29}\begin{bmatrix} -2 & -5 \\ -3 & 7 \end{bmatrix}.$$

The identity matrix on the left verifies that the inverse matrix has been calculated correctly.

Next, multiply each side of the matrix equation by the inverse matrix.

$$-\frac{1}{29}\begin{bmatrix} -2 & -5 \\ -3 & 7 \end{bmatrix} \cdot \begin{bmatrix} 7 & 5 \\ 3 & -2 \end{bmatrix} \cdot \begin{bmatrix} x \\ y \end{bmatrix} = -\frac{1}{29}\begin{bmatrix} -2 & -5 \\ -3 & 7 \end{bmatrix} \cdot \begin{bmatrix} 3 \\ 22 \end{bmatrix}$$

$$-\frac{1}{29}\begin{bmatrix} -29 & 0 \\ 0 & -29 \end{bmatrix} \cdot \begin{bmatrix} x \\ y \end{bmatrix} = -\frac{1}{29}\begin{bmatrix} -116 \\ 145 \end{bmatrix}$$

$$\begin{bmatrix} 1 & 0 \\ 0 & 1 \end{bmatrix} \cdot \begin{bmatrix} x \\ y \end{bmatrix} = \begin{bmatrix} 4 \\ -5 \end{bmatrix}$$

$$\begin{bmatrix} x \\ y \end{bmatrix} = \begin{bmatrix} 4 \\ -5 \end{bmatrix}$$

The solution is $(4, -5)$.

The graph at the right confirms the solution.

How might you check the solution?

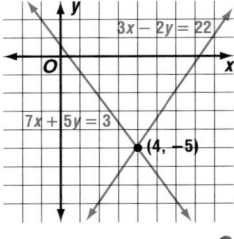

You will not be asked to find the inverse of a 3×3 matrix in this chapter.

To solve a system of equations with three variables, you will use the 3×3 identity matrix. However, as you may imagine, finding the inverse of a 3×3 matrix can be tedious. Graphing calculators and computer programs offer fast and accurate methods for performing the necessary calculations.

220 Chapter 4 Using Matrices

Alternative Learning Styles

Visual Have students make a flowchart for the solution of matrices involving inverses.

You can use a graphing calculator and a matrix equation to solve systems of equations. Consider the system of equations below.

$3x - 2y + z = 0$
$2x + 3y = 12$
$y + 4z = -18$

• Write the system so that each equation is in standard form and contains all three variables. Then write the coefficient matrix.

$$
\begin{aligned}
3x - 2y + 1z &= 0 \\
2x + 3y + 0z &= 12 \\
0x + 1y + 4z &= -18
\end{aligned}
\quad \rightarrow \quad
\begin{bmatrix} 3 & -2 & 1 \\ 2 & 3 & 0 \\ 0 & 1 & 4 \end{bmatrix}
$$

• Write the matrix equation in the form $AX = B$.

$$
\begin{bmatrix} 3 & -2 & 1 \\ 2 & 3 & 0 \\ 0 & 1 & 4 \end{bmatrix}
\cdot
\begin{bmatrix} x \\ y \\ z \end{bmatrix}
=
\begin{bmatrix} 0 \\ 12 \\ -18 \end{bmatrix}
$$

TECHNOLOGY Tips

You may need to use the arrow keys to see the entire matrix on the graphing calculator screen.

• Use a graphing calculator to find A^{-1}. The inverse is shown below.

```
[A]⁻¹
[[.2222222222...
[−.1481481481...
[.037037037...
■
```

• Now, find the product of A^{-1} and B.

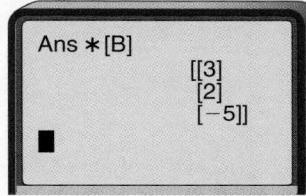

```
Ans * [B]
                [[3]
                [2]
                [−5]]
■
```

Therefore, $\begin{bmatrix} x \\ y \\ z \end{bmatrix} = \begin{bmatrix} 3 \\ 2 \\ -5 \end{bmatrix}$, and $x = 3$, $y = 2$, and $z = -5$.

Your Turn

Solve the matrix equation $AX = B$ for each value of A and B.

a. $A = \begin{bmatrix} 1 & -2 & 1 \\ 3 & 1 & -1 \\ 2 & 3 & 2 \end{bmatrix}$, $B = \begin{bmatrix} 7 \\ 2 \\ 7 \end{bmatrix}$

b. $A = \begin{bmatrix} 2 & 6 & 8 \\ -2 & 9 & -12 \\ 4 & 6 & -4 \end{bmatrix}$, $B = \begin{bmatrix} 5 \\ -1 \\ 3 \end{bmatrix}$

a. $x = 2$,
$y = -1$, $z = 3$
b. $x = \frac{1}{2}$,
$y = \frac{1}{3}$, $z = \frac{1}{4}$

You can use matrices to help solve problems that involve systems of equations. Matrices often simplify the process of solving these systems.

This Exploration integrates analytical problem-solving skills with graphing calculator skills. Understanding the theory of matrix equations is required in order to set up the problem, after which the graphing calculator facilitates computation.

Teaching Tip For Example 3, make sure students write the correct equations first. Then they can write matrices to solve the system.

In-Class Example

For Example 3
Dan bought 5 pieces of gum and 7 jawbreakers for 76 cents. Micah bought 7 pieces of gum and 4 jawbreakers for 60 cents. What was the cost of each piece of gum and each jawbreaker?
gum = 4 cents
jawbreaker = 8 cents

Example 3

APPLICATION

Business

Refer to the application at the beginning of the lesson. What combination of stuffed animals should Katie make each week to guarantee her a profit of $120?

Explore   Let b represent the number of bears, and let r represent the amount of rabbits. Therefore, $b + r = 15$.
The total number of animals must be 15.

Now, write an equation that represents Katie's profit.

$$9b + 5r = 120$$

Plan   Write a system of equations. Then write the system as a matrix equation.

$$\begin{array}{l} b + r = 15 \\ 9b + 5r = 120 \end{array} \quad \rightarrow \quad \begin{bmatrix} 1 & 1 \\ 9 & 5 \end{bmatrix} \cdot \begin{bmatrix} b \\ r \end{bmatrix} = \begin{bmatrix} 15 \\ 120 \end{bmatrix}$$

Solve   To solve the equation, first find the inverse of the coefficient matrix.

$$\frac{1}{ad - bc} \begin{bmatrix} d & -b \\ -c & a \end{bmatrix} \quad \rightarrow \quad -\frac{1}{4} \begin{bmatrix} 5 & -1 \\ -9 & 1 \end{bmatrix} \text{ or } \begin{bmatrix} -1.25 & 0.25 \\ 2.25 & -0.25 \end{bmatrix}$$

Now multiply each side of the matrix equation by the inverse and solve.

$$\begin{bmatrix} -1.25 & 0.25 \\ 2.25 & -0.25 \end{bmatrix} \cdot \begin{bmatrix} 1 & 1 \\ 9 & 5 \end{bmatrix} \cdot \begin{bmatrix} b \\ r \end{bmatrix} = \begin{bmatrix} -1.25 & 0.25 \\ 2.25 & -0.25 \end{bmatrix} \cdot \begin{bmatrix} 15 \\ 120 \end{bmatrix}$$

$$\begin{bmatrix} b \\ r \end{bmatrix} = \begin{bmatrix} 11.25 \\ 3.75 \end{bmatrix}$$

Examine   Since Katie cannot make a fraction of an animal, the solution (11.25, 3.75) is unreasonable. However, try $b = 11$, $r = 4$ and $b = 12$, $r = 3$ as possible solutions.

Bears	Rabbits	Profit
11	4	9(11) + 5(4) or $119
12	3	9(12) + 5(3) or $123 ✓

Therefore, one solution to the problem is 12 bears and 3 rabbits.

What other solutions are possible?

LOOK BACK

You can refer to Lesson 3-1 for information about consistent and inconsistent systems.

When the determinant of the coefficient matrix is 0, the system of equations has no unique solution. You can graph the equations to determine whether the system is consistent and has infinitely many solutions or is inconsistent and has no solutions.

Example **Solve the matrix equation** $\begin{bmatrix} 3 & 1 \\ 6 & 2 \end{bmatrix} \cdot \begin{bmatrix} x \\ y \end{bmatrix} = \begin{bmatrix} -2 \\ 10 \end{bmatrix}.$

The determinant of the coefficient matrix is 0, so there is no unique solution. Graph the system of equations.

The matrix equation represents the system of equations below.

$3x + y = -2$

$6x + 2y = 10$

Since the lines are parallel, this system has no solution. Therefore, the system is inconsistent.

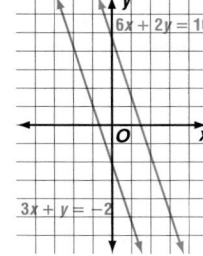

CHECK FOR UNDERSTANDING

Communicating Mathematics

Study the lesson. Then complete the following.

1. **Write** a matrix equation for the system.

   $2x - 8y = 3$ $\begin{bmatrix} 2 & -8 \\ 7 & -2 \end{bmatrix} \cdot \begin{bmatrix} x \\ y \end{bmatrix} = \begin{bmatrix} 3 \\ 5 \end{bmatrix}$
   $7x - 2y = 5$

2. $2r - 5s = 2$
   $3r + 8s = 9$

2. **Write** the matrix equation $\begin{bmatrix} 2 & -5 \\ 3 & 8 \end{bmatrix} \cdot \begin{bmatrix} r \\ s \end{bmatrix} = \begin{bmatrix} 2 \\ 9 \end{bmatrix}$ as a system of linear equations.

3. **List** the steps you would use to solve a system of linear equations with inverse matrices.   **See margin.**

4. **Sample answer:**
   $2x + 3y = 5$
   $4x + 6y = 10$

4. **Write** an example of a system of equations that does not have a unique solution.

Guided Practice

Write a matrix equation for each system.   5–7. See margin.

5. $4x - 7y = 2$ 6. $2a + 3b - 5c = 1$ 7. $y = 3x$
   $3x + 5y = 9$ $7a + 3c = 7$ $x + 2y = -21$
                          $3a - 6b + c = -5$

8. Given that the inverse of the coefficient matrix is $-\dfrac{1}{28}\begin{bmatrix} -3 & -8 \\ -2 & 4 \end{bmatrix}$, solve the matrix equation $\begin{bmatrix} 4 & 8 \\ 2 & -3 \end{bmatrix} \cdot \begin{bmatrix} x \\ y \end{bmatrix} = \begin{bmatrix} 7 \\ 0 \end{bmatrix}.$ $\left(\dfrac{3}{4}, \dfrac{1}{2}\right)$

Use a matrix equation to solve each system of equations.

9. $\left(-1, \dfrac{9}{2}\right)$ 10. $(1, 1.75)$

9. $x + 2y = 8$ 10. $5s + 4t = 12$
   $3x + 2y = 6$ $3s = -4 + 4t$

11. Determine whether the system of equations has *one* solution, *no* solution, or *infinitely many* solutions.

   $x + 2y = 5$
   $3x - 15 = -6y$ **infinitely many**

Example **4** **Solve the matrix equation** $\begin{bmatrix} 3 & 1 \\ 6 & 2 \end{bmatrix} \cdot \begin{bmatrix} x \\ y \end{bmatrix} = \begin{bmatrix} -2 \\ 10 \end{bmatrix}.$

In-Class Example

For Example 4
Solve the matrix equation
$\begin{bmatrix} 2 & 1 \\ 3 & -1 \end{bmatrix} \cdot \begin{bmatrix} x \\ y \end{bmatrix} = \begin{bmatrix} 6 \\ 9 \end{bmatrix}.$
(3, 0)

3 PRACTICE/APPLY

Check for Understanding

Exercises 1–11 are designed to help you assess your students' understanding through reading, writing, speaking, and modeling. You should work through Exercises 1–4 with your students and then monitor their work on Exercises 5–11.

Additional Answers

3. Find the inverse of the coefficient matrix and multiply both sides of the matrix equation by the inverse.

5. $\begin{bmatrix} 4 & -7 \\ 3 & 5 \end{bmatrix} \cdot \begin{bmatrix} x \\ y \end{bmatrix} = \begin{bmatrix} 2 \\ 9 \end{bmatrix}$

6. $\begin{bmatrix} 2 & 3 & -5 \\ 7 & 0 & 3 \\ 3 & -6 & 1 \end{bmatrix} \cdot \begin{bmatrix} a \\ b \\ c \end{bmatrix} = \begin{bmatrix} 1 \\ 7 \\ -5 \end{bmatrix}$

7. $\begin{bmatrix} -3 & 1 \\ 1 & 2 \end{bmatrix} \cdot \begin{bmatrix} x \\ y \end{bmatrix} = \begin{bmatrix} 0 \\ -21 \end{bmatrix}$

Study Guide Masters, p. 27

4-6   NAME_____   DATE_____
        Student Editio
Study Guide   Pages 219–22

Using Matrices to Solve Systems of Equations

You can use matrix equations to solve systems of equations. To solve matrix equations change the coefficient matrix into the appropriate identity matrix by multiplying each side of the matrix equation by the inverse of the coefficient matrix.

Example: Solve $\begin{cases} 3x - 2y + z = 0 \\ 2x + 3y = 12 \\ y + 4z = -18 \end{cases}$ if the inverse of the coefficient matrix is $\dfrac{1}{54}\begin{bmatrix} 12 & 9 & -3 \\ -8 & 12 & 2 \\ 2 & -3 & 13 \end{bmatrix}$

$\begin{bmatrix} 3 & -2 & 1 \\ 2 & 3 & 0 \\ 0 & 1 & 4 \end{bmatrix}\begin{bmatrix} x \\ y \\ z \end{bmatrix} = \begin{bmatrix} 0 \\ 12 \\ -18 \end{bmatrix}$

$\dfrac{1}{54}\begin{bmatrix} 12 & 9 & -3 \\ -8 & 12 & 2 \\ 2 & -3 & 13 \end{bmatrix}\begin{bmatrix} 3 & -2 & 1 \\ 2 & 3 & 0 \\ 0 & 1 & 4 \end{bmatrix}\begin{bmatrix} x \\ y \\ z \end{bmatrix} = \dfrac{1}{54}\begin{bmatrix} 12 & 9 & -3 \\ -8 & 12 & 2 \\ 2 & -3 & 13 \end{bmatrix}\begin{bmatrix} 0 \\ 12 \\ -18 \end{bmatrix}$

$\begin{bmatrix} 1 & 0 & 0 \\ 0 & 1 & 0 \\ 0 & 0 & 1 \end{bmatrix}\begin{bmatrix} x \\ y \\ z \end{bmatrix} = \dfrac{1}{54}\begin{bmatrix} 162 \\ 108 \\ -270 \end{bmatrix}$

$\begin{bmatrix} x \\ y \\ z \end{bmatrix} = \begin{bmatrix} 3 \\ 2 \\ -5 \end{bmatrix}$ The solution is (3, 2, −5).

Write the system of linear equations represented by each matrix equation.

1. $\begin{bmatrix} 4 & 6 \\ 5 & 8 \end{bmatrix}\begin{bmatrix} x \\ y \end{bmatrix} = \begin{bmatrix} 24 \\ 40 \end{bmatrix}$ 2. $\begin{bmatrix} 5 & 4 & 6 \\ 1 & 2 & 3 \\ -7 & 9 & 8 \end{bmatrix}\begin{bmatrix} x \\ y \\ z \end{bmatrix} = \begin{bmatrix} 40 \\ 6 \\ -72 \end{bmatrix}$
   $4x + 6y = 24,$ $5x + 4y + 6z = 40,$
   $5x + 8y = 40$ $x + 2y + 3z = 6,$
                          $-7x + 9y + 8z = -72$

Solve each matrix equation or system of equations by using inverse matrices.

3. $\begin{bmatrix} 1 & 2 \\ 3 & -1 \end{bmatrix}\begin{bmatrix} x \\ y \end{bmatrix} = \begin{bmatrix} 3 \\ -6 \end{bmatrix}$ 4. $\begin{bmatrix} -4 & -8 \\ 6 & 12 \end{bmatrix}\begin{bmatrix} x \\ y \end{bmatrix} = \begin{bmatrix} 16 \\ 12 \end{bmatrix}$
   $\left(-\dfrac{9}{7}, \dfrac{15}{7}\right)$ no solution

5. $4x - 2y = 22$ 6. $5x + 4y = 5$
   $6x + 4y = -2$ $9x - 8y = 0$
   $(3, -5)$ $\left(\dfrac{10}{19}, \dfrac{45}{76}\right)$

Reteaching

Using Substeps Follow the steps below to solve each system of equations by using matrices.

1. Write the matrix equation $AX = B$.
2. Find the inverse A^{-1} of the coefficient matrix A.
3. Multiply each side by the inverse and find a solution.

a. $3x - 2y = 12$
   $2x + y = -1$
   $\left(\dfrac{10}{7}, -\dfrac{27}{7}\right)$

b. $2x + 3y - z = 2$
   $x + 2y + z = 3$
   $-x - y + 3z = 1$
   $(-5, 4, 0)$

Assignment Guide

Core: 13–31 odd, 32, 33, 35–40
Enriched: 12–30 even, 32–40

For **Extra Practice**, see p. 884.

The red A, B, and C flags, printed only in the Teacher's Wraparound Edition, indicate the level of difficulty of the exercises.

Additional Answers

12. $\begin{bmatrix} 5 & -6 \\ 3 & 2 \end{bmatrix} \cdot \begin{bmatrix} a \\ b \end{bmatrix} = \begin{bmatrix} -47 \\ -17 \end{bmatrix}$

13. $\begin{bmatrix} 3 & -7 \\ 6 & 5 \end{bmatrix} \cdot \begin{bmatrix} m \\ n \end{bmatrix} = \begin{bmatrix} -43 \\ -10 \end{bmatrix}$

14. $\begin{bmatrix} 2 & 3 \\ -1 & 1 \end{bmatrix} \cdot \begin{bmatrix} r \\ s \end{bmatrix} = \begin{bmatrix} -17 \\ -4 \end{bmatrix}$

15. $\begin{bmatrix} -1 & -1 \\ 2 & -1 \end{bmatrix} \cdot \begin{bmatrix} x \\ y \end{bmatrix} = \begin{bmatrix} 0 \\ 0 \end{bmatrix}$

16. $\begin{bmatrix} 1 & -1 \\ 1 & 3 \end{bmatrix} \cdot \begin{bmatrix} x \\ y \end{bmatrix} = \begin{bmatrix} -3 \\ 5 \end{bmatrix}$

17. $\begin{bmatrix} 2 & -3 \\ 4 & -1 \end{bmatrix} \cdot \begin{bmatrix} x \\ y \end{bmatrix} = \begin{bmatrix} 0 \\ 5 \end{bmatrix}$

28.

$x + 3y = 6$

Practice Masters, p. 27

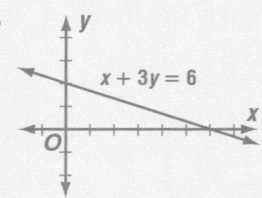

NAME_____ DATE _____

Student Edition
Pages 219–225

4-6 Practice

Using Matrices to Solve Systems of Equations

Write the system of linear equations represented by each matrix equation.

1. $\begin{bmatrix} 3 & -2 & 5 \\ 1 & 1 & -4 \\ -2 & 2 & 7 \end{bmatrix} \begin{bmatrix} x \\ y \\ z \end{bmatrix} = \begin{bmatrix} 3 \\ 2 \\ -5 \end{bmatrix}$ 2. $\begin{bmatrix} 2 & 1 & -3 \\ 5 & 2 & -2 \\ 3 & -3 & 5 \end{bmatrix} \begin{bmatrix} x \\ y \\ z \end{bmatrix} = \begin{bmatrix} -5 \\ 8 \\ 17 \end{bmatrix}$
$3x - 2y + 5z = 3$ $2x + y - 3z = -5$
$x + y - 4z = 0$ $5x + 2y - 2z = 8$
$-2x + 2y + 7z = -5$ $3x - 3y + 5z = 17$

Write a matrix equation for each system.

3. $-3x + 2y = 9$ 4. $6x - 2y = -2$
$5x - 3y = -13$ $3x + 3y = 10$
$\begin{bmatrix} -3 & 2 \\ 5 & -3 \end{bmatrix} \begin{bmatrix} x \\ y \end{bmatrix} = \begin{bmatrix} 9 \\ -13 \end{bmatrix}$ $\begin{bmatrix} 6 & -2 \\ 3 & 3 \end{bmatrix} \begin{bmatrix} x \\ y \end{bmatrix} = \begin{bmatrix} -2 \\ 10 \end{bmatrix}$

Solve each matrix equation by using inverse matrices.

5. $\begin{bmatrix} 2 & 1 \\ 3 & 2 \end{bmatrix} \cdot \begin{bmatrix} x \\ y \end{bmatrix} = \begin{bmatrix} 0 \\ -2 \end{bmatrix}$ $M^{-1} = \begin{bmatrix} 2 & -1 \\ -3 & 2 \end{bmatrix}$; $(2, -4)$

6. $\begin{bmatrix} 1 & 5 \\ 2 & -3 \end{bmatrix} \cdot \begin{bmatrix} x \\ y \end{bmatrix} = \begin{bmatrix} 10 \\ 7 \end{bmatrix}$ $M^{-1} = -\frac{1}{13}\begin{bmatrix} -3 & -5 \\ -2 & 1 \end{bmatrix}$; $(5, 1)$

7. $\begin{bmatrix} 1 & 3 & 2 \\ -1 & 2 & 1 \\ 4 & 1 & -2 \end{bmatrix} \begin{bmatrix} x \\ y \\ z \end{bmatrix} = \begin{bmatrix} 2 \\ -1 \\ -1 \end{bmatrix}$ $M^{-1} = -\frac{1}{17}\begin{bmatrix} -5 & 8 & -1 \\ 2 & -10 & -3 \\ -9 & 11 & 5 \end{bmatrix}$; $(1, -1, 2)$

8. $\begin{bmatrix} 2 & 3 & -1 \\ 4 & 1 & 5 \\ 1 & 2 & -1 \end{bmatrix} \begin{bmatrix} x \\ y \\ z \end{bmatrix} = \begin{bmatrix} 17 \\ -9 \\ 12 \end{bmatrix}$ $M^{-1} = \frac{1}{2}\begin{bmatrix} 11 & -1 & -16 \\ -9 & 1 & 14 \\ -7 & 1 & 10 \end{bmatrix}$ $(2, 3, -4)$

Practice

Write a matrix equation for each system.   **12–17. See margin.**

12. $5a - 6b = -47$ 13. $3m - 7n = -43$ 14. $2r + 3s = -17$
    $3a + 2b = -17$ $6m + 5n = -10$ $s = r - 4$

15. $y = -x$ 16. $y = x + 3$ 17. $2x = 3y$
    $y = 2x$ $3y + x = 5$ $y = 4x - 5$

Matrix M^{-1} is the inverse of the coefficient matrix. Use M^{-1} to solve each matrix equation.

18. $\begin{bmatrix} 3 & 1 \\ 4 & -2 \end{bmatrix} \cdot \begin{bmatrix} x \\ y \end{bmatrix} = \begin{bmatrix} 13 \\ 24 \end{bmatrix}$ $M^{-1} = -\frac{1}{10}\begin{bmatrix} -2 & -1 \\ -4 & 3 \end{bmatrix}$ $(5, -2)$

19. $\left(\frac{2}{9}, -\frac{4}{3}, -\frac{1}{3}\right)$

19. $\begin{bmatrix} 3 & 1 & 1 \\ -6 & 5 & 3 \\ 9 & -2 & -1 \end{bmatrix} \cdot \begin{bmatrix} x \\ y \\ z \end{bmatrix} = \begin{bmatrix} -1 \\ -9 \\ 5 \end{bmatrix}$ $M^{-1} = -\frac{1}{9}\begin{bmatrix} 1 & -1 & -2 \\ 21 & -12 & -15 \\ -33 & 15 & 21 \end{bmatrix}$

20. $\left(\frac{2}{3}, 1, -\frac{4}{3}\right)$

20. $\begin{bmatrix} 1 & 2 & 2 \\ 2 & -1 & 1 \\ 3 & -2 & 3 \end{bmatrix} \cdot \begin{bmatrix} a \\ b \\ c \end{bmatrix} = \begin{bmatrix} 0 \\ -1 \\ -4 \end{bmatrix}$ $M^{-1} = -\frac{1}{9}\begin{bmatrix} -1 & -10 & 4 \\ -3 & -3 & 3 \\ -1 & 8 & -5 \end{bmatrix}$

Solve each matrix equation or system of equations by using inverse matrices.

21. $\begin{bmatrix} 2 & 6 \\ 4 & -3 \end{bmatrix} \cdot \begin{bmatrix} x \\ y \end{bmatrix} = \begin{bmatrix} 3 \\ 1 \end{bmatrix}$ $\left(\frac{1}{2}, \frac{1}{3}\right)$ 22. $\begin{bmatrix} 8 & -1 \\ 2 & 3 \end{bmatrix} \cdot \begin{bmatrix} a \\ b \end{bmatrix} = \begin{bmatrix} 16 \\ -9 \end{bmatrix}$ $(1.5, -4)$

B

23. $\begin{bmatrix} 5 & -3 \\ 8 & 5 \end{bmatrix} \cdot \begin{bmatrix} a \\ b \end{bmatrix} = \begin{bmatrix} -30 \\ 1 \end{bmatrix}$ $(-3, 5)$ 24. $3x = 13 - y$ $(3, 4)$
                                                                          $2x - y = 2$

25. $6a + 2b = 11$ $\left(\frac{5}{3}, \frac{1}{2}\right)$ 26. $4x = -3y + 5$ $\left(\frac{3}{4}, \frac{2}{3}\right)$
    $3a = 8b + 1$ $8x = 9y$

28–29. See margin for graphs.

Determine whether each system has *one* unique solution, *no* solution, or *infinitely many* solutions. If it has one unique solution, name it. If it has no solution or many solutions, graph the system.

C

27. $3x - y = 4$ 28. $x + 3y = 6$ 29. $3x - 8y = 4$
    $6x + 2y = -8$ $3x - 18 = -9y$ $6x - 42 = 16y$
    $(0, -4)$ infinitely many   no solution

Graphing Calculator
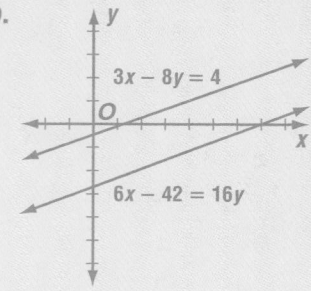

Use a graphing calculator to solve each system of equations.

30. $5x + y = 1$ $\left(\frac{1}{3}, -\frac{2}{3}\right)$ 31. $1.8x + 5y = 19.5$ $(2.5, 3)$
    $9x + 3y = 1$ $5.2x - 2.9y = 4.3$

Critical Thinking

32. See margin.

32. According to Cramer's rule, the solution of the system $\begin{cases} ax + by = e \\ cx + dy = f \end{cases}$ is

(x, y), where $x = \dfrac{\begin{vmatrix} e & b \\ f & d \end{vmatrix}}{\begin{vmatrix} a & b \\ c & d \end{vmatrix}}$, $y = \dfrac{\begin{vmatrix} a & e \\ c & f \end{vmatrix}}{\begin{vmatrix} a & b \\ c & d \end{vmatrix}}$, and $\begin{vmatrix} a & b \\ c & d \end{vmatrix} \neq 0$. Generalize Cramer's rule

to be used with a system of equations in three variables.

Additional Answers

29.

$3x - 8y = 4$

$6x - 42 = 16y$

32.

$x = \dfrac{\begin{vmatrix} r & b & c \\ s & e & f \\ t & h & i \end{vmatrix}}{\begin{vmatrix} a & b & c \\ d & e & f \\ g & h & i \end{vmatrix}}$, $y = \dfrac{\begin{vmatrix} a & r & c \\ d & s & f \\ g & t & i \end{vmatrix}}{\begin{vmatrix} a & b & c \\ d & e & f \\ g & h & i \end{vmatrix}}$, $z = \dfrac{\begin{vmatrix} a & b & r \\ d & c & s \\ g & h & t \end{vmatrix}}{\begin{vmatrix} a & b & c \\ d & e & f \\ g & h & i \end{vmatrix}}$

33. **Chemistry** Sonia Ramos is a chemist who is preparing an acid solution to be used as a cleaner for machine parts. The machine shop needs several 200-mL batches of solution at a 48% concentration. Sonia only has 60% and 40% concentration solutions. The two solutions can be combined in some ratio to make the 48% solution. How much of each solution should Sonia use to make 200 mL of solution?
80 mL of 60%; 120 mL of 40%

34. **Food Service** The manager of the Snack Shack is gathering information about the time it takes to make and serve hamburgers and chicken sandwiches. It takes 5 minutes to prepare a hamburger and 2 additional minutes to serve it with cheese, lettuce, and ketchup. It takes 7 minutes to prepare a chicken sandwich and 1 additional minute to serve it with lettuce, tomato, and mayonnaise. How many sandwiches can be prepared and served by one employee if 42 minutes is spent on preparation and 15 minutes is spent on serving? **7 hamburgers, 1 chicken sandwich**

Mixed Review

35. *True or false:* $\begin{bmatrix} \frac{9}{2} & \frac{1}{2} \\ 4 & \frac{2}{3} \end{bmatrix} \cdot \begin{bmatrix} \frac{2}{3} & -\frac{1}{2} \\ -4 & \frac{9}{2} \end{bmatrix} = I.$ (Lesson 4–5) **true**

36. Find $\begin{bmatrix} 2 \\ 9 \\ 0 \end{bmatrix} + 4\begin{bmatrix} -1 \\ 3 \\ 5 \end{bmatrix} + 3\begin{bmatrix} -6 \\ -3 \\ -1 \end{bmatrix}.$ (Lesson 4–2) $\begin{bmatrix} -20 \\ 12 \\ 17 \end{bmatrix}$

37. **Baseball** In a baseball game, a ball that lands to the right of the right field baseline or to the left of the left field baseline is a foul ball. If the ball lands on the line, it is a fair ball. Suppose a baseball diamond could be placed on a coordinate plane with home plate at the origin, first base on the x-axis, and third base on the y-axis. Write a system of inequalities that would describe foul territory. (Lesson 3–4) $y < 0$ **or** $x < 0$

38. Solve the system of equations by graphing. (Lesson 3–1) **(0, 2)**
$3x + 4y = 8$
$6y - 8x = 12$

39. **Oceanography** The Mariana Trench is the deepest point in any of the oceans. It is located in the western Pacific Ocean north of Australia. The deepest point in the trench is 36,198 feet, or about 6.8 miles below sea level. Water pressure in the ocean is represented by the function $f(x) = 1.15x$, where x is the depth in miles and $f(x)$ is the pressure in tons per square inch. Find the approximate water pressure at the deepest point in the Mariana Trench. (Lesson 2–2) **7.82 tons per square inch**

40. **Retail Sales** Leon bought a 10-speed bicycle on sale for 75% of its original price. The sale price was $41 less than the original price. Find the original price and the sale price. (Lesson 1–4) **$164, $123**

Extension

Reasoning Find the matrix M if
$$\begin{bmatrix} 4 & 1 \\ -3 & 2 \end{bmatrix} M = \begin{bmatrix} 8 & -9 \\ 5 & 4 \end{bmatrix}.$$

$M = \begin{bmatrix} 1 & -2 \\ 4 & -1 \end{bmatrix}$

Explain how you solved the problem.

---

4 ASSESS

Closing Activity

Speaking Separate the class into groups of four. Give each group the system of equations below to solve by using matrices.
$x - y + z = 3$
$2y - z = 1$
$2y - x + 1 = 0$
(3, 1, 1)
Have one student from each group explain how they solved the system.

Chapter 4, Quiz C (Lessons 4-5 and 4-6), is available in the *Assessment and Evaluation Masters*, p. 101.

Enrichment Masters, p. 27

4-6   NAME_____ DATE _____
      Enrichment   Student Edi
                                    Pages 219–

Properties of Matrices

Computing with matrices is different from computing with real numbers. Stated below are some properties of the real number system. Are these also true for matrices? In the problems on this page, you will investigate this question.

For all real numbers a and b, $ab = 0$ if and only if $a = 0$ or $b = 0$.
Multiplication is commutative. For all real numbers a and b, $ab = ba$.
Multiplication is associative. For all real numbers a, b, and c, $a(bc) = (ab)c$.

Use the matrices A, B, and C for the problems. Write whether each statement is true. Assume that a 2-by-2 matrix is the 0 matrix if and only if all of its elements are zero.

$A = \begin{bmatrix} 3 & 1 \\ 1 & 3 \end{bmatrix}$ $B = \begin{bmatrix} 1 & -3 \\ -1 & 3 \end{bmatrix}$ $C = \begin{bmatrix} 3 & 6 \\ 1 & 2 \end{bmatrix}$

1. $AB = 0$ no   2. $AC = 0$ no   3. $BC = 0$ yes
$AB = \begin{bmatrix} 2 & -6 \\ -2 & 6 \end{bmatrix}$ $AC = \begin{bmatrix} 10 & 20 \\ 6 & 12 \end{bmatrix}$ $BC = \begin{bmatrix} 0 & 0 \\ 0 & 0 \end{bmatrix}$

4. $AB = BA$ no   5. $AC = CA$ no   6. $BC = CB$ no
$BA = \begin{bmatrix} 0 & -8 \\ 0 & 8 \end{bmatrix}$ $CA = \begin{bmatrix} 15 & 21 \\ 5 & 7 \end{bmatrix}$ $CB = \begin{bmatrix} -3 & 9 \\ -1 & 3 \end{bmatrix}$
So, $AB \neq BA$.   So, $AC \neq CA$.   So, $BC \neq CB$.

7. $A(BC) = (AB)C$ yes   8. $B(CA) = (BC)A$ yes   9. $B(AC) = (BA)C$ eq
Both products equal   Both products equal   Both products eq
$\begin{bmatrix} 0 & 0 \\ 0 & 0 \end{bmatrix}$. $\begin{bmatrix} 0 & 0 \\ 0 & 0 \end{bmatrix}$ $\begin{bmatrix} -8 & -16 \\ 8 & 16 \end{bmatrix}$.

10. Write a statement summarizing your findings about the properties of matrix multiplication.
Based on these examples, matrix multiplication is associative, but not commutative. Two matrices may have a product of zero even if neither of the factors equals zero.

Instructional Resources

- Study Guide Master 4-7
- Practice Master 4-7
- Enrichment Master 4-7

 Transparency 4-7A contains the 5-Minute Check for this lesson; **Transparency 4-7B** contains a teaching aid for this lesson.

Recommended Pacing	
Standard Pacing	Day 10 of 14
Honors Pacing	Day 8 of 12
Block Scheduling*	Day 5 of 7

 *For more information on pacing and possible lesson plans, refer to the *Block Scheduling Booklet*.

1 FOCUS

 ### 5-Minute Check
(over Lesson 4-6)

1. Write a matrix equation for the system.
$5a - 2b = 16$
$-3a + b = -7$

$$\begin{bmatrix} 5 & -2 \\ -3 & 1 \end{bmatrix} \cdot \begin{bmatrix} a \\ b \end{bmatrix} = \begin{bmatrix} 16 \\ -7 \end{bmatrix}$$

2. Write the matrix equation as a system of linear equations.

$$\begin{bmatrix} 6 & 3 & 5 \\ -2 & 1 & 7 \\ 1 & -4 & -2 \end{bmatrix} \cdot \begin{bmatrix} r \\ s \\ t \end{bmatrix} = \begin{bmatrix} -2 \\ 5 \\ 11 \end{bmatrix}$$

$6r + 3s + 5t = -2$
$-2r + s + 7t = 5$
$r - 4s - 2t = 11$

3. Solve the matrix equation.

$$\begin{bmatrix} 3 & -2 \\ 4 & 1 \end{bmatrix} \cdot \begin{bmatrix} x \\ y \end{bmatrix} = \begin{bmatrix} 10 \\ 17 \end{bmatrix}$$

(4, 1)

 TEKS 2.a., 3.b., 3.c.

4-7

Using Augmented Matrices

What **YOU'LL LEARN**

- To solve systems of linear equations by using augmented matrices.

Why **IT'S IMPORTANT**

You can use augmented matrices to solve problems involving finance and business.

 **APPLICATION**
Investing

When Cleveland Jackson inherited $5000, he went to a financial planner for help in investing the money. The financial planner suggested that he invest the money in a stock fund that earns an average of 6%, a bond fund that earns an average of 7%, and a term fund that earns an average of 4%. The planner told Mr. Jackson that he shouldn't invest all the money in the highest paying fund, because although it would make more money, higher paying funds are more risky. Since the earnings from the stock fund will be available sooner, Mr. Jackson wants to earn three times as much from the stock fund as he will from the term fund. If he wants to earn a total of $300, how much should he invest in each fund? *This problem will be solved in Example 2.*

In the last lesson, you solved systems of equations using inverse matrices. A system of equations may also be solved using a matrix called an **augmented matrix**. The augmented matrix of a system contains the coefficient matrix with an extra column containing the constant terms. Study how the system below is written as an augmented matrix.

$$\begin{array}{l} x + 5y + 6z = -8 \\ 3x - 2y - 2z = 17 \\ 2x + 3y + 4z = 1 \end{array} \quad \rightarrow \quad \left[\begin{array}{ccc|c} 1 & 5 & 6 & -8 \\ 3 & -2 & -2 & 17 \\ 2 & 3 & 4 & 1 \end{array} \right]$$

The system of equations can be solved by manipulating the rows of the matrix rather than the equations themselves. For example, you could multiply each side of the first equation by -2. The result would be $-2x - 10y - 12z = 16$. The corresponding change in the matrix is that the first row becomes $[-2 \quad -10 \quad -12 \quad 16]$.

When you use an augmented matrix, you perform the same operations as you would in working with the equations, but you do not have to bother writing the variables or worrying about the order in which the terms are written—the organization of the matrix keeps all of this in its proper place. Here is a summary of the **row operations** that can be performed on an augmented matrix.

Notice that the row operations can only be performed on rows, not columns.

- Any two rows can be interchanged.
- Any row can be replaced with a nonzero multiple of that row.
- Any row can be replaced with the sum of that row and a multiple of another row.

The solution of the system of equations above is $(4, -3, 0.5)$; that is, $x = 4$, $y = -3$, and $z = 0.5$.

GLENCOE Technology

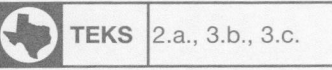 **CD-ROM**
Interaction

A multimedia simulation allows students to use matrix operations and transformations to program a jet to do a roll on a straight path. A blackline master activity with teacher's notes provides a follow-up to the CD-ROM simulation.

For Windows & Macintosh

Suppose we write these three equations in the form of an augmented matrix.

$$x = 4 \\ y = -3 \\ z = 0.5 \quad \rightarrow \quad \begin{bmatrix} 1 & 0 & 0 & | & 4 \\ 0 & 1 & 0 & | & -3 \\ 0 & 0 & 1 & | & 0.5 \end{bmatrix}$$

Notice that the first three columns are the same as a 3×3 identity matrix. When doing row operations, your goal should be to find an augmented identity matrix.

Just as there is no single order of steps to solve a system of equations, there is also no one single group of row operations that arrives at the correct solution. The order in which you solve a system may be different from the way a classmate solves it, but you may both be correct.

Example **①** Use an augmented matrix to solve the system of equations.
$$a + 2b + c = 0 \\ 2a + 5b + 4c = -1 \\ a - b - 9c = -5$$

Write the augmented matrix. $\begin{bmatrix} 1 & 2 & 1 & | & 0 \\ 2 & 5 & 4 & | & -1 \\ 1 & -1 & -9 & | & -5 \end{bmatrix}$ *The first element in row 1 is already 1.*

Multiply row 1 by -1 and add to row 3. $\begin{bmatrix} 1 & 2 & 1 & | & 0 \\ 2 & 5 & 4 & | & -1 \\ 0 & -3 & -10 & | & -5 \end{bmatrix}$ *The first element in row 3 is now 0.*

Multiply row 1 by -2 and add to row 2. $\begin{bmatrix} 1 & 2 & 1 & | & 0 \\ 0 & 1 & 2 & | & -1 \\ 0 & -3 & -10 & | & -5 \end{bmatrix}$ *The first element in row 2 is now 0, and the second element in row 2 is now 1.*

Multiply row 2 by -2 and add to row 1. $\begin{bmatrix} 1 & 0 & -3 & | & 2 \\ 0 & 1 & 2 & | & -1 \\ 0 & -3 & -10 & | & -5 \end{bmatrix}$ *The second element in row 1 is now 0.*

Multiply row 2 by 3 and add to row 3. $\begin{bmatrix} 1 & 0 & -3 & | & 2 \\ 0 & 1 & 2 & | & -1 \\ 0 & 0 & -4 & | & -8 \end{bmatrix}$ *The second element in row 3 is now 0.*

Notice that the matrix has all zeros in the "bottom triangle." The system can now be solved by setting $c = 2$ and substituting into the other equations.

Multiply row 3 by $-\frac{1}{4}$. $\begin{bmatrix} 1 & 0 & -3 & | & 2 \\ 0 & 1 & 2 & | & -1 \\ 0 & 0 & 1 & | & 2 \end{bmatrix}$ *The third element in row 3 is now 1.*

Multiply row 3 by 3 and add to row 1. $\begin{bmatrix} 1 & 0 & 0 & | & 8 \\ 0 & 1 & 2 & | & -1 \\ 0 & 0 & 1 & | & 2 \end{bmatrix}$ *The third element in row 1 is now 0.*

Multiply row 3 by -2 and add to row 2. $\begin{bmatrix} 1 & 0 & 0 & | & 8 \\ 0 & 1 & 0 & | & -5 \\ 0 & 0 & 1 & | & 2 \end{bmatrix}$ *This matrix contains an augmented identity matrix. Now you can read the solution.*

The solution is $(8, -5, 2)$.

The process of performing row operations to get the desired matrix is called **reducing a matrix**. The resulting matrix is called a **reduced matrix**. Reducing a matrix is the method used by computers to solve systems of equations with many variables and equations.

Motivating the Lesson

Questioning Given a system of equations in three variables, what effect will the following operations have on the system?

1. interchange the equations
   no effect
2. replace an equation with a nonzero multiple of that equation no effect
3. replace any equation with the sum of that equation and a multiple of another equation
   The system will have the same solution.

2 TEACH

Teaching Tip Point out that the row operations used in Example 1 are suggested by the techniques used when solving a system of equations by the elimination method.

In-Class Example

For Example 1
Use augmented matrices to solve each system of equations.

a. $8x - 16y = 32$
   $10x + 4y = 64$
   (6, 1)
b. $a + b - 2c = 4$
   $2a + b + 2c = 0$
   $a - 3b - 4c = -2$
   (0, 2, −1)

In-Class Example

For Example 2

The perimeter of a triangle is 72 centimeters. The sum of the two shorter sides is 8 more than the longest side. The sum of the two longer sides is 4 more than 3 times the shortest side. Find the length of each side. **32 cm, 23 cm, 17 cm**

CAREER CHOICES

The math used in banking varies from simple addition and subtraction for balancing a checkbook to exponential functions for determining depreciation or interest. Most math topics are related to banking in some way.

Example ❷

APPLICATION

Investing

Refer to the application at the beginning of the lesson. How much money should Mr. Jackson invest in each fund so that the total earnings will be $300?

Explore   Let s represent the amount in stocks, let b represent the amount in bonds, and let t represent the amount in the term fund.

Plan   Write a system of equations.

$s + b + t = 5000$ *The total amount invested is $5000.*

$0.06s + 0.07b + 0.04t = 300$ *The total amount earned is $300.*

$0.06s = 3(0.04)t$ *The amount earned from the stock fund is three times the amount earned from the term fund.*

Solve   Then write an augmented matrix.

$$
\begin{aligned}
s + b + t &= 5000 \\
0.06s + 0.07b + 0.04t &= 300 \\
0.06s &= 3(0.04)t
\end{aligned}
\quad \rightarrow \quad
\left[\begin{array}{ccc|c}
1 & 1 & 1 & 5000 \\
0.06 & 0.07 & 0.04 & 300 \\
0.06 & 0 & -0.12 & 0
\end{array}\right]
$$

After applying row operations on the matrix, we get the following.

$$
\left[\begin{array}{ccc|c}
1 & 0 & 0 & 2000 \\
0 & 1 & 0 & 2000 \\
0 & 0 & 1 & 1000
\end{array}\right]
$$

The solution is (2000, 2000, 1000), which means that Mr. Jackson should invest $2000 in the stock fund, $2000 in the bond fund, and $1000 in the term fund.

Examine   Examine this solution to see if it makes sense.

Stocks:	6% of $2000 =	$120
Bonds:	7% of $2000 =	$140
Term:	4% of $1000 =	$ 40
Total:		$300 ✓

Three times the amount earned in the term fund is 3($40) or $120.

CAREER CHOICES

The most common use of mathematical matrices may be the spreadsheet programs used in the **banking** industry. They are valuable in creating budgets, analyzing financial performance, and tracking loans, mortgages, and stocks.

For more information contact:

American Bankers Association 1120 Connecticut Ave, N.W. Washington, D.C. 20036

As with other methods of solving systems of equations, there is not always a unique solution. In systems where no solution or multiple solutions exist, solving by augmented matrices can identify these solutions. Study the solution of the system shown below.

$$
\begin{aligned}
x + y + 2z &= -5 \\
3x + y + 12z &= -19 \\
2x + y + 7z &= -12
\end{aligned}
\quad \rightarrow \quad
\left[\begin{array}{ccc|c}
1 & 1 & 2 & -5 \\
3 & 1 & 12 & -19 \\
2 & 1 & 7 & -12
\end{array}\right]
\quad \rightarrow \quad
\left[\begin{array}{ccc|c}
1 & 0 & 5 & -7 \\
0 & 1 & -3 & 2 \\
0 & 0 & 0 & 0
\end{array}\right]
$$

The row of zeros indicates that the last equation is some combination of the other two equations, meaning that this is a dependent system and there is no unique solution. However, there is a solution. In fact, there is an infinite number of solutions.

Let's write the equations represented by the matrix and solve each of them in terms of z.

$$x + 5z = -7 \qquad\qquad y - 3z = 2$$
$$x = -5z - 7 \qquad\qquad y = 3z + 2$$

The solution is the ordered triple $(-5z - 7, 3z + 2, z)$. By choosing any value for z, you can find coordinates of points on a line that are solutions to the system.

Let's look at another system of equations.

$$\begin{aligned} 3x - 5y + 2z &= -7 \\ x + 4y - z &= 10 \\ 6x + 7y - z &= -18 \end{aligned} \rightarrow \begin{bmatrix} 3 & -5 & 2 & \vdots & -7 \\ 1 & 4 & -1 & \vdots & 10 \\ 6 & 7 & -1 & \vdots & -18 \end{bmatrix} \rightarrow \begin{bmatrix} 1 & 4 & -1 & \vdots & 10 \\ 0 & -17 & 5 & \vdots & -37 \\ 0 & 0 & 0 & \vdots & 5 \end{bmatrix}$$

Notice the last row of the final matrix. This represents the equation $0 = 5$. Since this cannot be true, the system is inconsistent, and no solution exists.

CHECK FOR UNDERSTANDING

Communicating Mathematics

Study the lesson. Then complete the following.

1. **Discuss** the advantages and disadvantages of using an augmented matrix to solve a system of equations. See margin.

2. **Write** an augmented matrix for the system of equations.

   $$x + 3z = 5$$
   $$2x + y = 5$$
   $$-2x + 3y - z = 8$$

   $$\begin{bmatrix} 1 & 0 & 3 & \vdots & 5 \\ 2 & 1 & 0 & \vdots & 5 \\ -2 & 3 & -1 & \vdots & 8 \end{bmatrix}$$

3. **State** the row operations you would use to change $\begin{bmatrix} 4 & -1 & \vdots & -19 \\ 3 & 4 & \vdots & 19 \end{bmatrix}$ to $\begin{bmatrix} 1 & 0 & \vdots & -3 \\ 0 & 1 & \vdots & 7 \end{bmatrix}$. See margin.

4. **Choose** the operation that cannot be used with the augmented matrix below. c

   a. Multiply row 1 by -3 and add it to row 2.
   b. Switch row 2 and row 3.

   $$\begin{bmatrix} 1 & 5 & 6 & \vdots & -8 \\ 3 & -2 & -2 & \vdots & 17 \\ 2 & 3 & 4 & \vdots & 1 \end{bmatrix}$$

   c. Multiply column 3 by $\frac{1}{2}$.
   d. Multiply row 3 by 6.

5a. $(5, -2, 8)$
5b. no solution
5c. $(5 + 2z, 3 - 0.5z, z)$
6. See students' work.

5. **Describe** the solution for the system of equations represented by each reduced augmented matrix.

   a. $\begin{bmatrix} 1 & 0 & 0 & \vdots & 5 \\ 0 & 1 & 0 & \vdots & -2 \\ 0 & 0 & 1 & \vdots & 8 \end{bmatrix}$
   b. $\begin{bmatrix} 1 & 0 & 4 & \vdots & -3 \\ 0 & 0 & 0 & \vdots & 7 \\ 0 & 2 & -3 & \vdots & 8 \end{bmatrix}$
   c. $\begin{bmatrix} 1 & 0 & -2 & \vdots & 5 \\ 0 & 2 & 1 & \vdots & 6 \\ 0 & 0 & 0 & \vdots & 0 \end{bmatrix}$

 MATH JOURNAL

6. **Assess Yourself** List all of the algebraic methods that can be used to solve systems of equations. Which method do you prefer, and why?

Guided Practice

Write a system of equations represented by each augmented matrix. 8. $3x - 5y + 2z = 9$, $x - 7y + 3z = 11$, $4x - 3z = -1$

7. $\begin{bmatrix} 3 & -5 & \vdots & 25 \\ 2 & 4 & \vdots & 24 \end{bmatrix}$ $\begin{aligned} 3x - 5y &= 25 \\ 2x + 4y &= 24 \end{aligned}$

8. $\begin{bmatrix} 3 & -5 & 2 & \vdots & 9 \\ 1 & -7 & 3 & \vdots & 11 \\ 4 & 0 & -3 & \vdots & -1 \end{bmatrix}$

Reteaching

Using Alternative Methods Solve this 3×3 system of equations by elimination.

(1) $a + 2b + c = 0$
(2) $2a + 5b + 4c = -1$
(3) $a - b - 9c = -5$

Ask students what they would multiply the first equation by to eliminate the a terms from equations 2 and 3. $-2, -1$

Eliminate the a terms and rewrite the system. Ask students what they would multiply the second equation by to eliminate the b terms in equations 1 and 2. $-2, 3$ Eliminate the b terms and rewrite the system. Now have students identify the solution. Compare this to using augmented matrices.

---

3 PRACTICE/APPLY

Check for Understanding
Exercises 1–11 are designed to help you assess your students' understanding through reading, writing, speaking, and modeling. You should work through Exercises 1–6 with your students and then monitor their work on Exercises 7–11.

Additional Answers

1. **Advantage: can be used to solve equations with many variables. Disadvantage: requires many computations.**
3. **Sample answer: Multiply row 1 by 4 and add to row 2, then divide by 19. The resulting row is 1   0   −3. Multiply this row by −3 and add to row 2, then divide by 4. The resulting row is 0   1   7.**

Study Guide Masters, p. 28

4-7 NAME_____ DATE_____
Study Guide Student Edition Pages 226–231

Using Augmented Matrices

A system of three equations may be represented by a matrix called an **augmented matrix.** The system of equations can be solved by using the augmented matrix rather than the equations themselves. This matrix can be modified by transforming rows since each row represents an equation.

You may also use row operations on an augmented matrix. The resulting matrix yields the same solution as the original matrix.

System of Equations
$$\begin{aligned} 3x + 4y - 2z &= 5 \\ 2x + y - z &= 1 \\ -x - y - 2z &= -9 \end{aligned}$$

Augmented Matrix
$$\begin{bmatrix} 3 & 4 & -2 & \vdots & 5 \\ 2 & 1 & -1 & \vdots & 1 \\ -1 & -1 & -2 & \vdots & -9 \end{bmatrix}$$

Row Operations on Matrices
1. Interchange any two rows.
2. Replace any row with a nonzero multiple of that row.
3. Replace any row with the sum of that row and a multiple of another row.

Write an augmented matrix for each system of equations. Then solve each system.

1. $3x - 5y = 25$
   $2x + 4y = 24$
   $\begin{bmatrix} 3 & -5 & \vdots & 25 \\ 2 & 4 & \vdots & 24 \end{bmatrix}$, (10, 1)

2. $-3x - 2y = 6$
   $9x + 7y = 36$
   $\begin{bmatrix} -3 & -2 & \vdots & 6 \\ 9 & 7 & \vdots & 36 \end{bmatrix}$, (−38, 54)

3. $2m + 4n = 3$
   $5m - 3n = 6$
   $\begin{bmatrix} 2 & 4 & \vdots & 3 \\ 5 & -3 & \vdots & 6 \end{bmatrix}$, $\left(\frac{33}{26}, \frac{3}{26}\right)$

4. $12x - y + 12z = 6$
   $2x + y - 2z = -4$
   $9x + 2y + 3z = 3$
   $\begin{bmatrix} 12 & -1 & 12 & \vdots & 6 \\ 2 & 1 & -2 & \vdots & -4 \\ 9 & 2 & 3 & \vdots & 3 \end{bmatrix}$, (−2, 6, 3)

Assignment Guide

Core: 13–31 odd, 32–37
Enriched: 12–28 even, 29–37

For **Extra Practice,** see p. 885.

The red A, B, and C flags, printed only in the Teacher's Wraparound Edition, indicate the level of difficulty of the exercises.

Additional Answers

12. $\begin{bmatrix} 3 & 2 & | & 7 \\ 1 & -3 & | & 17 \end{bmatrix}$

13. $\begin{bmatrix} 4 & -3 & | & 5 \\ 2 & 9 & | & 6 \end{bmatrix}$

14. $\begin{bmatrix} 7 & -3 & | & 41 \\ 2 & 5 & | & 0 \end{bmatrix}$

15. $\begin{bmatrix} 2 & -1 & 4 & | & 6 \\ 1 & 5 & -2 & | & -6 \\ 3 & -2 & 6 & | & 8 \end{bmatrix}$

16. $\begin{bmatrix} 3 & -5 & 2 & | & 22 \\ 2 & 3 & -1 & | & -9 \\ 4 & 3 & 3 & | & 1 \end{bmatrix}$

17. $\begin{bmatrix} 2 & 1 & 1 & | & 2 \\ -1 & -1 & 2 & | & 7 \\ -3 & 2 & 3 & | & 7 \end{bmatrix}$

Practice Masters, p. 28

NAME_____ DATE_____

4-7 Practice

Student Edition
Pages 226–231

Using Augmented Matrices

Solve each system of equations by using augmented matrices.

1. $5x + 9y = 19$
   $2x - y = -20$
   $(-7, 6)$

2. $2x + y - 3z = -3$
   $3x + 2y + 4z = 5$
   $-4x - y + 2z = 4$
   $(-1, 2, 1)$

3. $4x - 3y - z = -3$
   $5x + 2y + 2z = 7$
   $3x + 3y + z = 10$
   $(1, 3, -2)$

4. $x + 2z = 11$
   $2x + y = 4$
   $x + 3y + z = 1$
   $(3, -2, 4)$

5. $2x + y + z = 2$
   $-x - y + 2z = 7$
   $-3x + 2y + 3z = 7$
   $(0, -1, 3)$

6. $3x - 2y + 5z = -14$
   $x + 5y - 3z = 18$
   $-2x - 3y + 8z = -8$
   $(-2, 4, 0)$

7. $2x - y + z = 4$
   $x + y - z = 11$
   $4x - 2y + 2z = 5$
   $\emptyset$

8. $3x - 2y + 4z = 8$
   $x + y - 3z = 1$
   $6x - 4y + 8z = 16$
   $\left(\frac{2}{5}z + 2, \frac{13}{5}z - 1, z\right)$

10. $\begin{bmatrix} 3 & -1 & 5 & | & -1 \\ 1 & 3 & -1 & | & 25 \\ 2 & 0 & 4 & | & 2 \end{bmatrix}$

$(5, 6, -2)$

Write an augmented matrix for each system. Then solve each system.

9. $4m - 7n = -19$ $\begin{bmatrix} 4 & -7 & | & -19 \\ 3 & 2 & | & 22 \end{bmatrix}$ 10. $3a - b + 5c = -1$
   $3m + 2n = 22$ $a + 3b - c = 25$
   $(4, 5)$ $2a + 4c = 2$

11. Describe the solution for the system of equations represented by

$\begin{bmatrix} 1 & 0 & -2 & | & 3 \\ 0 & 0 & 3 & | & 1 \\ 0 & 0 & 0 & | & 3 \end{bmatrix}$.   **no solution**

EXERCISES

Practice

Write an augmented matrix for each system of equations. Then solve each system.   12–17. See margin for matrices.

13. $\left(\frac{3}{2}, \frac{1}{3}\right)$
15. $(-6, 2, 5)$
16. $(1, -3, 2)$
17. $(0, -1, 3)$

12. $3x + 2y = 7$ 13. $4x - 3y = 5$ 14. $7m - 3n = 41$
    $x - 3y = 17$ $(5, -4)$ $2x + 9y = 6$ $2m = -5n$ $(5, -2)$

15. $2a - b + 4c = 6$ 16. $3x - 5y + 2z = 22$ 17. $2q + r + s = 2$
    $a + 5b - 2c = -6$ $2x + 3y - z = -9$ $-q - r + 2s = 7$
    $3a - 2b + 6c = 8$ $4x + 3y + 3z = 1$ $-3q + 2r + 3s = 7$

Describe the solution for the system of equations represented by each reduced augmented matrix.

19. $\left(-\frac{1}{4}z + 1, 2z + 5, z\right)$
21. no solution

18. $\begin{bmatrix} 3 & 0 & | & 6 \\ 0 & 2 & | & -8 \end{bmatrix}$ $(2, -4)$ 19. $\begin{bmatrix} 4 & 0 & 1 & | & 4 \\ 0 & 1 & -2 & | & 5 \\ 0 & 0 & 0 & | & 0 \end{bmatrix}$

20. $\begin{bmatrix} 4 & 0 & 0 & | & -8 \\ 0 & 0 & 1 & | & 3 \\ 0 & 2 & 0 & | & 5 \end{bmatrix}$ $\left(-2, \frac{5}{2}, 3\right)$ 21. $\begin{bmatrix} 1 & 0 & -7 & | & 2 \\ 0 & 0 & 5 & | & 0 \\ 0 & 0 & 0 & | & 2 \end{bmatrix}$

Solve each system of equations by using augmented matrices.

24. $(-5, 2, 8)$
25. $\left(-\frac{1}{6}, \frac{1}{2}, -\frac{2}{3}\right)$
26. $\left(-y + 2z + 1, z + \frac{4}{5}, z\right)$
27. no solution

22. $6a + 5b = -12$ 23. $6r + s = 9$ 24. $4m + 2n + 5p = 24$
    $12a + 10b = -20$ $3r = -2s$ $3m + 5n - p = -13$
    no solution $(2, -3)$ $m + 7n + 3p = 33$

25. $6x + 2y - 6z = 4$ 26. $2x - 3y + z = -2$ 27. $2a - b - c = 3$
    $3x - 5y - 3z = -1$ $x + y - 2z = 1$ $a + b - 3c = 5$
    $2x + 4y + z = 1$ $4x + 4y - 8z = 4$ $4a - 2b - 2c = -2$

28. **Geometry** In triangle ABC, the measure of $\angle A$ is twice the measure of $\angle B$. The measure of $\angle C$ exceeds four times the measure of $\angle B$ by 12 degrees. Find the measure of each angle.   **48°, 24°, 108°**

Critical Thinking

29. When one of the three rows in a reduced augmented matrix contains all zeros, the solution of the system of equations is a line. What kind of solution do you have when two rows contain all zeros? Explain your answer.   **a plane**

Mixed Review

30. Geometry The perimeter of a triangle is 83 inches. The longest side is three times the length of the shortest side and 17 inches more than one-half the sum of the other two sides. Use augmented matrices to find the length of each side. **39 in., 31 in., 13 in.**

31. Business The Yogurt Shoppe sells cones in three sizes: small, $0.89; medium, $1.19; and large, $1.39. One day, Kyle Miller sold 52 cones. He sold two more than twice as many medium cones as large cones. If he sold $58.98 in cones, how many of each size did he sell?
17 small, 24 medium, 11 large

32. Solve the system of equations by using an inverse matrix. (Lesson 4–6)

$3a + 2b = 7$
$-a - 7b = 23$ **(5, −4)**

33. Find the inverse of $\begin{bmatrix} 4 & -5 \\ 2 & -1 \end{bmatrix}$. (Lesson 4–5) $\frac{1}{6}\begin{bmatrix} -1 & 5 \\ -2 & 4 \end{bmatrix}$

34. Find $\begin{vmatrix} -2 & 0 \\ 7 & -6 \end{vmatrix}$. (Lesson 3–3)   **12**

35. Business The parking garage at Burrough's Department Store charges $1.50 for each hour or fraction of an hour for parking. What type of function does this relationship represent? (Lesson 2–6)   **a step function**

36. Graph $5 = 5x$. (Lesson 2–2)   **See margin.**

37. Evaluate $\dfrac{3ab^2 - c^3}{a + c}$ if $a = 3$, $b = 7$, and $c = -2$. (Lesson 1–1)   **449**

WORKING ON THE In·ves·ti·ga·tion

Refer to the Investigation on pages 180–181.

3-2-1-Blast-Off!

Conduct a shoot-off day. Create a shooting area with masking tape. Label the tape with a scale, marking distances 50 cm to 250 cm from the launching area.

The teacher selects a distance between 50 cm and 250 cm and announces that distance to the class. No test shots may be taken after the announcement. Groups are randomly selected to demonstrate their launch system. During these launches, the launcher should be shot from the floor, and the distance should be measured from the launcher's location to the spot where the Ping-Pong™ ball hits the floor.

Each group should shoot ten shots at the same distance. Then each group must accurately measure and record the shot distances.

1 State the target distance and list the ten distances shot by your launcher.

2 Create a matrix of the class results from the launcher shoot-off. The matrix should consist of all ten distances shot by each of the groups in the class.

3 Find the median, quartiles, greatest and least values, and interquartile range of each set of shots by each of the launchers.

4 How do these three measures compare to the target distance of your launcher? Explain.

5 How do these three measures help to determine which launcher was most accurate? Explain.

6 Make a box-and-whisker plot for each launcher. Which launcher would you consider to be the most accurate? Explain your reasoning.

Add the results of your work to your Investigation Folder.

Extension

Connections The general form of the equation of a parabola is $y = ax^2 + bx + c$. Find the equation of a parabola that contains the points (1, 9), (4, 6), and (6, 14). Substitute each ordered pair into the equation, and then solve the system of equations for a, b, and c. The equation is $y = x^2 - 6x + 14$.

In·ves·ti·ga·tion

Working on the Investigation

The Investigation on pages 180–181 is designed to be a long-term project that is completed over several days or weeks. Encourage students to keep their materials in their Investigation Folder as they work on the Investigation.

---

4 ASSESS

Closing Activity

Writing Have students write a paragraph explaining why there might be no solution for a system of equations.

Additional Answer

36.

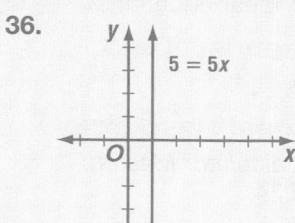

Enrichment Masters, p. 28

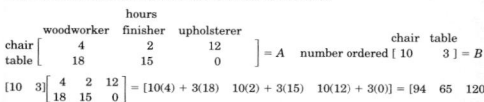

NCTM Standards: 1–5, 12

Objective

Use a graphing calculator to solve systems of linear equations.

Recommended Time

30 minutes

Instructional Resources

Graphing Calculator Masters, pp. 33 and 34

These masters provide keystroking instruction for this lesson for the TI-81 and Casio graphing calculators.

1 FOCUS

Motivating the Lesson

Have students look at the matrix functions on the TI-82 graphing calculator and guess what each function will do. Keep a tally of what the students say. Try to get them to be specific and to *define* what they think each function does.

An Extension of Lesson 4–6

You can solve a system of linear equations by using a graphing calculator and the MATRX function. The row operation functions are located in the MATH menu when you press the MATRX key. Each function is listed below with instructions on the keying procedures. Suppose your augmented matrix has been entered as matrix *A*.

Row Swap(

MATRX ▶ 8

Interchange two rows.
1. Enter the name of the matrix followed by a comma.
2. Enter one of the rows you want to interchange followed by a comma.
3. Enter the other row you want to interchange followed by) .

Example: To interchange rows 1 and 2 in matrix A, enter rowSwap([A], 1, 2).

*Row

MATRX ▶ 0

Multiply one row by a number.
1. Enter the number you want to multiply by, followed by a comma.
2. Enter the name of the matrix followed by a comma.
3. Enter the row you want multiplied, followed by) .

Example: To multiply row 2 by −3 in matrix A, enter *row(−3, [A], 2).

Row+ (

MATRX ▶ 9

Add two rows and store the result in the last row you entered.
1. Enter the name of the matrix followed by a comma.
2. Enter the row you want to add followed by a comma.
3. Enter the row you want it added to, followed by) .

Example: To add row 2 to row 1 in matrix A, enter row+([A], 2, 1).

*Row+ (

MATRX ▶

ALPHA A

Multiply one row by a number and add the result to another.
1. Enter the number you want to multiply by, followed by a comma.
2. Enter the name of the matrix followed by a comma.
3. Enter the row you want multiplied, followed by a comma.
4. Enter the row you want the result added to, followed by) .

*Example: To multiply row 1 by $\frac{1}{2}$ and add it to row 2 in matrix A,
enter* *row+(0.5, [A], 1, 2).

To perform one operation after another in completely reducing a matrix, let
ANS be your matrix name so the operations will be done on the matrix you
just finished.

Example Write an augmented matrix for the following system of equations. Then solve the system by reducing the matrix with a graphing calculator.

$15x + 11y = 36$
$4x - 3y = -26$

The augmented matrix $A = \begin{bmatrix} 15 & 11 & \vdots & 36 \\ 4 & -3 & \vdots & -26 \end{bmatrix}$.

Begin by entering the matrix.

Enter: MATRX ▶ ▶ ENTER

2 ENTER 3 ENTER 15 ENTER

11 ENTER 36 ENTER 4

ENTER (−) 3 ENTER (−) 26

ENTER 2nd QUIT

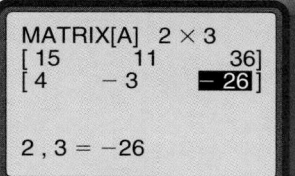

Multiply row 1 by 3.

Enter: MATRX ▶ 0 3 , MATRX

1 , 1) ENTER

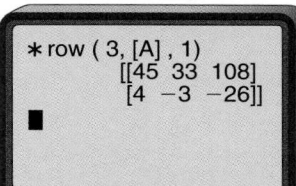

Multiply row 2 by 11 and add it to row 1.

Enter: MATRX ▶ ALPHA A 11

, 2nd ANS , 2 , 1

) ENTER

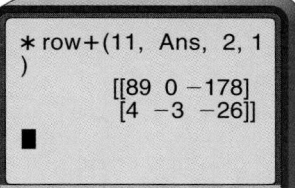

(continued on the next page)

Teaching Tip The opening parenthesis appears when you select the matrix function. The calculator will complete the matrix calculations whether or not the last parenthesis is inserted.

Teaching Tip In the Example, another method is to multiply row 1 by $\frac{1}{15}$; multiply row 2 by $\frac{1}{4}$; then add row 2 to row 1.

4 ASSESS

Observing students working with technology is an excellent method of assessment.

Multiply row 1 by $\frac{1}{89}$.

Enter: [MATRX] [▶] 0 89 [x⁻¹] [,]

[2nd] [ANS] [,] 1 [ )] [ENTER]

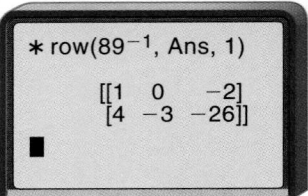

```
* row(89⁻¹, Ans, 1)
        [[1   0   −2]
         [4  −3  −26]]
■
```

Multiply row 1 by −4 and add it to row 2.

Enter: [MATRX] [▶] [ALPHA] [A] [(−)] 4

[,] [2nd] [ANS] [,] 1 [,] 2

[ )] [ENTER]

```
* row+(−4, Ans, 1, 2
)
        [[1   0   −2]
         [0  −3  −18]]
■
```

Multiply row 2 by $-\frac{1}{3}$.

Enter: [MATRX] [▶] 0 [(−)] 3 [x⁻¹] [,]

[2nd] [ANS] [,] 2 [ )] [ENTER]

```
* row(−3⁻¹, Ans, 2)
        [[1 0 −2]
         [0 1 6]]
■
```

The solution is $(-2, 6)$.

EXERCISES

2. $\left(\frac{8}{7}, -\frac{9}{7}\right)$

3. $\left(-\frac{1}{7}, -\frac{3}{7}\right)$

5. $\left(\frac{5}{4}, -\frac{1}{2}, \frac{1}{4}\right)$

6. $(-7, -9, 1)$

7. $(-2, -1, 3)$

8. $(1, -2, 1)$

9. $(-1, -6, 8)$

Write an augmented matrix for each system of equations. Then solve with a graphing calculator.

1. $3x + 2y = -2$
   $2x + 3y = 7$ $\quad(-4, 5)$

2. $x - 3y = 5$
   $2x + y = 1$

3. $3x - y = 0$
   $2x - 3y = 1$

4. $2x + y = 5$
   $2x - 3y = 1$
   $(2, 1)$

5. $x - y + z = 2$
   $x - z = 1$
   $y + 2z = 0$

6. $3x - 2y + z = -2$
   $x - y + 3z = 5$
   $-x + y + z = -1$

7. $3x + y + 3z = 2$
   $2x + y + 2z = 1$
   $4x + 2y + 5z = 5$

8. $-3x + y - 2z = -7$
   $2x - y - 3z = 1$
   $x + 2y + z = -2$

9. $-2x + y + z = 4$
   $4x - 3y - 2z = -2$
   $-3x + y + z = 5$

234 *Chapter 4 Using Matrices*

Using Technology
This lesson offers an excellent opportunity for using technology in your algebra classroom. For more information on using technology, see *Graphing Calculators in the Mathematics Classroom*, one of the titles in the Glencoe Mathematics Professional Series.

Integration: Statistics
Box-and-Whisker Plots

What YOU'LL LEARN

- To find the range, quartiles, and interquartile range for a set of data,
- to determine if any values in a set of data are outliers, and
- to represent data using box-and-whisker plots.

Why IT'S IMPORTANT

Box-and-whisker plots are a useful way to display data. They allow you to see important characteristics of the data at a glance.

APPLICATION
News Media

The 1994 edition of the *Editor and Publisher International Yearbook* lists the total number of morning and evening newspapers that are published in each state. One way to organize these data is to show them in a 1×50 matrix.

$$N = [26\ 7\ 22\ 32\ 104\ \ldots]$$

However, this is not the best way to display the data. A more convenient way is to organize them in the table below.

Number of Morning and Evening Newspapers in the United States

State	Number	State	Number	State	Number	State	Number
AL	26	IN	73	NE	18	SC	16
AK	7	IA	39	NV	8	SD	11
AZ	22	KS	47	NH	11	TN	27
AR	32	KY	23	NJ	21	TX	92
CA	104	LA	25	NM	18	UT	6
CO	28	ME	7	NY	71	VT	8
CT	19	MD	15	NC	49	VA	28
DE	3	MA	39	ND	10	WA	24
FL	40	MI	52	OH	84	WV	23
GA	34	MN	25	OK	46	WI	36
HI	6	MS	22	OR	19	WY	9
ID	12	MO	45	PA	89		
IL	68	MT	11	RI	6		

Even when the data are organized in a table, they are difficult to analyze because the values vary and there are no trends apparent in the data. However, there are several ways to measure variation in the data. The simplest is called the **range.**

Definition of Range	**The range of a set of data is the difference between the greatest and least values in the set.**

In this case, the greatest number of newspapers in any state is 104 in California, and the least is 3 in Delaware. So the range of the number of newspapers is $104 - 3$ or 101.

Because the range is the difference between the greatest and least values in a set of data, it is affected by extreme values. In these cases, it is not a good measure of variation.

Lesson 4-8  *Statistics* Box-and-Whisker Plots **235**

NCTM Standards: 1–4, 10

Instructional Resources

- Study Guide Master 4-8
- Practice Master 4-8
- Enrichment Master 4-8
- Assessment and Evaluation Masters, p. 101
- Real-World Applications, 11
- Science and Math Lab Manual, pp. 75–80

 Transparency 4-8A contains the 5-Minute Check for this lesson; **Transparency 4-8B** contains a teaching aid for this lesson.

Recommended Pacing

Standard Pacing	Day 12 of 14
Honors Pacing	Day 10 of 12
Block Scheduling*	Day 6 of 7

 *For more information on pacing and possible lesson plans, refer to the *Block Scheduling Booklet*.

1 FOCUS

 5-Minute Check
(over Lesson 4-7)

Describe the solution for the system of equations represented by each reduced augmented matrix.

1. $\begin{bmatrix} 1 & 0 & | & 3 \\ 0 & 1 & | & 5 \end{bmatrix}$ **(3, 5)**

2. $\begin{bmatrix} 1 & -3 & 5 & | & 2 \\ 0 & 0 & 0 & | & 3 \\ 0 & 0 & 1 & | & 2.6 \end{bmatrix}$ no solution

3. $\begin{bmatrix} 5 & 0 & 5 & | & 10 \\ 0 & 1 & -2 & | & 1 \\ 0 & 0 & 0 & | & 0 \end{bmatrix}$

   $(-z + 2, 2z + 1, z)$

Solve each system of equations by using augmented matrices.

4. $4x + 3y = 10$
   $5x - y = 3$ **(1, 2)**

5. $7m - 3n = 41$
   $2m + 5n = 0$ **(5, −2)**

Situational Problem Have the tallest person and the shortest person in the class stand side by side. Ask students to estimate the difference in the two heights. Measure and compare to the estimate. Ask students to list situations in which knowing the difference between the greatest and least measurements might be important.

2 TEACH

In-Class Example

For Example 1
The mean daily temperatures in San Francisco for each month of the year are 49°, 52°, 53°, 55°, 58°, 61°, 62°, 63°, 64°, 61°, 55°, 49°. Find the quartiles and interquartile range for the temperatures.
median: 56.5°
lower quartile: 52.5°
upper quartile: 61.5°
interquartile range: 9°

Teaching Tip Emphasize that while the range can be greatly affected by extreme values, the interquartile range usually is not.

The record for most Super Bowl losses is shared by three teams. The Minnesota Vikings, Denver Broncos, and Buffalo Bills have all been to the Super Bowl four times without a win.

Another way to analyze a set of data is to determine how the data are distributed between the least and greatest values. The **quartiles** are the values in a set that separate the data into four sections, each containing 25% of the data.

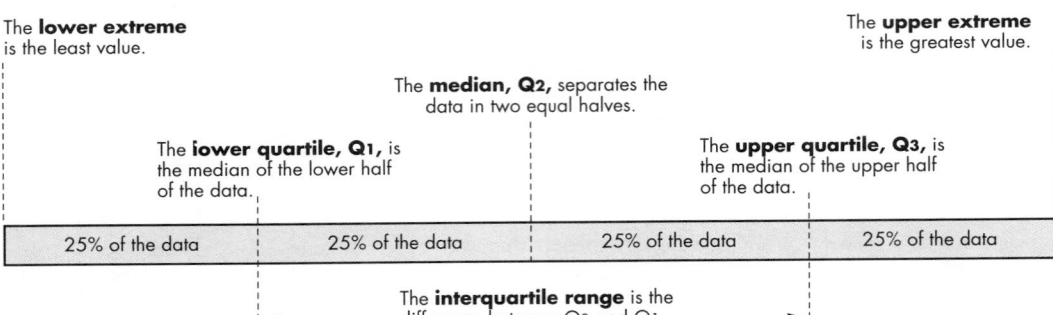

The **lower extreme** is the least value.

The **upper extreme** is the greatest value.

The **median, Q_2,** separates the data in two equal halves.

The **lower quartile, Q_1,** is the median of the lower half of the data.

The **upper quartile, Q_3,** is the median of the upper half of the data.

| 25% of the data | 25% of the data | 25% of the data | 25% of the data |

The **interquartile range** is the difference between Q_3 and Q_1.

Example 1

Sports

On January 29, 1995, the San Francisco 49ers became the first team to win five Super Bowls as they defeated the San Diego Chargers 49–26. The number of points scored by the winning teams in all Super Bowls through 1995 are as follows.

35, 33, 16, 23, 16, 24, 14, 24, 16, 21, 32, 27, 35, 31, 27, 26, 27, 38, 38, 46, 39, 42, 20, 55, 20, 37, 52, 30, 49

a. Find Q_1, Q_2, Q_3, the range, and the interquartile range.
b. Analyze how San Francisco's score in 1995 compares to the other winning scores.

a. First arrange the data in order.

14, 16, 16, 16, 20, 20, 21, 23, 24, 24, 26, 27, 27, 27, 30, 31, 32, 33, 35, 35, 37, 38, 38, 39, 42, 46, 49, 52, 55

The range is 55 − 14 or 41.

There are 29 values in all. The median, Q_2, is the middle, or 15th, value. Therefore, the median score is 30.

The lower quartile, Q_1, is the median of the lower half of the data. Since there are 14 values in the lower half, the lower quartile falls midway between the 7th and 8th value. The lower quartile is $\frac{21 + 23}{2}$ or 22.

The upper quartile, Q_3, is the median of the upper half of the data. It falls midway between the 22nd and 23rd values. Since both these values are 38, the upper quartile is 38.

The interquartile range is $Q_3 − Q_1 = 38 − 22$ or 16.
Fifty percent of the time, the number of points scored was between 22 and 38.

b. San Francisco's score of 49 is above the upper quartile. Therefore, it is in the upper 25% of the data.

Numerical data can often be represented using a **box-and-whisker plot**. In a box-and-whisker plot, the quartiles and the extreme values of a set of data are displayed using a number line.

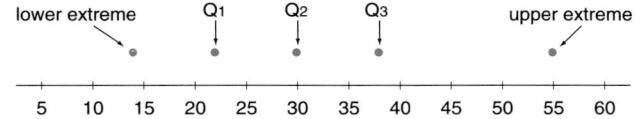

Thus, a box-and-whisker plot is a pictorial representation of the variability of the data and a way to summarize a data set with five points.

Example

APPLICATION

Sports

2 **Refer to the data in Example 1 about the Super Bowl winners. Make a box-and-whisker plot of the data.**

To make a box-and-whisker plot, draw a number line and plot the quartiles, the median, and the extreme values. The lower extreme is 14, the lower quartile is 22, the median is 30, the upper quartile is 38, and the upper extreme is 55.

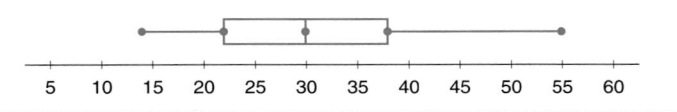

Draw a box to designate the interquartile range and mark the median by drawing a segment containing its point in the box. Draw segments (whiskers) connecting the lower quartile to the least value and the upper quartile to the greatest value.

The dimensions of the box-and-whisker plot can help you characterize the data. Each whisker and each small box contains 25% of the data. If the whisker or box is short, the data are concentrated over a narrower range of values. The longer the whisker or box, the more diverse the data. Extreme values are referred to as **outliers**.

Definition of Outlier	**An outlier is any value in the set of data that is at least 1.5 interquartile ranges beyond the upper or lower quartile.**

In-Class Example

For Example 2
Use the data from the In-Class Example for Example 1 concerning the mean daily temperatures by month for San Francisco to create a box-and-whisker plot.

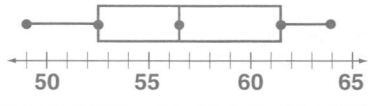

In-Class Example

For Example 3
The stem-and-leaf plot below represents the scores on a 100-point test in Mr. Porter's science class. Find any outliers in the scores. Then draw a box-and-whisker plot of the scores.

Stem	Leaf
10	0
9	
8	0 0 2 3 3
7	1 1 2 4 7 7 8
6	0 1 3 3 6 8 9
5	2 7
4	5
3	1

$4|5 = 45$

median: 71
lower quartile: 62
upper quartile: 79
interquartile range: 17
$79 + 1.5(17) = 104.5$
$62 - 1.5(17) = 36.5$
outlier: 31
greatest value: 100
least value not an outlier: 45

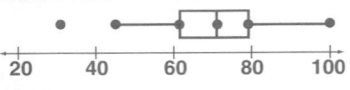

Example ③

APPLICATION
News Media

Refer to the data in the application at the beginning of the lesson about the number of newspapers in circulation.

a. Find Q1, Q2, Q3, and the interquartile range.

b. List any outliers.

c. Make a box-and-whisker plot.

d. If any outliers exist, analyze them to determine possible reasons why they exist.

a. First arrange the data in order.

3, 6, 6, 6, 7, 7, 8, 8, 9, 10, 11, 11, 11, 12, 15, 16, 18, 18, 19, 19, 21, 22, 22, 23, 23, 24, 25, 25, 26, 27, 28, 28, 32, 34, 36, 39, 39, 40, 45, 46, 47, 49, 52, 68, 71, 73, 84, 89, 92, 104

There are 50 values in all.

Q1 is the 13th value, 11.

Q2 is between the 25th value, 23, and the 26th value, 24. Therefore, Q2 is 23.5.

Q3 is the 38th value, 40.

The interquartile range is $40 - 11$ or 29.

b. Find the outliers.

$Q1 - 1.5(29) = 11 - 43.5$ or -32.5 *There are no values less than -32.5.*

$Q3 + 1.5(29) = 40 + 43.5$ or 83.5 *There are four values greater than 83.5.*

Therefore, 84, 89, 92, and 104 are outliers.

c. Draw a number line and plot the quartiles, the lower extreme, the upper extreme, and the outliers. Also, plot 73, since this is the last data value that is not an outlier. Extend the whiskers to the lower extreme, 14, and to 73. The outliers remain as single points.

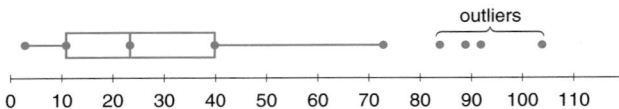

d. The outliers are from the states of Ohio, Pennsylvania, Texas, and California. All of these states have large populations that can support many daily newspapers.

In addition to showing how data within a set vary, box-and-whisker plots can be used to compare two or more sets of data.

Example **4**

The table below shows the median ages of men and women at the time of their first marriage for the decades of 1890 through 1990.

Year	Men	Women	Year	Men	Women
1890s	26.1	22.0	1950s	22.8	20.3
1900s	25.9	21.9	1960s	22.8	20.3
1910s	25.1	21.6	1970s	23.2	20.8
1920s	24.6	21.2	1980s	24.7	22.0
1930s	24.3	21.3	1990s	26.2	25.1
1940s	24.3	21.5			

a. Make a box-and-whisker plot for the men's and women's ages.
b. Analyze the information as it is displayed in the two plots.

a. For the men's data, the lower extreme is 22.8, the upper extreme is 26.2, and the quartiles are 23.2, 24.6, and 25.9. There are no outliers.

For the women's data, the lower extreme is 20.3, the upper extreme is 25.1, and the quartiles are 20.8, 21.5, and 22.0. There is one outlier, 25.1. The last value of the data that is not an outlier is 22.0.

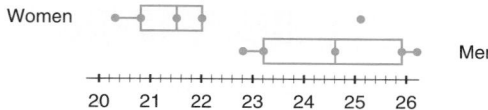

Women   Men

20   21   22   23   24   25   26

b. It appears from the data that over the years, men marry at a later age than women. It also appears that the interquartile range for the women is 1.2 years, but for the men it is 2.7 years. For 50% of the years, women married between the ages of 20.8 and 22.0. Thus, there is not much difference or spread in the ages at which women married, except in 1990. The ages at which men married varies much more.

In-Class Example

For Example 4
In Example 4, restrict the domain to exclude the data for the following years: 1890, 1900, 1980, and 1990. Then construct a box-and-whisker plot for the new data.

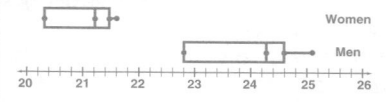

Women

Men

20   21   22   23   24   25   26

EXPLORATION

For a comparison, students might also construct stem-and-leaf plots for the data. Upon examining the two types of representations, students should conclude that the box-and-whisker plots show the spread of the data better.

EXPLORATION

GRAPHING CALCULATORS

The table below shows the 1990 populations of ten large cities and the predicted populations of those same cities for the year 2000.

City	1990 Population (millions)	2000 Population (millions)
Tokyo	27.0	30.0
Mexico City	20.2	27.9
Sao Paulo	18.1	25.4
Seoul	16.3	22.0
New York	14.6	14.6
Osaka	13.8	14.3
Bombay	11.8	15.4
Calcutta	11.7	14.1
Buenos Aires	11.5	12.9
Rio de Janeiro	11.4	14.2

Source: U.S. Bureau of the Census, International Data Base, 1994

(continued on the next page)

Check for Understanding
Exercises 1–10 are designed to help you assess your students' understanding through reading, writing, speaking, and modeling. You should work through Exercises 1–6 with your students and then monitor their work on Exercises 7–10.

Error Analysis
Students may be tempted to divide the number of numbers by 4 to get the place or position of the lower quartile (LQ) and upper quartile (UQ). But LQ and UQ are defined as the medians of the two sets of equal size (order) determined by the median. Demonstrate with sets having 10 or 12 members.

Additional Answers
4. $1.5(72.5 - 52.5) = 1.5(20)$ or 30. Any item of data greater than $72.5 + 30$ or less than $52.5 - 30$ is an outlier.

8. range = 19; $Q_1 = 12$; $Q_2 = 15$; $Q_3 = 19$; IR = 7; outliers = 1

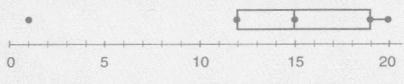

9. range = 19; $Q_1 = 25$; $Q_2 = 32.5$; $Q_3 = 38$; IR = 13; no outliers

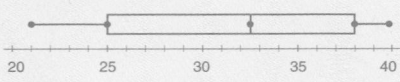

There are many ways in which these data could be displayed. You can make box-and-whisker plots using these data fairly quickly by using a graphing calculator.

Your Turn

a. Press STAT 1. Enter the 1990 population values into L1 and the 2000 population values into L2.

b. Press 2nd STAT PLOT 1. Turn on Plot 1 and define it as a box-and-whisker plot, using L1 and Frequency 1. Press 2nd STAT PLOT 2. Turn on Plot 2 and define it as a box-and-whisker plot, using L2 and Frequency 1.

c. Clear the Y= list and change the window settings to Xscl = 1, Ymin = 0, and Yscl = 0. Then press ZOOM 9.

d. Write a paragraph to describe the difference in the spread of the data between 1990 and 2000. **See students' work.**

CHECK FOR UNDERSTANDING

Communicating Mathematics

2. Sample answer: quartiles, range, outliers

3. See students' work.

4. See margin.

5. Sample answer: Data is clustered around the median.

Study the lesson. Then complete the following. 1. See students' work.

1. **Show** how a set of data can be separated into quartiles.

2. **Describe** what you can tell about a set of data from a box-and-whisker plot.

3. **Write** an example of two sets of data with the same lower and upper extreme but different interquartile ranges.

4. **Explain** how to find the outliers in a set of data if $Q_1 = 52.5$, $Q_2 = 60$, and $Q_3 = 72.5$.

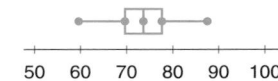

5. **Describe** how the data shown in the box-and-whisker plot at the right are distributed.

6. **You Decide** Michelle thinks that $Q_3 - Q_2 = Q_2 - Q_1$ for any set of data. Mei thinks that this isn't necessarily true. Who is correct? Explain your reasoning. **Mei; The data may be unevenly distributed around the median.**

Guided Practice

7. Use the box-and-whisker plot at the right to answer each question.

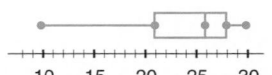

a. What is the range of the data? **20**
b. What is the median of the data? **26**
c. What percent of the data is greater than 28? **25%**
d. Between what two values of the data is the middle 50% of the data? **21 and 28**

Find the range, quartiles, interquartile range, and outliers for each set of data. Then make a box-and-whisker plot for each set of data.

8. {12, 19, 20, 1, 15, 14, 19} **See margin.**

9. {24, 32, 38, 38, 26, 33, 37, 39, 23, 31, 40, 21} **See margin.**

Reteaching

Using Alternative Examples Have students do research to find the number of members of the United States House of Representatives from each state. Have students determine the mean, mode, quartiles, range, interquartile range, and any outliers of this data and display the data using a box-and-whisker plot.

10. Astronomy The table at the right lists the approximate length of a day, in Earth hours, for each of the planets in our solar system.

Planet	Length of Day (Earth hours)
Mercury	1416
Venus	5832
Earth	24
Mars	24
Jupiter	10
Saturn	11
Uranus	22
Neptune	16
Pluto	153

a. Which planet's day length separates the data into two equal halves?
Mars or Earth

b. What is the median length of a day for the planets in our solar system?
24 hours

c. Fifty percent of the data lie between what two values? **784.5 and 13.5**

d. Estimate which value(s) may be outliers. Then determine if the data set has any outliers. **See students' work; outlier = 5832**

e. What problems would you encounter if you tried to make a box-and-whisker plot with these data? **Extreme variability of data makes it difficult to put all values on a number line.**

EXERCISES

Practice
A

11. Use box-and-whisker plot I to answer each question. **a. 50% b. 75%**

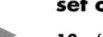

a. What percent of the data is less than 76?

b. What percent of the data is less than 92?

c. What percent of the data is greater than 64 and less than 92? **50%**

11d. The least value and lower quartile are same number.

d. Under what conditions would a set of data have this type of box-and-whisker plot?

12. Use box-and-whisker plot II to answer each question.

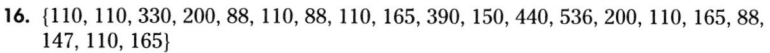

a. What is the range of the data? **210**

b. What values of the data are outliers? **670, 700**

c. What percent of the data is greater than 560? **50%**

d. What percent of the data is less than 580? **75%**

Find the range, quartiles, interquartile range, and outliers for each set of data. Then make a box-and-whisker plot for each set of data.

13–18. See margin. **B**

13. {25, 46, 31, 53, 39, 59, 48, 43, 68, 64, 29}

14. {25, 51, 29, 43, 32, 17, 21, 29, 36, 47}

15. {51, 69, 46, 27, 60, 53, 55, 39, 81, 54, 46, 23}

C

16. {110, 110, 330, 200, 88, 110, 88, 110, 165, 390, 150, 440, 536, 200, 110, 165, 88, 147, 110, 165}

17. {13.6, 15.1, 14.9, 15.7, 16.0, 14.1, 16.3, 14.3, 13.8}

18. {15.1, 11.5, 5.8, 6.2, 10.5, 7.6, 9.0, 8.5, 8.8, 8.5}

Assignment Guide

Core: 11–27 odd, 28–33
Enriched: 12–18 even, 20–33

For **Extra Practice,** see p. 885.

The red A, B, and C flags, printed only in the Teacher's Wraparound Edition, indicate the level of difficulty of the exercises.

Additional Answers

13. range = 43; Q_1 = 31; Q_2 = 46; Q_3 = 59; IR = 28; no outliers

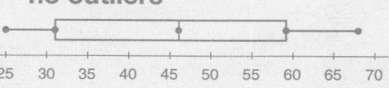

14. range = 34; Q_1 = 25; Q_2 = 30.5; Q_3 = 43; IR = 18; no outliers

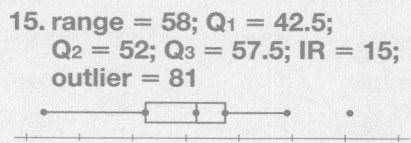

15. range = 58; Q_1 = 42.5; Q_2 = 52; Q_3 = 57.5; IR = 15; outlier = 81

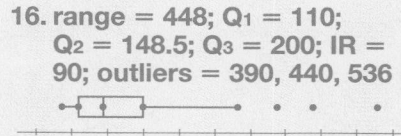

16. range = 448; Q_1 = 110; Q_2 = 148.5; Q_3 = 200; IR = 90; outliers = 390, 440, 536

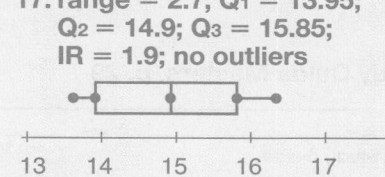

17. range = 2.7; Q_1 = 13.95; Q_2 = 14.9; Q_3 = 15.85; IR = 1.9; no outliers

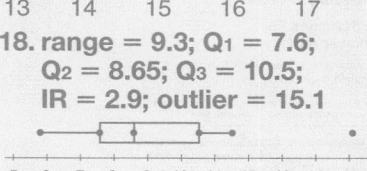

18. range = 9.3; Q_1 = 7.6; Q_2 = 8.65; Q_3 = 10.5; IR = 2.9; outlier = 15.1

Additional Answers

22e. 50% of the students in period 1 scored between 75 and 90; 50% of the students in period 2 scored between 60 and 85.

23a.

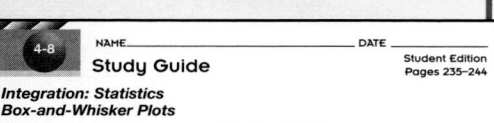

23b. Stem-and-leaf: advantage—all data are shown; disadvantage—difficult to see how data are dispersed.
Box-and-whisker: advantage—easy to see range, median, and so on; disadvantage—data are lost.

Graphing Calculator

19b. The median average high temperature for San Francisco is 63.5°; the median average high temperature for Springfield is 69.5°.

Critical Thinking

20. The data are clustered around the median with some extreme values.

Applications and Problem Solving

19. Meteorology San Francisco, California, and Springfield, Missouri, are both located at 37° N latitude. However, their average monthly high temperatures are very different.

a. Use a graphing calculator to make box-and-whisker plots for each set of data. **See margin.**

b. Write a sentence that compares the average monthly high temperatures in each city.

c. In which city would you prefer to live? Give reasons to support your answer. **See students' work.**

Average High Temperatures (°F)		
Month	San Francisco	Springfield
January	59	41
February	61	48
March	61	57
April	62	69
May	65	72
June	69	82
July	69	89
August	70	88
September	72	80
October	70	70
November	61	59
December	58	45

Source: *1995 Weather Almanac*

20. Suppose a set of data has a small interquartile range and a large range. What does this tell you about how the data are distributed?

21. Give an example of a set of data having ten values and containing at least one outlier at each end of the data. What conditions must be present for this to happen? **Sample answer: {1, 4, 4, 4, 5, 5, 5, 6, 6, 15}**

22. School Two geometry classes took the same exam, and their scores are shown in box-and-whisker plots below.

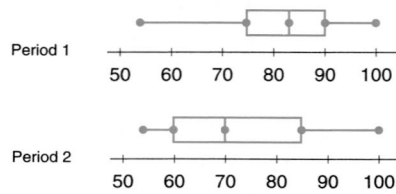

a. Which class has the higher median? **period 1**
b. Which class has the greater range? **They are equal.**
c. Which class has the greater interquartile range? **period 2**
d. Which class appears to have done better? **period 1**
e. Describe the spread of the scores in the two classes. **See margin.**

23. History The stem-and-leaf plot below represents the age at death of the presidents of the United States.

Stem	Leaf
4	6 9
5	3 6 6 7 8
6	0 0 3 3 4 4 5 6 7 7 7 8
7	0 1 1 2 3 4 7 8 8 9
8	0 1 3 5 8
9	0 0 $4|6 = 46$

a. Make a box-and-whisker plot of the data. **a–b. See margin.**
b. What are some advantages and disadvantages of representing these data in a stem-and-leaf plot? What are some advantages and disadvantages of representing these data in a box-and-whisker plot?

Study Guide Masters, p. 29

4-8

NAME_____ DATE _____

Study Guide

Student Edition
Pages 235–244

Integration: Statistics
Box-and-Whisker Plots

There are several ways to measure variation in a set of data. The simplest is called the **range**.

Definition of Range	The range of a set of data is the difference between the greatest and least values in the set.

Another way to measure a set of data is to use **quartiles**. Quartiles are the values in a set that separate the data into four sections, each containing 25% of the data.

| The lower extreme is the least value. | The lower quartile, Q₁, is the median of the lower half of the data | The median, Q₂, separates the data into two equal halves. | The upper quartile, Q₃, is the median of the upper half of the data | The upper extreme is the greatest value. |

Another way to organize and represent data is to use a **box-and-whisker plot**. In a box-and-whisker plot, the quartiles and the extreme values of a set of data are displayed using a number line. The extreme values are referred to as **outliers**.

Definition of Outlier	An outlier is any value in the set of data that is at least 1.5 interquartile ranges beyond the upper or lower quartile.

1. Use the box-and-whisker plot at the right to answer each question.
  a. What is the range of the data? **12**
  b. What are the upper and lower extremes? **4; 16**
  c. What is the median? **12**
  d. What is the interquartile range? **5**

Find the range, quartiles, interquartile range, and outliers for each set of data. Then make a box-and-whisker plot for each set of data.

2. {15, 16, 18, 10, 7, 30, 12} range = 23; Q₁ = 10; Q₃ = 18; interquartile range = 8; outliers = none

3. {2, 0, 5, 8, 14, 20, 100, 50, 1} range = 100; Q₁ = 1.5; Q₃ = 35; interquartile range = 33.5; outliers = 100

4. {7, 2, 3, 5, 8, 6, 10} range = 8; Q₁ = 3; Q₃ = 8; interquartile range = 5; outliers = none

242 Chapter 4

Additional Answer

19a.

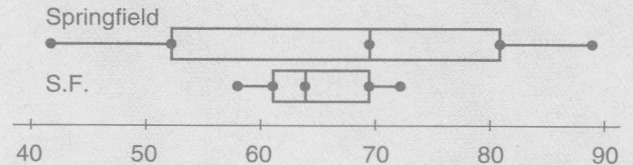

24. Food The number of Calories in a regular serving of French fries at different restaurants are listed below.

Restaurant	Calories	Restaurant	Calories
Burger Chef	250	Hardee's	239
Burger King	240	McDonald's	211
Carl's Jr.	220	Roy Rogers	240
Dairy Queen	200	Wendy's	327
Friendly's	125		

a. Make a box-and-whisker plot of the data. **See margin.**

b. Explain why this box-and-whisker plot has such short whiskers.
The least and greatest values are both outliers.

25. Literature Maya Angelou is a Reynolds Professor of African Studies at Wake Forest University in North Carolina and is well known for her poetry. She was commissioned by then President-elect Bill Clinton to write a poem for his 1993 inauguration. An excerpt from *On the Pulse of Morning* is shown below.

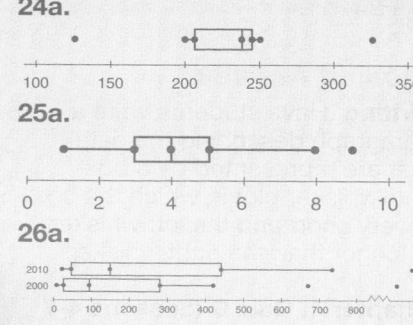

A Rock, A River, A Tree
Hosts to species long since departed,
Marked the mastodon,
The dinosaur, who left dried tokens
Of their sojourn here
On our planet floor,
Any broad alarm of their hastening doom
Is lost in the gloom of dust and ages.

a. Make a box-and-whisker plot that shows the number of letters in each word of this excerpt. **See margin.**

b. Find a newspaper article and make a box-and-whisker plot that shows the number of letters in each word of the article. **See students' work.**

c. Compare and contrast the two plots. **See students' work.**

26a. See margin.

26b. increase from 99,000 to 148,000

26c. increase from 260,500 to 393,000

26d. See students' work.

26. Demographics The chart at the right shows the Asian and Pacific Islander population projections for 2000 and 2010 in the western United States.

a. For each year, make a box-and-whisker plot.

b. How will the median population change from 2000 until 2010?

c. How will the interquartile range change from 2000 until 2010?

d. Write a sentence that summarizes how the population of Asian and Pacific Islanders is expected to change from 2000 to 2010.

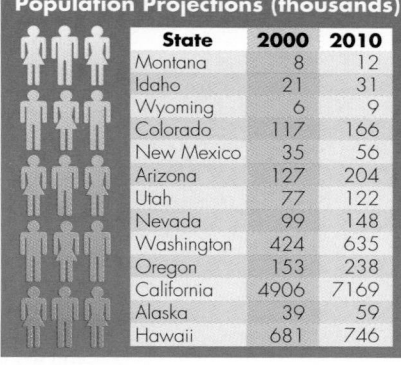

Population Projections (thousands)

State	2000	2010
Montana	8	12
Idaho	21	31
Wyoming	6	9
Colorado	117	166
New Mexico	35	56
Arizona	127	204
Utah	77	122
Nevada	99	148
Washington	424	635
Oregon	153	238
California	4906	7169
Alaska	39	59
Hawaii	681	746

Source: U.S. Bureau of the Census

Tech Prep

Demographer Students who are interested in a career in demographics may wish to do further research on the use of mathematics and statistics in that field, as mentioned in Exercise 26. For more information on tech prep, see the *Teacher's Handbook.*

Extension

Communication Ask students to set values for quartiles, range, and interquartile range. Then have them determine a set of data that would fit these values. Students should present this data in the form of a verbal problem.

Additional Answers

24a.
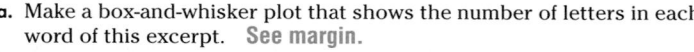

25a.

26a.

Practice Masters, p. 29

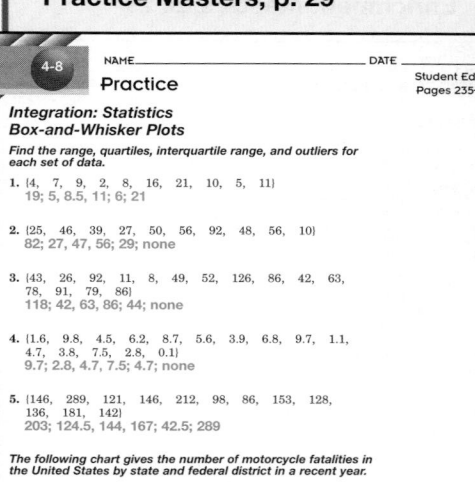

4-8 NAME_____ DATE_____
Practice
Student Edition Pages 235–244

Integration: Statistics
Box-and-Whisker Plots

Find the range, quartiles, interquartile range, and outliers for each set of data.

1. {4, 7, 9, 2, 8, 16, 21, 10, 5, 11}
19; 5, 8.5, 11; 6; 21

2. {25, 46, 39, 27, 50, 56, 92, 48, 56, 10}
82; 27, 47, 56; 29; none

3. {43, 26, 92, 11, 8, 49, 52, 126, 86, 42, 63, 78, 91, 79, 86}
118; 42, 63, 86; 44; none

4. {1.6, 9.8, 4.5, 6.2, 8.7, 5.6, 3.9, 6.8, 9.7, 1.1, 4.7, 3.8, 7.5, 2.8, 0.1}
9.7; 2.8, 4.7, 7.5; 4.7; none

5. {146, 289, 121, 146, 212, 98, 86, 153, 128, 136, 181, 142}
203; 124.5, 144, 167; 42.5; 289

The following chart gives the number of motorcycle fatalities in the United States by state and federal district in a recent year.

AL	39	FL	235	LA	45	NE	31	OK	46	VT	12
AK	1	GA	63	ME	21	NV	22	OR	70	VA	56
AZ	91	HI	13	MD	65	NH	24	PA	150	WA	90
AR	50	ID	27	MA	62	NJ	49	RI	18	WV	27
CA	767	IL	174	MI	105	NM	37	SC	56	WI	88
CO	62	IN	131	MN	54	NY	181	SD	14	WY	5
CT	65	IA	57	MS	30	NC	91	TN	83		
DE	14	KS	42	MO	60	ND	7	TX	297		
DC	4	KY	40	MT	26	OH	199	UT	30		

1. Make a box-and-whisker plot of the data. LV: 1, LQ: 26, M: 50, UQ: 88, GV: 181

2. Identify any outliers. 199, 235, 297, 767

Closing Activity

Writing Have students write a paragraph describing the data that are represented by a box-and-whisker plot in which the box is very short and the left whisker is longer than the right whisker.

Chapter 4, Quiz D (Lessons 4-7 and 4-8), is available in the *Assessment and Evaluation Masters*, p. 101.

Enrichment Masters, p. 29

4-8

NAME_____ DATE _____

Student Edition
Pages 235–244

Enrichment

Percentiles

This table shows test scores and their frequencies. The frequency is the number of people who had a particular score. The cumulative frequency is the total frequency up to that point, starting at the lowest score and adding up.

Score	Frequency	Cumulative Frequency
95	1	50
90	2	49
85	5	47
80	6	42
75	7	36
70	8	29
65	7	21
60	6	14
55	4	8
50	3	4
45	1	1

Example 1: What score is at the 16th percentile?

A score at the 16th percentile means the score just above the lowest 16% of the scores.
16% of the 50 scores is 8 scores.
The 8th score is 55.
The score just above this is 56.
The score at the 16th percentile is 56.

Notice that no one had a score of 56 points.

Use the table above to find the score at each percentile.

1. 42nd percentile _66_
2. 70th percentile _76_
3. 33rd percentile _66_
4. 90th percentile _86_
5. 58th percentile _71_
6. 80th percentile _81_

Example 2: At what percentile is a score of 75?

There are 29 scores below 75.

Seven scores are at 75. The fourth of these seven is the midpoint of this group.

Adding 4 scores to the 29 gives 33 scores.

33 out of 50 is 66%.

Thus, a score of 75 is at the 66th percentile.

Use the table above to find the percentile of each score.

7. a score of 50 _6th_
8. a score of 77 _72nd_
9. a score of 85 _90th_
10. a score of 58 _16th_
11. a score of 62 _28th_
12. a score of 81 _84th_

---

27. **Snacks** Who can resist the snack counter when you're at the movies? Not many people! But the Center for Science in the Public Interest reports that many snacks contain as many Calories and fat as a fast-food lunch. The chart below lists the Calories and fat content for several popular movie snacks.

Snack	Calories	Fat (grams)
KitKat Bar/4 oz	588	33
Twizzlers/5 oz	500	5
Butterfinger/4 oz	492	21
Reese's Peanut Butter Cups/3.2 oz	380	22
M&M's, peanut/2.6 oz	363	20
Junior Mints/3 oz	360	9
M&M's plain/2.6 oz	350	16
Goobers/2.2 oz	320	21
Skittles/2.6 oz	286	2
Raisinets/2.3 oz	270	10
Buttered popcorn popped in coconut oil/medium bucket	1221	97

a. Make box-and-whisker plots for the number of Calories and grams of fat.

b. Add the following values to the data.
   Unbuttered popcorn popped in coconut oil/medium bucket: 901 Calories, 60 grams fat
   Plain air-popped popcorn/medium bucket: 180 Calories, <1 gram fat
   How do these values affect the plot in part a?

c. Find a snack that would fall in the bottom 25% of the data for both number of Calories and grams of fat.

27a. See margin.

27b. Median is the same, box is longer.

27c. plain air-popped popcorn, Skittles

Mixed Review

28. (−2, −3, 7)

28. Solve the system of equations by using augmented matrices. (Lesson 4–7)
$$2x + y + z = 0$$
$$3x - 2y - 3z = -21$$
$$4x + 5y + 3z = -2$$

29. Find $[2 \ \ -6 \ \ 3] \cdot \begin{bmatrix} 3 & -3 \\ 9 & 0 \\ -2 & 4 \end{bmatrix}$. (Lesson 4–3) $[-54 \ \ 6]$

30. **Running** The length of a marathon was determined by the first marathon in the 1908 Olympic Games in London. The race began at Windsor Castle and ended in front of the royal box at London's Olympic Stadium, which was a distance of 26 miles 385 yards. Determine how many feet the marathon covers using the formula $f(m, y) = 5280m + 3y$, where m is the number of miles and y is the number of yards. (Lesson 3–5) **138,435 feet**

31. $\frac{2}{3}$

31. Find the slope of the line that passes through (5, 4) and (2, 2). (Lesson 2–3)

32. I, R

32. Name the sets of numbers to which 2.121221222 . . . belongs. (Lesson 1–2)

33. You are about to buy a new car. Your mother offers you a simple interest loan to finance it. Simple interest is calculated using the formula $I = prt$, where p represents the principal in dollars, r represents the annual interest rate, and t represents the time in years. Find the amount of interest you would pay for a two-year loan if the principal is $6000 and the rate is 12%. (Lesson 1–1) **$1440**

Additional Answer

27a.

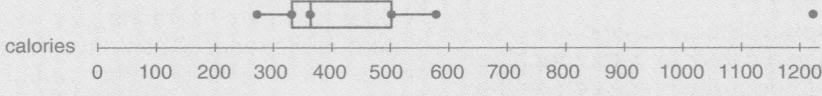

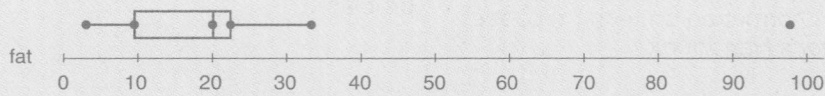

VOCABULARY

After completing this chapter, you should be able to define each term, property, or phrase and give an example or two of each.

Discrete Mathematics
addition of matrices (p. 195)
augmented matrix (p. 226)
coding matrix (p. 212)
column matrix (p. 187)
coordinate matrix (p. 189)
determinant (p. 205)
dimensions (p. 187)
discrete mathematics (p. 188)
element (p. 186)
equal matrices (p. 188)
expansion by minors (p. 205)
identity matrix (p. 213)
inverse of a matrix (p. 213)
matrix (p. 186)
matrix equation (p. 219)

minor (p. 205)
multiplying matrices (p. 199)
probability matrix (p. 200)
reduced matrix (p. 227)
reducing a matrix (p. 227)
row operations (p. 226)
row matrix (p. 187)
scalar (p. 188)
scalar multiplication (p. 188)
square matrix (p. 187)
third-order determinant (p. 205)
transition matrix (p. 200)
translation matrix (p. 196)

Problem Solving
use matrix logic (p. 187)

Geometry
dilation (p. 190)
rotation (p. 201)
transformation (p. 190)
translation (p. 195)

Statistics
box-and-whisker plot (p. 237)
interquartile range (p. 236)
lower extreme (p. 236)
lower quartile (p. 236)
median (p. 236)
outlier (p. 237)
quartiles (p. 236)
range (p. 235)
upper extreme (p. 236)
upper quartile (p. 236)

UNDERSTANDING AND USING THE VOCABULARY

Choose the correct term to complete each sentence.

1. The matrix $\begin{bmatrix} 1 & 0 & 0 \\ 0 & 1 & 0 \\ 0 & 0 & 1 \end{bmatrix}$ is a(n) __identity matrix__ for multiplication.

2. The matrix $\begin{bmatrix} 1 & 0 & | & 7 \\ 0 & 1 & | & -3 \end{bmatrix}$ is a(n) __reduced matrix__ .

3. __Scalar multiplication__ is the process of multiplying a matrix by a constant.

4. A(n) __rotation__ is when a figure is moved around a center point.

5. The __determinant__ of $\begin{bmatrix} -1 & 4 \\ 2 & -3 \end{bmatrix}$ is -5.

6. The matrix $\begin{bmatrix} 1 & 5 & 3 & | & 4 \\ 4 & -3 & 2 & | & 4 \\ 8 & -6 & 4 & | & 14 \end{bmatrix}$ is a(n) __augmented matrix__ .

7. The __dimensions__ of a matrix tell how many rows and columns are in the matrix.

8. A __translation__ occurs when a figure is moved from one location to another on the coordinate plane without changing its size, shape, or orientation.

9. The matrices $\begin{bmatrix} 3x \\ x + 2y \end{bmatrix}$ and $\begin{bmatrix} y \\ 7 \end{bmatrix}$ are __equal matrices__ if $x = 1$ and $y = 3$.

10. A __dilation__ is when a geometric figure is enlarged or reduced.

augmented matrix
determinant
dilation
dimensions
equal matrices
identity matrix
reduced matrix
rotation
scalar multiplication
translation

Chapter 4   Highlights   **245**

Using the CHAPTER HIGHLIGHTS

The Chapter Highlights begins with a listing of the new terms, properties, and phrases that were introduced in this chapter. Have students define each term and provide an example or two of it, if appropriate.

Assessment and Evaluation Masters, pp. 87–88

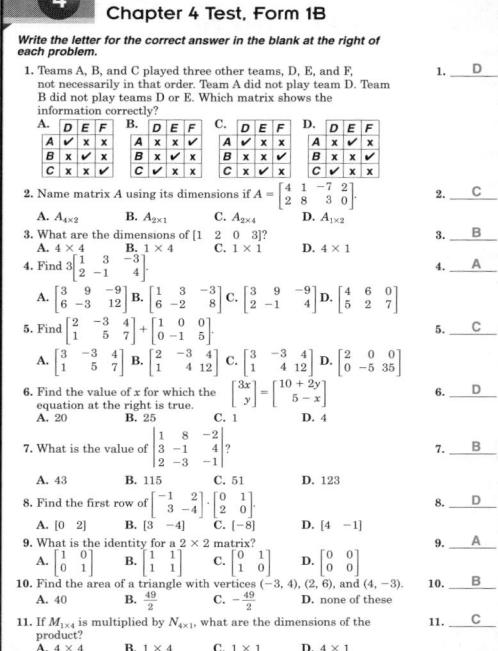

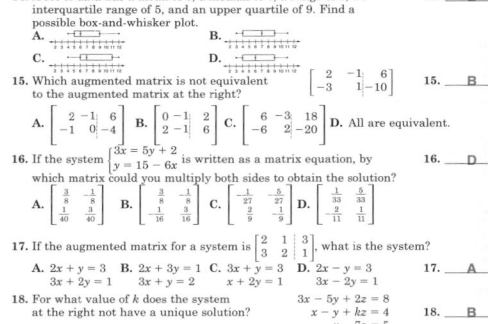

Instructional Resources

Three multiple-choice tests and three free-response tests are provided in the *Assessment and Evaluation Masters*. Forms 1A and 2A are for honors pacing, and Forms 1B, 1C, 2B, and 2C are for average pacing. Chapter 4 Test, Form 1B is shown at the right. Chapter 4 Test, Form 2B is shown on the next page.

Using the STUDY GUIDE AND ASSESSMENT

Skills and Concepts Encourage students to refer to the objectives and examples on the left as they complete the review exercises on the right.

Assessment and Evaluation Masters, pp. 93–94

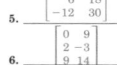
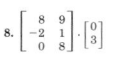

4 Chapter 4 Test, Form 2B

NAME_____ DATE_____

Name each matrix using its dimensions.

1. $R = \begin{bmatrix} 7 \\ 1 \\ -6 \end{bmatrix}$ 2. $S = \begin{bmatrix} -1 & 3 & 0 & 8 \\ 4 & -2 & 10 & -5 \end{bmatrix}$

1. _____ $R_{3\times1}$_____

2. _____ $S_{2\times4}$_____

Solve each equation.

3. $\begin{bmatrix} 5 & y \\ x & 10 \end{bmatrix} = \begin{bmatrix} 5 & -2 \\ 6 & z \end{bmatrix}$ 4. $\begin{bmatrix} 2x \\ 3y \end{bmatrix} + 3\begin{bmatrix} y-1 \\ x+2 \end{bmatrix} = \begin{bmatrix} -7 \\ 3 \end{bmatrix}$

3. _____ $x = 6, y = -2, z = 10$_____

4. _____ $(1, -2)$_____

Perform the indicated operations.

5. $6\begin{bmatrix} 1 & 3 \\ -2 & 5 \end{bmatrix}$ 6. $\begin{bmatrix} 1 & 5 \\ 2 & 0 \\ 3 & 6 \end{bmatrix} + \begin{bmatrix} -1 & 4 \\ 0 & -3 \\ 6 & 8 \end{bmatrix}$

5. _____ $\begin{bmatrix} 6 & 18 \\ -12 & 30 \end{bmatrix}$

6. _____ $\begin{bmatrix} 0 & 9 \\ 2 & -3 \\ 9 & 14 \end{bmatrix}$

7. $\begin{bmatrix} 6 & 8 & 3 \\ 5 & 2 & 9 \end{bmatrix} - \frac{1}{2}\begin{bmatrix} 4 & 16 & 8 \\ 0 & 6 & 2 \end{bmatrix}$ 8. $\begin{bmatrix} 8 & 9 \\ -2 & 1 \\ 0 & 8 \end{bmatrix} \cdot \begin{bmatrix} 0 \\ 3 \end{bmatrix}$

7. _____ $\begin{bmatrix} 4 & 0 & -1 \\ 5 & -1 & 8 \end{bmatrix}$

8. _____ $\begin{bmatrix} 27 \\ 3 \\ 24 \end{bmatrix}$

9. Evaluate $\begin{vmatrix} 4 & 0 & -1 \\ 5 & 3 & 6 \\ -2 & -5 & 2 \end{vmatrix}$.

9. _____ 163_____

10. Find the inverse of $\begin{bmatrix} 10 & 0 \\ 5 & 4 \end{bmatrix}$.

10. _____ $\begin{bmatrix} \frac{1}{10} & 0 \\ -\frac{1}{8} & \frac{1}{4} \end{bmatrix}$

11. What is the 3 × 3 identity matrix?

11. _____ $\begin{bmatrix} 1 & 0 & 0 \\ 0 & 1 & 0 \\ 0 & 0 & 1 \end{bmatrix}$

12. Find the area of a triangle with vertices (8, 0), (5, 6), and (−2, 10).

12. _____ 15_____

13. Make a box-and-whisker plot for the following set of data.

| 51 | 69 | 46 | 27 | 60 | 53 |
| 55 | 39 | 81 | 54 | 46 | 23 |

13. _____

4 Chapter 4 Test, Form 2B (continued)

NAME_____ DATE_____

14. A set of data has an upper quartile of 38 and an interquartile range of 12. Which, if any, of the following data items in the set are outliers?
5, 8, 50, 55, 57

14. _____ 5, 57_____

15. Write the system below as a matrix equation. Then use the inverse to solve.
$4x - 2y = -6$
$3x + y = -7$

15. _____ $(-2, -1)$_____

16. Write the system of linear equations represented by the matrix equation below. Do not solve.
$\begin{bmatrix} 1 & 1 & 1 \\ 5 & 3 & 2 \\ 5 & 6 & 8 \end{bmatrix} \cdot \begin{bmatrix} x \\ y \\ z \end{bmatrix} = \begin{bmatrix} 2 \\ 4 \\ 1 \end{bmatrix}$

16. _____ $x + y + z = 2$
$5x + 3y + 2z = 4$
$5x + 6y + 8z = 1$

17. Give the solution for a system with the augmented matrix shown below.
$\begin{bmatrix} 1 & 0 & 0 & | & 2 \\ 0 & 1 & 0 & | & -3 \\ 0 & 0 & 1 & | & 5 \end{bmatrix}$

17. _____ $(2, -3, 5)$_____

18. Write an augmented matrix for the system of equations shown below.
$a + b - 2c = 4$
$2a + b + 2c = 0$
$a - 3b - 4c = -2$

18. _____ $\begin{bmatrix} 1 & 1 & -2 & | & 4 \\ 2 & 1 & 2 & | & 0 \\ 1 & -3 & -4 & | & -2 \end{bmatrix}$

19. Solve the system in exercise 18 by using augmented matrices.

19. _____ $(0, 2, -1)$_____

20. Todd, Chris, and Lee Ann read three different books. One read a novel, one read a biography, and one read a science fiction book. Chris did not read a fictional book. Lee Ann never reads science fiction. Use matrix logic to find what books each person read.

20. _____ Todd: science fiction;
Chris: biography;
Lee Ann: novel

Bonus A triangle has an area of 6 square units. It has vertices with coordinates (1, 3), (4, 2), and a point on the *x*-axis. Find all possible coordinates for this point.

Bonus _____ $(-2, 0)$ or $(22, 0)$

SKILLS AND CONCEPTS

OBJECTIVES AND EXAMPLES

Upon completing this chapter, you should be able to:

• perform scalar multiplication on a matrix (Lesson 4–1)

$$4\begin{bmatrix} 2 & -3 \\ 4 & 1 \\ 0 & 3 \end{bmatrix} = \begin{bmatrix} 4(2) & 4(-3) \\ 2(4) & 4(1) \\ 4(0) & 4(3) \end{bmatrix} \text{ or } \begin{bmatrix} 8 & -12 \\ 16 & 4 \\ 0 & 12 \end{bmatrix}$$

11. $\begin{bmatrix} 24 & -9 & 6 \\ 12 & 3 & 21 \end{bmatrix}$ 12. $\begin{bmatrix} 15 & -10 \\ -30 & -20 \end{bmatrix}$

13. $\begin{bmatrix} 2 & \frac{1}{2} & -4 \end{bmatrix}$

• solve matrices for variables (Lesson 4–1)

To find x and y in $\begin{bmatrix} 2x \\ y \end{bmatrix} = \begin{bmatrix} 32 + 6y \\ 7 - x \end{bmatrix}$, solve the

system $2x = 32 + 6y$ and $y = 7 - x$.

$x = 9.25, y = -2.25$

• add and subtract matrices (Lesson 4–2)

$$2\begin{bmatrix} 8 & -1 \\ 3 & 4 \end{bmatrix} - 3\begin{bmatrix} 1 & 6 \\ -2 & -3 \end{bmatrix} = \begin{bmatrix} 16 & -2 \\ 6 & 8 \end{bmatrix} + \begin{bmatrix} -3 & -18 \\ 6 & 9 \end{bmatrix}$$
$$= \begin{bmatrix} 13 & -20 \\ 12 & 17 \end{bmatrix}$$

• multiply matrices (Lesson 4–3)

$$[6\ 4\ 1] \cdot \begin{bmatrix} 2 & 5 \\ -3 & 0 \\ -1 & 3 \end{bmatrix} = [12 - 12 - 1 \quad 30 + 0 + 3]$$
$$= [-1\ 33]$$

REVIEW EXERCISES

Use these exercises to review and prepare for the chapter test.

Find each product.

11. $3\begin{bmatrix} 8 & -3 & 2 \\ 4 & 1 & 7 \end{bmatrix}$ 12. $-5\begin{bmatrix} -3 & 2 \\ 6 & 4 \end{bmatrix}$ 14. $\begin{bmatrix} -2.4 \\ 0.36 \\ 1.2 \end{bmatrix}$

13. $\frac{2}{3}\begin{bmatrix} 3 & \frac{3}{4} & -6 \end{bmatrix}$ 14. $1.2\begin{bmatrix} -2 \\ 0.3 \\ 1 \end{bmatrix}$ 15. $\begin{bmatrix} 5.2 & 20 \\ -8 & -14 \\ -11.2 \end{bmatrix}$

15. $4\begin{bmatrix} 1.3 & 5.1 \\ -2 & -3.7 \\ -2.8 & 4.5 \end{bmatrix}$ 16. $-\frac{1}{2}\begin{bmatrix} -2 & 4 \\ -8 & 2 \end{bmatrix}$ 16. $\begin{bmatrix} 1 & -2 \\ 4 & -1 \end{bmatrix}$

Solve for the variables.

17. $\begin{bmatrix} 2y - x \\ x \end{bmatrix} = \begin{bmatrix} 3 \\ 4y - 1 \end{bmatrix}$ $x = -5, y = -1$

18. $\begin{bmatrix} 7x \\ x + y \end{bmatrix} = \begin{bmatrix} 5 + 2y \\ 11 \end{bmatrix}$ $x = 3, y = 8$

19. $\begin{bmatrix} 3x + y \\ x - 3y \end{bmatrix} = \begin{bmatrix} -3 \\ -1 \end{bmatrix}$ $x = -1, y = 0$

20. $\begin{bmatrix} 2x - y \\ 6x - y \end{bmatrix} = \begin{bmatrix} 2 \\ 22 \end{bmatrix}$ $x = 5, y = 8$

Perform the indicated operations.

21. $\begin{bmatrix} -4 & 3 \\ -5 & 2 \end{bmatrix} + \begin{bmatrix} 1 & -3 \\ 3 & -8 \end{bmatrix}\begin{bmatrix} -3 & 0 \\ -2 & -6 \end{bmatrix}$

22. $[0.2\ 1.3\ -0.4] - [2\ 1.7\ 2.6]\ [-1.8\ -0.4\ -3]$

23. $\begin{bmatrix} 1 & -5 \\ -2 & 3 \end{bmatrix} + \frac{3}{4}\begin{bmatrix} 0 & 4 \\ -16 & 8 \end{bmatrix}\begin{bmatrix} 1 & -2 \\ -14 & 9 \end{bmatrix}$

24. $\begin{bmatrix} 1 & 0 & -3 \\ 4 & -5 & 2 \end{bmatrix} - 2\begin{bmatrix} -2 & 3 & 5 \\ -3 & -1 & 2 \end{bmatrix}\begin{bmatrix} 5 & -6 & -13 \\ 10 & -3 & -2 \end{bmatrix}$

Perform the indicated operations, if possible.

25. $[2\ 7] \cdot \begin{bmatrix} 5 \\ -4 \end{bmatrix}$ $[-18]$

26. $\begin{bmatrix} 8 & -3 \\ 6 & 1 \end{bmatrix} \cdot \begin{bmatrix} 2 & -3 \\ 1 & -5 \end{bmatrix}\begin{bmatrix} 13 & -9 \\ 13 & -23 \end{bmatrix}$

27. $\begin{bmatrix} 3 & 4 \\ 1 & 0 \\ 2 & -5 \end{bmatrix} \cdot \begin{bmatrix} -2 & 4 & 5 \\ 3 & 0 & -1 \\ 1 & 0 & -1 \end{bmatrix}$ not possible to evaluate

246 Chapter 4 Study Guide and Assessment

GLENCOE Technology

Test and Review Software

You may use this software, a combination of an item generator and item bank, to create your own tests or worksheets. Types of items include free response, multiple choice, short answer, and open ended.

For IBM & Macintosh

• evaluate the determinant of a 3 × 3 matrix
(Lesson 4-4)

$$\begin{array}{ccc} 0 & -3 & 2 \\ \end{array}$$

$$\begin{vmatrix} 3 & 1 & 5 \\ 1 & -2 & 1 \\ 0 & -1 & 2 \end{vmatrix} \begin{matrix} 3 & 1 \\ 1 & -2 \\ 0 & -1 \end{matrix}$$

$$\begin{array}{ccc} -12 & 0 & -5 \\ \end{array}$$

$$= -12 + 0 + (-5) - 0 - (-3) - 2$$

$$= -16$$

Determine whether each matrix has a determinant. Write *yes* or *no*. If *yes*, find the value of the determinant.

28. $\begin{bmatrix} 4 & 11 \\ -7 & 8 \end{bmatrix}$ 109

29. $\begin{bmatrix} 7 & -4 & 5 \\ 1 & 3 & -6 \\ 5 & -1 & -2 \end{bmatrix}$ −52

30. $\begin{bmatrix} 5 & -1 & 2 \\ -6 & -7 & 3 \\ 7 & 0 & 4 \end{bmatrix}$ −87

31. $\begin{bmatrix} 2 & -3 & 1 \\ 0 & 7 & 8 \\ 2 & 1 & 3 \end{bmatrix}$ −36

32. $\begin{bmatrix} -2 & 9 \\ 7 & -4 \\ -6 & 1 \end{bmatrix}$ no

33. $\begin{bmatrix} 6 & 3 & -2 \\ -4 & 2 & 5 \\ -3 & -1 & 0 \end{bmatrix}$ −35

• find the inverse of a matrix   (Lesson 4-5)

Any matrix $M = \begin{bmatrix} a & b \\ c & d \end{bmatrix}$, will have an

inverse M^{-1} if and only if $\begin{vmatrix} a & b \\ c & d \end{vmatrix} \neq 0$.

Then $M^{-1} = \frac{1}{ad-bc} \begin{bmatrix} d & -b \\ -c & a \end{bmatrix}$.

Find the inverse of each matrix, if it exists. If it does not exist, explain why not.

34. $\begin{bmatrix} 3 & 2 \\ 4 & -2 \end{bmatrix}$ $\frac{1}{14}\begin{bmatrix} 2 & 2 \\ 4 & -3 \end{bmatrix}$

35. $\begin{bmatrix} 8 & 6 \\ 9 & 7 \end{bmatrix}$ $\frac{1}{2}\begin{bmatrix} 7 & -6 \\ -9 & 8 \end{bmatrix}$

36. $\begin{bmatrix} 2 & -4 \\ -3 & 6 \end{bmatrix}$ not possible

37. $\begin{bmatrix} -6 & 2 \\ 3 & 1 \end{bmatrix}$ $\frac{1}{12}\begin{bmatrix} -1 & 2 \\ 3 & 6 \end{bmatrix}$

38. $\begin{bmatrix} 0 & 2 \\ 5 & -4 \end{bmatrix}$ $\frac{1}{10}\begin{bmatrix} 4 & 2 \\ 5 & 0 \end{bmatrix}$

39. $\begin{bmatrix} 6 & -1 & 0 \\ 5 & 8 & -2 \end{bmatrix}$ not possible

---

• solve systems of linear equations by using inverse matrices   (Lesson 4-6)

$$\begin{bmatrix} 4 & 8 \\ 2 & -3 \end{bmatrix} \cdot \begin{bmatrix} x \\ y \end{bmatrix} = \begin{bmatrix} 7 \\ 0 \end{bmatrix}$$

$$-\frac{1}{28} \cdot \begin{bmatrix} -3 & -8 \\ -2 & 4 \end{bmatrix} \cdot \begin{bmatrix} 4 & 8 \\ 2 & -3 \end{bmatrix} \cdot \begin{bmatrix} x \\ y \end{bmatrix} = -\frac{1}{28} \cdot \begin{bmatrix} -3 & -8 \\ -2 & 4 \end{bmatrix} \cdot \begin{bmatrix} 7 \\ 0 \end{bmatrix}$$

$$-\frac{1}{28} \cdot \begin{bmatrix} -28 & 0 \\ 0 & -28 \end{bmatrix} \begin{bmatrix} x \\ y \end{bmatrix} = -\frac{1}{28} \cdot \begin{bmatrix} -21 \\ -14 \end{bmatrix}$$

$$\begin{bmatrix} 1 & 0 \\ 0 & 1 \end{bmatrix} \begin{bmatrix} x \\ y \end{bmatrix} = \begin{bmatrix} \frac{3}{4} \\ \frac{1}{2} \end{bmatrix} \text{ or } \begin{bmatrix} x \\ y \end{bmatrix} = \begin{bmatrix} \frac{3}{4} \\ \frac{1}{2} \end{bmatrix}$$

The solution is $\left(\frac{3}{4}, \frac{1}{2}\right)$.

Solve each matrix equation or system of equations by using inverse matrices.

40. $\begin{bmatrix} 5 & -2 \\ 1 & 3 \end{bmatrix} \cdot \begin{bmatrix} x \\ y \end{bmatrix} = \begin{bmatrix} 16 \\ 10 \end{bmatrix}$ (4, 2)

41. $\begin{bmatrix} 4 & 1 \\ 3 & -2 \end{bmatrix} \cdot \begin{bmatrix} a \\ b \end{bmatrix} = \begin{bmatrix} 9 \\ 4 \end{bmatrix}$ (2, 1)

42. $3x + 8 = -y$
    $4x - 2y = -14$ (−3, 1)

43. $3x - 5y = -13$
    $4x + 3y = 2$ (−1, 2)

Applications and Problem Solving Encourage students to work through the exercises in the Applications and Problem Solving section to strengthen their problem-solving skills.

OBJECTIVES AND EXAMPLES

• solve systems of linear equations by using augmented matrices (Lesson 4–7)

$5a - 3b = 7$

$3a + 9b = -3$

$$\begin{bmatrix} 5 & -3 & \vdots & 7 \\ 3 & 9 & \vdots & -3 \end{bmatrix} \rightarrow \begin{bmatrix} 1 & 0 & \vdots & 1 \\ 0 & 1 & \vdots & -\frac{2}{3} \end{bmatrix}$$

The solution is $\left(1, -\frac{2}{3}\right)$.

REVIEW EXERCISES

Solve each system of equations by using augmented matrices.

44. $9a - b = 1$ $\left(\frac{2}{3}, 5\right)$

$3a + 2b = 12$

45. $x + 5y = 14$ $(4, 2)$

$-2x + 6y = 4$

46. $6x - 7z = 13$ $(1, 2, -1)$

$8y + 2z = 14$

$7x + z = 6$

47. $2a - b - 3c = -20$ $\left(-\frac{1}{2}, 1, 6\right)$

$4a + 2b + c = 6$

$2a + b - c = -6$

• find the range, quartiles, and interquartile range for a set of data and represent the data using box-and-whisker plots (Lesson 4–8)

Find the range, interquartile range, and any outliers for the set of data below.

60, 61, 62, 72, 72, 78, 80, 82, 83, 83, 99

greatest value = 99   least value = 60
range = 39   median = 6th score, 78
lower quartile = 62   upper quartile = 83
interquartile range = 83 − 62 or 21

There are no outliers.

Find the range, quartiles, interquartile range, and outliers for each set of data. Then make a box-and-whisker plot for each set of data.

48. {90, 92, 78, 93, 79, 85, 89, 88, 84, 86}

49. {10, 50, 90, 40, 60, 40, 50, 90, 0}

50. {0.4, 0.2, 0.5, 0.9, 0.3 0.4, 0.5, 1.9, 0.5, 0.7, 0.8, 0.6, 0.2, 0.1, 0.4}   **1.8; 0.3, 0.5, 0.7; 0.4; 1.9**

51. {1055, 1075, 1095, 1125, 1005, 975, 1125, 1100, 1145, 1025, 1075}   **170; 1025, 1075, 1125; 100; no outliers**

48. 15; 84, 87, 90; 6; no outliers   49. 90; 25, 50, 75; 50; no outliers
48–51. See Solutions Manual for box-and-whisker plots.

APPLICATIONS AND PROBLEM SOLVING

52. Horticulture A rose garden is being planted as a border around two sides of a triangular shaped lawn in a city park. Two of the vertices of the triangle have coordinates $(-2, 4)$ and $(3, -5)$. The gardener wishes to locate the third vertex so that the lawn's area is 25 square feet. Find the value of f if the coordinates of the third vertex are $(3, f)$. (Lesson 4–4) **5**

A practice test for Chapter 4 is provided on page 915.

53. Auto Mechanics Ann Braun is inventory manager for a local repair shop. If she orders 6 batteries, 5 cases of spark plugs, and two dozen pairs of wiper blades, she will pay $830. If she orders 3 batteries, 7 cases of spark plugs, and 4 dozen pairs of wiper blades, she will pay $820. If the batteries are $22 less than twice the price of a dozen wiper blades, what is the cost of each item on her order? (Lesson 4–7) batteries, $74; spark plugs, $58; wiper blades, $48

ALTERNATIVE ASSESSMENT

COOPERATIVE LEARNING PROJECT

Who Owns Muffin? In this project, you will manipulate data by using logic. You will not need to use operational algebraic skills, but you will need to write things down, keep track of information, and analyze data. There are 16 pieces of information below. From this information, you are to figure out who owns Muffin and who has no children.

1. There are five houses in a row.
2. The owners of the FORD live in the RED house.
3. The VOLKSWAGEN owners have TWO children.
4. The family that lives in the GREEN house has a pet named SPOT.
5. The CHEVROLET owners' pet is called ROVER.
6. The GREEN house is just to the right of the WHITE house.
7. The family that owns a DUCK has FOUR children.
8. A PIG lives in the YELLOW house.
9. The family in the MIDDLE house has an animal named ROSIE.
10. The car at the FIRST house is a BUICK.
11. The CAT lives next door to the house with FIVE children.
12. The family that owns the PIG lives next door to the family with SEVEN children.
13. THOMAS, the GOAT, lives next door to SPOT.
14. The DODGE owners have a ZEBRA.
15. The BUICK's owners live next door to the BLUE house.
16. ROSIE's owners have a FORD.

Follow these steps to solve your problem.

- Set up a table.
- Determine what information you can be sure of and put it in the table.
- The remaining information will be retrieved by elimination and deduction.
- Continue in this manner until you have filled in the table.
- The two empty spaces point out where Muffin lives and where no children live.
- Write a paragraph describing your plan and how you attacked the problem.

THINKING CRITICALLY

- Find the new coordinates of quadrilateral *ROSE*, with vertices $R(-2, -1)$, $O(3, 0)$, $S(2, 2)$, and $E(-1, 2)$, if it is rotated 90° counterclockwise about the origin *twice*. Compare the new coordinates to the original ones. Make a conjecture about what effect this rotation has on any figure.

- If the determinant of a coefficient matrix is 0, can you use inverse matrices to solve the system of equations? Why or why not? Describe the graph of such a system of equations.

PORTFOLIO

Using the addition, subtraction, and multiplication operations with matrices, determine whether the following properties, when used with matrices, parallel these same properties under whole number operations.

- associative property
- commutative property
- distributive property

Write a convincing proof or argument for each property. Place this in your portfolio.

SELF EVALUATION

Are you a person that works independently or do you ask questions and also share your ideas with others? When you work independently, do you work for an answer or do you work to understand the problem or concept? Do you feel comfortable *learning* with others and not just *doing* with others?

Assess yourself. What type of a learner are you? Are you open to others' opinions and input or do you work and learn from your own experiences? Describe how you can become more or less dependent on yourself and more or less open to helping and/or receiving help from others both in your study of mathematics and in your daily life.

Chapter 4 Study Guide and Assessment **249**

Assessment and Evaluation Masters, pp. 98, 109

NAME _____ **DATE** _____

Chapter 4 Performance Assessment

Instructions: *Demonstrate your knowledge by giving a clear, concise solution to each problem. Be sure to include all relevant drawings and justify your answers. You may show your solution in more than one way or investigate beyond the requirements of the problem.*

1. A retailer sells three bicycle models. The Flyer sells for $225, and the retailer's cost is $150. The E-Z Rider retails for $175 and costs the retailer $100. A Young Flyer retails for $125 and costs the retailer $75.

   a. Represent the selling prices in a row matrix *A*.

   b. Represent the retailer's costs in a row matrix *B* such that each model's cost occupies the same column as its corresponding price in matrix *A*.

   c. Find $A - B$. Interpret the meaning of the matrix $A - B$.

   d. Represent the selling prices and retailer's costs in a matrix $C_{2 \times 3}$. Label the rows and columns.

   e. Multiply matrix *C* by 2. Interpret this product matrix. When would the retailer be interested in this matrix?

   f. Define matrix *D* as shown below.

   $$\text{Bicycles} \quad \begin{bmatrix} \text{Sold} & \text{Ordered} \\ 3 & -4 \end{bmatrix}$$

   Find $D \cdot C$ and explain what this product means.

2. **a.** Write a word problem that requires two equations in two variables to solve it.

   b. Solve your word problem using matrices. Explain each step.

3. Describe the data set used to make this box-and-whisker plot. What *can't* you tell about the data by looking at the box-and-whisker plot?

   500 550 600 650 700

Scoring Guide
Chapter 4
Performance Assessment

Level	Specific Criteria
3 Superior	• Shows thorough understanding of the concepts of *matrices, matrix subtraction and multiplication, solving equations using matrices,* and *box-and-whisker plot*. • Uses appropriate strategies to solve problems. • Computations are correct. • Written explanations are exemplary. • Word problem concerning two equations in two variables is appropriate and makes sense. • Goes beyond requirements of problems.
2 Satisfactory, with Minor Flaws	• Shows understanding of the concepts of *matrices, matrix subtraction and multiplication, solving equations using matrices,* and *box-and-whisker plot*. • Uses appropriate strategies to solve problems. • Computations are mostly correct. • Written explanations are effective. • Word problem concerning two equations in two variables is appropriate and makes sense. • Satisfies all requirements of problems.
1 Nearly Satisfactory, with Serious Flaws	• Shows understanding of most of the concepts of *matrices, matrix subtraction and multiplication, solving equations using matrices,* and *box-and-whisker plot*. • May not use appropriate strategies to solve problems. • Computations are mostly correct. • Written explanations are satisfactory. • Word problem concerning two equations in two variables is mostly appropriate and sensible. • Satisfies most requirements of problems.
0 Unsatisfactory	• Shows little or no understanding of the concepts of *matrices, matrix subtraction and multiplication, solving equations using matrices,* and *box-and-whisker plot*. • May not use appropriate strategies to solve problems. • Computations are incorrect. • Written explanations are not satisfactory. • Word problem concerning two equations in two variables is not appropriate or sensible. • Does not satisfy requirements of problems.

Alternative Assessment

The Alternative Assessment section provides students with the opportunity to assess their own work by thinking critically, working with others, keeping a portfolio, and honestly evaluating their own progress. For more information on alternative forms of assessment, see *Alternative Assessment in the Mathematics*

Classroom, one of the titles in the Glencoe Mathematics Professional Series.

Performance Assessment

Performance Assessment tasks for this chapter are included in the *Assessment and Evaluation Masters.* A scoring guide is also provided.

Using the
COLLEGE ENTRANCE EXAM PRACTICE

These two pages review the skills and concepts presented in Chapters 1–4. This review is formatted to reflect new trends in college entrance testing.

A more traditional cumulative review is provided in the *Assessment and Evaluation Masters*, pp. 103–104.

Assessment and Evaluation Masters, pp. 103–104

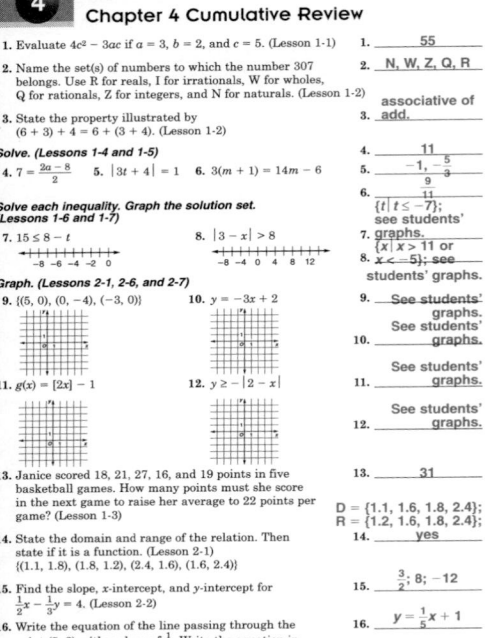

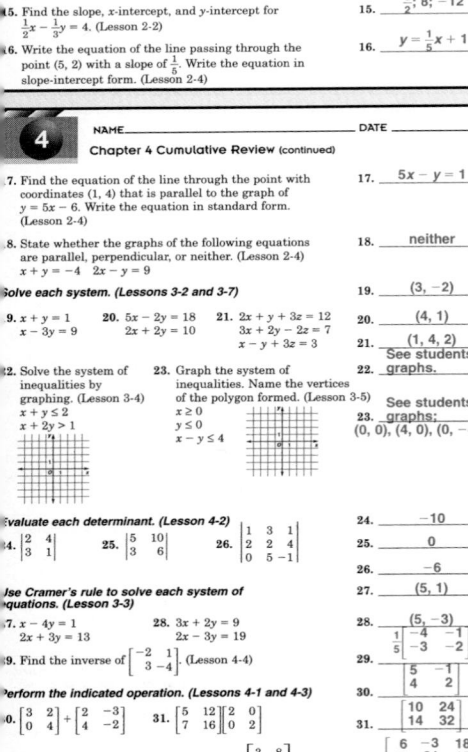

CHAPTERS 1–4

SECTION ONE: MULTIPLE CHOICE

There are eight multiple-choice questions in this section. After working each problem, write the letter of the correct answer on your paper.

1. Write the domain of $g = \{(9, 0), (3, 1), (12, 7), (1, -4), (12, 8), (-11, -3), (0, -6)\}$ and determine if g is a function.　C

   A. $\{9, 3, 12, 1, -11, 0\}$; g is a function.

   B. $\{0, 1, 7, -4, 8, -3, -6\}$; g is not a function.

   C. $\{9, 3, 12, 1, -11, 0\}$; g is not a function.

   D. $\{0, 1, 7, -4, 8, -3, -6\}$; g is a function.

2. The augmented matrix for a system is $\begin{bmatrix} 1 & 5 & 1 \\ 2 & -3 & 15 \end{bmatrix}$. What is the solution?　A

   A. $(6, -1)$ 　　　 B. $(1, 15)$

   C. $(5, -13)$ 　　 D. $(13, 1)$

3. Write an algebraic expression for the verbal expression, "twice the sum of a number and 5 is at most 18."　C

   A. $2x + 5 \geq 18$ 　　 B. $2(x + 5) > 18$

   C. $2(x + 5) \leq 18$ 　　 D. $2x + 2(5) = 18$

4. A set of data has a mean of 86.4, a median of 87, a range of 15, an interquartile range of 6, and an upper quartile of 90. Which box-and-whisker plot represents this information?　B

   A. 　　B.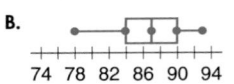

   74 78 82 86 90 94　　74 78 82 86 90 94

   C. 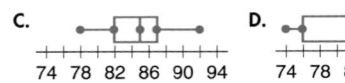　　D.

   74 78 82 86 90 94　　74 78 82 86 90 94

250 *College Entrance Exam Practice Chapters 1–4*

5. What is the slope-intercept form of a line that passes through $(1, -4)$ and is perpendicular to a line whose equation is $3x - 2y = 8$?　A

   A. $y = -\frac{2}{3}x - \frac{10}{3}$

   B. $2x + 3y = -10$

   C. $y = \frac{3}{2}x - 4$

   D. $y = \frac{2}{3}x - 4$

6. A feasible region has vertices $(0, 0), (4, 0), (5, 5)$, and $(0, 8)$. Find the maximum and minimum of the function $f(x,y) = x + 3y$ over this region.　A

   A. max: $f(0, 8) = 24$
      min: $f(0, 0) = 0$

   B. min: $f(0, 0) = 0$
      max: $f(5, 5) = 20$

   C. max: $f(5, 5) = 20$
      min: $f(0, 8) = 8$

   D. min: $f(4, 0) = 4$
      max: $f(0, 0) = 0$

7. Name all the sets of numbers to which -12 belongs.　D

   A. integers

   B. integers, rationals

   C. rationals, reals

   D. integers, rationals, reals

8. Find the value for a for which the graph of $y = ax - 3$ is perpendicular to the graph of $6x + y = 4$.　B

   A. $\frac{11}{4}$

   B. $\frac{1}{6}$

   C. $\frac{2}{3}$

   D. 6

Standardized Test Practice Questions are also provided in the *Assessment and Evaluation Masters*, p. 102.

SECTION TWO: SHORT ANSWER

This section contains seven questions for which you will provide short answers. Write your answer on your paper.

9. Create a system of inequalities for which the graph will be a regular hexagon with its interior located in the first quadrant.

Answers may vary.

10. Solve $\left| x - \frac{7}{3} \right| = 6$.

$-\frac{11}{3}, \frac{25}{3}$

11. Triangle ABC has vertices with coordinates $A(5, -2)$, $B(-3, 4)$, and $C(-2, -3)$. Find the coordinates of the vertices of triangle $A'B'C'$ if its perimeter is three times that of triangle ABC.

$A'(15, -6)$, $B'(-9, 12)$, $C'(-6, -9)$

12. Sherry bought 24 cans of soda at the store. She bought r cans at \$0.19 per can and t cans at \$0.29 per can. Find r and t if she spent \$5.46 on soda.

15, 9

13. During the seventh inning stretch at Fame Stadium Tuesday night, one concession stand sold 48 hot dogs and 72 soft drinks for a total of \$264. At the same time, another concession stand in the stadium sold 117 soft drinks and 54 hot dogs totaling \$387. Determine the individual price of a hot dog and a soft drink by using Cramer's Rule.

hot dog, \$1.75; soft drink, \$2.50

14. As an employee of Yogurt Delight, Maria is paid \$5.50 an hour less \$10 a week for cleaning her uniforms. Write an equation to describe her weekly pay and then find her pay for 32 hours of work.

$s = 5.5h - 10$; **\$166**

15. Latasha has a blueprint, as shown below, of a metal plate that is to be used in a sculpture. She needs to know the area of the quadrilateral in order to calculate the amount of ore needed to make the plate. Find the area.

53 units^2

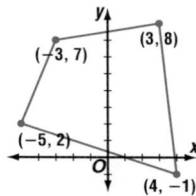

SECTION THREE: COMPARISON

This section contains five comparison problems that involve comparing two quantities, one in column A and one in column B. In certain questions, information related to one or both quantities is centered above them. All variables used represent real numbers.

Compare quantities A and B below.

- Write A if quantity A is greater.
- Write B if quantity B is greater.
- Write C if the two quantities are equal.
- Write D if there is not enough information to determine the relationship.

16. A   17. A   18. D   19. D   20. A

Column A	Column B
16. the value of x in $\begin{vmatrix} 3 & -2 & x \\ x & 1 & -5 \\ 2 & 0 & -1 \end{vmatrix} = 1$	the value of y in the system of equations $x + y + 3z = 7$ $2x - 2y - 3z = 2$ $3x - y - 2z = 1$

$$5a + 4b = -1$$
$$2a - b = 10$$

Column A	Column B
17. b	$\begin{vmatrix} -4 & 6 \\ -13 & 24 \end{vmatrix}$

$$t + 10 > 9$$

Column A	Column B
18. $3t - 2$	$-t + 2(t + 3)$

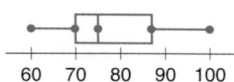

Column A	Column B
19. the mean of the data set	the median of the data set

$$2x + 3y = 7$$
$$3x - 4y = 2$$

Column A	Column B
20. x	y

Exploring Polynomials and Radical Expressions

PREVIEWING THE CHAPTER

This chapter reviews and extends students' knowledge of operations on monomials and polynomials. Addition, subtraction, and multiplication of polynomials are addressed. Methods for factoring polynomials are covered as well as methods for dividing polynomials, including synthetic division. Students also learn to simplify, add, subtract, multiply, and divide radicals. They make the connection between fractional exponents and radicals and then simplify expressions with fractional exponents. Complex numbers and operations on complex numbers are addressed, and students simplify expressions containing complex numbers.

Lesson (Pages)	Lesson Objectives	NCTM Standards	State/Local Objectives
5-1 (254–260)	Multiply and divide monomials. Represent numbers in scientific notation. Multiply and divide expressions written in scientific notation.	1–5	2.a.
5-2 (261–266)	Add, subtract, and multiply polynomials.	1–5	
5-3 (267–273)	Divide polynomials using long division. Divide polynomials by binomials using synthetic division.	1–5	
5-4 (274–280)	Factor polynomials. Use factoring to simplify polynomial quotients.	1–5	2.a.
5-5 (281–287)	Simplify radicals having various indices. Use a calculator to estimate roots of numbers.	1–5	
5-6 (288–295)	Simplify radical expressions. Rationalize the denominator of a fraction containing a radical expression. Add, subtract, multiply, and divide radical expressions.	1–5	9.a., 9.b., 9.c., 9.d., 9.e.
5-7 (296–302)	Solve problems by identifying and achieving subgoals. Write expressions with radical exponents in simplest radical form and vice versa. Evaluate expressions in either exponential or radical form.	1–5	2.a.
5-8 (303–309)	Solve equations containing radicals.	1–5	2.a., 9.c., 9.d.
5-9 (310–316)	Simplify square roots containing negative radicands. Solve quadratic equations that have pure imaginary solutions. Add, subtract, and multiply complex numbers.	1–5	
5-10 (317–321)	Simplify rational expressions containing complex numbers in the denominator.	1–5	

A complete, 1-page lesson plan is provided for each lesson in the *Lesson Planning Guide*. Answer keys for each lesson are available in the *Answer Key Masters*.

You may want to refer to the **Course Planning Calendar** on page T12 for detailed information on pacing.
PACING: **Standard**—16 days; **Honors**—12 days; **Block**—6 days

LESSON PLANNING CHART

| Lesson (Pages) | Materials/ Manipulatives | Extra Practice (Student Edition) | BLACKLINE MASTERS | | | | | | | | | Real-World Applications | Interactive Mathematics Tools Software | Teaching Transparencies |
			Study Guide	Practice	Enrichment	Assessment and Evaluation	Modeling Mathematics	Multicultural Activity	Tech Prep Applications	Graphing Calculator	Science and Math Lab Manual			
5-1 (254–260)	scientific calculator graphing calculator scissors	p. 885	p. 30	p. 30	p. 30			p. 9			pp. 81–86	12		5-1A 5-1B
5-2 (261–266)	rope algebra tiles*	p. 886	p. 31	p. 31	p. 31				p. 9					5-2A 5-2B
5-3 (267–273)	calculator graphing calculator	p. 886	p. 32	p. 32	p. 32	p. 128								5-3A 5-3B
5-4 (274–280)	algebra tiles* graphing calculator	p. 886	p. 33	p. 33	p. 33							13	5-4	5-4A 5-4B
5-5 (281–287)	calculator	p. 887	p. 34	p. 34	p. 34	pp. 127, 128	pp. 37–39							5-5A 5-5B
5-6 (288–295)	geoboards* geometric dot paper straightedge	p. 887	p. 35	p. 35	p. 35							14	5-6	5-6A 5-6B
5-7 (296–302)	calculator	p. 887	p. 36	p. 36	p. 36							15		5-7A 5-7B
5-8 (303–309)	calculator	p. 888	p. 37	p. 37	p. 37	p. 129							5-8	5-8A 5-8B
5-9 (310–316)	grid paper straightedge graphing calculator	p. 888	p. 38	p. 38	p. 38		p. 65			p. 10	p. 5			5-9A 5-9B
5-10 (317–321)		p. 888	p. 39	p. 39	p. 39	p. 129		p. 10						5-10A 5-10B
Study Guide/ Assessment (323–327)						pp. 113 –126, 130 –132								

*Included in Glencoe's Student Manipulative Kit and Overhead Manipulative Resources.

ORGANIZING THE CHAPTER

OTHER CHAPTER RESOURCES

Student Edition
Chapter Opener, pp. 252–253
Mathematics and Society, p. 295
Working on the Investigation,
pp. 273, 302
Closing the Investigation, p. 322

Teacher's Classroom Resources
Investigations and Projects Masters,
pp. 41–44

Technology
Teacher's Guide for Software
Resources
Test and Review Software (IBM
and Macintosh)
CD-ROM Interactions (Windows
and Macintosh)

Professional Publications
Block Scheduling Booklet
Glencoe Mathematics Professional
Series

OUTSIDE RESOURCES

Books/Periodicals
Algebra Problems: One Step Beyond, Dale
Seymour Publications
*Fractals for the Classroom: Introduction to
Fractals and Chaos*, NCTM

Software
*Bradford Algebra Software: Exponents, Roots, and
Radicals*, William K. Bradford Publishing
Koyn Fractal Studio, William K. Bradford Publishing

Videos/CD-ROMs
Multiplying Polynomials, Coronet, MTI

See the *Teacher's Guide for Software Resources* for software addresses.

ASSESSMENT RESOURCES

Student Edition
Math Journal, pp. 270, 284, 300
Mixed Review, pp. 260, 266,
273, 280, 286, 294, 302,
309, 316, 321
Self Test, p. 287
Chapter Highlights, p. 323
Chapter Study Guide and
Assessment, pp. 324–326
Alternative Assessment, p. 327
 Portfolio, p. 327

Teacher's Wraparound Edition
5-Minute Check, pp. 254, 261,
267, 274, 281, 288, 296, 303,
310, 317
Check for Understanding, pp. 258,
263, 270, 278, 284, 292, 300,
307, 314, 319
Closing Activity, pp. 260, 266,
273, 280, 286, 295, 302, 309,
316, 321
Cooperative Learning, pp. 276,
293

Assessment and Evaluation Masters
Multiple-Choice Tests, Forms 1A
(Honors), 1B (Average), 1C
(Basic), pp. 113–118
Free-Response Tests, Forms 2A
(Honors), 2B (Average), 2C
(Basic), pp. 119–124
Calculator-Based Test, p. 125
Performance Assessment, p. 126
Mid-Chapter Test, p. 127
Quizzes A–D, pp. 128–129
Standardized Test Practice, p. 130
Cumulative Review, pp. 131–132

ENHANCING THE CHAPTER

Examples of some of the materials for enhancing Chapter 5 are shown below.

DIVERSITY

Multicultural Activity Masters, pp. 9, 10

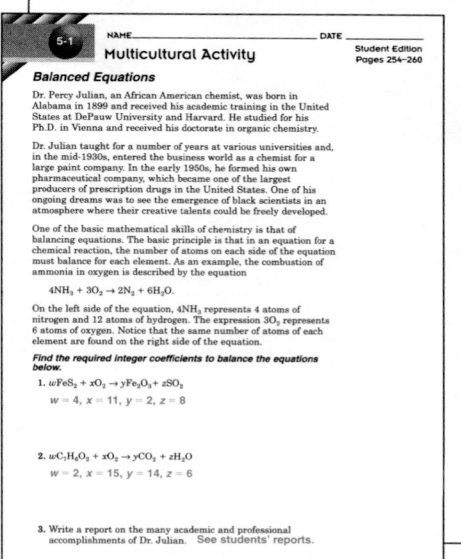

5-1 NAME_____ DATE_____
Multicultural Activity
Student Edition Pages 254–260

Balanced Equations

Dr. Percy Julian, an African American chemist, was born in Alabama in 1899 and received his academic training in the United States at DePauw University and Harvard. He studied for his Ph.D. in Vienna and received his doctorate in organic chemistry.

Dr. Julian taught for a number of years at various universities and, in the mid-1930s, entered the business world as a chemist for a large paint company. In the early 1950s, he formed his own pharmaceutical company, which became one of the largest producers of prescription drugs in the United States. One of his ongoing dreams was to see the emergence of black scientists in an atmosphere where their creative talents could be freely developed.

One of the basic mathematical skills of chemistry is that of balancing equations. The basic principle is that in an equation the number of atoms on each side of the equation must balance for each element. As an example, the combustion of ammonia in oxygen is described by the equation

$$4NH_3 + 3O_2 \rightarrow 2N_2 + 6H_2O.$$

On the left side of the equation, $4NH_3$ represents 4 atoms of nitrogen and 12 atoms of hydrogen. The expression $3O_2$ represents 6 atoms of oxygen. Notice that the same number of atoms of each element are found on the right side of the equation.

Find the required integer coefficients to balance the equations below.

1. $wFeS_2 + xO_2 \rightarrow yFe_2O_3 + zSO_2$
   $w = 4, x = 11, y = 2, z = 8$

2. $wC_7H_8O_2 + xO_2 \rightarrow yCO_2 + zH_2O$
   $w = 2, x = 15, y = 14, z = 6$

3. Write a report on the many academic and professional accomplishments of Dr. Julian. See students' reports.

APPLICATIONS

Real-World Applications, 12, 13, 14, 15

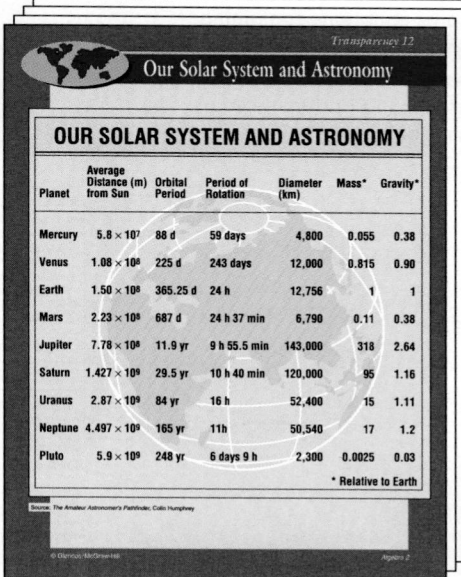

Transparency 12

Our Solar System and Astronomy

OUR SOLAR SYSTEM AND ASTRONOMY

Planet	Average Distance (m) from Sun	Orbital Period	Period of Rotation	Diameter (km)	Mass*	Gravity*
Mercury	5.8×10^7	88 d	59 days	4,800	0.055	0.38
Venus	1.08×10^8	225 d	243 days	12,000	0.815	0.90
Earth	1.50×10^8	365.25 d	24 h	12,756	1	1
Mars	2.23×10^8	687 d	24 h 37 min	6,790	0.11	0.38
Jupiter	7.78×10^8	11.9 yr	9 h 55.5 min	143,000	318	2.64
Saturn	1.427×10^9	29.5 yr	10 h 40 min	120,000	95	1.16
Uranus	2.87×10^9	84 yr	16 h	52,400	15	1.11
Neptune	4.497×10^9	165 yr	11h	50,540	17	1.2
Pluto	5.9×10^9	248 yr	6 days 9 h	2,300	0.0025	0.03

* Relative to Earth

Source: The Amateur Astronomer's Pathfinder, Colin Humphrey

© Glencoe/McGraw-Hill   Algebra 2

TECHNOLOGY

Graphing Calculator Masters, p. 5

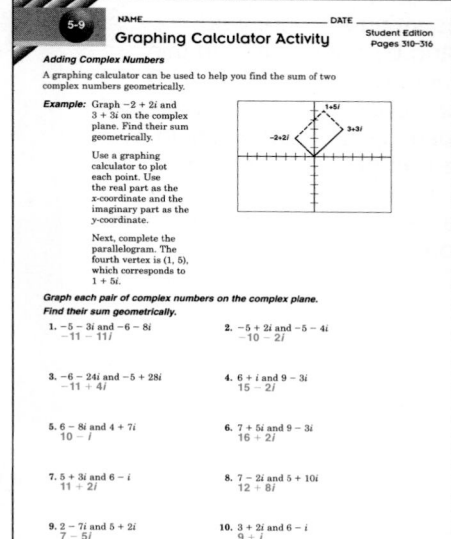

5-9 NAME_____ DATE_____
Graphing Calculator Activity
Student Edition Pages 310–316

Adding Complex Numbers

A graphing calculator can be used to help you find the sum of two complex numbers geometrically.

Example: Graph $-2 + 2i$ and $3 + 3i$ on the complex plane. Find their sum geometrically.

Use a graphing calculator to plot each point. Use the real part as the x-coordinate and the imaginary part as the y-coordinate.

Next, complete the parallelogram. The fourth vertex is (1, 5), which corresponds to $1 + 5i$.

Graph each pair of complex numbers on the complex plane. Find their sum geometrically.

1. $-5 - 3i$ and $-6 - 8i$
   $-11 - 11i$

2. $-5 + 2i$ and $-5 - 4i$
   $-10 - 2i$

3. $-6 - 24i$ and $-5 + 28i$
   $-11 + 4i$

4. $6 + i$ and $9 - 3i$
   $15 - 2i$

5. $6 - 8i$ and $4 + 7i$
   $10 - i$

6. $7 + 5i$ and $9 - 3i$
   $16 + 2i$

7. $5 + 3i$ and $6 - i$
   $11 + 2i$

8. $7 - 2i$ and $5 + 10i$
   $12 + 8i$

9. $2 - 7i$ and $5 + 2i$
   $7 - 5i$

10. $3 + 2i$ and $6 - i$
    $9 + i$

TECH PREP

Tech Prep Applications Masters, pp. 9, 10

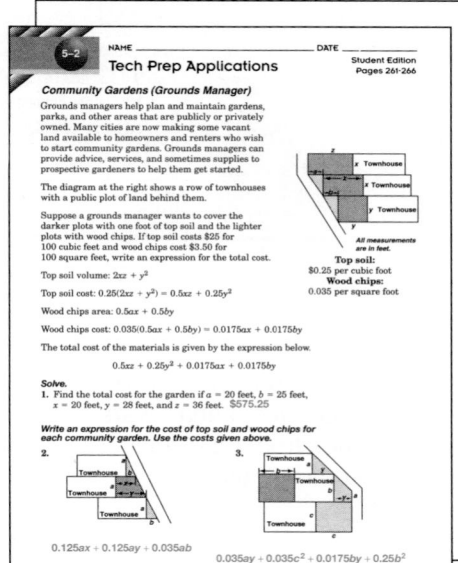

5-2 NAME_____ DATE_____
Tech Prep Applications
Student Edition Pages 261–266

Community Gardens (Grounds Manager)

Grounds managers help plan and maintain gardens, parks, and other areas that are publicly or privately owned. Many cities are now making some vacant land available to homeowners and renters who wish to start community gardens. Grounds managers can provide advice, services, and sometimes supplies to prospective gardeners to help them get started.

The diagram at the right shows a row of townhouses with a public plot of land behind them.

Suppose a grounds manager wants to cover the darker plots with one foot of top soil and the lighter plots with wood chips. If top soil costs $25 for 100 cubic feet and wood chips cost $3.50 for 100 square feet, write an expression for the total cost.

Top soil:
$0.25 per cubic foot
Wood chips:
0.035 per square foot

All measurements are in feet.

Top soil volume: $2xz + y^2$

Top soil cost: $0.25(2xz + y^2) = 0.5xz + 0.25y^2$

Wood chips area: $0.5xz + 0.5by$

Wood chips cost: $0.035(0.5az + 0.5by) = 0.0175az + 0.0175by$

The total cost of the materials is given by the expression below.

$$0.5xz + 0.25y^2 + 0.0175az + 0.0175by$$

Solve.
1. Find the total cost for the garden if $a = 20$ feet, $b = 25$ feet, $x = 20$ feet, $y = 28$ feet, and $z = 36$ feet. $575.25

Write an expression for the cost of top soil and wood chips for each community garden. Use the costs given above.

2. $0.125ax + 0.125ay + 0.035ab$

3. $0.035ay + 0.035c^2 + 0.0175by + 0.25b^2$

CONNECTIONS

Science and Math Lab Manual, pp. 81–86

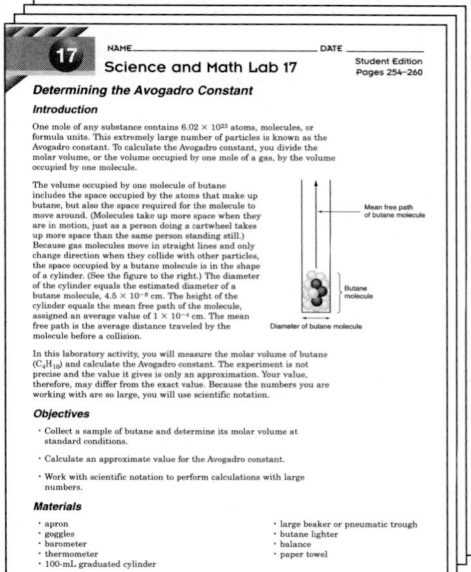

17 NAME_____ DATE_____
Science and Math Lab 17
Student Edition Pages 254–260

Determining the Avogadro Constant

Introduction

One mole of any substance contains 6.02×10^{23} atoms, molecules, or formula units. This extremely large number of particles is known as the Avogadro constant. To calculate the Avogadro constant, you divide the molar volume, or the volume occupied by one mole of a gas, by the volume occupied by one molecule.

The volume occupied by one molecule of butane includes the space occupied by the atoms that make up butane, but also the space required for the molecule to move around. (Molecules take up more space when they are in motion, just as a person doing a cartwheel takes up more space than the same person standing still.) Because gas molecules move in straight lines and only change direction when they collide with other particles, the space occupied by a butane molecule is in the shape of a cylinder. (See the figure to the right.) The diameter of the cylinder equals the estimated diameter of a butane molecule, 4.5×10^{-8} cm. The height of the cylinder equals the mean free path of the molecule, assigned an average value of 1×10^{-4} cm. The mean free path is the average distance traveled by the molecule before a collision.

In this laboratory activity, you will measure the molar volume of butane (C_4H_{10}) and calculate the Avogadro constant. The experiment is not precise and the value it gives is only an approximation. Your value, therefore, may differ from the exact value. Because the numbers you are working with are so large, you will use scientific notation.

Mean free path of butane molecule

Butane molecule

Diameter of butane molecule

Objectives

· Collect a sample of butane and determine its molar volume at standard conditions.

· Calculate an approximate value for the Avogadro constant.

· Work with scientific notation to perform calculations with large numbers.

Materials

· apron
· goggles
· barometer
· thermometer
· 100-mL graduated cylinder

· large beaker or pneumatic trough
· butane lighter
· balance
· paper towel

PROBLEM SOLVING

Problem of the Week Cards, 13, 14, 15

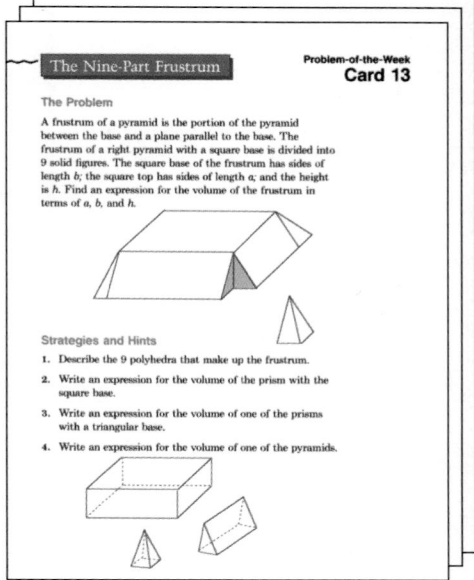

The Nine-Part Frustrum
Problem-of-the-Week Card 13

The Problem

A frustrum of a pyramid is the portion of the pyramid between the base and a plane parallel to the base. The frustrum of a right pyramid with a square base is divided into 9 solid figures. The square base of the frustrum has sides of length b; the square top has sides of length a; and the height is h. Find an expression for the volume of the frustrum in terms of a, b, and h.

Strategies and Hints

1. Describe the 9 polyhedra that make up the frustrum.

2. Write an expression for the volume of the prism with the square base.

3. Write an expression for the volume of one of the prisms with a triangular base.

4. Write an expression for the volume of one of the pyramids.

MAKING MATHEMATICS RELEVANT

This two-page introduction to the chapter provides students with an opportunity to explore contemporary topics and their applications to mathematics.

Background Information

Rising Use of Home PCs The data presented in the table are based on steady growth within the home computer market. The same study also presented an accelerated growth scenario, representing an increased demand by consumers. In this scenario, by the year 2010, 60 million households, more than half of those in the country, would own home computers. Ask students to think about what factors might influence the growth rate in home computer ownership.

Exploring Polynomials and Radical Expressions

Objectives

In this chapter, you will:

- simplify expressions containing polynomials, radicals, complex numbers, or rational exponents,
- factor polynomials,
- solve equations containing radicals, and
- solve problems by identifying and achieving subgoals.

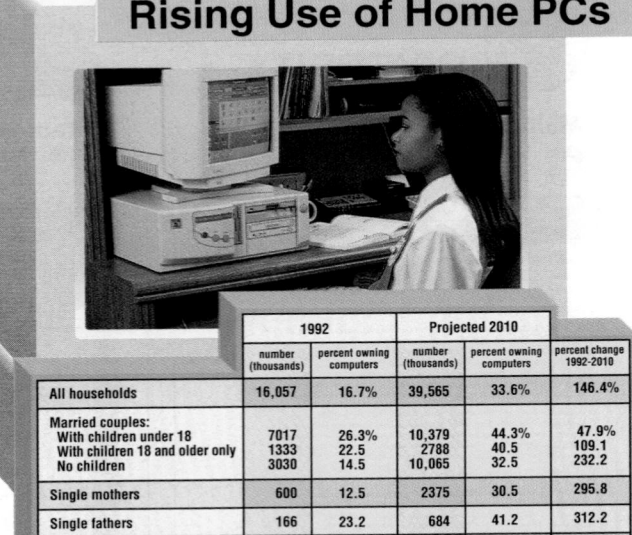

Rising Use of Home PCs

	1992		Projected 2010		
	number (thousands)	percent owning computers	number (thousands)	percent owning computers	percent change 1992-2010
All households	16,057	16.7%	39,565	33.6%	146.4%
Married couples:					
With children under 18	7017	26.3%	10,379	44.3%	47.9%
With children 18 and older only	1333	22.5	2788	40.5	109.1
No children	3030	14.5	10,065	32.5	232.2
Single mothers	600	12.5	2375	30.5	295.8
Single fathers	166	23.2	684	41.2	312.2
Men living alone	1119	12.3	3813	30.3	240.8
Women living alone	738	5.3	4328	23.3	486.5
Other households	2054	14.4	5133	32.4	149.9

Source: *American Demographics*, Feb. 1994

TIME Line

Home computer use is on the rise. Computer dependency has already become established in the workplace. Are you computer literate? Do you have a home computer? It may be very important to your future.

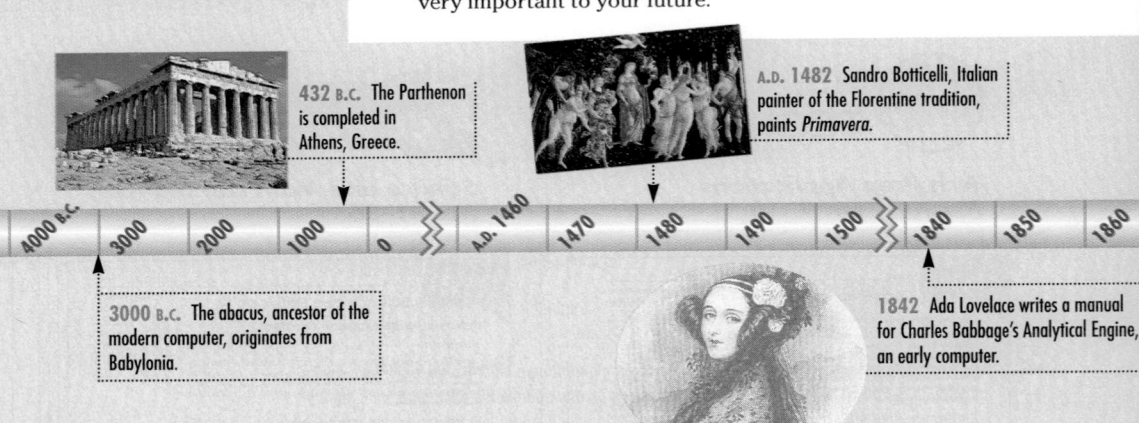

432 B.C. The Parthenon is completed in Athens, Greece.

A.D. 1482 Sandro Botticelli, Italian painter of the Florentine tradition, paints *Primavera*.

| 4000 B.C. | 3000 | 2000 | 1000 | 0 | A.D. 1460 | 1470 | 1480 | 1490 | 1500 | 1840 | 1850 | 1860 |

3000 B.C. The abacus, ancestor of the modern computer, originates from Babylonia.

1842 Ada Lovelace writes a manual for Charles Babbage's Analytical Engine, an early computer.

TIME Line

Students may wish to investigate the work of Charles Babbage, whose Analytical Engine, the world's first automatic digital computer, was never completed because the machining techniques of the time period were not yet precise enough to create the engine's metal parts.

interNET CONNECTION

Check out how computers fit into a small business with a shareware software index from the Small Business Administration.

World Wide Web
http://www.sbaonline.
sba.gov/shareware

Chapter Project

A business specialist is conducting a seminar for computer store managers so they can be more efficient in sales and customer service. The specialist tells the managers that the polynomial $2n^2 - 7n - 15$ can be used to estimate the profits on the sale of n computers. Suppose you are one of the managers attending this seminar.

- Determine how many computers you would have to sell to get a profit of $330.

- Determine the profit per computer for the sale of 10, 20, 30, 40, and 50 computers.

- Analyze the data from the sales of the different numbers of computers. Explain how this relates to computer superstores being able to sell computers at cheaper prices than smaller independent dealers.

- Include graphics and analyze the profit curve; i.e., when it is going up, going down, maximized, and so on.

When **David Bray** works on his home computer in Alexandria, Virginia, he gets things done. He recently won the grand prize in the largest science fair in the northern hemisphere for a computer program he created. His program deals with oil spills, how to predict their spread on water, and how to contain and remove them. This program also won "Best in Fair" at the International Youth Fair of Science and Technology in Argentina.

1960 Dr. Grace Hopper was first to demonstrate her company's version of COBOL on two computers.

1976 Seymour Cray develops the CRAY-1 computer system, the first supercomputer, which allowed great quantities of information to be processed quickly.

| 1890 | 1900 | 1910 | 1920 | 1930 | 1940 | 1950 | 1960 | 1970 | 1980 | 1990 | 2000 |

Antonín Dvořák SYMPHONIES NOS. 8 AND 9 ("NEW WORLD") in Full Score

1893 Antonín Dvořák, Bohemian composer, writes his *Symphony No. 9 in E Opus 95* ("From the New World").

1994 In an unprecedented achievement, every member of U.S. team earns a perfect score in the International Mathematical Olympiad.

Chapter 5 **253**

David worked 14 hours a week for 9 months developing his software to model oil spills. Computer programs are often used to model natural growth and decay processes.

Chapter Project

Cooperative Learning You may choose to have students pair off or arrange them in cooperative groups to discuss possible solutions for this activity. This project allows students to explore an example of a polynomial model of a real-world situation. It also introduces students to the end behavior of polynomial functions. According to this behavior, second-degree polynomials increase indefinitely as the independent variable increases.

Investigations and Projects Masters, p. 41

5 NAME _____ DATE _____

Chapter 5 Project A Student Edition Pages 254–32

Computers in the Classroom

1. Work with a partner to write a description of the ideal computer system for a high school mathematics classroom. If your classroom already has a computer, describe any changes in hardware or software you would like to make. Be sure to consider the amount of memory needed, the size of the hard drive needed, and any software that would be needed.

2. Visit several different electronics stores or look through catalogs to determine the cost of your system.

3. Write an expression that could be used to determine the cost of putting your system in x classrooms. Use this expression to estimate the cost of equipping every mathematics classroom in the United States with your system.

4. Write a report on the use of technology in high school classrooms today. Include a recommendation about what, if anything, needs to be done to better prepare students for the increasingly technological world beyond the classroom.

Alternative Chapter Projects ▬▬

Two other chapter projects are included in the *Investigations and Projects Masters.* In Chapter 5 Project A, pp. 41–42, students extend the topic in the chapter opener. In Chapter 5 Project B, pp. 43–44, students investigate specific fields of study within the realm of biotechnology.

1 FOCUS

NCTM Standards: 1–5

Instructional Resources

- Study Guide Master 5-1
- Practice Master 5-1
- Enrichment Master 5-1
- Multicultural Activity Masters, p. 9
- Real-World Applications, 12
- Science and Math Lab Manual, pp. 81–86

 Transparency 5-1A contains the 5-Minute Check for this lesson; **Transparency 5-1B** contains a teaching aid for this lesson.

Recommended Pacing	
Standard Pacing	Day 1 of 16
Honors Pacing	Day 1 of 12
Block Scheduling*	Day 1 of 6 (along with Lesson 5-2)

 *For more information on pacing and possible lesson plans, refer to the *Block Scheduling Booklet.*

 5-Minute Check
(over Chapter 4)

1. Evaluate the determinant of
$$\begin{bmatrix} -1 & 4 & 0 \\ 3 & -2 & -5 \\ -3 & 1 & 2 \end{bmatrix}.$$
35

2. If $A = \begin{bmatrix} 3 & -1 \\ 2 & 4 \end{bmatrix}$ and

$B = \begin{bmatrix} 4 & 0 & -3 \\ 7 & -5 & 9 \end{bmatrix}$, find AB.

$AB = \begin{bmatrix} 5 & 5 & -18 \\ 36 & -20 & 30 \end{bmatrix}$

3. Find the inverse of $\begin{bmatrix} 2 & 6 \\ 5 & 1 \end{bmatrix}$.
$\frac{1}{32} \begin{bmatrix} 1 & -6 \\ 5 & 2 \end{bmatrix}$

4. Solve the system by using Cramer's rule.
$2x - y + z = -2$
$x + 2y + 6z = 3$
$3x - y + 2z = -1$ **(3, 6, −2)**

5. Create a box-and-whisker plot for the following data:
62, 66, 64, 65, 70, 66, 69, 63, 69, 68, 72, 70, 58, 67, 65, 61, 64, 66, 63, 79, and 59.

Monomials

5-1

***What* YOU'LL LEARN**

- To multiply and divide monomials,
- to represent numbers in scientific notation, and
- to multiply and divide expressions written in scientific notation.

***Why* IT'S IMPORTANT**

You can use monomials to solve problems involving science and economics.

CONNECTION
Science

Exponents are used to express very large or very small numbers in **scientific notation**. A number is in scientific notation when it is in the form $a \times 10^n$, where $1 \le a < 10$ and n is an integer.

The table below shows examples of numbers written in scientific notation.

	Fact	Numeral	Scientific Notation
	The temperatures produced in the center of a thermonuclear fusion bomb are as high as 400 million degrees Celsius.	400,000,000	4.0×10^8
	The most powerful laser is the Nova at the Lawrence Hall of Science in California. It generates 100 trillion watts of power.	100,000,000,000,000	1.0×10^{14}
	The most powerful microscope was invented at IBM's research labs. It is capable of focusing to one-hundredth the diameter of an atom, measured in meters.	0.0000000003	3×10^{-10}

Notice that the last number in the table is written using negative exponents. Negative exponents are another way of expressing the inverse of a number. For example, $\frac{1}{x^2}$ can be written as x^{-2}.

Negative Exponents	For any real number a, and any integer n, where $a \ne 0$, $$a^{-n} = \frac{1}{a^n} \text{ and } \frac{1}{a^{-n}} = a^n.$$

Example **1** Express each number in scientific notation.
a. 2,340,000

$$2,340,000 = 2.34 \times 1,000,000$$
$$= 2.34 \times 10^6$$

b. 0.00012

$$0.00012 = 1.2 \times 0.0001$$
$$= 1.2 \times \frac{1}{10^4} \quad 0.0001 = \frac{1}{10,000} \text{ or } \frac{1}{10^4}$$
$$= 1.2 \times 10^{-4}$$

Answer for 5-Minute Check

5.

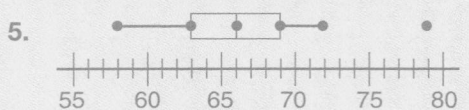

TEKS 2.a.

TECHNOLOGY Tips

To enter a number that is already in scientific notation into a graphing calculator,

use the $\boxed{10^x}$ key.

For example,

2.34×10^5 would be entered as $2.34 \boxed{\times} \boxed{10^x}$ 5.

EXPLORATION
PROGRAMMING

Use the following program to explore how a TI-82 graphing calculator expresses small numbers.

```
PROGRAM: SMALLNOS
:For (N,1000,10000,1000)
:Disp "1/N IF N IS",N,"EQUALS",1/N
:Pause
:End
```

The :For statement tells the calculator to evaluate N for values from 1000 to 10,000 in increments of 1000.

The calculator will pause after each calculation. Press ENTER to continue for the next value.   **a–c. See margin.**

Your Turn

a. How would you edit the program so that it will display N for values from 10,000 to 100,000 in increments of 1000? Rerun the program for these values.

b. How does your calculator display very small numbers? Give an example.

c. How might this differ from other scientific calculator displays?

Exponents are also used in algebraic expressions called **monomials.** A monomial is an expression that is a number, a variable, or the product of a number and one or more variables. Some examples of monomials are $5c$, $-a$, 17, x^3, and $\frac{1}{2}x^4y^2$. Monomials cannot contain variables whose exponents cannot be written as whole numbers. Thus, expressions such as $\frac{1}{n^2}$ and $\sqrt{n}$ are not monomials.   *Why?*

Constants are monomials that contain no variables. The numerical factor of a monomial is the **coefficient** of the variable. For example, the coefficient of m in $-6m$ is -6. The **degree** of a monomial is the sum of the exponents of its variables. For example, the degree of $12g^7h^4$ is $7 + 4$ or 11. The degree of a nonzero constant is 0.

The term power is sometimes used to refer to the exponent itself.

A **power** is an expression in the form of x^n. To **simplify** an expression containing powers means to rewrite the expression without parentheses or negative exponents.

Example ② Simplify $(2x^2y^3)(-5x^4y^2)$.

$$(2x^2y^3)(-5x^4y^2) = (2 \cdot x \cdot x \cdot y \cdot y \cdot y)(-5 \cdot x \cdot x \cdot x \cdot x \cdot y \cdot y) \quad \text{Definition of exponents}$$

$$= 2(-5) \cdot x \cdot x \cdot x \cdot x \cdot x \cdot x \cdot y \cdot y \cdot y \cdot y \cdot y \quad \text{Commutative property}$$

$$= -10x^6y^5$$

Example 2 suggests the following property of exponents.

Multiplying Powers	**For any real number a and integers m and n,** $a^m \cdot a^n = a^{m+n}$.

Motivating the Lesson

Questioning Ask questions about the size of the national debt, the population of the world, and the number of stars in our galaxy. Use an almanac to find very large or small numbers and discuss ways they can be written.

2 TEACH

In-Class Examples

For Example 1
Express each number in scientific notation.

a. 236,000 2.36×10^5
b. 0.01008 1.008×10^{-2}

For Example 2
Simplify.

a. $(2ab^2)(-4a^3b^3c)$ $-8a^4b^5c$
b. $(6x^2y^3)(xyz)$ $6x^3y^4z$

EXPLORATION

Provide, or have students bring in, other types of calculators. Have students compare the steps necessary to carry out the exercise on the various calculators.

Answers for the Exploration

a. :For (N, 10000,100000,1000)
b. It will display up to 10 decimal places in normal mode. After that, it uses E notation. If scientific mode is selected, all numbers are displayed in E notation. For example, 0.5×10^{-4} is displayed as 5 E−05.
c. Sample answer: 0.5^{-04}

Classroom Vignette

"Geometry Connection: Have students graph sets of ordered pairs that form common geometric figures and find the area and perimeter.

Example: Graph the ordered pairs $A(-3, -5)$, $B(3, -5)$, $C(3, 5)$, $D(-3, 5)$ and connect them to form a quadrilateral.
a. Identify the quadrilateral.
b. Find its perimeter.
c. Find its area."

Eva Gates
Independent Mathematics Consultant
Pearland, Texas

To multiply powers of the same variable, you add the exponents. Knowing this, it seems reasonable to expect that when dividing powers, you would subtract exponents. Consider $\dfrac{x^7}{x^4}$.

$$\dfrac{x^7}{x^4} = \dfrac{\overset{1\ \ 1\ \ 1\ \ 1}{x \cdot x \cdot x \cdot x \cdot x \cdot x \cdot x}}{\underset{1\ \ 1\ \ 1\ \ 1}{x \cdot x \cdot x \cdot x}} \qquad \textit{Remember that x cannot equal 0.}$$

$$= x \cdot x \cdot x$$

$$= x^3 \qquad\qquad \textit{Note that } x^3 = x^{7-4}.$$

It appears that our hypothesis is true. To divide powers of the same base, you subtract exponents. This is stated formally below.

Dividing Powers	For any real number a, except $a = 0$, and integers m and n, $\dfrac{a^m}{a^n} = a^{m-n}.$

In the next example, the check uses the definition of exponents to verify the rule for division of powers.

Example **3**   Simplify $\dfrac{p^5}{p^9}$. Assume that $p \neq 0$.

$$\dfrac{p^5}{p^9} = p^{5-9} \qquad \textit{Dividing powers}$$

$$= p^{-4} \text{ or } \dfrac{1}{p^4} \qquad \textit{Remember that a simplified expression cannot contain negative exponents.}$$

Check: $\dfrac{p^5}{p^9} = \dfrac{\overset{1\ \ 1\ \ 1\ \ 1\ \ 1}{p \cdot p \cdot p \cdot p \cdot p}}{\underset{1\ \ 1\ \ 1\ \ 1\ \ 1}{p \cdot p \cdot p \cdot p \cdot p \cdot p \cdot p \cdot p \cdot p}}$

$$= \dfrac{1}{p^4} \text{ or } p^{-4}$$

Let's use the property of division of powers and the definition of exponents to simplify $\dfrac{y^5}{y^5}$.

Method 1

$$\dfrac{y^5}{y^5} = y^{5-5} \quad \textit{Dividing powers}$$

$$= y^0$$

Method 2

$$\dfrac{y^5}{y^5} = \dfrac{\overset{1\ \ 1\ \ 1\ \ 1\ \ 1}{y \cdot y \cdot y \cdot y \cdot y}}{\underset{1\ \ 1\ \ 1\ \ 1\ \ 1}{y \cdot y \cdot y \cdot y \cdot y}}$$

$$= 1$$

Since $\dfrac{y^5}{y^5}$ cannot have two different values, we can conclude that $y^0 = 1$, where $y \neq 0$. In general, any nonzero number raised to the zero power is equal to 1.

The properties we have presented can be used to verify other properties of powers listed below.

> **Properties of Powers.**
>
> Suppose m and n are integers and a and b are real numbers. Then the following properties hold.
>
> **Power of a Power:** $(a^m)^n = a^{mn}$
>
> **Power of a Product:** $(ab)^m = a^m b^m$
>
> **Power of a Quotient:** $\left(\dfrac{a}{b}\right)^n = \dfrac{a^n}{b^n}$, $b \neq 0$ and
>
> $\left(\dfrac{a}{b}\right)^{-n} = \left(\dfrac{b}{a}\right)^n$ or $\dfrac{b^n}{a^n}$, $a \neq 0$, $b \neq 0$

Example **Simplify each expression.**

a. $(a^4)^5$

$$(a^4)^5 = a^{4(5)} \quad \text{Power of a power}$$
$$= a^{20}$$

b. $(-5p^2 s^4)^3$

$$(-5p^2 s^4)^3 = (-5)^3 \cdot (p^2)^3 \cdot (s^4)^3 \quad \text{Power of a product}$$
$$= -125 p^6 s^{12}$$

c. $\left(\dfrac{-2m}{n}\right)^4$

$$\left(\dfrac{-2m}{n}\right)^4 = \dfrac{(-2m)^4}{n^4} \quad \text{Power of a quotient}$$
$$= \dfrac{(-2)^4 \, m^4}{n^4}$$
$$= \dfrac{16m^4}{n^4}$$

d. $\left(\dfrac{a}{3}\right)^{-2}$

$$\left(\dfrac{a}{3}\right)^{-2} = \left(\dfrac{3}{a}\right)^2 \quad \text{Definition of negative exponent}$$
$$= \dfrac{3^2}{a^2} \text{ or } \dfrac{9}{a^2} \quad \text{Power of a quotient}$$

To simplify some expressions, you must use several of the properties of powers.

Example ⑤ **Simplify** $\left(\dfrac{-4x^{2n}}{x^{3n}z^2}\right)^3$.

Method 1

$$\left(\dfrac{-4x^{2n}}{x^{3n}z^2}\right)^3 = \dfrac{(-4x^{2n})^3}{(x^{3n}z^2)^3} \quad \text{Power of a quotient}$$
$$= \dfrac{(-4)^3(x^{2n})^3}{(x^{3n})^3(z^2)^3} \quad \text{Power of a product}$$
$$= \dfrac{-64x^{6n}}{x^{9n}z^6} \quad \text{Power of a power}$$
$$= \dfrac{-64x^{6n-9n}}{z^6} \quad \text{Dividing powers}$$
$$= \dfrac{-64x^{-3n}}{z^6} \text{ or } \dfrac{-64}{x^{3n}z^6}$$

Method 2

Simplify the fraction first before cubing.

$$\left(\dfrac{-4x^{2n}}{x^{3n}z^2}\right)^3 = \left(\dfrac{-4x^{2n-3n}}{z^2}\right)^3$$
$$= \left(\dfrac{-4}{x^n z^2}\right)^3$$
$$= \dfrac{(-4)^3}{(x^n)^3(z^2)^3}$$
$$= \dfrac{-64}{x^{3n}z^6}$$

You can also multiply and divide expressions involving numbers written in scientific notation. A calculator provides the most efficient method for finding the product or quotient.

In-Class Examples

For Example 4
Simplify.

a. $(x^2)^3$ x^6

b. $(6a^3 b^2)^4$ $1296a^{12}b^8$

c. $\left(\dfrac{3x^3 y^n}{x^5 y^{3n} z^2}\right)^2$

$\dfrac{9}{x^4 y^{4n} z^4}$ or $9x^{-4}y^{-4n}z^{-4}$

d. $\left(\dfrac{4}{n}\right)^{-3}$ $\dfrac{n^3}{64}$

For Example 5
Simplify $\left(\dfrac{3x^{3b}y}{-6x^b y^3}\right)^2 \cdot \dfrac{x^{4b}}{4y^4}$

Alternative Learning Styles

Kinesthetic Pieces of paper cut into different shapes can be used to represent a quotient of monomials. Use square pieces of paper to represent x and circular pieces of paper to represent y. The representation for the quotient of monomials $\dfrac{(2xy)^5}{(x^2 y)^2}$ is shown.

$$32 \; \square\bigcirc\square\bigcirc\square\bigcirc\square\bigcirc\square\bigcirc$$
$$\square\square\bigcirc\square\square\bigcirc$$

$$= 32 \; \square\bigcirc\bigcirc\bigcirc \longrightarrow 32xy^3$$

Teaching Tip If you multiply the numbers in scientific notation using pencil and paper, first group the integers and then group the powers of ten.

In-Class Examples

For Example 6
Use a scientific calculator to evaluate each expression.

a. $(1.4 \times 10^3)(2.3 \times 10^4)$
3.22×10^7 or 32,200,000

b. $(4.8 \times 10^{-5}) \div (1.6 \times 10^{-2})$
3×10^{-3} or 0.003

For Example 7
A chemist has performed an experiment that yields 1.2×10^{25} molecules of ethanol. There are 6.02×10^{23} molecules in a mole. How many moles of ethanol did the experiment yield?
$\approx 0.199 \times 10^2$ or 19.9 moles

GLOBAL CONNECTIONS

Levi's experiences in Auschwitz are depicted in his books *Survival in Auschwitz* and *Reawakening.*

Study Guide Masters, p. 30

5-1
NAME_____ DATE _____
Student Edition
Pages 254–260
Study Guide

Monomials
Refer to this table when simplifying monomials.

Property/Term	Definition	Example
Multiplying Powers	For any real number a and positive integers m and n, $a^m \cdot a^n = a^{m+n}$.	Simplify: $(x^3y^2)(x^4y^4)$ $(x^3y^2)(x^4y^4) = (xxxyy)(xxyyyy)$ $= (xxxxx)(yyyyyy)$ $= (x^5y^6)$
Raising a Power to a Power	For any real number a and positive integers m and n, $(a^m)^n = a^{mn}$.	Simplify: $(3^3)^3$ $(3^3)^3 = 3^3 \cdot 3^3 \cdot 3^3$ $= 3^{3+3+3}$ Multiplying Powers $= 3^9$
Finding a Power of a Product	For any real numbers a, b, and positive integer m, $(ab)^m = a^m b^m$.	Simplify: $(2ab)^3$ $(2ab)^3 = (2ab)(2ab)(2ab)$ $= 2 \cdot 2 \cdot 2 \cdot a \cdot a \cdot a \cdot b \cdot b \cdot b$ $= 8a^3b^3$
Dividing Powers	For any real number a and integers m and n, $\frac{a^m}{a^n} = a^{m-n}$ if $a \neq 0$.	Simplify: $\frac{x^7}{x^2}$ $\frac{x^7}{x^2} = x^{7-2}$ $= x^5$
Negative Exponents	For any real number a, where $a \neq 0$, and for any integer n, $a^{-n} = \frac{1}{a^n}$ and $\frac{1}{a^{-n}} = a^n$.	Simplify: $\frac{x^3}{x^5}$ $\frac{x^3}{x^5} = \frac{x \cdot x \cdot x}{x \cdot x \cdot x \cdot x \cdot x}$ $\frac{x^3}{x^5} = x^{3-5}$ $= \frac{1}{x \cdot x}$ or $\frac{1}{x^2}$ $= x^{-2}$

Simplify. Assume that no variable equals 0.

1. $18x^2 - 4y^2 - (-7x^2) - 6y^2$
   $25x^2 - 10y^2$
2. $2x^3 + 3x^3 + (-6x^3)$
   $-x^3$
3. $(a^4)^5$
   a^{20}

4. $\frac{1}{2}(2x^2)^2 + (5x^2)^2$
   $29x^4$
5. $\frac{1}{5}(-5a^2b^3)^2(abc)^2$
   $5a^6b^8c^2$
6. $m^7 \cdot m^8$
   m^{15}

7. $\frac{8m^3n^2}{4mn^2}$
   $\frac{2m^2}{n}$
8. $\frac{2^3c^4t^2}{2^3c^4t^2}$
   2
9. $\frac{m^{3a+3}}{m^{a-4}}$
   m^{a+7}

10. $(r^3s^2)^{-4}$
    $\frac{1}{r^8s^{12}}$
11. $a^{-3}(a^4 + a^3 + a)$
    $a^2 + 1 + \frac{1}{a}$
12. $\frac{(x+7)^{-1}}{(x^2-49)^{-1}}$
    $\frac{x-7}{x+7}$

Example 6 Use a scientific calculator to evaluate each expression.

a. $(3.69 \times 10^{-5})(4.1 \times 10^8)$

Estimate: $(4 \times 10^{-5})(4 \times 10^8) = 16 \times 10^3$ or 16,000

3.69 EXP +/− 5 × 4.1 EXP 8 = *15129*

b. $\frac{7.6 \times 10^2}{3.2 \times 10^{-6}}$

Estimate: $\frac{7 \times 10^2}{3.5 \times 10^{-6}} = 2 \times 10^8$ or 200,000,000

7.6 EXP 2 ÷ 3.2 EXP +/− 6 = *237500000*

Scientists use scientific notation because they often deal with very large or very small quantities.

Example 7
CONNECTION
Chemistry

A chemist works in a laboratory, doing research for a fertilizer company. For one batch of fertilizer, she needs 20 moles of sulfuric acid. A mole is a standard unit of measure in chemistry that contains 6.02×10^{23} molecules of a substance, Avogadro's constant. If she adds 1.08×10^{25} molecules of sulfuric acid, has she added enough to make one batch of fertilizer?

Divide the number of molecules she has by the number of molecules in a mole.

$$\frac{1.08 \times 10^{25} \text{ molecules}}{6.02 \times 10^{23} \text{ molecules/mole}} = \frac{1.08}{6.02} \cdot \frac{10^{25} \text{ molecules}}{10^{23} \text{ molecules/mole}}$$

$$\approx 0.179 \times 10^2 \text{ or } 17.9 \text{ moles} \quad \textit{Use a calculator.}$$

The chemist did not add enough sulfuric acid.

GLOBAL CONNECTIONS

Primo Levi (1919–1987) was born in Turin, Italy. His autobiography, *The Periodic Table*, is based on his life as a chemist with each chapter named after a different element. This award-winning author was a survivor of Auschwitz.

CHECK FOR UNDERSTANDING

Communicating Mathematics

Study the lesson. Then complete the following.

1. **Explain** why $a \neq 0$ in the expression $\frac{a^m}{a^n}$. You cannot divide by 0.

2. **Determine** if $4x^2$ and $(4x)^2$ are equivalent. No, $(4x)^2 = (4x)(4x)$ or $16x^2$.

4. No, it should not contain parentheses; $2x^6y^3$ is in simplest form.

3. **You Decide** Is a negative number raised to the 777th power a negative or positive number? Explain. Negative; a negative to an odd power is negative.

4. Is $2(x^2y)^3$ in simplest form? Explain your answer.

5. Write $3wz^{-4}$ without using negative exponents. $\quad \dfrac{3w}{z^4}$

Simplify. Assume that no variable equals 0.

6. $y^5 \cdot y^7 \quad y^{12}$

7. $(3a)^4 \quad 81a^4$

8. $(m^2)^2(m^{-2})^2 \quad 1$

9. $\dfrac{40x^4}{-5x^2} \quad -8x^2$

10. $\dfrac{-2c^3d^6}{24c^2d^2} \quad \dfrac{-cd^4}{12}$

11. $\dfrac{16s^6t^5}{(2s^2t)^2} \quad 4s^2t^3$

12. $\left(\dfrac{1}{x^3y^2}\right)^4 \quad \dfrac{1}{x^{12}y^8}$

13. $\left(\dfrac{bc}{2}\right)^{-3} \quad \dfrac{8}{b^3c^3}$

14. $\left(\dfrac{-6y^5}{3y^2}\right)^{-2} \quad \dfrac{9y^4}{36y^{10}}$ or $\dfrac{1}{4y^6}$

Express each number in scientific notation.

15. 386,000 $\quad 3.86 \times 10^5$

16. 0.000346 $\quad 3.46 \times 10^{-4}$

Evaluate. Express each answer in both scientific and decimal notation.

17. $\dfrac{8 \times 10^{-1}}{16 \times 10^{-2}} \quad 5 \times 10^0; 5$

18. $(3.42 \times 10^8)(1.1 \times 10^{-5})$
$3.762 \times 10^3; 3762$

EXERCISES

 Simplify. Assume that no variable equals 0.

19. $b^3 \cdot b^5 \quad b^8$

20. $x^2 \cdot x \cdot x^3 \quad x^6$

21. $(m^3)^3 \quad m^9$

22. $(-3y)^3 \quad -27y^3$

23. $\dfrac{an^6}{n^5} \quad an$

24. $\dfrac{-x^6y^6}{x^3y^4} \quad -x^3y^2$

26. $\dfrac{28x^4}{y^2}$

25. $(a^3b^3)(ab)^{-2} \quad ab$

26. $(4x^3y^{-4})(7xy^2)$

27. $(-3r^2s)^2(2rs^3)$

27. $18r^5s^5$ **28.** $-15a^5b^3$

28. $(3a^3b)(-5a^2b^2)$

29. $(2mn^2)(5m^2n)$

30. $(-5x^2y)(-2x^4y^7)$

29. $10\,m^3n^3$ **30.** $10x^6y^8$

31. $\left(-\dfrac{3}{4}m^2n^3\right)\left(\dfrac{8}{9}mn^4\right)$

32. $2b^2(2ab)^3 \quad 16a^3b^5$

33. $4x\,(-3x)^3 \quad -108x^4$

31. $-\dfrac{2}{3}m^3n^7$ **34.** $24a^4b^4$

34. $4a^2(3b^3)(2a^2b)$

35. $5mn^2(m^3n)(-3p^2)$

36. $5x(6x^2y)(3xy^3)$

35. $-15m^4n^3p^2$

37. $\dfrac{-6x^2y^3z^3}{24x^2y^7z^3} \quad \dfrac{-1}{4y^4}$

38. $\dfrac{2x^5y^3z^3}{8x^3y^7z} \quad \dfrac{x^2z^2}{4y^4}$

39. $\dfrac{-15m^5n^8\,(m^3n^2)}{45m^4n}$

36. $90x^4y^4$ **39.** $-\dfrac{m^4n^9}{3}$

40. $\dfrac{2a^3b}{(-2ab^3)^{-2}} \quad 8a^5b^7$

41. $\left(\dfrac{5a^3b}{10a^2b^2}\right)^4 \quad \dfrac{a^4}{16b^4}$

42. $\left(\dfrac{a}{b^{-1}}\right)^{-2} \quad \dfrac{1}{a^2b^2}$

47. 7.865×10^8

43. $\dfrac{40a^{-1}b^{-7}}{20a^{-5}b^{-9}} \quad 2a^4b^2$

44. $\dfrac{5^{2x}}{5^{2x+2}} \quad \dfrac{1}{25}$

45. $\dfrac{8}{m^0 + n^0} \quad 4$

52. 1.2460×10^{10};
12,460,000,000

Express each number in scientific notation. $\quad$ **48.** 8.742×10^{-4}

53. 4.02×10^{-5};
0.0000402

46. 810.4 $\quad 8.104 \times 10^2$

47. 786,500,000

48. 0.0008742

49. 0.001250

50. 901,010,000

51. 0.03331

54. 1.125×10^2; 112.5

1.25×10^{-3}

9.0101×10^8

3.331×10^{-2}

55. 9.025×10^7;
90,250,000

Evaluate. Express each answer in both scientific and decimal notations.

56. 4.93×10^0; 4.93

52. $(6.23 \times 10^4)(2.0 \times 10^5)$

53. $(2 \times 10^{-3})(2.01 \times 10^{-2})$

57. 3.1×10^8;
310,000,000

54. $(45,000)(0.0025)$

55. $(9.5 \times 10^3)^2$

56. $(6.9 \times 10^3)(1.4 \times 10^3)^{-1}$

57. $\dfrac{(93,000,000)(0.005)}{0.0015}$

Find the value of r that makes each sentence true.

 58. $y^{28} = y^{3r} \cdot y^7 \quad 7$

59. $2^{r+5} = 2^{2r-1} \quad 6$

60. $2^{2r+1} = 32 \quad 2$

61. $(x^3 \cdot x^r)^5 = x^{30} \quad 3$

62. $\dfrac{x^{2r}}{x^{-3r}} = x^{15} \quad 3$

63. $\dfrac{m^r}{m^{15}} = (m^3)^{r+2} \quad -\dfrac{21}{2}$

Reteaching

Using Substitution Have students substitute real values for m and n in each of the properties listed on page 257 and demonstrate how the property works. For example:

$(a^2)^3 = a^2 \cdot a^2 \cdot a^2$
$\qquad = (a \cdot a) \cdot (a \cdot a) \cdot (a \cdot a)$
$\qquad = a^6$ or $a^{2\cdot3}$.

---

3 PRACTICE/APPLY

Check for Understanding

Exercises 1–18 are designed to help you assess your students' understanding through reading, writing, speaking, and modeling. You should work through Exercises 1–4 with your students and then monitor their work on Exercises 5–18.

Error Analysis

Students sometimes think that $(2x)^3 = 2x^3$ and that $-2^4 = 16$. Point out that $(2x)^3$ means three factors of $(2x)$, or $(2x)(2x)(2x)$, which equals $8x^3$, as the exponent 3 refers to both the 2 and the x in $(2x)^3$. -2^4 means $-(2^4)$. In order to write -2 to the fourth power, parentheses must be used, $(-2)^4$.

Assignment Guide

Core: 19–67 odd, 68–79
Enriched: 20–64 even, 65–79

For **Extra Practice,** see p. 885.

The red A, B, and C flags, printed only in the Teacher's Wraparound Edition, indicate the level of difficulty of the exercises.

Practice Masters, p. 30

5-1 NAME_____ DATE_____
Practice
Student Edition
Pages 254–26

Monomials
Simplify. Assume that no variable equals 0.

1. $3n^2v^3 - n^2v^3 + 8v^3n^2 \quad 10n^2v^3$

2. $4r^4w^2 + 9r^2w^6 - r^4w^2 \quad 3r^4w^2 + 9r^2w^6$

3. $y^7 \cdot y^2 \cdot y^2 \quad y^{12}$

4. $(n^6)^3 \quad n^{18}$

5. $(2n)^4 + 2n^4 \quad 18n^4$

6. $\dfrac{12m^5y^4}{-9my^4} \quad \dfrac{4m^7y^2}{-3}$

7. $(4a^3c^2)^3(-3ac^4)^2 \quad 576a^{11}c^{14}$

8. $\left(\dfrac{3}{2}e^2f^4\right)^4\left(-\dfrac{4}{3}e^2f\right)^3\left(-\dfrac{1}{6}ef^2\right) \quad 2e^{24}f^{24}$

9. $-5v^3(2r^2v^2)(rv^3) - (-r^2)(16r^2v^7) \quad 6r^4v^7$

10. $(-n)^4(2xy^3n^2)^3 + (4xy^3n^2)^3(-3xn^2) \quad -40x^3y^9n^7$

11. $\dfrac{(3x^{-5}y^2)(5xy^{-4})}{(x^{-2})^3y^{-3}} \quad \dfrac{15x^{11}}{y^5}$

12. $(m^4n^6)^6(m^3n^3p^5)^6 \quad m^{34}n^{36}p^{30}$

13. $(3x^3y)(2xy^4) + (4xy^3)(3x^2y^3) \quad 18x^3y^5$

14. $t^{-5}(t^5 - t^4 + 5t) \quad \dfrac{1}{t^2} - \dfrac{1}{t} + \dfrac{5}{t^4}$

15. $\dfrac{-20(m^2v)(-v)^6}{5(-v)^4(-m^2)} \quad \dfrac{4v^3}{m^2}$

16. $\dfrac{x^{2s+1}}{x^{2s-1}} \quad x^2$

Evaluate. Express each answer in both scientific and decimal notation.

17. $(4.8 \times 10^2)(6.9 \times 10^4)$
3.312×10^7; 33,120,000

18. $(3.7 \times 10^9)(8.7 \times 10^2)$
3.219×10^{12}; 3,219,000,000,000

19. $\dfrac{4 \times 10^8}{1.6 \times 10^4}$
2.5×10^4; 25,000

20. $\dfrac{2.7 \times 10^9}{9 \times 10^{13}}$
3×10^{-5}; 0.00003

Astronomers disagree on the origins of our solar system's planetary moons. One theory holds that the moons were captured by their individual planets. Other astronomers believe that the moons broke away from their planets.

4 ASSESS

Closing Activity

Speaking Have students develop sentences, free of mathematical notation, that express the properties studied in the lesson. For example, the property $(ab)^m = a^m b^m$ can be expressed as "The power of a product is the product of the powers."

Additional Answer

68a.

15 16 17 18 19 20 21 22 23 24 25 26

Enrichment Masters, p. 30

5-1

NAME_____ DATE _____

Enrichment

Student Edition
Pages 254–260

Working with Exponents

The rules about powers and exponents are usually given with letters such as m, n, and k to represent exponents. For example, one rule states that $a^m \cdot a^n = a^{m+n}$.

In practice, such exponents are handled as algebraic expressions and the rules of algebra apply.

Example: Simplify $2a^3(a^{n+1} + a^{4n})$.

$2a^3(a^{n+1} + a^{4n}) = 2a^3 \cdot a^{n+1} + 2a^3 \cdot a^{4n}$ Use the distributive law.

$= 2a^{3+n+1} + 2a^{3+4n}$ Recall $a^m \cdot a^n = a^{m+n}$.

$= 2a^{n+3} + 2a^{3+4n}$ Simplify the exponent $2 + n + 1$ as $n + 3$.

It is important always to collect *like* terms only.

Example: Simplify $(a^n + b^n)^2$.

$(a^n + b^n)^2 = (a^n + b^n)(a^n + b^n)$

          F   O   I   L
$= a^n \cdot a^n + a^n \cdot b^n + a^n \cdot b^n + b^n \cdot b^n$ The second and third terms are like terms.

$= a^{2n} + 2a^n b^n + b^{2n}$

Simplify each expression by performing the indicated operations.

1. $2^2 2^m$ 2^{2+m}
2. $(a^3)^n$ a^{3n}
3. $(4^n b^2)^k$ $4^{nk} b^{2k}$
4. $(x^3 a^2)^m$ $x^{3m} a^{2m}$
5. $(-ay^3)^2$ $-a^3 y^{3n}$
6. $(-b^4 x)^2$ $-b^{2n} x^2$
7. $(c^2)^{4k}$ c^{2hk}
8. $(-2d^n)^5$ $-32d^{5n}$
9. $(a^3 b)(a^n b^2)$ $a^{2+n} b^3$
10. $(x^n y^m)(x^n y^n)$ $x^{n+m} y^{n+m}$
11. $\frac{a^n}{a^2}$ a^{n-2}
12. $\frac{12x^5}{4x^2}$ $3x^{5-2}$
13. $(ab^2 - a^2 b)(3a^n + 4b^n)$ $3a^{n+1} b^2 + 4ab^{n+2} - 3a^{n+2}b - 4a^2 b^{n+1}$
14. $ab^3(2a^2 b^{n-1} + 4ab^n + 6b^{n+1})$ $2a^3 b^{n+1} + 4a^2 b^{n+2} + 6ab^{n+3}$

260 *Chapter 5*

64. Which is greater, 100^{10} or 10^{100}? Explain your answer.

65. Express the quotient $\dfrac{x + x^2 + x^3 + x^4 + x^5 + x^6 + x^7}{x^{-3} + x^{-4} + x^{-5} + x^{-6} + x^{-7} + x^{-8} + x^{-9}}$ in simplest form. Assume that x is not equal to zero. (*Hint:* Simplify the denominator first.)

64. $100^{10} = (10^2)^{10}$ or 10^{20} and $10^{100} > 10^{20}$, so $10^{100} > 100^{10}$.   65. x^{10}

66. **Economics** In 1991, the U.S. government received approximately $468,000,000,000 in personal income taxes. The population of the country at that time was about 250,000,000. If everyone paid taxes, what was the average amount paid by each man, woman, and child?   **$1872**

Largest Planetary
Moons (diameter)
1. Ganymede, Jupiter (3273 miles)
2. Titan, Saturn (3200 miles)
3. Callisto, Jupiter (2995 miles)
4. Io, Jupiter (2257 miles)
5. Moon, Earth (2159 miles)

67. **Astronomy** In April of 1983, the space probe *Pioneer 10* was as far from Earth as the planet Pluto. *Pioneer 10* sent radio signals that traveled at the speed of light, 3.00×10^5 kilometers per second. If *Pioneer 10* was 4.58×10^9 kilometers from Earth, how long would it take a tracking station to send a message indicating a mid-course correction in the space probe's travel course? (Use $t = \dfrac{d}{r}$, where d is distance and r is rate.)   **about 1.53×10^4 seconds or 4.25 hours**

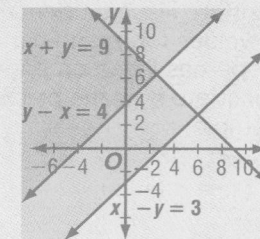

68. **Statistics** The chart at the right shows the percentage of the population that is made up of people in their twenties for 18 large U.S. cities. (Lesson 4–8)
   a. Make a box-and-whisker plot of the data.   **See margin.**

68b. See students' work.

   b. List three reasons why you think someone would want this information.

69. $\begin{bmatrix} 1 & 0 & 0 \\ 0 & 1 & 0 \\ 0 & 0 & 1 \end{bmatrix}$

69. Find M if $\begin{bmatrix} 3 & 6 & 1 \\ 2 & -1 & 0 \end{bmatrix} \cdot M = \begin{bmatrix} 3 & 6 & 1 \\ 2 & -1 & 0 \end{bmatrix}$.
   (Lesson 4–5)

Solve for the indicated variables.

70. $\begin{vmatrix} 5a & 3 \\ a & 5 \end{vmatrix} = 7$ (Lesson 4–4) $\dfrac{7}{22}$

71. 1, 5, 10

71. $y \begin{vmatrix} 3 & -4 \\ 2 & x \end{vmatrix} = \begin{vmatrix} 15 & -20 \\ z & 5 \end{vmatrix}$ (Lesson 4–1)

72. $\left(10, \dfrac{53}{2}, \dfrac{13}{2}\right)$

Solve each system algebraically or by graphing.   73. See margin for graph.

72. $8a - 3b + c = 7$
   $-2a + b - c = 0$
   $2a - 3b + 9c = -1$ (Lesson 3–7)

73. $x + y < 9$
   $x - y < 3$
   $y - x > 4$ (Lesson 3–4)

74. They are the same line.

74. Describe the graphs of two linear equations that are dependent. (Lesson 3–1)

75. Write an equation of the line that passes through (2, 2) and is parallel to the line $4x - y + 3 = 0$. (Lesson 2–5) $y = 4x - 6$

76. Find the x- and y-intercepts of $f(x) = 13x + 26$. (Lesson 2–3)   **-2, 26**

77. Graph $x - 3y = -3$. (Lesson 2–2)   **See Solutions Manual.**

78. Solve $-2(4 - 3x) > 4$. (Lesson 1–7) $\{x \mid x > 2\}$

79. Evaluate $15 - 3(2) \div 8 - 11$. (Lesson 1–1) $3\dfrac{1}{4}$

City	Percent of Population
Boston, MA	26%
Columbus, OH	24
San Diego, CA	22
Seattle, WA	20
Washington, DC	20
Nashville, TN	19
Anchorage, AK	18
Baltimore, MD	18
Chicago, IL	18
Indianapolis, IN	18
Jacksonville, FL	18
Milwaukee, WI	18
Philadelphia, PA	18
Phoenix, AZ	18
New York, NY	17
Detroit, MI	16
Honolulu, HI	16
U.S. Average	16

Extension

Problem Solving Solve $a^4 x \cdot a^{10} = a^9 x$ for x.   2
What properties are used to solve the equation?

Additional Answer

73.

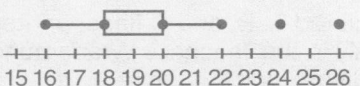

$x + y = 9$
$y - x = 4$
$x - y = 3$

Polynomials

What YOU'LL LEARN

• To add, subtract, and multiply polynomials.

Why IT'S IMPORTANT

You can use polynomials to solve problems involving biology and genetics.

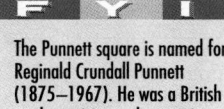

The Punnett square is named for Reginald Crundall Punnett (1875–1967). He was a British mathematician and geneticist.

Remember that a difference like $m^2 - 7mb - 12cd$ can be written as a sum, $m^2 + (-7mb) + (-12cd)$.

CONNECTION
Biology

Scientists can use algebraic expressions to summarize the possible outcomes in genetic breeding. Certain traits result from the pairing of two genes, one from the female parent and one from the male parent. For example, suppose a red-flowering, sweet pea plant has *genotype RR*, a white-flowering, sweet pea plant has genotype *WW*, and a pink-flowering, sweet pea plant has genotype *RW*. Each letter represents one of the two genes that make up the characteristic.

Suppose two pink-flowering plants are bred. The offspring can be expressed using algebra and a model called a *Punnett square*.

One gene from the mother pairs with one gene from the father for each possible offspring.

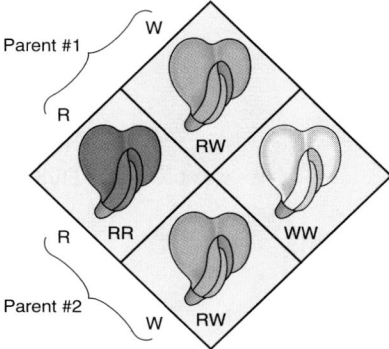

The sum of the possible results for four offspring can be written as $RR + RW + RW + WW$; that is, one red-, two pink-, and one white-flowering plants. Suppose we substitute *x* for *R* and *y* for *W*. The result would be a sum of four monomials, $xx + xy + xy + yy$, or $x^2 + 2xy + y^2$. The two monomials xy and xy can be combined because they are **like terms**. Like terms are two monomials that are the same, or differ only by their numerical coefficients.

The expression $x^2 + 2xy + y^2$ is called a **polynomial.** A polynomial is a monomial or a sum of monomials. The monomials that make up the polynomial are called the **terms** of the polynomial. An expression like $m^2 - 7mb - 12cd$ with three unlike terms is called a **trinomial.** An expression like $xy + b^3$ with two unlike terms is called a **binomial.** The *degree* of a polynomial is the degree of the monomial with the greatest degree. Thus, the degree of $x^2 + 2xy + y^2$ is 2.

Example **1** Determine whether or not each expression is a polynomial. Then state the degree of each polynomial.

a. $\frac{2}{7}x^4y^3 - 21x^3$

This expression is a polynomial. The degree of the first term is $4 + 3$ or 7, and the degree of the second term is 3. The degree of the polynomial is 7.

b. $9 + \sqrt{x} - 3$

This expression is not a polynomial because $\sqrt{x}$ is not a monomial.

F Y I

Punnett began his professional career researching the structural properties of marine worms. Later he teamed up with William Bateson, a great geneticist of the time.

NCTM Standards: 1–5

Instructional Resources

• Study Guide Master 5-2
• Practice Master 5-2
• Enrichment Master 5-2
• Tech Prep Applications Masters, p. 9

Transparency 5-2A contains the 5-Minute Check for this lesson; **Transparency 5-2B** contains a teaching aid for this lesson.

Recommended Pacing

Standard Pacing	Day 2 of 16
Honors Pacing	Day 2 of 12
Block Scheduling*	Day 1 of 6 (along with Lesson 5-1)

*For more information on pacing and possible lesson plans, refer to the *Block Scheduling Booklet*.

1 FOCUS

5-Minute Check
(over Lesson 5-1)

Simplify.

1. $7xyz^2 + 3xyz^2 - 12xyz^2 - 2xyz^2$

2. $\left(\frac{1}{2}x^2\right)^3$ $\frac{1}{8}x^6$

3. Multiply 1.8×10^3 by 42,000 using scientific notation. 7.56×10^7

Simplify.

4. $\frac{3(a^2b)^4}{(3ab)^3}$ $\frac{a^5b}{9}$

5. $\left(\frac{2x}{3z^2}\right)^{-4}$ $\frac{81z^8}{16x^4}$

Motivating the Lesson

Hands-On Activity Cut two pieces of rope of unknown lengths, *x* and *y*. Use these to mark off an area with a width of $x + y$ and a length of $2x + y$. Ask students how they would determine the area of the marked-off section in terms of the variables, without knowing the values of *x* and *y*.

In-Class Examples

For Example 1
Find the degree of each polynomial.

a. $x^2 - 3x^3 + 2x$ **3**
b. $7xy^2 - 7x^2y + 8x^3y - 16xy^4$ **5**

For Example 2
Find the perimeter of the triangle.

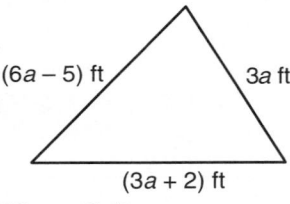

$(6a - 5)$ ft $3a$ ft $(3a + 2)$ ft

$(12a - 3)$ ft

For Example 3
Simplify.

a. $(-4x^3 - 3x + 10x^2) - (8x^2 + 2x - x^3 - x^4)$
$x^4 - 3x^3 + 2x^2 - 5x$
b. $(2x^2 - 3xy + 5y^2) - (4x^2 - 3xy - 2y^2)$
$-2x^2 + 7y^2$

For Example 4
Find $-9a^2(3a - 7b^3)$.
$-27a^3 + 63a^2b^3$

Teaching Tip In Example 3, remind students that when adding and subtracting like terms, the coefficients are combined, but the exponents do not change.

 **MODELING MATHEMATICS** This modeling activity provides students with a geometric interpretation of the product of two binomials. To reinforce the exercise, have students copy the diagram to their own sheet of paper. Then have them color the region of the diagram that corresponds to x^2 red, the region that corresponds to $7x$ blue, and the region that corresponds to 12 green.

To simplify a polynomial means to perform the operations indicated and combine like terms.

Example   **Find the perimeter of quadrilateral *ABCD*.**

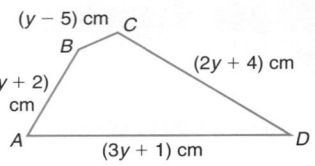

INTEGRATION
Geometry

The perimeter is the sum of the measures of the sides.

$$P = AB + BC + CD + DA$$
$$= (y + 2) + (y - 5) + (2y + 4) + (3y + 1)$$
$$= y + y + 2y + 3y + 2 - 5 + 4 + 1$$
$$= 7y + 2$$

The perimeter of quadrilateral *ABCD* is $(7y + 2)$ cm.

Example ③   **Simplify $(4x^2 - 3x) - (x^2 + 2x - 1)$.**

$$(4x^2 - 3x) - (x^2 + 2x - 1) = 4x^2 - 3x - x^2 - 2x + 1$$
$$= (4x^2 - x^2) + (-3x - 2x) + 1$$
$$= 3x^2 - 5x + 1$$

You can use the distributive property to multiply polynomials.

Example ④   **Find $3x(5x^4 - x^3 + 4x)$.**

$$3x(5x^4 - x^3 + 4x) = 3x(5x^4) + 3x(-x^3) + 3x(4x)$$
$$= 15x^5 - 3x^4 + 12x^2$$

You can use algebra tiles to make a geometric model of the product of two binomials.

MODELING MATHEMATICS   **Multiplying Binomials**

Materials: 📐 algebra tiles

Use algebra tiles to find the product of $x + 4$ and $x + 3$.

Your Turn

a. Draw a 90° angle on your paper.
b. Use an x-tile and a 1-tile to mark off a length equal to $x + 4$ along the top.
c. Use the tiles to mark off a length equal to $x + 3$ along the side.

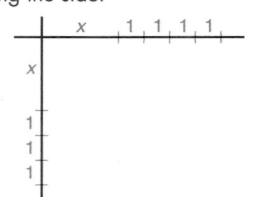

d. Draw lines to show the grid formed by these measures.
e. Fill in the lines with the appropriate tiles to show the area product. The model shows the polynomial $x^2 + 7x + 12$.

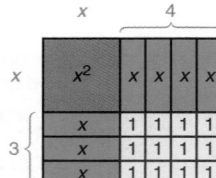

The area of the rectangle is the product of its length and width. Substituting the area, length, and width with the corresponding polynomials, we find that $x^2 + 7x + 12 = (x + 4)(x + 3)$.

In the following example, two different methods are used to multiply binomials.

Example **5** Find $(4n + 3)(3n + 1)$.

Method 1: Distributive Property

$$(4n + 3)(3n + 1) = 4n(3n + 1) + 3(3n + 1)$$
$$= 4n \cdot 3n + 4n \cdot 1 + 3 \cdot 3n + 3 \cdot 1$$
$$= 12n^2 + 4n + 9n + 3$$
$$= 12n^2 + 13n + 3$$

Method 2: FOIL Method

$$(4n + 3)(3n + 1) = \underbrace{4n \cdot 3n}_{First\ terms} + \underbrace{4n \cdot 1}_{Outside\ terms} + \underbrace{3 \cdot 3n}_{Inside\ terms} + \underbrace{3 \cdot 1}_{Last\ terms}$$
$$= 12n^2 + 13n + 3$$

The **FOIL method** is an application of the distributive property that makes the multiplication easier.

FOIL Method of Multiplying Polynomials	The product of two binomials is the sum of the products of
	F the *first* terms,
	O the *outer* terms,
	I the *inner* terms, and
	L the *last* terms.

Example **6** Find $(k^2 + 3k + 9)(k + 3)$.

$$(k^2 + 3k + 9)(k + 3)$$
$$= k^2(k + 3) + 3k(k + 3) + 9(k + 3) \qquad \textit{Distributive property}$$
$$= k^2 \cdot k + k^2 \cdot 3 + 3k \cdot k + 3k \cdot 3 + 9 \cdot k + 9 \cdot 3 \qquad \textit{Distributive property}$$
$$= k^3 + 3k^2 + 3k^2 + 9k + 9k + 27$$
$$= k^3 + 6k^2 + 18k + 27 \qquad \textit{Combine like terms.}$$

CHECK FOR UNDERSTANDING

Communicating Mathematics

Study the lesson. Then complete the following.   1–2. See margin.

1. **Demonstrate** the FOIL method by multiplying $(3a + 4b)$ and $(a - b)$.

2. **Show** another way to multiply the expression in Example 6 by distributing $(k^2 + 3k + 9)$ instead of $(k + 3)$.

3. Sample answer: $3x^4y^2 + x^3y^2 - 5xy + 20$

3. **Write** a polynomial of degree 6 that has four terms.

Lesson 5–2 Polynomials   **263**

Reteaching

Using Manipulatives Have students use algebra tiles to model the multiplication of a polynomial by a monomial, $x(x + 2)$.
Consider a rectangle with a width of x and a length of $x + 2$. Use the edge of a $1 \cdot x$ tile to mark off the dimensions of the rectangle. Then complete the rectangle by filling it in with tiles.

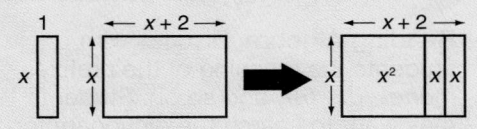

Now find the area of the large rectangle by adding the areas of the individual tiles. The area is $x^2 + 2x$.

In-Class Examples

For Example 5
Use the distributive property to find each product.

a. $(x + 8)(x + 12)$ $x^2 + 20x + 96$

b. $(x + 3)^2$ $x^2 + 6x + 9$

Use the FOIL method to find each product.

c. $(4c - 5)(2c - 3)$
$8c^2 - 22c + 15$

d. $(3y^2 - 2)(-2y + 1)$
$-6y^3 + 3y^2 + 4y - 2$

For Example 6
Find $(2x^2 + 10x - 4)(x - 12)$.
$2x^3 - 14x^2 - 124x + 48$

Teaching Tip In Example 6, you may want to show students the vertical form of multiplication as well as the horizontal form.

3 PRACTICE/APPLY

Check for Understanding
Exercises 1–17 are designed to help you assess your students' understanding through reading, writing, speaking, and modeling. You should work through Exercises 1–5 with your students and then monitor their work on Exercises 6–17.

Additional Answers

1. F: $3a(a)$ or $3a^2$, O: $3a(-b)$ or $-3ab$, I: $4b(a)$ or $4ab$, L: $4b(-b)$ or $-4b^2$; $3a^2 - 3ab + 4ab - 4b^2 = 3a^2 + ab - 4b^2$

2. $(k^2 + 3k + 9)(k + 3)$
$= (k^2 + 3k + 9)k + (k^2 + 3k + 9)3$
$= k^2 \cdot k + 3k \cdot k + 9 \cdot k + k^2 \cdot 3 + 3k \cdot 3 + 9 \cdot 3$
$= k^3 + 3k^2 + 9k + 3k^2 + 9k + 27$
$= k^3 + 6k^2 + 18k + 27$

Assignment Guide

Core: 19–65 odd, 66–76
Enriched: 18–58 even, 60–76

For **Extra Practice,** see p. 886.

The red A, B, and C flags, printed only in the Teacher's Wraparound Edition, indicate the level of difficulty of the exercises.

Additional Answer

4. Sample answer:

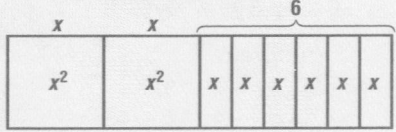

Study Guide Masters, p. 31

NAME_____ DATE _____

5-2
Study Guide
Student Edition
Pages 261–266

Polynomials

A polynomial is either a monomial or the sum of monomials. Each monomial in the polynomial is called a **term** of the polynomial. The **degree of a polynomial** is the degree of the monomial of the greatest degree. You can simplify polynomials with like terms by using the **distributive property,** by adding or subtracting like terms, or by using the **FOIL method.**

Example: Simplify $3x^2y + 2xy^3 + 6y + 5xy^3 - 8x^2y$.
First, group like terms.
$3x^2y + 2xy^3 + 6y + 5xy^3 - 8x^2y = (3x^2y - 8x^2y) + (2xy^3 + 5xy^3) + 6y$
$= -5x^2y + 7xy^3 + 6y$

Example: Find $3x(4xy^3 - 7x^2y - 3y)$.
Use the distributive property.
$3x(4xy^3 - 7x^2y - 3y) = 3x \cdot 4xy^3 - 3x \cdot 7x^2y - 3x \cdot 3y$
$= 12x^2y^3 - 21x^3y - 9xy$

FOIL Method for Multiplying Binomials
The product of two binomials is the sum of the products of
F the first terms
O the outer terms
I the inner terms
L the last terms.

Example: Find $(2x + 3)(x - 5)$.
$\begin{array}{ccccc} & F & O & I & L \\ (2x+3)(x-5) = & 2x \cdot x & + 2x \cdot (-5) & + 3 \cdot x & + 3 \cdot (-5) \\ = & 2x^2 & - 10x & + 3x & - 15 \\ = & 2x^2 & - 7x & & - 15 \end{array}$

Simplify.

1. $(-4m^2 - 6m) - (6m + 4m^2)$
   $-8m^2 - 12m$
2. $3(2a + 5c) - 2(4a - 6c)$
   $-2a + 27c$
3. $5a(7a^2b + 6ac^2 - 8ac)$
   $35a^3b + 30a^2c^2 - 40a^2c$

4. $15x^2y^3 + 8x^4y + 7x^2y^3$
   $22x^2y^3 + 8x^4y$
5. $2wy - 2w^2y - 2yw$
   $-2w^2y$
6. $2x(x + 5) - x^2(3 - x)$
   $x^3 - x^2 + 10x$

7. $(3t^2 - 8)(t^2 + 5)$
   $3t^4 + 7t^2 - 40$
8. $(2r + 7)^2$
   $4r^2 + 28r + 49$
9. $2(a - 6)(2a + 7)$
   $4a^2 - 10a - 84$

10. $(c + 7)(c - 3)$
    $c^2 + 4c - 21$
11. $(5a + 7)(5a - 7)$
    $25a^2 - 49$
12. $(2n^2 - 3)(n^3 + 5n - 1)$
    $2n^5 + 10n^3 - 5n^2 - 15n + 3$

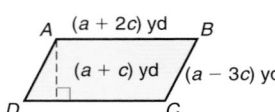

MODELING MATHEMATICS

4. **Draw** a geometric representation of $2x^2 + 6x$.   See margin.

5. **Write** two factors and a product for the model shown at the right.
   $(3x + 1)(x + 2) = 3x^2 + 7x + 2$

Guided Practice

Determine whether each expression is a polynomial. Write *yes* or *no* and explain your reasoning. Then state the degree of each polynomial.

6. $14x + 3y$ yes, 1
7. $\frac{y^3}{4} - 7x$ yes, 3
8. $\frac{ax^2 + 6}{by^3 + 5}$ no

Simplify.

9. $(5x - 7y) + (6x + 8y)$ $11x + y$
10. $(-2y^2 - 4y + 7) - (2y^2 + 4y - 7)$
11. $3y(2x + 6)$ $6xy + 18y$
12. $2m^2n(5mn - 3m^3n^2 + 4mn^4)$
13. $(x + 6)(x + 3)$ $x^2 + 9x + 18$
14. $(y - 10)(y + 7)$ $y^2 - 3y - 70$
15. $(3m - 1)(3m + 1)$ $9m^2 - 1$
16. $(2p - 3s)^2$ $4p^2 - 12ps + 9s^2$

17. **Geometry**   Quadrilateral *ABCD* is a parallelogram.   b. $(a^2 + 3ac + 2c^2)$ yd^2
   a. Find the perimeter of *ABCD*. $(4a - 2c)$ yd
   b. Find the area of *ABCD*.

A $(a + 2c)$ yd B
$(a + c)$ yd
$(a - 3c)$ yd
D C

EXERCISES

Practice

Determine whether each expression is a polynomial. Write *yes* or *no* and explain your reasoning. Then state the degree of each polynomial.

▲ 18. $x^2 + 2x + 3$ yes, 2
19. $y^3 + 3$ yes, 3
20. $\sqrt{s - 5}$ no
21. $\frac{3k^2}{2} + \frac{4k^7}{5}$ yes, 7
22. $\frac{4ab}{c} - \frac{2d}{x}$ no
23. $x\sqrt{3} + 8x^2y^4$ yes, 6

Simplify.

24. $(3r + s) - (r - s) - (r + 3s)$
25. $(z^2 - 6z - 10) + (2z^2 + 4z - 11)$
26. $(-12y - 6y^2) + (-7y + 6y^2)$
27. $(3m^2 + 5m - 6) + (7m^2 - 9)$
28. $(10x^2 - 3xy + 4y^2) - (3x^2 + 5xy)$
29. $(8r^2 + 5r + 14) - (7r^2 + 6r + 8)$
30. $4a(3a^2b)$ $12a^3b$
31. $4f(gf - bh)$ $4gf^2 - 4fbh$
▶ 32. $\frac{2}{3}x^2(6x + 9y - 12xy^2)$
33. $-5mn^2(-3m^2n + 6m^3n - 3m^4n^4)$
34. $(c^2 - 6cd - 2d^2) + (7c^2 - cd + 8d^2) - (-c^2 + 5cd - d^2)$
35. $(4x^2 - 3y^2 + 5xy) - (8xy + 6x^2 + 3y^2)$. $-2x^2 - 3xy - 6y^2$

Find the perimeter of each figure.

36. $(3y - 2)$ m
37. $(7m - 3n)$ ft
38.

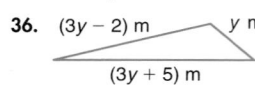

y m
$(3y + 5)$ m

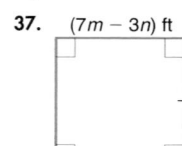

$(7m - 3n)$ ft

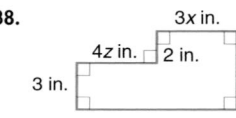

3x in.
4z in.   2 in.
3 in.

Answers (side column):

10. $-4y^2 - 8y + 14$
12. $10m^3n^2 - 6m^5n^3 + 8m^3n^5$

24. $r - s$ 26. $-19y$
25. $3z^2 - 2z - 21$
27. $10m^2 + 5m - 15$
28. $7x^2 - 8xy + 4y^2$
29. $r^2 - r + 6$
32. $4x^3 + 6x^2y - 8x^3y^2$
33. $15m^3n^3 - 30m^4n^3 + 15m^5n^6$
34. $9c^2 - 12cd + 7d^2$

36. $(7y + 3)$ m
37. $(28m - 12n)$ ft
38. $(8z + 6x + 10)$ in.

Alternative Teaching Strategies

Reading Algebra Discuss with students the meaning of the prefixes *mono-, bi-, tri-,* and so on. Students may want to search the dictionary for other words that begin with these prefixes.

43. $6y^2 + 5y - 56$

45. $g^2 - 2 + \dfrac{1}{g^4}$

46. $xy^3 + y + \dfrac{1}{x}$

50. $2w^4 - 7w^2 - 15$

Geometry

51. $(10y^2 + 6y)$ ft²

52. $(64x^2 - 4y^2)$ cm²

53. $\dfrac{9xy^2}{2}$ m²

Critical Thinking

61a. $(a + b + c)^2$, $a^2 + 2ab + b^2 + 2ac + 2bc + c^2$

Applications and Problem Solving

63a. $\dfrac{10x + 14}{9x - 2}$

Simplify.

39. $(q - 7)(q + 5)$ $q^2 - 2q - 35$
40. $(m + 7)(m + 2)$ $m^2 + 9m + 14$
41. $(5 - r)(5 + r)$ $25 - r^2$
42. $(2x + 7)(3x + 5)$ $6x^2 + 31x + 35$
43. $(3y - 8)(2y + 7)$
44. $(x^3 - y)(x^3 + y)$ $x^6 - y^2$
45. $g^{-3}(g^5 - 2g^3 + g^{-1})$
46. $x^{-3}y^2(yx^4 + y^{-1}x^3 + y^{-2}x^2)$
47. $(y - 3x)^2$ $y^2 - 6xy + 9x^2$
48. $(1 + 4m)^2$ $1 + 8m + 16m^2$
49. $(2p + q^3)^2$ $4p^2 + 4pq^3 + q^6$
50. $(w^2 - 5)(2w^2 + 3)$

Find the area of each figure.

51.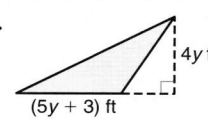
4y ft
(5y + 3) ft

52.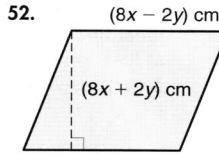
(8x − 2y) cm
(8x + 2y) cm

53.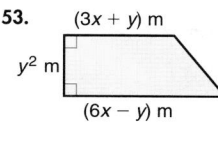
(3x + y) m
y² m
(6x − y) m

Simplify.   54. $9y^3 + 18y^2 - y - 2$

54. $(3y + 1)(3y - 1)(y + 2)$
55. $(x^2 + xy + y^2)(x - y)$ $x^3 - y^3$
56. $(2q + 1)(q - 2)^2$
57. $(x - 2)(x + 2)(x^2 + 5)$
58. $(3b - c)^3$
59. $(y + x)^2(y - x)^2$ $y^4 - 2x^2y^2 + x^4$

56. $2q^3 - 7q^2 + 4q + 4$ 57. $x^4 + x^2 - 20$ 58. $27b^3 - 27b^2c + 9bc^2 - c^3$

60. Draw a geometric representation of $(x + 3)(x - 3)$. Explain your results.   See margin.

61. a. Write two different polynomial expressions that represent the area of the figure at the right.
b. Write a polynomial for the perimeter of the figure. $4a + 4b + 4c$

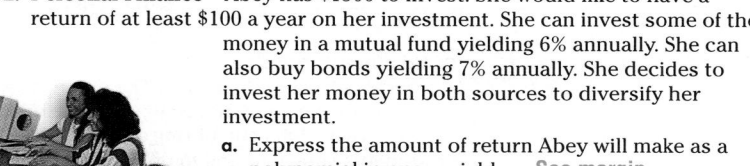

62. **Personal Finance**   Abey has $1500 to invest. She would like to have a return of at least $100 a year on her investment. She can invest some of the money in a mutual fund yielding 6% annually. She can also buy bonds yielding 7% annually. She decides to invest her money in both sources to diversify her investment.

a. Express the amount of return Abey will make as a polynomial in one variable.   See margin.

b. How much money should Abey place in each of these investments to have the desired return?
$1000 @ 7%, $500 @ 6%

63. **Geometry**   Recall that the measure of an angle inscribed in a circle is half the measure of its intercepted arc. That is, $m\angle B = \frac{1}{2}m\widehat{ADC}$.

a. Given a circle with inscribed quadrilateral $ABCD$ with the given arc measures, find the ratio of $m\angle A$ to $m\angle B$.

b. If $\widehat{mAB} + \widehat{mBC} + \widehat{mCD} + \widehat{mAD} = 360°$, find the value of x.   about 18.5°

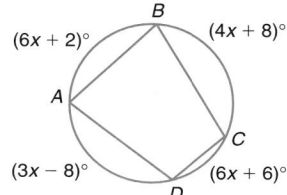
B   (4x + 8)°
(6x + 2)°
A
C
(3x − 8)°   (6x + 6)°
D

Additional Answers

60.

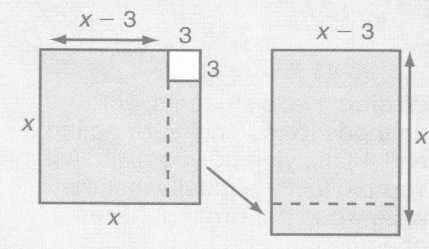

62a. Sample answer: Let x = amount invested at 6% and $1500 − x = amount invested at 7%. The return can be expressed as 0.06x + 0.07(1500 − x).

Practice Masters, p. 31

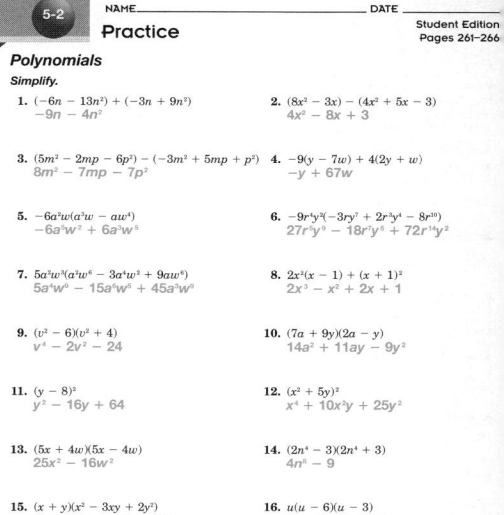

Closing Activity

Writing Have students write methods for adding, subtracting, and multiplying polynomials. Ask them to include pitfalls that may arise when performing these operations.

Enrichment Masters, p. 31

NAME_____ DATE _____

Enrichment

Student Edition
Pages 261–266

Polynomials with Fractional Coefficients

Polynomials may have fractional coefficients as long as there are no variables in the denominators. Computing with fractional coefficients is performed in the same way as computing with whole-number coefficients.

Add, subtract, or multiply. Write all coefficients as fractions.

1. Add $\frac{3}{4}a + \frac{2}{5}b - \frac{1}{3}c$ and $\frac{1}{6}a - \frac{4}{3}b + \frac{5}{7}c$.
$\frac{11}{12}a - \frac{14}{15}b + \frac{8}{21}c$

2. Subtract $\frac{7}{3}p - \frac{5}{2}m - \frac{3}{4}n$ from $\frac{3}{5}m - \frac{2}{7}p - \frac{1}{3}n$.
$\frac{31}{10}m + \frac{5}{12}n - \frac{55}{21}p$

3. Add $\frac{3}{2}x - \frac{4}{3}y - \frac{5}{4}z$, $-\frac{1}{4}x + y + \frac{2}{5}z$, and $-\frac{7}{8}x - \frac{6}{7}y + \frac{1}{2}z$.
$\frac{3}{8}x - \frac{25}{21}y - \frac{7}{20}z$

4. Add $\frac{1}{2}a^3 - \frac{1}{3}ab + \frac{1}{4}b^3$ and $\frac{5}{6}a^3 + \frac{2}{3}ab - \frac{3}{4}b^3$.
$\frac{4}{3}a^3 + \frac{1}{3}ab - \frac{1}{2}b^3$

5. From $\frac{1}{2}a^2 - \frac{1}{3}ab + \frac{1}{4}b^2$ take $\frac{1}{3}a^2 - \frac{1}{2}ab + \frac{5}{6}b^2$.
$\frac{1}{6}a^2 + \frac{1}{6}ab - \frac{7}{12}b^2$

6. Multiply $\frac{1}{2}a^2 - \frac{1}{3}ab + \frac{1}{4}b^2$ by $\frac{1}{2}a - \frac{2}{3}b$.
$\frac{1}{4}a^3 - \frac{1}{2}a^2b + \frac{25}{72}ab^2 - \frac{1}{6}b^3$

7. Multiply $\frac{2}{3}a^2 - \frac{1}{5}a + \frac{2}{7}$ by $\frac{3}{2}a^2 + \frac{1}{5}a^2 - \frac{2}{7}a$.
$\frac{4}{9}a^5 - \frac{1}{25}a^3 + \frac{4}{35}a^2 - \frac{4}{49}a$

8. Multiply $\frac{2}{3}x^2 - \frac{3}{4}x - 2$ by $\frac{4}{5}x - \frac{1}{6}x^2 - \frac{1}{2}$.
$-\frac{1}{9}x^4 + \frac{79}{120}x^3 - \frac{3}{5}x^2 - \frac{49}{40}x + 1$

9. Multiply $\frac{1}{6} + \frac{1}{3}x + \frac{1}{6}x^4 - \frac{1}{2}x^2$ by $\frac{1}{6}x^3 - \frac{1}{3} - \frac{1}{3}x$.
$\frac{1}{36}x^7 - \frac{5}{36}x^5 + \frac{7}{36}x^3 + \frac{1}{18}x^2 - \frac{1}{6}x - \frac{1}{18}$

---

64. **Make a Drawing** Suppose you were trying to model the product $(2x + 3y)(x + 5)$. Make a drawing of rectangles to represent each type of monomial in the product. Then make a drawing to illustrate the product and write the result. **See students' drawings; $2x^2 + 10x + 3xy + 15y$.**

65. **Genetics** Suppose p represents the ratio of dominant gene A in a population and q represents the ratio of recessive gene a in a population. The next generation is the result of $(p + q)^2$. This results in p^2 pure dominant genotypes (AA), q^2 pure recessive genotypes (aa), and $2pq$ hybrid genotypes (Aa). Since all members of the population must have at least one recessive gene or dominant gene present in their genotypes, $p + q = 1$.

Suppose that in the population of a certain village, the recessive left-handedness gene r had a frequency of 1:4 and the dominant right-handedness gene R had a frequency of 3:4. In the next generation, what would you predict the population genotypes to be?
9 out of 16, *RR*; 6 out of 16, *Rr*; 1 out of 16, *rr*

Mixed Review

66. Simplify $2(rk)^2(5rt^2) - k(2rk)(2rt)^2$. (Lesson 5–1) $2k^2r^3t^2$

67. Solve the system of equations by using augmented matrices. (Lesson 4–7)
$4x - y + z = 6$
$2x + y + 2z = 3$
$3x - 2y + z = 3$ **(2, 1, −1)**

68. Write a matrix equation for the system of equations. (Lesson 4–6)
$3x - y = 5$
$2x + 33y = 29$ $\begin{bmatrix} 3 & -1 \\ 2 & 33 \end{bmatrix} \cdot \begin{bmatrix} \ \\ \ \end{bmatrix} = \begin{bmatrix} 5 \\ 29 \end{bmatrix}$

69. If $A = \begin{bmatrix} 2 & -3 \end{bmatrix}$ and $B = \begin{bmatrix} -4 & 0 \end{bmatrix}$, find AB. (Lesson 4–3) $\begin{bmatrix} -14 & -15 \\ 4 & 20 \end{bmatrix}$

70. **Community Service** A theater where a drug abuse program is being presented seats 150 people. The proceeds will be donated to a local drug information center. Admission is $2.00 for adults and $1.00 for students. Every two adults must bring at least one student. How many adults and students should attend in order to raise the maximum amount of money? (Lesson 3–5) **100 adults and 50 students**

71. Solve the system of equations by using substitution. (Lesson 3–2) **(12, 2)**
$6x + 4y = 80$
$x - 7y = -2$

72. Solve the system of equations by graphing. (Lesson 3–1) **(−3, −3)**
$2x + 2y = -12$
$3x - 2y = -3$

73. Name the points, $(0, 0)$, $(-1, -3)$, or $(4, 0)$, that satisfy $4x - |y| \leq 12$. (Lesson 2–6) **(0, 0), (−1, −3)**

74. Find $h(-7)$ if $h(x) = \frac{3 + x}{4}$. (Lesson 2–1) **−1**

75. **Statistics** Find the mean, median, and mode of {45, 49, 40, 39, 39, 46, 44, 41, 42}. (Lesson 1–4) **42.778, 42, 39**

76. **Banking** Karen invests $7500 in a certificate of deposit at the Lombard Bank. The simple interest rate is 7.2% per year. How much will she make in 5 years? (Lesson 1–1) **$2700**

Extension

Communication Find
$(x^2 - y^2)(x^2 + y^2)$. $x^4 - y^4$
Discuss how knowing this and other special products can help in multiplying polynomials using mental math.

Dividing Polynomials

What YOU'LL LEARN

- To divide polynomials using long division, and
- to divide polynomials by binomials using synthetic division.

Why IT'S IMPORTANT

You can use polynomials to solve problems involving manufacturing and entertainment.

APPLICATION
Entertainment

Tionna, a senior at Franklin High School, spends one free period a day as a teacher's aide at the middle school that is located next to the high school. A magician was performing at the middle school and asked a member of the audience to participate in a number game. The magician said:

- Choose any number.
- Multiply your number by 3.
- Then add the sum of your number and 8 to the number you got when you multiplied.
- Now divide by the sum of your number and 2.

Then the magician said, "Without asking you what number you chose, I can tell you that your final result was . . . 4!"

Tionna wondered how the magician's trick worked. But magicians don't tell their secrets. So, she used her algebraic skills to write expressions that modeled the steps in the trick.

Choose a number.	x
Multiply by 3.	$3x$
Add the sum of your number and 8 to the previous result.	$3x + (x + 8)$ or $4x + 8$
Divide this result by your number plus 2.	$\dfrac{4x + 8}{x + 2}$

F Y I

The *Guinness Book of Records* lists the fastest magician as Eldon D. Wigton, alias Dr. Eldoonie. He performed 225 different tricks in 2 minutes in Kilbourne, Ohio, on April 21, 1991.

The final expression is $\dfrac{4x + 8}{x + 2}$. But how does this help Tionna solve the secret of the magician's trick? *You will be asked to solve the mystery in Exercise 3.*

In Lesson 5–1, you learned to divide monomials. You can divide a polynomial by a monomial by using those same skills.

Example ① **Simplify** $\dfrac{6r^2s^2 + 3rs^2 - 9r^2s}{3rs}$.

This expression means that each term in the numerator shares a common denominator. Rewrite the expression as a sum of quotients.

$$\frac{6r^2s^2 + 3rs^2 - 9r^2s}{3rs} = \frac{6r^2s^2}{3rs} + \frac{3rs^2}{3rs} - \frac{9r^2s}{3rs}$$

$$= \frac{6}{3} \cdot r^{2-1}s^{2-1} + \frac{3}{3} \cdot r^{1-1}s^{2-1} - \frac{9}{3} \cdot r^{2-1}s^{1-1}$$

$$= 2rs + s - 3r \quad r^{1-1} = r^0 \text{ or } 1$$

F Y I

In the past, the word *magic* had a very different meaning from the one we know today. Originally, the term referred to activity intended to influence human behavior or natural events by calling on external mystical forces. To avoid confusion, some people now use the term *conjuring* when referring to magic as a form of entertainment.

NCTM Standards: 1–5

Instructional Resources

- Study Guide Master 5-3
- Practice Master 5-3
- Enrichment Master 5-3
- Assessment and Evaluation Masters, p. 128

 Transparency 5-3A contains the 5-Minute Check for this lesson; **Transparency 5-3B** contains a teaching aid for this lesson.

Recommended Pacing	
Standard Pacing	Days 3 & 4 of 16
Honors Pacing	Day 3 of 12
Block Scheduling*	Day 2 of 6 (along with Lesson 5-4)

 *For more information on pacing and possible lesson plans, refer to the *Block Scheduling Booklet*.

1 FOCUS

 5-Minute Check
(over Lesson 5-2)

1. Find the degree of $6x^3y^2 - 12x^2y^3 - y^4 + 26$. **5**

Simplify.

2. $6x^2y + 3xy^4 + 7 + 5xy^4 - 9x^2y + 8y$ $-3x^2y + 8xy^4 + 8y + 7$

3. $(10a^3 - 6a^2b + 7ab^2 + b^3) - (5a^3 + 4a^2b - 3ab^2 - 1)$ $5a^3 - 10a^2b + 10ab^2 + b^3 + 1$

Use the FOIL method to find each product.

4. $(a - 4b)^2$ $a^2 - 8ab + 16b^2$

5. $(10r - 6s)(r + 2s)$ $10r^2 + 14rs - 12s^2$

Motivating the Lesson

Questioning Have students divide 11,106 by 9. **1234** Next, divide 1107 by 9. **123** Then divide 111,105 by 9. **12,345** Explain why the pattern is occurring. What would be the quotient of 111,111,102 and 9? **12,345,678**

Teaching Tip In Example 1, another approach is to factor the numerator and cancel.

In-Class Examples

For Example 1
Simplify.

a. $\dfrac{3a^2b + 6a^3b^2 + 18ab}{3ab}$

$a + 2a^2b + 6$

b. $\dfrac{12x^2y + 3x}{3x}$ $4xy + 1$

For Example 2

Simplify $\dfrac{x^2 - 5x - 24}{x + 3}$.

$x - 8$

For Example 3

Simplify
$(h^2 - 11h + 28)(h - 4)^{-1}$.

$h - 7$

For Example 4
The area of rectangle *ABEF* is represented by $2x^2 + 20x + 50$. Its width is represented by $x + 5$. Find the area and the length of the sides of square *ACDF*. Points *E* and *B* are midpoints of $\overline{FD}$ and $\overline{AC}$, respectively.
area = $4x^2 + 40x + 100$
length = $2x + 10$

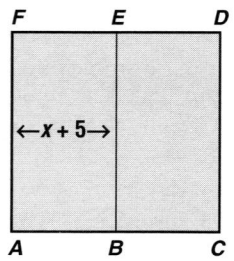

You can use a process similar to long division of whole numbers to divide a polynomial by a polynomial. When doing the division, remember that you can only add and subtract like terms.

Example  **2** Simplify $\dfrac{c^2 - c - 30}{c - 6}$.

In this lesson, assume that the denominator never equals zero.

$$
\begin{array}{r}
c \\
c - 6\overline{)c^2 - c - 30} \\
\underline{c^2 - 6c} \\
5c - 30
\end{array}
$$
$\quad -c - (-6c) = -c + 6c \text{ or } 5c$

$$
\begin{array}{r}
c + 5 \\
c - 6\overline{)c^2 - c - 30} \\
\underline{c^2 - 6c} \\
5c - 30 \\
\underline{5c - 30} \\
0
\end{array}
$$

Therefore, the quotient is $c + 5$.

Just as with the division of whole numbers, the division of two polynomials may result in a quotient with a remainder. Remember that $9 \div 4 = 2 + R1$ and is often written as $2\frac{1}{4}$. The division of polynomials with a remainder is presented in the same manner.

Example **3** Simplify $(s^2 + 4s - 16)(6 - s)^{-1}$.

$(s^2 + 4s - 16)(6 - s)^{-1} = \dfrac{s^2 + 4s - 16}{6 - s}$

$$
\begin{array}{r}
-s - 10 \\
-s + 6\overline{)s^2 + 4s - 16} \\
\underline{s^2 - 6s} \\
10s - 16 \\
\underline{10s - 60} \\
44
\end{array}
$$
For ease in dividing, rewrite $6 - s$ as $-s + 6$.

The quotient is $-s - 10 + \dfrac{44}{6 - s}$.   *The remainder is $\dfrac{44}{-s + 6}$ or $\dfrac{44}{6 - s}$.*

In Example 4, solving for a variable involves dividing polynomials.

Example **4**

INTEGRATION
Geometry

The area of triangle *ABC* is $(10y^2 + 6y)$ mm² and its base is $(5y + 3)$ mm. Find the measure of the altitude of the triangle.
An altitude of a triangle is a line segment from a vertex perpendicular to the line containing the opposite side. The measure of an altitude is the height *h* of the triangle.

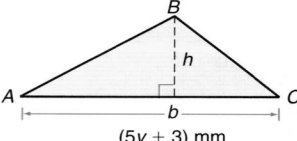

$A = \frac{1}{2}bh$

$10y^2 + 6y = \frac{1}{2}(5y + 3)(h)$ *$A = 10y^2 + 6y$, $b = 5y + 3$*

$20y^2 + 12y = (5y + 3)h$ *Multiply each side by 2.*

$\dfrac{20y^2 + 12y}{5y + 3} = h$ *Divide each side by $5y + 3$.* →

$4y = h$

$$
\begin{array}{r}
4y \\
5y + 3\overline{)20y^2 + 12y} \\
\underline{20y^2 + 12y} \\
0
\end{array}
$$

The length of the altitude is $4y$ mm.

A simpler process called **synthetic division** has been devised to divide a polynomial by a binomial. Suppose we wanted to divide $(6x^3 - 19x^2 + x + 6)$ by $(x - 3)$. Long division would produce the following result.

$$
\begin{array}{r}
6x^2 - 1x - 2 \\
x - 3\overline{)6x^3 - 19x^2 + x + 6} \\
\underline{(-)6x^3 - 18x^2} \\
-1x^2 + x + 6 \\
\underline{(-)-1x^2 + 3x} \\
-2x + 6 \\
\underline{(-)-2x + 6} \\
0
\end{array}
$$

Compare the coefficients in this division with those in Example 5.

Study the next example.

Example ⑤ Use synthetic division to find $(6x^3 - 19x^2 + x + 6) \div (x - 3)$.

Write the terms of the polynomial so that the degrees of the terms are in descending order. Then write just the coefficients as shown at the right. *There must be a coefficient for every possible power of the variable.*

$$6x^3 - 19x^2 + x + 6$$

$$6 \quad -19 \quad 1 \quad 6$$

Write the constant r of the divisor $x - r$ to the left.

$$
\begin{array}{r|rrrr}
3 & 6 & -19 & 1 & 6 \\
\hline
 & 6 & & & |
\end{array}
$$

In this case, $r = 3$.
Bring the first coefficient, 6, down as shown.

Multiply the first coefficient by r: $3 \cdot 6 = 18$.
Write the product under the second coefficient.
Then add the product and the second coefficient: $-19 + 18 = -1$.

$$
\begin{array}{r|rrrr}
3 & 6 & -19 & 1 & 6 \\
 & & 18 & & \\
\hline
 & 6 & -1 & & |
\end{array}
$$

Multiply the sum, -1, by r: $3(-1) = -3$.
Write the product under the next coefficient and add: $1 + (-3) = -2$.

$$
\begin{array}{r|rrrr}
3 & 6 & -19 & 1 & 6 \\
 & & 18 & -3 & \\
\hline
 & 6 & -1 & -2 & |
\end{array}
$$

Multiply the sum, -2, by r: $-2 \cdot 3 = -6$.
Write the product under the next coefficient and add: $6 + (-6) = 0$. The remainder is 0.

$$
\begin{array}{r|rrrr}
3 & 6 & -19 & 1 & 6 \\
 & & 18 & -3 & -6 \\
\hline
 & 6 & -1 & -2 & |\ 0
\end{array}
$$

Writing the quotient is easy. The numbers along the bottom row are the coefficients of the powers of x in descending order. Start with the power that is one less than that of the dividend. Thus, the result of this division is $6x^2 - x - 2$.

Check this result. Does $(x - 3)(6x^2 - x - 2) = 6x^3 - 19x^2 + x + 6$?

To use synthetic division, the divisor must have a leading coefficient of 1. You can rewrite other division expressions so you can use synthetic division.

In-Class Example

For Example 5
Use synthetic division to find each quotient.

a. $(-5x^5 - 21x^4 - 3x^3 + 4x^2 - 2x + 2) \div (x + 4)$
$-5x^4 - x^3 + x^2 - 2 + \dfrac{10}{x + 4}$

b. $(x^4 - 2x^3 + x - 1) \div (x + 1)$
$x^3 - 3x^2 + 3x - 2 + \dfrac{1}{x + 1}$

In-Class Example

For Example 6
Use synthetic division to find each quotient.

a. $(6n^2 - 2n + 4) \div (2n - 3)$

$3n + \dfrac{7}{2} + \dfrac{\frac{29}{4}}{n - \frac{3}{2}}$ or

$3n + \dfrac{7}{2} + \dfrac{29}{4n - 6}$

b. $(x^3 - x^2 + 2x - 7) \div (2x - 1)$

$\dfrac{1}{2}x^2 - \dfrac{1}{4}x + \dfrac{7}{8} - \dfrac{\frac{49}{16}}{x - \frac{1}{2}}$ or

$\dfrac{1}{2}x^2 - \dfrac{1}{4}x + \dfrac{7}{8} - \dfrac{49}{16x - 8}$

3 PRACTICE/APPLY

Check for Understanding

Exercises 1–14 are designed to help you assess your students' understanding through reading, writing, speaking, and modeling. You should work through Exercises 1–4 with your students and then monitor their work on Exercises 5–14.

Error Analysis

In long division of polynomials, students sometimes subtract the second or third terms of partial products incorrectly. For example:

$$\begin{array}{r} 6x - 8 \\ x-3\overline{)6x^2 + 10x + 24} \\ \underline{6x^2 - 18x} \\ -8x \\ \underline{-8x + 24} \end{array}$$

Point out that the whole binomial $6x^2 - 18x$ is being subtracted, not just $6x^2$. Subtracting $6x^2 - 18x$ means adding $-(6x^2 - 18x)$. The answer for the example is

$6x + 28 + \dfrac{108}{x - 3}$.

Additional Answers

2. Each position in synthetic division represents a power of the variable. If you do not put in zeros, then an expression like $x^4 + x^2 + 2$ is written as 1 1 2. This represents $x^2 + x + 2$.

3. Jocelyn is correct because $(4x + 8) \div (x + 2) = 4$, regardless of the value of x.

Example ⑥ Use synthetic division to find $(4x^4 - 5x^2 + 2x + 4) \div (2x - 1)$.

Use division to rewrite the divisor so it has a coefficient of 1.

$$\frac{4x^4 - 5x^2 + 2x + 4}{2x - 1} = \frac{(4x^4 - 5x^2 + 2x + 4) \div 2}{(2x - 1) \div 2} \text{ or } \frac{2x^4 - \frac{5}{2}x^2 + x + 2}{x - \frac{1}{2}}$$

Since the numerator does not contain all powers of x, you must include a 0 coefficient for the x^3 term.

Now use synthetic division.

$$\begin{array}{r|rrrrr} \frac{1}{2} & 2 & 0 & -\frac{5}{2} & 1 & 2 \\ & & 1 & \frac{1}{2} & -1 & 0 \\ \hline & 2 & 1 & -2 & 0 & | 2 \end{array}$$

$x - r = x - \frac{1}{2}$

The quotient is $2x^3 + x^2 - 2x + \dfrac{2}{x - \frac{1}{2}}$ or $2x^3 + x^2 - 2x + \dfrac{4}{2x - 1}$.

Check: Divide using long division.

$$\begin{array}{r} 2x^3 + x^2 - 2x \\ 2x - 1\overline{)4x^4 + 0x^3 - 5x^2 + 2x + 4} \\ \underline{4x^4 - 2x^3} \\ 2x^3 - 5x^2 \\ \underline{2x^3 - x^2} \\ -4x^2 + 2x \\ \underline{-4x^2 + 2x} \\ 0 + 4 \end{array}$$

The quotient is $2x^3 + x^2 - 2x + \dfrac{4}{2x - 1}$. ✓

CHECK FOR UNDERSTANDING

Communicating Mathematics

Study the lesson. Then complete the following.

1. **Show** how you would set up the synthetic division for $(5y^3 + y^2 - 7) \div (y + 1)$.

1. $\underline{-1|}\ 5\ \ 1\ \ 0\ \ -7$

2. **Illustrate** why it is necessary to include terms with zero coefficients in the row of numbers for synthetic division. **See margin.**

3. **You Decide** Refer to the magician's trick at the beginning of the lesson. Jocelyn says that the answer is always 4, regardless of the number chosen. Marie says that the magician knows a special way to compute numbers quickly and the answer depends on the number chosen. Who is correct, and why? **See margin.**

 MATH JOURNAL

4. **Assess Yourself** Compare the long division method of dividing polynomials with synthetic division. Are there any advantages to either method? Which do you prefer and why? **See students' work.**

Guided Practice

Simplify. 6. $6y - 3 + 2x$ 8. $3b + 5$ 10. $y^4 + 2y^3 + 4y^2 + 5y + 10$

5. $\dfrac{5xy^2 - 4xy + 7x^2y}{xy}$ $5y - 4 + 7x$ 6. $(6xy^2 - 3xy + 2x^2y)(xy)^{-1}$

7. $(a^2 - 10a - 24) \div (a + 2)$ $a - 12$ 8. $(9b^2 + 9b - 10) \div (3b - 2)$

9. $(a^3 + b^3) \div (a + b)$ $a^2 - ab + b^2$ 10. $(y^5 - 3y^2 - 20) \div (y - 2)$

Reteaching

Using Alternative Methods Use long division to solve $(3x^3 - 4x^2 - 3x - 2) \div (x - 3)$. $3x^2 + 5x + 12 + \dfrac{34}{x - 3}$

Now use synthetic division to solve the same problem. Compare the methods. Both use descending order for the dividend. In synthetic division, the coefficients are detached, subtraction is replaced by an equivalent addition, and the lines of numbers are compacted. Since synthetic division is a method for dividing a polynomial by the binomial $x - c$ (c is a constant), how could synthetic division by $x + 3$ be done? Use $x - (-3)$.

Use synthetic division to find each quotient.

11. $(3x^4 - 6x^3 - 2x^2 + x - 6) \div (x + 1)$ $3x^3 - 9x^2 + 7x - 6$

12. $(t^4 - 2t^3 + t^2 - 3t + 2)(t - 2)^{-1}$ $t^3 + t - 1$

13. $(12x^2 + 36x + 15) \div (6x + 3)$ $2x + 5$

14. $(x^3 + 13x^2 - 12x - 8) \div (x + 2)$ $x^2 + 11x - 34 + \dfrac{60}{x + 2}$

EXERCISES

Practice

Simplify.   16. $2n^2 + \dfrac{4m}{n} - 9m^2n$ 17. $4s^2 + 3rs - 5r$

15. $\dfrac{8x^2y^3 - 28x^3y^2}{4xy^2}$ $2xy - 7x^2$

16. $\dfrac{2mn^3 + 4m^2 - 9m^3n^2}{mn}$

18. $2k^2 - 3p + 4p^2$

19. $-a^2b + a - \dfrac{2}{b}$

20. $b^2 + 10b$

22. $n^2 - 2n + 3$

24. $2b^2 - b - 1 + \dfrac{4}{b+1}$

25. $3t^2 - 2t + 3$

26. $5a - 7b$

27. $5y^2 - 4y +$
$4 - \dfrac{11}{y+1}$

28. $h^2 - 4h + 17$

29. $2y + 7 + \dfrac{5}{y-3}$

32. $4x^2 + 2x + 1$

38. $6w^4 + 12w^3 +$
$24w^2 + 30w + 60$

39. $2m^3 + m^2 + 3m -$
$1 + \dfrac{5}{m-3}$

40. $a^3 - 6a^2 - 7a + 60$

17. $(12rs^3 + 9r^2s^2 - 15r^2s) \div (3rs)$

18. $(28k^3p - 42kp^2 + 56kp^3) \div (14kp)$

19. $(a^3b^2 - a^2b + 2a)(-ab)^{-1}$

20. $(b^3 + 8b^2 - 20b) \div (b - 2)$

21. $(x^2 - 12x - 45) \div (x + 3)$ $x - 15$

22. $(n^3 + 2n^2 - 5n + 12) \div (n + 4)$

23. $(g^2 + 8g + 15)(g + 3)^{-1}$ $g + 5$

24. $(2b^3 + b^2 - 2b + 3)(b + 1)^{-1}$

25. $(6t^3 + 5t^2 + 9) \div (2t + 3)$

26. $(50a^2 - 98b^2) \div (10a + 14b)$

27. $(5y^3 + y^2 - 7) \div (y + 1)$

28. $(2h^3 - 5h^2 + 22h + 51) \div (2h + 3)$

29. $(2y^2 + y - 16) \div (y - 3)$

30. $(x^3 - 4x^2) \div (x - 4)$ x^2

31. $(x^3 - 27) \div (x - 3)$ $x^2 + 3x + 9$

32. $(8x^3 - 1) \div (2x - 1)$

33. $3d^2 + 2d + 3 - \dfrac{2}{3d-2}$ 35. $2c^2 + c + 5 + \dfrac{6}{c-2}$ 36. $x^2 + x + 4$

Use synthetic division to find each quotient.

33. $\dfrac{9d^3 + 5d - 8}{3d - 2}$

34. $\dfrac{m^3 - 7m + 3m^2 - 21}{m + 3}$ $m^2 - 7$

35. $(2c^3 - 3c^2 + 3c - 4) \div (c - 2)$

36. $(2x^3 - x^2 + 5x - 12) \div (2x - 3)$

37. $(w^2 - w^3)(w - 1)^{-1}$ $-w^2$

38. $(6w^5 - 18w^2 - 120) \div (w - 2)$

39. $\dfrac{2m^4 - 5m^3 - 10m + 8}{m - 3}$

40. $\dfrac{a^4 - 5a^3 - 13a^2 + 53a + 60}{a + 1}$

41. $(y^5 + 32)(y + 2)^{-1}$

42. $(t^5 - 3t^2 - 20)(t - 2)^{-1}$

43. Solve $(b + 1)y = 2b^3 + b^2 - 2b + 3$ for y. $y = 2b^2 - b - 1 + \dfrac{4}{b+1}$

41. $y^4 - 2y^3 + 4y^2 - 8y + 16$ 42. $t^4 + 2t^3 + 4t^2 + 5t + 10$

Critical Thinking

44. Use synthetic division to find each quotient. Then evaluate the dividend for the value stated.   **a–b. See margin.**   c. $f(r) = $ the remainder

a. $\dfrac{3x^3 - 5x - 2}{x - 2}$, $x = 2$

b. $\dfrac{2x^4 - 3x^2 + 1}{x + 1}$, $x = -1$

c. Study the results of parts a and b. If the divisor represents $x - r$ and the dividend is $f(x)$, how is the division $\dfrac{f(x)}{x - r}$ related to $f(r)$?

45. $r^3 - 9r^2 + 27r - 28$ and $r - 3$

45. Suppose the quotient resulting from dividing one polynomial by another is $r^2 - 6r + 9 - \dfrac{1}{r - 3}$. What two polynomials were divided?

Assignment Guide

Core: 15–47 odd, 49–57
Enriched: 16–42 even, 44–57

For **Extra Practice**, see p. 886.

The red A, B, and C flags, printed only in the Teacher's Wraparound Edition, indicate the level of difficulty of the exercises.

Additional Answers

44a. $3x^2 + 6x + 7 + \dfrac{12}{x - 2}$; 12

44b. $2x^3 - 2x^2 - x + 1$; 0

Study Guide Masters, p. 32

5-3   **Study Guide**   NAME_____ DATE_____   Student Edition Pages 267–273

Dividing Polynomials

Properties of exponents are used to divide a monomial by a monomial and a polynomial by a monomial.

Example: $\dfrac{24x^4y - 12x^3y^2}{12x^2y} = \dfrac{24x^4y}{12x^2y} - \dfrac{12x^3y^2}{12x^2y}$

$= \dfrac{24}{12}x^{4-2}y^{1-1} - \dfrac{12}{12}x^{3-2}y^{2-1}$

$= 2x^2 - y$

Dividing a polynomial by a polynomial is similar to long division.

Example: $(x^2 + 3x - 18) \div (x - 3) \rightarrow x - 3\overline{)x^2 + 3x - 18}$
$\qquad\qquad \dfrac{x^2 - 3x}{6x - 18}$
$\qquad\qquad\quad \dfrac{6x - 18}{0}$

with quotient $x + 6$

Simplify.

1. $(x^3 - 1)(x^2 - 1)^{-1}$ $x + \dfrac{1}{x + 1}$

2. $(x^3 - 1) \div (x - 1)^{-1}$ $x^2 + x + 1$

3. $\dfrac{18a^3 + 30a^2}{3a}$ $2a(3a + 5)$

4. $\dfrac{12p^3t^4r - 21p^3qtr^4 - 9p^2tr}{3p^2tr}$ $4pt - 7qr^3 - 3p$

5. $\dfrac{c^3 + 4c - 21}{c + 7}$ $c - 3$

6. $\dfrac{24mn^4 - 40m^3n^3}{6n^2 \cdot 4m^3n^3}$ $\dfrac{6n^2}{m} - 10$

7. $(2x^2 - 5x - 3) \div (x - 3)$ $2x + 1$

8. $(m^2 - 3m - 7) \div (m + 2)$ $m - 5 + \dfrac{3}{m + 2}$

9. $(p^3 - 6) \div (p - 1)$ $p^2 + p + 1 - \dfrac{5}{p - 1}$

10. $(t^3 - 6t^2 + 1) \div (t + 2)$ $t^2 - 8t + 16 - \dfrac{31}{t + 2}$

11. $(x^5 - 1) \div (x - 1)$ $x^4 + x^3 + x^2 + x + 1$

12. $(p^3 - p^2 - p - 1) \div (p + 1)$ $p^2 - 2p + 1 - \dfrac{2}{p + 1}$

Using the Programming Exercises The program given in Exercise 46 is for use with a TI-82 graphing calculator. For other programmable calculators, have students consult their owner's manual for commands similar to those presented here.

Programming

46. The graphing calculator program below uses synthetic division to compute the coefficients of the quotient and the remainder when a polynomial is divided by a linear binomial. When prompted by a question mark, input the degree of the polynomial (N), the constant R for r in the divisor $x - r$, and the coefficients (C) of the polynomial. Press ENTER after each entry.

```
PROGRAM: SYNDIV                    : C → L1(X)
: ClrHome                         : End
: ClrList (L1, L2)                : L1(1) → L2(1)
: Disp "LET N = DEGREE",          : Disp "COEFFICIENTS OF",
  "OF POLYNOMIAL"                    "QUOTIENT ARE"
: Disp "LET R = CONSTANT",        : For (X, 1, N-1, 1)
  "IN DIVISOR X-R"                : L1 (X+1)+R*L2(X) →
: Prompt N, R                       L2 (X+1)
: Disp "ENTER COEFFICIENTS"       : End
: For (X, 1, N+1, 1)              : Disp L2
: Prompt C                        : Disp "REMAINDER",
                                    L1(N+1)+R*L2(N)
```

Use the program to find each quotient.

a. $2x^4 + x^3 - 7x^2 + 13x - 21 + \dfrac{24}{x+1}$

a. $(2x^5 + 3x^4 - 6x^3 + 6x^2 - 8x + 3) \div (x + 1)$

b. $(a^4 + 2a^3 - 7a^2 + 2a - 8) \div (a - 3)$ $a^3 + 5a^2 + 8a + 26 + \dfrac{70}{a-3}$

c. $(x^5 - 3x^2 - 20) \div (x - 2)$ $x^4 + 2x^3 + 4x^2 + 5x + 10$

Applications and Problem Solving

47. $\frac{1}{8}$ inch

47. Manufacturing A machinist who makes square metal pipes found a formula for the amount of metal she needed to make a pipe. She found that to make a pipe $8x$ inches long, she needed $32x^2 + x$ square inches of metal. In figuring the area needed, the machinist allowed some fixed length of metal for overlap of the seam. If the width of the finished pipe will be x inches, how much did the machinist leave for the seam?

Metal Needed

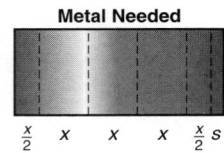

$\frac{x}{2}$ x x x $\frac{x}{2}$ s

s = width of seam

Finished Pipe

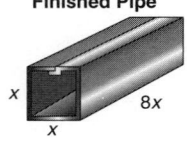

x $8x$

x

48. Health In the 1995 film *Outbreak*, a deadly disease threatens to wipe out the human race. Outbreaks of disease can become epidemics if there are no health preventatives available. The number of students and teachers at a large high school who will catch the flu during an outbreak in a certain year can be estimated by the formula $n = \dfrac{170t^2}{t^2 + 1}$, where t is the number of weeks from the beginning of the epidemic and n is the number of people who have become ill.

a. $170 - \dfrac{170}{t^2 + 1}$

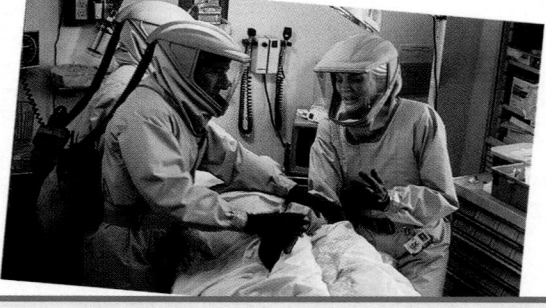

a. Perform the division indicated by $\dfrac{170t^2}{t^2 + 1}$.

b. Use the formula to estimate how many people will become ill during the first week. **85 people**

c. Use your calculator to evaluate increasingly greater values of t. What happens to the value of n as t becomes very great? **It approaches 170.**

Practice Masters, p. 32

5-3

NAME_____ DATE_____

Practice

Student Edition
Pages 267–273

Dividing Polynomials

Simplify.

1. $(-30x^4y + 12x^3y^2 - 18x^2y) \div (-6x^2y)$
$5x - 2y + 3$

2. $(2x^2 + 3x - 4) \div (x - 2)$
$2x + 7 + \frac{10}{x-2}$

3. $(4x^3 - 2x + 6)(2x - 3)^{-1}$
$2x + 2 + \frac{12}{2x-3}$

4. $(x^4 - 3x^3 + 5x - 6) \div (x + 2)$
$x^3 - 5x^2 + 10x - 15 + \frac{24}{x+2}$

5. $(6x^2 - x - 7) \div (3x + 1)$
$2x - 1 - \frac{6}{3x+1}$

6. $(2x^3 + 4x - 6) \div (x + 3)$
$2x^2 - 6x + 22 - \frac{72}{x+3}$

Use synthetic division to find each quotient.

7. $(2r^3 + 5r^2 - 2r - 15) \div (2r - 3)$
$r^2 + 4r + 5$

8. $(x^4 - 20) \div (x + 2)$
$x^3 - 2x^2 + 4x - 8 - \frac{4}{x+2}$

Tech Prep

Machinist Students who are interested in a career as a machinist may wish to do further research into the uses of math, as in Exercise 47, within this profession. For more information on tech prep, see the *Teacher's Handbook*.

49. Find $(a - b)^2$. (Lesson 5–2) $a^2 - 2ab + b^2$

50. Astronomy Earth is an average 1.496×10^8 kilometers from the sun. If light travels 3×10^5 kilometers per second, how long does it take sunlight to reach Earth? (Lesson 5–1)   **4.99×10^2 seconds or about 8 min 19 s**

51. Solve the system of equations by using augmented matrices. (Lesson 4–7)

$a + b + c = -2$
$2a - 3b + c = -11$
$-a + 2b - c = 8$ **$(-1, 2, -3)$**

52. Find $\begin{bmatrix} -2 & 1 \\ 3 & -6 \\ 4 & 5 \end{bmatrix} \cdot \begin{bmatrix} 1 & 2 & -3 & 7 \\ -3 & 2 & 9 & -1 \end{bmatrix}$. (Lesson 4–3) $\begin{bmatrix} -5 & -2 & 15 & -15 \\ 21 & -6 & -63 & 27 \\ -11 & 18 & 33 & 23 \end{bmatrix}$

53. Given $f(x, y) = 5x - 2y$, find $f(4, 1)$. (Lesson 3–5)   **18**

54. Photography The perimeter of a rectangular picture is 86 inches. Twice the width exceeds the length by 2 inches. What are the dimensions of the picture? (Lesson 3–2)   **15 in. × 28 in.**

55. Find $h\left(-\frac{1}{2}\right)$ if $h(x) = [3x + 7]$. (Lesson 2–6)   **5**

56. Write an equation in slope-intercept form for the line that has a slope of -2 and passes through the point at $(5, -3)$. (Lesson 2–4)   **$y = -2x + 7$**

57. Solve $|x - 7| = 13$. (Lesson 1–6)   **$-6, 20$**

4 ASSESS

Closing Activity

Writing Have students write a paragraph comparing long division and synthetic division for polynomials. They should include an example showing both ways and an explanation why they would choose one method over the other.

Chapter 5, Quiz A (Lessons 5-1 through 5-3), is available in the *Assessment and Evaluation Masters*, p. 128.

Enrichment Masters, p. 32

5-3   NAME_____   DATE_____
Enrichment   Student Edition Pages 267–273

Oblique Asymptotes

The graph of $y = ax + b$, where $a \neq 0$, is called an oblique asymptote of $y = f(x)$ if the graph of f comes closer and closer to the line as $x \to \infty$ or $x \to -\infty$.

For $f(x) = 3x + 4 + \frac{2}{x}$, $y = 3x + 4$ is an oblique asymptote because $f(x) - 3x - 4 = \frac{2}{x}$, and $\frac{2}{x} \to 0$ as $x \to \infty$ or $x \to -\infty$.

Example: Find the oblique asymptote for $f(x) = \frac{x^2 + 8x + 15}{x + 2}$.

$$\begin{array}{r} -2 | \quad 1 \quad 8 \quad 15 \\ \quad -2 \quad -12 \\ \hline \quad 1 \quad 6 \quad 3 \end{array}$$ Use synthetic division.

$y = \frac{x^2 + 8x + 15}{x + 2} = x + 6 + \frac{3}{x - 2}$

Since $\frac{3}{x - 2} \to 0$ as $x \to \infty$ or $x \to -\infty$, $y = x + 6$ is an oblique asymptote.

Use synthetic division to find the oblique asymptote for each of the following.

1. $y = \frac{8x^2 - 4x + 11}{x + 5}$ $y = 8x - 44$

2. $y = \frac{x^2 + 3x - 15}{x - 2}$ $y = x + 5$

3. $y = \frac{x^2 - 2x - 18}{x - 3}$ $y = x + 1$

4. $y = \frac{ax^2 + bx + c}{x - d}$ $y = ax + b + ad$

5. $y = \frac{ax^2 + bx + c}{x + d}$ $y = ax + b - ad$

3-2-1-Blast-Off!

WORKING ON THE Investigation

Refer to the Investigation on pages 180–181.

You are interested in using mathematics to further evaluate the performance of the launchers during the shoot-off. There are four measures you can use to help calculate accuracy around the given target.

Error Range The longest shot minus the shortest shot is the error range.

Tolerance All data must lie within a tolerance distance around the target (target distance ± tolerance), Therefore, the tolerance is the distance between the target distance and the farthest shot from the target.

Relative Error The ratio of the tolerance to the target distance. This is expressed as a percent.

Average Error Using the target distance and each of the distance shots, find the absolute value of the difference between each of these values. Calculate the mean of those differences, by adding all the absolute differences and dividing the sum by 10 shots.

1 Find these four measures for each of the launchers used in your class' shoot-off.

2 Compare these measures for each of the launchers. How do these four measures help to determine which launcher was most accurate? What do each of these measures represent when analyzing the data? Does a higher number or a lower number show more accuracy for each of the measures? Explain for each measure.

3 Consider all the data. From that information, which launcher would you consider to be the most accurate? Explain your reasoning.

Add the results of your work to your Investigation Folder.

Lesson 5-3 Dividing Polynomials **273**

Extension

Reasoning Have students make a chart to show the quotient of $3y^2 - 5y - 2$ divided by $x - 1$, $x - 2$, $x + 1$, $x + 2$, and $x + 3$. Do any of them have zeros for the remainder? What does that mean? Make charts for other division problems and see if there are any generalizations you can make.

Investigation

Working on the Investigation

The Investigation on pages 180–181 is designed to be a long-term project that is completed over several days or weeks. Encourage students to keep their materials in their Investigation Folder as they work on the Investigation.

Instructional Resources

- Study Guide Master 5-4
- Practice Master 5-4
- Enrichment Master 5-4
- Real-World Applications, 13

 Transparency 5-4A contains the 5-Minute Check for this lesson; **Transparency 5-4B** contains a teaching aid for this lesson.

Recommended Pacing	
Standard Pacing	Day 5 of 16
Honors Pacing	Day 4 of 12
Block Scheduling*	Day 2 of 6 (along with Lesson 5-3)

 *For more information on pacing and possible lesson plans, refer to the *Block Scheduling Booklet*.

1 FOCUS

 5-Minute Check
(over Lesson 5-3)

Simplify.

1. $\dfrac{36m^4y^4 - 18m^3y^3}{6m^2y}$

$6m^2y^3 - 3my^2$

2. $(x^3 + 4x - 4) \div (x + 2)$

$x^2 - 2x + 8 - \dfrac{20}{x + 2}$

Use synthetic division to find each quotient.

3. $(m^3 - 3m^2 - 18m + 40) \div (m + 4)$ $m^2 - 7m + 10$

4. $(16s^3 - 8s^2 - 40s + 15) \div (2s^2 - 5)$ $8s - 4 - \dfrac{5}{2s^2 - 5}$

Motivating the Lesson

Questioning Review with students how to find the greatest common factor. Have students solve the following GCF problems.

1. 10 and 25 **5**
2. 16 and 32 **16**
3. 24*ab* and 18*ab* **6*ab***
4. $3s^2t$, $4st^2$, st^3 **st**

Factoring

5-4

 *What* YOU'LL LEARN

- To factor polynomials, and
- to use factoring to simplify polynomial quotients.

Why IT'S IMPORTANT

You can use factoring to solve problems involving history and geometry.

F Y I

Leonard Euler (pronounced OI-ler) was a Swiss mathematician who discovered several polynomials that produced prime numbers up to a certain point.

CONNECTION
History

You would think that someone would have found a formula for computing all the possible prime numbers, but no one has. A **prime number** is a whole number greater than 1 whose only **factors** are 1 and itself. In 1963, a computer at the University of Illinois calculated the largest prime number known at that time. In honor of this accomplishment, the postage meter at the mathematics department printed the number on their mail in 1968.

As of 1993, the largest prime number discovered was $391{,}581 \times 2^{216{,}193} - 1$. It was generated by a computer at the Amdahl Corporation in 1989 and has 65,087 digits.

Prime numbers can be used to factor whole numbers, as in the example $36 = 2 \cdot 2 \cdot 3 \cdot 3$. Many polynomials can also be factored. Their factors, however, are other polynomials. Polynomials that cannot be factored are called *prime*. The table below summarizes the most common factoring techniques used with polynomials.

Any Number of Terms	
Greatest Common Factor (GCF)	$a^3b^2 + 2a^2b - 4ab^2 = ab(a^2b + 2a - 4b)$
Two Terms	
Difference of Two Squares **Sum of Two Cubes** **Difference of Two Cubes**	$a^2 - b^2 = (a + b)(a - b)$ $a^3 + b^3 = (a + b)(a^2 - ab + b^2)$ $a^3 - b^3 = (a - b)(a^2 + ab + b^2)$
Three Terms	
Perfect Square Trinomials	$a^2 + 2ab + b^2 = (a + b)^2$ $a^2 - 2ab + b^2 = (a - b)^2$
General Trinomials	$acx^2 + (ad + bc)x + bd = (ax + b)(cx + d)$
Four or More Terms	
Grouping	$ra + rb + sa + sb = r(a + b) + s(a + b)$ $= (r + s)(a + b)$

F Y I

Euler is responsible for most of our current notation in geometry, trigonometry, calculus, and algebra. He continued to produce new theories and proofs, even after becoming blind, by performing all of the calculations mentally.

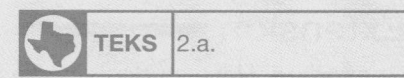 TEKS 2.a.

Whenever you factor a polynomial, always look for a common factor first. Then determine if the resulting polynomial factor can be factored again using one or more of the methods listed on the previous page.

Example  Factor $5k^3p - 3kp^2 + k^3p^5$.

$$5k^3p - 3kp^2 + k^3p^5 = (5 \cdot k \cdot k \cdot k \cdot p) - (3 \cdot k \cdot p \cdot p) + (k \cdot k \cdot k \cdot p \cdot p \cdot p \cdot p \cdot p)$$
$$= (kp \cdot 5k^2) - (kp \cdot 3p) + (kp \cdot k^2p^4)$$
$$= kp(5k^2 - 3p + k^2p^4)$$

The GCF is kp. The remaining polynomial is not factorable.

Check this result by finding the product.

The GCF is also used in grouping to factor a polynomial of four or more terms.

Example Factor $b^3 - 3b^2 + 4b - 12$.

$$b^3 - 3b^2 + 4b - 12 = (b^3 - 3b^2) + (4b - 12) \quad \textit{Group to find a GCF.}$$
$$= b^2(b - 3) + 4(b - 3) \quad \textit{Factor the GCF of each binomial.}$$
$$= (b - 3)(b^2 + 4) \quad \textit{Distributive property}$$

Check this result by finding the product.

You can use algebra tiles to model factoring a trinomial.

MODELING MATHEMATICS

Factoring Trinomials

Materials:  algebra tiles

Use algebra tiles to factor $2x^2 + 7x + 3$.

Your Turn

a. Use algebra tiles to model $2x^2 + 7x + 3$.

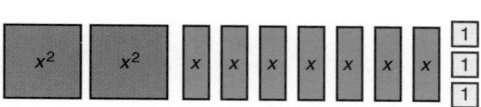

b. To find the product that resulted in this polynomial, arrange the tiles to form a rectangle.

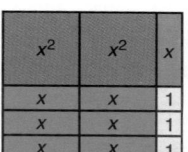

c. Determine the dimensions of the rectangle.

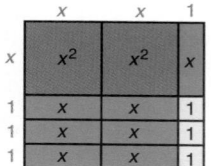

The rectangle is $2x + 1$ units long and $x + 3$ units wide. The area of the rectangle can be expressed as $(2x + 1)(x + 3)$. Since the area of the rectangle is also $2x^2 + 7x + 3$, we can say that $2x^2 + 7x + 3 = (2x + 1)(x + 3)$. *Verify by using FOIL.*

In-Class Examples

For Example 1
Factor $16m^2n + 12mn^2$.
$4mn (4m + 3n)$

For Example 2
Factor $a^2x - b^2x + a^2y - b^2y$.
$(a^2 - b^2)(x + y)$

Teaching Tip In Example 2, remind students to look for pairs of terms that have common factors. Another way of grouping this expression is $(b^3 + 4b) - (3b^2 + 12)$.

MODELING MATHEMATICS Remind students that the large squares represent the quadratic term, the long rectangles represent the linear term, and the small squares represent the constant term.

Classroom Vignette

"I like to show students how the model represents the FOIL method in reverse. I have the students divide the large rectangle into four smaller rectangles representing each part of FOIL. This model can be broken as shown below.

$2x \cdot x$ (F) $2x \cdot 3$ (0) $1 \cdot x$ (I) $1 \cdot 3$ (L)

The model now shows $2x^2 + 6x + x + 3$. Algebraically, we can factor these by grouping to arrive at the factors of the polynomial: $2x(x + 3) + 1(x + 3) = (2x + 1)(x + 3)$."

Eva Gates
Independent Mathematics Consultant
Pearland, Texas

In-Class Example

For Example 3
Factor each polynomial.

a. $4x^2 + 7x + 3$ $(4x + 3)(x + 1)$
b. $3a^2z - 27z$ $3z(a + 3)(a - 3)$
c. $x^3 + 125$
   $(x + 5)(x^2 - 5x + 25)$
d. $n^4 - 81$
   $(a^2 + 9)(a + 3)(a - 3)$

You have used FOIL to multiply two binomials. Thinking about FOIL can help you factor a polynomial into the product of two binomials. Study the following example.

$$(ax + b)(cx + d) = \overbrace{ax \cdot cx}^{F} + \overbrace{ax \cdot d}^{O} + \overbrace{b \cdot cx}^{I} + \overbrace{b \cdot d}^{L}$$
$$= acx^2 + (ad + bc)x + bd$$

Notice that the product of the *coefficient* of x^2 and the *constant* term is *abcd*. The product of the two coefficients of the x terms, *bc* and *ad*, is also *abcd*.

Example ③ **Factor each polynomial.**

a. $7x^2 - 16x + 4$

The product of the coefficient of the first term and the constant term is $7 \cdot 4$ or 28. So the two coefficients of the x terms must have a sum of -16 and a product of 28. You may need to use the guess-and-check strategy to find the two coefficients you need. The two coefficients must be -14 and -2 since $(-14)(-2) = 28$ and $-14 + (-2) = -16$.

Rewrite the expression using $-14x$ and $-2x$ in place of $-16x$ and factor by grouping.

$$\begin{aligned} 7x^2 - 16x + 4 &= 7x^2 - 14x - 2x + 4 & \textit{Substitute } -14x - 2x \textit{ for } -16x.\\ &= (7x^2 - 14x) + (-2x + 4) & \textit{Associative property}\\ &= 7x(x - 2) - 2(x - 2) & \textit{Factor out the GCF of each group.}\\ &= (7x - 2)(x - 2) & \textit{Distributive property} \end{aligned}$$

Check by using FOIL.

b. $2b^2x - 50x$

$$\begin{aligned} 2b^2x - 50x &= 2x(b^2 - 25) & \textit{Factor out the GCF.}\\ &= 2x(b + 5)(b - 5) & b^2 - 25 \textit{ is the difference of two squares.} \end{aligned}$$

c. $x^3y^3 + 64$

$x^3y^3 = (xy)^3$ and $64 = 4^3$. Thus, this is the sum of two cubes.
In this example, $a = xy$ and $b = 4$.
$$\begin{aligned} x^3y^3 + 64 &= (xy + 4)[(xy)^2 - 4(xy) + 4^2]\\ &= (xy + 4)(x^2y^2 - 4xy + 16) \end{aligned}$$

d. $a^6 - b^6$

This polynomial could be considered the difference of two squares or the difference of two cubes. The difference of two squares should always be done before the difference of two cubes.
$$\begin{aligned} a^6 - b^6 &= (a^3 + b^3)(a^3 - b^3) & \textit{Difference of two squares}\\ &= (a + b)(a^2 - ab + b^2)(a - b)(a^2 + ab + b^2) & \textit{Difference and sum of two cubes} \end{aligned}$$

Check by using the distributive property.

 ## Cooperative Learning

Think-Pair-Share Have students work in groups of four. Have them factor $3x^2 + 5x + 12x + 20$ three different ways. Students should be able to explain the steps they took in finding their solution. Which method would they choose to solve this problem?

For more information on the think-pair-share strategy, see *Cooperative Learning in the Mathematics Classroom*, one of the titles in the Glencoe Mathematics Professional Series, pages 24–25.

You can use a graphing calculator to check that the factored form of a polynomial is correct.

You can use this method to check the factoring you do in this lesson.

EXPLORATION
GRAPHING CALCULATORS

Is the factored form of $2x^2 - 11x - 21$ equal to $(2x - 7)(x + 3)$? You can graph the polynomial and then the factored expression. If the two graphs coincide, the factored form is probably correct.

a. Press $\boxed{Y=}$. Enter $2x^2 - 11x - 21$ for Y1 and $(2x - 7)(x + 3)$ for Y2.

b. Set your viewing window for $[-10, 10]$ by $[-40, 10]$.

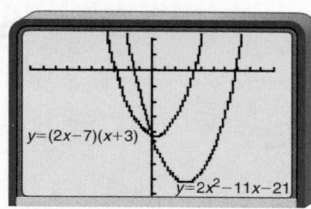

c. Press $\boxed{GRAPH}$. Notice that two different graphs appear. Thus, $2x^2 - 11x - 21 \neq (2x - 7)(x + 3)$.

Your Turn
b. In some cases, the graphs might be so close in shape that they seem to coincide but do not.

a. Determine if $x^2 + 5x - 6 = (x - 3)(x - 2)$ is a true statement. If it is not correct, state the correct factorization.   not true; $(x + 6)(x - 1)$

b. Why doesn't this method guarantee a way to check the factored form of a polynomial?

In Lesson 5–3, you learned to simplify the quotient of two polynomials by using long division or synthetic division. You can determine if one polynomial is a factor of another by using division.

Example **a.** Show that $4 - w$ is a factor of $w^3 - 6w^2 + 13w - 20$.
b. Find another factor of $w^3 - 6w^2 + 13w - 20$.

$$
\begin{array}{r}
-w^2 + 2w - 5 \\
-w + 4\overline{\smash{\big)}\ w^3 - 6w^2 + 13w - 20} \\
\end{array}
$$

a. $\quad 4 - w = -w + 4$

$$
\begin{array}{r}
\underline{w^3 - 4w^2} \\
-2w^2 + 13w \\
\underline{-2w^2 + 8w} \\
5w - 20 \\
\underline{5w - 20} \\
0
\end{array}
$$

Since the remainder is 0, $4 - w$ is a factor of $w^3 - 6w^2 + 13w - 20$.

b. The quotient in part a, $-w^2 + 2w - 5$, is another factor since $(4 - w)(-w^2 + 2w - 5) = w^3 - 6w^2 + 13w - 20$. Since $-w^2 + 2w - 5$ is not factorable, these are the only two factors of the polynomial.

Lesson 5–4 Factoring **277**

EXPLORATION

Tell students that this Exploration serves as a reminder that, as in much of algebra, students can usually check their work themselves using a variety of available methods.

In-Class Example

For Example 4

a. Show that $2 + x$ is a factor of $x^3 + 4x^2 + 7x + 6$.

$$
\begin{array}{r}
x^2 + 2x + 3 \\
x + 2\overline{\smash{\big)}\ x^3 + 4x^2 + 7x + 6} \\
\underline{x^3 + 2x^2} \\
2x^2 + 7x \\
\underline{2x^2 + 4x} \\
3x + 6 \\
\underline{3x + 6} \\
0
\end{array}
$$

b. Find another factor of $x^3 + 4x^2 + 7x + 6$.
$x^2 + 2x + 3$

GLENCOE Technology

Interactive Mathematics Tools Software

This multimedia software provides an interactive lesson that uses algebra tiles to factor trinomials. A **Computer Journal** gives students an opportunity to write about what they have learned.

For Windows & Macintosh

In-Class Example

For Example 5
Find the width of rectangle $EFGH$ if its area is $(2x^3 + 3x^2y + 3xy^2 + y^3)$ mm².

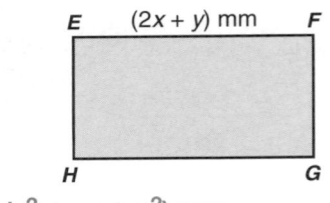

E — $(2x + y)$ mm — F

H ———————— G

$(x^2 + xy + y^2)$ mm

3 PRACTICE/APPLY

Check for Understanding
Exercises 1–17 are designed to help you assess your students' understanding through reading, writing, speaking, and modeling. You should work through Exercises 1–6 with your students and then monitor their work on Exercises 7–17.

Additional Answer

3. First factor the GCF:
$2(x^2 - 3x - 10)$.
Then factor the trinomial:
$2(x - 5)(x + 2)$.

Study Guide Masters, p. 33

Study Guide

NAME _____ DATE _____
Student Edition
Pages 274–280

Factoring
When factoring polynomials, there are general guidelines to follow.

Guidelines for Factoring
1. Check for the greatest common factor (GCF).
2. Check for special products. Remember, for any numbers a and b:
   a. Difference of two squares: $a^2 - b^2 = (a - b)(a + b)$
   b. Sum of two cubes: $a^3 + b^3 = (a + b)(a^2 - ab + b^2)$
   c. Difference of two cubes: $a^3 - b^3 = (a - b)(a^2 + ab + b^2)$
   d. Perfect square trinomials: $a^2 \pm 2ab + b^2 = (a \pm b)^2$
   e. General Trinomials: $acx^2 + (ad + bc)x + bd = (ax + b)(cx + d)$ FOIL method
3. If there are four or more terms, try grouping.

Example of Greatest Common Factor
$16x^3 - 32x^2y + 8xy^2 = 8x(2x^2 - 4xy + y^2)$

Examples of Grouping Method
a. $xm + xn + ym + yn =$
   $x(m + n) + y(m + n) = (x + y)(m + n)$
b. $x^3 - 12x^2y + 24x^2y^2 - 8xy^3 =$
   $x(x - 2y)(x^2 - 10xy + 4y^2)$

Examples of Special Products
a. $2m^2 - 98 = 2(m^2 - 49) =$
   $2(m - 7)(m + 7)$
b. $125c^6 + 1 = (5c^2 + 1)(25c^4 - 5c^2 + 1)$
c. $m^{15}n^3 - 27 =$
   $(m^5n - 3)(m^{10}n^2 + 3m^5n + 9)$
d. $121 + 22m + m^2 = (11 + m)^2$

Example of FOIL Method
$x^2 - 7x + 10$

Factors of 10	Sum of Factors
1, 10	11
-1, -10	-11
2, 5	7
-2, -5	-7

The two numbers are -2 and -5.
$x^2 - 7x + 10 = (x - 5)(x - 2)$

Factor.
1. $x^4 - 1$
   $(x^2 + 1)(x + 1)(x - 1)$
2. $35x^3y^4 - 60x^4y$
   $5x^3y(7y^3 - 12x)$
3. $2r^3 + 250$
   $2(r + 5)(r^2 - 5r + 25)$
4. $100m^4 - 9$
   $(10m^2 - 3)(10m^2 + 3)$
5. $3z^3 + 16z - 35$
   $(z + 7)(3z - 5)$
6. $162z^4 - 98$
   $2(9x^2 + 7)(9x^2 - 7)$
7. $4m^6 - 12m^3 + 9$
   $(2m^3 - 3)^2$
8. $x^3 - 343$
   $(x - 7)(x^2 + 7x + 49)$
9. $ac^4 - a^5c$
   $ac(c - a^4)$
10. $2m^5 - 12m^3 + 18m$
    $2m(m^2 - 3)^2$
11. $c^5 + c^3 - c^2 - c$
    $c(c + 1)^2(c - 1)$
12. $x^6 - 1$
    $(x + 1)(x - 1)(x^2 - x + 1)(x^2 + x + 1)$

278 Chapter 5

Example 5 Find the width of rectangle $ABCD$ if its area is $(3x^2 + 9xy + 6y^2)$ cm².

INTEGRATION
Geometry

A ——— $(3x + 6y)$ cm ——— D

B ——————————— C

$A = \ell w$

$w = \dfrac{A}{\ell}$ *Solve for w.*

$w = \dfrac{3x^2 + 9xy + 6y^2}{3x + 6y}$ $A = 3x^2 + 9xy + 6y^2, \ell = 3x + 6y$

$w = \dfrac{(3x + 6y)(x + y)}{3x + 6y}$ *Factor the numerator.*

$w = \dfrac{\overset{1}{\cancel{(3x + 6y)}}(x + y)}{\underset{1}{\cancel{3x + 6y}}}$

$w = x + y$

The width of the rectangle is $(x + y)$ cm.

CHECK FOR UNDERSTANDING

Communicating Mathematics

Study the lesson. Then complete the following.

1. **Decide** which of the following is the complete factorization of $12x^2 - 8x - 15$.   **c**
   a. $(4x + 3)(3x - 5)$
   b. $(6x - 5)(2x + 3)$
   c. $(6x + 5)(2x - 3)$
   d. cannot be factored

2. 1, 4, 9, 16, 25, 36, 49, 64, 81, 100; 1, 8, 27, 64, 125, 216, 343, 512, 729, 1000

2. **List** the cubes and squares of the numbers from 1 to 10. Explain how this list might help you in factoring.

3. **Explain** how to completely factor $2x^2 - 6x - 20$.   See margin.

5. $a^3 - b^3 = (a^2 - b^2)(a^4 + a^2b^2 + b^4) = (a - b)(a + b)(a^2 + ab + b^2)(a^2 - ab + b^2)$

4. **Show** another way to group the terms to factor the polynomial in Example 2. Was the final result the same? $(b^3 + 4b) - (3b^2 + 12)$; yes

5. **Factor** the polynomial in Example 3d by using the difference of two cubes. Explain why it is better to factor a difference of squares first.

MODELING MATHEMATICS

6. Draw two different geometric models of $2x^2 + 6x$.
   a. What property is shown in each model?   distributive
   b. What is the completely-factored form of the polynomial? $2x(x + 3)$

15. $(g + 20)(g^2 - 20g + 400)$

Guided Practice

Factor completely. If the polynomial is not factorable, write *prime*.

7. $-15x^2 - 5x$ $-5x(3x + 1)$
8. $m^2 - 6m + 8$ $(m - 4)(m - 2)$
9. $x^2 + xy + 3x$ $x(x + y + 3)$
10. $16r^2 - 169$ $(4r + 13)(4r - 13)$
11. $y^2 - 3y - 10$ $(y - 5)(y + 2)$
12. $a^2 + 5a + 6$ $(a + 3)(a + 2)$
13. $3h^2 - 48$ $3(h - 4)(h + 4)$
14. $2r^3 - 16s^3$ $2(r - 2s)(r^2 + 2rs + 4s^2)$
15. $g^3 + 8000$
16. $21 - 7y + 3x - xy$ $(x + 7)(3 - y)$
17. **Determine** if $3y - 2$ is a factor of $6y^3 - y^2 - 5y + 2$. If so, what is the other factor?   yes, $2y^2 + y - 1$ or $(2y - 1)(y + 1)$

Reteaching

Using Alternative Methods Students may use the reverse of FOIL to factor trinomials.
Given: $ax^2 + bx + c$

1. Find ac.
2. Find factors of ac that add or subtract (per sign of constant) to b.
3. Rewrite middle term bx as a sum or difference of factors of ac found in step 2.
4. Factor by grouping.

5. Check by using FOIL.
Example:
$6x^2 + x - 15$
$(6)(-15)$ *or* -90
factors of -90 that subtract (constant sign is "$-$") to 1; -9 and 10

$6x^2 + 1x - 15$
Rewrite $1x$ to get $6x^2 + 10x - 9x - 15$.
$2x(3x + 5) - 3(3x + 5)$
$(2x - 3)(3x + 5)$
$6x^2 + 10x - 9x - 15$

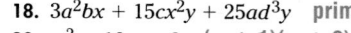

EXERCISES

Practice

Factor completely. If the polynomial is not factorable, write *prime*.

18. $3a^2bx + 15cx^2y + 25ad^3y$ prime
19. $10a^3b - 12a^2b^2$ $2a^2b(5a - 6b)$
20. $w^2 + 10w + 9$ $(w + 1)(w + 9)$
21. $16n^2 + 25m^2$ prime
22. $3x^2 - 3y^2$ $3(x + y)(x - y)$
23. $y^2 - 12y + 20$ $(y - 10)(y - 2)$

24. $2ab^2(6b - 4a + 5a^4b)$
24. $12ab^3 - 8a^2b^2 + 10a^5b^3$
25. $y^2 + 7y + 6$ $(y + 6)(y + 1)$
26. $x^2 - 5x + 4$ $(x - 4)(x - 1)$
27. $x^4 - y^2$ $(x^2 + y)(x^2 - y)$

28. $(2m + 3)(3m + 2)$
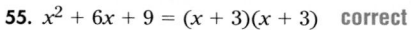
28. $6m^2 + 13m + 6$
29. $3n^2 + 21n - 24$ $3(n + 8)(n - 1)$
30. $3ay^2 + 9a$ $3a(y^2 + 3)$
31. $3a^2 - 27b^2$ $3(a - 3b)(a + 3b)$
32. $a^2 + 8ab + 16b^2$ $(a + 4b)^2$
33. $5x - 14 + x^2$ $(x + 7)(x - 2)$
34. $2x^2 + 3x + 1$ $(x + 1)(2x + 1)$
35. $5x^2 + 15x - 10$ $5(x^2 + 3x - 2)$
36. $2a^2 + 13a - 7$ $(a + 7)(2a - 1)$
37. $3a^2 + 24a + 45$ $3(a + 3)(a + 5)$
38. $12z^2 - z - 6$ $(4z - 3)(3z + 2)$
39. $m^2n^2 + mn + 1$ prime

40. $(2x - 3)(4a - 3)$
41. $(2a - 5b)(2x + 7y)$
42. $(2w - 3)(5w - 7v)$
40. $8ax - 6x - 12a + 9$
41. $4ax + 14ay - 10bx - 35by$
42. $10w^2 - 14wv - 15w + 21v$
43. $81y^2 - 49$ $(9y + 7)(9y - 7)$
44. $6a^2 + 27a - 15$ $3(2a - 1)(a + 5)$
45. $2x^4 + 4x^3 + 2x^2$ $2x^2(x + 1)^2$
46. $m^4 - 1$ $(m^2 + 1)(m + 1)(m - 1)$
47. $y^4 - 16$ $(y^2 + 4)(y + 2)(y - 2)$
48. $7mx^2 + 2nx^2 - 7my^2 - 2ny^2$ $(x - y)(x + y)(7m + 2n)$
49. $8a^2 + 8ab + 8ac + 3a + 3b + 3c$ $(8a + 3)(a + b + c)$
50. $5a^2x + 4aby + 3acz - 5abx - 4b^2y - 3bcz$ $(a - b)(5ax + 4by + 3cz)$
51. $3x^3 + 2x^2 - 5x + 9x^2y + 6xy - 15y$ $(x + 3y)(3x + 5)(x - 1)$

52. Determine the value of k so that $x - 4$ is a factor of $x^2 + 8x + k$. $k = -48$

53. Use factoring to simplify $\left(\dfrac{n^2 + 2n - 15}{n^2 + 3n - 10}\right)\left(\dfrac{n^2 - 9}{n^2 - 9n + 14}\right)^{-1}$. $\dfrac{n - 7}{n + 3}$

54. $m + k - 3$
54. One factor of $m^2 - k^2 + 6k - 9$ is $(m - k + 3)$. What is the other factor?

Graphing Calculator
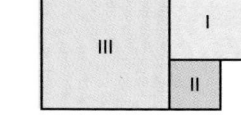

55–59. See margin for graphs.

Use a graphing calculator to determine if each polynomial is factored correctly. For each correct factorization, sketch the graph shown on the screen. For each incorrect factorization, write the correct factorization and sketch the graph.

55. $x^2 + 6x + 9 = (x + 3)(x + 3)$ correct
56. $3x^2 + 5x + 2 = (3x + 2)(x + 1)$ correct
57. $x^3 + 8 = (x + 2)(x^2 - x + 4)$ incorrect; $(x + 2)(x^2 - 2x + 4)$
58. $3x^2 - 48 = 3(x + 4)(x - 4)$ correct
59. $2x^2 - 5x - 3 = (x - 1)(2x + 3)$ incorrect; $(2x + 1)(x - 3)$

Critical Thinking

60. Factor $49p^{2n} + 14p^n + 1$. $(7p^n + 1)^2$

Applications and Problem Solving

61. **Geometry**   The figure at the right is made of three squares.
   a. Suppose the area of square I is y^2 square units and the perimeter of square II is $4x$ units. Write a polynomial for the area of square III. $(x^2 + 2xy + y^2)$ units^2
   b. Suppose the area of square I is 400 square units and the perimeter of square II is 44 units. Find the area of square III.   961 units^2

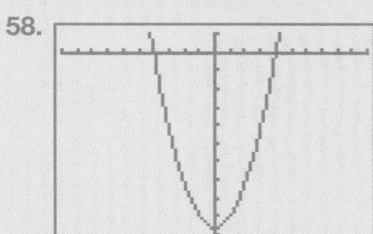

Additional Answers

58.

59.
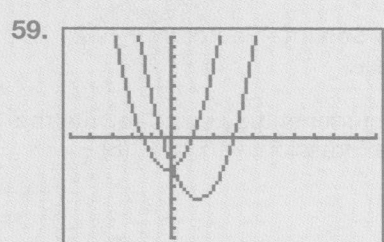

Assignment Guide
Core: 19–59 odd, 60, 61, 63–73
Enriched: 18–58 even, 60–73

For **Extra Practice,** see p. 886.

The red A, B, and C flags, printed only in the Teacher's Wraparound Edition, indicate the level of difficulty of the exercises.

Additional Answers

55.
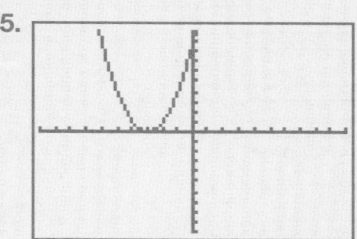

56.
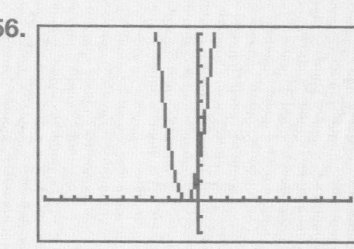

57.
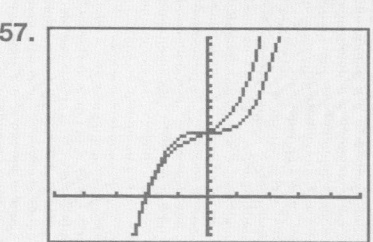

Practice Masters, p. 33

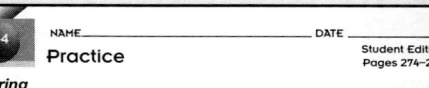

5-4   NAME_____   DATE_____
Practice   Student Edition Pages 274–280

Factoring
Factor completely.

1. $15a^5b - 10ab^5$
   $5ab(3a - 2b)$
2. $2x^5y - x^3y + 5xy^2 + xy^5$
   $xy(2x^4 - x^2 + 5y + y^4)$
3. $16r^2 - 169$
   $(4r + 13)(4r - 13)$
4. $c^2 - 49$
   $(c + 7)(c - 7)$
5. $2y^2 - 242$
   $2(y + 11)(y - 11)$
6. $x^3 + 8$
   $(x + 2)(x^2 - 2x + 4)$
7. $8m^3 - 1$
   $(2m - 1)(4m^2 + 2m + 1)$
8. $b^4 - 81$
   $(b^2 + 9)(b + 3)(b - 3)$
9. $x^2 - 3x - 10$
   $(x - 5)(x + 2)$
10. $r^3 + 3r^2 - 54r$
   $r(r + 9)(r - 6)$
11. $4a^2 + a - 3$
   $(4a - 3)(a + 1)$
12. $2t^3 + 32t^2 + 128t$
   $2t(t + 8)^2$
13. $y^2 + 20y + 96$
   $(y + 8)(y + 12)$
14. $6n^2 - 11n - 2$
   $(6n + 1)(n - 2)$
15. $x^2 - 8x + 16$
   $(x - 4)^2$
16. $21 - 7t + 3r - rt$
   $(r + 7)(3 - t)$
17. $x^2 + 2x - xy - 2y$
   $(x + 2)(x - y)$
18. $x^2 + 2xy + 2x + y^2 + 2y - 8$
   $(x + y + 4)(x + y - 2)$
19. $4x^6 - 4x^2$
   $4x^2(x^2 + 1)(x + 1)(x - 1)$
20. $k^3 - 2k^2r - 3kr^2$
   $k(k - 3r)(k + r)$
21. $45x^2 - 80y^2$
   $5(3x + 4y)(3x - 4y)$
22. $36a^3b^2 + 66a^2b^3 - 210ab^4$
   $6ab^2(3a - 5b)(2a + 7b)$
23. $4a^2 + 12ab + 9b^2 - 25c^2$
   $(2a + 3b + 5c)(2a + 3b - 5c)$
24. $81x^4 - 16$
   $(9x^2 + 4)(3x + 2)(3x - 2)$
25. $5y^5 + 135y^2$
   $5y^2(y + 3)(y^2 - 3y + 9)$
26. $18p^3 - 51p^2 - 135p$
   $3p(2p - 9)(3p + 5)$

4 ASSESS

Closing Activity

Modeling Using algebra tiles, model factoring the perfect square trinomial $x^2 + 4x + 4$.
$(x + 2)^2$

Enrichment Masters, p. 33

5-4	NAME_____ DATE_____
	Student Edition
Enrichment	Pages 274–280

Sums and Differences of Odd Powers
Study the patterns below for factoring the sum and the difference of cubes.
$a^3 + b^3 = (a + b)(a^2 - ab + b^2)$
$a^3 - b^3 = (a - b)(a^2 + ab + b^2)$
This pattern can be extended to other odd powers. Study these examples.

Example: Factor $a^5 + b^5$.
Extend the first pattern to obtain $a^5 + b^5 = (a + b)(a^4 - a^3b + a^2b^2 - ab^3 + b^4)$.
Check: $(a + b)(a^4 - a^3b + a^2b^2 - ab^3 + b^4) = a^5 - a^4b + a^3b^2 - a^2b^3 + ab^4$
$\qquad\qquad + a^4b - a^3b^2 + a^2b^3 - ab^4 + b^5$
$\qquad = a^5 \qquad\qquad\qquad\qquad\qquad + b^5$

Example: Factor $a^5 - b^5$.
Extend the second pattern to obtain $a^5 - b^5 = (a - b)(a^4 + a^3b + a^2b^2 + ab^3 + b^4)$.
Check: $(a - b)(a^4 + a^3b + a^2b^2 + ab^3 + b^4) = a^5 + a^4b + a^3b^2 + a^2b^3 + ab^4$
$\qquad\qquad - a^4b - a^3b^2 - a^2b^3 - ab^4 - b^5$
$\qquad = a^5 \qquad\qquad\qquad\qquad\qquad - b^5$

In general, if n is an odd integer, when you factor $a^n + b^n$ or $a^n - b^n$, one factor will be either $(a + b)$ or $(a - b)$, depending on the sign of the original expression. The other factor will have the following properties:
- The first term will be a^{n-1} and the last term will be b^{n-1}.
- The exponents of a will decrease by 1 as you go from left to right.
- The exponents of b will increase by 1 as you go from left to right.
- The degree of each term will be $n - 1$.
- If the original expression was $a^n + b^n$, the terms will alternately have + and – signs.
- If the original expression was $a^n - b^n$, the terms will all have + signs.

Use the patterns above to factor each expression.
1. $a^7 + b^7$ $(a + b)(a^6 - a^5b + a^4b^2 - a^3b^3 + a^2b^4 - ab^5 + b^6)$

2. $c^9 - d^9$ $(c - d)(c^8 + c^7d + c^6d^2 + c^5d^3 + c^4d^4 + c^3d^5 + c^2d^6 + cd^7 + d^8)$

3. $e^{11} + f^{11}$ $(e + f)(e^{10} - e^9f + e^8f^2 - e^7f^3 + e^6f^4 - e^5f^5 + e^4f^6 - e^3f^7 + e^2f^8 - ef^9 + f^{10})$

To factor an expression such as $x^{10} - y^{10}$, you can first change it to $(x^5 + y^5)(x^5 - y^5)$, then factor each part. Use this approach to factor each expression.
4. $x^{10} - y^{10}$ $(x + y)(x^4 - x^3y + x^2y^2 - xy^3 + y^4)(x - y)(x^4 + x^3y + x^2y^2 + xy^3 + y^4)$

5. $a^{14} - b^{14}$ $(a + b)(a^6 - a^5b + a^4b^2 - a^3b^3 + a^2b^4 - ab^5 + b^6)(a - b)(a^6 + a^5b + a^4b^2 + a^3b^3 + a^2b^4 + ab^5 + b^6)$

62b. 7171 m²; 344 m

62. Flags The largest flag flown from a flag-pole is a Brazilian national flag measuring 100 meters by 70 meters in Brasilia, the capital of Brazil.

a. Find the area and the perimeter of the flag. **7000 m²; 340 m**

b. Suppose a company made a flag 1 meter longer and wider than the Brazilian flag. What would be the area and the perimeter of that flag?

c. Suppose a company makes a flag and increases the length and width by x feet. Find the area and perimeter of that flag. Write your answers as polynomials. **$(x^2 + 170x + 7000)$ m²; $(340 + 4x)$ m**

Mixed Review

63. $t^2 - 2t + 1$
64. $14x^2 + 26x - 4$

66. $5x + 4y = -3$,
$3x - 5y = -24$

70a. $y = 5x - 187$

70c. 75.4 in.

73. distributive

63. Find $(t^3 - 3t + 2) \div (t + 2)$ by using synthetic division. (Lesson 5–3)

64. Use the FOIL method to find $(2x + 4)(7x - 1)$. (Lesson 5–2)

65. Physics Light from a laser travels about 300,000 kilometers per second. How many kilometers can it travel in a day? Write your answer in scientific notation. (Lesson 5–1) **2.592×10^{10} km**

66. Write the system of equations represented by $\begin{bmatrix} 5 & 4 \\ 3 & -5 \end{bmatrix} \cdot \begin{bmatrix} x \\ y \end{bmatrix} = \begin{bmatrix} -3 \\ -24 \end{bmatrix}$. (Lesson 4–6)

67. Find $-2\begin{bmatrix} \frac{1}{2} & 3 \\ 5 & 7 \end{bmatrix} + \begin{bmatrix} 1 & 2 \\ 3 & 4 \end{bmatrix}$. (Lesson 4–2) $\begin{bmatrix} 0 & -4 \\ -7 & -10 \end{bmatrix}$

68. Manufacturing Oaken Treasures makes two different kinds of chairs—rockers and swivels. Work on machines A and B is required to make both kinds of chairs. Machine A can run no more than 20 hours per day. Machine B is limited to 15 hours per day. The chart below shows the amount of time on each machine that is required to make one chair and the profit from each chair.

Chair	Machine A	Machine B	Profit
rocker	2 h	3 h	$12
swivel	4 h	1 h	$10

How many chairs of each kind should Oaken Treasures make each day to maximize their profit? (Lesson 3–6) **4 rockers, 3 swivels**

69. Solve the system of equations by using Cramer's Rule. (Lesson 3–3) **(7, −2)**
$2x + 3y - 8 = 0$
$3x + 2y - 17 = 0$

70. Statistics The table below shows the ideal weight for a man for a given height. (Lesson 2–5)

Height (inches)	66	68	70	72	74	76	78
Weight (pounds)	143	153	164	171	183	198	206

a. Use the information in the chart to write a prediction equation for the relationship between a man's height and his ideal weight.

b. Predict the ideal weight for a man who is 71 inches tall. **168 lb**

c. Predict the height of a man who is at his ideal weight of 190 pounds.

71. Write an equation for the line that passes through the point (2, 2) that is perpendicular to the graph of $2x + 3y - 1 = 4$. (Lesson 2–4) $y = \frac{3}{2}x - 1$

72. Write an algebraic expression to represent *the sum of a number and five times its square*. (Lesson 1–5) $a + 5a^2$

73. State the property illustrated by $(4 + 11)6 = 4(6) + 11(6)$. (Lesson 1–2)

280 Chapter 5 *Exploring Polynomials and Radical Expressions*

Extension

Problem Solving Factor $x^9 + 512$ completely.
$(x + 2)(x^2 - 2x + 4)(x^6 - 8x^3 + 64)$
Remind students they could rewrite the original expression as $(x^3)^3 + (8)^3$.

Roots of Real Numbers

What YOU'LL LEARN

- To simplify radicals having various indices, and
- to use a calculator to estimate roots of numbers.

Why IT'S IMPORTANT

You can use the roots of real numbers to solve problems involving baseball and tourism.

APPLICATION

Tourism

The table below lists the five highest mountain peaks in North America, according to the *World Almanac*.

Highest Peaks in North America

Height (feet)

20,320 — McKinley, Alaska
19,850 — Logan, Yukon Territory
18,700 — Citlaltepec (Orizaba), Mexico
18,008 — St. Elias, Alaska-Yukon
17,887 — Popocatepetl, Mexico

Peak and Location

Teresa and some of her friends are among a group of students visiting Mexico as a part of their study of Spanish. They are visiting Monte Albán in the Oaxaca Plateau of Mexico, which is near Orizaba. Monte Albán was the ancient religious center of the Zapotec Indians.

From an observation point at Monte Albán, Teresa and her friends can see a nearby river that is about 35 miles away. She guesses that the observation point is about 1000 feet high. Her friends guess the point to be higher than that. The formula for estimating the distance d (in miles) that can be seen from the top of a mountain of height h (in feet) is $d = 1.2\sqrt{h}$. Whose guess will be closer to the actual height of the observation point?

To determine the better estimate, we can rewrite the formula as $\sqrt{h} = \frac{d}{1.2}$. If $d = 35$ miles, then the following is true.

$$\sqrt{h} = \frac{35}{1.2} \qquad \textit{Estimate: Will } \sqrt{h} \textit{ be greater or less than 35?}$$

$$\sqrt{h} = 29.1\overline{6} \qquad \textit{Use a calculator.}$$

Now we need to determine a number h whose square root is $29.1\overline{6}$.

Finding the square root of a number and squaring a number are inverse operations. To find the square root of a number n, you must find a number whose square is n. For example, a square root of 36 is 6 since $6^2 = 36$. Since $(-6)^2 = 36$, -6 is also a square root of 36.

Definition of Square Root	For any real numbers a and b, if $a^2 = b$, then a is a square root of b.

Using the definition for the situation above, $29.1\overline{6}$ is the square root of h. So, $h = (29.1\overline{6})^2$ or about 850.7 feet. Teresa's estimate of the height is fairly close.

fabulous
FIRSTS

Alison Hargreaves (1962–1995)

Alison Hargreaves, a Scottish mountaineer, was the first woman to climb Mt. Everest alone and without oxygen. She reached the summit of Everest (29,028 ft) on May 13, 1995.

fabulous
FIRSTS

Mt. Everest, found in the Himalayan mountain range, is the highest mountain on Earth. The first people to reach its top were Sir Edmund Hillary of New Zealand and Tenzing Norgay of Nepal on May 29, 1953.

NCTM Standards: 1–5

Instructional Resources

- Study Guide Master 5-5
- Practice Master 5-5
- Enrichment Master 5-5
- Assessment and Evaluation Masters, pp. 127–128
- Modeling Mathematics Masters, pp. 37–39

 Transparency 5-5A contains the 5-Minute Check for this lesson; **Transparency 5-5B** contains a teaching aid for this lesson.

Recommended Pacing

Standard Pacing	Day 6 of 16
Honors Pacing	Day 5 of 12
Block Scheduling*	Day 3 of 6 (along with Lesson 5-6)

 *For more information on pacing and possible lesson plans, refer to the *Block Scheduling Booklet*.

1 FOCUS

 5-Minute Check
(over Lesson 5-4)

Factor.

1. $5x^2y - 20xy^2z + 35y^3z^2$
   $5y(x^2 - 4xyz + 7y^2z^2)$
2. $4a^2 - 9$ $(2a + 3)(2a - 3)$
3. $6y^3 + 13y^2 + 5y$
   $y(3y + 5)(2y + 1)$
4. $7a^2c - 175c$
   $7c(a + 5)(a - 5)$
5. $5cd^2 + 8ad^2 - 5cb^2 - 8ab^2$
   $(5c + 8a)(d - b)(d + b)$

Motivating the Lesson

Situational Problem Have students find the length of the sides of a cube with a volume of 64 cubic feet. **4 ft**
What does it mean to have a volume in cubic feet? **Each side of the solid can be measured in feet.**

Teaching Tip When going through the table listing powers, point out that the other powers do not have special names since they are not geometric figures such as squares and cubes.

Teaching Tip Stress that the inverse of raising a number to the *n*th power is finding an *n*th root. The power and inverse keys on a calculator may be used to find roots.

F Y I

While the symbol for the radical was not developed until the sixteenth century, the concepts of squares and square roots were known to the ancient Greek mathematicians.

F Y I

The radical sign was first introduced in 1525 by Christoff Rudolff in his algebra book *Die Cross.* This symbol was probably chosen because it resembled a small *r*, the first letter in the word *radix*, which means root.

Since finding the square root of a number and squaring a number are inverse operations, it makes sense that the inverse of raising a number to the *n*th power is finding the **nth root** of the number. For example, the table below shows the relationship between raising a number to a power and taking that root of the number.

Powers	Factors	Roots
$a^3 = 64$	$4 \cdot 4 \cdot 4 = 64$	4 is a cube root of 64
$a^4 = 16$	$2 \cdot 2 \cdot 2 \cdot 2 = 16$	2 is a fourth root of 16
$a^5 = 243$	$3 \cdot 3 \cdot 3 \cdot 3 \cdot 3 = 243$	3 is a fifth root of 243
$a^n = b$	$\underbrace{a \cdot a \cdot a \cdot a \cdots a}_{n \text{ factors of } a} = b$	*a* is an *n*th root of *b*

The pattern suggests the following formal definition of the *n*th root.

Definition of *n*th Root	For any real numbers *a* and *b*, and any positive integer *n*, if $a^n = b$, then *a* is an *n*th root of *b*.

$\sqrt[n]{98}$ *is read "the nth root of 98."*

The symbol $\sqrt[n]{}$ indicates an *n*th root.

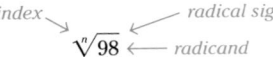

index → $\sqrt[n]{98}$ ← *radical sign* / ← *radicand*

Some numbers have more than one real *n*th root. For example, 49 has two square roots, 7 and -7. When there is more than one real root, the nonnegative root is called the **principal root**. When no index is given, as in $\sqrt{49}$, the radical sign indicates the principal square root. The symbol $\sqrt[n]{b}$ stands for the principal *n*th root of *b*. If *n* is odd and *b* is negative, there will be no nonnegative root. In this case, the principal root is negative.

$\sqrt{64} = 8$ $\sqrt{64}$ indicates the principal square root of 64.

$-\sqrt{64} = -8$ $-\sqrt{64}$ indicates the opposite of the principal square root of 64.

$\pm\sqrt{64} = \pm 8$ $\pm\sqrt{64}$ indicates both square roots of 64.
         ± means positive or negative.

$\sqrt[3]{-27} = -3$ $\sqrt[3]{-27}$ indicates the principal cube root of -27.

$-\sqrt[4]{16} = -2$ $-\sqrt[4]{16}$ indicates the opposite of the principal fourth root of 16.

The chart below gives a summary of the real *n*th roots of a number *b*.

Real *n*th Roots of *b*, $\sqrt[n]{b}$, or $-\sqrt[n]{b}$			
n	*b* > 0	*b* < 0	*b* = 0
even	one positive root one negative root	no real roots	one real root, 0
odd	one positive root no negative roots	no positive roots one negative root	

Example ❶ **Find each root.**

a. $\pm\sqrt{49x^8}$

$\pm\sqrt{49x^8} = \pm\sqrt{(7x^4)^2}$

$= \pm 7x^4$

The square roots of $49x^8$ are $\pm 7x^4$.

b. $-\sqrt{(a^2 + 1)^4}$

$-\sqrt{(a^2 + 1)^4} = -\sqrt{[(a^2 + 1)^2]^2}$

$= -(a^2 + 1)^2$

The opposite of the principal square root of $(a^2 + 1)^4$ is $-(a^2 + 1)^2$.

c. $\sqrt[5]{32x^{10}y^{15}}$

$\sqrt[5]{32x^{10}y^{15}} = \sqrt[5]{(2x^2y^3)^5}$

$= 2x^2y^3$

The principal fifth root of $32x^{10}y^{15}$ is $2x^2y^3$.

d. $\sqrt{-16}$

In this case of $\sqrt[n]{b}$, n is even and b is negative. Thus, $\sqrt{-16}$ has no real root.

When you find the nth root of an even power and an odd power is the result, you must take the absolute value of the result to ensure that the value is nonnegative.

$$\sqrt{(-3)^2} = |-3| \text{ or } 3 \qquad \sqrt{(-2)^{10}} = |(-2)^5| \text{ or } 32$$

If the result is an even power or you find the nth root of an odd power, there is no need to take the absolute value. *Why?*

Example ❷ **Find each root.**

a. $\sqrt[6]{x^6}$

Since $x^6 = x \cdot x \cdot x \cdot x \cdot x \cdot x$, x is the sixth root of x^6. The index is even, so the principal root is nonnegative. However, since x could be negative, we must take the absolute value of x to identify the principal root.

$\sqrt[6]{x^6} = |x|$

b. $\sqrt[4]{16(x + 3)^{12}}$

$\sqrt[4]{16(x + 13)^{12}} = \sqrt[4]{2^4[(x + 3)^3]^4}$

Since the index is even and the power is odd, we must use the absolute value of $(x + 3)^3$.

$\sqrt[4]{16(x + 3)^{12}} = 2|(x + 3)^3|$

LOOK BACK

You can review real and irrational numbers in Lesson 2-8.

Recall that real numbers that cannot be expressed as terminating or repeating decimals are *irrational numbers*. $\sqrt{2}$ and $\sqrt{3}$ are examples of irrational numbers. Decimal approximations for irrational numbers, such as 3.14 for π, are often used in applications. You can use a calculator to find decimal approximations.

Example ❸ **Use a calculator to find a decimal approximation for $\sqrt[5]{279}$.**

Use the root key. *It may be a second function key.*

Enter: 279 $\boxed{\sqrt[x]{y}}$ 5 $\boxed{=}$ *3.084045954*

Check: 3.084045954 $\boxed{y^x}$ 5 $\boxed{=}$ *279* ✓

In-Class Examples

For Example 1
Find each root.

a. $\pm\sqrt{169x^4}$ $\pm 13x^2$

b. $-\sqrt{(8x - 3)^4}$ $-(8x - 3)^2$

c. $\sqrt[3]{125a^6}$ $5a^2$

d. $\sqrt[3]{-m^3n^3}$ $-mn$

For Example 2
Find each root.

a. $\sqrt[4]{(an)^4}$ $|an|$

b. $\sqrt[6]{(xy^2)^6}$ $|x|y^2$

c. $\sqrt[6]{(3 - y^2)^{18}}$ $|3 - y^2|^3$

For Example 3
Use a calculator to approximate each value to three decimal places.

a. $\sqrt{973}$ 31.193

b. $\sqrt[3]{-870}$ -9.546

c. $\sqrt[5]{837}$ 3.842

Teaching Tip Students should exercise caution when using the function keys because some calculators compute values in a manner that creates approximation errors. The display may show a number that is slightly more or less than the actual value.

284 Chapter 5

In-Class Example

For Example 4

The volume of a sphere is given by $V = \frac{4}{3}\pi r^3$. Find the radius r of a sphere with a volume of 85 cubic feet. **2.728 feet**

3 PRACTICE/APPLY

Check for Understanding

Exercises 1–19 are designed to help you assess your students' understanding through reading, writing, speaking, and modeling. You should work through Exercises 1–5 with your students and then monitor their work on Exercises 6–19.

Additional Answers

1. An absolute value is not necessary if the root is a positive number, regardless of the value of the variable.
2. Taking the nth root and raising to the nth power are inverse operations.
3. The index is odd and the radicand is less than 0; there is one negative root, -2.
4a. No; if $x < 0$, then $\sqrt[4]{(-x)^4} = -x$.
4b. No; if $x < 0$, then $\sqrt[5]{(-x)^5} = -x$.

Example **4**

APPLICATION

Fishing

Carla, upon returning from a fishing trip, bragged to her friends that she caught a Pacific halibut that weighed 23 kilograms and was at least 2.5 meters long, but it got away as she was hauling it in. The length-to-weight relationship for Pacific halibut can be estimated by the formula $L = 0.46 \sqrt[3]{W}$, where W is the weight in kilograms and L is the length in meters. Is there a possibility that Carla told the truth, or is her story a little "fishy?"

Suppose that Carla is correct about the weight of her fish. Calculate the approximate length of a Pacific halibut that weighs 23 kilograms.

$L = 0.46 \sqrt[3]{W}$

$\quad = 0.46 \sqrt[3]{23}$

$\quad = 0.46(2.84)$

$\quad \approx 1.3064$ *Use a calculator.*

Carla's fish probably was a little more than 1 meter long. So her story is a little "fishy."

CHECK FOR UNDERSTANDING

Communicating Mathematics

Study the lesson. Then complete the following.   1–4. See margin.

1. **Explain** why it is not always necessary to take the absolute value of a result to indicate the principal root.

2. **Describe** how you would check the nth root of a number using your calculator.

3. **Explain** whether or not $\sqrt[5]{-32}$ is a real number.

4. **Determine** if each statement is true, regardless of the value of x. Explain your answers.

    a. $\sqrt[4]{(-x)^4} = x$ b. $\sqrt[5]{(-x)^5} = x$

 *MATH JOURNAL*

5. Copy and complete the table below. If there are things you do not understand about powers and roots, reread and study the lesson as necessary.

Powers	In words	Roots	In words
$2^3 = 2\cdot2\cdot2 = 8$	2 cubed is 8.	$\sqrt[3]{8} = \sqrt[3]{2\cdot2\cdot2} = 2$	The cube root of 8 is 2.
$8^4 = 4096$	8 to the fourth power is __?__. 4096	$\sqrt[4]{4096} = 8$	A fourth root of 4096 is 8.
$7^5 = 16{,}807$	7 to the fifth power is 16,807.	$\sqrt[5]{16{,}807} = 7$	The fifth root of 16,807 is 7.
$3^6 = 729$	3 to the sixth power is 729.	$\sqrt[6]{729} = $ __?__ 3	A sixth root of 729 is 3.
$a^n = b$	a to the nth power is b.	$\sqrt[n]{b} = a$	An nth root of b is a.

Reteaching

Using Reasoning The term $\sqrt[n]{a}$ is equal to a number b for which the property $\dfrac{\overbrace{b \times b \times \ldots \times b}^{n \text{ times}}}{} = a$ holds true.

If the number of b's being multiplied is even, then a must be positive. If n is odd, then a can be negative.

Use a calculator to approximate each value to three decimal places.

6. $\sqrt{99}$ 9.950   7. $-\sqrt[3]{23}$ -2.844 8. $\sqrt[4]{64}$ 2.828

Simplify. 17. $|3m - 2n|$

9. $\sqrt{(-3)^2}$ 3   10. $\sqrt[3]{27}$ 3   11. $\sqrt[5]{-32}$ -2

12. no real root

12. $\sqrt[4]{-10,000}$ 13. $\sqrt[3]{m^3}$ m 14. $\sqrt[4]{x^4}$ $|x|$

15. $-\sqrt{25x^6}$ $-5|x^3|$ 16. $\sqrt{25x^2y^4}$ $5|x|y^2$ 17. $\sqrt{(3m - 2n)^2}$

18. Find the principal fifth root of 32. 2

19. Find the principal third root of -125. -5

EXERCISES

Practice

Use a calculator to approximate each value to three decimal places.

A

20. $\sqrt{121}$ 11   21. $-\sqrt{144}$ -12 22. $\sqrt[3]{65}$ 4.021

23. $\sqrt{0.81}$ 0.9   24. $\sqrt[3]{-670}$ -8.750 25. $\sqrt[4]{625}$ 5

26. $\sqrt[7]{82,567}$ 5.040   27. $\sqrt[6]{(345)^3}$ 18.574   28. $\sqrt{(3600)^2}$ 60

Simplify. 32. no real roots

29. $\sqrt{16}$ 4   30. $\pm\sqrt{121}$ ±11 31. $\sqrt{196}$ 14

32. $\sqrt{-(-6)^2}$ 33. $\sqrt[4]{81}$ 3   34. $-\sqrt{121}$ -11

B

35. $\sqrt[4]{\left(-\frac{1}{2}\right)^4}$ $\frac{1}{2}$ 36. $\sqrt[3]{-27}$ -3 37. $\sqrt[3]{1000}$ 10

38. $\sqrt{0.36}$ 0.6   39. $\sqrt[3]{-0.125}$ -0.5 40. $\sqrt[7]{-1}$ -1

41. $\sqrt[3]{y^3}$ y 42. $\sqrt[4]{t^8}$ t^2 43. $-\sqrt[4]{x^4}$ $-|x|$

44. $\sqrt{(5f)^4}$ $25f^2$ 45. $\sqrt{36g^6}$ $6|g^3|$ 46. $\sqrt{64h^8}$ $8h^4$

47. $\sqrt[3]{m^6n^9z^{12}}$ $m^2n^3z^4$ 48. $\sqrt[3]{8b^3c^3}$ $2bc$ 49. $\sqrt[3]{-27a^9b^{12}}$ $-3a^3b^4$

50. $\pm|a^3 + 2|$

52. $|3x + y|$

53. $-|x + 1|$

54. $|x + 3|$

55. $\pm|s - t|$

57. no real roots

C

50. $\pm\sqrt{(a^3 + 2)^2}$ 51. $\sqrt[3]{(s + t)^3}$ $s + t$ 52. $\sqrt{(3x + y)^2}$

53. $-\sqrt{x^2 + 2x + 1}$ 54. $\sqrt{x^2 + 6x + 9}$ 55. $\pm\sqrt{s^2 - 2st + t^2}$

56. $\sqrt[5]{-(2m - 3n)^5}$ 57. $\sqrt{-4y^2 - 12y - 9}$ 56. $-(2m - 3n)$

58. $\pm\sqrt{16m^2 - 24mn + 9n^2}$ $\pm|4m - 3n|$

**Critical
Thinking**

59. Under what condition does $\sqrt{x^2 + y^2} = x + y$? $x = 0, y = 0$

**Applications and
Problem Solving**

60. **Aerospace Engineering** Scientists expect that in future space stations, artificial gravity will be created by rotating all or part of the space station. The formula $N = \frac{1}{2\pi}\sqrt{\frac{a}{r}}$ gives the number of rotations N required per second to maintain an acceleration of gravity of a meters per second squared on a satellite with a radius of r meters. The acceleration of gravity of Earth is 9.8 m/s². How many rotations per minute will produce an artificial gravity that is equal to half the acceleration of gravity on Earth in a space station with a 25-meter radius? about 4.2 rotations per minute

Assignment Guide

Core: 21–61 odd, 63–73
Enriched: 20–58 even, 59–73
All: Self Test, 1–11

For **Extra Practice,** see p. 887.

The red A, B, and C flags, printed only in the Teacher's Wraparound Edition, indicate the level of difficulty of the exercises.

Study Guide Masters, p. 34

Closing Activity

Speaking Have students discuss when they need to use absolute value signs in simplifying a radical.

Chapter 5, Quiz B (Lessons 5-4 and 5-5), is available in the *Assessment and Evaluation Masters,* p. 128.

Mid-Chapter Test (Lessons 5-1 through 5-5) is available in the *Assessment and Evaluation Masters,* p. 127.

Applications and Problem Solving

61. Baseball The Toronto Blue Jays defeated the Philadelphia Phillies four games to two in the 1993 World Series of baseball. During a practice session between games, the catcher for the Blue Jays practiced throwing the baseball to each of the bases. If a standard baseball diamond has sides 90 feet long, how far did the catcher have to throw the ball to reach second base? (*Hint:* Draw a diagram and use the Pythagorean formula $c = \sqrt{a^2 + b^2}$, where c is the length of the hypotenuse of a right triangle and a and b are the lengths of the legs.) **about 127.3 feet**

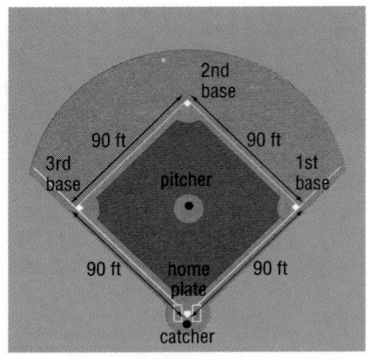

62. Physics Rashad and Alberto are part of the staff in a fun house at their school carnival that is raising money for Muscular Dystrophy. Their job is to drop water-filled balloons from a 25-foot wall on unsuspecting students as they stand on a particular spot in the fun house. The formula for determining the time t it takes a water balloon to reach the ground is $t = \sqrt{\dfrac{2d}{g}}$, where d is the height in feet from which the object is dropped and g is the acceleration due to gravity, which equals 32.2 ft/s². Migdalia and Lawanda have told Rashad and Alberto that they can avoid getting hit by a balloon by moving quickly out of the way. How much time do the girls have to avoid getting wet? (Assume very little air friction and the girls are about 5 feet tall.) **about 1.11 seconds**

Mixed Review

63. Simplify $\sqrt{(5b)^4}$. (Lesson 5–5) $25b^2$

64. Simplify $(2p + q^3)^2$. (Lesson 5–2) $4p^2 + 4pq^3 + q^6$

65. Simplify $y^2x^{-3}(yx^4 + y^{-1}x^3 + y^{-2}x^2)$. (Lesson 5–2) $xy^3 + y + \dfrac{1}{x}$

66. 3.84 × 10⁵ km

66. Astronomy Moonlight takes 1.28 seconds to reach Earth. If the speed of light is 3×10^5 kilometers per second, how far is the moon from Earth? (Lesson 5–1)

67. Solve $\begin{vmatrix} 5 & 7 \\ -2 & 2x \end{vmatrix} = 54$. (Lesson 4–4) 4

68. Find $\begin{bmatrix} 5 & -2 \\ \frac{1}{2} & -3 \end{bmatrix} \cdot \begin{bmatrix} 2 \\ 1 \end{bmatrix}$. (Lesson 4–3) $\begin{bmatrix} 8 \\ -2 \end{bmatrix}$

69. Graph the system below. Find the maximum and minimum values given the function for the following region. (Lesson 3–5)

$y \ge x$
$y \le x + 5$
$x \ge -3$
$y + 2x \le 5$
$f(x, y) = x - 2y$ max: $f(-3, -3) = 3$; min: $f(0, 5) = -10$

70. Solve the system of equations by graphing. (Lesson 3–1) $(-2, -4)$

$2x + 3y = -16$
$2y = 4x$

286 Chapter 5 *Exploring Polynomials and Radical Expressions*

Practice Masters, p. 34

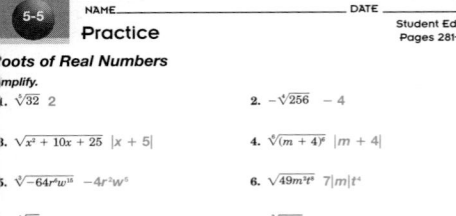

NAME_____ DATE _____
5-5
Practice
Student Edition
Pages 281–287

Roots of Real Numbers
Simplify.
1. $\sqrt{32}$ 2
2. $-\sqrt{256}$ −4
3. $\sqrt{x^2 + 10x + 25}$ $|x + 5|$
4. $\sqrt[4]{(m + 4)^4}$ $|m + 4|$
5. $\sqrt[3]{-64r^6w^{15}}$ $-4r^2w^5$
6. $\sqrt{49m^2t^4}$ $7|m|t^4$
7. $\sqrt{81}$ 3
8. $\sqrt[3]{-64}$ −4
9. $\sqrt{(2x)^8}$ $16x^4$
10. $-\sqrt[4]{625}$ −5
11. $\sqrt{216}$ 6
12. $\sqrt{676x^4y^2}$ $26x^2|y^3|$
13. $\sqrt[3]{(2x + 1)^3}$ $2x + 1$
14. $\sqrt[3]{-32x^3y^6}$ $-2xy^2$
15. $-\sqrt{144m^6n^2}$ $-12m^3|n^3|$
16. $\sqrt[3]{-27x^9y^3}$ $-3x^3y$
17. $\sqrt{243x^{10}}$ $3x^2$
18. $-\sqrt{49a^{10}b^6}$ $-7|a^3|b^6$
19. $\sqrt{(x - 5)^8}$ $(x - 5)^2$
20. $\sqrt[3]{343d^8}$ $7d^2$
21. $\sqrt{0.81}$ 0.9
22. $-\sqrt{0.0016}$ −0.04
23. $\sqrt{0.512}$ 0.8
24. $-\sqrt{0.6561}$ −0.9

Use a calculator to approximate each value to three decimal places.
25. $\sqrt{7.8}$ 2.793
26. $-\sqrt{89}$ −9.434
27. $\sqrt{25}$ 2.924
28. $\sqrt[3]{-4}$ −1.587

Extension

Connections The accompanying problem shows that given any two people, you can show that they are the same age!

What is wrong with the solution?
Taking the square root of an equation such as of $x^2 = y^2$ does not necessarily mean $x = y$, only that $|x| = |y|$ or $x = \pm y$.

Y = your age, M = my age
Average $A = \dfrac{M + Y}{2}$ or $2A = M + Y$
$2A(M - Y) = (M + Y)(M - Y)$
$2AM - 2AY = M^2 - Y^2$
$Y^2 - 2AY = M^2 - 2AM$
$Y^2 - 2AY + A^2 = M^2 - 2AM + A^2$
$(Y - A)(Y - A) = (M - A)(M - A)$
$(Y - A)^2 = (M - A)^2$
$Y - A = M - A$ or $Y = M$

Graph each equation. 71–72. See margin.

71. $b = 2[a] - 3$ (Lesson 2–6) **72.** $b = 2a - 3$ (Lesson 2–2)

73. Time Management The chart below illustrates the time in hours per week that unmarried young people between the ages of 12 and 17 and the ages of 18 and 29 spend on various activities. (Lesson 1–4)

Activity	12–17 Years	18–29 Years
Leisure activities:		
Eating	8.1	7.5
Sleeping	62.6	55.9
Attending sports events	0.8	0.3
Attending cultural events	0.3	0.4
Going to movies	0.6	0.7
Visiting, socializing	4.4	7.8
Participating in sports	3.3	1.8
Watching TV	17.7	14.2
Reading	1.3	1.9
Work/school activities:		
Attending classes	18.1	4.1
Cleaning, laundry	2.2	3.2
Doing homework	3.1	3.4
Washing, dressing	6.4	6.8
Working	2.8	29.0
Yardwork, repairs	1.9	1.2

a. Find the mean and median of the leisure activities for both age groups to the nearest tenth. **11.0, 3.3;10.1, 1.9**

b. Find the mean and median of the work/school activities for both age groups to the nearest tenth. **5.8, 3.0; 8.0, 3.8**

73c. Sample answer: Teens have more leisure time than adults.

c. Does the distribution of the data say anything to you about the priorities of these two groups? What can you say about the differences between the ways the two groups of people spend their time?

SELF TEST

1. **Astronomy** The distance from Earth to the sun is approximately 93,000,000 miles. Write this number in scientific notation. (Lesson 5–1) 9.3×10^7 **miles**

2. Write $8mn^{-5}$ without using negative exponents. (Lesson 5–1) $\dfrac{8m}{n^5}$

Simplify. (Lessons 5–1, 5–2, and 5–3) **6.** $d^2 + d - 3$

3. $(-3x^2y)^3(2x)^2$ $-108x^8y^3$

4. $(9x + 2y) - (7x - 3y)$ $2x + 5y$

5. $(n + 2)(n^2 - 3n + 1)$ $n^3 - n^2 - 5n + 2$

6. $(2d^4 + 2d^3 - 9d^2 - 3d + 9) \div (2d^2 - 3)$

7. Use synthetic division to find $(m^3 - 4m^2 - 3m - 7) \div (m - 4)$. (Lesson 5–3) $m^2 - 3 - \dfrac{19}{m - 4}$

Factor completely. (Lesson 5–4)

8. $ax^2 + 6ax + 9a$ $a(x + 3)^2$

9. $8r^3 - 64s^6$ $8(r - 2s^2)(r^2 + 2rs^2 + 4s^4)$

Simplify. (Lesson 5–5)

10. $\sqrt[3]{-64a^6b^9}$ $-4a^2b^3$

11. $\sqrt{4n^2 + 12n + 9}$ $|2n + 3|$

SELF TEST

The Self Test provides students with a brief review of the concepts and skills in Lessons 5-1 through 5-5. Lesson numbers are given to the right of exercises or instruction lines so students can review concepts not yet mastered.

Additional Answers

71.
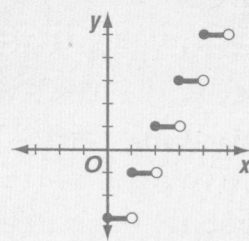

72.
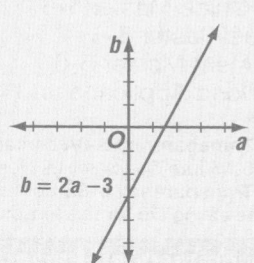
$b = 2a - 3$

Enrichment Masters, p. 34

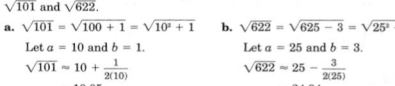

5-5 NAME _____ DATE _____

Enrichment Student Edition Pages 281–287

Approximating Square Roots

Consider the following expansion.

$$\left(a + \frac{b}{2a}\right)^2 = a^2 + \frac{2ab}{2a} + \frac{b^2}{4a^2}$$
$$= a^2 + b + \frac{b^2}{4a^2}$$

Think what happens if a is very great in comparison to b. The term $\frac{b^2}{4a^2}$ is very small and can be disregarded in an approximation.

$$\left(a + \frac{b}{2a}\right)^2 \approx a^2 + b$$
$$a + \frac{b}{2a} \approx \sqrt{a^2 + b}$$

Suppose a number can be expressed as $a^2 + b$, $a > b$. Then an approximate value of the square root is $a + \frac{b}{2a}$.

You should also see that $a - \frac{b}{2a} \approx \sqrt{a^2 - b}$.

Examples: Use the formula $\sqrt{a^2 \pm b} \approx a \pm \frac{b}{2a}$ to find approximations for $\sqrt{101}$ and $\sqrt{622}$.

a. $\sqrt{101} = \sqrt{100 + 1} = \sqrt{10^2 + 1}$

Let $a = 10$ and $b = 1$.

$\sqrt{101} \approx 10 + \frac{1}{2(10)}$

≈ 10.05

b. $\sqrt{622} = \sqrt{625 - 3} = \sqrt{25^2 - 3}$

Let $a = 25$ and $b = 3$.

$\sqrt{622} \approx 25 - \frac{3}{2(25)}$

≈ 24.94

Find an approximation for each square root to the nearest hundredth.

1. $\sqrt{626}$ 25.02

2. $\sqrt{99}$ 9.95

3. $\sqrt{402}$ 20.05

4. $\sqrt{1604}$ 40.05

5. $\sqrt{223}$ 14.93

6. $\sqrt{80}$ 8.94

7. $\sqrt{4890}$ 69.93

8. $\sqrt{2505}$ 50.05

9. $\sqrt{3575}$ 59.79

10. $\sqrt{1,441,100}$ 1200.42

11. $\sqrt{290}$ 17.03

12. $\sqrt{260}$ 16.12

13. Show that $a - \frac{b}{2a} \approx \sqrt{a^2 - b}$ for $a > b$. $\left(a - \frac{b}{2a}\right)^2 = a^2 - b + \frac{b^2}{4a^2}$

disregard $\frac{b^2}{4a^2}$; $\left(a - \frac{b}{2a}\right)^2 \approx a^2 - b$; $a - \frac{b}{2a} \approx \sqrt{a^2 - b}$

Radical Expressions

NCTM Standards: 1–5

Instructional Resources

- Study Guide Master 5-6
- Practice Master 5-6
- Enrichment Master 5-6
- Real-World Applications, 14

 Transparency 5-6A contains the 5-Minute Check for this lesson; **Transparency 5-6B** contains a teaching aid for this lesson.

Recommended Pacing

Standard Pacing	Days 7 & 8 of 16
Honors Pacing	Day 6 of 12
Block Scheduling*	Day 3 of 6 (along with Lesson 5-5)

 *For more information on pacing and possible lesson plans, refer to the *Block Scheduling Booklet*.

1 FOCUS

 ### 5-Minute Check
(over Lesson 5-5)

Simplify.

1. $\pm\sqrt{81a^4b^6}$ $\pm 9a^2\ b^3$

2. $\sqrt[3]{-27a^3y^9}$ $-3ay^3$

3. $\sqrt[4]{16x^4y^8}$ $2\ x\ y^2$

4. $\sqrt{m^2 - 8m + 16}$ $m - 4$

5. $\sqrt{4a^4 + 20a^2c^2 + 25c^4}$

   $2a^2 + 5c^2$

Motivating the Lesson

Questioning Discuss the equation $|a - b| = b - a$. What must be true? Discuss the use of absolute value for real roots.

1. An even root of an odd power will not require an absolute value symbol.

2. If $\sqrt[n]{x^p}$ is an even root of an even power, then absolute value is needed.

3. If $\sqrt[n]{x^p}$ is an odd root, then absolute value is not needed.

What YOU'LL LEARN

- To simplify radical expressions,
- to rationalize the denominator of a fraction containing a radical expression, and
- to add, subtract, multiply, and divide radical expressions.

Why IT'S IMPORTANT

You can use radical expressions to solve problems involving sports and low enforcement.

APPLICATION
Law Enforcement

The graph at the right illustrates the distance a car travels after the driver sees danger and applies the brakes. These distances are for good weather conditions. If the road is wet or if the car has worn brakes, the car will travel farther than the distances shown.

BRAKING DISTANCES
(after driver sees danger)

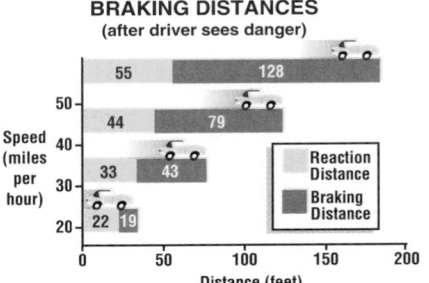

After an accident, police investigators use the formula $s = 2\sqrt{5\ell}$ to estimate the speed s of a car in miles per hour. The variable ℓ represents the length in feet of the tire skid marks on the pavement. On one occasion, an accident scene investigation team measured skid marks 120 feet long. How fast was the car traveling?

Let's explore two ways of applying the formula.

Method 1

$s = 2\sqrt{5\ell}$
$= 2\sqrt{5 \cdot 120}$
$= 2\sqrt{5} \cdot \sqrt{120}$
$\approx 2(2.2361)(10.9545)$
≈ 48.99

The car was going about 49 miles per hour. Using this method, we first find each of the roots and then multiply.

Method 2

$s = 2\sqrt{5\ell}$
$= 2\sqrt{5 \cdot 120}$
$= 2\sqrt{600}$
$\approx 2(24.4949)$
≈ 48.99

The car was going about 49 miles per hour. Using this method, we find the root of the product.

The result is the same using either method. These examples demonstrate the following property of radicals.

Product Property of Radicals	**For any real numbers a and b, and any integer n, $n > 1$,** 1. if n is even, then $\sqrt[n]{ab} = \sqrt[n]{a} \cdot \sqrt[n]{b}$ when a and b are both nonnegative, and 2. if n is odd, then $\sqrt[n]{ab} = \sqrt[n]{a} \cdot \sqrt[n]{b}$.

When you simplify a square root, first write the prime factorization of the radicand. Then use the product property to isolate the perfect squares. Then simplify each radical.

288 Chapter 5 *Exploring Polynomials and Radical Expressions*

 TEKS 9.a., 9.b., 9.c., 9.d., 9.e.

Example **1** Simplify $\sqrt{81p^4q^3}$.

$$\sqrt{81p^4q^3} = \sqrt{9^2 \cdot (p^2)^2 \cdot q^2 \cdot q}$$ *Factor into squares if possible.*

$$= \sqrt{9^2} \cdot \sqrt{(p^2)^2} \sqrt{q^2} \cdot \sqrt{q}$$ *Product property of radicals*

$$= 9 \cdot p^2 |q| \sqrt{q}$$

However, in order for $\sqrt{q}$ to be defined, q must be positive. Therefore, the absolute value is unnecessary.

$$\sqrt{81p^4q^3} = 9p^2q\sqrt{q}$$

Simplifying nth roots is very similar to simplifying square roots. Find the factors that are nth powers and use the product property.

Example **2** Simplify $7\sqrt[3]{27n^2} \cdot 4\sqrt[3]{8n}$.

$$7\sqrt[3]{27n^2} \cdot 4\sqrt[3]{8n} = 7 \cdot 4 \cdot \sqrt[3]{27n^2 \cdot 8n}$$ *Product property of radicals*

$$= 28 \cdot \sqrt[3]{3^3 \cdot 2^3 \cdot n^3}$$ *Factor into cubes where possible.*

$$= 28 \cdot \sqrt[3]{3^3} \cdot \sqrt[3]{2^3} \cdot \sqrt[3]{n^3}$$ *Product property of radicals*

$$= 28 \cdot 3 \cdot 2 \cdot n \text{ or } 168n$$

Let's look at the radicals that involve division to see if there is a quotient property of radicals similar to the product property. Consider $\sqrt{\dfrac{25}{16}}$. First simplify the radical using the product property of radicals. Then try what you think the quotient property of radicals might be.

Method 1: Product Property

$$\sqrt{\dfrac{25}{16}} = \sqrt{25 \cdot \dfrac{1}{16}}$$

$$= \sqrt{25} \cdot \sqrt{\dfrac{1}{16}}$$

$$= \sqrt{5^2} \cdot \sqrt{\left(\dfrac{1}{4}\right)^2}$$

$$= 5 \cdot \dfrac{1}{4} \text{ or } \dfrac{5}{4}$$

Method 2: Quotient Property

$$\sqrt{\dfrac{25}{16}} = \dfrac{\sqrt{25}}{\sqrt{16}}$$

$$= \dfrac{5}{4}$$

These results suggest that there is a quotient property of radicals.

Quotient Property of Radicals	For real numbers a and b, $b \neq 0$, and any integer n, $n > 1$, $$\sqrt[n]{\dfrac{a}{b}} = \dfrac{\sqrt[n]{a}}{\sqrt[n]{b}}, \text{ if all roots are defined.}$$

A radical expression is simplified when the following conditions are met.

- The index, n, is as small as possible.
- The radicand contains no factors (other than 1) that are nth powers of an integer or polynomial.
- The radicand contains no fractions.
- No radicals appear in the denominator.

In-Class Examples

For Example 1
Simplify.

a. $\sqrt{30a^3}$ $a\sqrt{30a}$

b. $\sqrt{54x^4y^5z^7}$ $3x^2y^2z^3\sqrt{6yz}$

c. $\sqrt[3]{54a^3b^7}$ $3ab^2\sqrt[3]{2b}$

d. $\sqrt{60xy^3}$ $2|y|\sqrt{15xy}$

For Example 2
Simplify.

a. $\sqrt{10x^2y} \cdot \sqrt{40xy^3}$ $20xy^2\sqrt{x}$

b. $\sqrt{12m^2n} \cdot \sqrt{6mn^2}$

    $6mn\sqrt{2mn}$

c. $\sqrt[4]{4t^3} \cdot \sqrt[4]{8t^2v^5}$ $2tv\sqrt[4]{2tv}$

GLENCOE *Technology*

Interactive Mathematics Tools Software

This multimedia software provides an interactive lesson by helping students observe the rules of simplifying radical expressions, both simple and complex. A **Computer Journal** gives students an opportunity to write about what they have learned.

For Windows & Macintosh

In-Class Example

For Example 3
Simplify.

a. $\sqrt{\dfrac{5}{4}}$ $\dfrac{\sqrt{5}}{2}$

b. $\dfrac{20\sqrt{8}}{2\sqrt{2}}$ 20

c. $\dfrac{5}{2\sqrt{2}}$ $\dfrac{5\sqrt{2}}{4}$

d. $\dfrac{6}{2\sqrt{3}}$ $\sqrt{3}$

e. $\dfrac{6}{\sqrt{2kn^3}}$ $\dfrac{3\sqrt{2kn}}{|k|n^2}$

f. $4\sqrt{\dfrac{5}{7x}}$ $\dfrac{4\sqrt{35x}}{7x}$

 **MODELING MATHEMATICS** Point out to students that this method works for $\sqrt{m}$ where m is the sum of two squares. For other values of m, other methods are needed.

To eliminate radicals from a denominator or fractions from a radicand, you can use a process called **rationalizing the denominator**. To rationalize a denominator, you must multiply the numerator and denominator by a quantity so that the radicand has an exact root. Study the examples below.

Example **Simplify each expression.**

a. $\dfrac{\sqrt{b^4}}{\sqrt{a^3}}$

b. $\sqrt[5]{\dfrac{3}{4s^2}}$

$\dfrac{\sqrt{b^4}}{\sqrt{a^3}} = \dfrac{\sqrt{b^2 \cdot b^2}}{\sqrt{a^2 \cdot a}}$

$= \dfrac{\sqrt{b^2} \cdot \sqrt{b^2}}{\sqrt{a^2} \cdot \sqrt{a}}$

$= \dfrac{b \cdot b}{a \cdot \sqrt{a}}$

$= \dfrac{b^2}{a\sqrt{a}} \cdot \dfrac{\sqrt{a}}{\sqrt{a}}$ *Rationalize the denominator.*

$= \dfrac{b^2\sqrt{a}}{a\sqrt{a^2}}$ or $\dfrac{b^2\sqrt{a}}{a^2}$

$\sqrt[5]{\dfrac{3}{4s^2}} = \dfrac{\sqrt[5]{3}}{\sqrt[5]{4s^2}} \cdot \dfrac{\sqrt[5]{8s^3}}{\sqrt[5]{8s^3}}$ *Why use* $\dfrac{\sqrt[5]{8s^3}}{\sqrt[5]{8s^3}}$?

$= \dfrac{\sqrt[5]{24s^3}}{\sqrt[5]{2^5 s^5}}$

$= \dfrac{\sqrt[5]{24s^3}}{2s}$ $4 = 2^2,\ 8 = 2^3$

Can you add radicals in the same way you multiply them? In other words, if $\sqrt{a} \cdot \sqrt{a} = \sqrt{a \cdot a}$, does $\sqrt{a} + \sqrt{a} = \sqrt{a + a}$?

MODELING MATHEMATICS   **Adding Radicals**

Materials: geometric dot paper   straightedge

You can use geometric dot paper to show the sum of two like radicals, such as $\sqrt{2} + \sqrt{2}$. Is $\sqrt{2} + \sqrt{2} = \sqrt{2 + 2}$ or 2?

a. First find the length $\sqrt{2}$ units by using the Pythagorean theorem with the dot paper.

$a^2 + b^2 = c^2$
$1^2 + 1^2 = c^2$
$2 = c^2$
$\sqrt{2} = c$

b. Extend the segment to a length twice the length of $\sqrt{2}$ to represent $\sqrt{2} + \sqrt{2}$.

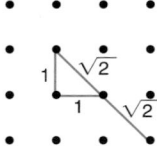

c. Is $\sqrt{2} + \sqrt{2} = \sqrt{2 + 2}$ or 2? Justify your answer.   No, it is longer than 2.

Your Turn

Try this method to model other irrational numbers.

In the activity on the previous page, you discovered that you do not add radicals in the same manner as you multiply them. You add radicals in the same manner as adding monomials. That is, you can add only like terms or like radicals.

Two radical expressions are called **like radical expressions** if both the indices and the radicands are alike. Some examples of like and unlike radical expressions are given below.

$\sqrt[3]{2}$ and $\sqrt{2}$ are not like expressions.   *Different indices*

$\sqrt[4]{3a}$ and $\sqrt[4]{3}$ are not like expressions   *Different radicands*

$3\sqrt[4]{2x}$ and $4\sqrt[4]{2x}$ are like expressions.   *Radicands are 2x; indices are 4.*

Example 4 Simplify $2\sqrt{20} - 2\sqrt{45} + 3\sqrt{80}$.

$2\sqrt{20} - 2\sqrt{45} + 3\sqrt{80}$

$= 2\sqrt{2^2 \cdot 5} - 2\sqrt{3^2 \cdot 5} + 3\sqrt{2^2 \cdot 2^2 \cdot 5}$ *Rewrite each radicand*
$= 2\sqrt{2^2} \cdot \sqrt{5} - 2\sqrt{3^2} \cdot \sqrt{5} + 3\sqrt{2^2} \cdot \sqrt{2^2} \cdot \sqrt{5}$ *using its factors.*
$= 2 \cdot 2\sqrt{5} - 2 \cdot 3\sqrt{5} + 3 \cdot 2 \cdot 2\sqrt{5}$
$= 4\sqrt{5} - 6\sqrt{5} + 12\sqrt{5}$ *These are like radicals.*
$= 10\sqrt{5}$

Example 5

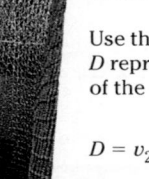
APPLICATION
Sports

As part of the tryout for a girls' softball team, each player must hit a series of balls in a batting cage. Ms. Johnson, the coach, determines the velocity of each hit with a speed gun. She uses the formula $d = v\sqrt{\dfrac{h}{4.9}}$ to estimate the distance the ball would have traveled if the ball had been hit in an open field. In the formula, v represents the velocity (in meters per second) of the baseball, and h is the height (in meters) from which the ball is hit. Zenobia hit two balls with speeds of 45 m/s and 47 m/s. If her bat is at a height of 0.8 meters from the ground, what is the difference between the distances these baseballs would have traveled?

Use the formula to express the differences of the two distances. Let D represent the difference of the distances, v_1 represent the velocity of the first hit, and v_2 represent the velocity of the second hit.

$D = v_2\sqrt{\dfrac{h}{4.9}} - v_1\sqrt{\dfrac{h}{4.9}}$

$= 47\sqrt{\dfrac{0.8}{4.9}} - 45\sqrt{\dfrac{0.8}{4.9}}$ *$h = 0.8$, $v_1 = 45$, and $v_2 = 47$*

$= (47 - 45)\sqrt{\dfrac{0.8}{4.9}}$ *Combine like radical expressions.*

$= 2\sqrt{\dfrac{0.8}{4.9}}$ *Estimate: Will the result be less than or greater than 2?*

Use a calculator to find an approximate value for this expression.

Enter: 2 ☒ ⦅ 0.8 ⊘ 4.9 ⦆ $\sqrt{x}$ ☰ *0.808122035*

There is a difference of about 0.8 meters between the two hits.

Teaching Tip For Example 4, remind students they need to find like terms. To determine if the terms are like, they need to simplify them first.

In-Class Examples

For Example 4
Simplify.

a. $2\sqrt{3} + 5 + 7\sqrt{3} - 2$
    $9\sqrt{3} + 3$

b. $10\sqrt{2} - 3\sqrt{2} + 7 + 6\sqrt{2}$
    $13\sqrt{2} + 7$

c. $3\sqrt{27} - 7\sqrt{3} - \sqrt{12}$ 0

d. $5\sqrt{6} - 3\sqrt{24} + \sqrt{150}$
    $4\sqrt{6}$

For Example 5
What would be the difference of the distances traveled of balls hit—at the same velocity as those in the example—by Cara, whose bat is at a height of 0.6 meters above the ground? Use a calculator to find an approximate value.

$2\sqrt{\dfrac{0.6}{4.9}} = 0.6998542122$
or about 0.7 meters

By Allison, whose bat is at a height of 1 meter above the ground?

$2\sqrt{\dfrac{1}{4.9}} = 0.903507903$ or about 1 meter

🔵 Alternative Learning Styles

Visual Use a geoboard as a model for the coordinate plane. Ask students to make a square.

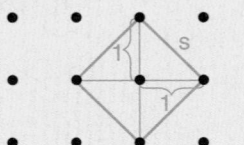

The length of each side of the square can be found by applying the Pythagorean theorem, $1^2 + 1^2 = s^2$. Thus, $s = \sqrt{2}$ cm. If two of the triangles are put together to form a square, the area of each square is 1 cm². So, the area of the large square is 2 cm². The area can also be represented by $A = s^2 = (\sqrt{2})^2$. Thus, $(\sqrt{2})^2 = \sqrt{2} \cdot \sqrt{2}$ or 2.

For Example 6
Simplify.

a. $\left(\sqrt{6} + \sqrt{3}\right)\left(\sqrt{3} + \sqrt{2}\right)$

   $3\sqrt{2} + 2\sqrt{3} + \sqrt{6} + 3$

b. $\left(2\sqrt{3} + 4\sqrt{5}\right)\left(\sqrt{3} + 6\sqrt{5}\right)$

   $126 + 16\sqrt{15}$

c. $\left(12 + \sqrt{3}\right)\left(12 - \sqrt{3}\right)$ 141

d. $\left(4\sqrt{5} + 2\sqrt{7}\right) \cdot$

   $\left(4\sqrt{5} - 2\sqrt{7}\right)$ 52

For Example 7
Simplify.

a. $\dfrac{\sqrt{3} + 2}{\sqrt{3} - 5}$ $\dfrac{-13 - 7\sqrt{3}}{22}$

b. $\dfrac{1 + 2\sqrt{5}}{6 - \sqrt{5}}$ $\dfrac{16 + 13\sqrt{5}}{31}$

---

3 PRACTICE/APPLY

Check for Understanding

Exercises 1–22 are designed to help you assess your students' understanding through reading, writing, speaking, and modeling. You should work through Exercises 1–8 with your students and then monitor their work on Exercises 9–22.

Additional Answers

2. The first and second terms do not have the same index. The second and third terms do not have the same radicand. The first and third terms do not have the same index or radicand.

4. The product of two conjugates yields the difference of two squares. Each square would produce a rational number and the difference of two rationals is a rational.

Just as you can add and subtract radicals like monomials, you can multiply radicals using FOIL like you multiply binomials.

Example **6** Simplify each expression.

a. $\left(2\sqrt{6} - 3\sqrt{2}\right)\left(3 + \sqrt{2}\right)$

$\qquad\qquad\qquad\qquad\quad F \qquad\quad O \qquad\quad I \qquad\quad L$

$\left(2\sqrt{6} - 3\sqrt{2}\right)\left(3 + \sqrt{2}\right) = 2\sqrt{6} \cdot 3 + 2\sqrt{6} \cdot \sqrt{2} - 3\sqrt{2} \cdot 3 - 3\sqrt{2} \cdot \sqrt{2}$

$\qquad\qquad\qquad\qquad = 6\sqrt{6} + 2\sqrt{2^2 \cdot 3} - 9\sqrt{2} - 3\sqrt{2^2}$

$\qquad\qquad\qquad\qquad = 6\sqrt{6} + 4\sqrt{3} - 9\sqrt{2} - 6$

b. $\left(3\sqrt{5} - 4\right)\left(3\sqrt{5} + 4\right)$

$\left(3\sqrt{5} - 4\right)\left(3\sqrt{5} + 4\right) = 3\sqrt{5} \cdot 3\sqrt{5} + 3\sqrt{5} \cdot 4 - 4 \cdot 3\sqrt{5} - 4 \cdot 4$

$\qquad\qquad\qquad\qquad = 9\sqrt{5^2} + 12\sqrt{5} - 12\sqrt{5} - 16$

$\qquad\qquad\qquad\qquad = 45 - 16$

$\qquad\qquad\qquad\qquad = 29$

Binomials like those in Example 6b, of the form $a\sqrt{b} + c\sqrt{d}$ and $a\sqrt{b} - c\sqrt{d}$ where a, b, c, and d are rational numbers, are called **conjugates** of each other. The product of conjugates is always a rational number. We can use conjugates to rationalize denominators.

Example **7** Simplify $\dfrac{\sqrt{2} - 3}{\sqrt{2} + 7}$.

$\dfrac{\sqrt{2} - 3}{\sqrt{2} + 7} = \dfrac{(\sqrt{2} - 3)(\sqrt{2} - 7)}{(\sqrt{2} + 7)(\sqrt{2} - 7)}$ *Multiply by $\dfrac{\sqrt{2} - 7}{\sqrt{2} - 7}$ because $\sqrt{2} - 7$ is*

$\qquad\quad = \dfrac{(\sqrt{2} - 3)(\sqrt{2} - 7)}{(\sqrt{2})^2 - 49}$ *the conjugate of $\sqrt{2} + 7$.*

$\qquad\quad = \dfrac{(\sqrt{2})^2 + \sqrt{2}(-7) + (-3)\sqrt{2} + (-3)(-7)}{-47}$

$\qquad\quad = \dfrac{2 - 7\sqrt{2} - 3\sqrt{2} + 21}{-47}$

$\qquad\quad = \dfrac{23 - 10\sqrt{2}}{-47}$

CHECK FOR UNDERSTANDING

Communicating Mathematics

1. Multiply by $\dfrac{\sqrt[3]{ac^2}}{\sqrt[3]{ac^2}}$.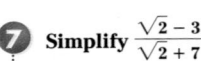

2. See margin.

4. See margin.

Study the lesson. Then complete the following.

1. **Explain** how you would rationalize the denominator of $\dfrac{1}{\sqrt[3]{a^2b^3c}}$.

2. **Explain** why $7\sqrt{3} - 4\sqrt[3]{3} + 2\sqrt[3]{4}$ cannot be simplified further.

3. **Write** examples for each of the following.

   a. two like radical expressions

   b. two unlike radical expressions

   c. two expressions that are conjugates of each other   Answers will vary.

4. **Explain** why the product of two conjugates is always a rational number.

292   Chapter 5   *Exploring Polynomials and Radical Expressions*

Reteaching

Using Tables/Charts Have students copy and complete the chart below.

x	$\sqrt{x^2}$	$(\sqrt{x})^2$	$\sqrt[3]{x^3}$	$(\sqrt[3]{x})^3$
1	1	1	1	1
−1	1	—	−1	−1
64	64	64	64	64
−64	64	—	−64	−64

Now generalize the results.

even$\sqrt{\ }$ negative = no real root

$\sqrt[n]{x^n} = x$

$(\sqrt[n]{x})^n = x$

5. Why is the product property of radicals for odd indices different than the product property for even indices? **See margin.**

6. **Replace** the $\underline{\ ?\ }$ in $\sqrt[n]{\dfrac{1}{c}}\ \underline{\ ?\ }\ \dfrac{1}{\sqrt[n]{c}}$ with an $=$ or $\neq$ to make the statement true. Write a reason for your answer. **See margin.**

7. **See Solutions Manual.**

MODELING MATHEMATICS

7. Use geometric dot paper to draw segments that represent each length.
   a. $\sqrt{10}$ b. $\sqrt{13}$ c. $\sqrt{17}$ d. $\sqrt{29}$

8. Describe how you could use models to show the sum $\sqrt{5} + \sqrt{10}$. Include a drawing in your explanation. **See margin.**

Guided Practice

Simplify.

12. $3|m|n^2\sqrt[4]{n}$

13. $-42\sqrt{15}$

14. $3x^2z^2\sqrt{5}$

17. $\left|\dfrac{y}{y-3}\right|\sqrt{y-3}$

18. $8\sqrt{2} + \sqrt[3]{2}$

20. $10 + 2\sqrt{3} - 5\sqrt{2} - \sqrt{6}$

21. $49 - 11y$

9. $\sqrt{80}$ $4\sqrt{5}$

10. $4\sqrt{54}$ $12\sqrt{6}$

11. $\sqrt[3]{64x^6y^3}$ $4x^2y$

12. $\sqrt[4]{81m^4n^5}$

13. $(7\sqrt{6})(-3\sqrt{10})$

14. $\sqrt{3x^2z^3} \cdot \sqrt{15x^2z}$

15. $\dfrac{\sqrt[3]{81}}{\sqrt[3]{9}}$ $\sqrt[3]{9}$

16. $\sqrt{\dfrac{5}{12a}}$ $\dfrac{\sqrt{15a}}{6a}$

17. $\sqrt{\dfrac{y^2}{y-3}}$

18. $\sqrt{2} + 5\sqrt[3]{2} + 7\sqrt{2} - 4\sqrt[3]{2}$

19. $5\sqrt[3]{135} - 2\sqrt[3]{81}$ $15\sqrt[3]{5} - 6\sqrt[3]{3}$

20. $(5 + \sqrt{3})(2 - \sqrt{2})$

21. $(7 + \sqrt{11y})(7 - \sqrt{11y})$

22. **Geometry** Find the perimeter and area of the rectangle shown at the right.
   $(6 + 16\sqrt{2})$ yd; $(24 + 6\sqrt{2})$ yd^2

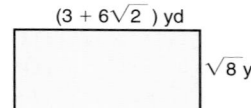
$(3 + 6\sqrt{2})$ yd
$\sqrt{8}$ yd

EXERCISES

Practice

Simplify.

30. $2|a|b\sqrt{2b}$

32. $11\sqrt[3]{6}$

33. $3xy^2\sqrt{10x}$

34. $6a^2b\sqrt[3]{7}$

41. $-42\sqrt{2} - 15\sqrt{14}$

43. $3\sqrt[3]{2x}$

44. $4\sqrt{5} + 23\sqrt{6}$

46. $25 - 5\sqrt{2} + 5\sqrt{6} - 2\sqrt{3}$

23. $\sqrt{32}$ $4\sqrt{2}$

24. $5\sqrt{50}$ $25\sqrt{2}$

25. $\sqrt[3]{16}$ $2\sqrt[3]{2}$

26. $\sqrt{98y^4}$ $7y^2\sqrt{2}$

27. $\sqrt[3]{32}$ $2\sqrt[3]{4}$

28. $\sqrt[4]{48}$ $2\sqrt[4]{3}$

29. $\sqrt{y^3}$ $y\sqrt{y}$

30. $\sqrt{8a^2b^3}$

31. $5\sqrt{3} - 4\sqrt{3}$ $\sqrt{3}$

32. $8\sqrt[3]{6} + 3\sqrt[3]{6}$

33. $\sqrt{90x^3y^4}$

34. $3\sqrt[3]{56a^6b^3}$

35. $(-3\sqrt{24})(5\sqrt{20})$ $-60\sqrt{30}$

36. $\sqrt{26} \cdot \sqrt[3]{39} \cdot \sqrt{14}$ $26\sqrt{21}$

37. $(4\sqrt{18})(2\sqrt{14})$ $48\sqrt{7}$

38. $8\sqrt{y^2} + 7\sqrt{y} - 4\sqrt{y}$ $8y + 3\sqrt{y}$

39. $\sqrt[3]{40} - 2\sqrt[3]{5}$ 0

40. $(\sqrt{10} - \sqrt{6})(\sqrt{5} + \sqrt{3})$ $2\sqrt{2}$

B
41. $-3\sqrt{7}(2\sqrt{14} + 5\sqrt{2})$

42. $\sqrt{a}(\sqrt{b} + \sqrt{ab})$ $\sqrt{ab} + a\sqrt{b}$

43. $8\sqrt[3]{2x} + 3\sqrt[3]{2x} - 8\sqrt[3]{2x}$

44. $5\sqrt{20} + \sqrt{24} - \sqrt{180} + 7\sqrt{54}$

45. $(6 - \sqrt{2})(6 + \sqrt{2})$ 34

46. $(5 + \sqrt{6})(5 - \sqrt{2})$

47. $(\sqrt{3} - \sqrt{5})^2$ $8 - 2\sqrt{15}$

48. $(x + \sqrt{y})^2$ $x^2 + 2x\sqrt{y} + y$

49. $\sqrt{98} - \sqrt{72} + \sqrt{32}$ $5\sqrt{2}$

50. $\sqrt[4]{a^2} + \sqrt[4]{a^6}$ $(1 + |a|)\sqrt[4]{a^2}$

51. $\sqrt{\dfrac{a^4}{b^3}}$ $\dfrac{a^2\sqrt{b}}{b^2}$

52. $\sqrt[4]{\dfrac{2}{3}}$ $\dfrac{\sqrt[4]{54}}{3}$

Lesson 5-6   Radical Expressions   **293**

Cooperative Learning

Numbered Heads Together Separate the class into groups of four. Give each group four problems that involve radicals. Each of the four operations should be used. Have each group explain how to do the problems step by step. You might have the groups each present one problem. The groups should make sure that every person in the group understands each problem before presenting them. For more information on the numbered heads together strategy, see *Cooperative Learning in the Mathematics Classroom*, one of the titles in the Glencoe Mathematics Professional Series, pages 9–12.

Assignment Guide

Core: 23–67 odd, 68–79
Enriched: 24–62 even, 63–79

For **Extra Practice,** see p. 887.

The red A, B, and C flags, printed only in the Teacher's Wraparound Edition, indicate the level of difficulty of the exercises.

Additional Answers

5. If a and b were allowed to be negative when n is even, they would have no real roots. a and b may be negative when n is odd because negative radicands can have real roots if n is odd.

6. Use $=$ because if $c \neq 0$, then
$$\sqrt[n]{\dfrac{1}{c}} = \dfrac{\sqrt[n]{1}}{\sqrt[n]{c}} = \dfrac{1}{\sqrt[n]{c}}.$$

8. First use dot paper to create segments that have lengths $\sqrt{5}$ and $\sqrt{10}$. Then use a compass to copy these two lengths end to end to create a segment $(\sqrt{5} + \sqrt{10})$ units long.

Study Guide Masters, p. 35

5-6
NAME_____ DATE_____

Student Edition
Pages 288–295

Study Guide

Radical Expressions

Radicals are added, subtracted, or multiplied the same way monomials are added, subtracted, or multiplied.

Use the following definitions and properties when multiplying and dividing radicals.

Term	Definition/Property	Example
Product Property of Radicals	For any real numbers a and b and any integer n, $n > 1$,	Simplify $\sqrt{63}$. $\sqrt{63} = \sqrt{9 \cdot 7}$
	1. if n is even, then $\sqrt[n]{ab} = \sqrt[n]{a} \cdot \sqrt[n]{b}$ when a and b are both nonnegative and	$= \sqrt{9} \cdot \sqrt{7}$ $= 3\sqrt{7}$
	2. if n is odd, then $\sqrt[n]{ab} = \sqrt[n]{a} \cdot \sqrt[n]{b}$.	
Quotient Property of Radicals	For any real numbers a and b, $b \neq 0$, and any integer n, $n > 1$, $\sqrt[n]{\dfrac{a}{b}} = \dfrac{\sqrt[n]{a}}{\sqrt[n]{b}}$ if all roots are defined.	Simplify $\sqrt{\dfrac{3}{8}}$. $\sqrt{\dfrac{3}{8}} = \dfrac{\sqrt{3}}{\sqrt{8}}$ $= \dfrac{\sqrt{3}}{2}$

Example: Simplify $4\sqrt{3} + 5\sqrt{12} - 7\sqrt{27}$.

$4\sqrt{3} + 5\sqrt{12} - 7\sqrt{27} = 4\sqrt{3} + 5\sqrt{2^2 \cdot 3}$
$\qquad - 7\sqrt{3^2 \cdot 3}$
$= 4\sqrt{3} + 5\sqrt{2^2}\sqrt{3}$
$\qquad - 7\sqrt{3^2}\sqrt{3}$
$= 4\sqrt{3} + 5 \cdot 2\sqrt{3}$
$\qquad - 7 \cdot 3\sqrt{3}$
$= 4\sqrt{3} + 10\sqrt{3}$
$\qquad - 21\sqrt{3}$
$= -7\sqrt{3}$

Example: Simplify $\dfrac{1 - \sqrt{2}}{6 + 5\sqrt{2}}$.

$\dfrac{1 - \sqrt{2}}{6 + 5\sqrt{2}} = \dfrac{1 - \sqrt{2}}{6 + 5\sqrt{2}} \cdot \dfrac{6 - 5\sqrt{2}}{6 - 5\sqrt{2}}$
$= \dfrac{6 - 5\sqrt{2} - 6\sqrt{2} + 5\sqrt{2^2}}{36 - (5\sqrt{2})^2}$
$= \dfrac{6 - 5\sqrt{2} - 6\sqrt{2} + 10}{36 - 25(2)}$
$= \dfrac{-16 + 11\sqrt{2}}{14}$

Simplify.

1. $5\sqrt{54}$
   $15\sqrt{6}$

2. $\sqrt[3]{24}$
   $2\sqrt[3]{3}$

3. $3\sqrt{2} + \sqrt{50} - 4\sqrt{8}$
   0

4. $\sqrt[3]{(-y)^6}$
   $-y\sqrt[3]{y^6}$

5. $\sqrt[3]{-27x^2}$
   $-3\sqrt[3]{x^2}$

6. $\sqrt[4]{2}(\sqrt[4]{4} + \sqrt[4]{12})$
   $2 + 2\sqrt[4]{3}$

7. $\dfrac{(5\sqrt{48} + \sqrt{75})}{5\sqrt{3}}$
   5

8. $\sqrt[3]{81}\sqrt[3]{24}$
   $6\sqrt[3]{9}$

9. $(4\sqrt{2} - 3\sqrt{5})(2\sqrt{20} + 5)$
   $40\sqrt{2} - 30\sqrt{5}$

F Y I

If students apply O'Carroll's formula (from Exercise 65) to Peng Liping, they will find that her handicapped weight W is 78.76, far greater than Akikta's or Francisco's.

Simplify.

53. $\sqrt{\frac{2}{5}} + \sqrt{40} + \sqrt{10}$ $\quad \frac{16\sqrt{10}}{5}$

54. $\frac{7}{4 - \sqrt{3}}$ $\quad \frac{28 + 7\sqrt{3}}{13}$

55. $\frac{\sqrt{6}}{5 + \sqrt{3}}$ $\quad \frac{5\sqrt{6} - 3\sqrt{2}}{22}$

56. $\frac{2 + \sqrt{6}}{2 - \sqrt{6}}$ $\quad -5 - 2\sqrt{6}$

57. $\frac{\sqrt{x+1}}{\sqrt{x-1}}$ $\quad \frac{\sqrt{x^2-1}}{x-1}$

58. $\frac{1}{\sqrt{x^2-1}}$ $\quad \frac{\sqrt{x^2-1}}{x^2-1}$

59. $\sqrt[4]{x^4} + \sqrt[3]{x^6} + \sqrt{x^8}$ $\quad |x| + x^2 + x^4$

60. $(4\sqrt{5} - 3\sqrt{2})(2\sqrt{5} + 2\sqrt{2})$ $\quad 28 + 2\sqrt{10}$

INTEGRATION
Geometry

61. Use the Pythagorean theorem to find the length of the hypotenuse of the right triangle shown at the right. $\quad 2y^2\sqrt{70}$ in.

$6y^2\sqrt{7}$ in.

$2y^2\sqrt{7}$ in.

62. Find the radius, r, of a sphere whose surface area S is 2464 square inches. Use the formula $r = \frac{1}{2}\sqrt{\frac{S}{\pi}}$. $\quad$ about 14 inches

63. when x and y are not negative

Critical Thinking

63. Under what conditions is the equation $\sqrt{x^3 y^2} = xy\sqrt{x}$ true?

64. Under what conditions is $\sqrt[n]{(-x)^n} = x$? $\quad$ when n is even and $x > 0$, or when n is any number and $x = 0$

Applications and Problem Solving

F Y I

Peng Liping of China won the Woman's World Weightlifting Championship in 1992. Her weight was in the 52 kg (114.5 lb) category, and she lifted 202.5 kg (446.25 lb).

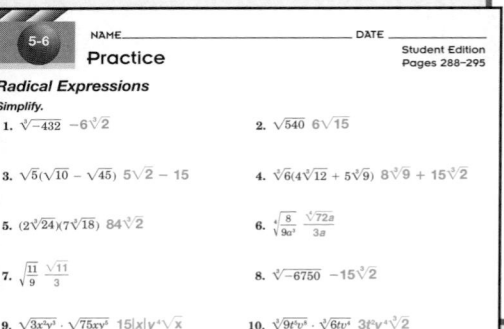

65. **Sports** Akikta and Francisco are in a weightlifting competition. They weigh 70 kg and 110 kg, respectively. Akikta's final and best lift is 190 kg, and Francisco's is 240 kg. The judges will use O'Carroll's formula for determining the superior weight lifter. The formula, $W = \frac{w}{\sqrt[3]{b-35}}$, involves the weight b of the lifter and the weight w lifted. W represents the handicapped weight.
   a. Calculate each lifter's rating. $\quad$ Akikta: 58.09, Francisco: 56.91
   b. Who will be the superior weight lifter, Akikta or Francisco? $\quad$ Akikta

66. **Physics** Find the time that it takes a pendulum to complete a swing if its length is 10 inches. Use the formula $T = 2\pi\sqrt{\frac{L}{384}}$, where T represents time in seconds, and L represents the length of the pendulum in inches. $\quad$ about 1 second

67. **Automotive Engineering** An automotive engineer is trying to design a safer car. The maximum force a road can exert on the tires of the car being redesigned is 2000 pounds. What is the maximum velocity v in ft/s at which this car can safely round a turn of radius 320 ft? Use the formula $v = \sqrt{\frac{F_c r}{100}}$, where F_c is the force the road exerts on the car and r is the radius of the turn. $\quad$ 80 ft/s or about 55 mph

Mixed Review

68. Simplify $\sqrt{(y+2)^2}$. (Lesson 5-5) $\quad |y+2|$

69. Factor $a + b + 3a^2 - 3b^2$. (Lesson 5-4) $\quad (a+b)(1+3a-3b)$

70. $n^3 - 3n^2 - 15n - 21$

71. $-6x^3 - 4x^2y + 13xy^2$

70. Find $(n^4 - 8n^3 + 54n + 105) \div (n-5)$ by using synthetic division. (Lesson 5-3)

71. Simplify $(x^3 - 3x^2y + 4xy^2 + y^3) - (7x^3 + x^2y - 9xy^2 + y^3)$. (Lesson 5-2)

Tech Prep

Automotive Engineering Technician
Students who are interested in automotive engineering may wish to do further research on the use of mathematics in that occupation, as mentioned in Exercise 67. For more information on tech prep, see the *Teacher's Handbook*.

Practice Masters, p. 35

5-6
NAME_____ DATE_____
Practice
Student Edition
Pages 288–295

Radical Expressions
Simplify.

1. $\sqrt[5]{-432}$ $\quad -6\sqrt[5]{2}$

2. $\sqrt{540}$ $\quad 6\sqrt{15}$

3. $\sqrt{5}(\sqrt{10} - \sqrt{45})$ $\quad 5\sqrt{2} - 15$

4. $\sqrt[4]{6}(4\sqrt[4]{12} + 5\sqrt[4]{9})$ $\quad 8\sqrt[4]{9} + 15\sqrt[4]{2}$

5. $(2\sqrt[4]{24})(7\sqrt[4]{18})$ $\quad 84\sqrt[4]{2}$

6. $\sqrt{\frac{8}{9a^2}}$ $\quad \frac{\sqrt{72a}}{3a}$

7. $\sqrt{\frac{11}{9}}$ $\quad \frac{\sqrt{11}}{3}$

8. $\sqrt[3]{-6750}$ $\quad -15\sqrt[3]{2}$

9. $\sqrt{3x^2y^3} \cdot \sqrt{75xy^3}$ $\quad 15|x|y^4\sqrt{x}$

10. $\sqrt[3]{9t^4v^4} \cdot \sqrt[3]{6tv^4}$ $\quad 3t^4v^4\sqrt[3]{2}$

11. $\sqrt{60} \cdot \sqrt{105}$ $\quad 30\sqrt{7}$

12. $\sqrt{3600} \cdot \sqrt{165}$ $\quad 30\sqrt{22}$

13. $\sqrt{810} + \sqrt{240} + \sqrt{135} - \sqrt{250}$ $\quad 4\sqrt{10} + 7\sqrt{15}$

14. $\sqrt[4]{216} - \sqrt{48} + \sqrt[4]{432}$ $\quad 6 - 2\sqrt{6} + 6\sqrt{2}$

15. $(\sqrt{12} - 2\sqrt{3})^2$ $\quad 0$

16. $(\sqrt{18} + 2\sqrt{3})^2$ $\quad 30 + 12\sqrt{6}$

17. $(\sqrt{5} - \sqrt{6})(\sqrt{5} + \sqrt{2})$ $\quad 5 + \sqrt{10} - \sqrt{30} - 2\sqrt{3}$

18. $(\sqrt{50} + \sqrt{27})(\sqrt{2} - \sqrt{6})$ $\quad 10 - 10\sqrt{3} + 3\sqrt{6} - 9\sqrt{2}$

19. $\frac{3}{2 - \sqrt{5}}$ $\quad -6 - 3\sqrt{5}$

20. $\frac{6}{\sqrt{2} - 1}$ $\quad 6\sqrt{2} + 6$

21. $\frac{5 + \sqrt{3}}{4 + \sqrt{3}}$ $\quad \frac{17 - \sqrt{3}}{13}$

22. $\frac{6}{2 - \sqrt{7}}$ $\quad -4 - 2\sqrt{7}$

23. $\sqrt[3]{144} + \sqrt[3]{\frac{2}{3}} - 5\sqrt[3]{18}$ $\quad -\frac{8}{3}\sqrt[3]{18}$

24. $\sqrt{\frac{3}{8}} + \sqrt{54} - \sqrt{6}$ $\quad \frac{9}{4}\sqrt{6}$

72. 1.9663×10^6
wavelengths

72. **Chemistry** Wavelengths of light are measured in Angstroms. An Angstrom is 10^{-8} centimeter. The wavelength of cadmium's green line is 5085.8 Angstroms. How many wavelengths of cadmium's green line are in one meter? (Lesson 5–1)

73. Find $\frac{2}{3}\begin{bmatrix} 9 & 0 \\ 12 & 15 \end{bmatrix} + \begin{bmatrix} -2 & 3 \\ -7 & -7 \end{bmatrix}$. (Lesson 4–2) $\begin{bmatrix} 4 & 3 \\ 1 & 3 \end{bmatrix}$

74. Solve the system of equations. (Lesson 3–7) **(−9, 2, 4)**

$x - 2y + z = -9$

$2y + 3z = 16$

$2y = 4$

75. Use Cramer's rule to solve the system of equations. (Lesson 3–3) **(2, 3)**

$s + t = 5$

$3s - t = 3$

76. Graph $y + 3x > -1$. (Lesson 2–7) **See margin.**

77. Find $f(-3)$ if $f(x) = x^2 - 3x - 9$. (Lesson 2–1) **9**

78. **Transportation** A San Antonio parking garage charges $1.50 for the first hour and $0.50 for each additional hour or part of an hour. For how many hours can you park your car if you only have $4.50? (Lesson 1–7) **7 hours**

79. Evaluate $\frac{3ab}{cd}$ if $a = 3$, $b = 7$, $c = -2$, and $d = 0.5$. (Lesson 1–1) **−63**

Divine Mathematics

Henry Wadsworth Longfellow (1807–1882) was one of America's most outstanding poets. He also was a lover of mathematics. Through one of the characters in his book *Kavanagh: A Tale*, published in 1965, Longfellow said the following.

> HOW DULL AND PROSAIC THE STUDY OF mathematics is made in our school-books; as if the grand science of numbers has been discovered and perfected merely to further the purpose of trade. There is something divine in the science of numbers . . . It holds the sea in the hollow of its hand. It measures the earth; it weighs the stars; it illumines the universe; it is law, it is order, it is beauty. And yet we imagine—that is, most of us—that its highest end and culminating point is book-keeping by double entry. It is our way of teaching it which makes it so prosaic. ∎

1. Explain in your own words what Longfellow was trying to say in this passage.

2. Longfellow enjoyed including mathematical problems in his poetry and prose. See if you can solve the following problems posed by Longfellow.

   a. "A tree one hundred cubits high is distant from a well two hundred cubits; from this tree one monkey descends and goes to the well; another monkey takes a leap upwards, and then descends by the hypotenuse; and both pass over an equal space." What is the height of the leap?

   b. "Ten times the square root of a flock of geese, seeing the clouds collect, flew to the Manus lake; one-eighth of the whole flew from the edge of the water amongst a multitude of water lilies; and three couples were observed playing in the water." How many geese were there in the flock?

Lesson 5–6 Radical Expressions **295**

Extension

Reasoning $\sqrt{-49a^3b^4} = -7ab^2\sqrt{-a}$
Is this equation true? **yes** Prove your answer.
Proof:

$$\sqrt{-49a^3b^4} = -7ab^2\sqrt{-a}$$

$$-49a^3b^4 = 49a^2b^4(-a)$$

$$-49a^3b^4 = -49a^3b^4$$

Mathematics and SOCIETY

Like Longfellow, mathematicians and philosophers in ancient Greece saw mathematics as divine. Even in our century, Albert Einstein held the view that God designed the universe according to mathematical laws.

---

4 ASSESS

Closing Activity
Writing Have students write a step-by-step process for adding and subtracting radical expressions.

Additional Answer
76.

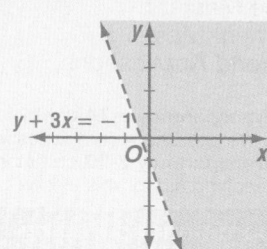

$y + 3x = -1$

Enrichment Masters, p. 35

5-6 NAME _____ DATE _____
Enrichment
Student Edition Pages 288–295

Special Products with Radicals
Notice that $(\sqrt{3})(\sqrt{3}) = 3$, or $(\sqrt{3})^2 = 3$.
In general, $(\sqrt{x})^2 = x$ when $x \geq 0$.
Also, notice that $(\sqrt{9})(\sqrt{4}) = \sqrt{36}$.
In general, $(\sqrt{x})(\sqrt{y}) = \sqrt{xy}$ when x and y are not negative.
You can use these ideas to find the special products below.
$(\sqrt{a} + \sqrt{b})(\sqrt{a} - \sqrt{b}) = (\sqrt{a})^2 - (\sqrt{b})^2 = a - b$
$(\sqrt{a} + \sqrt{b})^2 = (\sqrt{a})^2 + 2\sqrt{ab} + (\sqrt{b})^2 = a + 2\sqrt{ab} + b$
$(\sqrt{a} - \sqrt{b})^2 = (\sqrt{a})^2 - 2\sqrt{ab} + (\sqrt{b})^2 = a - 2\sqrt{ab} + b$

Example: Find the product: $(\sqrt{2} + \sqrt{5})(\sqrt{2} - \sqrt{5})$.
$(\sqrt{2} + \sqrt{5})(\sqrt{2} - \sqrt{5}) = (\sqrt{2})^2 - (\sqrt{5})^2 = 2 - 5 = -3$

Example: Evaluate $(\sqrt{2} + \sqrt{8})^2$.
$(\sqrt{2} + \sqrt{8})^2 = (\sqrt{2})^2 + 2\sqrt{2}\sqrt{8} + (\sqrt{8})^2$
$= 2 + 2\sqrt{16} + 8 = 2 + 2(4) + 8 = 2 + 8 + 8 = 18$

Multiply.
1. $(\sqrt{3} - \sqrt{7})(\sqrt{3} + \sqrt{7})$ −4
2. $(\sqrt{10} + \sqrt{2})(\sqrt{10} - \sqrt{2})$ 8
3. $(\sqrt{2x} - \sqrt{6})(\sqrt{2x} + \sqrt{6})$ 2x − 6
4. $(\sqrt{3} - \sqrt{27})^2$ 12
5. $(\sqrt{1000} + \sqrt{10})^2$ 1210
6. $(\sqrt{y} + \sqrt{5})(\sqrt{y} - \sqrt{5})$ y − 5
7. $(\sqrt{50} - \sqrt{x})^2$ 50 − 10√2x + x
8. $(\sqrt{x} + \sqrt{20})^2$ x + 4√5x + 20

You can extend these ideas to patterns for sums and differences of cubes. Study the pattern below.
$(\sqrt[3]{8} - \sqrt[3]{x})(\sqrt[3]{8^2} + \sqrt[3]{8x} + \sqrt[3]{x^2}) = (\sqrt[3]{8})^3 - (\sqrt[3]{x})^3 = 8 - x$

Multiply.
9. $(\sqrt[3]{2} - \sqrt[3]{5})(\sqrt[3]{2^2} + \sqrt[3]{10} + \sqrt[3]{5^2})$ −3
10. $(\sqrt[3]{y} + \sqrt[3]{w})(\sqrt[3]{y^2} - \sqrt[3]{yw} + \sqrt[3]{w^2})$ y + w
11. $(\sqrt[3]{7} + \sqrt[3]{20})(\sqrt[3]{7^2} - \sqrt[3]{140} + \sqrt[3]{20^2})$ 27
12. $(\sqrt[3]{11} - \sqrt[3]{8})(\sqrt[3]{11^2} + \sqrt[3]{88} + \sqrt[3]{8^2})$ 3

Rational Exponents

NCTM Standards: 1–5

Instructional Resources

- Study Guide Master 5-7
- Practice Master 5-7
- Enrichment Master 5-7
- Real-World Applications, 15

 Transparency 5-7A contains the 5-Minute Check for this lesson; **Transparency 5-7B** contains a teaching aid for this lesson.

Recommended Pacing

Standard Pacing	Days 9 & 10 of 16
Honors Pacing	Day 7 of 12
Block Scheduling*	Day 4 of 6 (along with Lesson 5-8)

 *For more information on pacing and possible lesson plans, refer to the *Block Scheduling Booklet.*

1 FOCUS

5-Minute Check
(over Lesson 5-6)

Simplify.

1. $\sqrt[4]{81a^8b^5c^3}$ $\quad 3a^2b\sqrt[4]{bc^3}$

2. $6\sqrt{2}(4\sqrt{3} - 3\sqrt{8})$

   $24\sqrt{6} - 72$

3. $\sqrt[3]{\frac{9}{4}m^2}$ $\quad \frac{\sqrt[3]{18m^2}}{2}$

4. $\sqrt[3]{192t} - \sqrt[3]{24t} + \sqrt[3]{5t}$

   $2\sqrt[3]{3t} + \sqrt[3]{5t}$

5. $(3\sqrt{5} - \sqrt{3})(3\sqrt{5} + \sqrt{3})$

   42

6. $\dfrac{4\sqrt{3} - 7}{5\sqrt{3} + 6}$ $\quad \dfrac{102 - 59\sqrt{3}}{39}$

Motivating the Lesson

Questioning Review the properties of exponents before discussing this lesson. If $(2^2)(2^4) = 2^6$, how can you rewrite $2^2 \times 2^{\frac{1}{2}}$? Discuss what students think $2^{\frac{1}{2}}$ means.

What YOU'LL LEARN

- To solve problems by identifying and achieving subgoals,
- to write expressions with rational exponents in simplest radical form and vice versa, and
- to evaluate expressions in either exponential or radical form.

Why IT'S IMPORTANT

You can use expressions with rational exponents to solve problems involving literature and music.

CONNECTION
Literature

In *The Pit and the Pendulum*, Edgar Allan Poe describes a situation in which a man is strapped to a wooden bench-like structure. A pendulum hangs from the ceiling that is "some thirty or forty feet overhead." The pendulum begins to swing, and with each swing the pendulum gets closer and closer to the man. The pendulum is at a right angle to his body, and a blade attached to the end of the pendulum is designed to cross right over his heart. As we read the story, we wonder if this man will be able to avoid being killed by the pendulum. Here is one way we can find out.

The formula describing the relationship of the length L of a pendulum to the time t it takes to make one swing (one full cycle back and forth) is given by $t = \sqrt{\frac{\pi^2 L}{8}}$. Suppose you wished to know how long it would take the pendulum to swing when it is 30 feet long and swinging right above the man's body.

Like a good mystery that unfolds little by little, page by page, a good problem solver approaches a problem using a series of small steps, or **subgoals.** By doing so, you make problem solving a simpler process.

Subgoal 1

Replace L by the values given in the story to obtain the possible range of time it takes the pendulum to swing.

30 feet overhead

$t = \sqrt{\frac{\pi^2(30)}{8}}$

$t \approx 6.08$ seconds

40 feet overhead

$t = \sqrt{\frac{\pi^2(40)}{8}}$

$t \approx 7.02$ seconds

It would have taken about 6 or 7 seconds for the pendulum to swing one cycle.

Subgoal 2

Determine if the man has enough time to escape the blade on the pendulum if the blade is just above his body and will strike him as it lowers for the next swing.

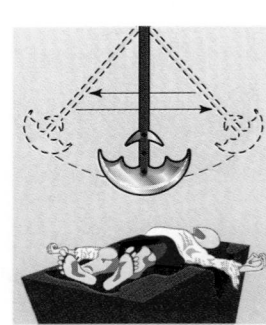

Since it takes at least 6 seconds for the pendulum to swing (that is, to move across to the other side and back to its original position), he would only have one-half the time to escape from the last safe pass of the blade over his body. One-half of 6 seconds is 3 seconds. Does this seem like enough time for him to escape?

 TEKS 2.a.

Scene from 1961 film version of *The Pit and the Pendulum,* starring Vincent Price and John Carr

2 TEACH

In-Class Example

For Example 1
Use subgoals to solve this problem.
Nina deposited $500 in her bank account. The account earns 8% interest per year. If she withdraws the money 6 months later, how much interest has she earned? The bank uses the formula $A = P(1+r)^t$ for finding the amount of money A in a compound interest account at the end of t years if P is the original amount of money deposited and r is the annual interest rate. **$19.62**

You have learned that squaring a number and taking the square root of a number are inverse operations. But how would we evaluate an expression that contains a fractional exponent? Assume that fractional exponents behave as integral exponents.

$$\text{For any number } a > 0, a^1 = a^{\frac{1}{2}(2)} \text{ or } \left(a^{\frac{1}{2}}\right)^2.$$

So, $a^{\frac{1}{2}}$ is a number that when squared equals a. Since $\left(\sqrt{a}\right)^2 = a$, it follows that $a^{\frac{1}{2}} = \sqrt{a}$. This suggests the following definition.

Definition of $b^{\frac{1}{n}}$	**For any real number b and for any integer $n > 1$,** $$b^{\frac{1}{n}} = \sqrt[n]{b}$$ **except when $b < 0$ and n is even.**

Example 1

PROBLEM SOLVING

Identify Subgoals

Economists refer to inflation as increases in the average cost of purchases. The formula $C = c(1 + r)^n$ can be used to predict the cost of consumer items at some projected time. In this formula, C represents the projected cost of the item at a given annual inflation rate, c the present cost of the item, r the rate of inflation (in decimal form), and n the number of years for the projection. Suppose a gallon of milk costs $2.69 now. How much would the price increase in 6 months with an inflation rate of 5.3%?

Subgoal 1: Identify the known values.

$c = \$2.69, r = 5.3\%$ or 0.053, and $n = 6$ months or $\frac{1}{2}$ year

Subgoal 2: Find the value of C.

$C = c(1 + r)^n$
$\quad = 2.69(1 + 0.053)^{\frac{1}{2}}$

Use a calculator to evaluate this expression.   *Remember that $a^{\frac{1}{2}} = \sqrt{a}$.*

Enter: 2.69 $\boxed{\times}$ $\boxed{(}$ 1 $\boxed{+}$ .053 $\boxed{)}$ $\boxed{\sqrt{x}}$ $\boxed{=}$ *2.760364704*

The cost of the milk in 6 months will be $2.76.

Subgoal 3: Find the increase in cost.

$C - c = \$2.76 - \$2.69$ or $\$0.07$

The increase in cost in 6 months is predicted to be 7 cents.

Teaching Tip You might wish to explain that "$(-16)^{\frac{1}{4}}$ is not defined" means that $(-16)^{\frac{1}{4}}$ is not a real number.

In-Class Example

For Example 2
Evaluate.

a. $36^{\frac{1}{2}}$ 6

b. $64^{\frac{1}{3}}$ 4

c. $49^{-\frac{1}{2}}$ $\frac{1}{7}$

d. $\left(\frac{1}{8}\right)^{-\frac{1}{3}}$ 2

e. $36^{\frac{3}{2}}$ 216

f. $27^{\frac{4}{3}}$ 81

Teaching Tip Point out that when the base is negative, the root must be odd. Otherwise there is no principal root.

From the definition of $b^{\frac{1}{n}}$, we can say that $7^{\frac{1}{4}} = \sqrt[4]{7}$ and $(-8)^{\frac{1}{3}} = \sqrt[3]{-8}$ or -2. The expression $(-16)^{\frac{1}{4}}$ is not defined since $-16 < 0$ and 4 is even. Why do we need this restriction?

In Example 2, each expression is evaluated in two ways. Method 1 uses the definition of $b^{\frac{1}{n}}$. Method 2 uses the properties of powers.

Example 2 Evaluate each expression.

a. $81^{-\frac{1}{4}}$

Method 1

$$81^{-\frac{1}{4}} = \frac{1}{81^{\frac{1}{4}}}$$

Remember that $b^{-n} = \frac{1}{b^n}$.

$$= \frac{1}{\sqrt[4]{81}}$$

$$= \frac{1}{\sqrt[4]{3^4}}$$

$$= \frac{1}{3}$$

Method 2

$$81^{-\frac{1}{4}} = (3^4)^{-\frac{1}{4}}$$

$$= 3^{4\left(-\frac{1}{4}\right)}$$

$$= 3^{-1}$$

$$= \frac{1}{3}$$

b. $32^{\frac{3}{5}}$

Method 1

$$32^{\frac{3}{5}} = 32^{3\left(\frac{1}{5}\right)}$$

$$= (32^3)^{\frac{1}{5}}$$

$$= \sqrt[5]{32^3}$$

$$= \sqrt[5]{(2^5)^3}$$

$$= \sqrt[5]{2^5 \cdot 2^5 \cdot 2^5}$$

$$= 2 \cdot 2 \cdot 2 \text{ or } 8$$

Method 2

$$32^{\frac{3}{5}} = (2^5)^{\frac{3}{5}}$$

$$= 2^{5\left(\frac{3}{5}\right)}$$

$$= 2^3$$

$$= 8$$

In part b of Example 2, Method 1 uses a combination of the definition of $b^{\frac{1}{n}}$ and the properties of powers. This example suggests the following general definition of rational exponents.

Definition of Rational Exponents	For any nonzero real number b, and any integers m and n, with $n > 1$, $$b^{\frac{m}{n}} = \sqrt[n]{b^m} = (\sqrt[n]{b})^m$$ except when $b < 0$ and n is even.

When simplifying expressions containing rational exponents, it is usually easier to leave the exponent in rational form rather than to write the expression as a radical. To simplify an expression, you must write the expression with all positive exponents. Furthermore, any exponents in the denominator of a fraction must be positive *integers*. That is, it may be necessary to rationalize a denominator.

All of the properties of powers you learned in Lesson 5-1 apply to rational exponents.

Example **Simplify each expression.**

a. $x^{\frac{2}{3}} \cdot x^{\frac{5}{3}}$

$$x^{\frac{2}{3}} \cdot x^{\frac{5}{3}} = x^{\left(\frac{2}{3}+\frac{5}{3}\right)}$$
$$= x^{\frac{7}{3}}$$

b. $y^{-\frac{5}{6}}$

$$y^{-\frac{5}{6}} = \frac{1}{y^{\frac{5}{6}}}$$
$$= \frac{1}{y^{\frac{5}{6}}} \cdot \frac{y^{\frac{1}{6}}}{y^{\frac{1}{6}}} \quad \text{Why use } \frac{y^{\frac{1}{6}}}{y^{\frac{1}{6}}} \text{?}$$
$$= \frac{y^{\frac{1}{6}}}{y^{\frac{6}{6}}}$$
$$= \frac{y^{\frac{1}{6}}}{y}$$

When simplifying a radical expression, always find the smallest index possible. Using rational exponents make this process easier.

Example **4** **Simplify each expression.**

a. $\dfrac{\sqrt[8]{16}}{\sqrt[6]{2}}$

$$\frac{\sqrt[8]{16}}{\sqrt[6]{2}} = \frac{16^{\frac{1}{8}}}{2^{\frac{1}{6}}}$$
$$= \frac{(2^4)^{\frac{1}{8}}}{2^{\frac{1}{6}}}$$
$$= \frac{2^{\frac{1}{2}}}{2^{\frac{1}{6}}}$$
$$= 2^{\left(\frac{1}{2}-\frac{1}{6}\right)}$$
$$= 2^{\frac{1}{3}} \text{ or } \sqrt[3]{2}$$

b. $\sqrt[4]{4n^2}$

$$\sqrt[4]{4n^2} = (4n^2)^{\frac{1}{4}}$$
$$= (2^2 \cdot n^2)^{\frac{1}{4}}$$
$$= 2^{2\left(\frac{1}{4}\right)} \cdot n^{2\left(\frac{1}{4}\right)}$$
$$= 2^{\frac{1}{2}} \cdot n^{\frac{1}{2}}$$
$$= \sqrt{2} \cdot \sqrt{n}$$
$$= \sqrt{2n}$$

c. $\dfrac{a^{\frac{1}{2}}+1}{a^{\frac{1}{2}}-1}$

$$\frac{a^{\frac{1}{2}}+1}{a^{\frac{1}{2}}-1} = \frac{a^{\frac{1}{2}}+1}{a^{\frac{1}{2}}-1} \cdot \frac{a^{\frac{1}{2}}+1}{a^{\frac{1}{2}}+1} \quad \text{The conjugate of } a^{\frac{1}{2}}-1 \text{ is } a^{\frac{1}{2}}+1.$$
$$= \frac{a + 2a^{\frac{1}{2}}+1}{a-1}$$

In summary, an expression is simplified when the following conditions are met.

- It has no negative exponents.
- It has no fractional exponents in the denominator.
- It is not a complex fraction.
- The index of any remaining radical is the least number possible.

In-Class Examples

For Example 3
Simplify.

a. $4^{\frac{1}{3}} \cdot a^{\frac{1}{2}} \cdot b^{\frac{5}{6}}$ $\sqrt[6]{16a^3b^5}$

b. $x^{\frac{1}{2}} \cdot x^{\frac{3}{4}} \cdot x^{\frac{1}{5}}$ $x\sqrt[20]{x^9}$

c. $w^{-\frac{4}{5}}$ $\dfrac{w^{\frac{1}{5}}}{w}$

d. $xy^{-\frac{1}{8}}$ $\dfrac{xy^{\frac{7}{8}}}{y}$

For Example 4
Simplify.

a. $\dfrac{\sqrt[10]{32}}{\sqrt[8]{4}}$ $\sqrt[4]{2}$

b. $\sqrt[6]{25n^4}$ $\sqrt[3]{5n^2}$

c. $\dfrac{a}{\left(a^{\frac{1}{2}}+b^{\frac{1}{2}}\right)}$ $\dfrac{a\left(a^{\frac{1}{2}}-b^{\frac{1}{2}}\right)}{a-b}$

Check for Understanding

Exercises 1–23 are designed to help you assess your students' understanding through reading, writing, speaking, and modeling. You should work through Exercises 1–5 with your students and then monitor their work on Exercises 6–23.

Additional Answer

4. To rationalize a denominator like $\dfrac{1}{x^{\frac{n}{m}}}$, multiply by 1 in the form $\dfrac{x^{\frac{m-n}{m}}}{x^{\frac{m-n}{m}}}$.

Study Guide Masters, p. 36

5-7

NAME_____ DATE_____
Student Edition
Pages 296–302

Study Guide

Rational Exponents

Definition of Rational Exponents

Definition	Example
For any real number b and for any integer n, $n > 1$, $b^{\frac{1}{n}} = \sqrt[n]{b}$ except when $b < 0$ and n is even.	Evaluate $27^{\frac{1}{3}}$. $27^{\frac{1}{3}} = \sqrt[3]{27}$ or $27^{\frac{1}{3}} = (3^3)^{\frac{1}{3}}$ $= \sqrt[3]{3^3}$ $= 3^1$ $= 3$ $= 3$
For any nonzero real number b and any integers m and n, $n > 1$, $b^{\frac{m}{n}} = \sqrt[n]{b^m} = (\sqrt[n]{b})^m$ except when $b < 0$ and n is even.	Evaluate $8^{\frac{5}{3}} \cdot 8^{\frac{5}{3}}$. $8^{\frac{5}{3}} \cdot 8^{\frac{5}{3}} = 8^{\frac{5}{3}}$ $8^{\frac{5}{3}} = (\sqrt[3]{8})^5$ or $8^{\frac{5}{3}} = (2^3)^{\frac{5}{3}}$ $= (2)^5$ $= 2^5$ $= 32$ $= 32$

A rational expression that contains a fractional exponent in the denominator must also be rationalized. When you simplify an expression, be sure your answer meets all of the given conditions.

Conditions for a Simplified Expression

1. It has no negative exponents.
2. It has no fractional exponents in the denominator.
3. It is not a complex fraction.
4. The index of any remaining radical is as small as possible.

Evaluate.

1. $27^{\frac{2}{3}}$ — 9
2. $\frac{5^{-\frac{1}{2}}}{2\sqrt{5}}$ — $\frac{1}{10}$
3. $(0.0004)^{\frac{1}{2}}$ — 0.02

Simplify.

4. $\frac{m^{\frac{1}{3}}n^{\frac{1}{4}}}{n\sqrt[4]{m^3n}}$
5. $\frac{a^{\frac{1}{2}}b^{\frac{1}{3}}c^{\frac{1}{4}}}{\sqrt[4]{a^2b^2c^3}}$
6. $\frac{\sqrt{2} \cdot \sqrt[4]{2^4}}{2\sqrt[4]{32}}$

7. $\frac{(4x)^{\frac{1}{2}}y^{\frac{1}{3}}}{\sqrt[3]{64x^3y^2}}$
8. $\frac{8^{\frac{1}{3}}32^{\frac{1}{2}}2^{\frac{1}{2}}}{16\sqrt{2}}$
9. $\frac{6^{\frac{1}{2}}y^{\frac{1}{3}}}{y\sqrt[3]{36y^3}}$

10. $(ab^{-2})^{-\frac{1}{2}}$ — $\frac{a^{\frac{1}{2}}b^{\frac{1}{3}}}{a}$
11. $(8x^3y^{-4})^{-\frac{1}{4}}$ — $\frac{y^4}{4x^4}$
12. $(m^{\frac{1}{3}}n^{\frac{1}{4}})^{-\frac{1}{2}}$ — $m^{\frac{1}{3}}n^{\frac{1}{4}}$

13. $\left(\frac{2x^{-4}}{x^{-\frac{1}{3}}}\right)^{-2}$ — $\frac{x}{4}$
14. $\frac{1}{m^{\frac{1}{3}}-1}$ — $\frac{m^{\frac{1}{3}}+1}{m-1}$
15. $\frac{c^{\frac{1}{3}}-c}{c^{\frac{1}{2}}}$ — $c^{\frac{1}{2}}-c^{\frac{2}{3}}$

Communicating Mathematics

3. The radical form $\sqrt[4]{-81}$ has an even index and negative radicand.

4. See margin.

 MATH JOURNAL

Guided Practice

9. $16^{\frac{1}{3}}a^{\frac{5}{3}}b^{\frac{7}{3}}$

19. $\dfrac{c(a-4b)^{\frac{1}{2}}}{a-4b}$

22. $x^{\frac{8}{3}}y^{\frac{1}{2}}$

Study the lesson. Then complete the following.

1. **Explain** how examining the subgoals helped to solve *The Pit and the Pendulum* application at the beginning of the lesson. **Answers will vary.**

2. **Determine** if $3 \cdot 4^{\frac{1}{6}}$ is the simplest form of $2916^{\frac{1}{6}}$. If not, tell why not and write the expression in simplest form.

3. **Explain** why $(-81)^{\frac{1}{4}}$ is not defined.

4. **Write** a general rule for rationalizing expressions such as $\dfrac{1}{x^{\frac{n}{m}}}$.

2. No, because $\sqrt[6]{2916} = (3^6 \cdot 2^2)^{\frac{1}{6}} = 3 \cdot 2^{\frac{1}{3}}$ or $3\sqrt[3]{2}$.

5. **Describe** the steps you go through when solving a complicated word problem. **See students' work.**

Express using rational exponents.

6. $\sqrt{14}$ — $14^{\frac{1}{2}}$
7. $\sqrt[4]{27}$ — $27^{\frac{1}{4}}$
8. $\sqrt[6]{b^3}$ — $b^{\frac{3}{6}}$ or $b^{\frac{1}{2}}$
9. $\sqrt[3]{16a^5b^7}$

Evaluate.

10. $16^{\frac{1}{4}}$ — 2
11. $8^{-\frac{1}{3}}$ — $\frac{1}{2}$
12. $64^{\frac{2}{3}}$ — 16
13. $\dfrac{16^{\frac{3}{4}}}{4^{\frac{1}{2}}}$ — 2

Simplify. 15. $xy^2z\sqrt[6]{x^3y^2z^3}$

14. $\sqrt[6]{9x^3}$ — $\sqrt[3]{3}\sqrt{x}$
15. $x^{\frac{3}{2}}y^{\frac{7}{3}}z^{\frac{9}{6}}$
16. $\dfrac{\sqrt[4]{125}}{\sqrt[3]{5}}$ — $\sqrt{5}$

17. $\dfrac{1}{5x^{\frac{1}{3}}}$ — $\dfrac{x^{\frac{2}{3}}}{5x}$
18. $(x^2y)^{-\frac{1}{3}}$ — $\dfrac{x^{\frac{1}{3}}y^{\frac{2}{3}}}{xy}$
19. $c(a-4b)^{-\frac{1}{2}}$

20. $x^{\frac{1}{3}} \cdot x^{\frac{3}{4}}$ — $x^{\frac{13}{12}}$
21. $\dfrac{y^{\frac{5}{6}}}{y^{\frac{1}{6}}}$ — $y^{\frac{2}{3}}$
22. $\dfrac{x^3}{y^{\frac{1}{2}}} \cdot \dfrac{y}{x^{\frac{1}{3}}}$

23. To what power do you have to raise
   a. 4 to get 2? — $\frac{1}{2}$
   b. 32 to get 8? — $\frac{3}{5}$
   c. x^3 to get x? — $\frac{1}{3}$

EXERCISES

Practice

27. $81^{\frac{13}{6}}$ or $9^{\frac{13}{3}}$ or $3^{\frac{26}{3}}$

 A

Evaluate.

24. $125^{\frac{1}{3}}$ — 5
25. $100^{-\frac{1}{2}}$ — $\frac{1}{10}$
26. $16^{-\frac{3}{4}}$ — $\frac{1}{8}$
27. $81^{\frac{2}{3}} \cdot 81^{\frac{3}{2}}$

28. $9^{\frac{5}{2}} \cdot 9^{\frac{3}{2}}$ — 6561
29. $(-64)^{-\frac{2}{3}}$ — $\frac{1}{16}$
30. $\left(\frac{16}{81}\right)^{\frac{1}{4}}$ — $\frac{2}{3}$
31. $\left(\frac{1}{32}\right)^{-\frac{3}{5}}$ — 8

32. $\left(\frac{27}{64}\right)^{-\frac{1}{3}}$ — $\frac{4}{3}$
33. $\dfrac{24}{6^{\frac{2}{3}}}$ — $4 \cdot 6^{\frac{1}{3}}$
34. $\dfrac{21}{7^{\frac{2}{3}}}$ — $3 \cdot 7^{\frac{1}{3}}$
35. $\dfrac{8}{3^{\frac{1}{2}}}$ — $\dfrac{8 \cdot 3^{\frac{1}{2}}}{3}$

Simplify.

B

36. $2^{\frac{5}{3}}a^{\frac{7}{3}}$ — $2a^2\sqrt[3]{4a}$
37. $(2m)^{\frac{1}{2}}m^{\frac{1}{2}}$ — $m\sqrt{2}$
38. $11^{\frac{1}{3}}p^{\frac{7}{3}}q^{\frac{2}{3}}$ — $p^2\sqrt[3]{11pq^2}$

39. $\dfrac{1}{w^{-\frac{4}{5}}}$ — $\dfrac{w^{\frac{5}{5}}}{w}$
40. $\dfrac{1}{(u-v)^{\frac{1}{3}}}$ — $\dfrac{(u-v)^{\frac{2}{3}}}{u-v}$
41. $x^{-\frac{5}{6}}$ — $\dfrac{x^{\frac{1}{6}}}{x}$

42. $\dfrac{1}{b^{\frac{1}{2}}+1}$ — $\dfrac{b^{\frac{1}{2}}-1}{b-1}$
43. $\dfrac{b^{-\frac{1}{2}}}{8b^{\frac{1}{3}} \cdot b^{-\frac{1}{4}}}$ — $\dfrac{b^{\frac{5}{12}}}{8b}$
44. $\dfrac{g^{\frac{3}{2}}+3g^{-\frac{1}{2}}}{g^{\frac{1}{2}}}$ — $\dfrac{g^2+3}{g}$

45. $\dfrac{3x^{-\frac{1}{3}}+x^{\frac{5}{3}}y}{x^{\frac{2}{3}}}$ — $\dfrac{x^2y+3}{x}$
46. $\dfrac{2a^{\frac{1}{2}}+a^{\frac{3}{2}}}{a^{\frac{1}{2}}}$ — $2+a$
47. $\dfrac{pq}{\sqrt[3]{r}}$ — $\dfrac{pqr^{\frac{2}{3}}}{r}$

300 Chapter 5 *Exploring Polynomials and Radical Expressions*

Reteaching

Using Questioning Ask students the following questions.

• By what can you multiply the denominator to eliminate the rational exponent? **the conjugate of the denominator**

• Then by what would you multiply the numerator to have an expression equivalent to the original? **the same**

expression by which you multiplied the denominator

• So you're really multiplying by a form of what number? **1**

48. $\left(m^{-\frac{2}{3}}\right)^{-\frac{1}{6}}$ $m^{\frac{1}{9}}$

49. $b^{-\frac{1}{3}} - b^{\frac{1}{3}}$ $\dfrac{b^{\frac{2}{3}}}{b} - b^{\frac{1}{3}}$

50. $\dfrac{z^{\frac{3}{2}}}{z^{\frac{1}{2}} + 2}$ $\dfrac{z^2 - 2z^{\frac{3}{2}}}{z - 4}$

51. $\left(\dfrac{m^{-2}n^{-6}}{121}\right)^{-\frac{1}{2}}$ $11mn^3$

52. $\dfrac{8^{\frac{1}{6}} - 9^{\frac{1}{4}}}{\sqrt{3} + \sqrt{2}}$ $2\sqrt{6} - 5$

53. $\dfrac{a^{\frac{5}{3}} - a^{\frac{1}{3}}b^{\frac{4}{3}}}{a^{\frac{2}{3}} + b^{\frac{2}{3}}}$ $a - a^{\frac{1}{3}}b^{\frac{2}{3}}$

54. $\sqrt[4]{49}$ $\sqrt{7}$

55. $r^{\frac{1}{2}}s^{\frac{1}{3}}$ $\sqrt[6]{r^3s^2}$

56. $\sqrt[6]{81p^4q^8}$ $\sqrt[3]{9p^2q^4}$

57. $13\sqrt[6]{13}$

57. $\sqrt{13} \cdot \sqrt[3]{13^2}$

58. $b^2c\sqrt[6]{a^5b^2c^3}$

58. $a^{\frac{5}{6}}b^{\frac{7}{3}}c^{\frac{3}{2}}$

59. $\sqrt[3]{\sqrt{27}}$ $\sqrt{3}$

61. 0.010000001

62. $1,000,000,100$

Evaluate $f(x) = x^{-\frac{2}{3}} + x^{-3}$ **for each value of x.**

60. $f(-8)$ $\dfrac{127}{512}$

61. $f(1000)$

62. $f(0.001)$

Calculator

Evaluate each expression to the nearest hundredth by using your calculator.

63. $45^{0.33}$ 3.51

64. $2.75^{\frac{2}{3}}$ 1.96

65. $\left(4\frac{1}{2}\right)^{0.075}$ 1.12

Critical Thinking

66. Explain how you would solve $9^x = 3^{x+\frac{1}{2}}$ for x.
See margin.

Applications and Problem Solving

67. Music On a piano, the frequency of the A note above middle C should be set at 440 vibrations per second. The frequency f_n of a note that is n notes above A should be $f_n = 440(\sqrt[12]{2})^{n-1}$.

  a. At what frequency should a piano tuner set the A that is one octave, or 12 notes, above the A above middle C? **831 vibrations per second**

  b. Middle C is nine notes below A that has a frequency 440 vibrations per second. What should the frequency of middle C be?
  247 vibrations per second

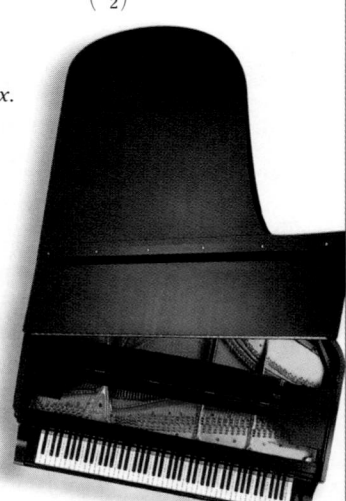

68. Environment When estimating the amount of pollutants contained in the hot gases released by a smokestack, EPA agents must take into account the phenomenon that the velocity of the gas varies throughout the cylindrical smokestack. In such situations, the gas near the center of a cross section of the smokestack has a greater velocity than the gas near the perimeter. This can be described algebraically by the formula $V = V_{max}\left[1 - \left(\dfrac{r}{r_0}\right)^2\right]$, where V_{max} is the maximum velocity of the gas, r_0 is the radius of the smokestack, and V is the velocity of the gas at a distance r from the center of the circular cross section of the smokestack. A cross section of a smokestack has a radius of 25 feet. The gas flowing from it has a measured velocity of 10 mph, and the velocity of the gas at a distance r from the center is 7 mph.

  a. Find the value of r. **about 13.7 feet**

68b. See students' work.

  b. Write the subgoals that you followed to solve the problem.

Assignment Guide

Core: 25–65 odd, 66, 67, 69–80
Enriched: 24–64 even, 66–80

For **Extra Practice,** see p. 887.

The red A, B, and C flags, printed only in the Teacher's Wraparound Edition, indicate the level of difficulty of the exercises.

Additional Answer

66. Rewrite the equation so that the bases are the same on each side.

$$9^x = 3^{x+\frac{1}{2}}$$
$$(3^2)^x = 3^{x+\frac{1}{2}}$$
$$3^{2x} = 3^{x+\frac{1}{2}}$$

Since the bases are the same and this is an equation, the exponents must be equal. Solve $2x = x + \frac{1}{2}$. Thus, $x = \frac{1}{2}$.

Practice Masters, p. 36

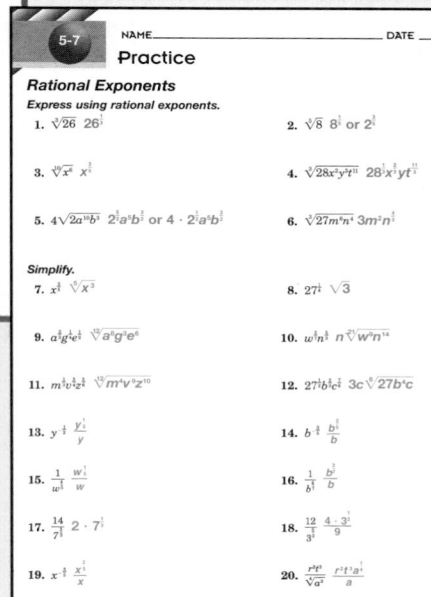

Closing Activity

Modeling Have students draw a model to show the equation
$$64^{\frac{1}{3}} = 4.$$
Students can show a cube with sides equal to 4.

74. No; only square matrices have inverses.

77. 83

Enrichment Masters, p. 36

5-7

NAME _____ DATE _____

Enrichment

Student Edition
Pages 296–302

Lesser-Known Geometric Formulas

Many geometric formulas involve radical expressions.

Make a drawing to illustrate each of the formulas given on this page.

1. The area of an isosceles triangle. Two sides have length a; the other side has length of c.
$A = \frac{c}{4}\sqrt{4a^2 - c^2}$

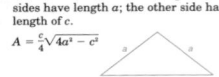

2. The area of an equilateral triangle with a side of length a.
$A = \frac{a^2}{4}\sqrt{3}$

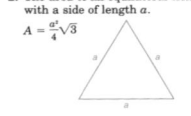

3. The area of a regular pentagon with a side of length a.
$A = \frac{a^2}{4}\sqrt{25 + 10\sqrt{5}}$

4. The area of a regular hexagon with a side of length a.
$A = \frac{3a^2}{2}\sqrt{3}$

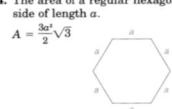

5. The volume of a regular tetrahedron with an edge of length a.
$V = \frac{a^3}{12}\sqrt{2}$

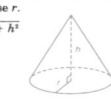

6. The area of the curved surface of a right cone with an altitude of h and radius of base r.
$S = \pi r \sqrt{r^2 + h^2}$

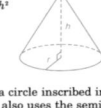

7. Heron's Formula for the area of a triangle uses the semi-perimeter s, where $s = \frac{a + b + c}{2}$. The sides of the triangle have lengths a, b, and c.
$A = \sqrt{s(s - a)(s - b)(s - c)}$

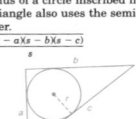

8. The radius of a circle inscribed in a given triangle also uses the semi-perimeter.
$r = \frac{\sqrt{s(s - a)(s - b)(s - c)}}{s}$

Mixed Review

69. Simplify $4\sqrt{(x - 5)^2}$. (Lesson 5–6) $4x - 20$

70. Simplify $\sqrt{\frac{9}{36}x^4}$. (Lesson 5–5) $\frac{1}{2}x^2$

71. Factor $a^3b^3 - 27$. (Lesson 5–4) $(ab - 3)(a^2b^2 + 3ab + 9)$

72. Simplify $\frac{-15r^5s^2}{5r^5s^{-4}}$. (Lesson 5–1) $-3s^6$

73. Solve the system by using augmented matrices. (Lesson 4–7) $(2, -4)$
$$2x + y = 0$$
$$3x - 4y = 22$$

74. Can a 3×4 matrix have an inverse? Explain your answer. (Lesson 4–5)

75. Three numbers have a sum of 6. The first number is twice the second, and the third is three times the second. What are the three numbers? (Lesson 3–7) **2, 1, 3**

76. Find a and b such that the solution of the system $2x + 3y = 7$ and $ax + by = -10$ is $(2, 1)$. (Lesson 3–1) **Sample answer: $a = -6$, $b = 2$**

77. Statistics A prediction equation in a study of the relationship between minutes spent studying s and test scores t is $t = 0.36s + 61.4$. Predict the score a student would receive if she spent 1 hour studying. (Lesson 2–5)

78. Find $h(m - 2)$ if $h(x) = \frac{x - 5}{7}$. (Lesson 2–1) $\frac{m - 7}{7}$

79. Solve $4 < 2x - 2 < 10$. (Lesson 1–6) $\{x \mid 3 < x < 6\}$

80. Name the property illustrated by $6 + a = 6 + a$. (Lesson 1–2) **reflexive (=)**

WORKING ON THE

In·ves·ti·ga·tion

Refer to the Investigation on pages 180–181.

Standard deviation is the most commonly used measure of variation. It is the average measure of how much each value in a set of data differs from the mean. To find the standard deviation, follow the steps below.

a. Find the mean of the set of data.

b. Find the difference between each value in the set of data and the mean.

c. Square each difference.

d. Find the mean of the squares.

e. Take the principal square root of this mean.

1 Find the standard deviation for each of the launchers used in your class shoot-off.

2 How does the standard deviation fit with the other measures you found for each of the launchers? Does its value change your analysis of which launcher is the most accurate? Explain.

3 Write a general formula for standard deviation. Also write it in a form with rational exponents.

4 Plot the data from each of the launchers used in your class shoot-off on box-and-whisker plots and relate the standard deviation to the length of the whiskers. Is there a correlation? Explain.

Add the results of your work to your Investigation Folder.

Extension

Problem Solving

Is $\sqrt[2]{4^2} = (\sqrt[2]{4})^2$?

no; $\sqrt[2]{4^2} = (+2)^2 = +4$

$(\sqrt[2]{4})^2 = \sqrt[2]{16} = \pm 4$

In·ves·ti·ga·tion

Working on the Investigation

The Investigation on pages 180–181 is designed to be a long-term project that is completed over several days or weeks. Encourage students to keep their materials in their Investigation Folder as they work on the Investigation.

Solving Radical Equations and Inequalities

What YOU'LL LEARN

- To solve equations and inequalities containing radicals.

Why IT'S IMPORTANT

You can use radical equations to solve problems involving aviation and manufacturing.

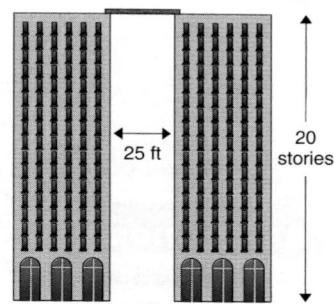

APPLICATION
Construction

At a building construction site, carts loaded with concrete must cross a 25-foot gap between two towers that are 20 stories high. The construction manager needs to select a beam strong enough to support a worker pushing a fully loaded cart. The beam must be at least 2 feet wide to accommodate the wheels of the cart. Will a beam 6 inches thick be able to safely support the load of the cart (865 lb) and the worker (250 lb maximum)?

25 ft

20 stories

The formula that expresses the relationship of the safe load s of a beam to its width w in feet and depth d in inches is $s = \frac{kwd^2}{\ell}$, where k is a constant equal to 576 and ℓ is the distance in feet between the supports. Since we wish to know the thickness or depth of the beam, let's solve the formula for d.

$$s = \frac{kwd^2}{\ell}$$

$$\ell s = kwd^2 \qquad \text{\textit{Multiply each side by } } \ell.$$

$$\frac{\ell s}{kw} = d^2 \qquad \text{\textit{Divide each side by kw.}}$$

$$\pm\sqrt{\frac{\ell s}{kw}} = d \qquad \text{\textit{Since d is squared, take the square root of each side.}}$$

The safe load s is the sum of the weight of the cart (865 lb) and the maximum weight of a construction worker (250 lb) or 1115 pounds.

$$d = \sqrt{\frac{25 \cdot 1115}{576 \cdot 2}} \approx 4.92 \qquad \ell = 25,\ s = 1115,\ k = 576,\ \text{and } w = 2$$

A beam at least 5 inches thick would safely support the load across the gap. A 6-inch beam would give an extra safety margin.

Some equations contain irrational numbers expressed as radicals. You can use the properties of radicals to solve these equations.

Example **Solve $x - 4 = x\sqrt{3}$.**

$$x - 4 = x\sqrt{3}$$
$$x - x\sqrt{3} = 4 \qquad \text{\textit{Isolate the variable on one side of the equation}}$$
$$x(1 - \sqrt{3}) = 4 \qquad \text{\textit{Factor the GCF.}}$$
$$x = \frac{4}{1 - \sqrt{3}}$$

(continued on the next page)

NCTM Standards: 1–5

Instructional Resources

- Study Guide Master 5-8
- Practice Master 5-8
- Enrichment Master 5-8
- Assessment and Evaluation Masters, p. 129

Transparency 5-7A contains the 5-Minute Check for this lesson; **Transparency 5-7B** contains a teaching aid for this lesson.

Recommended Pacing	
Standard Pacing	Day 11 of 16
Honors Pacing	Day 8 of 12
Block Scheduling*	Day 4 of 6 (along with Lesson 5-7)

*For more information on pacing and possible lesson plans, refer to the *Block Scheduling Booklet*.

1 FOCUS

5-Minute Check
(over Lesson 5-7)

Simplify.

1. $9^{-\frac{3}{2}}$ $\frac{1}{27}$

2. $\frac{x^{\frac{1}{2}} - y^{\frac{1}{2}}}{x^{\frac{1}{2}} - y^{\frac{1}{2}}}$ $\frac{x - 2x^{\frac{1}{2}}y^{\frac{1}{2}} + y}{x - y}$

3. Evaluate $16^{\frac{5}{4}}$.   **32**

4. Express $3^{\frac{1}{3}} \cdot x^{\frac{5}{6}} \cdot y^{\frac{1}{4}}$ in simplest radical form.
   $\sqrt[12]{81x^{10}y^3}$

5. Evaluate $\frac{9^{\frac{2}{3}}}{3}$. $3^{\frac{1}{3}}$

TEKS | 2.a., 9.c., 9.d.

Hands-On Activity Have students measure the sides and diagonal of a rectangular object, such as the classroom. Next position four desks as the vertices of a parallelogram and again have students measure the sides and diagonal of the figure. Finally, ask students to use the Pythagorean theorem to compute the diagonals for the two figures and check these calculations against their measurements.

2 TEACH

Teaching Tip In Example 1, remind students they need to rationalize the denominator because there is a radical in the denominator.

In-Class Examples

For Example 1
Solve each equation.

a. $x + 1 = x\sqrt{2}$ $\sqrt{2} + 1$

b. $a\sqrt{3} + 2 = 2a\sqrt{3} + 7$

$\dfrac{-5\sqrt{3}}{3}$

For Example 2
Suppose the student pilot instead flew due north 200 miles, then southeast 282 miles. How far east of the airport is she? **about 199 miles**

$$x = \frac{4}{(1 - \sqrt{3})} \cdot \frac{(1 + \sqrt{3})}{(1 + \sqrt{3})} \quad \text{\textit{Rationalize the denominator.}}$$

$$x = \frac{4(1 + \sqrt{3})}{1 - 3}$$

$$x = \frac{4 + 4\sqrt{3}}{-2} \text{ or } -2 - 2\sqrt{3}$$

Check:
$$x - 4 = x\sqrt{3}$$
$$-2 - 2\sqrt{3} - 4 \stackrel{?}{=} (-2 - 2\sqrt{3})(\sqrt{3})$$
$$-2\sqrt{3} - 6 = -2\sqrt{3} - 6 \checkmark$$

The solution is $-2 - 2\sqrt{3}$.

The Pythagorean theorem is often helpful when solving real-life problems.

Example 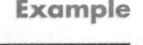 **2**

APPLICATION
Aviation

A student pilot leaves the Tamiami Municipal Airport at 9:00 A.M. on her first solo flight. She is traveling due west at 125 mph. At 10:00 A.M., she turns and flies in a southeasterly direction at the same speed. At noon, she notices that the fuel gauge indicates a low level of fuel. At this time, she is directly south of the airport. How far is it to the airport?

Explore First draw a diagram of the flight path. The problem gives us the following information.

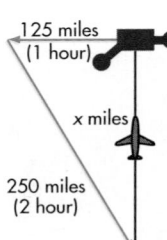

125 miles
(1 hour)

x miles

250 miles
(2 hour)

- She leaves the airport at 9:00 A.M.
- She flies west at 125 mph until 10:00 A.M.
- At 10:00, she turns southeast and flies until noon.
- At noon, the plane is directly south of the airport, and she turns north to return to the airport.

Plan Since the flight path makes a right triangle, we know we can use the Pythagorean theorem to find an expression for the length x of one of the legs of the triangle.

Solve
$$250^2 = 125^2 + x^2$$
$$250^2 - 125^2 = x^2 \quad \text{\textit{Subtract 125^2 from each side.}}$$
$$62{,}500 - 15{,}625 = x^2$$
$$46{,}875 = x^2$$
$$\pm\sqrt{46{,}875} = x \quad \text{\textit{Take the square root of each side.}}$$
$$\pm 216.5 \approx x \quad \text{\textit{Use your calculator.}}$$

Since distance cannot be negative, we know that the pilot is approximately 216.5 miles away from the airport.

Examine Use the Pythagorean theorem to examine the time involved.
$$1^2 + y^2 = 2^2 \quad \text{\textit{Let y represent the unknown time flying due north.}}$$
$$y^2 = 4 - 1 \text{ or } 3$$
$$y = \pm\sqrt{3}$$

The pilot flew $\sqrt{3}$ hours at 125 mph, or about 216.5 miles. $\checkmark$

---

304 *Chapter 5 Exploring Polynomials and Radical Expressions*

GLENCOE *Technology*

⊙ **Interactive Mathematics Tools Software**

This multimedia software provides an interactive lesson by helping students consider the real-life application of the relationship between the radius of an orbit and the time required to complete that orbit. A **Computer Journal** gives students an opportunity to write about what they have learned.

For Windows & Macintosh

Radical equations involving square roots are sometimes called <u>square root equations</u>.

Sometimes variables appear in the radicand. Equations with radicals like this are called **radical equations**. To solve this type of equation, you will need to raise each side of the equation to a power equal to the index to remove the variable from the radical.

Solving radical equations sometimes yields **extraneous solutions**, which are solutions that do not satisfy the original equation. You must check all the possible solutions in the *original* equation and disregard the extraneous solutions.

Example 3 Solve $\sqrt{x-3} = \sqrt{2} - \sqrt{x}$.

$$\sqrt{x-3} = \sqrt{2} - \sqrt{x}$$
$$(\sqrt{x-3})^2 = (\sqrt{2} - \sqrt{x})^2 \quad \text{Square each side.}$$
$$x - 3 = 2 - 2\sqrt{2x} + x$$
$$-5 = -2\sqrt{2x} \quad \text{Isolate the square root.}$$
$$(-5)^2 = (-2\sqrt{2x})^2 \quad \text{Square each side again.}$$
$$25 = 8x$$
$$\frac{25}{8} = x$$

Check:
$$\sqrt{x-3} = \sqrt{2} - \sqrt{x}$$
$$\sqrt{\frac{25}{8} - 3} \stackrel{?}{=} \sqrt{2} - \sqrt{\frac{25}{8}}$$
$$\sqrt{\frac{1}{8}} \stackrel{?}{=} \sqrt{2} - \sqrt{\frac{25}{8}}$$
$$\frac{1}{2}\sqrt{\frac{1}{2}} \stackrel{?}{=} \sqrt{2} - \frac{5}{2}\sqrt{\frac{1}{2}} \quad \frac{1}{8} = \frac{1}{2^2 \cdot 2}, \frac{25}{8} = \frac{5^2}{2^2 \cdot 2}$$
$$3\sqrt{\frac{1}{2}} \stackrel{?}{=} \sqrt{2} \quad \text{Add } \frac{5}{2}\sqrt{\frac{1}{2}} \text{ to each side.}$$
$$3\sqrt{\frac{1}{2} \cdot \frac{2}{2}} \stackrel{?}{=} \sqrt{2} \quad \text{Rationalize the denominator.}$$
$$\frac{3\sqrt{2}}{2} \neq \sqrt{2} \quad \text{Why?}$$

The solution does not check. The equation has no real solution.

You can apply the same methods used in solving square root equations to solving equations of *n*th roots. Remember to undo a square root, you squared the expression. To undo the *n*th root, you must raise the expression to the *n*th power.

Example 4 Solve $2(7n-1)^{\frac{1}{3}} - 4 = 0$.

In order to remove the cube root, we must first isolate it and then raise each side of the equation to the third power.

$$2(7n-1)^{\frac{1}{3}} - 4 = 0 \quad \text{Remember that } (7n-1)^{\frac{1}{3}} = \sqrt[3]{7n-1}.$$
$$2(7n-1)^{\frac{1}{3}} = 4 \quad \text{Add 4 to each side.}$$
$$(7n-1)^{\frac{1}{3}} = 2 \quad \text{Isolate the cube root.}$$
$$\left[(7n-1)^{\frac{1}{3}}\right]^3 = 2^3 \quad \text{Cube each side.}$$
$$7n - 1 = 8$$
$$7n = 9 \quad \text{Add 1 to each side.}$$
$$n = \frac{9}{7} \quad \text{Divide each side by 7.} \qquad \text{(continued on the next page)}$$

Lesson 5-8 Solving Radical Equations and Inequalities **305**

Teaching Tip When discussing the possibility of extraneous solutions, point out that while $x^2 = 4$ has two solutions, $x = 2$ has only one solution.
So, $x = 2$
$$x^2 = 2^2$$
$$x^2 = 4$$
Thus $x = \pm 2$ and there is an additional solution.

In-Class Examples

For Example 3
Solve each equation.
a. $\sqrt{x-2} = \sqrt{3} + \sqrt{x}$ $\frac{25}{12}$
b. $5\sqrt{n-2} = \sqrt{19n - 29} + 3$ 27

For Example 4
Solve each equation.
a. $(3y - 1)^{\frac{1}{3}} - 2 = 0$ 3
b. $(2t + 1)^{\frac{1}{4}} - 1 = 2$ 40

Alternative Learning Styles

Visual Have students develop a sense of the geometric meaning of square roots. To find $\sqrt{13}$, draw a diagonal of a 2×3 rectangle.

Another method: Construct a semicircle of diameter $2 + 3$ or 5. At the point of division between the 2 and 3, construct a perpendicular. This perpendicular is $\sqrt{6}$ units long.

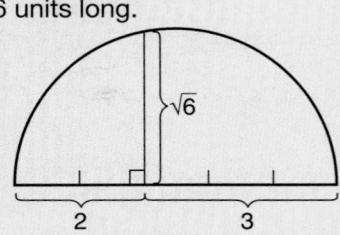

In-Class Example

For Example 5
Solve each inequality.

a. $\sqrt{2y - 1} \le 3$

$\dfrac{1}{2} \le y \le 5$

b. $-4 > \sqrt{3t - 2}$ $\varnothing$

Check: $2(7n - 1)^{\frac{1}{3}} - 4 \stackrel{?}{=} 0$

$2[7\left(\frac{9}{7}\right) - 1]^{\frac{1}{3}} - 4 \stackrel{?}{=} 0$

$2(8)^{\frac{1}{3}} - 4 \stackrel{?}{=} 0$

$2(2) - 4 \stackrel{?}{=} 0$

$0 = 0 \ \checkmark$

The solution is $\frac{9}{7}$.

You can use what you now know about solving square root equations to solve *square root inequalities*.

Example ⑤ **Solve $3 + \sqrt{4x - 5} \le 10$.**

Since the radicand of a radical expression must be greater than or equal to zero, first solve $4x - 5 \ge 0$.

$4x - 5 \ge 0$

$4x \ge 5$

$x \ge \dfrac{5}{4}$

Now solve $3 + \sqrt{4x - 5} \le 10$.

$3 + \sqrt{4x - 5} \le 10$

$\sqrt{4x - 5} \le 7$ *Subtract 3 from each side.*

$4x - 5 \le 49$ *Square each side.*

$4x \le 54$ *Add 5 to each side.*

$x \le 13\dfrac{1}{2}$ *Divide each side by 4 and simplify.*

It appears that $\frac{5}{4} \le x \le 13\frac{1}{2}$. Test values on each part of the number line below to check the result.

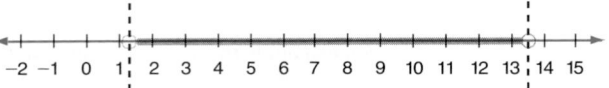

Try $x = 0$.

$3 + \sqrt{4x - 5} \le 10$

$3 + \sqrt{-5} \le 10$

False; negative square roots are not defined in the set of real numbers.

So, $\frac{5}{4} \le x \le 13\frac{1}{2}$.

Try $x = 7.5$.

$3 + \sqrt{4x - 5} \le 10$

$3 + \sqrt{30 - 5} \le 10$

$3 + 5 \le 10 \ \checkmark$
true

Try $x = 21.5$.

$3 + \sqrt{4x - 5} \le 10$

$3 + \sqrt{86 - 5} \le 10$

$3 + 9 \not\le 10$
false

To solve inequalities that involve radicals, complete the following steps.

1. Identify the excluded values.

2. Solve the inequality.

3. Test values to find the solution.

Communicating Mathematics

Study the lesson. Then complete the following. 1–3. See margin.

1. **Explain** how you would solve $\sqrt{2x-3} - \sqrt{x+3} = 0$.

2. **Explain** why you need to isolate the nth root before raising it to the nth power to remove it.

3. **You Decide** Pedro and Rochelle were working in pairs to solve the equation $(x+5)^{\frac{1}{4}} = -4$. Pedro said he could tell that there was no solution without even working the problem. Rochelle said they should solve the equation and then they could test their results to see if there was a solution. Who is correct and why?

Guided Practice

Solve each equation. Be sure to check for extraneous solutions.

4. $\sqrt{3d+1} = 4$ 5

5. $3 - (2-y)^{\frac{1}{2}} = 0$ -7

6. $1 + x\sqrt{2} = 0$ $\dfrac{-\sqrt{2}}{2}$

7. $\sqrt{a-4} - 3 = 0$ 13

8. $\dfrac{2}{3} \cdot (4m)^{\frac{1}{3}} = 4$ 54

9. $\sqrt[3]{y+1} = 2$ 7

10. $\sqrt{2x+3} - 4 \le -5$ no solution

11. $\sqrt{n+12} - \sqrt{n} > 2$ $0 \le n < 4$

12. Solve $\sqrt{x+9} = 9 - \sqrt{x}$. Choose the best answer.   d

    a. 4   **b.** ± 4 **c.** 2   **d.** 16

13. Solve $y = \sqrt{r^2 + s^2}$ for r. $r = \pm\sqrt{y^2 - s^2}$.

EXERCISES

Practice

Solve each equation. Be sure to check for extraneous solutions.

 A

14. $\sqrt{x} = 3$ 9

15. $\sqrt{q} - 8 = 0$ 64

16. $x^{\frac{1}{2}} + 4 = 0$ no solution

17. $7 + 6n\sqrt{5} = 0$ $-\dfrac{7\sqrt{5}}{30}$

18. $\sqrt[3]{r-1} = 3$ 28

19. $\sqrt[3]{2p+1} = 3$ 13

20. $\sqrt[4]{7+3z} = 2$ 3

21. $x\sqrt{x} = 8$ 4

22. $y\sqrt{3} - y = 7$ $\dfrac{7}{2}(\sqrt{3}+1)$

23. $\sqrt{2x-9} = -\dfrac{1}{3}$ no solution

B

24. $9 + \sqrt{4x+8} = 11$ -1

25. $3 + \sqrt{4n-5} = 10$ $\dfrac{54}{4}$

26. $6 - \sqrt{2y+1} < 3$ $y > 4$

27. $(7-5x)^{\frac{1}{2}} \ge 8$ $x \le -\dfrac{57}{5}$

28. $13 - 3r = r\sqrt{5}$ $\dfrac{39-13\sqrt{5}}{4}$

29. $3x + 5 = x\sqrt{3}$ $\dfrac{-15-5\sqrt{3}}{6}$

30. $\sqrt{g-4} = \sqrt{2g-3}$ no solution

31. $\sqrt{2r-6} = \sqrt{3+r}$ 9

C

32. $\sqrt{2} - \sqrt{x+6} \le -\sqrt{x}$ $x \ge 0$

33. $\sqrt{k+9} - \sqrt{k} > \sqrt{3}$ $k \ge 0$

34. $\sqrt{x-6} = 3 + \sqrt{x}$ no solution

35. $\sqrt{h+3} + \sqrt{h-1} = 5$ 5.41

36. $\sqrt{x+21} - 1 = \sqrt{x+12}$ 4

37. $\sqrt{4x+1} = 3 + \sqrt{4x-2}$

38. $(6g-5)^{\frac{1}{3}} + 2 = -3$ -20

39. $\sqrt{a+1} = \sqrt{a+6} - 1$ 3

40. $\sqrt{b+5} + \sqrt{b+10} > 2$ $b \ge -5$

41. $\sqrt{a-5} - \sqrt{a+7} \le 4$ $a \ge 5$

42. Explain why $\{25, 36\}$ is not the solution set for $x + \sqrt{x} - 30 = 0$.

37. no solution

42. 25 is an acceptable solution but 36 is not; $36 + \sqrt{36} - 30 \ne 0$.

Lesson 5–8 Solving Equations Containing Radicals   **307**

Reteaching

Using Alternative Methods An alternate approach to solving radical equations is to substitute a variable for each different radical expression.

$9 + \sqrt{x-1} = 1$

$\quad 9 + A = 1$

$\qquad\quad A = -8$

$\quad x - 1 = 64$

$\qquad\quad x = 65$

Check for extraneous roots.

Additional Answer

3. While Pedro's method will always work in checking for extraneous solutions, Rochelle can save herself time by observing the equation. Since it is a fourth root, the principal value will always be positive. The equation states that the fourth root is negative. This is not possible.

---

3 PRACTICE/APPLY

Check for Understanding

Exercises 1–13 are designed to help you assess your students' understanding through reading, writing, speaking, and modeling. You should work through Exercises 1–3 with your students and then monitor their work on Exercises 4–13.

Assignment Guide

Core: 15–53 odd, 55–64
Enriched: 14–46 even, 48–64

For **Extra Practice,** see p. 888.

The red A, B, and C flags, printed only in the Teacher's Wraparound Edition, indicate the level of difficulty of the exercises.

Additional Answers

1. Add $\sqrt{x+3}$ to each side of the equation. Square each side of the equation. Then solve for x.

2. When the radical is isolated, squaring will remove it. If it is not isolated, squaring will simply produce another radical term in the equation.

Study Guide Masters, p. 37

NAME _____ DATE _____

5-8 **Study Guide**   Student Edition Pages 303–309

Solving Equations Containing Radicals

The properties of radicals can be used to solve equations. Equations that contain variables in the radicand of a radical are called **radical equations**. Squaring each side of the equation may produce results that do not satisfy the original equation. All possible solutions must be checked.

Examples:

Solve $7 + \sqrt{a-3} = 1$.
$7 + \sqrt{a-3} = 1$
$\sqrt{a-3} = -6$ Isolate the radical.
$(\sqrt{a-3})^2 = (-6)^2$ Square each side.
$a - 3 = 36$
$a = 39$
The equation has no solutions.

Check: $7 + \sqrt{a-3} = 1$
$7 + \sqrt{39-3} \stackrel{?}{=} 1$
$7 + \sqrt{36} \stackrel{?}{=} 1$
$13 \ne 1$
The answer does not check.

Solve $\sqrt{2y-3} - \sqrt{2y+3} = -1$.
$\sqrt{2y-3} - \sqrt{2y+3} = -1$
$\sqrt{2y-3} = \sqrt{2y+3} - 1$
$2y - 3 = 2y + 3 - 2\sqrt{2y+3} + 1$
$-7 = -2\sqrt{2y+3}$
$\dfrac{7}{2} = \sqrt{2y+3}$
$\dfrac{49}{4} = 2y + 3$
$\dfrac{37}{4} = 2y$
$y = \dfrac{37}{8}$
The solution is $\dfrac{37}{8}$ or $4\dfrac{5}{8}$.

Check: $\sqrt{2y-3} - \sqrt{2y+3} = -1$
$\sqrt{2\left(\frac{37}{8}\right)-3} - \sqrt{2\left(\frac{37}{8}\right)+3} \stackrel{?}{=} -1$
$\sqrt{\dfrac{25}{4}} - \sqrt{\dfrac{49}{4}} \stackrel{?}{=} -1$
$\dfrac{5}{2} - \dfrac{7}{2} \stackrel{?}{=} -1$
$-1 = -1$

Solve each equation.

1. $3 + 2x\sqrt{3} = 5$ $\dfrac{\sqrt{3}}{3}$

2. $\sqrt{12-x} = \sqrt{x+6}$ 3

3. $2\sqrt{3x+4} + 1 = 15$ 15

4. $8 + \sqrt{x+1} = 2$ no solution

5. $\sqrt{5-x} - 4 = 6$ -95

6. $\sqrt{21} - \sqrt{5x-4} = 0$ 5

7. $\sqrt{2x} = \sqrt{\dfrac{x}{4}}$ 0

8. $\sqrt{x^2+7x} = \sqrt{7x-9}$ no solution

9. $\sqrt{x-8} + \sqrt{x+3} = 1$ no solution

Additional Answers

48. yes;

$$\sqrt[n]{b^m} = \left(b^m\right)^{\frac{1}{n}} = b^{\frac{m}{n}} =$$

$$\left(b^{\frac{1}{n}}\right)^m = \left(\sqrt[n]{b}\right)^m$$

49. yes;

$$\sqrt[k]{\sqrt[m]{b}} = \left(b^{\frac{1}{m}}\right)^{\frac{1}{k}} = b^{\frac{1}{km}} = \sqrt[km]{b}$$

Solve for the variable indicated.

43. $T = 2\pi\sqrt{\dfrac{\ell}{g}}$ for ℓ $\ell = g \cdot \dfrac{T^2}{4\pi^2}$

44. $t = \sqrt{\dfrac{2s}{g^2}}$ for s $s = \dfrac{t^2 g^2}{2}$

45. $m^2 = \sqrt[3]{\dfrac{rp}{g^2}}$ for p $p = \dfrac{m^6 g^2}{r}$

46. $r = \sqrt[3]{\dfrac{2mM}{c}}$ for c $c = \dfrac{2mM}{r^3}$

47. Geometry   The surface area of a cone can be found by using $S = \pi r\sqrt{r^2 + h^2}$, where r is the radius of the base and h is the height of the cone.

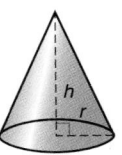

   a. Solve the equation for h. $h = \dfrac{\sqrt{S^2 - r^4\pi^2}}{\pi r}$

   b. Find h if $S = 225$ and $r = 5$.   **about 13.4**

Critical Thinking

48. Is $\sqrt[n]{b^m} = (\sqrt[n]{b})^m$? Justify your answer.   **See margin.**

49. Is $\sqrt[km]{b} = \sqrt[k]{\sqrt[m]{b}}$? Justify your answer.   **See margin.**

Applications and Problem Solving

50. Manufacturing   A company that manufactures ROM (Read Only Memory) chips for computers uses the formula $c = 100\sqrt[3]{n^2} + 1200$ to determine the cost of producing the chips, where c is the cost of production in dollars and n is the number produced. If a computer company places an order totaling \$10,000, how many chips will be produced?   **about 826 chips**

51. about 282 feet

51. Concerts   The organizers of a rock concert are preparing for the arrival of 50,000 enthusiastic fans in the open field where the concert will take place. It is reasonable to allow each person 5 square feet of space, so the organizers need to rope off a circular area of 250,000 square feet. Using the formula $A = \pi r^2$, where A represents the area of the circular region and r represents the radius of the region, find the radius of this region.

52. History   Johann Kepler (1571–1630) is known mainly as a mathematician of the sky. He is credited with several laws of planetary motion. His third law states that the square of the time of revolution of each planet (its period) is proportional to the cube of its mean distance from the sun. This can be expressed as $\dfrac{T_a}{T_b} = \left(\dfrac{r_a}{r_b}\right)^{\frac{3}{2}}$, where T_a is the time it takes one planet to orbit the sun, r_a is that planet's average distance from the sun, and T_b and r_b are another planet's period and average distance from the sun.

52a. $r_a = r_b\left(\dfrac{T_a}{T_b}\right)^{\frac{2}{3}}$

   a. Solve the formula for r_a.

   b. Find the distance (to the nearest million miles) that Jupiter is from the sun, if its period is 12 years. Mercury is 36 million miles from the sun and has a period of 88 days.   **about 487 million miles**

Practice Masters, p. 37

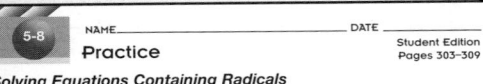

5-8   NAME_____ DATE_____

Student Edition
Pages 303–309

Practice

Solving Equations Containing Radicals

Solve each equation. Be sure to check for extraneous solutions.

1. $7x\sqrt{3} - 5 = 0$
$\dfrac{5\sqrt{3}}{21}$

2. $4x - x\sqrt{3} = 6$
$\dfrac{24 + 6\sqrt{3}}{13}$

3. $18 - 3x = x\sqrt{2}$
$\dfrac{54 - 18\sqrt{2}}{7}$

4. $\sqrt{x+8} - 5 = 0$
17

5. $\sqrt[3]{y} - 7 = 4$
71

6. $\sqrt[3]{3x} - 2 = 0$
$\dfrac{16}{3}$

7. $\sqrt{8n-5} - 1 = 2$
$\dfrac{7}{4}$

8. $\sqrt{1-4t} - 8 = -6$
$-\dfrac{3}{4}$

9. $\sqrt[3]{7v-2} + 12 = 7$
no real solution

10. $\sqrt[3]{6u-5} + 2 = -3$
-20

11. $\sqrt{6x-4} = \sqrt{2x+10}$
$\dfrac{7}{2}$

12. $\sqrt{9u-4} = \sqrt{7u-20}$
no real solution

13. $\sqrt{k+9} - \sqrt{k} = \sqrt{3}$
3

14. $\sqrt{x+10} + \sqrt{x-6} = 8$
15

15. $\sqrt{x+2} - 7 = \sqrt{x+9}$
no real solution

16. $\sqrt{4x^2 - 3x + 2} - 2x - 5 = 0$
-1

308   *Chapter 5*

53. $t = \dfrac{2\pi r \sqrt{GMr}}{GM}$

55. $5^{\frac{3}{7}}$

56. $3\sqrt{2} - 2\sqrt{3}$

57. $|x + 5|$

58. $2t^2 + 2t - \dfrac{3}{t-1}$

62. $a + b = 7,\ 30a + 20b = 160;\ (2, 5)$

53. Aerospace Engineering   The radius of the orbit of a satellite is found by $r = \sqrt[3]{\dfrac{GMt^2}{4\pi^2}}$, where t represents the time it takes for the satellite to complete one orbit, G represents the constant of universal gravitation, and M is the mass of the central object. Solve the formula for t.

54. Solar Energy   The energy of direct sunlight on a solar cell with an area of one square centimeter is converted into 0.01 watt of electrical energy. Suppose that a square solar cell must deliver 15 watts of energy. What should the dimensions of the cell be?   **$10\sqrt{15}$ or about 38.73 centimeters on each side**

Solar-powered car

Mixed Review

55. How would you write *the seventh root of 5 cubed* using exponents? (Lesson 5–7)

Simplify.

56. $\sqrt{3}(\sqrt{6} - 2)$ (Lesson 5–6)

57. $\sqrt{x^2 + 10x + 25}$ (Lesson 5–5)

58. $(2t^3 - 2t - 3) \div (t - 1)$ (Lesson 5–3)

59. $(y^5)^2$ (Lesson 5–1)   **y^{10}**

60. Write an augmented matrix for the system of equations. Then solve the system.   (Lesson 4–7)   **$(-4, 0, 7)$**

$x + 5y + 2z = 10$

$3x - 3y + 2z = 2$

$2x + 4y - z = -15$

61. Evaluate $\begin{vmatrix} 4 & -2 \\ 3 & 7 \end{vmatrix}$.   (Lesson 4–4)   **34**

62. Business   Mr. Whitner bought 7 drums of two different cleaning fluids for his dry-cleaning business. One of the fluids cost $30 per drum, and the other was $20 per drum. The total cost of the supplies was $160. How much of each fluid did Mr. Whitner buy? Write a system of equations and solve by graphing.   (Lesson 3–1)

63. Entertainment   Under the terms of a royalty agreement, a radio station is charged $60 per month for a new release plus $0.20 for each time the song is played. The songwriter gets $\frac{1}{4}$ of this amount.   (Lesson 2–2)

  a. If x is the number of times the song is played, write an equation that shows how much money y the songwriter gets.   **$y = 0.05x + 15$**

  b. How much would the songwriter get if the song was played 42 times in one month at the radio station?   **$17.10**

64. Statistics   The cost per cup of several different types of juices are given below.

11¢	9¢	6¢	9¢	12¢	4¢	4¢	8¢	6¢	4¢	16¢
12¢	11¢	19¢	7¢	19¢	7¢	19¢	4¢	6¢	5¢	6¢

Make a stem-and-leaf plot of the costs.   (Lesson 1–3)   **See margin.**

Extension ▬▬▬

Communication Have students create three radical equations, one with each of the following solutions.

  1. 2 solutions
  2. 1 solution
  3. no solution

Have students describe the procedure used for developing the equations.

---

4 ASSESS

Closing Activity

Speaking Have students explain how to solve $\sqrt{x} = \sqrt[3]{x}$. Students can take turns stating the next step and explaining why the next step is important.

$$\left(\sqrt{x}\right)^6 = \left(\sqrt[3]{x}\right)^6$$
$$x^3 = x^2$$
$$x^3 - x^2 = 0$$
$$x^2(x - 1) = 0$$
$$x = 0 \text{ or } x = 1$$

Chapter 5, Quiz C (Lessons 5-6 through 5-8), is available in the *Assessment and Evaluation Masters*, p. 129.

Additional Answer

64.

Stem	Leaf
0	4 4 4 4 5
•	6 6 6 6 7 7 8 9 9
1	1 1 2 2 6 9 9 9

$1|1 = 11$¢

Enrichment Masters, p. 37

NAME_____   DATE_____

5-8   **Enrichment**   Student Edition Pages 303–309

Doubling

According to Thomas H. McMahon in the July 1975 issue of *Scientific American*, the height of a tree varies directly with the $\frac{2}{3}$ power of the radius of the trunk at its base. ($h = kr^{\frac{2}{3}}$ where k is a constant.) Suppose you own a stand of trees that can be used for making paper. The amount of wood pulp and therefore the value of the trees should be proportional to the volume of the trees. If we approximate a tree without its branches as a right circular cone, the formula for the volume of the tree is $\frac{1}{3}\pi r^2 h = \frac{1}{3}\pi r^2(kr^{\frac{2}{3}}) = \frac{1}{3}\pi k r^{\frac{8}{3}}$.

If the trees on your land have radii of 3 inches and increase in radius one-fourth inch per year, it is possible to find the number of years it would take for the value of the trees to double.

volume of one tree now $= \frac{1}{3}\pi k(3)^{\frac{8}{3}} = \frac{1}{3}\pi k\left(3 + \frac{1}{4} \cdot 0\right)^{\frac{8}{3}}$

volume of one tree after 1 year $= \frac{1}{3}\pi k\left(3 + \frac{1}{4} \cdot 1\right)^{\frac{8}{3}}$

volume of one tree after 2 years $= \frac{1}{3}\pi k\left(3 + \frac{1}{4} \cdot 2\right)^{\frac{8}{3}}$

volume of one tree after y years $= \frac{1}{3}\pi k\left(3 + \frac{1}{4} \cdot y\right)^{\frac{8}{3}}$

We want the volume to double: 2(present volume) $= 2 \cdot \frac{1}{3}\pi k \cdot 3^{\frac{8}{3}}$.

Therefore, we are looking for the value of y which makes the following equation true.

$2 \cdot \frac{1}{3}\pi k \cdot 3^{\frac{8}{3}} = \frac{1}{3}\pi k\left(3 + \frac{1}{4}y\right)^{\frac{8}{3}}$ or $2 \cdot \frac{1}{3}\pi k \cdot \sqrt[3]{3^8} = \frac{1}{3}\pi k \sqrt[3]{\left(3 + \frac{1}{4}y\right)^8}$

Solve each problem.

1. Solve this equation for y, showing all work. Give a decimal approximation to the nearest tenth of a year. $y = 3.6$

2. According to the "Rule of 72," an investment at p% takes about $\frac{72}{p}$ years to double. In problem 1, what percent are you making on your investment? $3.6 = \frac{72}{p}$, 20%

3. Generalize the situation in problem 1. Let:
   $m =$ the number of times you want the value to increase (In problem 1, $m = 2$.)
   $r =$ the initial radius in inches (In problem 1, $r = 3$.)
   $n =$ the number of inches the radius increases per year $\left(\text{In problem 1, } n = \frac{1}{4}.\right)$

   Derive the following formula. $y = \frac{r}{n}(m^{\frac{3}{8}} - 1)$ $m \cdot \frac{1}{3}\pi k \cdot r^{\frac{8}{3}} = \frac{1}{3}\pi k(r + ny)^{\frac{8}{3}}$;

   $mr^{\frac{8}{3}} = (r + ny)^{\frac{8}{3}}$; $m^{\frac{3}{8}}r^8 = (r + ny)^8$; $m^{\frac{3}{8}}r = r + ny$; $\frac{r}{n}(m^{\frac{3}{8}} - 1) = y$

Complex Numbers

NCTM Standards: 1–5

Instructional Resources

- Study Guide Master 5-9
- Practice Master 5-9
- Enrichment Master 5-9
- Graphing Calculator Masters, p. 5
- Modeling Mathematics Masters, p. 65
- Tech Prep Applications Masters, p. 10

 Transparency 5-9A contains the 5-Minute Check for this lesson; **Transparency 5-9B** contains a teaching aid for this lesson.

Recommended Pacing

Standard Pacing	Days 12 & 13 of 16
Honors Pacing	Day 9 of 12
Block Scheduling*	Day 5 of 6 (along with Lesson 5-10)

 *For more information on pacing and possible lesson plans, refer to the *Block Scheduling Booklet.*

1 FOCUS

 ### 5-Minute Check
(over Lesson 5-8)

Solve.

1. $x + 2 = x\sqrt{3}$ $1 + \sqrt{3}$

2. $\sqrt{1 - 3y} - 3 = -10$ -16

3. $7 - \sqrt{5t + 4} = 0$ 9

4. $\sqrt[3]{5n + 2} + 2 = 0$ -2

5. $\sqrt{2x + 1} + \sqrt{4x - 2} = 4$ $\dfrac{3}{2}$

Motivating the Lesson

Situational Problem Have students solve the following equations.

1. $x^2 + 16 = 0$ no real solution

2. $5x^2 + 125 = 0$ no real solution

3. $1 + x\sqrt{2} = 0$ $\dfrac{-\sqrt{2}}{2}$

Which equations have no real solutions? Can the equations be rewritten to have a similar expression?

What YOU'LL LEARN

- To simplify square roots containing negative radicands,
- to solve quadratic equations that have pure imaginary solutions, and
- to add, subtract, and multiply complex numbers.

Why IT'S IMPORTANT

You can use complex numbers to solve problems involving electricity and physics.

To avoid $\sqrt{5} \cdot i$ being read as $\sqrt{5i}$, write $\sqrt{5} \cdot i$ as $i\sqrt{5}$.

Number Theory

Keesha and Juanita formed a study group for their algebra class. Their teacher, Mrs. Rodriguez, gave them an assignment that included solving the equation $3x^2 + 15 = 0$. Keesha and Juanita solved the equation as follows.

$$3x^2 + 15 = 0$$
$$3x^2 = -15$$
$$x^2 = -5$$

They were puzzled at the last step because they knew that there is no real number x that when squared results in a negative number. They were stumped! After checking with a few of their classmates, they found that everyone had the same difficulty. Is there a solution to the equation?

About 400 years ago, a solution to this type of equation was proposed by French mathematician René Descartes (1596–1650). He proposed that the solution to the equation $x^2 = -1$ be represented by a number i, where i is not a real number. Thus, $i = \sqrt{-1}$.

Keesha's class could now solve the equation.

$$x^2 = -5$$
$$x = \pm\sqrt{-5}$$
$$x = \pm\sqrt{5} \cdot \sqrt{-1} \quad \textit{Extension of product property of radicals}$$
$$x = \pm\sqrt{5} \cdot i \quad \sqrt{-1} = i$$
$$x = \pm i\sqrt{5}$$

Numbers such as $i\sqrt{5}$, $2i$, and $-5i$ are called **pure imaginary numbers**, and i is called the **imaginary unit**. Using i as you would any constant, you can define square roots of negative numbers.

Since $i = \sqrt{-1}$, it follows that $i^2 = -1$. Therefore,

$$(3i)^2 = 3^2 \cdot i^2 \text{ or } -9 \quad \rightarrow \quad \sqrt{-9} = \sqrt{9} \cdot \sqrt{-1} \text{ or } 3i$$
$$(i\sqrt{3})^2 = i^2(\sqrt{3})^2 \text{ or } -3 \quad \rightarrow \quad \sqrt{-3} = \sqrt{3} \cdot \sqrt{-1} \text{ or } i\sqrt{3}$$

Definition of Pure Imaginary Numbers	For any positive real number b, $\sqrt{-b^2} = \sqrt{b^2} \cdot \sqrt{-1}$ or bi, where i is the imaginary unit, and bi is called a pure imaginary number.

Example ① Simplify each expression.

a. $\sqrt{-12}$

$$\sqrt{-12} = \sqrt{2^2} \cdot \sqrt{3} \cdot \sqrt{-1}$$
$$= 2 \cdot \sqrt{3} \cdot i$$
$$= 2i\sqrt{3}$$

b. $\sqrt{-27x^3}$

$$\sqrt{-27x^3} = \sqrt{3^2} \cdot \sqrt{-3} \cdot \sqrt{x^2} \cdot \sqrt{x}$$
$$= 3x\sqrt{-3x}$$
$$= 3ix\sqrt{3x}$$

The commutative and associative properties for multiplication hold true for pure imaginary numbers.

Example **Simplify each expression.**

a. $-3i \cdot 8i$ b. $\sqrt{-6} \cdot \sqrt{-10}$

$\begin{aligned} -3i \cdot 8i &= -24i^2 \\ &= -24(-1) \quad i^2 = -1 \\ &= 24 \end{aligned}$

$\begin{aligned} \sqrt{-6} \cdot \sqrt{-10} &= i \cdot \sqrt{6}\, i \cdot \sqrt{10} \\ &= i^2 \sqrt{60} \\ &= -1 \cdot 2\sqrt{15} \text{ or } -2\sqrt{15} \end{aligned}$

You can use the properties of powers to simplify powers of *i*.

Example **Simplify i^{25}.**

LOOK BACK

You can review the properties of powers in Lesson 5-1.

$\begin{aligned} i^{25} &= i \cdot i^{24} && \text{Product of powers} \\ &= i \cdot (i^2)^{12} && \text{Power of a power} \\ &= i \cdot (-1)^{12} && i^2 = -1 \\ &= i \cdot 1 \text{ or } i \end{aligned}$

When you solve some equations, the answer may involve two pure imaginary numbers.

Example ④ **Solve $4x^2 + 36 = 0$.**

$\begin{aligned} 4x^2 + 36 &= 0 \\ 4x^2 &= -36 && \text{Subtract 36 from each side.} \\ x^2 &= -9 && \text{Divide each side by 4.} \\ x &= \pm\sqrt{-9} && \text{Take the square root of each side.} \\ x &= \pm 3i \end{aligned}$

Check:

$\begin{aligned} 4x^2 + 36 &= 0 \\ 4(3i)^2 + 36 &\overset{?}{=} 0 \\ 4 \cdot 9 \cdot i^2 + 36 &\overset{?}{=} 0 \\ -36 + 36 &\overset{?}{=} 0 \\ 0 &= 0 \checkmark \end{aligned}$

$\begin{aligned} 4x^2 + 36 &= 0 \\ 4(-3i)^2 + 36 &\overset{?}{=} 0 \\ 4 \cdot 9 \cdot i^2 + 36 &\overset{?}{=} 0 \\ -36 + 36 &\overset{?}{=} 0 \\ 0 &= 0 \checkmark \end{aligned}$

Suppose you were asked to simplify the expression $5 + 2i$. Since 5 is a real number and $2i$ is a pure imaginary number, the terms are not like terms and cannot be combined. This type of expression is called a **complex number.**

Definition of a Complex Number	A complex number is any number that can be written in the form $a + bi$, where a and b are real numbers and i is the imaginary unit; a is called the real part, and bi is called the imaginary part.

Teaching Tip Emphasize that *i* is not a variable. It is a symbol that stands for a specific number.

Teaching Tip An imaginary number is any number in simplest form that contains the imaginary unit.

In-Class Examples

For Example 1
Simplify.

a. $\sqrt{-81}$ $9i$

b. $\sqrt{-121x^5}$ $11ix^2\sqrt{x}$

For Example 2
Simplify.

a. $8i \cdot 3i$ -24

b. $\sqrt{-5} \cdot \sqrt{-20}$ -10

For Example 3
Simplify.

a. i^{12} 1

b. i^{17} i

For Example 4
Solve each equation.

a. $x^2 + 81 = 0$ $\pm 9i$

b. $a^2 + 72 = 0$ $\pm 6i\sqrt{2}$

Alternative Teaching Strategies

Student Diversity Separate the class into groups. Have each group develop the properties for complex numbers. They should find the properties and provide an example of each. Each group should write a report on its findings and include the structure of the complex numbers.

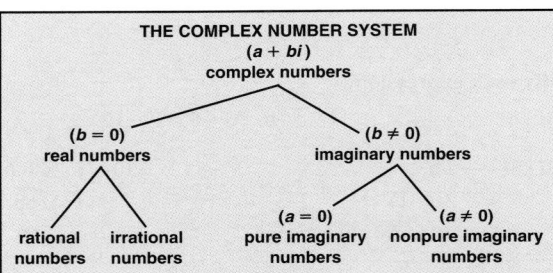

THE COMPLEX NUMBER SYSTEM
($a + bi$)
complex numbers

($b = 0$)
real numbers

($b \neq 0$)
imaginary numbers

rational numbers   irrational numbers

($a = 0$)
pure imaginary numbers

($a \neq 0$)
nonpure imaginary numbers

- If $b = 0$, a real number results.
- If $b \neq 0$, the number is imaginary.
- If $a = 0$, the number is a pure imaginary number.

Teaching Tip Explain that the set of complex numbers has two independent subsets—the real numbers and the imaginary numbers.

In-Class Example

For Example 5
Simplify.

a. $(8 + 7i) + (-12 + 11i)$
$-4 + 18i$

b. $(9 - 6i) - (12 + 2i)$ $-3 - 8i$

 **MODELING MATHEMATICS** Point out to students that the order in which the points are plotted does not matter. This geometric principle follows from the algebraic principle that the addition of complex numbers is commutative.

Two complex numbers are equal if and only if their real parts are equal and their imaginary parts are equal.

Definition of Equal Complex Numbers	$a + bi = c + di$ if and only if $a = c$ and $b = d$

To add or subtract complex numbers, combine like terms; that is, combine the real parts and combine the imaginary parts.

Example **Simplify each expression.**

a. $(8 - 5i) + (2 + i)$

b. $(4 + 7i) - (2 + 3i)$

$(8 - 5i) + (2 + i)$

$\quad = (8 + 2) + (-5i + i)$

$\quad = 10 - 4i$

$(4 + 7i) - (2 + 3i)$

$\quad = (4 - 2) + (7i - 3i)$

$\quad = 2 + 4i$

You can model the addition of complex numbers geometrically.

MODELING MATHEMATICS   **Adding Complex Numbers**

Materials: grid paper   straightedge

You can model the addition of complex numbers on a coordinate plane. The horizontal axis represents the real part a of the complex number and the vertical axis represents the coefficient b of the imaginary part. Use a coordinate plane to find $(5 + 3i) + (-2 + 2i)$.

- Create a coordinate plane and label the axes appropriately.
- Graph $5 + 3i$ by drawing a segment from the origin to $(5, 3)$ on the coordinate plane.
- Graph $-2 + 2i$ by drawing a segment from the origin to $(-2, 2)$ on the coordinate plane.
- Draw a parallelogram that has the two segments you drew as sides.
- The diagonal of the parallelogram drawn from the origin represents the sum of the two complex

numbers. The endpoint of the diagonal is $(3, 5)$, which represents $3 + 5i$. So, $(5 + 3i) + (-2 + 2i) = (3 + 5i)$.

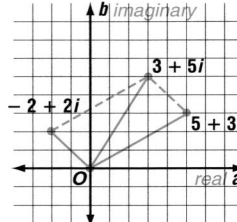

Your Turn

Model $(-2 + 3i) + (1 - 4i)$ on a coordinate plane.

Alternative Learning Styles

Auditory Lead a class discussion centering on the following questions.

1. In what sense are complex numbers not real? They have an imaginary part.

2. Are real numbers real? yes

3. Does anything in the physical world have a measure of $\sqrt{-1}$? no

You can multiply complex numbers by using the FOIL method.

Example **6** Simplify $(4 + 2i)(3 - 5i)$.

$$
\begin{array}{ccccc}
& F & O & I & L \\
(4 + 2i)(3 - 5i) = & 4(3) & - 4(5i) & + (2i)3 & - 2i(5i)
\end{array}
$$
$$
= 12 - 20i + 6i - 10i^2
$$
$$
= 12 - 14i - 10(-1)
$$
$$
= 22 - 14i
$$

One of the real-world uses of imaginary numbers is in electricity. However, electrical engineers use j instead of i to represent the imaginary unit. This avoids any confusion with the I used as a symbol for current. Imaginary numbers are used to represent the impedance of a circuit. The impedance is the resistance to the flow of electricity through the circuit.

Example **7**

APPLICATION
Electricity

F Y I

Millard Fuller, the founder and president for Habitat of Humanity International, was a self-made millionaire who gave most of his money away to charity. Since 1976, Habitat has built about 30,000 homes in more than 1000 U.S. cities and 40 foreign countries.

The Habitat for Humanity program utilizes volunteers to help build houses for low-income families who might otherwise not be able to afford the purchase of a home. At a recent site, Habitat workers built a small storage shed attached to the house. The electrical blueprints for the shed called for two AC circuits connected in series with a total voltage of 220 volts. One of the circuits must have an impedance of $7 - 10j$ ohms, and the other needs to have an impedance of $9 + 5j$. According to the building codes, the impedance cannot exceed $20 - 5j$ ohms. Will the circuits, as designed, meet the code?

Former President Jimmy Carter

Explore   First we need to understand the electricity terms used in the problem. In a simplified electrical circuit, there are three basic components to be considered:

- the flow of the electrical current, I
- the resistance to that flow, Z, called impedance, and
- the electromotive force, E, called voltage.

The formula $E = I \cdot Z$ illustrates the relationship among these components.

Plan   The total impedance is the sum of the individual impedances.

Solve
$$
(7 - 10j) + (9 + 5j) = 7 + 9 - 10j + 5j
$$
$$
= 16 + (-10 + 5)j
$$
$$
= 16 - 5j
$$

The total impedance is $16 - 5j$, which is less than $20 - 5j$. The circuits will meet the code.

Generally, you cannot order complex numbers that contain imaginary parts. However, if the imaginary parts of the two numbers are identical, you can compare the real number parts.

Examine   Since both numbers contain the same imaginary part, we can compare the real part. $16 < 20$, so the conclusion is correct.

Teaching Tip Point out with Example 6 that FOIL works for all complex numbers, real or imaginary.

In-Class Examples

For Example 6
Simplify.

a. $(8 + 5i)(2 - 3i)$ $31 - 14i$
b. $(-6 + 2i)(5 - 3i)$ $-24 + 28i$

For Example 7
Would two circuits in series with impedances of $8 - 5j$ ohms and $9 + j$ ohms meet the code? Yes; the total impedance is $17 - 4j$, which is less than $20 - 5j$.

F Y I

Each family invests hundreds of hours of labor into building its home and the homes of other families. Two of the most recognizable volunteers for Habitat for Humanity are former President Jimmy Carter and his wife Rosalyn. The pair has contributed physical labor at many of the organization's building sites.

Check for Understanding

Exercises 1–19 are designed to help you assess your students' understanding through reading, writing, speaking, and modeling. You should work through Exercises 1–5 with your students and then monitor their work on Exercises 6–19.

Error Analysis

Some students may be confused about the difference between complex and imaginary numbers. Numbers such as $7 - 3i$ and $8i$ are both complex and imaginary, but not real. Real numbers such as $\sqrt{2}$ and 6 are both complex and real, but not imaginary. To illustrate this, show a horizontal number line labeled *real* and a vertical one labeled *imaginary*.

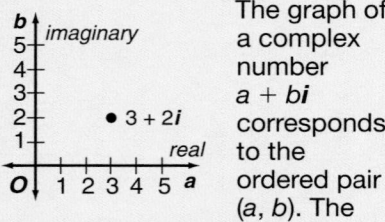

The graph of a complex number $a + bi$ corresponds to the ordered pair (a, b). The entire plane represents the set of complex numbers. All points not on the real axis are imaginary. All points on the vertical axis, except 0, are pure imaginary.

Study Guide Masters, p. 38

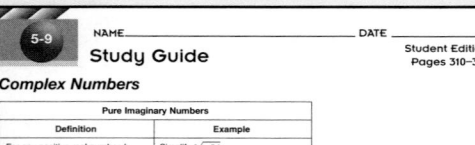

5-9
NAME_____ DATE _____
Student Edition
Pages 310–316

Study Guide

Complex Numbers

Communicating Mathematics

Study the lesson. Then complete the following.

1. **Determine** if each statement is true or false.
   a. Every real number is a complex number. true
   b. Every imaginary number is a complex number. true

2. **Show** where each of the following lies on the complex coordinate plane.
   a. real numbers along the real axis (*x*-axis)
   b. pure imaginary numbers along the imaginary axis (*y*-axis)

3. Which complex number is equivalent to $\sqrt{-50}$? c
   a. $-5i$ b. $25i$ c. $5i\sqrt{2}$ d. $-5i\sqrt{2}$

 MODELING MATHEMATICS

4. Identify the complex numbers and their sum shown in the graph at the right.
   $(-4 + 3i) + (5 + 2i) = 1 + 5i$

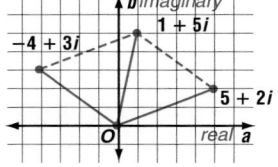

5. Graph the addends $(-2 + i)$ and $(4 + 4i)$ on the complex plane. Then find their sum geometrically. $2 + 5i$

Guided Practice

Simplify.

6. $\sqrt{-64}$ $8i$

7. $\sqrt{-98m^2n^2}$ $7i\,|mn|\,\sqrt{2}$

8. $(4i)(-3i)$ 12

9. $5\sqrt{-24} \cdot 3\sqrt{-18}$ $-180\sqrt{3}$

10. $\sqrt{3} \cdot \sqrt{-27}$ $9i$

11. i^{16} 1

12. $(15 + 10i) - (4 + 6i)$ $11 + 4i$

13. $(4 + 2i) + (1 + 3i)$ $5 + 5i$

14. $(4 - 3i)(5 + 7i)$ $41 + 13i$

15. $(3 + 2i)(3 - 2i)$ 13

16. Find the product $(2 - 4i)(3 + 9i)$. $42 + 6i$

17. Verify that $-2i\sqrt{2}$ is a solution for $5x^2 + 40 = 0$. Find the other solution.
    See margin.

Solve each equation.

18. $5x^2 + 30 = 5$ $\pm i\sqrt{5}$

19. $a^2 + 16 = 0$ $\pm 4i$

EXERCISES

Practice
A

Simplify.

24. $6m^2|\,n|\,i$
27. $-60i$
29. $-11\sqrt{2}$
30. $-\dfrac{5}{2}$

20. $\sqrt{-169}$ $13i$

21. $\sqrt{-\frac{4}{9}}$ $\frac{2}{3}i$

22. $\sqrt{-49}$ $7i$

23. $\sqrt{-100k^4}$ $10k^2i$

24. $\sqrt{-36m^4n^2}$

25. $\sqrt{-\frac{9x^3}{25y^8}}$ $\frac{3i|x|}{5y^4}\sqrt{x}$

26. $(2i)^2$ -4

27. $(-4i)(-5i)(3i)$

28. $5i(-2i)^2$ $-20i$

29. $(\sqrt{-11})(\sqrt{-22})$

30. $(2\sqrt{-50})(\frac{1}{8}\sqrt{-2})$

31. $\sqrt{-8} \cdot \sqrt{-18}$ -12

Reteaching

Using Writing Have students complete the following sentences.

1. Complex numbers are written in the form $a + bi$.
2. To add complex numbers, combine like terms.
3. $x + yi$ and $w + zi$ are equal if $x = w$ and $y = z$.
4. To graph $a + bi$, graph a on horizontal and b on vertical.

Additional Answer

17.
$$5x^2 + 40 = 0$$
$$5\left(-2i\sqrt{2}\right)^2 + 40 = 0$$
$$40i^2 + 40 = 0$$
$$40\,(-1) + 40 = 0$$
$$0 = 0$$

The other solution is $2i\sqrt{2}$.

34. $-10\sqrt{xy}$

32. $\sqrt{-5} \cdot \sqrt{20}$ $10i$ 33. $\sqrt{-8} \cdot \sqrt{6}$ $4i\sqrt{3}$ 34. $-2\sqrt{-x} \cdot -5\sqrt{-y}$

35. i^{17} i 36. i^{59} $-i$ 37. i^{34} -1

38. $2\sqrt{-18} + 3\sqrt{-2}$ $9i\sqrt{2}$ 39. $(4 - i) + (3 + 3i)$ $7 + 2i$

40. $(8 - 5i) - (2 + i)$ $6 - 6i$ 41. $(7 - 6i) - (5 - 6i)$ 2

43. $15 - i\sqrt{3} - i\sqrt{5}$

42. $(2 - 4i) + (2 + 4i)$ 4 43. $(11 - \sqrt{-3}) - (-4 + \sqrt{-5})$

44. $(4 + i)(4 - i)$ 17 45. $(4 - i)(3 + 2i)$ $14 + 5i$

B

46. $(3 - 4i)^2$ $-7 - 24i$ 47. $(2 - \sqrt{-3})(2 + \sqrt{-3})$ 7

48. $-21 - 2i$

48. $3(-5 - 2i) + 2(-3 + 2i)$ 49. $(3 + 2i)^2 + (3 + 4i)^2$ $-2 + 36i$

Solve each equation.

50. $-6x^2 - 30 = 0$ $\pm i\sqrt{5}$ 51. $5x^2 + 40 = 0$ $\pm 2i\sqrt{2}$

52. $3x^2 + 18 = 0$ $\pm i\sqrt{6}$ 53. $7x^2 + 84 = 0$ $\pm 2i\sqrt{3}$

54. $\frac{2}{3}x^2 + 30 = 0$ $\pm 3i\sqrt{5}$ 55. $4x^2 + 5 = 0$ $\pm i\frac{\sqrt{5}}{2}$

Simplify.

56. $-220 - 40i$ **C**

57. $148 - 222i$

58. $130 + 110i$

56. $(-6 + 2i)(7 - i)(4 + 3i)$ 57. $(7 - 5i)(7 + 5i)(2 - 3i)$

58. $(7 - i)(4 + 2i)(5 + 2i)$ 59. $(2 + i)(1 + 2i)(3 - 4i)$ $20 + 15i$

Find the values of m and n that make each equation true.

62. $3, 1$

63. $\frac{67}{11}, \frac{19}{11}$

60. $18 + 7i = 3m + 2ni$ $6, 3.5$ 61. $(2m + n) + (m - n)i = 7 - i$ $2, 3$

62. $(m + 2n) + (2m - n)i = 5 + 5i$ 63. $(2m - 3n)i + (m + 4n) = 13 + 7i$

64. Sample answer: $(2 + i)(2 - i) = 4 - i^2$ or 5

64. Give an example to demonstrate that the product of two complex numbers in the form $a + bi$, where $a \neq 0$ and $b \neq 0$ may not result in a complex number of the same form.

Graphing Calculator

65. Refer to the equations in Exercises 50–55.
  a. Replace 0 with y in each equation and write the equation in the form $y = ax^2 + c$. **a–d. See Solutions Manual.**
  b. Graph each equation and make a sketch of the graph.
  c. What characteristic(s) do all of the graphs have in common?
  d. How does the statement "the real roots of a function are its $x-$intercepts" relate to what you found in your graphs?

Critical Thinking

66. **Number Theory** Under which of the operations—addition, subtraction, or multiplication—is the set of imaginary numbers closed? Give examples to support your answer. **See margin.**

67. Show that $2 - 3i$ is a solution of $x^2 - 4x + 13 = 0$. Are there other solutions? Explain. **See margin.**

Applications and Problem Solving

68. **Electricity** Refer to the information in Example 7.
  a. A circuit has a current of $(7 + 3j)$ amps and an impedance of $(5 - j)$ ohms. What will the voltage of the circuit be? $38 + 8j$
  b. A circuit has been tested to have a current of $(10 + 5j)$ amps. The current needed to upgrade the circuit is $(50 + 20j)$ amps. How many additional amps are needed to upgrade the circuit? $(40 + 15j)$ amps

Lesson 5-9 Complex Numbers **315**

Assignment Guide

Core: 21–69 odd, 71–82
Enriched: 20–64 even, 65–82

For **Extra Practice**, see p. 888.

The red A, B, and C flags, printed only in the Teacher's Wraparound Edition, indicate the level of difficulty of the exercises.

Additional Answers

66. The imaginary numbers are not closed under any of these operations.
Addition:
$(2 + 3i) + (2 - 3i) = 4$
Subtraction:
$(1 + 2i) - (3 + 2i) = -2$
Multiplication:
$(3 + 2i)(3 - 2i) = 13$

67. $x^2 - 4x + 13 = 0$
$(2 - 3i)^2 - 4(2 - 3i) + 13 \overset{?}{=} 0$
$(4 - 12i + 9i^2)$
                $-8 + 12i + 13 \overset{?}{=} 0$
                $4 - 9 - 8 + 13 \overset{?}{=} 0$
                                $0 = 0$

Yes, $2 - 3i$, because solutions involving imaginary numbers occur in conjugate pairs.

Practice Masters, p. 38

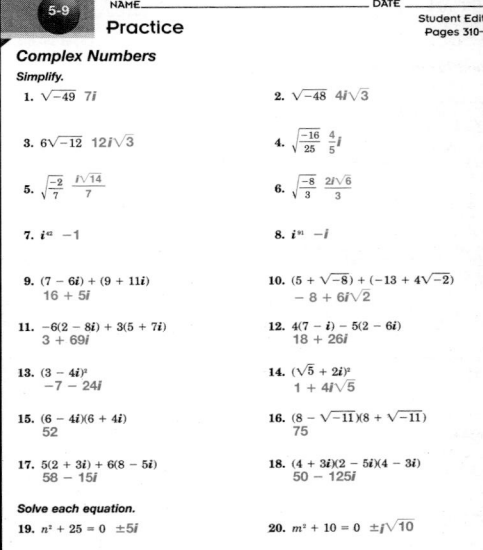

5-9 NAME_____ DATE_____
Practice   Student Edition Pages 310–316

Complex Numbers

Simplify.
1. $\sqrt{-49}$ $7i$ 2. $\sqrt{-48}$ $4i\sqrt{3}$

3. $6\sqrt{-12}$ $12i\sqrt{3}$ 4. $\sqrt{\frac{-16}{25}}$ $\frac{4}{5}i$

5. $\sqrt{\frac{-2}{7}}$ $\frac{i\sqrt{14}}{7}$ 6. $\sqrt{\frac{-8}{3}}$ $\frac{2i\sqrt{6}}{3}$

7. i^a -1 8. i^n $-i$

9. $(7 - 6i) + (9 + 11i)$ $16 + 5i$ 10. $(5 + \sqrt{-8}) + (-13 + 4\sqrt{-2})$ $-8 + 6i\sqrt{2}$

11. $-6(2 - 8i) + 3(5 + 7i)$ $3 + 69i$ 12. $4(7 - i) - 5(2 - 6i)$ $18 + 26i$

13. $(3 - 4i)^3$ $-7 - 24i$ 14. $(\sqrt{5} + 2i)^2$ $1 + 4i\sqrt{5}$

15. $(6 - 4i)(6 + 4i)$ 52 16. $(8 - \sqrt{-11})(8 + \sqrt{-11})$ 75

17. $5(2 + 3i) + 6(8 - 5i)$ $58 - 15i$ 18. $(4 + 3i)(2 - 5i)(4 - 3i)$ $50 - 125i$

Solve each equation.
19. $n^2 + 25 = 0$ $\pm 5i$ 20. $m^2 + 10 = 0$ $\pm i\sqrt{10}$

21. $6y^2 + 42 = 0$ $\pm i\sqrt{7}$ 22. $4r^2 + 64 = 0$ $\pm 4i$

Find the values of x and y for which each equation is true.
23. $3x - 5yi = 15 - 20i$ $x = 5$ $y = 4$ 24. $\sqrt{3}x + 7yi = 6 - 2i$ $x = 2\sqrt{3}$ $y = -\frac{2}{7}$

Closing Activity

Writing Write a paragraph explaining the concept of equality of two complex numbers.

Additional Answers

69a. $AB = D \cdot (BA)$

$$\begin{bmatrix} 0 & 1 \\ 1 & 0 \end{bmatrix} \cdot \begin{bmatrix} 0 & -i \\ i & 0 \end{bmatrix} \stackrel{?}{=} \begin{bmatrix} -1 & 0 \\ 0 & -1 \end{bmatrix} \cdot \left(\begin{bmatrix} 0 & -i \\ i & 0 \end{bmatrix} \cdot \begin{bmatrix} 0 & 1 \\ 1 & 0 \end{bmatrix} \right)$$

$$\begin{bmatrix} i & 0 \\ 0 & -i \end{bmatrix} \stackrel{?}{=} \begin{bmatrix} -1 & 0 \\ 0 & -1 \end{bmatrix} \cdot \begin{bmatrix} -i & 0 \\ 0 & i \end{bmatrix}$$

$$\begin{bmatrix} i & 0 \\ 0 & -i \end{bmatrix} = \begin{bmatrix} i & 0 \\ 0 & -i \end{bmatrix}$$

69b. $CB = D \cdot (BC)$

$$\begin{bmatrix} 1 & 0 \\ 0 & -1 \end{bmatrix} \cdot \begin{bmatrix} 0 & -i \\ i & 0 \end{bmatrix} \stackrel{?}{=} \begin{bmatrix} -1 & 0 \\ 0 & -1 \end{bmatrix} \cdot \left(\begin{bmatrix} 0 & -i \\ i & 0 \end{bmatrix} \cdot \begin{bmatrix} 1 & 0 \\ 0 & -1 \end{bmatrix} \right)$$

$$\begin{bmatrix} 0 & -i \\ -i & 0 \end{bmatrix} \stackrel{?}{=} \begin{bmatrix} -1 & 0 \\ 0 & -1 \end{bmatrix} \cdot \begin{bmatrix} i & 0 \\ 0 & i \end{bmatrix}$$

$$\begin{bmatrix} 0 & -i \\ -i & 0 \end{bmatrix} = \begin{bmatrix} 0 & -i \\ -i & 0 \end{bmatrix}$$

80.

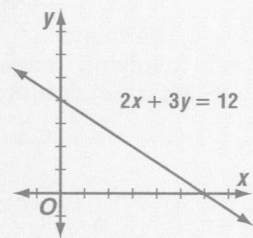

$2x + 3y = 12$

Enrichment Masters, p. 38

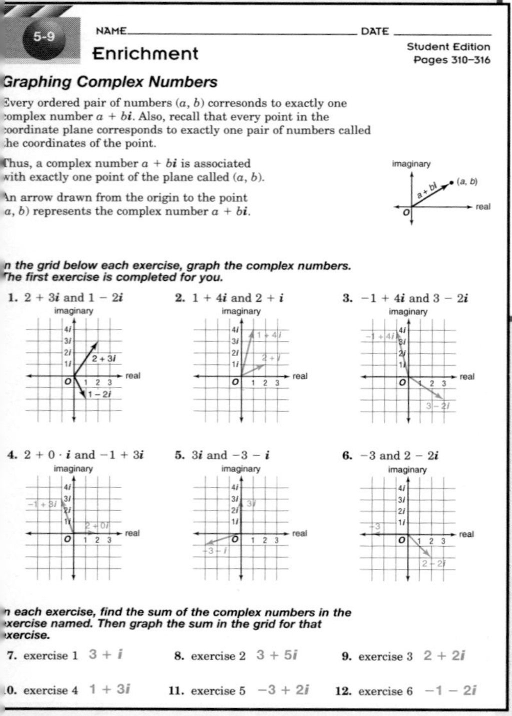

NAME_____ DATE_____

Enrichment

Student Edition
Pages 310–316

Graphing Complex Numbers

Every ordered pair of numbers (a, b) corresonds to exactly one complex number $a + bi$. Also, recall that every point in the coordinate plane corresponds to exactly one pair of numbers called the coordinates of the point.

Thus, a complex number $a + bi$ is associated with exactly one point of the plane called (a, b).

An arrow drawn from the origin to the point (a, b) represents the complex number $a + bi$.

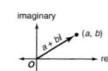

In the grid below each exercise, graph the complex numbers. The first exercise is completed for you.

1. $2 + 3i$ and $1 - 2i$ **2.** $1 + 4i$ and $2 + i$ **3.** $-1 + 4i$ and $3 - 2i$

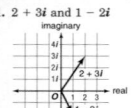   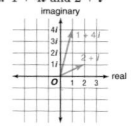   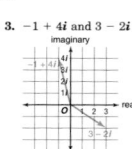

4. $2 + 0 \cdot i$ and $-1 + 3i$ **5.** $3i$ and $-3 - i$ **6.** -3 and $2 - 2i$

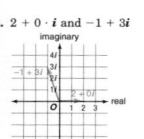   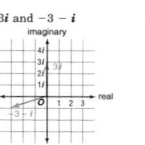   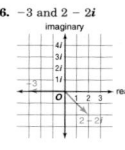

In each exercise, find the sum of the complex numbers in the exercise named. Then graph the sum in the grid for that exercise.

7. exercise 1 $3 + i$ **8.** exercise 2 $3 + 5i$ **9.** exercise 3 $2 + 2i$

10. exercise 4 $1 + 3i$ **11.** exercise 5 $-3 + 2i$ **12.** exercise 6 $-1 - 2i$

---

69. Quantum Mechanics Wolfgang Pauli (1900–1958) won the 1945 Nobel Prize for physics for his discovery of the Pauli exclusion principle. The principle states that in an atom, no two electrons can have the same energy. In his study of electron spin, he used matrices that have become known as the Pauli spin matrices. These matrices are $A = \begin{bmatrix} 0 & 1 \\ 1 & 0 \end{bmatrix}$, $B = \begin{bmatrix} 0 & -i \\ i & 0 \end{bmatrix}$, and $C = \begin{bmatrix} 1 & 0 \\ 0 & -1 \end{bmatrix}$. Suppose matrix $D = \begin{bmatrix} -1 & 0 \\ 0 & -1 \end{bmatrix}$.

  a. Verify that AB equals the product of D and BA.   See margin.

  b. Verify that CB equals the product of D and BC.   See margin.

70. Look for a Pattern Find the values for all of the powers of i from i^0 to i^{12}.

  a. What pattern do you notice in the values?

  b. Describe how you would simplify i^n, where n is a positive integer.

  c. Evaluate each expression. Assume that k is an integer.

    (1) i^{4k} 1   (2) i^{4k+1} i (3) i^{4k+2} -1 (4) i^{4k+3} $-i$

  d. Use your findings in part c to evaluate each expression.

    (1) i^{784} 1   (2) i^{503} $-i$ (3) $i^{8,413,634}$ -1

70b. Evaluate $(i^2)^{\frac{n}{2}}$.

71. Solve $\sqrt{3y^2 + 11y - 5} = y\sqrt{3} + 1$.   (Lesson 5–8)

72. Identify Subgoals What fraction of the perfect squares between 0 and 100 are odd?   (Lesson 5–7)

73. Physics If a stone is dropped from a cliff, the equation $t = \frac{1}{4}\sqrt{d}$ represents the time t in seconds that it takes for the stone to reach the ground. If d represents the distance in feet that the stone falls, find how long it would take for a stone to fall from a 150-foot cliff.   (Lesson 5–6)

74. Simplify $3p(p^2 - 2p + 3)$.   (Lesson 5–2) $3p^3 - 6p^2 + 9p$

75. Solve the system of equations by using augmented matrices.   (Lesson 4–7)

  $x + 3y - 2z = 9$

  $-x + 5y + 2z = 31$

  $2x - 9z = -32$ **(2, 5, 4)**

76. Find $3\begin{bmatrix} 3 & -2 & 5 \\ 2 & 7 & -5 \end{bmatrix} + 2\begin{bmatrix} -1 & 3 & 4 \\ 2 & -3 & 0 \end{bmatrix}$.   (Lesson 4–2) $\begin{bmatrix} 7 & 0 & 23 \\ 10 & 15 & -15 \end{bmatrix}$

77. Decorating Carol and Frank are buying some new living room furniture. A sofa, loveseat, and coffee table cost $2100. The sofa costs twice as much as the love seat. The sofa and the coffee table cost $1510. What are the prices of each piece of furniture?   (Lesson 3–7)

78. Solve the system of equations by using the elimination method. (Lesson 3–2)

  $3x - 2y = 7$

  $-3x + 9y = 14$

79. Write an equation in standard form for the line whose x-intercept is 6 and y-intercept is -5.   (Lesson 2–4) $5x - 6y = 30$

80. Graph $2x + 3y = 12$.   (Lesson 2–2)   **See margin.**

81. A number increased by 27 is 46. Find the number.   (Lesson 1–4)   **19**

82. State the property illustrated by $3 + (a + b) = (a + b) + 3$.   (Lesson 1–2)

Extension

Problem Solving Find the values for x and y such that $\sqrt{(x + 2)} + 3iy = \sqrt{3x} + 4i$. $x = 1$, $y = \frac{4}{3}$

What do you do first? Why? Justify your steps.

Answers (middle column):

70a. They all equal 1, i, -1, or $-i$.

71. $\dfrac{6(11 + 2\sqrt{3})}{109}$

72. $\dfrac{1}{2}$

73. 3.06 seconds

77. sofa, $1180; loveseat, $590; table, $330

78. $\left(\dfrac{13}{3}, 3\right)$

82. commutative $(+)$

5-10

Simplifying Expressions Containing Complex Numbers

What YOU'LL LEARN

• To simplify rational expressions containing complex numbers in the denominator.

Why IT'S IMPORTANT

You can use complex numbers to solve problems involving fractals and electricity.

APPLICATION
Electricity

We take electricity for granted as a part of our everyday life. In most third-world countries, only large metropolitan areas have access to electricity. The International Foundation for the Promotion of New and Emerging Sciences and Technology (NEST) has been working to bring electricity to smaller rural communities.

In the last lesson, you used the formula $E = I \cdot Z$ to solve problems dealing with electrical circuits. Impedance Z is the resistance to the flow of electricity and is measured in ohms. Voltage E refers to the electrical potential in a circuit and is measured in volts. Current I is measured in amperes (amps). If a circuit of 110 volts were to be installed in a house, what would the impedance be for a current of $15 + 3j$ amps?

$$E = I \cdot Z$$
$$110 = (15 + 3j)Z \quad E = 110, I = 15 + 3j$$
$$\frac{110}{15 + 3j} = Z \quad \textit{Divide each side by } (15 + 3j).$$

Remember that in electricity j is used instead of i to represent the imaginary unit.

Since j represents a radical, this expression is not in simplest form. *You will simplify this expression in Example 3.*

Remember that two radical expressions $a\sqrt{b} + c\sqrt{d}$ and $a\sqrt{b} - c\sqrt{d}$ are conjugates. Since imaginary numbers also involve radicals, numbers of the form $a + bi$ and $a - bi$ are called **complex conjugates**. Recall that the product of two radical conjugates is a rational number. Let's investigate the product of two complex conjugates.

Example **1** Simplify $(15 + 3i)(15 - 3i)$.

$$(15 + 3i)(15 - 3i) = 15^2 - 9i^2 \quad \textit{Difference of two squares}$$
$$= 225 - (-9) \quad 9i^2 = 9(-1)$$
$$= 234$$

F Y I

In Nepal, they are experimenting with microhydro-technology. During the day, these small hydroelectric units turn sugar-cane crushers, sawmills, and rice hullers, doing in 15 minutes what it took one person 3 days to do.

The product in Example 1 is rational. Let's explore the general case $(a + bi)(a - bi)$.

$$(a + bi)(a - bi) = a^2 - (bi)^2 \quad \textit{Difference of two squares}$$
$$= a^2 - b^2i^2$$
$$= a^2 + b^2 \quad b^2i^2 = b^2(-1)$$

Since a and b are real numbers, $a^2 + b^2$ will also be real. Thus, the product of complex conjugates is a real number.

Lesson 5–10 Simplifying Expressions Containing Complex Numbers **317**

5-10 LESSON NOTES

NCTM Standards: 1–5

Instructional Resources

• Study Guide Master 5-10
• Practice Master 5-10
• Enrichment Master 5-10
• Assessment and Evaluation Masters, p. 129
• Multicultural Activity Masters, p. 10

 Transparency 5-10A contains the 5-Minute Check for this lesson; **Transparency 5-10B** contains a teaching aid for this lesson.

Recommended Pacing

Standard Pacing	Day 14 of 16
Honors Pacing	Day 10 of 12
Block Scheduling*	Day 5 of 6 (along with Lesson 5-9)

 *For more information on pacing and possible lesson plans, refer to the *Block Scheduling Booklet*.

1 FOCUS

 5-Minute Check
(over Lesson 5-9)

Simplify.

1. $\sqrt{-49}$ $7i$
2. $5i \cdot 4i$ -20
3. $\sqrt{-6} \cdot \sqrt{-15}$ $-3\sqrt{10}$
4. $(7 + 6i)(4 - 2i)$ $40 + 10i$
5. $(1 + 8i) - (5 - 4i)$ $-4 + 12i$

F Y I

A world-wide organization, the Office of Appropriate Technology, helps to discover and disseminate new technologies to regions where larger, centralized technologies are not appropriate.

GLENCOE Technology

CD-ROM Interaction

A multimedia simulation links functions with the period of radius for Earth-orbiting satellites. A blackline master activity with teacher's notes provides a follow-up to the CD-ROM simulation.

For Windows & Macintosh

Motivating the Lesson

Questioning Ask students the following questions and discuss.

1. What are the conjugates of
$\frac{1}{3 + \sqrt{7}}$ and $\frac{2}{2 + \sqrt{5}}$?
$\frac{3 + \sqrt{7}}{2}$; $-4 + 2\sqrt{5}$

2. What are the products of conjugates involving irrational numbers? **If the real part is irrational, the product is irrational.**

3. What can you hypothesize about the conjugates of complex numbers? **To obtain the conjugate, reverse the sign of the imaginary part.**

2 TEACH

In-Class Examples

For Example 1
Simplify.

a. $(6 + 3i)(6 - 3i)$ 45
b. $(9 - 7i)(9 + 7i)$ 130

For Example 2
Simplify.

a. $\frac{3i}{2 - 4i}$ $\frac{3i - 6}{10}$

b. $\frac{3 + 7i}{2i}$ $\frac{7 - 3i}{2}$

For Example 3
Refer to the application at the beginning of the lesson. What would the impedance be for a current of $10 - 2j$ amps?
$10.58 + 2.12j$

Teaching Tip Note that in Example 2b, $\frac{-i}{-i}$ could have been used to rationalize the denominator.

We use conjugates of radicals to rationalize the denominators of expressions with radicals in the denominator. We can also use conjugates of complex numbers to rationalize denominators of expressions with complex numbers in the denominator.

Example **Simplify each expression.**

LOOK BACK

You can review rationalizing the denominator in Lesson 5-6.

a. $\frac{8i}{1 + 3i}$

$\frac{8i}{1 + 3i} = \frac{8i}{1 + 3i} \cdot \frac{1 - 3i}{1 - 3i}$ *$1 + 3i$ and $1 - 3i$ are conjugates.*

$= \frac{8i(1 - 3i)}{1 + 3^2}$

$= \frac{8i - 24i^2}{10}$

$= \frac{8i + 24}{10}$

$= \frac{4i + 12}{5}$ or $\frac{12 + 4i}{5}$

b. $\frac{2 + i}{5i}$

$\frac{2 + i}{5i} = \frac{2 + i}{5i} \cdot \frac{i}{i}$ *Why multiply by $\frac{i}{i}$ instead of $\frac{5i}{5i}$?*

$= \frac{2i + i^2}{5i^2}$

$= \frac{2i - 1}{-5}$ or $\frac{-1(1 - 2i)}{-1(5)}$

$= \frac{1 - 2i}{5}$

Example  **Refer to the application at the beginning of the lesson. What would the impedance Z be for a current of $15 + 3j$ amps in a 110-volt circuit?**

APPLICATION
Electricity

We found that $Z = \frac{110}{15 + 3j}$.

$Z = \frac{110}{15 + 3j} \cdot \frac{15 - 3j}{15 - 3j}$ *Rationalize the denominator.*

$= \frac{110(15 - 3j)}{234}$ *$(15 + 3j)(15 - 3j) = 15^2 + 3^2$ or 234*

$= \frac{1650 - 330j}{234}$

$\approx 7.05 - 1.41j$

The impedance would be approximately $7.05 - 1.41j$ ohms.

The picture at the left, called a **fractal,** was created with the aid of a computer. Benoit Mandelbrot coined the word *fractal* as a label for computer-generated, irregular and fragmented, self-similar shapes. Fractal objects are created using functions that are **iterated,** that is, repeated over and over. The function is evaluated for some initial value of *x*, and then the function is evaluated again using that result. Repeating this process and plotting the points produces interesting and sometimes beautiful pictures. Some of the most exciting fractals are created using this process with a number like $4 + 3i$ as the initial value.

318 *Chapter 5 Exploring Polynomials and Radical Expressions*

Classroom Vignette

"I like to have students explore iteration by making up a function *f(x)* and choosing a value for *x* to be iterated eight times. Students plot the iterations and study the pattern formed. They look for other functions that create interesting designs. Students artistically present their designs and display the most interesting ones in the classroom."

Carol Ann Van Galder

Carol Ann VanGalder
Milton High School
Milton, Wisconsin

Example ④ **Suppose the function** $f(x) = \frac{1}{x^2 + 1}$ **is to be iterated to produce a fractal.**

INTEGRATION

Fractal Geometry

Find the first two points of the iteration if the initial value is $(1 + i)$.

1st iteration

Replace x with $(1 + i)$.

$f(1 + i) = \dfrac{1}{(1 + i)^2 + 1}$

$= \dfrac{1}{1 + 2i - 1 + 1}$

$= \dfrac{1}{1 + 2i}$

$= \dfrac{1}{1 + 2i} \cdot \dfrac{1 - 2i}{1 - 2i}$

$= \dfrac{1 - 2i}{5}$ or $\dfrac{1}{5} - \dfrac{2i}{5}$

2nd iteration

Replace x with $\dfrac{1 - 2i}{5}$.

$f\left(\dfrac{1 - 2i}{5}\right) = \dfrac{1}{\left(\dfrac{1 - 2i}{5}\right)^2 + 1}$

$= \dfrac{1}{\dfrac{(1 - 4i - 4) + 25}{25}}$

$= \dfrac{25}{22 - 4i}$

$= \dfrac{25}{2(11 - 2i)} \cdot \dfrac{11 + 2i}{11 + 2i}$

$= \dfrac{275 + 50i}{2(121 + 4)}$

$= \dfrac{275 + 50i}{250}$ or $\dfrac{11}{10} + \dfrac{i}{5}$

The first two points of the iteration are $\dfrac{1}{5} - \dfrac{2i}{5}$ and $\dfrac{11}{10} + \dfrac{i}{5}$.

CHECK FOR UNDERSTANDING

Communicating Mathematics

Study the lesson. Then complete the following. 1–2. See margin.

1. **Describe** how to rationalize the denominator of $\dfrac{1}{a + bi}$.

2. **Explain** why the product of a complex number and its conjugate is always a real number.

3. **Evaluate** each expression if $z = 1 + 2i$.

    a. z^2 $-3 + 4i$ **b.** $\dfrac{1}{z}$ $\dfrac{1 - 2i}{5}$

3c. z or $1 + 2i$; see margin for verification.

    c. What would you think the product $z^2 \cdot \dfrac{1}{z}$ would be without substituting $1 + 2i$ for z? Use substitution to verify your answer.

4. Does every complex number have a multiplicative inverse and an additive inverse? **All have additive inverses, but 0 does not have a multiplicative inverse.**

Guided Practice

Find the conjugate of each complex number.

5. $7i$ $-7i$ 6. $3 + 5i$ $3 - 5i$

Find the product of each complex number and its conjugate.

7. $-10i$ 100 8. $12 + 5i$ 169

Simplify.

9. $\dfrac{7}{-2i}$ $\dfrac{7i}{2}$ 10. $\dfrac{9 + 3i}{2i}$ $\dfrac{3 - 9i}{2}$ 11. $\dfrac{5}{2 + i}$ $2 - i$

12. $\dfrac{5 + i}{1 + 2i}$ $\dfrac{7 - 9i}{5}$ 13. $\dfrac{3 - 2i}{1 - i}$ $\dfrac{5 + i}{2}$ 14. $\dfrac{7}{\sqrt{2} - 3i}$ $\dfrac{7\sqrt{2} + 21i}{11}$

15. $\left(\dfrac{7 + 3i}{1}\right)\left(\dfrac{7 - 3i}{58}\right) =$
$\dfrac{58}{58} = 1$

15. Show that $7 + 3i$ and $\dfrac{7 - 3i}{58}$ are multiplicative inverses of each other.

Lesson 5–10 Simplifying Expressions Containing Complex Numbers **319**

In-Class Example

For Example 4
Suppose the function $f(x) = \dfrac{1}{1 - x^2}$ is to be iterated to produce a fractal. Find the first two points of iteration if the initial value is $(i - 1)$.
$\dfrac{1}{5} - \dfrac{2i}{5}$; $\dfrac{1}{2} + i$

3 PRACTICE/APPLY

Check for Understanding
Exercises 1–15 are designed to help you assess your students' understanding through reading, writing, speaking, and modeling. You should work through Exercises 1–4 with your students and then monitor their work on Exercises 5–15.

Error Analysis
Students often think they have rationalized the denominator below

$\dfrac{1}{\sqrt[3]{2} + i\sqrt{3}} \cdot \dfrac{\sqrt[3]{2} - i\sqrt{3}}{\sqrt[3]{2} - i\sqrt{3}} =$

$\dfrac{\sqrt[3]{2} - i\sqrt{3}}{\sqrt[3]{4} - i^2 + 3}$ or $\dfrac{\sqrt[3]{2} - i\sqrt{3}}{\sqrt[3]{4} + 3}$

Instead, they have only changed it to a real number. It is still not in simplest form.

Study Guide Masters, p. 39

NAME_____ DATE _____

Student Edition
Pages 317–321

Study Guide

5-10

Simplifying Expressions Containing Complex Numbers

Complex numbers of the form $a + bi$ and $a - bi$ are called **conjugates** of each other. Notice that the product of complex conjugates is always a real number. Study the example to the right.

Example: Find $(5 + 2i)(5 - 2i)$.
$(5 + 2i)(5 - 2i) = 25 - 4i^2$
$= 25 - (-4)$
$= 29$

Sometimes rational expressions contain complex numbers. Since i represents a radical, rational numbers are usually written without imaginary numbers in the denominator. As with radicals, the denominator should be rationalized. Study the example to the right.

Example: Simplify $\dfrac{2 + 9i}{3i}$.
$\dfrac{2 + 9i}{3i} = \dfrac{2 + 9i}{3i} \cdot \dfrac{i}{i}$
$= \dfrac{2i + 9i^2}{3i^2}$
$= \dfrac{-9 + 2i}{-3}$ or $\dfrac{9 - 2i}{3}$

Find the conjugate of each complex number.

1. $4 - 2i$ $4 + 2i$ 2. $8 - 2i$ $8 + 2i$ 3. $6 + 3i$ $6 - 3i$

Find the product of each complex number and its conjugate.

4. $4 - 2i$ 20 5. $9 - 2i$ 85 6. $5 - 4i$ 41

Simplify.

7. $(5 - 7i)(5 + 7i)$ 74 8. $5 \div (3 + i)$ $\dfrac{3 - i}{2}$ 9. $7 - 13i \div 2i$ $\dfrac{1}{2}$

10. $\dfrac{3 + i\sqrt{5}}{3 - i\sqrt{5}}$ $\dfrac{2 + 3i\sqrt{5}}{7}$ 11. $\dfrac{4 - i\sqrt{2}}{i\sqrt{2}}$ $-1 - 2\sqrt{2}i$ 12. $\dfrac{\sqrt{6} + i\sqrt{3}}{\sqrt{2} - i}$ $\dfrac{\sqrt{12} - \sqrt{3} + 2i\sqrt{6}}{3}$

Reteaching

Using Reasoning Ask students to find a and b for each of the following:

1. $(8 + 2i)(a + bi) = 26 - 2i$
    $a = 3, b = -1$

2. $(5 - 3i) + (a + bi) = 9 + i$
    $a = 4, b = 4$

3. $(3 - 4i)^3 = a + bi$
    $a = -117, b = -44$

What properties justify your steps?

Additional Answers

1. To rationalize the denominator, multiply by 1 in the form of $\dfrac{a - bi}{a - bi}$.

2. The resulting product is a sum of two squares that are each real numbers.

3c.
$$z^2 \cdot \dfrac{1}{z} \overset{?}{=} z$$
$$(1 + 2i)^2\left(\dfrac{1}{1 + 2i}\right) \overset{?}{=} 1 + 2i$$
$$\dfrac{(1 + 2i)(1 + 2i)}{(1 + 2i)} \overset{?}{=} 1 + 2i$$
$$1 + 2i = 1 + 2i$$

Assignment Guide

Core: 17–59 odd, 60–69
Enriched: 16–54 even, 55–69

For **Extra Practice,** see p. 888.

The red A, B, and C flags, printed only in the Teacher's Wraparound Edition, indicate the level of difficulty of the exercises.

Additional Answers

55. $\overline{z \cdot w} = \overline{(a + bi) \cdot (c + di)}$
$= \overline{ac + adi + bci - bd}$
$= \overline{(ac - bd) + (ad + bc)i}$
$= (ac - bd) - (ad + bc)i$
$= ac - adi - bd - bci$
$= ac - adi + bdi^2 - bci$
$= a(c - di) - bi(-di + c)$
$= (a - bi)(c - di)$
$= \overline{z} \cdot \overline{w}$

56. $\left(\dfrac{-1 + i\sqrt{3}}{2}\right)^3$

$= \left(\dfrac{1 - 2i\sqrt{3} - 3}{4}\right)\left(\dfrac{-1 + i\sqrt{3}}{2}\right)$

$= \left(\dfrac{-1 - i\sqrt{3}}{2}\right)\left(\dfrac{-1 + i\sqrt{3}}{2}\right)$

$= \dfrac{1 + 3}{4}$ or 1

Practice Masters, p. 39

NAME_____ DATE _____
Student Edition
Pages 317–321

Practice

Simplifying Expressions Containing Complex Numbers

Simplify.

1. $\dfrac{2 - 4i}{1 + 3i}$ $-1 - i$
2. $\dfrac{3 - i}{2 - i}$ $\dfrac{7 + i}{5}$
3. $\dfrac{6 + 5i}{-2i}$ $\dfrac{-5 + 6i}{2}$
4. $\dfrac{1 + 6i}{5i}$ $\dfrac{6 - i}{5}$
5. $\dfrac{3 - 6i}{-4i}$ $\dfrac{6 + 3i}{4}$
6. $\dfrac{2 + 7i}{-5i}$ $\dfrac{-7 + 2i}{5}$
7. $\dfrac{3}{6 + 4i}$ $\dfrac{9 - 6i}{26}$
8. $\dfrac{2}{7 - 8i}$ $\dfrac{14 + 16i}{113}$
9. $\dfrac{3}{\sqrt{2} - 5i}$ $\dfrac{\sqrt{2} + 5i}{9}$
10. $\dfrac{2 + i\sqrt{3}}{1 + i\sqrt{3}}$ $\dfrac{5 - i\sqrt{3}}{4}$
11. $\dfrac{(1 - 2i)^2}{(2 - i)^2}$ $\dfrac{7 - 24i}{25}$
12. $\dfrac{2 + i}{(1 - i)^2}$ $\dfrac{-1 + 2i}{2}$
13. $\dfrac{3}{\sqrt{5} + 2i}$ $\dfrac{\sqrt{5} - 2i}{3}$
14. $\dfrac{2 - i}{\sqrt{2} + 2i}$ $\dfrac{-2 + 2\sqrt{2} - (4 + \sqrt{2})i}{6}$
15. $\dfrac{(1 + 3i)^2}{(4 - i)^2}$ $\dfrac{-168 + 26i}{289}$
16. $\dfrac{2 - i\sqrt{3}}{1 + i\sqrt{3}}$ $\dfrac{-1 - 3i\sqrt{3}}{4}$

Find the multiplicative inverse of each complex number.

17. $5 + 2i$ $\dfrac{5 - 2i}{29}$
18. $3 - i$ $\dfrac{3 + i}{10}$
19. $\dfrac{i}{7 + 4i}$ $4 - 7i$
20. $\dfrac{-6i}{4 - 5i}$ $\dfrac{5 + 4i}{6}$

320 Chapter 5

Practice

Find the conjugate of each complex number.

16. $10i$ $-10i$ **17.** $12 + i$ $12 - i$ **18.** $-15i$ $15i$

19. $10 - 4i$ $10 + 4i$ **20.** $7 + i\sqrt{5}$ $7 - i\sqrt{5}$ **21.** $6 + \sqrt{-7}$ $6 - i\sqrt{7}$

Find the product of each complex number and its conjugate.

22. $-2i$ 4 **23.** $5 - 2i$ 29 **24.** $4 + 6i$ 52

25. $1 + i$ 2 **26.** $3 + 5i\sqrt{2}$ 59 **27.** $8 - 2i$ 68

Simplify.

28. $\dfrac{2 + 8i}{3i}$ $\dfrac{8 - 2i}{3}$ **29.** $\dfrac{3 + 7i}{2i}$ $\dfrac{7 - 3i}{2}$ **30.** $\dfrac{11 + i}{2 - i}$ $\dfrac{21 + 13i}{5}$

31. $\dfrac{3i}{2 + i}$ $\dfrac{3 + 6i}{5}$ **32.** $\dfrac{-3i}{5 + 4i}$ $\dfrac{-12 - 15i}{41}$ **33.** $\dfrac{3}{6 + 4i}$ $\dfrac{9 - 6i}{26}$

B

34. $\dfrac{3 + 5i}{1 + i}$ $4 + i$ **35.** $\dfrac{2 + i}{3 - i}$ $\dfrac{1 + i}{2}$ **36.** $\dfrac{1 - i}{4 - 5i}$ $\dfrac{9 + i}{41}$

37. $\dfrac{2 + 3i}{3 - 2i}$ i **38.** $\dfrac{5 - 6i}{-3i}$ $\dfrac{6 + 5i}{3}$ **39.** $\dfrac{3 - 9i}{4 + 2i}$ $\dfrac{-3 - 21i}{10}$

40. $\dfrac{8}{\sqrt{2} + i}$ $\dfrac{8\sqrt{2} - 8i}{3}$ **41.** $\dfrac{1}{3 - i\sqrt{2}}$ $\dfrac{3 + i\sqrt{2}}{11}$ **42.** $\dfrac{4}{\sqrt{3} + 2i}$ $\dfrac{4\sqrt{3} - 8i}{7}$

Find the multiplicative inverse of each complex number.

43. $6 - 5i$ $\dfrac{6 + 5i}{61}$ **44.** $\dfrac{-i}{3 + 5i}$ $-5 + 3i$ **45.** $x + yi$ $\dfrac{x - yi}{x^2 + y^2}$

INTEGRATION
Fractal Geometry

Find the 1st and 2nd iteration of each function for the given initial value.

46. $f(x) = x^2 + 2$ for $x = 1 + i$ $2i + 2, 2 + 8i$

47. $f(x) = 3x^2 + 2$ for $x = 1 - i$ $2 - 6i, -94 - 72i$

48. $f(x) = x^2 - x$ for $x = i + 3$ $5 + 5i, -5 + 45i$

C

Simplify.

49. $\dfrac{3 - i\sqrt{5}}{3 + i\sqrt{5}}$ $\dfrac{2 - 3i\sqrt{5}}{7}$ **50.** $\dfrac{1 + i\sqrt{3}}{1 - i\sqrt{3}}$ $\dfrac{-1 + i\sqrt{3}}{2}$

51. $\dfrac{1 - i}{(1 + i)^2}$ $\dfrac{-1 - i}{2}$ **52.** $\left(\dfrac{\sqrt{3}}{2 + 3i}\right)^2$ $\dfrac{-15 - 36i}{169}$

53. $\dfrac{(2 + 3i)^2}{(3 + i)^2}$ $\dfrac{16 + 63i}{50}$ **54.** $\dfrac{(4 + 3i)^2}{(3 - 4i)^2}$ -1

Critical Thinking

55. If $z = a + bi$ and $w = c + di$ are complex numbers, then their conjugates are denoted by $\overline{z} = a - bi$ and $\overline{w} = c - di$, respectively. Determine if the conjugate of the product zw is equal to the product of the conjugates. That is, would $\overline{z \cdot w} = \overline{z} \cdot \overline{w}$? Why or why not?   See margin.

56. Show that $\dfrac{-1 + i\sqrt{3}}{2}$ is a cube root of 1.   See margin.

320   Chapter 5 Exploring Polynomials and Radical Expressions

Applications and Problem Solving

CAREER CHOICES

Engineers apply the principles of science and mathematics to solve practical technical problems. **Electrical engineers** design, develop, test, and supervise the manufacturing of electrical and electronic equipment. They comprise more than one fourth of all engineers. A bachelor's degree in engineering is the minimum requirement.

For more information, contact:

Institute of Electrical and Electronic Engineers
1828 L St. NW, Suite 1202
Washington, DC 20036

57. Electrical Engineering Refer to the application at the beginning of the lesson. Copy and complete the table.

	a.	b.	c.	d.
E (volts)	$60 + 112j$	$85 + 110j$	$-50 + 100j$	$-70 + 240j$
Z (ohms)	$10 + 6j$	$3 - 4j$	$\frac{25 - 25j}{2}$	$\frac{1310 - 920j}{41}$
I (amps)	$\frac{159 + 95j}{17}$	$\frac{-37 + 134j}{5}$	$-6 + 2j$	$-5 + 4j$

58. Electrical Circuitry In a two-battery flashlight, the positive terminal of the first battery touches the negative terminal of the second. The positive terminal of the second battery touches the center terminal of the light bulb. A metal strip connects the bulb to the switch, which is connected to the negative terminal of the first battery. When you turn the flashlight on, the switch completes the circuit, and the bulb lights up.

a. Suppose each of the batteries is 2.5 volts. What is the total impedance of the circuit in the flashlight if the current is $(1 + 2j\sqrt{2})$?

b. What is the total current if two 1.5 volt batteries are used and the impedance is $(2 + 3j)$ ohms?

58a. $\dfrac{5 - j10\sqrt{2}}{18}$ ohms

58b. $\dfrac{5 - 9j}{26}$ amps

59. Fractal Geometry Suppose the function $f(x) = x^2 - 1$ is to be iterated to produce a fractal. Find the first four points of the iteration if the initial value of x is $(1 + i)$. Write the points as ordered pairs.

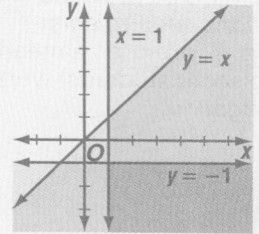

Mixed Review

Solve each equation. 60. $\pm 2i\sqrt{2}$

60. $3a^2 + 24 = 0$ (Lesson 5–9)

61. $2x + 7 = -x\sqrt{2}$ (Lesson 5–8)

62. Factor $(x + y)^2 - \frac{1}{4}$. (Lesson 5–4)

63. Retail The store Bunches of Boxes and Bags assembles boxes to package items for mailing. The store manager found that the volume of a box made from a piece of cardboard with a square of length x inches cut from each corner is $(4x^3 - 168x^2 + 1728x)$ in^3. If the piece of cardboard is 48 inches long, how wide is it? (Lesson 5–3) **36 in.**

64. Find the inverse of $\begin{bmatrix} 3 & 1 \\ -4 & 1 \end{bmatrix}$. (Lesson 4–5) $\frac{1}{7}\begin{bmatrix} 1 & -1 \\ 4 & 3 \end{bmatrix}$

Solve each system algebraically or by graphing.

65. $6x - 2y - 3z = -10$
$-6x + y + 9z = 3$
$8x - 3y = -16$ (Lesson 3–7)

66. $x > 1$
$y < -1$
$y < x$ (Lesson 3–4)

67. Is the relation $\{(0, 0), (1, 0)\}$ a function? Explain your answer. (Lesson 2–1)

68. Solve $3(2m - 3) \geq 9$. (Lesson 1–6) $\{m \mid m \geq 3\}$

69. Evaluate $[(-8 + 3) \times 4 - 2] \div 6$. (Lesson 1–1)

59. $(1 + i, -1 + 2i),$
$(-1 + 2i, -4 - 4i),$
$(-4 - 4i, -1 + 32i),$
$(-1 + 32i, -1024 - 64i)$

61. $\dfrac{7\sqrt{2} - 14}{2}$

62. $\left(x + y - \frac{1}{2}\right)\left(x + y + \frac{1}{2}\right)$

65. $\left(\frac{1}{4}, 6, -\frac{1}{6}\right)$

66. See margin.

67. Yes; each element of the domain is paired with exactly one element of the range.

69. $-\dfrac{11}{3}$

Extension

Reasoning Can the product of a conjugate and its complex number be an irrational number?

Yes; $\left(\sqrt[3]{2} + i\right)\left(\sqrt[3]{2} - i\right) = \sqrt[3]{4} + 1$ is irrational.

CAREER CHOICES

The first practical use of electricity was the telegraph, invented in 1837 by Samuel Morse. Forty years later, Alexander Graham Bell invented the telephone and in 1878, Thomas Edison created the light bulb.

4 ASSESS

Closing Activity

Writing Have students write one or two sentences describing how to rationalize the denominator of a fraction that contains imaginary numbers.

Chapter 5, Quiz D (Lessons 5-9 and 5-10), is available in the *Assessment and Evaluation Masters,* p. 129.

Additional Answer

66.

Enrichment Masters, p. 39

5-10   NAME_____   DATE_____
Enrichment   Student Edition
Pages 317–321

Conjugates and Absolute Value

When studying complex numbers, it is often convenient to represent a complex number by a single variable. For example, we might let $z = x + yi$. We denote the conjugate of z by $\bar{z}$. Thus, $\bar{z} = x - yi$.

We can define the absolute value of a complex number as follows.
$$|z| = |x + yi| = \sqrt{x^2 + y^2}$$
There are many important relationships involving conjugates and absolute values of complex numbers.

Example: Show $|z|^2 = z\bar{z}$ for any complex number z.
Let $z = x + yi$. Then,
$z\bar{z} = (x + yi)(x - yi)$
$= x^2 + y^2$
$= (\sqrt{x^2 + y^2})^2$
$= |z|^2$

Example: Show $\frac{\bar{z}}{|z|^2}$ is the multiplicative inverse for any nonzero complex number z.
We know $|z|^2 = z\bar{z}$. If $z \neq 0$, then we have $z\left(\frac{\bar{z}}{|z|^2}\right) = 1$.
Thus, $\frac{\bar{z}}{|z|^2}$ is the multiplicative inverse of z.

For each of the following complex numbers, find the absolute value and multiplicative inverse.

1. $2i$ $2; \frac{-i}{2}$
2. $-4 - 3i$ $5; \frac{-4 + 3i}{25}$
3. $12 - 5i$ $13; \frac{12 + 5i}{169}$
4. $5 - 12i$ $13; \frac{5 + 12i}{169}$
5. $1 + i$ $\sqrt{2}; \frac{1 - i}{2}$
6. $\sqrt{3} - i$ $2; \frac{\sqrt{3} + i}{4}$
7. $\frac{\sqrt{3}}{3} + \frac{\sqrt{3}}{3}i$
8. $\frac{\sqrt{2}}{2} - \frac{\sqrt{2}}{2}i$
9. $\frac{1}{2} - \frac{\sqrt{3}}{2}i$
$\frac{\sqrt{6}}{3}; \frac{\sqrt{3} - i\sqrt{3}}{2}$ $1; \frac{\sqrt{2}}{2} + \frac{\sqrt{2}}{2}i$ $1; \frac{1}{2} + \frac{\sqrt{3}}{3}i$

Closing the Investigation

This activity provides students an opportunity to bring their work on the Investigation to a close. For each Investigation, students should present their findings to the class. Here are some ways students can display their work.

- Conduct and report on an interview or survey.
- Write a letter, proposal, or report.
- Write an article for the school or local paper.
- Make a display, including graphs and/or charts.
- Plan an activity.

Assessment

To assess students' understanding of the concepts and topics explored in the Investigation and its follow-up activities, you may wish to examine students' Investigation Folders.

The scoring guide provided in the *Investigations and Projects Masters*, p. 7, provides a means for you to score students' work on the Investigation.

Investigations and Projects Masters, p. 7

Scoring Guide
Chapters 4 and 5
Investigation

Level	Specific Criteria
3 Superior	· Shows thorough understanding of using materials to design a launcher. Understands the concepts of *calibration, matrices, scatter plots, box-and-whisker plots, median, quartiles, greatest and least values, interquartile ranges, error range, tolerance, relative error, average error,* and *standard deviation.* · Uses appropriate strategies to solve problems. · Computations are correct. · Written explanations are exemplary. · Charts, graphs, and report are appropriate and sensible. · Goes beyond the requirements of some or all parts of the Investigation.
2 Satisfactory, with Minor Flaws	· Uses materials to design a launcher. Understands the concepts of *calibration, matrices, scatter plots, box-and-whisker plots, median, quartiles, greatest and least values, interquartile ranges, error range, tolerance, relative error, average error,* and *standard deviation.* · Uses appropriate strategies to solve problems. · Computations are mostly correct. · Written explanations are effective. · Charts, graphs, and report are appropriate and sensible. · Satisfies all requirements of the Investigation.
1 Nearly Satisfactory, with Obvious Flaws	· Uses materials to design a launcher. Understands most of the concepts of *calibration, matrices, scatter plots, box-and-whisker plots, median, quartiles, greatest and least values, interquartile ranges, error range, tolerance, relative error, average error,* and *standard deviation.* · May not use appropriate strategies to solve problems. · Computations are mostly correct. · Written explanations are satisfactory. · Charts, graphs, and report are appropriate and sensible. · Satisfies most requirements of the Investigation.
0 Unsatisfactory	· Shows little or no understanding of how to use materials to design a launcher, as well as the concepts of *calibration, matrices, scatter plots, box-and-whisker plots, median, quartiles, greatest and least values, interquartile ranges, error range, tolerance, relative error, average error,* and *standard deviation.* · May not use appropriate strategies to solve problems. · Computations are incorrect. · Written explanations are not satisfactory. · Charts, graphs, and report are not appropriate or sensible. · Does not satisfy the requirements of the Investigation.

3-2-1-Blast-Off!

Refer to the Investigation on pages 180–181.

When a new launch system is needed and a contract is given to a research company, the company employs engineers, scientists, physicists, drafters, and others to work together toward the final plans for the launcher. Accuracy is examined as well as the cost factor. Many of the skills you have used in this Investigation are used by professionals to design the right launcher for the job.

Analyze

You have conducted experiments and organized your data in various ways. It is now time to analyze your findings and state your conclusions.

PORTFOLIO ASSESSMENT

You may want to keep your work on this Investigation in your portfolio.

1. Look over the data and organize a table of all the data from the shoot-off including all the distances of each team.

2. Make a list of statistical measures and accuracy measures calculated from each team's data. These should include two sets of measures: the median, quartiles, least and greatest values, and interquartile range; the error range, tolerance, relative error, average error, and standard deviation. Did the data collected from the two sets of measures lead you to the same conclusion about the launcher's accuracy? Explain.

3. Analyze each of the launchers that were used in the shoot-off and rank them from most accurate to least accurate. Use mathematical measures to justify your rankings. Explain what measures you used and how you used them to evaluate the accuracy of the launchers.

Write

The government has asked you for a report on both the design and calibration of your launcher and an analysis of the results of the shoot-off.

4. Summarize the procedures you used to design the launcher. Describe the steps and procedures used to design your launcher, from the receipt of the instructions to the demonstration shoot-off.

5. Draw a detailed blueprint of the launch system that specifies its parts and the construction of the system.

6. Include in this report an operation manual that describes how the launcher operates. Include a description of the calibration system used for accuracy. A list or table that compares the launch system settings with actual shot distances should also be included. Describe the mathematical relationship between the settings and target distances.

7. Summarize the accuracy of the launch system. Include test data recorded from shots taken at each distance: 50 cm, 100 cm, 150 cm, 200 cm, and 250 cm. A graph depicting the location of the test shots and the target distance should also be included.

Using the CHAPTER HIGHLIGHTS

The Chapter Highlights begins with a listing of the new terms, properties, and phrases that were introduced in this chapter. Have students define each term and provide an example or two of it, if appropriate.

Assessment and Evaluation Masters, pp. 115–116

VOCABULARY

After completing this chapter, you should be able to define each term, property, or phrase and give an example or two of each.

Algebra
binomial (p. 261)
coefficient (p. 255)
complex conjugates (p. 317)
complex number (p. 311)
conjugates (p. 292)
constant (p. 255)
degree (p. 255)
extraneous solution (p. 305)
factors (p. 274)
FOIL method (p. 263)
imaginary unit (p. 310)
iterate (p. 318)

like radical expressions (p. 291)
like terms (p. 261)
monomial (p. 255)
nth root (p. 282)
polynomial (p. 261)
power (p. 255)
prime number (p. 274)
principal root (p. 282)
pure imaginary number (p. 310)
radical equations (p. 305)
radical inequalities (p. 306)
rational exponent (p. 298)

rationalizing the denominator (p. 290)
scientific notation (p. 254)
simplify (p. 255)
square root (p. 281)
synthetic division (p. 269)
term (p. 261)
trinomial (p. 261)

Geometry
fractal (p. 318)

Problem Solving
identify subgoals (p. 296)

UNDERSTANDING AND USING THE VOCABULARY

Choose a word or term that best completes each statement or phrase.

1. A number is expressed in <u>scientific notation</u> when it is in the form of $a \cdot 10^n$, where $1 \le a < 10$ and n is an integer.
2. Monomials that contain no variables are known as <u>constants</u>.
3. <u>Rationalizing the denominator</u> is the process used to eliminate radicals from the denominator or fractions from a radicand.
4. A shortcut method known as <u>synthetic division</u> is used to divide polynomials by binomials.
5. Real numbers that cannot be written as terminating or repeating decimals are <u>irrational numbers</u>.
6. The <u>FOIL method</u> is used to multiply two binomials.
7. In an algebraic term that is the product of a number and a variable, the number is the <u>coefficient</u> of the variable.
8. A <u>monomial</u> is an expression that is a number, a variable, or the product of a number and one or more variables.
9. A solution of a transformed equation that is not a solution of the original equation is an <u>extraneous solution</u>.
10. <u>Complex conjugates</u> are imaginary numbers of the form $a + b\mathbf{i}$ and $a - b\mathbf{i}$.
11. For any number a and b, if $a^2 = b$, then a is the <u>square root</u> of b.
12. A polynomial comprised of three unlike terms is known as a <u>trinomial</u>.
13. The <u>degree of a polynomial</u> is the degree of the monomial of the greatest degree.
14. When there is more than one root, the <u>principal root</u> is the nonnegative root.
15. <u>Fractals</u> are computer-generated, irregular and fragmented, self-similar shapes created using functions that are iterated—that is, repeated over and over.

Chapter 5 Highlights **323**

Instructional Resources

Three multiple-choice tests and three free-response tests are provided in the *Assessment and Evaluation Masters*. Forms 1A and 2A are for honors pacing, and Forms 1B, 1C, 2B, and 2C are for average pacing. Chapter 5 Test, Form 1B is shown at the right. Chapter 5 Test, Form 2B is shown on the next page.

5

NAME_____ DATE_____

Chapter 5 Test, Form 1B

Write the letter for the correct answer in the blank at the right of each problem.

1. Simplify $\frac{12m^6 t^{-5}}{15m^2 t^{-2}}$.
   A. $\frac{4m^4 t^3}{5}$ B. $-\frac{3m^4}{t^3}$ C. $\frac{4m^4}{5t^3}$ D. $\frac{m^4 t^3}{3}$ 1. __C__

2. Simplify $(7m - 8)^2$.
   A. $49m^2 + 64$ B. $49m^2 - 64$
   C. $49m^2 - 112m + 64$ D. $49m^2 - 30m + 64$ 2. __C__

3. Simplify $(3w^5)(-m)^4$.
   A. $3m^4 w^5$ B. $-3m^4 w^5$ C. $-12m^4 w^5$ D. $-3w^5 + m^4$ 3. __A__

4. Simplify $(x + 3)(x^2 + 5x - 4)$.
   A. $x^3 + 8x^2 + 11x - 12$ B. $x^3 + 5x - 12$
   C. $x^3 + 8x^2 + 4x - 12$ D. $x^3 + 8x^2 - 11x - 12$ 4. __A__

5. Simplify $\frac{a^2(r^{-3}s)^{-2}}{a^5 r^3 s^3}$.
   A. $\frac{1}{a^3 r^4 s^5}$ B. $\frac{r^3}{a^3 s^5}$ C. $\frac{r^3}{a^3 s}$ D. $\frac{a^3 s}{r^3}$ 5. __B__

6. Express 86,400,000 in scientific notation.
   A. 864×10^{-5} B. 864×10^5
   C. 8.64×10^{-7} D. 8.64×10^7 6. __D__

7. Simplify $\frac{4 - 2i}{7 + 3i}$.
   A. $\frac{11 - 13i}{29}$ B. $\frac{11 - 14i}{29}$ C. $\frac{13 - 17i}{29}$ D. $\frac{17 - 13i}{29}$ 7. __A__

8. Evaluate $\frac{4 \times 10^{-2}}{16 \times 10^{-4}}$. Express the answer in scientific notation.
   A. 0.25×10^2 B. 2.5×10^1 C. 2.5×10^3 D. 2.5×10^{-3} 8. __B__

9. Simplify $(3a^3 - 7a^2 + a) - (6a^3 - 4a^2 - 8)$.
   A. $-3a^6 - 3a^4 + a + 8$ B. $-3a^3 - 11a^2 + a - 8$
   C. $-3a^6 - 11a^4 + a - 8$ D. $-3a^3 - 3a^2 + a + 8$ 9. __D__

10. Simplify $\pm \sqrt{4x^2 - 4xy + y^2}$.
    A. $|2x - y|$ B. $\pm(2x - y)$ C. $\pm|2x - y|$ D. no real roots   10. __C__

11. Simplify $\sqrt[3]{-64n^3 w^3}$.
    A. $-4nw$ B. $-4|nw|$ C. $-8nw\sqrt[3]{nw}$ D. $-8|nw|$ 11. __A__

5

NAME_____ DATE_____

Chapter 5 Test, Form 1B (continued)

Factor each polynomial completely.

12. $y^3 - 64$
    A. $(y - 4)^3$ B. $(y - 4)(y^2 + 4y + 16)$
    C. $(y - 4)(y + 4)^2$ D. $(y - 8)(y^2 + 16y + 64)$ 12. __B__

13. $21x^2 + 29x - 10$
    A. $(3x - 2)(7x - 5)$ B. $(3x + 5)(7x - 2)$
    C. $(3x + 2)(7x + 5)$ D. $(3x - 5)(7x + 2)$ 13. __B__

14. $5y - 21x + 3xy - 35$
    A. $(y - 7)(3x + 5)$ B. $y(5 + 3x) + 7(-3x - 5)$
    C. $y(5 + 3x) - 7(3x - 5)$ D. not factorable   14. __A__

15. Simplify $\frac{6}{4 + \sqrt{2}}$.
    A. $\frac{12 - 6\sqrt{2}}{7}$ B. $\frac{4 - \sqrt{2}}{2}$ C. $\frac{4 - \sqrt{2}}{3}$ D. $\frac{12 - 3\sqrt{2}}{7}$ 15. __D__

16. Simplify $\frac{\frac{n}{v} - v}{\frac{1}{n^2} - \frac{1}{v^2}}$.
    A. $n^{\frac{1}{2}} + v^{\frac{1}{2}}$ B. $n^{\frac{1}{2}} - v^{\frac{1}{2}}$
    C. $\frac{n^{\frac{3}{2}} - v^{\frac{3}{2}} + nv^{\frac{1}{2}} - n^{\frac{1}{2}}v}{n - v}$ D. $\frac{n - 2n^{\frac{1}{2}}v^{\frac{1}{2}} + v}{n - v}$ 16. __C__

17. Divide using long division:
    $(4 - 7x^2 + 13x + x^4 + x^3) \div (x^2 + 4x + 1)$.
    A. $x^2 - 3x - 4 + \frac{32x + 8}{x^2 + 4x + 1}$ B. $x^2 + 3x - 18 + \frac{62x + 22}{x^2 + 4x + 1}$
    C. $x^2 - 3x + 4$ D. $x^2 - 3x + 4 - \frac{8}{x^2 + 4x + 1}$ 17. __C__

18. Solve $\sqrt[3]{x - 4} - 12 = -7$.
    A. $\{19\}$ B. $\{121\}$ C. $\{129\}$ D. $\varnothing$ 18. __C__

19. Simplify $(4 - 2i)^2$.
    A. 12 B. 20 C. $12 - 16i$ D. $20 - 16i$ 19. __C__

20. Divide using synthetic division: $(2x^4 + 6x^3 + 5x - 6) \div (x + 2)$.
    A. $2x^3 + 2x^2 - 4x + 13 - \frac{32}{x + 2}$ B. $2x^2 + 2x + x - 8$
    C. $2x^2 + 2x + x - \frac{8}{x + 2}$ D. $2x^3 + 2x^2 + x - \frac{8}{x + 2}$ 20. __A__

Bonus Find the value of k so $(x^3 - 2x^2 + kx + 6) \div (x + 2)$
has remainder 8.
A. -9 B. 9 C. 0 D. none of these   Bonus __A__

Skills and Concepts Encourage students to refer to the objectives and examples on the left as they complete the review exercises on the right.

Assessment and Evaluation Masters, pp. 121–122

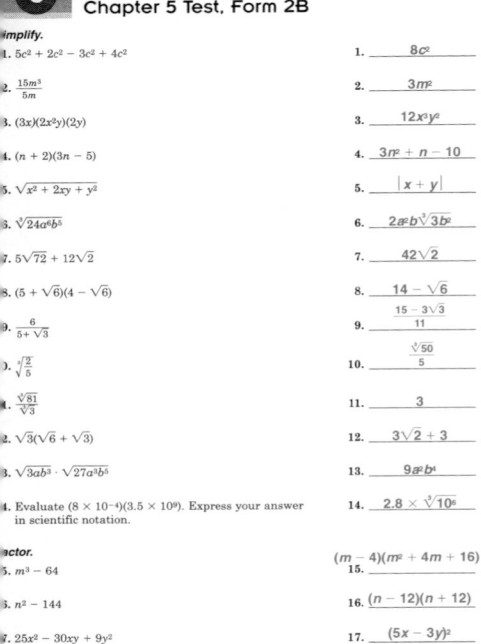

SKILLS AND CONCEPTS

Upon completing this chapter, you should be able to:

Use these exercises to review and prepare for the chapter test.

• multiply and divide monomials (Lesson 5–1)

$(3x^4y^6)(-8x^3y)$

$= (3)(-8)x^{4+3}y^{6+1}$ *Multiplying powers*

$= -24x^7y^7$ 20. $\frac{16}{15}c^4d^2f$ 21. $-\frac{3}{2}$

Simplify. Assume that no variable equals 0.

16. $m^3 \cdot m^5$ m^8 17. $f^{-7} \cdot f^4$ $\frac{1}{f^3}$

18. $(3x^2)^3$ $27x^6$ 19. $(2y)(4xy^3)$ $8xy^4$

20. $\left(\frac{3}{5}c^2f\right)\left(\frac{4}{3}cd\right)^2$ 21. $\frac{1}{x^0+y^0} - \frac{x^0+y^0}{1}$

22. $3(ab)^3(4ac^2) + c(4ab)(5a^3b^2c)$ $32a^4b^3c^2$

• represent numbers in scientific notation (Lesson 5–1)

$31,000 = 3.1 \times 10,000$

$= 3.1 \times 10^4$

$0.007 = 7 \times 0.001$

$= 7 \times 10^{-3}$

Evaluate. Express each answer in both scientific and decimal form.

23. $(2000)(85,000)$ $170,000,000; 1.7 \times 10^8$

24. $(0.0014)^2$ $0.00000196; 1.96 \times 10^{-6}$

25. $5,400,000 \div 6000$ $900; 9 \times 10^2$

• add, subtract, and multiply polynomials (Lesson 5–2)

$(5x^2 + 4x) - (3x^2 + 6x - 7)$

$= 5x^2 + 4x - 3x^2 - 6x + 7$

$= (5x^2 - 3x^2) + (4x - 6x) + 7$

$= 2x^2 - 2x + 7$

$(9k + 4)(7k - 6)$

$= (9k)(7k) + (9k)(-6) + (4)(7k) + (4)(-6)$

$= 63k^2 - 54k + 28k - 24$

$= 63k^2 - 26k - 24$

Simplify. 27. $4x^2 + 22x - 34$

26. $(4c - 5) - (c + 11) + (-6c + 17)$ $-3c + 1$

27. $(11x^2 + 13x - 15) - (7x^2 - 9x + 19)$

28. $-6m^2(3mn + 13m - 5n)$

29. $(d - 5)(d + 3)$ $d^2 - 2d - 15$

30. $x^{-8}y^{10}(x^{11}y^{-9} + x^{10}y^{-6})$ $x^3y + x^2y^4$

31. $(2a^2 + 6)^2$ $4a^4 + 24a^2 + 36$

32. $-5f^{12}(4f^3g + 2f)$ $-20f^{15}g - 10f^{13}$

33. $(2b - 3c)^3$ $8b^3 - 36b^2c + 54bc^2 - 27c^3$

28. $-18m^3n - 78m^3 + 30m^2n$

• divide polynomials by binomials using synthetic division (Lesson 5–3)

Find $(4x^4 - x^3 - 19x^2 + 11x - 2) \div (x - 2)$.

$4x^4 - x^3 - 19x^2 + 11x - 2$

$$
\begin{array}{r|rrrrr}
2 & 4 & -1 & -19 & 11 & -2 \\
& & 8 & 14 & -10 & 2 \\
\hline
& 4 & 7 & -5 & 1 & 0
\end{array}
$$

The quotient is $4x^3 + 7x^2 - 5x + 1$.

Find each quotient. 34. $2x^3 + x - \frac{3}{x-3}$

34. $(2x^4 - 6x^3 + x^2 - 3x - 3) \div (x - 3)$

35. $(10x^4 + 5x^3 + 4x^2 - 9) \div (x + 1)$

36. $(x^2 - 5x + 4) \div (x - 1)$ $x - 4$

37. $(5x^4 + 18x^3 + 10x^2 + 3x) \div (x^2 + 3x)$

35. $10x^3 - 5x^2 + 9x - 9$ 37. $5x^2 + 3x + 1$

Sidebar — Chapter 5 Test Form 2B

5 NAME_____ DATE_____

Chapter 5 Test, Form 2B

Simplify.

1. $5c^2 + 2c^2 - 3c^2 + 4c^2$ 1. $8c^2$

2. $\frac{15m^3}{5m}$ 2. $3m^2$

3. $(3x)(2x^2y)(2y)$ 3. $12x^3y^2$

4. $(n + 2)(3n - 5)$ 4. $3n^2 + n - 10$

5. $\sqrt{x^2 + 2xy + y^2}$ 5. $|x + y|$

6. $\sqrt[3]{24a^6b^5}$ 6. $2a^2b\sqrt[3]{3b^2}$

7. $5\sqrt{72} + 12\sqrt{2}$ 7. $42\sqrt{2}$

8. $(5 + \sqrt{6})(4 - \sqrt{6})$ 8. $14 - \sqrt{6}$

9. $\frac{6}{5 + \sqrt{3}}$ 9. $\frac{15 - 3\sqrt{3}}{11}$

10. $\sqrt{\frac{2}{5}}$ 10. $\frac{\sqrt{50}}{5}$

11. $\frac{\sqrt{81}}{\sqrt{3}}$ 11. 3

12. $2\sqrt{3}(\sqrt{6} + \sqrt{3})$ 12. $3\sqrt{2} + 3$

13. $\sqrt{3ab^3} \cdot \sqrt{27a^3b^5}$ 13. $9a^2b^4$

14. Evaluate $(8 \times 10^{-4})(3.5 \times 10^9)$. Express your answer in scientific notation. 14. $2.8 \times \sqrt[3]{10^6}$

Factor.

15. $m^3 - 64$ 15. $(m - 4)(m^2 + 4m + 16)$

16. $n^2 - 144$ 16. $(n - 12)(n + 12)$

17. $25x^2 - 30xy + 9y^2$ 17. $(5x - 3y)^2$

5 NAME_____ DATE_____

Chapter 5 Test, Form 2B (continued)

18. $7x^2 - 19x - 6$ 18. $(7x + 2)(x - 3)$

19. $x^3 + 3x^2 - 4x - 12$ 19. $(x + 2)(x - 2)(x + 3)$

20. Divide using synthetic division. $(x^3 + 4x^2 - 17x - 60) \div (x + 3)$ 20. $x^2 + x - 20$

21. Divide using long division. $(10y^3 - 9y^2 + 6y - 10) \div (2y + 3)$ 21. $5y^2 - 12y + 21 - \frac{73}{2y + 3}$

22. One factor of $a^3 + 10a^2 + 31a + 30$ is $a + 2$. Find the other factors. 22. $a + 5, a + 3$

23. Write $2^{\frac{1}{2}}x^{\frac{3}{3}}y^{\frac{1}{6}}$ as a single radical. 23. $\sqrt[6]{2^3x^4y}$

24. For what values of x and y is $x - 3i = 20 - 18yi$? 24. $x = 20, y = \frac{1}{6}$

25. Evaluate $\frac{12}{8^{\frac{2}{3}}}$. 25. 3

26. Simplify $\frac{x}{\frac{1}{x^2} + \frac{1}{y^2}}$. 26. $\frac{x - y}{x^2 - xy^2}$

27. Simplify $\frac{3}{4 + 7i}$. 27. $\frac{12 - 21i}{65}$

28. Simplify $(7 - 12i) + (15 - 7i)$. 28. $22 - 19i$

29. Find the solution set of the equation in the set of complex numbers. $\sqrt[3]{y} + 7 = 4$ 29. $y = 57$

30. Solve the following equation, if possible: $\sqrt{2d + 3} = -1$. If the equation has no real solution, write "no solution." 30. no solution

31. Write $\sqrt[5]{3x^3y^{10}z}$ in simplified form using rational exponents. 31. $3^{\frac{1}{5}}x^{\frac{3}{5}}y^2z^{\frac{1}{5}}$

32. Perform the following division. $(48x^5y^4 - 36x^3y^3 + 12x^2y^6) \div 6x^2y$ 32. $8x^3y^3 - 6xy^2 + 2y^5$

33. Simplify $\frac{x^{-\frac{3}{2}}\sqrt{y}}{x^{\frac{2}{3}}y^{-\frac{1}{2}}}$. 33. $\frac{y}{x}$

Bonus Factor $(x + 5)^2 - (x + 5)(y - 1) - 20(y - 1)^2$. Bonus $(x + 4y + 1)(x - 5y + 10)$

GLENCOE Technology

⊙ **Test and Review Software**

You may use this software, a combination of an item generator and item bank, to create your own tests or worksheets. Types of items include free response, multiple choice, short answer, and open ended.

For IBM & Macintosh

OBJECTIVES AND EXAMPLES

REVIEW EXERCISES

• factor polynomials (Lesson 5–4)

$4x^3 - 6x^2 + 10x - 15$

$= (4x^3 - 6x^2) + (10x - 15)$

$= 2x^2(2x - 3) + 5(2x - 3)$

$= (2x^2 + 5)(2x - 3)$

41. $(s + 8)(s^2 - 8s + 64)$ 42. prime

Factor completely. If the polynomial is not factorable, write *prime*.

38. $200x^2 - 50$ $50(2x + 1)(2x - 1)$
39. $10a^3 - 20a^2 - 2a + 4$ $2(5a^2 - 1)(a - 2)$
40. $5w^3 - 20w^2 + 3w - 12$ $(5w^2 + 3)(w - 4)$
41. $s^3 + 512$ 42. $x^2 - 7x + 5$

• simplify radicals having various indices
(Lesson 5–5)

$\pm\sqrt{81x^4} = \pm\sqrt{(9x^2)^2}$ or $\pm9x^2$

$\sqrt[7]{2187x^{14}y^{35}} = \sqrt[7]{(3x^2y^5)^7}$ or $3x^2y^5$

47. $\pm(x^4 - 3)$ 48. $512 + x^2$ 50. $|a - 5|$

Simplify.   45. no real roots

43. $\pm\sqrt{256}$ ±16
44. $\sqrt[3]{-216}$ -6
45. $\sqrt{-(-8)^2}$
46. $\sqrt[5]{c^5d^{15}}$ cd^3
47. $\pm\sqrt{(x^4 - 3)^2}$
48. $\sqrt[3]{(512 + x^2)^3}$
49. $\sqrt[4]{16m^8}$ $2m^2$
50. $\sqrt{a^2 - 10a + 25}$

• add, subtract, multiply, and divide radical
expressions (Lesson 5–6)

$6\sqrt[5]{32m^3} \cdot 5\sqrt[5]{1024m^2}$

$= 6 \cdot 5\sqrt[5]{(32m^3 \cdot 1024m^2)}$

$= 30\sqrt[5]{2^5 4^5 m^5}$

$= 30\sqrt[5]{2^5} \cdot \sqrt[5]{4^5} \cdot \sqrt[5]{m^5}$

$= 30 \cdot 2 \cdot 4 \cdot m$ or $240m$

Simplify.   53. $-5\sqrt{3}$ 54. $-2\sqrt[5]{11}$

51. $\sqrt[4]{64}$ $2\sqrt{2}$
52. $\sqrt{5} + \sqrt{20}$ $3\sqrt{5}$
53. $5\sqrt{12} - 3\sqrt{75}$
54. $6\sqrt[5]{11} - 8\sqrt[5]{11}$
55. $\left(\sqrt{8} + \sqrt{12}\right)^2$
56. $\sqrt{8} \cdot \sqrt{15} \cdot \sqrt{21}$
57. $\dfrac{1}{3 + \sqrt{5}}$ $\dfrac{3 - \sqrt{5}}{4}$
58. $\dfrac{\sqrt{10}}{4 + \sqrt{2}}$

55. $20 + 8\sqrt{6}$ 56. $6\sqrt{70}$ 58. $\dfrac{2\sqrt{10} - \sqrt{5}}{7}$

• evaluate expressions in either exponential or
radical form (Lesson 5–7)

$32^{\frac{4}{5}} \cdot 32^{\frac{2}{5}} = 32^{\left(\frac{4}{5} + \frac{2}{5}\right)}$

$\quad = 32^{\frac{6}{5}}$

$\quad = (2^5)^{\frac{6}{5}}$

$\quad = 2^6$ or 64

$\dfrac{3x}{y^{-\frac{3}{2}} \cdot \sqrt[3]{z}} = \dfrac{3xy^{\frac{3}{2}}}{z^{\frac{1}{3}}} \cdot \dfrac{z^{\frac{2}{3}}}{z^{\frac{2}{3}}}$

$\quad = \dfrac{3xy^{\frac{3}{2}}z^{\frac{2}{3}}}{z}$

Evaluate.

59. $27^{-\frac{2}{3}}$ $\dfrac{1}{9}$
60. $9^{\frac{1}{3}} \cdot 9^{\frac{5}{3}}$ 81
61. $\left(\dfrac{8}{27}\right)^{-\frac{2}{3}}$ $\dfrac{9}{4}$

Simplify.   64. $3x^{\frac{5}{3}} + 4x^{\frac{8}{3}}$

62. $\dfrac{1}{y^{\frac{2}{5}}}$ $\dfrac{y^{\frac{3}{5}}}{y}$
63. $\dfrac{xy}{\sqrt[3]{z}}$ $\dfrac{xyz^{\frac{2}{3}}}{z}$
64. $\dfrac{3x + 4x^2}{x^{-\frac{2}{3}}}$

• solve equations containing radicals (Lesson 5–8)

$\sqrt{3x - 8} + 1 = 3$

$\quad \sqrt{3x - 8} = 2$

$\quad (\sqrt{3x - 8})^2 = 2^2$

$\quad 3x - 8 = 4$

$\quad x = 4$

67. $-\sqrt{3}$

69. 1, 3

Solve each equation. Be sure to check for extraneous solutions.   66. no solution

65. $y^{\frac{1}{3}} - 7 = 0$ 343
66. $(x - 2)^{\frac{3}{2}} = -8$
67. $6 + 2x\sqrt{3} = 0$
68. $\sqrt{3t - 5} - 3 = 4$ 18
69. $\sqrt{1 + 8v} - 2 = v$
70. $\sqrt[4]{2x - 1} = 2$ 8.5
71. $\sqrt{y + 5} = \sqrt{2y - 3}$ 8
72. $\sqrt{y + 1} + \sqrt{y - 3} = 5$ 7.41

Applications and Problem Solving Encourage students to work through the exercises in the Applications and Problem Solving section to strengthen their problem-solving skills.

OBJECTIVES AND EXAMPLES

• add, subtract, and multiply complex numbers (Lesson 5–9)

$$(15 - 2i) + (5i - 11) = (15 - 11) + (-2i + 5i)$$
$$= 4 + 3i$$

$$(2 + 3i)(4i - 11) = (2)(4i) + (2)(-11) + (3i)(4i) + (3i)(-11)$$
$$= 8i - 22 + 12i^2 - 33i$$
$$= 8i - 22 + 12(-1) - 33i$$
$$= 8i - 33i - 22 - 12$$
$$= -34 - 25i$$

• simplify rational expressions containing complex numbers in the denominator   (Lesson 5–10)

$$\frac{7i}{2 + 4i} = \frac{7i}{2 + 4i} \cdot \frac{2 - 4i}{2 - 4i}$$
$$= \frac{7i(2 - 4i)}{4 + 4^2}$$
$$= \frac{14i - 28i^2}{20}$$
$$= \frac{14i + 28}{20} \text{ or } \frac{7}{5} + \frac{7}{10}i$$

REVIEW EXERCISES

Simplify.

73. $\sqrt{-256}$ $16i$

74. $\sqrt[6]{-64m^{12}}$ $2m^2 i$

75. $(13i - 2)5i$ $-65 - 10i$

76. $(7 - 4i) - (-3 + 6i)$ $10 - 10i$

77. $-6\sqrt{-a} \cdot 2\sqrt{-b}$ $12\sqrt{ab}$

78. i^6 -1

79. i^{85} i

80. $(3 + 4i)(5 - 2i)$ $23 + 14i$

81. $(\sqrt{6} + i)(\sqrt{6} - i)$ 7

Simplify.

82. $\frac{1 + i}{1 - i}$ i

83. $\frac{4 - 3i}{4 + 3i}$ $\frac{7 - 24i}{25}$

84. $\frac{4}{4 + 5i}$ $\frac{16 - 20i}{41}$

85. $\frac{1 + i\sqrt{2}}{1 - i\sqrt{2}}$ $\frac{-1 + 2i\sqrt{2}}{3}$

APPLICATIONS AND PROBLEM SOLVING

86. **Aerospace Engineering** Scientists expect that on future space stations, artificial gravity will be created by rotating all or part of the space station. The formula $N = \frac{1}{2\pi}\sqrt{\frac{a}{r}}$ gives the number of rotations N required per second to maintain an acceleration of gravity of a meters per second squared (m/s^2) on a satellite with a radius of r meters. The acceleration of gravity on Earth is 9.8 m/s^2. How many rotations per minute will produce an artificial gravity that is equal to half of the gravity on Earth in a space station 25 meters wide?   (Lesson 5–5)   **about 6 rotations per minute**

87. **Law Enforcement** A police investigator measured the skid marks left by a car to be approximately 120 feet. The driver of the car claims that she was not exceeding the 40-mph speed limit. Is she telling the truth? (Recall that $s = 2\sqrt{5\ell}$, where s represents speed, measured in miles per hour, and ℓ represents the length of the skidmarks, measured in feet.) How fast was she driving?   (Lesson 5–6)   **No, she is not telling the truth. She was going approximately 49 mph.**

88. **Archaeology** Since carbon-14 is present in all living organisms and decays at a predictable rate after death, archaeologists use the amount of carbon-14 left in a fossil to extimate the age of the fossil. This is commonly called *carbon dating*. The approximate number of milligrams A of carbon-14 left in a fossil after 5000 years can be found using the formula $A = A_0(2.7)^{-\frac{3}{5}}$, where A_0 is the initial amount of carbon-14 in the organism. Find the amount of carbon-14 left in an organism that contained 500 milligrams of carbon-14.   (Lesson 5–7)   **276 milligrams**

A practice test for Chapter 5 is provided on page 916.

ALTERNATIVE ASSESSMENT

PERFORMANCE ASSESSMENT TASK

Area and Volume   An open box can be made from a piece of cardboard 30 inches wide by 36 inches long by folding congruent square tabs from each corner.

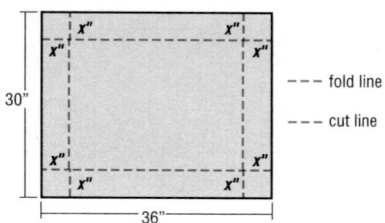

- - - fold line

- - - cut line

1. Obtain a piece of cardboard the same size as the one shown above. Mark the box as shown with 3-inch squares at each corner. Cut along the cut lines, fold in the tabs, and fold up the sides to make the box. What is the volume of the box?

2. Find the algebraic representation $V(x)$ of the volume of the box when x is the length of one side of the square tab in the corner. Make a table of values if the side length of the squares is 2, 4, 6, 8, 10, 12, and 14 inches. How does the volume of the box change when the size of the square tabs increases in size?

3. Find the algebraic representation $A(x)$ of the area of the bottom of the box. How does the area of the bottom of the box change when the size of the square tabs increases in size?

4. Is the measure of the area of the box ever equal to the measure of the volume of the box? What is the maximum volume of the box? What is the minimum volume of the box?

THINKING CRITICALLY

As you may recall, a set is closed under an operation if the result of performing the operation on any two elements of the set is an element of the set. For example, adding two whole numbers always results in a whole number.

Is the set of irrational numbers closed under any of the four basic operations? Give examples to support your answer.   **No; performing all four operations can result in a rational number.**

PORTFOLIO

Select one of the assignments from this chapter that you found to be difficult to master. Explain why you found this to be the case. How might this assignment be presented in a different way that may help other students having the same difficulty?

SELF EVALUATION

One characteristic of a good problem solver is knowing the language and properties of mathematics. If you don't understand something, do you seek clarification from you teacher or your parents?

Assess yourself. How well do you understand the language and properties of mathematics? Without looking first, write a paragraph about the language and properties of mathematics that you have learned in this chapter. When you're done, compare it to your notes or to your textbook. Note which lessons you need to study more in order to better understand the mathematics in this chapter.

Assessment and Evaluation Masters, pp. 126, 137

5   NAME_____   DATE_____

Chapter 5 Performance Assessment

Instructions: *Demonstrate your knowledge by giving a clear, concise solution to each problem. Be sure to include all relevant drawings and justify your answers. You may show your solution in more than one way or investigate beyond the requirements of the problem.*

1. Area models can be used to illustrate factoring polynomials. Represent $2x^2 + 3x + 1$ by the regions shown below.

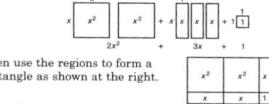

Then use the regions to form a rectangle as shown at the right.

Note that sides of length x are placed adjacent to one another and sides of length 1 are placed next to sides of length 1.

a. Use the area model above to find the factors of $2x^2 + 3x + 1$. Explain how you found each factor.

b. Use an area model to find the factors of $3x^2 + 4x + 1$. Explain each step.

c. Draw an area model for a polynomial. Then write the polynomial and its factors. Explain each step.

2. Explain how you would simplify $(\sqrt{6 + 3\sqrt{3}} - \sqrt{6 - 3\sqrt{3}})^2$. Justify each step.

3. a. Find two complex numbers whose difference is $2 - i$. Explain your reasoning.

b. Find the sum of the complex numbers you found in part a geometrically and algebraically. Show your work.

c. Explain in your own words how to find the quotient of two complex numbers.

d. Find the quotient of the two complex numbers you found in part a.

Scoring Guide
Chapter 5
Performance Assessment

Level	Specific Criteria
3 Superior	• Shows thorough understanding of the concepts of *using models to demonstrate factoring trinomials; simplifying radical expressions; and adding, subtracting, multiplying, and dividing complex numbers.* • Uses appropriate strategies to solve problems. • Computations are correct. • Written explanations are exemplary. • Diagrams and graphs are accurate and appropriate. • Goes beyond the requirements of problem.
2 Satisfactory, with Minor Flaws	• Shows understanding of the concepts of *using models to demonstrate factoring trinomials; simplifying radical expressions; and adding, subtracting, multiplying, and dividing complex numbers.* • Uses appropriate strategies to solve problems. • Computations are mostly correct. • Written explanations are effective. • Diagrams and graphs are mostly accurate and appropriate. • Satisfies all requirements of problem.
1 Nearly Satisfactory, with Serious Flaws	• Shows understanding of most of the concepts of *using models to demonstrate factoring trinomials; simplifying radical expressions; and adding, subtracting, multiplying, and dividing complex numbers.* • May not use appropriate strategies to solve problems. • Computations are mostly correct. • Written explanations are satisfactory. • Diagrams and graphs are mostly accurate and appropriate. • Satisfies most requirements of problem.
0 Unsatisfactory	• Shows little or no understanding of the concepts of *using models to demonstrate factoring trinomials; simplifying radical expressions; and adding, subtracting, multiplying, and dividing complex numbers.* • May not use appropriate strategies to solve problems. • Computations are incorrect. • Written explanations are not satisfactory. • Diagrams and graphs are not accurate or appropriate. • Does not satisfy requirements of problem.

Alternative Assessment

The Alternative Assessment section provides students with the opportunity to assess their own work by thinking critically, working with others, keeping a portfolio, and honestly evaluating their own progress. For more information on alternative forms of assessment, see *Alternative Assessment in the Mathematics Classroom,* one of the titles in the Glencoe Mathematics Professional Series.

Performance Assessment

Performance Assessment tasks for this chapter are included in the *Assessment and Evaluation Masters.* A scoring guide is also provided.

NCTM Standards: 1–8

This Investigation is designed to be completed over several days or weeks. It may be considered optional. You may want to assign the Investigation and the follow-up activities to be completed at the same time.

Objective

Use mathematics to design and construct a model bridge that incorporates a parabolic arch.

Mathematical Overview

This Investigation will use the following mathematical skills and concepts from Chapters 6 and 7.

- finding the equation of a parabola
- graphing a parabola
- determining a set of points that lies along a parabola

Recommended Time

Part	Pages	Time
Investigation	328–329	1 class period
Working on the Investigation	340, 375, 422, 455	20 minutes each
Closing the Investigation	468	1 class period

Instructional Resources

Investigations and Projects Masters, pp. 9–12

A recording sheet, teacher notes, and scoring guide are provided for each Investigation in the *Investigations and Projects Masters*.

1 MOTIVATION

This Investigation uses common materials to investigate the design and construction of large highway bridges. Ask students to describe the design of bridges that span large, deep canyons. Do such bridges normally have long supports anchored on the canyon bottom? If such supports are absent, what features provide support for the bridge?

the River Canyon Bridge

MATERIALS NEEDED

cardboard box

scissors

glue

ruler

toothpicks

string

pipe cleaners

straws

wooden craft sticks

You work in the engineering division of a company that builds bridges. Your company has just been awarded a contract to build a six-lane highway bridge across a deep river canyon. The canyon is 550 yards deep and 110 yards wide.

The walls of the canyon are very steep with an almost vertical drop. The river below the proposed bridge is very swift, with strong rapids, especially during the spring when the snow thaws. The river bed consists of soft sand.

Your team of four designers is contemplating the best design for this bridge. A traditional bridge built on stilts would be weak, especially in strong winds. The stilts would also be very expensive and difficult to construct, so you remove that design from consideration.

The company's consultant states that a bridge that includes a parabolic arch is best suited for this situation. Your task is to determine the dimensions of the bridge while ensuring that the arch is shaped like a parabola.

In this Investigation, you will examine several ways in which a bridge could be constructed over the river canyon.

328 *Investigation: The River Canyon Bridge*

Cooperative Learning

This Investigation offers an excellent opportunity for using cooperative learning groups. For more information on cooperative learning strategies and group management, see *Cooperative Learning in the Mathematics Classroom,* one of the titles in the Glencoe Mathematics Professional Series.

 TEKS | 5.b., 6.b.

2 SETUP

You may wish to have a student read the first three paragraphs of the Investigation to provide background information for the bridge-building project. You may then wish to read the next paragraph that explains what the class's task will be. Discuss the activity with your students. Then separate the class into groups of five or more.

3 MANAGEMENT

Each group member should be responsible for a specific task.

Recorder Writes proposal, collects data during durability tests.
Measurer Measures bridge dimensions and weights used during durability tests.
Illustrator Creates blueprint and other sketches of bridge.
Modelers Work together to create model bridge.

At the end of the activity, each member should turn in his or her respective equipment.

Investigations and Projects Masters, p. 12

········ **PLAN THE BRIDGE**

1 Think about several different bridge designs. Look in books, magazines, and travel brochures to find pictures of these bridges. Research the history of spanning spaces with bridges going back to Greek and Roman designs.

2 Discuss these designs with your classmates. Narrow the list to four designs that agree with the consultant's recommendation for this project.

3 Write a proposal in which you draw and explain the possible designs. Be sure to list the pros and cons of each design in your proposal. Include any historical references that may have influenced your choices.

········ **MODEL THE BRIDGE**

4 Use a box to simulate the canyon walls. Use toothpicks, straws, wooden craft sticks, glue, string, and/or any other building materials to build a bridge to span the river canyon.

5 Make a blueprint of your bridge. Include the measurements of the span of the bridge, its height, and where it attaches to the canyon wall.

6 Test your bridge with small weights to see how durable it is.

You will continue working on this Investigation throughout Chapters 6 and 7.

Be sure to keep your chart and materials in your Investigation Folder.

The River Canyon Bridge Investigation

Working on the Investigation
Lesson 6–1, p. 340
············
Working on the Investigation
Lesson 6–6, p. 375
············
Working on the Investigation
Lesson 7–2, p. 422
············
Working on the Investigation
Lesson 7–6, p. 455
············
Closing the Investigation
End of Chapter 7, p. 468
············

Investigation: The River Canyon Bridge **329**

6, 7 NAME_____ DATE_____
Investigation, Chapters 6 and 7   Student Edition Pages 328–329, 340, 375, 422, 455, 468

The River Canyon Bridge

Use this chart to record your data from page 375 in the Investigation. Then work with your group to answer the questions.

Design	Value for a	Value for b	Equation
1			
2			
3			
4			

Check with other groups and list other methods that they used to find a.

Why do you think that the consultant would suggest that the bridge design have a parabolic shape?

Which of the designs do you think would be strongest? Explain why you think so.

Use this chart to record your data from page 455 in the Investigation.

Design	Formula for Length of Strut	Length of Strut	Locations on Canyon Walls
1			
2			
3			
4			

Please keep this page and any other research in your Investigation folder.

Exploring Quadratic Functions and Inequalities

PREVIEWING THE CHAPTER

In this chapter, students learn to solve quadratic equations by using graphing technology, by factoring, by completing the square, and by using the quadratic formula. Students use the discriminant to determine the nature of the roots of a quadratic equation and then learn how to write a quadratic equation when two roots of the equation are known. The guess-and-check strategy is integrated into the chapter to help students solve problems involving quadratic equations. The chapter concludes with students finding the standard deviation of a set of data and solving problems involving normally distributed data.

Lesson (Pages)	Lesson Objectives	NCTM Standards	State/Local Objectives
6-1A (332–333)	Use a graphing calculator to graph and solve quadratic equations.	1–6	2.a., 4.a., 6.a., 6.b.
6-1 (334–340)	Write functions in quadratic form. Graph quadratic functions. Solve quadratic equations by graphing.	1–6	2.a., 6.b., 8.a., 8.c.
6-2 (341–345)	Solve problems by using the guess-and-check strategy. Solve quadratic equations by factoring.	1–5	2.a., 6.a., 6.b., 8.a., 8.c., 8.d.
6-3 (346–352)	Solve quadratic equations by completing the square.	1–5	2.a., 2.b., 5.e., 6.a., 6.b., 8.a., 8.c.
6-4 (353–358)	Solve quadratic equations by using the quadratic formula. Use discriminants to determine the nature of the roots of quadratic equations.	1–5	2.b., 6.a., 6.b., 8.a., 8.b., 8.c., 8.d.
6-5 (359–364)	Find the sum and product of the roots of quadratic equations. Find a quadratic equation to fit a given condition.	1–5	6.a., 6.b., 6.c., 8.a., 8.d.
6-6A (365–366)	Use a graphing calculator to graph and explore similarities between parabolas.	1–6	4.a., 4.b., 6.b., 7.a., 7.b.
6-6 (367–375)	Graph quadratic equations of the form $y = a(x - h)^2 + k$. Determine the equation of a parabola by using points on its graph.	1–6	1.a., 1.b., 4.a., 6.a., 6.b., 6.c., 7.a., 7.b., 8.a.
6-7A (376–377)	Use a graphing calculator to graph and solve quadratic inequalities.	1–5	2.a., 8.a., 8.d.
6-7 (378–383)	Graph quadratic inequalities. Solve quadratic inequalities in one variable.	1–5	2.a., 6.a., 6.b., 8.a., 8.d.
6-8 (384–391)	Find the standard deviation for a set of data.	1–4, 10	
6-9 (392–398)	Solve problems involving normally distributed data.	1–4, 10	

A complete, 1-page lesson plan is provided for each lesson in the *Lesson Planning Guide*. Answer keys for each lesson are available in the *Answer Key Masters*.

ORGANIZING THE CHAPTER

You may want to refer to the **Course Planning Calendar** on page T12 for detailed information on pacing.
PACING: Standard—17 days; **Honors**—14 days; **Block**—7 days

LESSON PLANNING CHART

| Lesson (Pages) | Materials/ Manipulatives | Extra Practice (Student Edition) | BLACKLINE MASTERS | | | | | | | | | Real-World Applications | Interactive Mathematics Tools Software | Teaching Transparencies |
			Study Guide	Practice	Enrichment	Assessment and Evaluation	Modeling Mathematics	Multicultural Activity	Tech Prep Applications	Graphing Calculator	Science and Math Lab Manual			
6-1A (332–333)	graphing calculator									pp. 35, 36				
6-1 (334–340)	ball stopwatch graphing calculator	p. 889	p. 40	p. 40	p. 40		p. 66			p. 6			6-1.1 6-1.2 6-1.3	6-1A 6-1B
6-2 (341–345)	toothpicks	p. 889	p. 41	p. 41	p. 41				p. 11					6-2A 6-2B
6-3 (346–352)	drawing paper scissors	p. 889	p. 42	p. 42	p. 42	p. 156	pp. 40–42						6-3	6-3A 6-3B
6-4 (353–358)	calculator	p. 890	p. 43	p. 43	p. 43			p. 11				16		6-4A 6-4B
6-5 (359–364)		p. 890	p. 44	p. 44	p. 44	pp. 155, 156						17		6-5A 6-5B
6-6A (365–366)	graphing calculator									pp. 37, 38				
6-6 (367–375)	graphing calculator	p. 890	p. 45	p. 45	p. 45		pp. 43–45	p. 12						6-6A 6-6B
6-7A (376–377)	graphing calculator									pp. 39, 40				
6-7 (378–383)		p. 891	p. 46	p. 46	p. 46	p. 157			p. 12			18		6-7A 6-7B
6-8 (384–391)	bull's-eye target blindfold	p. 891	p. 47	p. 47	p. 47						pp. 87–90		6-8	6-8A 6-8B
6-9 (392–398)	shakers pennies	p. 891	p. 48	p. 48	p. 48	p. 157						19		6-9A 6-9B
Study Guide/ Assessment (399–403)						pp. 141–154, 158–160								

ORGANIZING THE CHAPTER

OTHER CHAPTER RESOURCES

Student Edition
Investigation, pp. 328–329
Chapter Opener, pp. 330–331
Mathematics and Society, p. 364
Working on the Investigation,
pp. 340, 375

Teacher's Classroom Resources
Investigations and Projects Masters,
pp. 45–48

Technology
Teacher's Guide for Software
Resources
Test and Review Software (IBM
and Macintosh)
CD-ROM Interactions (Windows
and Macintosh)

Professional Publications
Block Scheduling Booklet
Glencoe Mathematics Professional
Series

OUTSIDE RESOURCES

Books/Periodicals
Algebra in the Real World, Dale Seymour
Publications
Posamentier, Alfred S. and Charles T. Salkind,
Challenging Problems in Algebra, Dale
Seymour Publications

Software
Green Globs and Graphing Equations, Sunburst
Review-It: Algebra II/Trigonometry, William K.
Bradford Publishing Company

Videos/CD-ROMs
Factor and Solve Quadratic Equations, ETA
Video Polynomials, Dale Seymour Publications

See the *Teacher's Guide for Software Resources* for software addresses.

ASSESSMENT RESOURCES

Student Edition
Math Journal, pp. 357, 362,
381, 395
Mixed Review, pp. 340, 345,
352, 358, 364, 375, 383,
391, 398
Self Test, p. 358
Chapter Highlights, p. 399
Chapter Study Guide and
Assessment, pp. 400–402
Alternative Assessment, p. 403
 Portfolio, p. 403

College Entrance Exam Practice,
pp. 404–405

Teacher's Wraparound Edition
5-Minute Check, pp. 334, 341,
346, 353, 359, 367, 378, 384,
392
Check for Understanding, pp. 338,
343, 350, 356, 362, 372, 381,
388, 395
Closing Activity, pp. 340, 345,
352, 358, 364, 375, 383, 390,
398
Cooperative Learning, pp. 348,
394

Assessment and Evaluation Masters
Multiple-Choice Tests, Forms 1A
(Honors), 1B (Average), 1C
(Basic), pp. 141–146
Free-Response Tests, Forms 2A
(Honors), 2B (Average), 2C
(Basic), pp. 147–152
Calculator-Based Test, p. 153
Performance Assessment, p. 154
Mid-Chapter Test, p. 155
Quizzes A–D, pp. 156–157
Standardized Test Practice, p. 158
Cumulative Review, pp. 159–160

ENHANCING THE CHAPTER

Examples of some of the materials for enhancing Chapter 6 are shown below.

DIVERSITY

Multicultural Activity Masters, pp. 11, 12

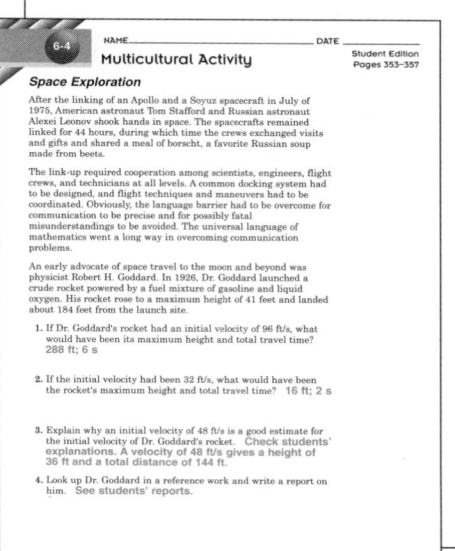

6-4 NAME_____ DATE_____ Student Edition Pages 353–357

Multicultural Activity

Space Exploration

After the linking of an Apollo and a Soyuz spacecraft in July of 1975, American astronaut Tom Stafford and Russian astronaut Alexei Leonov shook hands in space. The spacecrafts remained linked for 44 hours, during which time the crews exchanged visits and gifts and shared a meal of borscht, a favorite Russian soup made from beets.

The link-up required cooperation among scientists, engineers, flight crews, and technicians at all levels. A common docking system had to be designed, and flight techniques and maneuvers had to be coordinated. Obviously, the language barrier had to be overcome for communication to be precise and for possibly fatal misunderstandings to be avoided. The universal language of mathematics went a long way in overcoming communication problems.

An early advocate of space travel to the moon and beyond was physicist Robert H. Goddard. In 1926, Dr. Goddard launched a crude rocket powered by a fuel mixture of gasoline and liquid oxygen. His rocket rose to a maximum height of 41 feet and landed about 184 feet from the launch site.

1. If Dr. Goddard's rocket had an initial velocity of 96 ft/s, what would have been its maximum height and total travel time? **288 ft; 6 s**

2. If the initial velocity had been 32 ft/s, what would have been the rocket's maximum height and total travel time? **16 ft; 2 s**

3. Explain why an initial velocity of 48 ft/s is a good estimate for the initial velocity of Dr. Goddard's rocket. **Check students' explanations. A velocity of 48 ft/s gives a height of 36 ft and a total distance of 144 ft.**

4. Look up Dr. Goddard in a reference work and write a report on him. **See students' reports.**

APPLICATIONS

Real-World Applications, 16, 17, 18, 19

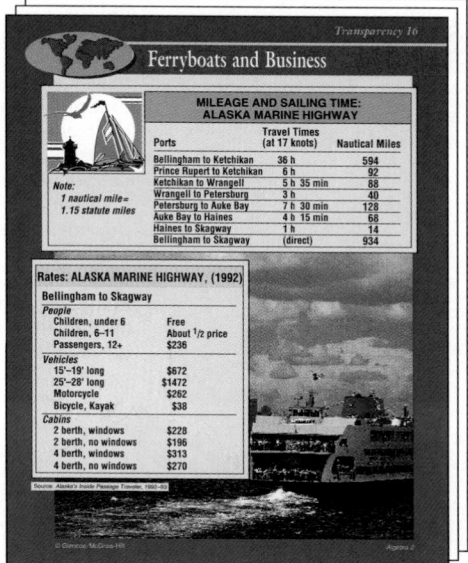

Transparency 16

Ferryboats and Business

MILEAGE AND SAILING TIME: ALASKA MARINE HIGHWAY

Ports	Travel Times (at 17 knots)	Nautical Miles
Bellingham to Ketchikan	36 h	594
Prince Rupert to Ketchikan	6 h	92
Ketchikan to Wrangell	5 h 35 min	88
Wrangell to Petersburg	3 h	40
Petersburg to Auke Bay	7 h 30 min	128
Auke Bay to Haines	4 h 15 min	68
Haines to Skagway	1 h	14
Bellingham to Skagway	(direct)	934

Note:
1 nautical mile =
1.15 statute miles

Rates: ALASKA MARINE HIGHWAY, (1992)

Bellingham to Skagway

People
Children, under 6	Free
Children, 6–11	About ½ price
Passengers, 12+	$236

Vehicles
15'–19' long	$672
25'–28' long	$1472
Motorcycle	$262
Bicycle, Kayak	$38

Cabins
2 berth, windows	$228
2 berth, no windows	$196
4 berth, windows	$313
4 berth, no windows	$270

Source: Alaska's Inside Passage Traveler, 1992–93.

TECHNOLOGY

Graphing Calculator Masters, p. 6

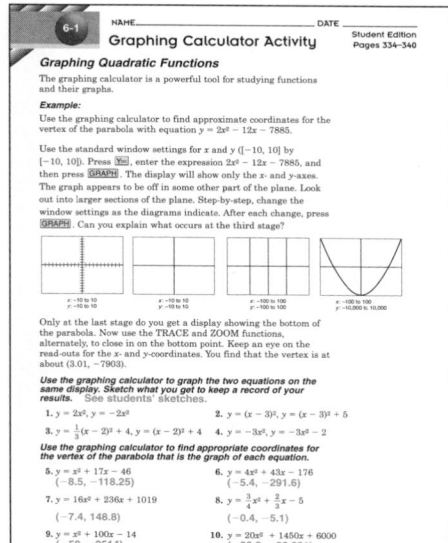

6-1 NAME_____ DATE_____ Student Edition Pages 334–340

Graphing Calculator Activity

Graphing Quadratic Functions

The graphing calculator is a powerful tool for studying functions and their graphs.

Example:
Use the graphing calculator to find approximate coordinates for the vertex of the parabola with equation $y = 2x^2 - 12x - 7885$.

Use the standard window settings for x and y ([−10, 10] by [−10, 10]). Press [Y=], enter the expression $2x^2 - 12x - 7885$, and then press [GRAPH]. The display will show only the x- and y-axes. The graph appears to be off in some other part of the plane. Look out into larger sections of the plane. Step-by-step, change the window settings as the diagrams indicate. After each change, press [GRAPH]. Can you explain what occurs at the third stage?

Only at the last stage do you get a display showing the bottom of the parabola. Now use the TRACE and ZOOM functions, alternately, to close in on the bottom point. Keep an eye on the read-outs for the x- and y-coordinates. You find that the vertex is at about $(3.01, -7903)$.

Use the graphing calculator to graph the two equations on the same display. Sketch what you get to keep a record of your results. **See students' sketches.**

1. $y = 2x^2, y = -2x^2$
2. $y = (x-3)^2, y = (x-3)^2 + 5$
3. $y = \frac{1}{3}(x-2)^2 + 4, y = (x-2)^2 + 4$
4. $y = -3x^2, y = -3x^2 - 2$

Use the graphing calculator to find appropriate coordinates for the vertex of the parabola that is the graph of each equation.

5. $y = x^2 + 17x - 46$ (−8.5, −118.25)
6. $y = 4x^2 + 43x - 176$ (−5.4, −291.6)
7. $y = 16x^2 + 236x + 1019$ (−7.4, 148.8)
8. $y = \frac{3}{4}x^2 + \frac{5}{3}x - 5$ (−0.4, −5.1)
9. $y = x^2 + 100x - 14$ (−50, −2514)
10. $y = 20x^2 + 1450x + 6000$ (−36.3, −20,281)

TECH PREP

Tech Prep Applications Masters, pp. 11, 12

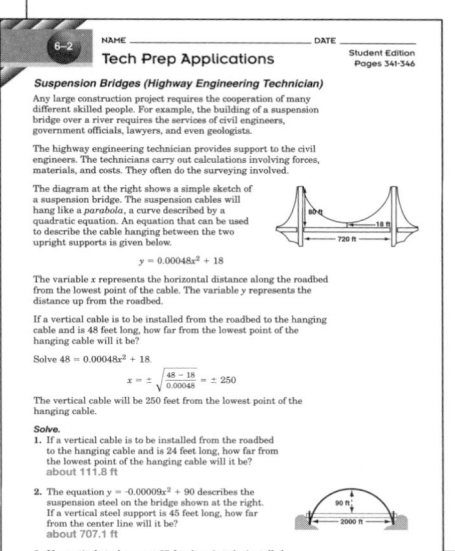

6-2 NAME_____ DATE_____ Student Edition Pages 341–346

Tech Prep Applications

Suspension Bridges (Highway Engineering Technician)

Any large construction project requires the cooperation of many different skilled people. For example, the building of a suspension bridge over a river requires the services of civil engineers, government officials, lawyers, and even geologists.

The highway engineering technician provides support to the civil engineers. The technicians carry out calculations involving forces, materials, and costs. They often do the surveying involved.

The diagram at the right shows a simple sketch of a suspension bridge. The suspension cables will hang like a *parabola*, a curve described by a quadratic equation. An equation that can be used to describe the cable hanging between the two upright supports is given below.

$$y = 0.00048x^2 + 18$$

The variable x represents the horizontal distance along the roadbed from the lowest point of the cable. The variable y represents the distance up from the roadbed.

If a vertical cable is to be installed from the roadbed to the hanging cable and is 48 feet long, how far from the lowest point of the hanging cable will it be?

Solve $48 = 0.00048x^2 + 18$.

$$x = \pm\sqrt{\frac{48-18}{0.00048}} = \pm 250$$

The vertical cable will be 250 feet from the lowest point of the hanging cable.

Solve.

1. If a vertical cable is to be installed from the roadbed to the hanging cable and is 24 feet long, how far from the lowest point of the hanging cable will it be? **about 111.8 ft**

2. The equation $y = -0.00009x^2 + 90$ describes the suspension steel on the bridge shown at the right. If a vertical steel support is 45 feet long, how far from the center line will it be? **about 707.1 ft**

3. If a vertical steel support 85 feet long is to be installed, how far from the center line will it be? **about 235.7 ft**

CONNECTIONS

Science and Math Lab Manual, pp. 87–90

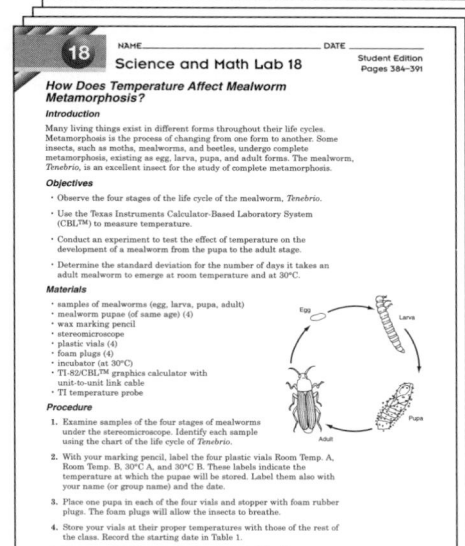

18 NAME_____ DATE_____ Student Edition Pages 384–391

Science and Math Lab 18

How Does Temperature Affect Mealworm Metamorphosis?

Introduction

Many living things exist in different forms throughout their life cycles. Metamorphosis is the process of changing from one form to another. Some insects, such as moths, mealworms, and beetles, undergo complete metamorphosis, existing as egg, larva, pupa, and adult forms. The mealworm, *Tenebrio*, is an excellent insect for the study of complete metamorphosis.

Objectives
- Observe the four stages of the life cycle of the mealworm, *Tenebrio*.
- Use the Texas Instruments Calculator-Based Laboratory System (CBL™) to measure temperature.
- Conduct an experiment to test the effect of temperature on the development of a mealworm from the pupa to the adult stage.
- Determine the standard deviation for the number of days it takes an adult mealworm to emerge at room temperature and at 30°C.

Materials
- samples of mealworms (egg, larva, pupa, adult)
- mealworm pupae (of same age) (4)
- wax marking pencil
- stereomicroscope
- plastic vials (4)
- foam plugs (4)
- incubator (at 30°C)
- TI-82/CBL™ graphics calculator with unit-to-unit link cable
- TI temperature probe

Procedure

1. Examine samples of the four stages of mealworms under the stereomicroscope. Identify each sample using the chart of the life cycle of *Tenebrio*.

2. With your marking pencil, label the four plastic vials Room Temp. A, Room Temp. B, 30°C A, and 30°C B. These labels indicate the temperature at which the pupae will be stored. Label them also with your name (or group name) and the date.

3. Place one pupa in each of the four vials and stopper with foam rubber plugs. The foam plugs will allow the insects to breathe.

4. Store your vials at their proper temperatures with those of the rest of the class. Record the starting date in Table 1.

5. Set up your CBL™ system. Use the unit-to-unit link cable to connect the CBL™ unit to your calculator. Use the I/O port located on the bottom edge of the unit.

(Egg, Larva, Pupa, Adult life cycle diagram shown at right)

PROBLEM SOLVING

Problem of the Week Cards, 16, 17

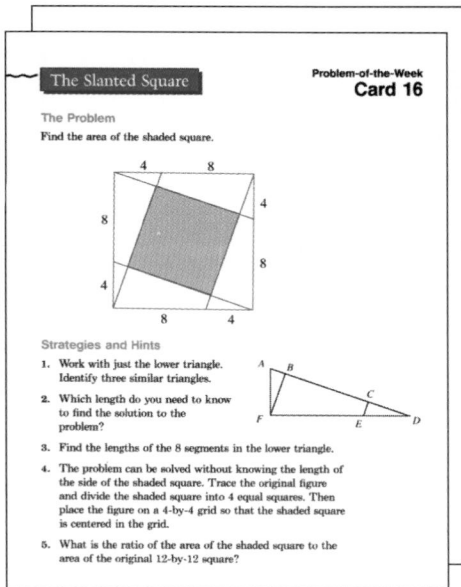

The Slanted Square — Problem-of-the-Week **Card 16**

The Problem

Find the area of the shaded square.

Strategies and Hints

1. Work with just the lower triangle. Identify three similar triangles.

2. Which length do you need to know to find the solution to the problem?

3. Find the lengths of the 8 segments in the lower triangle.

4. The problem can be solved without knowing the length of the side of the shaded square. Trace the original figure and divide the shaded square into 4 equal squares. Then place the figure on a 4-by-4 grid so that the shaded square is centered in the grid.

5. What is the ratio of the area of the shaded square to the area of the original 12-by-12 square?

MAKING MATHEMATICS RELEVANT

This two-page introduction to the chapter provides students with an opportunity to explore contemporary topics and their applications to mathematics.

Background Information
Why Teens Play an Instrument
Why do teenagers decide to begin playing a musical instrument, and why do some continue to play while others drop it? The table below reveals some interesting patterns. Encourage students to discuss how these findings relate to their own experiences.

What Motivates Teenagers			
Motivation to Start Playing	All Teens Who Are Current or Former Players %	Current Players %	Former Players %
Became interested on one's own	42	44	40
Parents encouraged	22	18	26
A teacher encouraged	16	11	21
Someone else	20	27	13
Total	100	100	100
Number of Interviews	(251)	(123)	(128)

Exploring Quadratic Functions and Inequalities

Objectives

In this chapter, you will:
- graph quadratic functions,
- solve quadratic equations
- solve problems using the guess-and-check strategy,
- analyze graphs of quadratic functions and inequalities, and
- solve problems involving standard deviation and the normal distribution.

Do you play an instrument? Many teens play an instrument, not because they have to, but because they enjoy it. Other teens have claimed that playing an instrument helps develop confidence and creativity, provides a way to make new friends, and instills a greater appreciation of other arts.

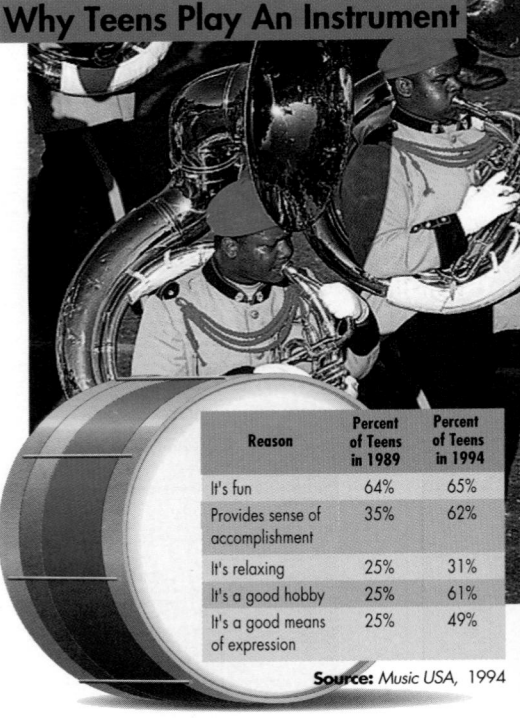

Why Teens Play An Instrument

Reason	Percent of Teens in 1989	Percent of Teens in 1994
It's fun	64%	65%
Provides sense of accomplishment	35%	62%
It's relaxing	25%	31%
It's a good hobby	25%	61%
It's a good means of expression	25%	49%

Source: *Music USA,* 1994

TIME Line

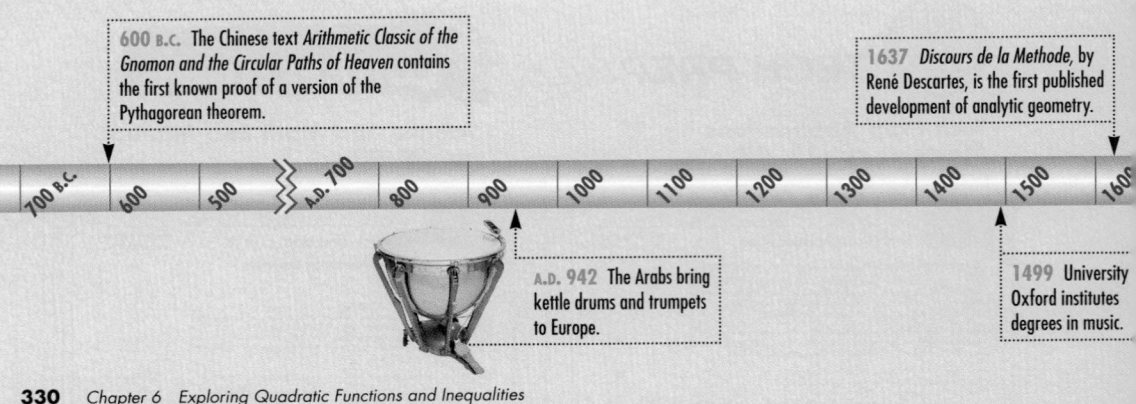

600 B.C. The Chinese text *Arithmetic Classic of the Gnomon and the Circular Paths of Heaven* contains the first known proof of a version of the Pythagorean theorem.

1637 *Discours de la Methode,* by René Descartes, is the first published development of analytic geometry.

A.D. 942 The Arabs bring kettle drums and trumpets to Europe.

1499 University Oxford institutes degrees in music.

TIME Line

One of the most important events in the history of mathematics was the development of analytic geometry by René Descartes. He combined the geometry of the Ancient Greeks with the algebra developed by the Persians. This synthesis became the foundation of all modern mathematical sciences.

interNET CONNECTION

Windplayer Online has news, articles, references, resources, and tips for saxophone, clarinet, flute, trumpet, and trombone players.

World Wide Web
http://www.windplayer.com/wp/instrument.html

Chapter Project

Form teams and conduct your own survey of various aspects of music and its significance in the lives of family and neighbors. Choose categories such as musical preference, CD and tape purchasing, time spent listening to or playing music, live performance attendance, instruments played, and the number of people who study music.

Keep track of the age, gender, and number of people questioned, their responses, and percentages of your sample for each question. Then see if you can make conclusions about the attitudes of people toward music.

Create charts or graphs using your data and report to the class on your findings.

Fourteen-year-old violin prodigy **Sarah Chang** began expressing herself through music in her hometown of Philadelphia at the age of 4. She has played with the New York Philharmonic, the Philadelphia Orchestra, the Chicago Symphony, and orchestras in several European cities. When she was 12, she had an album that hit the classical charts a month after it was released. Sarah, who doesn't mind practicing violin four hours a day, says, "I think performing is part of me, and I really love what I'm doing."

"I always wanted to play my dad's violin," Sarah says, recalling how she found her calling at age four. Her father, who was supportive and encouraging, provided her with her own violin instead. "I think performance is part of me, and I really love what I'm doing," she says. Clearly, following her natural calling, combined with the loving encouragement of her father, allowed her talent to flower and add beauty to the world.

Chapter Project

Cooperative Learning You may choose to have students pair off or arrange them in cooperative groups to discuss how to approach this project. This project gives the students experience with standard deviation in a simplified context. They might want to try to estimate the answer before doing the calculations.

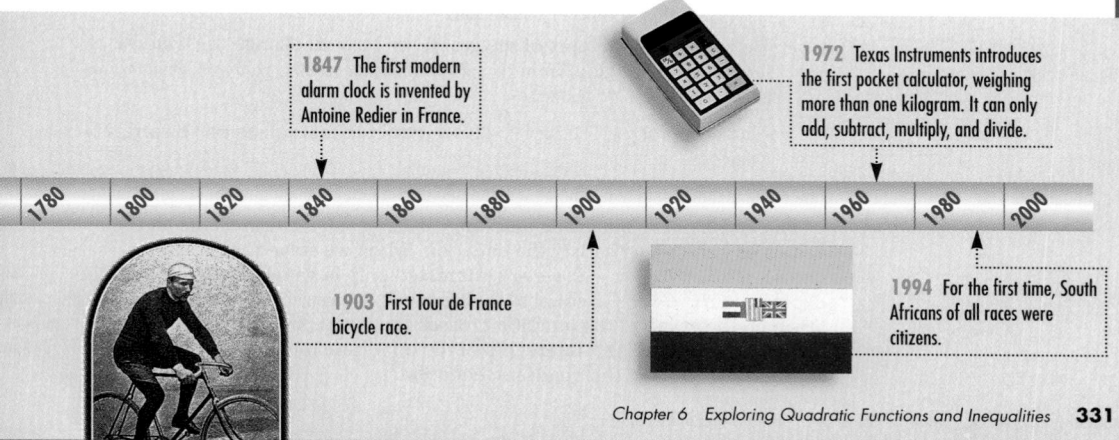

1847 The first modern alarm clock is invented by Antoine Redier in France.

1972 Texas Instruments introduces the first pocket calculator, weighing more than one kilogram. It can only add, subtract, multiply, and divide.

| 1780 | 1800 | 1820 | 1840 | 1860 | 1880 | 1900 | 1920 | 1940 | 1960 | 1980 | 2000 |

1903 First Tour de France bicycle race.

1994 For the first time, South Africans of all races were citizens.

Chapter 6 Exploring Quadratic Functions and Inequalities **331**

Alternative Chapter Projects

Two other chapter projects are included in the *Investigations and Projects Masters*. In Chapter 6 Project A, pp. 45–46, students extend the topic in the chapter opener. In Chapter 6 Project B, pp. 47–48, students gather data and use statistical methods to analyze the data.

Investigations and Projects Masters, p. 45

6

NAME_____ DATE _____

Student Edition Pages 332–398

Chapter 6 Project A

Preferred Music

1. Teens' musical tastes have changed dramatically over the past 35 years. Some teens' preferences change as new types of music are introduced. Work with a partner to make a list of the types of music you think are most popular among teens today.

2. Do research to find out about the most popular types of music over the past 35 years. Look for statistics about sales of recordings of the most popular music. Find information about attendance at concerts. As you complete your research, answer the following questions.
   - How has music changed over the past 35 years?
   - What types of music do teens listen to today?
   - How popular is the type of music you prefer?
   - What types of music, if any, were once popular among teens but no longer are?
   - What influence, if any, do you think popular music has had on teens in the past?
   - What influence, if any, do you think today's popular music has on teens?

3. Use statistical methods to analyze the data you collected in exercise 2. If possible, write equations to describe the data. Create charts and graphs to organize and explain the data.

4. Write an article for your school newspaper that summarizes your research. Be sure to include the equations, charts, and graphs you created in exercise 3.

NCTM Standards: 1–6

Objective
Use a graphing calculator to graph and solve quadratic equations.

Recommended Time
25 minutes

Instructional Resources
Graphing Calculator Masters, pp. 35 and 36

These masters provide keystroking instruction for this lesson for the TI-81 and Casio graphing calculators.

1 FOCUS

Motivating the Lesson
Draw the general shape of several graphs on the chalkboard or overhead. For example, draw an ellipse, a circle, a hyperbola, a parabola, and a cubic function on different coordinate planes. Ask students which picture is the graph of a quadratic equation and why.
The parabola, since it would graph equations of the form $y = ax^2 + bx + c$.

2 TEACH

Teaching Tip Many students do not realize that a parabola does not have to open up. A parabola can also open down, to the left, or to the right.

Teaching Tip You can clear the graphics screen by pressing

[Y=] and "turning off" equations instead of clearing them. You

can turn them off by using the

[▲] and [▼] keys to move

to the "=" and pressing [ENTER] to

make the sign not highlighted.

The graphing calculator is a powerful tool for studying graphs of functions. In this lesson, we will study graphs of functions of the form $y = ax^2 + bx + c$, where $a \neq 0$. These are called **quadratic functions,** and their graphs are called **parabolas.**

Example **1** **Graph each function in the standard viewing window.**

a. $y = x^2$

This function is of the form $y = ax^2 + bx + c$, where $a = 1$, $b = 0$, and $c = 0$.

Enter: [Y=] [X,T,θ] [x²]
[ZOOM] 6

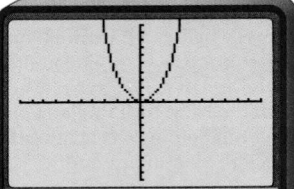

The graph of the function is shaped like a cup. This is the general shape of a parabola. *Notice that a > 0.*

b. $y = -0.3x^2 + 42$

The function $y = -0.3x^2 + 42$ is of the form $y = ax^2 + bx + c$, where $a = -0.3$, $b = 0$, and $c = 42$.

Enter: [Y=] [(−)] .3 [X,T,θ] [x²] [+] 42 [ZOOM] 6

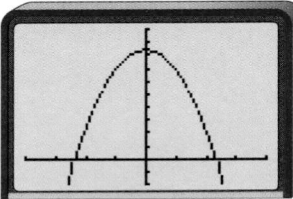

Nothing appears on the graphics screen. We must change the window to be able to view the complete graph. Press [TRACE] and notice that the coordinates of the vertex, (0, 42), are shown at the bottom of the screen. Since we cannot see the graph in the standard viewing window, change Ymax to 50. Then press [GRAPH].

To see both intercepts of the graph, we have to change the window again. Try changing Xmin to −20 and Xmax to 20. *You may want to use scale factors of 5 on both axes.*

The graph of $y = -0.3x^2 + 42$ is a parabola that opens downward. *Notice that a < 0.*

The graph of the quadratic function $y = ax^2 + bx + c$ represents all the values of x and y that satisfy the equation. When we solve the quadratic equation $ax^2 + bx + c = 0$, we are interested only in values of x that make the expression $ax^2 + bx + c$ equal to 0. These values are represented by the points at which the graph of the function crosses the x-axis, since the y values of these points are 0. The x-intercepts of the quadratic function are called the **solutions** or **roots** of the quadratic equation.

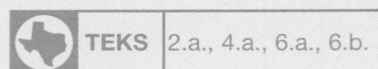
TEKS 2.a., 4.a., 6.a., 6.b.

There are three possible outcomes when solving a quadratic equation. The equation will have two real solutions, one real solution, or no real solutions.

Example ② Use a graphing calculator to solve $2x^2 - 6x - 4 = 0$ to the nearest hundredth.

Begin by graphing the related function $y = 2x^2 - 6x - 4$ in the standard viewing window.

Enter: [Y=] 2 [X,T,θ] [x²] [−] 6 [X,T,θ] [−] 4 [ZOOM] 6

TRACE to one of the x-intercepts and press [ZOOM] 2 [ENTER]. The more times you repeat this process, the more accurate your answer will be.

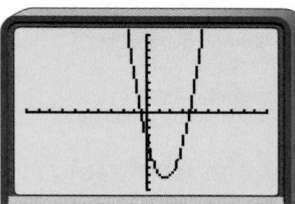

The solutions of this equation are -0.56 and 3.56, to the nearest hundredth.

You can also use the ROOT feature of the calculator to find the solutions automatically. This involves defining an interval that includes the root. A lower bound is a point on the graph just to the left of the solution and an upper bound is a point on the graph just to the right of the solution.

Enter: [2nd] [CALC] 2

Using the arrow keys, locate a lower bound for the first solution and press [ENTER]. Similarly, locate an upper bound for the root and press [ENTER]. Finally, after the Guess? prompt, press [ENTER].

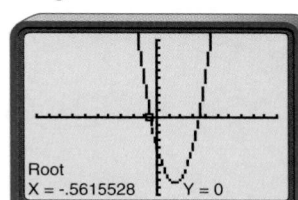

Root
X = -.5615528   Y = 0

Repeat this process for the second root.

It should be noted that solving equations graphically provides only approximate solutions. While approximate solutions are adequate for many applications, if an exact answer is required, an algebraic technique usually must be used.

EXERCISES

Determine a viewing window that gives a complete graph of each function. 1–6. See margin.

1. $y = 4x^2 + 11$
2. $y = 7.5x^2 + 9.5$
3. $y = 6x^2 + 250x + 725$
4. $y = x^2 + 4x - 15$
5. $y = -2x^2 - x - 15$
6. $y = x^2 + 30x + 225$

Solve each quadratic equation to the nearest hundredth by using a graphing calculator.

7. $4x^2 + 11 = 0$ no solution
8. $7.5x^2 + 9.5 = 0$ no solution
9. −3.14, −38.53   9. $6x^2 + 250x + 725 = 0$
10. $x^2 + 4x - 15 = 0$ −6.36, 2.36

3 PRACTICE/APPLY

Assignment Guide

Core: 1–10
Enriched: 1–10

4 ASSESS

Observing students working with technology is an excellent method of assessment.

Additional Answers

1–6. Sample answers are given.
1. Xmin = −10
   Xmax = 10
   Ymin = −10
   Ymax = 40
2. Xmin = −5
   Xmax = 5
   Ymin = −10
   Ymax = 40
3. Xmin = −50
   Xmax = 10
   Ymin = −2000
   Ymax = 500
4. Xmin = −10
   Xmax = 10
   Ymin = −25
   Ymax = 10
5. Xmin = −10
   Xmax = 10
   Ymin = −80
   Ymax = 5
6. Xmin = −50
   Xmax = 10
   Ymin = −100
   Ymax = 500

Using Technology

This lesson offers an excellent opportunity for using technology in your algebra classroom. For more information on using technology, see *Graphing Calculators in the Mathematics Classroom,* one of the titles in the Glencoe Mathematics Professional Series.

Instructional Resources

- Study Guide Master 6-1
- Practice Master 6-1
- Enrichment Master 6-1
- Graphing Calculator Masters, p. 6
- Modeling Mathematics Masters, p. 66

Transparency 6-1A contains the 5-Minute Check for this lesson; **Transparency 6-1B** contains a teaching aid for this lesson.

Recommended Pacing	
Standard Pacing	Day 2 of 17
Honors Pacing	Day 2 of 14
Block Scheduling*	Day 1 of 7

*For more information on pacing and possible lesson plans, refer to the *Block Scheduling Booklet*.

1 FOCUS

5-Minute Check
(over Chapter 5)

1. Simplify $(5m^6 + 3m^3 + 9m + 5) + (9m^6 - 2m^4 + 3m - 7)$. $14m^6 - 2m^4 + 3m^3 + 12m - 2$

2. Factor $2y^3 - 98y$. $2y(y + 7)(y - 7)$

3. Find $\dfrac{(m^3 - 3m^2 - 18m + 40)}{(m + 4)}$ using synthetic division. $m^2 - 7m + 10$

4. Evaluate $\left(\dfrac{1}{64}\right)^{-\frac{2}{3}}$. 16

5. Solve $\sqrt{r + 12} - \sqrt{r} = 2$. 4

6. Simplify $\dfrac{4 - 5i}{3 + 7i}$. $\dfrac{-23 - 43i}{58}$

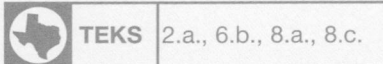

TEKS 2.a., 6.b., 8.a., 8.c.

6-1 Solving Quadratic Equations by Graphing

What YOU'LL LEARN

- To write functions in quadratic form,
- to graph quadratic functions, and
- to solve quadratic equations by graphing.

Why IT'S IMPORTANT

You can graph quadratic functions to solve problems involving space science and physics.

APPLICATION
Space Science

In the movie *Apollo 13,* actors Tom Hanks, Kevin Bacon, and Bill Paxton play real-life astronauts Jim Lovell, John Swigart, and Fred Haise in the story of the 1970 moon mission that nearly ended in disaster. During the filming of the movie, the actors trained on an airplane called the "Vomit Comet"—a stripped-down KC-135 used to help astronauts get accustomed to weightlessness. After climbing to a designated height, weightlessness begins as the jet arcs over a 36,000-foot peak and then dives toward the ground. For 23 seconds, the occupants are weightless.

The path of the Vomit Comet can be represented by the graph of a **quadratic function**. A quadratic function is a function described by an equation that can be written in the form $f(x) = ax^2 + bx + c$, where $a \neq 0$. In a quadratic function, ax^2 is called the **quadratic term**, bx is the **linear term,** and c is the **constant term.**

Example  **Write each function in quadratic form. Identify the quadratic term, the linear term, and the constant term.**

a. $f(x) = 2x^2 + 7 - 9x$

In quadratic form, the function is written as $f(x) = 2x^2 - 9x + 7$. The quadratic term is $2x^2$, the linear term is $-9x$, and the constant term is 7.

b. $f(x) = (x + 4)^2 - 20$

$$\begin{aligned} f(x) &= (x + 4)^2 - 20 \\ &= x^2 + 8x + 16 - 20 \quad \textit{Square } x + 4. \\ &= x^2 + 8x - 4 \quad \textit{Simplify.} \end{aligned}$$

The quadratic term is x^2, the linear term is $8x$, and the constant term is -4.

Suppose the flight of the Vomit Comet can be modeled by the quadratic function $h(t) = -16(t - 4)^2 + 36,000$.

To graph this function, we can create a table of values, as shown below.

Next, we can plot the points $(t, h(t))$, where height is in thousands of feet.

t	$-16(t - 4)^2 + 36,000$	$h(t)$
0	$-16(-4)^2 + 36,000$	35,744
4	$-16(0)^2 + 36,000$	36,000
8	$-16(4)^2 + 36,000$	35,744
12	$-16(8)^2 + 36,000$	34,976
16	$-16(12)^2 + 36,000$	33,696
20	$-16(16)^2 + 36,000$	31,904
24	$-16(20)^2 + 36,000$	29,600

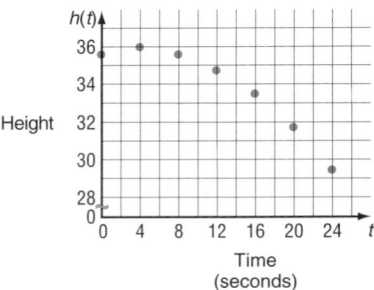

Height / Time (seconds)

Classroom Vignette

"To successfully graph quadratic equations, students need to know that the x-value of the vertex can be found by using $-\dfrac{b}{2a}$ for an equation written as $y = ax^2 + bx + c$. They can be sure to use this point as well as points greater and less than this value to complete their table of values."

Bonnie F. Wicker

Bonnie Wicker
Munford High School
Munford, Tennessee

CAREER CHOICES

An **astronaut** is a person trained to pilot a spacecraft, operate any of its various systems, or conduct scientific experiments aboard such a craft during space flights.

Today, most astronauts have advanced degrees in physics, chemistry, or the earth sciences.

For more information, contact:

NASA Center for Aerospace Information

800 Elkridge Landing Rd. Linthicum Heights, MD 21090

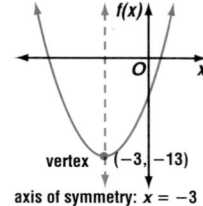

$$h(t) = -16(t-4)^2 + 36{,}000$$

Height (thousands of feet) / Time (seconds)

We can now connect the points in a smooth curve. The weightlessness begins when the jet arcs at an elevation of 36,000 feet. Weightlessness continues for 23 seconds. The jet then pulls out of the dive and climbs for another weightless session.

The graph of any quadratic function is a **parabola.** The graph of the Vomit Comet is part of a parabola. All parabolas have an **axis of symmetry.** The axis of symmetry is the line about which the parabola is symmetric. That is, if you could fold the coordinate plane along the axis of symmetry, the portions of the parabola on each side of the line would match. The axis of symmetry is named by the equation of the line. All parabolas have a **vertex** as well. The vertex is the point of intersection of the parabola and the axis of symmetry. Notice that this parabola intersects the x-axis twice. The x-coordinates of these intersection points are called the **zeros** of the function.

vertex $(-3, -13)$

axis of symmetry: $x = -3$

Example **2**

CONNECTION

Physics

An arrow is shot upward with an initial velocity of 64 feet per second. The height of the arrow $h(t)$ in terms of the time t since the arrow was released is $h(t) = 64t - 16t^2$.

a. Draw the graph of the function relating the height of the arrow to the time.

b. Name the axis of symmetry and the vertex.

c. How long after the arrow is released does it reach its maximum height? What is that height?

a. First find and graph the ordered pairs that satisfy the function $h(t) = 64t - 16t^2$. Then graph the parabola suggested by the points.

This is the graph of the function that describes the height at any given time. The actual path of the arrow is an entirely different parabola.

t	$h(t)$
0	0
0.5	28
1.0	48
1.5	60
2.0	64
2.5	60
3.0	48
3.5	28
4.0	0

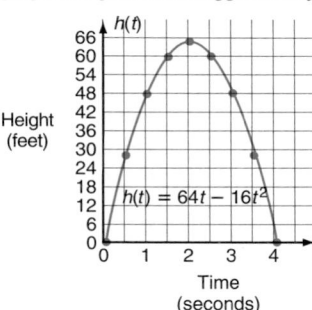

$$h(t) = 64t - 16t^2$$

Height (feet) / Time (seconds)

b. The equation of the axis of symmetry is $x = 2$. Since the vertex is the point of intersection of the parabola and the axis of symmetry, it is at $(2, 64)$.

c. You can see from the graph that the arrow reaches its maximum height at 2 seconds. The maximum height is 64 feet. *How does the vertex relate to the maximum height and the time of the maximum height?*

You can use quadratic functions to describe different mathematical situations as well as situations occurring in everyday life.

Lesson 6-1 Solving Quadratic Equations by Graphing **335**

Alternative Teaching Strategies

Reading Algebra Caution students that while the prefix *quad-* usually means "four," quadratic equations are polynomials of degree two and have, at most, two solutions.

GLENCOE Technology

Interactive Mathematics Tools Software

This multimedia software provides an interactive lesson by helping students observe the effects of changing the variables in $y = a(x - h)^2 + k$ form of a quadratic function on the graphs of a function. A **Computer Journal** gives students an opportunity to write about what they have learned. **For Windows & Macintosh**

Motivating the Lesson

Hands-On Activity Bring in a ball and a stopwatch. Throw the ball into the air. Have one student measure the time it takes the ball to return to your hand. Discuss what forces of nature affect the rising and falling of the ball. Discuss the equation $h = v_i t - \frac{1}{2}gt^2$, where h is the height of the ball at a given time, v_i is the initial velocity, t is time, and g is the acceleration of gravity.

2 TEACH

Teaching Tip Remind students that quadratic functions have a parabolic shape when graphed. Students may have to adjust the viewing window to see a parabola.

In-Class Examples

For Example 1
Write the function $f(x) = 3(x + 2)^2$ in quadratic form. Identify the quadratic term, the linear term, and the constant term. $f(x) = 3x^2 + 12x + 12; 3x^2; 12x; 12$

For Example 2
An arrow is shot upward with an initial velocity of 50 feet per second. The height of the arrow $h(t)$, in terms of the time since the arrow was released t, is $h(t) = 50t - 16t^2$. How long after the arrow is released does it reach its maximum height? What is that height? **1.56 seconds, 39.06 feet**

CAREER CHOICES

In the early years of the space program, astronauts were Air Force test pilots only. However, today the field has opened up. People from many different specialties now go into the astronaut training program.

In-Class Examples

For Example 3
Write a function for the area of a triangle if the height is 3 cm greater than the base. Then sketch the graph.

$$A = f(b) = \frac{b^2}{2} + \frac{3b}{2}$$

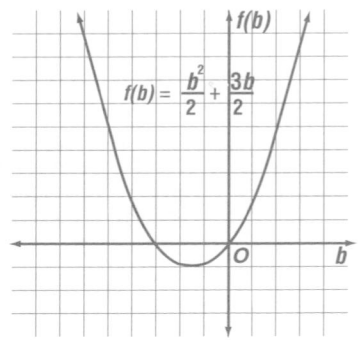

For Example 4
Solve $m^2 - 3m - 28 = 0$ by graphing.

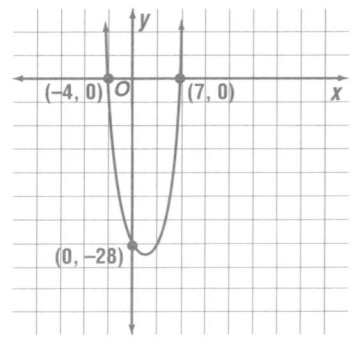

Example 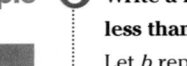 **3** **Write a function to represent the area of a triangle if the height is 5 cm less than the base. Then sketch the graph. Use $A = \frac{1}{2}bh$.**

INTEGRATION
Geometry

Let b represent the measure of the base of the triangle. Then $b - 5$ represents the height. Since the area is a function of the length of the base, let $f(b)$ represent the area.

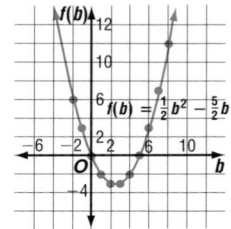

$$f(b) = \frac{1}{2}b(b - 5)$$
$$= \frac{1}{2}b^2 - \frac{5}{2}b$$

Find several ordered pairs that satisfy the quadratic function $f(b) = \frac{1}{2}b^2 - \frac{5}{2}b$. Then graph these ordered pairs and draw a parabola.

Which points on the graph could actually represent possible lengths of the base and areas of the triangles?

b	f(b)
−1	3
0	0
1	−2
2	−3
3	−3
4	−2
5	0
6	3
7	7
8	12

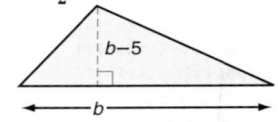

When a quadratic function is set equal to zero, the result is a **quadratic equation**. A quadratic equation is an equation that can be written in the form $ax^2 + bx + c = 0$, where $a \neq 0$. Since the largest exponent of the variable is 2, we say that a quadratic equation has a degree of 2. A quadratic equation contains only one variable, and all of the exponents are positive integers.

The **roots**, or solutions, of a quadratic equation are values of the variable that satisfy the equation. There are several methods you can use to find the roots of a quadratic equation. One method is to graph its related quadratic function. The related quadratic function of a quadratic equation in the form $ax^2 + bx + c = 0$ is $f(x) = ax^2 + bx + c$. The zeros of the function are the solutions of the equation, since $f(x) = 0$ at those points.

Example **4** **Solve $x^2 + 3x - 18 = 0$ by graphing.**

Graph the quadratic function $f(x) = x^2 + 3x - 18$ by finding and graphing the ordered pairs that satisfy the function. Then graph the parabola by connecting the points. Solve the equation by noting the points at which the graph intersects the x-axis.

x	f(x)
−9	36
−6	0
−3	−18
0	−18
3	0
6	36

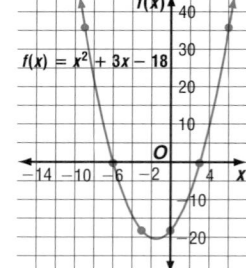

The table shows that $f(x) = 0$ when $x = -6$ and $x = 3$. The graph crosses the x-axis at −6 and 3. Thus, the solutions of the equation are −6 and 3.

GLENCOE *Technology*

 Interactive Mathematics Tools Software

This multimedia software provides an interactive lesson by having students determine the maximum height of a projectile and how it relates to its initial velocity. A **Computer Journal** gives students an opportunity to write about what they have learned.

For Windows & Macintosh

GLENCOE *Technology*

 Interactive Mathematics Tools Software

This multimedia software provides an interactive lesson by helping students discover the vertex and axis of symmetry of a function by using the equation. A **Computer Journal** gives students an opportunity to write about what they have learned.

For Windows & Macintosh

Check your solutions by substituting each solution into the equation to see if it is satisfied.

$$x^2 + 3x - 18 = 0$$
$$(-6)^2 + 3(-6) - 18 \stackrel{?}{=} 0$$
$$0 = 0 \;\checkmark$$

$$x^2 + 3x - 18 = 0$$
$$(3)^2 + 3(3) - 18 \stackrel{?}{=} 0$$
$$0 = 0 \;\checkmark$$

A spreadsheet is a tool that can be used to manipulate numbers easily. Accountants, insurance underwriters, and loan officers all use spreadsheets to simplify calculations.

EXPLORATION

SPREADSHEET

To solve the quadratic equation $2x^2 + x - 3 = 0$ by using a spreadsheet, first enter the coefficients 2, 1, and -3 into the cells. Establish a starting value for x. Then choose an increment for the values of x to increase. You can change any of these values by typing a different number into the cell. The spreadsheet automatically computes and updates all other values in the cells. The bottom row of cells contains the values of the equation for the given values of x. The spreadsheet below indicates that the roots are -1.5 and 1. *You can verify these solutions by graphing.*

Quadratic Equation									
2	X^2+	1	X+	-3	= 0				
Starting Value =			-2						
Increment =			0.5						
X	-2	-1.5	-1	-0.5	0	0.5	1	1.5	2
Y	3	0	-2	-3	-3	-2	0	3	7

Your Turn

a. Work through the other examples in this lesson by using a spreadsheet. **a–c. See students' work.**

b. Describe the difference between using a graphing calculator and using a spreadsheet to solve quadratic equations.

c. How did you determine the starting values and increments for x?

d. Find the roots of the equation $2x^2 + 2x - 12 = 0$ by using a spreadsheet. **$-3, 2$**

There are three possible outcomes when solving a quadratic equation. The equation will have two real solutions, one real solution, or no real solutions. When a quadratic equation has one real solution, it really has two solutions that are the same number. A graph of each of these outcomes is shown below.

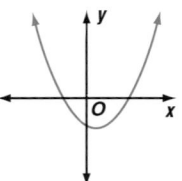

two real solutions

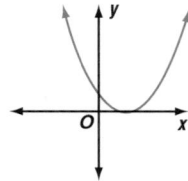

one real solution

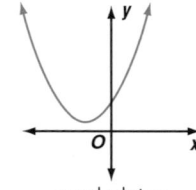

no real solutions

EXPLORATION

Students must be careful when selecting the starting values of x. They will probably begin with trial-and-error and then develop a pattern.

Classroom Vignette

"Show students that the line of symmetry can be described as the line where x equals the average of the roots of the quadratic equation.

That is, $x = \dfrac{r_1 + r_2}{2}$, where r_1 and r_2 are the roots of the equation."

Nancy Berkley

Nancy Berkley
North Stafford High School
Stafford, Virginia

In-Class Example

For Example 5
Solve $4x^2 - 12x = -9$ by graphing.

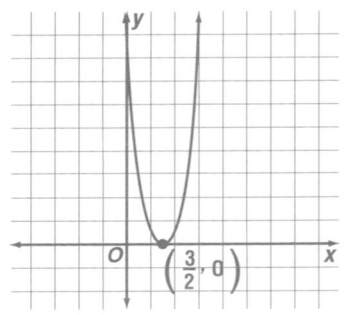

3 PRACTICE/APPLY

Check for Understanding
Exercises 1–15 are designed to help you assess your students' understanding through reading, writing, speaking, and modeling. You should work through Exercises 1–6 with your students and then monitor their work on Exercises 7–15.

Error Analysis
Students may perceive answers read from a graph as exact values, but all graphs have limited precision. When reading graphs, specify that values are approximate.

Study Guide Masters, p. 40

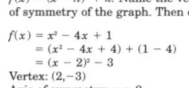 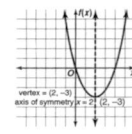

Study Guide
Student Edition
Pages 334–340

Solving Quadratic Equations by Graphing

| Definition of a Quadratic Function | A quadratic function is a function described by an equation that can be written in the form $f(x) = ax^2 + bx + c$ where $a \neq 0$. In a quadratic function, ax^2 is called the **quadratic term**, bx is called the **linear term**, and c is called the **constant term**. |

The graph of any quadratic function is a parabola. Parabolas have certain common characteristics. Study the chart below.

| Common Characteristics of Parabolas | 1. Axis of Symmetry: The line about which the parabola is symmetric. 2. Vertex: The point of the parabola where the parabola and the axis of symmetry intersect. 3. The graphs of all parabolas have the same general shape, a U shape. 4. A parabola whose equation is $y = (x - h)^2 + k$ has its vertex at (h, k) and axis of symmetry $x = h$. |

Example: Write $f(x) = x^2 - 4x + 1$ in the form $f(x) = (x - h)^2 + k$. Name the vertex and axis of symmetry of the graph. Then draw the graph.

$f(x) = x^2 - 4x + 1$
$= (x^2 - 4x + 4) + (1 - 4)$
$= (x - 2)^2 - 3$
Vertex: $(2, -3)$
Axis of symmetry: $x = 2$

Identify the quadratic term, the linear term, and the constant term in each function.
1. $f(x) = 4x^2 - 8x + 4$ 2. $m(p) = p^2 - 6p + 9$
   $4x^2; -8x; 4$ $p^2; -6p; 9$
3. $q(x) = -(x - 5)^2 - x^4$ 4. $f(x) = 5x^2 + (x - 4)^2$
   $-10x^2; 0; 25$ $6x^2; -8x; 16$

Graph each function. Name the vertex and the axis of symmetry. Identify the solutions of the related equation.
5. $f(x) = x^2 - 10x + 215$ 6. $f(x) = x^2 + 4x + 6$

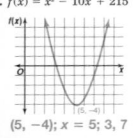 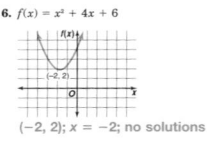

$(5, -4); x = 5; 3, 7$ $(-2, 2); x = -2;$ no solutions

338 Chapter 6

Example 5 illustrates a quadratic equation for which the solutions are the same number.

Example Solve $x^2 - 6x = -9$ by graphing.

Write the equation in standard form.
$$x^2 - 6x = -9 \quad \rightarrow \quad x^2 - 6x + 9 = 0$$

Find and graph the ordered pairs that satisfy the related function $f(x) = x^2 - 6x + 9$.

x	1	2	3	4	5	6
$f(x)$	4	1	0	1	4	9

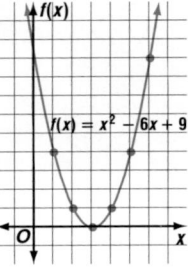

Notice that the graph has only one x-intercept, 3. Thus, the solution is 3.

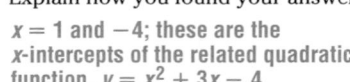

CHECK FOR UNDERSTANDING

Communicating Mathematics

1. No, because the degree of the equation is greater than 2.

3a. Three possible solutions are: $b = 10$, $h = 5$; $b = 12$, $h = 7$; $b = 7$, $h = 2$.

4. A quadratic function is an equation that equals $f(x)$, whereas a quadratic equation equals 0.

5. The graph of its related function is a parabola and cannot cross the x-axis more than twice.

Study the lesson. Then complete the following.

1. **Determine** if $3z^4 - 5z^3 + 6z - 6 = 0$ is a quadratic equation. Explain.
2. **Define** each term and explain how they are related.   See margin.
   a. solution   b. root   c. zero of a function   d. x-intercept
3. Refer to Example 3.   b. $b > 5$
   a. **List** three possible sets of dimensions for the triangle described.
   b. **Describe** the restrictions that must be placed on the graph of the function if you were to use it to solve the equation $\frac{1}{2}b^2 - \frac{5}{2}b = 0$.
4. **State** the difference between a quadratic equation and a quadratic function.
5. **Explain** why a quadratic equation cannot have more than two solutions.
6. **Determine** the solution of the equation $x^2 + 3x - 4 = 0$ from its related graph shown at the right. Explain how you found your answer.
   $x = 1$ and -4; these are the x-intercepts of the related quadratic function, $y = x^2 + 3x - 4$.

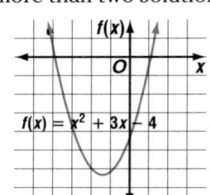

Guided Practice

9–11. See Solutions Manual for graphs.

9. $(2, 0)$, $x = 2$

10. $(0, 9)$, $x = 0$

11. $(-3, 0)$, $x = -3$

12. -2, -3

14. -1, $\frac{3}{2}$

Identify the quadratic term, the linear term, and the constant term in each function.   8. $-4x^2$; $-8x$; -9
7. $f(x) = x^2 + x - 4$ x^2; x; -4 8. $f(x) = -4x^2 - 8x - 9$

Graph each function. Name the vertex and the axis of symmetry.
9. $g(x) = x^2 - 4x + 4$ 10. $f(x) = x^2 + 9$ 11. $h(x) = x^2 + 6x + 9$

Solve each equation by graphing.   12–14. See Solutions Manual for graphs.
12. $d^2 + 5d + 6 = 0$ 13. $a^2 - 4a + 4 = 0$ 2   14. $2x^2 - x - 3 = 0$

15. A quadratic function $f(x)$ has values $f(3) = -4$, $f(6) = -7$, and $f(9) = 8$. Between which two x values is $f(x)$ sure to have a zero? Explain how you know.   See Solutions Manual.

338   Chapter 6   Exploring Quadratic Functions and Inequalities

Reteaching

Using Alternative Methods
Solve each equation by graphing.
$(x - 2)(x + 3) = 6$ $-4, 3$
$(x - 2)(x + 3) = -4$ $-2, 1$
$(x - 2)(x + 3) = 0$ $2, -3$
$(x - 2)(x + 3) = -6$ $0, -1$
First graph the related quadratic function $y = (x - 2)(x + 3)$. Then find where it intersects graphs of $y = 6$, $y = -4$, $y = 0$, and $y = -6$.

Additional Answers

2a. value that satisfies an equation
2b. solution to an equation
2c. x value of a function that makes the function equal to 0
2d. where the graph crosses the x-axis
All of these terms refer to the same values.

EXERCISES

Practice

Identify the quadratic term, the linear term, and the constant term in each function.

A

16. $g(x) = 5x^2 - 7x + 2$ $5x^2; -7x; 2$ **17.** $g(n) = 3n^2 - 1$ $3n^2; 0; -1$

18. $f(n) = \frac{1}{3}n^2 + 4$ $\frac{1}{3}n^2; 0; 4$ **19.** $f(z) = z^2 + 3z$ $z^2; 3z; 0$

B

20. $f(x) = (x + 3)^2$ $x^2; 6x; 9$ **21.** $f(t) = (3t + 1)^2 - 8$ $9t^2; 6t; -7$

Use the related graph of each equation to determine its solutions.

22. −2, 1
23. −4
24. 0, 16

22. $2x^2 + 2x - 4 = 0$ **23.** $x^2 + 8x + 16 = 0$ **24.** $x^2 - 16x = 0$

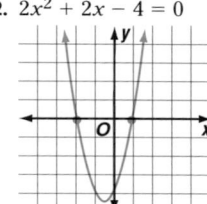 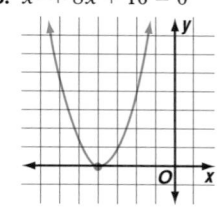 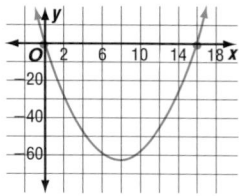

Graph each function. Name the vertex and the axis of symmetry.

25–33. See Solutions Manual.

25. $f(x) = x^2$ **26.** $f(x) = x^2 + 12x + 36$ **27.** $g(x) = x^2 - 9x + 9$

28. $h(x) = x^2 + 4$ **29.** $f(x) = x^2 - 9$ **30.** $h(x) = x^2 - 10x + 27$

C

31. $f(x) = x^2 + 20x + 93$ **32.** $g(x) = x^2 - \frac{2}{5}x + \frac{26}{25}$ **33.** $f(x) = x^2 + 3x - 0.95$

34–42. See Solutions Manual for graphs.

Solve each equation by graphing.

34. −7, 4   35. 6, −4
36. 3, $-\frac{5}{4}$ 39. −1.5, 3

40. $\frac{5}{2}$, $-\frac{1}{2}$ 41. −4, $\frac{3}{2}$

34. $m^2 + 3m = 28$ **35.** $p^2 - 2p - 24 = 0$ **36.** $4n^2 - 7n - 15 = 0$

37. $c^2 + 4c + 4 = 0$ −2   **38.** $n^2 - 3n = 0$ 0, 3   **39.** $2w^2 - 3w = 9$

40. $4v^2 - 8v - 5 = 0$ **41.** $2c^2 + 5c - 12 = 0$ **42.** $(3x + 4)(2x + 7) = 0$

Critical Thinking

42. $-\frac{4}{3}$, $-\frac{7}{2}$

43. Number Theory Although no one has found a formula that generates prime numbers, eighteenth-century Swiss mathematician Leonhard Euler discovered that $y = x^2 + x + 17$ produces prime numbers up to a certain point. **See margin.**

   a. Based on the graph of $f(x) = x^2 + x + 17$, what are the roots? Explain your answer.

   b. Describe how the nature of the graph relates to the equation for generating prime numbers.

Applications and Problem Solving

44. World Records In 1940, Emanual Zacchini of Italy was fired a record distance of 175 feet from a cannon while performing in the United States. Suppose his initial upward velocity was 80 feet per second. The height y can be represented by the function $y = 80x - 16x^2$, where x represents the number of seconds that have passed.

   a. Draw the graph of the function, relating heights Mr. Zacchini reaches to the time after he was shot from the cannon. **See margin.**

   b. How long after he was shot out of the cannon did he reach his maximum height? What was that height? **2.5 seconds, 100 feet**

45. Free-Falling In 1942, I.M. Chisov of the USSR bailed out of an airplane without a parachute at 21,980 feet and survived. The function $h(t) = -16t^2 + 21,980$ describes the relationship between height $h(t)$ in feet and time t in seconds. **b. about 37 seconds**

   a. Graph the function. **See margin.**

   b. About how many seconds did he fall before reaching the ground?

Lesson 6–1 Solving Quadratic Equations by Graphing **339**

Assignment Guide

Core: 17–45 odd, 46–53
Enriched: 16–42 even, 43–53

For **Extra Practice**, see p. 889.

The red A, B, and C flags, printed only in the Teacher's Wraparound Edition, indicate the level of difficulty of the exercises.

Additional Answers

43a. There are no roots because the graph does not touch the x-axis.

43b. Sample answer: There cannot be any negative prime numbers since the graph has no negative y values.

Additional Answers

44a.

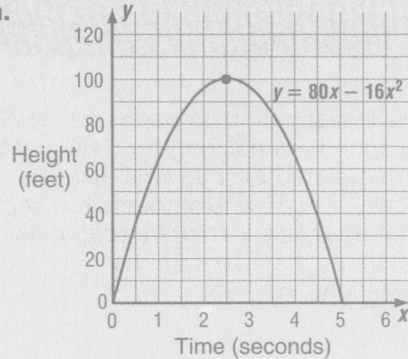

45a. $f(x) = x(x + 2)$

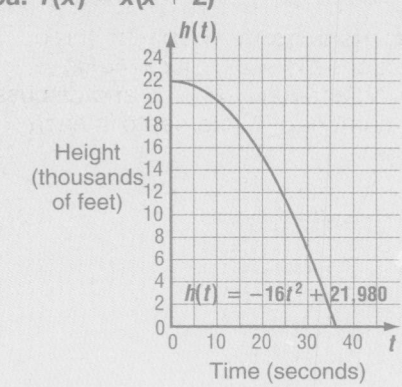

Practice Masters, p. 40

6-1 **Practice**
NAME_____ DATE_____
Student Edition Pages 334–

Solving Quadratic Equations by Graphing

Identify the quadratic term, the linear term, and the constant term in each function.

1. $f(x) = x^2 + 14x + 49$ $x^2; 14x; 49$ **2.** $f(x) = 54x^2 + 36x + 10$ $54x^2; 36x; 10$

3. $f(x) = -3(2x + 1)^2$ $-12x^2; -12x; -3$ **4.** $f(x) = -\frac{2}{3}(x - 6)^2 + 4$ $-\frac{2}{3}x^2; 8x; -20$

Graph each function. Name the vertex and the axis of symmetry.

5. $f(x) = x^2 - 10x + 25$ **6.** $f(x) = x^2 + 12x + 36$

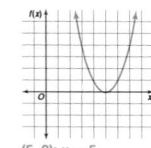 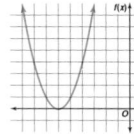

$(5, 0)$; $x = 5$ $(-6, 0)$; $x = -6$

Solve each equation by graphing.

7. $y = (x + 5)^2 - 1$ −6, −4   **8.** $x^2 + 2x = 0$ −2, 0

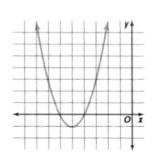 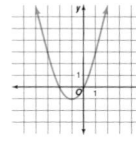

Chapter 6 **339**

4 ASSESS

Closing Activity
Writing Have students compare solving equations by spreadsheet and by graphing calculator. They should address the issue of accuracy.

Additional Answer

52.

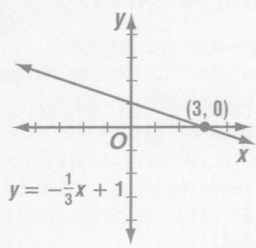

$$y = -\frac{1}{3}x + 1$$
(3, 0)

Enrichment Masters, p. 40

NAME_____ DATE _____

Enrichment   Student Edition Pages 334–340

Parametric Equations

Sometimes a graph is described by two equations rather than just one. For example, the coordinates (x, y) of a moving point are often described by two equations using the variable t for time.

$$x = t \qquad y = t^2$$

These are called **parametric equations** for the location of the point at time t. The variable t is the parameter.

Parametric equations are often used because an equation involving only x and y would be too complicated. Sometimes parameters provide the most straightforward description of the problem being solved.

Make a table of values and then sketch the graph of each set of parametric equations. The axes shown will help you choose appropriate values for t.

1. $x = t - 2$
   $y = 2t + 3$

2. $x = t$
   $y = t^2$

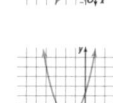 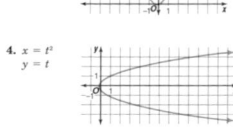

3. $x = t - 2$
   $y = t^2 - t + 1$

4. $x = t^2$
   $y = t$

5. $x = t^2 - 3t + 2$
   $y = t^2 + t - 1$

6. $x = t^3$
   $y = t^2$

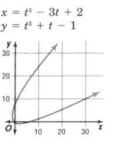 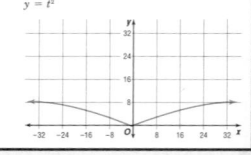

Mixed Review

46. $(148 - j64)$ volts

48. $\begin{bmatrix} 4 & 3 & 10 \\ 5 & -1 & 3 \end{bmatrix}$

50. 6, 9, 18

51. $y = -3x - 16$,
$3x + y = -16$

46. Electrical Engineering The relationship between the flow of electricity *I* in a circuit, the resistance to the flow *Z*, called impedance, and the electromotive force *E*, called voltage, is given by the formula $E = I \cdot Z$. Electrical engineers use *j* to represent the imaginary unit. An electrical engineer is designing a circuit that is to have a current of $(6 - j8)$ amps. If the impedance of the circuit is $(14 + j8)$ ohms, find the voltage. (Lesson 5–9)

47. Geometry The area of a square is $169x^2$. The length of one of its sides minus 14 is equal to 77. Solve for *x*. (Lesson 5–8) **7**

48. Write an augmented matrix for $4x + 3y = 10$ and $5x - y = 3$. Then solve the system of equations. (Lesson 4–6) **(1, 2)**

49. Evaluate the determinant of $\begin{bmatrix} \frac{1}{2} & -1 & 3 \\ -3 & 5 & -2 \\ 3 & 2 & 4 \end{bmatrix}$ using expansion by minors. (Lesson 4–5) **−57**

50. Jill has three sons. The age of the oldest son is 3 times the age of the youngest son, and the age of the middle son is half the age of the oldest son. The sum of their ages is 9 years less than the age of their mother. If the age of their mother is 42, find the ages of the three sons. (Lesson 3–7)

51. Write an equation in slope-intercept form and in standard form for the line that has a slope of -3 and passes through $(-7, 5)$. (Lesson 2–4)

52. Graph a line that passes through $(3, 0)$ and is perpendicular to $y - 3x = 1$. (Lesson 2–3) **See margin.**

53. Sonia's aquarium holds 31.5 L of water. The container she uses to fill the aquarium holds 1.5 L. How many full containers of water does it take to fill the aquarium? (Lesson 1–4) **21**

WORKING ON THE
In·ves·ti·ga·tion

Refer to the Investigation on pp. 328–329.

the River Canyon Bridge

After reviewing your proposal for four types of bridges, your company's consultant suggests a bridge that is supported by an arch as shown below.

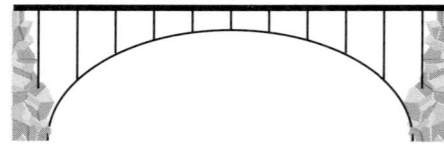

The arch would be in the shape of a parabola that opens downward with its vertex at the center of the bridge. The bridge would span the canyon and be anchored to the canyon walls.

It would be supported by a set of short struts that are anchored to the parabolic arch.

1 Draw a scaled blueprint of this bridge on grid paper. Let the road lie along the *x*-axis and let the vertex of the parabola lie on the *y*-axis.

2 Make a table of values for points that lie along the arch of the bridge.

3 Look for a pattern in your table and estimate at what points the arch of the bridge will touch the sides of the canyon.

4 How does this design compare with the bridges you considered?

Add the results of your work to your Investigation Folder.

Extension

Communication Graph the three functions $f(x) = x^2 - 4x + 4$, $f(x) = x^2 + 2$, and $f(x) = x^2 - 2$, and discuss the number of *x*-intercepts in each case.

In·ves·ti·ga·tion

Working on the Investigation
The Investigation on pages 328–329 is designed to be a long-term project that is completed over several days or weeks. Encourage students to keep their materials in their Investigation Folder as they work on the Investigation.

Solving Quadratic Equations by Factoring

What YOU'LL LEARN

- To solve problems by using the guess-and-check strategy, and
- to solve quadratic equations by factoring.

Why IT'S IMPORTANT

You can use quadratic equations to solve problems involving tennis, meteorology, and air travel.

APPLICATION
Tennis

In 1993, German tennis player Steffi Graf won three of the four biggest tournaments in tennis: Wimbledon, the French Open, and the U.S. Open. When an object, like a tennis ball, is hit straight up into the air, the height of the object is given by the function $h(t) = v_o t - 16t^2$, where $h(t)$ represents the height of the object, v_o represents the initial velocity, and t represents the time that the object has traveled. If a tennis ball is hit upward with an initial velocity of 48 feet per second, how long does it take for the ball to fall to the ground? To find the solution, substitute the known values into the formula $h(t) = v_o t - 16t^2$ to get the resulting function $h(t) = 48t - 16t^2$.

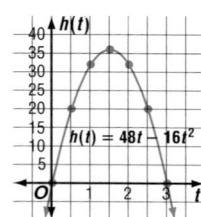

Players with the most Wimbledon titles
1. Billie Jean King, 20
2. Elizabeth Ryan, 19
3. Martina Navratilova, 18
4. Suzanne Lenglen, 15
5. William Renshaw, 14

There are several methods that you can use to find the solution. In the last lesson, you learned to find the solution by graphing.

t	0	0.5	1	1.5	2	2.5	3
$h(t)$	0	20	32	36	32	20	0

For this function, the zeros are 0 and 3. This means that the ball starts out at 0 feet and travels for 3 seconds before reaching the ground again.

Another way to solve a quadratic equation is by **factoring.** To solve by factoring, you must use the **zero product property.**

Zero Product Property	For any real numbers a and b, if $ab = 0$, then either $a = 0$, $b = 0$, or both.

We can solve the same equation by factoring that we solved above by graphing.

$$0 = 48t - 16t^2$$
$$0 = 16t(3 - t)$$

Since the product of $16t$ and $3 - t$ is 0, either $16t$ or $3 - t$ equals 0. So set each factor equal to 0 and solve.

$16t = 0$ or $3 - t = 0$ *Zero product property*
$t = 0$ $t = 3$

The solutions (or roots) are 0 and 3. These are the same as the zeros obtained when you graphed the related function, $h(t) = 48 - 16t^2$. These answers seem reasonable since a tennis ball might not stay in the air for more than 3 seconds.

Lesson 6–2 Solving Quadratic Equations by Factoring **341**

Wimbledon is the only grass court tournament of the four Grand Slam events.

6-2 LESSON NOTES

NCTM Standards: 1–5

Instructional Resources

- Study Guide Master 6-2
- Practice Master 6-2
- Enrichment Master 6-2
- Tech Prep Applications Masters, p. 11

Transparency 6-2A contains the 5-Minute Check for this lesson; **Transparency 6-2B** contains a teaching aid for this lesson.

Recommended Pacing	
Standard Pacing	Days 3 & 4 of 17
Honors Pacing	Day 3 of 14
Block Scheduling*	Day 2 of 7 (along with Lesson 6-3)

*For more information on pacing and possible lesson plans, refer to the *Block Scheduling Booklet*.

1 FOCUS

5-Minute Check
(over Lesson 6-1)

Solve each equation by graphing.

1. $x^2 = 4$ 2, −2
2. $x^2 + 4x = 0$ −4, 0
3. Write a function to represent the area of a triangle if the height is 4 cm less than the base. Then sketch the graph. $f(b) = \frac{1}{2}b^2 - 2b$

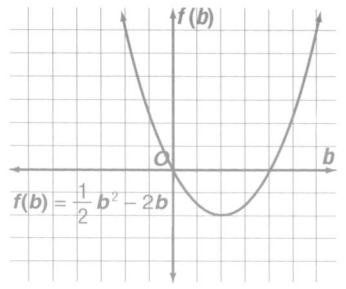

$f(b) = \frac{1}{2}b^2 - 2b$

TEKS | 2.a., 6.a., 6.b., 8.a., 8.c., 8.d.

Motivating the Lesson

Situational Problem Ask students to find the ways you can get 8 liters of water, given you have only two buckets. One of the buckets has a 3 liter and the other bucket a 7 liter capacity. Have students explain their method of solution. If someone says they guessed, point out that guessing is a valid method.

Teaching Tip Point out that in a problem such as the one in the application at the beginning of the lesson, a tennis ball would not begin its upward travel at 0 feet, but at some distance above the ground. The height above the ground at which the ball was hit would have to be added to any of the values determined by the equation.

2 TEACH

In-Class Examples

For Example 1
Solve $m^2 - 3m - 28 = 0$ by factoring. $-4, 7$

For Example 2
Craig Hoffheimer wants to build a swimming pool surrounded by a sidewalk of uniform width. He wants the dimensions of the pool and sidewalk to be 16 meters by 20 meters. The pool has an area of 192 square meters. How wide should the sidewalk be? **2 meters**

Teaching Tip Remind students that not all solutions to a quadratic equation may answer the application problem for which the equation was written.

The **guess-and-check** strategy can be useful when factoring quadratic equations. You may have to try several combinations of factors before finding the right one.

Example **Solve $x^2 + 6x - 16 = 0$ by factoring.**

Start guessing by using factors of 16: 2, 4, 8, or 16.

PROBLEM SOLVING
Guess and Check

Guess	Check	Correct?
$(x - 4)(x + 4)$	$x^2 - 16 = 0$	*No, the linear term is 0.*
$(x - 8)(x + 2)$	$x^2 - 6x - 16 = 0$	*No, the linear term is negative.*
$(x + 8)(x - 2)$	$x^2 + 6x - 16 = 0$	*Yes*

You can now solve the equation by using the zero product property to find the values of x.

$$(x + 8)(x - 2) = 0$$
$$x + 8 = 0 \quad \text{or} \quad x - 2 = 0$$
$$x = -8 \qquad\qquad x = 2$$

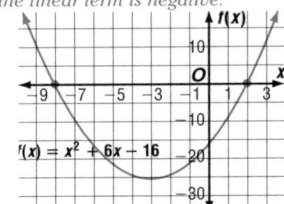

$f(x) = x^2 + 6x - 16$

The solutions are -8 and 2. You can check these solutions by graphing the related quadratic function and checking the x-intercepts.

When using factoring to solve a real-life problem, you need to examine each solution carefully to see if it is reasonable for that situation.

Example ② **APPLICATION**
Antiques

International auction houses sell hundreds of oriental rugs each year to collectors from all over the world. A 17th-century Mughal carpet was recently purchased from a museum for $253,000, despite having moth damage, corrosion, and holes. The rug has a border of uniform width depicting lilies, asters, and roses and a red center called a raspberry field. The auction brochure for the rug describes it as measuring 9 feet by 15 feet, with a raspberry field of 91 square feet. If you were interested in purchasing the rug, you might want to know how wide that beautiful border is. How wide is it?

Explore   Read the problem and make a drawing that models the Mughal carpet.

Let x feet be the width of the border.
The length of the red center is $15 - 2x$ feet.
The width of the red center is $9 - 2x$ feet.

Plan   Write an equation. The area of the red center can be expressed as the product of the length and width.

$$A = \ell w$$
$$= (15 - 2x)(9 - 2x) \quad \text{Substitute for } \ell \text{ and } w.$$
$$= 135 - 48x + 4x^2 \quad \text{Multiply the binomials.}$$
$$= 4x^2 - 48x + 135$$

Solve   Since the area of the red center is 91 square feet, replace A with 91 and solve this equation.

17th-Century Mughal carpet, sold for $253,000

Alternative Learning Styles

Kinesthetic If you have six toothpicks, how can you form four triangles so that they touch only at their endpoints? The toothpicks cannot cross. What problem-solving strategies did you use? Why?

TECHNOLOGY
Tips

You can use a graphing calculator and the TRACE function or [2nd] [CALC] root to find the zeros of the graphed function.

$A = 4x^2 - 48x + 135$

$91 = 4x^2 - 48x + 135$ *Replace A with 91.*

$0 = 4x^2 - 48x + 44$ *Subtract 91 from each side.*

$0 = x^2 - 12x + 11$ *Divide each side by 4.*

$0 = (x - 11)(x - 1)$ *Factor.*

$x - 11 = 0$ or $x - 1 = 0$

$x = 11$ $x = 1$

The solutions are 11 and 1. Use $x = 1$ since 11 is an unreasonable answer. Thus, the width of the floral border is 1 foot.

Examine   If the border is 1 foot wide all the way around, the width of the center is $9 - 2(1)$ or 7 and the length is $15 - 2(1)$ or 13. Since $7 \times 13 = 91$, the answer makes sense.

You have seen that a quadratic equation may have one solution. Factoring shows this is true because the two factors of the quadratic function are the same.

Example   ③   **Solve $x^2 + 10x = -25$ by factoring.**

$x^2 + 10x = -25$

$x^2 + 10x + 25 = 0$

$(x + 5)(x + 5) = 0$

$x + 5 = 0$ or $x + 5 = 0$

$x = -5$ $x = -5$

The only solution is -5.

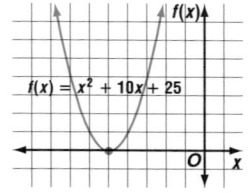

The graph of the related function intersects the x-axis in one point.

No matter which method you use, you can always check your solutions by substituting the values into the equation and simplifying.

Check: $x^2 + 10x = -25$

$(-5)^2 + 10(-5) \stackrel{?}{=} -25$

$-25 = -25$ ✓

CHECK FOR UNDERSTANDING

Communicating Mathematics

Study the lesson. Then complete the following.   1. See margin.

1. **Explain** why the solution of 11 feet is unreasonable in Example 2.

2. **State** the zeros of the function graphed at the right. Verify by solving the related equation by factoring. $-2, 4$

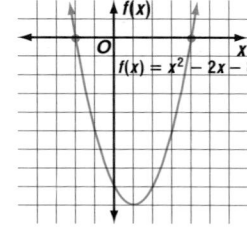

Lesson 6-2 Solving Quadratic Equations by Factoring   **343**

Reteaching

Using Models The model for factoring $x^2 - 2x - 15$ is shown. Notice that 3 pairs of tiles (3 positive, 3 negative) were added to form the representation. This model can now be used to solve $x^2 - 2x - 15 = 0$. One of the sides must represent 0. So, $x + 3 = 0$ or $x - 5 = 0$. Thus, the solutions are -3 or 5.

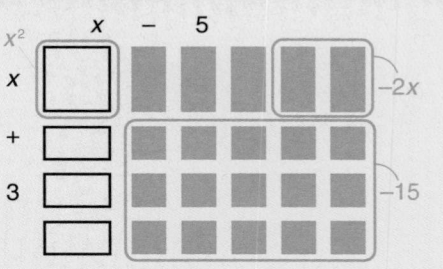

In-Class Example

For Example 3

Solve $x^2 + 4x = 12$ by factoring.

$-6, 2$

3 PRACTICE/APPLY

Check for Understanding

Exercises 1–10 are designed to help you assess your students' understanding through reading, writing, speaking, and modeling. You should work through Exercises 1–3 with your students and then monitor their work on Exercises 4–10.

Additional Answer

1. x cannot be 11 feet since $15 - 2x$ and $9 - 2x$ would lead to negative dimensions for the length and width of the carpet.

Study Guide Masters, p. 41

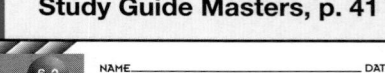

6-2   NAME _____ DATE _____

Study Guide   Student Edition Pages 341–3...

Solving Quadratic Equations by Factoring

The only way for the product of two numbers to equal 0 is for at least one of the factors to be 0. This fact is known as the **zero product property.** You use this property when you solve equations by factoring.

Zero Product Property	For any real numbers a and b, if $ab = 0$, then $a = 0$ or $b = 0$.

Example: Solve $x^2 - 4x = 12$ by factoring.

$x^2 - 4x - 12 = 0$ Rewrite the equation in standard form.

$(x - 6)(x + 2) = 0$ Factor.

$x - 6 = 0$ $x + 2 = 0$ Use the zero product property. Set each factor equal to zero and solve.

$x = 6$ $x = -2$

Solve each equation by factoring.

1. $z^2 - 12z + 27 = 0$ 9, 3

2. $x^2 + 13x + 40 = 0$ $-8, -5$

3. $x^2 - 7x - 44 = 0$ 11, -4

4. $x^2 + 3x - 130 = 0$ $-13, 10$

5. $x^2 - 12x = -36$ 6

6. $3s^2 - 13s = 10$ $\frac{-2}{3}$, 5

7. $16x^2 = 49$ $\frac{7}{4}, \frac{-7}{4}$

8. $3s^2 - 13s = -10$ $\frac{10}{3}$, 1

9. $4k^2 - 35k - 9 = 0$ 9, $-\frac{1}{4}$

10. $-2x^2 - 5x + 12 = 0$ $\frac{3}{2}, -4$

Assignment Guide

Core: 11–39 odd, 40–46
Enriched: 12–34 even, 35–46

For **Extra Practice,** see p. 889.

The red A, B, and C flags, printed only in the Teacher's Wraparound Edition, indicate the level of difficulty of the exercises.

Additional Answer

3. Carmen is right. Chelsea didn't factor correctly. $x^2 - 13x + 36 = 0$ factors to $(x - 9)(x - 4) = 0$, and the solutions for x are 9 and 4.

3. See margin.

5. $-\frac{7}{3}, -5$

9. $2, -\frac{7}{3}$

3. You Decide Chelsea was trying to find the zeros of the function $f(x) = x^2 - 13x + 36$. Carmen explained that she was making a mistake, but Chelsea insisted she was right. "All you have to do is make the $f(x)$ equal to zero and solve for x," Chelsea said. Look at her work below.

$$x^2 - 13x + 36 = 0$$
$$(x - 9)(x + 4) = 0$$
$$x - 9 = 0 \quad \text{or} \quad x + 4 = 0$$
$$x = 9 \qquad\qquad x = -4$$

Carmen said there was still something wrong. Who is correct? Explain.

Guided Practice

Solve each equation.

4. $(y - 8)(y + 6) = 0$ 8, -6
5. $(3y + 7)(y + 5) = 0$

Solve each equation by factoring.

6. $q^2 - 5q - 24 = 0$ 8, -3
7. $r^2 - 16r + 64 = 0$ 8
8. $a^3 = 81a$ $-9, 0, 9$
9. $3y^2 + y - 14 = 0$

10. **Physics** According to the the *Guinness Book of World Records,* the longest pendulum in the world is 73 feet $9\frac{3}{4}$ inches. It was installed in Tokyo, Japan, in 1983. The time in seconds t for a pendulum to swing back and forth is given by the formula $t^2 = 1.23L$, where L is the length of the pendulum in feet.

   a. What is the length of time needed for this pendulum to swing back and forth once?   9.53 seconds
   b. How long would it take for a pendulum that is 6 feet long to swing back and forth once?   2.72 seconds
   c. How long should the pendulum be if you want it to swing back and forth exactly 15 times a minute?   13 feet

EXERCISES

14. $\frac{5}{3}, -\frac{7}{2}$

20. $0, \frac{5}{3}$ 21. $-\frac{1}{6}, \frac{1}{3}$

22. $\frac{5}{2}, -\frac{5}{2}$

23. $-\frac{4}{3}$ 24. $-\frac{3}{4}, 4$

26. $\frac{1}{4}, 4$ 27. $-\frac{1}{4}, 3$

28. $\frac{1}{3}, -\frac{3}{2}$

29. $-\frac{3}{4}, -\frac{4}{3}$

30. $-\frac{5}{6}, 1$

33. $0, -\frac{6}{7}, \frac{2}{5}$

Practice

Solve each equation.

11. $(a + 4)(a + 1) = 0$ $-4, -1$
12. $z(z - 1) = 0$ 0, 1
13. $2x + 6)(x - 3) = 0$ $-3, 3$
14. $(3y - 5)(2y + 7) = 0$

Solve each equation by factoring.

15. $x^2 - x = 12$ 4, -3
16. $d^2 - 5d = 0$ 0, 5
17. $z^2 - 12z + 36 = 0$ 6
18. $y^2 + y - 30 = 0$ 5, -6
19. $r^2 - 3r = 4$ 4, -1
20. $3c^2 = 5c$
21. $18u^2 - 3u = 1$
22. $4y^2 = 25$
23. $9y^2 + 16 = -24y$
24. $4x^2 - 13x = 12$

Solve each equation by graphing or by factoring.

25. $b^2 + 3b = 40$ 5, -8
26. $4a^2 - 17a + 4 = 0$
27. $4s^2 - 11s = 3$
28. $6r^2 + 7r = 3$
29. $12m^2 + 25m + 12 = 0$
30. $18n^2 - 3n = 15$
31. $n^3 = 9n$ 0, 3, -3
32. $x^3 = 64x$ 0, 8, -8
33. $35z^3 + 16z^2 = 12z$
34. $18r^3 + 16r = 34r^2$ 0, 1, $\frac{8}{9}$

Critical Thinking

35. A parabola has intercepts at $x = -8$, $x = 4$, and $y = -8$. What is the equation of the parabola? $y = 0.25(x + 8)(x - 4)$ or $y = 0.25x^2 + x - 8$

344   Chapter 6   *Exploring Quadratic Functions and Inequalities*

Practice Masters, p. 41

 6-2

NAME_____ DATE_____
Practice
Student Edition
Pages 341–345

Solving Quadratic Equations by Factoring

Solve each equation by factoring.

1. $x^2 - 4x - 12 = 0$ 6, -2
2. $y^2 - 16y + 64 = 0$ 8
3. $n^2 + 25 = 10n$ 5
4. $9z = 10z^2$ 0, $\frac{9}{10}$
5. $7y^2 = 4y$ 0, $\frac{4}{7}$
6. $c^2 = 2c + 99$ $-9, 11$
7. $5w^2 - 35w + 60 = 0$ 3, 4
8. $3d^2 + 24d + 45 = 0$ $-5, -3$
9. $15v^2 + 19v + 6 = 0$ $-\frac{3}{5}, -\frac{2}{3}$
10. $4j^2 + 6 = 11j$ $\frac{3}{4}, 2$
11. $36k^2 = 25$ $\frac{5}{6}, -\frac{5}{6}$
12. $12m^3 - 8m^2 = 15m$ 0, $-\frac{5}{6}, \frac{3}{2}$
13. $6e^3 = 5e^2 + 6e$ 0, $\frac{3}{2}, -\frac{2}{3}$
14. $9 = 64p^2$ $\frac{3}{8}, -\frac{3}{8}$

Solve. Use any strategy.

15. At a cattle pen at the county fair, Jody counted 65 heads and 236 legs. How many cattle and how many workers were there in the pen at that time?
53 cattle, 12 workers

16. Replace each letter with a whole number so that the addition problem at the right is correct. Each letter represents a different number. (There are four possible answers.)
   A = 1, B = 2, C = 3, D = 4;
   A = 1, B = 3, C = 2, D = 4;
   A = 2, B = 4, C = 1, D = 3;
   A = 2, B = 1, C = 4, D = 3

```
  A B C D
+ D C B A
  5 5 5 5
```

36. Air Travel A Delta Airlines route map states the formula $(VM)^2 = 1.22A$, where VM represents the number of miles to the horizon you can see from an airplane if you are flying on a clear day. The altitude, in feet, is represented by A.

 a. Suppose you are flying at an altitude of 36,000 feet on a clear day. About how many miles are there to the horizon? **210 miles**

 b. Suppose the distance to the horizon is 236 miles. What is your altitude in feet? **45,652 feet**

  c. 42 miles

 c. The Sears Tower in Chicago is the tallest building in the world. The observation deck is 1454 feet above ground. About how far could you see on a clear day if you were standing on the observation deck?

37. Meteorology Weather forecasters can determine the approximate time that a thunderstorm will last if they know the diameter d of the storm in miles. The time t in hours can be found by using the formula $216t^2 = d^3$.

 a. Draw the graph of $y = 216t^2 - 5^3$ and use it to estimate how long a thunderstorm will last if its diameter is 5 miles. **about 45 minutes**

 b. Find how long a thunderstorm will last if its diameter is 5 miles and compare this time with your estimate in part a. **0.76 hour**

38. Guess and Check Find two integers whose sum is 15 and whose product is 54. **6, 9**

37a. See margin for graph.

39. Geometry The diagram below shows the relationship between the number of chords drawn through a circle and the maximum number of parts into which chords can divide a circle.

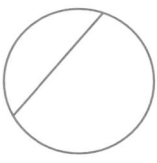
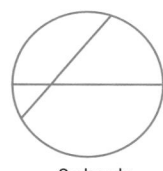
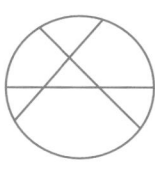

| 1 chord | 2 chords | 3 chords |
| 2 parts | 4 parts | 7 parts |

This relationship can be described by the formula $p = \frac{1}{2}x^2 + \frac{1}{2}x + 1$,

where p represents the number of parts and x represents the number of chords. How many chords would you have to draw to divide a circle into 37 parts? **8 chords**

Mixed Review

40. Geometry The length of a rectangle is 2 centimeters greater than its width. (Lesson 6–1)

 a. Write a function to represent the area of the rectangle. Then graph the function. **$A = w(w + 2)$; See margin for graph.**

 b. Use the graph to estimate the area of a rectangle whose width is 4 cm. Compare your estimate to the actual area. **24 cm²**

41. Solve $6y^2 = -96$. (Lesson 5–9) **$\pm 4i$**

42. Simplify $= \dfrac{rs}{r^{\frac{1}{2}} + r^{\frac{3}{2}}}$. (Lesson 5–7) $\dfrac{r^{\frac{1}{2}}s}{1 + r}$

43. Find the inverse of $\begin{bmatrix} 4 & -2 \\ -3 & 6 \end{bmatrix}$. (Lesson 4–4) $\dfrac{1}{18}\begin{bmatrix} 6 & 2 \\ 3 & 4 \end{bmatrix}$

44. Graph the system $3x - 2y = 10$ and $y - x = -1$ and state its solution. (Lesson 3–1) **(8, 7); See margin for graph.**

45. $\dfrac{4 - 27n}{5}$

45. Solve $3(2m + 9n) - (4 + 6m) = -5m$ for m. (Lesson 2–2)

46. Simplify $\frac{2}{3}\left(\frac{1}{2}a + 3b\right) + \frac{1}{2}\left(\frac{2}{3}a + b\right)$. (Lesson 1–2) $\dfrac{2}{3}a + \dfrac{5}{2}b$

Extension

Reasoning Suppose $a \neq 0$ and $b \neq 0$. If they are both positive, or both negative, the product is positive. If a and b are opposite signs, their product is negative. Have students make a table relating the signs within the equation to the signs in the factors.

Additional Answer

44.

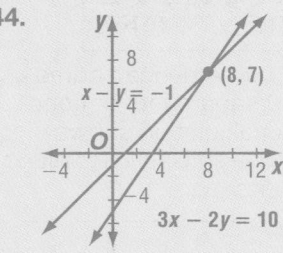

---

4 ASSESS

Closing Activity

Speaking Have students explain how they determine the values of a and b and their signs when factoring a quadratic expression into $(x + a)(x + b)$.

Additional Answers

37a.

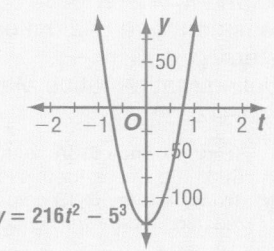

40a.

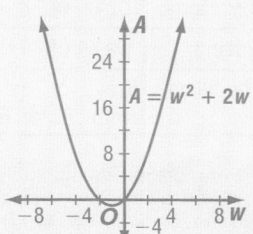

Enrichment Masters, p. 41

6-2 NAME _____ DATE _____
Student Edit
Enrichment Pages 341–3

Quadratic Form

Consider two methods for solving the following equation.
$$(y - 2)^2 - 5(y - 2) + 6 = 0$$
One way to solve the equation is to simplify first, then use factoring.
$$y^2 - 4y + 4 - 5y + 10 + 6 = 0$$
$$y^2 - 9y + 20 = 0$$
$$(y - 4)(y - 5) = 0$$
Thus, the solution set is {4, 5}.

Another way to solve the equation is first to replace $y - 2$ by a single variable. This will produce an equation that is easier to solve than the original equation. Let $t = y - 2$ and then solve the new equation.
$$(y - 2)^2 - 5(y - 2) + 6 = 0$$
$$t^2 - 5t + 6 = 0$$
$$(t - 2)(t - 3) = 0$$
Thus, t is 2 or 3. Since $t = y - 2$, the solution set of the original equation is {4, 5}.

Solve each equation using two different methods.

1. $(z + 2)^2 + 8(z + 2) + 7 = 0$ 2. $(3x - 1)^2 - (3x - 1) - 20 = 0$
{−3, −9}   {2, −1}

3. $(2t + 1)^2 - 4(2t + 1) + 3 = 0$ 4. $(y^2 - 1)^2 - (y^2 - 1) - 2 = 0$
{0, 1}   {0, $\pm\sqrt{3}$}

5. $(a^2 - 2)^2 - 2(a^2 - 2) - 3 = 0$ 6. $(1 + \sqrt{c})^2 + (1 + \sqrt{c}) - 6 = 0$
{±1, ±$\sqrt{5}$}   {1}

Completing the Square

NCTM Standards: 1–5

Instructional Resources

- Study Guide Master 6-3
- Practice Master 6-3
- Enrichment Master 6-3
- Assessment and Evaluation Masters, p. 156
- Modeling Mathematics Masters, pp. 40–42

Transparency 6-3A contains the 5-Minute Check for this lesson; **Transparency 6-3B** contains a teaching aid for this lesson.

Recommended Pacing

Standard Pacing	Day 5 of 17
Honors Pacing	Day 4 of 14
Block Scheduling*	Day 2 of 7 (along with Lesson 6-2)

*For more information on pacing and possible lesson plans, refer to the *Block Scheduling Booklet*.

1 FOCUS

5-Minute Check
(over Lesson 6-2)

Solve each equation by factoring.

1. $x^2 - x = 2$ **2, −1**
2. $c^2 - 16c + 64 = 0$ **8**
3. $z^3 = 16z$ **0, 4, −4**
4. $2x^2 + 5x + 3 = 0$ $-\frac{3}{2}, -1$
5. $12p^2 + 8p = 15$ $\frac{5}{6}, -\frac{3}{2}$

Motivating the Lesson

Hands-On Activity Have students draw a square. Have them cut off the same amount on two adjoining sides. They should then determine the dimensions and area of the new square. Have them write an equation to solve the problem.

TEKS 2.a., 2.b., 5.e., 6.a., 6.b., 8.a., 8.c.

**YOU'LL LEARN**

- To solve quadratic equations by completing the square.

**IT'S IMPORTANT**

You can complete the square to solve quadratic equations that involve architecture and law enforcement.

GLOBAL CONNECTIONS

The largest non-palatial residence is St. Emmeram Castle in Regensburg, Germany. It is valued at more than $177 million and contains 517 rooms with a floor space of 231,000 square feet. Only 95 rooms are personally used by the family of the late Prince Johannes von Thurn und Taxis.

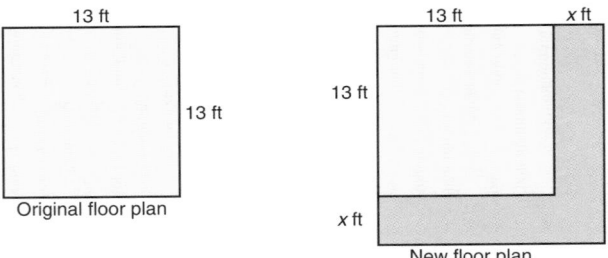

APPLICATION
Architecture

An architect for Windham Homes is changing the floor plan of a house to meet the needs of a new customer. The present floor plan calls for a square dining area that measures 13 feet by 13 feet. The customer would also like for the dining area to be square, but with an area of 250 square feet. How much will this add to the dimensions of the room?

A strip must be added to the length and width of the dining room as shown below. The width of the strip that will be added is represented by x feet. The length and width of the new dining area would then be $(13 + x)$ feet.

```
  13 ft                    13 ft    x ft
┌────────┐              ┌────────┬──┐
│        │              │        │  │
│        │13 ft     13 ft│        │  │
│        │              │        │  │
└────────┘              └────────┴──┘
Original floor plan        x ft
                        New floor plan
```

We can use the formula $A = s^2$ to find the area of the new dining room. Each side measures $13 + x$, and the new area is 250 square feet.

$$A = s^2$$
$$250 = (13 + x)^2 \quad \textit{Replace A with 250 and s with 13 + x.}$$
$$\pm\sqrt{250} = \sqrt{(13 + x)^2} \quad \textit{Take the square root of each side.}$$
$$\pm\sqrt{250} = 13 + x$$
$$\pm\sqrt{250} - 13 = x$$

Use a scientific calculator to find approximate values for x.

Enter: 250 $\boxed{\sqrt{x}}$ $\boxed{-}$ 13 $\boxed{=}$ *2.811388301*

Enter: 250 $\boxed{\sqrt{x}}$ $\boxed{+/-}$ $\boxed{-}$ 13 $\boxed{=}$ *−28.8113883*

Since we need the increased width of the dining area, we can ignore the negative solution. The width of the increase would be approximately 2.81 feet.

You can graph the related function to show that the answer is reasonable. Rewrite $250 = (13 + x)^2$ so that one side is zero. Then graph the related function.

$$250 = (13 - x)^2$$
$$(13 + x)^2 - 250 = 0 \quad \rightarrow \quad f(x) = (13 + x)^2 - 250$$
$$= x^2 + 26x - 81$$

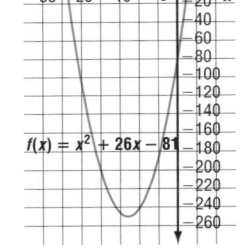

The estimated zeros are about −30 and 3. Thus, the answer 2.8 is reasonable.

GLOBAL CONNECTIONS

A typical $100,000 American home has about 2000 square feet of floor space. A quick calculation shows that the St. Emmeran Castle is valued at over $500 per square foot.

The quadratic equation $250 = (13 + x)^2$ contained one side that was a perfect square, $(13 + x)^2$. This allowed us to solve it by taking the square root of each side. When an equation does not contain a perfect square, you may create a perfect square by applying a process called **completing the square**.

In a perfect square, there is a relationship between the coefficient of the middle term and the constant term.

Specific Case

$(x + 9)^2 = x^2 + 18x + 81$

$9 = \frac{1}{2}(18) \rightarrow 9^2 = 81$

General Case

$(x + c)^2 = x^2 + 2cx + c^2$

$c = \frac{1}{2}(2c) \rightarrow c^2$

To complete the square in the expression below, you would use the same process. Using the pattern of coefficients, take half the coefficient of the linear term and square it.

$x^2 - 8x + \underline{\ ?\ }$

$\left(-\frac{8}{2}\right)^2 \rightarrow (-4)^2$ or 16   *$x^2 - 8x + 16$ is a perfect square trinomial, which can be written as $(x - 4)^2$.*

In Example 1, use the pattern of coefficients to make the trinomial a perfect square.

Example 1 Find the value of *c* that makes $x^2 + 14x + c$ a perfect square.

$c = \left(\frac{14}{2}\right)^2$ *Square half the coefficient of the linear term.*

$= 7^2$ or 49

The value of *c* is 49. Therefore, the trinomial $x^2 + 14x + 49$ is a perfect square. It can be written $(x + 7)^2$.

Example 2 Solve $x^2 - 6x = 40$ by completing the square.

First, you must find the term that completes the square on the left side of the equation. Then add that term to each side.

$x^2 - 6x + \square = 40 + \square$

$x^2 - 6x + 9 = 40 + 9$ $\left(-\frac{6}{2}\right)^2 = 9$

$(x - 3)^2 = 49$ *Factor the perfect square trinomial.*

$x - 3 = \pm 7$ *Take the square root of each side.*

$x - 3 = 7$ or $x - 3 = -7$

$x = 10$ $x = -4$

The solutions are 10 and -4.   *Check by factoring.*

A good way to help you visualize completing the square is to model the process using algebra tiles.

Lesson 6–3   Completing the Square **347**

GLENCOE *Technology*

Interactive Mathematics Tools Software

This multimedia software provides an interactive lesson that uses algebra tiles to determine what number will complete the square for various trinomials. A **Computer Journal** gives students an opportunity to write about what they have learned.

For Windows & Macintosh

2 TEACH

Teaching Tip Before completing Example 1, remind students what a perfect square trinomial is.

In-Class Examples

For Example 1
Find the value of c that makes $x^2 + 16x + c$ a perfect square.
64

For Example 2
Solve by completing the square.

a. $x^2 + 6x = 16$ $-8, 2$
b. $a^2 + 11a + 24 = 0$ $-8, -3$

MODELING
MATHEMATICS This modeling activity uses algebra tiles to visualize the process of completing the square. Point out that it is in Step 3 that the square is actually completed.

In-Class Example

For Example 3
Solve each equation by completing the square.

a. $2x^2 - 11x + 12 = 0$ $4, \frac{3}{2}$

b. $6x^2 - 7x - 5 = 0$ $-\frac{1}{2}, \frac{5}{3}$

MODELING MATHEMATICS

Completing the Square

Materials: algebra tiles   equation mat

Use algebra tiles to complete the square for the equation $x^2 + 6x + 2 = 0$.

Step 1 Subtract 2 from each side of the equation to model the equation $x^2 + 6x = -2$.

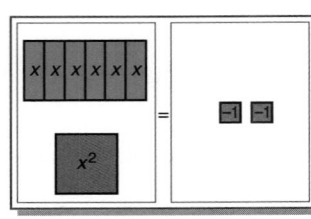

Step 2 Begin to arrange the x^2-tile and x-tiles into a square.

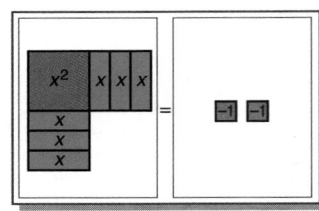

Step 3 To complete the square, add 9 1-tiles to the left side of the mat. Since it is an equation, add 9 1-tiles to the right side.

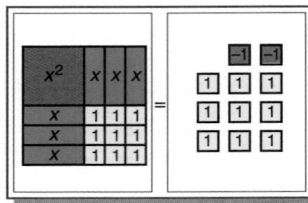

Step 4 Remove the zero pairs on the right side of the mat. After completing the square, the equation is $x^2 + 6x + 9 = 7$ or $(x + 3)^2 = 7$.

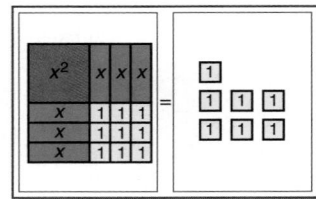

Your Turn

a. Use algebra tiles to complete the square for the equation $x^2 + 4x + 1 = 0$. $(x + 2)^2 - 3 = 0$

b. The equation $x^2 + 5x - 2 = 0$ has an odd number for the coefficient of x. Complete the square by using algebra tiles or by making a drawing. $\left(x + \frac{5}{2}\right)^2 - \frac{33}{4} = 0$

c. Write a paragraph explaining how you could complete the square with models without first rewriting the equation. Include a drawing. **See students' work.**

When the coefficient of the second-degree term is not 1, you must first divide the equation by that coefficient before completing the square.

Example **Solve $4x^2 - 5x - 21 = 0$ by completing the square.**

$$4x^2 - 5x - 21 = 0$$

$$x^2 - \frac{5}{4}x - \frac{21}{4} = 0 \qquad \textit{Divide each side by 4.}$$

$$x^2 - \frac{5}{4}x = \frac{21}{4} \qquad \textit{Isolate the constant on one side.}$$

$$x^2 - \frac{5}{4}x + \frac{25}{64} = \frac{21}{4} + \frac{25}{64} \qquad \textit{Add } \left(-\frac{5}{4} \div 2\right)^2 \textit{ or } \frac{25}{64} \textit{ to each side.}$$

$$\left(x - \frac{5}{8}\right)^2 = \frac{361}{64} \qquad \textit{Factor.}$$

348   *Chapter 6   Exploring Quadratic Functions and Inequalities*

 Cooperative Learning

Group Discussion Separate the class into groups. Have each group solve $x^2 - 2x - 8 = 0$ in three ways. Discuss which way seems easiest and why. Then have the groups make up problems that are easier to do the other two ways. For more information on the group discussion strategy, see *Cooperative Learning in the Mathematics Classroom*, one of the titles in the Glencoe Mathematics Professional Series, pages 30–31.

$$x - \frac{5}{8} = \pm\frac{19}{8}$$ *Take the square root of each side.*

$$x = \frac{5}{8} \pm \frac{19}{8}$$

$$x = \frac{5}{8} + \frac{19}{8} \qquad x = \frac{5}{8} - \frac{19}{8}$$

$$= \frac{24}{8} \text{ or } 3 \qquad = -\frac{14}{8} \text{ or } -\frac{7}{4}$$

The solutions are 3 and $-\frac{7}{4}$. *Verify using the graph of the related function.*

Not all roots of quadratic equations will be rational numbers. Roots that are irrational numbers may be written as *exact* answers in radical form or as *approximate* answers in decimal form when a calculator is used.

Example 4

CONNECTION

Physics

The distance *d* that an object travels can be calculated when the initial speed v_i, elapsed time *t*, and the rate of constant acceleration *a* are known. A formula that relates these factors is $d(t) = v_i t + \frac{1}{2}at^2$.

If a motorcycle has an initial speed of 30 m/s and a constant acceleration of 6 m/s², how much time will it take to travel 200 meters?

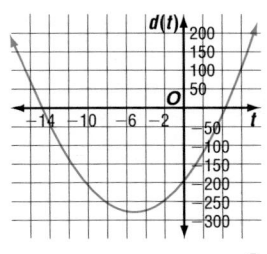

$$d(t) = v_i t + \frac{1}{2}at^2$$

$$200 = 30t + \frac{1}{2} \cdot 6t^2 \quad \text{\textit{Substitute the known values into the formula.}}$$

$$200 = 30t + 3t^2$$

$$\frac{200}{3} = 10t + t^2 \quad \text{\textit{Divide by 3.}}$$

$$\frac{200}{3} + 25 = t^2 + 10t + 25 \quad \text{\textit{Complete the square.}}$$

$$\frac{275}{3} = (t + 5)^2 \quad \text{\textit{Factor.}}$$

$$\pm\sqrt{\frac{275}{3}} = t + 5 \quad \text{\textit{Take the square root of each side.}}$$

$$\pm\sqrt{\frac{275}{3}} - 5 = t \quad \text{\textit{Subtract 5 from each side.}}$$

The solutions are $\sqrt{\frac{275}{3}} - 5$ or about 4.57 and $-\sqrt{\frac{275}{3}} - 5$, or about -14.57. Verify by looking at the graph of the related function.

We can eliminate -14.57 since negative time has no meaning in this example. Thus, the motorcycle will travel 200 meters in about 4.57 seconds.

In-Class Example

For Example 4
A car has an initial speed of 30 ft/s and has a constant acceleration of 6 ft/s². Determine the amount of time that will elapse if a distance of 576 feet has been traveled. Use $d(t) = v_i t + \frac{1}{2}at^2$.

$576 = 30t + \frac{1}{2}(6)t^2$;

9.73 seconds

Teaching Tip Ask students why, in Example 4, the solution with the radical is the exact solution.

In-Class Example

For Example 5
Solve each equation by completing the square.

a. $x^2 + 6x + 15 = 0$
$-3 + i\sqrt{6}, -3 - i\sqrt{6}$

b. $x^2 - x = -4$
$\frac{1}{2} + i\frac{\sqrt{15}}{2}, \frac{1}{2} - i\frac{\sqrt{15}}{2}$

3 PRACTICE/APPLY

Check for Understanding

Exercises 1–14 are designed to help you assess your students' understanding through reading, writing, speaking, and modeling. You should work through Exercises 1–5 with your students and then monitor their work on Exercises 6–14.

Error Analysis
When completing the square in a quadratic *function* $f(x) = x^2 + bx + c$, $\left(\frac{b}{2}\right)^2$ is added to and subtracted from the right side. This is different from completing the square in a quadratic *equation* $x^2 + bx + c = 0$. In this case, $\left(\frac{b}{2}\right)^2$ is added to each side of the equation.

Study Guide Masters, p. 42

6-3   NAME_____ DATE_____
Study Guide   Student Edition
Pages 346–352

Completing the Square
Quadratic equations can be solved by taking the square root of each side. First the expression that contains the variable must be the square of a binomial. If this is not already the case, then you can make it so by using a process called **completing the square.** You find half the coefficient of the linear term, square it, and add the result to each side.

Example: Solve $x^2 - 6x + 4 = 0$ by completing the square.

$x^2 - 6x + 4 = 0$
$x^2 - 6x = -4$ Isolate the terms with x on the left.
$x^2 - 6x + 9 = -4 + 9$ Add $\left(\frac{-6}{2}\right)^2$, or 9, to each side.
$(x - 3)^2 = 5$ Factor the left side (now a square).
$x - 3 = \pm\sqrt{5}$ Take the square root of each side.
$x = 3 \pm\sqrt{5}$ Add 3 to each side.

The solutions are $3 + \sqrt{5}$ and $3 - \sqrt{5}$.

If the equation does not have 1 as the coefficient of x^2, divide each side by the coefficient of x^2 to get a coefficient of 1 for x^2. Do this *before* you complete the square.

Find the exact solution for each equation by completing the square.
1. $y^2 - 4y - 5 = 0$ 2. $y^2 + 2y - 143 = 0$
   $-1, 5$ $-13, 11$

3. $x^2 + 4x + 1 = 0$ 4. $s^2 - 10s + 21 = 0$
   $-2 \pm\sqrt{3}$ $3, 7$

5. $y^2 + 12y + 4 = 0$ 6. $t^2 + 3t - 8 = 0$
   $-6 \pm 4\sqrt{2}$ $\frac{-3 \pm\sqrt{41}}{2}$

7. $2x^2 - 3x + 1 = 0$ 8. $-2x^2 + 13x + 7 = 0$
   $1, \frac{1}{2}$ $-\frac{1}{2}, 7$

350   Chapter 6

Not all solutions to quadratic equations are real. In some cases, the solutions are complex numbers of the form $a + bi$, where $b \neq 0$.

Example ⑤ Solve $x^2 + 8x + 20 = 0$ by completing the square.

$x^2 + 8x + 20 = 0$
$x^2 + 8x = -20$ *Subtract 20 from each side.*
$x^2 + 8x + 16 = -20 + 16$ $\left(\frac{8}{2}\right)^2 = 16$
$(x + 4)^2 = -4$ *Factor the left side.*
$x + 4 = \pm 2i$ *Take the square root of each side. Remember*
$x = -4 \pm 2i$ *that $\sqrt{-1} = i$.*

The roots are the complex numbers $-4 + 2i$ and $-4 - 2i$.

LOOK BACK
You can refer to Lesson 5-9 for information on complex numbers.

CHECK FOR UNDERSTANDING

Communicating Mathematics

Study the lesson. Then complete the following.

1. **Explain** how you would solve the equation $x^2 + 21x - 5 = 0$ by completing the square.   **See margin.**

2. **Discuss** how you can tell if a quadratic equation has imaginary roots just by looking at a sketch of its graph.   **The graph does not intersect the x-axis.**

3. No, $\left(\frac{5}{2}\right)^2 \neq 23$.

3. **State** whether $b^2 + 5b + 23$ is a perfect square. Explain.

4. **Write** a paragraph explaining why we sometimes eliminate negative answers to real-world applications.   **See students' work.**

MODELING MATHEMATICS

5. Use algebra tiles or make a drawing to solve the equation $x^2 + 4x - 5 = 0$ by completing the square. $-5, 1$

Guided Practice

Find the value of c that makes each trinomial a perfect square.

6. $x^2 + 12x + c$ 36

7. $x^2 - 7x + c$ $\frac{49}{4}$

9. $\frac{5}{3}, -\frac{1}{4}$

Find the exact solutions for each equation by completing the square.

11. $\frac{7 \pm \sqrt{33}}{2}$

8. $x^2 + 8x = 20$ 2, -10
9. $12t^2 - 17t = 5$
10. $r^2 + 14 = 8r$ $4 \pm \sqrt{2}$
11. $x^2 - 7x + 4 = 0$
12. $\frac{1}{2}x^2 - 4x + 8 = 0$ 4
13. $x^2 + 2x + 6 = 0$ $-1 \pm i\sqrt{5}$

14. 8 seconds

14. **Safety**   Juanita is driving a truck at an initial velocity of 60 ft/s. She sees a stop sign 240 feet ahead of her. If she begins to decelerate at the rate of $7\frac{1}{2}$ ft/s², how long will it take her before she stops at the stop sign? Use the formula $s = v_i t + \frac{1}{2}at^2$.

If acceleration is a positive number, what is deceleration?

350   Chapter 6   *Exploring Quadratic Functions and Inequalities*

Reteaching

Using Substeps Three methods of solving quadratic equations have been examined: graphing, factoring, and completing the square. Describe each method step by step.

Additional Answer

1. Sample answer: Add 5 to each side of the equation, add $\left(\frac{21}{2}\right)^2$ to each side, factor the left side, take the square root of each side, and then isolate the variable x. The solution is $-10.5 \pm \sqrt{115.25}$.

Practice

Find the value of c that makes each trinomial a perfect square.

18. $\frac{81}{4}$ 20. $\frac{225}{4}$

24. $\frac{-7 \pm 3\sqrt{13}}{2}$

28. $\frac{7 \pm i\sqrt{47}}{4}$

29. $\frac{-7 \pm i\sqrt{35}}{6}$

30. $\frac{-9 \pm i\sqrt{1199}}{32}$

31. $\frac{3 \pm \sqrt{89}}{2}$

15. $x^2 + 2x + c$ 1
16. $x^2 + 18x + c$ 81
17. $t^2 + 40t + c$ 400
18. $r^2 - 9r + c$
19. $a^2 - 100a + c$ 2500
20. $x^2 + 15x + c$

Find the exact solution for each equation by completing the square.

21. $x^2 + 3x - 18 = 0$ −6, 3
22. $x^2 + 2x - 120 = 0$ −12, 10
23. $x^2 - 8x + 11 = 0$ $4 \pm \sqrt{5}$
24. $x^2 + 7x - 17 = 0$
25. $x^2 + 9x + 20.25 = 0$ $-\frac{9}{2}$
26. $9x^2 + 96x + 256 = 0$ $-\frac{16}{3}$
27. $x^2 + 4x + 11 = 0$ $-2 \pm i\sqrt{7}$
28. $2x^2 - 7x + 12 = 0$
29. $3x^2 + 7x + 7 = 0$
30. $16x^2 + 9x + 20 = 0$
31. $x^2 - 3x - 20 = 0$
32. $2x^2 - x - 31 = 0$
33. $12x^2 - 13x - 35 = 0$ $\frac{7}{3}, -\frac{5}{4}$
34. $x^2 + 19x - 12 = 0$
35. $ax^2 + bx + c = 0$
36. $px^2 + rx + m = 0$

Programming

32. $\frac{1 \pm \sqrt{249}}{4}$

34. $\frac{-19 \pm \sqrt{409}}{2}$

35. $\frac{-b \pm \sqrt{b^2 - 4ac}}{2a}$

36. $\frac{-r \pm \sqrt{r^2 - 4pm}}{2p}$

38. $m = 7$ or $m = 3$; 2 roots

37. The graphing calculator program at the right determines if an equation written in standard form contains a perfect square trinomial. It uses the same process that you use when completing the square to determine if the expression is a perfect square trinomial.

Use the guess-and-check strategy in the program at the right to find the value for k that makes each expression a perfect square trinomial.

a. $x^2 + kx + 64$ ±16
b. $x^2 - 14x + k$ 49
c. $4x^2 - 12x + k$ 9
d. $16x^2 + 40x + k$ 25
e. $4x^2 + kx + 1$ ±4
f. $kx^2 - 20x + 4$ 25

```
PROGRAM:PERFSQR
: Prompt A, B, C
: If A < 0 or C < 0
: Then
: Goto 2
: End
: If √A ≠ int √A
: Then
: Goto 2
: End
: If √C ≠ int √C
: Then
: Goto 2
: End
: If B^2 = 4*A*C
: Then
: Disp "CONGRATULATIONS!",
  "IT IS A", "PERFECT SQUARE."
: Stop
: Lbl 2
: Disp "TRY AGAIN", "IT IS
  NOT A", "PERFECT SQUARE."
```

Critical Thinking

38. Find the values of m that make $f(x) = x^2 + (m + 5)x + (5m + 1)$ a perfect square trinomial function. How many roots does it have?

Applications and Problem Solving

39. **Physics**   When a moving car hits an object, the damage it can cause can be measured by the *collision impact*. For a certain car, the collision impact I can be represented by the formula $I = 2(s)^2$, where s represents the speed in kilometers per minute.

a. Sketch a graph of the function.   See margin.
b. What is the collision impact if the speed is 1 km/min? 2 km/min? 4 km/min?   2; 8; 32
c. As the speed doubles, explain what happens to the value of the collision impact.   The impact of the collision quadruples.

Lesson 6–3 Completing the Square   **351**

Assignment Guide

Core: 15–37 odd, 38, 39, 41–48
Enriched: 16–36 even, 37–48

For **Extra Practice,** see p. 889.

The red A, B, and C flags, printed only in the Teacher's Wraparound Edition, indicate the level of difficulty of the exercises.

Additional Answer

39a.

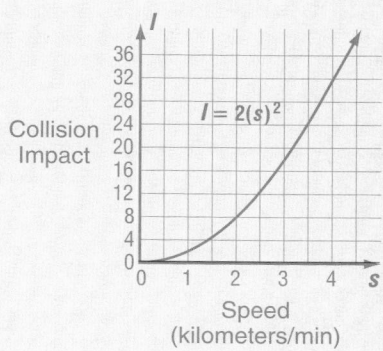

Using the Programming

Exercises The program given in Exercise 37 is for use with a TI-82 graphing calculator. For other programmable calculators, have students consult their owner's manual for commands similar to those presented here.

Practice Masters, p. 42

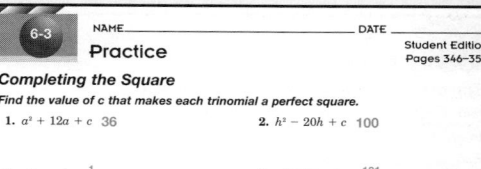

Closing Activity
Writing Have students make a flowchart showing the steps needed to complete the square.

Chapter 6, Quiz A (Lessons 6-1 through 6-3), is available in the *Assessment and Evaluation Masters*, p. 156.

Additional Answers

45.

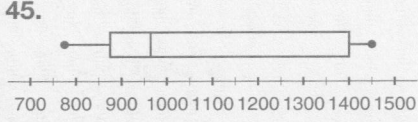

700 800 900 1000 1100 1200 1300 1400 1500

46.

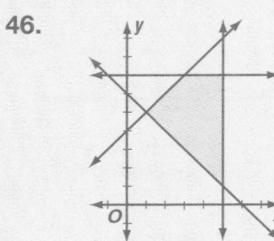

48.

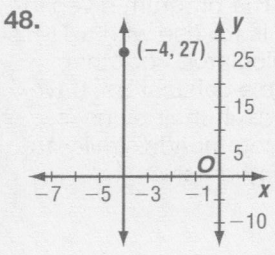

Enrichment Masters, p. 42

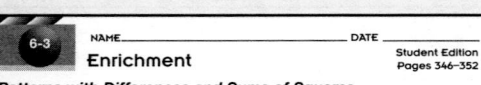

6-3	NAME_____ DATE_____
	Enrichment	Student Edition Pages 346-352

Patterns with Differences and Sums of Squares
Some whole numbers can be written as the difference of two squares and some cannot. Formulas can be developed to describe the sets of numbers algebraically.

If possible, write each number as the difference of two squares. Look for patterns.

1. 0 $0^2 - 0^2$
2. 1 $1^2 - 0^2$
3. 2 cannot
4. 3 $2^2 - 1^2$
5. 4 $2^2 - 0^2$
6. 5 $3^2 - 2^2$
7. 6 cannot
8. 7 $4^2 - 3^2$
9. 8 $3^2 - 1^2$
10. 9 $3^2 - 0^2$
11. 10 cannot
12. 11 $6^2 - 5^2$
13. 12 $4^2 - 2^2$
14. 13 $7^2 - 6^2$
15. 14 cannot
16. 15 $4^2 - 1^2$

Even numbers can be written as 2n, where n is one of the numbers 0, 1, 2, 3, and so on. Odd numbers can be written 2n + 1. Use these expressions for these problems.

17. Show that any odd number can be written as the difference of two squares.
   $2n + 1 = (n + 1)^2 - n^2$
18. Show that the even numbers can be divided into two sets: those that can be written in the form 4n and those that can be written in the form 2 + 4n.
   Find 4n for n = 0, 1, 2, and so on. You get {0, 4, 8, 12, ...}. For 2 + 4n, you get {2, 6, 10, 12, ...}. Together these sets include all even numbers.
19. Describe the even numbers that cannot be written as the difference of two squares.
   2 + 4n, for n = 0, 1, 2, 3, ...
20. Show that the other even numbers can be written as the difference of two squares.
   $4n = (n + 1)^2 - (n - 1)^2$

Every whole number can be written as the sum of squares. It is never necessary to use more than four squares. Show that this is true for the whole numbers from 0 through 15 by writing each one as the sum of the least number of squares.

21. 0 0^2
22. 1 1^2
23. 2 $1^2 + 1^2$
24. 3 $1^2 + 1^2 + 1^2$
25. 4 2^2
26. 5 $1^2 + 2^2$
27. 6 $1^2 + 1^2 + 2^2$
28. 7 $1^2 + 1^2 + 1^2 + 2^2$
29. 8 $2^2 + 2^2$
30. 9 3^2
31. 10 $1^2 + 3^2$
32. 11 $1^2 + 1^2 + 3^2$
33. 12 $1^2 + 1^2 + 1^2 + 3^2$
34. 13 $2^2 + 3^2$
35. 14 $1^2 + 2^2 + 3^2$
36. 15 $1^2 + 1^2 + 2^2 + 3^2$

---

40. Law Enforcement The police can use the length of skid marks to help determine the speed of a vehicle before the brakes were applied. If the skid marks were on concrete, the formula $\frac{s^2}{24} = d$ can be used to approximate the speed of the vehicle. In the formula, s represents the speed in miles per hour, and d represents the length of the skid marks in feet. If the length of a car's skid marks on dry concrete were 50 feet, how fast was the car traveling when the brakes were applied? **about 35 mph**

Mixed Review

41. Physics A ball is thrown straight up with an initial velocity of 56 feet per second. The height of the ball t seconds after it is thrown is given by the formula $h(t) = 56t - 16t^2$. (Lesson 6–2)
   a. What is the height of the ball after 1 second? **40 ft**
   b. What is its maximum height? **49 ft**
   c. After how many seconds will it return to the ground? **3.5 s**

42. Forestry A forester is often responsible for choosing which stands of trees will be harvested. The formula $V = 0.0027Ld^2 + 0.0027L\left(d + \frac{L}{A}\right)^2$ can be used to estimate how many cubic feet of wood will come from one log. In the equation, V represents the volume of the log in cubic feet, L represents the length of the log in feet, d represents the diameter of the top of the log in inches, and A represents the length of the log required for 1 inch of taper. Suppose that a 16-foot long log has a 1-inch taper over an 8-foot length. What diameter log does the forester want to find if he needs to get 150 cubic feet of wood out of one log? (Lesson 6–1) **about 41 in.**

43. Simplify $\sqrt[4]{5m^3n^5} \cdot \sqrt[4]{125m^2n^3}$. (Lesson 5–6) $5mn^2 \cdot \sqrt[4]{m}$

44. Factor $2ab(c - d) + 10d(c - d)$. (Lesson 5–4) $2(ab + 5d)(c - d)$

45. Consumerism The prices of 14 video cameras are listed below.

$877	$819	$1100	$1450	$812	$973	$1399
$890	$1409	$949	$900	$775	$1299	$1399

Make a box-and-whisker plot of the prices. (Lesson 4–8) **See margin.**

46. See margin for graph.

46. Graph the system of inequalities. Name the vertices of the polygon formed. Find the maximum and minimum values of the given function. (Lesson 3–5)

$y \le 7$
$y \ge -x + 6$
$y \le x + 4$
$x \le 5$
$f(x, y) = 2x - 3y$ **(1, 5), (3, 7), (5, 7), (5, 1); max: f(5, 1) = 7; min: f(3, 7) = −15**

47. (−4, −3)

47. Use Cramer's rule to solve $3m - 4n = 0$ and $n + 7 = -m$. (Lesson 3–3)

48. Graph a line that only goes through Quadrants II and III and passes through the point (−4, 27). (Lesson 2–3) **See margin.**

Extension

Reasoning Find the values of m that make $x^2 + (m + 5)x + (5m + 1)$ a perfect square. **7, 3**
How many roots would each related quadratic equation have? **1**

6-4

The Quadratic Formula and the Discriminant

What YOU'LL LEARN

- To solve quadratic equations by using the quadratic formula, and
- to use discriminants to determine the nature of the roots of quadratic equations.

Why IT'S IMPORTANT

You can use the quadratic formula to solve quadratic equations that involve health and probability.

Landmarks

The Golden Gate Bridge in San Francisco, California, is a magnificent structure that was completed on May 27, 1937, after more than four years of construction and a cost of approximately $27 million. The Golden Gate is the tallest bridge in the world, with its towers extending 746 feet above the water and the floor of the bridge extending 200 feet above the water.

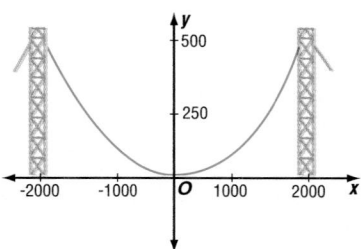

The two supporting cables that pass over the tops of the towers are each 7650 feet long and 36.5 inches in diameter. They are the largest bridge cables ever made. These supporting cables approximate the shape of a parabola with the lowest point reaching about 6 feet above the floor of the bridge. This parabola can be approximated by the quadratic function $y = 0.00012244898x^2 + 6$, where x represents the distance from the axis of symmetry and y represents the height of the cables.

How would you solve the quadratic equation $0.00012244898x^2 + 6 = 0$? In Lessons 6–1, 6–2, and 6–3, you learned several ways to solve quadratic equations. But it would be difficult to use any of those techniques to solve this equation. You might ask, "Isn't there a formula that will work for any quadratic equation?" The answer is yes! This formula can be derived by solving the general form of a quadratic equation for x.

$$ax^2 + bx + c = 0$$

$$x^2 + \frac{b}{a}x + \frac{c}{a} = 0 \qquad \textit{Divide each side by a.}$$

$$x^2 + \frac{b}{a}x = -\frac{c}{a} \qquad \textit{Subtract } \frac{c}{a} \textit{ from each side.}$$

$$x^2 + \frac{b}{a}x + \frac{b^2}{4a^2} = -\frac{c}{a} + \frac{b^2}{4a^2} \qquad \textit{Complete the square.}$$

$$\left(x + \frac{b}{2a}\right)^2 = \frac{b^2 - 4ac}{4a^2} \qquad \textit{Simplify.}$$

$$\sqrt{\left(x + \frac{b}{2a}\right)^2} = \pm\sqrt{\frac{b^2 - 4ac}{4a^2}} \qquad \textit{Take the square root of each side.}$$

$$x + \frac{b}{2a} = \frac{\pm\sqrt{b^2 - 4ac}}{2a} \qquad \textit{Simplify.}$$

$$x = \frac{-b \pm\sqrt{b^2 - 4ac}}{2a} \qquad \textit{Subtract } \frac{b}{2a} \textit{ from each side.}$$

Lesson 6–4 The Quadratic Formula and the Discriminant **353**

By June 30, 1992, more than 1,313,887,324 vehicles had crossed the Golden Gate Bridge.

Completed in 1937, the Golden Gate Bridge has a main span of 4200 feet and is suspended from two cables that are 746 feet apart.

6-4 LESSON NOTES

NCTM Standards: 1–5

Instructional Resources

- Study Guide Master 6-4
- Practice Master 6-4
- Enrichment Master 6-4
- Multicultural Activity Masters, p. 11
- Real-World Applications, 16

Transparency 6-4A contains the 5-Minute Check for this lesson; **Transparency 6-4B** contains a teaching aid for this lesson.

Recommended Pacing	
Standard Pacing	Days 6 & 7 of 17
Honors Pacing	Day 5 of 14
Block Scheduling*	Day 3 of 7 (along with Lesson 6-5)

*For more information on pacing and possible lesson plans, refer to the *Block Scheduling Booklet*.

1 FOCUS

5-Minute Check
(over Lesson 6-3)

Solve each equation by completing the square.

1. $x^2 - 2x - 15 = 0$ $5, -3$
2. $x^2 + 4x + 29 = 0$ $-2 \pm 5i$
3. $c^2 + 3c - 130 = 0$ $-13, 10$

Motivating the Lesson

Situational Problem Give students the general equation $ax^2 + bx + c = 0$, where $a \neq 0$. Have students determine what they need to add to each side in order to complete the square. Have students then determine the value for several equations such as $x^2 + 5x + 6 = 0$ and $x^2 + 10x + 16 = 0$.

TEKS	2.b., 6.a., 6.b., 8.a., 8.b., 8.c., 8.d.

Teaching Tip Ask students to determine the restrictions for the quadratic formula.

In-Class Examples

For Example 1
Solve each equation by using the quadratic formula.

a. $t^2 - 10t = 24$ $12, -2$
b. $2y^2 + 4y = 30$ $3, -5$

For Example 2
Solve each equation by using the quadratic formula.

a. $x^2 - 3x - 2 = 0$
$$\frac{3 \pm \sqrt{17}}{2}$$

b. $x^2 - 7x + 1 = 0$
$$\frac{7 \pm 3\sqrt{5}}{2}$$

This equation is known as the **quadratic formula**.

The Quadratic Formula	The solutions of a quadratic equation of the form $ax^2 + bx + c = 0$, where $a \neq 0$, are given by the following formula. $$x = \frac{-b \pm \sqrt{b^2 - 4ac}}{2a}$$

Example   Solve $r^2 - 7r = 18$ by using the quadratic formula.

First, write the equation in standard form. $r^2 - 7r = 18 \rightarrow r^2 - 7r - 18 = 0$

Then, substitute the values of a, b, and c directly into the quadratic formula. $a = 1$, $b = -7$, and $c = -18$

$$r = \frac{-b \pm \sqrt{b^2 - 4ac}}{2a}$$

$$= \frac{-(-7) \pm \sqrt{(-7)^2 - 4(1)(-18)}}{2(1)}$$

$$= \frac{7 \pm \sqrt{121}}{2} \text{ or } \frac{7 \pm 11}{2}$$

$$r = \frac{7 + 11}{2} \text{ or } 9 \quad \text{and} \quad r = \frac{7 - 11}{2} \text{ or } -2$$

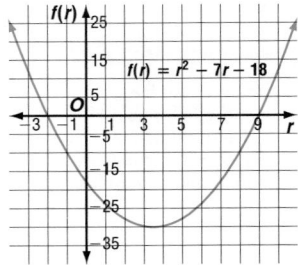

The solutions are 9 and -2.
Check these solutions.

The graph of the related function shows that there are two solutions.

Sometimes roots are irrational. You can express these roots exactly by writing them in radical form.

Example   Solve $x^2 + 9x - 11 = 0$ by using the quadratic formula.

The equation is in standard form. Substitute the values of a, b, and c directly into the quadratic formula. $a = 1$, $b = 9$, and $c = -11$

$$x = \frac{-b \pm \sqrt{b^2 - 4ac}}{2a}$$

$$= \frac{-9 \pm \sqrt{9^2 - (4)(1)(-11)}}{2(1)} \text{ or } \frac{-9 \pm \sqrt{125}}{2}$$

The solutions are $\dfrac{-9 + 5\sqrt{5}}{2}$ and $\dfrac{-9 - 5\sqrt{5}}{2}$.

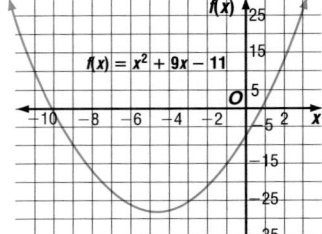

The graph of the related function shows that there are two solutions.

You can use a scientific calculator to help you find approximate solutions.
First evaluate the radical part of the expression $\dfrac{-9 \pm \sqrt{9^2 - (4)(1)(-11)}}{2(1)}$ and store the result in memory.

Enter: 9 [x^2] [$-$] 4 [$\times$] 11 [$+/-$] [$=$] [2nd] [$\sqrt{x}$] [STO▶]   *11.18033989*

Alternative Teaching Strategies

Student Diversity Explain to students that each type of scientific calculator has a different system of storing information. Before teaching calculator use, review with students the functions on their calculators and the vocabulary that explains them.

Now find the solutions.

Enter: 9 [+/−] [+] [RCL] [=] [÷] 2 [=] *1.090169944*

Enter: 9 [+/−] [−] [RCL] [=] [÷] 2 [=] *−10.09016994*

The two solutions are approximately 1.1 and −10.1.
How do these solutions compare with the graph?

When using the quadratic formula, if the radical contains a negative value, the solutions will be imaginary. Imaginary solutions always appear in conjugate pairs.

Example Solve $-3x^2 + 4x - 4 = 0$ by using the quadratic formula.

Substitute the values of a, b, and c directly into the quadratic formula.
$a = -3$, $b = 4$, and $c = -4$

$$x = \frac{-b \pm \sqrt{b^2 - 4ac}}{2a}$$

$$= \frac{-4 \pm \sqrt{(4)^2 - 4(-3)(-4)}}{2(-3)}$$

$$= \frac{-4 \pm \sqrt{-32}}{-6}$$

$$= -\frac{4 \pm 4i\sqrt{2}}{-6} \text{ or } \frac{2 \pm 2i\sqrt{2}}{3}$$

The solutions are the imaginary numbers $\frac{2 + 2i\sqrt{2}}{3}$ and $\frac{2 - 2i\sqrt{2}}{3}$.

A graph of the related function shows that the solutions are imaginary.

Example  A car is traveling at 26 meters per second (m/s) and accelerating at -13 m/s². After traveling 26 m, the driver brings the car to a complete stop. The equation $26 = 26t - \frac{13}{2}t^2$, where t is the time it takes to stop, can be used to represent this situation. How long did it take the driver to stop the car?

First, write the equation in standard form. $-\frac{13}{2}t^2 + 26t - 26 = 0$

Then, substitute directly into the quadratic formula.
$a = -\frac{13}{2}$, $b = 26$, and $c = -26$

$$t = \frac{-b \pm \sqrt{b^2 - 4ac}}{2a}$$

$$= \frac{-26 \pm \sqrt{(26)^2 - 4\left(-\frac{13}{2}\right)(-26)}}{2\left(-\frac{13}{2}\right)}$$

$$= \frac{-26 \pm \sqrt{0}}{-13}$$

$$= 2$$

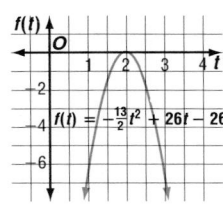

It took 2 seconds to stop the car.

A graph of the related function shows that there is one solution.

Lesson 6–4   The Quadratic Formula and the Discriminant   **355**

CONNECTION
Physics

Classroom Vignette

"I have students use graphing calculators to graph each of the examples as a quadratic function. They then use TRACE to determine the *x*-intercepts and make a comparison of the results with the related roots and discriminants."

William L. Crosby
Riverside High School
Parsons, Tennessee

William L. Crosby

In-Class Examples

For Example 3
Solve each equation by using the quadratic formula.

a. $x^2 - 3x + 7 = 0$

$\dfrac{3 + i\sqrt{19}}{2}$, $\dfrac{3 - i\sqrt{19}}{2}$

b. $5m^2 + 7m = -3$

$\dfrac{-7 + i\sqrt{11}}{10}$, $\dfrac{-7 - i\sqrt{11}}{10}$

For Example 4
A farmer wants to build a rectangular pen using a side of a barn and 60 feet of fence. Find the dimensions and area of the largest such pen.
30 ft by 15 ft, 450 sq ft

Teaching Tip The number of real roots of a quadratic equation is equal to the number of times that the graph of the related function intersects the *x*-axis.

In-Class Example

For Example 5
Find the value of the discriminant for each quadratic equation. Then describe the nature of the roots.

a. $4x^2 = -25 + 20x$
0; There is one real root, and it is rational.

b. $3x^2 + 2 = 5x$
1; There are two real roots, and they are rational.

3 PRACTICE/APPLY

Check for Understanding

Exercises 1–15 are designed to help you assess your students' understanding through reading, writing, speaking, and modeling. You should work through Exercises 1–5 with your students and then monitor their work on Exercises 6–15.

Study Guide Masters, p. 43

6-4 NAME _____ DATE _____
Student Edition
Pages 353–358

Study Guide

The Quadratic Formula and the Discriminant

The method of completing the square can be used to develop a general formula called the *quadratic formula* that can be used to solve any quadratic equation.

The Quadratic Formula
The roots of a quadratic equation of the form $ax^2 + bx + c = 0$, where $a \neq 0$, are given by:
$$x = \frac{-b \pm \sqrt{b^2 - 4ac}}{2a}$$

In the quadratic formula, the expression $b^2 - 4ac$ is called the **discriminant**. The discriminant is used to determine how many real roots there are.

Nature of Roots of a Quadratic Equation

Discriminant	Nature of Roots
$b^2 - 4ac > 0$	two distinct real roots
$b^2 - 4ac = 0$	one distinct real root
$b^2 - 4ac < 0$	no real roots

Find the value of the discriminant and describe the nature of the roots of each quadratic equation. Then solve the equation.

1. $3x^2 + 5x = 2$
   49; two real roots; $-2, \frac{1}{3}$

2. $2y^2 + y - 15 = 0$
   121; two real roots; $\frac{5}{2}, -3$

3. $r^2 - \frac{3r}{5} + \frac{2}{25} = 0$
   $\frac{1}{25}$; two real roots; $\frac{2}{5}, \frac{1}{5}$

4. $3t^2 - \frac{5}{2}t - \frac{1}{2} = 0$
   $\frac{121}{16}$; two real roots; $\frac{2}{3}, -\frac{1}{4}$

5. $m^2 - 8m = -14$
   8; two real roots;
   $4 + \sqrt{2}, 4 - \sqrt{2}$

6. $p^2 + 12p = -4$
   128; two real roots;
   $-6 + 4\sqrt{2}, -6 - 4\sqrt{2}$

7. $2x^2 - 7 = -3x$
   65; two real roots;
   $\frac{-3 + \sqrt{65}}{4}, \frac{-3 - \sqrt{65}}{4}$

8. $-2b^2 + b - 5 = 0$
   -36; no real roots;

356 Chapter 6

Study Examples 1, 2, 3, and 4 and observe the relationship between the expression under the radical, $b^2 - 4ac$, and the roots of the quadratic equation. This expression, $b^2 - 4ac$, is called the **discriminant.** The value of the discriminant determines the nature of the roots of a quadratic equation. The table below summarizes all the possibilities.

Example	Value of $b^2 - 4ac$	Discriminant a Perfect Square?	Nature of Root(s)	Nature of Related Graph
1	$b^2 - 4ac > 0$	yes	2 real, rational	intersects x-axis twice
2	$b^2 - 4ac > 0$	no	2 real, irrational	intersects x-axis twice
3	$b^2 - 4ac < 0$	—	2 imaginary	does not intersect x-axis
4	$b^2 - 4ac = 0$	—	1 real	intersects x-axis once

Example ⑤ Find the value of the discriminant for each quadratic equation. Then describe the nature of the roots.

a. $x^2 - 8x + 16 = 0$

$a = 1, b = -8, c = 16$
$b^2 - 4ac = (-8)^2 - 4(1)(16)$
$= 64 - 64$
$= 0$

The value of the discriminant is 0, so there is one real root.

b. $5x^2 + 42 = 0$

$a = 5, b = 0, c = 42$
$b^2 - 4ac = (0)^2 - 4(5)(42)$
$= 0 - 840$
$= -840$

The value of the discriminant is negative, so there are two imaginary roots.

c. $x^2 - 5x - 50 = 0$

$a = 1, b = -5, c = -50$
$b^2 - 4ac = (-5)^2 - 4(1)(-50)$
$= 25 + 200$
$= 225$

The value of the discriminant is 225, which is a perfect square. There are two real, rational roots.

d. $2x^2 - 9x + 8 = 0$

$a = 2, b = -9, c = 8$
$b^2 - 4ac = (-9)^2 - 4(2)(8)$
$= 81 - 64$
$= 17$

The value of the discriminant is 17, which is not a perfect square. There are two real, irrational roots.

CHECK FOR UNDERSTANDING

Communicating Mathematics

Study the lesson. Then complete the following.

1. **Explain** why the roots of a quadratic equation are imaginary if the value of the discriminant is less than 0. See margin.

2. **Draw** graphs to illustrate the relationship between the nature of the roots determined by the discriminant and the number of times the graph of the related function intersects the x-axis. See students' work.

3. Refer to the application at the beginning of the lesson. Calculate the value of the discriminant for the equation of the supporting cables for the Golden Gate Bridge. What does it mean? See margin.

4. The discriminant is 0; there is one real root.

4. **Describe** the value of the discriminant for the equation whose graph is at the right. How many real roots are there?

356 Chapter 6 Exploring Quadratic Functions and Inequalities

Reteaching

Checking Solutions Have students verify by substitution that both solutions to the general quadratic equation $ax^2 + bx + c = 0$ are indeed roots. To make the check less cumbersome, use D for the discriminant until the radicals are cleared.

Additional Answers

1. The square root of a negative number is an imaginary number.

3. -0.0029387755; This means that the cables do not touch the floor of the bridge, since the graph does not intersect the x-axis and the roots are imaginary.

MATH JOURNAL

Guided Practice

7. 3, −5, −2; 49
8. 1, −24, 144; 0
9. 1, 5, 7; −3
12. 21; 2 R, I;
$\frac{-1 \pm \sqrt{21}}{2}$; 1.79, −2.79
13. −15; 2 C;
$\frac{-5 \pm i\sqrt{15}}{2}$
14. See margin.
16. 16; 2 R, Q; −8, −4
18. 12; 2 R, I; 2 ± √3;
3.73, 0.27
19. 49; 2 R, Q; −2, $\frac{1}{3}$
21. 73; 2 R, I;
$\frac{-11 \pm \sqrt{73}}{6}$; −0.41,
−3.26
22. −24; 2 C; 6 ± i√6
24. 137; 2 R, I;
$\frac{-7 \pm \sqrt{137}}{4}$; 1.18, −4.68

5. **Assess Yourself** Of the methods you have used to solve quadratic equations—graphing, factoring, completing the square, and the quadratic formula—which do you prefer? Why? See students' work.

6. Which equation shows how to solve $3x^2 - x + 2 = 0$ by using the quadratic formula? **C**

   a. $x = \frac{1 \pm \sqrt{3^2 - 4(3)(2)}}{2(3)}$ **b.** $x = \frac{-2 \pm \sqrt{(-1)^2 - 4(3)(2)}}{2}$

   c. $x = \frac{1 \pm \sqrt{1^2 - 4(3)(2)}}{2(3)}$ **d.** $x = \frac{-1 \pm \sqrt{(-1)^2 - 4(3)(2)}}{2}$

State the values of *a*, *b*, and *c* for each equation. Then find the value of the discriminant.

7. $3x^2 - 5x = 2$ 8. $x^2 - 24x + 144 = 0$ 9. $x^2 + 7 = -5x$

For Exercises 10–13, R = real, C = imaginary, Q = rational, and I = irrational.

Find the value of the discriminant and describe the nature of the roots (real, imaginary, rational, irrational) of each quadratic equation. Then solve the equation. Express irrational roots as exact and approximate to the nearest hundredth.

10. $x^2 + 10x = -25$ 0; 1 R, Q; −5   11. $2x^2 = 72$ 576; 2 R, Q; 6, −6
12. $x^2 + x - 5 = 0$ 13. $x^2 + 5x + 10 = 0$

14. If the discriminant of the equation of a parabola is 2025, how many times does the graph of the equation intersect the *x*-axis? Justify your answer.

15. Solve $x^2 + 2x - 5 = 0$.

   a. How many roots does the function $y = x^2 + 2x - 5$ have? What are they?   2 roots, −1 ± √6 (1.4 and −3.4)

   b. Approximately where does the graph of $y = x^2 + 2x - 5$ cross the *x*-axis?   1.4 and −3.4

For Exercises 16–29, R = real, C = imaginary, Q = rational, I = irrational.

EXERCISES

Practice

25. −116; 2 C; $\frac{4 \pm i\sqrt{29}}{5}$
26. 1.48; 2 R, I;
$\frac{-1 \pm \sqrt{1.48}}{0.8}$; 0.271,
−2.77
28. 240; 2 R, I;
8 ± 2√15;
15.75, 0.25
29. −31; 2 C;
$\frac{9 \pm i\sqrt{31}}{8}$

Find the value of the discriminant and describe the nature of the roots (real, imaginary, rational, irrational) of each quadratic equation. Then solve the equation. Express irrational roots as exact and approximate to the nearest hundredth.   22. −24; 2 C; 6 ± i√6

A
16. $x^2 + 12x + 32 = 0$ 17. $2x^2 - 12x + 18 = 0$ 0; 1 R, Q; 3
18. $x^2 - 4x + 1 = 0$ 19. $3x^2 + 5x - 2 = 0$
20. $x^2 - 2x + 5 = 0$ −16, 2 C; 1 ± 2*i*   21. $3x^2 + 11x + 4 = 0$

B
22. $x^2 - 12x + 42 = 0$ 23. $x^2 = 6x$ 36; 2 R, Q; 0, 6
24. $2x^2 + 7x - 11 = 0$ 25. $5x^2 - 8x + 9 = 0$
26. $0.4x^2 + x = 0.3$ 27. $2x^2 - 13x = 7$ 225; 2 R, Q; 7, $-\frac{1}{2}$

C
28. $x^2 - 16x + 4 = 0$ 29. $4x^2 - 9x = -7$

Critical Thinking

30. **Probability** Suppose you picked an integer at random from 1 through 12 as a value for *c* in the equation $y = x^2 + 6x + c$. What is the probability that the resulting equation will have imaginary roots?

Applications and Problem Solving

30. $\frac{1}{4}$

31. **Health** A person's blood pressure depends on his or her age. For women, normal systolic blood pressure is given by the formula $P = 0.01A^2 + 0.05A + 107$, where *P* is the normal blood pressure in millimeters of mercury (mm Hg) and *A* is the age. For men, the normal systolic blood pressure is given by the formula $P = 0.006A^2 - 0.02A + 120$.

(continued on the next page)

Tech Prep

Lab Technician Students who are interested in the health profession may wish to do further research on the data provided in Exercise 31 and explore the potential growth of this career. For more information on tech prep, see the *Teacher's Handbook*.

Assignment Guide

Core: 17–29 odd, 30, 31, 33–38
Enriched: 16–28 even, 30–38
All: Self Test, 1–10

For **Extra Practice,** see p. 890.

The red A, B, and C flags, printed only in the Teacher's Wraparound Edition, indicate the level of difficulty of the exercises.

Additional Answer

14. The graph will cross the *x*-axis twice since 2025 is a positive square root.

Practice Masters, p. 43

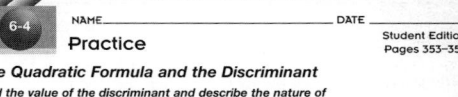

6-4   NAME_____   DATE_____
Student Edition
Practice   Pages 353–357

The Quadratic Formula and the Discriminant
Find the value of the discriminant and describe the nature of the roots of each quadratic equation. Then solve the equation. Express irrational roots as exact and approximate to the nearest hundredth.

1. $x^2 - 9x + 14 = 0$ 2. $r^2 = 3r$
   25; 2 real, rational; 7, 2   9; 2 real, rational; 0, 3

3. $9u^2 - 24u + 16 = 0$ 4. $n^2 - 3n = 40$
   0; 1 real, rational; $\frac{4}{3}$ 169; 2 real, rational; −5, 8

5. $3t^2 + 9t - 2 = 0$ 6. $7u^2 + 6u + 2 = 0$
   105; 2 real, irrational; $\frac{-9 \pm \sqrt{105}}{6}$;   −20; 2 imaginary; $\frac{-3 \pm \sqrt{5}i}{7}$
   0.21, −3.21

7. $5w^2 - 2w + 4 = 0$ 8. $12x^2 - x - 6 = 0$
   −76; 2 imaginary; $\frac{1 \pm \sqrt{19}i}{5}$ 289; 2 real, rational; $\frac{3}{4}$, $-\frac{2}{3}$

9. $2m^2 + 7m = 0$ 10. $x^2 - \frac{1}{2}x + \frac{1}{16} = 0$
   49; 2 real, rational; 0, $-\frac{7}{2}$ 0; 1 real, rational; $\frac{1}{4}$

11. $12x^2 + 2x - 4 = 0$ 12. $6w^2 - 2w - 1 = 0$
   196; 2 real, rational; $\frac{1}{2}$, $-\frac{2}{3}$ 28; 2 real, irrational; $\frac{1 \pm \sqrt{7}}{6}$;
   0.61, −0.27

Closing Activity

Speaking Read several quadratic equations to the class. Have students determine the discriminant of each equation. They should be able to describe to the class the nature of the roots for each problem.

Additional Answer

31a.

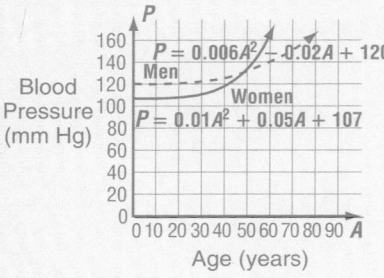

$P = 0.006A^2 - 0.02A + 120$
Men
Blood Pressure (mm Hg)
Women
$P = 0.01A^2 + 0.05A + 107$
Age (years)

The graph representing the normal blood pressure of women is more narrow than the graph of men's blood pressure. Initially, women's blood pressure is lower than men's, but it increases at a faster rate.

Enrichment Masters, p. 43

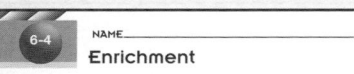

6-4   NAME _____ DATE _____

Enrichment   Student Edition Pages 353–357

The Golden Quadratic Equations

A **golden rectangle** has the property that its length can be written as $a + b$, where a is the width of the rectangle and

$$\frac{a+b}{a} = \frac{a}{b}.$$

Any golden rectangle can be divided into a square and a smaller golden rectangle.

There are two quadratic equations that can be derived from the proportion used to define golden rectangles. These are sometimes called *golden quadratic equations*.

Solve each problem.

1. In the proportion for the golden rectangle, let a equal 1. Write the resulting quadratic equation and solve for b.
$b^2 + b - 1 = 0$

$b = \frac{-1 + \sqrt{5}}{2}$

2. In the proportion, let b equal 1. Write the resulting quadratic equation and solve for a.
$a^2 - a - 1 = 0$

$a = \frac{1 + \sqrt{5}}{2}$

3. Describe the difference between the two golden quadratic equations you found in exercises 1 and 2.
The signs of the first-degree terms are opposite.

4. Show that the positive solutions of the two equations in exercises 1 and 2 are reciprocals.
$\left(\frac{-1 + \sqrt{5}}{2}\right)\left(\frac{1 + \sqrt{5}}{2}\right) = $
$\frac{-(1)^2 + (\sqrt{5})^2}{4} = \frac{-1 + 5}{4} = 1$

5. Use the Pythagorean theorem to find a radical expression for the diagonal of a golden rectangle with short side x and long side 1.
$d = \frac{\sqrt{10 - 2\sqrt{5}}}{2}$

6. Find a radical expression for the diagonal of a golden rectangle with long side x and short side 1.
$d = \frac{\sqrt{10 + 2\sqrt{5}}}{2}$

---

a. Graph both functions on the same set of axes. Describe the differences between the graphs and explain how the differences reflect the blood pressures of men and women. **See margin.**   **b. 121 mm Hg**

31c. 50 years

b. Find the normal blood pressure of a woman who is 35 years old.

c. Find the approximate age of a man whose blood pressure is 134 mm Hg.

32. **Business** Bryan Starr is a 17-year-old high school senior from Upper Arlington, Ohio, who started his own lawn service when he was 12. His business has grown substantially and he has been able to put away money for college, buy a truck, and invest in new lawn equipment to keep up with the growing demand for his services. Suppose his weekly revenue R can be represented by the formula $R = -p^2 + 50p - 125$, where p is the average price he charges for each lawn. **a, b, d. See Solutions Manual.**

  a. Sketch a graph of the related function. Explain why it behaves like it does, considering Bryan's business.

  b. Explain how Bryan could earn $400 each week.

  c. What price should he charge to earn the maximum revenue? What would be his revenue? **$25, $500**

  d. Use the discriminant to find if there is a price he could charge that would make his weekly revenue $600. Explain.

Mixed Review

34. $\frac{5}{3}, -3$

33. **Geometry** The area of a square plus its perimeter minus 12 is equal to 0. Find x if the area is $4x^2$. (Lesson 6–3)   **1**

34. Solve $3t^2 + 4t = 15$ by factoring. (Lesson 6–2)

35. Simplify $\sqrt{x^2 + 6x + 9}$. (Lesson 5–5) $|x + 3|$

36. **Ecology** On an average day, 958,904,100 photocopies are made. Of these, 356,164,384 are unnecessary. On an average day, how many photocopies are necessary? Round your answer to the nearest million and express it in scientific notation. (Lesson 5–1) 6.03×10^8

37. Solve the system $x - y = 10$ and $2y - 3x = -1$ by using a matrix equation. (Lesson 4–6) $(-19, -29)$

38. Solve $|2x - 5| \leq 9$. (Lesson 1–7) $\{x \mid -2 \leq x \leq 7\}$

SELF TEST

Solve each equation by graphing. (Lesson 6–1)   **1–2. See Solutions Manual for graphs.**

1. $z^2 + 4z + 3 = 0$ $-3, -1$ 2. $m^2 + 6m = 27$ $-9, 3$

Solve each equation by factoring. (Lesson 6–2)

3. $x^2 + 5x - 36 = 0$ $4, -9$ 4. $2x^2 + 7x = -3$ $-\frac{1}{2}, -3$

Solve each equation by completing the square. (Lesson 6–3)

5. $x^2 + 6x = 55$ $-11, 5$ 6. $x^2 - 7x + 21 = 0$ $\frac{7 \pm i\sqrt{35}}{2}$

7. Find the value of the discriminant for the equation $x^2 - 8x + 2 = 0$ and describe the nature of the roots. (Lesson 6–4)   **56, 2 real, irrational roots**

Solve each equation by using the quadratic formula. (Lesson 6–4)

8. $3x^2 + 5x - 1 = 0$ $\frac{-5 \pm \sqrt{37}}{6}$ 9. $2x^2 - 25x + 72 = 0$ $\frac{9}{2}, 8$

10. **Horticulture** The length of a tropical garden at a local conservatory is 5 feet more than its width. A walkway 2 feet wide surrounds the outside of the garden. If the total area of the walkway and garden is 594 square feet, find the dimensions of the garden. (Lesson 6–2)   **18 feet by 23 feet**

SELF TEST

The Self Test provides students with a brief review of the concepts and skills in Lessons 6-1 through 6-4. Lesson numbers are given to the right of exercises or instruction lines so students can review concepts not yet mastered.

Extension

Reasoning Show that if a and c have different signs, then $ax^2 + bx + c = 0$ $(a \neq 0)$ has two real roots. Since $ac < 0$, then $-4ac > 0$. Thus, $b^2 - 4ac > 0$, and $ax^2 + bx + c = 0$ has two real roots.

Sum and Product of Roots

What YOU'LL LEARN

- To find the sum and product of the roots of quadratic equations, and
- to find a quadratic equation to fit a given condition.

Why IT'S IMPORTANT

You can use the sum and product of roots to write quadratic equations involving space flight and engineering.

APPLICATION

Engineering

One of the major tasks of civil engineers is to design roads that are safe and comfortable. In highway design, the quadratic function $y = ax^2 + bx + c$ is called a *transition curve* because it has properties that provide a smooth transition between peaks and valleys.

A road with an initial gradient, or slope, of 3% can be represented by the formula $y = ax^2 + 0.03x + c$, where y is the elevation and x is the distance along the curve. Suppose the elevation of the road is 1105 feet at points 200 feet and 1000 feet along the curve. You can find the equation of the transition curve. *This problem will be solved in Example 4.*

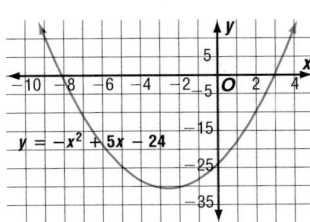

As in the situation above, you may know the roots of a quadratic equation without knowing the equation itself. For example, suppose the roots of a quadratic equation are 3 and -8 and you want to find the equation. In a previous lesson, you used factoring to solve an equation. You applied the zero product property and set both equations equal to 0 to find the solutions. You can work backward to find the equation when you know the solutions.

$$x = 3 \quad \text{or} \quad x = -8 \qquad \textit{Start with the solutions.}$$
$$x - 3 = 0 \qquad x + 8 = 0 \qquad \textit{Rewrite equations equal to 0.}$$

$$(x - 3)(x + 8) = 0 \qquad \textit{Multiplicative property of zero}$$
$$x^2 + 5x - 24 = 0 \qquad \textit{Multiply.}$$

The last equation has roots 3 and -8 and is written in standard form. The sum and product of the roots can help to develop the equation in another way.

Add the roots. $\quad 3 + (-8) = -5 \quad$ *-5 is the opposite of the coefficient of x.*

Multiply the roots. $\quad 3(-8) = -24 \quad$ *-24 is the constant term.* $\quad x^2 + 5x - 24 = 0$

This pattern can be generalized for any quadratic equation by using the roots defined by the quadratic formula. Let s_1 and s_2 represent the roots.

$$s_1 = \frac{-b + \sqrt{b^2 - 4ac}}{2a} \qquad\qquad s_2 = \frac{-b - \sqrt{b^2 - 4ac}}{2a} \quad \textit{Quadratic formula}$$

Lesson 6–5   Sum and Product of Roots   **359**

6-5 LESSON NOTES

NCTM Standards: 1–5

Instructional Resources

- Study Guide Master 6-5
- Practice Master 6-5
- Enrichment Master 6-5
- Assessment and Evaluation Masters, pp. 155, 156
- Real-World Applications, 17

 Transparency 6-5A contains the 5-Minute Check for this lesson; **Transparency 6-5B** contains a teaching aid for this lesson.

Recommended Pacing

Standard Pacing	Day 8 of 17
Honors Pacing	Day 6 of 14
Block Scheduling*	Day 3 of 7 (along with Lesson 6-4)

 *For more information on pacing and possible lesson plans, refer to the *Block Scheduling Booklet*.

1 FOCUS

5-Minute Check
(over Lesson 6-4)

Solve $m^2 - 8m + 15 = 0$

1. by completing the square
   3, 5
2. by using the quadratic formula **3, 5**

Find the value of the discriminant and describe the nature of the roots (real, imaginary, rational, irrational) of each quadratic equation. Then solve the equation.

3. $x^2 - 9x + 21 = 0 \quad -3; 2$
   imaginary roots; $\dfrac{9 \pm i\sqrt{3}}{2}$

4. $5x^2 - x - 4 = 0 \quad 81; 2$
   real, rational roots; $1, -\dfrac{4}{5}$

 **TEKS** | 6.a., 6.b., 6.c., 8.a., 8.d.

Questioning Separate the class into four groups. Have each group graph one of the following equations and determine the roots.

$5x^2 + x - 4 = 0$
$x^2 + 2x - 8 = 0$
$2x^2 + 4x - 16 = 0$
$8 - 2x - x^2 = 0$

Discuss how different equations have the same roots and differently shaped graphs.

2 TEACH

In-Class Example

For Example 1
Write a quadratic equation that has the given roots.

a. $-\dfrac{3}{8}$ and 5 $8x^2 - 37x - 15 = 0$

b. $\dfrac{1}{3}$ and $\dfrac{1}{2}$ $6x^2 - 5x + 1 = 0$

Teaching Tip Emphasize that fractions for the sum and product must be written with the same denominator. Then, a, b, and c are recognizable. Do not simplify unless it is necessary.

Teaching Tip When finding the product of s_1 and s_2, note that

$\dfrac{-b + \sqrt{b^2 - 4ac}}{2a}$ and $\dfrac{-b - \sqrt{b^2 - 4ac}}{2a}$

can be written as $\dfrac{-b}{2a} + \dfrac{\sqrt{b^2 - 4ac}}{2a}$

and $\dfrac{-b}{2a} - \dfrac{\sqrt{b^2 - 4ac}}{2a}$. So you can use the difference of squares to find the product.

Their sum can be represented as follows.

$$s_1 + s_2 = \frac{-b + \sqrt{b^2 - 4ac}}{2a} + \frac{-b - \sqrt{b^2 - 4ac}}{2a} \qquad \textit{Add the roots.}$$

$$= \frac{-2b + 0}{2a} \text{ or } -\frac{b}{a} \qquad \textit{Simplify.}$$

The sum of the roots is $-\dfrac{b}{a}$.

The product of the roots may be represented as follows.

$$s_1(s_2) = \left(\frac{-b + \sqrt{b^2 - 4ac}}{2a}\right)\left(\frac{-b - \sqrt{b^2 - 4ac}}{2a}\right)$$

$$= \frac{b^2 - (b^2 - 4ac)}{4a^2} \qquad \textit{Multiply.}$$

$$= \frac{b^2 - b^2 + 4ac}{4a^2} \qquad \textit{Use the distributive property.}$$

$$= \frac{4ac}{4a^2} \text{ or } \frac{c}{a}$$

The product of the roots is $\dfrac{c}{a}$.

The rule below can help you find a quadratic equation if you know the roots.

Sum and Product of Roots	If the roots of $ax^2 + bx + c = 0$ with $a \neq 0$ are s_1 and s_2, then $s_1 + s_2 = -\dfrac{b}{a}$ and $s_1 \cdot s_2 = \dfrac{c}{a}$.

Example ❶ Write a quadratic equation that has roots $\dfrac{3}{4}$ and $-\dfrac{12}{5}$.

Find the sum and product of the roots. Begin by expressing the sum and product of the roots with the same denominator.

$$s_1 + s_2 = \frac{3}{4} + \left(-\frac{12}{5}\right)$$

$$= \frac{15}{20} - \frac{48}{20} \text{ or } -\frac{33}{20}$$

$$s_1 \cdot s_2 = \left(\frac{3}{4}\right)\left(-\frac{12}{5}\right)$$

$$= -\frac{36}{20}$$

So, $-\dfrac{33}{20} = -\dfrac{b}{a}$ and $-\dfrac{36}{20} = \dfrac{c}{a}$.

Therefore, $a = 20$, $b = 33$, and $c = -36$.   The equation is $20x^2 + 33x - 36 = 0$.

Check by solving the equation by factoring.

$20x^2 + 33x - 36 = 0$
$(4x - 3)(5x + 12) = 0$
$4x - 3 = 0$ or $5x + 12 = 0$
$\quad 4x = 3$ $\quad 5x = -12$
$\quad\ x = \dfrac{3}{4}$ ✓ $\quad\ x = -\dfrac{12}{5}$ ✓

The method used in Example 1 can also be used with equations whose roots are imaginary.

Example ② Write a quadratic equation that has roots $7 - 3i$ and $7 + 3i$.

$$s_1 + s_2 = (7 - 3i) + (7 + 3i)$$
$$= 14 \quad -\frac{b}{a} = \frac{14}{1}$$
$$s_1(s_2) = (7 - 3i)(7 + 3i)$$
$$= 49 + 9 \text{ or } 58 \quad \frac{c}{a} = \frac{58}{1}$$

Since $-\frac{b}{a} = \frac{14}{1}$ and $\frac{c}{a} = \frac{58}{1}$, $a = 1$, $b = -14$, $c = 58$. Replace a, b, and c in

$ax^2 + bx + c = 0$ with these values. The resulting equation is
$x^2 - 14x + 58 = 0$.

You can also use the sum and product of roots to check the solutions of an equation.

Example ③ Solve $2x^2 - 7x + 3 = 0$. Check by using the sum and product of the roots.

$$x = \frac{-b + \sqrt{b^2 - 4ac}}{2a}$$

$$= \frac{-(-7) \pm \sqrt{(-7)^2 - 4(2)(3)}}{2(2)} \quad a = 2,\ b = -7,\text{ and } c = 3$$

$$= \frac{7 \pm \sqrt{25}}{4} \text{ or } \frac{7 \pm 5}{4}$$

The solutions are $\frac{7 + 5}{4}$ and $\frac{7 - 5}{4}$ or 3 and $\frac{1}{2}$.

Check: The sum of the roots, $s_1 + s_2$, should be $-\frac{b}{a}$ or $\frac{7}{2}$.

The product or the roots, $s_1 s_2$, should be $\frac{c}{a}$ or $\frac{3}{2}$.

$$3 + \frac{1}{2} = \frac{7}{2} \checkmark \qquad\qquad 3\left(\frac{1}{2}\right) = \frac{3}{2} \checkmark$$

You can use the sum and product of roots to solve real-world problems.

Example ④ Refer to the application at the beginning of the lesson. Find the equation of the transition curve if the formula for a road with a gradient of 3% is $y = ax^2 + 0.03x + c$.

APPLICATION
Engineering

Explore Read the problem and determine two points on the road. The points on the road are $(200, 1105)$ and $(1000, 1105)$. So $y = 1105$ when $x = 200$ and $x = 1000$.

(continued on the next page)

Lesson 6–5 Sum and Product of Roots **361**

Alternative Learning Styles

Auditory Read aloud the civil engineering application in Example 4. Encourage students to suggest ways to describe the problem before attempting to solve it.

In-Class Examples

For Example 2
Write a quadratic equation that has the given roots.

a. $7 - 2i$ and $7 + 2i$
$x^2 - 14x + 53 = 0$

b. $5 + i\sqrt{3}$ and $5 - i\sqrt{3}$
$x^2 - 10x + 28 = 0$

For Example 3
Solve each equation. Check by using the sum and product of the roots.

a. $3x^2 - 10x + 3 = 0$ $3, \frac{1}{3}$;

$$s_1 + s_2 = \frac{10}{3} = -\frac{b}{a}$$
$$s_1 s_2 = 1 = \frac{c}{a}$$

b. $y^2 - 10y = 11$ $11, -1$;

$$s_1 + s_2 = 10 = -\frac{b}{a}$$
$$s_1 s_2 = -11 = \frac{c}{a}$$

For Example 4
A rocket is launched at the Kennedy Space Center. Listening to the radio, Connie hears the liftoff of the rocket and starts her stopwatch. From an observation tower, she observes the rocket 3 seconds after liftoff at the same height of the tower. Thirteen seconds later, she observes the rocket returning to Earth and at the same height of the tower. What was the initial velocity of the rocket and what was the height of the tower?

$$h = v_0 t - \frac{1}{2} g t^2$$
$$\text{or } -\frac{1}{2}(32)t^2 + v_0 t - h = 0$$
$$-16t^2 + v_0 t + (-h) = 0$$

$$s_1 + s_2 = -\frac{b}{a} \qquad s_1 s_2 = \frac{c}{a}$$
$$3 + 13 = -\frac{b}{-16} \qquad 3 \cdot 13 = \frac{c}{-16}$$
$$16 = \frac{b}{16} \qquad 39 = \frac{c}{-16}$$
$$256 = b \qquad -624 = c$$

$v_0 = 256$ ft/s, $h = 624$ ft

Check for Understanding

Exercises 1–16 are designed to help you assess your students' understanding through reading, writing, speaking, and modeling. You should work through Exercises 1–4 with your students and then monitor their work on Exercises 5–16.

Additional Answers

2. Set the sum of the roots equal to $\frac{-b}{a}$. Set the product of the roots equal to $\frac{c}{a}$. This will tell you the values of a, b, and c. Substitute the values of a, b, and c in $ax^2 + bx + c = 0$.

3. Set the sum of the roots equal to $\frac{-b}{a}$ and the product of the roots equal to $\frac{c}{a}$. Substitute this into $x^2 + -\frac{b}{a}x + \frac{c}{a} = 0$. Put this equation in standard form by multiplying both sides of the equation by a.

9. $x^2 - 8x + 11 = 0$
10. $x^2 - 2\sqrt{5}x + 69 = 0$
11. $3x^2 + 19x - 14 = 0$
12. $32x^2 + 4x - 15 = 0$

Study Guide Masters, p. 44

6-5

NAME_____ DATE_____

Student Edition
Pages 359–364

Study Guide

Sum and Product of Roots

The quadratic formula gives the roots of $ax^2 + bx + c = 0$, with $a \neq 0$, as

$$\frac{-b + \sqrt{b^2 - 4ac}}{2a} \quad \text{and} \quad \frac{-b - \sqrt{b^2 - 4ac}}{2a}.$$

You can add and simplify these expressions, then multiply and simplify to find expressions for the sum and the product of the roots.

Sum and Product of Roots
If the roots of $ax^2 + bx + c = 0$, with $a \neq 0$, are S_1 and S_2, then $S_1 + S_2 = -\frac{b}{a}$ and $S_1 S_2 = \frac{c}{a}$.

You can usually find the values of the expressions $-\frac{b}{a}$ and $\frac{c}{a}$ by merely glancing at the quadratic equation. Therefore, they give a quick check on the correctness of the solutions you obtain when you solve a quadratic equation.

Example: Tell what the sum and product of the roots of $9x^2 + 9x - 10 = 0$ will be and use the results to check whether $\frac{2}{3}$ and $\frac{5}{3}$ are correct solutions.

The sum of the roots will be $-\frac{9}{9}$ or -1. The product of the roots will be $-\frac{10}{9}$. Since $\frac{2}{3} + \frac{5}{3}$ does not equal -1 and $\frac{2}{3} \cdot \frac{5}{3}$ does not equal $-\frac{10}{9}$, the proposed solutions are *not* correct.

Without solving the equation, state the sum and the product of the roots of each quadratic equation.

1. $x^2 + 2x - 15 = 0$ $-2, -15$
2. $x^2 + 3x - 28 = 0$ $-3, -28$
3. $x^2 - x + 1 = 0$ $1, 1$
4. $7x^2 + 14x - 3 = 0$ $-2, -\frac{3}{7}$
5. $-2x^2 - 5x = 6$ $-\frac{5}{2}, 3$
6. $16x^2 + 18x - 12 = 0$ $-\frac{9}{8}, -\frac{3}{4}$

Solve each equation. Then find the sum and the product of the roots to check your solutions.

7. $x^2 - 7x = 18$ $9, -2$
8. $25x^2 = 36$ $-\frac{6}{5}, \frac{6}{5}$
9. $7p^2 - 11p = 6$ $-\frac{3}{7}, 2$
10. $3c^2 + 7c - 2 = 0$
    $\frac{-7 + \sqrt{73}}{6}, \frac{-7 - \sqrt{73}}{6}$

Plan   Since $y = 1105$, rewrite the equation equal to 0.

$1105 = ax^2 + 0.03x + c$ *Substitute 1105 for y.*
$0 = ax^2 + 0.03x + (c - 1105)$ *Rewrite equation equal to 0.*

Let $b = 0.03$, $s_1 = 200$, and $s_2 = 1000$.

Solve   Use the sum and product of the roots to find the equation.

$$s_1 + s_2 = -\frac{b}{a} \qquad\qquad s_1 \cdot s_2 = \frac{c}{a}$$

$$200 + 1000 = -\frac{(0.03)}{a} \qquad 200 \cdot 1000 = \frac{c - 1105}{a} \quad \text{\textit{Why substitute}}$$
$$\text{\textit{c −1105 for c?}}$$

$$1200 = -\frac{0.03}{a} \qquad\qquad 200,000 = \frac{c - 1105}{-0.000025}$$

$$a = -0.000025 \qquad\qquad -5 = c - 1105$$

$$1100 = c$$

Thus, the equation of the transition curve is $y = -0.000025x^2 + 0.03x + 1100$.

Examine   Check to see if the equation makes sense. Substitute $x = 200$ and $x = 1000$ into the equation $y = -0.000025x^2 + 0.03x + 1100$.

CHECK FOR UNDERSTANDING

Communicating Mathematics

Study the lesson. Then complete the following.   1. $-\frac{b}{a}, \frac{c}{a}$

1. **Write** the sum and the product of the roots of a quadratic equation expressed in terms of a, b, and c.

2. **Explain** how to use the zero product property to form a quadratic equation when its roots are known.   See margin.

3. **Describe** how to create an equation when only the sum and product of the roots are known.   See margin.

4. When might it be difficult to find an equation using the sum and product of roots? Give some examples.   See students' work.

Guided Practice

State the sum and product of the roots of each quadratic equation.

5. $x^2 - 12x + 22 = 0$ 12, 22
6. $x^2 - 22 = 0$ 0, −22
7. $3x^2 + 75 = 0$ 0, 25
8. $2x^2 - \frac{1}{4}x = \frac{4}{15}$ $\frac{-8}{8}, \frac{1}{8}, \frac{4}{15}$

Write a quadratic equation that has the given roots.   9–12. See margin.

9. $4 \pm \sqrt{5}$
10. $\sqrt{5} \pm 8i$
11. $-7, \frac{2}{3}$
12. $\frac{-3}{4}, \frac{5}{8}$

Solve each equation. Check by using the sum and product of the roots.

13. 7, −7   14. $\frac{3}{2}$, −9   15. $\frac{9}{4}, -\frac{9}{4}$

13. $x^2 - 49 = 0$
14. $2x^2 + 15x = 27$
15. $16x^2 - 81 = 0$

16. Suppose a quadratic equation has two real roots, r_1 and r_2. If the sum of the roots is $-\frac{19}{2}$ and the product of the roots is -30, write a quadratic equation that has roots r_1 and r_2. $2x^2 + 19x - 60 = 0$

Reteaching

Using Visual Models Graph several quadratic equations with two real roots. For each graph, locate the x-intercepts, add the values together, and show that they equal $-\frac{b}{a}$. Multiply them and show that the product equals $\frac{c}{a}$.

Practice

Write a quadratic equation that has the given roots. 17–28. See margin.

17. $6, -9$ 18. $5, -1$ 19. $2, \frac{5}{8}$ 20. $6, 6$

21. $-\frac{2}{5}, \frac{2}{5}$ 22. $-\frac{2}{5}, \frac{2}{7}$ 23. $-4, -\frac{2}{3}$ 24. $\frac{4}{3}, -\frac{1}{6}$

25. $4 \pm \sqrt{3}$ 26. $\frac{3}{7} \pm 2i$ 27. $\frac{-2 \pm 5i}{4}$ 28. $\frac{-2 \pm 3\sqrt{5}}{7}$

Solve each equation. Check by using the sum and product of the roots.

29. $-4, -\frac{3}{2}$ 30. $6, \frac{4}{3}$

36. $\frac{-5 \pm \sqrt{5}}{2}$

37. $9, -\frac{5}{4}$

38. $\frac{\pm i \sqrt{51}}{3}$

39a. $12x^2 - 48x + 13 = 0$

39b. $42x^2 - 7x + 10 = 0$

29. $-2x^2 - 11x - 12 = 0$
30. $-3x^2 + 22x - 24 = 0$
31. $x^2 - 8x = 0$ $0, 8$
32. $x^2 - 16 = 0$ ± 4
33. $x^2 + \frac{1}{6}x - \frac{1}{3} = 0$ $\frac{1}{2}, -\frac{2}{3}$
34. $\frac{1}{2}x^2 - \frac{13}{20}x - \frac{3}{20} = 0$ $\frac{3}{2}, -\frac{1}{5}$
35. $x^2 - 8x - 18 = 0$ $4 \pm \sqrt{34}$
36. $2x^2 + 10x = -10$
37. $4x^2 - 31x - 45 = 0$
38. $3x^2 + 17 = 0$

39. Write a quadratic equation whose roots satisfy the following conditions.

   a. The sum of the roots is 4. The product of the roots is $\frac{13}{12}$.

   b. The sum of the roots is $\frac{1}{6}$. The product of the roots is $\frac{5}{21}$.

Critical Thinking

40. Find a value k such that -3 is a root of $2x^2 + kx - 21 = 0$. -1
41. Find a value k such that $\frac{1}{2}$ is a root of $2x^2 + 11x = -k$. -6
42. List all possible integral roots of $x^2 + bx - 24 = 0$. Assume that b represents an integer.   24, −1; −24, 1; 12, −2; −12, 2; 8, −3; −8, 3; 6, −4; −6, 4

Applications and Problem Solving

43. **Space Flight**   The United States is currently researching a project called the National Aerospace Plane, which would be able to regularly fly passengers directly into space. If the space plane is successful, it will be able to take off from an airport and rocket to orbit by accelerating to Mach 25 or 17,700 miles per hour. Scientists exploring the concepts of velocity and acceleration in space launch a model rocket that returns to Earth 18 seconds after takeoff. Use the formula $h = v_i t - \frac{1}{2}gt^2$, where $g = 9.8$ m/s², to determine the initial velocity of the rocket.   *Remember that the rocket starts on Earth when $t = 0$.*   **88.2 m/s**

44. **Geometry**   Imagine that square *AEFD* is cut off the end of rectangle *ABCD* at the right. The remaining rectangle *EBCF* has the same ratio of length to width as the original rectangle *ABCD*. A rectangle with those similarities is called a "golden rectangle." Because of their pleasing shape, golden rectangles can be found in ancient and modern architecture.

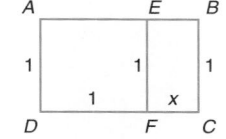

   a. Find the ratio of length to width for each rectangle. $\frac{1+x}{1}, \frac{1}{x}$

   b. Set the ratios equal, write the equation, and solve for *x*.   *Remember that measures cannot be negative.*   **0.618**

   c. Substitute the value of *x* into the ratios you found in part a. What number do you get? This number is known as the *golden ratio*.   **1.618**

Extension

Problem Solving   Find k such that $-\frac{13}{3}$ is a root of $3x^2 - kx - (k + 73) = 0$. $k = 5$

Have students give the justification for the steps in their solution.

Assignment Guide

Core: 17–43 odd, 45–52
Enriched: 18–38 even, 40–52

For **Extra Practice,** see p. 890.

The red A, B, and C flags, printed only in the Teacher's Wraparound Edition, indicate the level of difficulty of the exercises.

Additional Answers

17. $x^2 + 3x - 54 = 0$
18. $x^2 - 4x - 5 = 0$
19. $8x^2 - 21x + 10 = 0$
20. $x^2 - 12x + 36 = 0$
21. $25x^2 - 4 = 0$
22. $35x^2 + 4x - 4 = 0$
23. $3x^2 + 14x + 8 = 0$
24. $18x^2 - 21x - 4 = 0$
25. $x^2 - 8x + 13 = 0$
26. $49x^2 - 42x + 205 = 0$
27. $16x^2 + 16x + 29 = 0$
28. $49x^2 + 28x - 41 = 0$

Practice Masters, p. 44

6-5   NAME_____   DATE _____
Practice   Student Edition
Pages 359–36

Sum and Product of Roots

Solve each equation. Then find the sum and the product of the roots to check your solutions.

1. $x^2 - 7x + 4 = 0$ $\frac{7 \pm \sqrt{33}}{2}$; 7; 4
2. $x^2 + 3x + 6 = 0$ $\frac{-3 \pm \sqrt{15}i}{2}$; −3, 6
3. $2n^2 + 5n + 6 = 0$ $\frac{-5 \pm \sqrt{23}i}{4}$; $-\frac{5}{3}$; 3
4. $7x^2 - 5x = 0$ $0, \frac{5}{7}; \frac{5}{7}; 0$
5. $4r^2 - 9 = 0$ $\frac{3}{2}, -\frac{3}{2}; 0; -\frac{9}{4}$
6. $-5x^2 - x + 4 = 0$ $-1, \frac{4}{5}; -\frac{1}{5}; -\frac{4}{5}$
7. $3x^2 + 8x = 3$ $\frac{1}{3}, -3; -\frac{8}{3}; -1$
8. $\frac{2}{3}x^2 - \frac{1}{2}x - 1 = 0$ $\frac{3 \pm \sqrt{105}}{8}, \frac{3}{4}; -\frac{3}{2}$

Write a quadratic equation that has the given roots.

9. $7, -3$ $x^2 - 4x - 21 = 0$
10. $4, \frac{1}{3}$ $3x^2 - 13x + 4 = 0$
11. $-\frac{2}{3}, -\frac{4}{5}$ $15x^2 + 22x + 8 = 0$
12. $-2\sqrt{5}, 4\sqrt{5}$ $x^2 - 2\sqrt{5}x - 40 = 0$
13. $3 - \sqrt{6}, 3 + \sqrt{6}$ $x^2 - 6x + 3 = 0$
14. $7 - 2i, 7 + 2i$ $x^2 - 14x + 53 = 0$
15. $7i, -7i$ $x^2 + 49 = 0$
16. $\frac{2 + \sqrt{10}}{5}, \frac{2 - \sqrt{10}}{5}$ $25x^2 - 20x - 6 = 0$
17. $2 + i\sqrt{11}, 2 - i\sqrt{11}$ $x^2 - 4x + 15 = 0$
18. $\frac{1 + 6i}{4}, \frac{1 - 6i}{4}$ $16x^2 - 8x + 37 = 0$

Find k such that the number given is a root of the equation.

19. $7; 2x^2 + kx - 21 = 0$ −11
20. $-2; x^2 - 13x + k = 0$ −30

Closing Activity

Writing Give students three pairs of roots. Make one pair integers, one pair fractions, and one pair imaginary. Have students determine a quadratic equation for each pair.

Chapter 6, Quiz B (Lessons 6-4 and 6-5), is available in the *Assessment and Evaluation Masters,* p. 156.

Mid-Chapter Test (Lessons 6-1 through 6-5) is available in the *Assessment and Evaluation Masters,* p. 155.

Answers for Mathematics and Society

1. The paths of the objects being tossed are parabolas, quadratic equations.
2. Sample answers: how many objects are being thrown, how far apart the people are who are juggling, how heavy the objects are
3. Answers will vary.

Enrichment Masters, p. 44

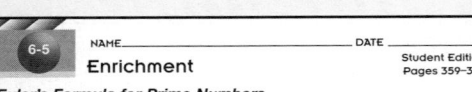

6-5

NAME_____ DATE_____

Enrichment

Student Edition
Pages 359–364

Euler's Formula for Prime Numbers

Many mathematicians have searched for a formula that would generate prime numbers. One such formula was proposed by Euler and uses a quadratic polynomial:

$$x^2 + x + 41.$$

Find the values of $x^2 + x + 41$ for the given values of x. State whether each value of the polynomial is or is not a prime number.

1. $x = 0$
41, prime

2. $x = 1$
43, prime

3. $x = 2$
47, prime

4. $x = 3$
53, prime

5. $x = 4$
61, prime

6. $x = 5$
71, prime

7. $x = 6$
83, prime

8. $x = 17$
347, prime

9. $x = 28$
853, prime

10. $x = 29$
911, prime

11. $x = 30$
971, prime

12. $x = 35$
1301, prime

13. Does the formula produce all prime numbers greater than 40? Give examples in your answer.
No. Among the primes omitted are 59, 67, 73, 79, 89, 101, 103, 107, 109, and 127.

14. Euler's formula produces primes for many values of x, but it does not work for all of them. Find the first value of x for which the formula fails. (*Hint:* Try multiples of ten.)
$x = 40$ gives 1681, which equals 41^2.

Mixed Review

45. Solve $x^2 - 2x - 35 = 0$ by using the quadratic formula. (Lesson 6–4) **7, −5**

46. Solve $m^2 + 3m - 180 = 0$ by completing the square. (Lesson 6–3) **−15, 12**

47. Graph the function $f(x) = x^2 + 8x - 5$. Name the vertex and axis of symmetry. (Lesson 6–1) **(−4, −21); x = −4; See Solutions Manual for graph.**

48. Simplify $\sqrt{108} - \sqrt{48} + (\sqrt{3})^3$. (Lesson 5–6) **$5\sqrt{3}$**

49. Factor $4x^2 - 9$. (Lesson 5–4) **(2x − 3)(2x + 3)**

50. Solve the system $3a - b + 2c = 7$, $-a + 4b - c = 3$, and $a + 4b - c = 1$ by using augmented matrices. (Lesson 4–7) **(−1, 2, 6)**

51. Solve for a. (Lesson 4–5) **$\frac{21}{8}$**
$$\begin{vmatrix} a & 2 & -1 \\ 4a & -7 & -1 \\ 2 & 2 & -2 \end{vmatrix} = 45$$

52. Graph $y = -|5x - 12| + 1$. (Lesson 2–6) **See Solutions Manual.**

Mathematics and Juggling

The excerpt below appeared in an article in *New Scientist* on March 18, 1995.

MATHEMATICS AND MUSIC, IT IS SAID, often go together. Mathematicians are also reputed to be unusually good at chess. But there is a less well-known activity that also enjoys a time-honoured association with mathematics: juggling. Although the connection may seem tenuous at first sight, there has recently been a rush to apply mathematics to juggling, as mathematicians have come up with a clever way to invent new juggling patterns. . . . The pure mathematics of juggling concerns itself only with the patterns of throws, ignoring detail such as the precise timings, the exact trajectories and even the objects being thrown. Some theoretically minded jugglers recently introduced an idea called "site swaps" to describe the patterns in a compact form. And last year, four mathematicians—turned it into a mathematical theory. . . . (Site swap notation) is an easy way to remember a wide range of patterns that look very impressive when performed. The advantage for mathematicians is that a neat, compact notation makes it easier to count or classify patterns. ■

1–3. See margin.

1. What are the characteristics of the motions of objects being juggled?
2. If you were to construct a mathematical theory about juggling, what are some of the variables that might be involved?
3. Use your creativity to design a new juggling pattern that could actually be performed. What are some factors that limit any pattern design?

Mathematics and SOCIETY

We can develop a simplified notation if all but the following three factors are considered. An object is either in the juggler's left hand, right hand, or in the air. A table can be used to represent many configurations.

Location	Object 1	Object 2	Object 3
in air		X	X
left hand			
right hand	X		

The table represents the fact that one object is in his right hand, the other two are still in the air. A series of tables represents a juggling routine. Discuss models of some simple routines.

6-6A Graphing Technology
Families of Parabolas

A Preview of Lesson 6–6

The equations for the parabolas in a family are closely related. In the general form of a quadratic equation, $y = a(x - h)^2 + k$, a, h, and k may change. Changing the value of a, h, or k results in a different parabola in the family.

Example ❶ **Graph the following equations on the same screen in the standard viewing window. Describe any similarities and differences among the graphs.**

The parent graph in this example is the graph of $y = x^2$.

$y = x^2, y = x^2 + 4, y = x^2 - 2$

Enter: Y= | X,T,θ | x^2 | ENTER
X,T,θ | x^2 | + | 4 | ENTER
X,T,θ | x^2 | − | 2 | ZOOM | 6

You can also graph the three equations by entering the following single equation.

Enter: Y= | X,T,θ | x^2 | + | 2nd | { | 0 | ,
4 | , | (−) | 2 | 2nd | } | ZOOM | 6

The graphs have the same shape and all open upward. The vertex of each graph is on the y-axis. However, the graphs have different vertical positions.

Example 1 shows how changing the value of k in the equation $y = a(x - h)^2 + k$ translates the parabola along the y-axis. If $k > 0$, the parabola is translated k units upward, and if $k < 0$, it is translated k units downward. How do you think changing the value of h will change the graphs in a family of parabolas?

Example ❷ **Graph the following equations in the standard viewing window and describe any similarities and differences among the graphs.**

The parent graph in this example is the graph of $y = x^2$.

$y = x^2, y = (x + 4)^2, y = (x - 2)^2$

Enter: Y= | X,T,θ | x^2 | ENTER | (
X,T,θ | + | 4 |) | x^2 | ENTER | (
X,T,θ | − | 2 |) | x^2 | ZOOM | 6

You can also graph the three equations by entering the following single equation.

Enter: Y= | (| X,T,θ | + | 2nd
{ | 0 | , | 4 | , | (−) | 2 | 2nd | } |) | x^2 | ZOOM | 6

The graphs have the same shape and all open upward. The vertex of each graph is on the x-axis. However, the graphs have different horizontal positions.

NCTM Standards: 1–6

Objective
Use a graphing calculator to graph and explore similarities between parabolas.

Recommended Time
25 minutes

Instructional Resources
Graphing Calculator Masters, pp. 37 and 38

These masters provide keystroking instruction for this lesson for the TI-81 and Casio graphing calculators.

1 FOCUS

Motivating the Lesson
Ask each student to sketch a parabola in a standard viewing window drawn on a piece of paper. Then draw a standard viewing window on the chalkboard or overhead and have each student draw his or her parabola on it. Explain that all of these are related and are members of the family of parabolas.

2 TEACH

Teaching Tip Make sure that all three graphs are turned on (or the "=" are highlighted) when you graph the functions in Examples 1 and 2.

3 PRACTICE/APPLY

Assignment Guide
Core: 1–15
Enriched: 1–15

 TEKS | 4.a., 4.b., 6.b., 7.a., 7.b.

Observing students working with technology is an excellent method of assessment.

Additional Answers

1. The value of k determines the vertical position of the graph. As you change k, the graph will slide up or down the coordinate plane. Examples will vary.

2. The value of h determines the horizontal position of the graph. As you change h, the graph will slide to the right or the left on the coordinate plane. Examples will vary.

3. Both graphs have the same shape and vertex, but the first graph opens upward and the second graph opens downward. Examples will vary.

4. Both graphs have the same shape, but the graph of $y = (x + 6)^2$ is 6 units to the left of the graph of $y = x^2$.

5. Both graphs have the same shape, but the graph of $y = (x - 8)^2$ is 8 units to the right of the graph of $y = x^2$.

6. Both graphs have the same shape, but the graph of $y = x^2 + 1.5$ is 1.5 units above the graph of $y = x^2$.

7. Both graphs have the same shape, but the graph of $y = x^2 - 11$ is 11 units below the graph of $y = x^2$.

8. Both graphs open downward, but the graph of $y = -5x^2$ is more narrow than the graph of $y = -x^2$.

9. The graph of $y = -2x^2$ opens downward and is more narrow than the graph of $y = x^2$.

10. The graph of $y = -\frac{1}{2}x^2 + 4$ opens downward, it is wider, and it is 4 units above the graph of $y = x^2$.

11. Both graphs have the same shape, but the graph of $y = -\frac{1}{3}x^2 + 2$ is 2 units above the graph of $y = -\frac{1}{3}x^2$.

12. The graph of $y = -6(x + 1)^2 - 11$ opens downward, is more narrow than the graph of $y = x^2$, and it is 11 units down and 1 unit to the left.

Example 2 demonstrates that changing the value of h in $y = a(x - h)^2 + k$ translates the graph horizontally. If $h > 0$, the graph translates to the right h units. If $h < 0$, the graph translates to the left h units.

Changing the value of a in $y = a(x - h)^2 + k$ affects the direction of the opening and the shape of the graph. If $a > 0$, the graph opens upward, and if $a < 0$, the graph opens downward. If $|a| < 1$, the graph is wider than the graph of $y = x^2$, and if $|a| > 1$, then the graph is narrower than the graph of $y = x^2$. Graphs of equations with a values that have the same absolute value, such as $y = 2x^2$ and $y = -2x^2$, have the same shape.

Example **Graph the following equations in the standard viewing window and describe any similarities and differences among the graphs.**

The parent graph in this example is the graph of $y = x^2$.

$y = x^2$, $y = -x^2$, $y = 2x^2$, $y = -2x^2$, $y = 0.5x^2$, $y = -0.5x^2$

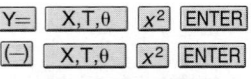

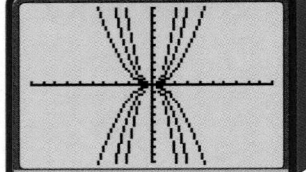

The graphs of $y = x^2$, $y = 2x^2$, and $y = 0.5x^2$ open upward, while the graphs of $y = -x^2$, $y = -2x^2$, and $y = -0.5x^2$ open downward. The graphs of $y = 2x^2$ and $y = -2x^2$ are narrower than the graph of $y = x^2$, while the graphs of $y = 0.5x^2$ and $y = -0.5x^2$ are wider than the graph of $y = x^2$.

EXERCISES

Study the lesson. Then complete the following.   1–15. See margin.

1. Describe the effect that changing the value of k in an equation of the form $y = a(x - h)^2 + k$ has on the graph of the equation. Give an example.

2. Describe the effect that changing the value of h in an equation of the form $y = a(x - h)^2 + k$ has on the graph of the equation. Give an example.

3. How do the graphs of $y = a(x - h)^2 + k$ and $y = -a(x - h)^2 + k$ compare? Give an example.

Examine each pair of equations below and predict the graphs for each. Then use a graphing calculator to confirm your results. Write one sentence that compares the two graphs.

4. $y = x^2$, $y = (x + 6)^2$ 5. $y = x^2$, $y = (x - 8)^2$

6. $y = x^2$, $y = x^2 + 1.5$ 7. $y = x^2$, $y = x^2 - 11$

8. $y = -x^2$, $y = -5x^2$ 9. $y = x^2$, $y = -2x^2$

10. $y = x^2$, $y = -\frac{1}{2}x^2 + 4$ 11. $y = -\frac{1}{3}x^2$, $y = -\frac{1}{3}x^2 + 2$

12. $y = x^2$, $y = -6(x + 1)^2 - 11$ 13. $y = (x + 2)^2 + 1$, $y = (x + 2)^2 - 4$

14. $y = 2(x + 3)^2 + 1$,   15. $y = 2(x - 4)^2 + 3$,
    $y = 4(x + 3)^2 + 1$ $y = \frac{1}{2}(x - 4)^2 - 5$

---

13. Both graphs have the same shape, but the graph of $y = (x + 2)^2 - 4$ is 5 units below the graph of $y = (x + 2)^2 + 1$.

14. The graph of $y = 4(x + 3)^2 + 1$ is more narrow than the graph of $y = 2(x + 3)^2 + 1$.

15. The graph of $y = \frac{1}{2}(x - 4)^2 - 5$ is 8 units below and is wider than the graph of $y = 2(x - 4)^2 + 3$.

Using Technology

This lesson offers an excellent opportunity for using technology in your algebra classroom. For more information on using technology, see *Graphing Calculators in the Mathematics Classroom,* one of the titles in the Glencoe Mathematics Professional Series.

Analyzing Graphs of Quadratic Functions

APPLICATION
World Cultures

A recent article in *National Geographic* featured the Cherokee Indians living in Oklahoma. The Cherokee Nation is a federally recognized sovereign nation that has its own court system, legislature, and tax commission. The Cherokee are working toward self-sufficiency while trying to preserve their cultural identity.

One of the people featured in the *National Geographic* article was Lorene Drywater of Tahlequah, Oklahoma. She makes buffalo grass dolls, a craft she learned from her mother. She sells the dolls to tourists for additional income. As anyone who sells things can tell you, deciding on an appropriate price is very important. If your price is too low, you will not make much of a profit. If your price is too high, you will also probably not make much of a profit because fewer people will buy what you are selling. The best price is the price that leads to the maximum profit.

Suppose Ms. Drywater's profit $P(x)$ can be found by $P(x) = -x^2 + 24x - 60$, where x represents the price of each doll. What price should she charge to receive the maximum profit?

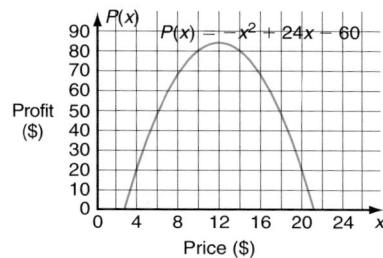

You can see from this graph that the vertex is (12, 84) and the axis of symmetry is $x = 12$. Thus, she should charge $12 for each doll to receive the maximum profit of $84. Is there a way to find this information without graphing the function?

You know that the graph of $ax^2 + bx + c = 0$ is a parabola. Quadratic functions can also be expressed in the general form $y = a(x - h)^2 + k$. We can write $P(x) = -x^2 + 24x - 60$ in the general form by completing the square.

$$\begin{aligned}
P(x) &= -x^2 + 24x - 60 \\
&= -1(x^2 - 24x) - 60 \\
&= -1(x^2 - 24x + 144) - 60 + 144 \quad \textit{Add and subtract } \left(\tfrac{-24}{2}\right)^2 \textit{ or 144 to} \\
&= -1(x - 12)^2 + 84 \qquad\qquad\qquad\quad \textit{obtain an equivalent equation.}
\end{aligned}$$

In this equation, $h = 12$ and $k = 84$. Compare these values with the coordinates of the vertex and axis of symmetry you found above by graphing. What pattern do you notice?

What YOU'LL LEARN

- To graph quadratic functions of the form $y = a(x - h)^2 + k$, and
- to determine the equation of a parabola by using points on its graph.

Why IT'S IMPORTANT

You can graph quadratic functions to solve problems involving biology and number theory.

F Y I

Cherokee Nation Industries, Inc. employs nearly 300 workers, most of whom are Cherokee. These skilled technicians work on equipment for commercial aircraft, M1 Abrams tanks, multilaunch rocket systems, and NATO spy planes.

F Y I

The Cherokee people are originally from the Great Lakes region. But today most surviving members of the Cherokee nation live in Oklahoma and North Carolina.

GLENCOE Technology

CD-ROM Interaction

A multimedia simulation connects data collection, graphing, and finding the line of best fit with finding the maximum profit for a fireworks factory. A blackline master activity with teacher's notes provides a follow-up to the CD-ROM simulation.

For Windows & Macintosh

6-6 LESSON NOTES

NCTM Standards: 1–6

Instructional Resources

- Study Guide Master 6-6
- Practice Master 6-6
- Enrichment Master 6-6
- Modeling Mathematics Masters, pp. 43–45
- Multicultural Activity Masters, p. 12

 Transparency 6-6A contains the 5-Minute Check for this lesson; **Transparency 6-6B** contains a teaching aid for this lesson.

Recommended Pacing

Standard Pacing	Day 10 of 17
Honors Pacing	Day 8 of 14
Block Scheduling*	Day 4 of 7

*For more information on pacing and possible lesson plans, refer to the *Block Scheduling Booklet*.

1 FOCUS

5-Minute Check
(over Lesson 6-5)

Find the sum and product of the roots of each quadratic equation.

1. $4x^2 - 2x + 3 = 0$ $\frac{1}{2}; \frac{3}{4}$
2. $12x^2 + 19x + 4 = 0$ $-\frac{19}{12}; \frac{1}{3}$
3. Find the sum and product of the roots of $y^2 + 9y + 25 = 0$. Then solve the equation. $-9; 25; \dfrac{-9 \pm i\sqrt{19}}{2}$

Find the quadratic equation with the given roots.

4. $3, -1$ $x^2 - 2x - 3 = 0$
5. $2 + \sqrt{5}, 2 - \sqrt{5}$ $x^2 - 4x - 1 = 0$

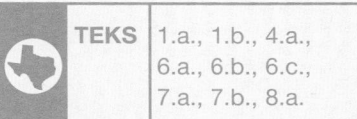 **TEKS** 1.a., 1.b., 4.a., 6.a., 6.b., 6.c., 7.a., 7.b., 8.a.

2 TEACH

In-Class Example

For Example 1
Name the vertex and the axis of symmetry for the graph of $f(x) = (x + 11)^2 + 8$. How is the graph of this function different from the graph of $f(x) = x^2$?
$(-11, 8)$; $x = -11$; it is translated 11 units left and 8 units up.

fabulous
FIRSTS

Chief Mankiller's life story is a tale of overcoming adversity. She was born into poverty and has undergone over 20 medical operations, including a kidney transplant. She also survived a near-fatal auto accident.

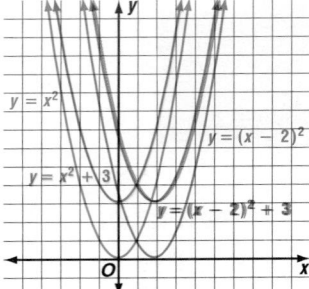

fabulous
FIRSTS

Wilma Mankiller (1945–)

Wilma Mankiller was the first and only woman elected chief of the Cherokee Nation, the second largest Native American tribe in the U.S. She served as chief for ten years. She resigned her position in 1995.

The graphs of $y = x^2$, $y = (x - 2)^2$, $y = x^2 + 3$, and $y = (x - 2)^2$ are shown at the right on the same set of axes. Study these graphs.

Equation	Vertex	Axis of Symmetry
$y = x^2$	$(0, 0)$	$x = 0$
$y = (x - 2)^2$	$(2, 0)$	$x = 2$
$y = x^2 + 3$	$(0, 3)$	$x = 0$
$y = (x - 2)^2 + 3$	$(2, 3)$	$x = 2$

Notice that the graphs all have the same shape. The difference is their position.

We can express the equations for these parabolas in the general form $y = (x - h)^2 + k$. When a quadratic function is written in this form, the vertex is (h, k), and the equation of the axis of symmetry is $x = h$.

Equation	General Form	h	k
$y = x^2$	$y = (x - 0)^2 + 0$	0	0
$y = (x - 2)^2$	$y = (x - 2)^2 + 0$	2	0
$y = x^2 + 3$	$y = (x - 0)^2 + 3$	0	3
$y = (x - 2)^2 + 3$	$y = (x - 2)^2 + 3$	2	3

In Chapter 4, you learned that a translation slides a figure on the coordinate plane without changing its shape or size. As the values of h and k change, the graph of $y = a(x - h)^2 + k$ is the graph of $y = x^2$ translated $|h|$ units left or right and $|k|$ units up or down. If h is positive, the parabola is translated to the right. If h is negative, it is translated to the left. Likewise, for k, the translation is up if k is positive and down if k is negative.

Example **Name the vertex and the axis of symmetry for the graph of $f(x) = (x + 6)^2 - 3$. Then graph the function. How is this graph different from the graph of $f(x) = x^2$?**

This function can be rewritten as $f(x) = [x - (-6)]^2 + (-3)$. Then $h = -6$ and $k = -3$. The vertex is at $(-6, -3)$, and the axis of symmetry is $x = -6$.

Finding several points on the graph makes graphing easier.

It is helpful to choose points that are close to h and on either side of h.

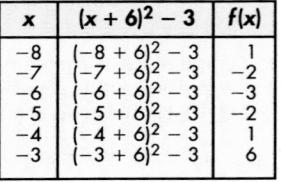

x	$(x + 6)^2 - 3$	$f(x)$
-8	$(-8 + 6)^2 - 3$	1
-7	$(-7 + 6)^2 - 3$	-2
-6	$(-6 + 6)^2 - 3$	-3
-5	$(-5 + 6)^2 - 3$	-2
-4	$(-4 + 6)^2 - 3$	1
-3	$(-3 + 6)^2 - 3$	6

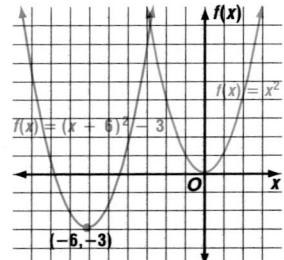

The shape of the graph is the same as the shape of the graph of $f(x) = x^2$, but it is translated 6 units left and 3 units down. *Notice that points with the same y-coordinates are the same distance from the axis of symmetry, $x = -6$.*

How does the value of *a* in the general form $y = a(x - h)^2 + k$ affect a parabola? Consider the equation in the application at the beginning of the lesson.

Graph $P(x) = -1(x - 12)^2 + 84$ and $P(x) = 1(x - 12)^2 + 84$ on the same coordinate plane and compare the graphs.

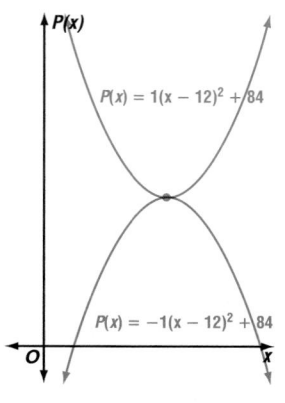

The graphs have the same vertex and are shaped the same. The graph of $P(x) = -1(x - 12)^2 + 84$ opens downward, and the graph of $P(x) = 1(x - 12)^2 + 84$ opens upward.

Graph the following functions to further investigate the relationships between similar functions. What do you find?

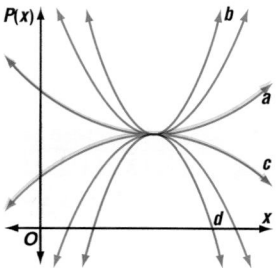

a. $P(x) = \frac{1}{4}(x - 12)^2 + 84$

b. $P(x) = 2(x - 12)^2 + 84$

c. $P(x) = -\frac{1}{4}(x - 12)^2 + 84$

d. $P(x) = -2(x - 12)^2 + 84$

All of the graphs for quadratic functions a, b, c, and d have the vertex (12, 84) and the axis of symmetry $x = 12$. When *a* is negative, the graph opens downward. When *a* is positive, the graph opens upward. As the value of $|a|$ increases, the graph becomes narrower.

The chart below summarizes the characteristics of the graph of $y = a(x - h)^2 + k$.

$y = a(x - h)^2 + k$	*a* is positive.	*a* is negative.
Vertex	(*h, k*)	(*h, k*)
Axis of Symmetry	$x = h$	$x = h$
Direction of Opening	upward	downward
As the value of $|a|$ increases, the graph of $y = a(x - h)^2 + k$ narrows.		

Example ② Graph $f(x) = -5x^2 + 80x - 319$. Name the vertex, axis of symmetry, and direction of opening for the graph.

Write the function in the form $f(x) = a(x - h)^2 + k$ by completing the square.

$$f(x) = -5x^2 + 80x - 319$$
$$= -5(x^2 - 16x) - 319$$
$$= -5(x^2 - 16x + 64) - 319 - (-5)(64) \quad \textit{Why subtract } (-5)(64)?$$
$$= -5(x - 8)^2 + 1$$

The general form of this function is $f(x) = -5(x - 8)^2 + 1$. So, $a = -5$, $h = 8$, and $k = 1$. The vertex is at (8, 1), and the axis of symmetry is $x = 8$. Since $a = -5$, the graph opens downward and is narrower than the graph of $f(x) = (x - 8)^2$.

(continued on the next page)

Teaching Tip Point out that as $|a|$ decreases, the graphs of $y = a(x - h)^2 + k$ widen.

Teaching Tip You may want to verify the conclusions in the chart by looking at each graph on page 369 and identifying the values of *a*, *h*, and *k*.

Teaching Tip Emphasize that in Example 2, restating the equation in the form $f(x) = (x - h)^2 + k$ enables students to determine the vertex and axis of symmetry more easily.

In-Class Example

For Example 2
Graph $f(x) = 4(x + 3)^2$. Name the vertex, axis of symmetry, and direction of opening for the graph.

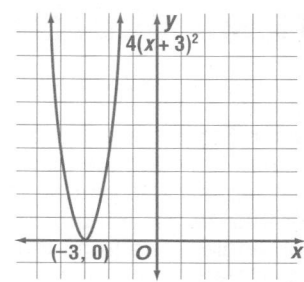

vertex $(-3, 0)$
axis of symmetry: $x = -3$
graph opens up

In-Class Examples

For Example 3

Write the equation of the parabola shown below.

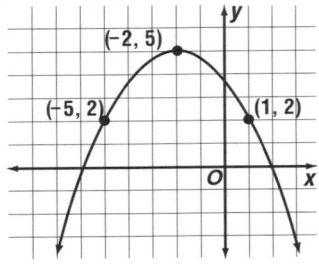

$y = -\frac{1}{3}(x + 2)^2 + 5$

For Example 4

Write the equation of the parabola that passes through the points at $(9, -3)$, $(6, 3)$, and $(4, 27)$. $f(x) = 2(x - 8)^2 - 5$

F Y I

Evolutionary theory purports to be able to explain such behavior. Frogs that can cover the maximum distance in their jump could escape predators better than frogs with other launch angles. The frogs that escaped had the highest probability of survival.

x	$-5(x - 8)^2 + 1$	$f(x)$
6	$-5(6 - 8)^2 + 1$	-19
7	$-5(7 - 8)^2 + 1$	-4
8	$-5(8 - 8)^2 + 1$	1
9	$-5(9 - 8)^2 + 1$	-4
10	$-5(10 - 8)^2 + 1$	-19

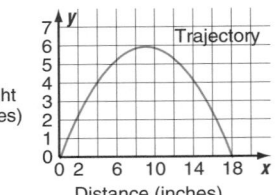

$f(x) = -5x^2 + 80x - 319$

One way to find the equation of a parabola is by using the values of the vertex and one other point on the graph.

Example 3

Biology

A deadly frog found in an area of rain forest in western Colombia can be lethal even to the touch because it exudes a toxic substance. Suppose the graph below represents the path, or trajectory, that one of the frogs takes while hopping through the rain forest. Write the equation of the parabola.

F Y I

The launch angle of a frog's jump is approximately 45°. This helps the frog cover maximum distance on flat ground.

The vertex of the parabola is at $(9, 6)$. So $h = 9$ and $k = 6$.

Substitute the values of h and k and the coordinates of one other point on the graph into the general form of the equation and solve for a.

Use $(0, 0)$.

$y = a(x - h)^2 + k$
$0 = a(0 - 9)^2 + 6$ *Substitute 9 for h, 6 for k,*
$-6 = a(-9)^2$ *0 for x, and 0 for y.*
$a = -\frac{6}{81}$ or $-\frac{2}{27}$

The equation of the parabola is
$y = -\frac{2}{27}(x - 9)^2 + 6$ or $y = -\frac{2}{27}x^2 + \frac{4}{3}x$.

It is also possible to write the equation of a parabola if you know three of its points.

Example 4

Write the equation of the parabola that passes through the points at $(0, -3)$, $(1, 4)$, and $(2, 15)$.

Each point should satisfy the equation of the parabola. Using the form of the equation $y = ax^2 + bx + c$, find a, b, and c by substituting the coordinates of the points into the quadratic form of the equation.

Ordered Pairs	Substitution	Simplify
$(0, -3)$	$-3 = a(0)^2 + b(0) + c$	$-3 = c$
$(1, 4)$	$4 = a(1)^2 + b(1) + c$	$4 = a + b + c$
$(2, 15)$	$15 = a(2)^2 + b(2) + c$	$15 = 4a + 2b + c$

Alternative Learning Styles

Visual The graphing calculator gives an opportunity to investigate transformations. The values of h and k define a translation. Many students will have difficulty understanding why the parabola will move to the right or in a positive direction if the value of h in $x - h$ is positive and to the left or in a negative direction if h is negative. Explain using the parent equation. If h is positive, the $x - h$ will remain this way, but if h is negative, we will be looking at $x - (-h)$ or $x + h$.

LOOK BACK

Refer to Lesson 3-7 for information on solving systems of equations in three variables.

Now solve the system of equations. From the first equation, $c = -3$, so substitute -3 for c in the other two equations.

$$4 = a + b - 3 \quad \rightarrow \quad 7 = a + b$$
$$15 = 4a + 2b - 3 \quad \rightarrow \quad 18 = 4a + 2b$$

Solve by using elimination.

$7 = a + b$	**Multiply by -2.**	$-14 = -2a - 2b$
$18 = 4a + 2b$		$18 = 4a + 2b$
		$4 = 2a$
		$2 = a$

Now substitute 2 for a and solve for b.

$$7 = 2 + b$$
$$b = 5$$

The solution to the system is $(2, 5, -3)$. So the equation of the parabola is $y = 2x^2 + 5x - 3$. *Check to see if each of the three points satisfies the equation.*

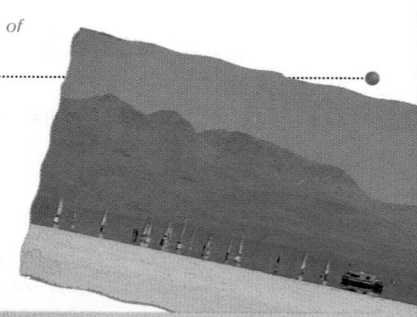

You can use a graphing calculator to model real-world data.

EXPLORATION

This data will vary with different races. Skin pigmentation is due in part to the amount of melanin, which provides protection from the sun's rays.

EXPLORATION
GRAPHING CALCULATORS

The *Mesa Tribune* (Mesa, Arizona) printed the sun intensity guide at the right on August 8, 1993. The data represent the average number of minutes of exposure to the sun required to redden untanned Caucasian skin.

Time of Day	Number of Minutes
9 A.M.	34
10 A.M.	20
11 A.M.	15
noon	13
1 P.M.	14
2 P.M.	18
3 P.M.	32
4 P.M.	60

Your Turn

a. Use the Edit option on the STAT menu feature to list the ordered pairs. Let x represent the number of hours since 8 A.M. Use the window $[-1, 9]$ with a scale factor of 1 and $[0, 65]$ with a scale factor of 5. Then press ⟨2nd⟩ ⟨STAT PLOT⟩ 1 ⟨ENTER⟩ ⟨▼⟩ ⟨ENTER⟩ ⟨GRAPH⟩.

b. To find a quadratic equation whose graph best fits the data, go to the CALC option on the STAT menu. Then choose 6, for QuadReg, and enter ⟨2nd⟩ ⟨L1⟩ , ⟨2nd⟩ ⟨L2⟩ . Then press ⟨ENTER⟩.

c. Write the equation of the graph that best fits the data. Then press ⟨Y=⟩ ⟨VARS⟩ 5 ⟨▶⟩ ⟨▶⟩ 7 ⟨GRAPH⟩.

d. How well do you feel the graph of the equation fits the data? Justify your answer. **See students' work.**

b. $a = 2.833333333$, $b = -22.5$, $c = 54.75$

c. $y = 2.83x^2 - 22.5x + 54.75$

Lesson 6-6 Analyzing Graphs of Quadratic Functions **371**

Classroom Vignette

"As an alternative assessment, I ask students to research real-world applications of quadratic functions and share their findings with the class, incorporating information and techniques from this chapter."

Anne Licciardi
Foxborough High School
Foxborough, Massachusetts

Check for Understanding

Exercises 1–17 are designed to help you assess your students' understanding through reading, writing, speaking, and modeling. You should work through Exercises 1–5 with your students and then monitor their work on Exercises 6–17.

Additional Answers

1. The graph of each function has a vertex at $(-6, -2)$ and an axis of symmetry at $x = -6$. The graph of $y = 4(x + 6)^2 - 2$ is narrow and opens upward; the graph of $y = -\frac{1}{2}(x + 6)^2 - 2$ is wider and opens downward.

2. To find the equation of a parabola, you would need the vertex and one point, three points, or the vertex and the value of a.

3. Vertex $(-4, 7)$; axis of symmetry $x = -4$; graph opens downward and is wide.

6. $(-3, 0)$, $x = -3$, down

7. $(0, -6)$, $x = 0$, up

8. $f(x) = (x - 2)^2 + 1$; $(2, 1)$, $x = 2$, up

9. $f(x) = -3(x - 2)^2 + 12$; $(2, 12)$, $x = 2$, down

14.

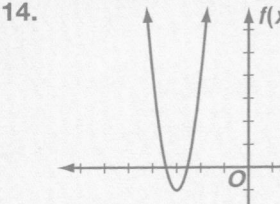

$f(x) = 5(x + 3)^2 - 1$

15.

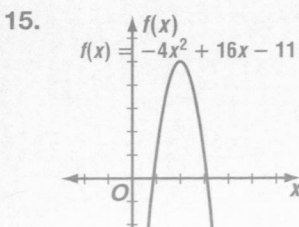

$f(x) = -4x^2 + 16x - 11$

16.

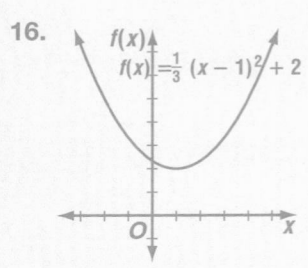

$f(x) = \frac{1}{3}(x - 1)^2 + 2$

CHECK FOR UNDERSTANDING

Communicating Mathematics

Study the lesson. Then complete the following.   1–3. See margin.

1. **Describe** the difference between the graphs of $y = 4(x + 6)^2 - 2$ and $y = -\frac{1}{2}(x + 6)^2 - 2$.

2. **List** the information you need to find the equation of a parabola.

3. **Analyze** the equation $y = -\frac{1}{6}(x + 4)^2 + 7$ and sketch its graph.

4. **Write** the equation of the function whose graph is 1 unit to the right and 4 units down from the graph shown at the right. $y = 5(x - 1)^2 - 4$

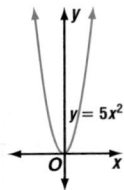

$y = 5x^2$

5. Marisel is correct. To complete the square, Leticia should have subtracted 2(9) or 18, not 9.

5. **You Decide**   Leticia and Marisel both wrote the equation $f(x) = 2x^2 - 12x - 3$ in general form by completing the square. However, they each got different answers. Look at their solutions and find which one is correct. Describe the error in the other person's solution.

Leticia	Marisel
$f(x) = 2x^2 - 12x - 3$	$f(x) = 2x^2 - 12x - 3$
$= 2(x^2 - 6x) - 3$	$= 2(x^2 - 6x) - 3$
$= 2(x^2 - 6x + 9) - 3 - 9$	$= 2(x^2 - 6x + 9) - 3 - 18$
$= 2(x - 3)^2 - 12$	$= 2(x - 3)^2 - 21$

Guided Practice

Write each equation in the form $y = a(x - h)^2 + k$ if not already in that form. Then name the vertex, axis of symmetry, and direction of opening for the graph of each quadratic function.   6–9. See margin.

6. $f(x) = -2(x + 3)^2$

7. $f(x) = 5x^2 - 6$

8. $f(x) = x^2 - 4x + 5$

9. $f(x) = -3x^2 + 12x$

Write an equation for each parabola.

10.

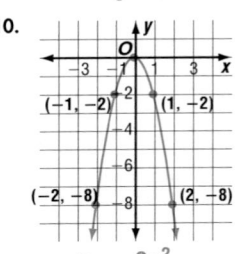

$y = -2x^2$

11.

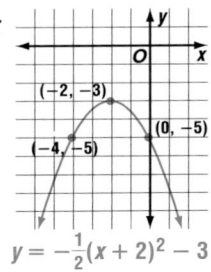

$y = -\frac{1}{2}(x + 2)^2 - 3$

Write an equation for the parabola that passes through the given points.

12. $y = \frac{2}{3}x^2 - \frac{4}{3}x + 2$

12. $(0, 2)$, $(2, 2)$, $(3, 4)$

13. $y = 3x^2 - 4x + 7$

13. $(1, 6)$, $(-2, 27)$, $(2, 11)$

Graph each function.   14–16. See margin.

14. $f(x) = 5(x + 3)^2 - 1$ 15. $f(x) = -4x^2 + 16x - 11$ 16. $f(x) = \frac{1}{3}(x - 1)^2 + 2$

17. Write the equation of a parabola with position 5 units below the parabola with equation $f(x) = 3x^2$. $f(x) = 3x^2 - 5$

Reteaching

Using Data   Given either the vertex and one point, three points, or the vertex and the value of a, write the equation of the parabola in the form $y = a(x - h)^2 + k$. Then check to see if the graph of the equation fits the given features of the parabola by using a graphing calculator or graphing software.

EXERCISES

Practice

Write each equation in the form $y = a(x - h)^2 + k$ if not already in that form. Then name the vertex, axis of symmetry, and direction of opening for the graph of each quadratic function. **18–29. See margin.**

18. $f(x) = 4(x + 3)^2 + 1$
19. $f(x) = -(x + 11)^2 - 6$
20. $f(x) = -2(x - 2)^2 - 2$
21. $f(x) = 3(x - \frac{1}{2})^2 + \frac{1}{4}$
22. $f(x) = x^2 + 6x - 3$
23. $f(x) = -x^2 - 4x + 8$
24. $f(x) = 4x^2 + 24x$
25. $f(x) = -6x^2 + 24x$
26. $f(x) = 3x^2 - 18x + 11$
27. $f(x) = -2x^2 - 20x - 50$
28. $f(x) = -\frac{1}{2}x^2 + 5x - \frac{27}{2}$
29. $f(x) = \frac{1}{3}x^2 - 4x + 15$

Write an equation for each parabola.

30.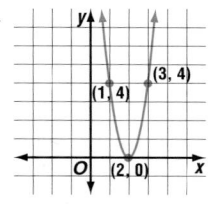

$y = 4(x - 2)^2$

31.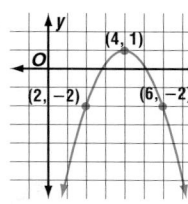

$y = -\frac{3}{4}(x - 4)^2 + 1$

32.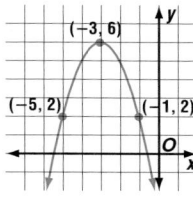

$y = -(x + 3)^2 + 6$

33.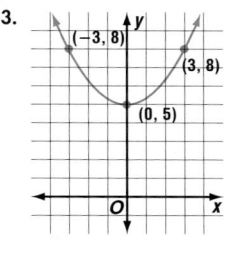

$y = \frac{1}{3}x^2 + 5$

34.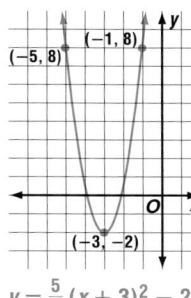

$y = \frac{5}{2}(x + 3)^2 - 2$

35.

$y = -3(x - 5)^2 + 4$

Write an equation for the parabola that passes through the given points.

36. $y = 2x^2 - x$
37. $y = \frac{1}{2}x^2 - 2x - 1$
38. $y = 7x^2 - 9x + 2$
39. $y = \frac{25}{3}x^2 + \frac{73}{3}x + 6$

36. $(0, 0), (2, 6), (-1, 3)$
37. $(2, -3), (0, -1), \left(-1, \frac{3}{2}\right)$
38. $(1, 0), (3, 38), (-2, 48)$
39. $(-1, -10), (0, 6), (2, 88)$

Graph each function. 40–49. See Solutions Manual.

40. $f(x) = 3(x + 3)^2$
41. $f(x) = 2(x + 3)^2 - 5$
42. $f(x) = \frac{1}{2}(x + 3)^2 - 5$
43. $f(x) = \frac{1}{3}(x - 1)^2 + 3$
44. $f(x) = x^2 + 6x + 2$
45. $f(x) = -2x^2 + 16x - 31$
46. $f(x) = -5x^2 - 40x - 80$
47. $f(x) = 2x^2 + 8x + 10$
48. $f(x) = -9x^2 - 18x - 6$
49. $f(x) = -0.25x^2 - 2.5x - 0.25$

50. Write an equation for a parabola whose vertex is at $(6, 1)$ and for which $a = 9$. $y = 9(x - 6)^2 + 1$

51. $f(x) = -2(x - 2)^2 + 9$

51. Write the equation of a parabola with position 2 units to the right and 9 units above the parabola with equation $f(x) = -2x^2$.

Lesson 6–6 Analyzing Graphs of Quadratic Functions   **373**

Assignment Guide

Core: 19–55 odd, 57–66
Enriched: 18–52 even, 53–66

For **Extra Practice,** see p. 890.

The red A, B, and C flags, printed only in the Teacher's Wraparound Edition, indicate the level of difficulty of the exercises.

Additional Answers

18. $(-3, 1)$, $x = -3$, up
19. $(-11, -6)$, $x = -11$, down
20. $(2, -2)$, $x = 2$, down
21. $\left(\frac{1}{2}, \frac{1}{4}\right)$, $x = \frac{1}{2}$, up
22. $f(x) = (x + 3)^2 - 12$; $(-3, -12)$, $x = -3$, up
23. $f(x) = -(x + 2)^2 + 12$; $(-2, 12)$, $x = -2$, down
24. $f(x) = 4(x + 3)^2 - 36$; $(-3, -36)$, $x = -3$, up
25. $f(x) = -6(x - 2)^2 + 24$; $(2, 24)$, $x = 2$, down
26. $f(x) = 3(x - 3)^2 - 16$; $(3, -16)$, $x = 3$, up
27. $f(x) = -2(x + 5)^2$; $(-5, 0)$, $x = -5$, down
28. $f(x) = -\frac{1}{2}(x - 5)^2 - 1$; $(5, -1)$, $x = 5$, down
29. $f(x) = \frac{1}{3}(x - 6)^2 + 3$; $(6, 3)$, $x = 6$, up

Study Guide Masters, p. 45

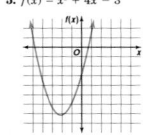
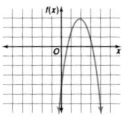

Additional Answers

52a. $y = -1.58x^2 + 21.30x + 37.23$

54.

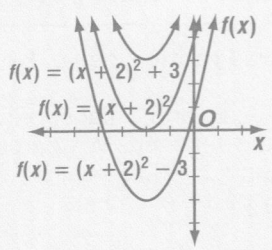

$f(x) = (x + 2)^2 + 3$
$f(x) = (x + 2)^2$
$f(x) = (x + 2)^2 - 3$

The first equation has 0 real roots, the second equation has 1 real root, and the third equation has 2 real roots.

55c.

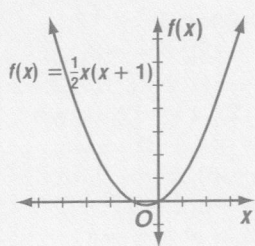

$f(x) = \frac{1}{2}x(x + 1)$

56c.

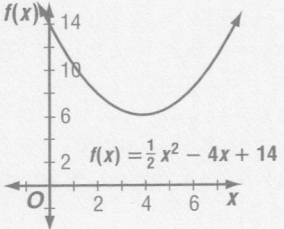

$f(x) = \frac{1}{2}x^2 - 4x + 14$

Practice Masters, p. 45

  NAME_____ DATE_____
Practice   Student Edition
                                     Pages 367–375

Analyzing Graphs of Quadratic Functions

Write each equation in the form $f(x) = a(x − h)^2 + k$. Then name the vertex, axis of symmetry, and direction of opening for the graph of each quadratic function.

1. $f(x) = -6x^2$
   $f(x) = -6x^2$; (0, 0);
   $x = 0$; down

2. $y = -2x^2 - 16x - 32$
   $f(x) = -2(x + 4)^2$; (-4, 0);
   $x = -4$; down

3. $h(x) = \frac{2}{3}x^2 + 4x + 6$
   $f(x) = \frac{2}{3}(x + 3)^2$; (-3, 0);
   $x = -3$; up

4. $y = 2x^2 + 16x + 29$
   $f(x) = 2(x + 4)^2 - 3$;
   (-4, -3); $x = -4$; up

5. $g(x) = -9x^2 + 12x - 4$
   $g(x) = -9\left(x - \frac{2}{3}\right)^2$; $\left(\frac{2}{3}, 0\right)$;
   $x = \frac{2}{3}$; down

6. $y = -3x^2 + 6x - 5$
   $f(x) = -3(x - 1)^2 - 2$;
   (1, -2); $x = 1$; down

Write the equation of the parabola that passes through the given points.

7. (0, 1), (2, -1), (1, 3)
   $f(x) = -3x^2 + 5x + 1$

8. (0, 0), (2, 3), (-1, 4)
   $f(x) = \frac{11}{6}x^2 - \frac{13}{6}x$

Graph each function.

9. $f(x) = -2x^2 + 1$

10. $f(x) = -3x^2 + 6x - 5$

Graphing Calculators

52. A recent article in *USA Today* listed the average high temperatures for Death Valley, California, the hottest place in the United States. **a. See margin.**

Month	Temperature (°F)
January	65
February	73
March	81
April	88
May	100
June	110
July	116
August	113
September	106
October	91
November	75
December	66

Average High Temperatures for Death Valley

   a. Use a graphing calculator to model the data at the right. Find a quadratic equation whose graph best fits the data.

   b. Do you think the graph of the equation fits the data? Justify your answer.

   c. How would you expect a graph representing the average low temperatures to compare with the graph you found above? **See students' wo**

52b. See students' work.

53. $h = -\frac{b}{2a}$,

$k = \frac{4ac - b^2}{4a}$ or $c - \frac{b^2}{4a}$

Critical Thinking

53. Given $f(x) = ax^2 + bx + c$ with $a \neq 0$, complete the square and rewrite the equation in the form $f(x) = a(x - h)^2 + k$. State an expression for h and k in terms of a, b, and c.

54. Sketch the family of graphs $y = (x + 2)^2 + 3$, $y = (x + 2)^2$, and $y = (x + 2)^2 - 3$. Fully describe the nature of the graphs and the roots of each equation. **See margin.**

Applications and Problem Solving

55. **Number Theory** *Triangular numbers* are numbers that can be represented by a triangular array of m dots, with n dots on each side.

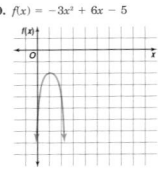

$n = 1$ $n = 2$ $n = 3$ $n = 4$
$m = 1$ $m = 3$ $m = 6$ $m = 10$

55a. Since the domain is the number of dots on a side, it is the set of integers greater than 0. Likewise, since the range is the total number of dots, it is also the set of integers greater than 0.

55b. $f(x) = \frac{1}{2}x(x + 1)$

55c. 0; See margin for graph.

   a. The relationship between the number of dots on each side and the total number of dots can be modeled by a quadratic function. Identify a reasonable domain and range for this function.

   b. Write the quadratic function.

   c. Graph the function. What is the least triangular number?

56. **Entertainment** Did you know that Tarzan has been featured in 43 movies? The story of the man who swings through the trees has fascinated us for years. Suppose Tarzan is in a tree 14 meters above the ground and he decides to use a vine to swing to another tree. One second after he begins his swing, he is 10.5 meters above the ground. Three seconds after he begins his swing, he is 6.5 meters above the ground.

56a. (0, 14), (1, 10.5), (3, 6.5)

56b. $f(x) = \frac{1}{2}x^2 - 4x + 14$

   a. Write three ordered pairs to represent the situation.

   b. Write an equation for the parabola that passes through these points.

   c. Sketch the graph of the parabola. **See margin.**

   d. It seems that Tarzan gets pretty close to the ground as he swings through the trees. How close does he actually get? **6 meters**

Extension

Reasoning Describe the graph of $f(x) = ax^2 + bx + \frac{b^2}{4a}$, where $a \neq 0$.

A parabola is in the form $f(x) = a\left(x + \frac{b}{2a}\right)^2$. The vertex is $\left(-\frac{b}{2a}, 0\right)$. The axis of symmetry is $x = \frac{-b}{2a}$. The graph opens upward if $a > 0$ and downward if $a < 0$. The graph is tangent to the x-axis.

Teaching Tip In Exercise 56,

Tarzan's swing may actually follow a circular path. However, a parabola is a close approximation of the swing.

58. $\dfrac{2 \pm 3i}{2}$

60. If x is your number, you can write the expression $\dfrac{3x + (x + 8)}{(x + 2)}$, which equals 4.

57. Horticulture Helene Jonson has a rectangular garden 25 feet by 50 feet. She wants to increase the garden on all sides by an equal amount. If the area of the garden will be increased by 400 square feet, by how much will each dimension be increased? (Lesson 6–5) **5 ft**

58. Solve $4x^2 - 8x + 13 = 0$ by using the quadratic formula. (Lesson 6–4)

59. Graph $h(x) = x^2 - 2x + 5$. Name the vertex and the axis of symmetry. (Lesson 6–1) **(1, 4), $x = 1$; See margin for graph.**

60. Entertainment A magician asked a member of his audience to choose any number. He said, "Multiply your number by 3. Add the sum of your number and 8 to that result. Now divide by the sum of your number and 2." The magician announced the final answer without asking the original number. What was the final answer and how did he know what it was? (Lesson 5–3) **4**

61. Simplify $(-x + 4)(-2 - 3x)$. (Lesson 5–2) $3x^2 - 10x - 8$

62. Find $\begin{bmatrix} -6 & 3 \\ 4 & 7 \end{bmatrix} \cdot \begin{bmatrix} 2 & -5 \\ -3 & 6 \end{bmatrix}$. (Lesson 4–3) $\begin{bmatrix} -21 & 48 \\ -13 & 22 \end{bmatrix}$

63. Find $-2\begin{bmatrix} -3 & 0 & 12 \\ -7 & \frac{1}{3} & 4 \end{bmatrix}$. (Lesson 4–1) $\begin{bmatrix} 6 & 0 & -24 \\ 14 & -\frac{2}{3} & -8 \end{bmatrix}$

64. Solve the system of equations. (Lesson 3–7) $(-7, 3, 6)$

$x + 2y - z = -7$

$3x + y + z = -12$

$4z = 24$

65. Refer to the graph at the right. The slope of $\overleftrightarrow{AB}$ is $\frac{4}{3}$. Line $\overleftrightarrow{EF}$ is perpendicular to $\overleftrightarrow{AB}$ and has a y-intercept of -2. Write the equation of $\overleftrightarrow{EF}$. (Lesson 2–4) $3x + 4y = -8$

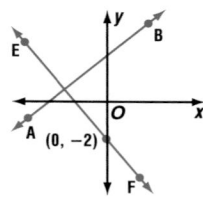

66. Solve $23x - 7 > 62$. (Lesson 1–6) $\{x \mid x > 3\}$

WORKING ON THE
In·ves·ti·ga·tion

Refer to the Investigation on pages 328–329.

the River Canyon Bridge

The formula for a parabolic curve whose vertex lies along the y-axis is $ax^2 + y = b$, where b represents the y-coordinate of the vertex.

1 Knowing the value of b, how might you determine the value of a for a particular bridge design? Describe your method for finding a.

2 Depending on the arch of the bridge, the value of a varies. For the bridges you might consider,

the value of a must be within certain ranges. Describe possible values for a and justify your answer.

3 Determine the values of a and b for each of your designs and for the design proposed by the consultant in the Investigation in Lesson 6–1. With this information, write an equation for the parabolic curve of the arch in each design.

Add the results of your work to your Investigation Folder.

Lesson 6–6 Analyzing Graphs of Quadratic Functions **375**

In·ves·ti·ga·tion

Working on the Investigation

The Investigation on pages 328–329 is designed to be a long-term project that is completed over several days or weeks. Encourage students to keep their materials in their Investigation Folder as they work on the Investigation.

---

4 ASSESS

Closing Activity
Modeling Have students draw four parabolas that have the same vertex, while two open downward and two open upward. Make sure students can tell you the equation of each graph.

Additional Answer
59.

$h(x) = x^2 - 2x + 5$, vertex (1, 4)

Enrichment Masters, p. 45

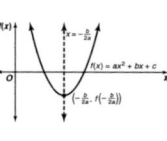

6-6 Enrichment NAME_____ DATE_____ Student Edition Pages 367–375

Finding the Axis of Symmetry of a Parabola

As you know, if $f(x) = ax^2 + bx + c$ is a quadratic function, the values of x that make $f(x)$ equal to zero are

$$\frac{-b + \sqrt{b^2 - 4ac}}{2a} \text{ and } \frac{-b - \sqrt{b^2 - 4ac}}{2a}.$$

The average of these two number values is $-\frac{b}{2a}$. The function $f(x)$ has its maximum or minimum value when $x = -\frac{b}{2a}$. Since the axis of symmetry of the graph of $f(x)$ passes through the point where the maximum or minimum occurs, the axis of symmetry has the equation $x = -\frac{b}{2a}$.

Example: Find the vertex and axis of symmetry for $f(x) = 5x^2 + 10x - 7$.

Use $x = -\frac{b}{2a}$.

$x = -\frac{10}{2(5)} = -1$ The x-coordinate of the vertex is -1.

Substitute $x = -1$ in $f(x) = 5x^2 + 10x - 7$.

$f(-1) = 5(-1)^2 + 10(-1) - 7 = -12$

The vertex is $(-1, -12)$.

The axis of symmetry is $x = -\frac{b}{2a}$, or $x = -1$.

Find the vertex and axis of symmetry for the graph of each function using $x = -\frac{b}{2a}$.

1. $f(x) = x^2 - 4x - 8$ $(2, -12); x = 2$
2. $g(x) = -4x^2 - 8x + 3$ $(-1, 7); x = -1$
3. $y = -x^2 + 8x + 3$ $(4, 19); x = 4$
4. $f(x) = 2x^2 + 6x + 5$ $\left(-\frac{3}{2}, \frac{1}{2}\right); x = -\frac{3}{2}$
5. $A(x) = x^2 + 12x + 36$ $(-6, 0); x = -6$
6. $k(x) = -2x^2 + 2x - 6$ $\left(\frac{1}{2}, -5\frac{1}{2}\right); x = \frac{1}{2}$

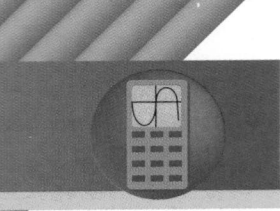

6–7A Graphing Technology
Quadratic Inequalities

A Preview of Lesson 6–7

Objective
Use a graphing calculator to graph and solve quadratic inequalities.

Recommended Time
25 minutes

Instructional Resources
Graphing Calculator Masters, pp. 39 and 40

These masters provide keystroking instruction for this lesson for the TI-81 and Casio graphing calculators.

1 FOCUS

Motivating the Lesson
Remind students that if *a* in $ax^2 + bx + c$ is positive, the parabola opens up and if *a* is negative, the parabola opens down. An estimate of the maximum or minimum will help students select an appropriate viewing window.

2 TEACH

Teaching Tip Point out that if one point above the parabola satisfies the inequality, then all points above the parabola satisfy it. If one point below the parabola satisfies the inequality, all points below it satisfy the inequality.

TEKS 2.a., 8.a., 8.d.

To graph quadratic inequalities in two variables, we will use a procedure similar to that discussed in Lesson 2-7A on graphing linear inequalities. We will utilize the SHADE(feature found in the DRAW menu.

Example   Graph $y \leq 0.5x^2 + x - 3$ in the standard viewing window.

You will recall that you must enter two functions when graphing an inequality in two variables. The calculator shades between the designated functions. The first function entered is the lower boundary of the region to be shaded and the second function is the upper boundary of the region.

Since the inequality asks for all points such that *y is less than or equal to* $0.5x^2 + x - 3$, we will shade below the parabola. The lower boundary will be $y = -10$, and the upper boundary will be $y = 0.5x^2 + x - 3$.

Before you begin, clear any functions stored in the Y = list. Then clear the DRAW menu by pressing [2nd] [DRAW] [ENTER] [ENTER] [CLEAR].

Make sure Ymin is greater than or equal to −10.

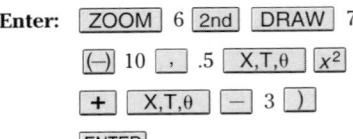

Enter: [ZOOM] 6 [2nd] [DRAW] 7
[(−)] 10 [,] .5 [X,T,θ] [x²]
[+] [X,T,θ] [−] 3 [)]
[ENTER]

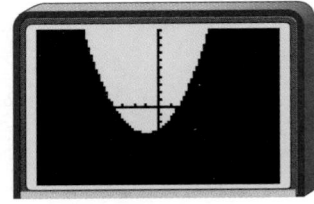

To graph an inequality that has a > or ≥ sign, the function itself will be the lower boundary.

Example   Graph $y \geq x^2 - 4x + 1$ in the standard viewing window.

Since the inequality asks for all points such that *y is greater than or equal to* $x^2 - 4x + 1$, we will shade above the parabola. The lower boundary will be $x^2 - 4x + 1$, and the upper boundary will be $y = 10$. *Be sure to clear the DRAW menu first.*

Make sure Ymax is less than or equal to 10.

Enter: [ZOOM] 6 [2nd] [DRAW] 7
[X,T,θ] [x²] [−] 4 [X,T,θ]
[+] 1 [,] 10 [)] [ENTER]

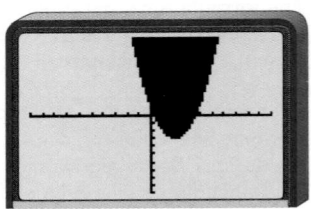

Sometimes you will want to be able to trace the graphs drawn or use other graphing features of the calculator. This often occurs when solving inequalities in one variable. In this case, equations should be entered in the $Y =$ list.

Example ③ **Solve $2x^2 + 3x - 4 < 0$ to the nearest hundredth using a graphing calculator.**

Begin by obtaining a graph of $y = 2x^2 + 3x - 4$. We are interested in determining values for x so that $2x^2 + 3x - 4$ is less than 0. So, we look for points where the y value is less than 0, or where the graph falls below the x-axis.

Graphing calculators cannot show dashed lines for inequalities involving less than or greater than signs.

Enter: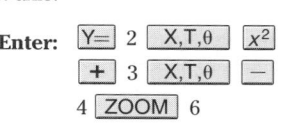

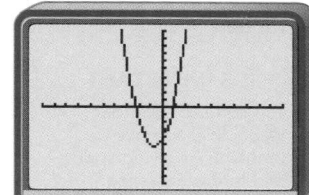

Zooming in on the x-intercepts, we find that $2x^2 + 3x - 4 < 0$ when $-2.35 < x < 0.85$.

EXERCISES

1–6. See margin.

Use a graphing calculator to graph each inequality.

1. $y \geq x^2 + 11x - 3$
2. $y \leq -0.5x^2 + 9$
3. $y \leq 1.2x^2 + 15x$
4. $y \geq 6x^2 - 15x + 7$
5. $y > -x^2 + 6x + 8$
6. $y > -4x^2 - 3x - 6$

Use a graphing calculator to solve each inequality to the nearest hundredth. 7–12. See margin.

7. $x^2 + 4x - 21 > 0$
8. $2x^2 - 4x + 1 \leq 0$
9. $x(2x + 1) \geq 0$
10. $x^2 - 3 > 0$
11. $x^2 - 9x < 4$
12. $0.5x^2 > 1.8x$

13. **Geometry** A length of a rectangle is 4 inches longer than the width. Find the possible dimensions of the rectangle if the area must be at least 28 square inches.
$w \geq 3.66, \ell \geq 7.66$

---

3 PRACTICE/APPLY

Assignment Guide

Core: 1–13
Enriched: 1–13

4 ASSESS

Observing students working with technology is an excellent method of assessment.

Additional Answers

1.
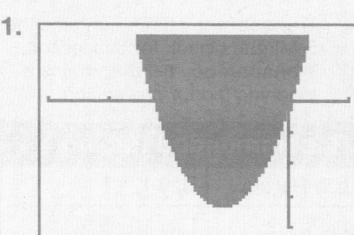

2.
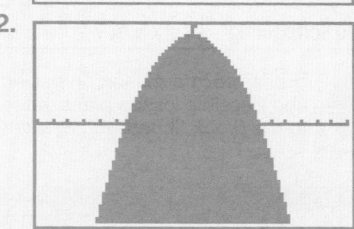

3.
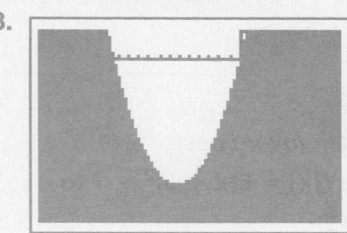

4.
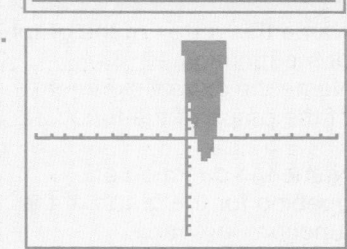

5.
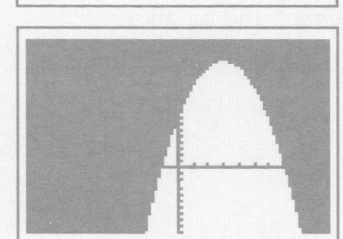

Using Technology

This lesson offers an excellent opportunity for using technology in your algebra classroom. For more information on using technology, see *Graphing Calculators in the Mathematics Classroom*, one of the titles in the Glencoe Mathematics Professional Series.

6.

7. $\{x \mid x < -7 \text{ or } x > 3\}$
8. $\{x \mid 0.29 \leq x \leq 1.71\}$
9. $\{x \mid x \leq -0.50 \text{ or } x \geq 0\}$
10. $\{x \mid x < -1.73 \text{ or } x > 1.73\}$
11. $\{x \mid -0.42 < x < 9.42\}$
12. $\{x \mid x < 0 \text{ or } x > 3.6\}$

NCTM Standards: 1–5

Instructional Resources

- Study Guide Master 6-7
- Practice Master 6-7
- Enrichment Master 6-7
- Assessment and Evaluation Masters, p. 157
- Real-World Applications, 18
- Tech Prep Applications Masters, p. 12

 Transparency 6-7A contains the 5-Minute Check for this lesson; **Transparency 6-7B** contains a teaching aid for this lesson.

Recommended Pacing

Standard Pacing	Day 12 of 17
Honors Pacing	Day 10 of 14
Block Scheduling*	Day 5 of 7

 *For more information on pacing and possible lesson plans, refer to the *Block Scheduling Booklet*.

1 FOCUS

 ### 5-Minute Check
(over Lesson 6-6)

Use $f(x) = 5(x + 3)^2 - 1$ to solve.

1. Name the vertex of the graph of the function. $(-3, -1)$
2. Name the axis of symmetry of the graph of the function. $x = -3$
3. Name the direction of opening for the graph of the function. **upward**
4. Graph the function.

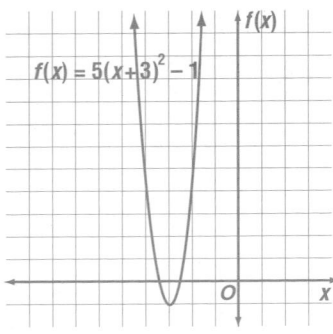

$f(x) = 5(x+3)^2 - 1$

6-7

Graphing and Solving Quadratic Inequalities

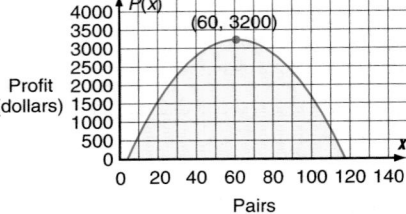

What YOU'LL LEARN

- To graph quadratic inequalities, and
- to solve quadratic inequalities in one variable.

Why IT'S IMPORTANT

You can use quadratic inequalities to solve problems involving sports and forensic science.

LOOK BACK

You can refer to Lesson 2-7 to review linear inequalities.

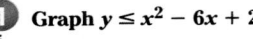 **APPLICATION**

Business

Athletic Advantage, Inc. makes athletic shoes for aerobics and running. According to recent sales figures, their profit $P(x)$ on x pairs of shoes can be found by the inequality $P(x) \leq -x^2 + 120x - 400$. The relation is an inequality because the wholesale price is lower for large orders.

The graph of this inequality is the part of the plane enclosed by the parabola whose equation is $P(x) = -x^2 + 120x - 400$. The parabola is the **boundary** of each region. Points on the parabola represent the profit if all the shoes are sold at the list price. Points in the interior of the curve represent profits if some of the shoes are sold at a discount.

You can graph **quadratic inequalities** using the same techniques you used to graph linear inequalities.

1. Graph the boundary. Determine if it should be solid or dashed.
2. Test a point in each region.
3. Shade the region whose ordered pair results in a true inequality.

Example 1 **Graph $y \leq x^2 - 6x + 2$.**

The boundary will be the graph of $y = -x^2 - 6x + 2$.

$y = -x^2 - 6x + 2$
$= -(x^2 + 6x) + 2$
$= -(x^2 + 6x + 9) + 2 + 9$ *Complete the square.*
$= -(x + 3)^2 + 11$

The boundary is a parabola that opens downward with its vertex at $(-3, 11)$. The boundary is included in the graph, so it should be solid. Test points not on the parabola to see whether points inside or outside the parabola belong to the graph.

Region inside parabola

Test $(-1, 0)$: $y \leq -x^2 - 6x + 2$
$0 \overset{?}{\leq} -(-1)^2 - 6(-1) + 2$
$0 \leq -1 + 6 + 2$
$0 \leq 7$ true

The point at $(-1, 0)$ does belong.

Region outside parabola

Test $(0, 5)$: $y \leq -x^2 - 6x + 2$
$5 \overset{?}{\leq} -(0)^2 - 6(0) + 2$
$5 \leq 0 - 0 + 2$
$5 \leq 2$ false

The point at $(0, 5)$ does not belong.

Since $(-1, 0)$ is part of the solution and $(0, 5)$ is not, shade the region inside the parabola.

$y = -x^2 - 6x + 2$

378 Chapter 6 *Exploring Quadratic Functions and Inequalities*

TEKS 2.a., 6.a., 6.b., 8.a., 8.d.

Example 2

INTEGRATION

Geometry

A rectangle is 6 centimeters longer than it is wide. Find the possible dimensions if the area of the rectangle is more than 216 square centimeters.

Draw a diagram of the rectangle. Let w represent the width of the rectangle. Then $w + 6$ represents the length and $w(w + 6)$ represents the area.

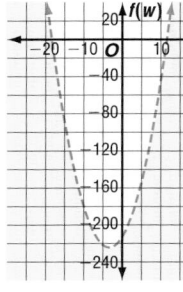

w cm

$(w + 6)$ cm

$$w(w + 6) > 216$$
$$w^2 + 6w > 216$$
$$w^2 + 6w - 216 > 0$$
$$(w^2 + 6w + 9) - 216 - 9 > 0 \qquad \textit{Complete the square.}$$
$$(w + 3)^2 - 225 > 0$$

The boundary of the graph of this inequality is a parabola that opens upward with its vertex at $(-3, -225)$. Test a point not on the boundary to determine which region should be included in the graph.

Test (0, 0): $\quad w(w + 6) > 216$
$$0(0 + 6) > 216$$
$$0 > 216 \quad \text{false}$$

Since the graph of $(0, 0)$ is inside the parabola and it does not satisfy the inequality, the region outside the parabola is included in the graph.

The points on the graph outside Quadrant I should be disregarded since length cannot be negative. So the width of the rectangle should be greater than 12 cm and the length should be greater than 18 cm.

Just as you solve a quadratic equation by graphing its related quadratic function, you can solve a quadratic inequality in one variable by graphing its related quadratic inequality in two variables. For example, to solve $0 > x^2 - 6x - 7$, you can graph $y > x^2 - 6x - 7$. The solutions of the inequality are each point on the x-axis that is included in the graph.

You can also solve quadratic inequalities algebraically.

Example 3

Solve $0 > x^2 - 6x - 7$.

Method 1: Graphing
Graph the related inequality $y > x^2 - 6x - 7$. First complete the square and rewrite the inequality as $y > (x - 3)^2 - 16$. The graph of the $y = (x - 3)^2 - 16$ is a parabola that opens upward with its vertex at $(3, -16)$.

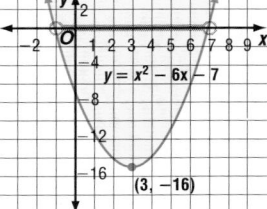

$y = x^2 - 6x - 7$

$(3, -16)$

The points on the x-axis that satisfy $y > x^2 - 6x - 7$ are solutions to the inequality $0 > x^2 - 6x - 7$. Those solutions are $\{x \mid -1 < x < 7\}$.

(continued on the next page)

Motivating the Lesson

Questioning Have students draw a graph for $y > x^2 + 2x + 1$.

1 What would be the first step in graphing the inequality?
2. How can you decide which side of the boundary to shade without testing a point? Can you decide without testing a point?
3. Which point would be the easiest to test in each case? Why?

2 TEACH

Teaching Tip Emphasize that the process for graphing quadratic inequalities is the same process as the process for graphing linear inequalities.

Teaching Tip Ask students if the graph in Example 1 has a maximum or minimum. How can they determine this from the graph?

In-Class Examples

For Example 1
Graph $y < x^2 + 3x - 4$.

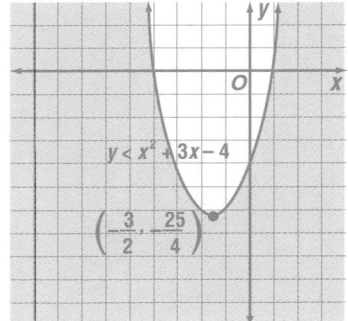

$y < x^2 + 3x - 4$

$\left(-\dfrac{3}{2}, -\dfrac{25}{4}\right)$

For Example 2
A flower bed is 3 feet longer than it is wide. Find the possible dimensions if the area of the flower bed is at least 40 square feet. **length $\geq$ 8 ft; width 3 ft less than the length**

For Example 3
Solve $0 < x^2 - 3x - 10$.
$\{x \mid -2 < x < 5\}$

In-Class Example

For Example 4
Solve $x^2 + 9x + 14 < 0$.
$\{x \mid -7 < x < -2\}$

Teaching Tip Caution students that $0 < ab$ does not mean $0 < a$ or $0 < b$. Students may be tempted to apply this faulty reasoning in Example 4.

Method 2:   Factoring

$0 < x^2 - 6x - 7$
$0 < (x - 7)(x + 1)$

Since the product of two numbers is negative if one number is negative and one is positive, we can write the following.

$(x - 7)$ is negative and $(x + 1)$ is positive:	**or**	$(x - 7)$ is positive and $(x + 1)$ is negative:

$x - 7 < 0$ and $x + 1 > 0$ $x - 7 > 0$ and $x + 1 < 0$
$\quad x < 7 \qquad\qquad x > -1$ $\quad x > 7 \qquad\qquad x < -1$
$\qquad\quad -1 < x < 7$

The graphs of $x > 7$ and $x < -1$ never intersect, so $x > 7$ __and__ $x < -1$ can never be true.

You can also solve quadratic inequalities by using three test points.

Example ④ **Solve $x^2 - x - 12 > 0$.**

First solve the equation $x^2 - x - 12 = 0$ by factoring.

$x^2 - x - 12 = 0$
$(x - 4)(x + 3) = 0$
$x - 4 = 0$ or $x + 3 = 0$
$\quad x = 4 \qquad\qquad x = -3$

The points at 4 and -3 separate the x-axis into three regions: $x < -3$, $-3 < x < 4$, and $x > 4$.

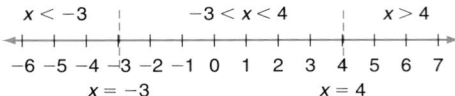

Choose a value from each part and substitute it into $x^2 - x - 12 > 0$. Determine if the result is true or false. Organize your results in a table.

Part of x-axis	Chosen point, x	$x^2 - x - 12$	Is $x^2 - x - 12 > 0$?
$x < -3$	-5	$(-5)^2 - (-5) - 12 = 18$	yes
$-3 < x < 4$	1	$(1)^2 - 1 - 12 = -12$	no
$x > 4$	6	$(6)^2 - 6 - 12 = 18$	yes

The solution set to the inequality $x^2 - x - 12 > 0$ is $\{x \mid x < -3 \text{ or } x > 4\}$, as shown on the number line below.

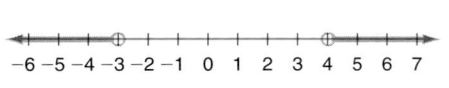

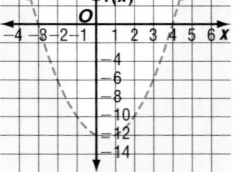

The graph of the related inequality $x^2 - x - 12 > y$, shown above, confirms the solutions.

Classroom Vignette

"Example 4 can also be solved using a sign graph for each factor and then for the product. This method is fairly easy for students to understand. $(x + 3)(x - 4) > 0$

sign of $(x - 4)$ in the intervals

sign of $(x + 3)$ in the intervals

sign of the product of the factors in the intervals

The solution is greater than 0, so it occurs where the sign of the product is positive."

Nancy Barr
Monterey High School
Lubbock, Texas

Communicating Mathematics

Study the lesson. Then complete the following. 1–4. See margin.

1. The equation $y = x^2 - 5x + 4$ is graphed at the right.
   a. If you were to graph the inequality $y \geq x^2 - 5x + 4$, would you include the region inside or outside of the parabola? Explain why.
   b. What are the solutions of $0 \geq x^2 - 5x + 4$?

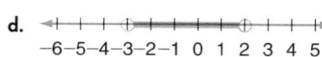

$y = x^2 - 5x + 4$

2. **State** the points you would test to find the solution to $(x - 8)(x + 2) > 0$.

3. **Rewrite** Example 2 so that the region inside the parabola will be included in the graph instead of the region outside the parabola.

4. **Explain** how factoring can help determine the solution set of a quadratic inequality.

MATH JOURNAL

5. **Write** what you have learned about graphing quadratic inequalities. Explain why some boundaries are contained in the region and some are not included. How can you determine if the graph is a region inside or outside of the boundary? See students' work.

Guided Practice

Determine if the ordered pair is a solution of the given inequality.

6. $y < 2x^2 + 4$, $(3, 5)$ yes
7. $y \geq x^2 - 9$, $(0, 5)$ yes
8. $y \leq 2x^2 - 3x + 1$, $(-1, 4)$ yes
9. $y > 5x^2 + 2x - 3$, $(-1, -1)$ no

10. Which of the following is the graph of the solution set for $x^2 < x + 6$? b
   a. [number line: -5-4-3-2-1 0 1 2 3 4 5 6]
   b. [number line: -5-4-3-2-1 0 1 2 3 4 5 6]
   c. [number line: -6-5-4-3-2-1 0 1 2 3 4 5]
   d. [number line: -6-5-4-3-2-1 0 1 2 3 4 5]

Graph each inequality. 11–14. See Solutions Manual.

11. $y \leq x^2 + 4x + 4$
12. $y > x^2 - 36$
13. $y \leq -x^2 + 7x + 8$
14. $y \leq -x^2 - 3x + 10$

Use the related graph of each inequality to write its solutions.

15. $x^2 - 4x - 12 \leq 0$

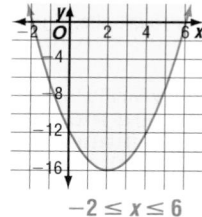

$-2 \leq x \leq 6$

16. $x^2 - 9 > 0$

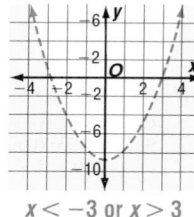

$x < -3$ or $x > 3$

17. $-x^2 + 10x - 25 \geq 0$

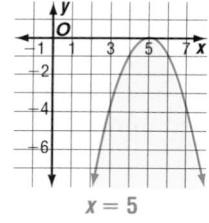

$x = 5$

Solve each inequality.

18. $(x + 11)(x - 3) > 0$
19. $(n - 2.5)(n + 3.8) \geq 0$
20. $x^2 - 4x \leq 0$ $\{x \mid 0 \leq x \leq 4\}$
21. $b^2 \geq 10b - 25$ {all reals}
22. $2x^2 > 25$
23. $2b^2 - b < 6$

18. $\{x \mid x < -11$ or $x > 3\}$
19. $\{n \mid n \geq 2.5$ or $n \leq -3.8\}$
22. $\left\{x \mid x > \dfrac{5\sqrt{2}}{2}\right.$ or $\left. x < \dfrac{-5\sqrt{2}}{2}\right\}$
23. $\left\{b \mid -\dfrac{3}{2} < b < 2\right\}$

Lesson 6-7 Graphing and Solving Quadratic Inequalities **381**

Reteaching

Using Alternative Methods An alternate strategy to solve polynomial inequalities is to use a sign chart of the factors and product.

Example: $(x - 7)(x + 2) > 0$

value of x	-6	-4	-2	0	1	3	5	7	9
sign of $(x-7)$	–	–	–	–	–	–	–	0	+
sign of $(x+2)$	–	–	0	+	+	+	+	+	+
sign of product	+	+	0	–	–	–	–	0	+
points on graph where product is > 0		-6 -4 -2 0 1 3 5 7 9							

---

3 PRACTICE/APPLY

Check for Understanding

Exercises 1–25 are designed to help you assess your students' understanding through reading, writing, speaking, and modeling. You should work through Exercises 1–5 with your students and then monitor their work on Exercises 6–25.

Additional Answers

1a. Inside; the test point of (3, 0), which is inside the graph, gives a true statement.

1b. $\{x \mid 1 \leq x \leq 4\}$

2. Sample answer: any number less than −2, one between −2 and 8, and one greater than 8

3. Find the possible dimensions if the area of the rectangle is less than 216 square centimeters.

4. Sample answer: Factoring gives test points that can be used to find the solution.

Study Guide Masters, p. 46

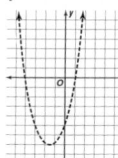

6-7

NAME_____ DATE_____

Study Guide

Student Edition Pages 378–383

Graphing and Solving Quadratic Inequalities

The graph of the equation $y = x^2 + 3x - 4$ separates the plane into two regions. The graph of $y > x^2 + 3x - 4$ is the region *inside* the parabola. The graph of $y < x^2 + 3x - 4$ is the region *outside* the parabola. The parabola itself is called the boundary of each region. To show that the parabola is part of a graphed inequality, we use a smooth, solid curve. When it is *not* part of the graph, we use a curve made up of dashes.

Methods of Solving Quadratic Inequalities	
1. Graphing Method	Using the quadratic function and letting $y = 0$, find the zeros of the function (x-intercepts).
2. Algebraic Method	Write the inequality with 0 on one side and a quadratic expression on the other. Next factor the quadratic expression in one variable. Recall that the product of two factors is positive only when both factors are positive or both factors are negative. Also recall that the product of two factors is negative only if one factor is positive and the other is negative.

Graph each inequality.

1. $y \geq x^2 + 5x + 4$

2. $y > -2x^2 + 4x$

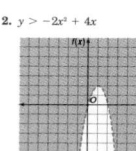

Solve each inequality.

3. $x^2 + 2x < 0$
   $\{x \mid -2 < x < 0\}$

4. $x^2 - 16 < 0$
   $\{x \mid -4 < x < 4\}$

5. $0 < 6x - x^2 - 5$
   $\{x \mid 1 < x < 5\}$

6. $c^2 \leq 4$
   $\{c \mid -2 \leq c \leq 2\}$

7. $2m^2 - m < 1$
   $\{m \mid -\frac{1}{2} < m < 1\}$

8. $y^2 < -8$
   $\emptyset$

Assignment Guide

Core: 27–55 odd, 56, 57, 59, 61–71

Enriched: 26–54 even, 56–71

For **Extra Practice,** see p. 891.

The red A, B, and C flags, printed only in the Teacher's Wraparound Edition, indicate the level of difficulty of the exercises.

Additional Answers

51. $\left\{ t \mid \dfrac{-1-\sqrt{10}}{2} \le t \le \dfrac{-1+\sqrt{10}}{2} \right\}$

52. $\{x \mid -4 < x < 1 \text{ or } x > 3\}$

53. $\{x \mid x \le -4 \text{ or } -2 \le x \le 8\}$

54. $\{x \mid x < -5 \text{ or } -1 < x < 4 \text{ or } x > 6\}$

55. $\{x \mid x \le -3 \text{ or } -2 \le x \le 1 \text{ or } x \ge 2\}$

56.
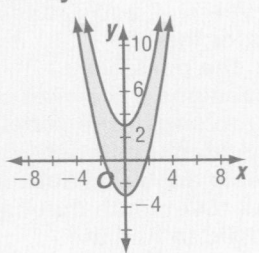

Practice Masters, p. 46

NAME_____ DATE _____

Student Edition
Pages 378–383

Practice

Graphing and Solving Quadratic Inequalities

Graph each inequality.

1. $y \le x^2 + 4$

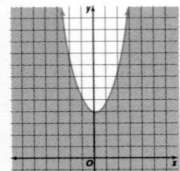

2. $y < x^2 + 8x - 5$

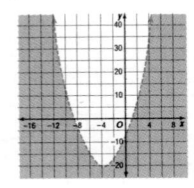

Solve each inequality.

3. $x^2 - x - 20 > 0$
  $\{x \mid x > 5 \text{ or } x < -4\}$

4. $x^2 - 10x + 16 < 0$
  $\{x \mid 2 < x < 8\}$

5. $5x^2 + 10 \ge 27x$
  $\{x \mid x \ge 5 \text{ or } x \le \frac{2}{5}\}$

6. $9x^2 + 31x + 12 \le 0$
  $\{x \mid -3 \le x \le -\frac{4}{9}\}$

7. $9z \le 12z^2$
  $\{z \mid z \ge \frac{3}{4} \text{ or } z \le 0\}$

8. $4x^2 + 4x + 1 > 0$
  $\{x \mid x \ne -\frac{1}{2}\}$

9. $x^2 + 64 \ge 16x$
  all reals

10. $x^2 + \frac{4}{3}x + \frac{4}{9} < 0$
  no solution

11. $9x^2 + 6x + 1 \le 0$
  $\{-\frac{1}{3}\}$

12. $2x^2 + 3 \le 8x$
  $\{x \mid \frac{4-\sqrt{10}}{2} \le x \le \frac{4+\sqrt{10}}{2}\}$

24. The graph of the quadratic function $y = x^2 - 4x - 5$ is shown at the right.

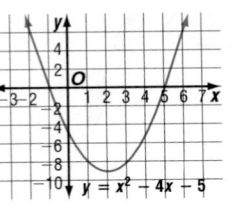

  a. What are the solutions of the equation $0 = x^2 - 4x - 5$? $x = -1, 5$
  b. What are the solutions of the inequality $0 \le x^2 - 4x - 5$? $x \le -1 \text{ or } x \ge 5$
  c. What are the solutions of the inequality $0 \ge x^2 - 4x - 5$? $-1 \le x \le 5$

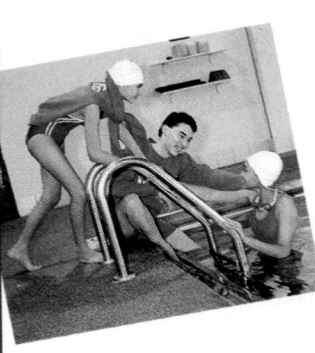

25. **Recreation**   The YMCA has a 40-foot by 60-foot area in which to build a swimming pool. The pool will be surrounded by a concrete sidewalk of uniform width. What could the width of the sidewalk surrounding the pool be if organizers want the pool to be at least 1500 square feet? $0 \le w \le 5$

EXERCISES

Practice

Graph each inequality.   26–37. See Solutions Manual.

Ⓐ
26. $y \ge x^2 - 10x + 25$
27. $y < x^2 - 16$
28. $y \le x^2 - x - 20$
29. $y \ge x^2 + 3x - 18$
30. $y \ge 2x^2 + x - 3$
31. $y \le -x^2 + 5x + 6$
32. $y > 2x^2 + 3x - 5$
33. $y < -x^2 + 13x - 36$
34. $y \le -x^2 + 5x + 14$
35. $y \ge -3x^2 + 5x + 2$
36. $y > 4x^2 - 8x + 3$
37. $y \le -x^2 - 7x + 10$

Solve each inequality.   51–55. See margin.

38. $\{x \mid -7 < x < 4\}$

39. $\{x \mid x < -3 \text{ or } x > 6\}$

40. $\{m \mid m > 2 \text{ or } m < -3\}$

41. $\{q \mid q \le -6 \text{ or } q \ge 4\}$

Ⓑ

43. $\left\{ x \mid -4 \le x \le \frac{3}{2} \right\}$

44. $\left\{ s \mid s < -\frac{4}{3} \text{ or } s > \frac{1}{2} \right\}$

46. $\left\{ v \mid v = \frac{1}{3} \right\}$

47. $\left\{ g \mid -\frac{1}{2} < g < 3 \right\}$

Ⓒ

38. $(x - 4)(x + 7) < 0$
39. $x^2 - 3x - 18 > 0$
40. $m^2 + m - 6 > 0$
41. $q^2 + 2q \ge 24$
42. $p^2 - 4p \le 5$ $\{p \mid -1 \le p \le 5\}$
43. $2x^2 + 5x - 12 \le 0$
44. $6s^2 + 5s > 4$
45. $w^2 \ge 2w$ $\{w \mid w \le 0 \text{ or } w \ge 2\}$
46. $9v^2 - 6v + 1 \le 0$
47. $2g^2 - 5g - 3 < 0$
48. $f^2 + 12f + 36 < 0$ $\varnothing$
49. $n^2 \le 3$ $\{n \mid -\sqrt{3} \le n \le \sqrt{3}\}$
50. $8d + d^2 \ge -16$ {all reals}
51. $4t^2 - 9 \le -4t$
52. $(x - 1)(x + 4)(x - 3) > 0$
53. $(x + 2)(x + 4)(x - 8) \le 0$
54. $(x + 5)(x + 1)(x - 4)(x - 6) > 0$
55. $(x - 2)(x + 2)(x - 1)(x + 3) \ge 0$

Critical Thinking

56. Find the intersection of the graphs of $y \ge x^2 - 3$ and $y \le x^2 + 3$. See margin.

Applications and Problem Solving

57. **Sports**   The instant replay facility at the Superdome in New Orleans, Louisiana, was moved because it was hit by a high punt kicked by Oakland Raider Ray Guy. The original position of the facility was 90 feet above the playing field. Cody, a high school punter, can kick a football with an initial velocity of 65 feet per second. The height of the football t seconds after he kicks it is found by the function $h(t) = -16t^2 + 65t$.

57a. No, the maximum height of the ball is 66 feet.

  a. If Cody were to have kicked a football in the Superdome before the instant replay facility was moved, would he have been able to hit it? Explain.
  b. What was the speed of the ball Ray Guy punted if it hit the facility in 3 seconds?   78 feet per second

Additional Answer

60a.

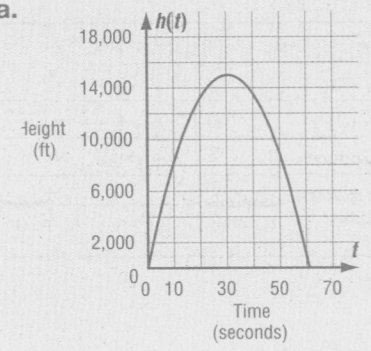

58. **Geometry** A rectangle is 5 centimeters longer than it is wide. Find the possible dimensions if the area of the rectangle is more than 104 square centimeters.

59. **Business** Lorena drives a shuttle bus for the National Park Service. The charge is $1.00 to ride from the parking lot to one of the major attractions in the National Park. During the winter months, about 100 people ride the bus each day. It is estimated that 5 more passengers will ride per day for each $0.20 decrease in fare. The cost of operating the shuttle bus is $66 per day. How many $0.20 decreases in fare could be made and still allow the shuttle bus to make a profit? **1 decrease of $0.20**

60. **Forensic Science** Police are investigating the shooting of a police helicopter. They found a weapon at the scene of the crime that has a suspect's fingerprints on it. Forensic experts have deduced that the weapon is capable of firing with an initial velocity of 980 feet per second. So the height of the bullet t seconds after firing is found by the function $h(t) = -16t^2 + 980t$.

58. The width is greater than 8 centimeters. The length is greater than 13 centimeters.

   a. Draw a graph to represent this situation. **See margin.**
   b. If the helicopter was flying at an altitude of 7000 feet at the time it was shot, is it possible that this weapon shot the helicopter? Explain your answer. **Yes, the bullet reaches a height of approximately 15,006 feet.**

Mixed Review

61a. $f(x) = -\frac{2}{315}$ $(x - 315)^2 + 630$

61. **Architecture** The Gateway Arch of the Jefferson National Expansion Memorial in St. Louis is shaped like a parabola whose equation is $f(x) = \frac{1}{315}(-2x^2 + 1260x)$. (Lesson 6–6)

   a. Write the equation in the form $y = a(x - h)^2 + k$.
   b. If the bases of the arch are 630 feet apart, how tall is the arch? **630 ft**
   c. Graph $f(x)$. Compare your graph to a photo of the Gateway Arch. Describe what you observe. **See margin.**

62. Find a value k such that 1 is a root of $x^2 + kx - 5 = 0$. (Lesson 6–5) **4**

63. $\frac{6 \pm \sqrt{146}}{11}$

63. Solve $11m^2 - 12m = 10$ by using the quadratic formula. (Lesson 6–4)

64. $\frac{-b \pm \sqrt{b^2 - 4c}}{2}$

64. Solve $x^2 + bx + c = 0$ by completing the square. (Lesson 6–3)

65. Simplify $(5 + \sqrt{8})^2$. (Lesson 5–6) **$33 + 20\sqrt{2}$**

66. $y^3 + 1 - \frac{4}{y + 3}$

66. Divide $(y^4 + 3y^3 + y - 1) \div (y + 3)$ by using synthetic division. (Lesson 5–3)

67. Simplify $(5a - 3)(1 - 3a)$. (Lesson 5–2) **$-15a^2 + 14a - 3$**

68. Find the inverse of $\begin{bmatrix} 4 & 6 \\ -1 & 5 \end{bmatrix}$. (Lesson 4–4) $\frac{1}{26}\begin{bmatrix} 5 & -6 \\ 1 & 4 \end{bmatrix}$

69. Solve the system of equations using Cramer's rule. (Lesson 3–3) **$(4, -2)$**
   $6x + 7y = 10$
   $3x - 4y = 20$

70. $m = \frac{3}{2}$, $x: \frac{8}{3}$, $y: -4$

70. Graph $3x - 2y = 8$. Find the slope, the x-intercept, and the y-intercept. (Lesson 2–3)

71. Solve $4x - (2x + 8) + 3x = 5x - 8$. (Lesson 1–4) **all reals**

Lesson 6–7 Graphing and Solving Quadratic Inequalities **383**

Extension

Reasoning Solve $(x - 1)^3(x + 1) \le (x - 1)(x + 1)^3$.
$\{ |x| \ -1 \le x \le 0 \text{ or } x \ge 1 \}$

Tech Prep

Forensic Investigator Students who are interested in forensic science may wish to do further research on the information provided in Exercise 60 and explore the potential growth of this career. For more information on tech prep, see the *Teacher's Handbook*.

---

4 ASSESS

Closing Activity

Writing Have students write a paragraph to explain how to solve a quadratic inequality. Have them determine whether the region above or below the graph of $y > ax^2$ should be shaded.
If $a > 0$, the inside is shaded.
If $a < 0$, the outside is shaded.

Chapter 6, Quiz C (Lessons 6-6 and 6-7), is available in the *Assessment and Evaluation Masters*, p. 157.

Additional Answer

61c.
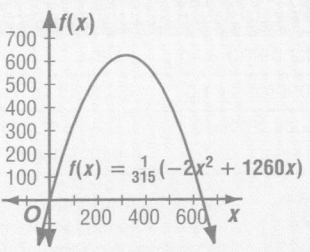

See students' work for comparisons.

Enrichment Masters, p. 46

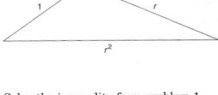

6-7 Enrichment
Student Edition Pages 378–383

Quadratic Relationships in Triangles

The **triangle inequality** states that the sum of any two sides of a triangle is greater than the length of the third side. For the triangle in the diagram, the sides measure 1, r, and r^2.

Solve each problem.

1. Write an equality comparing the sum of the two shorter sides to the longest side. $1 + r > r^2$
2. Solve the inequality from problem 1 for r. $r < \frac{1 + \sqrt{5}}{2}$
3. Compare the sum of the two longer sides to the shortest side. $r^2 + r > 1$
4. Solve the inequality in problem 3 for r. $r > \frac{-1 + \sqrt{5}}{2}$
5. What possible values can r have in the triangle? $\frac{-1 + \sqrt{5}}{2} < r < \frac{1 + \sqrt{5}}{2}$
6. A golden rectangle has sides r and 1 that satisfy the proportion $r : 1 = (r + 1) : r$. Solve for r and relate this answer to the results of problem 5. $r = \frac{1 + \sqrt{5}}{2}$; the range of values for r in the triangle lies between $\frac{1 + \sqrt{5}}{2}$ and $\frac{-1 + \sqrt{5}}{2}$.

Look for the so-called golden ratio, $\frac{1 + \sqrt{5}}{2}$, to appear as you solve the following problems. Triangles ABC and A'B'C' are both isosceles, with $AY = XB$ and $A'Y' = X'B'$.

7. Write a proportion showing that the sides of triangles ABC and ACX form equal ratios. Use b for the length of the long side of triangle ABC. $\frac{a}{b} = \frac{b - a}{a}$

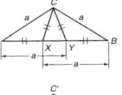

8. Let the ratio $b:a$ equal r. Solve the proportion in problem 7 for r. $\frac{a}{b} = \frac{b}{a} - 1$, so $\frac{1}{r} = r - 1$; $r = \frac{1 + \sqrt{5}}{2}$

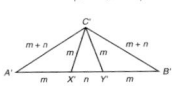

9. Show that triangles ABC and $A'B'C'$ are similar by finding the ratio r' in the triangle $A'B'C'$. $\frac{m + n}{2m + n} = \frac{m}{m + n}$; for $r' = \frac{2m + n}{m + n}$, $\frac{m + n}{2m + n} = \frac{2m + n}{m + n} - \frac{m + n}{m + n}$ and $\frac{1}{r'} = r' - 1$. So, $r = r'$ and the figures are similar.

Chapter 6 **383**

NCTM Standards 1–4, 10

Instructional Resources

- Study Guide Master 6-8
- Practice Master 6-8
- Enrichment Master 6-8
- Science and Math Lab Manual, pp. 87–90

 Transparency 6-8A contains the 5-Minute Check for this lesson; **Transparency 6-8B** contains a teaching aid for this lesson.

Recommended Pacing	
Standard Pacing	Days 13 & 14 of 17
Honors Pacing	Day 11 of 14
Block Scheduling*	Day 6 of 7 (along with Lesson 6-9)

 *For more information on pacing and possible lesson plans, refer to the *Block Scheduling Booklet*.

1 FOCUS

 5-Minute Check
(over Lesson 6-7)

1. Graph $y \leq -0.5x^2 - 2x - 2$.

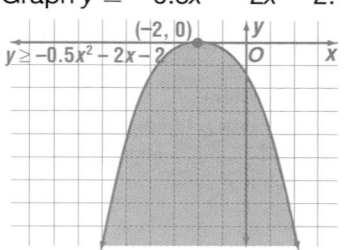

Solve each inequality.
2. $(x - 10)(x + 1) < 0$
   $\{x \mid -1 < x < 10\}$
3. $x^2 + 8x - 9 > 0$
   $\{x \mid x < -9 \text{ or } x > 1\}$
4. $x^2 - 20x \geq -100$
   $\{$all real numbers$\}$

Integration: Statistics
Standard Deviation

 **APPLICATION**
Lifestyles

 **What YOU'LL LEARN**
- To find the standard deviation for a set of data.

Why IT'S IMPORTANT
Standard deviation can help you describe the spread of a set of data.

As we grow older, we spend our money in different ways. The chart below shows the money people spend on selected items each year in the United States for several age groups.

Item/Age Group	under 25	35–44	55–64	75 and up
Food at home	$1410	$3324	$2639	$1864
Food away from home	1140	2129	1634	703
Own a home	421	4549	3433	1587
Rent a home	2465	1733	751	1091
Footwear	158	315	206	153
Vehicle purchases	1916	2682	2215	528
Public transportation	181	340	378	156
Health insurance	144	583	749	1152
Electronic items	393	503	404	163
Pets and toys	139	577	442	172
Education	871	507	465	38

It appears that expenses for people in the under 25 category vary less than those in the 35–44 category. But how can you tell for sure?

Sometimes you need information about the spread, or variation, of data. A measure of variation called the **standard deviation** measures how much each value in a set of data differs from the mean. The symbol commonly used for standard deviation is SD or the lowercase Greek letter sigma, σ. The mean is usually labeled with the symbol $\bar{x}$ read "x bar."

To find the standard deviation of a set of data, follow these steps.
1. Find the mean, $\bar{x}$.
2. Find the difference between each value in the set of data and the mean.
3. Square each difference.
4. Find the mean of the squares.
5. Take the principal square root of this mean.

Standard Deviation	From a set of data with n values, where x_1 represents the first term and x_n represents the nth term, if $\bar{x}$ represents the mean, then the standard deviation can be found as follows. $$\text{SD or } \sigma_{\bar{x}} = \sqrt{\frac{(x_1 - \bar{x})^2 + (x_2 - \bar{x})^2 + \dots + (x_n - \bar{x})^2}{n}}$$

To find the standard deviation of the data given for people under 25 and people aged 35-44, first find the mean of the expenses for both groups.

under 25:

$$\overline{x} = \frac{1410 + 1140 + 421 + 2465 + 158 + 1916 + 181 + 144 + 393 + 139 + 871}{11}$$

$$\approx 839.82$$

35–44:

$$\overline{x} = \frac{3324 + 2129 + 4549 + 1733 + 315 + 2682 + 340 + 583 + 503 + 577 + 507}{11}$$

$$\approx 1567.45$$

Then substitute each mean into the formula for standard deviation.

under 25:

$$SD = \sqrt{\frac{(1410 - 839.82)^2 + (1140 - 839.82)^2 + \ldots + (139 - 839.82)^2 + (871 - 839.82)^2}{11}}$$

$$= \sqrt{\frac{(570.18)^2 + (300.18)^2 + \ldots + (-700.82)^2 + (31.18)^2}{11}}$$

$$\approx 766.63$$

35–44:

$$SD = \sqrt{\frac{(3324 - 1567.45)^2 + (2129 - 1567.45)^2 + \ldots + (577 - 1567.45)^2 + (507 - 1567.45)^2}{11}}$$

$$= \sqrt{\frac{(1756.55)^2 + (561.55)^2 + \ldots + (990.45)^2 + (1060.45)^2}{11}}$$

$$\approx 1376.53$$

The standard deviation for the under–25 age group is about $766.63. The standard deviation for the 35–44 age group is about $1376.53. So the expenses for the under–25 age group are closer to their mean than those in the 35–44 age group, and they vary less.

Most of the members of a set of data are within 1 standard deviation from the mean. The under 25 age group expenses can be broken down as shown in the diagram below.

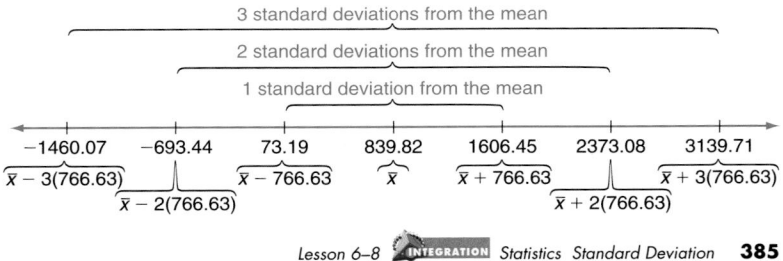

Hands-On Activity Draw or post a bull's-eye target on the chalkboard. Blindfold several student volunteers. One at a time, have each of these students make a mark where he or she thinks the bull's-eye is located. Elicit student responses regarding the variance of the marks from the bull's-eye. Ask if the location of the other rings gives us a reference for determining variance.

GLENCOE *Technology*

Interactive Mathematics Tools Software

This multimedia software provides an interactive lesson by helping students observe the relationship between the standard deviation and the mean of a set of data by manipulating the data on a histogram. A **Computer Journal** gives students an opportunity to write about what they have learned.
For Windows & Macintosh

For Example 1

A study about the effects of different fertilizers on tree growth is being conducted. The trees planted last year are now 59 cm, 59 cm, 65 cm, 54 cm, 60 cm, 58 cm, 50 cm, and 66 cm tall. Calculate the mean height of the trees and find the standard deviation of the data.

60 cm, ≈ 3.61

Standard deviation is often used to classify large sets of data.

Example ❶

APPLICATION

Sports

A day at a National Football League game for a family of four represents the most expensive outing in professional sports, averaging $184.19, according to *Team Marketing Report*, a Chicago-based newsletter. The cost in 1994 represented a 6.2% increase over the previous year, when the average was $173.37. The average ticket price for each NFL team for 1994 is listed in the table below.

Team	1994 Average	Team	1994 Average
Arizona	$27.69	LA Rams	$29.13
Atlanta	27.00	Miami	29.65
Buffalo	33.73	Minnesota	29.79
Chicago	32.23	New England	34.34
Cincinnati	28.43	New Orleans	26.71
Cleveland	27.27	N.Y. Giants	35.59
Dallas	32.85	N.Y. Jets	25.00
Denver	32.34	Philadelphia	40.00
Detroit	30.04	Pittsburgh	30.99
Green Bay	26.13	San Diego	33.86
Houston	31.88	San Francisco	39.75
Indianapolis	26.48	Seattle	28.00
Kansas City	29.16	Tampa Bay	29.57
LA Raiders	31.32	Washington	35.70

a. **Estimate the mean ticket price.**

b. **Calculate the mean ticket price.**

c. **Find the standard deviation of the data.**

a. A quick glance at the data shows that about half of the data are above $30 and about half are below $30. So the mean will probably be about $30.

b. You can use a scientific calculator to perform the arithmetic necessary to calculate the mean and the standard deviation. However, your calculator may also have a statistics mode that simplifies this calculation. Press ⃞MODE and ⃞STAT to put your calculator in statistics mode. *The statistics functions are often second key functions.*

Enter the data by entering each number and then pressing the ⃞Σ+ key. This provides a cumulative sum.

Enter: 27.69 ⃞Σ+ 27 ⃞Σ+ 33.73 ⃞Σ+ ... 35.70 ⃞Σ+

Wrong entries can be deleted by using ⃞Σ−.

The display will show how many numbers were entered.

To find the mean, press ⃞2nd ⃞x̄ . *30.87964286*

The mean is $30.88.

c. Find the standard deviation.

Enter: ⃞2nd ⃞σn *3.793188898*

The standard deviation is $3.79.

When studying the standard deviation of a set of data, it is very important to keep the mean in mind. For example, suppose a company that sells video equipment found that the standard deviation of monthly prices of their equipment over the last two years was $50. If the mean of the prices over those two years was $200, then the standard deviation indicates a significant variation or change. However, if the mean was $900, then the standard deviation of $50 indicates a much smaller variation.

You can use a graphing calculator to calculate the mean and standard deviation of a set of data.

EXPLORATION

GRAPHING CALCULATORS

First, enter the elements of the data set into the calculator as follows. Press the STAT key and choose 1: Edit. Now you may enter the data into List 1 (L1). After each entry, press ENTER. After the data entry is complete, press STAT and choose CALC. Then choose 1: 1-Var Stats. Enter the name of the list that you are using. Press 2nd L1. Then press ENTER. $\bar{x}$ and σ_x will be displayed on the screen along with other information.

Your Turn

a. Solve Example 1 by using a graphing calculator.

b. Practice the above process until you can explain it to a friend in your own words. Then write out your explanation.

c. Find the mean and standard deviation of the set of data below by using a graphing calculator.

16, 42, 21, 19, 18.6, 41, 37, 24, 29.2, 26, 35

Example Corn production (in billions of bushels) in the United States from 1984 to 1993 is shown in the graph below. Find the mean corn production and the standard deviation of the data.

APPLICATION
Agriculture

U.S. Corn Production in Billions of Bushels

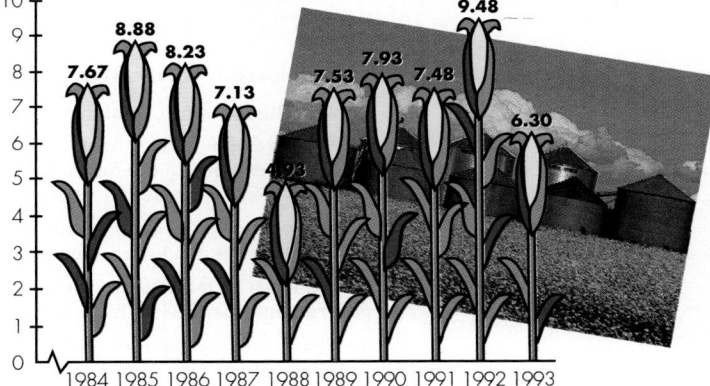

Source: *Weatherwise Magazine, 1994*

(continued on the next page)

Lesson 6–8 **INTEGRATION** *Statistics Standard Deviation* **387**

EXPLORATION

Have students apply the same approach to Example 1.

In-Class Example

For Example 2

The average prices received by U.S. farmers for a dozen eggs during the years 1984 through 1992 are as follows: 72¢, 57¢, 61¢, 55¢, 53¢, 69¢, 71¢, 68¢, 58¢. Find the mean and standard deviation. **62.67¢, 6.9¢**

Teaching Tip You may want to have students plot the data for Example 2 on box-and-whisker plots and relate the standard deviation to the length of the whiskers.

Check for Understanding

Exercises 1–9 are designed to help you assess your students' understanding through reading, writing, speaking, and modeling. You should work through Exercises 1–4 with your students and then monitor their work on Exercises 5–9.

We can use a spreadsheet to do the calculations as follows.

Year	Billions of Bushels	Difference from Mean	Square of Difference
1984	7.67	0.114	0.012996
1985	8.88	1.324	1.752976
1986	8.23	0.674	0.454276
1987	7.13	−0.426	0.181476
1988	4.93	−2.626	6.895876
1989	7.53	−0.026	0.000676
1990	7.93	0.374	0.139876
1991	7.48	−0.076	0.005776
1992	9.48	1.924	3.701776
1993	6.30	−1.256	1.577536
Total	75.56	Total	14.72324
Mean = B12/10		7.556	
SD = $\sqrt{(D12/10)}$		1.2133935	

The mean is 7.556, and the standard deviation is 1.213.

So the average corn production in the 10-year period 1984–1993 was 7.556 billion bushels. In most of the years, the production was between 7.556 − 1.213 or 6.343 billion and 7.556 + 1.213 or 8.769 billion bushels.

CHECK FOR UNDERSTANDING

Communicating Mathematics

Study the lesson. Then complete the following.   1. See students' work.

1. **Explain** the meaning of standard deviation in your own words.

2. Refer to Example 1. Find the number of ticket prices that were within one standard deviation of the mean. What percent of the total number of ticket prices is this?   **19 ticket prices; 68%**

3. Answers will vary. Sample answer: floods along Mississippi River

3. **Write** a paragraph describing the events that occurred in the summer of 1993 that resulted in lower than usual corn production in the United States.

4. Over the last 12 months, the mean number of full-time employees in a city government was 2783 with a standard deviation of 43.

   a. What does this say about the variation of the number of employees in the government?   **Variation is small.**

   b. If the standard deviation were 430, what would that say about the variation of the number of employees?   **Variation is large.**

388   *Chapter 6   Exploring Quadratic Functions and Inequalities*

Reteaching

Using Graphics Graph several examples from the exercises. For each graph, show the points on the horizontal axis that represent one standard deviation and those that represent two standard deviations. Point out how few data points lie outside these limits.

Find the mean and standard deviation to the nearest hundredth for each set of data.

5. {110, 70, 20, 40, 10}   **50; 36.33**

6. {48, 36, 40, 29, 45, 51, 38, 47, 39, 37}   **41; 6.32**

7. {43, 56, 78, 81, 47, 42, 34, 22, 78, 98, 38, 46, 54, 67, 58, 92, 55}   **58.18; 20.60**

8.

Stem	Leaf
4	3 5 6 8
5	2 4 5 6
6	1 2 4 5 5 6 7 7 7 $5|2 = 5.2$

5.78; 0.83

9. Quality Control   A coffee machine is designed to dispense 250 mL for each cup. The actual measures in milliliters for a sample of 10 cups were 251, 246, 252, 249, 250, 248, 246, 253, 250, and 251.

a. Find the standard deviation of the amounts.   **2.24**

b. Do you think the variation is large or small?   **small**

c. How do you think the variation would change if someone poured each cup of coffee, rather than used a machine?   **Answers will vary.**

EXERCISES

Find the mean and standard deviation to the nearest hundredth for each set of data.   **15. 57.41; 9.11**   **16. 6.55; 0.66**   **17. 3.87; 0.55**

10. {45, 65, 145, 85, 25, 25}   **65; 41.63**

11. {400, 300, 325, 275, 425, 375, 350}   **350; 50**

12. {5, 4, 5, 5, 5, 5, 6, 6, 6, 6, 7, 7, 7, 7, 8, 9}   **6.13; 1.27**

13. {234, 345, 123, 368, 279, 876, 456, 235, 333, 444}   **369.30; 194.14**

14. {13, 14, 15, 16, 17, 18, 19, 20, 21, 23, 67, 56, 34, 99, 44, 55}   **33.19, 23.86**

15.

Stem	Leaf
4	4 5 6 7 7
5	3 5 6 7 8 9
6	7 7 8 9 9 9 $4|5 = 45$

16.

Stem	Leaf
5	7 7 7 8 9
6	3 4 5 5 6 7
7	2 3 4 5 6 $6|3 = 6.3$

18. 60.27; 10.64

17.

Stem	Leaf
3	0 0 1 2 4
•	5 6 6 6 8 9
4	1 1 3 4 4
•	5 5 6 7 $3|4 = 3.4$

18.

Stem	Leaf
4	1 3 9
5	2 3 6 9
6	4 4 5 7 8
7	2 4 7 $5|2 = 52$

19. {76, 78, 89, 90, 34, 56, 50}   **67.57; 19.68**

21. 0; no variation from the mean

20. {321, 322, 323, 324, 325, 326, 327, 328, 329, 330}   **325.50; 2.87**

21. Suppose you have a set of data in which all elements are the same. What is the standard deviation of this data? Explain your answer.

Assignment Guide

Core: 11–25 odd, 26–30
Enriched: 10–20 even, 21–30

For **Extra Practice,** see p. 891.

The red A, B, and C flags, printed only in the Teacher's Wraparound Edition, indicate the level of difficulty of the exercises.

Study Guide Masters, p. 47

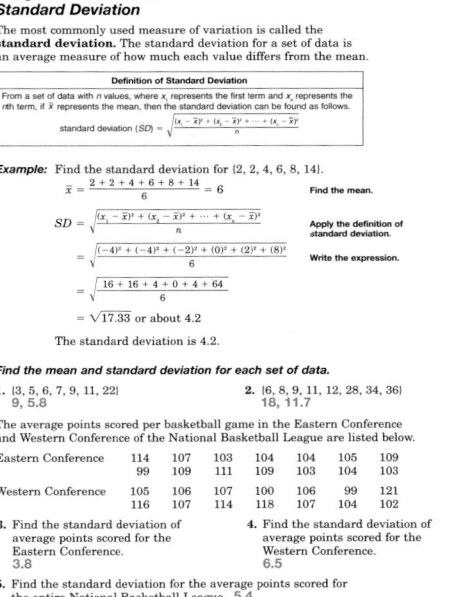

6-8   NAME_____ DATE_____
Study Guide   Student Edition Pages 384–391

Integration: Statistics
Standard Deviation

The most commonly used measure of variation is called the **standard deviation.** The standard deviation for a set of data is an average measure of how much each value differs from the mean.

Definition of Standard Deviation

From a set of data with n values, where x_1 represents the first term and x_n represents the nth term, if $\bar{x}$ represents the mean, then the standard deviation can be found as follows.

$$\text{standard deviation } (SD) = \sqrt{\frac{(x_1 - \bar{x})^2 + (x_2 - \bar{x})^2 + \cdots + (x_n - \bar{x})^2}{n}}$$

Example: Find the standard deviation for {2, 2, 4, 6, 8, 14}.

$$\bar{x} = \frac{2 + 2 + 4 + 6 + 8 + 14}{6} = 6 \qquad \text{Find the mean.}$$

$$SD = \sqrt{\frac{(x_1 - \bar{x})^2 + (x_2 - \bar{x})^2 + \cdots + (x_n - \bar{x})^2}{n}} \qquad \text{Apply the definition of standard deviation.}$$

$$= \sqrt{\frac{(-4)^2 + (-4)^2 + (-2)^2 + (0)^2 + (2)^2 + (8)^2}{6}} \qquad \text{Write the expression.}$$

$$= \sqrt{\frac{16 + 16 + 4 + 0 + 4 + 64}{6}}$$

$$= \sqrt{17.33} \text{ or about } 4.2$$

The standard deviation is 4.2.

Find the mean and standard deviation for each set of data.

1. {3, 5, 6, 7, 9, 11, 22}
9, 5.8

2. {6, 8, 9, 11, 12, 28, 34, 36}
18, 11.7

The average points scored per basketball game in the Eastern Conference and Western Conference of the National Basketball League are listed below.

Eastern Conference	114	107	103	104	104	105	109
	99	109	111	109	103	104	103
Western Conference	105	106	107	100	106	99	121
	116	107	114	118	107	104	102

3. Find the standard deviation of average points scored for the Eastern Conference.
3.8

4. Find the standard deviation of average points scored for the Western Conference.
6.5

5. Find the standard deviation for the average points scored for the entire National Basketball League.   5.4

Closing Activity

Speaking Have each student explain to a partner how he or she would determine the standard deviation of the heights of the students in the class.

Additional Answer

24e. The new standard deviation is the same as the original standard deviation since the prices of all the jeans are lowered by the same amount.

Practice Masters, p. 47

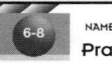

NAME _____ DATE _____

Student Edition
Pages 384–391

6-8

Practice

Integration: Statistics
Standard Deviation

Find the mean and standard deviation to the nearest hundredth for each set of data.

Accept answers reasonably close to those given here. Slight variations can result from differences in calculator models.

1. {3, 5, 2, 6, 5, 9, 5, 2, 8, 6} 5.1, 2.21

2. {6.1, 2.5, 4.8, 3.8, 7.1, 6.1, 5.9} 5.19, 1.47

3. {0.050, 0.048, 0.051, 0.047, 0.048, 0.053, 0.044, 0.048, 0.052, 0.046} 0.05, 0.002950

4. {26, 37, 89, 42, 56, 43, 27, 18, 72, 83} 49.3, 23.53

5. {156, 283, 102, 127, 136, 145, 154, 129, 110, 152, 181, 193} 155.67, 45.88

6. {1246, 8492, 5673, 1491, 2467, 4531, 3798, 1288, 4543, 5896} 3942.5, 2252.58

7.
Stem	Leaf
2	5 6 8
3	0 4
5	3 8
7	2
9	4 7 9

56, 28.68

8.
Stem	Leaf
2	00 46
3	23 79 86
4	51 80
5	32 49 97

414.3, 124.77

9.
Stem	Leaf
42	1 3 7 9
48	2 4
50	9
52	0 3 5

474.3, 42.60

10.
Stem	Leaf
11	00 23 59
12	27 63
13	42 57
14	14 98 99

1298.2, 139.53

390 Chapter 6

Applications and Problem Solving

22. Sports The weights, in pounds, of the starting players for the basketball teams of three high schools are given below.

Jonesboro: 150, 145, 120, 168, 175
Hillview: 124, 157, 195, 205, 177
Murrayville: 146, 155, 176, 186, 199

a. Find the standard deviation for the weights of the players on the Jonesboro basketball team. **19.29**

b. Find the standard deviation for the weights of the players on the Hillview basketball team. **28.88**

c. Find the standard deviation for the weights of the players on the Murrayville basketball team. **19.52**

d. Which team has the most variation in weight? How do you think this variation will impact their play? **Hillview; See students' work.**

23. Airlines The on-time performance of the nation's nine largest airlines declined in 1993, although complaints also dropped.

Airline	Percent of flights arriving on time	Complaints per 100,000 fliers
Southwest	88.7%	0.29
Northwest	84.8	0.68
TWA	83.0	1.09
United	80.5	0.64
American	80.0	0.38
Continental	77.9	1.93
Delta	75.4	0.45
USAir	73.5	0.83
America West	71.9	0.74

a. What are the mean and standard deviation of percent of flights arriving on time? **79.52; 5.16**

23b. **0.78; 0.47**

b. What are the mean and standard deviation of the complaints?

c. Write a paragraph that explains the relationship between on-time flights and passenger complaints. **See students' work.**

24. Sales In 1991, *Zillions* magazine tested jeans for durability and quality in their laboratory. The following table gives the top five lab test winners for men's and women's jeans along with the price of each pair.

Men's	Price	Women's	Price
Wrangler ProRodeo Cowboy Cut	$20	Sears Jeans That Fit	$19
Wrangler American Hero	$17	Wrangler ProRodeo Cowboy Cut	$26
Levi's 509	$31	Chic Heavenly Blues	$48
Wrangler Rustler	$15	PS Gitano	$21
J. C. Penney Long Haul	$23	Gap Straight Leg	$30

24a. **$21.20, $5.60**

a. Find the mean and standard deviation of the prices of the men's jeans.

b. Find the mean and standard deviation of the prices of the women's jeans. **$28.80, $10.34**

c. Which had the greatest variation in price? **women's jeans**

24d. **See students' work.**

d. Survey 10 students in your school lunchroom and determine the brand of jeans that they wear. Compare your results with the tests above.

e. Suppose during end-of-year clearance sales, the stores lower the prices of all women's jeans by $5. How will the new standard deviation compare with the original standard deviation? Why do you think this occurs? **See margin.**

390 Chapter 6 Exploring Quadratic Functions and Inequalities

25. Food Professionally-trained food testers working for *Zillions* magazine dipped into several brands of potato chips three times a day, four days a week, for five weeks in 1994. The result of their work is listed in the table below.

Very Good	Price per ounce (¢)	Good	Price per ounce (¢)
Lady Lee	14	Ruffles Light	25
Cape Cod	20	Kroger	12
Jays	18	Wise	17
Cape Cod Unsalted	20	Charles Chips	21
Eagle Idaho Russet	23	Pringles Original	21
Albertsons	12	Lay's	21
Ruffles	21	Pringles Light Original	24
Lay's Crunch Taters	23	Golden Flake	17
Vons	13	Pathmark	10
		Michael Season's	28
		Wise Cottage Fries	21
		Pringles Idaho Rippled	22
		Barrell O'Fun	20
		New York Deli	24
		Keebler Ripplin's	19
		O'Boisie's	25
		Lay's Unsalted	21

a. Find the mean and standard deviation of the prices of the chips rated "Very Good." **18.22¢; 3.99¢**

b. Find the mean and standard deviation of the prices of the chips rated "Good." **20.47¢; 4.43¢**

Mixed Review

26. Solve $(3x - 9)(x + 12) < 0$. (Lesson 6–7) $\{x \mid -12 < x < 3\}$

27. Architecture Look at the diagram below of a suspension bridge.

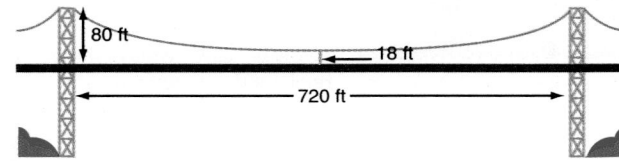

27. 250 ft

The equation $y = 0.00048x^2 + 18$ can be used to describe the cable hanging between the two upright supports, where x represents the horizontal distance along the roadbed from the lowest point of the cable and y represents the distance up from the roadbed. If a vertical cable is to be installed from the roadbed to the hanging cable and is 48 feet long, how far from the lowest point of the hanging cable will it be? (Lesson 6–2)

28. Simplify $(2r^2 + r - 3) \div (2r + 3)$. (Lesson 5-3) $(r - 1)$

29. $\begin{bmatrix} 3 & 4 & \vdots & 22 \\ 7 & -1 & \vdots & 10 \end{bmatrix}$

29. Write an augmented matrix for the system of equations. Then solve. (Lesson 4–7) $(2, 4)$

$$3x + 4y = 22$$
$$7x - y = 10$$

30. Given the function $f(x, y) = 6x - 3y$, find $f(-5, 2)$. (Lesson 3–5) -36

Extension

Communication Have students research standard deviation and use of quality control in production of consumer products. Have them write a short report including several common examples. For example, steel used for a specific purpose should contain a certain amount of carbon. Samples with carbon contents that vary more than a specified standard deviation are rejected.

Enrichment Masters, p. 47

6-8 NAME _____ DATE _____
Enrichment
Student Edition
Pages 384–391

Correlation

There is a useful number, called the **correlation coefficient**, that gives a measure of how well a group of data items is clustered around a line. If the values of y are almost in direct proportion to the values of x, then the data points in a graph will cluster around a line and the correlation coefficient, r, will be close to 1. If the values of y are inversely proportional to x and closely bunched around a line, the correlation coefficient r will be close to -1. If there is no close correlation, $r = 0$.

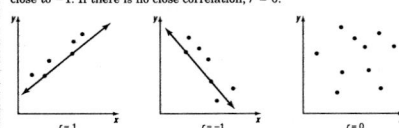

$r = 1$ $r = -1$ $r = 0$

The correlation coefficient is calculated as follows.

$$S_{xx} = \Sigma x^2 - \frac{(\Sigma x)^2}{n}$$

Note: Σx^2 is shorthand for $\sum\limits_{i=1}^{n} x_i^2$.

$$r = \frac{S_{xy}}{\sqrt{S_{xx} \cdot S_{yy}}}$$

$$S_{yy} = \Sigma y^2 - \frac{(\Sigma y)^2}{n}$$

$$S_{xy} = \Sigma xy - \frac{\Sigma x \Sigma y}{n}$$

Use the formula to find the correlation coefficient for the following students scores in math and English.

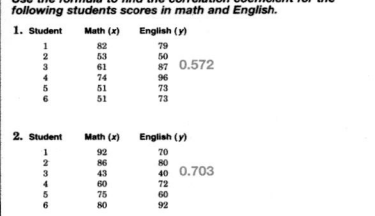

1. | Student | Math (x) | English (y) |
| 1 | 82 | 79 |
| 2 | 53 | 50 |
| 3 | 61 | 87 | 0.572
4	74	96
5	51	73
6	51	73

2. | Student | Math (x) | English (y) |
| 1 | 92 | 70 |
| 2 | 86 | 80 |
| 3 | 43 | 40 | 0.703
4	60	72
5	75	60
6	80	92

NCTM Standards 1–4, 10

Instructional Resources

- Study Guide Master 6-9
- Practice Master 6-9
- Enrichment Master 6-9
- Assessment and Evaluation Masters, p. 157
- Real-World Applications, 19

 Transparency 6-9A contains the 5-Minute Check for this lesson; **Transparency 6-9B** contains a teaching aid for this lesson.

Recommended Pacing	
Standard Pacing	Day 15 of 17
Honors Pacing	Day 12 of 14
Block Scheduling*	Day 6 of 7 (along with Lesson 6-8)

 *For more information on pacing and possible lesson plans, refer to the *Block Scheduling Booklet*.

1 FOCUS

 5-Minute Check
(over Lesson 6-8)

Use the stem-and-leaf plot below to solve each problem.

Monthly Precipitation

Stem	Leaf
2	68
3	00133468
4	22

$2 \mid 8 = 2.8$ inches

1. Find the mean of the data. about 3.4
2. Find the standard deviation of the data. about 0.49

Motivating the Lesson

Questioning Ask students if they have ever had a teacher who graded "on the curve." Ask if students know how the teacher knew how many students got each grade.

6-9

Integration: Statistics
The Normal Distribution

What YOU'LL LEARN

- To solve problems involving normally-distributed data.

Why IT'S IMPORTANT

The normal distribution is used to help analyze and describe data.

APPLICATION
Basketball

In professional basketball, a power forward is responsible for rebounding and scoring close to the basket. So, it makes sense that most power forwards are very tall. Forty NBA power forwards and their heights are listed in the table below.

Name	Height	Name	Height	Name	Height
Barkley	78″	Hill	81″	Perkins	81″
Brickowski	82″	Johnson	79″	Pinckney	81″
Bryant	81″	Jones	80″	Reid	81″
Cage	81″	Laettner	83″	Rodman	80″
Campbell	83″	Long	80″	Smith	82″
Coleman	82″	Lynch	80″	Thorpe	82″
Cummings	81″	Malone	81″	Tisdale	81″
A. Davis	81″	Mason	79″	Vaught	81″
D. Davis	83″	McDaniel	79″	Weatherspoon	78″
Ellis	80″	Mills	82″	Br. Williams	83″
Gilliam	81″	Nance	82″	Bu. Williams	80″
Grant	82″	Oakley	81″	J. Williams	82″
Green	81″	Owens	81″	Willis	84″
Gugliotta	82″				

One way of analyzing data is to consider how frequently each value occurs. The table below shows the frequencies of the heights of the forty basketball players. The graph below visually displays the frequencies of the heights in the table.

Height	Frequency
78″	2
79″	3
80″	6
81″	15
82″	9
83″	4
84″	1

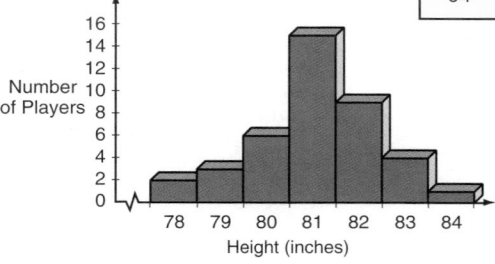

The bar graph shows a **frequency distribution** of the heights. That is, it shows how the heights are spread out over the range from 78 inches to 84 inches. A graph like this one that shows a frequency distribution is called a **histogram**.

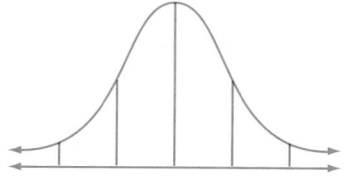

Curves are very useful in displaying information. You used parabolas to represent related data. Curves are also used to show frequency distributions, especially when the distribution contains a large number of values. While the curves may be of any shape, many distributions have graphs shaped like the one at the left. Many distributions with this type of graph are **normal distributions.**

The curve of the graph of a normal distribution is symmetric and is often called a **bell curve.** The shape of the curve indicates that the frequencies in a normal distribution are concentrated around the center portion of the distribution. What does this tell you about the mean?

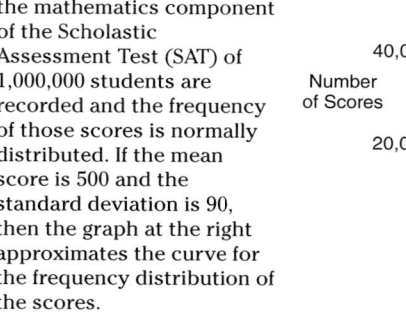

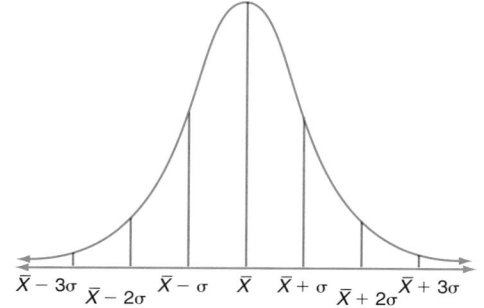

Normal distributions have these properties.

1. The graph is maximized at the mean.
2. The mean, median, and mode are about equal.
3. The data are symmetrical about the mean.
4. About 68% of the values are within one standard deviation from the mean.
5. About 95% of the values are within two standard deviations from the mean.
6. About 99% of the values are within three standard deviations from the mean.

Suppose the scores on the mathematics component of the Scholastic Assessment Test (SAT) of 1,000,000 students are recorded and the frequency of those scores is normally distributed. If the mean score is 500 and the standard deviation is 90, then the graph at the right approximates the curve for the frequency distribution of the scores.

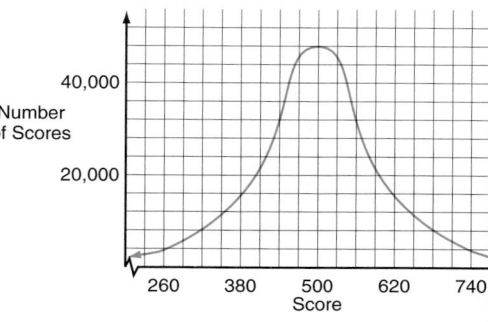

As shown by the graph, the mean is the most frequent score. Of the 1,000,000 students, the following is true.

- About 680,000 scored between 410 and 590 points.
- About 950,000 students scored between 320 and 680 points.
- About 990,000 students scored between 230 and 770 points.

Normal distributions occur quite frequently in real life. In addition to test scores, the lengths of newborn babies, cholesterol levels, the useful life and size of manufactured items, and production levels can be represented by normal distributions. In all of these cases, the number of data items must be large for the distribution to be normal.

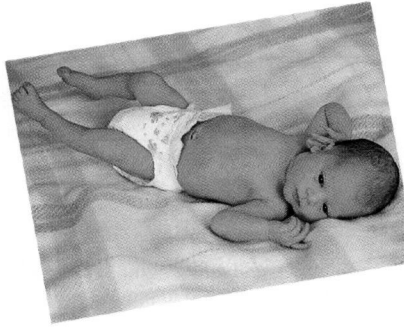

 Alternative Teaching Strategies

Student Diversity Review the vocabulary words from the lesson: *frequency distribution, histogram, normal distribution, bell curve, skewed distribution.* After discussing the types of distributions, sketch several graphs and have students identify the distribution as normal, positively skewed, or negatively skewed.

Teaching Tip If the curve in Example 1 were expressed on a graph, the *x*-coordinate of the maximum point would be the mean of the set of data. The total area under the curve and above the *x*-axis represents the total probability of the distribution, or 1.

In-Class Examples

For Example 1
The monthly incomes of 10,000 workers in Gahanna are distributed normally. Suppose the mean monthly income is $1250 and the standard deviation is $250.

a. How many workers earn more than $1500 per month?
   1600

b. How many workers earn less than $750 per month? 250

c. What percentage of the 10,000 workers earn between $500 and $1750 a month? 97%

d. What percentage of the workers earn less than $1750 a month? 97.5%

For Example 2
A grading scale is set up for 1000 students' test scores. It is assumed that the scores are normally distributed with a mean score of 75 and a standard deviation of 15.

a. How many students will have scores between 45 and 75?
   $1000 \times 47.5\% = 475$

b. If 60 is the lowest passing score, how many students are expected to pass the test?
   $1000(34\% + 50\%) = 840$

 Example **1** The useful lives of 10,000 batteries are normally distributed. The mean useful life is 20 hours, and the standard deviation is 4 hours.
   a. Sketch a normal curve showing the useful life at one, two, and three standard deviations from the mean.
   b. How many batteries will last between 16 and 24 hours?
   c. How many batteries will last less than 12 hours?

a. Draw a normal curve with 20 hours as the mean.
   one standard deviation from the mean: $\overline{x} - 4$ and $\overline{x} + 4$ or 16–24 hours

   two standard deviations from the mean: $\overline{x} - 2(4)$ and $\overline{x} + 2(4)$ or 12–28 hours

   three standard deviations from the mean: $\overline{x} - 3(4)$ and $\overline{x} + 3(4)$ or 8–30 hours

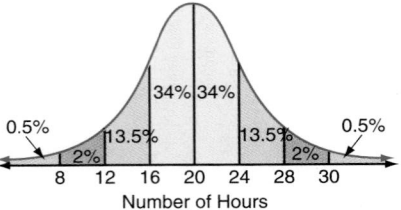

b. The percentage of batteries lasting between 16 and 24 hours is 34% + 34% or 68% of the batteries.
   $10,000 \times 68\% = 6800$ batteries

c. The percentage of batteries lasting less than 12 hours is 0.5% + 2% or 2.5%.
   $10,000 \times 2.5\% = 250$ batteries

You can use normal distributions to estimate the probabilities of certain events occurring.

 Example **2**

APPLICATION
Medicine

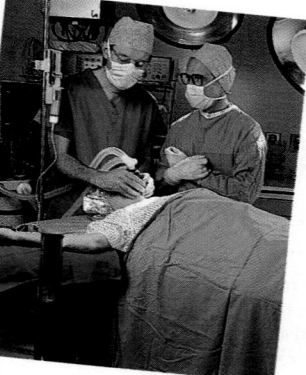

The correct number of milligrams of anesthetic an anesthesiologist must administer to a patient is normally distributed. The mean is 100 milligrams, and the standard deviation is 20 milligrams.
   a. Of a sample of 200 patients, about how many people require more than 120 milligrams of anesthetic for a response?
   b. What is the probability that a patient chosen at random will require between 80 and 120 milligrams?

a. This frequency distribution is shown by the curve below. The percentages represent the percentages of patients requiring the dosage within the given interval.

The percentage of people requiring more than 120 milligrams of anesthetic is 13.5% + 2% + 0.5% or 16%.
   $200 \times 16\% = 32$
So about 32 of the 200 patients require more than 120 milligrams of anesthetic.

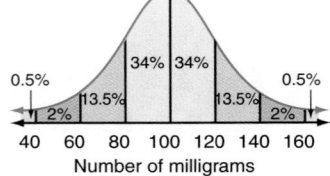

b. The percentage of people requiring between 80 and 120 milligrams of anesthetic is 68%. So the probability that a patient chosen at random will require such amounts of anesthetic is 68%.

 ## Cooperative Learning

Numbered Heads Together Have groups of students draw a normal curve for and solve the following problem.
500 deer were tagged and their heights recorded. If the heights were normally distributed, if the mean height was 4.5 feet, and if the standard deviation was 0.5 feet, how many deer were taller than 5 feet? 80 deer

For more information on the numbered heads together strategy, see *Cooperative Learning in the Mathematics Classroom*, one of the titles in the Glencoe Mathematics Professional Series, pages 30–31.

The histogram at the right shows the number of urban cities in 1990 in the United States for varying population sizes. You can see that the resulting curve displays a **skewed** distribution. A skewed curve that is high at the left and has a tail at the right like this one is *positively skewed*. A skewed curve that is high at the right and has a tail to the left is *negatively skewed*.

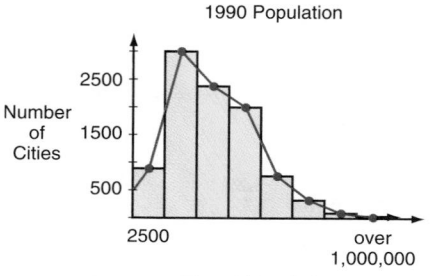

1990 Population

Size of Population

CHECK FOR UNDERSTANDING

Communicating Mathematics

Study the lesson. Then complete the following.   1–3. See margin.

1. **Refer** to the application at the beginning of the lesson. Explain why the heights of the power forwards approximate a normal distribution. Explain why the histogram approximates a normal curve.

2. **Sketch** a negatively skewed graph. Describe a situation in which you would expect data to be distributed this way.

3. **Compare and contrast** the means and standard deviations of the graphs.

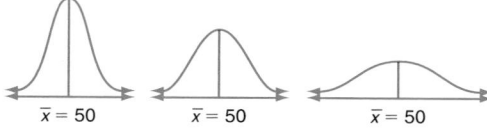

$\bar{x} = 50$ $\bar{x} = 50$ $\bar{x} = 50$

4. Explain why you think that the SAT scores of the students in your class would be skewed or why they would be normal.   **See students' work.**

Guided Practice

5. The table at the right shows female mathematics SAT scores in 1990.

   a. State whether the tables of data would result in a graph that is positively skewed, is negatively skewed, or appears to be normally distributed.   **normally distributed**

   b. Sketch a histogram of the data.

5b. See margin.

Scores	Percent of Females
200–290	5
300–390	18
400–490	26
500–590	26
600–690	18
700–800	7

6. Mrs. Sung gave a test in her trigonometry class. The scores were normally distributed with a mean of 85% and a standard deviation of 3%.

   a. What percentage would you expect to score between 82% and 88%?   **68%**

   b. What percentage would you expect to score between 88% and 91%?

6b. 13.5%

   c. What is the probability that a student chosen at random scored between 79% and 91%?   **95%**

7. **Quality Control**   The useful life of a radial tire is normally distributed with a mean of 30,000 miles and a standard deviation of 5000 miles. The company makes 10,000 tires a month.   a. **6800 tires**

   a. About how many tires will last between 25,000 and 35,000 miles?

   b. About how many tires will last more than 40,000 miles?   **250 tires**

   c. About how many tires will last less than 25,000 miles?   **1600 tires**

   d. What is the probability that if you buy a radial tire at random, it will last between 20,000 and 35,000 miles?   **81.5%**

Lesson 6-9   **INTEGRATION** Statistics The Normal Distribution   **395**

Reteaching ▬▬▬▬

Using Hands-On Activity Give each pair of students a shaker of 20 pennies. Each pair is to record the number of heads obtained in each of 5 throws. Find the standard deviation for the number of heads in 20 coins. How often are these outcomes expected: 5 heads, 2 heads, 0 heads?

5b.

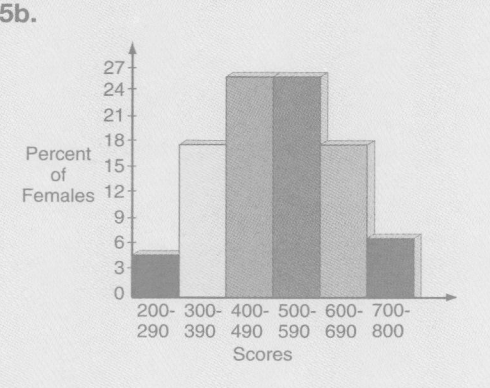

3 PRACTICE/APPLY

Check for Understanding

Exercises 1–7 are designed to help you assess your students' understanding through reading, writing, speaking, and modeling. You should work through Exercises 1–4 with your students and then monitor their work on Exercises 5–7.

Error Analysis

Students sometimes think that a statistical experiment has a "right" answer, but unlikely events do happen. Some discussion of mathematical expectancy and the law of large numbers would be appropriate here.

Additional Answers

1. **Sample answer:** The height of power forwards in basketball will fall within a certain range due to the fact that they have to be a certain height to play that position effectively. For the same reason, a histogram will approximate a normal curve. The mean, median, and mode of the data are very close to each other.

2.

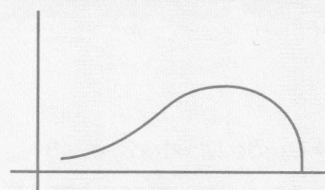

   Sample answer: As age increases, the average yearly income increases.

3. The means of the three graphs are the same, but the standard deviations of the three are different. The first graph has the least standard deviation, the middle graph's standard deviation will be slightly greater, and the last graph will have the greatest standard deviation.

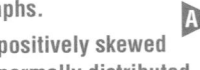
Assignment Guide

Core: 9–13 odd, 14, 15, 17, 19–24
Enriched: 8–14 even, 15–24

For **Extra Practice,** see p. 891.

The red A, B, and C flags, printed only in the Teacher's Wraparound Edition, indicate the level of difficulty of the exercises.

Additional Answers

8.

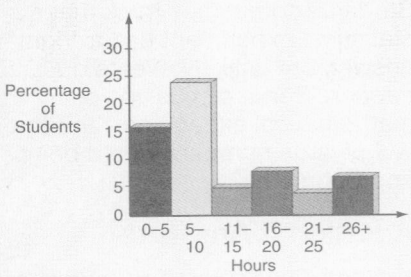

9.

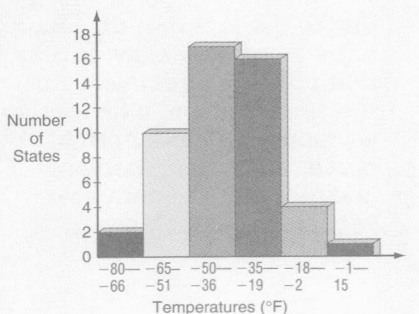

Study Guide Masters, p. 48

NAME_____ DATE_____
Study Guide
Student Edition
Pages 392–398

Integration: Statistics
The Normal Distribution

One way to analyze data is to consider the frequency with which each value occurs. Often this is done on a bar graph called a **histogram.** Often the frequency distributions are shown by curves of many different shapes. A curve that is bell-shaped and symmetric indicates a **normal distribution.**

Normal Distribution Properties

1. The graph is maximized at the mean.
2. About 68% of the items are within one standard deviation from the mean. Of the 68%, 34% are greater than the mean and 34% are less than the mean.
3. About 95% of the items are within two standard deviations from the mean. Of the 95%, 47.5% are greater than the mean and 47.5% are less than the mean.
4. About 99% of the items are within three standard deviations from the mean. Of the 99%, 49.5% are greater than the mean and 49.5% are less than the mean.

The number of hours that students studied for final exams was normally distributed. Of the 200 students surveyed, the mean number of hours they studied was 12 hours. The standard deviation was 3 hours.

1. Make the curve to represent the frequency distribution.

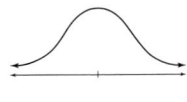

2. Of the 200 students surveyed, how many studied less than 9 hours?
   32
3. Of the 200 students surveyed, how many studied between 9 and 15 hours?
   136
4. Of the 200 students surveyed, how many studied at least 3 hours?
   199
5. What percentage of the students studied 3 hours or less?
   0.5%
6. What percentage of the students studied at least 9 hours?
   84%
7. How many students studied less than 12 hours?
   100

EXERCISES

Practice

8–9. See margin for graphs.
8. positively skewed
9. normally distributed

State whether the tables of data would result in a graph that is **positively skewed, negatively skewed,** or appears to be **normally distributed.** Then sketch a histogram of the data.

8. the number of hours of TV students watch in a week

Hours	Percentage
0–5	16
6–10	24
11–15	5
16–20	8
21–25	4
26+	7

Source: *The Elementary Mathematician*

9. the record low temperatures in the fifty states

Temperature (°F)	Number of States
−80 to −66	2
−65 to −51	10
−50 to −36	17
−35 to −19	16
−18 to −2	4
−1 to 15	1

Source: *The World Almanac, 1995*

10a. 68%
10b. 34%

10. The shelf life of a particular dairy product is normally distributed with a mean of 12 days and a standard deviation of 3.0 days.
   a. About what percentage of the products last between 9 and 15 days?
   b. About what percentage of the products last between 12 and 15 days?
   c. About what percentage of the products last 3 days or less? 0.5%
   d. About what percentage of the products last 15 or more days? 16%

11. The vending machine in the basement of McMicken Hall usually dispenses about 6 oz of soft drink. Lately, it is not working properly and the variability in how much of the soft drink it dispenses has been getting greater. The amounts are normally distributed with a standard deviation of 0.2 oz. **a. 50% b. 50%**
   a. What percent of the time will you have more than 6 oz of soft drink?
   b. What percent of the time will you have less than 6 oz of soft drink?
   c. What percent of the time will you have between 5.6 and 6.4 oz of soft drink? 95%

12. The Floppy Disk Company makes 3.5" floppy disks for disk drives that are 3.7" wide. The size of a manufactured disk is normally distributed with a standard deviation of 0.1". The company manufactures 1000 disks every hour. **a. 2.5% c. about 25 disks**
   a. What percentage of the disks would you expect to be greater than 3.7"?
   b. In one hour, how many disks would you expect to be between 3.4" and 3.7"? 815 disks
   c. About how many disks will be unable to fit in the disk drive?

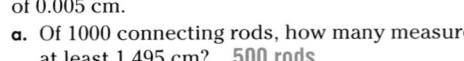
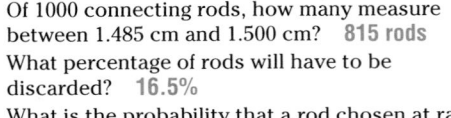

13. The diameter of the connecting rod in a certain imported sports car must be between 1.480 and 1.500 cm, inclusive, to be usable. The diameters of the connecting rods are normally distributed with a mean of 1.495 cm and a standard deviation of 0.005 cm.
   a. Of 1000 connecting rods, how many measure at least 1.495 cm? **500 rods**
   b. Of 1000 connecting rods, how many measure between 1.485 cm and 1.500 cm? **815 rods**
   c. What percentage of rods will have to be discarded? **16.5%**

13d. 83.5%

   d. What is the probability that a rod chosen at random will be usable?

396 Chapter 6 *Exploring Quadratic Functions and Inequalities*

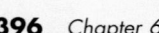

14. Suppose the weights of the books used in your school were normally distributed.   **a–c. See margin.**

  a. Where on the normal curve would you find the weight of your Algebra 2 textbook?

  b. Which textbook would be three standard deviations to the left of the mean (extremely light)?

  c. Which textbook would be three standard deviations to the right of the mean (extremely heavy)?

**Applications and
Problem Solving**

15. Sample answer: The
statistician was using
standard deviations.

15. Humor   The following quote appeared in *Chance* magazine in Winter, 1995.

> Someone asked an accountant, a mathematician, an engineer, a statistician, and an actuary how much 2 + 2 was. The accountant said "4." The mathematician said "it depends on your number base." The engineer took out his slide-rule and said "approximately 3.99." The statistician consulted his tables and said "I am 95% confident that it lies between 3.95 and 4.05." The actuary said "What do you want it to add up to?"

How did each person's perspective affect his or her answer? Describe the information the statistician used to give his answer.

16. Health   A recent study showed that the systolic blood pressure of high school students ages 14–17 is normally distributed with a mean of 120 mm Hg and a standard deviation of 12 mm Hg. Suppose a high school has 800 students.

  a. About what percentage of the students have blood pressure below 108 mm Hg?   **16%**

  b. About how many students have blood pressure between 108 and 144 mm Hg?   **652 students**

17. Noise Level   Airplane pilots often suffer from hearing loss as a result of being exposed to high noise levels. A team of researchers measured the cockpit noise levels of 16 commercial aircraft. The results are listed in the table below.

Plane	Decibels of Noise Level	Plane	Decibels of Noise Level
1	80	9	85
2	83	10	80
3	83	11	75
4	86	12	75
5	72	13	74
6	90	14	77
7	87	15	80
8	83	16	82

Source: *Archives of Environmental Health*

17c. See margin.

  a. Calculate the mean and standard deviation of the data.   **80.75; 4.94**

  b. Construct a histogram for the noise levels of the planes. Use the intervals 70-73, 74-77, 78-81, 82-85, 86-89, and 90-93.   **See margin.**

  c. Do you think the data appear to be normally distributed? Explain.

Additional Answers

14a. Sample answer: The Algebra 2 textbook will be one standard deviation to the right of the mean.

14b. Sample answer: A paperback novel would be about three standard deviations to the left of the mean.

14c. Sample answer: A literature book or history book would be about three standard deviations to the right of the mean.

17b.

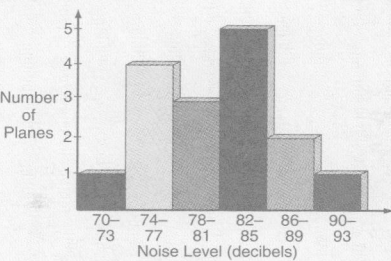

17c. Sample answer: The data do not appear to be normally distributed since they are not symmetrical about the mean.

Practice Masters, p. 48

6-9   NAME_____ DATE _____

Practice   Student Edition Pages 392–398

Integration: Statistics
The Normal Distribution

The weights of eggs produced on a farm are normally distributed with a mean of 1.4 ounces and a standard deviation of 0.4 ounces.

1. What percent of the eggs weigh at least 1 ounce?   84%

2. How many of 1200 eggs are within 2 standard deviations of the mean?   1140 eggs

3. To be graded extra large, an egg must weigh at least 2.2 ounces. What is the probability that an egg from this farm will be graded extra large?   0.025

A bottle of fruit punch must contain at least 16 fluid ounces. The machine that fills the bottles is set so that the mean volume is 16.4 fluid ounces. The volumes in the bottles are normally distributed.

4. What percent of the bottles are underfilled if the standard deviation is 0.2 fluid ounces?   2.5%

5. What percent of the bottles are underfilled if the standard deviation is 0.4 fluid ounces?   16%

6. If the standard deviation is 0.2 fluid ounces, find the mean volume that will ensure only 0.5% of the bottles will be underfilled.   16.6 fluid ounces

A battery has an average life span of 50 hours, with a standard deviation of 3 hours. The life span of the batteries is normally distributed.

7. What percent of the batteries last at least 44 hours?   97.5%

8. How many of 1500 batteries are within 1 standard deviation of the mean?   1020 batteries

9. What percent of the batteries will last at least 53 hours?   16%

Closing Activity

Modeling Have students model verbal problems using a normal curve.

Chapter 6, Quiz D (Lessons 6-8 and 6-9), is available in the *Assessment and Evaluation Masters*, p. 157.

Additional Answers

18a.

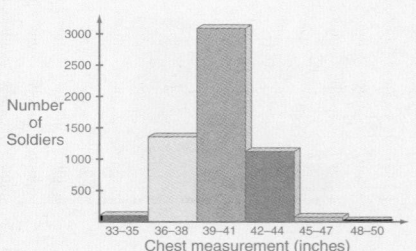

19a.

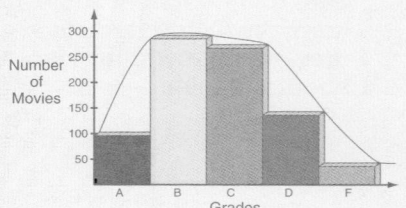

19b. no, positively skewed

Enrichment Masters, p. 48

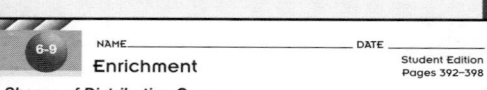

6-9	NAME_____ DATE _____
	Enrichment Student Edition Pages 392–398

Shapes of Distribution Curves

Graphs of frequency distributions can be described as either symmetric or skewed.

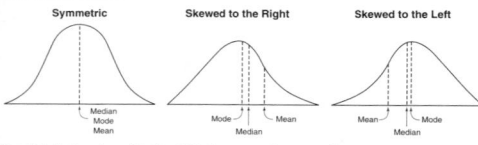

In a distribution skewed to the right, there are a larger number of high values. The long "tail" extends to the right.

In a distribution skewed to the left, there are a larger number of low values. The "tail" extends to the left.

For each of the following, state whether the distribution is symmetric or skewed. If it is skewed, tell whether it is skewed to the right or to the left.

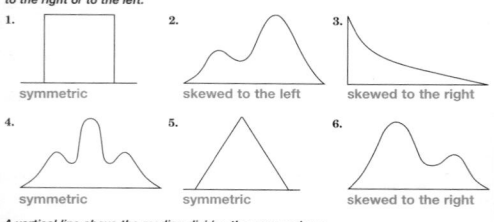

A vertical line above the median divides the area under a frequency curve in half.

7. Where is the median in a symmetric distribution?
in the middle of the range; It is the same as the mean.

8. Where is the median in a skewed distribution?
to the left of the middle if skewed to the right; to the right of the middle if skewed to the left

---

18. **Physiology** Nineteenth-century Belgian scholar Lambert Adolphe Jacques Quetelet discovered that if you take a large group of people and measure a physical characteristic such as height, weight, or arm length, the data will be nearly normally distributed. Below is a set of data Quetelet collected in 1846. They are the chest measurements of 5738 Scottish soldiers.

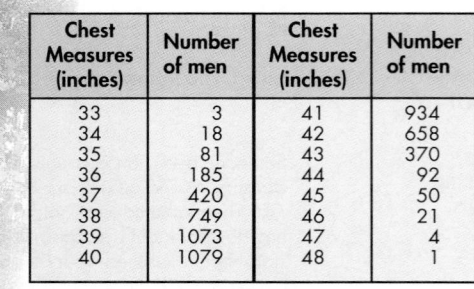

Chest Measures (inches)	Number of men	Chest Measures (inches)	Number of men
33	3	41	934
34	18	42	658
35	81	43	370
36	185	44	92
37	420	45	50
38	749	46	21
39	1073	47	4
40	1079	48	1

Source: *Lettres sur la Theorie des Probabilites, appliquee aux Sciences Morales et Politiques*

The mean measurement to the nearest inch is 40 inches and the standard deviation is 2 inches.   **a. See margin.**

a. Construct a histogram for the chest measurements of Scottish soldiers.

b. If the data represented a perfectly normal distribution, what percentage of Scottish soldiers would have chest measurements that were within two standard deviations of the mean? **95%**

c. What percentage of soldiers actually had chest measurements that were within two standard deviations of the mean? **96.9%**

19. **Entertainment** The 5th Anniversary Issue of *Entertainment Weekly* gave a summary of grades their critics have awarded the movies reviewed since the magazine's premiere issue. The grades were 96 As, 285 Bs, 267 Cs, 136 Ds, and 36 Fs.   **a. See margin.**

a. Construct a histogram for these data and sketch a curve showing the distribution.

b. Do the data appear to be normally distributed? Explain.

Mixed Review

20. Find the mean and the standard deviation for the following set of data.
7, 16, 9, 4, 12, 3, 9, 4 (Lesson 6–8) **8, 4.2**

21. **Football** The price of a Super Bowl ticket from Super Bowl I in 1967 to Super Bowl XXIX in 1995 can be described by the function $y = \frac{2}{5}x^2 - 6x + 32$, where y represents the price and x represents the year, with $x = 1$ representing 1967. (Lesson 6–6)

a. Write the equation in the form $y = a(x - h)^2 + k$ and graph the function.

b. What was the approximate price of tickets for Super Bowl XXIX in 1995?

c. What will be the approximate price of tickets for Super Bowl XXXV in 2001? **$312**

21a. $y = 0.4(x - 7.5)^2 + 9.5$; See Solutions Manual for Graph.

21b. $194.40

22. Write a quadratic equation with the roots $2 \pm \sqrt{3}$. (Lesson 6–5)

22. $x^2 - 4x + 1 = 0$

23. Simplify $(-x - 8)(3x + 4)$. (Lesson 5–2) **$-3x^2 - 28x - 32$**

24. Solve $6(3x - 5y) + (2 + 8x) = -11x$ for x. (Lesson 2–2)

24. $\frac{30y - 2}{37}$

398 Chapter 6 *Exploring Quadratic Functions and Inequalities*

Extension

Problem Solving The burning time of a fabricated fire log is normally distributed with a mean of 5 hours and a standard deviation of 0.25 hours. A camping store has 1000 logs to sell. How many of these logs will burn longer than 4.5 hours? **975**

VOCABULARY

After completing this chapter, you should be able to define each term, property, or phrase and give an example or two of each.

Algebra
axis of symmetry (p. 335)
boundary (p. 378)
completing the square (p. 347)
constant term (p. 334)
discriminant (p. 356)
factoring (p. 341)
linear term (p. 334)
parabola (p. 335)

quadratic equation (p. 336)
quadratic formula (p. 354)
quadratic function (p. 334)
quadratic inequality (p. 378)
quadratic term (p. 334)
roots (p. 336)
vertex (p. 335)
zero product property (p. 341)
zeros (p. 335)

Statistics
bell curve (p. 393)
frequency distribution (p. 392)
histogram (p. 392)
normal distribution (p. 393)
skewed (p. 395)
standard deviation (p. 384)

Problem Solving
guess and check (p. 342)

UNDERSTANDING AND USING THE VOCABULARY

Choose the letter of the term that best matches each statement or phrase.

1. the graph of any quadratic function

2. a process whereby the middle term of a quadratic equation of the form $ax^2 + bx + c = 0$ is altered to help solve the quadratic equation **b**

3. the vertical line passing through the vertex of a parabola and dividing the parabola into two mirror images **a**

4. a function described by an equation of the form $f(x) = ax^2 + bx + c$, where $a \neq o$ **h**

5. the solutions of an equation **i**

6. a bell-shaped symmetric graph with about 68% of the items within one standard deviation from the mean, about 95% of the items within two standard deviations from the mean, and about 99% of the items within three standard deviations of the mean **e**

a. axis of symmetry
b. completing the square
c. discriminant
d. factoring
e. normal distribution
f. parabola
g. quadratic formula
h. quadratic function
i. roots
j. standard deviation

7. the process whereby a polynomial of degree 2 or more is simplified into the product of monomials, binomials, or a combination thereof **d**

8. in the quadratic formula, the expression under the radical sign, $b^2 - 4ac$ **c**

9. The solution(s) of a quadratic equation of the form $ax^2 + bx + c = 0$ with $a \neq 0$ are given by $x = \dfrac{-b \pm \sqrt{b^2 - 4ac}}{2a}$. **g**

10. For a set of data with n values, if x_i represents a value such that $1 \leq i \leq n$, and $\overline{x}$ represents the mean, then $\sqrt{\dfrac{(x_1 - \overline{x})^2 + (x_2 - \overline{x})^2 + \cdots + (x_n - \overline{x})^2}{n}}$ represents this value. **j**

Chapter 6 Highlights **399**

Using the CHAPTER HIGHLIGHTS

The Chapter Highlights begins with a listing of the new terms, properties, and phrases that were introduced in this chapter. Have students define each term and provide an example or two of it, if appropriate.

Assessment and Evaluation Masters, pp. 143–144

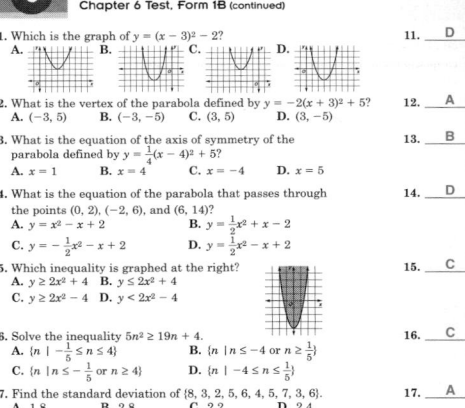

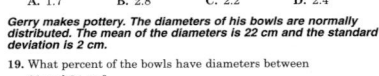

Instructional Resources

Three multiple-choice tests and three free-response tests are provided in the *Assessment and Evaluation Masters.* Forms 1A and 2A are for honors pacing, and Forms 1B, 1C, 2B, and 2C are for average pacing. Chapter 6 Test, Form 1B is shown at the right. Chapter 6 Test, Form 2B is shown on the next page.

Using the
STUDY GUIDE
AND ASSESSMENT

Skills and Concepts Encourage students to refer to the objectives and examples on the left as they complete the review exercises on the right.

Assessment and Evaluation Masters, pp. 149–150

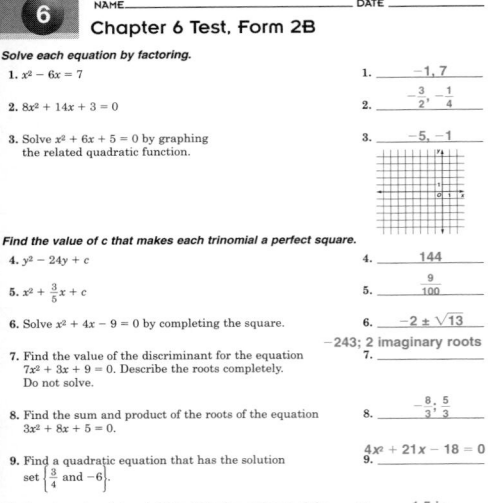

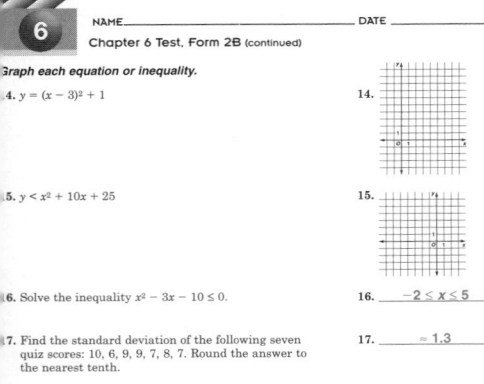

SKILLS AND CONCEPTS

OBJECTIVES AND EXAMPLES

Upon completing this chapter, you should be able to:

• solve quadratic equations by graphing
(Lesson 6–1)

Solve $x^2 + 4x - 12 = 0$ by graphing.

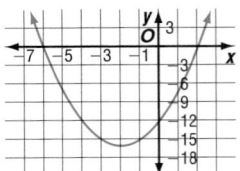

The graph crosses the x-axis at -6 and 2. Thus, the solutions of the equation are -6 and 2.

• solve quadratic equations by factoring
(Lesson 6–2)

Solve $x^2 + 9x + 20 = 0$.

$(x + 4)(x + 5) = 0$

$\quad x + 4 = 0 \quad$ or $\quad x + 5 = 0$

$\quad\quad x = -4 \quad\quad\quad\quad x = -5$

The solutions are -4 and -5.

• solve quadratic equations by completing the square   (Lesson 6–3)

Solve $x^2 + 10x - 39 = 0$ by completing the square.

$x^2 + 10x + \square = 39 + \square$

$x^2 + 10x + 25 = 39 + 25$

$\quad (x + 5)^2 = 64$

$\quad\quad x + 5 = \pm 8$

$\quad x + 5 = 8 \quad$ or $\quad x + 5 = -8$

$\quad\quad x = 3 \quad\quad\quad\quad x = -13$

The solutions are -13 and 3.

REVIEW EXERCISES

Use these exercises to review and prepare for the chapter test.

Solve each equation by graphing.

11. $x^2 + 6x - 40 = 0$ $\quad$ **−10, 4**

12. $x^2 - 2x - 15 = 0$ $\quad$ **−3, 5**

13. $a^2 - 8a - 20 = 0$ $\quad$ **−2, 10**

14. $3m^2 + 9m + 6 = 0$ $\quad$ **−2, −1**

15. $x^2 + 12x + 35 = 0$ $\quad$ **−7, −5**

16. $0.5x^2 + 0.5x - 15 = 0$ $\quad$ **−6, 5**

11–16. See Solutions Manual for graphs.

Solve each equation by factoring.

17. $x^2 - 4x - 32 = 0$ $\quad$ **−4, 8**

18. $3x^2 + 6x + 3 = 0$ $\quad$ **−1**

19. $5y^2 = 80$ $\quad$ **−4, 4**

20. $2c^2 + 18c - 44 = 0$ $\quad$ **−11, 2**

21. $d^2 + 29d + 100 = 0$ $\quad$ **−25, −4**

22. $v^3 = 49v$ $\quad$ **−7, 0, 7**

23. $25x^3 - 25x^2 = 36x$ $\quad$ **$-\frac{4}{5}, 0, \frac{9}{5}$**

24. $r^2 - 3r - 70 = 0$ $\quad$ **−7, 10**

Solve each equation by completing the square.

25. $-5x^2 - 5x + 9 = 0$ $\quad$ **$-\frac{1}{2} \pm \frac{\sqrt{205}}{10}$**

26. $k^2 + 6k - 4 = 0$ $\quad$ **$-3 \pm \sqrt{13}$**

27. $b^2 + 4 = 6b$ $\quad$ **$3 \pm \sqrt{5}$**

28. $n^2 - 10n = 23$ $\quad$ **$5 \pm 4\sqrt{3}$**

29. $h^2 - 4h - 7 = 0$ $\quad$ **$2 \pm \sqrt{11}$**

30. $5x^2 - 15x - 9 = 2$ $\quad$ **$\frac{3}{2} \pm \frac{\sqrt{445}}{10}$**

GLENCOE Technology

Test and Review Software

You may use this software, a combination of an item generator and item bank, to create your own tests or worksheets. Types of items include free response, multiple choice, short answer, and open ended.

For IBM & Macintosh

OBJECTIVES AND EXAMPLES

- solve quadratic equations by using the quadratic formula (Lesson 6–4)

Solve $x^2 - 5x - 66 = 0$.

$$x = \frac{-b \pm \sqrt{b^2 - 4ac}}{2a}$$

$$= \frac{-(-5) \pm \sqrt{(-5)^2 - 4(1)(-66)}}{2(1)}$$

$$= \frac{5 \pm 17}{2}$$

$x = \frac{5 + 17}{2}$ or 11   and $x = \frac{5 - 17}{2}$ or -6

- find a quadratic equation to fit a given condition (Lesson 6–5)

Write an equation that has roots of $-\frac{5}{2}$ and 3.

$s_1 = -\frac{5}{2}$ $s_2 = 3$

$s_1 + s_2 = -\frac{5}{2} + 3 = \frac{1}{2} = -\frac{b}{a}$

$s_1 s_2 = -\frac{5}{2} \cdot 3 = -\frac{15}{2} = \frac{c}{a}$

Therefore $a = 2$, $b = -1$, and $c = -15$.
The equation is $2x^2 - x - 15 = 0$.

- graph quadratic functions of the form $y = a(x - h)^2 + k$ (Lesson 6–6)

Name the vertex, axis of symmetry, and direction of opening for the graph of $f(x) = 3x^2 + 42x + 142$.

$f(x) = 3x^2 + 42x + 142$
$= 3(x^2 + 14x) + 142$
$= 3(x^2 + 14x + 49) + 142 - 3(49)$
$= 3(x + 7)^2 - 5$

So $a = 3$, $h = -7$, and $k = -5$. The vertex is at $(-7, -5)$, and the axis of symmetry is $x = -7$. Since $a = 3$, the graph opens upward.

- graph quadratic inequalities (Lesson 6–7)

Graph $y \le -2x^2 - 28x - 89$.

REVIEW EXERCISES

Solve each equation by using the quadratic formula.

31. $x^2 + 2x + 7 = 0$ $-1 \pm \sqrt{6}i$

32. $x + 2x^2 + 1 = -1 - x$ $-\frac{1}{2} \pm \frac{\sqrt{3}}{2}i$

33. $-x^2 + 5x - 9 = 0$ $\frac{5}{2} \pm \frac{\sqrt{11}}{2}i$

34. $-2x^2 + 12x - 5 = 0$ $3 \pm \frac{\sqrt{26}}{2}$

35. $3c^2 + 7c - 2 = 0$ $-\frac{7}{6} \pm \frac{\sqrt{73}}{6}$

36. $8b^2 - b - 15 = 0$ $\frac{1}{16} \pm \frac{\sqrt{481}}{16}$

Find a quadratic equation that has the given roots.

37. $7, -6$ $x^2 - x - 42 = 0$

38. $11, 14$ $x^2 - 25x + 154 = 0$

39. $-\frac{13}{2}, -4$ $2x^2 + 21x + 52 = 0$

40. $\frac{3}{4}, \frac{9}{2}$ $8x^2 - 42x + 27 = 0$

41. $-2.5, 5.25$ $8x^2 - 22x - 105 = 0$

42. $-0.25, 0.25$ $16x^2 - 1 = 0$

Write each equation in the form $f(x) = a(x - h)^2 + k$ if not already in that form. Name the vertex, axis of symmetry, and direction of opening for the graph of each quadratic function. Then graph it.

43. $f(x) = -6(x + 2)^2 + 3$

44. $f(x) = 4(x - 5)^2 - 7$

45. $f(x) = 5x^2 - 35x + 58$

46. $f(x) = -9x^2 + 54x - 8$

47. $f(x) = -\frac{1}{3}x^2 + 8x$ **43–48. See margin.**

48. $f(x) = 0.25x^2 - 6x - 16$

Graph each inequality.   **49–54. See Solutions Manual.**

49. $y > x^2 - 5x + 15$

50. $y < -3x^2 + 48$

51. $y \le 4x^2 - 36x + 17$

52. $y \ge -x^2 + 7x - 11$

53. $y < x^2 + 5x + 6$

54. $y \ge 3x^2 - 15x + 22$

48. $f(x) = 0.25(x - 12)^2 - 52$;
(12, −52), $x = 12$, up

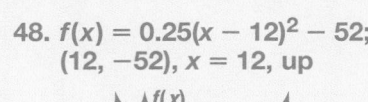

Additional Answers

43. $(-2, 3)$, $x = -2$, down

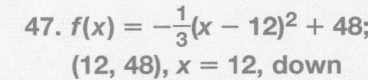

44. $(5, -7)$, $x = 5$, up

45. $f(x) = 5\left(x - \frac{7}{2}\right)^2 - \frac{13}{4}$; $\left(\frac{7}{2}, \frac{13}{4}\right)$, $x = \frac{7}{2}$, up

46. $f(x) = -9(x - 3)^2 + 73$;
(3, 73), $x = 3$, down

47. $f(x) = -\frac{1}{3}(x - 12)^2 + 48$;
(12, 48), $x = 12$, down

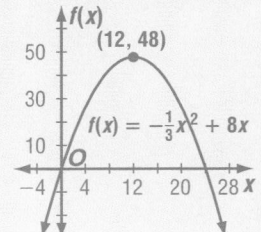

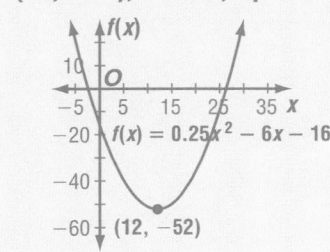

Applications and Problem Solving Encourage students to work through the exercises in the Applications and Problem Solving section to strengthen their problem-solving skills.

OBJECTIVES AND EXAMPLES

- find the standard deviation for a set of data
  (Lesson 6–8)

To find the standard deviation of this set of data, follow the steps below.

1. Find the mean of the data.
2. Find the difference between each value in the set of data and the mean.
3. Square each difference.
4. Find the mean of the squares.
5. Take the principal root of this mean.

REVIEW EXERCISES

Find the mean and the standard deviation to the nearest hundredth for each set of data.

55. {100, 156, 158, 159, 162, 165, 170, 190}
    $\bar{x} = 157.5$, $\sigma = 23.98$

56. {56, 56, 57, 58, 58, 58, 59, 61}
    $\bar{x} = 57.88$, $\sigma = 1.54$

57. {302, 310, 331, 298, 348, 305, 314, 284, 321, 337}
    $\bar{x} = 315$, $\sigma = 18.47$

58. {3.4, 4.2, 8.6, 5.1, 3.6, 2.8, 7.1, 4.4, 5.2, 5.6}
    $\bar{x} = 5$, $\sigma = 1.68$

- solve problems involving normally-distributed data (Lesson 6–9)

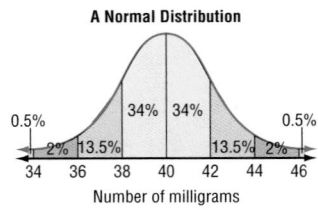

A Normal Distribution

0.5%   34% | 34%   0.5%
2% | 13.5%   13.5% | 2%
34   36   38   40   42   44   46
Number of milligrams

59. Mr. Byrum gave an exam to his 30 Algebra 2 students at the end of the first semester. The scores were normally distributed with a mean of 78% and a standard deviation of 6%.

   a. What percentage of the class would you expect to have scored between 72% and 84% on the test? **68%**

   b. What percentage of the class would you expect to have scored between 90% and 96% on the test? **2%**

   c. Approximately how many students scored between 84% and 90%? **4 students**

   d. What percentage of the class would you expect to score less than 60%? **0.5%**

   e. Approximately how many students scored between 72% and 84%? **20 students**

APPLICATIONS AND PROBLEM SOLVING

60. **Space Exploration** The Apollo 11 spacecraft propelled the first men to the moon and contained three stages of rockets. The first stage dropped off 2 min 40 s after takeoff and the second stage ignited. The initial velocity of the second stage was 2760 m/s with a constant acceleration of 200 m/s². How long did it take the second stage to travel 7040 m? (Lesson 6–3)
    about 2.35 seconds

61. **Physics** The Empire State Building is 1250 feet tall. If an object is thrown upward from the top of the building at an initial velocity of 35 feet per second, its height t seconds after it is thrown is given by the function $h(t) = -16t^2 + 35t + 1250$. How long will it be before the object hits the ground? (Lesson 6–2) **10 seconds**

62. **Work** The monthly incomes of 10,000 workers at the ProComm plant are distributed normally. Suppose the mean monthly income is $1250 and the standard deviation is $250. (Lesson 6–9)

   a. How many workers earn more than $1500 per month? **1600 workers**

   b. How many workers earn less than $750 per month? **250 workers**

   c. What percentage of the workers earn between $500 and $1750 per month? **97%**

   d. What percentage of the workers earn less than $1750 per month? **97.5%**

A practice test for Chapter 6 is provided on page 917.

ALTERNATIVE ASSESSMENT

COOPERATIVE LEARNING PROJECT

Statistics So far in this text, you have learned several methods of statistical analysis.

- *Standard deviation* is the average measure of how much each value in a set of data differs from the mean.
- A *bar graph* that shows the frequency distribution of data is called a histogram.
- In a *stem-and-leaf plot*, each piece of data is separated into two number columns that are used to form the stem and leaf.
- The *normal distribution* is a symmetric curve of a graph that is often bell-shaped.

In this project, you will have the opportunity to gather data and complete your own statistical analysis using one of the four methods listed above. Your teacher will separate you into groups of four and assign each of you a method of statistical analysis. Once you are assigned to a group and a method, your group should decide which teacher in the school you would like to approach to provide you with a list of his or her latest test scores. Tell the teacher that this is a math project and that only a list of the scores is necessary to complete the project. Be sure to tell the teacher that no names are to be given with any of the test scores. Also, have the teacher provide you with the method by which the test scores were achieved: for example, multiple-choice, true-false, matching, essay, and so on.

Once you have obtained the test scores, begin your analysis of the scores using the method assigned to you by your teacher. Remember, statistics can be used to prove any point an individual wants to make.

When your statistical analysis is complete, share your results with the rest of your group. Are there any similarities and/or differences between the various methods of analysis?

Now share your results with someone in another group who used the same method of analysis as you did. Are there any similarities and/or differences between methods of the same type of analysis? Can any conclusions be drawn about the statistical analysis and the method of testing used by the teacher? Does one method of testing yield better statistical results than another?

THINKING CRITICALLY

Find values of k that meet the following conditions.

a. $x^2 - 7x + k = 0$ has two real roots. $k < \frac{49}{4}$

b. $kx^2 - 5x + 7 = 0$ has two imaginary roots.

c. $3x^2 - kx + 15 = 0$ has one root. $k = \pm 2\sqrt{45}$

b. $k > \frac{25}{28}$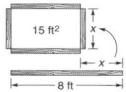

PORTFOLIO

Select an item from this chapter that shows your best work and place it in your portfolio. Explain why you believe it to be your best work and how you came to choose this particular piece.

SELF EVALUATION

Every day you are required to make decisions. Some may be as simple as what you should wear to school or what kind of cereal you want to have for breakfast. Others such as what classes to take in school next year or where to apply for a part-time job are a little tougher.

Assess yourself. How do you handle decision-making? It may be helpful to make a list of all your choices and write the pros and cons of each one. Also remember to seek input from friends and family members who have experience in the area. Once you make your decision, accept responsibility for it and move forward.

Assessment and Evaluation Masters, pp. 154, 165

6 NAME _____ DATE _____

Chapter 6 Performance Assessment

Instructions: *Demonstrate your knowledge by giving a clear, concise solution to each problem. Be sure to include all relevant drawings and justify your answers. You may show your solution in more than one way or investigate beyond the requirements of the problem.*

1. Mr. Babb is cutting timbers to outline a rectangular flower bed for his wife. He is using two 8-foot pieces of timber to outline the bed. He will cut each piece as shown below.

   a. Write a quadratic equation to represent the situation. Solve the equation graphically and then by factoring. Show your work. Where should he make his cut if the area of each flower bed is to be 15 square feet?

   b. Do both answers make sense? Why or why not?

   c. Where should Mr. Babb cut the timbers to outline an 18-square-foot flower bed? Identify a, b, and c and use the quadratic formula to solve.

   d. Do both answers make sense? Why or why not?

2. a. Write a quadratic function whose graph has its vertex in the second quadrant.

   b. Name the vertex, give the equation of the axis of symmetry, and tell whether the graph opens up or down. Justify your reasoning.

3. a. Write a word problem for the inequality $(x - 2)^2 < 121$.

   b. Solve and explain each step.

Scoring Guide
Chapter 6
Performance Assessment

Level	Specific Criteria
3 Superior	• Shows thorough understanding of the concepts of *solving quadratic equations by graphing, factoring, and using the quadratic formula; vertex; direction of opening of parabolas;* and *solving quadratic inequalities.* • Uses appropriate strategies to solve problems. • Computations are correct. • Written explanations are exemplary. • Diagrams are accurate and appropriate. • Goes beyond requirements of problem.
2 Satisfactory, with Minor Flaws	• Shows understanding of the concepts of *solving quadratic equations by graphing, factoring, and using the quadratic formula; vertex; direction of opening of parabolas;* and *solving quadratic inequalities.* • Uses appropriate strategies to solve problems. • Computations are mostly correct. • Written explanations are effective. • Diagrams are mostly accurate and appropriate. • Satisfies all requirements of problem.
1 Nearly Satisfactory, with Serious Flaws	• Shows understanding of most of the concepts of *solving quadratic equations by graphing, factoring, and using the quadratic formula; vertex; direction of opening of parabolas;* and *solving quadratic inequalities.* • May not use appropriate strategies to solve problems. • Computations are mostly correct. • Written explanations are satisfactory. • Diagrams are mostly accurate and appropriate. • Satisfies most requirements of problem.
0 Unsatisfactory	• Shows little or no understanding of the concepts of *solving quadratic equations by graphing, factoring, and using the quadratic formula; vertex; direction of opening of parabolas;* and *solving quadratic inequalities.* • May not use appropriate strategies to solve problems. • Computations are incorrect. • Written explanations are not satisfactory. • Diagrams are not accurate or appropriate. • Does not satisfy requirements of problem.

Alternative Assessment

The Alternative Assessment section provides students with the opportunity to assess their own work by thinking critically, working with others, keeping a portfolio, and honestly evaluating their own progress. For more information on alternative forms of assessment, see *Alternative Assessment in the Mathematics Classroom,* one of the titles in the Glencoe Mathematics Professional Series.

Performance Assessment

Performance Assessment tasks for this chapter are included in the *Assessment and Evaluation Masters.* A scoring guide is also provided.

These two pages review the skills and concepts presented in Chapters 1–6. This review is formatted to reflect new trends in college entrance testing.

A more traditional cumulative review is provided in the *Assessment and Evaluation Masters,* pp. 159–160.

Assessment and Evaluation Masters, pp. 159–160

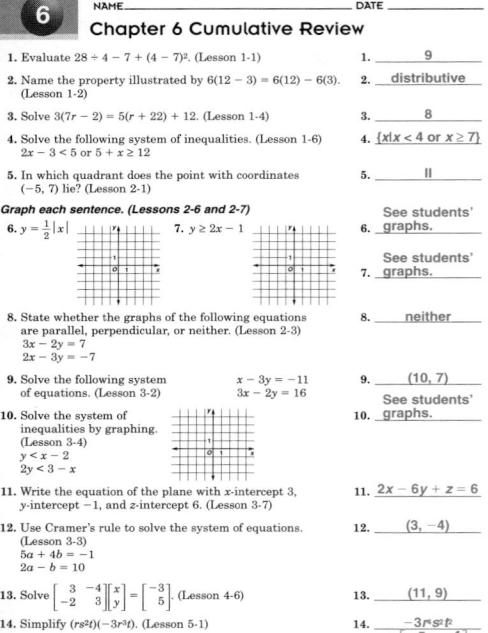

COLLEGE ENTRANCE EXAM PRACTICE

CHAPTERS 1–6

SECTION ONE: MULTIPLE CHOICE

There are eight multiple-choice questions in this section. After working each problem, write the letter of the correct answer on your paper.

1. Evaluate $(4.5 \times 10^4)(3.33 \times 10^2)$. Express the answer in scientific notation and in standard notation. **D**

A. 1.4985×10^6; 1,498,500

B. 14.985×10^6; 14,985,000,000

C. 1.4985×10^7; 149,850,000,000

D. 1.4985×10^7; 14,985,000

2. Which matrix below represents translated $\triangle D'E'F'$ if $\triangle DEF$ with $D(7, -2)$, $E(4, 5)$, and $F(-3, 4)$ is moved 5 units left and 1 unit up? **B**

A. $\begin{bmatrix} 8 & 5 & -2 \\ -7 & 0 & -1 \end{bmatrix}$

B. $\begin{bmatrix} 2 & -1 & -8 \\ -1 & 6 & 5 \end{bmatrix}$

C. $\begin{bmatrix} -1 & 6 & 5 \\ 8 & 5 & 2 \end{bmatrix}$

D. $\begin{bmatrix} 2 & -1 & -8 \\ -7 & 0 & -1 \end{bmatrix}$

3. Choose the equation that represents a parabola that is 1 unit to the right and 8 units below the parabola with equation $f(x) = 5x^2$. **C**

A. $f(x) = 5(x - 8)^2 + 1$

B. $f(x) = 5x^2 - 8$

C. $f(x) = 5(x - 1)^2 - 8$

D. $f(x) = 5(x - 1)^2 + 8$

4. Find the area of a rectangle with length $3\sqrt{3} - \sqrt{2}$ units and width $\sqrt{3} + 3\sqrt{2}$ units. **A**

A. $3 + 8\sqrt{6}$

B. 27

C. $11\sqrt{6}$

D. $3 + 8\sqrt{5}$

5. Simplify $4(5x + 2y) + 9(x - 2y)$. **B**

A. $10xy$

B. $29x - 10y$

C. $54x + 13y$

D. $29x$

6. Choose the system of inequalities whose solution is represented by the graph below. **C**

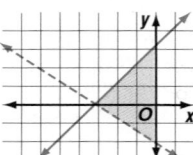

A. $y > -\dfrac{3}{2}x - 2$

$x < 0$

$y \le \dfrac{1}{2}x - 6$

B. $-2 < y \le 3$

$x > -3$

C. $y \le x + 3$

$y > -\dfrac{2}{3}x - 2$

$x \le 0$

D. $y \ge -2x$

$y < -4x + 3$

7. Choose the false statement regarding the value of the discriminant of a quadratic equation. **B**

A. If it is a perfect square, two real rational roots exist.

B. If it is zero, infinitely many roots exist.

C. If it is negative, two complex roots exist.

D. If it is not a perfect square, two real irrational roots exist.

8. Find the next number in the pattern 2, 8, 18, 32, 50, __?__. **D**

A. 54

B. 68

C. 98

D. 72

404 *College Entrance Exam Practice   Chapters 1–6*

Standardized Test Practice Questions are also provided in the *Assessment and Evaluation Masters,* p. 158.

SECTION TWO: SHORT ANSWER

This section contains seven questions for which you will provide short answers. Write your answer on your paper.

9. Find the mean and the standard deviation for {13.7, 15.0, 13.7, 16.9, 13.6, 14.3, 14.8, 14.8, 15.1, 15.4, 14.9}.   **14.7, 0.9**

10. Joseph works at Angelino's Pizza. His last three orders were 5 slices of pizza, 2 salads, and 2 sodas for $9.75; 3 slices of pizza, 2 salads, and 1 soda for $7.15; and 2 slices of pizza, 1 salad, and 1 soda, for a total of $4.35. What are the individual prices for pizza, salad, and soda at Angelino's?
                        pizza–$1.05, salad–$1.75, soda–$0.50

11. Simplify $\dfrac{(4 + 3i)^2}{(3 - i)^2}$. $\dfrac{-44 + 117i}{50}$

12. Determine the slope of the line that passes through $(2, 0)$ and $(-3, 5)$.   **−1**

13. An object is fired upwards from the top of a 200-foot tower at a velocity of 80 feet per second. The height of the object t seconds after firing is given by the formula $h(t) = -16t^2 + 80t + 200$. Find the maximum height reached by the object and the time that height is reached.   **300 ft; 2.5 seconds**

14. Two and one-half years ago, Miko deposited the $1500 she earned at a summer job into her bank account. Her account earns 7.5% interest annually. Now she is withdrawing the money and the interest to buy a car. Use the formula $A = P(1 + r)^t$, where A is the amount of money in the account after t years if the interest rate is r and the beginning balance is P, to find how much money Miko has to buy the car.
                        $1797.27

15. Determine the range, quartiles, and interquartile range of the data. Then make a box-and-whisker plot.

Stem	Leaf
4	1 3 9
5	2 3 6 9
6	4 4 5
7	2 4 7 *7	2 = 72*

36; 50.5, 59, 68.5; 18; See Solutions Manual for box-and-whisker plot.

SECTION THREE: COMPARISON

This section contains five comparison problems that involve comparing two quantities, one in column A and one in column B. In certain questions, information related to one or both quantities is centered above them. All variables used represent real numbers.

Compare quantities A and B below.

- Write A if quantity A is greater.

- Write B if quantity B is greater.

- Write C if the two quantities are equal.

- Write D if there is not enough information to determine the relationship.

16. A   17. D   18. C   19. A   20. B

Column A	Column B
16. $(a - 10)(a - 3) \le 0$	$a^2 + 4a - 21 < 0$

$$i^x = -i$$

Column A	Column B
17. 8	x

Column A	Column B
18. $\dfrac{2(3 + 7)^2}{2^3 + 3 \cdot 4}$	$(6 + 7 \cdot 2) - 10 - 8 \div 2 + 4$

Column A	Column B
19. $\dfrac{m^3 + 7m^2 + 17m + 35}{m^2 + 2m + 7}$	$\dfrac{3m^3 - m^2 - 14m + 8}{3m^2 + 5m - 4}$

Column A	Column B
20. $\sqrt[3]{2x + 1} = 3$	$\sqrt[3]{2}\left(3\sqrt[3]{4} + 2\sqrt[3]{32}\right) = x$

7

Analyzing Conic Sections

PREVIEWING THE CHAPTER

This chapter opens with the development of the formulas for finding the distance between two points and finding the midpoint of a line segment. Students identify and graph parabolas, circles, ellipses, and hyperbolas. They also write the equations for these curves given certain properties or the graph of the curve. Conic sections are classified, and students learn to identify a conic section from its quadratic equation written in standard form. Modeling lessons provide students with hands-on activities relating to chapter concepts. Finally, students solve systems in which one or more of the equations are quadratic equations.

Lesson (Pages)	Lesson Objectives	NCTM Standards	State/Local Objectives
7-1 (408–414)	Find the distance between two points in the coordinate plane. Find the midpoint of a line segment in the coordinate plane.	1–5, 8	
7-2 (415–422)	Write equations of parabolas. Graph parabolas having certain properties.	1–5, 8	5.a., 5.b., 5.c., 5.e., 6.b., 6.c., 7.a., 7.b., 8.a., 8.c., 8.d.
7-3 (423–429)	Write equations of circles. Graph circles having certain properties.	1–5, 8	5.b., 5.c., 5.e.
7-4A (430)	Draw an ellipse using simple materials.	1–5, 8	
7-4 (431–439)	Write equations of ellipses. Graph ellipses having certain properties.	1–5, 8	5.b., 5.c., 5.e.
7-5 (440–447)	Write equations of hyperbolas. Graph hyperbolas having certain properties.	1–5, 8	5.b., 5.c., 5.e.
7-6A (448–449)	Use a graphing calculator to graph conic sections.	1–5, 8	
7-6 (450–455)	Write equations of conic sections in standard form. Identify conic sections from their equations. Use simulation to solve problems.	1–5, 8	5.a., 5.b., 5.c., 5.d., 5.e.
7-6B (456–457)	Draw conic sections using conic graph paper.	1–5	
7-7A (458–459)	Use a graphing calculator to solve systems of quadratic equations and inequalities by graphing.	1–5, 8	3.b., 3.c.
7-7 (460–467)	Solve systems of equations involving quadratics graphically and algebraically. Solve systems of inequalities involving quadratics graphically.	1–5, 8	3.a., 3.b., 3.c.

ORGANIZING THE CHAPTER

You may want to refer to the **Course Planning Calendar** on page T12 for detailed information on pacing.
PACING: Standard—15 days; **Honors**—13 days; **Block**—7 days

LESSON PLANNING CHART

Lesson (Pages)	Materials/ Manipulatives	Extra Practice (Student Edition)	Study Guide	Practice	Enrichment	Assessment and Evaluation	Modeling Mathematics	Multicultural Activity	Tech Prep Applications	Graphing Calculator	Science and Math Lab Manual	Real-World Applications	Interactive Mathematics Tools Software	Teaching Transparencies
7-1 (408–414)	graphing calculator	p. 892	p. 49	p. 49	p. 49								7-1	7-1A 7-1B
7-2 (415–422)	wax paper	p. 892	p. 50	p. 50	p. 50	p. 184	p. 67		p. 13		pp. 91–94		7-2	7-2A 7-2B
7-3 (423–429)	graphing calculator	p. 892	p. 51	p. 51	p. 51			p. 13				20		7-3A 7-3B
7-4A (430)	thumbtacks string cardboard grid paper						p. 22						7-4A	
7-4 (431–439)	grid paper compass*	p. 893	p. 52	p. 52	p. 52	pp. 183, 184								7-4A 7-4B
7-5 (440–447)	graphing calculator	p. 893	p. 53	p. 53	p. 53							21		7-5A 7-5B
7-6A (448–449)	graphing calculator									pp. 41, 42				
7-6 (450–455)	graphing calculator	p. 893	p. 54	p. 54	p. 54	p. 185	pp. 46–48	p. 14		p. 7				7-6A 7-6B
7-6B (456–457)	conic graph paper						p. 23							
7-7A (458–459)	graphing calculator									pp. 43, 44				
7-7 (460–467)	graphing calculator	p. 894	p. 55	p. 55	p. 55	p. 185			p. 14					7-7A 7-7B
Study Guide/ Assessment (469–473)						pp. 169–182, 186–188								

*Included in Glencoe's Student Manipulative Kit and Overhead Manipulative Resources.

ORGANIZING THE CHAPTER

OTHER CHAPTER RESOURCES

Student Edition
Chapter Opener, pp. 406–407
Mathematics and Society, p. 467
Working on the Investigation,
  pp. 422, 455
Closing the Investigation, p. 468

Teacher's Classroom Resources
Investigations and Projects Masters,
  pp. 49–52

Technology
Teacher's Guide for Software
  Resources
Test and Review Software (IBM
  and Macintosh)
CD-ROM Interactions (Windows
  and Macintosh)

Professional Publications
Block Scheduling Booklet
Glencoe Mathematics Professional
  Series

OUTSIDE RESOURCES

Books/Periodicals
High School Template, Activity Resources
  Company
Practical Conic Sections, Dale Seymour
  Publications

Software
Graph Whiz, William K. Bradford Publishing Co.
Math Connections: Algebra II, Sunburst
Tools of Mathematics: Advanced Algebra, William
  K. Bradford Publishing Co.

Videos/CD-ROMs
Polynomials, Dale Seymour Publications

See the *Teacher's Guide for Software Resources* for software addresses.

ASSESSMENT RESOURCES

Student Edition
Math Journal, pp. 426, 453, 464
Mixed Review, pp. 414, 422,
  429, 438, 447, 455, 467
Self Test, p. 439
Chapter Highlights, p. 469
Chapter Study Guide and
  Assessment, pp. 470–472
Alternative Assessment, p. 473
  Portfolio, p. 473

Teacher's Wraparound Edition
5-Minute Check, pp. 408, 415,
  423, 431, 440, 450, 460
Check for Understanding, pp. 411,
  419, 426, 436, 444, 453, 464
Closing Activity, pp. 414, 422,
  429, 439, 447, 455, 467
Cooperative Learning, pp. 409,
  444

Assessment and Evaluation Masters
Multiple-Choice Tests, Forms 1A
  (Honors), 1B (Average), 1C
  (Basic), pp. 169–174
Free-Response Tests, Forms 2A
  (Honors), 2B (Average), 2C
  (Basic), pp. 175–180
Calculator-Based Test, p. 181
Performance Assessment, p. 182
Mid-Chapter Test, p. 183
Quizzes A–D, pp. 184–185
Standardized Test Practice, p. 186
Cumulative Review, pp. 187–188

ENHANCING THE CHAPTER

Examples of some of the materials for enhancing Chapter 7 are shown below.

DIVERSITY

Multicultural Activity Masters, pp. 13, 14

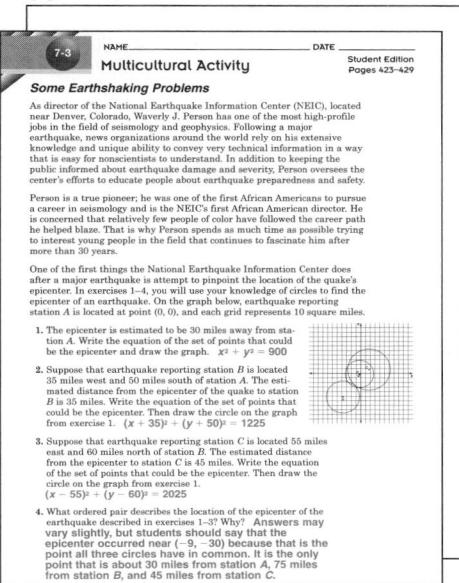

7-3 NAME_____ DATE_____ Student Edition Pages 423–429

Multicultural Activity

Some Earthshaking Problems

As director of the National Earthquake Information Center (NEIC), located near Denver, Colorado, Waverly J. Person has one of the most high-profile jobs in the field of seismology and geophysics. Following a major earthquake, news organizations around the world rely on his extensive knowledge and unusual ability to convey very technical information in a way that is easy for nonscientists to understand. In addition to keeping the public informed about earthquake damage and severity, Person oversees the center's efforts to educate people about earthquake preparedness and safety.

Person is a true pioneer; he was one of the first African Americans to pursue a career in seismology and is the NEIC's first African American director. He is concerned that relatively few people of color have followed the career path he helped blaze. That is why Person spends as much time as possible trying to interest young people in the field that continues to fascinate him after more than 30 years.

One of the first things the National Earthquake Information Center does after a major earthquake is attempt to pinpoint the location of the quake's epicenter. In exercises 1–4, you will use your knowledge of circles to find the epicenter of an earthquake. On the graph below, earthquake reporting station A is located at point $(0, 0)$, and each grid represents 10 square miles.

1. The epicenter is estimated to be 30 miles away from station A. Write the equation of the set of points that could be the epicenter and draw the graph. $x^2 + y^2 = 900$

2. Suppose that earthquake reporting station B is located 35 miles west and 50 miles south of station A. The estimated distance from the epicenter of the quake to station B is 35 miles. Write the equation of the set of points that could be the epicenter. Then draw the circle on the graph from exercise 1. $(x + 35)^2 + (y + 50)^2 = 1225$

3. Suppose that earthquake reporting station C is located 55 miles east and 60 miles north of station B. The estimated distance from the epicenter to station C is 45 miles. Write the equation of the set of points that could be the epicenter. Then draw the circle on the graph from exercise 1. $(x − 55)^2 + (y − 60)^2 = 2025$

4. What ordered pair describes the location of the epicenter of the earthquake described in exercises 1–3? Why? Answers may vary slightly, but students should say that the epicenter occurred near $(−9, −30)$ because that is the point all three circles have in common. It is the only point that is about 30 miles from station A, 75 miles from station B, and 45 miles from station C.

APPLICATIONS

Real-World Applications, 20, 21

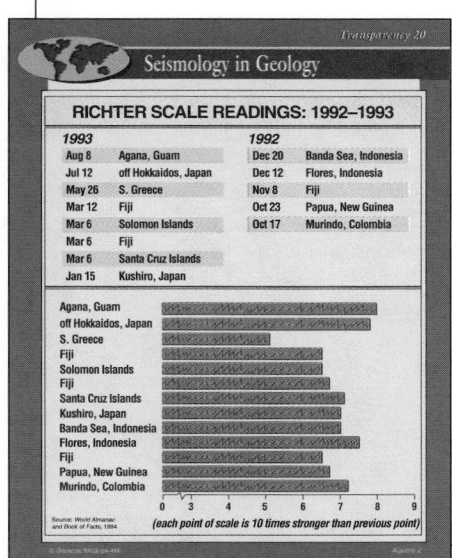

Transparency 20

Seismology in Geology

RICHTER SCALE READINGS: 1992–1993

1993		1992	
Aug 8	Agana, Guam	Dec 20	Banda Sea, Indonesia
Jul 12	off Hokkaidos, Japan	Dec 12	Flores, Indonesia
May 26	S. Greece	Nov 8	Fiji
Mar 12	Fiji	Oct 23	Papua, New Guinea
Mar 6	Solomon Islands	Oct 17	Murindo, Colombia
Mar 6	Fiji		
Mar 6	Santa Cruz Islands		
Jan 15	Kushiro, Japan		

Source: World Almanac and Book of Facts, 1994

(each point of scale is 10 times stronger than previous point)

TECHNOLOGY

Graphing Calculator Masters, p. 7

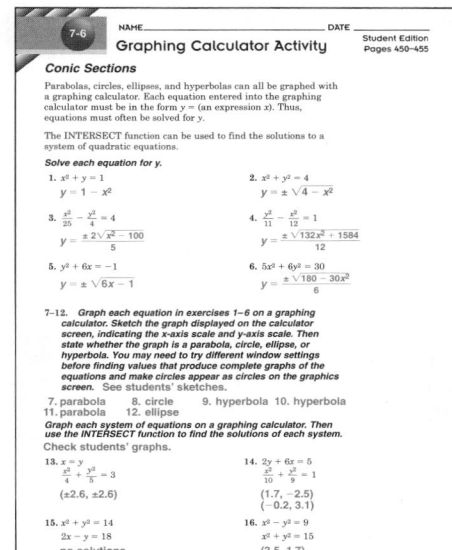

7-6 NAME_____ DATE_____ Student Edition Pages 450–455

Graphing Calculator Activity

Conic Sections

Parabolas, circles, ellipses, and hyperbolas can all be graphed with a graphing calculator. Each equation entered into the graphing calculator must be in the form y = (an expression x). Thus, equations must often be solved for y.

The INTERSECT function can be used to find the solutions to a system of quadratic equations.

Solve each equation for y.

1. $x^2 + y = 1$
   $y = 1 − x^2$

2. $x^2 + y^2 = 4$
   $y = \pm \sqrt{4 − x^2}$

3. $\frac{x^2}{25} − \frac{y^2}{4} = 4$
   $y = \pm \frac{2\sqrt{x^2 − 100}}{5}$

4. $\frac{x^2}{11} − \frac{y^2}{12} = 1$
   $y = \pm \frac{\sqrt{132x^2 + 1584}}{12}$

5. $y^2 + 6x = −1$
   $y = \pm \sqrt{6x − 1}$

6. $5x^2 + 6y^2 = 30$
   $y = \pm \frac{\sqrt{180 − 30x^2}}{6}$

7–12. Graph each equation in exercises 1–6 on a graphing calculator. Sketch the graph displayed on the calculator screen, indicating the x-axis scale and y-axis scale. Then state whether the graph is a parabola, circle, ellipse, or hyperbola. You may need to try different window settings before finding values that produce complete graphs of the equations and make circles appear as circles on the graphics screen. See students' sketches.

7. parabola 8. circle 9. hyperbola 10. hyperbola
11. parabola 12. ellipse

Graph each system of equations on a graphing calculator. Then use the INTERSECT function to find the solutions of each system. Check students' graphs.

13. $x = y$
   $\frac{x^2}{4} + \frac{y^2}{5} = 3$
   $(\pm 2.6, \pm 2.6)$

14. $2y + 6x = 5$
   $\frac{x^2}{10} + \frac{y^2}{9} = 1$
   $(1.7, −2.5)$
   $(−0.2, 3.1)$

15. $x^2 + y^2 = 14$
   $2x − y = 18$
   no solutions

16. $x^2 − y^2 = 9$
   $x^2 + y^2 = 15$
   $(3.5, 1.7)$

TECH PREP

Tech Prep Applications Masters, pp. 13, 14

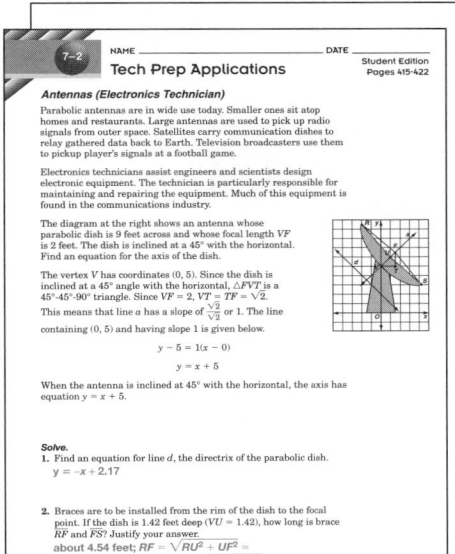

7-2 NAME_____ DATE_____ Student Edition Pages 415–422

Tech Prep Applications

Antennas (Electronics Technician)

Parabolic antennas are in wide use today. Smaller ones sit atop homes and restaurants. Large antennas are used to pick up radio signals from outer space. Satellites carry communication dishes to relay gathered data back to Earth. Television broadcasters use them to pickup player's signals at a football game.

Electronics technicians assist engineers and scientists design electronic equipment. The technician is particularly responsible for maintaining and repairing the equipment. Much of this equipment is found in the communications industry.

The diagram at the right shows an antenna whose parabolic dish is 9 feet across and whose focal length VF is 2 feet. The dish is inclined at a 45° with the horizontal. Find an equation for the axis of the dish.

The vertex V has coordinates $(0, 5)$. Since the dish is inclined at a 45° angle with the horizontal, $\triangle FVT$ is a 45°-45°-90° triangle. Since $VF = 2$, $VT = TF = \sqrt{2}$. This means that line a has a slope of $\frac{\sqrt{2}}{\sqrt{2}}$ or 1. The line containing $(0, 5)$ and having slope 1 is given below.

$$y − 5 = 1(x − 0)$$
$$y = x + 5$$

When the antenna is inclined at 45° with the horizontal, the axis has equation $y = x + 5$.

Solve.
1. Find an equation for line d, the directrix of the parabolic dish.
   $y = −x + 2.17$

2. Braces are to be installed from the rim of the dish to the focal point. If the dish is 1.42 feet deep ($VU = 1.42$), how long is brace $\overline{RF}$ and $\overline{FS}$? Justify your answer.
   about 4.54 feet; $RF = \sqrt{RU^2 + UF^2} = \sqrt{4.5^2 + (2 − 1.42)^2} = \sqrt{20.25 + 0.3364} \approx 4.54$

CONNECTIONS

Science and Math Lab Manual, pp. 91–94

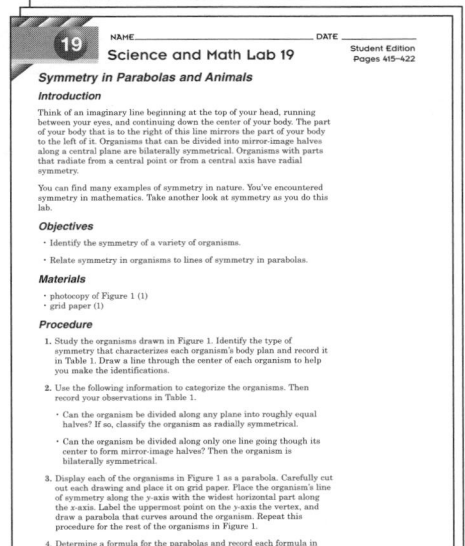

19 NAME_____ DATE_____ Student Edition Pages 415–422

Science and Math Lab 19

Symmetry in Parabolas and Animals

Introduction

Think of an imaginary line beginning at the top of your head, running between your eyes, and continuing down the center of your body. The part of your body that is to the right of this line mirrors the part of your body to the left of it. Organisms that can be divided into mirror-image halves along a central line are bilaterally symmetrical. Organisms with parts that radiate from a central point or from a central axis have radial symmetry.

You can find many examples of symmetry in nature. You've encountered symmetry in mathematics. Take another look at symmetry as you do this lab.

Objectives
· Identify the symmetry of a variety of organisms.
· Relate symmetry in organisms to lines of symmetry in parabolas.

Materials
· photocopy of Figure 1 (1)
· grid paper (1)

Procedure

1. Study the organisms drawn in Figure 1. Identify the type of symmetry that characterizes each organism's body plan and record it in Table 1. Draw a line through the center of each organism to help you make the identifications.

2. Use the following information to categorize the organisms. Then record your observations in Table 1.

· Can the organism be divided along any plane into roughly equal halves? If so, classify the organism as radially symmetrical.

· Can the organism be divided along only one line going though its center to form mirror-image halves? Then the organism is bilaterally symmetrical.

3. Display each of the organisms in Figure 1 as a parabola. Carefully cut out each drawing and place it on grid paper. Place the organism's line of symmetry along the y-axis with the widest horizontal part along the x-axis. Label the uppermost point on the y-axis the vertex, and draw a parabola that curves around the organism. Repeat this procedure for the rest of the organisms in Figure 1.

4. Determine a formula for the parabolas and record each formula in Table 1. Identify the axis of symmetry, the vertex, the focus, and the directrix.

PROBLEM SOLVING

Problem of the Week Cards, 18, 19

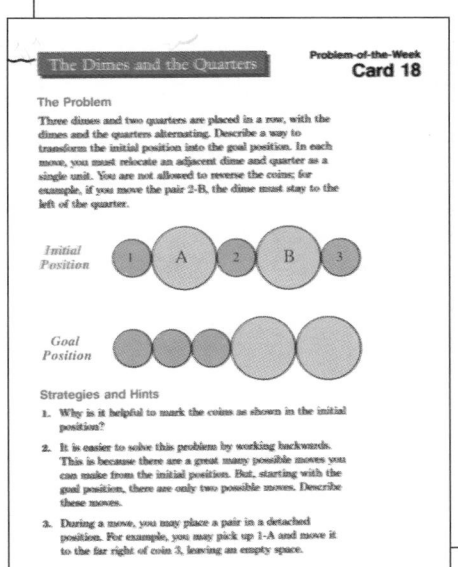

The Dimes and the Quarters

Problem-of-the-Week Card 18

The Problem

Three dimes and two quarters are placed in a row, with the dimes and the quarters alternating. Describe a way to transform the initial position into the goal position. In each move, you must relocate an adjacent dime and quarter as a single unit. You are not allowed to reverse the coins; for example, if you move the pair 2-B, the dime must stay to the left of the quarter.

Initial Position

① Ⓐ ② Ⓑ ③

Goal Position

Strategies and Hints

1. Why is it helpful to mark the coins as shown in the initial position?

2. It is easier to solve this problem by working backwards. This is because there are a great many possible moves you can make from the initial position. But, starting with the goal position, there are only two possible moves. Describe these moves.

3. During a move, you may place a pair in a detached position. For example, you may pick up 1-A and move it to the far right of coin 3, leaving an empty space.

MAKING MATHEMATICS RELEVANT

This two-page introduction to the chapter provides students with an opportunity to explore contemporary topics and their applications to mathematics.

Background Information
Education: Comparing the U.S. with Other Countries Use the table provided to stimulate a discussion based on the following questions.

A. Because country A provides more mathematics instruction time than country B, does it follow that country A's students learn more?

B. What might you infer about math instruction in the United States from the following facts? A team of U.S. students recently beat teams from all over the world in a difficult math competition, yet average math scores in the United States are lower than in many other countries.

CHAPTER 7

Analyzing Conic Sections

Objectives

In this chapter, you will:

- find the distance between two points in the coordinate plane,
- find the midpoint of a line segment in the coordinate plane,
- write equations of conic sections having certain properties,
- graph conic sections,
- use simulations to solve problems, and
- solve systems of quadratic equations and inequalities.

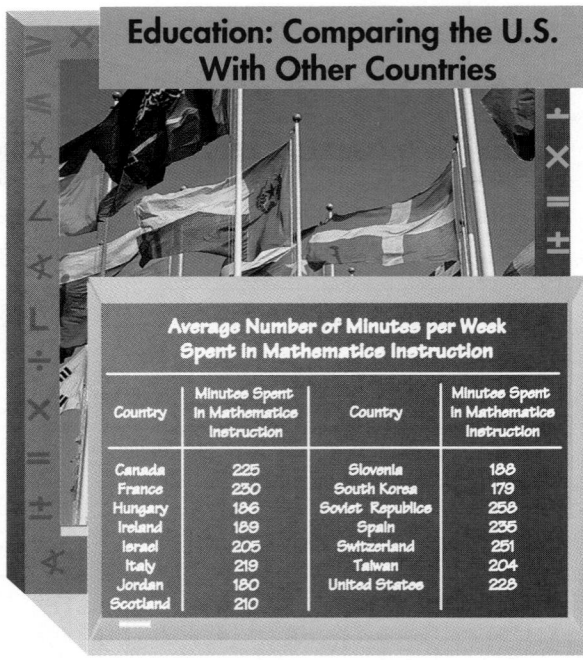

Education: Comparing the U.S. With Other Countries

Average Number of Minutes per Week Spent in Mathematics Instruction

Country	Minutes Spent in Mathematics Instruction	Country	Minutes Spent in Mathematics Instruction
Canada	225	Slovenia	188
France	230	South Korea	179
Hungary	186	Soviet Republic	258
Ireland	189	Spain	235
Israel	205	Switzerland	251
Italy	219	Taiwan	204
Jordan	180	United States	228
Scotland	210		

Source: Bureau of the Census, *Statistical Abstract of the United States*

The best and the brightest of U.S. high school students can match up with their international competition in mathematics. How about in geographic knowledge? Can America's educational system still produce the best? Do you know where the Windward Passage is or the location of the Amur River?

TIME Line

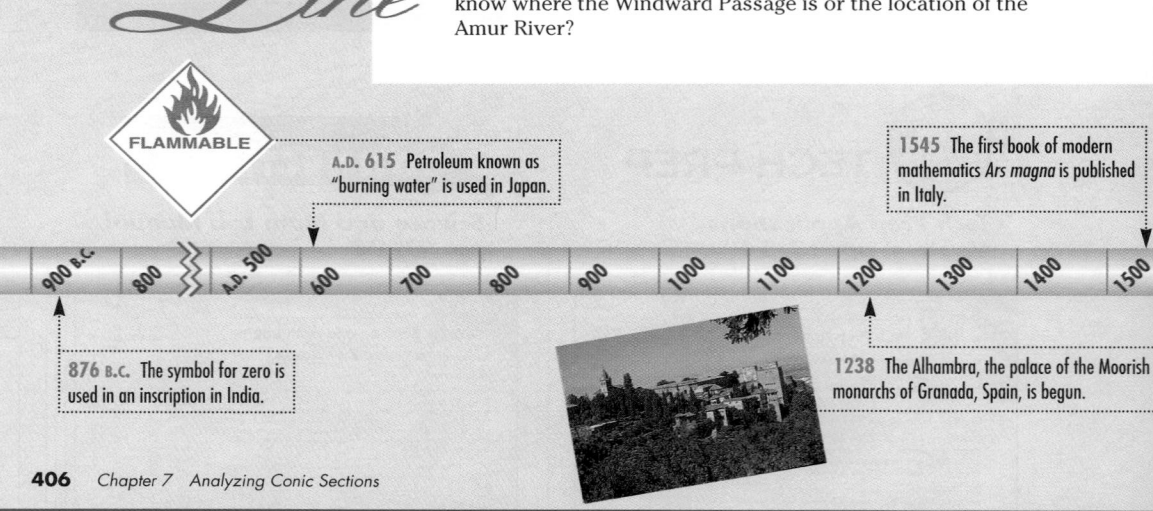

876 B.C. The symbol for zero is used in an inscription in India.

A.D. 615 Petroleum known as "burning water" is used in Japan.

1238 The Alhambra, the palace of the Moorish monarchs of Granada, Spain, is begun.

1545 The first book of modern mathematics *Ars magna* is published in Italy.

TIME Line

Students may be interested in researching one of the mathematical topics found on the time line, such as the first reference to zero in 876 B.C., the publication of the *Ars Magna* in 1545, or the introduction of the Greek letter π for a mathematical constant.

interNET CONNECTION

27th International Physics Olympiad home pages include background information, competition details, and information on the host city and nation.

World Wide Web
http://www.anu.edu.au/Physics/IPhO/Welcome.html

CHRIS GALE
Mic

Chris Galeczka knew that the official languages of Afghanistan are Pashtu and Dari. This knowledge earned him a $25,000 scholarship and a first-place victory in the 1995 National Geography Bee held in Washington, D.C. The 13-year-old from Sterling Heights, Michigan, was chosen from some six million students competing in every state and six territories. These were narrowed to 57 finalists for the contest at the National Geographic Society headquarters, hosted by *Jeopardy!*'s Alex Trebek.

Knowing every country, their capitals, languages, religions, and governments paid off for Chris. His next competition was an international geography contest, also sponsored by the National Geographic Society, at Epcot at Walt Disney World in Orlando, Florida.

Chapter Project

Organize a match of Conic Jeopardy to test your classmates' tournament skills.

- Use four categories for your Jeopardy game: parabolas, circles, ellipses, and hyperbolas.
- Write five problems for each category in varying degrees of difficulty.

- Construct a Jeopardy grid on the chalkboard and assign points to the various levels.
- Challenge your classmates to a game of Conic Jeopardy.
- Use different sets of questions for each round of the game.

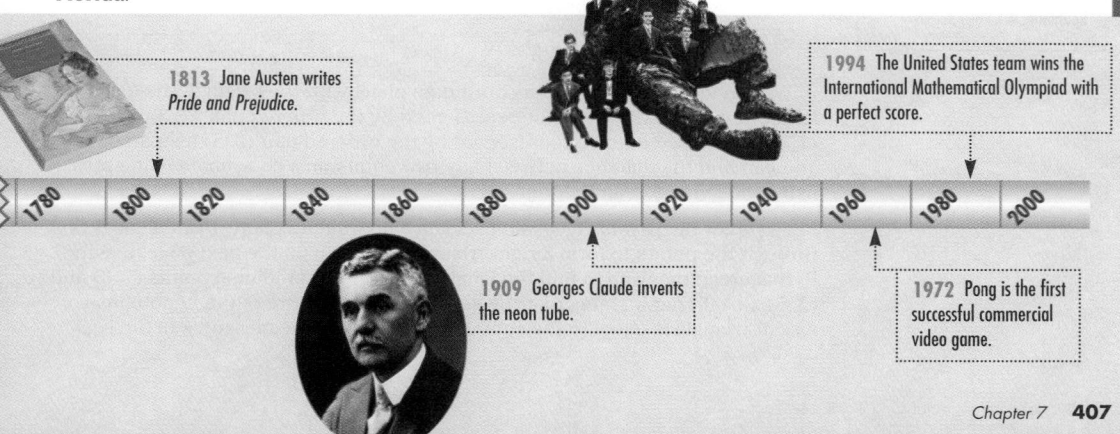

1813 Jane Austen writes *Pride and Prejudice*.

1994 The United States team wins the International Mathematical Olympiad with a perfect score.

1780 1800 1820 1840 1860 1880 1900 1920 1940 1960 1980 2000

1909 Georges Claude invents the neon tube.

1972 Pong is the first successful commercial video game.

Chapter 7 **407**

Alternative Chapter Projects

Two other chapter projects are included in the *Investigations and Projects Masters*. In Chapter 7 Project A, pp. 49–50, students extend the topic in the chapter opener. In Chapter 7 Project B, pp. 51–52, students investigate applications of conic sections.

Emphasize to students that to win a geography bee requires knowledge in many different areas. These include geomorphology, climatology, biogeography, oceanography, soil geography, cultural geography, population geography, social geography, urban geography, economic geography, political geography, and historical geography.

Chapter Project

Cooperative Learning Questions can best be developed in small groups. In a group of five students, each student can make up one question. Each student is timed while trying to work the problems. Average the solution times and rank them accordingly.

Investigations and Projects Masters, p. 49

---

7 NAME_____ DATE _____

Chapter 7 Project A

Student Edition
Pages 408–468

No Contest

1. Here is a problem that might be used in a mathematics contest.

   A roller coaster ride at Cedar Point Amusement Park passes through a tunnel constructed in the shape of a semicircle with a diameter of 6 meters. Give the equation for this semicircle. Find the height of the tunnel 1 meter from the middle.

   Spend 15 minutes working on the solution to this problem by yourself.

2. Work with a partner or small group of students who have also spent 15 minutes on the problem. Take turns sharing your work thus far. Then work together to solve the problem and check your work.

3. Prepare a presentation of your solution in the form of a written or an oral report. Be sure to state the problem, give its solution, and describe how the problem was solved.

4. Write a separate report about how the group worked together on this project. What were some advantages and disadvantages of working together? Based on your experiences, write a list of do's and don'ts for a math team working on a contest problem.

Instructional Resources

- Study Guide Master 7-1
- Practice Master 7-1
- Enrichment Master 7-1

Transparency 7-1A contains the 5-Minute Check for this lesson; **Transparency 7-1B** contains a teaching aid for this lesson.

Recommended Pacing	
Standard Pacing	Day 1 of 15
Honors Pacing	Day 1 of 13
Block Scheduling*	Day 1 of 7 (along with Lesson 7-2)

*For more information on pacing and possible lesson plans, refer to the *Block Scheduling Booklet.*

1 FOCUS

5-Minute Check
(over Chapter 6)

1. Express $f(x) = -4(2x - 1)^2$ in quadratic form.
   $f(x) = -16x^2 + 16x - 4$
2. Name the vertex and axis of symmetry for the graph of $f(x) = (x - 2)^2 + 6$.
   (2, 6); x = 2
3. Name the direction of opening for the graph of $f(x) = -\frac{4}{5}(x + 2)^2 - 3$.
   downward
4. Write an equation of the parabola that passes through (0, 15), (−1, 8), and (−6, 3).
   $f(x) = x^2 + 8x + 15$

Motivating the Lesson

Situational Problem If Luba lives 5 miles from Zina and Zina lives 3 miles from Connie, how far does Luba live from Connie?

Have students draw sketches of possible answers. Students should realize that there are a multitude of answers to the problem as it is stated.

7–1

What YOU'LL LEARN

- To find the distance between two points in the coordinate plane, and
- to find the midpoint of a line segment in the coordinate plane.

Why IT'S IMPORTANT

You can use the distance and midpoint formulas to solve problems involving geography and transportation.

CAREER CHOICES

An **aircraft mechanic** makes repairs, performs scheduled maintenance, and completes required inspections on airplanes.

Aircraft mechanics must graduate from a trade school, obtain work experience, and pass tests to gain certification from the Federal Aviation Administration.

For further information, contact:

Aviation Maintenance Foundation
P.O. Box 2826
Redmond, WV 98073

Integration: Geometry
The Distance and Midpoint Formulas

APPLICATION
Aviation

Each July, Browning, Montana, hosts the North American Indian Days. Browning is located just east of Glacier National Park and is on one of the four reservations for the Blackfeet Indians. The other three reservations are located in Canada.

Yoomee wants to fly her small plane from Miles City, Montana, to Browning to participate in the celebration. First, she needs to estimate the distance from Miles City to Browning. A square grid is superimposed on the map of Montana. Each side of a square on the grid represents 70 miles. Miles City appears at 7C on the map, and Browning appears at 3A on the map. How can we use this grid to help the pilot estimate the distance from Miles City to Browning?

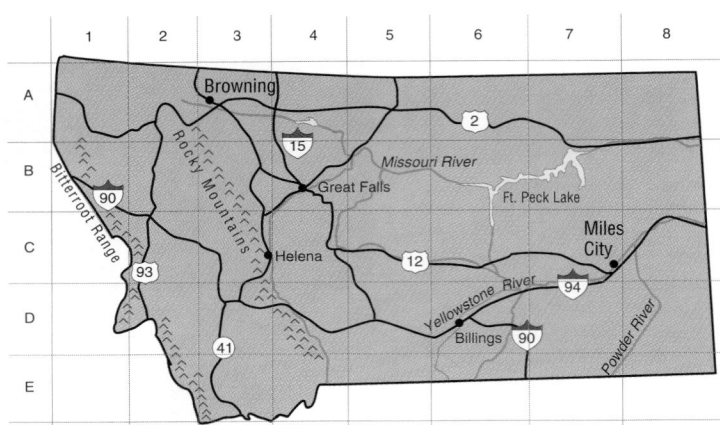

We can look at the map as a coordinate plane with the origin in the lower left corner. Miles City could be represented by the ordered pair (7, 3) instead of 7C. Browning could be represented by the ordered pair (3, 5) instead of 3A. You can find the distance between any two points on a coordinate plane by using the Pythagorean theorem.

First plot the points (7, 3) and (3, 5) on a coordinate plane. Draw segments through the points to form a right triangle as shown on the next page. Use the Pythagorean theorem to find the length of the segment joining points (7, 3) and (3, 5). Recall that it states that the square of the measure of the hypotenuse of a right triangle is equal to the sum of the squares of the measures of the legs $(a^2 + b^2 = c^2)$.

CAREER CHOICES

The median annual salary for aircraft mechanics was $32,500 in 1992, with the top 10% earning over $47,500.

You can find the horizontal or vertical distance between two points by using absolute value. The distance between two points on a number line whose coordinates are a and b is $|a - b|$ or $|b - a|$. The length of the horizontal leg is $|7 - 3|$ or 4 units, and the length of the vertical leg is $|3 - 5|$ or 2 units.

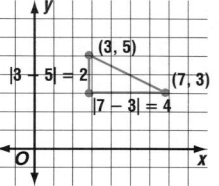

$$c^2 = a^2 + b^2 \quad \textit{Pythagorean theorem}$$

$$d^2 = 4^2 + 2^2 \quad \textit{Replace c with d, a with 4, and b with 2.}$$

$$d^2 = 16 + 4$$

$$d^2 = 20$$

$$d = \sqrt{20}$$

$$d \approx 4.47 \quad \textit{Distance is nonnegative.}$$

The map distance is about 4.47 units. Each unit equals 70 miles. So, the actual distance is about 4.47(70) or 312.9 miles.

The solution for this application suggests a method for finding the distance between any two points on a coordinate plane. Suppose (x_1, y_1) and (x_2, y_2) name two points in the coordinate plane. We can form a right triangle by drawing a vertical line through point (x_1, y_1) and a horizontal line through point (x_2, y_2). The lines will intersect at the third vertex of the triangle, (x_1, y_2). *Why?*

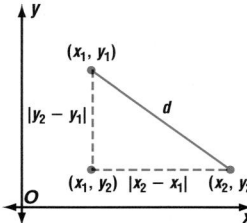

Use the Pythagorean theorem to find the distance, d, between the two points.

$$c^2 = a^2 + b^2 \quad \textit{Pythagorean theorem}$$

$$d^2 = |x_2 - x_1|^2 + |y_2 - y_1|^2 \quad \textit{Replace c with d, a with } |x_2 - x_1|, \textit{ and b with } |y_2 - y_1|.$$

$$d^2 = (x_2 - x_1)^2 + (y_2 - y_1)^2 \quad \textit{Why can } (x_2 - x_1)^2 \textit{ be substituted for } |x_2 - x_1|^2?$$

$$d = \sqrt{(x_2 - x_1)^2 + (y_2 - y_1)^2}$$

Distance Formula for Two Points in a Plane	The distance between two points with coordinates (x_1, y_1) and (x_2, y_2) is given by $d = \sqrt{(x_2 - x_1)^2 + (y_2 - y_1)^2}$.

Example Find the distance between points at $(-5, 7)$ and $(9, -11)$.

$$d = \sqrt{(x_2 - x_1)^2 + (y_2 - y_1)^2} \quad \textit{Distance formula}$$

$$= \sqrt{[9 - (-5)]^2 + (-11 - 7)^2} \quad \textit{Replace } x_2 \textit{ with 9, } x_1 \textit{ with } -5, y_2 \textit{ with } -11, \textit{ and } y_1 \textit{ with 7.}$$

$$= \sqrt{(14)^2 + (-18)^2}$$

$$= \sqrt{196 + 324}$$

$$= \sqrt{520} \text{ or } 2\sqrt{130}$$

The distance is $2\sqrt{130}$ or about 22.8 units.

 Cooperative Learning

Numbered Heads Together Separate the class into groups of four. Give each group a geoboard. Have them make several right triangles. Have them find the length of the hypotenuse of the right triangles formed. Then have them generalize the results. Discuss the results and the formula on this page. For more information on the numbered heads together strategy, see *Cooperative Learning in the Mathematics Classroom*, one of the titles in the Glencoe Mathematics Professional Series, pages 9–12.

Teaching Tip A good way to introduce distance is with the use of a geoboard. Using an overhead projector geoboard, squares can easily be counted and distance calculated using the Pythagorean theorem.

In-Class Example

For Example 1
Find the distance between the points at $(4, 4)$ and $(-6, -2)$.
$2\sqrt{34}$

Teaching Tip In Example 2, you may want to remind students that the midpoint is half the distance.

In-Class Examples

For Example 2
Show that $P(5.5, 5.5)$ is the midpoint of the segment joining $A(4, 2)$ and $B(7, 9)$.
slope AP = slope $AB = \frac{7}{3}$;

$AP = BP = \frac{\sqrt{58}}{2}$

For Example 3
Circle X has a diameter $\overline{MN}$. If M is at $(-4, 2)$ and the center is at $(-6, 3)$, find the coordinates of N.
$(-8, 4)$

Example Show that $P(5, 3)$ is the midpoint of the segment joining $M(-1, 6)$ and $N(11, 0)$.

First, we must show that P is on $\overline{MN}$. It is sufficient to show that $\overline{MP}$ and $\overline{MN}$ have the same slope.

slope of $\overline{MP} = \frac{6-3}{-1-5}$

$= \frac{3}{-6}$ or $-\frac{1}{2}$

slope of $\overline{MN} = \frac{6-0}{-1-11}$

$= \frac{6}{-12}$ or $-\frac{1}{2}$

Next, we must show that the distance from M to P is the same as the distance from N to P. The length of $\overline{MP}$ is represented by MP, and the length of $\overline{MN}$ by MN.

distance from M to P

$MP = \sqrt{(-1-5)^2 + (6-3)^2}$

$= \sqrt{(-6)^2 + 3^2}$

$= \sqrt{36 + 9}$

$= \sqrt{45}$ or $3\sqrt{5}$

distance from N to P

$NP = \sqrt{(11-5)^2 + (0-3)^2}$

$= \sqrt{6^2 + (-3)^2}$

$= \sqrt{36 + 9}$

$= \sqrt{45}$ or $3\sqrt{5}$

Since the distances are the same, P is the midpoint of $\overline{MN}$.

In Example 2, the coordinates of the endpoints of $\overline{MN}$ are $(-1, 6)$ and $(11, 0)$. Find the mean of the x-coordinates and the mean of the y-coordinates. What do you observe? This suggests the following.

Midpoint of a Line Segment	If a line segment has endpoints at (x_1, y_1) and (x_2, y_2), then the midpoint of the line segment has coordinates $\left(\frac{x_1 + x_2}{2}, \frac{y_1 + y_2}{2}\right)$.

Example Circle P has a diameter $\overline{AB}$. If A is at $(-3, -5)$ and the center is at $(2, 3)$, find the coordinates of B.

Explore Read the problem. You know the coordinates for one endpoint of a diameter and the coordinates for the center of the circle. You want to know the coordinates for the other endpoint of the diameter.

Plan The center of the circle is the midpoint of the diameter. Use the formula for the midpoint of a line segment to find the coordinates of the other endpoint. Let (x, y) be the coordinates of B.

Solve $(x, y) = \left(\frac{x_1 + x_2}{2}, \frac{y_1 + y_2}{2}\right)$

$(2, 3) = \left(\frac{-3 + x}{2}, \frac{-5 + y}{2}\right)$

$2 = \frac{-3 + x}{2}$ and $3 = \frac{-5 + y}{2}$

$4 = -3 + x$ $\qquad 6 = -5 + y$

$7 = x$ $\qquad\qquad 11 = y$

The coordinates of B are $(7, 11)$.

GLENCOE Technology

Interactive Mathematics Tools Software

This multimedia software provides an interactive lesson that allows students to derive the distance formula and to practice the skill by substituting coordinates into the formula. A **Computer Journal** gives students an opportunity to write about what they have learned.

For Windows & Macintosh

Examine If (2, 3) is the center of the circle, then it must be equidistant from (−3, −5) and (7, 11). Use the distance formula to check your answer.

$$d = \sqrt{(-3 - 2)^2 + (-5 - 3)^2} = \sqrt{89} \text{ or about } 9.43$$

$$d = \sqrt{(7 - 2)^2 + (11 - 3)^2} = \sqrt{89} \text{ or about } 9.43$$

The distances are the same, so (2, 3) must be the midpoint of the diameter or the center of the circle.

CHECK FOR UNDERSTANDING

Communicating Mathematics

1a. Substitute values into the midpoint formula and solve for the other endpoint.

Study the lesson. Then complete the following.

1. a. **Describe** how you would find the coordinates of the endpoint of a segment given the midpoint and the other endpoint.

   b. **Demonstrate** your method by finding the endpoint of a segment with midpoint (−4, 13) and endpoint (20, 31).   **See margin.**

2. **Describe** a situation in which a point is equidistant from the endpoints of a segment but is not the midpoint.   **See margin.**

3. **Explain** why it is not important which endpoint is chosen as (x_1, y_1) and which is chosen as (x_2, y_2) when using the distance formula.
$(x_2 - x_1)^2 = (x_1 - x_2)^2$ and $(y_2 - y_1)^2 = (y_1 - y_2)^2$

Guided Practice

Find the distance between each pair of points with the given coordinates.

4. (7, 8), (−4, 9) $\sqrt{122}$ units

5. (0.5, 1.4), (1.1, 2.9) $\sqrt{2.61}$ units

6. $(2\sqrt{3}, -5), (-3\sqrt{3}, 9)$ $\sqrt{271}$ units

Find the midpoint of each line segment if the coordinates of the endpoints are given.

7. $\left(\frac{5}{2}, \frac{9}{4}\right)$

8. $\left(\frac{5\sqrt{2}}{2}, \frac{5\sqrt{5}}{2}\right)$

9. $AB = 2\sqrt{5},$ $BC = 2\sqrt{10},$ $AC = 2\sqrt{5}$

7. (8, 9), (−3, −4.5)

8. $(-3\sqrt{2}, -4\sqrt{5}), (8\sqrt{2}, 9\sqrt{5})$

9. **Geometry**   Show that the triangle with vertices $A(-3, 0)$, $B(-1, 4)$, and $C(1, -2)$ is isosceles.

10. **Geometry**   Triangle MNO has vertices $M(3, 5)$, $N(-2, 8)$, and $O(7, -4)$. Find the coordinates of the midpoints of each side.
$\left(\frac{1}{2}, \frac{13}{2}\right), \left(\frac{5}{2}, 2\right), \left(5, \frac{1}{2}\right)$

EXERCISES

Practice

Find the distance between each pair of points with the given coordinates.

15. 16 units
16. $5\sqrt{3}$ units
17. $\sqrt{65}$ units
18. $\frac{\sqrt{813}}{12}$ units

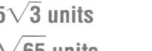

11. (−4, 9), (1, −3)   13 units

12. (−4, −10), (−3, −11) $\sqrt{2}$ units

13. (9, −2), (12, −14) $3\sqrt{17}$ units

14. (0.23, 0.4), (0.68, −0.2)   0.75 units

15. $(-2\sqrt{7}, 10), (4\sqrt{7}, 8)$

16. $(2\sqrt{3}, 4\sqrt{3}), (2\sqrt{3}, -\sqrt{3})$

17. $\left(-3, \frac{-2}{11}\right), \left(5, \frac{9}{11}\right)$

18. $\left(\frac{2\sqrt{3}}{3}, \frac{\sqrt{5}}{4}\right), \left(\frac{-2\sqrt{3}}{3}, \frac{\sqrt{5}}{2}\right)$

Lesson 7–1 **INTEGRATION** *Geometry   The Distance and Midpoint Formulas*   **411**

3 PRACTICE/APPLY

Check for Understanding
Exercises 1–10 are designed to help you assess your students' understanding through reading, writing, speaking, and modeling. You should work through Exercises 1–3 with your students and then monitor their work on Exercises 4–10.

Error Analysis
Students may subtract the coordinates of a point in different orders when using the distance formula. It is important that the coordinates be subtracted in the correct order, $(x_2 - x_1)$ and $(y_2 - y_1)$, regardless of which point is chosen to be (x_1, y_1).

Additional Answers

1b. $x = \frac{x_1 + x_2}{2}$ $y = \frac{y_1 + y_2}{2}$

$-4 = \frac{x_1 + 20}{2}$ $13 = \frac{y_1 + 31}{2}$

$-8 = x_1 + 20$ $26 = y_1 + 31$

$-28 = x_1$ $-5 = y_1$

The other endpoint is at (−28, −5).

2. any point on the perpendicular bisector of the segment, but not on the segment

Assignment Guide
Core: 11–39 odd, 40, 41, 43–51
Enriched: 12–38 even, 39–51

For **Extra Practice,** see p. 892.

The red A, B, and C flags, printed only in the Teacher's Wraparound Edition, indicate the level of difficulty of the exercises.

Reteaching

Using Graphics Develop the formula for the coordinates of the midpoint of a line segment from the graph at the right.

$$x_m = x_1 + \frac{x_2 - x_1}{2}$$

and $y_m = y_1 + \frac{y_2 - y_1}{2}$

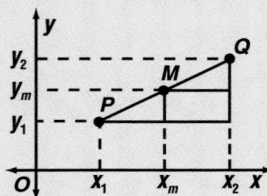

Additional Answer

38b.

$$AQ = \sqrt{\left[-2-\left(\frac{9}{2}\right)\right]^2 + (4-7)^2}$$

$$= \sqrt{\left(-\frac{13}{2}\right)^2 + (-3)^2}$$

$$= \sqrt{\frac{169}{4} + 9}$$

$$= \frac{\sqrt{205}}{2}$$

$$QY = \sqrt{\left[-2-\left(\frac{9}{2}\right)\right]^2 + (10-7)^2}$$

$$= \sqrt{\left(-\frac{13}{2}\right)^2 + 3^2}$$

$$= \sqrt{\frac{169}{4} + 9}$$

$$= \sqrt{\frac{205}{4}}$$

$$= \frac{\sqrt{205}}{2}$$

$$AY = \sqrt{[-2-(-2)]^2 + (4-10)^2}$$

$$= \sqrt{0^2 + (-6)^2}$$

$$= \sqrt{0 + 36}$$

$$= \sqrt{36}$$

$$= 6$$

Study Guide Masters, p. 49

NAME _____ DATE _____

7-1

Study Guide

Student Edition
Pages 408–414

Integration: Geometry
The Distance and Midpoint Formulas

For number lines, you can use absolute value and averages to find distances and locate midpoints. You can do the same in the coordinate plane, though to find distances you need to use the Pythagorean theorem.

Number Line	Coordinate Plane
A: coordinate a B: coordinate b	P: coordinates (x_1, y_1) Q: coordinates (x_2, y_2)
distance: $AB = |a - b|$ or $|b - a|$	distance: $PQ = \sqrt{(x_2 - x_1)^2 + (y_2 - y_1)^2}$
midpoint: $\frac{a+b}{2}$ (average)	midpoint: $\left(\frac{x_1+x_2}{2}, \frac{y_1+y_2}{2}\right)$

Example: Find the distance from P to Q and the midpoint of $\overline{PQ}$ if P has coordinates $(-2, 7)$ and Q has coordinates $(9, 3)$.

You can choose either point for (x_1, y_1).

Use the other point for (x_2, y_2). Let (x_1, y_1) be $(-2, 7)$. Then (x_2, y_2) is $(9, 3)$.

$PQ = \sqrt{(x_2 - x_1)^2 + (y_2 - y_1)^2}$ midpoint of $\overline{PQ} = \left(\frac{x_1+x_2}{2}, \frac{y_1+y_2}{2}\right)$

$= \sqrt{(9-(-2))^2 + (3-7)^2}$ $= \left(\frac{(-2)+9}{2}, \frac{7+3}{2}\right)$

$= \sqrt{121 + 16}$ $= \left(\frac{7}{2}, 5\right)$

$= \sqrt{137}$

Find the distance between each pair of points with the given coordinates.

1. $(-3, 4), (6, -11)$
   $3\sqrt{34}$
2. $(13, 9), (11, 15)$
   $2\sqrt{10}$
3. $(-15, -7), (2, 12)$
   $5\sqrt{26}$
4. $\left(\frac{1}{2}, 2\right), \left(-\frac{1}{2}, 1\right)$
   $\sqrt{2}$
5. $\left(\frac{1}{4}, \frac{1}{2}\right), \left(\frac{1}{2}, \frac{1}{4}\right)$
   $\frac{1}{4}\sqrt{2}$
6. $(1.0, -0.31), (-0.2, 0.19)$
   1.3

Find the midpoint of each line segment if the coordinates of the endpoints are given.

7. $(3, 5), (-6, 11)$
   $\left(-\frac{3}{2}, 8\right)$
8. $(8, -15), (-7, 13)$
   $\left(\frac{1}{2}, -1\right)$
9. $(2.5, -6.1), (7.9, 13.7)$
   $(5.2, 3.8)$
10. $(-7, -6), (-1, 24)$
    $(-4, 9)$
11. $(3, -10), (30, -20)$
    $\left(\frac{33}{2}, -15\right)$
12. $(-9, 1.7), (-11, 1.3)$
    $(-10, 1.5)$

412 *Chapter 7*

---

20. $\left(\frac{17}{2}, \frac{27}{2}\right)$

31. $(-4.3, 2.8)$

33a. $y = -\frac{2}{5}x - 2$

33b. $\sqrt{29}$ units

33c. $\left(-\frac{5}{2}, -1\right)$

34a. $(6, 0), (1, -2), (-1, 7)$

34d. $\sqrt{29} + 7\sqrt{2} + \sqrt{85}$

37a. $2\sqrt{58}$ and $6\sqrt{2}$ units

Find the midpoint of each line segment if the coordinates of the endpoints are given.

19. $(8, 3), (16, 7)$ $(12, 5)$
20. $(5, 9), (12, 18)$
21. $(-5, 3), (-3, -7)$ $(-4, -2)$
22. $(6, -5), (-2, -7)$ $(2, -6)$
23. $(0.45, 7), (-0.3, -9)$
    $(0.075, -1)$
24. $(-3, -12), (-8, 0.34)$
    $(-5.5, -5.83)$

Find the value of a so that the distance between points with the given coordinates is 10 units.

 B

25. $(-7, 3), (a, 11)$ -1 or -13
26. $(7, 2), (-1, a)$ -4 or 8
27. $(6, 3), (8, a)$
    about 12.8 or -6.8
28. $(-8, 8), (a, 11)$
    about 1.5 or -17.5

Given the coordinates of one endpoint of $\overline{AB}$ and its midpoint, M, find the coordinates of the other endpoint.

29. $A(9, 3), M(4, 2)$ $(-1, 1)$
30. $B(2, 5), M(-1, 7)$ $(-4, 9)$
31. $M(-0.8, 3.85), B(2.7, 4.9)$
32. $M\left(\frac{9}{16}, \frac{5}{4}\right), A\left(\frac{1}{4}, 3\right)$ $\left(\frac{7}{8}, -\frac{1}{2}\right)$

C

33. A graph of line AB is shown at the right.
    a. Write an equation for this line.
    b. Find the length of $\overline{AB}$.
    c. Find the coordinates of the midpoint of $\overline{AB}$.

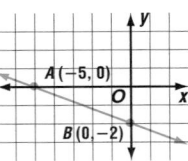

34. Triangle CAT has vertices $C(4, 9)$, $A(8, -9)$, and $T(-6, 5)$.
    a. Find the coordinates of the midpoints of each side of the triangle.
    b. The *median* of a triangle is a segment that joins a vertex of the triangle and the midpoint of the side opposite that vertex. Find the length of the median from point C to $\overline{TA}$. $\sqrt{130}$ units
    c. Find the perimeter of $\triangle CAT$. $2\sqrt{29} + 14\sqrt{2} + 2\sqrt{85}$ units
    d. Find the perimeter of the triangle formed in part a above.
    e. How do the perimeters in parts c and d compare?
    The perimeter in part c is twice the perimeter in part d.

35. Find the perimeter of the quadrilateral shown at the right.
    $\sqrt{65} + 2\sqrt{2} + \sqrt{122} + \sqrt{277}$ units
36. Find the center of the circle whose diameter has endpoints at $(9, 0)$ and $(11, -14)$. $(10, -7)$

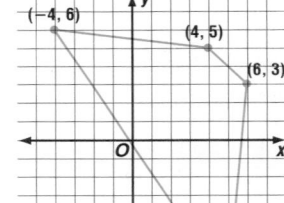

37. The vertices of a parallelogram are $M(2, 2)$ $A(12, 2)$, $T(16, 8)$, and $H(6, 8)$.
    a. Find the length of each diagonal.
    b. Find the coordinates of the point of intersection of the diagonals. $(9, 5)$

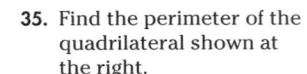

38a. $Q\left(\frac{9}{2}, 7\right)$

38b. Isosceles; see margin for evidence.

38. Triangle *MAY* is a right triangle.
  a. Find the midpoint of the hypotenuse. Call it point *Q*.
  b. Classify △*AQY* according to the length of its sides. Include sufficient evidence to support your conclusion.
  c. Classify △*AQM* according to its angles. **obtuse**

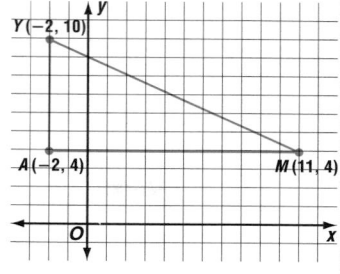

Programming

39. The graphing calculator program at the right can help you find the distance between points with coordinates (x_1, y_1) and (x_2, y_2).
  a. Use the program to find the distance between the points at (1, 5) and (5, 2). **5 units**

39b. about 18.97 units
  b. Use the program to find the distance between the points at (−3, 6) and (−9, −12).

39c. See margin.
  c. Modify the program to find the midpoint of a segment.
  d. Test your program by finding the midpoint of the segment with endpoints at (12, 8) and (−5, −11). **(3.5, −1.5)**

```
PROGRAM:DISTFORM
: ClrHome
: Disp "X1 ="
: Input A
: Disp "Y1 ="
: Input B
: Disp "X2 ="
: Input C
: Disp "Y2 ="
: Input E
: C - A → X
: E - B → Y
: √ (X² + Y²) → D
: Disp "DISTANCE"
: Disp "BETWEEN"
: Disp "(X1, Y1) AND"
: Disp "(X2, Y2) IS ="
: Disp D
```

Critical Thinking

40. $\left(\frac{7}{2}, -\frac{9}{2}\right)$

40. Find the coordinates of the point that is three-fourths of the way from $P(-1, 12)$ to $Q(5, -10)$.

Applications and Problem Solving

41a. about 300 miles

41. Transportation
A grid is superimposed on a map of a portion of the state of Florida.
  a. About how far is it from Orlando, Florida, to Tallahassee, Florida, if each unit on the grid represents 70 miles?
  b. How long will it take a plane to fly from Tallahassee, Florida, to Daytona Beach, Florida, if its speed averages 180 miles per hour? **about 1.6 hours**

Lake Eola, Orlando, Florida

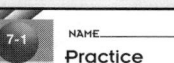

Lesson 7–1 **INTEGRATION** *Geometry The Distance and Midpoint Formulas* **413**

Using the Programming Exercises The program given in Exercise 39 is for use with a TI-82 graphing calculator. For other programmable calculators, have students consult their owner's manual for commands similar to those presented here.

Additional Answer

39c. : ClrHome
  : Disp "X1 ="
  : Input A
  : Disp "Y1 = "
  : Input B
  : Disp "X2 = "
  : Input C
  : Disp "Y2 = "
  : Input D
  : $\frac{(A + C)}{2}$ → X
  : $\frac{(B + D)}{2}$ → Y
  : Disp "X VALUE OF MIDPOINT IS"
  : Disp X
  : Disp "Y VALUE OF MIDPOINT IS"
  : Disp Y

Practice Masters, p. 49

NAME _____ DATE _____

7-1 **Practice**   Student Edition Pages 408–414

Integration: Geometry
The Distance and Midpoint Formulas

Find the distance between each pair of points with the given coordinates.

1. $(-3, 5), (2, 8)$ $\sqrt{34}$

2. $(6, -1), (-3, -2)$ $\sqrt{82}$

3. $\left(\frac{2}{5}, 3\right), \left(\frac{3}{4}, \frac{5}{2}\right)$ $\frac{\sqrt{149}}{20}$

4. $(-4\sqrt{2}, -\sqrt{8}), (-5\sqrt{2}, \sqrt{18})$ $2\sqrt{13}$

5. $(3\sqrt{5}, 4\sqrt{2}), (-2\sqrt{5}, 3\sqrt{8})$ $\sqrt{133}$

6. $\left(\frac{1}{2}, \frac{2}{3}\right), \left(\frac{4}{5}, \frac{9}{10}\right)$ $\frac{\sqrt{130}}{30}$

Find the value of c such that the distance between points with the given coordinates is 5 units.

7. $(5, 2), (c, -3)$ 5

8. $(-2, c), (2, -1)$ −4 or 2

9. $(0, c), (3, 1)$ −3 or 5

10. $(c, 0), (-4, 1)$ $-4 + 2\sqrt{6}$ or $-4 - 2\sqrt{6}$

Find the midpoint of each line segment if the coordinates of the endpoints are given.

11. $(8, -3), (-6, -11)$ $(1, -7)$

12. $(-14, 5), (10, 6)$ $\left(-2, \frac{11}{2}\right)$

13. $\left(-\frac{1}{2}, \sqrt{27}\right), (3, 5\sqrt{3})$ $\left(\frac{5}{4}, 4\sqrt{3}\right)$

14. $(1.3, -0.6), (4, -8)$ $(2.65, -4.3)$

15. $(2.6, -4.7), (8.4, 2.5)$ $(5.5, -1.1)$

16. $(5, 8\sqrt{6}), (9, -2\sqrt{24})$ $(7, 2\sqrt{6})$

Chapter 7 **413**

Closing Activity

Modeling On a geoboard, select three vertices of a right triangle where no sides are parallel to either axis. Use the Pythagorean theorem to determine that it is a right triangle.

Additional Answers

43a. Sample answer: Draw several lines across the U.S. One should go from the northeast corner to the southwest corner, another should go from the southeast corner to the northwest corner, another should go across the middle of the U.S. from east to west, etc. Find the centers of these lines. Find a point that represents all of the points.

43d. Sample answer: Cut out Alaska and Hawaii and place them next to the continental U.S. Follow the procedure described in Exercise 43a.

Enrichment Masters, p. 49

7-1	NAME _____ DATE _____
Enrichment	Student Edition Pages 408–414

Reading Algebra

If two mathematical problems have basic structural similarities, they are said to be **analogous.** Using analogies is one way of discovering and proving new theorems.

The following numbered sentences discuss a three-dimensional analogy to the Pythagorean theorem.

01 Consider a tetrahedron with three perpendicular faces that meet at vertex O.

02 Suppose you want to know how the areas A, B, and C of the three faces that meet at vertex O are related to the area D of the face opposite vertex O.

03 It is natural to expect a formula analogous to the Pythagorean theorem $z^2 = x^2 + y^2$, which is true for a similar situation in two dimensions.

04 To explore the three-dimensional case, you might guess a formula and then try to prove it.

05 Two reasonable guesses are $D^3 = A^3 + B^3 + C^3$ and $D^2 = A^2 + B^2 + C^2$.

Refer to the numbered sentences to answer the questions.

1. Use sentence 01 and the top diagram. The prefix *tetra-* means four. Write an informal definition of tetrahedron.
a three-dimensional figure with four faces

2. Use sentence 02 and the top diagram. What are the lengths of the sides of each face of the tetrahedron?
a, b, and c; a, q, and r; b, p, and r; c, p, and q

3. Rewrite sentence 01 to state a two-dimensional analogue. Consider a triangle with two perpendicular sides that meet at vertex C.

4. Refer to the top diagram and write expressions for the areas A, B, and C mentioned in sentence 02.
Possible answer: $A = \frac{1}{2}pr$, $B = \frac{1}{2}pq$, $C = \frac{1}{2}rq$

5. To explore the three-dimensional case, you might begin by expressing a, b, and c in terms of p, q, and r. Use the Pythagorean theorem to do this.
$a^2 = q^2 + r^2$, $b^2 = r^2 + p^2$, $c^2 = p^2 + q^2$

6. Which guess in sentence 05 seems more likely? Justify your answer. See students' explanations.

---

42. Sports In a field goal attempt, a football was kicked from a hash mark on the twenty-yard line. If the ball passed midway between the goal posts, what was the ground distance traveled by the ball from the point that it was kicked to the point on the ground below where it crossed the goal post? **about 93.87 ft**

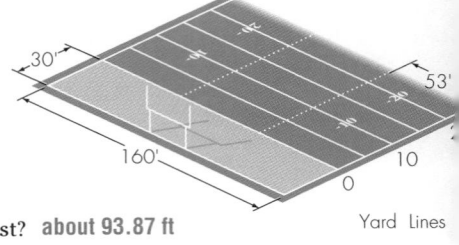
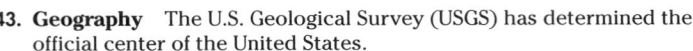

Yard Lines

43. Geography The U.S. Geological Survey (USGS) has determined the official center of the United States.

le Fourche, South Dakota   The Center of the Nation

a. Describe a method that might be used to determine the geographical center of the continental United States. **See margin.**

b. Use a map of the continental United States to determine the geographical center. **See students' work.**

c. USGS has located the geographical center of the continental United States in Kansas. How does the result of your method compare to result of the USGS method? **See students' work.**

d. How could you determine the geographical center of the United States if the land masses of Alaska and Hawaii are included? **See margin.**

e. USGS has declared the geographical center of the *entire* United States to be near Belle Fourche, South Dakota. Would you agree with this location? Explain. **See students' work.**

f. How do you think the geographical center compares to the population center? **Sample answer: Because certain sections of the U.S. are more populated, the geographical and population centers differ.**

Mixed Review

44. Conservation On September 3, 1964, President Lyndon B. Johnson signed the Wilderness Act, thereby establishing a national wilderness preservation system of the public lands of the United States. The public lands in Illinois are listed in the table at the right. (Lesson 6–8)

Park	Number of Acres
Bald Knob	5863
Bay Creek	2866
Burden Falls	3671
Clear Springs	4730
Crab Orchard	4050
Garden of the Gods	3268
Lusk Creek	4466
Panther Den	685

a. Find the mean of the public land acreage. **3700 acres**

b. Find the standard deviation of the public land acreage. **1432.7 acres**

c. Does the standard deviation indicate a large or small variation in the number of public land acres? Explain. **Sample answer: large variation**

45. Find $(t^2 - 3t + 2) \div (t + 2)$ by using synthetic division. (Lesson 5–3)

45. $t - 5 + \dfrac{12}{t+2}$

46. Simplify $(s + 3)^2$. (Lesson 5–2) $s^2 + 6s + 9$

47. Solve the system of equations by using augmented matrices. (Lesson 4–7)
$$2a - b + c = 44$$
$$-a + 3b - 2c = -53$$
$$5a - 6b - c = 19 \quad \textbf{(11, 2, 24)}$$

48. Find $3\begin{bmatrix} 4 & -2 \\ 5 & 7 \end{bmatrix} + 2\begin{bmatrix} -3 & 5 \\ -4 & 3 \end{bmatrix}$. (Lesson 4–2) $\begin{bmatrix} 6 & 4 \\ 7 & 27 \end{bmatrix}$

49. Photography The perimeter of a rectangular picture is 86 inches. Twice the width exceeds the length by 2 inches. What are the dimensions of the picture? (Lesson 3–2) **15 inches by 28 inches**

50. Find a value of a for which the graph of $y = ax + 9$ is perpendicular to the graph of $x + 3y = 14$. (Lesson 2–3) **3**

51. Evaluate $2|-3x| - 9$ if $x = 5$. (Lesson 1–5) **21**

Extension

Reasoning Show that the points $A(5, -1)$, $B(3, 2)$, and $C(9, 6)$ are vertices of a right triangle.

$AB = \sqrt{13}$, $BC = 2\sqrt{13}$,
$AC = \sqrt{65}$, hypotenuse $= \sqrt{65}$

$$\left(\sqrt{65}\right)^2 = \left(\sqrt{13}\right)^2 + \left(2\sqrt{13}\right)^2$$
$$65 = 13 + 52$$
$$65 = 65$$

Satisfies the Pythagorean theorem.

Parabolas

APPLICATION

Law Enforcement

What YOU'LL LEARN

- To write equations of parabolas, and
- to graph parabolas having certain properties.

Why IT'S IMPORTANT

You can graph parabolas to solve problems involving manufacturing and communications.

Have you ever driven around a corner and observed a police officer pointing a radar gun at your car? The radar gun has a reflector that sends out and receives rays. This reflector is in the shape of a *parabola*.

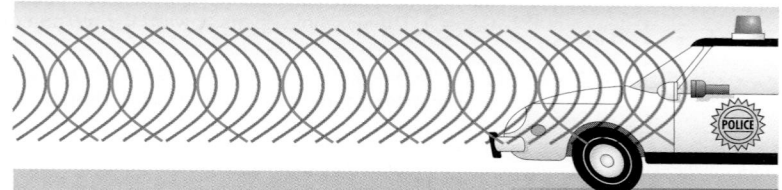

A parabola is a shape formed by slicing a double cone on a slant as shown at the right. Any figure that can be formed by slicing a double cone is called a **conic section**. Other conic sections are shown below.

parabola

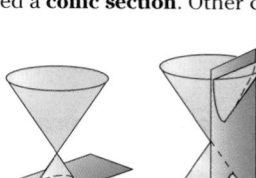

circle   ellipse   hyperbola

A parabola can be defined in terms of the location of a point called the **focus** and a line called the **directrix**.

Definition of a Parabola	**A parabola is the set of all points in a plane that are the same distance from a given point called the *focus* and a given line called the *directrix*.**

The directrix is named by the equation of the line.

The parabola at the right has a focus at (3, 4) and a directrix with equation $y = -2$. We can use the distance formula and the definition of a parabola to find the equation of this parabola.

Let (x, y) be any point on the parabola. The distance from this point to the focus must be the same as its distance from the directrix. The distance from a point to a line is measured along the perpendicular from the point to the line.

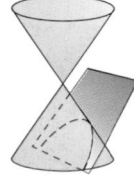

Lesson 7-2 Parabolas **415**

Alternative Learning Styles

Visual Draw a coordinate grid on graph paper with the *x* values going from -12 to 12 and the *y* values going from 4 to -22. For positive *x* values, draw segments that connect the points $(n, 0)$ and $(12, -2n)$. For negative *x* values, draw segments that connect the points $(n, 0)$ and $(-12, 2n)$. What figure is suggested? Have students experiment with other ordered pairs.

TEKS	5.a., 5.b., 5.c., 5.e., 6.b., 6.c., 7.a., 7.b., 8.a., 8.c., 8.d.

NCTM Standards: 1–5, 8

Instructional Resources

- Study Guide Master 7-2
- Practice Master 7-2
- Enrichment Master 7-2
- Assessment and Evaluation Masters, p. 184
- Modeling Mathematics Masters, p. 67
- Science and Math Lab Manual, pp. 91–94
- Tech Prep Applications Masters, p. 13

Transparency 7-2A contains the 5-Minute Check for this lesson; **Transparency 7-2B** contains a teaching aid for this lesson.

Recommended Pacing	
Standard Pacing	Day 2 of 15
Honors Pacing	Day 2 of 13
Block Scheduling*	Day 1 of 7 (along with Lesson 7-1)

*For more information on pacing and possible lesson plans, refer to the *Block Scheduling Booklet*.

1 FOCUS

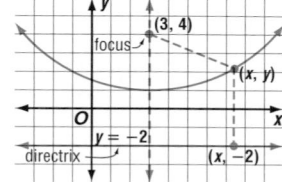

5-Minute Check
(over Lesson 7-1)

1. Use the Pythagorean theorem to find the distance between two points with coordinates (9, 7) and (6, 3). **5**
2. Use the distance formula to find the distance between two points with coordinates (6, 4) and (1, 1). $\sqrt{34}$
3. Find the midpoint of the line segment whose endpoints are at (11, 8) and (1, 4). **(6, 6)**
4. Show that $P(4, 3)$ is the midpoint of the segment joining $A(-2, 7)$ and $B(10, -1)$.
   slope AP = slope $AB = -\frac{2}{3}$; $AP = BP = 2\sqrt{13}$
5. Circle H has a diameter $\overline{CD}$. If C is at (13, 12) and the center is at (9.5, 9.5), find the coordinates of D. **(6, 7)**

416 Chapter 7

Motivating the Lesson

Hands-On Activity Ask the class how an automobile headlight works. Be sure they understand that any other point as a light source (focus) will cause the rays to be directed differently. This is how low beam and high beam can be created within the same headlight reflector. Bring in a double filament headlight bulb to show how the focus is in different positions.

2 TEACH

Teaching Tip As mentioned in the application, radar works by transmitting waves (usually electromagnetic or microwave) and receiving the echoes. Radar is used in law enforcement (checking speed), protection (motion detection), marine biology (making a map of the ocean floor), and many other careers.

In-Class Example

For Example 1
Write $y = x^2 + 4x + 1$ in the form $y = a(x - h)^2 + k$. Name the vertex, the axis of symmetry, and the direction of opening of the parabola.
$y = [x - (-2)]^2 - 3$; $(-2, -3)$; $x = -2$; up

MODELING  This hands-on project will help students recognize that a parabola is defined by the distance between the focus and directrix. You may wish to use an overhead projector to show the wax paper parabolas to the class. Have students randomly select a point for the focus, then select those that show the changes for demonstration purposes.

Answer for Modeling Mathematics

d. As the distance between the directrix and the focus increases, the parabola becomes wider.

$$\text{distance between } (x, y) \text{ and } (3, 4) = \text{distance between } (x, y) \text{ and } (x, -2)$$
$$\sqrt{(x - 3)^2 + (y - 4)^2} = \sqrt{(x - x)^2 + [y - (-2)]^2}$$
$$(x - 3)^2 + (y - 4)^2 = (0)^2 + (y + 2)^2 \quad \textit{Square each side.}$$
$$(x - 3)^2 + y^2 - 8y + 16 = y^2 + 4y + 4$$
$$(x - 3)^2 + 12 = 12y$$
$$\frac{1}{12}(x - 3)^2 + 1 = y$$

The equation of a parabola with focus at $(3, 4)$ and directrix with equation $y = -2$ is $y = \frac{1}{12}(x - 3)^2 + 1$. The equation of the *axis of symmetry* for this parabola is $x = 3$. Notice that the axis of symmetry and the directrix are perpendicular to each other. The axis of symmetry intersects the parabola at a point called the *vertex*. The vertex of this parabola is at $(3, 1)$. The parabola opens upward, since $\frac{1}{12}$ is positive.

In general, given the equation of a parabola written in the form $y = a(x - h)^2 + k$, the vertex is at (h, k), and the equation of the axis of symmetry is $x = h$. The parabola opens upward if $a > 0$ and opens downward if $a < 0$.

Example ❶ Write $y = 2x^2 + 12x + 14$ in the form $y = a(x - h)^2 + k$. Name the vertex, the axis of symmetry, and the direction of opening of the parabola.

$$y = 2x^2 + 12x + 14$$
$$y = 2(x^2 + 6x) + 14 \qquad \textit{Factor 2 from the x terms.}$$
$$y = 2(x^2 + 6x + \square) + 14 - 2\square \qquad \textit{Complete the square on the right side.}$$
$$y = 2(x^2 + 6x + 9) + 14 - 2(9) \qquad \textit{The 9 added when you complete the square}$$
$$y = 2(x + 3)^2 - 4 \qquad \textit{is multiplied by 2.}$$
$$y = 2[x - (-3)]^2 - 4 \qquad (h, k) = (-3, -4)$$

The vertex of this parabola is located at $(-3, -4)$, and the equation of the axis of symmetry is $x = -3$. The parabola opens upward.

MODELING MATHEMATICS

Parabolas

Materials: 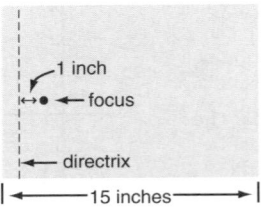 wax paper

You can make parabolas by folding wax paper.

Your Turn

a. Start with a sheet of wax paper that is about 15 inches long and 12 inches wide. Make a line that is perpendicular to the sides of the sheet by folding the sheet near one end. Open up the paper again. This line is the directrix. Mark a point about midway between the sides of the

sheet so that the distance from the directrix is about 1 inch. This point is the focus.

Put the focus on top of any point on the directrix and crease the paper. Make about 20 more creases by placing the focus on top of other points on the directrix. The lines form the outline of a parabola.   a–c. See students' work.

b. Start with a new sheet of wax paper. Form another outline of a parabola with a focus that is about 3 inches from the directrix.

c. On a new sheet of paper, form a third outline of a parabola with a focus that is about 5 inches from the directrix.

d. Compare the shapes of the three parabolas. How does the distance between the focus and the directrix affect the parabola?   See margin.

1 inch
• ← focus
← directrix
|←——— 15 inches ———→|

416 Chapter 7 Analyzing Conic Sections

Classroom Vignette

"Patty paper (used to separate hamburger patties and purchased from restaurant supply companies) is great to use for paper-folding activities. It is square in shape, not heavily waxed, and while it is not as transparent as waxed paper, it is very economical and convenient."

Nancy Lee King
Greenwood High School
Midland, Texas

Nancy Lee King

The line segment through the focus of a parabola and perpendicular to the axis of symmetry is called the **latus rectum**. The endpoints of the latus rectum lie on the parabola. In the figure at the right, the latus rectum is $\overline{AB}$. The length of the latus rectum of the parabola with equation $y = a(x - h)^2 + k$ is $\left|\frac{1}{a}\right|$ units. The endpoints of the latus rectum are $\left|\frac{1}{2a}\right|$ units from the focus.

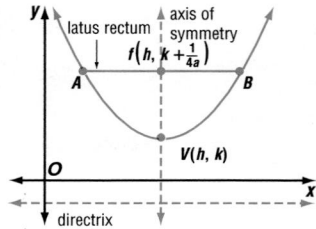

Equations of parabolas with a vertical axis of symmetry are in the form $y = a(x - h)^2 + k$ and are functions. Equations of parabolas with a horizontal axis of symmetry are in the form $x = a(y - k)^2 + h$ and are not functions.   *Why?*

Information about Parabolas

form of equation	$y = a(x - h)^2 + k$	$x = a(y - k)^2 + h$
axis of symmetry	$x = h$	$y = k$
vertex	(h, k)	(h, k)
focus	$\left(h, k + \frac{1}{4a}\right)$	$\left(h + \frac{1}{4a}, k\right)$
directrix	$y = k - \frac{1}{4a}$	$x = h - \frac{1}{4a}$
direction of opening	upward if $a > 0$ downward if $a < 0$	right if $a > 0$ left if $a < 0$
length of latus rectum	$\left|\frac{1}{a}\right|$ units	$\left|\frac{1}{a}\right|$ units

Example   **Graph $3x - y^2 = 8y + 31$.**

First write the equation in the form $x = a(y - k)^2 + h$.
$$3x - y^2 = 8y + 31 \qquad \textit{There is a } y^2 \textit{ term.}$$
$$3x = y^2 + 8y + 31 \qquad \textit{Isolate the y terms.}$$
$$3x = (y^2 + 8y + \square) + 31 - \square \qquad \textit{Complete the square.}$$
$$3x = (y^2 + 8y + 16) + 31 - 16$$
$$3x = (y + 4)^2 + 15$$
$$x = \frac{1}{3}(y + 4)^2 + 5 \qquad (h, k) = (5, -4)$$

Then use the following information to draw the graph.
vertex: $(5, -4)$
axis of symmetry: $y = -4$

focus: $\left(5 + \dfrac{1}{4\left(\frac{1}{3}\right)}, -4\right)$ or $\left(5\frac{3}{4}, -4\right)$

directrix: $x = 5 - \dfrac{1}{4\left(\frac{1}{3}\right)}$ or $4\frac{1}{4}$

direction of opening: right, since $a > 0$

length of latus rectum: $\left|\dfrac{1}{\frac{1}{3}}\right|$ or 3 units

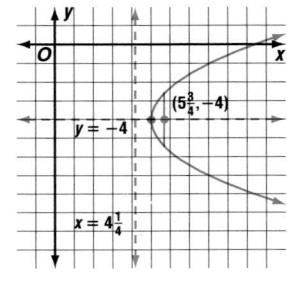

GLENCOE *Technology*

 Interactive Mathematics Tools Software

This multimedia software provides an interactive lesson by helping students observe horizontal parabolas as their equations are manipulated. A **Computer Journal** gives students an opportunity to write about what they have learned.

For Windows & Macintosh

Teaching Tip The latus rectum is sometimes called the "focal chord." It is helpful in determining the shape of the curve.

In-Class Example

For Example 2
Graph $5x = y^2 + 4y - 26$.
vertex: $(-6, -2)$; axis of symmetry: $y = -2$; focus: $\left(-4\frac{3}{4}, -2\right)$; directrix: $x = -7.25$; direction of opening: to the right; length of latus rectum: 5 units

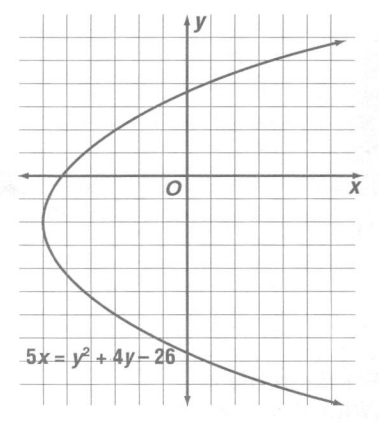

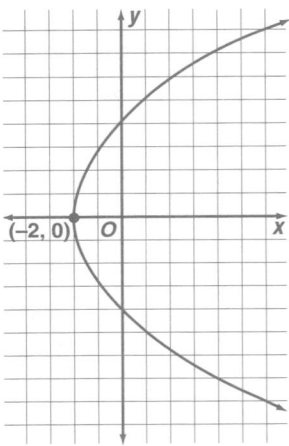

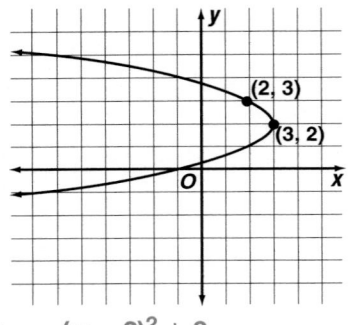

In-Class Examples

For Example 3
Write the equation of the cross-section of a satellite dish with a focus 2 units from the vertex and a latus rectum 8 units long. Assume that the focus is at the origin and the parabola opens to the right. Then use this information to draw a graph.

$x = \frac{1}{8}y^2 - 2$

For Example 4
Write an equation for the parabola shown below.

$x = -(y - 2)^2 + 3$

Example ③

APPLICATION
Solar Energy

Solar energy may be harnessed by using parabolic mirrors. The mirrors reflect the rays from the sun to the focus of the parabola. In the Mojave Desert in California, such mirrors are used to heat oil that flows through tubes placed at the focus. The focus of each parabolic mirror at this facility is 6.25 feet above the vertex. The latus rectum is 25 feet long.

a. **Assume that the focus is at the origin and write an equation for the parabola formed by each mirror.**

b. **Then graph the equation.**

a. In order for the mirrors to collect the sun's energy, the parabola must open upward. Therefore, the vertex must be below the focus.

focus: $(0, 0)$ vertex: $(0, -6.25)$

The measure of the latus rectum is 25. So $25 = \left|\frac{1}{a}\right|$, and $a = \frac{1}{25}$.

Write the equation using the form $y = a(x - h)^2 + k$.

An equation for the parabola formed by each mirror is $y = \frac{1}{25}x^2 - 6.25$.

b. Now use all of the information to draw a graph.

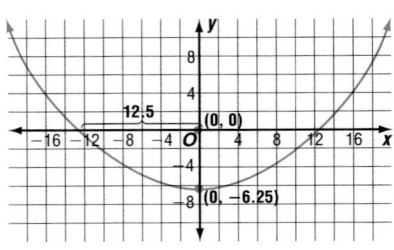

Example ④ **Write an equation for the parabola shown below.**

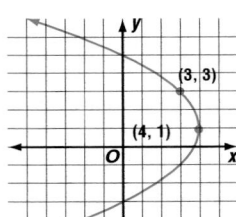

The vertex is at $(4, 1)$. Use the equation $x = a(y - k)^2 + h$.

$$x = a(y - 1)^2 + 4$$

The parabola passes through the point at $(3, 3)$. Use this information to solve for a.

$$3 = a(3 - 1)^2 + 4 \quad x = 3, y = 3$$
$$3 = 4a + 4$$
$$-1 = 4a$$
$$-\frac{1}{4} = a$$

An equation for the parabola is $x = -\frac{1}{4}(y - 1)^2 + 4$.

Communicating Mathematics

Study the lesson. Then complete the following.

1. **Describe** the relationships among the directrix, the focus, the vertex, the axis of symmetry, and the latus rectum.   See margin.

2. Shanice; both $(x - 3)^2$ and $(3 - x)^2$ equal $x^2 - 6x + 9$.

2. **You Decide**   Ralph says that the graphs of the equations $y = 4(x - 3)^2 - 7$ and $y = 4(3 - x)^2 - 7$ are different. Shanice says they are the same. Who is right? Explain your answer.

3. **Compare and contrast** the equations of parabolas that open right or left and those that open up or down. Tell which equations, if any, are functions.   See margin.

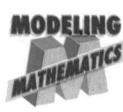

4. Suppose you used wax paper folding to create outlines of two parabolas. If one has a focus 10 centimeters from the directrix and the other has a focus 5 centimeters from the directrix, how will the parabolas compare?
The parabola with the focus 10 cm away will be wider than the other one.

Guided Practice

Express each equation in the form $y = a(x - h)^2 + k$ or $x = a(y - k)^2 + h$.

5. $y = 2x^2 - 12x + 6$
$y = 2(x - 3)^2 - 12$

6. $y = \frac{1}{2}x^2 + 12x - 8$
$y = \frac{1}{2}(x + 12)^2 - 80$

7. $x = 3y^2 + 5y - 9$
$x = 3\left(y + \frac{5}{6}\right)^2 - 11\frac{1}{12}$

8. $x = y^2 + 14y + 20$
$x = (y + 7)^2 - 29$

Name the coordinates of the vertex and focus, the equations of the axis of symmetry and directrix, and the direction of opening of the parabola with the given equation. Then find the length of the latus rectum and graph the parabola.   9–12. See Solutions Manual.

9. $y = (x - 3)^2 - 4$

10. $y = 2(x + 7)^2 + 3$

11. $y = 3x^2 - 8x + 6$

12. $y = \frac{2}{3}x^2 - 6x + 12$

13. Write an equation for the graph shown at the right. $y = -2x^2 + 3$

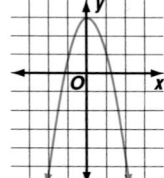

14. Write an equation of the parabola with its focus at $(3, 8)$ and $y = 4$ as the equation for its directrix. Then draw the graph. $y = \frac{1}{8}(x - 3)^2 + 6$

15. Write an equation of the parabola with its vertex at $(5, -1)$ and its focus at $(3, -1)$. Then draw the graph. $x = -\frac{1}{8}(y + 1)^2 + 5$

Reteaching

Using Alternative Methods Given the focus and the directrix, find the equation of a parabola in two ways. First, use the definition of a parabola and the distance formula to find the equation. Second, use formulas for the focus and directrix to find values of h, k, and a. Then write the equation.

Check for Understanding

Exercises 1–15 are designed to help you assess your students' understanding through reading, writing, speaking, and modeling. You should work through Exercises 1–4 with your students and then monitor their work on Exercises 5–15.

Additional Answers

1. The axis of symmetry passes through the vertex and is perpendicular to the latus rectum and the directrix. The focus is also on the axis of symmetry. The latus rectum contains the focus, joins two points on the parabola, and is parallel to the directrix. The vertex is equidistant from the focus and the directrix.

3. The equation of a parabola opening up or down is $y = a(x - h)^2 + k$. The parabola opens upward if $a > 0$ and downward if $a < 0$. These equations are functions. The equation of a parabola opening right or left is $x = a(y - k)^2 + h$. The parabola opens to the right if $a > 0$ and to the left if $a < 0$. These equations are not functions.

14.
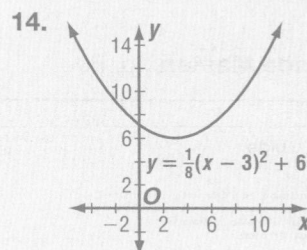
$y = \frac{1}{8}(x - 3)^2 + 6$

15.
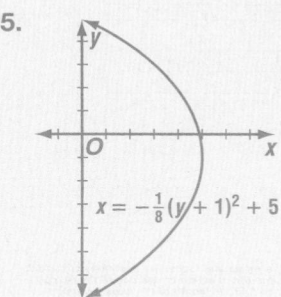
$x = -\frac{1}{8}(y + 1)^2 + 5$

Assignment Guide

Core: 17–49 odd, 51–59
Enriched: 16–44 even, 45–59

For **Extra Practice,** see p. 892.

The red A, B, and C flags, printed only in the Teacher's Wraparound Edition, indicate the level of difficulty of the exercises.

Additional Answers

32.

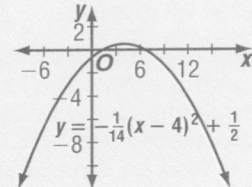

$$y = -\frac{1}{14}(x-4)^2 + \frac{1}{2}$$

33.

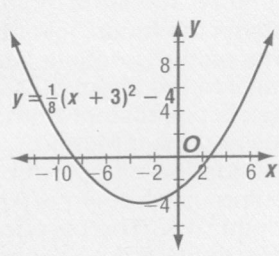

$$y = \frac{1}{8}(x+3)^2 - 4$$

Study Guide Masters, p. 50

NAME _____ DATE _____
7-2 **Study Guide**
Student Edition
Pages 415–422

Parabolas

A **parabola** is a curve consisting of all points in the coordinate plane that are the same distance from a given point (the focus) and a given line (the directrix). The chart summarizes important information about parabolas.

	Information about Parabolas	
Form of equation	$y = a(x-h)^2 + k$	$x = a(y-k)^2 + h$
Axis of symmetry	$x = h$	$y = k$
Vertex	(h, k)	(h, k)
Focus	$\left(h, k+\frac{1}{4a}\right)$	$\left(h+\frac{1}{4a}, k\right)$
Directrix	$y = k - \frac{1}{4a}$	$x = h - \frac{1}{4a}$
Direction of opening	up $(a>0)$; down $(a<0)$	right $(a>0)$; left $(a<0)$
Length of latus rectum	$\left|\frac{1}{a}\right|$ units	$\left|\frac{1}{a}\right|$ units

Example: Graph $y = \frac{1}{4}(x-2)^2 - 3$.
vertex: $(2, -3)$
axis of symmetry: $x = 2$
focus: $(2, -3 + 1)$ or $(2, -2)$
directrix: $y = -3 - 1$ or $y = -4$
direction of opening: upward, since $a > 0$
length of latus rectum: $\left|\frac{1}{\frac{1}{4}}\right|$ or 4 units

Name the coordinates of the vertex and focus, the equations of the axis of symmetry and directrix, and the direction of opening of the parabola with the given equation. Then find the length of the latus rectum.

1. $x^2 = 2y$
$(0, 0); x = 0; \left(0, \frac{1}{2}\right);$
$y = -\frac{1}{2};$ upward; 2

2. $x^2 = y + 2$
$(0, -2); x = 0; \left(0, -1\frac{3}{4}\right);$
$y = -2\frac{1}{4};$ upward; 1

3. $y = x^2 + 4x + 3$
$(-2, -1); x = -2;$
$\left(-2, -\frac{3}{4}\right); y = -1\frac{1}{4};$
upward; 1

The coordinates of the focus and the equation of the directrix of a parabola are given. Write an equation for each parabola. Then draw the graph.

4. $(3, 5), y = 1$
5. $(4, -4), y = -6$
6. $(5, -1), x = 3$

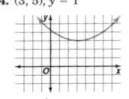 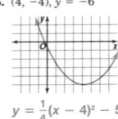 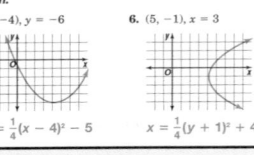

$y = \frac{1}{8}(x-3)^2 + 3$
$y = \frac{1}{4}(x-4)^2 - 5$
$x = \frac{1}{4}(y+1)^2 + 4$

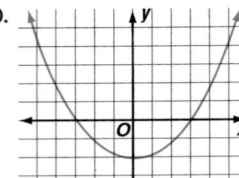

EXERCISES

Practice Name the coordinates of the vertex and focus, the equations of the axis of symmetry and directrix, and the direction of opening of the parabola with the given equation. Then find the length of the latus rectum and graph the parabola. **16–29. See Solutions Manual.**

16. $-6y = x^2$
17. $3(y-3) = (x+6)^2$
18. $-2(x-4) = (y-1)^2$
19. $4(x-2) = (y+3)^2$
20. $(y-8)^2 = -4(x-4)$
21. $y = x^2 - 12x + 20$
22. $x = y^2 - 14y + 25$
23. $y = -2x^2 + 5x - 10$
B 24. $x = 5y^2 - 25y + 60$
25. $y = 3x^2 - 24x + 50$
26. $\frac{1}{2}(y+1) = (x-8)^2$
27. $x = -\frac{1}{3}y^2 - 12y + 15$
28. $y = \frac{1}{2}x^2 - 3x + \frac{19}{2}$
29. $x = \frac{1}{4}y^2 - \frac{1}{2}y - 3$

Write an equation for each graph.

30. $y = \frac{2}{9}x^2 - 2$
31. $x = 2(y-2)^2 + 1$

30.
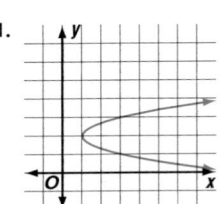

31.

The coordinates of the focus and equation of the directrix of a parabola are given. Write an equation for each parabola. Then draw the graph.

32–37. See margin.

32. $(4, -3); y = 4$
33. $(-3, -2); y = -6$
34. $(3, 0); x = -2$
35. $(4, -3); y = 6$
C 36. $(10, -4); x = 5$
37. $(4, 0); x = -2$

Write an equation of each parabola described below. Then draw the graph. **38–43. See Solutions Manual.**

38. vertex, $(0, 1)$; focus, $(0, 5)$
39. vertex, $(8, 6)$; focus, $(2, 6)$
40. focus, $(-4, -2)$; directrix, $x = -8$
41. vertex, $(1, 7)$; directrix, $y = 3$
42. vertex, $(-7, 4)$; axis of symmetry, $x = -7$; measure of latus rectum, 6; $a < 0$
43. vertex, $(4, 3)$; axis of symmetry, $y = 3$; measure of latus rectum, 4; $a > 0$

44c. -1 and $-\frac{1}{3}$

44d. $y = -\frac{2}{3}$

44e. $\left(-\frac{1}{3}, -\frac{2}{3}\right)$

44. **a.** Draw the graph of $x = 3y^2 + 4y + 1$. **See margin.**
b. Find the x-intercept(s). 1
c. Find the y-intercept(s).
d. What is the equation of the axis of symmetry?
e. What are the coordinates of the vertex?

Additional Answers

34.
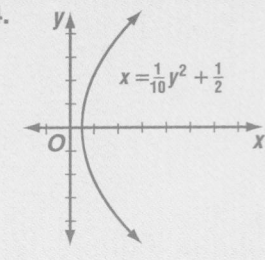

$$x = \frac{1}{10}y^2 + \frac{1}{2}$$

35.
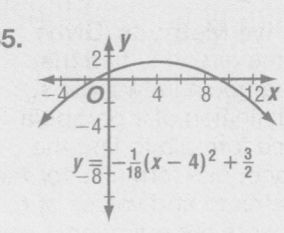

$$y = -\frac{1}{18}(x-4)^2 + \frac{3}{2}$$

45. The graph of the equation

$$y = -\frac{1}{8}(x - 8)^2 + 2 \text{ is shown}$$

at the right.

What values of x make each statement true?

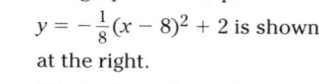

a. $-\frac{1}{8}(x - 8)^2 + 2 = 0$ **4 and 12**

b. $-\frac{1}{8}(x - 8)^2 + 2 > 0$ **4 < x < 12**

c. $-\frac{1}{8}(x - 8)^2 + 2 < 0$ **x < 4 or x > 12**

46. $y = -\frac{1}{4}(x + 3)^2 + 1$
and $x = 2(y - 1)^2 - 3$

46. Suppose two different parabolas have their vertex at $(-3, 1)$ and contain the point with coordinates $(-1, 0)$. Find their equations.

Applications and Problem Solving

47. Manufacturing An automobile headlight contains a parabolic reflector. A special bulb with two filaments is used to produce the high and low beams. The filament placed at the focus produces the high beam and the filament placed off the focus produces the low beam. The equation of the cross section of the reflector is $y = \frac{1}{12}x^2$. How far from the vertex should the filament for the high beam be placed? **3 units**

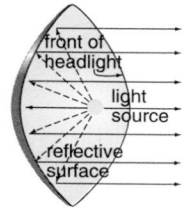

48. Communications A microphone is placed at the focus of a parabolic reflector to collect sounds for the television broadcast of the World Cup Soccer final game. The focus of the parabola that is a cross section of the reflector is 6 inches from the vertex. The latus rectum is 24 inches in length. Assume the focus is at the origin and the parabola opens to the right. Write an equation for the cross section.

48. $x = \frac{1}{24}y^2 - 6$

49. $y = -\frac{1}{26,200}x^2 + 6550$

49. Space Science A spacecraft is in a circular orbit 150 kilometers above Earth. Once it obtains the velocity needed to escape Earth's gravity, the spacecraft will follow a parabolic path with the focus at the center of Earth, as shown below. Suppose it obtains its escape velocity above the North Pole. Assume the center of Earth is at the origin and the radius of Earth is 6400 kilometers. Write an equation for the parabolic path of the spacecraft.

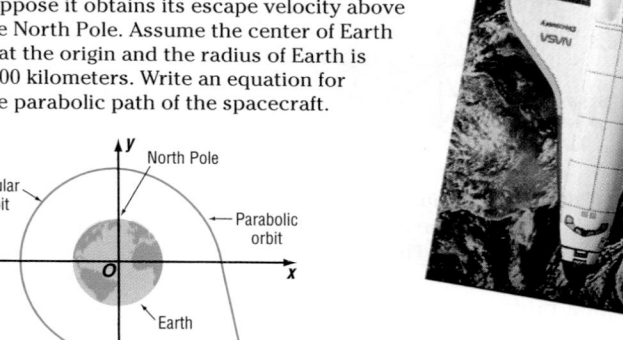

50. $y = -\frac{1}{200}x^2 + 50$

50. Baseball When a ball is thrown, the path it travels is a parabola. Suppose a baseball is thrown from ground level, reaches a maximum height of 50 feet, and hits the ground 200 feet from where it was thrown. Assuming this situation could be modeled on a coordinate plane with the focus of the parabola at the origin, find the equation of the (parabolic) path of the ball. (*Hint:* The focus is on ground level.)

Additional Answers

36.

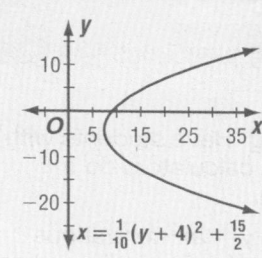

$$x = \frac{1}{10}(y + 4)^2 + \frac{15}{2}$$

37.

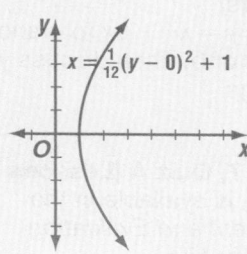

$$x = \frac{1}{12}(y - 0)^2 + 1$$

44a.

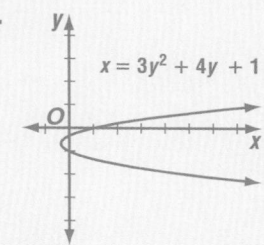

$$x = 3y^2 + 4y + 1$$

Practice Masters, p. 50

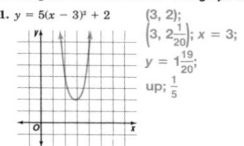
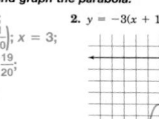
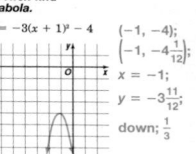
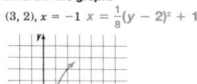
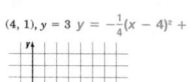
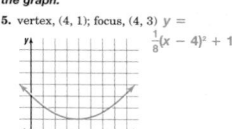
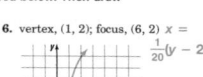

Closing Activity

Modeling Have students with graphing calculators do the following.

1. Graph $y = ax^2$ for various values of a. Then discuss your findings.
2. Graph $y = x^2 + bx$ for various values of b. Then discuss your findings.

Chapter 7, Quiz A (Lessons 7-1 and 7-2), is available in the *Assessment and Evaluation Masters*, p. 184.

Enrichment Masters, p. 50

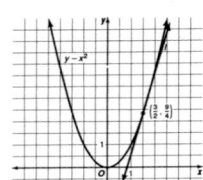

7-2 NAME_____ DATE_____
Enrichment
Student Edition
Pages 415–422

Tangents to Parabolas

A line that intersects a parabola in exactly one point without crossing the curve is a **tangent** to the parabola. The point where a tangent line touches a parabola is the **point of tangency**. The line perpendicular to a tangent to a parabola at the point of tangency is called the **normal** to the parabola at that point. In the diagram, line l is tangent to the parabola that is the graph of $y = x^2$ at $\left(\frac{3}{2}, \frac{9}{4}\right)$. The x-axis is tangent to the parabola at O, and the y-axis is the normal to the parabola at O.

Solve each problem.

1. Find an equation for line l in the diagram. *Hint:* A nonvertical line with an equation of the form $y = mx + b$ will be tangent to the graph of $y = x^2$ at $\left(\frac{3}{2}, \frac{9}{4}\right)$ if and only if $\left(\frac{3}{2}, \frac{9}{4}\right)$ is the only pair of numbers that satisfies both $y = x^2$ and $y = mx + b$.
$m = 3, b = -\frac{9}{4}, y = 3x - \frac{9}{4}$

2. If a is any real number, then (a, a^2) belongs to the graph of $y = x^2$. Express m and b in terms of a to find an equation of the form $y = mx + b$ for the line that is tangent to the graph of $y = x^2$ at (a, a^2).
$m = 2a, b = a^2, y = (2a)x + (-a^2)$ or $y = 2ax - a^2$

3. Find an equation for the normal to the graph of $y = x^2$ at $\left(\frac{3}{2}, \frac{9}{4}\right)$.
$y = -\frac{1}{3}x + \frac{11}{4}$

4. If a is a nonzero real number, find an equation for the normal to the graph of $y = x^2$ at (a, a^2).
$y = \left(-\frac{1}{2a}\right)x + \left(a^2 + \frac{1}{2}\right)$

Mixed Review

51. **Draw a Diagram** A hole in a compact disc needs to be at the center of the disc. If the hole is to be $\frac{7}{16}$ inch in diameter and the diameter of the disc is $4\frac{3}{4}$ inches, how far from the edge of the disc will the edge of the hole be placed? (Lesson 7-1) $2\frac{5}{32}$ inches

52. Write the equation of a parabola with position 3 units to the right of the parabola with equation $f(x) = x^2$. (Lesson 6-6) $f(x) = (x-3)^2$

53. $-7 \pm \sqrt{61}$
53. Solve $x^2 + 14x - 12 = 0$ by completing the square. (Lesson 6-3)

54. Simplify $(3 + 2i)(4 + 5i)$. (Lesson 5-9) $2 + 23i$

55. $201{,}600; 2.016 \times 10^5$
55. **Health** Ty's heart rate is usually 120 beats per minute when he runs. If he runs for 2 hours every day, about how many beats will his heart make during the equivalent of two weeks of exercise sessions? Express the answer in both decimal and scientific notation. (Lesson 5-1)

56. Find $-3\begin{bmatrix} \frac{5}{6} & 3 \\ -2 & \frac{2}{9} \end{bmatrix}$. (Lesson 4-3) $\begin{bmatrix} -\frac{5}{2} & -9 \\ 6 & -\frac{2}{3} \end{bmatrix}$

57. Given $f(x, y) = -3y + 4x$, find $f(-7, -4)$. (Lesson 3-5) -16

58. $c = 10\left(h - \frac{1}{2}\right) + 35$
58. **Business** The Friendly Fix-It Company charges \$35 for any in-home repair. In addition, the technician charges \$10 per hour after the first half-hour. What would be the cost C of an in-home repair of h hours? (Lesson 2-4)

59. If $a = 2, b = -6, c = 3$, and $a^3b^2 + 4ac + 2d \geq 6c^2 - 4ab$, solve for d. (Lesson 1-6) $d \geq -105$

WORKING ON THE In·ves·ti·ga·tion

Refer to the Investigation on pages 328–329.

the River Canyon Bridge

After much discussion, your group of designers decides to proceed with the design proposed by the company's consultant. The consultant's suggestion is a general one, and your group must now design a bridge with more exact specifications.

1 Verify that the arch in each of your designs is parabolic. Use the definition of a parabola as your guide.

2 Suppose the directrix of your parabola is the roadway above it. The focus would be inside the parabola. Experiment with different foci to see how the degree of steepness of the parabola changes.

3 Show four different designs in which the steepness of the parabola is different. Indicate the distance between the focus and the directrix in each design.

4 Write an equation for each of the parabolic designs you test.

5 Make a blueprint of each of the four designs. Include the lengths of the struts and how far apart they are located.

Add the results of your work to your Investigation Folder.

422 *Chapter 7 Analyzing Conic Sections*

Extension

Reasoning Write the equation of the parabola whose latus rectum has endpoints at $(6, 0)$ and $(-6, 0)$, and $a > 0$.

$y = \frac{1}{12}x^2 - 3$

In·ves·ti·ga·tion

Working on the Investigation

The Investigation on pages 328–329 is designed to be a long-term project that is completed over several days or weeks. Encourage students to keep their materials in their Investigation Folder as they work on the Investigation.

7-3

Circles

What YOU'LL LEARN

- To write equations of circles, and
- to graph circles having certain properties.

Why IT'S IMPORTANT

You can graph circles to solve problems involving seismology and aviation.

FYI

The strongest earthquake in American history measured 8.4 on the Richter scale. It occurred on March 27, 1964 near Prince William Sound, Alaska. It killed 131 people and caused an estimated $750 million in property damage.

APPLICATION
Seismology

When an earthquake occurs, the most serious property damage usually occurs at or near the center of the quake, called the *epicenter*. The damage is usually less severe as the distance from the epicenter increases. Shock waves radiate from the epicenter in a circular pattern. The earthquake in California on January 17, 1994, resulted in severe damage to buildings and roads near the epicenter, which was near the city of Northridge.

A **circle** is the set of all points in a plane that are equidistant from a given point in the plane, called the **center**. Any segment whose endpoints are the center and a point on the circle is a **radius** of the circle. *The measure of a radius is also called a radius.*

Assume that (x, y) names any point on the circle at the right. The center is at (h, k), and the radius is represented by r. We can find an equation for the circle by using the distance formula.

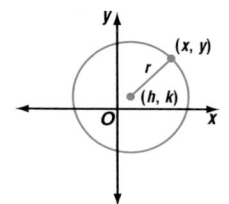

$$\sqrt{(x_2 - x_1)^2 + (y_2 - y_1)^2} = d$$

Substitute the coordinates of (x, y) and (h, k) into the formula. The distance from the center at (h, k) to a point at (x, y) on the circle is the radius r.

$$\sqrt{(x - h)^2 + (y - k)^2} = r$$

$(x - h)^2 + (y - k)^2 = r^2$ *Square each side.*

Equation of a Circle	The equation of a circle with center (h, k) and radius r units is $$(x - h)^2 + (y - k)^2 = r^2.$$

FYI

The deadliest earthquake in history occurred on January 24, 1556, in the Shanxi province of China. An estimated 830,000 people were killed.

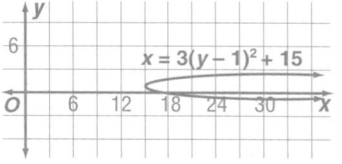 **TEKS** 5.b., 5.c., 5.e.

7-3 LESSON NOTES

NCTM Standards: 1–5, 8

Instructional Resources

- Study Guide Master 7-3
- Practice Master 7-3
- Enrichment Master 7-3
- Multicultural Activity Masters, p. 13
- Real-World Applications, 20

Transparency 7-3A contains the 5-Minute Check for this lesson; **Transparency 7-3B** contains a teaching aid for this lesson.

Recommended Pacing	
Standard Pacing	Day 3 of 15
Honors Pacing	Day 3 of 13
Block Scheduling*	Day 2 of 7

*For more information on pacing and possible lesson plans, refer to the *Block Scheduling Booklet*.

1 FOCUS

5-Minute Check *(over Lesson 7-2)*

Use the equation $x = 3(y - 1)^2 + 15$ for Exercises 1–5.

1. Name the coordinates of the vertex and the equation of the axis of symmetry of its graph. **(15, 1); $y = 1$**
2. Name the coordinates of the focus and the equation of the directrix of its graph. $\left(15\frac{1}{2}, 1\right); x = 14\frac{11}{12}$
3. Toward what direction does its graph open? **right**
4. What is the length of the latus rectum of its graph? $\frac{1}{3}$ **units**
5. Graph the equation.

$x = 3(y - 1)^2 + 15$

Chapter 7 **423**

Motivating the Lesson

Hands-On Activity Have students use a pencil, a piece of string, and a tack to make a circle. Place the tack on a piece of graph paper at a particular point. Draw the circle. Have students pick some points on the circle and find the distance from the center to each point.

2 TEACH

In-Class Examples

For Example 1
A dog is tied in a yard using a 15-foot leash. The leash is anchored 6 feet south and 9 feet west of the dog's food and water bowls. Assuming the bowls are at the origin, write the equation for the set of points at which the dog will be at the maximum length of the leash. Then draw the graph.
$(x + 9)^2 + (y + 6)^2 = 225$

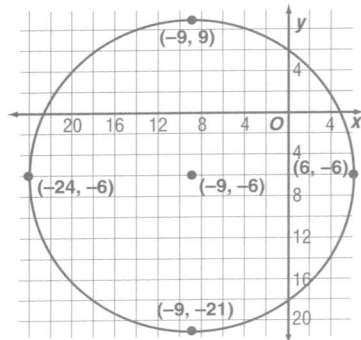

For Example 2
Find the center and radius of a circle with equation
$x^2 + 2x + y^2 + 4y - 11 = 0$.
Then graph the circle.
$(x + 1)^2 + (y + 2)^2 = 16$
$C(-1, -2); r = 4$

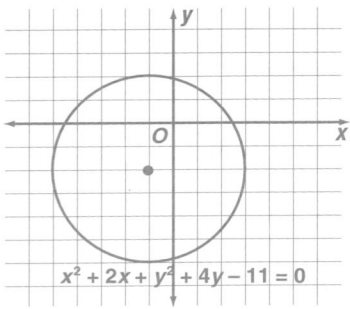

Teaching Tip Before completing Example 2, you may need to review with students how to complete a square.

Example ❶

APPLICATION
Seismology

The University of Southern California (USC) is located about 4 kilometers west and about 4.5 kilometers south of downtown Los Angeles. A seismograph on the campus indicated that an earthquake occurred, and it is estimated that the epicenter of the quake was about 60 kilometers from the university. Assume that the origin of a coordinate plane is located at the center of Los Angeles. Write an equation of the set of points that could be the epicenter of the quake and draw the graph.

Any point that is 60 kilometers from the university could be the epicenter. So the circle whose center is at the university and whose radius is 60 kilometers is the solution set. The center of the circle is at $(-4, -4.5)$.

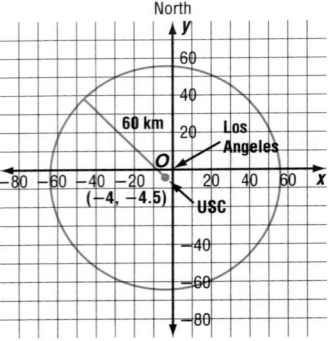

$$[x - (-4)]^2 + [y - (-4.5)]^2 = (60)^2$$
$$(x + 4)^2 + (y + 4.5)^2 = 3600$$

The equation is
$(x + 4)^2 + (y + 4.5)^2 = 3600$.

The equation $x^2 + y^2 + 2x - 12y = 35$ also describes a circle. If we were to complete the square for each variable and write the equation in the form $(x - h)^2 + (y - k)^2 = r^2$, the result would be $(x + 1)^2 + (y - 6)^2 = 72$. This circle has its center at $(-1, 6)$, and its radius is $\sqrt{72}$ or $6\sqrt{2}$ units long.

Example ❷ Find the center and radius of a circle with equation $x^2 + y^2 + 16x - 22y - 20 = 0$. Then graph the circle.

Solve by completing the square.

$$x^2 + y^2 + 16x - 22y - 20 = 0$$
$$x^2 + 16x + \square + y^2 - 22y + \square = 20 + \square + \square$$
$$x^2 + 16x + 64 + y^2 - 22y + 121 = 20 + 64 + 121$$
$$(x + 8)^2 + (y - 11)^2 = 205$$

The center of the circle is at $(-8, 11)$.
The radius is $\sqrt{205}$ or about 14.32 units.

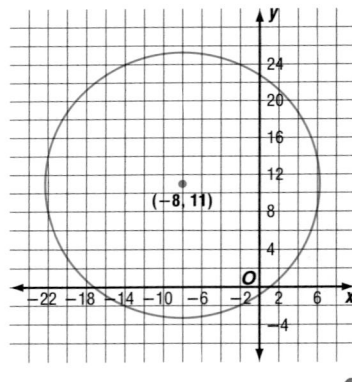

Alternative Learning Styles

Auditory Guide a discussion using the following questions.

1. What are circles and their components?
2. How can we relate distance formulas to finding the radius? **Given the coordinates of a point on the circle and the coordinates of the center, you can find the length of the radius.**
3. Is a circle the graph of a function? **No; there are two points for most x values with a point on the circle.**

A line in the plane of a circle can intersect the circle in zero, one, or two points. A line that intersects the circle in exactly one point is said to be **tangent** to the circle. The line and the circle are tangent to each other at this point.

Example Write an equation of the circle with its center at $(-6, 11)$ and that is tangent to the y-axis.

To visualize the circle, draw a sketch. Since the circle is tangent to the y-axis, its radius is 6 units.

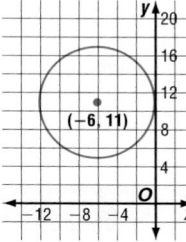

The equation is $(x + 6)^2 + (y - 11)^2 = 36$.

Example Write an equation of a circle if the endpoints of a diameter are at $(-7, 11)$ and $(5, -10)$.

The center of the circle is the midpoint of the diameter.

$$(h, k) = \left(\frac{x_1 + x_2}{2}, \frac{y_1 + y_2}{2}\right)$$

$$= \left(\frac{-7 + 5}{2}, \frac{11 + (-10)}{2}\right)$$

$$= \left(\frac{-2}{2}, \frac{1}{2}\right) \text{ or } \left(-1, \frac{1}{2}\right)$$

The radius is the distance from the center to one endpoint of the diameter. Use the distance formula.

$$r = \sqrt{[5 - (-1)]^2 + \left(-10 - \frac{1}{2}\right)^2}$$

$$= \sqrt{6^2 + (-10.5)^2}$$

$$= \sqrt{146.25} \text{ or about } 12.1$$

The radius of the circle is about 12.1 units, and r^2 is 146.25.

An equation of the circle is $(x + 1)^2 + \left(y - \frac{1}{2}\right)^2 = 146.25$.

In-Class Examples

For Example 3
Write an equation of the circle that has its center at $(2, -4)$ and is tangent to the x-axis.
$(x - 2)^2 + (y + 4)^2 = 16$

For Example 4
Write an equation of a circle if the endpoints of a diameter are at $(1, 8)$ and $(1, -6)$.
$(x - 1)^2 + (y - 1)^2 = 49$

EXPLORATION

This Exploration demonstrates that while a graphing calculator cannot graph a relation that is not a function, it is possible to break down the relation into parts that are functions and graph all parts simultaneously.

Answers for the Exploration

c. Solve the equation for y:
$y = \pm\sqrt{49 - x^2}$. Then graph the positive and negative answers.

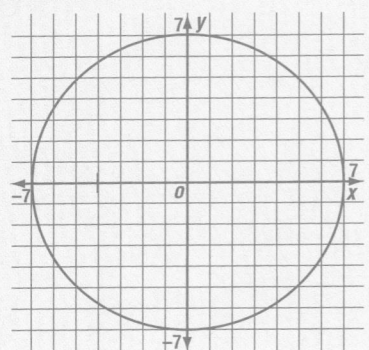

d.

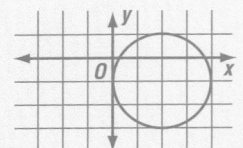

3 PRACTICE/APPLY

Check for Understanding

Exercises 1–16 are designed to help you assess your students' understanding through reading, writing, speaking, and modeling. You should work through Exercises 1–6 with your students and then monitor their work on Exercises 7–16.

Additional Answers

1. They have the same radius, 4 units, but different centers, $(-3, 4)$ and $(3, 2)$.
2. Answers will vary. Sample answer:
$(x - 2)^2 + (y - 3)^2 = 25$
$(x - 2)^2 + (y - 3)^2 = 36$

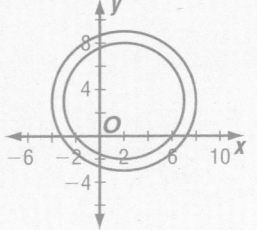

EXPLORATION

Graph the two equations below on the same screen.

$$y = \sqrt{9 - x^2} \qquad y = -\sqrt{9 - x^2}$$

Your Turn e. See students' work.

a. Describe the graph formed by the union of these two graphs. **a circle**

b. Write an equation for the union of the two graphs. $x^2 + y^2 = 9$

c. Most graphing calculators cannot graph the equation $x^2 + y^2 = 49$ directly. Describe a way to use a graphing calculator to graph the equation. Then graph the equation. **c–d. See margin.**

d. Use a graphing calculator to graph the equation $(x - 2)^2 + (y + 1)^2 = 4$.

e. Do you think it is easier to graph the equation in Step d using graph paper and a pencil or using a graphing calculator? Explain?

CHECK FOR UNDERSTANDING

Communicating Mathematics

Study the lesson. Then complete the following. 1–5. See margin.

1. **Describe** the similarities and differences between the graphs of $(x + 3)^2 + (y - 4)^2 = 16$ and $(x - 3)^2 + (y - 2)^2 = 16$.

2. **Concentric circles** are defined as circles with the same center, but *not* necessarily the same radius. Write equations of two concentric circles. Then graph the circles.

3. **Explain** why the phrase "in a plane" is included in the definition of a circle. What would be defined if the phrase were *not* included?

4. **You Decide** Jean says that you can take the square root of each side of an equation. Therefore, she decides that $(x - 2)^2 + (y + 3)^2 = 36$ and $(x - 2) + (y + 3) = 6$ are equivalent equations. Marco says that the equations are *not* equivalent. Who is right? Explain your answer.

5. How many axes of symmetry does a circle have? Explain your answer.

MATH JOURNAL

6. The circle with equation $(x - a)^2 + (y - b)^2 = r^2$ lies in the first quadrant and is tangent to both the x-axis and the y-axis. Make a sketch of the circle. Describe the possible values of a, b, and r. Do the same for a circle in Quadrants II, III, and IV. **See Solutions Manual.**

9–14. See Solutions Manual for graphs.

Guided Practice

Write an equation for each circle if the coordinates of the center and the length of the radius are given.

9. $(4, 1)$, 3 units

10. $(0, 14)$, $\sqrt{34}$ units

11. $(4, 0)$, $\frac{4}{5}$ units

12. $\left(-\frac{2}{3}, \frac{1}{2}\right)$, $\frac{2\sqrt{2}}{3}$ unit

13. $(-4, 3)$, 5 units

14. $(-2, 0)$, $2\sqrt{3}$ units

7. center $(-12, 0)$, $r = \sqrt{23}$ units
$(x + 12)^2 + y^2 = 23$

8. center $(8, -9.5)$, $r = \frac{1}{2}$ unit
$(x - 8)^2 + (y + 9.5)^2 = \frac{1}{4}$

Find the coordinates of the center and the radius of each circle whose equation is given. Then draw the graph.

9. $(x - 4)^2 + (y - 1)^2 = 9$

10. $x^2 + (y - 14)^2 = 34$

11. $(x - 4)^2 + y^2 = \frac{16}{25}$

12. $\left(x + \frac{2}{3}\right)^2 + \left(y - \frac{1}{2}\right)^2 = \frac{8}{9}$

13. $x^2 + y^2 + 8x - 6y = 0$

14. $x^2 + y^2 + 4x - 8 = 0$

Reteaching ———

Using Alternative Methods Given the coordinates of three points on a circle, find the center of the circle, its radius, and its equation. Verify that the three given points do indeed lie on the circle. If needed, remind students that the center lies on the perpendicular bisectors of chords.

Additional Answers

3. If the phrase were not included, the figure would be a sphere.

4. Marco; the square root of $(x - 2)^2 + (y + 3)^2$ is not $(x - 2) + (y + 3)$.

5. Infinite number; every line passing through the center of the circle is an axis of symmetry.

15. $(x-3)^2 + (y+1)^2 = 9$

15. Write an equation for the graph below.

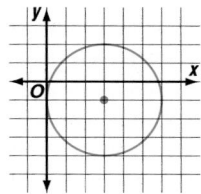

16. Write an equation for a circle that has its center at $(4, -2)$ and passes through $(5, 3)$. $(x-4)^2 + (y+2)^2 = 26$

Assignment Guide

Core: 17–57 odd, 59–68
Enriched: 18–54 even, 55–68

For **Extra Practice,** see p. 892.

The red A, B, and C flags, printed only in the Teacher's Wraparound Edition, indicate the level of difficulty of the exercises.

EXERCISES

Practice

17. $(x+1)^2 + (y+5)^2 = 4$

18. $x^2 + (y-3)^2 = 49$

19. $(x+8)^2 + (y-7)^2 = \frac{1}{4}$

20. $(x+3)^2 + (y+9)^2 = \frac{25}{36}$

23–40. See Solutions Manual for graphs.

23. $(0, -2)$, 2 units

24. $(0, 0)$, 12 units

25. $(3, 1)$, 5 units

26. $(-3, -7)$, 9 units

27. $(3, 0)$, 4 units

28. $(3, -7)$, $5\sqrt{2}$ units

29. $(-\sqrt{5}, 4)$, 5 units

30. $(-2, 0)$, $\sqrt{13}$ units

31. $(-7, -3)$, $2\sqrt{2}$ units

32. $(0, 3)$, 5 units

33. $(-1, 0)$, $\sqrt{11}$ units

34. $(9, 9)$, $\sqrt{109}$ units

35. $\left(0, -\frac{9}{2}\right)$, $\sqrt{19}$ units

36. $\left(-\frac{9}{2}, 4\right)$, $\frac{\sqrt{129}}{2}$ units

37. $\left(\frac{3}{2}, -4\right)$, $\frac{3\sqrt{17}}{2}$ units

38. $(6, 8)$, 4 units

Write an equation for each circle if the coordinates of the center and length of the radius are given.

17. center, $(-1, -5)$; $r = 2$ units

18. center, $(0, 3)$; $r = 7$ units

19. center, $(-8, 7)$; $r = \frac{1}{2}$ unit

20. center, $(-3, -9)$; $r = \frac{5}{6}$ unit

21. center, $(0.5, 0.7)$; $r = 13.5$ units
$(x - 0.5)^2 + (y - 0.7)^2 = 182.25$

22. center, $\left(\sqrt{2}, 3\sqrt{7}\right)$; $r = 0.25$ unit
$\left(x - \sqrt{2}\right)^2 + \left(y - 3\sqrt{7}\right)^2 = 0.0625$

Find the coordinates of the center and the radius of each circle whose equation is given. Then draw the graph.

23. $x^2 + (y+2)^2 = 4$

24. $x^2 + y^2 = 144$

25. $(x-3)^2 + (y-1)^2 = 25$

26. $(x+3)^2 + (y+7)^2 = 81$

27. $(x-3)^2 + y^2 = 16$

28. $(x-3)^2 + (y+7)^2 = 50$

29. $\left(x+\sqrt{5}\right)^2 + y^2 - 8y = 9$

30. $x^2 + y^2 + 4x = 9$

31. $x^2 + y^2 + 6y = -50 - 14x$

32. $x^2 + y^2 - 6y - 16 = 0$

33. $x^2 + y^2 + 2x - 10 = 0$

34. $x^2 + y^2 - 18x - 18y + 53 = 0$

35. $4x^2 + 4y^2 + 36y + 5 = 0$

36. $x^2 + y^2 + 9x - 8y + 4 = 0$

37. $x^2 + y^2 - 3x + 8y = 20$

38. $x^2 - 12x + 84 = -y^2 + 16y$

39. $x^2 + y^2 + 2x + 4y = 9$
$(-1, -2)$, $\sqrt{14}$ units

40. $x^2 + 2\sqrt{7}x + 7 + \left(y - \sqrt{11}\right)^2 = 11$
$(-\sqrt{7}, \sqrt{11})$, $\sqrt{11}$ units

41. $(x-2)^2 + (y+1)^2 = 4$ **42.** $(x+1)^2 + (y-1)^2 = 16$ **43.** $(x+3)^2 + (y+2)^2 = 1$

Write an equation for each graph.

41.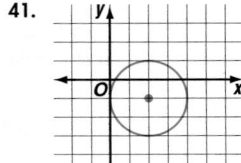

42.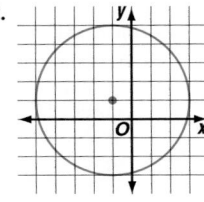

43.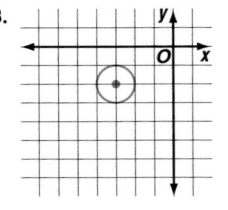

Lesson 7–3   Circles   **427**

Study Guide Masters, p. 51

NAME _____ DATE _____

7-3 **Study Guide**

Student Edition
Pages 423–429

Circles

A **circle** is the set of all points in a plane that are equidistant from a given point, called the **center.** The distance from the center to any point on the circle is called the **radius.**

Equation of Circle with Center at (h, k), radius r
$(x - h)^2 + (y - k)^2 = r^2$

Example: Find the center and radius of the circle whose equation is $x^2 + 2x + y^2 + 4y = 11$. Then graph the circle.

Complete the square for each variable.
$x^2 + 2x + y^2 + 4y = 11$
$x^2 + 2x + \blacksquare + y^2 + 4y + \square = 11 + \blacksquare + \square$

Write the equation in the form $(x - h)^2 + (y - k)^2 = r^2$
$x^2 + 2x + 1 + y^2 + 4y + 4 = 11 + 1 + 4$
$(x + 1)^2 + (y + 2)^2 = 16$

The circle has its center at $(-1, -2)$ and a radius of 4.

Find the coordinates of the center and the radius of each circle whose equation is given. Then draw the graph.

1. $(x-3)^2 + y^2 = 9$ **2.** $x^2 + (y+5)^2 = 4$ **3.** $(x-1)^2 + (y+3)^2 = 9$

$(3, 0), r = 3$ $(0, -5), r = 2$ $(1, -3), r = 3$

4. $(x-2)^2 + (y+4)^2 = 16$ **5.** $x^2 + 14x + y^2 + 2y = -40$ **6.** $x^2 + y^2 - 10x + 8y + 16 = 0$

$(2, -4), r = 4$ $(-7, -1), r = \sqrt{10}$ $(5, -4), r = 5$

Write an equation for each circle if the coordinates of the center and length of the radius are given.

7. $(-3, 5)$, 7 units
$(x + 3)^2 + (y - 5)^2 = 49$

8. $(-4, -6)$, 5 units
$(x + 4)^2 + (y + 6)^2 = 25$

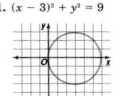

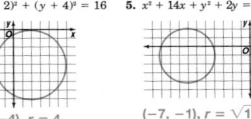

Additional Answers

50b.

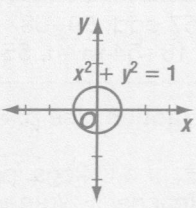

$x^2 + y^2 = 1$

51.

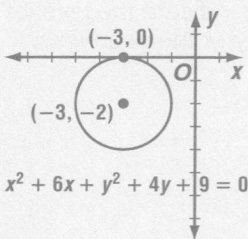

$(-3, 0)$

$(-3, -2)$

$x^2 + 6x + y^2 + 4y + 9 = 0$

Practice Masters, p. 51

Practice

NAME_____ DATE _____

Student Edition
Pages 423–429

Circles

Find the coordinates of the center and the radius of each circle whose equation is given. Then draw the graph.

1. $(x + 3)^2 + y^2 = 16$ $(-3, 0)$; 4   **2.** $3x^2 + 3y^2 = 12$ $(0, 0)$; 2

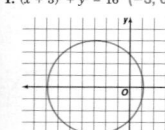 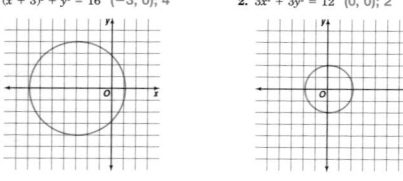

3. $x^2 + y^2 - 6x - 12y + 36 = 0$ $(3, 6)$; 3   **4.** $x^2 + y^2 + 2x + 6y = 26$ $(-1, -3)$; 6

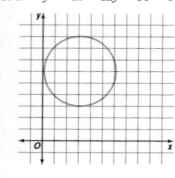 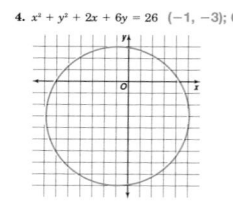

Write an equation for each circle if the coordinates of the center and length of the radius are given.

5. center $(-4, 2)$; radius 8
$(x + 4)^2 + (y - 2)^2 = 64$

6. center $(5, -6)$; radius 11
$(x - 5)^2 + (y + 6)^2 = 121$

7. center $\left(-\frac{1}{4}, -\sqrt{3}\right)$; radius $5\sqrt{2}$
$\left(x + \frac{1}{4}\right)^2 + (y + \sqrt{3})^2 = 50$

8. center $\left(3.8, 1\frac{1}{3}\right)$; radius $\frac{3}{7}$
$(x - 3.8)^2 + \left(y - 1\frac{1}{3}\right)^2 = \frac{9}{49}$

428 Chapter 7

44. $(x - 8)^2 + (y + 9)^2 = 1130$

45. $(x + \sqrt{13})^2 + (y - 42)^2 = 1777$

46. $(x + 1.25)^2 + (y + 0.5)^2 = 492.3125$

47. $(x + 8)^2 + (y + 7)^2 = 64$

49. $(x + 3)^2 + (y + 6)^2 = 9$

51. $y = 0$; See margin for graph.

52a. $(0, 5)$, $(4, 3)$, $(0, -5)$

52b. Yes, the vertices of the triangle are on the circle and a diameter is on the y-axis.

56. $(x - 5)^2 + (y - 10)^2 = 400$

57a. $x^2 + y^2 = 841,000,000$

57b. See margin.

Write an equation for each circle described below.

44. The circle has its center at $(8, -9)$ and passes through the point at $(21, 22)$.

45. The circle passes through the origin and has its center at $\left(-\sqrt{13}, 42\right)$.

46. The endpoints of a diameter are at $(11, 18)$ and $(-13.5, -19)$.

47. The circle is tangent to the y-axis and has its center at $(-8, -7)$.

48. The circle is tangent to $x = -3$, $x = 5$, and the x-axis. The center of the circle is in the first quadrant. $(x - 1)^2 + (y - 4)^2 = 16$

49. The circle is tangent to the y-axis and has a radius of 3 units. The center of the circle is in the third quadrant and lies on the graph of $y = 2x$.

50. A *unit circle* is a circle with a radius of 1 unit.   **a.** $x^2 + y^2 = 1$

   a. Write an equation for a unit circle with its center at the origin.

   b. Graph the equation.   **See margin.**

   c. Find the area of the circle. π square units

   d. Find the circumference of the circle. 2π units

51. Draw the circle whose equation is $x^2 + 6x + y^2 + 4y + 9 = 0$. What is the equation of the line that is tangent to the circle at $(-3, 0)$?

52. Geometry   The equation for the circle at the right is $x^2 + y^2 = 25$. The triangle is formed by the y-axis and the lines whose equations are

$$y = -\frac{1}{2}x + 5 \text{ and } y = 2x - 5.$$

   a. Find the coordinates of the vertices of the triangle.

   b. Recall from geometry that if a triangle is inscribed in a circle and one of its sides is a diameter of the circle, the triangle is a right triangle. Using this information, do you think the triangle in the diagram is a right triangle? Explain.

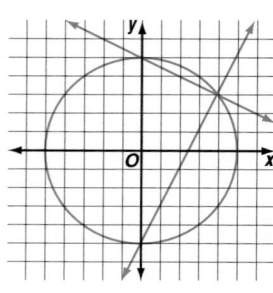

53–54. See Solutions Manual.

Graphing Calculator

Write the equations needed to graph each equation on a graphing calculator. Then graph the equations on a graphing calculator.

53. $x^2 + y^2 = 4$ **54.** $(x + 3)^2 + (y - 1)^2 = 8$

Critical Thinking

55. Consider the graphs whose equations are of the form $(x - 3)^2 + (y - a)^2 = 64$. Assign three different values for a and graph each equation. Describe all graphs whose equations have this form.   **circles with a radius of 8 and centers on the graph of $x = 3$**

Applications and Problem Solving

56. Air Traffic Control   The radar for a county airport control tower is located at $(5, 10)$ on the map. It can detect a plane up to 20 miles away. Write an equation for outside limits that a plane can be detected.

57. Satellites   A satellite is in a circular orbit 25,000 miles above Earth.

   a. Write an equation for the orbit of this satellite if the origin is at the center of Earth. Use 8000 miles as the diameter of Earth.

   b. Draw a sketch of Earth and the orbit to scale. Label your sketch.

Additional Answer

57b.

Earth

Satellite

25,000 miles

8000 miles

33,000 miles

Extension

Problem Solving Write an equation for a circle with a center on the x-axis and the radius 5 units long, passing through $(2, -2)$.

center at $\left(2 + \sqrt{21}, 0\right)$ or $\left(2 - \sqrt{21}, 0\right)$

58. Sports The maintenance personnel for the Onalaska, Wisconsin, School District needed to mark off an arc, AB, as a boundary on an empty lot to be converted to a baseball field. The figure at the right shows the details. The center C of the circle was located within a building on an adjacent lot. The supervisor needed to know what set of points the crew might connect to form the arc.

a. If the location of points A, B, and C were known, how could the work crew determine the other points needed to draw arc AB accurately? (*Hint:* Let point A be the origin and let $\overline{AB}$ lie along the x-axis. Then determine the coordinates of the center of the circle. Use the center and radius to form the equation of the circle.)

b. Explain how the equation can be used to draw arc AB. **See margin.**
a. $(x - 200)^2 + (y + 275)^2 = 340^2$; $y = \sqrt{-x^2 + 400x + 75{,}600} - 275$

Mixed Review

59. Write $y^2 = 6x$ in the form $x = a(y - k)^2 + h$. (Lesson 7–2)

59. $x = \frac{1}{6}y^2$

60. Solve $x^2 - 3x + 1 = 0$. Then find the sum and product of the roots to check your solutions. (Lesson 6–5)

60. $\frac{3 \pm \sqrt{5}}{2}$

61. Simplify $\frac{3}{4 - i}$. (Lesson 5–10) $\frac{12 + 3i}{17}$

62. Business Dawn is writing a computer program to find the salaries of her employees after their annual raise. The percentage of increase is represented by p. Marty's salary is $23,450 now. Write a polynomial to represent Marty's salary in one year and another to represent Marty's salary after three years. Assume that the rate of increase will be the same for the three years. (Lesson 5–2) $23{,}450(1 + p)$; $23{,}450(1 + p)^3$

63. Solve $\begin{vmatrix} x^2 & x \\ 3 & 1 \end{vmatrix} = 4$. (Lesson 4–4) $4, -1$

64. Solve the system of equations. (Lesson 3–7) $(3, -4, 0)$

$2a + b = 2$

$5a = 15$

$a + b + c = -1$

65. The sum of Kari's age and her mother's age is 52. Kari's mother is 20 years older than Kari. How old is each? (Lesson 3–2) **16, 36**

66. What is the slope of the line perpendicular to the line that passes through $(5, 1)$ and $(8, 2)$? (Lesson 2–3) -3

67. Health The optimum heart rate is the rate that a person should achieve during exercise to be most beneficial. The prediction equation $r = 0.6(220 - a)$, where a represents age, can be used to find a person's optimum heart rate r. If Josh is 20 years old, find his optimum heart rate. (Lesson 2–2) **120**

68. Simplify $\sqrt{9} \div \sqrt{4}$. (Lesson 1–1) $\frac{3}{2}$

Lesson 7–3 Circles **429**

Classroom Vignette

"The situation in Exercise 58 is a real-life problem from the maintenance department in the Onalaska, Wisconsin, School District that was presented to the math department. We have students work in cooperative groups to solve this problem while we are studying the conics chapter."

Leah Wisnewski Leah Wisnewski, Richard Kyes, Robert Deml
Onalaska High School
Onalaska, Wisconsin

4 ASSESS

Closing Activity

Speaking Have students randomly place a circular object on a piece of graph paper with the x-axis and y-axis defined ahead of time. Students should then trace around the object to form a circle on the graph paper. Have them discuss how they would determine the exact coordinates of the center.

Additional Answer

58b. Using a coordinate plane with origin at point A, mark all the points that satisfy the equation from $(0, 0)$ to $(400, 0)$.

Enrichment Masters, p. 51

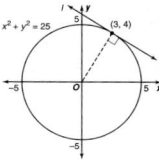

7-3 NAME _____ DATE _____
Enrichment Student Edition Pages 423–429

Tangents to Circles

A line that intersects a circle in exactly one point is a **tangent** to the circle. In the diagram, line l is tangent to the circle with equation $x^2 + y^2 = 25$ at the point whose coordinates are $(3, 4)$.

A line is tangent to a circle at a point P on the circle if and only if the line is perpendicular to the radius from the center of the circle to point P. This fact enables you to find an equation of the tangent to a circle at a point P if you know an equation for the circle and the coordinates of P.

Use the diagram above to solve each problem.

1. What is the slope of the radius to the point with coordinates $(3, 4)$? What is the slope of the tangent to that point? $\frac{4}{3}$, $-\frac{3}{4}$

2. Find an equation of the line l that is tangent to the circle at $(3, 4)$. $y = -\frac{3}{4}x + \frac{25}{4}$

3. If k is a real number between -5 and 5, how many points on the circle have x-coordinate k? State the coordinates of these points in terms of k. two, $(k, \pm \sqrt{25 - k^2})$

4. Describe how you can find equations for the tangents to the points you named for Exercise 3.
Use the coordinates of $(0, 0)$ and of one of the given points. Find the slope of the radius to that point. Use the slope of the radius to find what the slope of the tangent must be. Use the slope of the tangent and the coordinates of the point on the circle to find an equation for the tangent.

5. Find an equation for the tangent at $(-3, 4)$. $y = \frac{3}{4}x + \frac{25}{x}$

Chapter 7 **429**

NCTM Standards: 1–5, 8

Objective
Draw an ellipse using simple materials.

Recommended Time
Demonstration and discussion: 15 minutes; Exercises: 30 minutes

Instructional Resources
For each student or group of students
Modeling Mathematics Masters
• p. 15 (grid paper)
• p. 22 (worksheet)
For teacher demonstration
Algebra and Geometry Overhead Manipulative Resources

1 FOCUS

Motivating the Lesson
Explain that an ellipse can be viewed as a generalization of a circle. Every point on the circumference of a circle is equidistant from the center. Ask students to imagine what the circumference of a circle with two centers would look like.

2 TEACH

Teaching Tip Have students make the two foci coincide. After drawing the figure, students will see that they have traced a circle.

Teaching Tip On wax paper, draw a circle and use the center as one focus. Insert another point any place in the circle for the second focus. Fold the paper so that all points on the circle (one at a time) lie on the focus that is not the center of the circle.

3 PRACTICE/APPLY

Assignment Guide

Core: 1–4
Enriched: 1–4

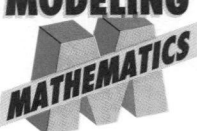

7-4A Drawing Ellipses

Materials: thumbtacks string cardboard

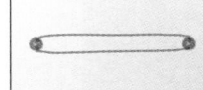 grid paper

A Preview of Lesson 7–4

To draw an ellipse, tie a knot in a piece of string and loop it around the thumbtacks as shown.

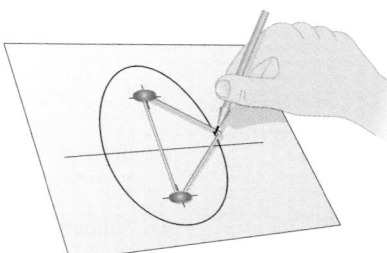

Place your pencil in the string as shown in the diagram. Begin at some point. Keep the string tight and draw a curve. Continue drawing until you return to your starting point. Pick a point on the circle and measure the distance between the point and each thumbtack. Add these numbers together. Pick two more points and repeat this process. What is true about the sum of the distances from the two thumbtacks for all points on the curve?

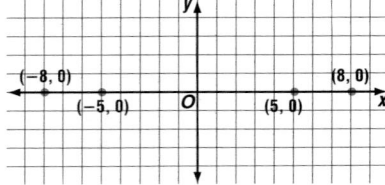

The two thumbtacks are located at the foci of the ellipse. *Foci is the plural of focus.*

Activity   **Place a large piece of grid paper on the cardboard.**

a. Place the thumbtacks at (8, 0) and (−8, 0). Choose a string of appropriate length. Draw the ellipse.

b. Repeat part a, but place the thumbtacks at (5, 0) and (−5, 0). Use the same piece of string and draw an ellipse. How does this ellipse compare to the one drawn in part a?

Model   **Place the thumbtacks at each set of points and draw an ellipse.**

1. A(12, 0) and B(−12, 0)   **2.** C(2, 0) and D(−2, 0)   **3.** E(14, 4) and F(−10, 4)
1–3. See Solutions Manual for sample graphs.

Write   **4.** Write a paragraph describing what happens to the shape of an ellipse when each of the following changes are made.   a-c. See Solutions Manual.

   a. The thumbtacks are moved closer together or farther apart.

   b. Both thumbtacks are placed at the same point.

   c. The length of the piece of string is changed.

4 ASSESS

Observing students working in cooperative groups is an excellent method of assessment.

GLENCOE Technology

Interactive Mathematics Tools Software

This multimedia software provides an interactive lesson by adjusting the height of the foci of an orbit and having students observe their effect on the shape of the ellipse. A **Computer Journal** gives students an opportunity to write about what they have learned.

For Windows & Macintosh

7-4

Ellipses

What YOU'LL LEARN

- To write equations of ellipses, and
- to graph ellipses having certain properties.

Why IT'S IMPORTANT

You can graph ellipses to solve problems involving medicine and astronomy.

APPLICATION
Museums

A cross section of the whispering chamber at the Museum of Science and Industry in Chicago is shaped like an **ellipse.** In this chamber, a person standing at a focus point can hear a person standing at the other focus point whispering, even though they are 43.42 feet apart.

Museum of Science and Industry, Chicago, Illinois

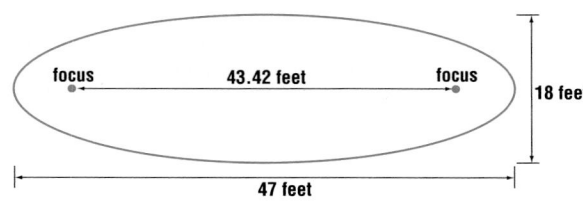

focus · ———— 43.42 feet ———— · focus | 18 feet
|—————————— 47 feet ——————————|

The architect for the whispering chamber used an important property of ellipses. Rays emanating from one of the two foci of an ellipse are reflected to the other focus. As you discovered in Lesson 7–4A, the sum of the distances from the two foci of an ellipse is always the same.

Definition of Ellipse	An ellipse is the set of all points in a plane such that the sum of the distances from the foci is constant.

The ellipse at the right has foci at $(8, 0)$ and $(-8, 0)$. The sum of the distances from any point with coordinates (x, y) on the ellipse to the foci is 24 units.

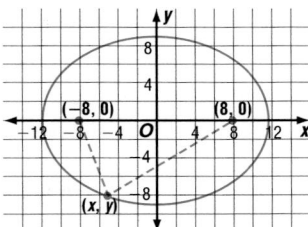

Use the distance formula and the definition of an ellipse to find the equation of the ellipse. Let (x, y) be the coordinates of any point on the ellipse. The sum of the distance between the points at (x, y) and $(8, 0)$ and the distance between the points at (x, y) and $(-8, 0)$ is 24 units.

Lesson 7–4 Ellipses **431**

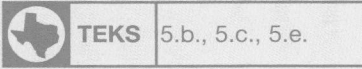

TEKS | 5.b., 5.c., 5.e.

NCTM Standards: 1–5, 8

Instructional Resources

- Study Guide Master 7-4
- Practice Master 7-4
- Enrichment Master 7-4
- Assessment and Evaluation Masters, pp. 183–184

 Transparency 7-4A contains the 5-Minute Check for this lesson; **Transparency 7-4B** contains a teaching aid for this lesson.

Recommended Pacing	
Standard Pacing	Day 5 of 15
Honors Pacing	Day 5 of 13
Block Scheduling*	Day 3 of 7

 *For more information on pacing and possible lesson plans, refer to the *Block Scheduling Booklet.*

1 FOCUS

 5-Minute Check
(over Lesson 7-3)

Write an equation for each circle if the coordinates of the center and length of the radius are given.

1. center, $(5, 0)$; $r = 6$ units
   $(x - 5)^2 + y^2 = 36$
2. center, $(-3, -2)$; $r = \frac{3}{2}$ units
   $(x + 3)^2 + (y + 2)^2 = \frac{9}{4}$
3. Find the coordinates of the center and the length of the radius for the circle whose equation is given. Then draw the graph.
   $x^2 + (y - 3)^2 = 16$
   $(0, 3)$, 4 units

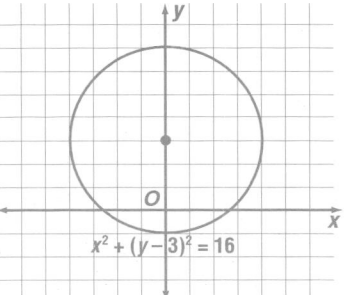

$x^2 + (y - 3)^2 = 16$

Motivating the Lesson

Hands-On Activity Bring in a flashlight. Show how to form a circle (beam perpendicular to the wall), ellipse (beam at an angle to the wall), and parabola (flashlight parallel to the wall). Discuss what happens as you move the flashlight slowly through the different positions.

2 TEACH

Teaching Tip For $\frac{x^2}{144} + \frac{y^2}{80} = 1$, the length of the major axis is $2a$ or $2\sqrt{144}$ or 24. The length of the minor axis is $2\sqrt{80}$ or $8\sqrt{5}$.

$$\underset{(x, y) \text{ and } (-8, 0)}{\text{distance between}} + \underset{(x, y) \text{ and } (8, 0)}{\text{distance between}} = 24$$

$$\sqrt{(x + 8)^2 + y^2} + \sqrt{(x - 8)^2 + y^2} = 24$$

$$\sqrt{(x + 8)^2 + y^2} = 24 - \sqrt{(x - 8)^2 + y^2}$$

$$(x + 8)^2 + y^2 = 576 - 48\sqrt{(x - 8)^2 + y^2} + (x - 8)^2 + y^2 \quad \textit{Square each side.}$$

$$x^2 + 16x + 64 + y^2 = 576 - 48\sqrt{(x - 8)^2 + y^2} + x^2 - 16x + 64 + y^2$$

$$32x - 576 = -48\sqrt{(x - 8)^2 + y^2} \quad \textit{Simplify.}$$

$$2x - 36 = -3\sqrt{(x - 8)^2 + y^2} \quad \textit{Divide each side by 16, the GCF.}$$

$$4x^2 - 144x + 1296 = 9[(x - 8)^2 + y^2] \quad \textit{Square each side.}$$

$$4x^2 - 144x + 1296 = 9x^2 - 144x + 576 + 9y^2 \quad \textit{Distributive property}$$

$$5x^2 + 9y^2 = 720 \quad \textit{Simplify.}$$

$$\frac{x^2}{144} + \frac{y^2}{80} = 1 \quad \textit{Divide each side by 720.}$$

The equation of this ellipse is $\frac{x^2}{144} + \frac{y^2}{80} = 1$.

Every ellipse has two axes of symmetry. The points at which the ellipse intersect the axes define two segments with endpoints on the ellipse. The longer segment is called the **major axis**, and the shorter segment is called the **minor axis**. The foci always lie on the major axis. The intersection of the two axes is the **center** of the ellipse.

Study the ellipse at the right. The sum of the distances from the foci to any point on the ellipse is $2a$ units. The distance from the center to either focus is c units. We can calculate the value of b by using the Pythagorean theorem, $b^2 = a^2 - c^2$.

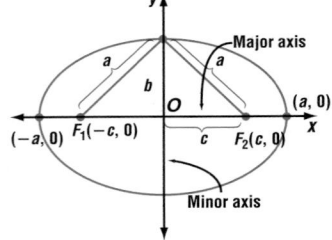

If we found the equation of this general ellipse, we would have the standard equation of an ellipse.

The length of the major axis is $2a$.
The length of the minor axis is $2b$.
Notice that $a > b$.

Standard Equations of Ellipses with Center at the Origin

- If an ellipse has foci at $(-c, 0)$ and $(c, 0)$ and the sum of the distances from the foci to any point on the ellipse is $2a$ units, then the standard equation of an ellipse is $\frac{x^2}{a^2} + \frac{y^2}{b^2} = 1$, where $b^2 = a^2 - c^2$.

  In this case, the major axis is horizontal.

- If an ellipse has foci at $(0, -c)$ and $(0, c)$ and the sum of the distances from the foci to any point on the ellipse is $2a$ units, then the standard equation of an ellipse is $\frac{x^2}{b^2} + \frac{y^2}{a^2} = 1$, where $b^2 = a^2 - c^2$.

  In this case, the major axis is vertical.

For the equation of an ellipse, $a^2 > b^2$. You can decide if the foci are on the *x*-axis or the *y*-axis by observing the equation. If a^2 is the denominator of the x^2 term, the foci are on the *x*-axis. If a^2 is the denominator of the y^2 term, the foci are on the *y*-axis.

Example ❶ Find the coordinates of the foci and the lengths of the major and minor axes of an ellipse whose equation is $16x^2 + 4y^2 = 144$. Then draw the graph.

Write the equation in standard form.

$16x^2 + 4y^2 = 144$

$\frac{x^2}{9} + \frac{y^2}{36} = 1$ *Divide each side by 144.*

Since $36 > 9$, the foci are on the *y*-axis, with $a = 6$ and $b = 3$.

$b^2 = a^2 - c^2$

$9 = 36 - c^2$

$c^2 = 27$

$c = 3\sqrt{3}$ or about 5.2

The foci are at $(0, 3\sqrt{3})$ and $(0, -3\sqrt{3})$.

The length of the major axis, $2a$, is 12 units.

The length of the minor axis, $2b$, is 6 units.

You can use this information to draw the ellipse.

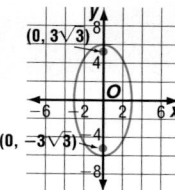

Example ❷ Write the equation of the ellipse shown below.

The length of the major axis is the distance between the points at $(7, 0)$ and $(-7, 0)$. This distance is 14 units.

$2a = 14$

$a = 7$

The foci are located at $(4, 0)$ and $(-4, 0)$. The value of c is 4.

$b^2 = a^2 - c^2$

$b^2 = 7^2 - 4^2$ or 33

Now, write the equation in the form   *The major axis is horizontal.*

$\frac{x^2}{a^2} + \frac{y^2}{b^2} = 1$, where $a^2 = 49$ and $b^2 = 33$.

The equation of the ellipse is $\frac{x^2}{49} + \frac{y^2}{33} = 1$

Planets, satellites, moons, and comets all have orbits that have the shape of a conic section. The most common orbit is in the form of an ellipse.

Lesson 7–4 Ellipses **433**

In-Class Examples

For Example 1
Find the coordinates of the foci and the lengths of the major and minor axes of an ellipse whose equation is $49x^2 + 16y^2 = 784$. Then draw the graph.

foci: $\left(0, \sqrt{33}\right), \left(0, -\sqrt{33}\right)$;

major axis = 14 units; minor axis = 8 units

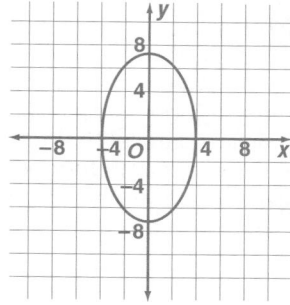

For Example 2
Write the equation of the ellipse shown below.

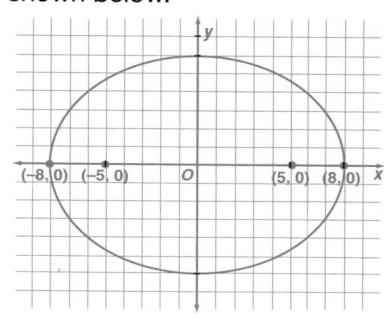

$\frac{x^2}{64} + \frac{y^2}{39} = 1$

 Alternative Learning Styles

Kinesthetic Use the procedure described for drawing an ellipse to show students that as the foci of an ellipse get closer together, the shape of the ellipse approaches the shape of a circle. As a result of this activity, students will see that when the foci and the center become one point, the figure is a circle.

1. Under what conditions is the graph of $\frac{x^2}{a^2} + \frac{y^2}{b^2} = 1$ a circle?
   when $a = b$

2. What happens to the foci and the center of this ellipse? They become one point—the center of the circle—since $c^2 = a^2 - b^2 = 0$.
Note that a circle, then, is a special case of an ellipse.

In-Class Example

For Example 3

Venus follows an elliptical orbit around the sun. Its closest point is 66.8 million miles; its farthest point is 67.7 million miles. Find the equation of Venus' orbit.

$$\frac{x^2}{4.5226 \times 10^{15}} + \frac{y^2}{4.522560475 \times 10^{15}} = 1$$

MODELING MATHEMATICS This activity emphasizes the connection between a circle and an ellipse. Point out to students that the line $y = 5$ is a line parallel to the major axis of the ellipse and tangent to the ellipse. The line $y = -5$ also would have worked.

Answer for Modeling Mathematics

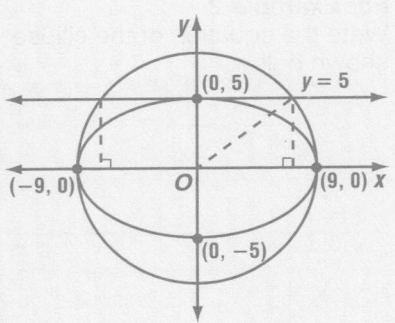

Example 3

APPLICATION
Astronomy

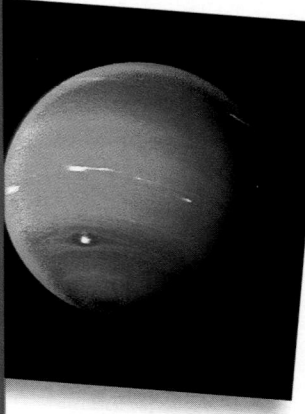

Mercury follows an ellipse-shaped, or *elliptical*, orbit around the sun. At its closest point, Mercury is 29.0 million miles from the center of the sun. At its farthest point, Mercury is 43.8 million miles from the center of the sun. Assume that the center of this orbit lies at the origin, the center of the sun is a focus of this ellipse, and the sun lies on the x-axis.

a. Draw a sketch of Mercury's orbit.
b. Write an equation for the orbit.

a. A sketch of Mercury's orbit is shown at the right.

b. The length of the major axis is 29.0 + 43.8 or 72.8 million miles. Use this information to find the value of a.

$$2a = 72,800,000$$
$$a = 36,400,000$$

The distance from the center of the orbit to the center of the sun is $36.4 - 29.0$ or 7.4 million miles. This is the value of c, the distance from the center to the focus.

$$b^2 = a^2 - c^2$$
$$= (36,400,000)^2 - (7,400,000)^2$$
$$= 1,324,960,000,000,000 - 54,760,000,000,000$$
$$= 1,270,200,000,000,000 \text{ or } 1.2702 \times 10^{15}$$

Now we can write the equation.

$$\frac{x^2}{a^2} + \frac{y^2}{b^2} = 1$$

$$\frac{x^2}{(36,400,000)^2} + \frac{y^2}{1,270,200,000,000,000} = 1$$

$$\frac{x^2}{1.32496 \times 10^{15}} + \frac{y^2}{1.2702 \times 10^{15}} = 1 \quad (36,400,000)^2 = 1.32496 \times 10^{15}$$

An equation for the orbit is $\dfrac{x^2}{1.32496 \times 10^{15}} + \dfrac{y^2}{1.2702 \times 10^{15}} = 1$.

A circle can be used to find the foci of an ellipse.

MODELING MATHEMATICS

Locating Foci

Materials:  grid paper  compass

See margin for sample diagram.
a–f. See students' work.

Your Turn

a. On a coordinate plane, draw an ellipse with its center at the origin. Let the endpoints of the major axis be at $(-9, 0)$ and $(9, 0)$, and let the endpoints of the minor axis be at $(0, -5)$ and $(0, 5)$.

b. Estimate the locations of the foci and mark these points.

c. Use a compass to draw a circle with center at $(0, 0)$ and radius of 9 units.

d. Draw the line $y = 5$ and mark the points at which the line intersects the circle.

e. Draw perpendicular lines from the points of intersection to the x-axis. The foci are located at the points where the perpendicular lines intersect the x-axis.

f. Draw another ellipse and locate its foci using this method. Why does this method work?

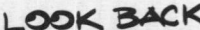

LOOK BACK

You can refer to Lesson 4-2 for more information on translations.

An ellipse with its center at the origin is represented by an equation in the form $\frac{x^2}{a^2} + \frac{y^2}{b^2} = 1$ or $\frac{x^2}{b^2} + \frac{y^2}{a^2} = 1$. The ellipse could be translated h units to the left or right and k units up or down. This would move the center to the point (h, k). Such a move would be equivalent to replacing x with $(x - h)$ and replacing y with $(y - k)$.

Standard Equations of Ellipses with Center at (h, k)

- The standard equation of an ellipse with its center at (h, k) and with a horizontal major axis is $\frac{(x - h)^2}{a^2} + \frac{(y - k)^2}{b^2} = 1$.

- The standard equation of an ellipse with center at (h, k) and with a vertical major axis is $\frac{(x - h)^2}{b^2} + \frac{(y - k)^2}{a^2} = 1$.

Example Graph $\frac{(x + 4)^2}{25} + \frac{(y - 3)^2}{4} = 1$.

The graph has the same shape as the graph of $\frac{x^2}{25} + \frac{y^2}{4} = 1$. The center, however, is at $(-4, 3)$.

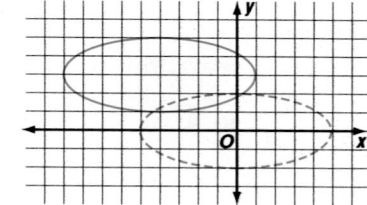

Draw the graph of $\frac{x^2}{25} + \frac{y^2}{4} = 1$.

Then translate the graph 4 units to the left and 3 units up.

Sometimes equations of ellipses are written in expanded form as they were for circles. You need to complete the square for each variable to write the equation in standard form.

Example An equation of an ellipse is $x^2 + 9y^2 - 4x + 54y + 49 = 0$. Find the coordinates of the center and foci and the lengths of the major and minor axes. Then draw the graph.

$$x^2 + 9y^2 - 4x + 54y + 49 = 0$$
$$(x^2 - 4x + \square) + 9(y^2 + 6y + \square) = -49 + \square + 9(\square) \quad \textit{Complete the squares.}$$
$$(x^2 - 4x + 4) + 9(y^2 + 6y + 9) = -49 + 4 + 9(9)$$
$$(x - 2)^2 + 9(y + 3)^2 = 36 \quad \textit{Standard form}$$
$$\frac{(x - 2)^2}{36} + \frac{(y + 3)^2}{4} = 1$$

The coordinates of the center are $(2, -3)$.

Since $36 > 4$, the foci are on the horizontal axis.

$$b^2 = a^2 - c^2$$
$$4 = 36 - c^2 \quad \textit{a = 6 and b = 2}$$
$$c^2 = 32$$
$$c = 4\sqrt{2} \text{ or about } 5.66$$

(continued on the next page)

For Example 4

Graph $\frac{(x + 1)^2}{4} + \frac{(y + 2)^2}{9} = 1$.

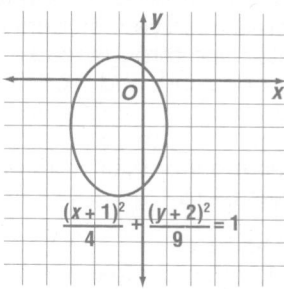

For Example 5

An equation of an ellipse is $16y^2 + 9x^2 - 96y - 90x = -225$. Find the coordinates of the center and foci and the lengths of the major and minor axes. Then draw the graph.

center: (5, 3)

foci: $\left(5 + \sqrt{7}, 3\right), \left(5 - \sqrt{7}, 3\right)$

major axis length: 8
minor axis length: 6

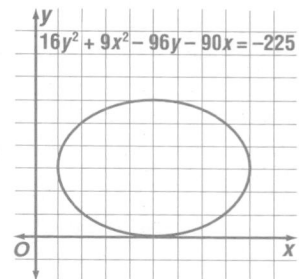

Check for Understanding

Exercises 1–15 are designed to help you assess your students' understanding through reading, writing, speaking, and modeling. You should work through Exercises 1–5 with your students and then monitor their work on Exercises 6–15.

Error Analysis

Students often confuse the $b^2 = a^2 - c^2$ relation from an ellipse with the Pythagorean relationship $a^2 + b^2 = c^2$. In the ellipse labeling, the letter a represents the hypotenuse. This labeling choice is useful in defining eccentricity for ellipses and hyperbolas $\left(e = \dfrac{c}{a}\right)$.

Additional Answers

1. Sample answer: For the equation $\dfrac{x^2}{m^2} + \dfrac{y^2}{n^2} = 1$, if $m^2 > n^2$, then the major axis is horizontal. If $m^2 < n^2$, then the major axis is vertical.

2. If the major and minor axes are the same length, the ellipse is a circle.

3. The equation in this form allows easy determination of the length of the major and minor axes and the coordinates of the center.

4. The shortest distance from the center of the sun plus the longest distance from the center of the sun gives the major axis.

10.

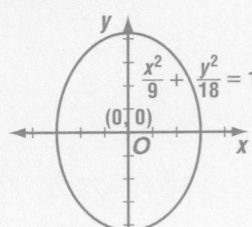

11.

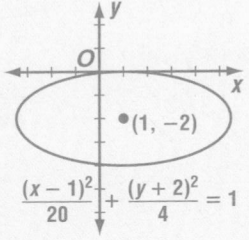

The foci are at $(2 + 4\sqrt{2}, -3)$ and $(2 - 4\sqrt{2}, -3)$ or about $(7.66, -3)$ and $(-3.66, -3)$.

Since $a = 6$, the length of the major axis is $2a$ or 12 units. Since $b = 2$, the length of the minor axis is $2b$ or 4 units.

Use this information to draw the graph.

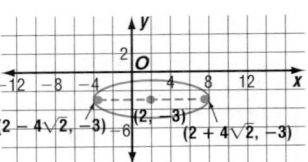

CHECK FOR UNDERSTANDING

Communicating Mathematics

Study the lesson. Then complete the following.   1–4. See margin.

1. **Describe** how you can tell from the equation of an ellipse which is the major and minor axis.

2. **Describe** how circles and ellipses are related.

3. **Explain** why one side of an equation is always 1 when the equation of an ellipse is written in standard form.

4. **Explain** how the length of the major axis was determined in Example 3.

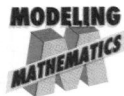
MODELING MATHEMATICS

5. Draw an ellipse. Then use a circle and lines to find the foci of the ellipse. See students' work.

6. (0, 0), vertical   7. (4, −6), horizontal

Guided Practice

The equation of an ellipse is given. Find the coordinates of the center and state whether the major axis is vertical or horizontal.

6. $\dfrac{x^2}{5} + \dfrac{y^2}{20} = 1$ 7. $\dfrac{(x-4)^2}{42} + \dfrac{(y+6)^2}{23} = 1$

Write an equation for each ellipse in standard form.

8. $\dfrac{x^2}{4} + \dfrac{y^2}{20} = 1$

8. $10x^2 + 2y^2 = 40$ 9. $x^2 + 6y^2 - 2x + 12y - 23 = 0$

9. $\dfrac{(x-1)^2}{30} + \dfrac{(y+1)^2}{5} = 1$

Find the coordinates of the center and foci and the lengths of the major and minor axes for each ellipse whose equation is given. Then draw the graph.   10–13. See margin for graphs.

10. (0, 0); (0, ±3); $6\sqrt{2}$; 6

10. $\dfrac{x^2}{9} + \dfrac{y^2}{18} = 1$ 11. $\dfrac{(x-1)^2}{20} + \dfrac{(y+2)^2}{4} = 1$

11. (1, −2); (−3, −2), (5, −2); $4\sqrt{5}$; 4

12. $4x^2 + 8y^2 = 32$ 13. $x^2 + 25y^2 - 8x + 100y + 91 = 0$

12. (0, 0); (±2, 0); $4\sqrt{2}$; 4

13. (4, −2); $(4 \pm 2\sqrt{6}, -2)$; 10; 2

14. Write an equation for the graph at the right. $\dfrac{x^2}{36} + \dfrac{y^2}{20} = 1$

15. Write an equation of an ellipse whose endpoints of the major axis are at (0, 10) and (0, −10) and whose foci are at (0, 8) and (0, −8). $\dfrac{x^2}{36} + \dfrac{y^2}{100} = 1$

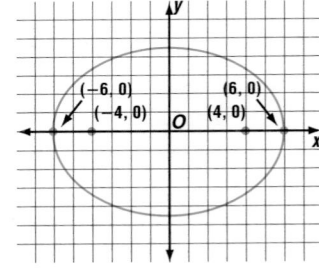

Reteaching

Using Alternative Methods Given the foci and the sum of the distances from the foci to any point on an ellipse, find the standard form of its equation in two ways. First use the definition of an ellipse and the distance formula to find the equation. Then use relationships to find h, k, b, and c.

EXERCISES

Practice

A

Write an equation for each ellipse.

19. $(0, 0)$; $(0, \pm\sqrt{5})$;
$2\sqrt{10}$; $2\sqrt{5}$

20. $(0, 0)$; $(\pm4, 0)$; 10; 6

21. $(5, -11)$; $(5, -11 \pm \sqrt{23})$; 24; 22

22. $(-8, 2)$; $(-8 \pm 3\sqrt{7}, 2)$; 24; 18

23. $(0, 0)$; $(\pm3\sqrt{5}, 0)$; 18; 12

24. $(0, 0)$; $(0, \pm\sqrt{6})$; 6; $2\sqrt{3}$

25. $(0, 0)$; $(0, \pm\sqrt{7})$; 8; 6

26. $(0, 0)$;
B
$(\pm\sqrt{6}, 0)$; 6; $2\sqrt{3}$

27. $(-3, 1)$; $(-3, 5)$, $(-3, -3)$; $4\sqrt{6}$; $4\sqrt{2}$

28. $(-2, 7)$; $(-2 \pm 4\sqrt{2}, 7)$; $4\sqrt{10}$; $4\sqrt{2}$

29. $(2, 2)$; $(2, 4)$, $(2, 0)$; $2\sqrt{7}$; $2\sqrt{3}$

30. $(-1, 3)$; $(2, 3)$, **C**
$(-4, 3)$; 10; 8

16.

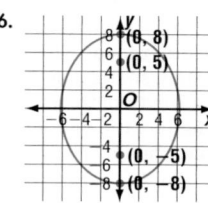

$\dfrac{x^2}{39} + \dfrac{y^2}{64} = 1$

17.

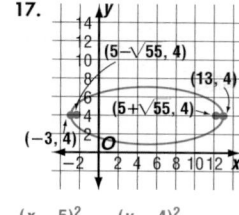

$\dfrac{(x-5)^2}{64} + \dfrac{(y-4)^2}{9} = 1$

18.

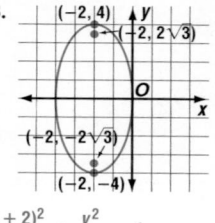

$\dfrac{(x+2)^2}{4} + \dfrac{y^2}{16} = 1$

Find the coordinates of the center and foci, and the lengths of the major and minor axes for each ellipse whose equation is given. Then draw the graph. 19–32. See Solutions Manual for graphs.

19. $\dfrac{x^2}{5} + \dfrac{y^2}{10} = 1$

20. $\dfrac{x^2}{25} + \dfrac{y^2}{9} = 1$

21. $\dfrac{(x-5)^2}{121} + \dfrac{(y+11)^2}{144} = 1$

22. $\dfrac{(x+8)^2}{144} + \dfrac{(y-2)^2}{81} = 1$

23. $36x^2 + 81y^2 = 2916$

24. $27x^2 + 9y^2 = 81$

25. $16x^2 + 9y^2 = 144$

26. $3x^2 + 9y^2 = 27$

27. $3x^2 + y^2 + 18x - 2y + 4 = 0$

28. $x^2 + 5y^2 + 4x - 70y + 209 = 0$

29. $7x^2 + 3y^2 - 28x - 12y = -19$

30. $16x^2 + 25y^2 + 32x - 150y = 159$

31. $9x^2 + 16y^2 - 18x + 64y = 71$
$(1, -2)$; $(1 \pm \sqrt{7}, -2)$; 8; 6

32. $4x^2 + 9y^2 + 16x - 18y - 11 = 0$
$(-2, 1)$; $(-2 \pm \sqrt{5}, 1)$; 6; 4

33–38. See margin.

Write an equation for each ellipse described below.

33. The endpoints of the major axis are at $(10, 2)$ and $(-8, 2)$. The foci are at $(6, 2)$ and $(-4, 2)$.

34. The major axis is 20 units in length and parallel to the y-axis. The minor axis is 6 units in length. The center is located at $(4, 2)$.

35. The foci are at $(12, 0)$ and $(-12, 0)$. The endpoints of the minor axis are at $(0, 5)$ and $(0, -5)$.

36. The endpoints of the major axis are at $(-11, 5)$ and $(7, 5)$. The endpoints of the minor axis are at $(-2, 9)$ and $(-2, 1)$.

37. The endpoints of the major axis are at $(2, 12)$ and $(2, -4)$. The endpoints of the minor axis are at $(4, 4)$ and $(0, 4)$.

38. The major axis is 16 units long and parallel to the x-axis. The center is at $(5, 4)$ and minor axis is 9 units long.

39–40. See margin.

Critical Thinking

For each equation, replace k with four different values greater than one. Graph the four resulting equations on a graphing calculator. Describe what happens to the graph as the value of k increases.

39. $\dfrac{x^2}{k^2} + \dfrac{y^2}{1} = 1$

40. $\dfrac{x^2}{25} + \dfrac{y^2}{4} = k$

Assignment Guide

Core: 17–45 odd, 46–53
Enriched: 16–38 even, 39–53
All: Self Test, 1–10

For **Extra Practice**, see p. 893.

The red A, B, and C flags, printed only in the Teacher's Wraparound Edition, indicate the level of difficulty of the exercises.

Additional Answers

33. $\dfrac{(x-1)^2}{81} + \dfrac{(y-2)^2}{56} = 1$

34. $\dfrac{(x-4)^2}{9} + \dfrac{(y-2)^2}{100} = 1$

35. $\dfrac{x^2}{169} + \dfrac{y^2}{25} = 1$

36. $\dfrac{(x+2)^2}{81} + \dfrac{(y-5)^2}{16} = 1$

37. $\dfrac{(x-2)^2}{4} + \dfrac{(y-4)^2}{64} = 1$

38. $\dfrac{(x-5)^2}{64} + \dfrac{(y-4)^2}{20.25} = 1$

39. As k increases, the length of the major axis increases, but the minor axis length stays the same.

40. As k increases, the shape of the ellipse remains similar, and the size increases.

Study Guide Masters, p. 52

7-4   NAME_____ DATE_____

Study Guide   Student Edition Pages 431–439

Ellipses

An ellipse is the set of all points in a plane such that the sum of the distances from two given points in the plane, called the **foci**, is constant. An ellipse has two axes of symmetry. The intersection of the two axes is the **center of the ellipse**. The ellipse intersects the axes to define two segments whose endpoints lie on the ellipse. The longer segment is called the **major axis**, and the shorter segment is called the **minor axis**.

Standard Equations for Ellipses with Center at (h, k)		
Horizontal Major Axis:	$\dfrac{(x-h)^2}{a^2} + \dfrac{(y-k)^2}{b^2} = 1$	$(a^2 > b^2)$
Vertical Major Axis:	$\dfrac{(x-h)^2}{b^2} + \dfrac{(y-k)^2}{a^2} = 1$	$(a^2 > b^2)$

Example: Write the equation of the ellipse. First find the length of the major axis. The distance between $(-5, 0)$ and $(5, 0)$ is 10 units.
$2a = 10$
$a = 5$ so $a^2 = 25$
Since the foci are at $(-3, 0)$ and $(3, 0)$, $c = 3$.
$b^2 = a^2 - c^2$
$b^2 = 5^2 - 3^2$ so $b^2 = 16$
The equation is $\dfrac{x^2}{25} + \dfrac{y^2}{16} = 1$.

Write an equation for each ellipse.

1. 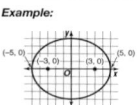 2. 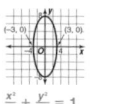 3.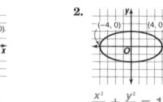

$\dfrac{x^2}{9} + \dfrac{y^2}{64} = 1$ $\dfrac{x^2}{16} + \dfrac{y^2}{4} = 1$ $\dfrac{(x+3)^2}{4} + \dfrac{(y+1)^2}{9} = 1$

Find the coordinates of the center and foci, and the lengths of the major axis and minor axis for each ellipse whose equation is given. Then draw the graph.

4. $\dfrac{x^2}{4} + \dfrac{y^2}{25} = 1$ 5. $9x^2 + 16y^2 = 144$ 6. $x^2 + 4y^2 + 24y = -32$

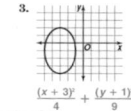 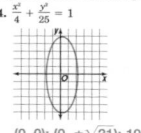 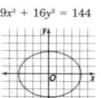

$(0, 0)$; $(0, \pm\sqrt{21})$; 10, 4 $(0, 0)$; $(\pm\sqrt{7}, 0)$; 8, 6 $(0, -3)$; $(\pm\sqrt{3}, 0)$; 4, 2

Additional Answers

12.

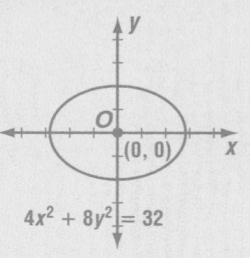

$4x^2 + 8y^2 = 32$

13.

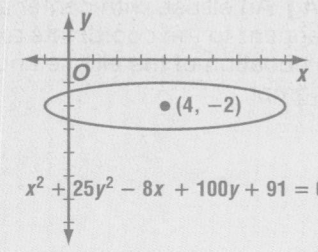

$x^2 + 25y^2 - 8x + 100y + 91 = 0$

Additional Answers

45a.

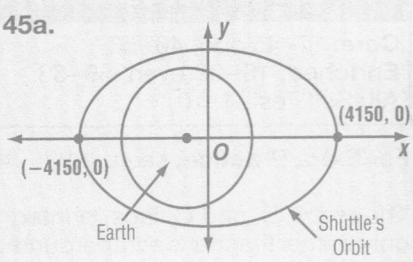

47.

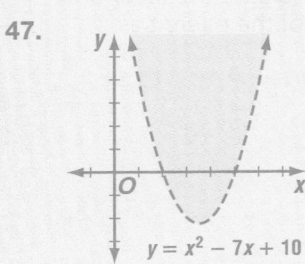

$y = x^2 - 7x + 10$

Applications and Problem Solving

41. Medicine A lithotriper can be used to break up kidney stones so that they no longer pose a health threat. This instrument uses the properties of ellipses. An electrode sends shock waves out from one focus of an ellipse. The waves are then reflected off an elliptical surface to the other focus where the kidney stone is located, shattering the stone. Suppose that the length of the major axis of the ellipse is 40 centimeters and the length of the minor axis is 20 centimeters. How far from the kidney stone should the electrode be placed in order to shatter it? $20\sqrt{3}$ cm or about 34.6 cm

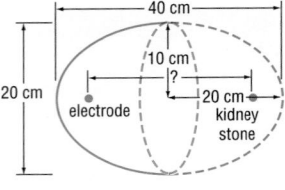

42. National Landmarks The United States Capitol building contains an elliptical room. It is 96 feet in length and 46 feet in width.

a. Write an equation to describe the shape of the room. Assume that it is centered at the origin and the major axis is horizontal.

b. John Quincy Adams discovered that he could overhear the conversations being held at the opposing party leader's desk if he stood in a certain spot in the elliptical chamber. Describe the position of the desk and how far away Adams had to stand to overhear.

42a. $\dfrac{x^2}{2304} + \dfrac{y^2}{529} = 1$

42b. The desk is at one focus; about 84 feet from Adams at the other.

43. about $\dfrac{x^2}{2.02 \times 10^{16}} + \dfrac{y^2}{2.00 \times 10^{16}} = 1$

43. Astronomy Find the equation of the elliptical orbit of Mars as it travels around the sun. Assume the radius of the sun is 400,000 miles.

Planet	Shortest Distance from Sun (miles)	Greatest Distance from Sun (miles)
Mercury	28,600,000	43,400,000
Venus	66,800,000	67,700,000
Earth	91,400,000	94,500,000
Mars	128,500,000	155,000,000

44. $\dfrac{x^2}{552.25} + \dfrac{y^2}{81} = 1$

44. Museums Find the equation of the cross section of the whispering chamber described in the application at the beginning of this lesson. The length of the major axis is 47 feet, and the length of the minor axis is 18 feet. Assume that the center of the ellipse is at the origin and the major axis is horizontal.

45b. $\dfrac{x^2}{17,222,500} + \dfrac{y^2}{17,220,000} = 1$

45. Space Science The space shuttle travels in an elliptical orbit around Earth. The center of Earth is one focus of the ellipse, and the high and low points of the orbit are both on the major axis. Suppose a shuttle is orbiting Earth so that its high point is 200 miles above Earth's surface and its low point is 100 miles above the surface. Let the x-axis be the major axis.

a. Find the equation of the path of the shuttle, using the center of the ellipse, not the center of Earth, as the origin. Note that Earth's diameter is about 8000 miles. Draw a diagram and label it. **See margin.**

b. Find the equation of the path of the shuttle, using the center of Earth as the origin. (*Hint:* Where would the center of the ellipse be then?)

Mixed Review

46. Write an equation for the circle whose center is at $(6, 2)$ and whose radius is 5 units. (Lesson 7–3) $(x - 6)^2 + (y - 2)^2 = 25$

47. Graph $y > x^2 - 7x + 10$. (Lesson 6–7) **See margin.**

438 Chapter 7 Analyzing Conic Sections

Practice Masters, p. 52

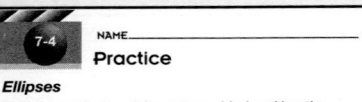

| 7-4 | NAME_____ DATE _____ |
| Practice | Student Edition Pages 431–439 |

Ellipses

Find the coordinates of the center and foci, and lengths of the major and minor axes for each ellipse whose equation is given. Then draw the graph.

1. $\frac{x^2}{9} + \frac{y^2}{16} = 1$ (0, 0); (0, ±√7); 8; 6

2. $16x^2 + y^2 = 64$ (0, 0); (0, ±2√15); 16; 4

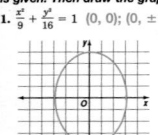
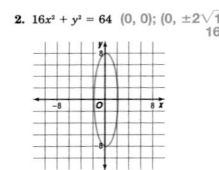

3. $\frac{(x-3)^2}{1} + \frac{(y-1)^2}{36} = 1$ (3, 1); (3, 1 ± √35); 12; 2

4. $\frac{(x+4)^2}{49} + \frac{(y+3)^2}{25} = 1$ (−4, −3); (−4 ± 2√6, −3); 14; 10

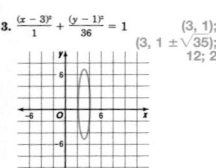
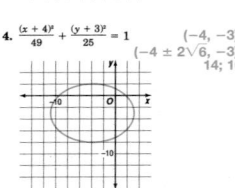

Write the equation for each ellipse described below.

5. The foci are at (4, 0) and (−4, 0). Then endpoints of the minor axis are at (0, 2) and (0, −2).
$\frac{x^2}{20} + \frac{y^2}{4} = 1$

6. The center has coordinates (2, −4). The minor axis is parallel to the x-axis with a length of 6. The major axis has a length of 10.
$\frac{(x-2)^2}{9} + \frac{(y+4)^2}{25} = 1$

Extension ━━━━━━━━━

Reasoning An ellipse with center at (4, 9) is tangent to the coordinate axes. Write the equation of the ellipse and draw the graph.

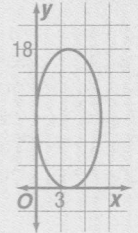

$\dfrac{(x-4)^2}{16} + \dfrac{(y-9)^2}{81} = 1$

48. Simplify $\left(\sqrt[6]{5a^{\frac{7}{4}}b^{-\frac{2}{3}}}\right)12.$ (Lesson 5–7) $\dfrac{25a^{21}}{b^8}$

49. 6.25×10^{-11}

49. Technology Computers today are built to perform millions of operations per second. It takes an electric impulse one billionth of a second to travel 8 inches. One billionth of a second, also known as a *nanosecond*, is the measurement used to measure time on computers. One nanosecond equals 10^{-9} seconds. How much time does it take an electric impulse to travel half an inch? Write your answer in scientific notation. (Lesson 5–1)

50. $\left(\dfrac{1}{5}, \dfrac{2}{5}, -\dfrac{3}{5}\right)$

50. Solve the system of equations by using matrices. (Lesson 4–6)

$2x - y - 5z = 3$
$x + 4y - 2z = 3$
$5x + 3y + 2z = 1$

51. Solve the system of equations by using Cramer's rule. (Lesson 3–3)

$6a + 7b = -10.15$
$9.2a - 6b = 69.944$ $\quad(4.27, -5.11)$

52. Find the slope of the line perpendicular to the line that passes through $(0, 0)$ and $(4, -2)$. (Lesson 2–4) **2**

53. 19°F; 16°F; about 18.5°F

53. Statistics During a cold spell lasting 43 days, the following high temperatures (in °F) were recorded in Chicago. Find the median, mode, and mean of the temperatures. (Lesson 1–3)

26	17	12	5	4	25	17	23	13	6	25
19	27	22	26	20	31	24	12	27	16	27
16	30	7	31	16	5	29	18	16	22	29
8	31	13	24	5	-7	20	29	18	12	

SELF TEST

Find the distance between each pair of points with the given coordinates. (Lesson 7–1)

1. $(9, 5), (4, -7)$ **13 units**

2. $(0, -5), (10, -3)$ $2\sqrt{26}$ **units**

Find the midpoint of each line segment if the coordinates of the endpoints are given. (Lesson 7–1)

3. $(8, 0), (-5, 12)$ $\left(\dfrac{3}{2}, 6\right)$

4. $(5, -7), (3, -1)$ $(4, -4)$

Name the coordinates of the vertex and focus, the equations of the axis of symmetry and directrix, and the direction of opening of the parabola with the given equation. Then find the length of the latus rectum and graph the parabola. (Lesson 7–2)

5. $y^2 = 6x$

6. $y = x^2 + 8x + 20$ **5–6. See margin.**

Find the coordinates of the center and the radius of each circle whose equation is given. Then draw the graph. (Lesson 7–3) **7–8. See Solutions Manual for graphs.**

7. $x^2 + (y - 4)^2 = 49$ **(0, 4), 7 units**

8. $3x^2 + 3y^2 + 6y + 9x = 2$ $\left(-\dfrac{3}{2}, -1\right), \dfrac{\sqrt{141}}{6}$ **units**

9. An equation of an ellipse is $8x^2 + 4y^2 - 16x - 20y = 7$. Write this equation in standard form. (Lesson 7–4) $\dfrac{(x-1)^2}{5} + \dfrac{(y-2.5)^2}{10} = 1$

10. Write an equation of an ellipse whose foci are at $(3, 8)$ and $(3, -6)$ and whose major axis is 18 units long. (Lesson 7–4) $\dfrac{(x-3)^2}{32} + \dfrac{(y-1)^2}{81} = 1$

SELF TEST

The Self Test provides students with a brief review of the concepts and skills in Lessons 7-1 through 7-4. Lesson numbers are given to the right of exercises or instruction lines so students can review concepts not yet mastered.

Answer for the Self Test

6. $(-4, 4); \left(-4, \dfrac{17}{4}\right); x = -4; y = \dfrac{15}{4};$ up; 1

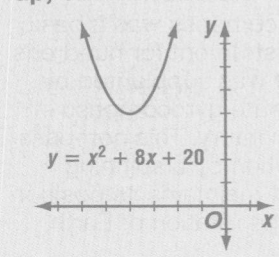

$y = x^2 + 8x + 20$

---

4 ASSESS

Closing Activity

Modeling Make an elliptical chamber for the class. Point out the foci and the major and minor axes. Make sure you include the equation that describes the ellipse formed.

Chapter 7, Quiz B (Lessons 7-3 and 7-4), is available in the *Assessment and Evaluation Masters,* p. 184.

Mid-Chapter Test (Lessons 7-1 through 7-4) is available in the *Assessment and Evaluation Masters*, p. 183.

Answer for the Self Test

5. $(0, 0) \left(\dfrac{3}{2}, 0\right); y = 0; x = -\dfrac{3}{2};$ right; 6

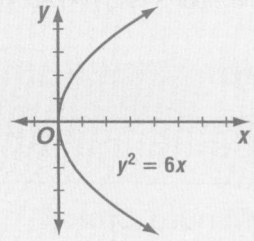

$y^2 = 6x$

Enrichment Masters, p. 52

7-4 NAME _____ DATE _____
Student Edit
Enrichment Pages 431–

Superellipses

The circle and the ellipse are members of an interesting family of curves that were first studied by the French physicist and mathematician Gabriel Lamé (1795–1870). The general equation for the family is $\left|\dfrac{x}{a}\right|^n + \left|\dfrac{y}{b}\right|^n = 1$, with $a \neq 0$, $b \neq 0$, and $n > 0$. For even values of n greater than 2, the curves are called **superellipses.**

1. Consider two curves that are *not* superellipses. Graph each equation on the grid at the right. State the type of curve produced each time.

a. $\left|\dfrac{x}{2}\right|^2 + \left|\dfrac{y}{2}\right|^2 = 1$ circle

b. $\left|\dfrac{x}{3}\right|^2 + \left|\dfrac{y}{2}\right|^2 = 1$ ellipse

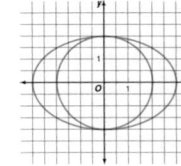

2. In each of the following cases you are given values of a, b, and n to use in the general equation. Write the resulting equation. Then graph. Sketch each graph on the grid at the right.

a. $a = 2, b = 3, n = 4$ See
b. $a = 2, b = 3, n = 6$ students'
c. $a = 2, b = 3, n = 8$ graphs.

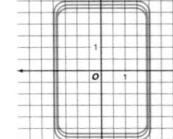

3. What shape will the graph of $\left|\dfrac{x}{2}\right|^n + \left|\dfrac{y}{3}\right|^n$ approximate for greater and greater even, whole-number values of n?
a rectangle that is 6 units long and 4 units wide, centered at the origin

Instructional Resources

- Study Guide Master 7-5
- Practice Master 7-5
- Enrichment Master 7-5
- Real-World Applications, 21

Transparency 7-5A contains the 5-Minute Check for this lesson; **Transparency 7-5B** contains a teaching aid for this lesson.

Recommended Pacing	
Standard Pacing	Day 6 of 15
Honors Pacing	Day 6 of 13
Block Scheduling*	Day 4 of 7

*For more information on pacing and possible lesson plans, refer to the *Block Scheduling Booklet*.

1 FOCUS

5-Minute Check
(over Lesson 7-4)

Use the equation $\frac{x^2}{16} + \frac{y^2}{4} = 1$

for Exercises 1–5.

1. Find the coordinates of the center of the graph of the equation. **(0, 0)**
2. Find the coordinates of the foci of the graph of the equation. $\left(2\sqrt{3}, 0\right),$ $\left(-2\sqrt{3}, 0\right)$
3. Find the length of the major axis. **8**
4. Find the length of the minor axis. **4**
5. Graph the equation.

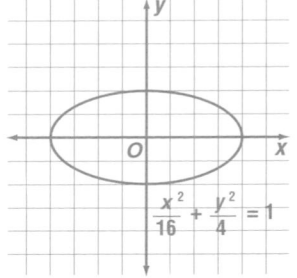

$$\frac{x^2}{16} + \frac{y^2}{4} = 1$$

Hyperbolas

What YOU'LL LEARN

- To write equations of hyperbolas, and
- to graph hyperbolas having certain properties.

Why IT'S IMPORTANT

You can graph hyperbolas to solve problems involving forestry and navigation.

APPLICATION
Navigation

During World War I and II, the Long Range Navigational system (LORAN) was developed and used. This system is based on the shape of a **hyperbola**.

Two stations send out different signals at the same time. A ship receives these signals and notes the difference between the time it received one of the signals and the time it received the other. This information is used to locate the ship on a hyperbola with foci located at the two stations. Another set of signals can locate the ship on another hyperbola, and the ship's location is the intersection of the two hyperbolas.

GLOBAL CONNECTIONS

In 1044, Tseng Kong-liang described the use of magnetized iron "fish" that float in water and can be used to find south. The Chinese began to use the south-pointing compass for navigation about this time. Later, its use spread to the Arab world and then to Europe.

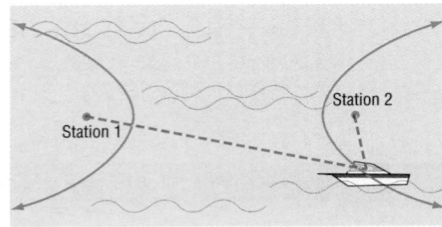

Since this system does *not* rely on land sightings, it can be used for successful navigation at night or for long missions over the ocean.

Definition of Hyperbola	A hyperbola is the set of all points in a plane such that the absolute value of the difference of the distances from any point on the hyperbola to two given points, called the *foci*, is constant.

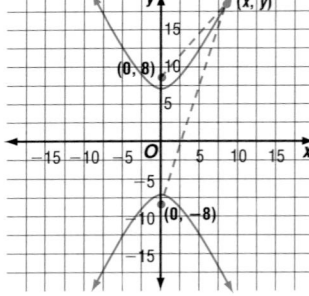

The hyperbola at the left has foci at $(0, 8)$ and $(0, -8)$. The absolute value of the differences of the distances from the foci to any point on the hyperbola is 14. We can use the distance formula and the definition of a hyperbola to find the equation of this hyperbola.

Let (x, y) be the coordinates of any point on the hyperbola. The distance between the points at (x, y) and $(0, 8)$ minus the distance between the points at (x, y) and $(0, -8)$ is ± 14 units.

GLOBAL CONNECTIONS

The magnetic compass was a basic navigational instrument for hundreds of years until it was supplanted by the more accurate gyrocompass in the twentieth century. This compass indicates direction by a spinning gyroscope that maintains its position regardless of the rotation of Earth.

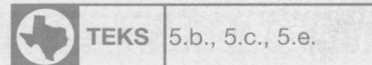

TEKS 5.b., 5.c., 5.e.

$$\underset{\substack{\text{distance between} \\ (x, y) \text{ and } (0, 8)}}{} - \underset{\substack{\text{distance between} \\ (x, y) \text{ and } (0, -8)}}{} = \pm 14$$

$$\sqrt{x^2 + (y - 8)^2} - \sqrt{x^2 + (y + 8)^2} = \pm 14$$

$$\sqrt{x^2 + (y - 8)^2} = \pm 14 + \sqrt{x^2 + (y + 8)^2}$$

$$x^2 + (y - 8)^2 = 196 \pm 28\sqrt{x^2 + (y + 8)^2} + x^2 + (y + 8)^2 \qquad \textit{Square each side.}$$

$$x^2 + y^2 - 16y + 64 = 196 \pm 28\sqrt{x^2 + (y + 8)^2} + x^2 + y^2 + 16y + 64$$

$$-32y - 196 = \pm 28\sqrt{x^2 + (y + 8)^2} \qquad \textit{Simplify.}$$

$$8y + 49 = \pm 7\sqrt{x^2 + (y + 8)^2} \qquad \textit{Divide each side by } -4.$$

$$64y^2 + 784y + 2401 = 49[x^2 + (y + 8)^2] \qquad \textit{Square each side.}$$

$$64y^2 + 784y + 2401 = 49x^2 + 49y^2 + 784y + 3136 \qquad \textit{Distributive property}$$

$$15y^2 - 49x^2 = 735 \qquad \textit{Simplify.}$$

$$\frac{y^2}{49} - \frac{x^2}{15} = 1 \qquad \textit{Divide each side by 735.}$$

The equation of the hyperbola is $\frac{y^2}{49} - \frac{x^2}{15} = 1$.

Let's take a closer look at the parts of a hyperbola. The midpoint of the segment connecting the foci of a hyperbola is the **center** of the hyperbola. The point on each branch of the hyperbola that is nearest the center is a **vertex**. As a hyperbola recedes from the center, the branches approach lines called the **asymptotes**.

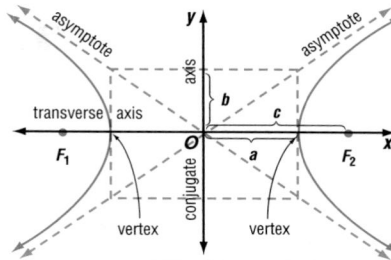

A hyperbola has many similarities to an ellipse. The distance to the center from a vertex is a units. The distance to the center from a focus is c units. There are two axes of symmetry. The **transverse axis** is a segment of length $2a$ whose endpoints are the vertices of the hyperbola. The **conjugate axis** is a segment of length $2b$ units that is perpendicular to the transverse axis at the center. The lengths of a, b, and c are related differently for a hyperbola than for an ellipse. For a hyperbola, $a^2 + b^2 = c^2$.

Standard Equations of Hyperbolas with Center at the Origin	• If a hyperbola has foci at $(-c, 0)$ and $(c, 0)$ and if the absolute value of the difference of the distances from any point on the hyperbola to the two foci is $2a$ units, then the standard equation of the hyperbola is $\frac{x^2}{a^2} - \frac{y^2}{b^2} = 1$, where $c^2 = a^2 + b^2$. *In this case, the transverse axis is horizontal.* • If a hyperbola has foci at $(0, -c)$ and $(0, c)$ and if the absolute value of the difference of the distances from any point on the hyperbola to the two foci is $2a$ units, then the standard equation of the hyperbola is $\frac{y^2}{a^2} - \frac{x^2}{b^2} = 1$, where $c^2 = a^2 + b^2$. *In this case, the transverse axis is vertical.*

Questioning Explore the effect of rotating a circle in space. Use a circular ring (like a key ring) and place it on an overhead projector. Lift one edge to form an ellipse. Ask students what could be done to form a hyperbola.

2 TEACH

Teaching Tip You may want to introduce the latus rectum as an aid to graphing. The latera recta are segments perpendicular to the transverse axis that passes through the foci. Each latus rectum is $\frac{2b^2}{a}$ units long. The distance from the focus to the point of intersection with the branch of the hyperbola is $\frac{b^2}{a}$ units.

In-Class Examples

For Example 1
Write an equation of a hyperbola with foci at (0, 7) and (−7, 0) if the length of the transverse axis is 6 units. Then draw the graph.

$\dfrac{y^2}{9} - \dfrac{x^2}{40} = 1$

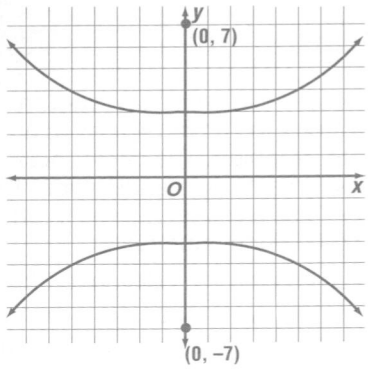

For Example 2
A comet travels along a path that is a branch of the hyperbola whose equation is

$\dfrac{x^2}{144} - \dfrac{y^2}{324} = 1$.

Find the coordinates of the vertices and foci and the equations of the asymptotes. Then draw the graph.

vertices: (12, 0), (−12, 0)

foci: $\left(6\sqrt{13}, 0\right), \left(-6\sqrt{13}, 0\right)$

asymptotes: $y = \dfrac{\pm 9x}{4}$

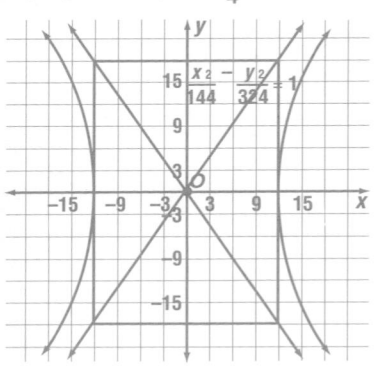

It's easier to graph a hyperbola if the asymptotes are drawn first. To draw the asymptotes, use the values of a and b and draw a rectangle with dimensions $2a$ and $2b$. The point of intersection of the diagonals is the center of the hyperbola. The diagonals are a subset of the asymptotes. The chart below shows the equations of the asymptotes for different hyperbolas.

Equation of Hyperbola	$\dfrac{x^2}{a^2} - \dfrac{y^2}{b^2} = 1$	$\dfrac{y^2}{a^2} - \dfrac{x^2}{b^2} = 1$
Equation of Asymptote	$y = \pm\dfrac{b}{a}x$	$y = \pm\dfrac{a}{b}x$
Transverse Axis	horizontal	vertical

Example Write an equation of a hyperbola with foci at (6, 0) and (−6, 0) if the length of the transverse axis is 8 units. Then draw the graph.

Half the length of the transverse axis is the distance, a, from the center to a vertex of the hyperbola. The distance from the center to a focus point is represented by c. In this hyperbola, $c = 6$, and $a = 4$.

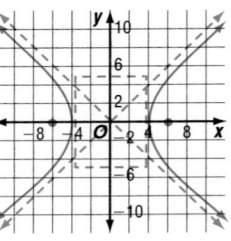

$c^2 = a^2 + b^2$

$6^2 = 4^2 + b^2$

$36 = 16 + b^2$

$b^2 = 20$

$b = \pm 2\sqrt{5}$ or about ± 4.5

An equation of the hyperbola is $\dfrac{x^2}{16} - \dfrac{y^2}{20} = 1$.

Example  A comet travels along a path that is one branch of a hyperbola. The equation of the hyperbola is $\dfrac{y^2}{225} - \dfrac{x^2}{400} = 1$. Find the coordinates of the vertices and foci and the equations of the asymptotes. Then draw the graph.

APPLICATION

Astronomy

F Y I

For a full week in July, 1994, fragments from a comet crashed into Jupiter's atmosphere. These fragments entered the atmosphere at speeds of about 130,000 miles per hour and caused fireballs larger than Earth.

The center of the hyperbola is at (0, 0). It has a vertical transverse axis, and $a = \sqrt{225}$ or 15 and $b = \sqrt{400}$ or 20.

Since $a = 15$, the distance from the center to each vertex is 15 units. Thus, the vertices are at (0, 15) and (0, −15).

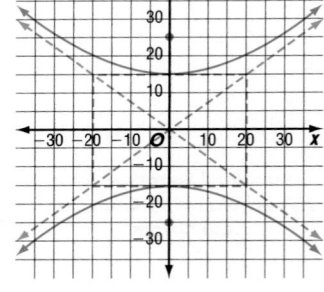

To find the foci, first find the value of c.

$c^2 = a^2 + b^2$

$c^2 = 225 + 400$

$c^2 = 625$

$c = 25$

The foci are at (0, 25) and (0, −25).

The equations of the asymptotes are $y = \pm\dfrac{3}{4}x$. Use the information to draw the graph.

F Y I

The comet that struck Jupiter, Shoemaker-Levy 9, was discovered by amateur astronomer David Levy while working with the professional astronomers Eugene and Carolyn Shoemaker. This team of astronomers is credited with the discovery of 12 comets.

So far, we have studied hyperbolas that are centered at the origin. The center of a hyperbola may be located somewhere other than at the origin. If the center is at (h, k), then the standard equation is found by replacing x with $(x - h)$ and y with $(y - k)$. The slopes of the asymptotes are calculated in the same way as if the hyperbola was centered at the origin. Keep in mind that the asymptotes always pass through the center of the hyperbola.

Standard Equations of Hyperbolas with Center at (h, k)

- **The equation of a hyperbola with center at (h, k) and with a horizontal transverse axis is** $\frac{(x - h)^2}{a^2} - \frac{(y - k)^2}{b^2} = 1$.
- **The equation of a hyperbola with center at (h, k) and with a vertical transverse axis is** $\frac{(y - k)^2}{a^2} - \frac{(x - h)^2}{b^2} = 1$.

Example 3 Draw the graph of $\frac{(x + 2)^2}{16} - \frac{(y - 5)^2}{25} = 1$.

The graph is congruent to the graph of $\frac{x^2}{16} - \frac{y^2}{25} = 1$, but its center is at $(-2, 5)$.

Draw the graph of $\frac{x^2}{16} - \frac{y^2}{25} = 1$. Then translate the graph 2 units left and 5 units up.

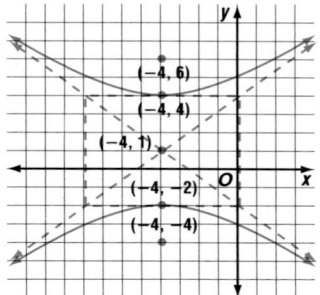

Example 4 Write the equation of the hyperbola shown at the right.

The center of the hyperbola is located at $(-4, 1)$, and the transverse axis is vertical.

The vertices are located 3 units above and below the center, so $a = 3$. The foci are located 5 units above and below the center, so $c = 5$.

Use this information to find the value of b^2.

$c^2 = a^2 + b^2$
$5^2 = 3^2 + b^2$
$b^2 = 16$

Now write the equation.

$\frac{(y - k)^2}{a^2} - \frac{(x - h)^2}{b^2} = 1$ *Standard equation of hyperbola with vertical transverse axis*

$\frac{(y - 1)^2}{3^2} - \frac{[x - (-4)]^2}{16} = 1$ *Substitute values for a^2, b^2, h, and k.*

The equation of the hyperbola is $\frac{(y - 1)^2}{9} - \frac{(x + 4)^2}{16} = 1$.

Lesson 7–5 Hyperbolas **443**

In-Class Examples

For Example 3

Draw the graph of $\frac{(y + 2)^2}{16} - \frac{(x - 3)^2}{25} = 1$.

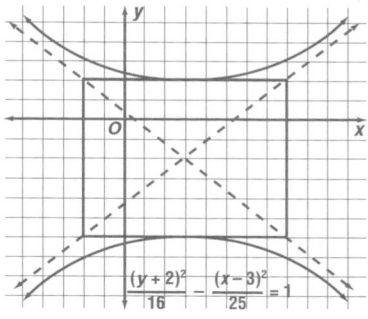

For Example 4
Write the equation of the hyperbola shown below.

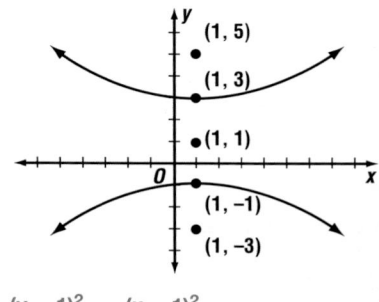

$\frac{(y - 1)^2}{4} - \frac{(x - 1)^2}{12} = 1$

Alternative Teaching Strategies

Reading Algebra *Conic* sections are so named because each results from cutting a cross-section of a *cone*. The concept of conic sections was discovered by the Greek mathematician Apollonius.

In-Class Example

For Example 5
The graph of $144y^2 - 25x^2 - 576y - 150x = 3249$ is a hyperbola.

a. Find the standard form of the equation.
$$\frac{(y-2)^2}{25} - \frac{(x+3)^2}{144} = 1$$

b. Find the coordinates of the vertices and foci.
vertices: $(-3, 7)$, $(-3, -3)$
foci: $(-3, 15)$, $(-3, -11)$

c. Find the equations of the asymptotes.
$$y = \frac{5}{12}x + \frac{9}{4};\ y = -\frac{5}{12}x + \frac{9}{4}$$

d. Draw the graph.

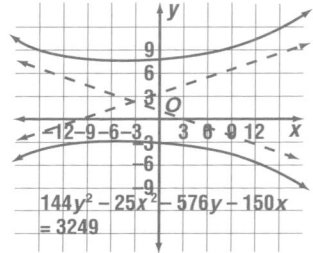

3 PRACTICE/APPLY

Check for Understanding

Exercises 1–15 are designed to help you assess your students' understanding through reading, writing, speaking, and modeling. You should work through Exercises 1–4 with your students and then monitor their work on Exercises 5–15.

Error Analysis
Students sometimes confuse the relationship of a, b, and c in the ellipse and the hyperbola.

Conic	Relationship
ellipse	$b^2 = a^2 - c^2$
hyperbola	$c^2 = a^2 + b^2$

The hyperbola's labels are the same as those in the Pythagorean theorem.

Just as equations of circles and ellipses are sometimes written in expanded form, so are the equations of hyperbolas. You need to complete the square for each variable to write the equation in standard form.

Example The graph of $25x^2 - 4y^2 + 100x + 24y - 36 = 0$ is a hyperbola.
  a. Find the standard form of the equation.
  b. Find the coordinates of the vertices and foci.
  c. Find the equations of the asymptotes.
  d. Draw the graph.

a. $\qquad 25x^2 - 4y^2 + 100x + 24y - 36 = 0$

$25(x^2 + 4x + \square) - 4(y^2 - 6y + \square) = 36 + 25(\square) - 4(\square)$ *Complete the squares.*

$25(x^2 + 4x + 4) - 4(y^2 - 6y + 9) = 36 + 25(4) - 4(9)$

$25(x + 2)^2 - 4(y - 3)^2 = 100$

$\frac{(x + 2)^2}{4} - \frac{(y - 3)^2}{25} = 1$

The standard form of the equation is $\frac{(x+2)^2}{4} - \frac{(y-3)^2}{25} = 1$.

b. The center of this hyperbola is at $(-2, 3)$, and the transverse axis is horizontal. Since the value of a is 2, the vertices are 2 units to the right and left of the center along the transverse axis. The vertices are at $(0, 3)$ and $(-4, 3)$.

Use $a = 2$ and $b = 5$ to find c.
$c^2 = a^2 + b^2$
$c^2 = 2^2 + 5^2$
$c^2 = 29$
$c = \sqrt{29}$

The foci are at $(-2 + \sqrt{29}, 3)$ and $(-2 - \sqrt{29}, 3)$ or about $(3.39, 3)$ and $(-7.39, 3)$.

c. The asymptotes pass through the center at $(-2, 3)$. The slopes of the asymptotes are $\pm\frac{b}{a}$ or $\pm\frac{5}{2}$.

$y - y_1 = m(x - x_1)$ $y - y_1 = m(x - x_1)$

$y - 3 = \frac{5}{2}[x - (-2)]$ *Let $(x, y) = (-2, 3)$.* $y - 3 = -\frac{5}{2}[x - (-2)]$

$y - 3 = \frac{5}{2}x + 5$ $y - 3 = -\frac{5}{2}x - 5$

$y = \frac{5}{2}x + 8$ $y = -\frac{5}{2}x - 2$

The equations of the asymptotes are $y = \frac{5}{2}x + 8$ and $y = -\frac{5}{2}x - 2$.

d. Use this information to draw the graph.

Cooperative Learning

Trade-A-Problem Have students work in small groups. Each group should draw a hyperbola and determine its equation. Then have groups exchange drawings and determine the equations for the other groups' hyperbola. Group members should agree on the equation before they check their answer with the other group. For more information on the trade-a-problem strategy, see *Cooperative Learning in the Mathematics Classroom*, one of the titles in the Glencoe Mathematics Professional Series, pages 25–26.

Communicating Mathematics

Study the lesson. Then complete the following. 1–4. See margin.

1. **Compare and contrast** hyperbolas and parabolas.

2. **Compare and contrast** hyperbolas and ellipses.

3. How would you know if the graph of an equation is an ellipse or a hyperbola?

4. **Describe** the steps you would follow to draw the graph of the equation $\frac{(y-5)^2}{36} - \frac{(x+2)^2}{9} = 1$.

Guided Practice

State whether the graph of each equation is an ellipse or a hyperbola.

5. $\frac{x^2}{24} - \frac{y^2}{36} = 1$
hyperbola

6. $\frac{x^2}{100} + \frac{y^2}{25} = 1$
ellipse

7. $\frac{y^2}{20} - \frac{x^2}{32} = 1$
hyperbola

Write an equation for each hyperbola in standard form.

9. $\frac{(y+3)^2}{24} - \frac{(x-1)^2}{8} = 1$

8. $6x^2 - 12y^2 = 108$ $\frac{x^2}{18} - \frac{y^2}{9} = 1$

9. $y^2 - 3x^2 + 6x + 6y = 18$

Find the coordinates of the vertices and the foci and the slopes of the asymptotes for each hyperbola whose equation is given. Then draw the graph. 10–13. See Solutions Manual for graphs.

10. $(0, \pm 3\sqrt{2})$; $(0, \pm\sqrt{38})$; $\pm\frac{3\sqrt{10}}{10}$

10. $\frac{y^2}{18} - \frac{x^2}{20} = 1$

11. $x^2 - 36y^2 = 36$

11. $(\pm 6, 0)$; $(\pm\sqrt{37}, 0)$; $\pm\frac{1}{6}$

12. $\frac{(y+6)^2}{20} - \frac{(x-1)^2}{25} = 1$

13. $5x^2 - 4y^2 - 40x - 16y = 36$

12. $(1, -6 \pm 2\sqrt{5})$; $(1, -6 \pm 3\sqrt{5})$; $\pm\frac{2\sqrt{5}}{5}$

14. Write an equation for the graph at the right.

$\frac{y^2}{4} - \frac{x^2}{21} = 1$

13. $(4 \pm 2\sqrt{5}, -2)$; $(4 \pm 3\sqrt{5}, -2)$; $\pm\frac{\sqrt{5}}{2}$

15. $\frac{x^2}{1} - \frac{y^2}{16} = 1$

15. A hyperbola is centered at the origin with a horizontal transverse axis. The value of a is 1, and the value of b is 4. Write an equation for the hyperbola.

Practice

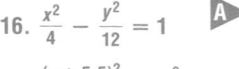

Write an equation for each hyperbola.

16. $\frac{x^2}{4} - \frac{y^2}{12} = 1$

17. $\frac{(y+5.5)^2}{6.25} - \frac{x^2}{6} = 1$

18. $\frac{(x-3)^2}{4} - \frac{(y+5)^2}{9} = 1$

16.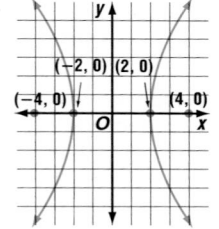

17.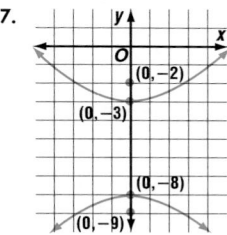

18.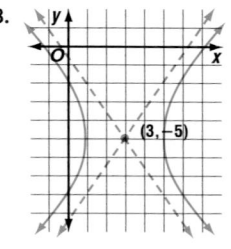

Lesson 7–5 Hyperbolas **445**

Reteaching ───────

Using Alternative Methods Given the foci and the difference of the distances from the foci to any point on a hyperbola, find the standard form of its equation in two ways. First use the definition of a hyperbola and the distance formula to find the equation. Then use given values to find h, k, a, and b.

Additional Answer

4. a. Determine that the center is at $(-2, 5)$.
   b. Determine that the transverse axis is vertical.
   c. Determine that the transverse axis is 12 units.
   d. Locate the vertices at $(-2, 11)$ and $(-2, -1)$.
   e. Determine that the conjugate axis is 6 units.
   f. Use a rectangle to draw the asymptotes.
   g. Sketch the graph.

Additional Answers

1. Similarities:
   a. Both have foci.
   b. Both are curves.
   c. The equations for both have squared terms.
   d. Both are U-shaped.
   Differences:
   a. A parabola has one focus; a hyperbola has 2 foci.
   b. A parabola is one curve; a hyperbola has 2 branches.
   c. The equations for hyperbolas contain both x^2 and y^2 terms; a parabola has just one of these terms.

2. Similarities:
   a. Both have two axes of symmetry.
   b. Both have 2 foci.
   c. The equations for both have two squared terms.
   Differences:
   a. Standard equation for an ellipse contains addition; standard equation for a hyperbola contains subtraction.
   b. An ellipse is a closed figure; a hyperbola is not closed.
   c. For an ellipse, $b^2 = a^2 - c^2$; for a hyperbola, $c^2 = a^2 + b^2$.
   d. Hyperbolas have asymptotes; ellipses do not.

3. The equation for an ellipse contains addition; the equation for a hyperbola contains subtraction.

Study Guide Masters, p. 53

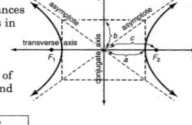

7-5   NAME_____ DATE_____
Study Guide   Student Edition Pages 440–447

Hyperbolas

A **hyperbola** is the set of all points in a plane such that the absolute value of the difference of the distances from any point on the hyperbola to two given points in the plane, called the **foci**, is constant. Key features of a hyperbola are the foci, vertex, asymptotes, transverse axis, and conjugate axis, shown in the figure. The **center of a hyperbola** is the midpoint of the segment connecting the foci. The lengths a, b, and c are related by the formula $c^2 = a^2 + b^2$.

Equation of the Hyperbola	$\frac{(x-h)^2}{a^2} - \frac{(y-k)^2}{b^2} = 1$	$\frac{(y-k)^2}{a^2} - \frac{(x-h)^2}{b^2} = 1$
Slopes of the Asymptotes	$\pm\frac{b}{a}$	$\pm\frac{a}{b}$
Transverse Axis	Horizontal	Vertical
Foci	$(h - c, k), (h + c, k)$	$(h, k - c), (h, k + c)$
Vertices	$(h - a, k), (h + a, k)$	$(h, k - b), (h, k + b)$

Find the coordinates of the vertices and foci and the slopes of the asymptotes for each hyperbola whose equation is given. Then draw the graph.

1. $\frac{x^2}{4} - \frac{y^2}{16} = 1$

2. $\frac{(y-3)^2}{1} - \frac{(x+2)^2}{9} = 1$

3. $36x^2 - 25y^2 = 900$

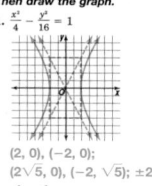

$(2, 0), (-2, 0)$; $(2\sqrt{5}, 0), (-2, \sqrt{5})$; ±2

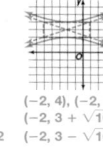

$(-2, 4), (-2, 2)$; $(-2, 3 + \sqrt{10}), (-2, 3 - \sqrt{10})$; $\pm\frac{1}{3}$

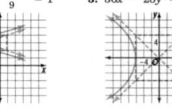

$(5, 0), (-5, 0)$; $(\sqrt{61}, 0), (-\sqrt{61}, 0)$; $\pm\frac{6}{5}$

4. $\frac{y^2}{16} - \frac{x^2}{9} = 1$

5. $6(x-3)^2 - 4(y+1)^2 = 96$

6. $y^2 - 2x^2 + 6y + 4x = 9$

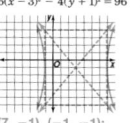

$(0, 4), (0, -4)$; $(0, 5), (0, -5)$; $\pm\frac{4}{3}$

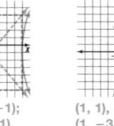

$(7, -1), (-1, -1)$; $(3 - 2\sqrt{10}, -1), (3 + 2\sqrt{10}, -1)$; $\pm\frac{\sqrt{6}}{2}$

$(1, 1), (1, -7)$; $(1, -3 + 2\sqrt{6}), (1, -3 - 2\sqrt{6})$; $\pm\sqrt{2}$

Chapter 7 **445**

Assignment Guide

Core: 17–45 odd, 46, 47, 49–57
Enriched: 16–42 even, 43–57

For **Extra Practice,** see p. 893.

The red A, B, and C flags, printed only in the Teacher's Wraparound Edition, indicate the level of difficulty of the exercises.

Teaching Tip For Exercises 39–42, encourage students to graph these equations by checking many values for x and y. Discuss when the rectangular hyperbola lies in quadrants I and III. when $c > 0$ When is it in quadrants II and IV? when $c < 0$ What happens as c increases? hyperbola moves farther from origin

Additional Answers

35. $\frac{(x-2)^2}{49} - \frac{(y+3)^2}{4} = 1$
36. $\frac{(y-5)^2}{16} - \frac{(x+4)^2}{81} = 1$
37. $\frac{x^2}{25} - \frac{y^2}{36} = 1$
38. $\frac{y^2}{16} - \frac{x^2}{49} = 1$
43. One branch is always in the first quadrant and the other is always in the third quadrant. As the value of c increases, the vertices move away from the origin.

Practice Masters, p. 53

7-5 NAME________ DATE ________

Practice — Student Edition Pages 440–447

Hyperbolas

Find the coordinates of the vertices and foci and the slopes of the asymptotes for each hyperbola whose equation is given. Then draw the graph.

1. $\frac{y^2}{9} - \frac{x^2}{36} = 1$ $(0, \pm 3)$; $(0, \pm 3\sqrt{5})$; $\pm\frac{1}{2}$

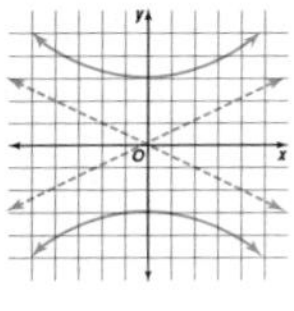

2. $y^2 - 4x^2 = 16$ $(0, \pm 4)$; $(0, \pm 2\sqrt{5})$; ± 2

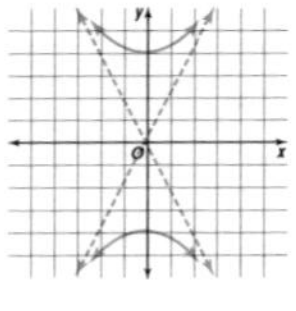

3. $\frac{(y-2)^2}{9} - \frac{(x+3)^2}{25} = 1$

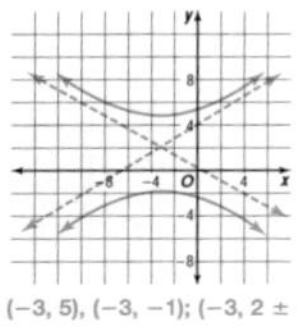

$(-3, 5), (-3, -1)$; $(-3, 2 \pm \sqrt{34})$; $\pm\frac{3}{5}$

4. $\frac{(x-1)^2}{64} - \frac{(y+4)^2}{16} = 1$

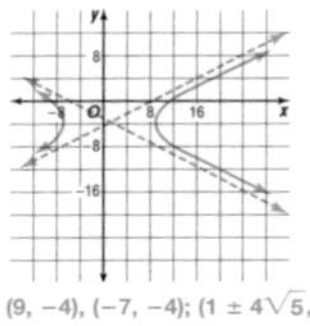

$(9, -4), (-7, -4)$; $(1 \pm 4\sqrt{5}, -4)$; $\pm\frac{1}{2}$

5. $4y^2 - x^2 - 16y + 2x + 11 = 0$

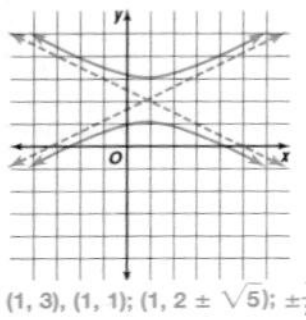

$(1, 3), (1, 1)$; $(1, 2 \pm \sqrt{5})$; $\pm\frac{1}{2}$

6. $3y^2 - 4x^2 + 12y + 24x = 36$

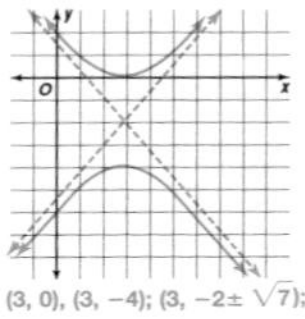

$(3, 0), (3, -4)$; $(3, -2 \pm \sqrt{7})$; $\pm\frac{2\sqrt{3}}{3}$

19. $(\pm 9, 0)$; $(\pm\sqrt{130}, 0)$; $\pm\frac{7}{9}$
20. $(0, \pm 6)$; $(0, \pm 2\sqrt{10})$; ± 3
21. $(\pm 3, 0)$; $(\pm\sqrt{34}, 0)$; $\pm\frac{5}{3}$
22. $(0, \pm 4)$; $(0, \pm\sqrt{41})$; $\pm\frac{4}{5}$
23. $(\pm\sqrt{2}, 0)$; $(\pm\sqrt{3}, 0)$; $\pm\frac{\sqrt{2}}{2}$
24. $(0, \pm 6)$; $(0, \pm 3\sqrt{5})$; ± 2
25. $(\pm 2, 0)$; $(\pm 2\sqrt{2}, 0)$; ± 1
26. $(\pm\sqrt{6}, 0)$; $(\pm 2\sqrt{2}, 0)$; $\pm\frac{\sqrt{3}}{3}$
27. $(-2, 0), (-2, 8)$; $(-2, -1), (-2, 9)$; $\pm\frac{4}{3}$
28. $(2, -2), (2, 8)$; $(2, 3 \pm \sqrt{41})$; $\pm\frac{5}{4}$
29. $(-3, -3), (1, -3)$; $(-1 \pm \sqrt{13}, -3)$; $\pm\frac{3}{2}$
30. $(0, -3), (-12, -3)$; $(-6 \pm 3\sqrt{5}, -3)$; $\pm\frac{1}{2}$
31. $(-5, 2), (-1, 2)$; $(-3 \pm \sqrt{5}, 2)$; $\pm\frac{1}{2}$
32. $(0, 3 \pm 2\sqrt{30})$; $(0, 3 \pm \sqrt{129})$; $\pm\frac{2\sqrt{30}}{3}$

Find the coordinates of the vertices and foci and the slopes of the asymptotes for each hyperbola whose equation is given. Then draw the graph. 19–34. See Solutions Manual for graphs.

19. $\frac{x^2}{81} - \frac{y^2}{49} = 1$
20. $\frac{y^2}{36} - \frac{x^2}{4} = 1$
21. $\frac{x^2}{9} - \frac{y^2}{25} = 1$
22. $\frac{y^2}{16} - \frac{x^2}{25} = 1$
23. $x^2 - 2y^2 = 2$
24. $y^2 = 36 + 4x^2$
25. $x^2 - y^2 = 4$
26. $2x^2 - 6y^2 = 12$
27. $\frac{(y-4)^2}{16} - \frac{(x+2)^2}{9} = 1$
28. $\frac{(y-3)^2}{25} - \frac{(x-2)^2}{16} = 1$
29. $\frac{(x+1)^2}{4} - \frac{(y+3)^2}{9} = 1$
30. $\frac{(x+6)^2}{36} - \frac{(y+3)^2}{9} = 1$
31. $(x+3)^2 - 4(y-2)^2 = 4$
32. $9y^2 - 120x^2 - 54y = 999$
33. $y^2 - 3x^2 + 6y + 6x = 18$ $(1, -3 \pm 2\sqrt{6})$; $(1, -3 \pm 4\sqrt{2})$; $\pm\sqrt{3}$
34. $4x^2 - 25y^2 - 8x - 96 = 0$ $(6, 0), (-4, 0)$; $(1 \pm \sqrt{29}, 0)$; $\pm\frac{2}{5}$

Write an equation for each hyperbola described below.

35. The hyperbola is centered at $(2, -3)$ and has a horizontal transverse axis. The value of a is 7 and the value of b is 2. 35–38. See margin.
36. The hyperbola is centered at $(-4, 5)$ and has a vertical transverse axis. The value of a is 4 and the value of b is 9.
37. The vertices of the hyperbola are at $(-5, 0)$ and $(5, 0)$. The conjugate axis has a length of 12 units.
38. The vertices of the hyperbola are at $(0, -4)$ and $(0, 4)$. The conjugate axis has a length of 14 units.

39–42. See Solutions Manual.
An equation of the form $xy = c$ is a hyperbola with the x- and y-axes as asymptotes. Sketch the graph of each hyperbola.

39. $xy = 3$
40. $xy = 8$
41. $xy = -5$
42. $xy = -12$

Graphing Calculator

43–45. See margin.
For the equation $xy = c$, replace c with different values. Graph the resulting equations on a graphing calculator. Answer each question.

43. Suppose $c > 0$. How are the graphs similar and how are they different?
44. Suppose $c < 0$. How are the graphs similar and how are they different?
45. What happens to the graph if $c = 0$?

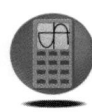

Critical Thinking

46. A hyperbola with a horizontal transverse axis contains the point at $(4, 3)$. The equations of the asymptotes are $y - x = 1$ and $y + x = 5$. Write the equation of the hyperbola. See margin.

Applications and Problem Solving

47. **Chemistry** Boyle's Law states that if the temperature of a gas is constant, then the volume of the gas is inversely proportional to the pressure exerted by the gas. This law is represented by the equation $PV = k$. In this equation, P represents the pressure, V represents the volume, and k is a constant. The constant for a certain gas is 22,500. Graph $PV = k$ for the gas. See margin.

Additional Answers

44. One branch is always in the second quadrant and the other is always in the fourth quadrant. As the value of c decreases, the vertices move away from the origin.
45. The graph becomes the x- and y-axes.
46. $\frac{(x-2)^2}{4} - \frac{(y-3)^2}{4} = 1$
47.

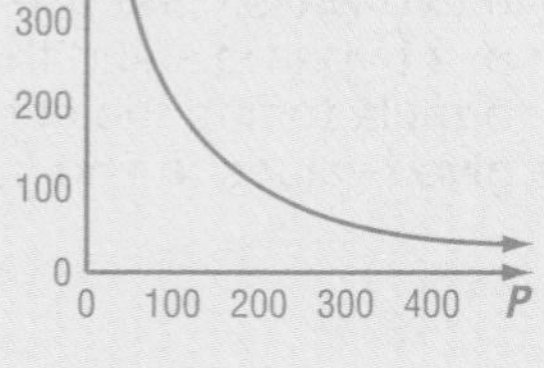

48a. $\frac{x^2}{1.1025} - \frac{y^2}{7.8975} = 1$

Largest national forests in the United States
1. Tongass National Forest, AK
2. Chugach National Forest, AK
3. Toiyabe National Forest, NV
4. Tonto Naitonal Forest, AZ
5. Boise National Forest, ID

48. Forestry A forest ranger at an outpost and another ranger at the primary station both heard an explosion. The outpost and the primary station are 6 kilometers apart.

   a. If one ranger heard the explosion 6 seconds before the other, write an equation that describes all the possible locations of the explosion. Place the two ranger stations on the *x*-axis with the midpoint between the stations at the origin. The transverse axis is horizontal. (*Hint*: The speed of sound is about 0.35 km per second.)

   b. Draw a sketch of the possible locations of the explosion. Include the ranger stations in the drawing. **See Solutions Manual.**

Mixed Review

49. $\frac{(x-1)^2}{25} + \frac{(y-4)^2}{9} = 1$

51. $-7, \frac{3}{2}$
52. 1.32×10^9 km

49. Write the equation of the ellipse whose foci are at (5, 4) and (−3, 4). The major axis is 10 units long. (Lesson 7–4)

50. Name the vertex and the axis of symmetry for the graph of $f(x) = (x + 2)^2$. (Lesson 6–6) **(−2, 0); x = −2**

51. Solve $2q^2 + 11q = 21$ by factoring. (Lesson 6–2)

52. Astronomy Venus has an average distance of 1.08×10^8 kilometers from the sun. Saturn has an average distance of 1.428×10^9 kilometers from the sun. About how much closer to the sun is Venus? (Lesson 5–1)

53. Statistics The number of years of life expected at birth for women in certain countries is given below. Make a box-and-whisker plot of the data, labeling any outliers. (Lesson 4–8) **See Solutions Manual.**

77.2	76.8	76.0	74.3	77.5	78.8	78.4	75.4	77.5
76.0	73.7	75.6	77.2	79.5	79.5	75.0	72.9	76.2
79.9	79.6	74.0	77.6	75.6	75.9	73.2		

54. Solve the system of equations. (Lesson 3–7) **(5, 3, 7)**

   $r + s + t = 15$
   $r + t = 12$
   $s + t = 10$

55. If $h(x) = [5x − 4]$, find $h(−1.5)$. (Lesson 2–6) **−12**

56. Business Derringer Cleaners charges $52 to clean a wedding dress. If the equation relating time spent in hours to the cost in dollars is $C = 12 + 20t$, find the time spent cleaning the dress. (Lesson 2–1) **2 hours**

57. Simplify $7x + 8y + 9y − 5x$. (Lesson 1–2) **2x + 17y**

Extension

Reasoning If the difference of the distances from any point on the hyperbola to the two foci, (−12, 0) and (12, 0), is 20 units, what is the equation of the hyperbola?

$\frac{x^2}{100} - \frac{y^2}{44} = 1$

Tech Prep

Forest Ranger Students who are interested in a career in forestry may wish to do further research into the use of mathematics within that occupation, as mentioned in Exercise 48. For more information on tech prep, see the *Teacher's Handbook*.

The highest producers of roundwood in million cubic meters are as follows.
1. Russia   361.4
2. United States 345.3
3. India   216.0
4. Brazil   212.7
5. China   212.5

4 ASSESS

Closing Activity

Writing Find the values of *a* and *b* for which the asymptotes of $\frac{x^2}{a^2} - \frac{y^2}{b^2} = 1$ are perpendicular. Explain in writing how you found these values.

If $y = \frac{b}{a}x$ and $y = -\frac{b}{a}x$ are perpendicular, then $\frac{b}{a} = -\frac{1}{\left(-\frac{b}{a}\right)}$.

Since *a* and *b* are positive, $a = b$.

Enrichment Masters, p. 53

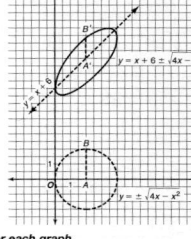

7-5 NAME _____ DATE _____
Enrichment   Student Edition
                            Pages 440–447

Graphing with Addition of y-Coordinates

Equations of parabolas, ellipses, and hyperbolas that are "tipped" with respect to the *x*- and *y*-axes are more difficult to graph than the equations you have been studying.

Often, however, you can use the graphs of two simpler equations to graph a more complicated equation. For example, the graph of the ellipse in the diagram at the right is obtained by adding the *y*-coordinate of each point on the circle and the *y*-coordinate of the corresponding point of the line.

Graph each equation. State the type of curve for each graph.

1. $y = 6 - x \pm \sqrt{4 - x^2}$ ellipse
2. $y = x \pm \sqrt{x}$ parabola

Use a separate sheet of graph paper to graph these equations. State the type of curve for each graph.

3. $y = 2x \pm \sqrt{7 + 6x - x^2}$ ellipse
   See students' graphs.
4. $y = -2x \pm \sqrt{-2x}$ parabola
   See students' graphs.

7–6A Graphing Technology
Conic Sections

A Preview of Lesson 7–6

NCTM Standards: 1–5, 8

Objective

Use a graphing calculator to graph conic sections.

Recommended Time

25 minutes

Instructional Resources

Graphing Calculator Masters, pp. 41 and 42

These masters provide keystroking instruction for this lesson for the TI-81 and Casio graphing calculators.

1 FOCUS

Motivating the Lesson

Write an equation of a conic section on the chalkboard or overhead. Tell students to graph it on their graphing calculators. Ask students if the equation *can* be graphed. Tally how many students say yes and how many say no.

2 TEACH

Teaching Tip A parabola is the only conic section that can be a function.

Teaching Tip A circle is not a function, but a semi-circle can be. In Example 1, you are entering halves of the circle.

Teaching Tip Students may wonder why a complete circle does not appear on their viewing screen in Example 1. The viewing screen is made up of pixels, each of which represents a point on the coordinate plane. The pixels near the *x*-axis often do not represent ordered pairs that fit the equation of the circle. Therefore, those pixels are not blackened and a gap results.

Most conic sections are relations, not functions. Since most graphing calculators plot functions, we must manipulate the equations before entering them into the calculator. For example, the equation for a circle, $x^2 + y^2 = 16$, cannot be entered directly into the calculator since it requires that the equation be entered in a Y= format.

Example **Graph $x^2 + y^2 = 16$ in the standard viewing window.**

First solve the equation for *y*.

$$x^2 + y^2 = 16$$
$$y^2 = 16 - x^2$$
$$y = \pm \sqrt{16 - x^2}$$

Now enter the equations $y = \sqrt{16 - x^2}$ and $y = -\sqrt{16 - x^2}$ separately, since there is no $\pm$ key.

Enter: [Y=] [2nd] [√] [(] 16

[–] [X,T,θ] [x^2] [)] [ENTER]

[(–)] [2nd] [√] [(] 16

[–] [X,T,θ] [x^2] [)] [ZOOM] 6

The graph appears to be an ellipse. The calculator screen can be set so that units on the *x*- and *y*-axes are equal length. To do this quickly, enter [ZOOM] 5. The graph no longer appears distorted and shows the circle.

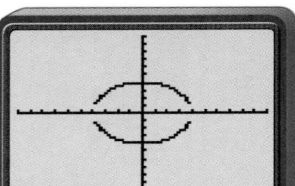

To save time entering equations, you can define Y1 as $\sqrt{16 - x^2}$ and Y2 as −Y1. To do this, enter Y1 as shown above. Then move the cursor to Y2 and enter the following.

Enter: [(–)] [2nd] [Y-VARS] 1 1

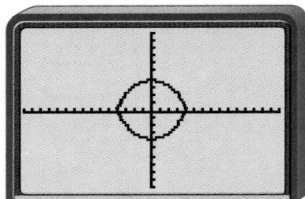

Example ② Graph the hyperbola $9y^2 + 36y - x^2 + 6x - 54 = 0$ in the $[-10, 15]$ by $[-0, 10]$ viewing window.

Rewrite the equation by completing the square and solving for y.

$$y = -2 \pm \sqrt{\frac{81 + (x-3)^2}{9}}$$

To enter the equations into the calculator efficiently, let Y1 = $\sqrt{\frac{81 + (x-3)^2}{9}}$, Y2 = -2 + Y1, and Y3 = -2 − Y1.

Enter: [Y=] [2nd] [√] [(] [(] 81

[+] [(] [X,T,θ] [−] 3 [)]

[x²] [)] [÷] 9 [)] [ENTER]

[(−)] 2 [+] [2nd] [Y-VARS]

1 1 [ENTER]

[(−)] 2 [−] [2nd] [Y-VARS] 1 1

Then deselect Y1 and enter GRAPH. *To deselect Y1, press* [Y=] *and highlight the equals sign next to Y1. Then press* [ENTER].

1–10. See Solutions Manual for graphs.

EXERCISES

Use a graphing calculator to graph each conic section. Name the conic section and sketch the graph that appears.

1. $y = x^2 + 9x - 12$ parabola
2. $(x-3)^2 + y^2 = 25$ circle
3. $16x^2 + 4y^2 = 48$ ellipse
4. $10x^2 - 7y^2 - 70 = 0$ hyperbola
5. $25x^2 + 4y^2 - 24y = 64$ ellipse
6. $x^2 - 8x + y^2 = 25$ circle
7. $4x^2 + y^2 - 100 = 0$ ellipse
8. $y^2 + 5 = x^2 + 2y + 1$ hyperbola
9. $y^2 - 12y - x + 25 = 0$ parabola
10. $(y+1)^2 - x^2 - 4 = 0$ hyperbola

Assignment Guide

Core: 1–10
Enriched: 1–10

4 ASSESS

Observing students working with technology is an excellent method of assessment.

Using Technology

This lesson offers an excellent opportunity for using technology in your algebra classroom. For more information on using technology, see *Graphing Calculators in the Mathematics Classroom,* one of the titles in the Glencoe Mathematics Professional Series.

Instructional Resources

- Study Guide Master 7-6
- Practice Master 7-6
- Enrichment Master 7-6
- Assessment and Evaluation Masters, p. 185
- Graphing Calculator Masters, p. 7
- Modeling Mathematics Masters, pp. 46–48
- Multicultural Activity Masters, p. 14

 Transparency 7-6A contains the 5-Minute Check for this lesson; **Transparency 7-6B** contains a teaching aid for this lesson.

Recommended Pacing	
Standard Pacing	Days 8 & 9 of 15
Honors Pacing	Day 8 of 13
Block Scheduling*	Day 5 of 7

 *For more information on pacing and possible lesson plans, refer to the *Block Scheduling Booklet*.

1 FOCUS

 ### 5-Minute Check
(over Lesson 7-5)

Use the hyperbola with equation $25y^2 - 64x^2 = 1600$ for Exercises 1–3.

1. Find the coordinates of the vertices. **(0, 8), (0, −8)**

2. Find the coordinates of the foci. **$(0, \sqrt{89}), (0, -\sqrt{89})$**

3. Find the slopes of the asymptotes. **$\frac{8}{5}, -\frac{8}{5}$**

4. Write an equation for a hyperbola centered at $(-2, -1)$ with a vertical transverse axis. The value of a is 4 and the value of b is 5.

$$\frac{(y + 1)^2}{16} - \frac{(x + 2)^2}{25} = 1$$

7-6

What YOU'LL LEARN

- To write equations of conic sections in standard form,
- to identify conic sections from their equations, and
- to use simulation to solve problems.

Why IT'S IMPORTANT

You can graph conic sections to solve problems involving aeronautics and space science.

Conic Sections

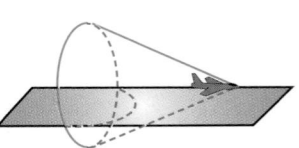

APPLICATION
Aeronautics

The F-15 Eagle can reach speeds in excess of Mach 2.5. Mach 1 is the speed of sound, and Mach 2.5 is 2.5 times the speed of sound.

A plane like the F-15 Eagle, flying faster than the speed of sound, produces a shock wave in the shape of a cone. When the shock wave hits the ground, a sonic boom is heard. If the plane is flying parallel to the ground, the sonic boom is heard at points that form one branch of a hyperbola. What shape would the points form if the plane is climbing and *not* flying parallel to the ground? What shape would be formed if the plane could fly vertically?

Recall that parabolas, circles, ellipses, and hyperbolas are called conic sections, because they are the cross sections formed when a double cone is sliced by a plane.

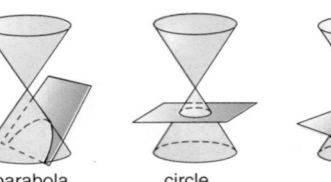  

parabola   circle   ellipse   hyperbola

The conic sections can all be described by a general quadratic equation.

Equation of a Conic Section	The equation of a conic section can be written in the form $Ax^2 + Bxy + Cy^2 + Dx + Ey + F = 0$, where A, B, and C are *not* all zero.

You can identify the conic section that is represented by a given equation by writing the equation in one of the standard forms you have learned.

Conic Section	Standard Form of Equation
parabola	$y = a(x - h)^2 + k$ or $x = a(y - k)^2 + h$
circle	$(x - h)^2 + (y - k)^2 = r^2$
ellipse	$\frac{(x - h)^2}{a^2} + \frac{(y - k)^2}{b^2} = 1$ or $\frac{(x - h)^2}{b^2} + \frac{(y - k)^2}{a^2} = 1$ $a \neq b$
hyperbola	$\frac{(x - h)^2}{a^2} - \frac{(y - k)^2}{b^2} = 1$ or $\frac{(y - k)^2}{a^2} - \frac{(x - h)^2}{b^2} = 1$ or $xy = c$, when $c \neq 0$

 **F Y I**

Some of Apollonius' books are summaries of work by Euclid and Aristaeus. However, he expanded upon their work and developed new theorems and terminology.

 **TEKS** | 5.a., 5.b., 5.c., 5.d., 5.e.

Example **1** **Identify the graph of** $y^2 - 3x + 6y + 12 = 0$ **as a parabola, a circle, an ellipse, or a hyperbola. Then graph the equation.**

Complete the square to write the equation in standard form.

$$y^2 - 3x + 6y + 12 = 0$$
$$3x = y^2 + 6y + 12$$
$$3x = (y^2 + 6y + \square) + 12 - \square$$
$$3x = (y^2 + 6y + 9) + 12 - 9$$
$$3x = (y + 3)^2 + 3 \qquad \textit{Factor.}$$
$$x = \tfrac{1}{3}(y + 3)^2 + 1 \qquad \textit{Divide by 3.}$$

This equation has the standard form of $x = a(y - k)^2 + h$. So the graph of the equation $y^2 - 3x + 6y + 12 = 0$ is a parabola with vertex at $(1, -3)$ and opening to the right.

Example **2** **The shock wave generated by a jet plane intersects the ground in a curve with equation** $x^2 - 14x + 4 = 9y^2 - 36y$. **What is the shape of the curve? Sketch the curve.**

APPLICATION
Aeronautics

To determine the shape of the curve, complete the squares and write the equation in standard form.

$$x^2 - 14x + 4 = 9y^2 - 36y$$
$$x^2 - 14x - 9y^2 + 36y = -4$$
$$(x^2 - 14x + \square) - 9(y^2 - 4y + \square) = -4 + \square - 9(\square) \qquad \textit{Complete the squares.}$$
$$(x^2 - 14x + 49) - 9(y^2 - 4y + 4) = -4 + 49 - 9(4)$$
$$(x - 7)^2 - 9(y - 2)^2 = 9$$
$$\frac{(x - 7)^2}{9} - \frac{(y - 2)^2}{1} = 1 \qquad \textit{Divide each side by 9.}$$

The curve is a hyperbola. The center of the hyperbola is at $(7, 2)$. Since the value of a is 3, the vertices are 3 units to the right and left of the center along the transverse axis. The vertices are located at $(4, 2)$ and $(10, 2)$. The value of b is 1.

The slopes of the asymptotes are $\pm\frac{1}{3}$. Use all of this information to sketch the curve.

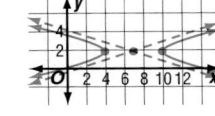

Of course, the shock wave will only generate one half of the hyperbola.

F Y I

The years from 300 to 200 B.C. are called the "Golden Age" of Greek mathematics. Apollonius is particularly known for his work on conics. He wrote eight books on the subject and was considered "the great geometer" by his peers.

You can easily determine the type of conic section represented by an equation of the form $Ax^2 + Bxy + Cy^2 + Dx + Ey + F = 0$ when $B = 0$ by looking at A and C.

Conic Section	Relationship of A and C
parabola	$A = 0$ or $C = 0$, but not both.
circle	$A = C$
ellipse	A and C have the same sign and $A \neq C$.
hyperbola	A and C have opposite signs.

Classroom Vignette

"Play Doh® and dental floss can be used to allow students individually to slice a cone and get a conic section."

Cindy Boyd
Abilene High School
Abilene, Texas

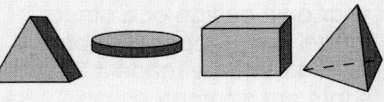

Motivating the Lesson
Questioning Conceal the top of the overhead projector from the students' view and use some of the following blocks and figures for them to identify.

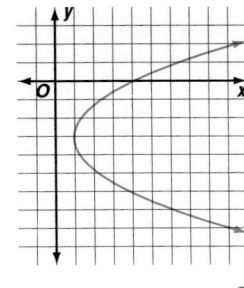

By placing the figures in different positions, they will appear to be different. This helps a student to realize that a figure's appearance and properties can change. Do the same with a circular or elliptical ring.

2 TEACH

Teaching Tip An equation of the form $Ax^2 + Bxy + Cy^2 + Dx + Ey + F = 0$ may not always represent a conic section. The equation may be an example of a degenerate case or it may not represent anything.

In-Class Examples

For Example 1
Identify the graph of $9x^2 + 16y^2 - 54x + 64y + 1 = 0$ as a parabola, a circle, an ellipse, or a hyperbola. Then graph the equation. **ellipse**

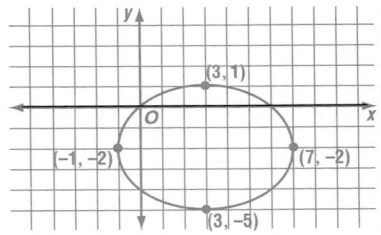

For Example 2
The shock wave generated by a supersonic jet intersects the ground in a curve whose equation is $(y - 1)^2 = -5(x - 3)$. What shape is the curve? **parabola**

Teaching Tip A shock wave is a pressure wave caused by faster-than-sound movement through a medium. It is stronger and faster than a sound wave but dissipates more quickly. Sound wave variation is referred to as the Doppler effect. A car horn changes pitch as it passes because the distance the sound waves travel varies as the car moves.

Chapter 7 **451**

For Example 3
Statistically, a certain basketball team makes 2 out of every 3 foul shots. Use a spinner of your own design or a die to model the number of shots predicted to be made if 24 shots are attempted. **Answers will vary depending on the simulation.**

3 PRACTICE/APPLY

Check for Understanding
Exercises 1–13 are designed to help you assess your students' understanding through reading, writing, speaking, and modeling. You should work through Exercises 1–4 with your students and then monitor their work on Exercises 5–13.

Assignment Guide
Core: 15–39 odd, 40–46
Enriched: 14–34 even, 36–46

For **Extra Practice,** see p. 893.

Additional Answers

1. Slice the cone with a plane that is not perpendicular to the axis.
2. Slice the double cone with a plane that contains the axis.
9. $y = \left(x + \frac{3}{2}\right)^2 - \frac{5}{4}$; parabola

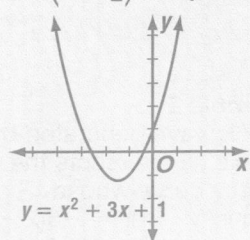

$$y = x^2 + 3x + 1$$

10. $\frac{y^2}{16} - \frac{x^2}{8} = 1$; hyperbola

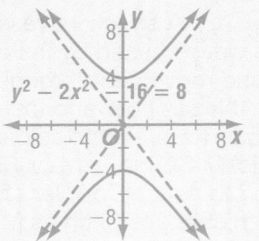

$$y^2 - 2x^2 - 16 = 8$$

Conic sections can be modeled by slicing a double cone. Sometimes it helps to **use a simulation** to model other mathematical situations that are difficult to solve directly.

Example ③

Use a Simulation

The roll of a die simulates buying one box of cereal.

DeLIGHTful Cereal has placed contest tickets that are printed with two consecutive letters from the name of the cereal in their cereal boxes, that is, DE, LI, GH, TF, and UL. To win an official Olympic poster, you must collect all five different tickets whose letters spell the name of the cereal. The total number of each kind of ticket is the same. How many boxes would you expect to have to buy to win the contest?

Explore Read the problem. In order to win the poster, you must collect five different tickets. If you are very lucky, you could win after buying only five boxes of cereal. However, most people will need to buy more than five boxes. How many boxes will you have to buy to win the poster?

Plan It would be expensive and inconvenient, but you could buy lots of boxes of cereal to see how many it takes to win. Instead, you could simulate these purchases by assigning each of the tickets a number from 1 to 5. Then roll a die to simulate buying one box and to determine the prize in the box. If you roll a 6, ignore it. Keep rolling until all 5 numbers appear. Several simulations should be tried.

Solve Five simulations are recorded below.

Rolls	Number of Rolls (Boxes Bought) to Win
5 1 4 3 4 3 5 3 3 1 4 2	12
4 3 2 5 5 4 4 4 3 2 4 4 1	13
1 2 1 5 5 5 4 3	8
3 5 5 4 1 3 1 1 3 1 2	11
4 3 5 1 3 4 3 4 3 4 1 1 3 2	14

Find the mean to estimate of the number of boxes you would need to buy.

$$\frac{12 + 13 + 8 + 11 + 14}{5} = 11.6 \text{ or about } 12$$

Our estimate is that you would have to buy about 12 boxes to win the poster.

Examine When you simulate a situation in this way, the more trials you conduct, the better your estimate. You may wish to conduct more trials to see if the answer is reasonable.

Alternative Teaching Strategies

Student Diversity Expand upon the Classroom Vignette on page 451 by making different sizes of cones and comparing shapes and sizes of the conic sections. Have students compare their sections to the drawings on page 450.

Communicating Mathematics

Study the lesson. Then complete the following. 1–2. See margin.

1. **Describe** how a parabola is formed by slicing a cone.

2. **Explain** how to slice a double cone so that the cross section will be two straight intersecting lines.

3. **Describe** a problem that might be solved by using a model or simulation. a problem that is difficult or impossible to solve directly

 MATH JOURNAL

4. **Assess Yourself** Draw an example of each of the four conic sections you have studied. Write a sentence or two describing the properties of each of these curves. Which conic section is your "favorite?" Explain your answer. See students' work.

Guided Practice

State whether the graph of each equation is a parabola, a circle, an ellipse, or a hyperbola.

5. $x^2 + y^2 = 20$ circle

6. $x = (y - 5)^2 + 9$ parabola

7. $\frac{x^2}{23} - \frac{(y - 8)^2}{34} = 1$ hyperbola

8. $\frac{(y - 7)^2}{3} + \frac{(x + 2)^2}{2} = 1$ ellipse

Write each equation in standard form. State whether the graph of the equation is a parabola, a circle, an ellipse, or a hyperbola. Then graph the equation. 9–13. See margin.

9. $y = x^2 + 3x + 1$

10. $y^2 - 2x^2 - 16 = 0$

11. $x^2 + y^2 = x + 2$

12. $x^2 + 4y^2 + 2x - 24y + 33 = 0$

13. Write $x + 2 = x^2 + y$ in standard form. Then graph the equation.

Practice

Write each equation in standard form. State whether the graph of the equation is a parabola, a circle, an ellipse, or a hyperbola. Then graph the equation. 14–31. See Solutions Manual.

A

14. $6x^2 + 6y^2 = 162$

15. $x^2 = 8y$

16. $4x^2 + 2y^2 = 8$

17. $4y^2 - x^2 + 4 = 0$

18. $(x - 1)^2 + 9(y - 4)^2 = 36$

19. $y + 4 = (x - 2)^2$

20. $x^2 + y^2 + 6y + 13 = 40$

21. $x^2 - y^2 + 8x = 16$

B

22. $x^2 + y^2 + 4x - 6y = -4$

23. $y + x^2 = -(8x + 23)$

24. $3x^2 + 4y^2 + 8y = 8$

25. $(y - 4)^2 = 9(x - 4)$

26. $x^2 - 8y + y^2 + 11 = 0$

27. $25y^2 + 9x^2 - 50y - 54x = 119$

28. $x^2 + 4y^2 - 11 = 2(4y - x)$

29. $9y^2 + 18y = 25x^2 + 216$

30. $x^2 + y^2 = 2x + 8$

31. $6x^2 - 24x - 5y^2 - 10y - 11 = 0$

The graph of an equation of the form $Ax^2 + Bxy + Cy^2 + Dx + Ey + F = 0$ is either a conic section or a *degenerate case*. The degenerate cases for the conic sections are stated below. Graph each equation and identify the result.

32–34. See Solutions Manual for graphs.

C

32. $4x^2 - y^2 = 0$

33. $4y^2 + 3x^2 + 32y - 6x = -67$

34. $x^2 - x = 0$

32. intersecting lines
33. isolated point
34. parallel lines

Conic	Degenerate Case
ellipse or circle	isolated point
hyperbola	two intersecting lines
parabola	two parallel lines or one line

Lesson 7-6 Conic Sections **453**

Reteaching

Using Alternative Methods The graph of every second-degree equation of the form $Ax^2 = Bxy + Cy^2 + Dx + Ey + F = 0$ is a conic section (or a degenerate case). The sign of the discriminant $D = B^2 - 4AC$ can be used to determine the conic section.

$D < 0$ ellipse (one point or 0)
$D = 0$ parabola (parallel lines)
$D > 0$ hyperbola (intersecting lines)

Additional Answers

11. $\left(x - \frac{1}{2}\right)^2 + y^2 = \frac{9}{4}$; circle

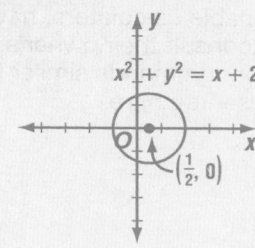

$x^2 + y^2 = x + 2$

$\left(\frac{1}{2}, 0\right)$

12. $\frac{(x + 1)^2}{4} + \frac{(y - 3)^2}{1} = 1$; ellipse

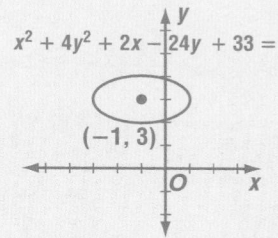

$x^2 + 4y^2 + 2x - 24y + 33 = 0$

$(-1, 3)$

13. $y = -\left(x - \frac{1}{2}\right)^2 + \frac{9}{4}$; parabola

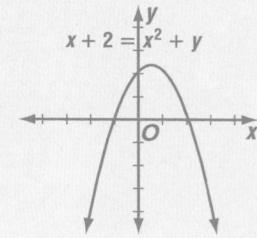

$x + 2 = x^2 + y$

Study Guide Masters, p. 54

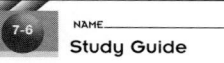

NAME _____ DATE _____

7-6   **Study Guide**   Student Edition Pages 450–455

Conic Sections

Parabolas, circles, ellipses, and hyperbolas are known as **conic sections.** Any conic section in the coordinate plane can be described by an equation of the form $Ax^2 + Bxy + Cy^2 + Dx + Ey + F = 0$, where A, B, and C are not all zero. When $B = 0$, the coefficients of x^2 and y^2 tell you what kind of conic section the equation will have for its graph.

$A = C$	circle
$A \ne C$, but have same sign	ellipse
$A \ne C$, but have opposite signs	hyperbola
$A = 0$ or $C = 0$, but not both	parabola

Example: Write $x^2 = 4y^2 + 16$ in the form $Ax^2 + Bxy + Cy^2 + Dx + Ey + F = 0$. Tell what kind of conic section the graph will be. Then change the equation to the standard form for that conic section and graph the equation.

$x^2 = 4y^2 + 16$
$x^2 - 4y^2 = 16$

Since A and C have opposite signs, the graph will be a hyperbola.

Next change $x^2 - 4y^2 = 16$ to the standard form for a hyperbola. Divide each side by 16.
$\frac{x^2}{16} - \frac{y^2}{4} = 1$

Write each equation in standard form. State whether the graph of the equation is a parabola, a circle, an ellipse, or a hyperbola. Then graph the equation.

1. $x^2 - 2x + y^2 + 8y = 8$

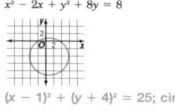

2. $y = x^2 - 2x - 8$

$(x - 1)^2 + (y + 4)^2 = 25$; circle

$y = (x - 1)^2 - 9$; parabola

3. $9(x + 4)^2 + 4(y - 1)^2 = 36$

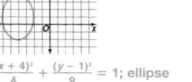

4. $x^2 = 2x + y^2 - 4y + 7$

$\frac{(x + 4)^2}{4} + \frac{(y - 1)^2}{9} = 1$; ellipse

$\frac{(x - 1)^2}{4} - \frac{(y - 2)^2}{4} = 1$; hyperbola

Chapter 7 **453**

Using the Programming Exercises The program given in Exercise 35 is for use with a TI-82 graphing calculator. For other programmable calculators, have students consult their owner's manual for commands similar to those presented here.

Programming

35. The program below determines the type of graph represented by an equation of the form $Ax^2 + Bxy + Cy^2 + Dx + Ey + F = 0$, where $B = 0$.

```
PROGRAM: CONICS
: Prompt A, C, D, E, F          : End
: If A≠0                         : Lbl 2
: Then                          : If A=C
: Goto 1                        : Then
: End                          : Disp "CIRCLE"
: If D=0                        : Stop
: Then                          : End
: Disp"DEGENERATE","CASE"       : If AC>0
: Goto 2                        : Then
: End                          : Disp "ELLIPSE"
: Goto 2                        : Stop
: Lbl 1                         : End
: If C≠0                        : If AC<0
: Then                          : Then
: D²/(4A)+E²/(4C)→G             : Disp "HYPERBOLA"
: End                          : Stop
: If G≠F                        : End
: Then                          : Disp "PARABOLA"
: Goto 2
```

Use the program to determine the type of conic section each equation represents. a. ellipse b. hyperbola

a. $12x^2 + 36x + 16y^2 + 32y - 5 = 0$
b. $25x^2 - 4y^2 = 100$
c. $x^2 + 12x + y^2 - 8y = -44$ circle
d. $(y + 3)^2 = -12(x - 2)$ parabola

Critical Thinking

36a. The vertices move closer to the center.

36. Graph $\frac{x^2}{16} - \frac{y^2}{9} = 1$ on a graphing calculator. Then graph $\frac{x^2}{16} - \frac{y^2}{9} = k$ for $k = \frac{1}{2}, \frac{1}{4}, \frac{1}{8}, \frac{1}{16}, \frac{1}{32}$, and so on. Answer each question.

a. What happens as the value of k approaches 0?
b. Identify the graph when $k = 0$. 2 intersecting lines

37. The equation of an ellipse is $\frac{x^2}{16} + \frac{y^2}{4} = 1$. The directrix of a parabola is tangent to the ellipse at one endpoint of the minor axis. If the focus of the parabola is located at the other endpoint of the minor axis, write all possible equations of the parabola. $y = \pm\frac{1}{8}x^2$

Applications and Problem Solving

38. **Space Science** The orbits of comets follow the paths of the conic sections. For example, Halley's Comet follows an elliptical orbit with the sun located at one of its foci. What type of orbits pass by Earth only once?

parabolas and hyperbolas

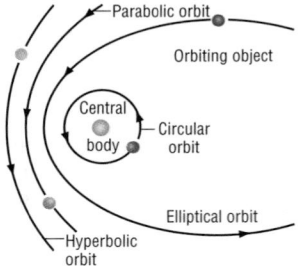
Parabolic orbit
Orbiting object
Central body
Circular orbit
Elliptical orbit
Hyperbolic orbit

39. **Use a Simulation** A baseball card manufacturer is packaging a puzzle piece in each package of cards. The total number of each piece is the same.

a. If there are 6 different puzzle pieces, design a simulation to determine how many packages of baseball cards you would need to buy to collect all the pieces.
b. Use your simulation to estimate the number of packages you would need to buy to collect all the pieces. a–b. Answers will vary.

Practice Masters, p. 54

| 7-6 | NAME_____ DATE_____ |
| | **Practice** | Student Edition Pages 450–455 |

Conic Sections

Write each equation in standard form. State whether the graph of the equation is a parabola, a circle, an ellipse, or a hyperbola. Then graph the equation.

1. $y^2 = -3x$

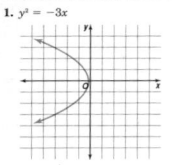

$x = -\frac{1}{3}(y - 0)^2 + 0$; parabola

2. $x^2 + y^2 + 6x = 7$

$(x + 3)^2 + (y - 0)^2 = 16$; circle

3. $5x^2 - 6y^2 - 30x - 12y + 9 = 0$

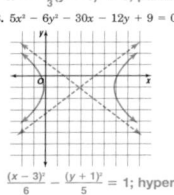

$\frac{(x - 3)^2}{6} - \frac{(y + 1)^2}{5} = 1$; hyperbola

4. $3x^2 = 8 - 4y^2 - 8y$

$\frac{(x - 0)^2}{4} + \frac{(y + 1)^2}{3} = 1$; ellipse

5. $5y^2 = 10 - 4x^2$

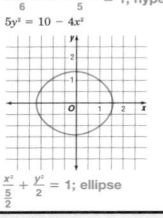

$\frac{x^2}{\frac{5}{2}} + \frac{y^2}{2} = 1$; ellipse

6. $5x^2 + 2y^2 + 30x - 16y + 67 = 0$

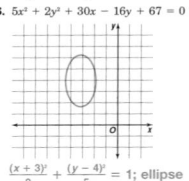

$\frac{(x + 3)^2}{2} + \frac{(y - 4)^2}{5} = 1$; ellipse

40. $\dfrac{(y-4)^2}{36} - \dfrac{(x-5)^2}{16} = 1$

41. quadratic, $4x^2$; linear, $-8x$; constant, -2

44. 30 footballs, 0 basketballs

40. Write an equation of the hyperbola with center at (5, 4) if its transverse axis is vertical, $a = 6$, and $b = 4$. (Lesson 7–5)

41. Identify the quadratic term, the linear term, and the constant term of $f(x) = 4x^2 - 8x - 2$. (Lesson 6–1)

42. Simplify $(m^5 n^{-3})^2 m^2 n^7$. (Lesson 5–1) $m^{12}n$

43. Evaluate the determinant of $\begin{bmatrix} 4 & -7 & 2 \\ 3 & -3 & 3 \\ 2 & 7 & 5 \end{bmatrix}$. (Lesson 4–4) -27

44. Manufacturing The Oklahoma City division of SuperSports, Inc. produces footballs and basketballs. It takes 4 hours on machine A and 2 hours on machine B to make a football. Producing a basketball requires 6 hours on machine A, 6 hours on machine B, and 1 hour on machine C. Machine A is available 120 hours per week, machine B is available 72 hours per week, and machine C is available 10 hours per week. If the company makes \$3 profit on each football and \$2 profit on each basketball, how many of each should they make to maximize their profit? (Lesson 3–6)

45. Graph $4y - x \le 6$. (Lesson 2–7) **See margin.**

46. Evaluate $7 - 4^2 + 27 - 1$. (Lesson 1–1) **17**

Refer to the Investigation on pages 328–329.

WORKING ON THE In·ves·ti·ga·tion

the River Canyon Bridge

Once you have determined the parabolic equation for an arch, you can find other equations that might be helpful in determining the dimensions of the bridge.

1 Using the equations for the parabolas, determine a general formula for finding the length of a strut from any point under the roadway. Explain how you found the formula. Then find specific formulas for all four of your designs.

2 Use your formula to find the lengths of the struts on each bridge. How do these measurements compare with your initial blueprints?

3 For each design, determine the locations on the canyon walls at which the ends of the arch will be anchored. State each location in terms of the distance from the top of the canyon (where the roadway is located). Explain how you determined each location.

4 Revise your blueprints as necessary with your new data.

Add the results of your work to your Investigation Folder.

Lesson 7–6 Conic Sections **455**

Extension

Reasoning Which coefficient(s) must be zero if $Ax^2 + Bxy + Cy^2 + Dx + Ey + F = 0$

a. is a function? *C*
b. is a line? *A, B, and C*

In·ves·ti·ga·tion

Working on the Investigation

The Investigation on pages 328–329 is designed to be a long-term project that is completed over several days or weeks. Encourage students to keep their materials in their Investigation Folder as they work on the Investigation.

---

4 ASSESS

Closing Activity

Writing Have students write a paragraph explaining the equations for the conic sections.

Chapter 7, Quiz C (Lessons 7-5 and 7-6), is available in the *Assessment and Evaluation Masters*, p. 185.

Additional Answer

45.

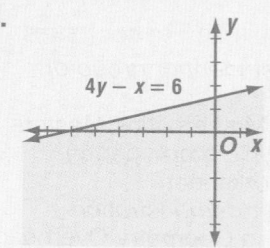

$4y - x = 6$

Enrichment Masters, p. 54

7-6 NAME_____ DATE_____
Enrichment Student Edition Pages 450–455

Loci

A *locus* (plural, *loci*) is the set of all points, and only those points, that satisfy a given set of conditions. In geometry, figures often are defined as loci. For example, a circle is the locus of points of a plane that are a given distance from a given point. The definition leads naturally to an equation whose graph is the curve described.

Example: Write an equation of the locus of points that are the same distance from (3, 4) and $y = -4$.

Recognizing that the locus is a parabola with focus (3, 4) and directrix $y = -4$, you can find that $h = 3$, $k = 0$, and $a = 4$ where (h, k) is the vertex and 4 units is the distance from the vertex to both the focus and directrix.

Thus, an equation for the parabola is $y = \frac{1}{16}(x - 3)^2$.

The problem also may be approached analytically as follows:

Let (x, y) be a point of the locus.

The distance from (3, 4) to (x, y) = the distance from $y = -4$ to (x, y).

$$\sqrt{(x-3)^2 + (y-4)^2} = \sqrt{(x-x)^2 + (y-(-4))^2}$$
$$(x-3)^2 + y^2 - 8y + 16 = y^2 + 8y + 16$$
$$(x-3)^2 = 16y$$
$$\frac{1}{16}(x-3)^2 = y$$

State what type of curve each locus is. Then write an equation for the locus.

1. All points that are the same distance from (0, 5) and (4, 5). line, $x = 2$

2. All points that are 4 units from the origin. circle, $x^2 + y^2 = 4$

3. All points that are the same distance from $(-2, -1)$ and $x = 2$. parabola, $x = \frac{-1}{8}(y^2 + 2y + 1)$

4. The locus of points such that the sum of the distances from $(-2, 0)$ and $(2, 0)$ is 6. ellipse, $\frac{x^2}{9} + \frac{y^2}{5} = 1$

5. The locus of points such that the absolute value of the difference of the distances from $(-3, 0)$ and $(3, 0)$ is 2. hyperbola, $\frac{x^2}{1} - \frac{y^2}{8} = 1$

Objective

Draw conic sections using conic graph paper.

Recommended Time

Demonstration and discussion: 30 minutes; Exercises: 30 minutes

Instructional Resources

For each student or group of students
Modeling Mathematics Masters
• p. 18 (conic graph paper)
• p. 23 (worksheet)
For teacher demonstration
Algebra and Geometry Overhead Manipulative Resources

1 FOCUS

Motivating the Lesson

Display a sheet of regular graph paper. Ask students how they would create a parabola on that paper. They should suggest finding an equation for the parabola and then plotting pairs of points. Then display a sheet of conic graph paper, such as that used in Activity 1. Ask students how they might create a parabola on that paper. Students may realize that the lines and concentric circles can help to more easily draw a figure such as a parabola.

2 TEACH

Teaching Tip Remind students that the conics represented contain an infinite number of points and not just the finite number of points illustrated in the graphs.

Teaching Tip Suggest that students use colored pencils in Activity 1.

MODELING MATHEMATICS

An Extension of Lesson 7–6

7–6B Conic Sections

Materials: conic graph paper

Recall that a parabola is the set of all points that are equally distant from the focus and the directrix.

You can draw a parabola based on this definition by using special conic graph paper. This graph paper contains a series of concentric circles equally spaced from each other and a series of parallel lines tangent to each circle.

Number the circles consecutively beginning with the smallest circle. Number the lines with consecutive integers as shown in the sample at the right. Be sure that line 1 is tangent to circle 1.

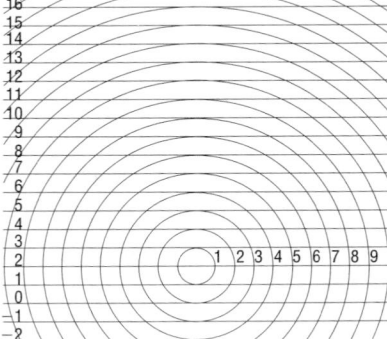

Activity 1

Mark the point at the intersection of circle 1 and line 1. Mark both points that are on line 2 and circle 2. Continue this process marking both points on line 3 and circle 3, and so on. Now connect the points with a smooth curve.

Look at the diagram at the right. What is the graph? Note that every point on the graph is equally distant from the center of the small circle and from the line labeled 0. The center of the small circle is the focus of the parabola, and line 0 is the directrix.

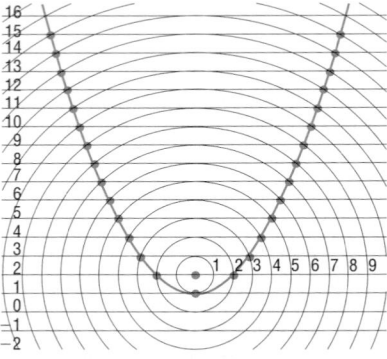

---

456 Chapter 7 Analyzing Conic Sections

Activity 2

An ellipse is the set of points such that the sum of their distances from two fixed points is constant. The two fixed points are called the foci.

Use graph paper like that shown below. It contains two small circles and a series of concentric circles from each. The concentric circles are tangent to each other as shown.

Choose the constant 13. Mark the points at the intersections of circle 9 and circle 4, because $9 + 4 = 13$. Continue this process until you have marked the intersection of all circles whose sum is 13.

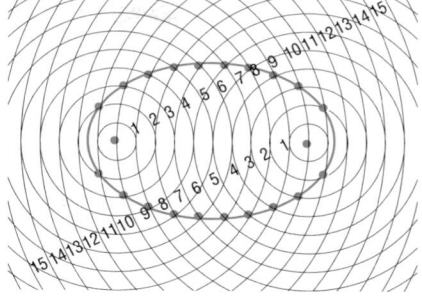

Connect the points to form an ellipse. The foci are the centers of the two small circles on the graph paper.

Activity 3

A hyperbola is the set of points such that the difference of their distances from two fixed points is constant. The two fixed points are called the foci.

Choose the same graph paper that you used for the ellipse. Choose the constant 7. Mark the points at the intersections of circle 9 and circle 2, because $9 - 2 = 7$. Continue this process until you have marked the intersection of all circles whose difference is 7.

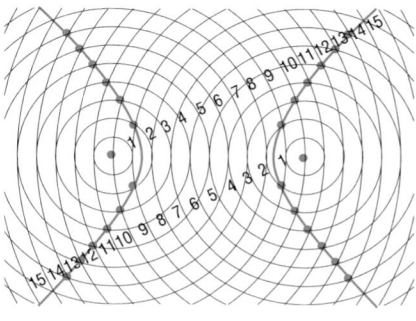

Connect the points to form a hyperbola.

Model

1. Use the paper from Activity 1. Mark the intersection of line 0 and circle 2. Then mark the two points on line 1 and circle 3, the two points on line 2 and circle 4, and so on. Draw the new parabola. Continue this process and make as many parabolas as you can on one sheet of conic graph paper. The focus is always the center of the small circle. Why are the resulting graphs parabolas? **1–3. See margin.**

2. In Activity 2, we drew an ellipse such that the sum of the distances from two fixed points was 13. Choose 9, 10, 11, 12, 14, and so on for that sum, and draw as many ellipses as you can on one piece of conic graph paper. What happens as the sum increases? decreases?

3. In Activity 3, we drew a hyperbola such that the difference from two fixed points was 7. Choose other numbers and draw as many hyperbolas as you can on one piece of graph paper. What happens as the difference increases? decreases?

3 PRACTICE/APPLY

Assignment Guide

Core: 1–3
Enriched: 1–3

Additional Answers

1. The points are equidistant from the focus and the directrix.
2. The ellipses become more circular; the ellipses become more oblong.
3. Each branch of the hyperbola becomes more narrow, and the vertices become farther apart. Each branch of the hyperbola becomes wider, and the vertices become closer.

4 ASSESS

Observing students working in cooperative groups is an excellent method of assessment.

Using Manipulatives

The inclusion of manipulative activities in the algebra classroom offers students the opportunity to use models to bridge the gap from the concrete to the abstract. For more information on using manipulatives, see *Manipulatives in the Mathematics Classroom*, one of the titles in the Glencoe Mathematics Professional Series.

7-7A Graphing Technology
Solving Quadratic Systems

A Preview of Lesson 7-7

Objective

Use a graphing calculator to solve systems of quadratic equations and inequalities by graphing.

Recommended Time

25 minutes

Instructional Resources

Graphing Calculator Masters,
pp. 43 and 44

These masters provide keystroking instruction for this lesson for the TI-81 and Casio graphing calculators.

1 FOCUS

Motivating the Lesson

Write two conic section equations on the chalkboard or overhead. Then ask students how they would solve them graphically. Try to get them to apply what they learned in previous Graphing Technology lessons.

2 TEACH

Teaching Tip In Example 1, students should note that they will actually be entering three equations on their calculators.

As you know, the graphing calculator is capable of graphing several equations on the screen at one time. You can use this capability with the TRACE or "intersect" features to determine approximate solutions of a system of quadratic equations, if a solution exists.

Example ❶ **Solve the system of equations with a graphing calculator. Round the answer to the nearest hundredth.**
$$2y = 12 - x^2$$
$$x^2 - y^2 = 25$$

First, solve each equation for y.

$$2y = 12 - x^2 \qquad\qquad x^2 - y^2 = 25$$
$$y = \frac{1}{2}(12 - x^2) \qquad\qquad x^2 - 25 = y^2$$
$$\qquad\qquad\qquad \pm\sqrt{x^2 - 25} = y$$

Now, enter the equations into the calculator and graph in the standard viewing window. Any points where the graphs intersect represent solutions to the system of equations.

Enter: [Y=] .5 [(] 12 [−] [X,T,θ]

[x²] [)] [ENTER]

[2nd] [√] [(] [X,T,θ] [x²] [−]

25 [)] [ENTER]

[(−)] [2nd] [Y-VARS] 1 2

[ZOOM] 6

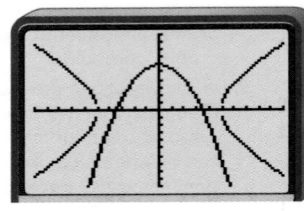

We see that the graphs do not intersect. Therefore, there is no solution to this system of equations.

TEKS | 3.b., 3.c.

Example **2** Solve the system of equations with a graphing calculator. Round the coordinates to the nearest hundredth.

$$x^2 + y^2 = 25$$
$$x^2 - y^2 = 1$$

Solve each equation for y.

$$x^2 + y^2 = 25 \qquad\qquad x^2 - y^2 = 1$$
$$y^2 = 25 - x^2 \qquad\qquad x^2 - 1 = y^2$$
$$y = \pm\sqrt{25 - x^2} \qquad \pm\sqrt{x^2 - 1} = y$$

Now, enter the equations into the calculator and graph in the "square" viewing window. Any points where the graphs intersect represent solutions to the system of equations.

Enter: 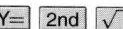 25

 ENTER

(−) 2nd Y-VARS 1 1

ENTER

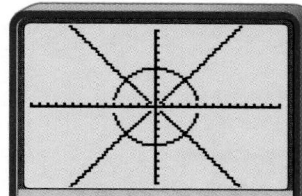

− 1) ENTER (−)

2nd Y-VARS 1 3 ZOOM 5

We see from the graph that there are four points of intersection. Use ZOOM and TRACE to determine the points of intersection. The solutions are approximately $(-3.61, 3.46)$, $(3.61, 3.46)$, $(3.61, -3.46)$, and $(-3.61, -3.46)$.

EXERCISES

Use a graphing calculator to solve each system of equations. Round the coordinates to the nearest hundredth.

1. $x^2 + y^2 = 16$
$y = 2x^2 - 2$ $\quad(\pm 1.68, 3.63)$

2. $9x^2 - 4y^2 = 36$
$x^2 + 4y^2 = 36$ $\quad(\pm 2.68, \pm 2.68)$

3. $x^2 + 9y^2 = 9$
$y = x^2 - 1$ $\quad(0, -1), (\pm 1.36, 0.85)$

4. $x^2 + y^2 = 64$
$9y^2 - 4x^2 = 1$ $\quad(\pm 6.65, \pm 4.45)$

5. $(x - 1)^2 + y^2 = 9$
$x^2 + 64y^2 = 64$ $\quad(\pm 2.98, \pm 0.93)$

6. $y = -x^2 + 7$
$y = x^2 - 7$ $\quad(\pm 2.65, 0)$

7. $x = y^2 - 10y + 25$
$x^2 + y^2 = 25$ $\quad(0, 5), (4, 3)$

8. $x^2 + y^2 = 1$
$x^2 + y^2 = 45$ $\quad$ no solution

Lesson 7-7A Graphing Technology: Solving Quadratic Systems **459**

Assignment Guide

Core: 1–8
Enriched: 1–8

4 ASSESS

Observing students working with technology is an excellent method of assessment.

Using Technology
This lesson offers an excellent opportunity for using technology in your algebra classroom. For more information on using technology, see *Graphing Calculators in the Mathematics Classroom*, one of the titles in the Glencoe Mathematics Professional Series.

7-7 Solving Quadratic Systems

NCTM Standards: 1–5, 8

Instructional Resources

- Study Guide Master 7-7
- Practice Master 7-7
- Enrichment Master 7-7
- Assessment and Evaluation Masters, p. 185
- Tech Prep Applications Masters, p. 14

Transparency 7-7A contains the 5-Minute Check for this lesson; **Transparency 7-7B** contains a teaching aid for this lesson.

Recommended Pacing

Standard Pacing	Days 12 & 13 of 15
Honors Pacing	Day 11 of 13
Block Scheduling*	Day 6 of 7

*For more information on pacing and possible lesson plans, refer to the *Block Scheduling Booklet*.

1 FOCUS

5-Minute Check
(over Lesson 7-6)

Write each equation in standard form. State whether the graph of each equation is a hyperbola, a parabola, a circle, an ellipse, or none of these.

1. $\frac{(x-1)^2}{25} + (y+5)^2 = 1$ **ellipse**
2. $x^2 + y^2 = -9$ **none**
3. $x^2 - 4y^2 = 4$ **hyperbola**
4. $x^2 + 2x - 7 = y$ **parabola**
5. $x^2 - 8x - 3 = 4 - 6y - y^2$ **circle**

TEKS 3.a., 3.b., 3.c.

What YOU'LL LEARN

- To solve systems of equations involving quadratics graphically and algebraically, and
- to solve systems of inequalities involving quadratics graphically.

Why IT'S IMPORTANT

You can use quadratic systems of equations to solve problems involving chemistry and advertising.

fabulous FIRSTS

Rachel F. Brown (1898–1980)

Rachel F. Brown was the first woman to receive the Pioneer Chemist Award from the American Institute of Chemists. She discovered a vaccine for pneumonia and helped to isolate an antibiotic against fungal diseases.

CONNECTION
Chemistry

An important concept in chemistry, Boyle's Law, states that if the temperature of a gas is constant, the pressure exerted by the gas varies inversely as the volume. So, $PV = k$, where P represents pressure in kilopascals, V represents volume in cubic decimeters, and k is a constant. A medical technologist provides oxygen for patients with respiratory problems through a tank containing compressed oxygen. The constant for oxygen at 25°C is 504. The volume of the tank is 12 cubic decimeters. What is the pressure of the oxygen in the tank?

We can solve the system of equations described above by graphing to find the pressure in the tank. First write the system of equations.

$PV = k$ *Boyle's Law*
$PV = 504$ *The constant for oxygen at 25° C is 504.*
$V = 12$ *The volume of the tank is 12 dm³.*

Now graph $PV = 504$ and $V = 12$.

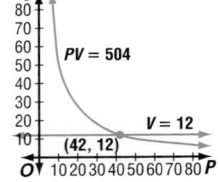

The point at which the line intersects the hyperbola is the solution.

The pressure is 42 kilopascals when the volume is 12 cubic decimeters.

Since a negative pressure or volume is impossible, we will only consider positive values of P and V.

If the graphs of a system of equations are a conic section and a straight line, the system will have zero, one, or two solutions.

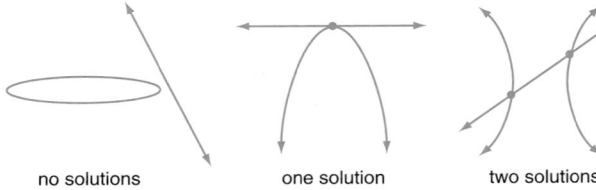

no solutions   one solution   two solutions

fabulous FIRSTS

Rachel Brown and Elizabeth Hazen announced the discovery of the antibiotic mystatin in 1950. It is used to cure athlete's foot, ringworm, and Dutch elm disease.

We have solved systems of linear equations graphically and algebraically. We can use similar methods to solve systems involving quadratic equations.

Example Solve the system of equations.
$$x^2 + 4y^2 = 25$$
$$2y + x = 1$$

Method 1: Graphing

The graph of the equation $x^2 + 4y^2 = 25$ is an ellipse with its center at the origin, a major axis of 10 units, and a minor axis of 5 units. The graph of the equation $2y + x = 1$ is a line with slope $-\frac{1}{2}$ and y-intercept $\frac{1}{2}$. The graph shows that there are two solutions for this system of equations. You can use the graph to estimate solutions of $(-3, 2)$ and $\left(4, -1\frac{1}{2}\right)$.

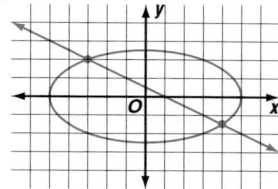

Method 2: Algebra

Use substitution to solve the system algebraically. First rewrite $2y + x = 1$ as $x = 1 - 2y$.

$$x^2 + 4y^2 = 25$$
$$(1 - 2y)^2 + 4y^2 = 25 \quad \text{\textit{Substitute } } 1 - 2y \text{ \textit{for} } x.$$
$$8y^2 - 4y - 24 = 0 \quad \text{\textit{Simplify.}}$$
$$2y^2 - y - 6 = 0 \quad \text{\textit{Divide each side by 4.}}$$
$$(2y + 3)(y - 2) = 0 \quad \text{\textit{Factor.}}$$

$$2y + 3 = 0 \quad \text{or} \quad y - 2 = 0 \quad \text{\textit{Zero product property}}$$
$$y = -\frac{3}{2} \qquad\qquad y = 2$$

Now solve for x.

$$x = 1 - 2y \qquad\qquad x = 1 - 2y$$
$$x = 1 - 2\left(-\frac{3}{2}\right) \qquad x = 1 - 2(2)$$
$$x = 4 \qquad\qquad\qquad x = -3$$

The solutions of the system of equations are $\left(4, -1\frac{1}{2}\right)$ and $(-3, 2)$.

Compare these to the graphical estimate.

If the graphs of a system of equations are two conic sections, the system will have zero, one, two, three, or four solutions.

no solutions

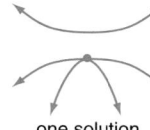
one solution

two solutions

three solutions

four solutions

Lesson 7–7   Solving Quadratic Systems **461**

GLENCOE Technology

 CD-ROM Interaction

A multimedia simulation links systems of quadratic equations with determining the path of an orbiting satellite. A blackline master activity with teacher's notes provides a follow-up to the CD-ROM simulation.

For Windows & Macintosh

Motivating the Lesson
Hands-On Activity Place twelve 1-cm squares on the overhead projector. The total area is 12 cm². Arrange them as 1 by 12, 2 by 6, and 3 by 4. Ask students to notice that the area remains constant but the perimeter changes. What is the greatest possible perimeter and the least possible perimeter? Try the same idea with a piece of string. Here, the perimeter remains constant and the area changes. What observations can they make? Make a graph with the data. Draw a best-fit curve. Discuss what the points on the graph represent and what the rest of the graph means.

2 TEACH

In-Class Example

For Example 1
Solve the system of equations by graphing and by algebra.
$$y = (x - 2)^2 + 1$$
$$y = -4x + 5 \quad (0, 5)$$

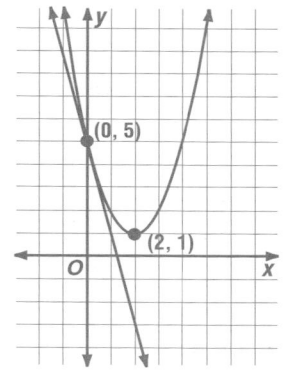

Teaching Tip Encourage students to check the solutions by substituting the values into both equations.

In-Class Examples

For Example 2
Solve the system of equations by graphing and by algebra.
$$4x^2 - y^2 = 36$$
$$(x - 5)^2 + y^2 = 64$$
$$(-3, 0), (5, 8), (5, -8)$$

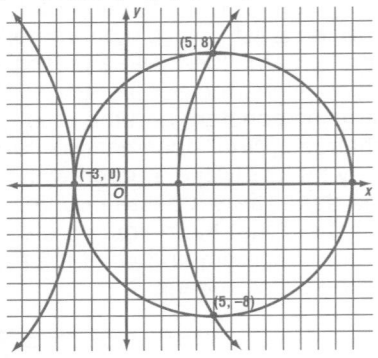

For Example 3
Solve the system of equations by any method. Use a graphing calculator to determine if the results are reasonable.
$$x^2 + y^2 = 9$$
$$5x - y = 0$$
$$\left(\frac{3}{\sqrt{26}}, \frac{15}{\sqrt{26}}\right),$$
$$\left(\frac{-3}{\sqrt{26}}, \frac{-15}{\sqrt{26}}\right)$$

Example ② Solve the system of equations.
$$5x^2 + y^2 = 30$$
$$y^2 - 16 = 9x^2$$

Method 1: Graphing

The graph of the equation $5x^2 + y^2 = 30$ is an ellipse with its center at the origin, a major axis of $2\sqrt{30}$ units, and a minor axis of $2\sqrt{6}$ units. The graph of the equation $y^2 - 16 = 9x^2$ is a hyperbola with its center at the origin, $a = 4$ and $b = \frac{4}{3}$.

The graph shows that there are four solutions for this system of equation, which appear to be $(1, 5)$, $(-1, 5)$, $(1, -5)$, and $(-1, -5)$.

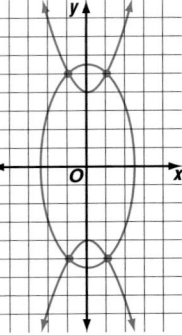

Method 2: Algebra

Use the elimination method to solve the system algebraically.

$$5x^2 + y^2 = 30 \qquad \rightarrow \qquad 5x^2 + y^2 = 30$$
$$y^2 - 16 = 9x^2 \qquad\qquad\qquad \underline{(+)\ 9x^2 - y^2 = -16}$$
$$ 14x^2 = 14$$
$$x^2 = 1$$
$$x = \pm 1$$

Substitute 1 and -1 for x and solve for y.

$$5x^2 + y^2 = 30 \qquad\qquad\qquad\qquad 5x^2 + y^2 = 30$$
$$5(1)^2 + y^2 = 30 \qquad\qquad\qquad\qquad 5(-1)^2 + y^2 = 30$$
$$y^2 = 25 \qquad\qquad\qquad\qquad y^2 = 25$$
$$y = \pm 5 \qquad\qquad\qquad\qquad y = \pm 5$$

The solutions are $(1, 5)$, $(-1, 5)$, $(1, -5)$, and $(-1, -5)$, which agree with the graph.

Example ③ **Solve the system of equations by any method. Use a graphing calculator to determine if the results are reasonable.**
$$x + 4 = (y - 2)^2$$
$$2y + x = 0$$

Rewrite $2y + x = 0$ as $x = -2y$.

$$x + 4 = (y - 2)^2$$
$$-2y + 4 = (y - 2)^2 \qquad\qquad \textit{Substitute } -2y \textit{ for x.}$$
$$-2y + 4 = y^2 - 4y + 4$$
$$y^2 - 2y = 0$$
$$y(y - 2) = 0 \qquad\qquad\qquad \textit{Factor.}$$

$$y = 0 \quad \text{ or } \quad y - 2 = 0 \qquad \textit{Zero product property}$$
$$y = 2$$

If $y = 0$, then $x = -2(0)$ or 0. If $y = 2$, then $x = -2(2)$ or -4. Thus, the solutions are $(0, 0)$ and $(-4, 2)$.

Check by graphing in the standard viewing window. First solve each equation for y.

$$x + 4 = (y - 2)^2 \qquad 2y + x = 0$$
$$\pm\sqrt{x + 4} = y - 2 \qquad 2y = -x$$
$$\pm\sqrt{x + 4} + 2 = y \qquad y = -\frac{x}{2}$$

Enter: [Y=] [(−)] [X,T,θ] [÷] 2 [ENTER]

[2nd] [√] [(] [X,T,θ] [+] 4

[)] [+] 2 [ENTER] [(−)] [2nd] [√]

[(] [X,T,θ] [+] 4 [)] [+]

2 [ZOOM] 6

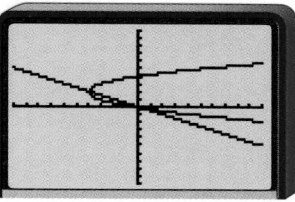

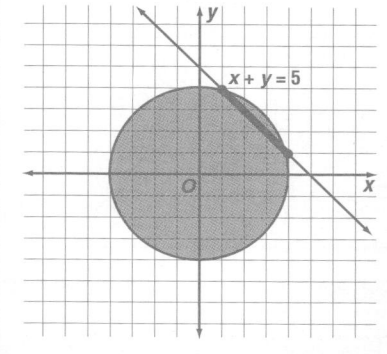

In-Class Example

For Example 4
A spring shower brings rain to a circular area with a radius of 4 miles. Assume the center of the circle is at the origin. If a walker walks on a path described by $x + y = 5$, show when the walker needs rain gear.

Example ④

APPLICATION

Mirrors

A hyperbolic mirror is a mirror in the shape of one branch of a hyperbola. Such a mirror reflects light rays directed at one focus toward the other focus. Suppose a hyperbolic mirror is modeled by the upper branch of the hyperbola whose equation is $\frac{y^2}{9} - \frac{x^2}{16} = 1$. A light source is located at $(-8, 0)$. Where should the light from this source hit the mirror so that the light will be reflected to $(0, -5)$?

The foci of the hyperbola are at $(0, 5)$ and $(0, -5)$. In order for the light to be reflected to the focus at $(0, -5)$, it must be directed at the other focus at $(0, 5)$. The equation of the line that passes through $(-8, 0)$ and $(0, 5)$ is $y = \frac{5}{8}x + 5$. Solve the system of equations $\frac{y^2}{9} - \frac{x^2}{16} = 1$ and $y = \frac{5}{8}x + 5$ by using substitution.

$$\frac{y^2}{9} - \frac{x^2}{16} = 1$$
$$16y^2 - 9x^2 = 144 \quad \textit{Multiply each side by 144.}$$
$$16\left(\frac{5}{8}x + 5\right)^2 - 9x^2 = 144 \quad \textit{Substitute } \left(\frac{5}{8}x + 5\right) \textit{ for y.}$$
$$\frac{25}{4}x^2 + 100x + 400 - 9x^2 = 144 \quad \textit{Simplify.}$$
$$25x^2 + 400x + 1600 - 36x^2 = 576 \quad \textit{Multiply each side by 4.}$$
$$11x^2 - 400x - 1024 = 0$$

Use the quadratic formula.

$$x = \frac{-(-400) \pm \sqrt{(-400)^2 - 4(11)(-1024)}}{2(11)} \quad \textit{a = 11, b = -400, and c = -1024.}$$
$$= \frac{200 \pm 24\sqrt{89}}{11}$$

The value of x is about 38.8 or about -2.4. The closest point for the light to hit the mirror is where x equals about -2.4 and y equals about $\frac{5}{8}(-2.4) + 5$ or 3.5.

In-Class Example

For Example 5
Solve the system of inequalities by graphing.
$10 \geq (x - 5)^2 + 2y$
$y \geq -2x + 9$

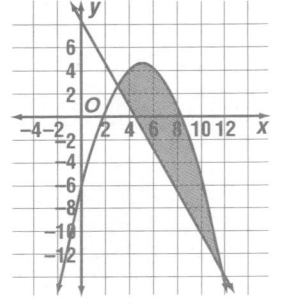

You have learned how to solve systems of linear inequalities by graphing. You can use a similar method when the inequalities involve conic sections.

Example **5** **Solve the system of inequalities by graphing.**

$9x^2 + y^2 < 81$
$x^2 + y^2 \geq 16$

The graph of $9x^2 + y^2 < 81$ is the interior of the ellipse $9x^2 + y^2 = 81$. This region is shaded in blue.

The graph of $x^2 + y^2 \geq 16$ is the circle $x^2 + y^2 = 16$ and its exterior. This region is shaded in yellow.

The intersection of these two graphs represents the solutions for the system of inequalities.

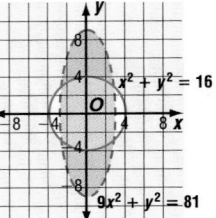

3 PRACTICE/APPLY

Check for Understanding
Exercises 1–14 are designed to help you assess your students' understanding through reading, writing, speaking, and modeling. You should work through Exercises 1–5 with your students and then monitor their work on Exercises 6–14.

Additional Answers

1. Problems whose answers are *not* easily determined by looking at the graph; the graph helps to determine the number of answers and their approximate values.
2. There is no solution. You may get a complex solution when solving the system algebraically.
3. Sample answer:
   $y = x^2$
   $(x - 4)^2 + (y - 4)^2 = 4$
   $\dfrac{(x - 6)^2}{16} + \dfrac{(y - 4)^2}{4} = 1$

CHECK FOR UNDERSTANDING

Communicating Mathematics

Study the lesson. Then complete the following.   1–3. See margin.

1. **Describe** a situation in which you would choose to solve a system of quadratic equations algebraically rather than graphically. How would a graph of the equations help you to find the algebraic solutions?

2. **Describe** the algebraic solution if the graphs of a system of quadratic equations do *not* intersect.

3. **Write** equations for two different conic sections that intersect at the point (2, 4).

4. The blue region of the graph at the right represents the solution of $x^2 + y^2 \leq 25$ and the yellow region represents the solution of $4y + x^2 \leq 25$. What does the green region represent?   the solution of the system of inequalities or the points that are solutions to both inequalities

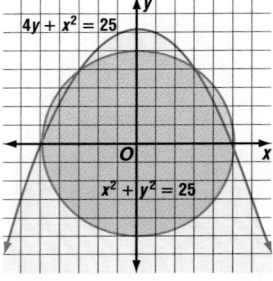

5. List the possible number of intersections for each pair of graphs and then draw an example for each possibility.   a–d. See Solutions Manual.

   a. a circle and a line
   b. a parabola and a circle
   c. an ellipse and a hyperbola
   d. a parabola and a hyperbola

Guided Practice

Name the type of conic section represented by each equation. Then solve the system algebraically.

6. circle, line; (3, 4), (−4, −3)
7. ellipse, hyperbola; $\left(\dfrac{\pm\sqrt{39}}{2}, \dfrac{\pm\sqrt{3}}{2} \right)$

6. $x^2 + y^2 = 25$
   $y - x = 1$

7. $x^2 + 3y^2 = 12$
   $x^2 - y^2 = 9$

8. $2x^2 - 2y^2 = 72$ hyperbola,
   $4y^2 + x^2 = 25$ ellipse; no solution

9. $3x = 8y^2$ parabola, hyperbola; no
   $8y^2 - 2x^2 = 16$ solution

Reteaching

Using Predictions After students solve a quadratic system algebraically, have them predict or sketch the graph of the quadratic system. Then use a graphing utility (graphing calculator or computer program) to see the solutions.

Solve each system of equations algebraically. Check your solutions with a graphing calculator.

10. $y = x + 2$
$y = x^2$ $(-1, 1), (2, 4)$

11. $5x^2 + y^2 = 30$
$9x^2 - y^2 = -16$ $(\pm 1, \pm 5)$

Solve each system of inequalities by graphing.   12–13. See margin.

12. $x^2 + y^2 < 25$
$4x^2 - 9y^2 < 36$

13. $y^2 < x$
$x^2 - 4y^2 < 16$

14. Write the system of equations represented by the graph at the right. $y = x^2 - 4, y = 3x$

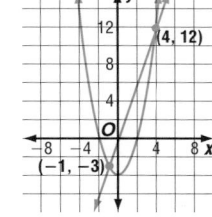

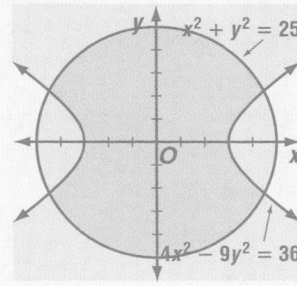

Assignment Guide

Core: 15–53 odd, 54–63
Enriched: 16–50 even, 51–63

For **Extra Practice,** see p. 894.

The red A, B, and C flags, printed only in the Teacher's Wraparound Edition, indicate the level of difficulty of the exercises.

Additional Answers

12.

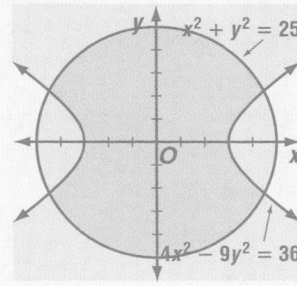

13.

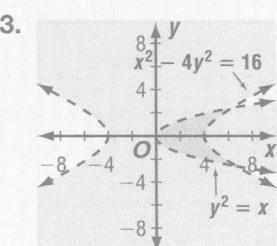

EXERCISES

Practice

Solve each system of equations algebraically. Check your solutions with a graphing calculator.

16. $\left(\frac{3}{2}, \frac{9}{2}\right), (-1, 2)$ **A**

15. $y = 6$
$y^2 = x^2 + 9$ $(\pm 3\sqrt{3}, 6)$

16. $y = 2x^2$
$y = x + 3$

17. $y^2 = x^2 - 25$
$x^2 - y^2 = 7$ no solution

18. $4x^2 + y^2 = 100$
$4x + y^2 = 20$ $(5, 0), (-4, \pm 6)$

19. $x^2 + y^2 = 64$
$x^2 + 64y^2 = 64$ $(\pm 8, 0)$

20. $x + 4 = (y - 1)^2$
$x + y + 1 = 0$ $(-3, 2), (0, -1)$

21. $y^2 = x^2 - 7$
$x^2 + y^2 = 25$ $(\pm 4, \pm 3)$

22. $y = 7 - x$
$y^2 + x^2 = 9$ no solution

23. $(5, \pm 2), (-1, \pm 4)$

23. $x^2 + 2y^2 = 33$
$x^2 + y^2 - 19 = 2x$

24. $x = (y - 3)^2 + 2$
$y + x = 5$ $(2, 3), (3, 2)$

B

25. $\frac{x^2}{30} + \frac{y^2}{6} = 1$
$x = y$ $(\sqrt{5}, \sqrt{5}), (-\sqrt{5}, -\sqrt{5})$

26. $\frac{x^2}{36} - \frac{y^2}{4} = 1$
$x = y$ no solution

27. $(-1+\sqrt{17}, 1+\sqrt{17}), (-1-\sqrt{17}, 1-\sqrt{17})$

28. $(\pm 2, \pm \sqrt{3})$

27. $x^2 + y^2 = 36$
$y = x + 2$

28. $3x^2 - y^2 = 9$
$x^2 + 2y^2 = 10$

29. $x^2 + y^2 = 36$
$8y = x^2 - 79$ no solution

30. $y = -x^2 + 3$
$x^2 + 4y^2 = 36$ $(0, 3), (\pm 2.40; -2.75)$

32. $(6, 3), (6, 1), (-4, 0), (-4, 4)$

31. $x^2 + 2y^2 = 16$
$y^2 + 2x^2 = 17$ $(\pm \sqrt{6}, \pm \sqrt{5})$

32. $3x^2 - 20y^2 - 12x + 80y - 96 = 0$
$3x^2 + 20y^2 = 80y + 48$

33–38. See Solutions Manual.

Solve each system of inequalities by graphing.

33. $x^2 + y^2 \geq 4$
$x^2 + y^2 \leq 36$

34. $x^2 + y^2 \leq 25$
$x + 2y \geq 1$

35. $x + y = 4$
$9x^2 - 4y^2 \geq 36$

36. $4x^2 + 9y^2 \geq 36$
$4y^2 + 9x^2 \leq 36$

37. $(y - 3)^2 \geq x + 2$
$x^2 \leq y + 4$

38. $(x + 2)^2 + 16(y + 3)^2 \geq 16$
$x + y = 0$

Lesson 7–7 Solving Quadratic Systems   **465**

Study Guide Masters, p. 55

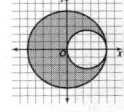

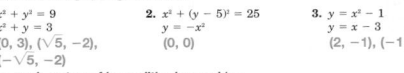

NAME_____ DATE _____

7-7   **Study Guide**   Student Edition Pages 460–467

Solving Quadratic Systems

You can use algebra to find exact solutions for systems of quadratic equations. For systems of inequalities, it is usually best to show the solution set with a graph.

Example: Use algebra to find the solutions of the system $\begin{cases} x^2 + y^2 = 25 \\ y - x = 1 \end{cases}$.

Solve $y - x = 1$ to get $y = x + 1$.

$x^2 + (x + 1)^2 = 25$	Substitute $x + 1$ for y.
$2x^2 + 2x - 24 = 0$	Simplify. Add -25 to both sides.
$2(x + 4)(x - 3) = 0$	Factor.
$x + 4 = 0$ or $x - 3 = 0$	Zero Product Property
$x = -4$ $x = 3$	Solve for x.
$y = -3$ $y = 4$	Substitute for x in $y = 1 + x$.

The solutions are $(-4, -3)$ and $(3, 4)$.

Example: Solve the system $\begin{cases} x^2 + y^2 \leq 25 \\ \left(x - \frac{5}{2}\right)^2 + y^2 \geq \frac{25}{4} \end{cases}$ by graphing.

The graph of $x^2 + y^2 \leq 25$ consists of all points on or inside the circle with center $(0, 0)$ and radius 5. The graph of $\left(x - \frac{5}{2}\right)^2 + y^2 \geq \frac{25}{4}$ consists of all points on or outside the circle with center $\left(\frac{5}{2}, 0\right)$ and radius $\frac{5}{2}$. The solution of the system is the set of points in both regions.

Solve each system of equations, algebraically. Check your solutions with a graphing calculator.

1. $x^2 + y^2 = 9$
$x^2 + y = 3$
$(0, 3), (\sqrt{5}, -2), (-\sqrt{5}, -2)$

2. $x^2 + (y - 5)^2 = 25$
$y = -x^2$
$(0, 0)$

3. $y = x^2 - 1$
$y = x - 3$
$(2, -1), (-1, -4)$

Solve each system of inequalities by graphing.

4. $x^2 + y^2 \leq 169$
$x^2 + 9y^2 \leq 225$

5. $\frac{x^2}{16} + \frac{y^2}{4} \leq 1$
$y > \frac{1}{2}x - 2$

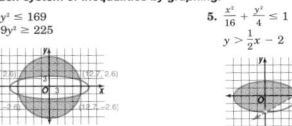

Additional Answers

39. $y = -x - 1$
   $x = (y - 1)^2 - 4$

40. $\frac{x^2}{16} - \frac{y^2}{4} = 1$
   $y = 3x - 3$

41. $y = -2x^2$
   $x^2 + y^2 = 5$

42. $x^2 + y^2 \geq 9$
   $y \geq \frac{1}{2}x + 1$

43. $x^2 + y^2 \geq 25$
   $x^2 + y^2 \leq 100$

44. $x^2 + y^2 \geq 16$
   $x + y = 2$

46. $y = x^2$
   $x = (y - 2)^2$

47. $x^2 + y^2 = 36$
   $\frac{(x + 2)^2}{16} - \frac{y^2}{4} = 1$

48. $x^2 + y^2 = 100$
   $\frac{x^2}{16} + \frac{y^2}{4} = 1$

49. $x^2 + y^2 = 81$
   $\frac{x^2}{4} + \frac{y^2}{100} = 1$

50. $\frac{x^2}{64} + \frac{y^2}{36} = 1$
   $\frac{x^2}{64} - \frac{y^2}{16} = 1$

Practice Masters, p. 55

NAME_____ DATE _____

7-7 **Practice** Student Edition Pages 460–467

Solving Quadratic Systems

Solve each system of equations.

1. $(x - 2)^2 + y^2 = 5$
   $x - y = 1$
   $(0, -1), (3, 2)$

2. $x = 2(y + 1)^2 - 6$
   $x + 3y = 5$
   $(2, 1), \left(\frac{37}{2}, -\frac{9}{2}\right)$

3. $y^2 - 3x^2 = 6$
   $y = 2x - 1$
   $(-1, -3), (5, 9)$

4. $x + 2y^2 = 4$
   $y = -x + 1$
   $(2, -1), \left(-\frac{1}{2}, \frac{3}{2}\right)$

Graph each system of equations. Then find the solutions of each system.

5. $y = x^2$
   $y = -x + 2$ $(-2, 4), (1, 1)$

6. $4y^2 - 9x^2 = 36$
   $4x^2 - 9y^2 = 36$ No solutions

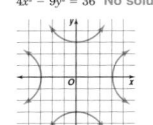

Solve each system of inequalities by graphing.

7. $x^2 + y^2 < 36$
   $x^2 + y^2 \geq 16$

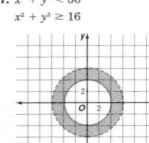

8. $\frac{(x + 2)^2}{4} + \frac{(y - 3)^2}{16} \leq 1$
   $(x + 1)^2 + (y - 2)^2 \leq 4$

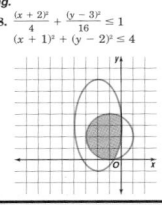

39–44. See margin.

Write the system of equations or inequalities represented by each graph.

39.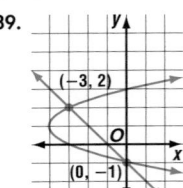

40.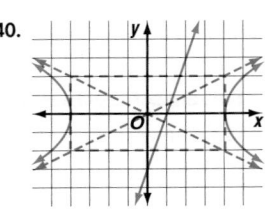

41.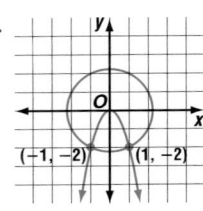

42.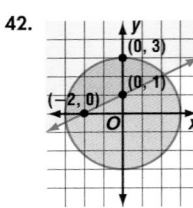

43.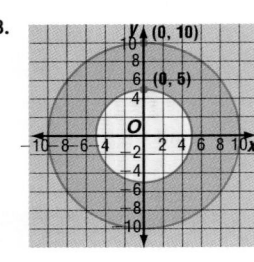

44.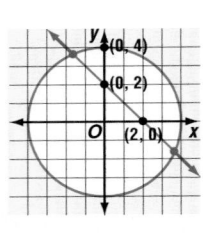

46–50. See margin for sample answers.

Graphing Calculator

Write a system of equations that will satisfy each condition stated. Use a graphing calculator to verify that you are correct.

45. two circles that intersect in three points   impossible

46. two parabolas that intersect in two points

47. a hyperbola and a circle that intersect in three points

48. a circle and an ellipse that do not intersect

49. a circle and an ellipse that intersect in four points

50. a hyperbola and an ellipse that intersect in two points

Critical Thinking

51. Solve each system of equations.

a. $x + y^2 = 2$
   $2y - 2\sqrt{2} = x(\sqrt{2} + 2)$
   $(-2, -2), (0, \sqrt{2})$

b. $x^2 + y^2 = 1$
   $y = 3x + 1$
   $x^2 + (y + 1)^2 = 4$ (0, 1)

Applications and Problem Solving

52. **Advertising**   The corporate logo for CBS Inc. is shown at the right. It is similar to a small circle and its interior, an ellipse and its exterior, and a large circle and its interior. Write three inequalities that, when graphed, will model the CBS logo on a coordinate plane.   Sample answer:
$x^2 + y^2 \leq 4$, $\frac{x^2}{16} + \frac{y^2}{4} \geq 1$, $x^2 + y^2 \leq 16$

53. (40, 30)

53. **Seismology**   Three tracking stations have detected an earthquake in an area. The first station is located at the origin on the map. Each grid in the map represents one square mile. The second tracking station is located at (0, 30) while the third station is located at (35, 18). The epicenter was 50 miles from the first station, 40 miles from the second station, and 13 miles from the third station. Where was the epicenter of the earthquake located?

Extension

Problem Solving   Find a such that there is a unique point of intersection of the two circles represented by $x^2 + y^2 = 4$ and $(x - 2)^2 + (y - 2)^2 = a$.
$a = 12 - 8\sqrt{2}$ or $a = 12 + 8\sqrt{2}$

Tech Prep

Navigator   Students who are interested in navigation—the science of guiding ships, airplanes, or spacecraft—may wish to do further research into the use of mathematics within that field, as mentioned in Exercise 54. For more information on tech prep, see the *Teacher's Handbook*.

Mixed Review

54. **Astronomy** In the early 1600s, Johann Kepler studied the orbits of the planets and determined that they were elliptical. It is now known that orbits can take the shape of any of the conic sections. The equations of different orbits are listed below. State the shape of each orbit. (Lesson 7–6)
 a. $x^2 + y^2 = 75,000$ **circle**   **b.** $y - x^2 = 3x + 5$ **parabola**

55. Find the standard deviation for {5.2, 5.7, 6.0, 5.6, 2.4}. (Lesson 6–8) **1.3**

56. Graph $2x^2 - x - 6 < y$. (Lesson 6–7) **See margin.**

57. Simplify $\frac{5ab^2 - 4ab + 7a^2b}{ab}$. (Lesson 5–3) $5b - 4 + 7a$

58. Find $[2\ -5\ 7] - [-3\ 8\ -1]$. (Lesson 4–2) $[5\ -13\ 8]$

59. Solve the system of equations algebraically. (Lesson 3–2) **(2, 3)**
$$\tfrac{1}{2}x + \tfrac{1}{3}y = 2$$
$$x - y = -1$$

60. Find a and b so there is no solution to the system $5x - 4y = 12$ and $bx + ay = 3$. (Lesson 3–1) **Sample answer: $a = -4$, $b = 5$**

61a. See margin for graph; Sample answer: $y = 4.4x - 8305$

61b. Sample answer: 8 h 15 min

62. $m = \frac{7}{3}n - 2$

61. **Statistics** The chart at the right shows the average amount of time each day that people watch television for the given years. (Lesson 2–5)
 a. Draw a scatter plot and find a prediction equation for the data.
 b. Predict the viewing time for the year 2000.

62. Solve $3m + 2 = 7n - 4$ for m. (Lesson 2–2)

63. Solve $-\frac{16}{19}k = 8$. (Lesson 1–4) $-\frac{19}{2}$

Year	Average Viewing Time
1950	4 h 35 min
1955	4 h 51 min
1960	5 h 6 min
1965	5 h 29 min
1970	5 h 56 min
1975	6 h 7 min
1980	6 h 36 min
1985	7 h 10 min

Mathematics and SOCIETY

Asteroids and Comets

The article below appeared in *Science News* on February 5, 1994.

AN ESTIMATED 2,000 ASTEROIDS LARGER than 1 kilometer follow orbits that cross that of Earth. Are any of these rocky missiles headed on a collision course with our planet? The impact, equivalent to the destructive power of 10,000 megatons of TNT, would dramatically disrupt life on our planet. . . . Clark R. Chapman of the Planetary Science Institute in Tucson, Ariz., and David Morrison of NASA's Ames Research Center in Mountain View, Calif., calculate that there is a 1-in-10,000 chance that a 2-km-wide asteroid or comet will collide with Earth during the next century. . . . A rocky body measuring 100 meters across could hit home about once every 100 to 200 years. ■

1–3. See Solutions Manual.

1. How do you think scientists can calculate the probability that Earth will be struck by an asteroid or comet?

2. What types of damage could result if a large asteroid or comet collided with Earth? What would affect the amount of damage?

3. If we discovered that a large asteroid or comet were on a collision course with Earth, what, if anything, could be done about it?

Lesson 7–7 Solving Quadratic Systems **467**

Mathematics and SOCIETY

Asteroids are relatively small rocky objects that orbit the sun between Mars and Jupiter. Their origin is still unknown, though there are two dominant theories. The first theory regards asteroids as the debris from a broken-up planet. The second theory regards asteroids as particles that never fused into a planet when the solar system was forming.

---

4 ASSESS

Closing Activity
Speaking Describe what you would do to decide which method to use to solve a system of equations.

Chapter 7, Quiz D (Lesson 7-7), is available in the *Assessment and Evaluation Masters*, p. 185.

Additional Answers

56.
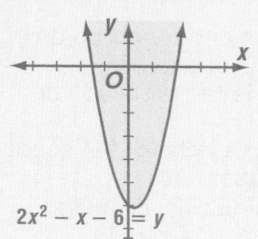
$2x^2 - x - 6 = y$

61a.
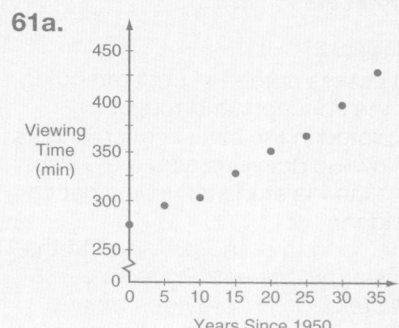
Years Since 1950

Enrichment Masters, p. 55

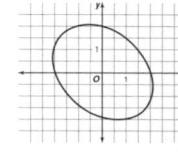

7-7 NAME_____ DATE_____
Enrichment Student Edition Pages 460–467

Graphing Quadratic Equations with xy-Terms

You can use a graphing calculator to examine graphs of quadratic equations that contain xy-terms.

Example: Use a graphing calculator to display the graph of $x^2 + xy + y^2 = 4$.

Solve the equation for y in terms of x by using the quadratic formula.
$$y^2 + xy + (x^2 - 4) = 0$$

To use the formula, let $a = 1$, $b = x$, and $c = (x^2 - 4)$.
$$y = \frac{-x \pm \sqrt{x^2 - 4(1)(x^2 - 4)}}{2}$$
$$y = \frac{-x \pm \sqrt{16 - 3x^2}}{2}$$

To graph the equation on the graphing calculator, enter the two equations:
$$y = \frac{-x + \sqrt{16 - 3x^2}}{2} \text{ and } y = \frac{-x - \sqrt{16 - 3x^2}}{2}$$

Use a graphing calculator to display the graphs of the following equations. State the type of curve each graph represents.

1. $y^2 + xy = 8$ hyperbola
2. $x^2 + y^2 - 2xy - x = 0$ parabola
3. $x^2 - xy + y^2 = 15$ ellipse
4. $x^2 + xy + y^2 = -9$ graph is ∅
5. $2x^2 - 2xy - y^2 + 4x = 20$ hyperbola
6. $x^2 - xy - 2y^2 + 2x + 5y - 3 = 0$ two intersecting lines

Chapter 7 **467**

In·ves·ti·ga·tion

TEACHER NOTES

Closing the Investigation

This activity provides students an opportunity to bring their work on the Investigation to a close. For each Investigation, students should present their findings to the class. Here are some ways students can display their work.

- Conduct and report on an interview or survey.
- Write a letter, proposal, or report.
- Write an article for the school or local paper.
- Make a display, including graphs and/or charts.
- Plan an activity.

Assessment

To assess students' understanding of the concepts and topics explored in the Investigation and its follow-up activities, you may wish to examine students' Investigation Folders.

The scoring guide provided in the *Investigations and Projects Masters*, p. 11, provides means for you to score students' work on the Investigation.

Investigations and Projects Masters, p. 11

Scoring Guide
Chapters 6 and 7
Investigation

Level	Specific Criteria
3 Superior	• Shows thorough understanding of the concepts of a *parabola, vertex, focus, writing an equation,* and *using a formula*. • Uses appropriate strategies to solve problems. • Computations are correct. • Written explanations are exemplary. • Formulas and blueprints are appropriate and sensible. • Goes beyond the requirements of some or all problems.
2 Satisfactory, with Minor Flaws	• Shows understanding of the concepts of a *parabola, vertex, focus, writing an equation,* and *using a formula*. • Uses appropriate strategies to solve problems. • Computations are mostly correct. • Written explanations are effective. • Formulas and blueprints are appropriate and sensible. • Satisfies the requirements of problems.
1 Nearly Satisfactory, with Obvious Flaws	• Shows understanding of most of the concepts of a *parabola, vertex, focus, writing an equation,* and *using a formula*. • May not use appropriate strategies to solve problems. • Computations are mostly correct. • Written explanations are satisfactory. • Formulas and blueprints are appropriate and sensible. • Satisfies the requirements of problems.
0 Unsatisfactory	• Shows little or no understanding of the concepts of a *parabola, vertex, focus, writing an equation,* and *using a formula*. • May not use appropriate strategies to solve problems. • Computations are incorrect. • Written explanations are not satisfactory. • Formulas and blueprints are not appropriate or sensible. • Does not satisfy the requirements of problems.

---

the River Canyon Bridge

Refer to the Investigation on pages 328–329.

When a bridge project is proposed to a department of highways, the department employs engineers, geologists, surveyors, engineers, and electronic draftsmen to work together to develop the plans for the bridge. Cost factors are examined as well as the feasibility of the building site. Traffic patterns are studied and weight limits are imposed. Many of the skills you have used in the exploration are used by the professionals to determine the correct bridge for the canyon highway.

Analyze

You have conducted experiments and organized your data in various ways. It is now time to analyze your findings and state your conclusions.

PORTFOLIO ASSESSMENT

You may want to keep your work on this Investigation in your portfolio.

1 Select one of your designs or create a new design that represents the best bridge for this location.

2 Build a two-dimensional model of the bridge using the building materials described in the Investigation. Cut a large rectangle from the cardboard box. Draw in a picture of the canyon. Build the model on top of the cardboard by using glue to anchor the pipe cleaners and string. Measure and calculate accurately, following your blueprint as closely as possible.

3 How does this model compare with the one you originally built in the Investigation?

468 Chapter 7 Analyzing Conic Sections

Write

Once your model is completed, finish the project by completing the following.

4 Write a narrative describing the features and dimensions of your bridge. Justify why this design was chosen and why others were discarded.

5 Explain how you designed your model and how you used mathematics to plan its construction. Discuss the design of your bridge and why you believe it is sturdy and structurally sound.

6 Explain the process you used to construct your model.

A completed project should include:

- an accurately drawn blueprint, complete with labeled dimensions of the bridge and the parabolic equations that represent the arch of the bridge,

- a model of the bridge over the canyon, constructed to scale and following the designs and dimensions of your blueprint, and a well-written narrative describing the features, dimensions, and process of construction as outlined above.

VOCABULARY

After completing this chapter, you should be able to define each term, property, or phrase and give an example or two of each.

Algebra

asymptotes (p. 441)
center of a circle (p. 423)
center of an ellipse (p. 432)
center of an hyperbola (p. 441)
circle (p. 423)
concentric circles (p. 426)
conic section (p. 415)
conjugate axis (p. 441)

directrix (p. 415)
distance formula (p. 409)
ellipse (p. 431)
foci of an ellipse (p. 431)
foci of a hyperbola (p. 440)
focus of a parabola (p. 415)
hyperbola (p. 440)
latus rectum (p. 417)
major axis (p. 432)
midpoint formula (p. 410)

minor axis (p. 432)
parabola (p. 415)
radius (p. 423)
tangent (p. 425)
transverse axis (p. 441)
vertex (p. 441)

Problem Solving

use a simulation (p. 452)

1–15. See Solutions Manual for correct statements.

UNDERSTANDING AND USING THE VOCABULARY

Tell whether each statement is true or false. If the statement is false, correct it to make it true. 5. true

1. An ellipse is the set of all points in a plane such that the sum of the distances from two given points in the plane, called the foci, is constant. **true**

2. The equation of a circle is $(x - k)^2 - (y - h)^2 = r^2$. **false**

3. The transverse axis is the line segment of a hyperbola of length $2a$ that has its endpoints at the vertices of the hyperbola. **true**

4. The major axis is the longer of the two axes of symmetry of an ellipse. **true**

5. The formula used to find the distance between two points is given by $d = \sqrt{(x_2 - x_1)^2 + (y_2 - y_1)^2}$.

6. A tangent line is a line that intersects a circle in exactly two points. **false**

7. A parabola is the set of all points that are the same distance from a given point called the directrix and a given line called the focus. **false**

8. The radius is the distance from the center of a circle to any point on the circle. **true**

9. The conjugate axis is the line segment parallel to the transverse axis. **false**

10. A conic section is formed by slicing a hollow double cone with a plane. **true**

11. A hyperbola is the set of all points in a plane such that the absolute values of the sum of the distances from any point on the hyperbola to two given points is twice the distance of the conjugate axis. **false**

12. An asymptote is a line that a curve approaches before changing directions. **false**

13. The midpoint formula is given by the following: $\left(\dfrac{x_1 - x_2}{2}, \dfrac{y_1 - y_2}{2}\right)$. **false**

14. The set of all points in a plane that are equidistant from a given point in a plane, called the center, form a circle. **true**

15. The equation of a conic section is given by $Ax^2 + Bxy + Cy^2 + Dx + Ey + F = 0$. **true**

Instructional Resources

Three multiple-choice tests and three free-response tests are provided in the *Assessment and Evaluation Masters*. Forms 1A and 2A are for honors pacing, and Forms 1B, 1C, 2B, and 2C are for average pacing. Chapter 7 Test, Form 1B is shown at the right. Chapter 7 Test, Form 2B is shown on the next page.

Using the CHAPTER HIGHLIGHTS

The Chapter Highlights begins with a listing of the new terms, properties, and phrases that were introduced in this chapter. Have students define each term and provide an example or two of it, if appropriate.

Assessment and Evaluation Masters, pp. 171, 172

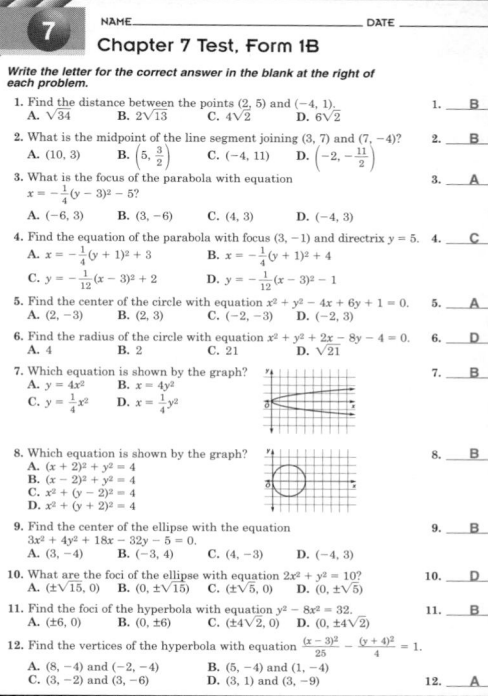

7 NAME_____ DATE_____

Chapter 7 Test, Form 1B

Write the letter for the correct answer in the blank at the right of each problem.

1. Find the distance between the points $(2, 5)$ and $(-4, 1)$.   1. __B__
   A. $\sqrt{34}$ B. $2\sqrt{13}$ C. $4\sqrt{2}$ D. $6\sqrt{2}$

2. What is the midpoint of the line segment joining $(3, 7)$ and $(7, -4)$?   2. __B__
   A. $(10, 3)$ B. $\left(5, \frac{3}{2}\right)$ C. $(-4, 11)$ D. $\left(-2, -\frac{11}{2}\right)$

3. What is the focus of the parabola with equation $x = -\frac{1}{4}(y - 3)^2 - 5$?   3. __A__
   A. $(-6, 3)$ B. $(3, -6)$ C. $(4, 3)$ D. $(-4, 3)$

4. Find the equation of the parabola with focus $(3, -1)$ and directrix $y = 5$.   4. __C__
   A. $x = -\frac{1}{4}(y + 1)^2 + 3$ B. $x = -\frac{1}{4}(y + 1)^2 + 4$
   C. $y = -\frac{1}{12}(x - 3)^2 + 2$ D. $y = -\frac{1}{12}(x - 3)^2 - 1$

5. Find the center of the circle with equation $x^2 + y^2 - 4x + 6y + 1 = 0$.   5. __A__
   A. $(2, -3)$ B. $(2, 3)$ C. $(-2, -3)$ D. $(-2, 3)$

6. Find the radius of the circle with equation $x^2 + y^2 + 2x - 8y - 4 = 0$.   6. __D__
   A. 4   B. 2   C. 21   D. $\sqrt{21}$

7. Which equation is shown by the graph?   7. __B__
   A. $y = 4x^2$ B. $x = 4y^2$
   C. $y = \frac{1}{4}x^2$ D. $x = \frac{1}{4}y^2$

8. Which equation is shown by the graph?   8. __B__
   A. $(x + 2)^2 + y^2 = 4$
   B. $(x - 2)^2 + y^2 = 4$
   C. $x^2 + (y - 2)^2 = 4$
   D. $x^2 + (y + 2)^2 = 4$

9. Find the center of the ellipse with the equation $3x^2 + 4y^2 + 18x - 32y - 5 = 0$.   9. __B__
   A. $(3, -4)$ B. $(-3, 4)$ C. $(4, -3)$ D. $(-4, 3)$

10. What are the foci of the ellipse with equation $2x^2 + y^2 = 10$?   10. __D__
    A. $(\pm\sqrt{15}, 0)$ B. $(0, \pm\sqrt{15})$ C. $(\pm\sqrt{5}, 0)$ D. $(0, \pm\sqrt{5})$

11. Find the foci of the hyperbola with equation $y^2 - 8x^2 = 32$.   11. __B__
    A. $(\pm 6, 0)$ B. $(0, \pm 6)$ C. $(\pm 4\sqrt{2}, 0)$ D. $(0, \pm 4\sqrt{2})$

12. Find the vertices of the hyperbola with equation $\frac{(x - 3)^2}{25} - \frac{(y + 4)^2}{4} = 1$.   12. __A__
    A. $(8, -4)$ and $(-2, -4)$ B. $(5, -4)$ and $(1, -4)$
    C. $(3, -2)$ and $(3, -6)$ D. $(3, 1)$ and $(3, -9)$

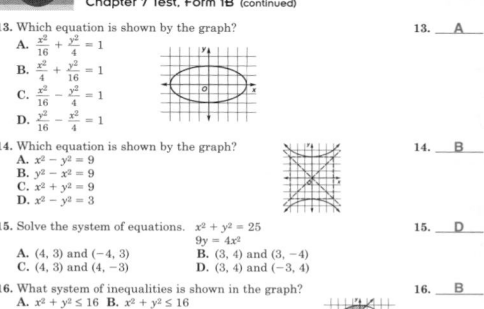

7 NAME_____ DATE_____

Chapter 7 Test, Form 1B (continued)

13. Which equation is shown by the graph?   13. __A__
    A. $\frac{x^2}{16} + \frac{y^2}{4} = 1$
    B. $\frac{x^2}{4} + \frac{y^2}{16} = 1$
    C. $\frac{x^2}{16} - \frac{y^2}{4} = 1$
    D. $\frac{x^2}{16} - \frac{y^2}{4} = 1$

14. Which equation is shown by the graph?   14. __B__
    A. $x^2 - y^2 = 9$
    B. $y^2 - x^2 = 9$
    C. $x^2 + y^2 = 9$
    D. $x^2 - y^2 = 3$

15. Solve the system of equations. $x^2 + y^2 = 25$, $9y = 4x^2$ 15. __D__
    A. $(4, 3)$ and $(-4, 3)$ B. $(3, 4)$ and $(3, -4)$
    C. $(4, 3)$ and $(4, -3)$ D. $(3, 4)$ and $(-3, 4)$

16. What system of inequalities is shown in the graph?   16. __B__
    A. $x^2 + y^2 \leq 16$ B. $x^2 + y^2 \leq 16$
    $x - y > -3$ $x - y < -3$
    C. $x^2 + y^2 \geq 16$ D. $x^2 + y^2 \geq 16$
    $x - y > -3$ $x - y < -3$

17. What is the graph of $4x^2 = y^2 + 8y + 32$?   17. __D__
    A. parabola   B. circle   C. ellipse   D. hyperbola

18. What is the graph of $5x^2 + 10x + 5y^2 = 9$?   18. __B__
    A. parabola   B. circle   C. ellipse   D. hyperbola

19. What is the graph of $4x^2 = y - 24x + 35$?   19. __A__
    A. parabola   B. circle   C. ellipse   D. hyperbola

20. Which is a true statement about using simulations to solve problems?   20. __D__
    A. Flipping a coin is sometimes useful.
    B. Rolling a die is sometimes helpful.
    C. Simulations can help when a direct solution is too difficult.
    D. All of the above are true.

Bonus Which equation has a graph that is an ellipse that is tangent to the x-axis and y-axis and has center $(5, -1)$?   Bonus __C__
    A. $(x - 5)^2 + (y + 1)^2 = 1$ B. $\frac{(x - 5)^2}{1} + \frac{(y + 1)^2}{25} = 1$
    C. $\frac{(x - 5)^2}{25} + \frac{(y + 1)^2}{1} = 1$ D. $\frac{(x + 5)^2}{25} + \frac{(y - 1)^2}{1} = 1$

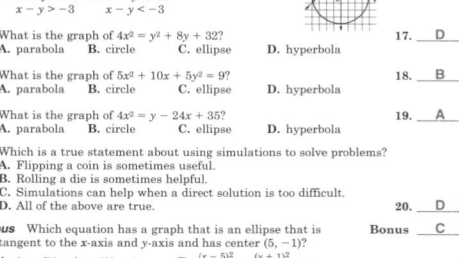

Skills and Concepts Encourage students to refer to the objectives and examples on the left as they complete the review exercises on the right.

Assessment and Evaluation Masters, pp. 177–178

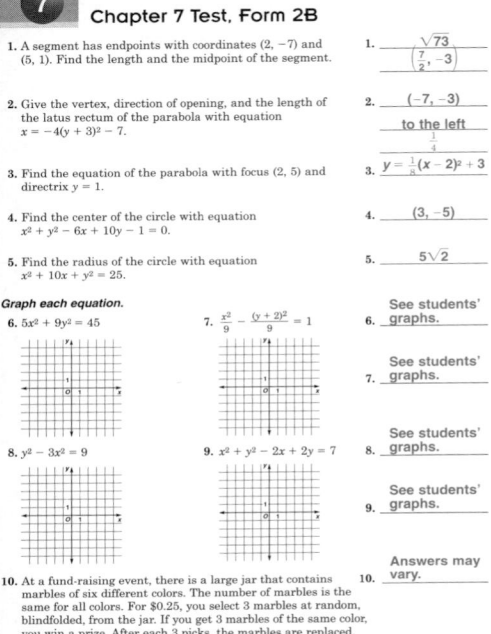

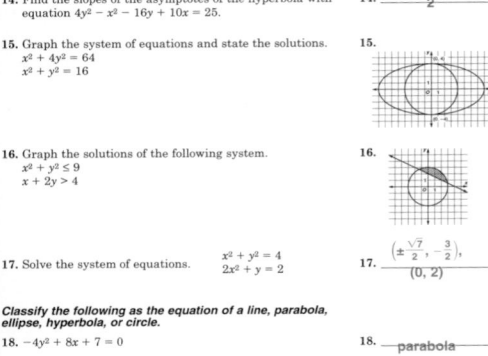

SKILLS AND CONCEPTS

OBJECTIVES AND EXAMPLES

Upon completing this chapter, you should be able to:

- find the distance between two points in the coordinate plane   (Lesson 7–1)

  Find the distance between the points at $(6, -4)$ and $(-3, 8)$.

  $$d = \sqrt{(x_2 - x_1)^2 + (y_2 - y_1)^2}$$
  $$= \sqrt{(-3 - 6)^2 + [8 - (-4)]^2}$$
  $$= \sqrt{81 + 144}$$
  $$= \sqrt{225} \text{ or } 15$$

- find the midpoint of a line segment in the coordinate plane   (Lesson 7–1)

  Find the midpoint of the segment whose endpoints are at $(-5, 9)$ and $(11, -1)$.

  $$\left(\frac{x_1 + x_2}{2}, \frac{y_1 + y_2}{2}\right) = \left(\frac{-5 + 11}{2}, \frac{9 + (-1)}{2}\right)$$
  $$= \left(\frac{6}{2}, \frac{8}{2}\right) \text{ or } (3, 4)$$

- graph parabolas having certain properties (Lesson 7–2)

  Graph $4y - x^2 = 14x - 27$.

  First write the equation in the form

  $$y = a(x - h)^2 + k^2.$$

  $$4y - x^2 = 14x - 27 \quad \rightarrow \quad y = \frac{1}{4}(x + 7)^2 - 19$$

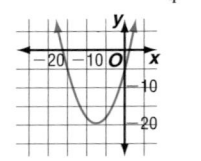

REVIEW EXERCISES

Use these exercises to review and prepare for the chapter test.

Find the distance between each pair of points with the given coordinates.

16. $(-2, 10)$ and $(-2, 13)$ **3**
17. $(8, 5)$ and $(-9, 4)$ $\sqrt{290}$
18. $\left(3\sqrt{3}, 5\sqrt{3}\right)$ and $\left(-4\sqrt{3}, -7\sqrt{3}\right)$ $\sqrt{579}$
19. $(7, -3)$ and $(1, 2)$ $\sqrt{61}$
20. $(-13, 16)$ and $(5, -8)$ **30**

Find the midpoint of each line segment if the coordinates of the endpoints are given.

21. $(1, 2)$ and $(4, 6)$
22. $(-8, 0)$ and $(-2, 3)$ 21. $\left(\frac{5}{2}, 4\right)$ 22. $\left(-5, \frac{3}{2}\right)$
23. $(7a, -5b)$ and $(a, -3b)$ $(4a, -4b)$
24. $\left(\frac{3}{5}, -\frac{7}{4}\right)$ and $\left(\frac{1}{4}, -\frac{2}{5}\right)$ $\left(\frac{17}{40}, -\frac{43}{40}\right)$

Name the coordinates of the vertex and focus, the equations of the axis of symmetry and directrix, and the direction of opening of the parabola with the given equation. Then find the length of the latus rectum and graph the parabola.

25. $(x - 1)^2 = 12(y - 1)$
26. $(y + 6) = 16(x - 3)^2$
27. $x^2 - 8x + 8y + 32 = 0$
28. $x = 16y^2$

25–28. See Solutions Manual.

GLENCOE Technology

Test and Review Software

You may use this software, a combination of an item generator and item bank, to create your own tests or worksheets. Types of items include free response, multiple choice, short answer, and open ended.

For IBM & Macintosh

OBJECTIVES AND EXAMPLES

- graph circles having certain properties
  (Lesson 7–3)

  Graph $x^2 + y^2 + 8x - 24y + 16 = 0$.

  First write the equation in the form $(x - h)^2 + (y - k)^2 = r^2$: $(x + 4)^2 + (y - 12)^2 = 144$.

  Then draw the graph.

  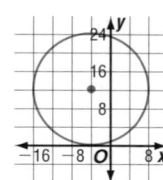

- graph ellipses having certain properties
  (Lesson 7–4)

  Graph $x^2 + 3y^2 - 16x + 24y + 31 = 0$.

  First write the equation in standard form.
  $$\frac{(x - 8)^2}{81} + \frac{(y + 8)^2}{27} = 1$$
  Then draw the graph.

  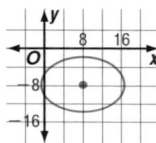

- graph hyperbolas having certain properties
  (Lesson 7–5)

  Graph $9x^2 - 4y^2 + 18x + 32y - 91 = 0$.

  First write the equation in standard form.
  $$\frac{(x + 1)^2}{4} - \frac{(y - 4)^2}{9} = 1$$
  Then draw the graph.

  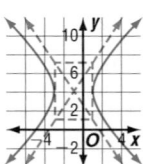

REVIEW EXERCISES

Find the coordinates of the center and the radius of each circle whose equation is given. Then draw the graph.

29. $x^2 + y^2 = 169$ 29–32. See margin.
30. $(x + 5)^2 + (y - 11)^2 = 49$
31. $x^2 + y^2 - 6x + 16y - 152 = 0$
32. $x^2 + y^2 + 6x - 2y - 15 = 0$

Find the coordinates of the center and foci, and the lengths of the major and minor axes for each ellipse whose equation is given. Then draw the graph.

33. $49x^2 + 16y^2 = 784$
34. $9x^2 + 4y^2 = 36$
35. $25x^2 + 64y^2 = 1600$
36. $\frac{x^2}{16} + \frac{y^2}{25} = 1$

33–36. See Solutions Manual.

Find the coordinates of the vertices and foci and the slopes of the asymptotes for each hyperbola whose equation is given. Then draw the graph.

37. $9y^2 - 4x^2 = 36$
38. $25x^2 - 4y^2 = 100$
39. $9y^2 - 16x^2 = 144$
40. $x^2 - 25y^2 = 25$

37–40. See Solutions Manual.

Additional Answers

29. (0, 0); 13 units

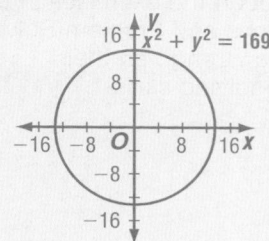

30. (−5, 11); 7 units

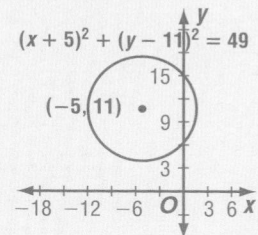

31. (3, −8); 15 units

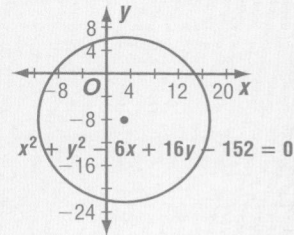

32. (−3, 1); $\sqrt{23}$ units

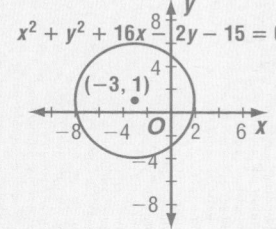

Applications and Problem Solving Encourage students to work through the exercises in the Applications and Problem Solving section to strengthen their problem-solving skills.

OBJECTIVES AND EXAMPLES

- identify conic sections from their equations (Lesson 7–6)

$$Ax^2 + Bxy + Cy^2 + Dx + Ey + F = 0 \quad (B = 0)$$

Conic Section	Relationship of A and C
parabola	$A = 0$ or $C = 0$, but not both.
circle	$A = C$
ellipse	A and C have the same sign and $A \neq C$.
hyperbola	A and C have opposite signs.

REVIEW EXERCISES

State whether the graph of each equation is a parabola, a circle, an ellipse, or a hyperbola.

41. $7x^2 + 9y^2 = 63$ ellipse
42. $11x^2 + 11y^2 = 55$ circle
43. $(x - 4)^2 = 6y$ parabola
44. $5y^2 - 13x^2 = 81$ hyperbola
45. $x^2 + y^2 = 289$ circle

- solve systems of equations involving quadratics graphically and algebraically   (Lesson 7–7)

A system of equations whose graphs are a line and a conic section can have zero, one, or two solutions. A system of equations whose graphs are two conic sections can have zero, one, two, three, or four solutions.

Solve each system of equations algebraically. Check your solution with a graphing calculator.

46. $x^2 + y^2 - 18x + 24y + 200 = 0$
    $4x + 3y = 0$ (6, −8), (12, −16)
47. $4x^2 + y^2 - 48x - 2y + 129 = 0$
    $x^2 + y^2 - 2x - 2y - 7 = 0$ (4, 1)
48. $x^2 + y^2 + 2x - 12y + 12 = 0$
    $y + x = 0$ (−1, 1), (−6, 6)

APPLICATIONS AND PROBLEM SOLVING

49. **Transportation**   A piano delivery truck traveled 45 miles north on Interstate 71 before turning east on Interstate 70. After traveling 60 miles on I-70, about how far is the truck from its original starting point?   (Lesson 7–1)
    75 miles

50. $y = \frac{1}{12}x^2$

50. **Telecommunications**   The cross-section of a satellite dish is in the shape of a parabola. For this dish, the receiver is located at the focus and is 3 feet above the vertex. Find an equation for the cross-section. Assume that the vertex is at the origin.   (Lesson 7–2)

51. **Aviation**   The control tower for the Metro Blairsville Airport is located at (9, 23) on the county map. The radar used at the airport can detect airplanes up to 45 miles away. Write an equation for the position of the most distant plane that the people in the control tower can detect in terms of the county map.   (Lesson 7–3)
    $(x - 9)^2 + (y - 23)^2 = 2025$

A practice test for Chapter 7 is provided on page 918.

ALTERNATIVE ASSESSMENT

PERFORMANCE ASSESSMENT TASK

Architectural Geometry   You have been commissioned to design a circular theater with circular rows surrounding a circular central stage. The floor of the building is a square 1500 feet on each side. You are interested in maximizing the seating capacity of this theater, without sacrificing the comfort of the patrons who will purchase theater tickets.

Consider three different options.
• a stage with a 75-foot diameter
• a stage with a 100-foot diameter
• a stage with a 150-foot diameter

The marketing division of your company believes that an average price of $25 per ticket is the best price for this theater. Write a proposal for the width of the rows, taking into careful consideration the advantages and disadvantages of the different widths. Compare your row width with each size of stage. Which size of stage along with which row width will allow for the most patrons and the greatest comfort?

The people who will see your proposals are impressed with facts and figures, so be sure to include tables and graphs to illustrate which proposal you believe would be best for the theater and its patrons.

THINKING CRITICALLY

• Write equations for two parabolas that do not intersect.
• Write equations for a line and a parabola that intersect only at the point (2, 5).
• Write equations for a parabola and a circle that intersect the line $y = 2x + 3$ in the same point.
• Write equations for a line, a parabola, and a circle that each contain the points (3, 0) and (0, −3).

PORTFOLIO

Describe what you have learned about conic sections, including how they are related. List the four different types of conic sections, comparing each standard equation to the others.

Write an example of an equation for each type of conic section. Then draw each on a separate coordinate grid, labeling important characteristics such as center, foci, vertex, axes of symmetry, and so on. Place these in your portfolio.

SELF EVALUATION

"I dare you." Did you ever hear or say these words when you were younger? How daring are you? A good problem solver is willing to try new ways of approaching problems.

Assess yourself. Do you try new ways to solve problems? Taking risks and not using familiar ways of solving problems can be scary. However, if you learn to take risks, you will be rewarded with a thorough understanding of the concepts you are taught.

Assessment and Evaluation Masters, pp. 182, 193

NAME_____ DATE _____

7   **Chapter 7 Performance Assessment**

Instructions: *Demonstrate your knowledge by giving a clear, concise solution to each problem. Be sure to include all relevant drawings and justify your answers. You may show your solution in more than one way or investigate beyond the requirements of the problem.*

1. The graph of a hyperbola is shown at the right. The vertices are at (−1, 2) and (7, 8) and the foci are at $\left(-3, \frac{1}{2}\right)$ and $\left(9, \frac{19}{2}\right)$.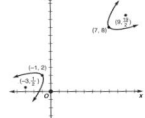

   a. Explain how to find the midpoint of a line segment. Find the center of the hyperbola. Show your work.

   b. Explain how to find the distance between two points. Find the values of a and c for the hyperbola. Show your work.

   c. Define the relationship among a, b, and c for a hyperbola. Then find the value of b. Show your work.

2. a. Explain how you can determine whether an equation of the form $Ax^2 + Bxy + Cy^2 + Dx + Ey + F = 0$ represents a circle, ellipse, parabola, or hyperbola.

   b. Identify the conic section represented by the equation $y^2 + 2y + 1 = 6x - x^2$. Write the standard form of the equation and draw the graph. Show your work.

   c. Identify the conic section represented by the equation $x^2 + 4x - 12y - 8 = 0$. Write the standard form of the equation and draw the graph.

   d. If the equation in part c is an ellipse or hyperbola, find the values of a, b, and c. If the equation is a parabola, give the coordinates of the focus and the equation of the directrix.

   e. Write an equation for an ellipse in standard form. Give the coordinates of the center and foci and the length of the major axis. Graph the ellipse.

Scoring Guide
Chapter 7
Performance Assessment

Level	Specific Criteria
3 Superior	• Shows thorough understanding of the concepts of *distance between two points, midpoint of a segment, identifying and graphing conic sections from their equations,* and *finding the center, focus, and directrix.* • Computations are correct. • Written explanations are exemplary. • Graphs are accurate and appropriate. • Goes beyond requirements of problem.
2 Satisfactory, with Minor Flaws	• Shows understanding of the concepts of *distance between two points, midpoint of a segment, identifying and graphing conic sections from their equations,* and *finding the center, focus, and directrix.* • Computations are mostly correct. • Written explanations are effective. • Graphs are mostly accurate and appropriate. • Satisfies all requirements of problem.
1 Nearly Satisfactory, with Serious Flaws	• Shows understanding of most of the concepts of *distance between two points, midpoint of a segment, identifying and graphing conic sections from their equations,* and *finding the center, focus, and directrix.* • Computations are mostly correct. • Written explanations are satisfactory. • Graphs are mostly accurate and appropriate. • Satisfies most requirements of problem.
0 Unsatisfactory	• Shows little or no understanding of the concepts of *distance between two points, midpoint of a segment, identifying and graphing conic sections from their equations,* and *finding the center, focus, and directrix.* • Computations are incorrect. • Written explanations are not satisfactory. • Graphs are not accurate or appropriate. • Does not satisfy requirements of problem.

Alternative Assessment

The Alternative Assessment section provides students with the opportunity to assess their own work by thinking critically, working with others, keeping a portfolio, and honestly evaluating their own progress. For more information on alternative forms of assessment, see *Alternative Assessment in the Mathematics Classroom,* one of the titles in the Glencoe Mathematics Professional Series.

Performance Assessment

Performance Assessment tasks for this chapter are included in the *Assessment and Evaluation Masters.* A scoring guide is also provided.

This Investigation is designed to be completed over several days or weeks. It may be considered optional. You may want to assign the Investigation and the follow-up activities to be completed at the same time.

Objective
Use algebraic methods to investigate the volume of a container and find a way to measure its contents.

Mathematical Overview
This Investigation will use the following mathematical skills and concepts from Chapters 8 and 9.

- making charts and graphs
- finding the inverse of a relation or function
- determining if a graph represents a function

Recommended Time		
Part	**Pages**	**Time**
Investigation	474–475	1 class period
Working on the Investigation	501, 538, 555, 575	20 minutes each
Closing the Investigation	584	1 class period

Instructional Resources
Investigations and Projects Masters, pp. 13–16

A recording sheet, teacher notes, and scoring guide are provided for each Investigation in the *Investigations and Projects Masters*.

1 MOTIVATION

This Investigation uses common household items to model the process used to measure the volume of a liquid in large underground storage tanks. Explain that in some cases, such as underground gasoline tanks, it is not possible to see how much of the contents remains. Sometimes the use of a calibrated dipstick is the preferred method of measurement.

Fill It Up!

MATERIALS NEEDED

2 sizes of coffee cans

wooden chopsticks

duct tape

large nail

hammer

metal snips

metric ruler

funnel

metric measuring cup

Imagine you work for a major petroleum company as a technical support representative for all of the gas stations in a certain region. Gasoline is stored in underground cylindrical tanks just below the surface of the station. The tanks are positioned with their circular bases perpendicular to the surface. An opening on the top center of the tank is used to fill and measure the gasoline in the tank. A pipe at the bottom of the tank transfers gasoline to the pumps.

A dipstick measures the amount of gasoline left in the storage tank. It is lowered through the opening in the storage tank until it touches the bottom of the tank. Then it is removed. The wet part of the stick indicates how many gallons of gasoline are left in the storage tank according to the markings on the stick. It is similar to the oil dipstick used in a car.

The owner of one of the gas stations that you service has misplaced his dipstick for one of his tanks. He could order a replacement stick, but since the tank is an odd size, the dipstick is very expensive. He asks you to design a stick with the appropriate scale marked on it.

In this Investigation, you will begin to research the problem by experimenting with coffee cans and wooden chopsticks. The coffee cans will represent the gas tanks, and the chopsticks will represent dipsticks.

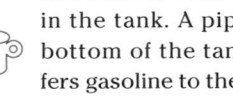

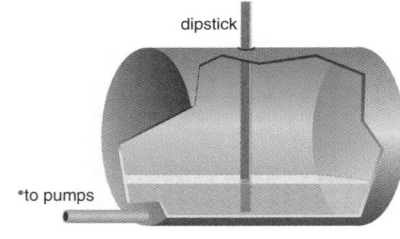

dipstick

*to pumps

.... **SET UP**

1 Make a model of a gas tank by using a coffee can with the plastic lid taped securely onto the can with duct tape.

2 Punch a hole in the side of the coffee can using a nail and hammer. Using a pair of metal snips, make the hole big enough to insert a funnel.

 Cooperative Learning

This Investigation offers an excellent opportunity for using cooperative learning groups. For more information on cooperative learning strategies and group management, see *Cooperative Learning in the Mathematics Classroom*, one of the titles in the Glencoe Mathematics Professional Series.

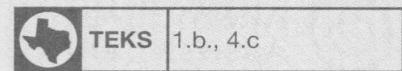 TEKS | 1.b., 4.c

COFFEE CAN EXPERIMENT

radius of can:	length of can:			capacity of can:	
water in can (mL)	measure on dipstick (cm)	% of can filled		% of dipstick covered	% change in capacity
50 mL					
100 mL					
⋮					

3 Copy the chart above onto a sheet of paper.

COLLECT DATA

4 Measure the radius of the lid and the length of the coffee can. Record these data in your chart.

5 Use a funnel and a metric measuring cup to pour 50 mL of water into the coffee can through the hole on its side. Lower the chopstick into the hole until it touches the bottom and pull it out. With a metric ruler, measure the distance on the chopstick that is wet and record the measurement in your chart.

6 Repeat this process, adding 50 mL at a time, until the coffee can is full. Did you use all of the last 50 mL? What is the capacity of the coffee can in mL? Record this value in your chart.

7 Estimate how much water is in the can when it is one-half full, one-fourth full, and three-fourths full. Make a note of these numbers.

8 For each 50-mL increment, calculate the ratio of the amount of water in the coffee can to the capacity of the coffee can. Convert these ratios to percents of a full coffee can. Record these data in your chart. Were your estimates correct for the amount of water when the can is one-half full, one-fourth full, and three-fourths full?

9 For each increment, calculate the ratio of the measure on the dipstick to the total length of the dipstick. Convert these ratios to percents of a fully-covered dipstick. Record these data in your chart.

10 Make a drawing to illustrate the measurement scale for a dipstick for this coffee can. Include markings for one-fourth, one-half, and three-fourths full.

11 How does the height of the water change as the amount of water in the can changes? Determine the change in the percent of water in the tank at each 50-mL increment. Record these data in your chart.

Make an Investigation Folder in which you can store all of your work on this Investigation for future use. Be sure to keep your chart and materials in your Investigation Folder.

You will continue working on this Investigation throughout Chapters 8 and 9.

Fill It Up! Investigation

Working on the Investigation
Lesson 8–3, p. 499

Working on the Investigation
Lesson 8–8, p. 534

Working on the Investigation
Lesson 9–1, p. 555

Working on the Investigation
Lesson 9–4, p. 575

Closing the Investigation
End of Chapter 9, p. 584

Investigation: Fill It Up! **475**

2 SETUP

You may have a student read the first three paragraphs of the Investigation to provide information on underground tanks and the measurement of their contents. You may then read the fourth paragraph, which introduces the procedure to be used. Discuss the activity with your students. Then separate the class into groups of three.

3 MANAGEMENT

Each group member should be responsible for a specific task.

Recorder Collects data.
Measurer Measures/adds water to coffee can, measures water mark on stick.
Illustrator Draws accompanying drawings, graphs.

At the end of the activity, each member should turn in his or her respective equipment.

Sample Answers

Answers will vary as they are based on the size of the coffee can used by each group.

Investigations and Projects Masters, p. 16

8, 9

NAME _____ DATE _____

Investigation, Chapters 8 and 9 Student Edition Pages 474–475, 501, 538, 555, 575, 584

Fill It Up!

Use this section to record your calculations from Working on the Investigation from Lesson 9-4.

	% of tank that is full	% of dipstick that is wet
Rational expression	_____	_____
Verification	_____	_____
Rational expression showing how you calculated the change in volume percent	_____	
Verification	_____	

Work with your group to add to the list of questions to be considered.

• A tank is 24 feet in length and 18 feet in diameter. What is the volume of the tank?

• What is the volume of the tank in gallons?

• Where on the dipstick would be the marking showing the tank was $\frac{1}{4}$ full?

_____
_____
_____
_____

Exploring Polynomial Functions

PREVIEWING THE CHAPTER

This chapter opens with a lesson on evaluating polynomial functions. Students then learn to determine the factors of polynomials by using the factor theorem and synthetic division. Zeros are approximated and polynomial functions are graphed using synthetic division to find significant points. Students learn and apply a number of algebraic principles to determine the number and type of zeros for a function, integrating two or more strategies when necessary. The rational zero theorem is used to identify possible rational zeros of a function. Students then apply their knowledge of quadratic functions to solve polynomial functions. Finally, the composition of functions is studied, and the inverses of functions are determined and graphed.

ORGANIZING THE CHAPTER

> A complete, 1-page lesson plan is provided for each lesson in the *Lesson Planning Guide*. Answer keys for each lesson are available in the *Answer Key Masters*.

You may want to refer to the **Course Planning Calendar** on page T12 for detailed information on pacing.
PACING: **Standard**—15 days; **Honors**—14 days; **Block**—7 days

LESSON PLANNING CHART

Lesson (Pages)	Materials/ Manipulatives	Extra Practice (Student Edition)	Study Guide	Practice	Enrichment	Assessment and Evaluation	Modeling Mathematics	Multicultural Activity	Tech Prep Applications	Graphing Calculator	Science and Math Lab Manual	Real-World Applications	Interactive Mathematics Tools Software	Teaching Transparencies
8-1 (478–484)	graphing calculator	p. 894	p. 56	p. 56	p. 56								8-1	8-1A 8-1B
8-2 (485–490)		p. 894	p. 57	p. 57	p. 57	p. 212					pp. 43–48			8-2A 8-2B
8-3A (491–492)	graphing calculator									pp. 45, 46				
8-3 (493–499)	scientific calculator graphing calculator	p. 895	p. 58	p. 58	p. 58					p. 8		22		8-3A 8-3B
8-3B (500–501)	graphing calculator									pp. 47, 48				
8-4 (502–508)	scientific calculator graphing calculator	p. 895	p. 59	p. 59	p. 59	pp. 211, 212	p. 68	p. 15						8-4A 8-4B
8-5 (509–514)		p. 895	p. 60	p. 60	p. 60									8-5A 8-5B
8-6 (515–519)		p. 896	p. 61	p. 61	p. 61	p. 213		p. 16				23		8-6A 8-6B
8-7 (520–525)		p. 896	p. 62	p. 62	p. 62				p. 15			24	8-7	8-7A 8-7B
8-7B (526–527)	grid paper					p.24								
8-8 (528–534)	reflective mirror* grid paper straightedge* graphing calculator	p. 896	p. 63	p. 63	p. 63	p. 213	pp. 49–51	p. 16					8-8	8-8A 8-8B
8-8B (535–538)	graphing calculator													
Study Guide/ Assessment (539–543)						pp. 197–210, 214								

*Included in Glencoe's Student Manipulative Kit and Overhead Manipulative Resources.

ORGANIZING THE CHAPTER

OTHER CHAPTER RESOURCES

Student Edition
Investigation, pp. 474–475
Chapter Opener, pp. 476–477
Working on the Investigation,
pp. 499, 534

Teacher's Classroom Resources
Investigations and Projects Masters,
pp. 53–56

Technology
Teacher's Guide for Software
Resources
Test and Review Software (IBM
and Macintosh)
CD-ROM Interactions (Macintosh
and Windows)

Professional Publications
Block Scheduling Booklet
Glencoe Mathematics Professional
Series

OUTSIDE RESOURCES

Books/Periodicals
*Algebra Experiments II: Exploring Nonlinear
Functions,* Addison-Wesley
The Language of Functions and Graphs, Shell
Center for Mathematical Education

Software
The Function Supposer: Explorations in Algebra,
Sunburst
Tools of Mathematics: Advanced Algebra, William
K. Bradford Publishing

Videos/CD-ROMs
Polynomials, Dale Seymour Publications

See the *Teacher's Guide for Software Resources* for software addresses.

ASSESSMENT RESOURCES

Student Edition
Math Journal, pp. 482, 488, 523
Mixed Review, pp. 484, 490,
499, 508, 514, 519, 525, 533
Self Test, p. 508
Chapter Highlights, p. 539
Chapter Study Guide and
Assessment, pp. 540–542
Alternative Assessment, p. 543
 Portfolio, p. 543

College Entrance Exam Practice,
pp. 544–545

Teacher's Wraparound Edition
5-Minute Check, pp. 478, 485,
493, 502, 509, 515, 520, 528
Check for Understanding, pp. 481,
488, 497, 506, 512, 518, 523,
531
Closing Activity, pp. 484, 490,
499, 508, 514, 519, 525, 534
Cooperative Learning, pp. 487,
503

Assessment and Evaluation Masters
Multiple-Choice Tests, Forms 1A
(Honors), 1B (Average), 1C
(Basic), pp. 197–202
Free-Response Tests, Forms 2A
(Honors), 2B (Average), 2C
(Basic), pp. 203–208
Calculator-Based Test, p. 209
Performance Assessment, p. 210
Mid-Chapter Test, p. 211
Quizzes A–D, pp. 212–213
Standardized Test Practice, p. 214
Cumulative Review, pp. 215–216

Examples of some of the materials for enhancing Chapter 8 are shown below.

DIVERSITY

Multicultural Activity Masters, pp. 15, 16

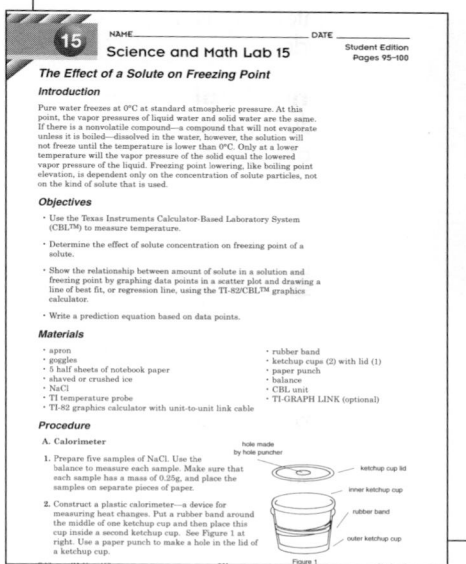

APPLICATIONS

Real-World Applications, 22, 23, 24

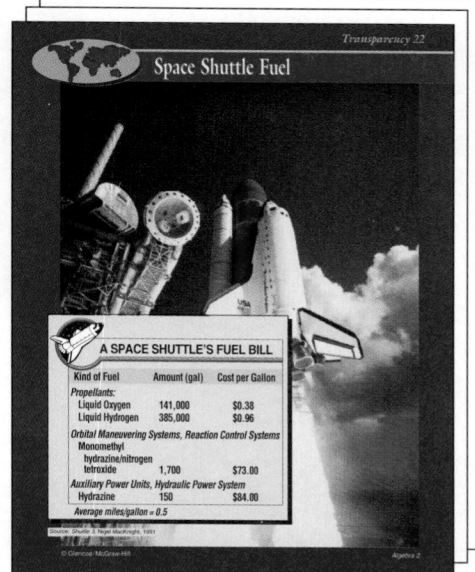

TECHNOLOGY

Graphing Calculator Masters, p. 8

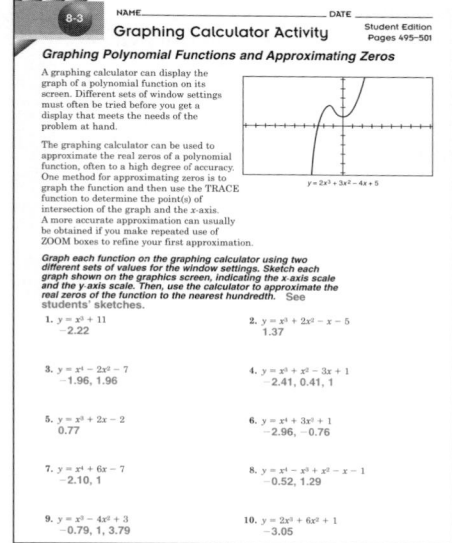

TECH PREP

Tech Prep Applications Masters, pp. 15, 16

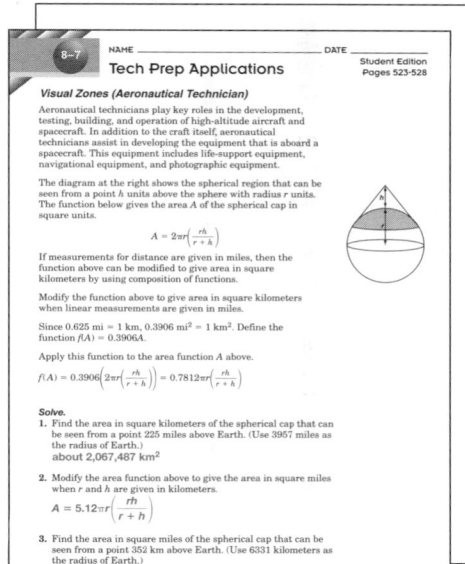

CONNECTIONS

Science and Math Lab Manual, pp. 43–48

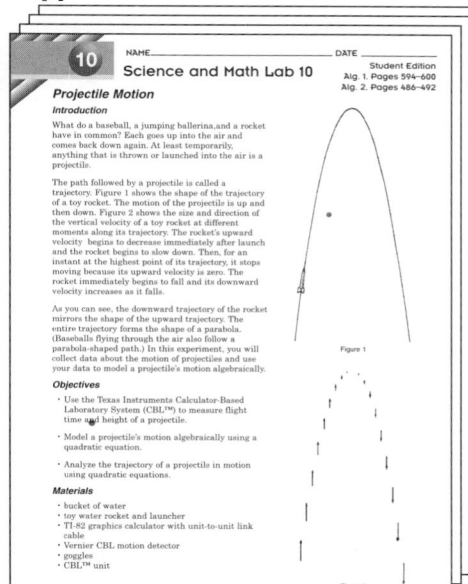

PROBLEM SOLVING

Problem of the Week Cards, 20, 21

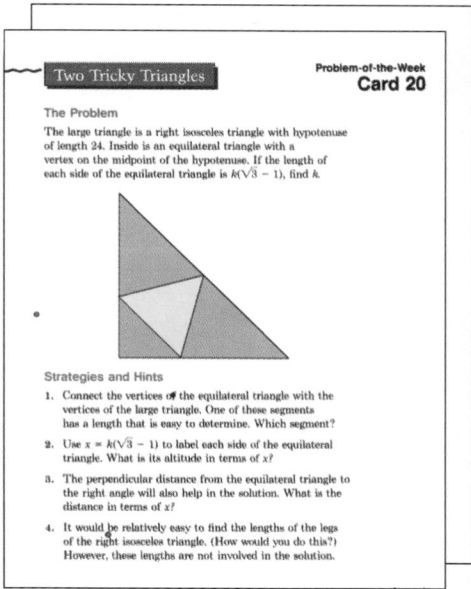

MAKING MATHEMATICS RELEVANT

This two-page introduction to the chapter provides students with an opportunity to explore contemporary topics and their applications to mathematics.

Background Information

The Information Highway A host of useful information—as well as lots of fun stuff—is available on the Internet. On the Net, one can gain access to current U.S. weather information, Census Bureau statistics, universities, libraries, bookstores, a variety of shopping networks, and the Smithsonian Photo Archive. One of the most popular uses of the Internet is as a vehicle for conversation between individuals with similar interests.

CHAPTER

8

Exploring Polynomial Functions

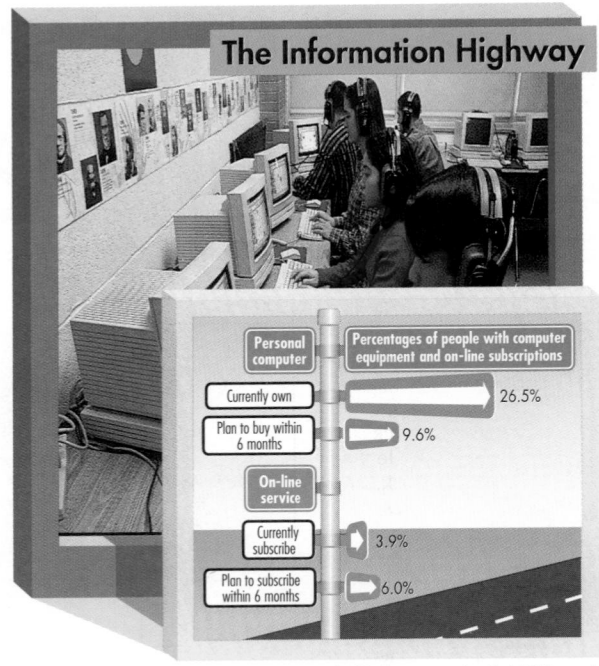

The Information Highway

Personal computer	Percentages of people with computer equipment and on-line subscriptions
Currently own	26.5%
Plan to buy within 6 months	9.6%
On-line service	
Currently subscribe	3.9%
Plan to subscribe within 6 months	6.0%

Source: Bruskin/Goldring research poll of 1015 people

Objectives

In this chapter, you will:

- find factors and zeros of polynomial functions,
- approximate real zeros of polynomial functions,
- graph polynomial functions,
- find the composition of functions,
- determine the inverses of functions or relations, and
- work backward to solve problems.

The Internet began in 1969 as a network for military sites, universities, and research institutions. Since the beginning, the Internet has been free and open, having no restrictions on who has access or what information is shared. Now Congress may decide to regulate the Net with the Communications Decency Act. Should the government protect minors from harm or should cyberspace be free of government regulation?

TIME *Line*

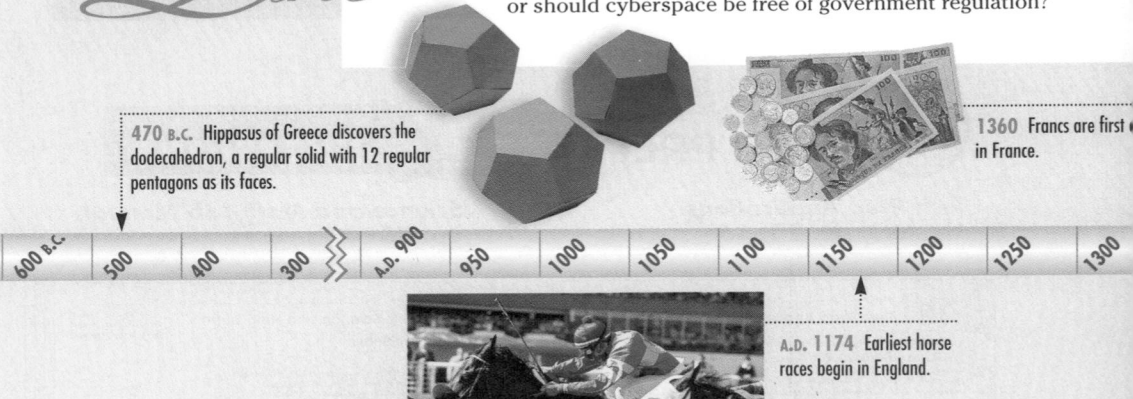

470 B.C. Hippasus of Greece discovers the dodecahedron, a regular solid with 12 regular pentagons as its faces.

1360 Francs are first • in France.

| 600 B.C. | 500 | 400 | 300 | A.D. 900 | 950 | 1000 | 1050 | 1100 | 1150 | 1200 | 1250 | 1300 |

A.D. 1174 Earliest horse races begin in England.

TIME *Line*

Students might find it interesting to research and write a report on the regular solids, of which the dodecahedron is only one example. These solids have a fascinating mathematical history.

*inter*NET
CONNECTION

An introduction to the Internet tells what makes up the Internet, who governs it, who pays for it, and what is in store for its future.

World Wide Web
http://www.dsu.edu/
internet/internet.html

Chapter Project

In small groups, plan an Internet research project. Have one person do research on the history of the Internet, its origins, early participants, and social implications for society. Another person should research the current Internet and its uses, business, educational, and personal. Investigate procedures for going online, who provides access, costs, and benefits of linking in cyberspace. The question of government regulation could be researched listing arguments for and against censorship and the political history involved. Group members should present and discuss their findings.

At age 21, while at the University of Illinois' National Center for Supercomputer Applications, **Marc Andreessen** helped create the Internet browsing program Mosaic, which helps people point and click their way around the World Wide Web. In 1994, he joined Jim Clark, the founder of Silicon Graphics, to form a new company, Netscape, in California. He improved the Mosaic program, now called Navigator, and captured 70% of the Internet market, approaching 10 million customers. In the summer of 1995, Netscape went public on the NASDAQ market, and Marc became the owner of $565 million worth of stocks in the company.

Marc Andreessen has often been compared to Bill Gates, CEO of Microsoft. Just as Microsoft has dominated the software market for PCs, Netscape has dominated the Internet market. But while he is enjoying his success, Marc does worry that somewhere there is a 20-something genius about to create the next revolution in the computer market.

Chapter Project

Cooperative Learning Separate the class into two groups. Give each group a list of questions that requires research to answer. Have one group answer the questions using traditional library methods. Have the other group get on the Internet to research. Have panels discuss which method is easier, more practical, more cost effective, and so on.

1942 The first electronic brain or automatic computer is developed in the U.S.

1989 Computer viruses infect computer networks worldwide.

| 1450 | 1500 | 1550 | 1600 | 1650 | 1700 | 1750 | 1800 | 1850 | 1900 | 1950 | 2000 |

1619 Spanish painter Diego Velázquez, at the age of 20, creates his canvas *The Water Carrier of Seville.*

1784 The first school for the blind is founded in Paris.

1991 Gertrude Elion becomes the first woman inducted into the Inventors Hall of Fame.

Chapter 8 **477**

Alternative Chapter Projects ▬

Two other chapter projects are included in the *Investigations and Projects Masters.* In Chapter 8 Project A, pp. 53–54, students extend the topic in the chapter opener. In Chapter 8 Project B, pp. 55–56, students assume the role of financial planners.

Investigations and Projects Masters, p. 53

8

NAME _____ DATE _____

Chapter 8 Project A

Student Edition
Pages 478–538

Surfing the Net

1. Many companies now offer access to the Internet. Do research to determine the differences between local Internet providers and commercial online services that provide access to the Internet.

2. Choose two local Internet providers and two commercial online services. Make a list of the features and services each company provides. Obtain information about the rates charged by each of these companies. Write a function to describe the cost of each service.

3. Use the functions you wrote in exercise 2 and the chart below to compare the costs of the four companies you selected.

Number of Hours per Month	Internet Providers		Commercial Online Services	
1				
2				
3				
4				
5				
6				
7				
8				

4. Write an article for the school newspaper that will help other students figure out the best way for them to start exploring the Net. Be sure to include the chart you made in exercise 3.

NCTM Standards: 1–6

Instructional Resources

- Study Guide Master 8-1
- Practice Master 8-1
- Enrichment Master 8-1

Transparency 8-1A contains the 5-Minute Check for this lesson; **Transparency 8-1B** contains a teaching aid for this lesson.

Recommended Pacing	
Standard Pacing	Day 1 of 15
Honors Pacing	Day 1 of 14
Block Scheduling*	Day 1 of 7 (along with Lesson 8-2)

*For more information on pacing and possible lesson plans, refer to the *Block Scheduling Booklet.*

1 FOCUS

5-Minute Check
(over Chapter 7)

1. Find the distance between (3, 6) and (7, −8). $2\sqrt{53}$
2. Find the midpoint of the line segment whose endpoints are $A(17, -8)$ and $B(-13, 1)$. $\left(2, -\frac{7}{2}\right)$
3. State whether the graph of $(x - 3)^2 = 4y - 4$ is a parabola, a circle, an ellipse, or a hyperbola. **parabola**
4. Find the solution of the system of equations. $(x - 2)^2 + y^2 = 16$ $y - x = 2$ **(−2, 0), (2, 4)**
5. Find the equation of the parabola with vertex at (6, −1) and focus at (3, −1). $x = -\frac{1}{12}(y + 1)^2 + 6$

TEKS | 1.a., 4.a., 4.b.

Polynomial Functions

8-1

What YOU'LL LEARN

- To evaluate polynomial functions, and
- to identify general shapes of the graphs of polynomial functions.

Why IT'S IMPORTANT

You can use polynomial functions to solve problems involving biology and energy.

CONNECTION
Biology

Calvin and Hobbes
by Bill Watterson

Calvin has to give up his ambition of migrating with the wildebeests when he learns that they live on another continent. The Serengeti Plain is a wild game reserve in Africa where herds of wildebeests, or gnus, roam. The population of wildebeests on the Serengeti Plain can be described by the function $f(x) = -0.125x^5 + 3.125x^4 + 58,000$, where x represents the number of years since 1990. The graph at the right shows this function. The expression $-0.125x^5 + 3.125x^4 + 58,000$ is a **polynomial in one variable.** *You will find the population of wildebeests in Example 2.*

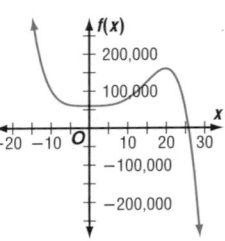

Definition of a Polynomial in One Variable	A polynomial of degree n in one variable x is an expression of the form $a_0x^n + a_1x^{n-1} + \ldots + a_{n-2}x^2 + a_{n-1}x + a_n$, where the coefficients $a_0, a_1, a_2, \ldots, a_n$ represent real numbers, a_0 is not zero, and n represents a nonnegative integer.

In Chapter 2, linear functions, which are degree 1, were identified and graphed. In Chapter 6, quadratic functions, which are degree 2, were identified and graphed. In general, the degree of a polynomial in one variable is determined by the greatest exponent of its variable.

Remember that $4 = 4x^0$ and $x + 8 = x^1 + 8x^0$.

Polynomial	Expression	Degree
Constant	4	0
Linear	$x + 8$	1
Quadratic	$3x^2 + 4x - 3$	2
Cubic	$4x^3 - 5$	3
General	$a_0x^n + a_1x^{n-1} + \ldots + a_{n-2}x^2 + a_{n-1}x + a_n$	n

Alternative Learning Styles

Auditory Encourage discussion about the differences between rational numbers, real numbers, and imaginary numbers. In this chapter, students need to know the difference between rational zeros and real zeros.

Example **1** Determine if each expression is a polynomial in one variable. If so, determine its degree.

a. $6x^4 + 3x^2 + 4x - 8$

This is a polynomial in one variable, x. The degree is 4.

b. $9x^3y^5 + 2x^2y^6 - 4$

This is not a polynomial in one variable. It contains two variables, x and y.

c. $t^{-3} + 4t^2 - 1$

This is not a polynomial, because the variable has a negative exponent.

d. $5x^7 + 3x^2 + \frac{2}{x}$

This is not a polynomial, because the term $\frac{2}{x}$ cannot be written in the form x^n, where n is a nonnegative integer.

fabulous

FIRSTS

Joshua Stewart (1983–)

Eleven-year-old Joshua Stewart became the youngest climber to reach the 19,340-foot summit of Kilimanjaro, when he reached the peak with his father and African guides in 1994. This mountain, located near the Serengeti Plain in Tanzania, is the highest peak in Africa.

When a polynomial equation is used to represent a function, the function is a **polynomial function**. For example, the equation $f(x) = 4x^2 - 5x + 2$ describes a quadratic polynomial function, and the equation $p(x) = 2x^3 + 4x^2 - 5x + 7$ describes a cubic polynomial function. These and other polynomial functions can be defined by the following general rule.

Definition of a Polynomial Function	A polynomial function of degree n can be described by an equation of the form $P(x) = a_0x^n + a_1x^{n-1} + \ldots + a_{n-2}x^2 + a_{n-1}x + a_n$, where the coefficients $a_0, a_1, a_2, \ldots, a_{n-1}$, and a_n represent real numbers, a_0 is not zero, and n represents a nonnegative integer.

If you know an element in the domain of any polynomial function, you can find the corresponding value in the range. Remember that if $f(x)$ is the function and 4 is an element in the domain, the corresponding element in the range is $f(4)$. To find $f(4)$, evaluate the function for $x = 4$.

Example **2**

CONNECTION

Biology

Refer to the application at the beginning of the lesson. Use the polynomial function to estimate the population of wildebeests in 1995.

x represents the number of years since 1990, 1995−1990 or 5.

$f(x) = -0.125x^5 + 3.125x^4 + 58{,}000$

$f(5) = -0.125(5)^5 + 3.125(5)^4 + 58{,}000$ *Replace x with 5.*

$= -390.625 + 1953.125 + 58{,}000$ or $59{,}562.5$ *Evaluate.*

Therefore, in 1995, there were approximately 59,562 wildebeests.

Example **3** a. Find $p(a + 2)$ if $p(x) = x^3 - 2x + 1$.

$p(a + 2) = (a + 2)^3 - 2(a + 2) + 1$ *Substitute a + 2 for x.*

$= a^3 + 6a^2 + 12a + 8 - 2a - 4 + 1$

$= a^3 + 6a^2 + 10a + 5$

              (continued on the next page)

---

fabulous

FIRSTS

Kilimanjaro is an extinct volcano. At its peak is a crater about 600 feet deep. Kilimanjaro's peak is covered by snow and ice year-round, and its slopes hold several large glaciers.

Motivating the Lesson

Questioning Have students list objects that increase in value over time. Such items could include baseball cards, stamps, antique cars, and paintings with high rates of appreciation. Discuss how to compute the total value of an object using the formula $A = P(1 + r)^t$ where P is the original amount, A is the amount of money at the end of a specified time, t is time in years, and r is the yearly interest rate.

2 TEACH

In-Class Examples

For Example 1
Determine if each expression is a polynomial in one variable. If so, determine its degree.

a. $x^2 + 2xy + y^2$ no

b. $2a^2 - 2a + \frac{1}{4}$
yes; degree −2

c. $12 - \frac{2}{n} + n^2$ no

d. $34 + 18c^4 + 15c^6$
yes; degree −6

For Example 2
Use the given function to estimate the population of wildebeests in the year 2000.
76,750

Teaching Tip You may want to list several polynomials and state the values of $n, a_0, \ldots, a_n$ for each polynomial to help students understand the notation.

In-Class Example

For Example 3

a. Find $p(m + 2)$ if
$p(x) = 3x - 8x^2 + x^3$.
$m^3 - 2m^2 - 17m - 18$

b. Find $f(3) - f(-3)$ if
$f(x) = 2x^2 - 4x + 6$. -24

b. Find $-2p(a) + p(a + 1)$ if $p(x) = x^3 + 3x^2 - 5$.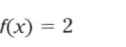

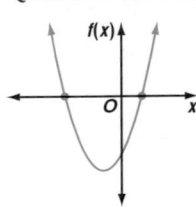

$$-2p(a) + p(a + 1) = [-2(a^3 + 3a^2 - 5)] + [(a + 1)^3 + 3(a + 1)^2 - 5]$$
$$= -2a^3 - 6a^2 + 10 + a^3 + 3a^2 + 3a + 1 + 3(a^2 + 2a + 1) - 5$$
$$= -2a^3 - 6a^2 + 10 + a^3 + 3a^2 + 3a + 1 + 3a^2 + 6a + 3 - 5$$
$$= -a^3 + 9a + 9$$

Remember that the x-coordinate of a point at which the graph crosses the x-axis is called a <u>zero</u> of the function. On the coordinate plane, these zeros are real numbers.

The graphs of several polynomial functions are shown below. Notice how many times the graph of each function intersects the x-axis. In each case, this is the maximum number of real zeros the function may have. How does the degree compare to the maximum number of real zeros?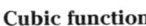

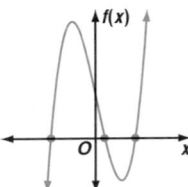

Constant function
$f(x) = 2$
Degree 0

Linear function
$f(x) = \frac{3}{2}x - 3$
Degree 1

Quadratic function
$f(x) = x^2 + 2x - 3$
Degree 2

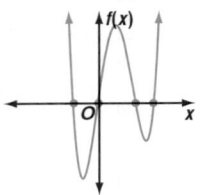

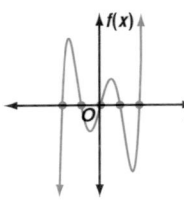

Cubic function
$f(x) = x^3 - 5x + 2$
Degree 3

Quartic function
$f(x) = x^4 - 3x^3 - 2x^2 + 7x + 1$
Degree 4

Quintic function
$f(x) = x^5 - 5x^3 + 4x$
Degree 5

These are the general shapes of the graphs for polynomial functions with degree greater than 0 and positive **leading coefficients**. The leading coefficient is the coefficient of the term with the highest degree. So, for the function $f(x) = 5x^3 + 2x^2 + 8x - 1$, the leading coefficient is 5.

Notice that the simplest polynomial graphs have equations in the form $f(x) = x^n$, where n is a positive number. Note the general shapes of the graphs for even-degree polynomial functions and odd-degree polynomial functions.

even-degree polynomial functions

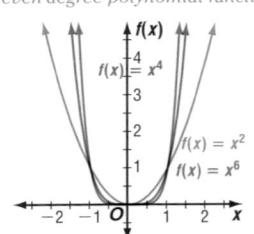

odd-degree polynomial functions

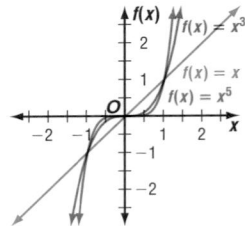

GLENCOE Technology

Interactive Mathematics Tools Software

This multimedia software provides an interactive lesson by helping students determine the degree of a function by its graph. A **Computer Journal** gives students an opportunity to write about what they have learned.

For Windows & Macintosh

LOOK BACK

Refer to Lesson 6-1 for a review of roots of quadratic equations.

Note that the even-degree functions are tangent to the *x*-axis at the origin. When this happens, the function has two zeros or roots that are the same number. For example, $x^2 - 6x + 9 = 0$ can be factored as $(x - 3)(x - 3) = 0$. So 3 is the root of the equation.

An even-degree function may or may not intersect the *x*-axis, depending on its location in the coordinate plane. If it does not intersect the *x*-axis, its roots are all imaginary. An odd-degree function always crosses the *x*-axis at least once. *Why?*

Example **4** Determine if each graph represents an odd-degree function or an even-degree function. Then state how many real zeros each function has.

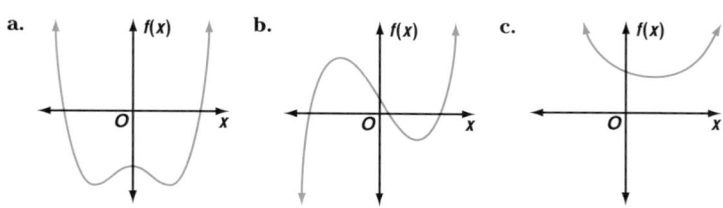

a. b. c.

Graph	left-most y values	right-most y values	degree of function	times graph crosses x-axis	number of real zeros
a.	positive	positive	even	2	2
b.	negative	positive	odd	3	3
c.	positive	positive	even	0	0

In Chapter 2, you studied families of graphs of linear equations. In Chapter 6, you studied families of parabolas. Some families of graphs of polynomial equations are shown below. The equation below each graph is the equation of the parent graph for that family.

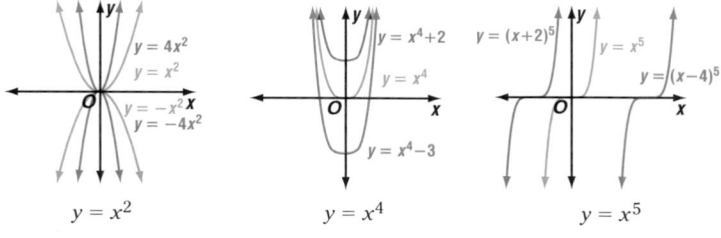

$y = x^2$ $y = x^4$ $y = x^5$

CHECK FOR UNDERSTANDING

Communicating Mathematics

Study the lesson. Then complete the following.

1. Refer to Example 4. What appears to be the degree of each function? **4, 3, 2**

2. **Describe** the characteristics of the graphs of odd-degree and even-degree polynomial functions whose leading coefficients are positive. **See margin.**

3. **State** how many real zeros are possible for each polynomial function.

   a. quartic **4** b. linear **1** c. quadratic **2** d. quintic **5** e. cubic **3**

Alternative Teaching Strategies

Student Diversity To help students relate the terms used in the lesson to their visual representations, have students quickly sketch graphs for a number of functions that you describe orally, such as a "quartic function," or a "function of degree 4," or an "even degree function with no real zeros." Students' graphs may vary, but all should show the correct orientation.

In-Class Example

For Example 4
Determine if each graph represents an odd-degree function or an even-degree function. Then state how many real zeros each function has.

a.
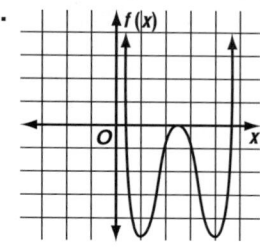

even; 3

b.
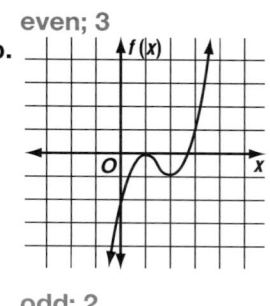

odd; 2

Additional Answer

2. Sample answer: Even-degree polynomial functions with positive leading coefficients have graphs whose leftmost points and rightmost points have positive values for $f(x)$. Odd-degree polynomial functions with positive leading coefficients have graphs whose leftmost points have negative values for $f(x)$ and whose rightmost points have positive values for $f(x)$.

Check for Understanding

Exercises 1–23 are designed to help you assess your students' understanding through reading, writing, speaking, and modeling. You should work through Exercises 1–6 with your students and then monitor their work on Exercises 7–23.

Additional Answers

4.

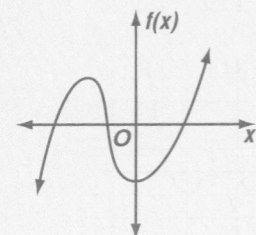

5. Zach is correct. For example, the graph of the function $y = x^2 + 4x + 4$ is tangent to the x-axis at one point, and the graph of the function $y = x^2 + 2$ does not intersect the x-axis at any point.

6. Sample answer: When the leading coefficient is positive, the graph's leftmost points go downward and the right-most points go upward.

(continued in bottom margin)

udy Guide Masters, p. 56

8-1   NAME_____ DATE _____

Student Edition
Pages 478–485

Study Guide

Polynomial Functions

A polynomial function is one whose value, for each number a, is equal to the value of a polynomial for the value a of its variable. The function $p(x) = x^3 + 2x^2 - 5x + 7$ is a polynomial function. To find the value of $p(x)$ for a particular value of x, evaluate $x^3 + 2x^2 - 5x + 7$ for value of x.

Example: Find $p(3)$ if $p(x) = x^3 + 2x^2 - 5x + 7$.

$p(3) = (3)^3 + 2(3)^2 - 5(3) + 7$ Replace x with 3.
$= 27 + 2 \cdot 9 - 15 + 7$ Simplify.
$= 27 + 18 - 15 + 7$
$= 37$

Find f(−3) for each function.

1. $f(x) = 6x + 10$ −8
2. $f(x) = -x^3 + 4x^2 + 37$ 316
3. $f(x) = x^4 + 2x^3 + 4x - 1$ 14
4. $f(x) = \frac{2}{3}x^3 - x$ 57
5. $f(x) = 7x^3 + \frac{1}{9}x^2 - 50$ −238
6. $f(x) = x^3 - x^2 - x + 4$ −29

Find f(x + h) for each function.

7. $f(x) = \frac{1}{2}x$ $\frac{1}{2}x + \frac{1}{2}h$
8. $f(x) = 5x^2 - 3$ $5x^2 + 10xh + 5h^2 - 3$
9. $f(x) = x^2 - 7x + 4$ $x^2 + 2xh + h^2 - 7x - 7h + 4$
10. $f(x) = x^3 + 4x$ $x^3 + 3x^2h + 3xh^2 + h^3 + 4x$
11. $f(x) = x^2 - \frac{2}{5}x$ $x^2 + 2xh + h^2 - \frac{2}{5}x - \frac{2}{5}h$
12. $f(x) = x^3 - x^2$ $x^3 + 3x^2h + 3xh^2 + h^3 - x^2 - 2xh - h^2$
13. $f(x) = (x - h)^2 + x$ $x^2 + x - h$
14. $f(x) = x^2 + 2x - h^2$ $x^2 + 2xh + 2x + 2h$

---

4. Sketch the graph of an odd-degree function with a positive leading coefficient and three real roots.   **See margin for sample graph.**

5. You Decide   Carlos explains to his friend Zach, "The graphs of odd-degree polynomial functions always intersect the x-axis an odd number of times, and the graphs of even-degree functions always intersect the x-axis an even number of times." Zach doesn't believe this is always the case. Who is correct? Give an example to support your answer.   **See margin.**

 MATH JOURNAL

6. Look at the family of graphs at the right for the function $f(x) = x^3$. Investigate the relationship between the similar functions and their graphs. **See margin.**

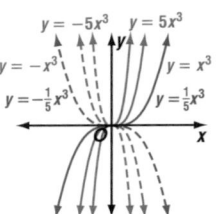

Guided Practice

8. No, the polynomial contains two variables, a and b.

11. quintic, 5, 5

13. quartic, 4, 4

Find the degree of each polynomial in one variable. If it is not a polynomial in one variable, explain why.

7. $4t^3 + 8t^2 + 2t - 1$ **3**   **8.** $9ab^2 + 4ab + 3$ **9.** $7x^3 - 8x^5 + 8x - 7$ **5**

Identify each polynomial function as *linear, quadratic, cubic, quartic,* or *quintic*. State the degree and how many real zeros are possible.

10. $f(x) = 6x^3 + 8x + 7$ **cubic, 3, 3**   **11.** $f(x) = 3x^5 + 7x^4 - 5x^3 + 6x + 9$

12. $f(x) = 2x + 5$ **linear, 1, 1**   **13.** $f(x) = 5x^3 + 6x^2 - 8x^4 - 10x + 17$

Match the polynomial and its functional value.

14. $p(x) = 3x^2 + 4x + 5$ **b**
15. $p(x) = x^4 - 7x^3 + 8x - 6$ **a**
16. $p(x) = 7x^2 - 9x + 10$ **d**
17. $p(x) = 4x^3 - 2x^2 - 6x + 5$ **c**

a. $p(4) = -166$
b. $p(5) = 100$
c. $p(-4) = -259$
d. $p(-2) = 56$

18. Refer to the graph at the right.
   a. Determine whether the degree of the function is even or odd.   **even**
   b. How many real zeros does the polynomial function have?   **3**

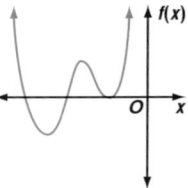

Find p(2) and p(−1) for each function.

19. $p(x) = 2x^2 + 6x - 8$ **12, −12**   **20.** $p(x) = -3x^4 + 1$ **−47, −2**

Find f(x + h) for each function.

21. $f(x) = 2x - 3$ **$2x + 2h - 3$**   **22.** $f(x) = 4x^2$ **$4x^2 + 8xh + 4h^2$**

23. Energy   The power generated by a windmill is a function of the speed of the wind. The approximate power is given by the function $P(s) = \frac{s^3}{1000}$, where s represents the speed of the wind in kilometers per hour. Find the units of power generated by a windmill when the wind speed is 25 kilometers per hour.   **15.625 units**

Reteaching

Using Reasoning To focus on the scheme for naming coefficients in a polynomial, ask for the exponent of x for the term with coefficient a_r, $(a_r x^?)$.

$n - r$

Contrast the scheme given with

$b_n x^n + b_{n-1} x^{n-1} + b_{n-2} x^{n-2} + \ldots$

$b_r x^r + \ldots b_1 x + b_0$.

Additional Answer

6. continued

When the leading coefficient is negative, the graph's leftmost points go upward and the rightmost points go downward. As the leading coefficient decreases, the graph stretches out and approaches the x-axis. As the leading coefficient increases, the graph narrows and approaches the y-axis.

Practice

Determine whether the degree of the function represented by each graph is even or odd. How many real zeros does each polynomial function have?

24.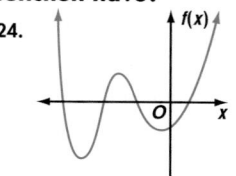

25.

26.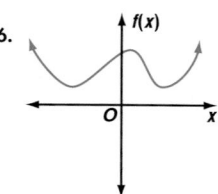

24. even, 4
25. odd, 2
26. even, 0

Find $p(3)$ and $p(-2)$ for each function.

27. $p(x) = 5x + 6$ 21, −4
28. $p(x) = x^2 - 2x + 1$ 4, 9
29. $p(x) = 2x^3 - x^2 - 3x + 1$ 37, −13
30. $p(x) = x^5 - x^2$ 234, −36
31. $p(x) = -x^4 + 53$ −28, 37
32. $p(x) = x^5 + 5x^4 - 15x^2 - 8$
   505, −20

Find $f(x + h)$ for each function.

33. $f(x) = x + 2$ $x + h + 2$
34. $f(x) = x - 4$ $x + h - 4$

36. $x^2 + 2xh + h^2 -$
$2x - 2h + 5$

35. $f(x) = 5x^2$ $5x^2 + 10xh + 5h^2$
36. $f(x) = x^2 - 2x + 5$

37. $3x^2 + 6xh + 3h^2 + 7$

37. $f(x) = 3x^2 + 7$
38. $f(x) = x^3 + x$

38. $x^3 + 3x^2h + 3xh^2 + h^3 + x + h$

Find $4[p(x)]$ for each function.   39. $4x^2 + 20$ 40. $24x^3 - 16x^2 + 8$

41. $x^3 + \dfrac{x^2}{4} - 8$

39. $p(x) = x^2 + 5$
40. $p(x) = 6x^3 - 4x^2 + 2$
41. $p(x) = \dfrac{x^3}{4} + \dfrac{x^2}{16} - 2$

Find an equation for each graph.

42.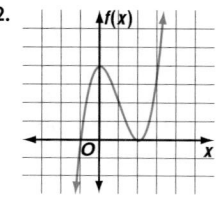

43.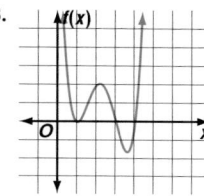

44.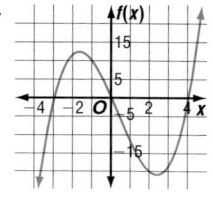

42. $f(x) = x^3 - 3x^2 + 4$
43. $9x^3 + 27x^2 - 31x + 12$
44. $f(x) = x^3 - x^2 - 12x$

45. Sketch a graph of a polynomial function $f(x)$ that has the indicated number and type of zeros. **See Solutions Manual for sample graphs.**
   a. 5 real   **b.** 3 real, 2 imaginary   **c.** 4 imaginary

Find $2p(a) + p(a - 1)$ for each function.

46. $p(x) = 4x + 1$
   $12a - 1$
47. $p(x) = x^2 + 3$
   $3a^2 - 2a + 10$
48. $p(x) = x^2 - 5x + 8$
   $3a^2 - 17a + 30$

Find $2[f(x + 3)]$ for each function.

49. $f(x) = 2x + 9$
   $4x + 30$
50. $f(x) = x^2 - 6$
   $2x^2 + 12x + 6$
51. $f(x) = x^2 + 3x + 12$
   $2x^2 + 18x + 60$

Graphing Calculator

52. Sketch a graph that matches each description. Write an equation for the graph of each function. **See Solutions Manual for sample graphs.**
   a. a quadratic function with zeros at −1 and 2. $f(x) = x^2 - x - 2$
   b. a cubic function with zeros at −2, −1, and 2. $f(x) = x^3 + x^2 - 4x - 4$
   c. a quartic function with zeros at −2, −1, 1, and 2. $f(x) = x^4 - 5x^2 + 4$
   d. a quintic function with zeros at −2, −1, 0, 1, and 2. $f(x) = x^5 - 5x^3 + 4x$

Extension

Reasoning Find
$\dfrac{f(x + h) - f(x)}{h}$ if $f(x) = x^4$.

$4x^3 + 6x^2h + 4xh^2 + h^3$

Assignment Guide

Core: 25–55 odd, 57–66
Enriched: 24–52 even, 53–66

For **Extra Practice,** see p. 894.

The red A, B, and C flags, printed only in the Teacher's Wraparound Edition, indicate the level of difficulty of the exercises.

Practice Masters, p. 56

8-1   NAME_____   DATE_____
Practice   Student Editio
Pages 478–48

Polynomial Functions
Find f(3) for each function.
1. $f(x) = x^3 - 6x + 2$ −7
2. $f(x) = x^4 - x^3$ 72

3. $f(x) = -5x^3 + 6x^2 - x - 4$ −88
4. $f(x) = \frac{x^2}{6} + 4x - 10$ $\frac{7}{2}$

Find h(−2) for each function.
5. $h(x) = x^3 - x^5$ 24
6. $h(x) = -7x^3 + 5x + 9$ −29

7. $h(x) = x^3 - \frac{5x}{4} + 6$ $\frac{25}{2}$
8. $h(x) = 3x^3 - 7x^2 + 2x - 5$ −61

Find g(x + h) for each function.
9. $g(x) = 6x - 7$ $6x + 6h - 7$
10. $g(x) = 3x^2 - 4x + 6$
   $3x^2 + 6xh + 3h^2 - 4x - 4h + 6$

11. $g(x) = -2x^2 + 5x - 4$
   $-2x^2 - 4xh - 2h^2 + 5x + 5h - 4$
12. $g(x) = x^3 - 2x$
   $x^3 + 3x^2h + 3xh^2 + h^3 - 2x - 2h$

Find 5[f(x + 2)] for each function.
13. $f(x) = 3x^2 - 4$ $15x^2 + 60x + 40$
14. $f(x) = x + 8$ $5x + 50$

15. $f(x) = 3x - 4$
   $15x + 10$
16. $f(x) = 2x^2 - 5x + 1$
   $10x^2 + 15x - 5$

Closing Activity

Speaking Have students form small groups. Give each group the same principal and a different rate of interest and ask them to determine the amount of the total investment. Each group will then share the total investment with the class and discuss how the same amount of principal with different rates will provide greater income.

Additional Answers

54b.

$f(x) = \frac{1}{2}x(x - 4)(x + 1)$

56c. $h = 3(1)^2 - 3(1) + 1$ or 1
$h = 3(2)^2 - 3(2) + 1$ or 7
$h = 3(3)^2 - 3(3) + 1$ or 19
The domain is the total number of rings and the range is the number of hexagons.

Enrichment Masters, p. 56

8-1

NAME_____ DATE _____

Enrichment

Student Edition
Pages 480–487

Approximation by Means of Polynomials

Many scientific experiments produce pairs of numbers $[x, f(x)]$ that one would like to see related by some kind of formula. If the pairs form a function, you can fit a polynomial to the pairs in exactly one way. Consider the pairs given by the following table.

x	1	2	4	7
f(x)	6	11	39	-54

We will assume the polynomial is of degree three. Substitute the given values into this expression.

$f(x) = A + B(x - x_0) + C(x - x_0)(x - x_1) + D(x - x_0)(x - x_1)(x - x_2)$

You will get the system of equations shown at the right. You can solve this system and use the values for A, B, C, and D to find the desired polynomial.

$6 = A$
$11 = A + B$
$39 = A + 3B + 6C$
$-54 = A + 6B + 30C + 90D$

Solve each problem.

1. Solve the system of equations for the values A, B, C, and D.
$A = 6, B = 5, C = 3, D = -2$

2. Find the polynomial that represents the four ordered pairs. Write your answer in the form $y = a + bx + cx^2 + dx^3$.
$y = -2x^3 + 17x^2 - 32x + 23$

3. Find the polynomial that gives the following values.

x	8	12	15	20
f(x)	-207	169	976	3801

$A = -207, B = 94, C = 25, D = 1; y = x^3 - 10x^2 - 10x + 1$

4. A scientist measured the volume $f(x)$ of carbon dioxide gas that can be absorbed by one cubic centimeter of charcoal at pressure x.

x	120	340	534	698
f(x)	3.1	5.5	7.1	8.3

Find the values for A, B, C, and D.
$A = 3.1, B = 0.01091,$
$C = -0.00000643, D = 0.0000000066$

53. There is no real number x that can make the equation $0 = x^4 + x^2 + 1$ true.

Applications and Problem Solving

56b.

Number of Rings	Number of Hexagons
1	1
2	7
3	19
4	37

57. See margin.

58. $\frac{x^2}{4} + \frac{y^2}{1} = 1$, Ellipse; see margin for graph.

61. $1.6 \times 10^6; 1.7 \times 10^6$

53. Although a fourth-degree function can have as many as four real zeros, $P(x) = x^4 + x^2 + 1$ has no real zeros. Can you explain why?

54. The graph of the polynomial function $f(x) = ax(x - 4)(x + 1)$ goes through the point at (5, 15).

   a. Find the value of a. $\frac{1}{2}$

   b. Sketch the graph of the function. **See margin.**

55. **Biology** The intensity of light emitted by a firefly can be determined by the polynomial function $L(t) = 10 + 0.3t + 0.4t^2 - 0.01t^3$, where t is the temperature in Celsius and $L(t)$ is the light intensity in lumens. If the temperature is 30° C, find the light intensity. **109 lumens**

56. **Patterns** If you look at a cross section of a honeycomb, you see a pattern of hexagons. This pattern has one hexagon surrounded by six more hexagons. Surrounding these is a third "ring" of 12 hexagons, and so on. Assume that the pattern continues.

   a. Find the number of hexagons in the 4th ring. **18**

   b. Make a table that shows the total number of hexagons in the first ring, the first two rings, the first three rings, and the first four rings.

   c. Show that the polynomial function $h = 3r^2 - 3r + 1$ gives the total number of hexagons when $r = 1, 2, 3$. Identify the domain and range of this function. **See margin.**

   d. Use the equation to find the total number of hexagons in a honeycomb with 12 rings. **397**

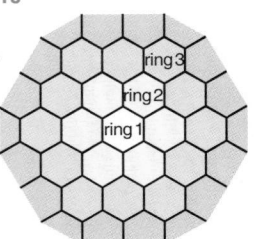

57. **Seismology** Two tracking stations have detected an earthquake. The first station determined that the epicenter was 25 miles away. The second station determined that the epicenter was 42 miles away. If the first station is located at the origin and the second station is 50 miles due east of the first station, where could the epicenter have been? (Lesson 7–7)

58. Write the standard form of the equation $x^2 + 4y^2 = 4$. Graph the equation and state whether the graph is a parabola, a circle, an ellipse, or a hyperbola. (Lesson 7–6)

59. Find two numbers whose difference is -40 and whose product is a minimum. (Lesson 6–4) **−20, 20**

60. Solve $\sqrt{n + 12} - \sqrt{n} = 2$. (Lesson 5–8) **4**

61. **Biology** The average human has between 1,600,000 and 1,700,000 sweat glands, mostly located in the palms of the hand and soles of the feet. Express both of these figures in scientific notation. (Lesson 5–1)

62. Determine the dimensions of the product $A_{4\times2} \cdot B_{2\times3}$. (Lesson 4–3) **4 × 3**

63. Find $\begin{bmatrix} -9 & 6 \\ 5 & 19 \end{bmatrix} - \begin{bmatrix} -3 & 18 \\ -4 & 12 \end{bmatrix}$. (Lesson 4–2) $\begin{bmatrix} -6 & -12 \\ 9 & 7 \end{bmatrix}$

64. In which octant does the point at $(7, -2, 9)$ lie? (Lesson 3–7) **2**

65. Solve the system of equations by using either the substitution or elimination method. (Lesson 3–2) **(4, −28)**
$2x - y = 36$
$3x - \frac{1}{2}y = 26$

66. Evaluate $2|-3x| - 9$ if $x = 5$. (Lesson 1–5) **21**

Additional Answers

57. Approximately (13.6, 21) or (13.6, −21); that is, the epicenter could have been 13.6 miles east and 21 miles north or south of the first station.

58.

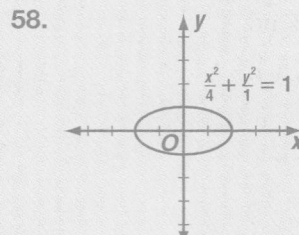

$\frac{x^2}{4} + \frac{y^2}{1} = 1$

The Remainder and Factor Theorems

What YOU'LL LEARN

• To find factors of polynomials by using the factor theorem and synthetic division.

Why IT'S IMPORTANT

You can use the remainder and factor theorems to find factors of polynomials that model situations in engineering and architecture.

APPLICATION
Sports

A javelin is usually thrown from about shoulder height, around 5 feet off the ground. It is not unusual for the javelin to start off with an upward velocity of about 74 feet per second. Based on this information, one can determine that the height of a javelin t seconds after it is thrown can be described by the function $h(t) = -16t^2 + 74t + 5$, if the effect of air resistance is ignored. The 16 in the function is associated with the strength of the Earth's gravity; if the javelin were thrown on another planet, there would be a different number in the equation.

The graph of $h(t)$ is shown at the right. Notice that when $t = 0$, the value of $h(t)$ is 5. Suppose we find the height of the javelin after 3 seconds.

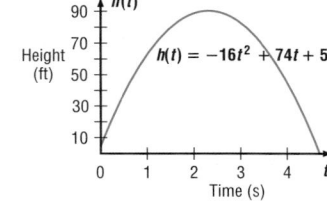

$h(t) = -16t^2 + 74t + 5$

$h(3) = -16(3)^2 + 74(3) + 5$ *Replace t with 3.*

$= -144 + 222 + 5$

$= 83$

After 3 seconds, the height of the javelin is 83 feet.

Divide the polynomial in the function by $t - 3$, and compare the remainder to $h(3)$.

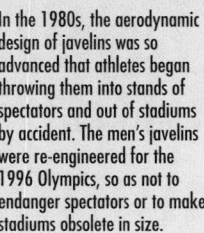

F Y I

In the 1980s, the aerodynamic design of javelins was so advanced that athletes began throwing them into stands of spectators and out of stadiums by accident. The men's javelins were re-engineered for the 1996 Olympics, so as not to endanger spectators or to make stadiums obsolete in size.

Method 1: Long Division

$$\begin{array}{r} -16t + 26 \\ t - 3 \overline{)-16t^2 + 74t + 5} \\ \underline{-16t^2 + 48t} \\ 26t + 5 \\ \underline{26t - 78} \\ 83 \end{array}$$

Method 2: Synthetic Division

$$\begin{array}{c|rrr} 3 & -16 & 74 & 5 \\ & & -48 & 78 \\ \hline & -16 & 26 & \underline{83} \end{array}$$

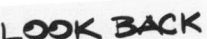

LOOK BACK

Refer to Lesson 5-3 for a review of synthetic division.

Notice that the value of $h(3)$ is the same as the remainder when the polynomial is divided by $t - 3$. This illustrates the **remainder theorem.**

The Remainder Theorem	If a polynomial $f(x)$ is divided by $x - a$, the remainder is the constant $f(a)$, and dividend = quotient · divisor + remainder $f(x) = q(x) \cdot (x - a) + f(a)$, where $q(x)$ is a polynomial with degree one less than the degree of $f(x)$.

Lesson 8–2   The Remainder and Factor Theorems   **485**

F Y I

According to Olympic regulations, a javelin must be at least 260 centimeters long for men and 220 centimeters long for women. A man's javelin weighs 800 grams while a woman's javelin weighs 600 grams.

8-2 LESSON NOTES

NCTM Standards: 1–5

Instructional Resources

• Study Guide Master 8-2
• Practice Master 8-2
• Enrichment Master 8-2
• Assessment and Evaluation Masters, p. 212
• Science and Math Lab Manual, pp. 43–48

Transparency 8-2A contains the 5-Minute Check for this lesson; **Transparency 8-2B** contains a teaching aid for this lesson.

Recommended Pacing	
Standard Pacing	Day 2 of 15
Honors Pacing	Day 2 of 14
Block Scheduling*	Day 1 of 7 (along with Lesson 8-1)

*For more information on pacing and possible lesson plans, refer to the *Block Scheduling Booklet.*

1 FOCUS

5-Minute Check
(over Lesson 8-1)

1. Determine whether the degree of the function represented in the graph is even or odd. State how many real zeros the polynomial function has.

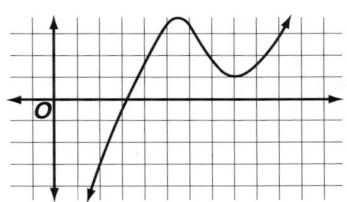

odd, 1

2. Find $f(4)$ if $f(x) = 3x^2 + 4x - 5$. 59

3. Find $p(3)$ if $p(x) = x^3 - x^2 - x - 1$. 14

4. Find $3 \cdot p(x - 1)$ if $p(x) = x^2 - 4x - 9$.
$3x^2 - 18x - 12$

Motivating the Lesson

Questioning Have students do two division problems. One problem should be long division with whole numbers, and the other problem should be long division with variables. Compare the steps of each problem.

Teaching Tip Another way of interpreting the remainder theorem is as follows. For any polynomial $f(x)$, $f(a)$ is always the same value as the remainder when $f(x)$ is divided by $x - a$.

Teaching Tip Remind students that in the remainder theorem the divisor must be in the form $x - a$.

In-Class Examples

For Example 1
Show that $f(0)$ is the remainder when $f(x)$ is divided by x if $f(x) = x^3 - x^2 + x + 1$.

$$\underline{0}\begin{array}{rrrr} 1 & -1 & 1 & 1 \\ & 0 & 0 & 0 \\ \hline 1 & -1 & 1 & | \; 1 \end{array}$$

$f(0) = 0^3 - 0^2 + 0 + 1$ or 1
The result is the same as the remainder.

For Example 2
a. If $f(x) = x^4 - 6x^3 + 8x^2 + 5x + 13$, find $f(4)$. **33**
b. If $f(x) = 3x^5 - 5x^3 + 57$, find $f(-2)$. **1**

Example ① Let $f(x) = 3x^4 - x^3 + 2x - 6$. Show that $f(2)$ is the remainder when $f(x)$ is divided by $x - 2$.

Use synthetic division to divide by $x - 2$.

$$\underline{2|}\begin{array}{rrrrr} 3 & -1 & 0 & 2 & -6 \\ & 6 & 10 & 20 & 44 \\ \hline 3 & 5 & 10 & 22 & | \; 38 \end{array}$$ *Long division could also be used.*

The quotient is $3x^3 + 5x^2 + 10x + 22$ with a remainder of 38.

Now find $f(2)$.　　$f(2) = 3(2)^4 - (2)^3 + 2(2) - 6$
　　　　　　　　　　$= 48 - 8 + 4 - 6$ or 38

Thus, $f(2) = 38$, the same number as the remainder after division by $x - 2$.

As illustrated in Example 1, synthetic division can be used to find the value of a function. When synthetic division is used to find the value of a function, it is called **synthetic substitution**. This is a convenient way of finding the value of a function, especially when the degree of the polynomial is greater than 2.

Example ② If $f(x) = x^4 + 2x^3 - 10x^2 + 5x - 7$, find $f(8)$.

Method 1: Synthetic Substitution

When $f(x)$ is divided by $x - 8$, the remainder is $f(8)$.

$$\underline{8|}\begin{array}{rrrrr} 1 & 2 & -10 & 5 & -7 \\ & 8 & 80 & 560 & 4520 \\ \hline 1 & 10 & 70 & 565 & | \; 4513 \end{array}$$

The remainder is 4513. Thus, by synthetic substitution, $f(8) = 4513$.

Method 2: Direct Substitution

$$f(8) = (8)^4 + 2(8)^3 - 10(8)^2 + 5(8) - 7$$
$$= 4096 + 1024 - 640 + 40 - 7 \text{ or } 4513$$

By substitution, $f(8) = 4513$, the same result as by synthetic substitution.

Consider $f(x) = x^4 + x^3 - 13x^2 - 25x - 12$. If $f(x)$ is divided by $x - 4$, then the remainder is 0. Therefore, 4 is a zero of $f(x)$.

$$\underline{4|}\begin{array}{rrrrr} 1 & 1 & -13 & -25 & -12 \\ & 4 & 20 & 28 & 12 \\ \hline 1 & 5 & 7 & 3 & | \; 0 \end{array}$$

The quotient of $f(x)$ and $x - 4$ is $x^3 + 5x^2 + 7x + 3$.

Check:　$f(x) = x^4 + x^3 - 13x^2 - 25x - 12$
　　　　　$f(4) \overset{?}{=} (4)^4 + (4)^3 - 13(4)^2 - 25(4) - 12$
　　　　　　$0 \overset{?}{=} 256 + 64 - 208 - 100 - 12$
　　　　　　$0 = 0$ ✓

From the results of the division and by using the remainder theorem, we can make the following statement.

$$\underset{\text{dividend}}{x^4 + x^3 - 13x^2 - 25x - 12} = \underset{\text{quotient}}{(x^3 + 5x^2 + 7x + 3)} \cdot \underset{\text{divisor}}{(x - 4)} + \underset{\text{remainder}}{0}$$

Since the remainder is 0, $x - 4$ is a factor of $x^4 + x^3 - 13x^2 - 25x - 12$. This illustrates the **factor theorem,** which is a special case of the remainder theorem.

The Factor Theorem	The binomial $x - a$ is a factor of the polynomial $f(x)$ if and only if $f(a) = 0$.

Suppose you wanted to find the zeros of $f(x) = x^3 - 6x^2 + 3x + 10$. From the graph at the right, you can see that the graph crosses the x-axis at -1, 2, and 5. These are the zeros of the function. Using these zeros and the zero product property, we can express the polynomial in factored form.

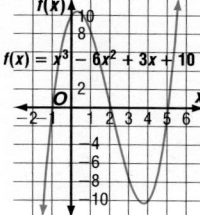

$$f(x) = (x + 1)(x - 2)(x - 5)$$

Many polynomial functions are not easily graphed and once graphed, the exact zeros are often difficult to determine. The factor theorem can help you find all the factors of a polynomial. Suppose we wanted to determine if $x - 3$ is a factor of $x^3 + 5x^2 - 12x - 36$ and, if it is, what the other factors are.

Let $f(x) = x^3 + 5x^2 - 12x - 36$. The binomial $x - 3$ is a factor of the polynomial if 3 is a zero. Use the factor theorem.

$$
\begin{array}{c|cccc}
3 & 1 & 5 & -12 & -36 \\
  &   & 3 & 24 & 36 \\
\hline
  & 1 & 8 & 12 & 0
\end{array}
$$

Since the remainder is 0, $x - 3$ is a factor of the polynomial. Further, since $x - 3$ is a factor of the polynomial, it follows that the remainder is 0.

When you divide a polynomial by one of its binomial factors, the quotient is called a **depressed polynomial.** The polynomial $x^3 + 5x^2 - 12x - 36$ can be factored as $(x - 3)(x^2 + 8x + 12)$. The polynomial $x^2 + 8x + 12$ is the depressed polynomial, which also may be factorable.

$$x^2 + 8x + 12 = (x + 2)(x + 6)$$

So, $x^3 + 5x^2 - 12x - 36 = (x - 3)(x + 2)(x + 6)$.

Example

APPLICATION
Engineering

When a certain type of plastic is cut into sections, the length of each section determines the strength of the plastic. The function $f(x) = x^4 - 14x^3 + 69x^2 - 140x + 100$ can describe the relative strength of a section of length x feet. Sections of plastic x feet long, where $f(x) = 0$, are extremely weak. After testing the plastic, engineers discovered that sections 2 feet long and 5 feet long were extremely weak.
a. Show that $x - 2$ and $x - 5$ are factors of the polynomial function.
b. Find other lengths of plastic that are extremely weak, if they exist.

(continued on the next page)

Cooperative Learning

Group Discussion Have students work in small groups. Half of each group should solve a division problem using long division; the others should use synthetic division. When finished, group members should compare their answers and discuss the advantages of each method. For more information on the group discussion strategy, see *Cooperative Learning in the Mathematics Classroom*, one of the titles in the Glencoe Mathematics Professional Series, page 31.

In-Class Example

For Example 3

a. Is $x - 2$ a factor of
$x^4 - x^3 + 2x - 2$?
$(x - 2)$ is not a factor.

b. Show that $x - 2$ is a factor of
$x^3 + 7x^2 + 2x - 40$. Then
find the remaining factors.
$(x - 2)(x + 4)(x + 5)$

3 PRACTICE/APPLY

Check for Understanding
Exercises 1–15 are designed to
help you assess your students'
understanding through reading,
writing, speaking, and modeling.
You should work through
Exercises 1–5 with your students
and then monitor their work on
Exercises 6–15.

Error Analysis
Given two linear factors of $p(x)$,
students sometimes divide $p(x)$ by
one factor and then divide $p(x)$
again by the other factor. The
second known factor should be
divided into the depressed
polynomial. Another error some
students make is to not check for
multiple factors.

Study Guide Masters, p. 57

8-2	NAME_____ DATE _____	Student Edition

Study Guide — Pages 486–492

The Remainder and Factor Theorems

Two important theorems concerning division of a polynomial by
a binomial are the remainder theorem and the factor theorem.

The Remainder Theorem

If a polynomial $f(x)$ is divided by $x - a$, the remainder is the constant $f(a)$, and
dividend = quotient · divisor + remainder
$f(x) = q(x) · (x - a) + f(a)$
where $q(x)$ is a polynomial with degree one less than the degree of $f(x)$.

The Factor Theorem

The binomial $x - a$ is a factor of the polynomial $f(x)$
if and only if $f(a) = 0$.

Suppose you need to find the value of a polynomial for a particular
value, a, of its variable. You can use long division or synthetic
substitution to find the remainder that results if you divide the
polynomial by $x - a$.

Example: Use synthetic substitution to find $f(1)$ if
$f(x) = x^4 + 3x^2 + 4x - 1$.

```
1 | 1  0  3  4  -1     Use the setup for synthetic division by x - 1.
  |    1  1  4   8
  --------------------
    1  1  4  8 |  7     The remainder is 7.
```
Since the remainder is 7, you know that $f(1) = 7$.

Use synthetic substitution to find $f(-5)$ and $f(\frac{1}{2})$ for each function.

1. $f(x) = -3x^2 + 5x - 1$ **2.** $f(x) = x^4 + 11x^2 - 1$
$-101; \frac{3}{4}$ $-181; \frac{37}{8}$

3. $f(x) = -x^3 + 3x^2 - 5$ $195; -\frac{35}{8}$ **4.** $f(x) = 4x^3 + 6x - 7$ $63; -3$

**Given a polynomial and one of its factors, find the remaining
factors of the polynomial.**

5. $x^3 - 4x^2 + 12x - 27; x - 3$ **6.** $x^3 + 4x^2 - x - 4; x + 4$
$x^2 - x + 9$ $x + 1, x - 1$

Find values for k so that each remainder is 5.

7. $(x^2 + 6x + k) \div (x + 1)$ 10   **8.** $(2x^2 + 5x + k) \div (x + 2)$ 1

a.
```
2 | 1  -14   69  -140   100
  |     2   -24   90   -100
  ---------------------------
    1  -12   45   -50 |   0
```

The remainder is 0, so $x - 2$ is a factor of $x^4 - 14x^3 + 69x^2 - 140x + 100$.

So, $x^4 - 14x^3 + 69x^2 - 140x + 100 = (x^3 - 12x^2 + 45x - 50)(x - 2)$.

```
5 | 1  -12   45  -50
  |      5  -35   50
  --------------------
    1   -7   10 |  0
```

The remainder is 0, so $(x - 5)$ is a factor of $x^4 - 14x^3 + 69x^2 - 140x + 100$.

So, $x^4 - 14x^3 + 69x^2 - 140x + 100 = (x - 2)(x - 5)(x^2 - 7x + 10)$.

b. Are there other values of x at which $f(x) = 0$? If so, sections of plastic
with these lengths will be extremely weak.

Factor the depressed polynomial, if possible.

$x^2 - 7x + 10 = (x - 2)(x - 5)$

So, $x^4 - 14x^3 + 69x^2 - 140x + 100 =$
$(x - 2)(x - 5)(x - 2)(x - 5)$ or
$(x - 2)^2 (x - 5)^2$.

The graph of the polynomial function
touches the x-axis at 2 and 5. Thus,
the only lengths of plastic that are
extremely weak are 2 feet and
5 feet long.

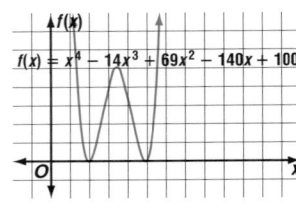

$f(x) = x^4 - 14x^3 + 69x^2 - 140x + 100$

CHECK FOR UNDERSTANDING

Communicating Mathematics

Study the lesson. Then complete the following.

1. If the divisor is a factor of a polynomial, then what is the remainder after
division?

2. **You Decide** Jack tells Mayuko that if $x - 6$ is a factor of a polynomial
$f(x)$, then $f(6) = 0$. Mayuko argues that if $x - 6$ is a factor of $f(x)$, then
$f(-6) = 0$. Who is correct? Explain.

3. **a.** **State** the zeros of the polynomial $P(x)$ whose
graph is shown at the right.

   b. **Describe** what $P(x) + 100$ would look like.
How many real zeros would it have?

4. **State** the degree of each polynomial. Then state
the degree of the depressed polynomial that
would result from dividing the polynomial by
one of its binomial factors.

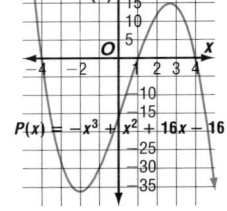

$P(x) = -x^3 + x^2 + 16x - 16$

   a. $4x^4 + 3x^3 - 5x^2 + 8$ **b.** $5x^2 + 7x^5 - 8x - 2$

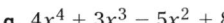

MATH JOURNAL

5. **Assess Yourself** A depressed polynomial of degree 2 is the result of
synthetic substitution. What options do you have to find the remaining
factors? Which would you choose to use first? Explain.

Guided Practice

Divide using synthetic division and write your answer in the form *dividend = quotient · divisor + remainder.* Is the binomial a factor of the polynomial? 6–7. See margin.

6. $(x^3 - 4x^2 + 2x - 6) \div (x - 4)$ **7.** $(x^4 - 16) \div (x - 2)$

Use synthetic substitution to find $g(2)$ and $g(-1)$ for each function.

8. $g(x) = x^3 - 5x + 2$ **0, 6**   **9.** $g(x) = x^4 - 6x - 8$ **−4, −1**

Given a polynomial and one of its factors, find the remaining factors of the polynomial. Some factors may not be binomials.

10. $x^3 + 2x^2 - x - 2; x - 1$ **11.** $x^3 - 6x^2 + 11x - 6; x - 2$

12. $2x^3 + 7x^2 - 53x - 28; (x + 7)$ **13.** $x^4 + 2x^3 + 2x^2 - 2x - 3; x + 1$

10. $x + 1, x + 2$
11. $x - 3, x - 1$
12. $2x + 1, x - 4$
13. $x - 1; x^2 + 2x + 3$

14. Use the graph of the polynomial function at the right to determine at least one binomial factor of the polynomial. Then find all factors of the polynomial. $(x - 2)(x + 2)(x^2 + 1)$

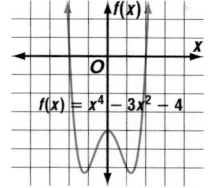
$f(x) = x^4 - 3x^2 - 4$

15. Use synthetic substitution to show that $x - 8$ is a factor of $x^3 - 4x^2 - 29x - 24$. Then find any remaining factors. $x + 1, x + 3$

EXERCISES

Practice

Divide using synthetic division and write your answer in the form *dividend = quotient · divisor + remainder.* Is the binomial a factor of the polynomial? 16–23. See margin.

16. $(x^3 - 6x^2 + 2x - 4) \div (x - 2)$ **17.** $(x^3 - 2x^2 - 5x + 6) \div (x - 3)$

18. $(2x^3 + 8x^2 - 3x - 1) \div (x - 2)$ **19.** $(x^3 + 27) \div (x + 3)$

20. $(2x^3 + x^2 - 8x + 16) \div (x + 4)$ **21.** $(6x^3 + 9x^2 - 6x + 2) \div (x + 2)$

22. $(x^3 - 64) \div (x - 4)$ **23.** $(4x^4 - 2x^2 + x + 1) \div (x - 1)$

Use synthetic substitution to find $f(2)$ and $f(-1)$ for each function.

24. $f(x) = x^3 - 2x^2 - x + 1$ **−1, −1** **25.** $f(x) = 2x^2 - 8x + 6$ **−2, 16**

26. $f(x) = x^3 + 2x^2 - 3x + 1$ **11, 5** **27.** $f(x) = x^3 - 8x^2 - 2x + 5$

28. $f(x) = 5x^4 - 6x^2 + 2$ **58, 1** **29.** $f(x) = 3x^4 + x^3 - 2x^2 + x + 12$ **62, 11**

27. −23, −2

Given a polynomial and one of its factors, find the remaining factors of the polynomial. Some factors may not be binomials.

30. $x^3 - x^2 - 5x - 3; x + 1$ **31.** $x^3 - 3x + 2; x - 1$

32. $x^3 + x^2 - 16x - 16; x - 4$ **33.** $6x^3 - 25x^2 + 2x + 8; 3x - 2$

34. $2x^3 + 17x^2 + 23x - 42; 2x + 7$ **35.** $x^4 + 2x^3 - 8x - 16; x + 2$

36. $8x^4 + 32x^3 + x + 4; 2x + 1$ **37.** $16x^5 - 32x^4 - 81x + 162; x - 2$
$x + 4, 4x^2 - 2x + 1$ $2x - 3, 2x + 3, 4x^2 + 9$

30. $x + 1, x - 3$
31. $x - 1, x + 2$
32. $x + 4, x + 1$
33. $2x + 1, x - 4$
34. $x - 1, x + 6$
35. $x - 2, x^2 + 2x + 4$

Use the graph of each polynomial function to determine at least one binomial factor of the polynomial. Then find all of the factors.

38. $f(x) = x^5 + x^4 - 3x^3 - 3x^2 - 4x - 4$ **39.** $f(x) = x^4 + 7x^3 + 15x^2 + 13x + 4$

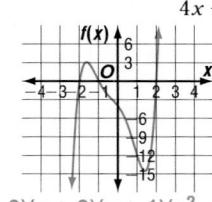   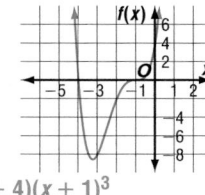

$(x - 2)(x + 2)(x + 1)(x^2 + 1)$ $(x + 4)(x + 1)^3$

Lesson 8-2 The Remainder and Factor Theorems **489**

Reteaching

Using Substeps Discuss the steps for dividing polynomials. List the steps on the board and use them to work a few examples. Encourage students to use the steps to do their homework.

Assignment Guide

Core: 17–43 odd, 44, 45, 47–54
Enriched: 16–42 even, 44–54

For **Extra Practice,** see p. 894.

The red A, B, and C flags, printed only in the Teacher's Wraparound Edition, indicate the level of difficulty of the exercises.

Additional Answers

6. $(x^3 - 4x^2 + 2x - 6) = (x^2 + 2)(x - 4) + 2$; no

7. $(x^4 - 16) = (x^3 + 2x^2 + 4x + 8)(x - 2) + 0$; yes

16. $(x^3 - 6x^2 + 2x - 4) = (x^2 - 4x - 6)(x - 2) - 16$; no

17. $(x^3 - 2x^2 - 5x + 6) = (x^2 + x - 2)(x - 3) + 0$; yes

18. $(2x^3 + 8x^2 - 3x - 1) = (2x^2 + 12x + 21)(x - 2) + 41$; no

19. $(x^3 + 27) = (x^2 - 3x + 9)(x + 3) + 0$; yes

20. $(2x^3 + x^2 - 8x + 16) = (2x^2 - 7x + 20)(x + 4) - 64$; no

21. $(6x^3 + 9x^2 - 6x + 2) = (6x^2 - 3x)(x + 2) + 2$; no

22. $(x^3 - 64) = (x^2 + 4x + 16)(x - 4) + 0$; yes

23. $(4x^4 - 2x^2 + x + 1) = (4x^3 + 4x^2 + 2x + 3)(x - 1) + 4$; no

Practice Masters, p. 57

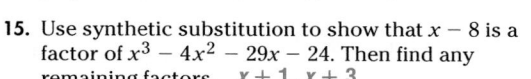

8-2   NAME_____   DATE_____
Practice   Student Edition
Pages 486–492

The Remainder and Factor Theorems

Divide using synthetic division and write your answer in the form dividend = quotient · divisor + remainder. Is the binomial a factor of the polynomial?

1. $(4x^3 - 9x^2 - 10x - 2) \div (x - 3)$
$4x^3 - 9x^2 - 10x - 2 =$
$(4x^2 + 3x - 1)(x - 3) - 5$; no

2. $(2x^3 + 5x^2 - 9x + 20) \div (x + 4)$
$2x^3 + 5x^2 - 9x + 20 =$
$(2x^2 - 3x + 3)(x + 4) + 8$; no

3. $(x^4 - 6x^3 - 2x - 10) \div (x + 1)$
$x^4 - 6x^3 - 2x - 10 =$
$(x^3 - 7x^2 + 7x - 9)(x + 1) - 1$; no

4. $(3x^4 - 9x^3 - 32x^2 + 54) \div (x - 5)$
$3x^4 - 9x^3 - 32x^2 + 54 =$
$(3x^3 + 6x^2 - 2x - 10)(x - 5) + 4$; no

Given a polynomial and one of its factors, find the remaining factors of the polynomial. Some factors may not be binomials.

5. $x^3 + 6x^2 - x - 30; x + 5$
$x + 3, x - 2$

6. $x^3 - 11x^2 + 36x - 36; x - 6$
$x - 3, x - 2$

7. $2x^3 + 3x^2 - 65x + 84; x - 4$
$2x - 3, x + 7$

8. $2x^3 + 15x^2 - 14x - 48; x - 2$
$2x + 3, x + 8$

9. $16x^5 + 32x^4 - x - 2; x + 2$
$4x^2 + 1, 2x + 1, 2x - 1$

10. $x^4 - 3x^3 + 27x - 81; x - 3$
$x + 3, x^2 - 3x + 9$

Find values for k so that each remainder is 5.

11. $(2x^2 - 8x + k) \div (x - 7)$
−37

12. $(x^3 + 4x^2 + kx + 8) \div (x + 2)$
5.5

13. $(x^4 + kx^3 - 7x^2 + 8x + 25) \div (x - 2)$
−3

14. $(x^2 + 2x + 6) \div (x + k)$
1

Chapter 8 **489**

Closing Activity

Speaking Ask students to describe the methods, step by step, for performing long division and for performing synthetic division.

Chapter 8, Quiz A (Lessons 8-1 and 8-2), is available in the *Assessment and Evaluation Masters*, p. 212.

Enrichment Masters, p. 57

8-2

NAME _____ DATE _____

Enrichment

Student Edition
Pages 488–494

Miniature Golf

In miniature golf, the object of the game is to roll the golf ball into the hole in as few shots as possible. As in the diagram at the right, the hole is often placed so that a direct shot is impossible. Reflections can be used to help determine the direction that the ball should be rolled in order to score a hole-in-one.

• Ball

• Hole

Example: Using wall $\overline{EF}$, find the path to use to score a hole-in-one.

Find the reflection image of the "hole" with respect to $\overline{EF}$ and label it H'. The intersection of $\overline{BH'}$ with wall $\overline{EF}$ is the point at which the shot should be directed.

• Ball

• Hole

E   F
            • H'

Example: For the hole at the right, find a path to score a hole-in-one.

Find the reflection image of H with respect to $\overline{EF}$ and label it H'. In this case, $\overline{BH'}$ intersects $\overline{JK}$ before intersecting $\overline{EF}$. Thus, this path cannot be used. To find a usable path, find the reflection image of H' with respect to $\overline{GF}$ and label it H''. Now, the intersection of $\overline{BH''}$ with wall $\overline{GF}$ is the point at which the shot should be directed.

• H'

Copy each figure. Then, use reflections to determine a possible path for a hole-in-one.

1. 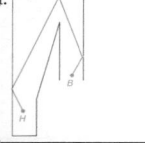   2. 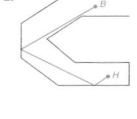   3.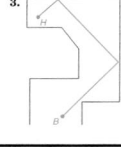

490 Chapter 8

Find values for k so that each remainder is 3.

40. $(x^2 - x + k) \div (x - 1)$ 3
41. $(x^2 + kx - 17) \div (x - 2)$ 8
42. $(x^3 + 4x^2 + x + k) \div (x + 2)$ −3
43. $(x^2 + 5x + 7) \div (x + k)$ 1, 4

Critical Thinking

44a. $f(-4) = -18$,
$f(-2) = 4$, $f(0) = -6$,
$f(2) = 0$, $f(4) = 70$

44c. 3 times, yes

44. Consider the function $f(x) = x^3 + 2x^2 - 5x - 6$.
  a. Use synthetic substitution to find $f(-4)$, $f(-2)$, $f(0)$, $f(2)$, and $f(4)$.
  b. On a coordinate plane, graph the ordered pairs of the form $(x, f(x))$ you found and connect them to make a smooth curve. **See margin.**
  c. How many times does the graph cross the x-axis? Does this agree with what you learned in Lesson 8-1 about graphs of polynomial functions?

Applications and Problem Solving

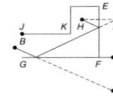

45. Architecture According to the *Guinness Book of Records,* the 1454-foot Sears Tower in Chicago, Illinois, is the tallest office building in the world. It has 110 floors and 18 elevators. The elevators traveling from one floor to the next do not travel at a constant speed. Suppose the speed of an elevator in feet per second is given by the function $F(t) = -0.5t^4 + 4t^3 - 12t^2 + 16t$, where t is the time in seconds.
  a. Find the speed of the elevator at 1, 2, and 3 seconds. **7.5, 8, 7.5**
  b. It takes 4 seconds for the elevator to go from one floor to the next. Use synthetic substitution to find $f(4)$. Explain what this means. **0; The elevator is stopping or is stopped.**

46. Technology The graph at the right shows how the cost of computer viruses in the U.S. has drastically increased since 1990. The function $C(x) = 0.03x^3 - 0.02x^2 + 0.2x + 0.1$ estimates this cost over the interval shown, with $x = 0$ representing the year 1990. Estimate the cost of computer viruses in the year 1999. **$22 billion**

Computer Bugs (in billions)

$2.7

$1.4

$0.1 $0.3 $0.7

'90 '91 '92 '93 '94

Source: National Computer Security Association

Mixed Review

48. (0, ±9);
$\left(0, \pm\sqrt{106}\right)$; $\pm\dfrac{9}{5}$

49. yes

50. $\dfrac{5 \pm i\sqrt{7}}{4}$

47. Art Joyce Jackson purchases works of art for an art gallery. Two years ago, she bought a painting for $20,000, and last year, she bought one for $35,000. If these paintings appreciate at 14% per year, how much are the two paintings worth now? (Lesson 8–1) **$65,892**

48. Find the coordinates of the vertices and foci and the slopes of the asymptotes for the hyperbola given by the equation $\dfrac{y^2}{81} - \dfrac{x^2}{25} = 1$. (Lesson 7–5)

49. Is $(4, -4)$ a solution to the quadratic inequality $-y \leq -x^2 + 5x$? (Lesson 6–7)

50. Solve $2x^2 - 5x + 4 = 0$ by using the quadratic formula. (Lesson 6–4)

51. Find $(6x^3 - 5x^2 - 12x - 4) \div (3x + 2)$. (Lesson 5–3) $2x^2 - 3x - 2$

52. Find $7\begin{bmatrix} -1 & 4 \\ 8 & -6 \end{bmatrix} + 2\begin{bmatrix} 6 & -5 \\ 1 & 8 \end{bmatrix}$. (Lesson 4–2) $\begin{bmatrix} 5 & 18 \\ 58 & -26 \end{bmatrix}$

53. Solve $\begin{bmatrix} 2x \\ y + 1 \end{bmatrix} = \begin{bmatrix} y \\ 3 \end{bmatrix}$ for x and y. (Lesson 4–1) **(1, 2)**

54. If $a = -1$, $b = 7$, $c = 4$, and $-a^3b^2 + 2ab + 3d \geq \dfrac{1}{2}c^3$, solve for d. (Lesson 1–6) $d \geq -1$

Extension

Reasoning

If $p(x) = 2x^3 + k^2x^2 - 4kx + 5$, find values for k so that $p(-1) = 0$.
−3 or −1

Additional Answer

44b.

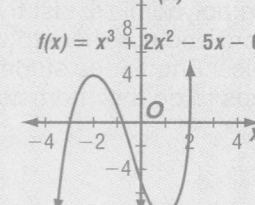

$f(x) = x^3 + 2x^2 - 5x - 6$

8–3A Graphing Technology
Polynomial Functions

A Preview of Lesson 8–3

You can use a graphing calculator to graph polynomial functions and approximate the real zeros of the function. When using a calculator to approximate zeros, it is important to view a complete graph of the function before zooming in on a certain point. Otherwise, zeros may be overlooked because they were not in the viewing window. Remember that a complete graph of a function shows all the characteristics of the graph such as all x- and y-intercepts, relative maximum and minimum points, and the end behavior of the graph.

Example Use a graphing calculator to obtain a complete graph of $f(x) = 2x^3 + 6x^2 - 14x + 12$. Then approximate each real zero to the nearest hundredth.

Let's try graphing in the standard viewing window.

Enter: [Y=] 2 [X,T,θ] [∧] 3 [+]

6 [X,T,θ] [x²] [−] 14

[X,T,θ] [+] 12 [ZOOM] 6

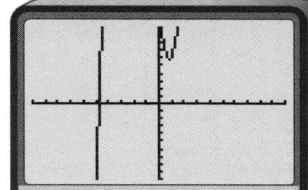

We see that this viewing window does not contain a complete graph. Change the viewing window to $[-10, 10]$ by $[-10, 60]$ with a scale factor of 1 for the x-axis and 5 for the y-axis.

This window can accommodate the complete graph.

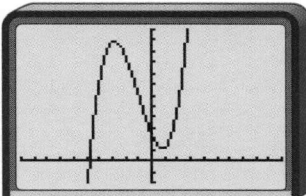

LOOK BACK

Refer to Lesson 6-1A for information on using the automatic ROOT feature.

According to the graph, there is one x-intercept (real zero) for this function. There are three zeros for any third-degree polynomial, so two of the zeros for this function must be imaginary. Use ZOOM, TRACE, or ROOT to approximate the real zero.

The only real zero is approximately -4.74.

When using a graphing calculator to approximate real zeros, it is helpful to know that a function with degree n has at most n real zeros. Thus, a function with degree 5 has at most five real zeros. If you can see five x-intercepts in the viewing window, you know you have found all of the zeros and that they are all real. However, if there are fewer than five x-intercepts, there are duplicate real zeros or the zeros are not all real. Complex or imaginary zeros occur in conjugate pairs, so a fifth-degree function may have one, three, or five real zeros.

Lesson 8–3A Graphing Technology: Polynomial Functions **491**

NCTM Standards: 1–6

Objective
Use a graphing calculator to graph polynomial functions and approximate the real zeros of the functions.

Recommended Time
25 minutes

Instructional Resources
Graphing Calculator Masters, pp. 45 and 46

These masters provide keystroking instruction for this lesson for the TI-81 and Casio graphing calculators.

1 FOCUS

Motivating the Lesson
Help students recall that an n-degree polynomial has n roots. These roots may be rational, real, or imaginary. Point out that a graphing calculator will reveal only real roots.

2 TEACH

Teaching Tip To ensure that the graph is complete, repeatedly zoom out until all the characteristics necessary to interpret the graph are in the viewing window.

3 PRACTICE/APPLY

Assignment Guide
Core: 1–10
Enriched: 1–10

Observing students working with technology is an excellent method of assessment.

Additional Answers

5.

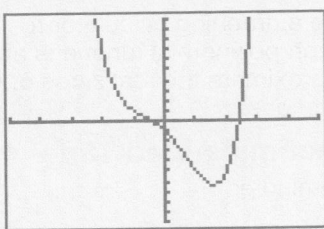

6.

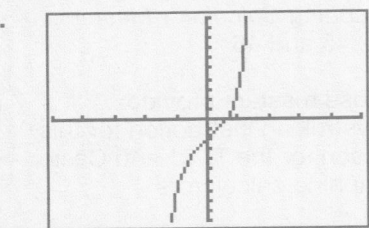

7.

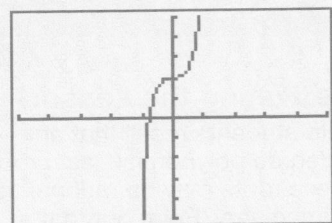

8.

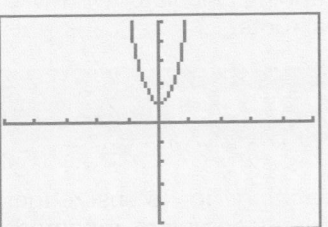

9.

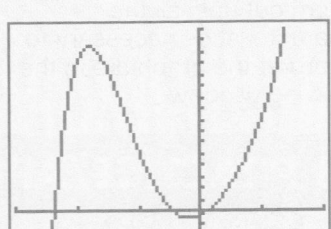

10.

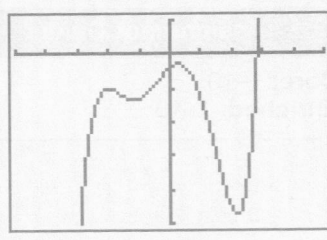

Example ❷ Use a graphing calculator to obtain a complete graph of $f(x) = 3x^5 - 5x^4 - 2x^3 + x^2 - 6x + 8$. Then approximate each real zero to the nearest hundredth.

First, try graphing in the standard viewing window.

Enter: 3 [X,T,θ] [∧] 5 [−] 5 [X,T,θ]

[∧] 4 [−] 2 [X,T,θ] [∧] 3 [+]

[X,T,θ] [x²] [−] 6 [X,T,θ] [+]

8 [ZOOM] 6

The standard viewing window does not accommodate the complete graph. The view shown at the right uses the window $[-5, 5]$ by $[-10, 15]$.

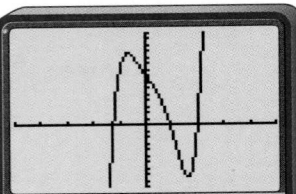

According to the graph, there are three real zeros for this function. Use ZOOM, TRACE, or ROOT to approximate the real zeros. They are approximately -1.24, 0.93, and 2.

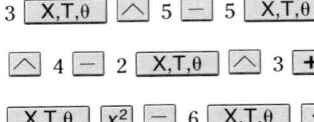
EXERCISES

Use a graphing calculator to obtain a complete graph of each polynomial function. Describe your viewing window and state the number of real zeros.

1. $f(x) = 2x^3 - 3x^2 - 12x + 17$

2. $f(x) = 3x^4 - 8x^3 - 35x^2 + 72x + 47$

3. $j(x) = 0.1x^4 + x^3 - x^2 + 3x + 18$

4. $g(x) = x^5 - 4x^4 + 2x^3 - 7x + 15$

Graph each function so that a complete graph is shown. Then approximate each of the real zeros to the nearest hundredth.

5. $f(x) = x^4 - 3x^2 - 6x - 2$

6. $h(x) = 2x^5 + 3x - 2$

7. $c(x) = 3x^{13} + 4x^3 + 2$

8. $m(x) = 2x^8 + 4x^2 + 1$

9. $p(x) = 8x^5 - 20x^3 + 73x^2 + 28x - 4$

10. $f(x) = x^5 + x^4 - 8x^3 - 10x^2 + 7x - 4$

492 Chapter 8 *Exploring Polynomial Functions*

Using Technology

This lesson offers an excellent opportunity for using technology in your algebra classroom. For more information on using technology, see *Graphing Calculators in the Mathematics Classroom*, one of the titles in the Glencoe Mathematics Professional Series.

Graphing Polynomial Functions and Approximating Zeros

INTEGRATION
Geometry

What YOU'LL LEARN

- To approximate the real zeros of polynomial functions,
- to find maxima and minima of polynomial functions, and
- to graph polynomial functions.

Why IT'S IMPORTANT

You can graph polynomial functions to solve problems involving geometry and physical fitness.

In her geometry class, Hillary Borchers has a project in which she must create cracker shapes that form a tessellation in the same manner as some Keebler crackers. For her art class, she must design a special packaging box for the crackers. In order to best display the tessellation, the bottom of the box will be a square, and it will be open at the top so that the crackers can be seen through cellophane.

Hillary is to use a 108 square-inch sheet of a special metallic paper to cover the sides and bottom of the box. What will be the dimensions of the box if it is to hold a maximum volume of crackers? You can use a graph to solve this problem.

First, write polynomial equations to describe the surface area and volume of the box. Let x represent the length of the side of the square on the bottom, and let h represent the height of the box.

$$\underbrace{Surface\ Area}\ =\ \underbrace{area\ of\ the\ base}\ +\ \underbrace{area\ of\ the\ four\ sides}$$

$$SA\ =\ x^2\ +\ 4xh$$
$$108\ =\ x^2 + 4xh \quad \textit{Replace SA with 108.}$$

$$\underbrace{Volume}\ =\ \underbrace{area\ of\ the\ base}\ \cdot\ \underbrace{height}$$
$$V\ =\ x^2\ \cdot\ h$$

In order to find the volume by graphing, we need to express the volume in terms of one variable. First, solve the surface area formula for h in terms of x.

$$x^2 + 4xh = 108$$
$$4xh = 108 - x^2$$
$$h = \frac{108 - x^2}{4x}$$

Then, substitute the value of h in the formula for volume.

$$V = x^2 h$$
$$= x^2\left(\frac{108 - x^2}{4x}\right) \quad \textit{Replace h with } \frac{108 - x^2}{4x}.$$
$$= \frac{108x^2 - x^4}{4x} \quad \textit{Simplify.}$$
$$= 27x - \frac{x^3}{4}$$

Let $V(x) = 27x - \dfrac{x^3}{4}$.

Lesson 8–3 Graphing Polynomial Functions and Approximating Zeros **493**

CAREER CHOICES

Industrial designers develop and design manufactured products and their packaging. They combine artistic talent with research on product use to create the most appealing and functional design.

A bachelor's degree is required and training in computer-aided design (CAD) is very helpful.

For more information, contact:
Industrial Designers Society of America
1142 E Walker Rd.
Great Falls, VA 22066

CAREER CHOICES

The average entry-level salary for industrial designers in 1992 was $27,900. Designers with 6 years of experience earned $38,100; those with 10 years of experience earned $44,500, while those in managerial positions averaged $75,000.

8-3 LESSON NOTES

NCTM Standards: 1–6

Instructional Resources

- Study Guide Master 8-3
- Practice Master 8-3
- Enrichment Master 8-3
- Graphing Calculator Masters, p. 8
- Real-World Applications, 22

Transparency 8-3A contains the 5-Minute Check for this lesson; **Transparency 8-3B** contains a teaching aid for this lesson.

Recommended Pacing	
Standard Pacing	Day 4 of 15
Honors Pacing	Day 4 of 14
Block Scheduling*	Day 2 of 7

*For more information on pacing and possible lesson plans, refer to the *Block Scheduling Booklet*.

1 FOCUS

5-Minute Check
(over Lesson 8-2)

1. Use synthetic substitution to find $f(3)$ for $f(x) = x^3 + 4x^2 + 3x - 2$. **70**
2. Use synthetic substitution to find $f(-3)$ for $f(x) = x^4 - 4x^2 + 4$. **49**
3. Divide $(x^3 - 4x^2 - 22x + 36)$ by $(x - 5)$. $x^2 + x - 17$; **R −49**
4. Is $(x - 7)$ a factor of $x^3 - 2x^2 - 39x + 28$? **yes**
5. Is $(x + 2)$ a factor of $6x^3 + 9x^2 - 6x + 2$? **no**

Motivating the Lesson

Hands-On Activity Have students sketch graphs given the following conditions.

1. third-degree with one real zero
2. third-degree with two real zeros
3. third-degree with three real zeros

Discuss the similarities and differences in this family of graphs.

Teaching Tip Emphasize that the location principle is true if it is assumed that the graph of a polynomial is a smooth continuous curve.

Make a table of values.

x	V(x)
−11	**35.75**
−10	**−20**
−9	−60.75
−8	−88
−7	−103.25
−6	−108
−5	−103.75
−4	−92

A zero is between $x = -11$ and $x = -10$.

x	V(x)
−3	−74.25
−2	−52
−1	−26.75
0	**0**
1	26.75
2	52
3	74.25
4	92

A zero is at $x = 0$.

x	V(x)
5	103.75
6	108
7	103.25
8	88
9	60.75
10	**20**
11	**−35.75**
12	−108

Greatest value for $V(x)$

A zero is between $x = 10$ and $x = 11$.

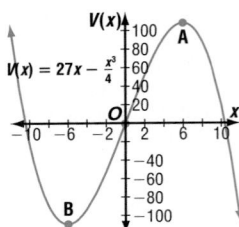

$V(x) = 27x - \dfrac{x^3}{4}$

Sketch the graph of the function $V(x)$ by connecting those points with a smooth curve. The graph will cross the x-axis somewhere between the pairs of x values where the corresponding $V(x)$ values change sign. Since the x-intercepts are zeros of the function, there is a zero between each pair of these x values. This strategy is called the **location principle.**

The Location Principle	Suppose $y = f(x)$ represents a polynomial function and a and b are two numbers such that $f(a) < 0$ and $f(b) > 0$. Then the function has at least one real zero between a and b.

The plurals of maximum and minimum are __maxima__ and __minima__.

The graph above shows the shape of the graph of a general third-degree polynomial function. Point A on the graph is a **relative maximum** of the cubic function, since no other nearby points have a greater y-coordinate. Likewise, point B is a **relative minimum,** since no other nearby points have a lesser y-coordinate. You can also see from the tables of values where there is a relative maximum and a relative minimum. You can use this information to help graph functions that have imaginary zeros.

You can use the coordinates of the relative maximum to determine the point at which the box has the maximum volume. In the tables of values, the point at (6, 108) appears to have the greatest y-coordinate. To check whether it is truly the relative maximum, compute the y values for an x value on either side of this point.

Find $V(5.9)$ and $V(6.1)$.

$$V(x) = 27x - \frac{x^3}{4}$$

$$V(5.9) = 27(5.9) - \frac{5.9^3}{4}$$

$$\approx 107.96$$

$$V(x) = 27x - \frac{x^3}{4}$$

$$V(6.1) = 27(6.1) - \frac{6.1^3}{4}$$

$$\approx 107.95$$

Since both y values are less than the y value for the maximum, the point at (6, 108) is a relative maximum. So, in order for the box to have a maximum volume, the side of the box has to be 6 inches long. The box would have a maximum volume of 108 cubic inches.

Classroom Vignette

"In addition to the traditional way of graphing polynomial functions, I like to have my students work in cooperative groups using a spreadsheet program or computer graphing program to study polynomial functions."

Sara Davis
Riverton High School
Riverton, Kansas

Sara Davis

To determine the height of the box, substitute 6 for x in the surface area equation.

$$h = \frac{108 - x^2}{4x}$$

$$= \frac{108 - 6^2}{4(6)} \quad \textit{Replace x with 6.}$$

$$= 3$$

The box must be 3 inches tall to have maximum volume. Thus, the dimensions of Hillary's cracker box are 6 inches by 6 inches by 3 inches.

Example 1

CONNECTION

Physics

Under certain conditions, the velocity of an object as a function of time is described by the function $V(t) = 9t^3 - 93t^2 + 238t - 120$. Approximate the zeros of $V(t)$ to the nearest tenth and draw the graph.

Evaluate the function for several successive values of t to locate the zeros. Then plot the points and connect them to form a smooth graph.

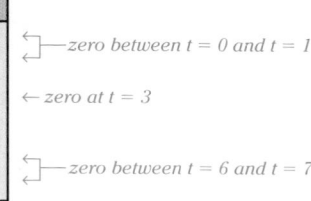

t	$V(t)$
0	**−120**
1	**34**
2	56
3	**0**
4	−80
5	−130
6	**−96**
7	**76**

zero between $t = 0$ and $t = 1$

zero at $t = 3$

zero between $t = 6$ and $t = 7$

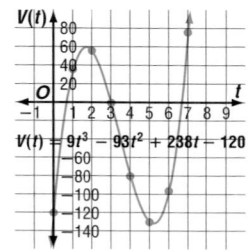

$V(t) = 9t^3 - 93t^2 + 238t - 120$

One zero lies between 0 and 1. Another zero is 3. A third zero lies between 6 and 7.

To approximate the zeros to the nearest tenth, you have to repeat the process of evaluating $V(t) = 9t^3 - 93t^2 + 238t - 120$ for successive values of t expressed in tenths, as we did in the application at the beginning of the lesson. Using a scientific calculator will help find these values more easily.

To evaluate $V(0.5)$, do the following.

Enter: 9 $\boxed{\times}$ .5 $\boxed{y^x}$ 3 $\boxed{-}$ 93 $\boxed{\times}$
.5 $\boxed{x^2}$ $\boxed{+}$ 238 $\boxed{\times}$ .5 $\boxed{-}$
120 $\boxed{=}$ -23.125

Following this procedure for the rest of the values in the chart, you will find that the zeros approximated to the nearest tenth are 0.7 and 6.7.

t	$V(t)$	
0.5	−23.125	
0.6	−8.736	zero
0.7	4.117	
6.5	−30.625	
6.6	−12.816	zero
6.7	6.697	

In-Class Example

For Example 1
Approximate to the nearest tenth the real zeros for $g(x) = -2x^3 - 5x^2 + 3x + 2$. Then draw the graph.
The real zeros are approximately −2.9, −0.4, and 0.8.

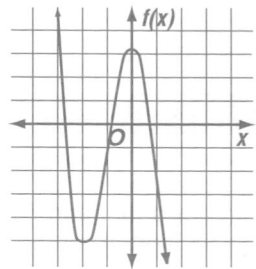

For Example 2
Graph $f(x) = x^3 + x^2 - 4x - 4$.

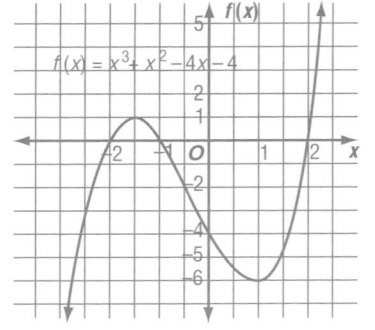

EXPLORATION

In this activity, students first use a graph to estimate the relative minimum for a function. They then learn a feature of the graphing calculator that finds a more accurate value for the relative minimum or maximum, provided a value below and above the minimum or maximum is given.

---

3 PRACTICE/APPLY

Check for Understanding

Exercises 1–14 are designed to help you assess your students' understanding through reading, writing, speaking, and modeling. You should work through Exercises 1–4 with your students and then monitor their work on Exercises 5–14.

Error Analysis
Students often overlook the possibility of real roots between integers m and $m + 1$ where $f(m)$ and $f(m + 1)$ have the same sign. Contrast this with the situation in which all x_1 and x_2 are in $[m, m + 1]$ are $f(x_1)$ and $f(x_2)$ have the same sign.

Example **Graph $f(x) = x^3 - 5x^2 + 3x + 12$.**

In order to graph the function, you need to find several points and then connect them to make a smooth curve. Since $f(x)$ is a third-degree polynomial function, it will have 3 or 1 real zeros. Also, its left-most points will have negative values for y, and its right-most points will have positive values for y.

Make a table and evaluate several successive values of x to locate the zeros and to find the relative maximum and relative minimum.

x	$f(x)$
-2	-22
-1	3
0	**12**
0.5	**12.375**
1	**11**
2	6
2.9	**3.039**
3	**3**
4	8

— zero between $x = -2$ and $x = -1$

} indicates a relative maximum

} indicates a relative minimum

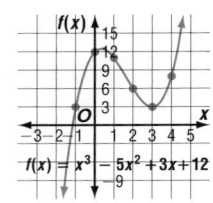

$f(x) = x^3 - 5x^2 + 3x + 12$

The function has one relative maximum and one relative minimum. The values of $f(0.5)$ and $f(2.9)$ were calculated to approximate the maximum and minimum more closely. There is a zero between -2 and -1. *Use a graphing calculator to check the graph.*

A graphing calculator can be helpful in finding the relative maximum and relative minimum of a function.

EXPLORATION
GRAPHING CALCULATORS

To find the relative maximum and relative minimum of $f(x) = x^3 - 6x^2 + 6x + 5$, press $\boxed{Y=}$ and enter the equation. Then press $\boxed{\text{ZOOM}}$ 6. The graph appears to have a relative minimum between 3 and 4 and a relative maximum between 0 and 1. To find the actual relative minimum, follow these steps.

Enter: $\boxed{\text{MATH}}$ 6 $\boxed{\text{2nd}}$ $\boxed{\text{Y-VARS}}$ 1 $\boxed{\text{ENTER}}$ $\boxed{,}$ $\boxed{\text{X,T,}\theta}$ $\boxed{,}$ 3 $\boxed{,}$ 4 $\boxed{)}$ $\boxed{\text{ENTER}}$ 3.414214414

Thus, there is a relative minimum at $x \approx 3.41$.

Your Turn

a. Find the y-coordinate of the relative minimum to the nearest hundredth.

b. Find the coordinates of the relative maximum of the function to the nearest hundredth. (*Hint*: Use the fMax feature by pressing $\boxed{\text{MATH}}$ 7.)

c. Graph the function $f(x) = x^3 + x^2 - 7x - 3$, and find the relative maximum and relative minimum to the nearest hundredth.

Reteaching ———

Using Graphing Graph $f(x) = x^2$ on a sheet of tissue paper. Move the function around axes drawn on grid paper to show that there can be zero, one, or two real zeros. Do the same with $f(x) = x^3 - 4x$. Show that it can have zero, one, two, or three real zeros.

Tech Prep

Pharmacist Students who are interested in pharmacy may wish to do further research into the use of mathematics in determining dosages in that occupation, as mentioned in Exercise 14. For more information on tech prep, see the *Teacher's Handbook*.

Communicating Mathematics

Study the lesson. Then complete the following.

1. **State** the greatest number of relative minima that are possible for each condition.
   a. a third-degree polynomial with a positive leading coefficient
   b. a third-degree polynomial with a negative leading coefficient
   c. a fourth-degree polynomial with a positive leading coefficient
   d. a fourth-degree polynomial with a negative leading coefficient

2. Refer to the application at the beginning of the lesson. Why did we not choose one of the negative zeros for the volume of the box?

3. **Sketch** a graph of each polynomial.
   a. even-degree polynomial function with one relative maximum and two relative minima
   b. odd-degree polynomial function with one relative maximum and one relative minimum; the leading coefficient is negative
   c. even-degree polynomial function with four relative maxima and three relative minima
   d. odd-degree polynomial function with three relative maxima and three relative minima; the left-most points are negative

4. Consider the function $f(x) = x^4 - 8x^2 + 10$.
   a. Evaluate $f(x)$ for successive integers between -4 and 4 inclusive.
   b. Between what successive integers do the zeros appear? Approximate those zeros to the nearest tenth.
   c. State the ranges of x values where the values of $f(x)$ are negative and ranges where the values of $f(x)$ are positive.
   d. State the relative maximum(s) and relative minimum(s).
   e. Graph the function.

Guided Practice

Approximate the real zeros of each function to the nearest tenth.

5. $f(x) = x^3 - x^2 + 1$

6. $g(x) = x^4 + 3x^3 - 5$

Graph each function.

7. $f(x) = x^3$

8. $f(x) = x^3 - x^2 - 4x + 4$

9. $f(x) = -3x^3 + 20x^2 - 36x + 16$

10. $f(x) = x^4 - 7x^2 + x + 5$

State whether each graph is of odd degree or even degree. State the number of relative minima and relative maxima.

11.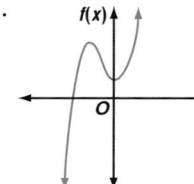

12.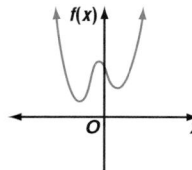

13.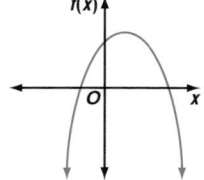

14. **Pharmacy** A syringe is to deliver an injection of 2 cubic centimeters of medication. If the plunger is pulled out two centimeters to have the proper dosage, approximate the radius of the inside of the syringe to the nearest hundredth of a centimeter. Use the formula for the volume of a cylinder, $V = \pi r^2 h$.

Lesson 8–3 Graphing Polynomial Functions and Approximating Zeros **497**

Additional Answers

4a.

x	f(x)
−4	138
−3	19
−2	−6
−1	3
0	10
1	3
2	−6
3	19
4	138

4c. negative between −2.5 and −1.2 and between 1.2 and 2.5; positive between −1.2 and 1.2, less than −2.5, and greater than 2.5

7.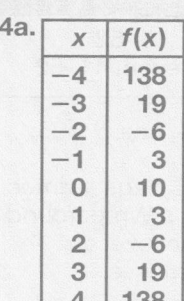

$f(x) = x^3$

8.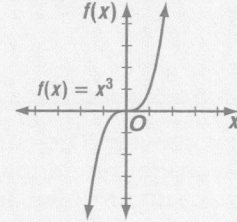

$f(x) = x^3 - x^2 - 4x + 4$

Study Guide Masters, p. 58

8-3 NAME_____ DATE_____
Student Edition
Study Guide Pages 495–501

Graphing Polynomial Functions and Approximating Zeros

Imagine a point that moves along the graph of a polynomial function. If the point is below the x-axis for a certain value of x and later, for a greater value of x, above the x-axis, the point must have crossed the x-axis somewhere in between.

| The Location Principle | Suppose $y = f(x)$ represents a polynomial function and a and b are two numbers such that $f(a) < 0$ and $f(b) > 0$. Then the function has at least one real zero between a and b. |

By narrowing in on places where a polynomial function changes from negative to positive values (or vice versa), you can find approximate values for real zeros.

Example: Approximate the real zero of $f(x) = \frac{1}{10}x^4 + x^3 - 3x^2 - \frac{1}{2}$ to the nearest tenth.

The first table below helps you see that there is a zero between 2 and 3. The second table shows that the graph intersects the x-axis between 2.4 and 2.5, a little closer to 2.5 than to 2.4.

The real zero of $f(x)$ is approximately 2.4.

x	f(x)	x	f(x)
1	−4.4	2.2	−2.029
0	−0.5	2.3	−1.405
1	−2.4	2.4	−0.638
2	−2.9	2.5	0.282
3	7.6		

Approximate the real zeros of each function to the nearest tenth.

1. $f(x) = x^3 - 5x^2 + 6x + 1$ −0.1

2. $f(x) = 6x^4 - 5x^3 + 2x^2 - 5x - 4$ −0.5 and 1.3

Graph each function.

3. $f(x) = x^4 - 7x - 3$

4. $f(x) = 2x^4 - 11x^2 - x + 4$

Additional Answers

9.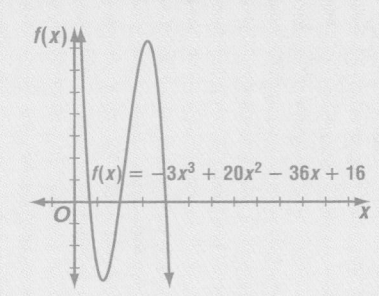

$f(x) = -3x^3 + 20x^2 - 36x + 16$

10.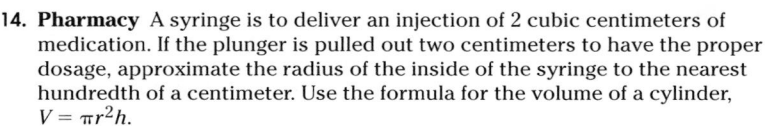

$f(x) = x^4 - 7x^2 + x + 5$

Assignment Guide

Core: 15–43 odd, 45–52
Enriched: 16–40 even, 41–52

For **Extra Practice,** see p. 895.

The red A, B, and C flags, printed only in the Teacher's Wraparound Edition, indicate the level of difficulty of the exercises.

Additional Answers

39a.

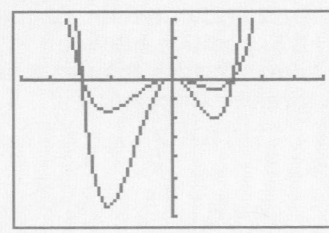

41. Sample answer: The ends of an even-degree function both point up or down, and the ends of an odd-degree function point in opposite directions.

Practice Masters, p. 58

NAME_____ DATE_____

8-3 Practice   Student Edition
                                                    Pages 495–501

Graphing Polynomial Functions and Approximating Zeros

Approximate the real zeros of each function to the nearest tenth.

1. $f(x) = x^3 - 3x^2 + 4$ 2. $f(x) = x^3 - 7x + 6$
   −1.0, 2.0   −3.0, 1.0, 2.0

3. $f(x) = x^3 + 6x^2 + 11x + 3$ 4. $f(x) = x^3 - 6x^2 + 8x - 2$
   −0.3   0.3, 1.5, 4.2

5. $f(x) = x^3 + 3x^2 - 4x - 6$ 6. $f(x) = x^3 + x^2 - x + 15$
   −3.6, −1, 1.6   −3.0

7. $f(x) = x^4 - 2x^3 + 2x^2 - 5x + 4$ 8. $f(x) = x^4 + 2x^4 - x^2 - 4$
   1.0, 1.7   −1.1, 1.1

Graph each function.

9. $f(x) = (x - 2)^3$ 10. $f(x) = (x + 1)^4 - 3$

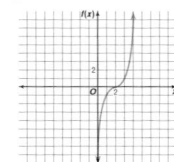   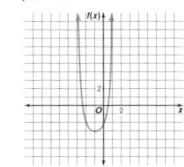

11. $f(x) = x^3 - 3x^2 - x + 3$ 12. $f(x) = x^4 - 9x^2$

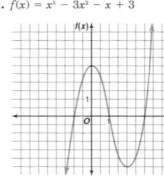   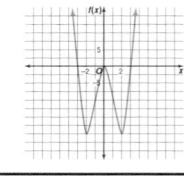

498 Chapter 8

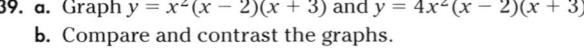

EXERCISES

Practice

Approximate the real zeros of each function to the nearest tenth.

15. $f(x) = x^3 - 2x^2 + 6$ 16. $h(x) = 2x^5 + 3x - 2$
17. $r(x) = x^5 - 6$ 18. $g(x) = x^3 + 1$
19. $f(x) = x^4 + 2x^3 - x^2 - 3$ 20. $p(x) = x^3 + 2x^2 - 3x - 5$
21. $n(x) = 3x^3 - 16x^2 + 12x + 6$ 22. $h(x) = x^4 - 4x^2 + 2$

Graph each function.

23. $f(x) = 4x^6$ 24. $f(x) = 3x^5$ 25. $f(x) = x^3 - x$
26. $f(x) = -x^3 - 4x^2$ 27. $f(x) = x^3 + 5$ 28. $f(x) = x^4 - 81$
29. $f(x) = 15x^3 - 16x^2 - x + 2$ 30. $f(x) = x^4 - 10x^2 + 9$
31. $f(x) = -x^4 + x^3 + 8x^2 - 3$ 32. $f(x) = x^3 - x^2 - 8x + 12$

Approximate the real zeros of each function to the nearest tenth. Then use the functional values to graph the function.

33. $r(x) = x^5 + 4x^4 - x^3 - 9x^2 + 3$ 34. $g(x) = x^4 - 9x^3 + 25x^2 - 24x + 6$
35. $h(x) = x^3 - 3x^2 + 2$ 36. $f(x) = x^3 + 5x^2 - 9$
37. $f(x) = x^4 + 7x + 1$ 38. $p(x) = x^5 + x^4 - 2x^3 + 1$

Graphing Calculator

39. **a.** Graph $y = x^2(x - 2)(x + 3)$ and $y = 4x^2(x - 2)(x + 3)$.
    b. Compare and contrast the graphs.

40. Find the relative maxima and relative minima of each function.
    a. $f(x) = x^3 - 4x^2 + 8$ **b.** $f(x) = x^3 + 3x^2 - 12x$

Critical Thinking

41. Study the graphs for Exercises 23–32. Write a statement comparing the graphs of functions of even degree with those of functions of odd degree.

Applications and Problem Solving

42. **Geometry**   A function that represents the volume of a pyramid with a height of the same measure as the side of its square base is $V(s) = \frac{1}{3}s^3$.

    a. Graph the function.
    b. Find the zeros of the function.
    c. Find the maximum and minimum of the function.
    d. Make a conjecture about how all of this data relates.

43. **Aerospace Engineering**   The space shuttle has an external tank for the fuel that the main engines need for the launch. This tank is shaped like a capsule, a cylinder with a hemispherical dome at either end. The cylindrical part of the tank has a volume of 1170 cubic meters and a height of 17 meters more than the radius of the tank. What are the dimensions of the tank to the nearest tenth of a meter? (*Hint:* Use the formula for the volume of a cylinder.)

44. **Physical Fitness**   An indoor running track is being built at a physical fitness center. It will consist of a rectangular region with a semicircle on each end. If the perimeter of the room is to be a 200-meter running track, find the dimensions that will make the area of the rectangular region as large as possible.

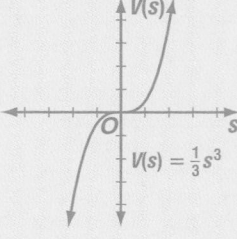

498   Chapter 8   *Exploring Polynomial Functions*

Additional Answers

42a.

$$V(s) = \frac{1}{3}s^3$$

42d. All three zeros occur at 0. However, since $V(s) \neq 0$, we are not interested in zeros. There is no maximum or minimum volume for any value of s.

11. $4, 1 + i, 1 - i$
12. $-2, -2 + 3i,$
    $-2i - 3i$
15. $f(x) = x^3 - 2x^2 -$
    $19x + 20$
16. $f(x) = x^3 - 11x^2 +$
    $23x - 45$

State the number of positive real zeros, negative real zeros, and imaginary zeros for each function.

9. $f(x) = x^3 - 6x^2 + 1$
   2 or 0; 1; 0 or 2

10. $f(x) = x^4 + 5x^3 + 2x^2 - 7x - 9$
    1; 3 or 1; 0 or 2

Given a function and one of its zeros, find all of the zeros of the function.

11. $h(x) = x^3 - 6x^2 + 10x - 8; 4$
12. $g(x) = x^3 + 6x^2 + 21x + 26; -2$
13. $f(x) = x^3 + 7x^2 + 25x + 175; 5i$ $5i, -5i, -7$
14. $p(x) = x^4 - 9x^3 + 24x^2 - 6x - 40; 3 - i$ $3 - i, 3 + i, 4, -1$

Write the polynomial function of least degree with integral coefficients that has the given zeros.

15. $-4, 1, 5$
16. $9, 1 + 2i$

17. **Manufacturing**   The volume of a candy carton is 120 in³. To hold the correct number of candy bars, the carton must be 3 inches longer than it is wide. The height is 2 inches less than the width. Find the dimensions of the carton. $\ell = 8$ in., $w = 5$ in., $h = 3$ in.

EXERCISES

Practice

State the number of positive real zeros, negative real zeros, and imaginary zeros for each function.   18–25. See margin.

18. $f(x) = 5x^3 + 8x^2 - 4x + 3$
19. $g(x) = x^4 + x^3 + 2x^2 - 3x - 1$
20. $h(x) = 4x^3 - 6x^2 + 8x - 5$
21. $f(x) = x^4 - 9$
22. $r(x) = x^5 - x^3 - x + 1$
23. $g(x) = x^{14} + x^{10} - x^9 + x - 1$
24. $p(x) = x^5 - 6x^4 - 3x^3 + 7x^2 - 8x + 1$
25. $f(x) = x^{10} - x^8 + x^6 - x^4 + x^2 - 1$

26. $-4, 1 + 2i, 1 - 2i$

27. $2, 1 + i, 1 - i$

28. $2i, -2i, 3$

29. $2i, -2i, \dfrac{i}{2}, -\dfrac{i}{2}$

30. $-\dfrac{3}{2}, 1 + 4i, 1 - 4i$

31. $\dfrac{1}{2}, 4 + 5i, 4 - 5i$

Given a function and one of its zeros, find all of the zeros of the function.

26. $p(x) = x^3 + 2x^2 - 3x + 20; -4$
27. $f(x) = x^3 - 4x^2 + 6x - 4; 2$
28. $v(x) = x^3 - 3x^2 + 4x - 12; 2i$
29. $h(x) = 4x^4 + 17x^2 + 4; 2i$
30. $g(x) = 2x^3 - x^2 + 28x + 51; -\dfrac{3}{2}$
31. $q(x) = 2x^3 - 17x^2 + 90x - 41; \dfrac{1}{2}$
32. $f(x) = x^3 - 3x^2 + 9x + 13; 2 + 3i$ $2 + 3i, 2 - 3i, -1$
33. $r(x) = x^4 - 6x^3 + 12x^2 + 6x - 13; 3 + 2i$ $3 - 2i, 3 + 2i, -1, 1$
34. $h(x) = x^4 - 15x^3 + 70x^2 - 70x - 156; 5 - i$ $5 - i, 5 + i, -1, 6$

Write the polynomial function of least degree with integral coefficients that has the given zeros.   35–40. See margin.

35. $-2, 1, 3$
36. $2, 4i$
37. $4i, 3, -3$
38. $3, 1 + i$
39. $2i, 3i, 1$
40. $6, 2 + 2i$

Critical Thinking

41. If $f(x) = x^3 + kx^2 - 7x - 15$, find the value of k so that $-2 - i$ is a zero of $f(x)$.   1

42. Suppose a fifth-degree polynomial has exactly two x-intercepts. Describe the nature of the roots of the function. Sketch some examples to support your reasoning.   See Solutions Manual.

Extension

Reasoning
If $g(x) = x^3 + kx^2 - 7x - 15$, find the value of k so that $-2 + i$ is a zero of $g(x)$.   1

Assignment Guide

Core: 19–43 odd, 45–52
Enriched: 18–40 even, 41–52
All: Self Test, 1–10

For **Extra Practice**, see p. 895.

The red A, B, and C flags, printed only in the Teacher's Wraparound Edition, indicate the level of difficulty of the exercises.

Additional Answers

35. $y = x^3 - 2x^2 - 5x + 6$
36. $y = x^3 - 2x^2 + 16x - 32$
37. $y = x^4 + 7x^2 - 144$
38. $y = x^3 - 5x^2 + 8x - 6$
39. $y = x^5 - x^4 + 13x^3 - 13x^2 + 36x - 36$
40. $y = x^3 - 10x^2 + 32x - 48$

Practice Masters, p. 59

NAME_____ DATE_____

Practice   Student Edition Pages 504–510

Roots and Zeros

For each function, state the number of positive real zeros, negative real zeros, and imaginary zeros.

1. $f(x) = 2x^4 - 2x^3 + 2x^2 - x - 1$
   3 or 1; 1; 0 or 2
2. $f(x) = 4x^3 - 2x^2 + x + 3$
   2 or 0; 1; 0 or 2

3. $f(x) = 3x^4 + x^3 - 3x^2 + 7x + 5$
   2 or 0; 2 or 0; 0, 2, or 4
4. $f(x) = 7x^4 + 3x^3 - 2x^2 - x + 1$
   2 or 0; 2 or 0; 0, 2, or 4

5. $f(x) = 5x^6 + 7x^4 + 8x^2 + 3$
   0; 0; 6
6. $f(x) = x^5 - x^4 + x^3 + x - 7$
   3 or 1; 0; 2 or 4

Given a function and one of its zeros, find all of the zeros of the function.

7. $f(x) = x^3 - 7x^2 + 17x - 15; 2 + i$
   $2 - i, 3$
8. $f(x) = x^3 + 6x + 20; 1 - 3i$
   $1 + 3i, -2$

9. $g(x) = x^4 - 6x^3 + 6x^2 + 24x - 40; 3 + i$
   $3 - i, 2, -2$
10. $g(x) = x^3 - 3x^2 + 9x - 7; 1$
    $1 + i\sqrt{6}, 1 - i\sqrt{6}$

Write the polynomial function of least degree with integral coefficients that has the given zeros.

11. $6, 2i$
    $f(x) = x^3 - 6x^2 + 4x - 24$
12. $4, -1, -3i$
    $f(x) = x^4 - 3x^3 + 5x^2 - 27x - 36$

13. $i, -5i$
    $f(x) = x^4 + 26x^2 + 25$
14. $1 + 2i, 1 - i$
    $f(x) = x^4 - 4x^3 + 11x^2 - 14x + 10$

Solve.

15. On the first day of school, Kyle lost his class schedule. He remembers that math is not the first class. History is before English and band. Band is after history and English. Neither math nor English is the fourth class, and math is before English. Reconstruct Kyle's class schedule.
    1st: History
    2nd: Math
    3rd: English
    4th: Band

Closing Activity

Speaking Separate the class into two groups, those who gathered information on Gauss and those who gathered information on Descartes. Select one person to be the leader of each group and another to be the recorder. Allow each group member to share one accomplishment of the mathematician they researched. Then have each group share the information with the class.

Chapter 8, Quiz B (Lessons 8-3 and 8-4), is available in the *Assessment and Evaluation Masters*, p. 212.

Mid-Chapter Test (Lessons 8-1 through 8-4) is available in the *Assessment and Evaluation Masters*, p. 211.

SELF TEST

The Self Test provides students with a brief review of the concepts and skills in Lessons 8-1 through 8-4. Lesson numbers are given to the right of exercises or instruction lines so students can review concepts not yet mastered.

Enrichment Masters, p. 59

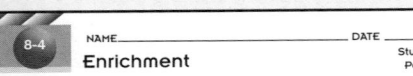

8-4 NAME_____ DATE_____
Student Edition
Enrichment Pages 506–511

Using Maximum Values

Many times maximum solutions are needed for different situations. For instance, what is the area of the largest rectangular field that can be enclosed with 2000 feet of fencing?

Let x and y denote the length and width of the field, respectively.

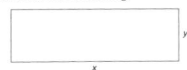

y

x

Perimeter: $2x + 2y = 2000 \rightarrow y = 1000 - x$
Area: $A = xy = x(1000 - x) = -x^2 + 1000x$

This problem is equivalent to finding the highest point on the graph of $A(x) = -x^2 + 1000x$ shown on the right.

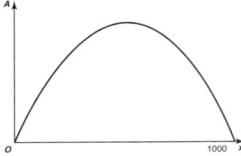

Complete the square for $-x^2 + 1000x$.

$A = -(x^2 - 1000x + 500^2) + 500^2$
$= -(x - 500)^2 + 500^2$

Because the term $-(x - 500)^2$ is either negative or 0, the greatest value of A is 500^2. The maximum area enclosed is 500^2 or 250,000 square feet.

Solve each problem.

1. Find the area of the largest rectangular garden that can be enclosed by 300 feet of fence. **5625 sq ft**

2. A farmer will make a rectangular pen with 100 feet of fence using part of his barn for one side of the pen. What is the largest area he can enclose? **1250 sq ft**

3. An area along a straight stone wall is to be fenced. There are 600 meters of fencing available. What is the greatest rectangular area that can be enclosed? **45,000 m²**

Applications and Problem Solving

43. Medicine Doctors can measure cardiac output in patients at high risk for a heart attack by monitoring the concentration of dye injected into a vein near the heart. A normal heart's dye concentration is approximated by $d(x) = -0.006x^4 - 0.140x^3 - 0.053x^2 + 1.79x$, where x is the time in seconds.

  a. Find all real zeros by graphing. Then verify them by using synthetic division. **−22.3, −4.2, 0, 3.2; See margin for graph.**

  b. Which root makes sense for an answer to this problem? Why? **3.2**

44. Physiology During a five-second respiratory cycle, the volume of air in liters in the human lungs can be described by the function $A(t) = 0.1729t + 0.1522t^2 - 0.0374t^3$, where t is the time in seconds. Find the volume of air held by the lungs at 3 seconds. **0.8787 liter**

Mixed Review

45. Graph $f(x) = x^3 - 5x + 7$. (Lesson 8–3) **See Solutions Manual.**

46. Find the center and radius of a circle whose equation is $x^2 + (y - 3)^2 - 4x - 77 = 0$. (Lesson 7–3) **(2, 3); 9**

47. Write a quadratic equation that has roots 3 and −5. (Lesson 6–5)

47. $x^2 + 2x - 15$

48. Find $\begin{bmatrix} -2 & \frac{2}{3} \\ -\frac{1}{4} & 3 \end{bmatrix} + \begin{bmatrix} 5 & \frac{4}{9} \\ \frac{1}{2} & -9 \end{bmatrix}$. (Lesson 4–2) $\begin{bmatrix} 3 & \frac{10}{9} \\ \frac{1}{4} & -6 \end{bmatrix}$

49. See Solutions Manual.

49. Design Marco is designing a new dartboard. The center of the board is defined by the inequality $|x| + |y| \leq 2$. Draw the graph of this inequality to see what Marco's new dartboard will look like. (Lesson 3–4)

50. Name which ordered pairs, (7, −3), (−4, −1), or (12, −6), satisfy $-2|x| - 5y < 3$. (Lesson 2–7) **(7, −3) and (−4, −1)**

51. Find the value of $f(12)$ when $f(x) = \frac{19}{23 - x}$. (Lesson 2–1) $\frac{19}{11}$

52. Evaluate $-4|-5x| + 17$ if $x = 2$. (Lesson 1–5) **−23**

SELF TEST

Find each value if $p(x) = 4x^3 - 3x^2 + 2x - 5$. (Lesson 8–1)

1. $p(a^2)$ $4a^6 - 3a^4 + 2a^2 - 5$
2. $p(x + 1)$ $4x^3 + 9x^2 + 8x - 2$

Given a polynomial and one of its factors, find the remaining factors of the polynomial. (Lesson 8–2)

3. $x^3 + x^2 - 24x + 36; x - 3$ $x + 6, x - 2$
4. $2x^3 + 13x^2 + x - 70; x - 2$ $2x + 7, x + 5$

Graph each function. (Lesson 8–3) **5–6. See margin.**

5. $g(x) = x^5 - 5$
6. $h(x) = x^3 - x^2 + 4$

State the number of positive real zeros, negative real zeros, and imaginary zeros for each function. (Lesson 8–4)

7. $f(x) = x^3 + 8x^2 - 7x + 10$ **2 or 0; 1; 2 or 0**
8. $f(x) = 6x^4 + 18x^3 + 4x - 9$ **1; 1; 2**

9. Determine whether the degree of the function represented by the graph at the right is even or odd. How many real zeros does the polynomial function have? (Lesson 8–1) **even, 4**

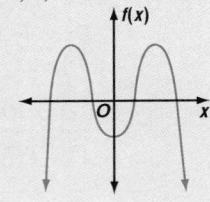

10. **Manufacturing** The height of a certain juice can is 4 times the radius of the top of the can. Determine the dimensions of the can if the volume is approximately 17.89 cubic inches. (*Hint*: The formula for the volume of a right circular cylinder is $V = \pi r^2 h$.) (Lesson 8–4) $r \approx 1.125$ in., $h \approx 4.5$ in.

Additional Answer

43a.

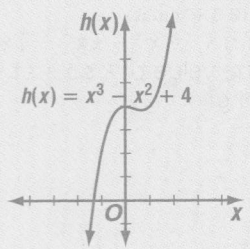

Answers for the Self Test

5.

$g(x) = x^5 - 5$

6.

$h(x) = x^3 - x^2 + 4$

Rational Zero Theorem

What YOU'LL LEARN

- To identify all possible rational zeros of a polynomial function by using the rational zero theorem, and
- to find zeros of polynomial functions.

Why IT'S IMPORTANT

You can use the rational zero theorem to find zeros of polynomials that model situations in finance and food production.

APPLICATION
Architecture

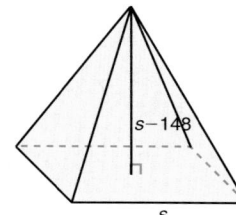

The largest pyramid in the United States is the Luxor Hotel and Casino in Las Vegas, Nevada. The volume of this unique hotel and casino is 28,933,800, or about 29 million cubic feet. The height of the pyramid is 148 feet less than the length of the building. The base of the building is square. What are the dimensions of this building?

The formula for the volume of a pyramid is $V = \frac{1}{3}Bh$, where B represents the area of the base and h represents the height. Let's set up an equation to find the dimensions of the pyramid. Let s represent the length of one side of the base of the pyramid. Then the height is $s - 148$.

$$V = \frac{1}{3}Bh$$
$$28{,}933{,}800 = \frac{1}{3}(s^2)(s - 148)$$
$$86{,}801{,}400 = s^2(s - 148) \quad \text{Multiply each side by 3.}$$
$$86{,}801{,}400 = s^3 - 148s^2 \quad \text{Distributive property}$$
$$0 = s^3 - 148s^2 - 86{,}801{,}400$$

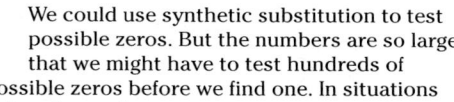

We could use synthetic substitution to test possible zeros. But the numbers are so large that we might have to test hundreds of possible zeros before we find one. In situations like this, the **rational zero theorem** can give us some direction in testing possible zeros. This theorem and a corollary are stated below.

Rational Zero Theorem	Let $f(x) = a_0x^n + a_1x^{n-1} + \ldots + a_{n-1}x + a_n$ represent a polynomial function with integral coefficients. If $\frac{p}{q}$ is a rational number in simplest form and is a zero of $y = f(x)$, then p is a factor of a_n and q is a factor of a_0.
Corollary (Integral Zero Theorem)	If the coefficients of a polynomial function are integers such that $a_0 = 1$ and $a_n \neq 0$, any rational zeros of the function must be factors of a_n.

F Y I

The Luxor Hotel in Las Vegas is large enough to hold 11 Boeing 747's.

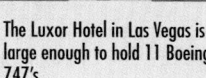

F Y I

The base of the Great Pyramid of Khufu at Giza, the largest of the ancient Egyptian pyramids, measures 754 feet square. The pyramid is thought to have originally stood 481 feet high.

8-5 LESSON NOTES

NCTM Standards: 1–5, 14

Instructional Resources

- Study Guide Master 8-5
- Practice Master 8-5
- Enrichment Master 8-5

 Transparency 8-5A contains the 5-Minute Check for this lesson; **Transparency 8-5B** contains a teaching aid for this lesson.

Recommended Pacing	
Standard Pacing	Days 8 & 9 of 15
Honors Pacing	Days 7 & 8 of 14
Block Scheduling*	Day 3 of 7 (along with Lesson 8-4)

 *For more information on pacing and possible lesson plans, refer to the *Block Scheduling Booklet*.

1 FOCUS

 5-Minute Check *(over Lesson 8-4)*

State the number of positive real zeros, negative real zeros, and imaginary zeros for each function.

1. $f(x) = 4x^3 - 2x^2 + x + 3$
   2 or 0; 1; 2 or 0
2. $h(x) = 3x^4 + 2x^3 - 3x^2 - 4x + 1$
   2 or 0; 2 or 0; 0, 2, or 4

Given a function and one of its zeros, find all the zeros of the function.

3. $x^3 - 7x^2 + 17x - 15$; $2 + i$
   $2 - i$, 3
4. $x^3 - 6x^2 + 10x - 8$; 4
   $1 + i$, $1 - i$

Write the polynomial function of least degree with integral coefficients that has the given zeros.

5. 3, $2i$
   $f(x) = x^3 - 3x^2 + 4x - 12$

Hands-On Activity Separate the class into groups. Give each group a container to find its volume. Have each group write a problem that defines the dimensions of the container in relationship to one of the sides. Students should then write the equation and discuss its solution.

2 TEACH

In-Class Example

For Example 1
List all possible rational zeros for each function and state whether they are positive or negative.

a. $h(x) = 3x^4 - 2x^3 - 5$

$\pm 1, \pm\frac{1}{3}, \pm 5, \pm\frac{5}{3}$; one positive real zero, one negative real zero

b. $g(x) = 2x^3 - 5x^2 + 3x - 8$

$\pm 1, \pm 2, \pm 4, \pm 8, \pm\frac{1}{2}$; three or one positive real zero; no negative real zero

---

Let $V(s) = s^3 - 148s^2 - 86,801,400$ be the related function for $0 = s^3 - 148s^2 - 86,801,400$. All coefficients are integers, $a_0 = 1$, and $a_n = 86,801,400$. The graph of $V(x)$ is shown at the right.

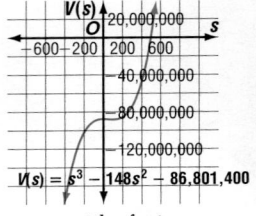

$V(s) = s^3 - 148s^2 - 86,801,400$

According to the integral zero theorem, any rational zeros must be factors of 86,801,400.

$$86,801,400 = 2^3 \times 3^2 \times 5^2 \times 7 \times 83^2$$

So the possible zeros in this case are ± 1 through ± 10, ± 12, ± 14, ± 15, $\pm 18, \ldots, \pm 175, \pm 300, \pm 450, \pm 489, \pm 498$, and so on, to $\pm 86,801,400$.

According to Descartes' rule of signs, there will be only one positive real zero and no negative real zeros. The graph of this function crosses the x-axis one time. We can use synthetic substitution to test for possible zeros, and we can stop testing when we find the first zero. Let's make a chart. Since $s - 148 = h$ and h must be positive, we need to consider only values for s that are greater than 148.

s	1	-148	0	$-86,801,400$
175	1	27	4725	$-85,974,525$
300	1	152	45,600	$-73,121,400$
450	1	302	135,900	$-25,646,400$
498	1	350	174,300	**0**

One zero is 498. Thus, $s - 498$ is a factor of the polynomial, and 498 is a root of the equation. The dimensions are 498 feet by 498 feet by $498 - 148$ or 350 feet. *Verify the dimensions by substituting them into the formula for the volume of a pyramid.*

Example **List all possible rational zeros of $f(x) = 3x^3 + 9x^2 + x - 10$, and state whether they are positive or negative.**

Since $a_0 \neq 1$, we cannot use the integral zero theorem. If $\frac{p}{q}$ is a rational root, then p is a factor of -10 and q is a factor of 3. The possible values of p are $\pm 1, \pm 2, \pm 5$, and ± 10. The possible values of q are ± 1 and ± 3. So all the possible rational zeros are as follows.

$\pm 1, \pm 2, \pm 5, \pm 10, \pm\frac{1}{3}, \pm\frac{5}{3}$, and $\pm\frac{10}{3}$

Now use Descartes' rule of signs.

$f(x) = 3x^3 + 9x^2 + x - 10$

Since there is one sign change, there is one positive real zero.

$f(x) = -3x^3 + 9x^2 - x - 10$

Since there are two sign changes, there are two or no negative real zeros.

$f(x) = 3x^3 + 9x^2 + x - 10$

The graph of the function shown above verifies that there is one positive real zero and two negative real zeros. *Note that the two negative real zeros are the same number.*

Classroom Vignette

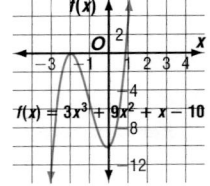

"I put the following problems on the board so that students can see they are all solved the same way.
(1) Solve $x^3 - x^2 - 34x - 56 = 0$.
(2) Find the zeros of $f(x) = x^3 - x^2 - 34x - 56$.
(3) Find the roots of $x^3 - x^2 - 34x - 56 = 0$.
(4) Where does $f(x) = x^3 - x^2 - 34x - 56$ cross the x-axis?
(5) Factor $x^3 - x^2 - 34x - 56$."

Gail Gardner
New Bern High School
New Bern, North Carolina

Example ❷ The volume of a rectangular solid is 1430 cubic centimeters. The width is 1 centimeter less than the length, and the height is 2 centimeters greater than the length. Find the dimensions of the solid.

Explore   Read the problem and define the variable.

Let ℓ represent the length of the solid.

Plan   Write an equation.

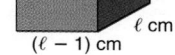

$Volume = length \times width \times height$

$V = \ell(\ell - 1)(\ell + 2)$

Solve $V = \ell(\ell - 1)(\ell + 2)$

$1430 = \ell^3 + \ell^2 - 2\ell$ *Replace V with 1430.*

$0 = \ell^3 + \ell^2 - 2\ell - 1430$ *Subtract 1430 from each side.*

Possible rational zeros are ± 1, ± 2, ± 5, ± 10, ± 11, and ± 13. Since measures must be positive and according to Descartes' rule of signs there is one positive real zero, we can stop testing possible zeros when we find the first one. Let's make a table and test each possible rational zero.

$\frac{p}{q}$	1	1	-2	-1430
1	1	2	0	-1430
2	1	3	4	-1422
5	1	6	28	-1290
10	1	11	108	-350
11	1	12	130	**0**

One zero is 11. The other dimensions are $11 - 1$ or 10 cm and $11 + 2$ or 13 cm.

Examine   Check to see if the dimensions are correct.

$10 \times 11 \times 13 = 1430$ ✓

You have learned many rules to help you determine the number and characteristics of the zeros of a function. Example 3 shows how many of them can be used.

Example ❸ Find all zeros of $f(x) = 4x^4 - 13x^3 - 13x^2 + 28x - 6$.

• From the corollary to the fundamental theorem of algebra, we know there are exactly 4 complex roots.

• According to Descartes' rule of signs, there are either 3 or 1 positive real zeros and exactly 1 negative real zero.

• According to the rational zero theorem, the possible rational zeros are $\pm\frac{1}{4}$, $\pm\frac{1}{2}$, $\pm\frac{3}{4}$, ± 1, $\pm\frac{3}{2}$, ± 2, ± 3, and ± 6.

• Use synthetic substitution and a chart to find at least one zero.

$\frac{p}{q}$	4	-13	-13	28	-6
$\frac{1}{4}$	4	-12	-16	24	0

One zero is $\frac{1}{4}$.

(continued on the next page)

In-Class Examples

For Example 2
The volume of a rectangular solid is 60 cubic inches. The height is 3 inches less than the width, and the length is 1 inch longer than the width. Find the dimensions of the solid.
The zero is 5. The solid is 2 in. × 5 in. × 6 in.

For Example 3
Find all zeros of $g(x) = x^3 - 4x^2 - 2x + 20$.
−2; 3 + i; 3 − i

Teaching Tip In Example 3, emphasize the continued division using the depressed polynomial until degree two is reached.

GLENCOE *Technology*

CD-ROM Interaction

A multimedia simulation allows students to graph polynomials and analyze their slopes to design a roller coaster. A blackline master activity with teacher's notes provides a follow-up to the CD-ROM simulation.

For Windows & Macintosh

Check for Understanding

Exercises 1–15 are designed to help you assess your students' understanding through reading, writing, speaking, and modeling. You should work through Exercises 1–6 with your students and then monitor their work on Exercises 7–15.

Additional Answers

2. Yes, if the length were 1, the width would be $1 - 1$ or 0.

4a. There are only 2 changes in sign for the coefficients of $p(x)$.

4b. There are no changes in sign for the coefficients of $p(x)$.

5. 1–10, 12, 14–15, 18, 20–21, 22, 24–25, 28, 30, 35, 36, 40, 42, 45, 50, 56, 60, 63, 70, 72, 75, 83, 84, 90, and 100.

Study Guide Masters, p. 60

| 8-5 | NAME_____ DATE_____ | Student Edition Pages 511–516 |

Study Guide

Rational Zero Theorem

From the factored form of a polynomial equation, you can look back to say what the original polynomial was. You can also look forward to say what the final solutions will be by setting each factor equal to 0 and solving. Without doing all the multiplication, you can say what the first and last terms of the original polynomial were.

$$(5x + 3)(7x + 2)(4x - 11)(8x - 5) = 0$$

original polynomial   **final solutions**

$(5 \cdot 7 \cdot 4 \cdot 8)x^4 + \cdots + (3 \cdot 2 \cdot -11 \cdot -5)$ $-\frac{3}{5}, -\frac{2}{7}, \frac{11}{4}, \frac{5}{8}$

Notice that the coefficient of the x^4 term is the product of the *denominators* of the final solutions. The constant term is similarly related to the product of the *numerators* of the solutions. This example gives some insight into the rational zero theorem.

| Rational Zero Theorem | Let $f(x) = a_n x^n + a_{n-1}x^{n-1} + \cdots + a_1 x + a_0$ represent a polynomial function with integral coefficients. If $\frac{p}{q}$ is a rational number in simplest form and is a zero of $y = f(x)$, then p is a factor of a_0 and q is a factor of a_n. |

The rational zero theorem allows you to list all possible rational zeros of a polynomial function with integral coefficients. Descartes' rule of signs can help you narrow the field still further.

Example: State all possible rational zeros of
$f(x) = 6x^3 + 11x^2 - 3x - 2$.
The coefficient of x^3 is 6, with has factors $\pm 1, \pm 2, \pm 3,$ and ± 6.
The constant term is -2, which has factors ± 1 and ± 2.
Therefore, the possible rational zeros are
$\pm 1, \pm 2, \pm \frac{1}{2}, \pm \frac{1}{3}, \pm \frac{2}{3},$ and $\pm \frac{1}{6}$.

Find all of the rational zeros for each function.

1. $f(x) = x^3 + 4x^2 - 25x - 28$ 2. $f(x) = x^3 + 6x^2 + 4x + 24$
$-1, 4, -7$ -6

3. $f(x) = 12x^2 - 7x + 1$ 4. $f(x) = x^3 - 9x^2 - 5x + 45$
$\frac{1}{3}, \frac{1}{4}$ 9

Find all of the zeros of each function.

5. $f(x) = x^4 + 2x^3 - 11x^2 + 8x - 60$ 6. $f(x) = 5x^4 + 28x^3 - 82x^2 + 108x - 32$
$3, 5, \pm 2i$ $\frac{2}{5}, -8, 1 \pm i$

The depressed polynomial after division by $x - \frac{1}{4}$ is
$4x^3 - 12x^2 - 16x + 24$. Now use a synthetic division chart with this polynomial.

x	4	-12	-16	24
$\frac{1}{2}$	4	-10	-21	$\frac{27}{2}$
$\frac{3}{4}$	4	-9	$-\frac{91}{4}$	$\frac{111}{16}$
1	4	-8	-24	**0**

Another zero is 1.

The new depressed polynomial is $4x^2 - 8x - 24$. Use the quadratic formula to find other possible zeros.

$$x = \frac{-(-8) \pm \sqrt{(-8)^2 - 4(4)(-24)}}{2(4)} \qquad a = 4, b = 8, c = -24$$

$$= \frac{8 \pm \sqrt{448}}{8} \text{ or } 1 \pm \sqrt{7}$$

The zeros are $\frac{1}{4}, 1, 1 + \sqrt{7},$ and $1 - \sqrt{7}$.

The approximate values of the irrational zeros are 3.65 and -1.65. So, there are 3 positive real zeros and 1 negative zero.

The graph of the function shown at the right crosses the x-axis 4 times, confirming that there are 4 real roots.

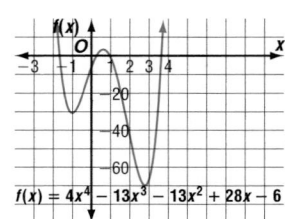

$$f(x) = 4x^4 - 13x^3 - 13x^2 + 28x - 6$$

Communicating Mathematics

1a. when leading coefficient is 1

1b. You limit the number of possible solutions.

3. Sample answer:
$f(x) = x^4 + 2x^3 - 3x^2 + 2x - 1$

4a–b. See margin.

Study the lesson. Then complete the following.

1. a. **Explain** when you can use the integral zero theorem to determine possible rational zeros for a polynomial function.

   b. Why is it helpful to use the rational zero theorem while finding the zeros of a polynomial function?

2. Refer to Example 2. When testing possible zeros, would starting with a number greater than 1 have made more sense? Explain.   **See margin.**

3. **Write** a polynomial function with four possible rational zeros.

4. a. **Explain** why there cannot be three positive zeros for $p(x) = x^3 + 4x^2 - 3x + 2$.

   b. **Explain** why there cannot be four positive zeros for $p(x) = x^3 + 2x^2 + 3x + 1$.

5. Refer to the application at the beginning of the lesson. List all of the possible roots between 0 and 100.   **See margin.**

6. Write a polynomial function that has possible rational zeros of $\pm 1, \pm 3, \pm \frac{1}{2},$ and $\pm \frac{3}{2}$.   **Sample answer:** $f(x) = 2x^2 + x + 3$

Guided Practice

List all of the possible rational zeros for each function.   7. $\pm 1, \pm 2, \pm 3, \pm 6$

8. $\pm 1, \pm 2, \pm \frac{1}{2}, \pm \frac{1}{3}, \pm \frac{1}{6}, \pm \frac{2}{3}$

7. $h(x) = x^3 + 8x + 6$ 8. $d(x) = 6x^3 + 6x^2 - 15x - 2$

Reteaching

Using Cooperative Learning Have each student pick four numbers, two of which are fractions, to use as roots of a polynomial equation. Have them find the equation that has these roots. Then, have students exchange equations, check answers together, and solve them.

9. $-2, -4, 7$

12. $\frac{1}{2}, -\frac{1}{3}, -2$

13. $3, \frac{2}{3}, -\frac{2}{3}, \frac{-3 \pm \sqrt{13}}{2}$

Find all of the rational zeros for each function.

9. $f(x) = x^3 - x^2 - 34x - 56$

10. $p(x) = x^3 - 3x - 2$ $-1, -1, 2$

11. $g(x) = x^4 - 3x^3 + x^2 - 3x$ $0, 3$

12. $h(x) = 6x^3 + 11x^2 - 3x - 2$

13. Find all of the zeros of $h(x) = 9x^5 - 94x^3 + 27x^2 + 40x - 12$.

14. Write a polynomial function of least degree that has zeros -3, 2, and 5.
$f(x) = x^3 - 4x^2 - 11x + 30$

15. Geometry The volume of the figure at the right is 384 cm³. Find the dimensions.
12 cm by 8 cm by 4 cm

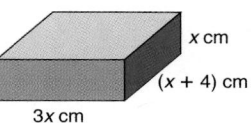
x cm
$(x + 4)$ cm
$3x$ cm

EXERCISES

Practice

18. $\pm 1, \pm 2, \pm 3, \pm 6,$ $\pm 9, \pm 18$

19. $\pm 1, \pm \frac{1}{3}, \pm 3$

20. $\pm 1, \pm 3, \pm 5, \pm 15,$ $\pm \frac{1}{3}, \pm \frac{5}{3}$

22. $-4, 2, 7$

23. $-6, -5, 10$

24. $0, 9$

25. $3, 3, -\frac{1}{2}$

26. $\frac{1}{2}, -1, 1$

27. $-2, -4$

29. $2, -2, 3, -3$

30. $-1, -1, 1, 4$

31. $-7, 1, 3$

33. $-\frac{1}{2}, \frac{1}{3}, \frac{1}{2}, \frac{3}{4}$

List all of the possible rational zeros for each function.

16. $f(x) = x^3 + 6x + 2$ $\pm 1, \pm 2$

17. $p(x) = x^4 - 10$ $\pm 1, \pm 2, \pm 5, \pm 10$

18. $n(x) = x^5 + 6x^3 - 12x + 18$

19. $p(x) = 3x^3 - 5x^2 - 11x + 3$

20. $f(x) = 3x^4 + 15$

21. $h(x) = 9x^6 - 5x^3 + 27$
$\pm 1, \pm \frac{1}{3}, \pm \frac{1}{9}, \pm 3, \pm 9, \pm 27$

Find all of the rational zeros for each function.

22. $p(x) = x^3 - 5x^2 - 22x + 56$

23. $f(x) = x^3 + x^2 - 80x - 300$

24. $g(x) = x^4 - 3x^3 - 53x^2 - 9x$

25. $h(x) = 2x^3 - 11x^2 + 12x + 9$

26. $f(x) = 2x^5 - x^4 - 2x + 1$

27. $p(x) = x^4 + 10x^3 + 33x^2 + 38x + 8$

28. $n(x) = x^4 + x^2 - 2$ $1, -1$

29. $t(x) = x^4 - 13x^2 + 36$

30. $h(x) = x^4 - 3x^3 - 5x^2 + 3x + 4$

31. $p(x) = x^3 + 3x^2 - 25x + 21$

32. $f(x) = x^5 - 6x^3 + 8x$ $0, 2, -2$

33. $g(x) = 48x^4 - 52x^3 + 13x - 3$

Find all of the zeros of each function. 34–37. See margin.

34. $f(x) = 6x^3 + 5x^2 - 9x + 2$

35. $p(x) = 6x^4 + 22x^3 + 11x^2 - 38x - 40$

36. $g(x) = 5x^4 - 29x^3 + 55x^2 - 28x$

37. $p(x) = x^5 - 2x^4 - 12x^3 - 12x^2 - 13x - 10$

Critical Thinking

38. Suppose k and $2k$ are zeros of $f(x) = x^3 + 4x^2 + 9kx - 90$. Find k and all three zeros of $f(x)$. $k = -3; -3, -6, 5$

Applications and Problem Solving

39. Stock Market In 1994, IBM's research lab discovered a flaw in Intel's Pentium™ chip that could have caused an error as often as once every 24 days. Intel's stock was affected on the day the flaw was discovered, as shown in the graph at the right. The function $f(x) = -0.002x^4 + 0.05x^3 - 0.3x^2 - 0.4x + 63$ can be used to model Intel's stock prices at time x, where $x = 0$ represents 9:30 A.M., $x = 1$ represents 10:00 A.M., and so on.

  a. Use $f(x)$ to estimate the price of Intel's stock at 2:30 P.M. $59

39b. They are the same.

  b. Compare this value to an estimate of the value from the graph.

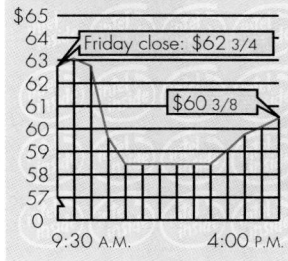
Price of Intel Stock
Monday, Dec.12,1994
Friday close: $62 3/4
$60 3/8
9:30 A.M.   4:00 P.M.

Source: *Bloomberg Business News*

Lesson 8-5 Rational Zero Theorem **513**

Assignment Guide

Core: 17–37 odd, 38, 39, 41–50
Enriched: 16–36 even, 38–50

For **Extra Practice,** see p. 895.

The red A, B, and C flags, printed only in the Teacher's Wraparound Edition, indicate the level of difficulty of the exercises.

Additional Answers

34. $\frac{2}{3}, \frac{-3 \pm \sqrt{17}}{4}$

35. $-2, \frac{4}{3}, \frac{-3 \pm i}{2}$

36. $0, \frac{4}{5}, \frac{5 \pm i\sqrt{3}}{2}$

37. $-1, -2, 5, i, -i$

Practice Masters, p. 60

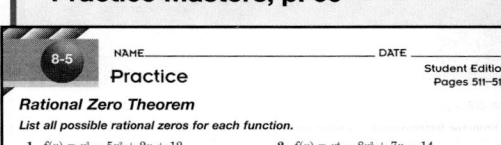

4 ASSESS

Closing Activity

Writing Have students determine the zeros of a third-degree equation and sketch a graph of the function.

Additional Answer

41a.

Enrichment Masters, p. 60

8-5

NAME_____ DATE_____

Enrichment

Student Edition
Pages 513–518

The Bisection Method for Approximating Real Zeros

The **bisection method** can be used to approximate zeros of polynomial functions like $f(x) = x^3 + x^2 - 3x - 3$. Since $f(1) = -4$ and $f(2) = 3$, there is at least one real zero between 1 and 2. The midpoint of this interval is $\frac{1+2}{2} = 1.5$. Since $f(1.5) = -1.875$, the zero is between 1.5 and 2. The midpoint of this interval is $\frac{1.5+2}{2} = 1.75$. Since $f(1.75)$ is about 0.172, the zero is between 1.5 and 1.75. The midpoint of this interval is $\frac{1.5+1.75}{2} = 1.625$ and $f(1.625)$ is about -0.94. The zero is between 1.625 and 1.75. The midpoint of this interval is $\frac{1.625+1.75}{2} = 1.6875$. Since $f(1.6875)$ is about -0.41, the zero is between 1.6875 and 1.75. Therefore, the zero is 1.7 to the nearest tenth. The diagram below summarizes the results obtained by the bisection method.

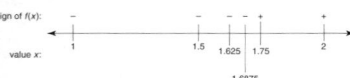

Using the bisection method, approximate to the nearest tenth the zero between the two integral values of x for each function.

1. $f(x) = x^3 - 4x^2 - 11x + 2, f(0) = 2, f(1) = -12$ 0.2

2. $f(x) = 2x^4 + x^2 - 15, f(1) = -12, f(2) = 21$ 1.6

3. $f(x) = x^5 - 2x^3 - 12, f(1) = -13, f(2) = 4$ 1.9

4. $f(x) = 4x^3 - 2x + 7, f(-2) = -21, f(-1) = 5$ −1.3

5. $f(x) = 3x^3 - 14x^2 - 27x + 126, f(4) = -14, f(5) = 16$ 4.7

514 Chapter 8

40. Food Production I.C. Dreams makes ice cream cones. The volume of each cone is about 5.24 cubic inches, and the height is 4 inches more than the radius of the opening of the cone. Find the dimensions of the cone. Use the formula for the volume of a cone, $V = \frac{1}{3}\pi r^2 h$. $r = 1$ in., $h = 5$ in.

41. Patterns The diagrams below show the number of regions formed by connecting the points on a circle.

 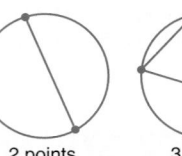 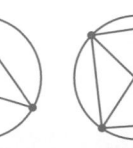

| 1 point | 2 points | 3 points | 4 points |
| 1 region | 2 regions | 4 regions | 8 regions |

The number of regions formed by connecting n points of a circle can be described by the function $f(n) = \frac{1}{24}(n^4 - 6n^3 + 23n^2 - 18n + 24)$.

41a. See margin for diagram.

a. Find the number of regions formed by connecting 5 points of a circle. Draw a diagram to verify your solution. **16 regions**

b. How many points would you have to connect to form 99 regions? **8 points**

Mixed Review

42. Write a polynomial function of least degree with integral coefficients that has -2 and $2 + 3i$ as zeros. (Lesson 8–4) $f(x) = x^3 - 2x^2 + 5x + 26$

43. Write $2y^2 = 14x$ in the form $x = a(y - k)^2 + h$. (Lesson 7–2) $x = \frac{1}{7}y^2$

44. Solve $c^2 - 9c - 58 = -7c + 5$ by factoring. (Lesson 6–2) $-7, 9$

45. Physics A model airplane is fixed on a string so that it flies around in a circle. The designers of the plane want to find the time it takes for the airplane to make a complete circle. They know that the formula $F_c = m\left(\frac{4\pi^2 r}{T^2}\right)$ describes the force required to keep the airplane going in a circle, m represents the mass of the plane, r represents the radius of the circle, and T represents the time for a revolution. Solve the formula for T. Write the answer in simplest radical form. (Lesson 5–8)

45. $T = \dfrac{2\pi\sqrt{mrF_c}}{F_c}$

46. Use augmented matrices to solve the system of equations. (Lesson 4–7)

$5x - 7y + z = 29$

$-2x - 3y + 5z = 20$

$x - 9y + 3z = 13$ **(7, 2, 8)**

47. Solve $\begin{bmatrix} -5x \\ 9x + 4 \end{bmatrix} = \begin{bmatrix} 15y \\ -31y \end{bmatrix}$ for x and y. (Lesson 4–1) **(3, −1)**

48. Given the function $f(x, y) = 9x - 3y$, find $f(-3, 7)$. (Lesson 3–6) **−48**

49. Marcia and Roberto want to build a ramp that they can use while rollerblading. If they want the ramp to have a base of 8 feet and slope of $\frac{1}{2}$, how tall will their ramp be? (Lesson 2–3) **4 feet**

50. Margie is 6 years older than Max. Moira is 19 years younger than Margie. If Max is 17, how old is Moira? (Lesson 1–4) **4**

514 Chapter 8 Exploring Polynomial Functions

Extension

Communication Do all polynomial functions with real coefficients have at least one real root if they have odd degree? **Yes, complex numbers appear in pairs (conjugates), so if there are an odd number of roots, at least one must be real.**

Using Quadratic Techniques to Solve Polynomial Equations

What YOU'LL LEARN

* To solve nonquadratic equations by using quadratic techniques.

Why IT'S IMPORTANT

You can solve polynomial equations that model situations in finance and geometry.

APPLICATION

Finance

On his seventeenth birthday, Montel received $100. On his eighteenth birthday, he received $150. One year ago, on his nineteenth birthday, he received $200. Montel put his birthday money into an account paying 6% interest, compounded annually, and did not withdraw or add any additional money. Determine the amount of money currently in his account.

We can use the formula for compound interest, $A = P(1 + r)^t$, where P is the original amount of money deposited, r is the interest rate (written as a decimal), and t is the number of years invested. The amount of money currently in his account is the sum of the amounts he received on his last three birthdays, plus interest.

The interest rate is 6%, so $r = 0.06$. Let $x = 1 + r$ or 1.06, and let $T(x)$ represent the total amount of money currently in the account. Find $T(1.06)$.

$$
\begin{array}{ccccccc}
 & & \text{money from} & & \text{money from} & & \text{money from} \\
\text{Total} & = & \text{17th birthday} & + & \text{18th birthday} & + & \text{19th birthday}
\end{array}
$$

$$T(x) = 100x^3 + 150x^2 + 200x$$

$$T(1.06) = 100(1.06)^3 + 150(1.06)^2 + 200(1.06) \quad \textit{Replace x with 1.06.}$$

$$= \$499.64 \quad \text{The amount of money in Montel's account is \$499.64.}$$

LOOK BACK

Refer to Lessons 6-1 through 6-4 for information on quadratic functions.

Note that the polynomial function contains a factor that is a quadratic since $T(x) = 100x^3 + 150x^2 + 200x$ or $50x(2x^2 + 3x + 4)$.

In some cases, we can rewrite polynomial equations and use quadratic techniques to solve them. For example, $x^4 - 38x^2 + 72 = 0$ can be written as $(x^2)^2 - 38(x^2) + 72 = 0$. Equations that can be written in the form $a[f(x)]^2 + b[f(x)] + c = 0$ are said to be in **quadratic form.**

Definition of Quadratic Form	For any numbers a, b, and c, except $a = 0$, an equation that can be written as $a[f(x)]^2 + b[f(x)] + c = 0$, where $f(x)$ is some expression in x, is in quadratic form.

Example 1 Solve $x^4 - 17x^2 + 16 = 0$.

The graph of $y = x^4 - 17x^2 + 16$ crosses the x-axis 4 times, so there are 4 real zeros.

$$x^4 - 17x^2 + 16 = 0$$

$$(x^2)^2 - 17(x^2) + 16 = 0 \quad \textit{Quadratic form}$$

$$(x^2 - 16)(x^2 - 1) = 0$$

$$(x - 4)(x + 4)(x - 1)(x + 1) = 0$$

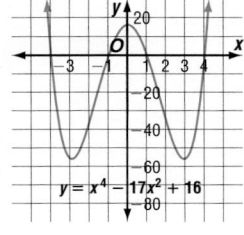

$y = x^4 - 17x^2 + 16$

(continued on the next page)

Lesson 8–6 Using Quadratic Techniques to Solve Polynomial Equations **515**

Alternative Learning Styles

Kinesthetic Have students make three or four rectangular prisms. They should measure the sides and determine the volume. Then they should label one side x, write expressions (for example, $x + 6$ and $x - 2$) for the other sides, and write an algebraic expression for the volume. Have students exchange labeled prisms and then solve for the volume using an algebraic method.

Instructional Resources

* Study Guide Master 8-6
* Practice Master 8-6
* Enrichment Master 8-6
* Assessment and Evaluation Masters, p. 213
* Multicultural Activity Masters, p. 16
* Real-World Applications, 23

 Transparency 8-6A contains the 5-Minute Check for this lesson; **Transparency 8-6B** contains a teaching aid for this lesson.

Recommended Pacing	
Standard Pacing	Day 10 of 15
Honors Pacing	Day 9 of 14
Block Scheduling*	Day 4 of 7

 *For more information on pacing and possible lesson plans, refer to the *Block Scheduling Booklet*.

1 FOCUS

 5-Minute Check
(over Lesson 8-5)

List all the possible rational zeros for each function.

1. $f(x) = x^3 + 2x^2 - 3x + 5$
$\pm 1, \pm 5$

2. $p(x) = 6x^3 + 4x^2 - 14x + 4$
$\pm 1, \pm \frac{1}{2}, \pm \frac{1}{3}, \pm \frac{1}{6}, \pm 2, \pm \frac{2}{3},$
$\pm 4, \pm \frac{4}{3}$

Find all the zeros of each function.

3. $h(x) = 3x^3 - 4x^2 - 17x + 6$
$-2, 3, \frac{1}{3}$

4. $j(x) = x^3 - 3x^2 - 53x - 9$
$9, -3 + 2\sqrt{2}, -3 - 2\sqrt{2}$

 **TEKS** 2.a., 8.b., 8.d.

2 TEACH

In-Class Examples

For Example 1

a. Solve $x^4 + 3x^3 - 18x^2 = 0$.
$0, -6, 3$

b. Solve $x^4 - 7x^2 + 12 = 0$.
$2, -2, \sqrt{3}, -\sqrt{3}$

For Example 2

Solve $t^3 - 216 = 0$.
$6, -3 + 3i\sqrt{3}, -3 - 3i\sqrt{3}$

For Example 3

Suppose $1000 is deposited on August 1 and the account has grown to $1092 on April 1 of the following year. What interest rate did the account pay? **14%**

Teaching Tip Review the meaning of quadratic form.

Use the zero product property.

$x - 4 = 0$ or $x + 4 = 0$ or $x - 1 = 0$ or $x + 1 = 0$

$x = 4$ $x = -4$ $x = 1$ $x = -1$

The roots are $-4, 4, -1$, and 1, which are verified on the graph.

You can solve cubic equations with the quadratic formula if a quadratic factor can be found.

Example **Solve $x^3 + 64 = 0$.**

$$x^3 + 64 = 0$$

$(x + 4)(x^2 - 4x + 16) = 0$ *Factor.*

Use the zero product property.

$x + 4 = 0$ or $x^2 - 4x + 16 = 0$

$x = -4$ $x = \dfrac{4 \pm \sqrt{(-4)^2 - 4(1)(16)}}{2(1)}$

$= \dfrac{4 \pm \sqrt{-48}}{2}$ or $2 \pm 2i\sqrt{3}$

The roots are -4 and $2 \pm 2i\sqrt{3}$.

The only real root is -4.

The graph of the related function crosses the x-axis only once at -4.

You have studied the rule $(a^m)^n = a^{mn}$ in Chapter 5. This property of exponents is often used to solve equations that have terms with rational exponents.

Example  **APPLICATION Finance**

Isabel earned $1000 from her summer job, and on August 1 she decided to put it in the bank to save it for a cruise she wants to take during the next spring break, which starts on April 1. The cruise costs $1046, but Isabel figures that if her money earns some interest she may have enough money by April. As she shops around for interest rates at various banks, what interest rate should she be looking for so that her $1000 on August 1 will grow to $1046 by April 1? Use the interest formula $A = P(1 + r)^t$.

Let x represent $1 + r$ and substitute the known values into the formula: $A = \$1046$, $P = \$1000$, and $t = 8$ months or $\frac{2}{3}$ year.

$$A = P(1 + r)^t$$

$1046 = 1000x^{\frac{2}{3}}$ *Substitute.*

$1.046 = x^{\frac{2}{3}}$ *Divide each side by 1000.*

$(1.046)^3 = \left(x^{\frac{2}{3}}\right)^3$ *Cube each side.*

$1.14 = x^2$

$\pm\sqrt{1.14}$ or $\pm 1.07 = x$ *Take the square root of each side. Why $\pm$?*

Since $x = 1 + r$, then $r = 0.07$ or $r = -2.07$. Since interest rates cannot be negative, the interest rate is 0.07 or 7%.

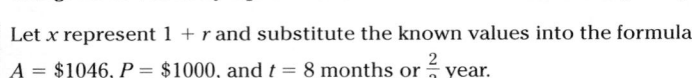

Some equations involving rational exponents can be written in quadratic form.

Example **4** **Solve** $x^{\frac{1}{2}} - 8x^{\frac{1}{4}} + 15 = 0$.

$x^{\frac{1}{2}} - 8x^{\frac{1}{4}} + 15 = 0$

$\left(x^{\frac{1}{4}}\right)^2 - 8\left(x^{\frac{1}{4}}\right) + 15 = 0$ *Quadratic form*

$\left(x^{\frac{1}{4}} - 5\right)\left(x^{\frac{1}{4}} - 3\right) = 0$ *Factor.*

Use the zero product property.

$x^{\frac{1}{4}} - 5 = 0$ or $x^{\frac{1}{4}} - 3 = 0$

$x^{\frac{1}{4}} = 5$ $x^{\frac{1}{4}} = 3$

$\left(x^{\frac{1}{4}}\right)^4 = 5^4$ $\left(x^{\frac{1}{4}}\right)^4 = 3^4$

$x = 625$ $x = 81$

Check: $x^{\frac{1}{2}} - 8x^{\frac{1}{4}} + 15 = 0$

$625^{\frac{1}{2}} - 8(625)^{\frac{1}{4}} + 15 \stackrel{?}{=} 0$

$25 - 40 + 15 \stackrel{?}{=} 0$

$0 = 0$ ✓

$81^{\frac{1}{2}} - 8(81)^{\frac{1}{4}} + 15 = 0$

$9 - 24 + 15 \stackrel{?}{=} 0$

$0 = 0$ ✓

The real roots are 81 and 625.

Example **5** **Solve** $x - 2\sqrt{x} - 3 = 0$.

$x - 2\sqrt{x} - 3 = 0$

$\left(\sqrt{x}\right)^2 - 2(\sqrt{x}) - 3 = 0$ *Quadratic form*

$\sqrt{x} = \dfrac{-b \pm \sqrt{b^2 - 4ac}}{2a}$ *Use the quadratic formula.*

$\sqrt{x} = \dfrac{2 \pm \sqrt{(-2)^2 - 4(1)(-3)}}{2(1)}$ *a = 1, b = –2, and c = –3*

$\sqrt{x} = \dfrac{2 \pm \sqrt{16}}{2}$

$\sqrt{x} = 3$ or $\sqrt{x} = -1$

$x = 9$

There is no real number x such that $\sqrt{x} = -1$. The only real solution is 9.

CHECK FOR UNDERSTANDING

Communicating Mathematics

Study the lesson. Then complete the following.

1. **Explain** why the graph in Example 2 crosses the *x*-axis only once when three roots are given.

2. **Explain** the steps you would take to solve $\sqrt{x^4 + 48} = 4x$.

3. **Write** three examples of equations that are not quadratic but can be written in quadratic form. Then write them in quadratic form.

Guided Practice

Factor each polynomial. Identify the quadratic factor if one exists.

4. $x^4 - 3x^3 + 6x^2$

5. $2x^3 + 7x^2 - 8x$

6. $4m^3 + 9m - 16m^2$

7. $y^3 - y^5 - 100y$

8. $x^7 + x^{\frac{7}{2}} + x^5$

9. $x^3 - 729$

Write each equation in quadratic form if possible. If not, explain why not.

10. $3r + 7\sqrt{r} = 11$

11. $a^8 + 10a^4 - 16 = 0$

For Example 4

a. Solve $x^{\frac{2}{3}} - 8x^{\frac{1}{3}} + 15 = 0$.
125, 27

b. Solve $y^{\frac{4}{3}} - 13y^{\frac{2}{3}} + 36 = 0$.
8, 27

For Example 5

a. Solve $y - 8\sqrt{y} + 7 = 0$.
1, 49

b. Solve $s - 13\sqrt{s} + 36 = 0$.
81, 16

3 PRACTICE/APPLY

Check for Understanding
Exercises 1–16 are designed to help you assess your students' understanding through reading, writing, speaking, and modeling. You should work through Exercises 1–3 with your students and then monitor their work on Exercises 4–16.

Error Analysis
Remind students that the radical sign indicates only the positive square root. Caution students to be careful to watch when squaring both sides of any equation. Note that $-4 \neq 4$ but $(-4)^2 = (4)^2$.

Study Guide Masters, p. 61

NAME_____ DATE _____

8-6

Study Guide

Student Edition
Pages 517–522

Using Quadratic Techniques to Solve Polynomial Equations

Many equations look very much like quadratic equations when, in fact, they are not. For example, $5(x^{\frac{1}{2}})^2 + x^{\frac{1}{2}} - 4 = 0$ has the rough form of a quadratic equation even though the expression on the left side of the equation is not a polynomial.

Definition of Quadratic Form

An equation is in quadratic form if it is in the form
$a[f(x)]^2 + b[f(x)] + c = 0$
where $f(x)$ is some expression in x,
and a, b, and c are numbers with $a \neq 0$.

Equations that are in quadratic form can often be solved with the same techniques that work for quadratic equations.

Example: Solve $x^4 - 29x^2 + 100 = 0$.
$x^4 - 29x^2 + 100 = 0$
$(x^2)^2 - 29(x^2) + 100 = 0$ Write the equation in quadratic form.
$(x^2 - 25)(x^2 - 4) = 0$ Factor.
$x^2 - 25 = 0$ or $x^2 - 4 = 0$ Use the zero product property.
$(x + 5)(x - 5) = 0$ or $(x + 2)(x - 2) = 0$ Factor each equation.
$x = -5$ or $x = 5$ or $x = -2$ or $x = 2$ Use the zero product property again.
The solutions are $-5, -2, 2,$ and 5.

Write each equation in quadratic form.

1. $x^4 + 6x^2 - 8 = 0$
   $(x^2)^2 + 6(x^2) - 8 = 0$

2. $4p^4 + 6p^2 + 8 = 0$
   $4(p^2)^2 + 6(p^2) + 8 = 0$

3. $x^4 + 2x^2 + 1 = 0$
   $(x^2)^2 + 2(x^2) + 1 = 0$

4. $x^{\frac{1}{2}} + 2x^{\frac{1}{4}} + 1 = 0$
   $(x^{\frac{1}{4}})^2 + 2(x^{\frac{1}{4}}) + 1 = 0$

Solve each equation.

5. $x^2 = 49$
   $\pm\sqrt{7}, \pm i\sqrt{7}$

6. $x^4 - 6x^2 = -8$
   $\pm 2, \pm\sqrt{2}$

7. $m^6 - 16m^3 + 64 = 0$
   $2, 1 \pm i\sqrt{3}$

8. $y^4 - 5y^2 + 4 = 0$
   $\pm 1, \pm 2$

9. $\frac{1}{x^2} - \frac{7}{x} + 12 = 0$ $\frac{1}{3}, \frac{1}{4}$

10. $x - 5\sqrt{x} + 6 = 0$ 4, 9

Assignment Guide

Core: 17–35 odd, 36, 37, 39–46
Enriched: 18–34 even, 36–46

For **Extra Practice,** see p. 896.

The red A, B, and C flags, printed only in the Teacher's Wraparound Edition, indicate the level of difficulty of the exercises.

Additional Answer

36. Sample answer: Write the equation in quadratic form, factor, use the zero product property to solve for a.

19. $84(n^2)^2 - 62(n^2) = 0$

20. $7\left(\sqrt{q}\right)^2 + 8\left(\sqrt{q}\right) - 13 = 0$

26. $\sqrt{3}, -\sqrt{3}, -2, 2$

33. $3.2, -4.7, 0$

Practice Masters, p. 61

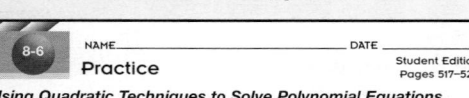

8-6   NAME_____ DATE _____
    Practice   Student Edition
                    Pages 517–522

Using Quadratic Techniques to Solve Polynomial Equations
Solve each equation.

1. $x^4 - 50x^2 + 49 = 0$ 2. $t^4 - 21t^2 + 80 = 0$
   $\pm 7, \pm 1$ $\pm\sqrt{5}, \pm 4$

3. $m^4 - 625 = 0$ 4. $n^4 - 49n^2 = 0$
   $\pm 5, \pm 5i$ $0, \pm 7$

5. $w - 12\sqrt{w} + 27 = 0$ 6. $n - 10\sqrt{n} + 25 = 0$
   $9, 81$ 25

7. $y^4 - 8y^2 = 0$ 8. $n^6 - 1 = 0$
   $0, 2, -1 \pm i\sqrt{3}$ $\pm 1, \frac{-1 \pm i\sqrt{3}}{2}, \frac{1 \pm i\sqrt{3}}{2}$

9. $x^{\frac{1}{2}} - 5x^{\frac{1}{4}} + 6 = 0$ 10. $r^{\frac{2}{3}} - r^{\frac{1}{3}} - 20 = 0$
   $16, 81$ $125, -64$

11. $x^{\frac{2}{3}} - 29x^{\frac{1}{3}} + 100 = 0$ 12. $y^3 - 28y^{\frac{3}{2}} + 27 = 0$
    $8, 125$ $1, 9$

13. $y^{-1} - 8y^{-\frac{1}{2}} + 12 = 0$ 14. $y^{\frac{2}{3}} - 7y^{\frac{1}{3}} + 12 = 0$
    $\frac{1}{36}, \frac{1}{4}$ $\frac{1}{27}, \frac{1}{64}$

Solve each equation.

12. $x - 16x^{\frac{1}{2}} = -64$ **64**   13. $m^4 + 7m^3 + 12m^2 = 0$ **0, −4, −3**

14. $3m^{\frac{3}{2}} - 81 = 0$ **9**   15. $y^3 = 26.6y - 3.2y^2$ **3.8, −7, 0**

16. **Geometry** The width of a rectangular prism is w centimeters. The height is 2 centimeters less than the width. The length is 4 centimeters more than the width. If the volume of the prism is 8 times the measure of the length, find the dimensions of the prism. $w = 4$ cm, $\ell = 8$ cm, $h = 2$ cm

EXERCISES

Practice

Write each equation in quadratic form if possible. If not, explain why not.   17. $(x^4)^2 + 10(x^4) + 13.2 = 0$

17. $x^8 + 10x^4 = -13.2$ 18. $11x^4 + 3x = -8$ **impossible**

19. $84n^4 - 62n^2 = 0$ 20. $7q + 8\sqrt{q} = 13$

21. $5y^4 + 7y = 8$ **impossible**   22. $11n^4 = -44n^2$ $11(n^2)^2 + 44(n^2) = 0$

Solve each equation.

23. $x^3 - 3x^2 - 10x = 0$ **−2, 0, 5**   24. $n^3 + 12n^2 + 32n = 0$ **−8, −4, 0**

25. $b^3 = 1331$ **11**, $\frac{-11 \pm 11i\sqrt{3}}{2}$ 26. $m^4 - 7m^2 + 12 = 0$

27. $z - 8\sqrt{z} - 240 = 0$ **400**   28. $y^3 - 729 = 0$ **9**, $\frac{-9 \pm 9i\sqrt{3}}{2}$

29. $y^{\frac{2}{3}} - 9y^{\frac{1}{3}} + 20 = 0$ **125, 64**   30. $r - 19r^{\frac{1}{2}} + 60 = 0$ **225, 16**

31. $6.25m^3 - 12.25m = 0$ **0, 1.4, −1.4**   32. $y^{\frac{1}{3}} = 7.5$ **421.875**

33. $m^5 + 1.5m^4 = 15.04m^3$ 34. $p^{\frac{2}{3}} + 11p^{\frac{1}{3}} + 28 = 0$ **−343, −64**

35. Write an equation for a polynomial that has roots −3, 0, and 2.
    $x^3 + x^2 - 6x = 0$

Critical Thinking

36. Write an explanation about how you would solve the equation $|a - 3|^2 - 9|a - 3| = -8$. Then solve the equation.   **11, 4, 2, −5;**
    See margin for explanation.

Applications and Problem Solving

37. **Geometry** The formula for the area of an ellipse is $A = \pi ab$. Find the measure of a and b to the nearest hundredth of an inch if an ellipse has an area of 8.85 square inches and the measure of b is 2.3 inches greater than a. $a = 0.885$ in.; $b = 3.185$ in.

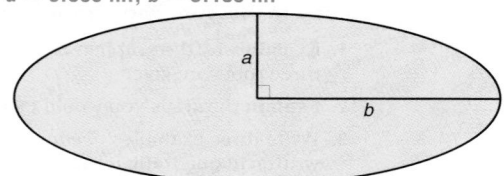

38. **Geometry** A piece of wire is cut into two pieces. One piece is bent into the shape of a square, and the other into the shape of an equilateral triangle. The side of the square and a side of the equilateral triangle have the same length, and the measure of that length, in inches, is an integer. The original piece of wire was less than 50 inches long before it was cut.

    a. Find all possible integral measurements for the length of the side of the square and the triangle.   **1 in., 2 in., 3 in., 4 in., 5 in., 6 in., 7 in.**

    b. What is the shortest possible length for the original piece of wire?   **7 in.**

    c. What is the longest possible length for the original piece of wire?   **49 in.**

Reteaching

Using Alternative Methods Present this general method for solving equations in quadratic form. Use a variable to represent $f(x)$ in $a[f(x)]^2 + b[f(x)] + c = 0$.
Example: $x^4 - 13x^2 + 36 = 0$
Let $A = x^2$.
$A^2 + 13A + 36 = 0$
    $A = 9$ or $A = 4$

Substitute x^2 for A.
$x^2 = 9$ or $x^2 = 4$
$x = \pm\sqrt{9}$ or ± 3
$x = \pm\sqrt{4}$ or ± 2

39. Aerospace The force of gravity decreases with the square of the distance from the center of Earth. So, as an object moves further from Earth, its weight decreases. The radius of Earth is approximately 3960 miles. The formula relating weight and distance is

$(3960 + r)^2 = \dfrac{3960^2 \cdot W_E}{W_S}$, where W_E represents

the weight of a body on Earth, W_S represents the weight of a body a certain distance from the center of Earth, and r represents the distance of an object above Earth's surface.

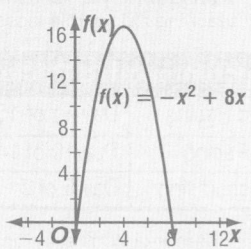

a. An astronaut weighs 140 pounds on Earth and 120 pounds in space. How far is he above Earth's surface? **317.29 miles**

b. An astronaut weighs 125 pounds on Earth. What is her weight in space if she is 99 miles above the surface of Earth? **119 pounds**

Mixed Review

40. 5 in. by 5 in. by 8 in.

40. Manufacturing The volume of a milk carton is 200 cubic inches. The base of the carton is square, and the height is 3 inches more than the length of the base. What are the dimensions of the carton? (Lesson 8–5)

41. Find the value of c such that the points at $(7, 2)$ and $(3, c)$ are 5 units apart. (Lesson 7–1) **5 or −1**

42. Agriculture The function $f(x) = -x^2 + 8x$, where x is the number of apple trees planted in a given area and $f(x)$ is the number of pounds of apples produced per day, can be used to determine how many apples are to be planted in a certain area. (Lesson 6–7)

a. Graph $f(x) = -x^2 + 8x$. **See margin.**

b. If Wessel Farm wants to produce at least 12 pounds of apples per day, how many trees should they plant in the area? Write as an inequality.

c. According to the graph of $f(x)$, production is low if few or many trees are planted and production is high if a medium number of trees is planted. Give some possible reasons why this might be true in real life.

42b. $2 \le x \le 6$

42c. See margin.

43. Physics The formula for finding the time t that it takes an object dropped

from a height of h feet to reach the ground is $t = \sqrt{\dfrac{2h}{g}}$, where g represents

the acceleration due to gravity. All objects in free fall near Earth's surface have an acceleration due to gravity of 32 feet per second squared. If a plant falls off a windowsill 64 feet from the ground, how long will it take the plant to reach the ground? (Lesson 5–5) **4 seconds**

44. Find M if $\begin{bmatrix} -9 & 12 \\ 4 & -7 \end{bmatrix} \cdot M = \begin{bmatrix} -9 & 12 \\ 4 & -7 \end{bmatrix}$. (Lesson 4–5) $\begin{bmatrix} 1 & 0 \\ 0 & 1 \end{bmatrix}$

45. Use Cramer's rule to solve the system of equations. (Lesson 3–3)
$\dfrac{x}{2} - \dfrac{2y}{3} = 2\dfrac{1}{3}$
$3x + 4y = -50$ **(−6, −8)**

46. Geography The following numbers are the percent of people in the South American countries who live in urban areas. (Lesson 1–3)
84, 87, 51, 76, 65, 54, 46, 70, 86, 83, 35

46a. See margin.

a. Make a stem-and-leaf plot of this data.

b. How many countries are less than 60% urban? **4**

46c. 87%

c. Argentina is the most urbanized country in South America. What percent of it is urban?

d. Guyana is the least urbanized country in South America. What percent of it is urban?

Lesson 8–6 Using Quadratic Techniques to Solve Polynomial Equations **519**

Extension ■

Connections Encourage students to look through their science books to find examples of polynomial functions.

Additional Answer

46a.

Stem	Leaf
3	5
4	6
5	1 4
6	5
7	0 6
8	3 4 6 7

4 6 = 46

4 ASSESS

Closing Activity

Modeling Use a graphing calculator to estimate the roots of several polynomial functions of quadratic form. Then use analytical techniques to find exact solutions.

Chapter 8, Quiz C (Lessons 8-5 and 8-6), is available in the *Assessment and Evaluation Masters,* p. 213.

Additional Answers

42a.

42c. **Sample answer: If few trees are planted, production will be low since there will be fewer trees producing apples. If many trees are planted, production might be low because there are more trees to maintain, with less time paid to production.**

Enrichment Masters, p. 61

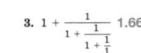

8-6 NAME_____ DATE_____

Enrichment Student Edition Pages 519–524

Infinite Continued Fractions

Some infinite expressions are actually equal to real numbers! The infinite continued fraction at the right is one example.

$x = 1 + \cfrac{1}{1 + \cfrac{1}{1 + \cfrac{1}{1 + \cfrac{1}{1 + \dots}}}}$

If you use x to stand for the infinite fraction, then the entire denominator of the first fraction on the right is also equal to x. This observation leads to the following equation:

$x = 1 + \dfrac{1}{x}$

Write a decimal for each continued fraction.

1. $1 + \dfrac{1}{1}$ 2

2. $1 + \dfrac{1}{1 + \frac{1}{1}}$ 1.5

3. $1 + \cfrac{1}{1 + \cfrac{1}{1 + \frac{1}{1}}}$ 1.666

4. $1 + \cfrac{1}{1 + \cfrac{1}{1 + \frac{1}{1}}}$ 1.6

5. $1 + \cfrac{1}{1 + \cfrac{1}{1 + \frac{1}{1}}}$ 1.625

6. The more terms you add to the fractions above, the closer their value approaches the value of the infinite continued fraction. What value do the fractions seem to be approaching? about 1.6

7. Rewrite $x = 1 + \frac{1}{x}$ as a quadratic equation and solve for x.
$x^2 - x - 1 = 0; x = \frac{1 \pm \sqrt{5}}{2}; x \approx 1.618$ or -0.618
(The positive root is the value of the infinite fraction, because the original fraction is clearly not negative.)

8. Find the value of the following infinite continued fraction.
$3 + \cfrac{1}{3 + \cfrac{1}{3 + \cfrac{1}{3 + \dots}}}$ $x = 3 + \frac{1}{x}; x = \frac{3 + \sqrt{13}}{2}$ or about 3.30

Chapter 8 **519**

NCTM Standards: 1–6

Instructional Resources

- Study Guide Master 8-7
- Practice Master 8-7
- Enrichment Master 8-7
- Real-World Applications, 24
- Tech Prep Applications Masters, p. 15

 Transparency 8-7A contains the 5-Minute Check for this lesson; **Transparency 8-7B** contains a teaching aid for this lesson.

Recommended Pacing

Standard Pacing	Day 11 of 15
Honors Pacing	Day 10 of 14
Block Scheduling*	Day 5 of 7

 *For more information on pacing and possible lesson plans, refer to the *Block Scheduling Booklet.*

1 FOCUS

 5-Minute Check
(over Lesson 8-6)

Solve each equation.

1. $x^4 + 3x^3 - 18x^2 = 0$ $0, -6, 3$
2. $x^4 - 7x^2 + 12 = 0$
   $2, -2, \sqrt{3}, -\sqrt{3}$
3. $x^{\frac{2}{5}} = 9$ 243
4. $x^{\frac{2}{3}} - 8x^{\frac{1}{3}} + 15 = 0$ $125, 27$
5. $x^{\frac{4}{3}} - 13x^{\frac{2}{3}} + 36 = 0$ $8, 27$

Motivating the Lesson

Hands-On Activity Bring in a Kelvin thermometer, a Celsius thermometer, and a Fahrenheit thermometer. Also bring in a hot plate, a container for water, and water for the container. Heat the water, taking the temperature of the water on all three scales as it rises. Write a formula to convert the temperature from one scale to the other.

 **What YOU'LL LEARN**

- To find the composition of functions.

Why IT'S IMPORTANT

You can use composition of functions to solve problems involving biology and foreign currency.

Composition of Functions

8-7

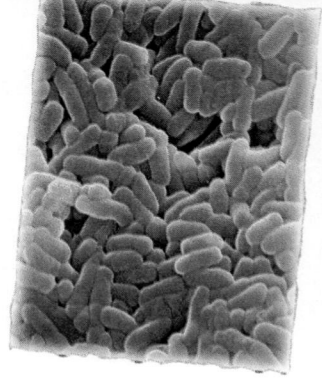

CONNECTION
Biology

Temperature is measured in different units in different countries. An American scientist and a German scientist are working on incubating a bacterium in their respective countries. They are sharing their findings with each other through the Internet. The last message from the German scientist says that her bacterium died at a temperature of 312° K, which she discovered was not warm enough. The American scientist's temperature for incubation is 98.2° F. Should the American scientist be worried? *This problem will be solved in Example 5.*

Let $K(x)$ be the function for converting Celsius temperatures to Kelvin, and let $C(x)$ be the function for converting Fahrenheit temperatures to Celsius.

$K(x) = x + 273$ *Converting Celsius to Kelvin*

$C(x) = \frac{5}{9}(x - 32)$ *Converting Fahrenheit to Celsius*

Using **composition of functions** is one way to solve the problem.

Composition of Functions	**Suppose f and g are functions such that the range of g is a subset of the domain of f. Then the composite function $f \circ g$ can be described by the equation $[f \circ g](x) = f[g(x)]$.**

$[f \circ g](x)$ and $f[g(x)]$ are both read "f of g of x."

Given two functions f and g, you can find $f \circ g$ and $g \circ f$ if the range of each function is a subset of the domain of the other function.

Example **1**   If $f = \{(1, 2), (3, 4), (5, 4)\}$ and $g = \{(2, 5), (4, 3)\}$, find $f \circ g$ and $g \circ f$.

$f[g(2)] = f(5)$ or 4 $g(2) = 5$	$g[f(1)] = g(2)$ or 5 $f(1) = 2$
$f[g(4)] = f(3)$ or 4 $g(4) = 3$	$g[f(3)] = g(4)$ or 3 $f(3) = 4$
	$g[f(5)] = g(4)$ or 3 $f(5) = 4$
$f \circ g = \{(2, 4), (4, 4)\}$	$g \circ f = \{(1, 5), (3, 3), (5, 3)\}$

The composition of functions can be shown by mappings. Suppose $f = \{(6, 2), (4, 5), (0, -2)\}$ and $g = \{(5, 4), (-2, 6), (2, 0)\}$. The composition of these functions is shown below.

LOOK BACK

Refer to Lesson 2-1 for information on mappings.

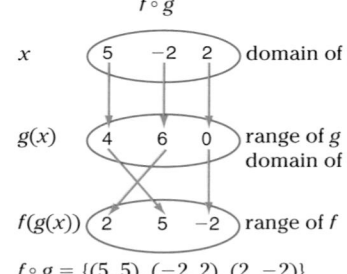

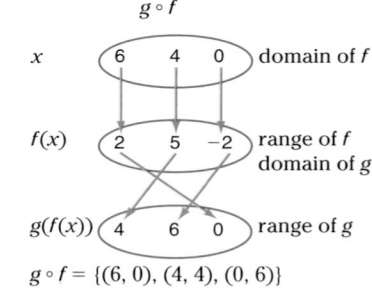

$f \circ g = \{(5, 5), (-2, 2), (2, -2)\}$ $g \circ f = \{(6, 0), (4, 4), (0, 6)\}$

 Alternative Learning Styles

Visual Have students draw boxes using markers of different colors to illustrate the domain and range of each of the following functions.
$f = \{(2, 5), (8, 4), (-3, 4)\}$
$g = \{(5, -3), (4, 8)\}$
Then have students match the boxes to show the mapping of $f \circ g$, as shown at the right. Then have them use the cards to show the mapping of $g \circ f$.

5			4	Domain of g
−3			8	Range of g
−3		2	8	Domain of f
4		5	4	Range of f

Thus, $f \circ g = \{(5, 4), (4, 4)\}$

The composition of two functions may not exist. Look back at the definition of the composition of functions. The composition of functions f and g, $f \circ g$, is defined when the range of g is a subset of the domain of f. If this condition is not met, the composition is not defined.

Example If $h = \{(4, 6), (2, 4), (6, 8), (8, 10)\}$ and $k = \{(4, 5), (6, 5), (8, 12), (10, 12)\}$, find $h \circ k$ and $k \circ h$, if they exist.

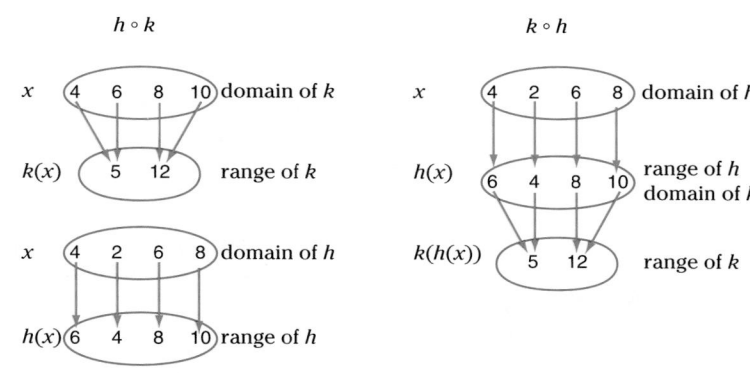

$h \circ k$ does not exist.

$k \circ h = \{(4, 5), (2, 5), (6, 12), (8, 12)\}$

The range of k is not a subset of the domain of h. Why not?

Sometimes, when two functions are composed, the graph of the composition resembles the graph of one of the original functions.

Example If $f(x) = x^2 - 4$ and $g(x) = 4x - 1$, find $[f \circ g](x)$.

$$[f \circ g](x) = f[g(x)]$$
$$= f(4x - 1) \qquad \text{Substitute } 4x - 1 \text{ for } g(x).$$
$$= (4x - 1)^2 - 4 \qquad \text{Evaluate } f \text{ when } x \text{ is } (4x - 1).$$
$$= 16x^2 - 8x + 1 - 4$$
$$= 16x^2 - 8x - 3 \qquad \text{Simplify.}$$

The graphs of each function are shown below.

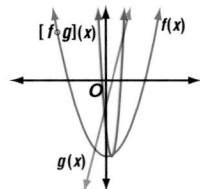

$f(x)$ is quadratic.
$g(x)$ is linear.
$[f \circ g](x)$ is quadratic.

In-Class Examples

For Example 1
If $f = \{(1, 4), (10, 5), (6, -3)\}$ and $g = \{(5, 1), (4, 6), (-3, 10)\}$, find $f \circ g$ and $g \circ f$.
$f \circ g = \{(5, 4), (4, -3), (-3, 5)\}$;
$g \circ f = \{(1, 6), (10, 1), (6, 10)\}$

For Example 2
If $f = \{(1, 3), (2, 7), (3, -2)\}$ and $g = \{(7, 11), (3, -6), (-2, -3)\}$, find $f \circ g$ and $g \circ f$, if they exist.
$f \circ g$ does not exist;
$g \circ f = \{(1, -6), (2, 11), (3, -3)\}$

For Example 3
If $f(x) = 2x^3 + 3$ and $g(x) = x + 7$, find $[f \circ g](x)$.
$2(x + 7)^3 + 3 = 2x^3 + 42x^2 + 294x + 686$

Teaching Tip In Example 3, emphasize that the function symbol "closest" to the variable is applied first, rather than working from left to right. Thus, g is applied to x first when evaluating $(f \circ g)(x)$.

GLENCOE *Technology*

Interactive Mathematics Tools Software

This multimedia software provides an interactive lesson by having students observe the tax savings, when investing a certain sum of money, as the interest rates and tax rates are manipulated. A **Computer Journal** gives students an opportunity to write about what they have learned.

For Windows & Macintosh

For Example 4
If $f(x) = x + 7$ and $g(x) = x^2 - 4$, find $[f \circ g](2)$ and $[g \circ f](2)$. **7, 77**

For Example 5
When converting to the metric system, we often need to convert inches into meters. Let $M(x)$ be the conversion of centimeters to meters, and let $C(x)$ be the conversion of inches to centimeters.

$M(x) = \frac{x}{100}$

$C(x) = 2.54x$

If Margarita is 67 inches tall, what is her metric height?

$[M \circ C](67) = \frac{(2.54)(67)}{100} = 1.7$ m

For Example 6
Find $f(4)$ if $f(0) = 7$ and $f(n) = f(n - 1) + 2n$. **27**

Example **4** If $f(x) = x + 5$ and $g(x) = x^2 - 2$, find $[f \circ g](3)$ and $[g \circ f](3)$.

$[f \circ g](3) = f[g(3)]$

$\qquad = f(3^2 - 2)$ \quad *Substitute $3^2 - 2$ for $g(3)$.*

$\qquad = f(7)$ \quad *Simplify.*

$\qquad = 7 + 5$ or 12 \quad *Evaluate f when x is 7.*

$[g \circ f](3) = g[f(3)]$

$\qquad = g(3 + 5)$ \quad *Substitute $3 + 5$ for $f(3)$.*

$\qquad = g(8)$ \quad *Simplify.*

$\qquad = 8^2 - 2$ or 62 \quad *Evaluate g when x is 8.*

Example **5**

CONNECTION
Biology

Refer to the application at the beginning of the lesson. Should the American scientist be worried that her incubation temperature is not warm enough?

In order to compare the two temperatures, we need to convert the American scientist's temperature from Fahrenheit to Kelvin. To do this, convert the temperature from Fahrenheit to Celsius and then from Celsius to Kelvin. This can be written as $[K \circ C](x)$ or $K[C(x)]$.

$[K \circ C](x) = K[C(x)]$

$\qquad = K\left[\frac{5}{9}(x - 32)\right]$ \quad *Substitute $\frac{5}{9}(x - 32)$ for $C(x)$.*

$\qquad = \left[\frac{5}{9}(x - 32)\right] + 273$

$[K \circ C](98.2) = \left[\frac{5}{9}(98.2 - 32)\right] + 273$ \quad *Replace x with 98.2.*

$\qquad \approx 309.8$ \quad *Simplify*

The American scientist is incubating her bacterium at $309.8°$ K. This is $2.2°$ K cooler than the German scientist's incubation temperature in which the bacterium died, so she should be worried.

Iteration is a special type of composition, the composition of a function with itself.

Example **6** Find $f(4)$ if $f(0) = 2$ and $f(n) = f(n - 1) + n$.

$f(0) = 2$

$f(1) = f(1 - 1) + 1 = f(0) + 1 = 3$ \quad *Use f(0) to find f(1).*

$f(2) = f(2 - 1) + 2 = f(1) + 2 = 5$ \quad *Use f(1) to find f(2).*

$f(3) = f(3 - 1) + 3 = f(2) + 3 = 8$ \quad *Use f(2) to find f(3).*

$f(4) = f(4 - 1) + 4 = f(3) + 4 = 12$ \quad *Use f(3) to find f(4).*

Communicating Mathematics

Study the lesson. Then complete the following.

1. **Write** out how you would read $[g \circ h](x)$.

2. In Example 2, what values would the domain of h need for $h \circ k$ to exist?

3. Look at the mapping of $[f \circ g](x)$ at the right.

    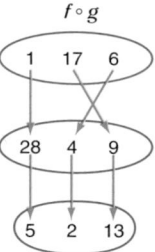

    $f \circ g$

    a. State the domain and the range of f and g.

    b. Write the functions f and g as a set of ordered pairs.

    c. Does $[g \circ f](x)$ exist? Explain.

4. Refer to Example 3. What type of function is $[g \circ f](x)$?

5. **Show** that if $f(x) = x^2$ and $g(x) = x - 4$, then $[f \circ g](x) \neq [g \circ f](x)$.

6. **Write** two functions $f(x)$ and $g(x)$ such that $f[g(x)] = x^2 - 6$.

7. **Explain** how you could find $f(2)$ and $f(3)$ if $f(x)$ is defined by $f(x + 1) = \frac{1}{4}f(x)$ and $f(1) = 24$.

MATH JOURNAL

8. Draw your family tree. Explain how your family tree could be a composition of functions.

Guided Practice

Find $[f \circ g](2)$ and $[g \circ f](2)$.

9. $f(x) = x + 6$

    $g(x) = x - 3$

10. $f(x) = x^2 + 3$

    $g(x) = x + 1$

Find $g[h(x)]$ and $h[g(x)]$.

11. $g(x) = 4x$

    $h(x) = 2x - 1$

12. $g(x) = x + 2$

    $h(x) = x^2$

If $f(x) = x^2$, $g(x) = 3x$, and $h(x) = x + 2$, find each value.

13. $f[g(1)]$

14. $[f \circ h](4)$

15. $h[f(x)]$

Find the first four iterations of each function, given the initial value.

16. $f(0) = 1, f(n) = f(n - 1) + 3$

17. $f(1) = 3, f(n) = 2f(n - 1)$

18. **Bonus** A sales representative for a furniture manufacturer is paid an annual salary plus a bonus of 3% of her sales *over* $275,000. Let $f(x) = x - 275,000$ and let $h(x) = 0.03x$.

    a. If x is greater than 275,000, is her bonus represented by $f[h(x)]$ or $h[f(x)]$? Explain.

    b. Find her bonus if her sales for the year are $400,000.

Lesson 8–7 Composition of Functions **523**

Reteaching

Using Alternative Methods Given $f(x)$ and $g(x)$, have students compute the value obtained by applying g and then f to a value of x in two ways. Find $f[g(3)]$ and $[f \circ g](3)$.
For example, let $f(x) = 2x + 3$ and $g(x) = x^2 - x - 2$.

$f(g(3))$

$f(3^2 - 3 - 2)$

$f(4)$

11

$[f \circ g](x) = 2(x^2 - x - 2) + 3$

$[f \circ g](x) = 2x^2 - 2x - 1$

$[f \circ g](3) = 2 \cdot 9 - 6 - 1$

$[f \circ g](3) = 11$

---

3 PRACTICE/APPLY

Check for Understanding
Exercises 1–18 are designed to help you assess your students' understanding through reading, writing, speaking, and modeling. You should work through Exercises 1–8 with your students and then monitor their work on Exercises 9–18.

Additional Answers

3a. domain of g: 1, 17, 6
    range of g: 28, 4, 9
    domain of f: 28, 4, 9
    range of f: 5, 2, 13

3b. $g = \{(1, 28), (17, 9), (6, 4)\}$
    $f = \{(28, 5), (4, 2), (9, 13)\}$

3c. $[g \circ f](x)$ does not exist because the range of f is not a subset of the domain of g.

5. $[f \circ g](x) = f[g(x)]$
    $\quad\quad\quad\quad = f[x - 4]$
    $\quad\quad\quad\quad = (x - 4)^2$
    $\quad\quad\quad\quad = x^2 - 8x + 16$

    $[g \circ f](x) = g[f(x)]$
    $\quad\quad\quad\quad = g[x^2]$
    $\quad\quad\quad\quad = (x^2) - 4$
    $\quad\quad\quad\quad = x^2 - 4$

Study Guide Masters, p. 62

8-7   NAME_____ DATE_____

Study Guide Student Edition
Pages 523–528

Composition of Functions

Composition of Functions
Suppose f and g are functions such that the range of g is a subset of the domain of f. Then the composite function, $f \circ g$, can be described by the equation $[f \circ g](x) = f[g(x)]$.

Example: If $f(x) = x + 7$ and $g(x) = 3 + 2x$, find $[f \circ g](x)$ and $[g \circ f](x)$.

$[f \circ g](x) = f[3 + 2x]$ $[g \circ f](x) = g[x + 7]$
$\quad\quad = (3 + 2x) + 7$ $\quad\quad = 3 + 2(x + 7)$
$\quad\quad = 2x + 10$ $\quad\quad = 2x + 17$

Find $[f \circ g](x)$ and $[g \circ f](x)$.

1. $f(x) = 2x + 7$
   $g(x) = -5x - 1$
   $[f \circ g](x) = -10x + 5$
   $[g \circ f](x) = -10x - 36$

2. $f(x) = x^2 - 1$
   $g(x) = -4x^2$
   $[f \circ g](x) = 16x^4 - 1$
   $[g \circ f](x) = -4x^4 + 8x^2 - 4$

3. $f(x) = x^2 + 2x$
   $g(x) = x - 9$
   $[f \circ g](x) = x^2 - 16x + 63$
   $[g \circ f](x) = x^2 + 2x - 9$

4. $f(x) = 5x + 4$
   $g(x) = 3 - x$
   $[f \circ g](x) = 19 - 5x$
   $[g \circ f](x) = -1 - 5x$

5. $f(x) = x^2$
   $g(x) = 2x^2 + 2x - 1$
   $[f \circ g](x) = 4x^4 + 8x^3 - 4x + 1$
   $[g \circ f](x) = 2x^4 + 2x^2 - 1$

6. $f(x) = 7x + 6$
   $g(x) = 6x + 7$
   $[f \circ g](x) = 42x + 55$
   $[g \circ f](x) = 42x + 43$

If $f(x) = x^2 + 5$, $g(x) = 9x - 1$, and $h(x) = -2x$, find each value.

7. $[f \circ g](-2)$
   366

8. $[h \circ g](-3)$
   56

9. $[f \circ (g \circ h)](2)$
   1374

10. $[g \circ h](-3)$
    53

Assignment Guide

Core: 19–51 odd, 53–61
Enriched: 20–46 even, 48–61

For **Extra Practice,** see p. 896.

The red A, B, and C flags, printed only in the Teacher's Wraparound Edition, indicate the level of difficulty of the exercises.

Additional Answers

46. $f \circ g = \{(1, -3), (-3, 1), (2, 1)\}$
    $g \circ f = \{(1, 0), (0, 1)\}$
47. $f \circ g$ does not exist
    $g \circ f = \{(3, 6), (4, 4), (6, 6), (7, 8)\}$

25. $x + 11, x + 11$
26. $10x, 10x$
27. $x^2 - 2, x^2 - 4x + 4$

28. $6x - 2, 6x + 1$
29. $x^3 + 1, x^3 + 3x^2 + 3x + 1$
30. $|x - 3|, |x| - 3$
39. $16x^2 - 32x + 16$

40. $-1, -6, -11, -16$
41. $6, 18, 54, 162$
42. $11, 23, 39, 59$
43. $0.2, 0.4, 1.2, 4.8$
44. $-8, -28, -90, -278$
45. $25, 104, 425, 1716$

46–47. See margin.

EXERCISES

Practice

Find $[f \circ g](3)$ and $[g \circ f](3)$.

19. $f(x) = x$
    $g(x) = -x$ $-3, -3$

20. $f(x) = x^2$
    $g(x) = x^3$ $729, 729$

21. $f(x) = x + 1$
    $g(x) = x^2 + 6$ $16, 22$

22. $f = \{(1, -7), (2, 3), (3, 0)\}$
    $g = \{(0, 11), (3, 1)\}$ $-7, 11$

23. $f = \{(-1, 9), (3, 6)\}$
    $g = \{(-5, 3), (6, 12), (3, -1)\}$ $9, 12$

24. $f(x) = 7x - 5$
    $g(x) = x^2 - 3x + 7$ $44, 215$

Find $g[h(x)]$ and $h[g(x)]$.

B

25. $g(x) = x + 7$
    $h(x) = x + 4$

26. $g(x) = 5x$
    $h(x) = 2x$

27. $g(x) = x - 2$
    $h(x) = x^2$

28. $g(x) = -2x$
    $h(x) = -3x + 1$

29. $g(x) = x + 1$
    $h(x) = x^3$

30. $g(x) = |x|$
    $h(x) = x - 3$

If $f(x) = x^2$, $g(x) = 4x$, and $h(x) = x - 1$, find each value.

31. $h[g(2)]$ 7
32. $[f \circ g](4)$ 256
33. $[h \circ f](3)$ 8

34. $[f \circ h](-3)$ 16
35. $h[g(-2)]$ -9
36. $h[f(-4)]$ 15

37. $g[f(x)]$ $4x^2$
38. $[f \circ g](x)$ $16x^2$
39. $[f \circ (g \circ h)](x)$

Find the first four iterations of each function, given the initial value.

40. $f(0) = 4, f(n) = f(n - 1) - 5$
41. $f(1) = 2, f(n) = 3f(n - 1)$
42. $f(1) = 3, f(n) = f(n - 1) + 4n$
43. $f(0) = 0.2, f(n) = n(f(n - 1))$
44. $f(0) = -2, f(n) = 3f(n - 1) - 2n$
45. $f(0) = 6, f(n) = 4f(n - 1) + n^2$

Express $f \circ g$ and $g \circ f$, if they exist, as sets of ordered pairs.

C

46. $f = \{(1, 1), (0, -3)\}$
    $g = \{(1, 0), (-3, 1), (2, 1)\}$

47. $f = \{(3, 8), (4, 0), (6, 3), (7, -1)\}$
    $g = \{(0, 4), (8, 6), (3, 6), (-1, 8)\}$

Critical Thinking

48. Name two functions f and g such that $f[g(x)] = g[f(x)]$.
49. If $f(0) = 4$ and $f(x + 1) = 3f(x) - 2$, find $f(4)$. 244

Applications and Problem Solving

48. Sample answer: $f(x) = x, g(x) = -x$

50. **Foreign Currency**   The British Isles, located northwest of the European mainland, consist of two large islands, Great Britain and Ireland, and many smaller islands. Carolyn Martinez took a trip to the British Isles during the summer of 1995 and needed to exchange American dollars for British pounds. After she arrived in Ireland, she needed to exchange her British pounds for Irish punts. Look at the functions below.

$B(x) = 0.9733x$ *Converting British pounds to Irish punts*

$A(x) = 0.6252x$ *Converting American dollars to British pounds*

50a. It represents converting American dollars to Irish punts.

a. Find the equation of the composition function $B[A(x)]$. Explain what this composition represents. $B[A(x)] = 0.9733(0.6252x) = 0.6085x$

b. How many Irish punts will she get for $500? about 304.25

524   Chapter 8   *Exploring Polynomial Functions*

Practice Masters, p. 62

NAME_____   DATE _____

8-7
Practice

Student Edition
Pages 523–528

Composition of Functions

Find $[f \circ g](2)$ and $[g \circ f](2)$.

1. $f(x) = 2x - 1$
   $g(x) = -3x$ $-13; -9$

2. $f(x) = x^2 - 5$
   $g(x) = 3x^2 + 1$ $164; 4$

Find $f[g(x)]$ and $g[f(x)]$.

3. $f(x) = x - 8$
   $g(x) = x + 8$ $x; x$

4. $f(x) = x^2 - x + 3$
   $g(x) = |x|$ $x^2 - |x| + 3; |x^2 - x + 3|$

Find $f[g(-3)]$ and $g[f(-3)]$.

5. $f(x) = 9$
   $g(x) = \frac{1}{x}$ $9; \frac{1}{9}$

6. $f(x) = \sqrt{x + 5}$
   $g(x) = 2x + 8$ $\sqrt{7}; 2\sqrt{2} + 8$

If $f(x) = x^2$, $g(x) = 5x$, and $h(x) = x + 4$, find each value.

7. $f[g(1)]$ 25
8. $g[h(-2)]$ 10

9. $h[f(4)]$ 20
10. $f[h(-9)]$ 25

Express $g \circ f$ and $f \circ g$, if they exist, as sets of ordered pairs.

11. $f = \{(3, 8), (2, 5), (4, -5), (9, 3)\}$
    $g = \{(9, 2), (-5, 3), (5, 9), (8, 10), (1, 9)\}$
    $g \circ f$ doesn't exist
    $f \circ g$ doesn't exist

12. $f = \{(1, 4), (10, 5), (6, -3)\}$
    $g = \{(5, 1), (4, 6), (-3, 10)\}$
    $g \circ f = \{(1, 6), (10, 1), (6, 10)\}$
    $f \circ g = \{(5, 4), (4, -3), (-3, 5)\}$

51. **Discounts** Jeanette bought a new electric wok that was originally priced at $38. The department store advertised a rebate of $5 as well as a discount of 25% off all small appliances.

  a. Express the price of the wok after the rebate and the price after the discount using function notation. Let x represent the price of the wok, $r(x)$ represent the price after the rebate, and $p(x)$ represent the price after the discount.

  b. Find $r[p(x)]$ and explain what this value represents.

  c. Find $p[r(x)]$ and explain what this value represents.

52. **Finance** Nashota pays $30 each month on a credit card that charges 1.4% interest monthly. She has a balance of $450. The balance at the beginning of the nth month is given by the following function that is defined recursively.

  $f(1) = 450$

  $f(n) = f(n - 1) + 0.014f(n - 1) - 30$

  Find the balances at the beginning of the first five months.

Mixed Review

53. Write $x^6 + 3x^3 - 10 = 0$ in quadratic form. (Lesson 8–6)

54. Write $y^2 = 6x$ in the form $x = a(y - k)^2 + h$. (Lesson 7–2)

55. **Statistics** An astronomer made ten measurements in minutes of degrees (') of the angular distance between two stars. The measurements were 11.20', 11.17', 10.92', 11.06', 11.19', 10.97', 11.09', 11.05', 11.22', and 11.03'. Find the mean and the standard deviation of the measurements. (Lesson 6–8)

56. Find the product $(m + 7)^2$. (Lesson 5–2)

57. Find $\begin{bmatrix} 4 & 5 \\ -2 & 9 \\ -1 & 4 \end{bmatrix} \cdot \begin{bmatrix} 5 & 3 & -6 & 0 \\ -2 & 1 & 4 & -1 \end{bmatrix}$. (Lesson 4–3)

58. **Art** Cecilia would like to place a picture of her triangle-shaped painting in the center of a page in her portfolio. She would like the longest side on the bottom. The lengths of the sides of the picture are 4 inches, 3 inches, and 3 inches. Suppose the center of her page is represented by the origin. Find a system of inequalities that describes the points her picture would occupy on the page, so that the top and bottom of the picture are at an equal distance above and below the origin, and the left and right corners are at an equal distance from the origin. (Lesson 3–5)

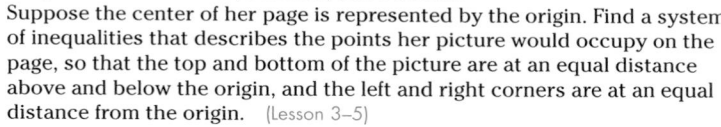

Molecular cloud from which new stars emerge

59. What type of special function is $f(x) = x$? (Lesson 2–6)

  a. constant   b. identity   c. absolute value   d. step

60. Find a value of b for which the graph of $y = bx - 7$ is perpendicular to the graph of $x - 2y = 18$. (Lesson 2–3)

61. Simplify $-4(3a + 2b) - 3(-7a - 6b)$. (Lesson 1–2)

Extension

Connections Have students show that when $C(x) = \frac{5}{9}(x - 32)$ and $F(x) = \frac{9}{5}x + 32$, $[C \circ F](x) = x$.

$[C \circ F](x) = C\left(\frac{9}{5}x + 32\right) =$

$\frac{5}{9}\left[\left(\frac{9}{5}x + 32\right) - 32\right] = \frac{5}{9}\left[\frac{9}{5}x\right] = x$

Relate this to the general concept of inverse functions.

Closing Activity

Writing Write an explanation of how to find $f \circ g$ and $g \circ f$. Include the domain and range of each function and the composite.

Enrichment Masters, p. 62

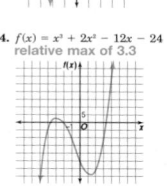

NAME_____ DATE _____

8-7

Student Editi
Pages 525–5

Enrichment

Relative Maximum Values

The graph shows a relative maximum value somewhere between $f(-2)$ and $f(-1)$. You can obtain a closer approximation by comparing values such as those shown in the table.

$f(x) = x^3 - 6x - 9$

x	$f(x)$
-2	-5
-1.5	-3.375
-1.4	-3.344
-1.3	-3.397
-1	-4

To the nearest tenth a relative maximum value for $f(x)$ is -3.3.

Using a calculator to find points, graph each function. To the nearest tenth, find a relative maximum value of the function.

1. $f(x) = x(x^2 - 3)$
   relative max of 2.0

2. $f(x) = x^3 - 3x - 3$
   relative max of -1.0

3. $f(x) = x^3 - 9x - 2$
   relative max of 8.4

4. $f(x) = x^3 + 2x^2 - 12x - 24$
   relative max of 3.3

Objective

Graph the iterations of a function.

Recommended Time

Demonstration and discussion: 30 minutes; Exercises: 30 minutes

Instructional Resources

For each student or group of students
Modeling Mathematics Masters
• p. 15 (grid paper)
• p. 24 (worksheet)
For teacher demonstration
Algebra and Geometry Overhead Manipulative Resources

1 FOCUS

Motivating the Lesson

To help introduce the concept of iteration, have students use a scientific calculator for Activity 1. Have them first enter the constant value 2. Then they should apply the remaining operations, multiplying the constant by $\frac{1}{2}$, and then adding five repeatedly. List the results of the first five applications. **2, 6, 8, 9, 9.5**

2 TEACH

Teaching Tip While this lesson explores only iterative applications of linear functions, remind students that the concept is valid for any type of function.

3 PRACTICE/APPLY

Assignment Guide

Core: 1–12
Enriched: 1–12

MODELING MATHEMATICS

An Extension of Lesson 8–7

8-7B Exploring Iteration

Materials: grid paper

Each result of the iteration process is called an **iterate.** To iterate a function $f(x)$, begin with a starting value x_0, find $f(x_0)$, and call the result x_1. Then find $f(x_1)$, and call the result x_2. Find $f(x_2)$ and call the result x_3, and so on.

Activity 1 Find the first three iterates, x_1, x_2, and x_3, of the function $f(x) = \frac{1}{2}x + 5$ for an initial value of $x_0 = 2$.

Step 1 To obtain the first iterate, find the value of the function for $x_0 = 2$.
$f(x_0) = f(2)$
$\qquad = \frac{1}{2}(2) + 5$ or 6   So, $x_1 = 6$.

Step 2 To obtain the second iterate x_2, substitute the function value for the first iterate, x_1, for x.
$f(x_1) = f(6)$
$\qquad = \frac{1}{2}(6) + 5$ or 8   So, $x_2 = 8$.

Step 3 Now find the third iterate, x_3, by substituting x_2 for x.
$f(x_2) = f(8)$
$\qquad = \frac{1}{2}(8) + 5$ or 9   So, $x_3 = 9$.

Therefore, the first three iterates for the function $f(x) = \frac{1}{2}x + 5$ for an initial value of $x_0 = 2$ are 6, 8, 9.

Graphing the iterations of a function can help us understand the process of iteration better. Follow these steps.

• Graph a function $g(x)$ and the line $f(x) = x$ on the coordinate plane.

• Choose an initial value, x_0, and locate the point $(x_0, 0)$.

• Draw a vertical line from $(x_0, 0)$ to the graph of $g(x)$. This will be the segment from the point $(x_0, 0)$ to $(x_0, g(x_0))$.

• Now draw a horizontal segment from this point to the graph of the line $f(x) = x$. This will be the segment from $(x_0, g(x_0))$ to $(g(x_0), g(x_0))$.

• Repeat the process for many iterations.

This process is called **graphical iteration.**

You can think of the line $f(x) = x$ as a mirror that reflects each function value to become the input for the next iteration of the function. The points at which the graph of the function $g(x)$ intersects the graph of the line $f(x) = x$ are called **fixed points.** If you try to iterate the initial value that corresponds to the x-coordinate of a fixed point, the iterates will all be the same.

Cooperative Learning

This lesson offers an excellent opportunity for using cooperative learning groups. For more information on cooperative learning strategies and group management, see *Cooperative Learning in the Mathematics Classroom*, one of the titles in the Glencoe Mathematics Professional Series.

Four basic paths are possible when a linear function is iterated.

Staircase Out
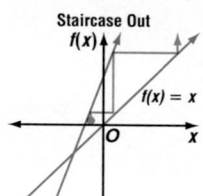

Staircase In
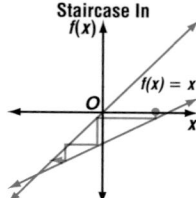

Spiral Out
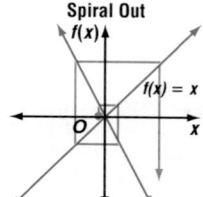

Spiral In
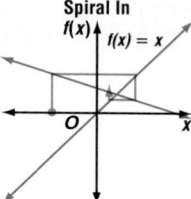

Activity 2 Perform graphical iteration on the function $g(x) = 4x$ for the first three iterates if the initial value is $x_0 = 0.25$. Which of the four types of paths does the iteration take?

Step 1 To do the graphical iteration, first graph the functions $f(x) = x$ and $g(x) = 4x$.

Step 2 Start at the point $(0.25, 0)$ and draw a vertical line to the graph of $g(x) = 4x$. From that point, draw a horizontal line to the graph of $f(x) = x$.

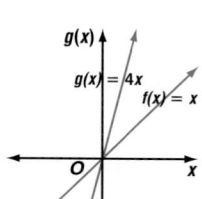

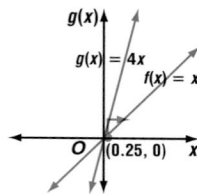

Step 3 Repeat the process from the point on $f(x) = x$. Then repeat again.

The path of the iterations staircases out.

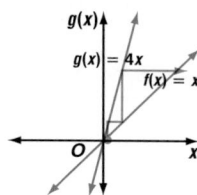

Model Find the first three iterates of each function using the given initial value. If necessary, round your answers to the nearest hundredth.

1. $g(x) = 5x$; $x_0 = 0.2$ 1, 5, 25
2. $g(x) = -2x + 1$; $x_0 = -0.5$ 2, -3, 7
3. $g(x) = 3 - 0.4x$; $x_0 = -4$
   4.6, 1.16, 2.54
4. $g(x) = 3x - 0.5x^2$; $x_0 = 1$
   2.5, 4.38, 3.55

Draw Graph each function and the function $f(x) = x$ on the same set of axes. Then draw the graphical iteration for $x_0 = 1$. State the slope of the linear function and tell what type of path the graphical iteration forms.

5. $g(x) = 4x + 12$ 4, staircase out
6. $g(x) = \frac{3}{5}x + 2$ $\frac{3}{5}$, staircase in
7. $g(x) = -2x - 3$ -2, spiral out
8. $g(x) = 5x - 7$ 5, staircase out
9. $g(x) = \frac{1}{4}x + 1$ $\frac{1}{4}$, staircase in
10. $g(x) = -\frac{1}{3}x + 4$ $-\frac{1}{3}$, spiral in

5–10. See margin for graphs.

Write
11–12. See margin.

11. Write a paragraph explaining the relationship between the slope of a linear function and the type of path that the graphical iteration forms.
12. What type of path do you think is formed when you perform the graphical iteration on the function $f(x) = 5x - x^2$? How does it compare to the iteration of linear functions?

4 ASSESS

Observing students working in cooperative groups is an excellent method of assessment.

Additional Answers

5.
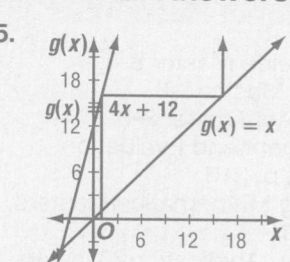

6.
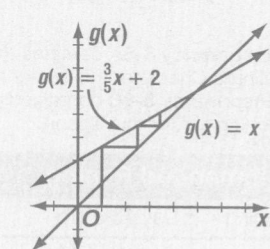

7.
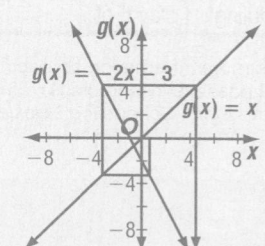

8.
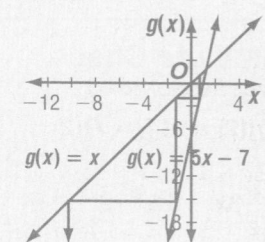

9.
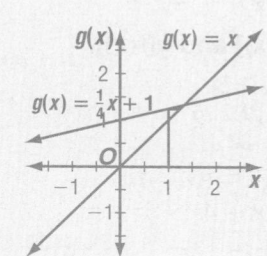

Additional Answers

10.

$g(x) = x$

$g(x) = -\frac{1}{3}x + 4$

11. Sample answer: Functions whose slopes are positive form staircase paths; functions whose slopes are negative form spiral paths.
12. It initially forms a staircase pattern, then settles into a cyclical pattern.

NCTM Standards: 1–6

Instructional Resources

- Study Guide Master 8-8
- Practice Master 8-8
- Enrichment Master 8-8
- Assessment and Evaluation Masters, p. 213
- Modeling Mathematics Masters, pp. 49–51
- Tech Prep Applications Masters, p. 16

 Transparency 8-8A contains the 5-Minute Check for this lesson; **Transparency 8-8B** contains a teaching aid for this lesson.

Recommended Pacing	
Standard Pacing	Day 13 of 15
Honors Pacing	Day 12 of 14
Block Scheduling*	Day 6 of 7

 *For more information on pacing and possible lesson plans, refer to the *Block Scheduling Booklet*.

1 FOCUS

 5-Minute Check
(over Lesson 8-7)

Find $[f \circ g](2)$ and $[g \circ f](2)$.

1. $f(x) = 2x - 1$
$g(x) = -3x$ $-13, -9$
2. $f(x) = x^2 + 1$
$g(x) = x + 1$ $10, 6$

Find $f[g(x)]$ and $g[f(x)]$.

3. $f(x) = x + 3$
$g(x) = x^2 - 2$
$x^2 + 1, x^2 + 6x + 7$
4. $f(x) = x^2 - 3x + 7$
$g(x) = x + 4$
$x^2 + 5x + 11, x^2 - 3x + 11$
5. If $f = \{(2, 5), (8, 4), (-3, 4)\}$ and $g = \{(5, -3), (4, 8)\}$, find $f \circ g$ and $g \circ f$.
$f \circ g = \{(5, 4), (4, 4)\}; g \circ f = \{(2, -3), (8, 8), (-3, 8)\}$

Inverse Functions and Relations

The Tāj Mahal, Āgra, India

What YOU'LL LEARN

- To determine the inverse of a function or relation,
- to graph functions and their inverses, and
- to work backward to solve problems.

Why IT'S IMPORTANT

You can use inverses to solve problems involving shopping and world cultures.

 **APPLICATION**
World Cultures

The ancient Hindus loved to do number puzzles. Aryabhata, a mathematician who lived in India during the sixth century A.D., was especially drawn to these puzzles. Look at the number puzzle below.

> Choose a number between 1 and 10.
> Multiply that number by 4.
> Add 6 to the resulting number.
> Divide by 2.
> Then subtract 5.

Aryabhata could have correctly told you your original number. How? Suppose your original number was 8. The chart below shows the steps of the puzzle.

Verbal Instructions	Number	Functional Representation
Choose a number between 1 and 10.	8	$f(x) = x$
Multiply that number by 4.	8 × 4 or 32	$g(x) = 4[f(x)] = 4x$
Add 6.	32 + 6 or 38	$h(x) = g(x) + 6 = 4x + 6$
Divide by 2.	38 ÷ 2 or 19	$j(x) = h(x) \div 2 = \frac{4x+6}{2}$
Then subtract 5.	19 − 5 or 14	$k(x) = j(x) - 5 = \frac{4x+6}{2} - 5$

To tell you the original number, Aryabhata would **work backward** and do the inverse, or opposite, of the steps as he went along. Subtraction is the inverse operation of addition, and division is the inverse operation of multiplication.

The chart below shows the inverse of the puzzle shown above.

Verbal Instructions	Number	Functional Representation
Tell me the number that you ended with.	14	$p(x) = x$
Add 5 to the number.	14 + 5 or 19	$r(x) = p(x) + 5 = x + 5$
Multiply by 2.	19 × 2 or 38	$t(x) = r(x) \times 2 = 2x + 10$
Subtract 6.	38 − 6 or 32	$v(x) = t(x) - 6 = 2x + 4$
Divide by 4.	32 ÷ 4 or 8	$w(x) = \frac{v(x)}{4} = \frac{1}{2}x + 1$

The functions $k(x) = \frac{4x+6}{2} - 5$ and $w(x) = \frac{1}{2}x + 1$ are **inverse functions.**

Definition of Inverse Functions	Two functions f and g are inverse functions if and only if both of their compositions are the identity function. That is, $$[f \circ g](x) = x \text{ and } [g \circ f](x) = x.$$

GLOBAL CONNECTIONS

Aryabhata I (476–550), a Hindu mathematician and astronomer, was the most important early scholar in Indian mathematics. In his work *Aryabhatiya*, he gave a value of 3.1416 for π, used the decimal and place-value system, and supplied a variety of rules for algebra.

GLOBAL CONNECTIONS

On April 19, 1975, India launched its first orbiting satellite. Its mission was to explore the ionosphere, measure neutron and gamma rays from the sun, and perform x-ray astronomy experiments. The satellite's name is *Aryabhata,* after the famous mathematician and astronomer.

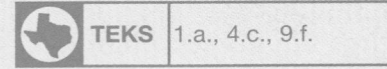 **TEKS** | 1.a., 4.c., 9.f.

You can determine if two functions are inverse functions by finding both of their compositions. If both compositions equal the identity function $h(x) = x$, then the functions are inverse functions.

You can also determine if two functions are inverse functions by graphing. The graphs of a function and its inverse are mirror images, or reflections, of each other with respect to the graph of the identity function $h(x) = x$. Its graph is the line of symmetry.

Example Determine whether $f(x) = 3x - 4$ and $g(x) = \frac{x+4}{3}$ are inverse functions.

Method 1: Finding Compositions

Find $[f \circ g](x)$ and $[g \circ f](x)$ to determine whether these functions are inverse functions.

$$[f \circ g](x) = f[g(x)] \qquad\qquad [g \circ f](x) = g[f(x)]$$

$$= f\left(\frac{x+4}{3}\right) \qquad\qquad\qquad = g(3x - 4)$$

$$= 3\left(\frac{x+4}{3}\right) - 4 \qquad\qquad = \frac{(3x-4)+4}{3}$$

$$= x \qquad\qquad\qquad\qquad\qquad = x$$

Since both $[f \circ g](x)$ and $[g \circ f](x)$ equal x, then $f(x)$ and $g(x)$ are inverse functions. That is, f is the inverse of g and g is the inverse of f.

Method 2: Graphing

Graph both functions.

Suppose the plane containing the graphs could be folded along the line $h(x) = x$. Then the graphs would coincide. This verifies that the functions are inverses.

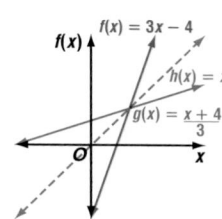

We can write f is the inverse of g and g is the inverse of f using the notation $f = g^{-1}$ and $g = f^{-1}$. The symbol g^{-1} is read "g inverse" or "the inverse of g." By the definition of inverse functions, we can write the following.

The -1 is not an exponent.

$$[f \circ f^{-1}](x) = x \text{ and } [f^{-1} \circ f](x) = x$$

The ordered pairs of inverse functions are related. Use the functions in Example 1 and evaluate $f(5)$. Then find $f^{-1}[f(5)]$.

$f(5) = 3(5) - 4 \text{ or } 11$ $\qquad\qquad$ $f^{-1}[f(5)] = f^{-1}(11)$

The ordered pair (5, 11) $\qquad\qquad\qquad = \frac{(11)+4}{3}$ or 5
belongs to f.

$\qquad\qquad\qquad$ The ordered pair (11, 5)
$\qquad\qquad\qquad$ belongs to f^{-1}.

So, the inverse of a function can be found by exchanging the domain and range of the function.

Property of Inverse Functions	Suppose f and f^{-1} are inverse functions. Then $f(a) = b$ if and only if $f^{-1}(b) = a$.

Motivating the Lesson

Questioning Discuss the following questions.

1. Why is 0 the additive identity? **Any number plus 0 equals the number itself.**
2. Why is 1 the multiplicative identity? **Any number times 1 equals the number itself.**
3. Tell what it means for two numbers to be additive inverses of one another. **Their sum is zero.**
4. Tell what it means for two numbers to be multiplicative inverses of one another. **Their product is 1.**

2 TEACH

In-Class Example

For Example 1

Determine whether $f(x) = 6 - 2x$ and $g(x) = \frac{6-x}{2}$ are inverse functions. **yes**

GLENCOE *Technology*

Interactive Mathematics Tools Software

This multimedia software provides an interactive lesson by leading students through strategies of finding the inverse of a function. A **Computer Journal** gives students an opportunity to write about what they have learned.

For Windows & Macintosh

In-Class Example

For Example 2
Find the inverse of $f(x) = x + 3$. Then verify that f and f^{-1} are inverse functions and graph both functions. $f^{-1}(x) = x - 3$. **They are inverse functions because $[f \circ f^{-1}](x) = [f^{-1} \circ f](x) = x$.**

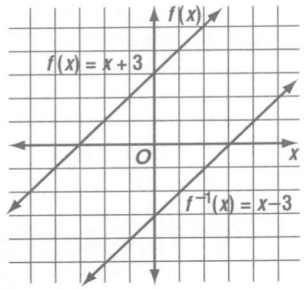

For Example 3
Find the inverse of $f(x) = x^2 - 4x + 4$. Determine whether the inverse is a function.

$f^{-1}(x) = \pm\sqrt{x} + 2$; not a function

Teaching Tip Remind students that if the inverse of a function is not a function, they should not use the $f^{-1}(x)$ notation to indicate the inverse, since this indicates the inverse is also a function.

To find the inverse of a function f, you can interchange the variables in the equation $y = f(x)$.

Example ② **Find the inverse of $f(x) = 3x + 6$. Then verify that f and f^{-1} are inverse functions.**

Method 1: Algebra

$y = 3x + 6$ *Rewrite $f(x) = 3x + 6$ as $y = 3x + 6$.*

$x = 3y + 6$ *Interchange x and y.*

$y = \dfrac{x - 6}{3}$ *The inverse is also a function.*

The inverse of $f(x) = 3x + 6$ is $f^{-1}(x) = \dfrac{x - 6}{3}$.

Check: To verify that f and f^{-1} are inverses, show that the compositions of f and f^{-1} are identity functions.

$$[f \circ f^{-1}](x) = f[f^{-1}(x)] \qquad\qquad [f^{-1} \circ f](x) = f^{-1}[f(x)]$$

$$= f\left(\frac{x - 6}{3}\right) \qquad\qquad\qquad = f^{-1}(3x + 6)$$

$$= 3\left(\frac{x - 6}{3}\right) + 6 \qquad\qquad\quad = \frac{(3x + 6) - 6}{3}$$

$$= x \qquad\qquad\qquad\qquad\qquad = x$$

The functions are inverses, since both $[f \circ f^{-1}](x)$ and $[f^{-1} \circ f](x)$ equal x.

Method 2: Graphing

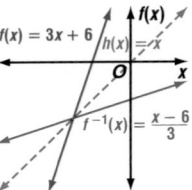

Now graph both functions.

The graphs are reflections of each other over the line $h(x) = x$. This verifies that the functions are inverses.

In Example 2, f and f^{-1} were both functions. However, the inverse of a function is not always a function.

Example ③ **Find the inverse of $f(x) = x^2 + 4$. Determine whether the inverse is a function.**

Rewrite $f(x)$ as $y = x^2 + 4$.

To make the inverse of a quadratic function a function, only nonnegative values of the range are considered. Using only these values, the inverse is called a <u>square root function</u>. In Example 3, the square root function is $y = \sqrt{x - 4}$.

$x = y^2 + 4$ *Interchange x and y.*

$\pm\sqrt{x - 4} = y$ *Solve for y.*

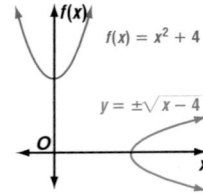

The inverse of $f(x) = x^2 + 4$ is $y = \pm\sqrt{x - 4}$. This inverse is not a function, since the graph does not pass the vertical line test for functions.

Check this result.

MODELING MATHEMATICS

Inverses of Functions

Materials:  geomirror grid paper ✎ straightedge

f. $y = (x + 5)^{\frac{1}{3}}$; Yes, the graph passes the vertical line test.

Use a full sheet of grid paper. Draw axes in the center of the page, and label each mark on each axis as one unit.

e. $y = \frac{1}{2}(x + 8)$

Your Turn   a–d. See margin.

a. Use a straightedge to graph $y = 2x - 8$ on the grid paper. Label the graph with its equation.

b. On the same set of axes, use a straightedge to graph $y = x$ as a dashed line.

c. Place the reflective mirror so that the drawing edge is on the line $y = x$ and carefully plot points that are part of the reflection of the original line with respect to the line of symmetry.

d. Draw a line through the points. This is the inverse of the original function.

e. What is the equation of the inverse?

f. Try this activity with the function $y = x^3 - 5$. Is the inverse also a function? Explain.

MODELING MATHEMATICS This modeling activity introduces, in a hands-on manner, the concept that the inverse of a function is its reflection through the $y = x$ line.

Answers for Modeling Mathematics

a–d.

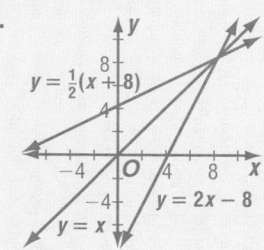

You may recall that a relation is a set of ordered pairs. The **inverse relation** is the set of ordered pairs obtained by reversing the coordinates of each original ordered pair.

Definition of Inverse Relations	Two relations are inverse relations if and only if whenever one relation contains the element (a, b), the other relation contains the element (b, a).

Example ④

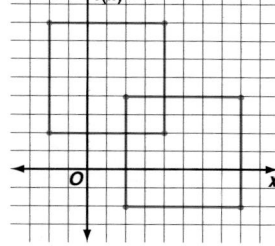

INTEGRATION

Geometry

The vertices of square $ABCD$ form the relation $\{(2, 4), (8, 4), (2, -2), (8, -2)\}$. Find the inverse of this relation and determine if the resulting ordered pairs are also the vertices of a square.

To find the inverse of this relation, reverse the coordinates of the ordered pairs.

The inverse of the relation is $\{(4, 2), (4, 8), (-2, 2), (-2, 8)\}$.

Plotting the points shows that the ordered pairs are also vertices of a square.

2. Switch x and y in the equation and solve for y.

3. See margin.

In-Class Example

For Example 4

The vertices of triangle *EFG* form the relation $\{(5, 1), (1, 8), (-1, 4)\}$. Find the inverse of this relation and determine by graphing if the resulting ordered pairs are also the vertices of a triangle.   inverse = $\{(1, 5), (8, 1), (4, -1)\}$; yes

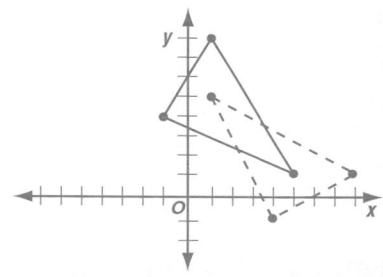

CHECK FOR UNDERSTANDING

Communicating Mathematics

4. The graphs are reflections of each other over the line of symmetry, $y = x$.

Study the lesson. Then complete the following.

1. **Explain** the difference between inverse functions and inverse relations. Are inverse functions also inverse relations? Explain.   See margin.

2. **Describe** in your own words how to find the inverse of a function.

3. **Explain** why the inverse relation in Example 4 is not a function.

4. **Explain** how the graph of a function is related to the graph of its inverse.

Lesson 8–8   Inverse Functions and Relations   **531**

Reteaching

Using Reasoning Note that just as a rational number and its additive inverse yield the additive identity, the composition of a function and its inverse yield the identity function. Show that the inverse of a function can be found by reversing the order of each pair in the given function.

Additional Answers

1. Inverse functions have both their compositions equal to the identity function. Inverse relations contain ordered pairs such that the coordinates of one relation are in reverse order of the coordinates of the other. Inverse functions are also inverse relations, but inverse relations are not always functions.

3. The graph does not pass the vertical line test for functions.

3 PRACTICE/APPLY

Check for Understanding

Exercises 1–14 are designed to help you assess your students' understanding through reading, writing, speaking, and modeling. You should work through Exercises 1–6 with your students and then monitor their work on Exercises 7–14.

Additional Answers

5. **The inverse is a function because it passes the vertical line test.**

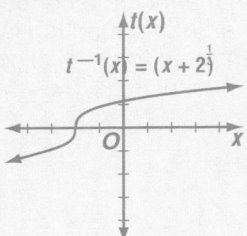

9.

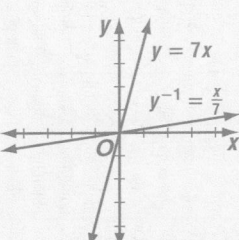

10.

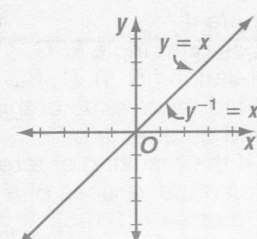

11.

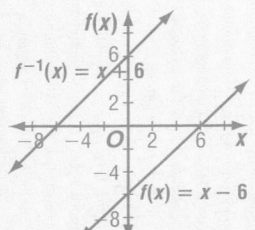

Study Guide Masters, p. 63

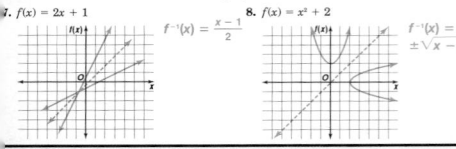

8-8

NAME_____ DATE_____

Study Guide

Student Edition
Pages 531–538

Inverse Functions and Relations

The function $I(x) = x$ is called the **identity function**, since for any function f, $[f \circ I](x) = f(x)$ and $[I \circ f](x) = f(x)$. Two functions are **inverse functions** if both their compositions are the identity function.

| **Definition of Inverse Functions** |
| Two functions, f and g, are inverse functions if and only if both their compositions are the identity function. That is, $[f \circ g](x) = x$ and $[g \circ f](x) = x$. |

A special notation is used to show that two functions f and g are inverse functions.

$$g = f^{-1} \text{ and } f = g^{-1}.$$

Suppose f and f^{-1} are inverse functions. Then $f(a) = b$ if and only if $f^{-1}(b) = a$. The inverse function can be found by reversing the order in each pair in the given function or as shown in the example below. In general, the graph of a relation and its inverse are mirror images, or reflections of each other with respect to the graph of the identity function $I(x) = x$.

Example: Find the inverse of $f(x) = 4x + 1$.
Rewrite $f(x)$ as $y = 4x + 1$.
$x = 4y + 1$ Interchange x and y.
$4y = x - 1$ Solve for y.
$y = \frac{x-1}{4}$
Thus, the inverse of $f(x)$ is the function $f^{-1}(x) = \frac{x-1}{4}$.

Find the inverse of each relation and determine whether the inverse is a function.

1. $f(x) = \frac{2}{3}x - \frac{1}{4}$ $f^{-1}(x) = \frac{3}{2}x + \frac{3}{8}$; yes
2. $h(x) = 5x + \frac{1}{4}$ $h^{-1}(x) = \frac{1}{5}x - \frac{1}{20}$; yes
3. $f(x) = \frac{2}{3}x + 5$ $f^{-1}(x) = \frac{3}{2}x - \frac{15}{2}$; yes
4. $y = x^3 - 8$ $y = \sqrt[3]{x + 8}$; no
5. $g(x) = (x + 10)^2$ $g^{-1}(x) = \pm\sqrt{x} - 10$; no
6. $f(x) = \frac{x-7}{2}$ $f^{-1}(x) = 2x + 7$; yes

Find the inverse of each function. Then graph each function and its inverse.

7. $f(x) = 2x + 1$
8. $f(x) = x^2 + 2$

6. $f^{-1}(x) = \pm\sqrt{2x + 6}$; See students' work.
8. $\{(8, 3), (-2, 4), (-3, 5)\}$, yes

21. $f^{-1}(x) = \frac{1}{4}x - 1$
22. $g^{-1}(x) = 2x - 4$
23. $f^{-1}(x) = -x$
24. $g^{-1}(x) = x + 2$

25. $y^{-1} = \pm\sqrt{x + 9}$
26. $y^{-1} = \pm\sqrt{x + 9}$
27. $f^{-1}(x) = \frac{3x + 1}{2}$
28. $y^{-1} = \pm\sqrt{x - 1}$
29. $y^{-1} = \pm\sqrt{x + 4}$
30. $y^{-1} = \pm\sqrt{x + 3} - 2$

5. **Sketch** the graph of the inverse of $t(x)$, shown at the right. Is the inverse a function? Explain.   **See margin.**

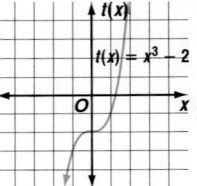

6. Use a reflective mirror and grid paper to graph the inverse of the function $f(x) = \frac{1}{2}x^2 - 3$.

Guided Practice

Find the inverse of each relation and determine whether the inverse is a function.

7. $\{(3, 2), (4, 2)\}$ $\{(2, 3), (2, 4)\}$, no
8. $\{(3, 8), (4, -2), (5, -3)\}$

Find the inverse of each function. Then graph the function and its inverse.   **9–12. See margin for graphs.**

9. $y = 7x$ $y^{-1} = \frac{x}{7}$
10. $y = x$ $y^{-1} = x$
11. $f(x) = x - 6$ $f^{-1}(x) = x + 6$
12. $y = -2x - 1$ $y^{-1} = \frac{-x-1}{2}$

13. Determine whether $f(x) = 6x + 2$ and $g(x) = \frac{x+2}{6}$ are inverse functions.   **no**

14. **Temperature**   Refer to the application at the beginning of Lesson 8-7. The formula for converting Fahrenheit to Celsius is $C(x) = \frac{5}{9}(x - 32)$. Find $C^{-1}(x)$, the inverse of $C(x)$, and explain what practical purpose the inverse serves.
$C^{-1}(x) = \frac{9}{5}x + 32$, and it can be used to convert Celsius to Fahrenheit.

EXERCISES

Practice

Find the inverse of each relation and determine whether the inverse is a function.   **15–18. See margin.**

A

15. $\{(2, 4), (-3, 1), (2, 8)\}$
16. $\{(-1, -2), (-3, -2), (-1, -4), (0, 6)\}$
17. $\{(1, 3), (1, -1), (1, -3), (1, 1)\}$
18. $\{(6, 11), (-2, 7), (0, 3), (-5, 3)\}$

Find the inverse of each function. Then graph the function and its inverse.   **19–30. See Solutions Manual for graphs.**

B

19. $y = 6$ $x = 6$
20. $y = 4x$ $y^{-1} = \frac{x}{4}$
21. $f(x) = 4x + 4$
22. $g(x) = \frac{1}{2}x + 2$
23. $f(x) = -x$
24. $g(x) = x - 2$

C

25. $y = x^2 - 9$
26. $y = (x - 9)^2$
27. $f(x) = \frac{2x - 1}{3}$
28. $y = x^2 + 1$
29. $y = (x - 4)^2$
30. $y = (x + 2)^2 - 3$

Determine whether each pair of functions are inverse functions.

31. $f(x) = x + 7$
    $g(x) = x - 7$ yes
32. $g(x) = 2x - 3$
    $h(x) = -2x + 3$ no
33. $f(x) = \frac{x - 2}{3}$
    $g(x) = 3x - 2$ no
34. $f(x) = \frac{x - 1}{2}$
    $g(x) = 2x + 1$ yes

Additional Answers

12.

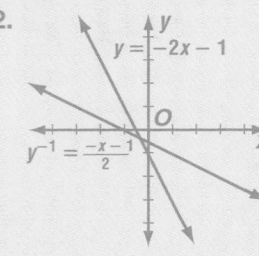

15. $\{(4, 2), (1, -3), (8, 2)\}$, yes
16. $\{(-2, -1), (-2, -3), (-4, -1), (6, 0)\}$, no
17. $\{(3, 1), (-1, 1), (-3, 1), (1, 1)\}$, yes
18. $\{(11, 6), (7, -2), (3, 0), (3, -5)\}$, no

35. yes

36. no

37. no

Sketch the graph of the inverse of each relation. Then determine if the inverse is a function. 35–37. See margin for graphs.

35. 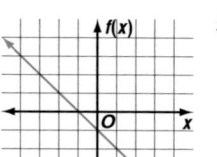 36. 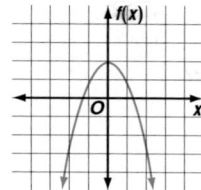 37.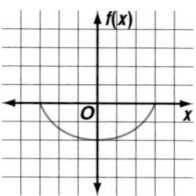

Programming

38. The graphing calculator program at the right evaluates $f[g(x)]$ and $g[f(x)]$ if $f(x) = 2x - 1$ and $g(x) = x^2 + 1$. The calculator prompts you to enter a value for x and finds the values of $f[g(x)]$ and $g[f(x)]$. It also tells you if the functions are inverses. To use this program for other pairs of functions, change the second and third lines to reflect the expressions for $f[g(x)]$ and $g[f(x)]$.

```
Program: INVERSES
: Prompt X
: 2(X² + 1) - 1→A
: (2X - 1)² + 1→B
: Disp "F(G(X)) = ",A
: Disp "G(F(X)) = ",B
: If A = B
: Then
: Disp "INVERSES"
: Else
: Disp "NOT INVERSES"
```

Use this program and a chart to determine if each pair of functions are inverses of each other.

a. $f(x) = x + 1$
   $g(x) = x - 1$ yes

b. $f(x) = \frac{1}{2}x^2 + 4$
   $g(x) = 2x + 8$ no

c. $g(x) = \frac{1}{5}(x + 7)$
   $h(x) = 5x - 7$ yes

Critical Thinking

39. Find a function that is its own inverse. Can you find more than one?
   Sample answer: $f(x) = x$ and $f^{-1}(x) = x$ or $f(x) = -x$ and $f^{-1}(x) = -x$.

Applications and Problem Solving

40. **Consumerism** LaKisha bought a stereo on sale from Electronics Unlimited. She used a $40 gift certificate to help pay for the stereo. If the stereo was on sale at 25% off and the final bill was $522.50 plus tax, what is its regular price? $750

41. **Work Backward** Jake asked Cynthia to choose a number between 1 and 20. He told her to add 7 to that number, then multiply by 4, then subtract 6, then divide by 2. Cynthia told Jake that her final number was 35. What was her original number? 12

42. **Sales** Sales associates at Electronics Unlimited earn $8 an hour plus a 4% commission on the merchandise they sell. Write a function to describe their weekly income and find how much merchandise they must sell in order to earn $500 in a 40-hour week. $I(m) = 320 + 0.04m$; $4500

Mixed Review

43. **Chemistry** While performing an experiment, Joy Chen found the temperature of a solution at different times. She needs to record the temperature in degrees Kelvin, but only has a thermometer with a Fahrenheit scale. Joy knows that a Kelvin temperature is 273 degrees greater than an equivalent Celsius temperature and that the formula $C = \frac{5}{9}(F - 32)$ converts a Fahrenheit temperature to Celsius.

   What will she record when the thermometer reads 59° F?
   (Lesson 8–7) 288° K

44. $y = -\frac{1}{4}(x - 2)^2 + 5$; See margin for graph.

44. Write an equation for the parabola with focus at (2, 4) and directrix $y = 6$. Then draw the graph. (Lesson 7–2)

Lesson 8–8 Inverse Functions and Relations **533**

Assignment Guide

Core: 15–41 odd, 43–50
Enriched: 16–38 even, 39–50

For **Extra Practice,** see p. 896.

The red A, B, and C flags, printed only in the Teacher's Wraparound Edition, indicate the level of difficulty of the exercises.

Using the Programming Exercises The program given in Exercise 38 is for use with a TI-82 graphing calculator. For other programmable calculators, have students consult their owner's manual for commands similar to those presented here.

Additional Answers

35.
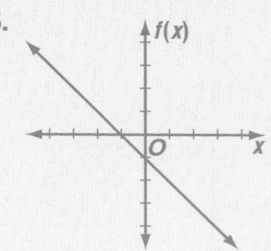

36.
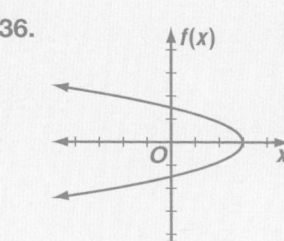

Practice Masters, p. 63

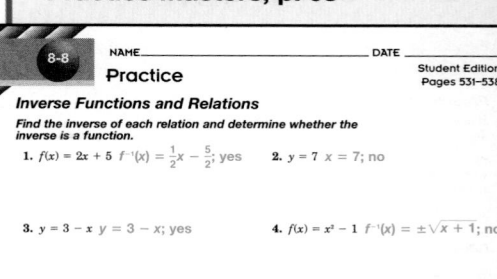

8-8 Practice

NAME _____ DATE _____
Student Edition Pages 531–538

Inverse Functions and Relations

Find the inverse of each relation and determine whether the inverse is a function.

1. $f(x) = 2x + 5$ $f^{-1}(x) = \frac{1}{2}x - \frac{5}{2}$; yes
2. $y = 7$ $x = 7$; no

3. $y = 3 - x$ $y = 3 - x$; yes
4. $f(x) = x^2 - 1$ $f^{-1}(x) = \pm\sqrt{x + 1}$; no

Determine whether each pair of functions are inverse functions.

5. $f(x) = x + 5$
   $g(x) = x - 5$ yes
6. $f(x) = \frac{1}{2}x + 2$
   $g(x) = 2x - 4$ yes

7. $f(x) = 4 - x$
   $g(x) = 4 + x$ no
8. $f(x) = 3x - 9$
   $g(x) = -3x + 9$ no

Find the inverse of each function. Then graph each function and its inverse.

9. $f(x) = x^2 - 3$ $f^{-1}(x) = \pm\sqrt{x + 3}$
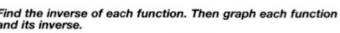
10. $f(x) = -4x$ $f^{-1}(x) = -\frac{1}{4}x$
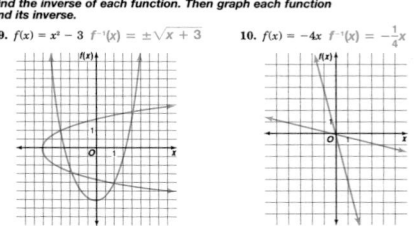

Tech Prep

Sales Associate Students who are interested in a career in sales may wish to do further research into the use of mathematics in that occupation, as mentioned in Exercise 42. For more information on tech prep, see the *Teacher's Handbook*.

Additional Answers

37.
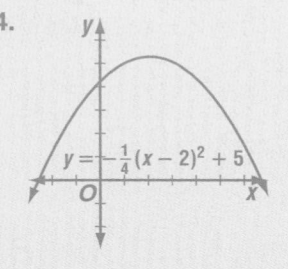

44.

Closing Activity

Speaking Separate the class into groups of four. Have each group member supply one of the steps in a "guess the number" procedure, like that found in the application at the beginning of the lesson. After completing the procedure, allow one group to present it to another group.

Chapter 8, Quiz D (Lessons 8-7 and 8-8), is available in the *Assessment and Evaluation Masters,* p. 213.

Additional Answer

48.

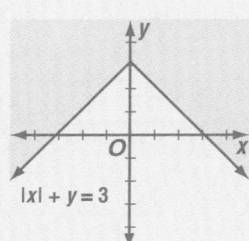

$|x| + y = 3$

Enrichment Masters, p. 63

| 8-8 | NAME _____ DATE _____ | Student Edition Pages 533–540 |

Enrichment

Proof by Induction

Mathematical induction is a useful tool when you want to prove that a statement is true for all natural numbers.

The three steps in using induction are:
1. Prove that the statement is true for $n = 1$.
2. Prove that if the statement is true for the natural number n, it must also be true for $n + 1$.
3. Conclude that the statement is true for all natural numbers.

Follow the steps to complete each proof.

Theorem A: The sum of the first n odd natural numbers is equal to n^2.

1. Show that the theorem is true for $n = 1$.
   $1 = (1)^2$

2. Suppose $1 + 3 + 5 + \cdots + (2n - 1) = n^2$. Show that
   $1 + 3 + 5 + \cdots + (2n - 1) + (2n + 1) = (n + 1)^2$.
   Add $2n + 1$ to each side of the equation whose truth was assumed: $1 + 3 + 5 + \cdots + (2n - 1) + (2n + 1) = n^2 + (2n + 1) = (n + 1)^2$

3. Summarize the results of problems 1 and 2.
   The theorem is true for $n = 1$. If the sum of the first n odd numbers equals n^2, then it is true that the sum of the first $n + 1$ odd numbers equals $(n + 1)^2$. Therefore, the theorem is true for all natural numbers.

Theorem B: Show that $a^n - b^n$ is exactly divisible by $a - b$ for n equal to 1, 2, 3, and all natural numbers.

4. Show that the theorem is true for $n = 1$.
   $(a^1 - b^1) \div (a - b) = 1$

5. The expression $a^{n+1} - b^{n+1}$ can be rewritten as $a(a^n - b^n) + b^n(a - b)$. Verify that this is true.
   $a(a^n - b^n) + b^n(a - b) = a^{n+1} - ab^n + ab^n - b^{n+1} = a^{n+1} - b^{n+1}$

6. Suppose $a - b$ is a factor of $a^n - b^n$. Use the result in problem 5 to show that $a - b$ must then also be a factor of $a^{n+1} - b^{n+1}$.
   $a^{n+1} - b^{n+1} = a(a^n - b^n) + b^n(a - b)$; $a - b$ is a factor of both addends on the right side. So, $a - b$ is also a factor of the left side.

7. Summarize the results of problems 4 through 6.
   The theorem is true for $n = 1$. If $a - b$ is a factor of $a^n - b^n$, it is also a factor of $a^{n+1} - b^{n+1}$. So, the theorem is true for all natural numbers n.

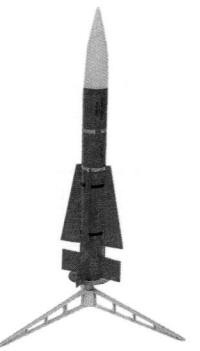

45. **Physics** A toy rocket is fired upwards from the top of a 200-foot tower at a velocity of 80 feet per second. The height of the rocket t seconds after firing is given by the formula $h(t) = -16t^2 + 80t + 200$. Find the maximum height reached by the rocket and the time at which that height is reached. (Lesson 6–4) **300 ft, 2.5 seconds**

46. Divide $(n^3 - n^2 + 4n + 6)$ by $(n + 1)$ using synthetic division. (Lesson 5–3)

47. Find $-2\begin{bmatrix} 0 & 3 \\ -5 & 3 \end{bmatrix} + \begin{bmatrix} 5 & 3 \\ -3 & 9 \end{bmatrix}$. (Lesson 4–2) $\begin{bmatrix} 5 & -3 \\ 7 & 3 \end{bmatrix}$

48. Graph $|x| + y \geq 3$. (Lesson 2–7) **See margin.**

49. State the domain and range of the relation $\{(9, 0), (3, 1), (12, 7), (1, -4), (12, 8), (-11, -3), (0, -6)\}$. Is this relation a function? (Lesson 2–1)

46. $n^2 - 2n + 6$
49. D = {-11, 0, 1, 3, 9, 12}, R = {-6, -4, -3, 0, 1, 7, 8}; no

50. **Manufacturing** A company manufactures auto parts. The diameter of a piston cannot vary more than 0.001 cm. Write an inequality to represent the diameter of a piston if its diameter is supposed to be 10 cm. (Lesson 1–7) $9.999 \leq d \leq 10.001$

WORKING ON THE In·ves·ti·ga·tion

Refer to the Investigation on pages 474–475.

Now that you have performed your own experiments on coffee cans of different sizes, you decide to get some data on the markings on a real gasoline tank from another colleague. The length of the tank is 20 feet and its radius is 10 feet. The table shows the distance in feet measured on the dipstick, the volume in cubic feet of gasoline in the tank, the percent of the tank that is full, and the percent of the dipstick that is wet.

meas. on stick (ft)	vol. of gas in tank (ft³)	% of vol. in tank	% of stick covered	change in vol. %
0	0.0	0.0	0	
1	327.0	5.2	10	
2	894.6	14.2	20	
3	1585.3	25.2	30	
4	2347.0	37.4	40	
5	3141.6	50.0	50	
6	3936.2	62.6	60	
7	4697.8	74.8	70	
8	5388.6	85.8	80	
9	5956.2	94.8	90	
10	6283.2	100.0	100	

1 What are the differences and similarities in your charts and this chart? Are there any differences in the dipstick measurement increments and the volume measurement increments in your data and these data? Explain.

2 What is the volume of this tank in cubic feet?

3 Where on the dipstick would the markings be to show that the tank is one-half full, one-fourth full, and three-fourths full? Does this coincide with the locations at which you found the markings should be for your data?

4 Copy and complete the table.

5 Make a graph of the change in percentage of capacity for each increment. Describe the graph. How does this graph differ from those you made in your experiments? How is this graph similar to the graphs you made in your experiments?

6 Graph the inverse of this relation. Does the original graph represent a function? Does the graph of the inverse represent a function?

Add the results of your work to your Investigation Folder.

Extension

Problem Solving Find the inverse of $f(x) = 2 - x$. $f^{-1}(x) = 2 - x$

In·ves·ti·ga·tion

Working on the Investigation

The Investigation on pages 474–475 is designed to be a long-term project that is completed over several days or weeks. Encourage students to keep their materials in their Investigation Folder as they work on the Investigation.

8–8B Square Root Functions and Relations

APPLICATION
Weather

The function $d = \sqrt{\frac{3h}{2}}$ represents the greatest distance d in miles that a person h feet high can see on a clear day. Suppose Kenyatta is standing on the 102nd floor observation deck of the Empire State Building, 1250 feet high, on a clear day. What is the greatest distance that he can see? *You will solve this problem in Example 2.*

Because the function described above involves a square root, it is called a **square root function.** In order for a square root to be a real number, the radicand cannot be negative. When graphing a square root function, determine when the radicand would be negative and remember to exclude those values from the domain.

In Lesson 8-8, you learned that the inverse of a quadratic function is a square root function if only the nonnegative range is considered. Look at the graph at the right. Notice that for a square root function, negative values are excluded from the range.

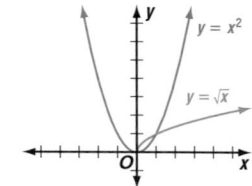

For many families of square root functions, the parent function is $y = \sqrt{x}$.

What YOU'LL LEARN

- To graph and analyze square root functions, and
- to graph square root inequalities.

Why IT'S IMPORTANT

You can use square root functions to solve problems involving weather and oceanography.

EXPLORATION
GRAPHING CALCULATORS

To graph square root function like $y = \sqrt{x - 1}$, use the $\sqrt{}$ key.

Enter: [Y=] [2nd] [√] [( ] [X,T,θ]

[−] [1] [ )] [ZOOM] [6]

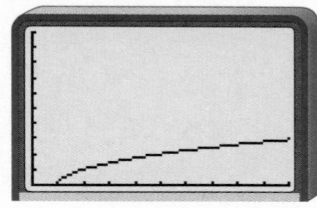

Your Turn

a. Graph $y = \sqrt{x}$, $y = \sqrt{x} + 1$, and $y = \sqrt{x} - 2$ in the viewing window [−2, 8] by [−4, 6]. State the domain and range of each function and describe the similarities and differences among the graphs.

b. Graph $y = \sqrt{x}$, $y = \sqrt{2x}$, and $y = \sqrt{8x}$ in the viewing window [0, 10] by [0, 10]. State the domain and range of each function and describe the similarities and differences among the graphs.

---

1 FOCUS

5-Minute Check
(over Lesson 8-8)

Find the inverse of each relation and determine whether the inverse is a function.

1. {(2, 3), (5, 3), (2, 5), (6, 7)}
   {(3, 2), (3, 5), (5, 2), (7, 6)};
   no
1. {(1, 2), (2, 3), (3, 4), (4, 1)}
   {(2, 1), (3, 2), (4, 3), (1, 4)};
   yes

Find the inverse of each function.

3. $y = 8$ $x = 8$
4. $h(x) = x^3$ $y = \sqrt[3]{x}$
5. Are $y = x + 2$ and $y = -x - 2$ inverse functions?   no

Motivating the Lesson

Questioning In Lesson 6-2, Exercise 36 (page 345), students used the formula $(VM)^2 = 1.22A$, where *VM* represents the number of miles to the horizon you can see from an airplane if you are flying on a clear day. Ask students why they think that formula and the fomula they will use at the beginning of this lesson are different.

TEKS   1.a., 4.a., 9.a., 9.b., 9.c., 9.d., 9.e., 9.f.

EXPLORATION

In this activity, students learn how to use a graphing calculator to graph square root functions. They also study families of graphs involving square root functions and describe the similarities and differences between graphs in this family.

Answers for the Exploration
a. For $y = \sqrt{x}$, D: $x \geq 0$; R: $y \geq 0$.
   For $y = \sqrt{x} + 1$, the graph of $y = \sqrt{x}$ is translated up 1 unit; D: $x \geq 0$;
   R: $y \geq 1$. For $y = \sqrt{x} - 2$, the graph of $y = \sqrt{x}$ is translated down 2 units;
   D: $x \geq 0$; R: $y \geq -2$.
b. The domain of each function is $x \geq 0$. The range of each function is $y \geq 0$. The graph of $y = \sqrt{2x}$ is slightly wider than the graph of $y = \sqrt{x}$. The graph of $y = \sqrt{8x}$ is a lot wider than the graph of $y = \sqrt{x}$.

In-Class Example

For Example 1

Graph $y = \sqrt{3x - 4}$. State the domain, range, and x- and y-intercepts.

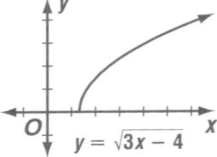

The domain is $x \geq \frac{4}{3}$, and the range is $y \geq 0$. The x-intercept is $\frac{4}{3}$, and there is no y-intercept.

For Example 2

Graph $y = \sqrt{\dfrac{2x}{5}}$. State the domain and range.

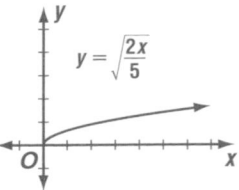

The domain and range are both all positive real numbers.

Check for Understanding

Exercises 1–10 are designed to help you assess your students' understanding through reading, writing, speaking, and modeling. You should work through Exercises 1–3 with your students and then monitor their work on Exercises 4–10.

Example **Graph $y = \sqrt{6x + 5}$. State the domain, range, and x- and y-intercepts.**

Since the radicand cannot be negative, identify the domain.

$$6x + 5 \geq 0$$
$$6x \geq -5$$
$$x \geq -\frac{5}{6}$$

Thus, the x-intercept is $-\frac{5}{6}$. Generate a table of values and graph the function.

x	y
$-\frac{5}{6}$	0
0	2.2
2	4.1
4	5.4
6	6.4
8	7.3
10	8.1

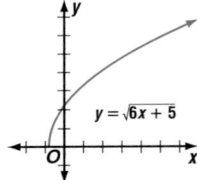

The domain is $x \geq -\frac{5}{6}$, and the range is $y \geq 0$. The y-intercept is $\sqrt{5}$ or about 2.24.

Example **2** **Refer to the application at the beginning of the lesson.**

APPLICATION
Weather

a. Graph the function $d = \sqrt{\dfrac{3h}{2}}$. State the domain and range.

b. Find the greatest distance that Kenyatta can see.

a. Make a table of values and graph the function.

h	d
0	0
2	$\sqrt{3}$ or 1.73
4	$\sqrt{6}$ or 2.45
6	$\sqrt{9}$ or 3.00
8	$\sqrt{12}$ or 3.46
10	$\sqrt{15}$ or 3.87

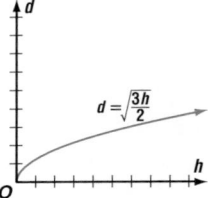

The domain and range of the function are both all nonnegative real numbers.

b. If the observation deck is 1250 feet high, then the greatest distance Kenyatta can see is $\sqrt{\dfrac{3(1250)}{2}}$ or about 43.3 miles. *Check this result against the graph.*

You can use what you know about square root functions to graph *square root inequalities*.

Example ❸ Graph $y < \sqrt{2x + 4}$.

Generate a table of values and graph the relation. Since the boundary should not be included, the graph should be dashed.

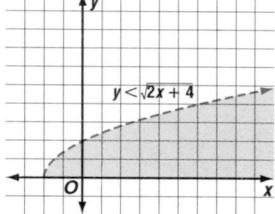
$y < \sqrt{2x + 4}$

Because the range includes only nonnegative real numbers, the graph is only in the first and second quadrants. Select a point on one of the half-planes and test its ordered pair. For example, use $(1, 1)$. Since $1 < \sqrt{2(1) + 4}$, the half-plane containing $(1, 1)$ should be shaded.

CHECK FOR UNDERSTANDING

Communicating Mathematics

1. See margin.

2. $-\dfrac{3}{2}$

3a. $y \le \sqrt{\dfrac{3h}{2}}$

Guided Practice

4-7. See Solutions Manual for graphs.

c. See margin for graph.

Study the lesson. Then complete the following.

1. **Describe** the differences between the graphs of $y = \sqrt{x} - 6$ and $y = \sqrt{x - 6}$.

2. **Find** the minimum value in the domain for $y = \sqrt{2x + 3}$.

3. Refer to the application at the beginning of the lesson.
   a. Write a mathematical sentence that describes *all* of the distances Kenyatta would be able to see.
   b. Graph the relation that you came up with in part a.   See margin.

Graph each function. State the domain and range of each function.

4. $y = -\sqrt{x}$ D: $x \ge 0$; R: $y \le 0$
5. $y = \sqrt{7x}$ D: $x \ge 0$; R: $y \ge 0$

6. $y = \sqrt{x - 1} + 5$ D: $x \ge 1$; R: $y \ge 5$
7. $y = \sqrt{5x + 1}$ D: $x \ge 0$; R: $y \ge 1$

Graph each inequality.   8-9. See margin.

8. $y > \sqrt{x + 9} - 8$
9. $y \le \sqrt{3x + 4} - 4$

10. **Oceanography**   A *tsunami* is a large ocean wave generated by an undersea earthquake. The formula for a tsunami's speed s in meters per second is $s = 3.1\sqrt{d}$, where d is the depth of the ocean in meters.
    a. Describe the domain and range of the function.   D: $d \ge 0$; R: $s \ge 0$
    b. Determine the speed of a tsunami if the earthquake occurs in a part of the ocean that is 10,000 meters deep.   310 m/s
    c. Graph the function and use the graph to verify your answer to part b.

Lesson 8–8B   Square Root Functions and Relations   **537**

Reteaching

Using Reasoning Remind students that the square root function:

- cannot have a negative radicand, and
- involves only the positive or negative square root, but not both.

Additional Answers

1. The graph of $y = \sqrt{x} - 6$ has no x-intercept and its y-intercept is -6. The graph of $y = \sqrt{x - 6}$ has no y-intercept and its x-intercept is 6.

3b.
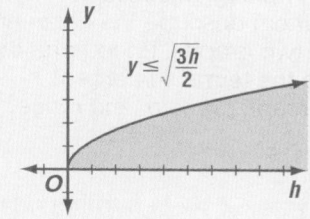
$y \le \sqrt{\dfrac{3h}{2}}$

8.
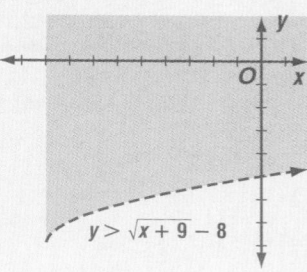
$y > \sqrt{x + 9} - 8$

9.
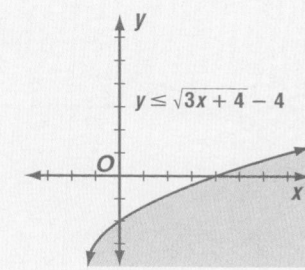
$y \le \sqrt{3x + 4} - 4$

10c.
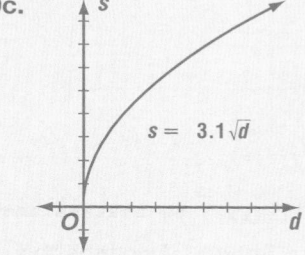
$s = 3.1\sqrt{d}$

Assignment Guide

Core: 11–31 odd
Enriched: 12–28 even, 29–31

The red A, B, and C flags, printed only in the Teacher's Wraparound Edition, indicate the level of difficulty of the exercises.

Closing Activity

Writing Have students graph $y = \sqrt{x^2 + 4}$ and $y = \sqrt{x^2 - 4}$ on their graphing calculators. Then have them describe the differences in the two graphs. Encourage them to use the terms *x-intercept*, *y-intercept*, *domain*, and *range*.

Additional Answers

29b. $y = -2\sqrt{x}$ is a little wider than $y = \sqrt{x}$, and falls downward to the right. $y = \sqrt{x} - 4$ begins at (4, 0). $y = \sqrt{x} + 3$ begins at (0, 3). $y = 3\sqrt{x} - 1 + 5$ is wider than $y = \sqrt{x}$, and begins at (1, 5).

30d.

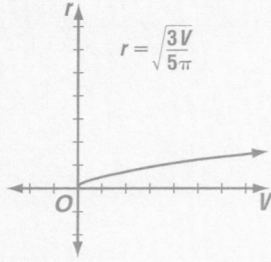

31c.

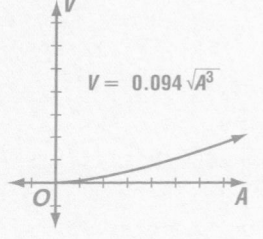

Extension

Problem Solving Describe the graph of $y = \sqrt[3]{x}$.   It looks like the graph of $y = x^3$, but turned on its side.

Practice   **Graph each function. State the domain and range of each function.**

11. $y = \sqrt{3x}$ D: $x \geq 0$; R: $y \geq 0$ **12.** $y = -\sqrt{4x}$ D: $x \geq 0$; R: $y \leq 0$

13. $y = -2\sqrt{x}$ D: $x \geq 0$; R: $y \leq 0$ **14.** $y = 5\sqrt{x}$ D: $x \geq 0$; R: $y \geq 0$

15. $y = \sqrt{x + 2}$ D: $x \geq 0$; R: $y \geq 0$ **16.** $y = \sqrt{x - 7}$ D: $x \geq 0$; R: $y \geq 0$

17. $y = -\sqrt{2x + 1}$ **18.** $y = \sqrt{3x - 2}$

19. $y = \sqrt{x + 6} - 5$ **20.** $y = \sqrt{x - 5} + 3$

21. $y = \sqrt{7x - 1} + 2$ **22.** $y = 2\sqrt{3 - 4x} + 6$

11-22. See Solutions Manual for graphs.

17. D: $x \geq -\frac{1}{2}$;
R: $y \leq 0$

18. D: $x \geq \frac{2}{3}$;
R: $y \geq 0$

19. D: $x \geq -6$;
R: $y \geq -5$

20. D: $x \geq 5$; R: $y \geq 3$

21. D: $x \geq \frac{1}{7}$; R: $y \geq 2$

22. D: $x \leq \frac{3}{4}$; R: $y \geq 6$

Graph each inequality.   23-28. See Solutions Manual.

23. $y \leq -6\sqrt{x}$ **24.** $y < \sqrt{x + 8}$

25. $y > \sqrt{5x + 7}$ **26.** $y \geq \sqrt{2x - 7}$

27. $y \geq \sqrt{x - 3} + 4$ **28.** $y < \sqrt{6x - 2} + 3$

Critical Thinking

29. In Lesson 6-6A, you investigated the role that a, h, and k played in the graph of a quadratic function of the form $y = a(x - h)^2 + k$.

a. Describe the roles a, h, and k play for the family of square root functions of the form $y = a\sqrt{x - h} + k$.   a-b. See margin.

b. Use what you found in part a to describe the graphs of the functions below without graphing them. Relate your answers to the graph of the parent function $y = \sqrt{x}$.

$$y = -2\sqrt{x} \qquad y = \sqrt{x - 4} \qquad y = \sqrt{x} + 3 \qquad y = 3\sqrt{x - 1} + 5$$

Applications and Problem Solving

30a. $r = \sqrt{\dfrac{3V}{5\pi}}$

30d. See margin.

30. Geometry   There are several sizes of ice cream cones available at Johnson's Real Ice Cream Shoppe, but all of them are 5 inches long.

a. Write a square root function that expresses the radius r of the cones as a function of volume V. Use the formula $V = \frac{1}{3}\pi r^2 h$, where h is the height.

b. Describe the domain and range of the function.   D: $V \geq 0$; R: $r \geq 0$

c. Determine the volume of a cone that has a radius of 2 inches.   20.9 in³

d. Graph the function and use the graph to verify your answer to part c.

31c. See margin for graph.

31d. No; the radicand is cubed.

31. Geometry   The volume V and the surface area A of a soap bubble are related by the formula $V = 0.094\sqrt{A^3}$.

a. Describe the domain and range of the function.   D: $x \geq 0$; R: $y \geq 0$

b. Determine the volume of a soap bubble that has a surface area of 12 cm².   about 3.9 cm³

c. Graph the function and use the graph to verify your answer to part b.

d. Does this graph look like the graphs of the other square root functions you have graphed in this lesson? Why or why not?

Additional Answers

29b.

If:	$h > 0$	$h < 0$	$k > 0$	$k < 0$
$a > 0$	h is minimum value in domain.	$-h$ is minimum value in domain.	k is minimum value in range.	
$a < 0$			k is maximum value in range.	

Using the CHAPTER HIGHLIGHTS

The Chapter Highlights begins with a listing of the new terms, properties, and phrases that were introduced in this chapter. Have students define each term and provide an example or two of it, if appropriate.

VOCABULARY

After completing this chapter, you should be able to define each term, property, or phrase and give an example or two of each.

Algebra

complex conjugates theorem   (p. 504)
composition of functions   (p. 520)
depressed polynomial   (p. 487)
Descartes' rule of signs   (p. 505)
factor theorem   (p. 487)
fundamental theorem of algebra   (p. 503)
integral zero theorem   (p. 509)
inverse function   (p. 528)
inverse relation   (p. 531)
leading coefficient   (p. 480)
location principle   (p. 494)
polynomial function   (p. 479)
polynomial in one variable   (p. 478)
quadratic form   (p. 515)

rational zero theorem   (p. 509)
relative maximum   (p. 494)
relative minimum   (p. 494)
remainder theorem   (p. 485)
square root function   (p. 531)
synthetic substitution   (p. 486)

Discrete Mathematics

fixed points   (p. 526)
graphical iteration   (p. 526)
iterate   (p. 526)
iteration   (p. 522)

Problem Solving

work backward   (p. 528)

Assessment and Evaluation Masters, pp. 199–200

UNDERSTANDING AND USING THE VOCABULARY

Choose the letter of the term that best matches each statement or phrase.

1. A point on the graph of a polynomial function that has no other nearby points with lesser y-coordinates is the ___?___.   **h**

2. The ___?___ is the factor in the term in a polynomial function with the highest degree.   **e**

3. The ___?___ says that in any polynomial function, if an imaginary number is a zero of that function, then its conjugate is also a zero.   **a**

4. When a polynomial is divided by one of its binomial factors, the quotient is called a ___?___.   **c**

5. A point on the graph of a polynomial function that has no other nearby points with a greater y-coordinate is the ___?___.   **g**

6. $f \circ g\ (x) = f[g(x)]$ represents a ___?___.   **b**

7. $(x^2)^2 - 17(x^2) + 16 = 0$ is written in ___?___.   **f**

8. $f(x) = 6x - 2$ and $g(x) = \dfrac{x + 2}{6}$ are ___?___ since $[f \circ g](x) = x$ and $[g \circ f](x) = x$.   **d**

a. complex conjugates theorem
b. composition of functions
c. depressed polynomial
d. inverse functions
e. leading coefficient
f. quadratic form
g. relative maximum
h. relative minimum

Instructional Resources

Three multiple-choice tests and three free-response tests are provided in the *Assessment and Evaluation Masters*. Forms 1A and 2A are for honors pacing, and Forms 1B, 1C, 2B, and 2C are for average pacing. Chapter 8 Test, Form 1B is shown at the right. Chapter 8 Test, Form 2B is shown on the next page.

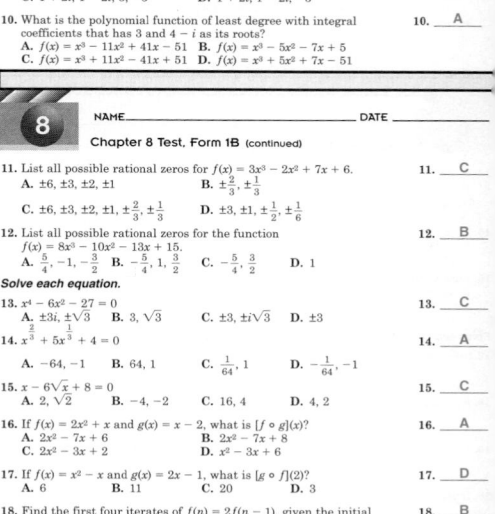

8   NAME_____ DATE _____

Chapter 8 Test, Form 1B

Write the letter for the correct answer in the blank at the right of each problem.

1. Find $f(x + h)$ for the function $f(x) = 2x^2 - 3$.   1. __A__
   A. $2x^2 + 4xh + 2h^2 - 3$ B. $2x^2 + 2h^2 - 3$
   C. $2x^2 + 4xh + 2h^2$ D. $2x^2 + 4xh + h^2 - 3$

2. Find $3p(a) + p(a + 2)$ for $p(x) = x^2 - 3$.   2. __C__
   A. $4a^2 - 8a - 4$ B. $4a^2 - 8a - 4$
   C. $4a^2 + 4a - 8$ D. $4a^2 - 12a + 12$

3. Which of the following could be a function for the graph?   3. __D__
   A. $f(x) = -x^3 - x^2$ B. $f(x) = x^3 + x^2$
   C. $f(x) = x^3 + 4x^2 + x - 2$ D. $f(x) = -x^3 - 4x^2 - x + 2$

4. Divide using synthetic division and write your answer in the form   4. __A__
   dividend = quotient · divisor + remainder.
   $(2x^4 - 3x^3 - 6x^2 - 8x - 3) \div (x - 3)$
   A. $2x^4 - 3x^3 - 6x^2 - 8x - 3 = (2x^3 + 3x^2 + 3x + 1)(x - 3)$
   B. $2x^4 - 3x^3 - 6x^2 - 8x - 3 = (-2x^3 - 3x^2 - 3x - 1)(x - 3)$
   C. $2x^4 - 3x^3 - 6x^2 - 8x - 3 = (2x^3 - 9x^2 + 21x - 71)(x - 3) + 210$
   D. $2x^4 - 3x^3 - 6x^2 - 8x - 3 = (2x^3 + 3x + 3)(x - 3) + 1$

5. Use synthetic substitution to find $f(-2)$.   5. __B__
   $f(x) = 2x^4 - 3x^3 + x^2 - x + 5$.
   A. 15   B. 67   C. −53   D. 3

6. One factor of $x^3 - 3x^2 - 4x + 12$ is $x + 2$. What are the other two?   6. __D__
   A. $x + 2, x + 3$ B. $x + 2, x - 3$
   C. $x - 2, x + 3$ D. $x - 2, x - 3$

7. What are the real zeros for $f(x) = x^3 - 3x^2 + 8$? (Approximate the   7. __C__
   zeros to the nearest tenth.)
   A. −1   B. −2   C. −1.4   D. −1.5

8. Which of the following is the graph of $f(x) = x^4 - 4x^2 + 4$?   8. __B__
   A.   B.   C.   D.

9. What are all the zeros for $f(x) = x^3 + x^2 - x + 15$ if $1 + 2i$ is one zero?   9. __D__
   A. $1 + 2i, 3, -3$ B. $1 + 2i, 1 - 2i, 3$
   C. $1 + 2i, 1 - 2i, -3$ D. $1 + 2i, 1 - 2i, -3$

10. What is the polynomial function of least degree with integral   10. __A__
    coefficients that has 3 and $4 - i$ as its roots?
    A. $f(x) = x^3 - 11x^2 + 41x - 51$ B. $f(x) = x^3 - 5x^2 - 7x + 5$
    C. $f(x) = x^3 + 11x^2 - 41x + 51$ D. $f(x) = x^3 + 5x^2 + 7x - 51$

8   NAME_____ DATE _____

Chapter 8 Test, Form 1B (continued)

11. List all possible rational zeros for $f(x) = 3x^3 - 2x^2 + 7x + 6$.   11. __C__
    A. $\pm 6, \pm 3, \pm 2, \pm 1$ B. $\pm \frac{2}{3}, \pm \frac{1}{3}$
    C. $\pm 6, \pm 3, \pm 2, \pm 1, \pm \frac{2}{3}, \pm \frac{1}{3}$ D. $\pm 3, \pm 1, \pm \frac{1}{2}, \pm \frac{1}{6}$

12. List all possible rational zeros for the function   12. __B__
    $f(x) = 8x^3 - 10x^2 - 13x + 15$.
    A. $\frac{5}{4}, -1, -\frac{3}{2}$ B. $-\frac{5}{4}, 1, \frac{3}{2}$ C. $-\frac{5}{4}, \frac{3}{2}$ D. 1

Solve each equation.

13. $x^4 - 6x^2 - 27 = 0$ 13. __C__
    A. $\pm 3i, \pm \sqrt{3}$ B. $3, \sqrt{3}$ C. $\pm 3, \pm i\sqrt{3}$ D. ± 3

14. $x^{\frac{2}{3}} + 5x^{\frac{1}{3}} + 4 = 0$ 14. __A__
    A. $-64, -1$ B. $64, 1$ C. $\frac{1}{64}, 1$ D. $-\frac{1}{64}, -1$

15. $x - 6\sqrt{x} + 8 = 0$ 15. __C__
    A. $2, \sqrt{2}$ B. $-4, -2$ C. $16, 4$ D. $4, 2$

16. If $f(x) = 2x^2 + x$ and $g(x) = x - 2$, what is $[f \circ g](x)$?   16. __A__
    A. $2x^2 - 7x + 6$ B. $2x^2 - 7x + 8$
    C. $2x^2 - 3x + 2$ D. $x^2 - 3x + 6$

17. If $f(x) = x^2 - x$ and $g(x) = 2x - 1$, what is $[g \circ f](2)$?   17. __D__
    A. 6   B. 11   C. 20   D. 3

18. Find the first four iterates of $f(n) = 2f(n - 1)$, given the initial   18. __B__
    value $f(0) = 1$.
    A. $1, 3, 5, 7$ B. $1, 2, 4, 8$ C. $2, 4, 8, 16$ D. $0, 2, 4, 8$

19. What is the inverse of $f(x) = -5x + 2$?   19. __B__
    A. $f^{-1}(x) = \frac{x - 2}{5}$ B. $f^{-1}(x) = \frac{2 - x}{5}$
    C. $f^{-1}(x) = \frac{1}{2 - 5x}$ D. $f^{-1}(x) = \frac{1}{5x - 2}$

20. Which is the graph of the inverse of $y = 3x - 1$?   20. __C__
    A.   B.   C.   D.

Bonus   If $f(x) = 3x + 4$, solve for x: $f[f(x)] = f(x)$.   Bonus __B__
    A. 2   B. −2   C. −1   D. 1

Using the STUDY GUIDE AND ASSESSMENT

Skills and Concepts Encourage students to refer to the objectives and examples on the left as they complete the review exercises on the right.

Assessment and Evaluation Masters, pp. 205–206

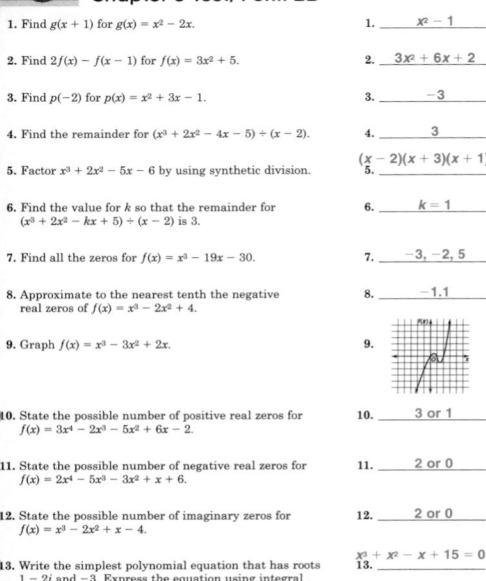

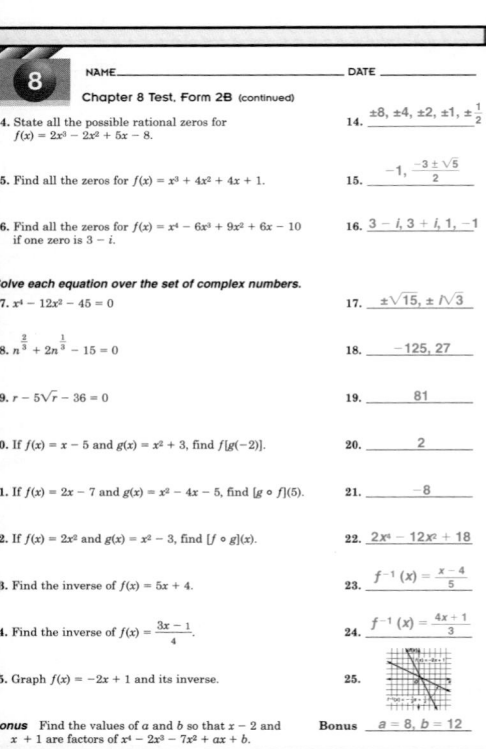

SKILLS AND CONCEPTS

OBJECTIVES AND EXAMPLES	REVIEW EXERCISES

Upon completing this chapter, you should be able to:

Use these exercises to review and prepare for the chapter test.

• evaluate polynomial functions (Lesson 8–1)

Find $p(a + 1)$ if $p(x) = 5x - x^2 + 3x^3$.

$p(a + 1) = 5(a + 1) - (a + 1)^2 + 3(a + 1)^3$

$= 5a + 5 - (a^2 + 2a + 1) + 3(a +1)(a^2 + 2a + 1)$

$= 5a + 5 - a^2 - 2a - 1 + 3(a^3 + 3a^2 + 3a + 1)$

$= 5a + 5 - a^2 - 2a - 1 + 3a^3 + 9a^2 + 9a + 3$

$= 3a^3 + 8a^2 + 12a + 7$

Find $p(-4)$ and $p(x + h)$ for each function.

9. $p(x) = x - 2$ $-6, x + h - 2$

10. $p(x) = -x + 4$ $8, -x - h + 4$

11. $p(x) = 6x + 3$ $-21, 6x + 6h + 3$

12. $p(x) = x^2 + 5$ $21, x^2 + 2xh + h^2 + 5$

13. $p(x) = x^2 - x$ $20, x^2 + 2xh + h^2 - x - h$

14. $p(x) = 2x^3 - 1$

   $-129, 2x^3 + 6x^2h + 6xh^2 + 2h^3 - 1$

• find factors of polynomials by using the factor theorem and synthetic division   (Lesson 8–2)

Show that $x + 2$ is a factor of $x^3 - 2x^2 - 5x + 6$. Then find any remaining factors.

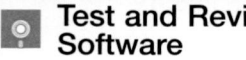

-2	1	-2	-5	6
		-2	8	-6
	1	-4	3	0

The remainder is 0, so $x + 2$ is a factor of $x^3 - 2x^2 - 5x + 6$, and $x^3 - 2x^2 - 5x + 6 = (x + 2)(x^2 - 4x + 3)$.

Since $x^2 - 4x + 3 = (x - 3)(x - 1)$,
$x^3 - 2x^2 - 5x + 6 = (x + 2)(x - 3)(x - 1)$.

22. $x + 1, x - 3, x - 5$

Use synthetic substitution to find $f(3)$ and $f(-2)$ for each function.

15. $f(x) = x^2 - 5$ $4, -1$

16. $f(x) = x^2 - 4x + 4$ $1, 16$

17. $f(x) = x^3 - 3x^2 + 4x + 8$ $20, -20$

18. $f(x) = x^4 - 5x + 2$ $68, 28$

Given a polynomial and one of its factors, find the remaining factors of the polynomial. Some factors may not be binomials.

19. $x^3 + 5x^2 + 8x + 4; x + 1$ $x + 2, x + 2$

20. $x^3 + 4x^2 + 7x + 6; x + 2$ $x^2 + 2x + 3$

21. $x^3 - x^2 - 4x + 4; x + 2$ $x - 1, x - 2$

22. $x^4 - 6x^3 + 22x + 15; x + 1$

• approximate the real zeros of polynomial functions   (Lesson 8–3)

The location principle states that if $y = f(x)$ represents a polynomial function, and a and b are two numbers such that $f(a) < 0$ and $f(b) > 0$, then the function has at least one zero between a and b.

23–28. See margin for graphs.

Approximate the real zeros of each function to the nearest tenth. Then use the functional values to graph the function.

23. $h(x) = x^3 - 6x - 9$ 3

24. $f(x) = x^4 + 7x + 1$ $-1.9, -0.1$

25. $p(x) = x^5 + x^4 - 2x^3 + 1$ -2.0

26. $g(x) = x^3 - x^2 + 1$ -0.8

27. $r(x) = 4x^3 + x^2 - 11x + 3$ $-1.9, 0.3, 1.4$

28. $f(x) = x^3 + 4x^2 + x - 2$ $-1, -3.6, 0.6$

GLENCOE Technology

Test and Review Software

You may use this software, a combination of an item generator and item bank, to create your own tests or worksheets. Types of items include free response, multiple choice, short answer, and open ended.

For IBM & Macintosh

Additional Answer

23.

h(x) graph with $h(x) = x^3 - 6x - 9$

OBJECTIVES AND EXAMPLES

• find the number and type of zeros of a polynomial function   (Lesson 8–4)

State the number of positive real zeros and negative real zeros for $f(x) = 5x^4 + 6x^3 - 8x + 12$.

Since $f(x)$ has two sign changes, there are 2 or 0 real positive zeros.

$f(-x) = 5x^4 - 6x^3 + 8x + 12$

Since $f(-x)$ has two sign changes, there are 0 or 2 negative real zeros.

• find zeros of polynomial functions   (Lesson 8–5)

Find all of the zeros of $f(x) = x^3 + 7x^2 - 36$.

There are exactly 3 complex zeros.

There are either 1 or 3 positive real zeros and 2 or 0 negative real zeros.

The possible rational zeros are $\pm 1, \pm 2, \pm 3, \pm 4, \pm 6, \pm 9, \pm 12, \pm 18, \pm 36$.

$$\begin{array}{r|rrrr} 2 & 1 & 7 & 0 & -36 \\ & & 2 & 18 & 36 \\ \hline & 1 & 9 & 18 & 0 \end{array}$$

$x^3 + 7x^2 - 36 = (x - 2)(x^2 + 9x + 18) = (x - 2)(x + 3)(x + 6)$

Therefore, the zeros are 2, −3, and −6.

• solve nonquadratic equations by using quadratic techniques   (Lesson 8–6)

$x^3 - 3x^2 - 54x = 0$

$x(x^2 - 3x - 54) = 0$

$x(x - 9)(x + 6) = 0$

$x = 0, x = 9, x = -6$

$y - 4\sqrt{y} - 45 = 0$

$(\sqrt{y})^2 - 4(\sqrt{y}) - 45 = 0$

$(\sqrt{y} - 9)(\sqrt{y} + 5) = 0$

$\sqrt{y} - 9 = 0$ or $\sqrt{y} + 5 = 0$

$y = 81$ no real solution

REVIEW EXERCISES

State the number of positive real zeros, negative real zeros, and imaginary zeros for each function.

29. $f(x) = 2x^4 - x^3 + 5x^2 + 3x - 9$ 3 or 1; 1; 2 or 0

30. $f(x) = 7x^3 + 5x - 1$ 1; 0; 2

31. $f(x) = -4x^4 - x^2 - x - 1$ 0; 0 or 2; 4 or 2

32. $f(x) = 3x^4 - x^3 + 8x^2 + x - 7$ 3 or 1; 1; 0 or 2

33. $f(x) = x^4 + x^3 - 7x + 1$ 2 or 0; 2 or 0; 4, 2, or 0

Find all of the rational zeros for each function.

34. $f(x) = 2x^3 - 13x^2 + 17x + 12$ $\frac{-1}{2}$, 3, 4

35. $f(x) = x^4 + 5x^3 + 15x^2 + 19x + 8$ −1, −1

36. $f(x) = x^3 - 3x^2 - 10x + 24$ −3, 2, 4

37. $f(x) = 2x^3 - 5x^2 - 28x + 15$ −3, 5, $\frac{1}{2}$

38. $f(x) = 2x^4 - 9x^3 + 2x^2 + 21x - 10$ $\frac{1}{2}$, 2

Solve each equation.

39. $3x^3 + 4x^2 - 15x = 0$ $\frac{5}{3}$, −3, 0

40. $m^4 + 3m^3 = 40m^2$ 0, 5, −8

41. $a^3 - 64 = 0$ 4, $-2 \pm 2i\sqrt{3}$

42. $r + 9\sqrt{r} = -8$ ∅

43. $x^4 - 8x^2 + 16 = 0$ 2, −2

44. $x^{\frac{2}{3}} - 9x^{\frac{1}{3}} + 20 = 0$ 64, 125

Additional Answers

24.
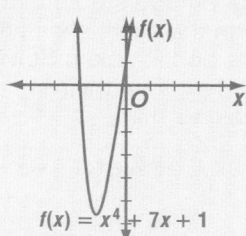
$f(x) = x^4 + 7x + 1$

25.
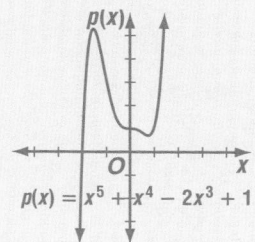
$p(x) = x^5 + x^4 - 2x^3 + 1$

26.
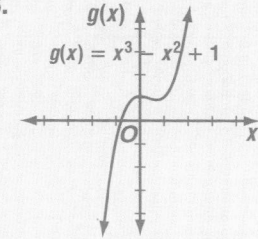
$g(x) = x^3 - x^2 + 1$

27.
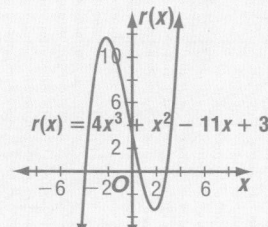
$r(x) = 4x^3 + x^2 - 11x + 3$

28.
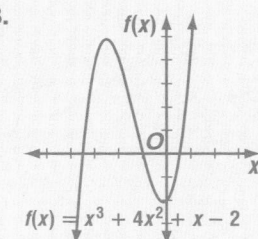
$f(x) = x^3 + 4x^2 + x - 2$

Applications and Problem
Solving Encourage students to
work through the exercises in the
Applications and Problem Solving
section to strengthen their
problem-solving skills.

Additional Answers

51.

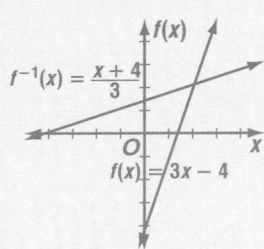

$f^{-1}(x) = \frac{x+4}{3}$

$f(x) = 3x - 4$

52.

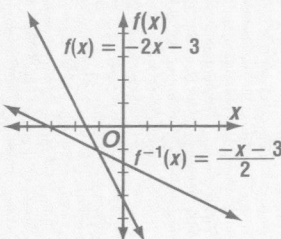

$f(x) = -2x - 3$

$f^{-1}(x) = \frac{-x-3}{2}$

53.

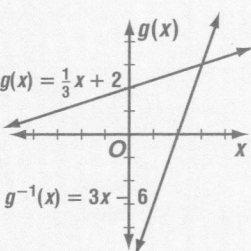

$g(x) = \frac{1}{3}x + 2$

$g^{-1}(x) = 3x - 6$

54.

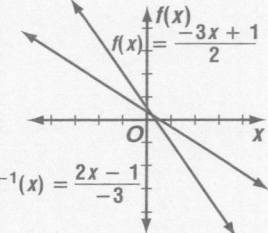

$f(x) = \frac{-3x+1}{2}$

$f^{-1}(x) = \frac{2x-1}{-3}$

55.

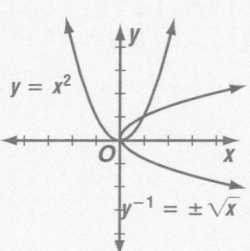

$y = x^2$

$y^{-1} = \pm\sqrt{x}$

56.

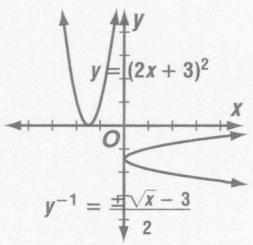

$y = (2x + 3)^2$

$y^{-1} = \frac{\pm\sqrt{x} - 3}{2}$

CHAPTER 8   STUDY GUIDE AND ASSESSMENT

OBJECTIVES AND EXAMPLES

• find the composition of functions   (Lesson 8–7)

If $f(x) = x^2 - 2$ and $g(x) = 8x - 1$, find $g[f(x)]$
and $f[g(x)]$.

$$g[f(x)] = 8(x^2 - 2) - 1$$
$$= 8x^2 - 16 - 1$$
$$= 8x^2 - 17$$
$$f[g(x)] = (8x - 1)^2 - 2$$
$$= (64x^2 - 16x + 1) - 2$$
$$= 64x^2 - 16x - 1$$

REVIEW EXERCISES

Find $g[h(x)]$ and $h[g(x)]$.

45. $h(x) = 2x - 1$
$g(x) = 3x + 4$
$6x + 1, 6x + 7$

46. $h(x) = x^2 + 2$
$g(x) = x - 3$
$x^2 - 1, x^2 - 6x + 11$

47. $h(x) = x^2 + 1$
$g(x) = -2x + 1$
$-2x^2 - 1, 4x^2 - 4x + 2$

48. $h(x) = -5x$
$g(x) = 3x - 5$
$-15x - 5, -15x + 25$

49. $h(x) = x^3$
$g(x) = x - 2$
$x^3 - 2, x^3 - 6x^2 + 12x - 8$

50. $h(x) = x + 4$
$g(x) = |x|$
$|x + 4|, |x| + 4$

• determine the inverse of a function or relation
(Lesson 8–8)

Find the inverse of $f(x) = -3x + 1$.

Rewrite $f(x)$ as $y = -3x + 1$. Then interchange
the variables and solve for y.

$$x = -3y + 1 \qquad \text{51–56. See margin for graphs.}$$
$$3y = -x + 1$$
$$y = \frac{-x+1}{3}$$
$$f^{-1}(x) = \frac{-x+1}{3}$$

**Find the inverse of each function. Then
graph the function and its inverse.**

51. $f(x) = 3x - 4$ $f^{-1}(x) = \frac{x+4}{3}$

52. $f(x) = -2x - 3$ $f^{-1}(x) = \frac{-x-3}{2}$

53. $g(x) = \frac{1}{3}x + 2$ $g^{-1}(x) = 3x - 6$

54. $f(x) = \frac{-3x+1}{2}$ $f^{-1}(x) = \frac{2x-1}{-3}$

55. $y = x^2$ $y^{-1} = \pm\sqrt{x}$

56. $y = (2x + 3)^2$ $y^{-1} = \frac{\pm\sqrt{x} - 3}{2}$

APPLICATIONS AND PROBLEM SOLVING

57a. $A = 1000(1 + r)^6 + 1000(1 + r)^5 + 1000(1 + r)^4 + 1200(1 + r)^3 + 1200(1 + r)^2 + 2000(1 + r)$

57. Financial Planning Jo Phillips, a financial
advisor, is helping Toshi's parents develop a
plan to save money for his college education.
Toshi will start college in six years. According
to Ms. Phillip's plan, Toshi's parents will save
$1000 each year for the next three years.
During the fourth and fifth years, they will save
$1200 each year. During the last year before he
starts college, they will save $2000.
(Lesson 8–2)

a. In the formula $A = P(1 + r)^t$, A = the
balance, P = the amount invested, r = the
interest rate, and t = the number of years
the money has been invested. Use this
formula to write a polynomial equation to
describe the balance of the account when
Toshi starts college.

b. Find the balance of the account if the
interest rate is 6%. **$8916.76**

58. Manufacturing The DrinKone Company
makes paper cups that are cone-shaped. The
volume of a cone is about 7.07 cubic inches. The
diameter of the top of the cone is equal to
the height of the cone. Determine the
dimensions of the cone. (*Hint:* The formula for
the volume of a cone is $V = \frac{1}{3}\pi r^2 h$.)
(Lesson 8–5) **diameter = 3 inches,
height = 3 inches**

59. Business The CD Menagerie adds a 100%
markup to the wholesale price of compact
discs before placing them in the store for sale.
If a CD is on sale for 20% off and the customer
pays $12 for it, what is its wholesale price?
(Lesson 8–7) **$7.50**

**A practice test for Chapter 8 is provided on
page 919.**

ALTERNATIVE ASSESSMENT

COOPERATIVE LEARNING PROJECT

Designing a Package   In this project, imagine that you are a packaging engineer. Packaging engineers determine the ideal shape and substance for a container based on what it will hold and how it will be used. You are the lead designer for a series of new containers to hold note paper. Each container should have twice the volume of the next smaller size. The container should use as little material as possible because of the need to find new ways to save material, reduce waste, encourage recycling, and limit packaging that could be dangerous for the environment. Prepare your new containers, including models and/or diagrams.

Each container will be made from material that starts out as a flat square or rectangle shape. Each container will then be formed by cutting out a square of the same size from each corner and then the edges will be folded up to form the container.

Follow these steps to accomplish your task.

- Make a model and/or draw diagrams of the containers.

- Write an algebraic equation to describe a relation between the length, width, and height of each of your containers and their volume.

- Write an algebraic equation to describe the amount of material that is left over after the container is constructed.

- Determine the amount of wasted material for each of your containers.

- Prepare a written presentation.

You may also want to investigate why soft drink companies have changed the size of their 24-pack packages to cubes. Focus on the following factors.

- marketing advantages

- customer convenience

- cost savings for materials

THINKING CRITICALLY

Do all polynomial functions with real coefficients have at least one real root if they have odd degree? Explain. Support your answers with examples.

PORTFOLIO

If you are given a problem to solve and there are two or more processes that can be used, how do you determine which one is most efficient for that situation? Long division and synthetic division are both methods used to divide polynomials by a first-degree binomial.

Write a comparative analysis for the two methods.

- Describe the advantages and disadvantages to both methods.

- Describe the set-up that must be used for each method

- List common errors that occur when using each of the methods

- Describe the relationship between the two methods.

Place this in your portfolio.

SELF EVALUATION

What type of learner are you? There are a variety of learning styles that researchers have identified. A few of these models are: auditory (by hearing), visual (by seeing), tactile (by touching), kinesthetic (by moving), and linguistic (by speaking).

Assess yourself. Under which style or styles do you learn best?

- Are you the type of person that is very hands-on?

- Do you like to do modeling or manipulating?

- Do you prefer to see a graph or diagram?

- Do you enjoy listening to an explanation?

- Or are you a good memory person?

Describe how you best learn under a particular style and relate it to both mathematics and your daily life.

Assessment and Evaluation Masters, pp. 210, 221

8   NAME_____ DATE_____

Chapter 8 Performance Assessment

Instructions: Demonstrate your knowledge by giving a clear, concise solution to each problem. Be sure to include all relevant drawings and justify your answers. You may show your solution in more than one way or investigate beyond the requirements of the problem.

1. The following questions refer to the polynomial functions $f(x) = x^5 - x^4 + 40x^2 - x - 39$ and $h(x) = 2x^4 + 7x^3 - 3x^2 - 14x - 6$.

   a. How many roots do $f(x)$ and $h(x)$ each have in the complex numbers? Justify your answers.

   b. Find $f(2)$ in two ways.

   c. Find the number of possible positive real zeros $f(x)$ and $h(x)$ each have. Justify your answer.

   d. Explain how you can determine the number of possible negative real zeros of a function. Find the number of possible negative real zeros for $f(x)$ and $h(x)$.

   e. Two zeros of $f(x)$ are -1 and $2 - 3i$. Find all the zeros of the function.

   f. Explain how you find all the possible rational zeros of a function. Find the possible rational zeros of $h(x)$.

   g. Use synthetic division to find the rational zeros of $h(x)$.

2. a. Write a polynomial function $f(x)$ of second degree.

   b. Find $[f \circ g](x)$ and $[g \circ f](x)$ if $g(x) = 2x + 3$. Show your work.

   c. Describe how you find the inverse of a function.

   d. Tell in your own words how the graphs of a function and its inverse are related.

   e. Find the inverse of the function you wrote in part a and draw its graph. Is it a function? Why or why not?

Scoring Guide
Chapter 8
Performance Assessment

Level	Specific Criteria
3 Superior	• Shows thorough understanding of the concepts *possible positive and negative real zeros, possible rational zeros, approximating irrational zeros,* and *composition and inver of functions.* • Computations are correct. • Written explanations are exemplary. • Graphs are accurate and appropriate. • Goes beyond requirements of problem.
2 Satisfactory, with Minor Flaws	• Shows understanding of the concepts *possible positive and negative real zeros, possible rational zeros, approximating irrational zeros,* and *composition and inver of functions.* • Computations are mostly correct. • Written explanations are effective. • Graphs are mostly accurate and appropriate. • Satisfies all requirements of problem.
1 Nearly Satisfactory, with Serious Flaws	• Shows understanding of most of the concepts *possible positive and negative real zeros, possible rational zeros, approximating irrational zeros,* and *composition and inver of functions.* • Computations are mostly correct. • Written explanations are satisfactory. • Graphs are mostly accurate and appropriate. • Satisfies most requirements of problem.
0 Unsatisfactory	• Shows little or no understanding of the concepts *possible positive and negative real zeros, possible rational zeros, approximating irrational zeros,* and *composition and inver of functions.* • Computations are incorrect. • Written explanations are not satisfactory. • Graphs are not accurate or appropriate. • Does not satisfy requirements of problem.

 **Alternative Assessment**

The Alternative Assessment section provides students with the opportunity to assess their own work by thinking critically, working with others, keeping a portfolio, and honestly evaluating their own progress. For more information on alternative forms of assessment, see *Alternative Assessment in the Mathematics Classroom,* one of the titles in the Glencoe Mathematics Professional Series.

Performance Assessment

Performance Assessment tasks for this chapter are included in the *Assessment and Evaluation Masters.* A scoring guide is also provided.

Using the
COLLEGE ENTRANCE EXAM PRACTICE

These two pages review the skills and concepts presented in Chapters 1–8. This review is formatted to reflect new trends in college entrance testing.

A more traditional cumulative review is provided in the *Assessment and Evaluation Masters,* pp. 215–216.

Assessment and Evaluation Masters, pp. 215–216

CHAPTERS 1–8

SECTION ONE: MULTIPLE CHOICE

There are eight multiple-choice questions in this section. After working each problem, write the letter of the correct answer on your paper.

1. Evaluate $\dfrac{2[15 - 9 \div 3 + 2]}{(7 + 5) \div 4}$. **A**

   A. $\dfrac{28}{3}$ **B.** $\dfrac{8}{3}$

   C. $\dfrac{4}{5}$ **D.** 2

2. The epicenter of an earthquake is located at $(3, 11)$ on a state map. Severe property damage occurred as far as 7 miles away from the epicenter. Choose the equation for the most distant point at which severe property damage occurred. **B**

   A. $(x - 7)^2 + (y - 3)^2 = 49$

   B. $(x - 3)^2 + (y - 11)^2 = 49$

   C. $\sqrt{(x - 3)^2 + (y - 11)^2} = 49$

   D. $(x - 3) + (y - 11) = 7$

3. Which augmented matrix is not equivalent to the augmented matrix below? **D**

$$\begin{bmatrix} 1 & -2 & 1 & | & 6 \\ 3 & 2 & -1 & | & 0 \\ 2 & 1 & -6 & | & -2 \end{bmatrix}$$

   A. $\begin{bmatrix} 1 & -2 & 1 & | & 6 \\ 0 & 8 & -4 & | & -18 \\ 4 & 2 & -12 & | & -4 \end{bmatrix}$

   B. $\begin{bmatrix} 5 & -5 & -3 & | & 16 \\ 3 & 2 & -1 & | & 0 \\ 1 & -2 & 1 & | & 6 \end{bmatrix}$

   C. $\begin{bmatrix} -9 & -6 & 3 & | & 0 \\ 2 & 1 & -6 & | & -2 \\ 1 & -2 & 1 & | & -2 \end{bmatrix}$

   D. $\begin{bmatrix} 3 & -6 & 3 & | & 18 \\ 15 & 12 & -7 & | & 0 \\ 8 & 4 & -24 & | & -8 \end{bmatrix}$

4. Casey hit a foul ball straight up over the plate that reached a height of 112 feet. How long will it be before the ball reaches the ground? The formula for the total time is $t = \sqrt{\dfrac{2h}{g}}$, where h is the height of the ball in feet and g is the acceleration due to gravity, or 32 ft/s². **A**

   A. $2\sqrt{7}$ seconds **B.** $2\sqrt{\dfrac{4}{7}}$ seconds

   C. 14 seconds **D.** 7 seconds

5. Which equation is true for the polynomial function $g(x) = x^2 - x + 5$? **C**

   A. $g(-2) = 7$

   B. $2[g(a - 1)] = 2a^2 - 6a + 6$

   C. $g(h + 3) = h^2 + 5h + 11$

   D. $g(b) - g(2b) = -b^2 + b$

6. Which graph represents a quadratic function? **B**

   A. 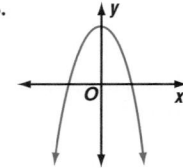 **B.**

   C. **D.**
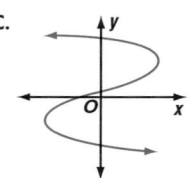
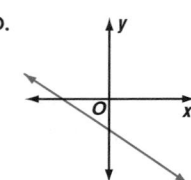

7. Which formula could be used to find the distance between the points at $(3, -5)$ and $(-4, -2)$? **D**

   A. $\sqrt{(-4 - 3)^2 + (-5 - 2)^2}$

   B. $\left(\dfrac{3 - 4}{2}, \dfrac{-5 - 2}{2}\right)$

   C. $\left(\dfrac{-4 - 3}{2}, \dfrac{-2 + 5}{2}\right)$

   D. $\sqrt{(-4 - 3)^2 + [-2 - (-5)]^2}$

Standardized Test Practice Questions are also provided in the *Assessment and Evaluation Masters,* p. 214.

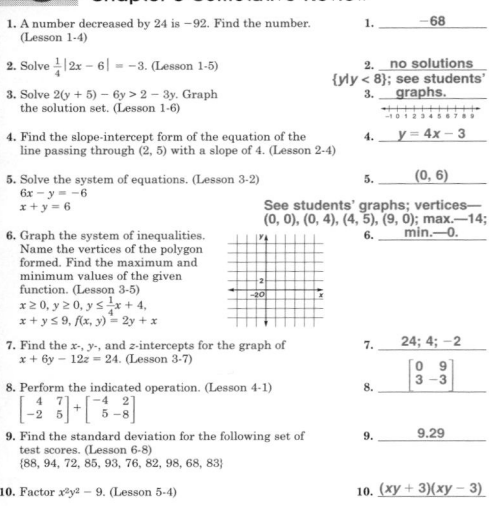

8
NAME _____ **DATE** _____

Chapter 8 Cumulative Review

1. A number decreased by 24 is −92. Find the number. (Lesson 1-4)
   1. __−68__

2. Solve $\frac{1}{4}|2x - 6| = -3$. (Lesson 1-5)
   2. __no solutions {y|y < 8}; see students'__

3. Solve $2(y + 5) - 6y > 2 - 3y$. Graph the solution set. (Lesson 1-6)
   3. __graphs.__

4. Find the slope-intercept form of the equation of the line passing through (2, 5) with a slope of 4. (Lesson 2-4)
   4. __y = 4x − 3__

5. Solve the system of equations. (Lesson 3-2)
   $6x - y = -6$
   $x + y = 6$
   5. __(0, 6)__

6. Graph the system of inequalities. Name the vertices of the polygon formed. Find the maximum and minimum values of the given function. (Lesson 3-5)
   $x \geq 0, y \geq 0, y \leq \frac{1}{4}x + 4,$
   $x + y \leq 9, f(x, y) = 2y + x$
   6. See students' graphs; vertices— (0, 0), (0, 4), (4, 5), (9, 0); max.—14; min.—0.

7. Find the x-, y-, and z-intercepts for the graph of $x + 6y - 12z = 24$. (Lesson 3-7)
   7. __24; 4; −2__

8. Perform the indicated operation. (Lesson 4-1)
   $\begin{bmatrix} 4 & 7 \\ -2 & 5 \end{bmatrix} + \begin{bmatrix} -4 & 2 \\ 5 & -8 \end{bmatrix}$
   8. $\begin{bmatrix} 0 & 9 \\ 3 & -3 \end{bmatrix}$

9. Find the standard deviation for the following set of test scores. (Lesson 6-8) {88, 94, 72, 85, 93, 76, 82, 98, 68, 83}
   9. __9.29__

10. Factor $x^2y^2 - 9$. (Lesson 5-4)
    10. __(xy + 3)(xy − 3)__

11. Simplify $\sqrt[3]{40a^3b^2}$. (Lesson 5-6)
    11. $2a\sqrt[3]{5b^2}$

12. Simplify $n^{\frac{3}{4}}$. (Lesson 5-7)
    12. $\frac{n^{\frac{1}{4}}}{n}$ or $\frac{\sqrt[4]{n}}{n}$

13. Simplify $(4 - 5i) + (3 + 2i)$. (Lesson 5-10)
    13. __7 − 3i__

14. Find the value of c that makes $b^2 + 7b + c$ a perfect square. (Lesson 6-3)
    14. $\frac{49}{4}$

8
NAME _____ **DATE** _____

Chapter 8 Cumulative Review (continued)

15. Find the value of the discriminant for $4x^2 + 3x + 1 = 0$. Then describe the nature of the roots and solve the equation. (Lesson 6-4)
    15. −7; 2 imaginary roots; $\frac{-3 \pm i\sqrt{7}}{8}$

16. Solve $x^{\frac{4}{3}} = 2\sqrt[3]{2}$. (Lesson 5-8)
    16. __2__

17. Write $f(x) - (5x - 1)^2$ in quadratic form. Then identify the quadratic term, the linear term, and the constant. (Lesson 7-2)
    17. $f(x) = 25x^2 - 10x + 1$; $25x^2$; $-10x$; 1

18. Write the equation $f(x) - 2x^2 + 8x + 8$ in the form $f(x) = a(x - h)^2$. Name the vertex, the axis of symmetry, and the direction of opening of the graph. (Lesson 7-2)
    18. $f(x) = 2(x + 2)^2$; $(-2, 0)$; $x = -2$; up

19. Annette Howard has 220 feet of fence to enclose her rectangular garden courtyard. If she leaves two 10-foot openings at opposite ends for gates, what would be the length and width for maximum area? (Lesson 7-2)
    19. length: 160 ft; width: 60 ft

20. Find the coordinates of the vertices and foci, and slopes of the asymptotes for the hyperbola whose equation is $\frac{x^2}{36} - \frac{y^2}{16} = 1$. (Lesson 7-5)
    20. $(0, \pm 6)$; $(0, \pm 2\sqrt{13})$; $\pm\frac{3}{2}$

21. State whether the following is the equation of a circle, parabola, ellipse, or hyperbola. (Lesson 7-6)
    $x^2 + y^2 + 6x + 2 - 12y = 4$
    21. __circle__

22. Find the solutions of the system of equations. (Lesson 7-7)
    $(x + 1)^2 + y^2 = 36$
    $y - 6x = 42$
    22. $\left(\frac{-247}{37}, \frac{72}{37}\right)$, $(-7, 0)$

23. Find $p(-2)$ for $p(x) = x^2 - 2x + 6$. (Lesson 8-1)
    23. __14__

24. State the possible number of positive real zeros, negative real zeros, and imaginary zeros for $f(x) = x^3 - 7x^2 + 17x - 15$. (Lesson 8-4)
    24. __3 or 1; 0; 2 or 0__

25. Find $[f \circ g](x)$ and $[g \circ f](x)$. (Lesson 8-7)
    $f(x) = x^2 + 5$
    $g(x) = x - 2$
    25. $[f \circ g](x) = x^2 - 4x + 9$; $[g \circ f](x) = x^2 + 3$

8. Choose the system of equations that Lorenzo solved if he used Cramer's rule to solve for y as follows. **C**

$$y = \frac{\begin{vmatrix} 2 & 2 \\ 3 & -5 \end{vmatrix}}{\begin{vmatrix} 2 & -6 \\ 3 & 4 \end{vmatrix}}$$

A. $2x - 6y = 2$ **B.** $2x + 2y = -6$
   $-5x + 4y = 3$ $3x - 5y = 4$

C. $2x - 6y = 2$ **D.** $-6x + 2y = 2$
   $3x + 5y = -5$ $4x - 5y = 3$

SECTION TWO: SHORT ANSWER

This section contains seven questions for which you will provide short answers. Write your answer on your paper.

9. A walkway of uniform width will be constructed along the inside edges of a rectangular lawn that measures 24 meters by 32 meters. The remaining lawn will have an area of 425 square meters. How wide is the walkway?   **3.5 m**

10. Solve the system of equations by graphing.

$4x^2 + 9y^2 = 36$

$4x^2 - 9y^2 = 36$ **See margin.**

11. Find the values for x and y that make the equation $(x + 2y) + (2x - y)i = 5 + 5i$ true. $x = 3, y = 1$

12. Write the standard form of the equation $6x^2 - 24x - 5y^2 - 10y = 11$. Then state whether the graph of the equation is a parabola, a circle, an ellipse, or a hyperbola. $\dfrac{(x-2)^2}{5} - \dfrac{(y+1)^2}{6} = 1$; **hyperbola**

13. Find the value of k so that the remainder of $(x^2 + 5x + 7) \div (x + k)$ is 3.   **1, 4**

14. Solve the system of equations by using a matrix equation.

$3x + 2y = 9$

$x - 2y = 11$ $(5, -3)$

15. The camera store at City Mall adds a 40% markup to the wholesale price of its cameras. If Mario chooses a camera that is $325 wholesale and uses a 15% off coupon, how much will he pay for the camera?   **$386.75**

SECTION THREE: COMPARISON

This section contains five comparison problems which involve comparing two quantities, one in column A and one in column B. In certain questions, information related to one or both quantities is centered above or between them. All variables used represent real numbers.

Compare quantities A and B below.

- Write A if quantity A is greater.
- Write B if quantity B is greater.
- Write C if the two quantities are equal.
- Write D if there is not enough information to determine the relationship.

16. B   17. B   18. A   19. B   20. B

Column A	Column B
16. the standard deviation for $\{5, 7, 3, 4, 2, 4, 4, 4, 4, 5, 4, 3, 4, 3, 4\}$	the value of $g(-3)$ if $g(x) = \dfrac{x^2}{2} - 3$
17. the x-intercept of the line that passes through $(6, 1)$ and $(6, 7)$	$[9\ 4\ 2] \cdot \begin{bmatrix} 2 \\ 6 \\ 11 \end{bmatrix}$
18. $x < 0$ x^2	x^3
19. $A(3, -2), B(-2, 1), C(5, 5)$ the distance from A to C	the distance from B to C
20. $\sqrt[3]{-8000}$	$-\sqrt[4]{256}$

Exploring Rational Expressions

PREVIEWING THE CHAPTER

Students use the concepts of the asymptotes to help them sketch and graph rational functions. Next, they study direct, inverse, and joint variation. Students are introduced to addition, subtraction, multiplication, and division of rational expressions and then solve rational equations. The chapter concludes with students organizing data to solve real-world problems.

Lesson (Pages)	Lesson Objectives	NCTM Standards	State/Local Objectives
9-1A (548–549)	Use a graphing calculator to explore graphs of rational functions.	1–6, 13	4.a., 10.a., 10.c., 10.d.
9-1 (550–555)	Graph rational functions.	1–6, 13	1.a., 4.a., 10.a., 10.b., 10.c., 10.e.
9-2 (556–561)	Solve problems involving direct, inverse, and joint variation.	1–6, 13	10.f.
9-3 (562–568)	Simplify rational expressions. Simplify complex fractions.	1–5, 7	
9-4 (569–575)	Find the least common denominator of two or more algebraic expressions. Add and subtract rational expressions.	1–5	10.e.
9-5 (576–583)	Solve rational equations and inequalities.	1–5	1.a., 2.a., 10.c., 10.d., 10.e.

ORGANIZING THE CHAPTER

A complete, 1-page lesson plan is provided for each lesson in the *Lesson Planning Guide*. Answer keys for each lesson are available in the *Answer Key Masters*.

You may want to refer to the **Course Planning Calendar** on page T12 for detailed information on pacing.
PACING: Standard—10 days; **Honors**—9 days; **Block**—4 days

LESSON PLANNING CHART

| Lesson (Pages) | Materials/ Manipulatives | Extra Practice (Student Edition) | BLACKLINE MASTERS | | | | | | | | | Real-World Applications | Interactive Mathematics Tools Software | Teaching Transparencies |
			Study Guide	Practice	Enrichment	Assessment and Evaluation	Modeling Mathematics	Multicultural Activity	Tech Prep Applications	Graphing Calculator	Science and Math Lab Manual			
9-1A (548–549)	graphing calculator									pp. 49, 50				
9-1 (550–555)	balances* metric measuring cups* liquids	p. 897	p. 64	p. 64	p. 64		p. 69	p. 17	p. 17	p. 9			9-1	9-1A 9-1B
9-2 (556–561)		p. 897	p. 65	p. 65	p. 65	p. 240		p. 18	p. 18		pp. 95–98			9-2A 9-2B
9-3 (562–568)		p. 897	p. 66	p. 66	p. 66	pp. 239, 240						25		9-3A 9-3B
9-4 (569–575)	*MET* software	p. 898	p. 67	p. 67	p. 67	p. 241								9-4A 9-4B
9-5 (576–583)		p. 898	p. 68	p. 68	p. 68	p. 241						26		9-5A 9-5B
Study Guide/ Assessment (585–589)						pp. 225 –238, 242 –244								

*Included in Glencoe's Student Manipulative Kit and Overhead Manipulative Resources.

ORGANIZING THE CHAPTER

OTHER CHAPTER RESOURCES

Student Edition
Chapter Opener, pp. 546–547
Mathematics and Society, p. 583
Working on the Investigation,
   pp. 555, 575
Closing the Investigation, p. 584

Teacher's Classroom Resources
Investigations and Projects Masters,
   pp. 57–60

Technology
Teacher's Guide for Software
   Resources
Test and Review Software (IBM
   and Macintosh)
CD-ROM Interactions (Windows
   and Macintosh)

Professional Publications
Block Scheduling Booklet
Glencoe Mathematics Professional
   Series

OUTSIDE RESOURCES

Books/Periodicals
Borenson, Henry, "The Graphics Calculator: A
   Helpful Tool," *Mathematics Teacher,* Nov., 1990
The Language of Functions and Graphs, Dale
Seymour Publications

Software
*Math Grapher: Plotting Equations and Trig
   Functions,* J. Weston Walch

Videos/CD-ROMs
Calculators for Classrooms, NCTM
Polynomials, NCTM

See the *Teacher's Guide for Software Resources* for software addresses.

ASSESSMENT RESOURCES

Student Edition
Math Journal, pp. 572, 581
Mixed Review, pp. 555, 561,
   567, 574, 583
Self Test, p. 568
Chapter Highlights, p. 585
Chapter Study Guide and
   Assessment, pp. 586–588
Alternative Assessment, p. 589
 Portfolio, p. 589

Teacher's Wraparound Edition
5-Minute Check, pp. 550, 556,
   562, 569, 576
Check for Understanding, pp. 553,
   559, 565, 572, 581
Closing Activity, pp. 555, 561,
   568, 574, 583
Cooperative Learning, pp. 563,
   577

Assessment and Evaluation Masters
Multiple-Choice Tests, Forms 1A
   (Honors), 1B (Average), 1C
   (Basic), pp. 225–230
Free-Response Tests, Forms 2A
   (Honors), 2B (Average), 2C
   (Basic), pp. 231–236
Calculator-Based Test, p. 237
Performance Assessment, p. 238
Mid-Chapter Test, p. 239
Quizzes A–D, pp. 240–241
Standardized Test Practice, p. 242
Cumulative Review, pp. 243–244

ENHANCING THE CHAPTER

Examples of some of the materials for enhancing Chapter 9 are shown below.

DIVERSITY

Multicultural Activity Masters, pp. 17, 18

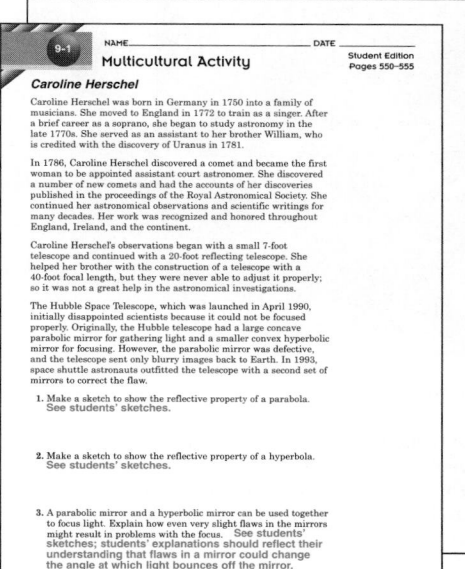

9-1 NAME _____ DATE _____
Multicultural Activity
Student Edition Pages 550–555

Caroline Herschel

Caroline Herschel was born in Germany in 1750 into a family of musicians. She moved to England in 1772 to train as a singer. After a brief career as a soprano, she began to study astronomy in the late 1770s. She served as an assistant to her brother William, who is credited with the discovery of Uranus in 1781.

In 1786, Caroline Herschel discovered a comet and became the first woman to be appointed assistant court astronomer. She discovered a number of new comets and had the accounts of her discoveries published in the proceedings of the Royal Astronomical Society. She continued her astronomical observations and scientific writings for many decades. Her work was recognized and honored throughout England, Ireland, and the continent.

Caroline Herschel's observations began with a small 7-foot telescope and continued with a 20-foot reflecting telescope. She helped her brother with the construction of a telescope with a 40-foot focal length, but they were never able to adjust it properly; so it was not a great help in the astronomical investigations.

The Hubble Space Telescope, which was launched in April 1990, initially disappointed scientists because it could not be focused properly. Originally, the Hubble telescope had a large concave parabolic mirror for gathering light and a smaller convex hyperbolic mirror for focusing. However, the parabolic mirror was defective, and the telescope sent only blurry images back to Earth. In 1993, space shuttle astronauts outfitted the telescope with a second set of mirrors to correct the flaw.

1. Make a sketch to show the reflective property of a parabola.
   See students' sketches.

2. Make a sketch to show the reflective property of a hyperbola.
   See students' sketches.

3. A parabolic mirror and a hyperbolic mirror can be used together to focus light. Explain how even very slight flaws in the mirrors might result in problems with the focus. See students' sketches; students' explanations should reflect their understanding that flaws in a mirror could change the angle at which light bounces off the mirror.

APPLICATIONS

Real-World Applications, 25, 26

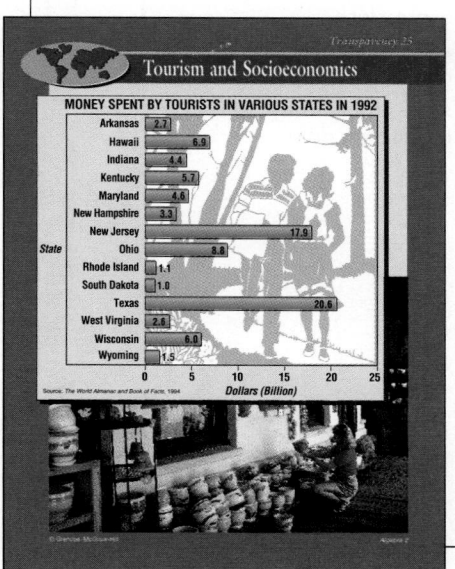

Transparency 25

Tourism and Socioeconomics

MONEY SPENT BY TOURISTS IN VARIOUS STATES IN 1992

State	Dollars (Billion)
Arkansas	2.7
Hawaii	6.9
Indiana	4.4
Kentucky	5.7
Maryland	4.6
New Hampshire	3.3
New Jersey	17.9
Ohio	8.8
Rhode Island	1.1
South Dakota	1.0
Texas	20.6
West Virginia	2.6
Wisconsin	6.0
Wyoming	1.5

Source: The World Almanac and Book of Facts, 1994

Algebra 2

TECHNOLOGY

Graphing Calculator Masters, p. 9

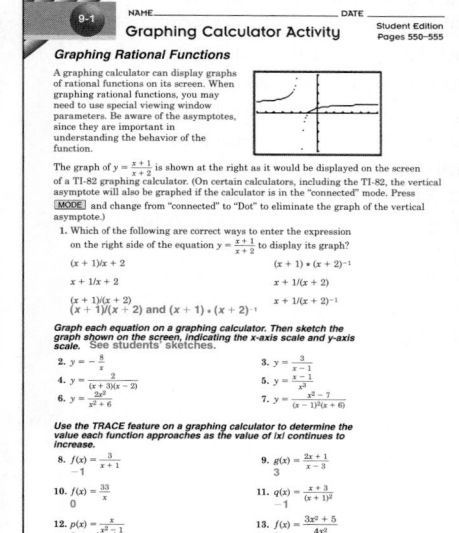

9-1 NAME _____ DATE _____
Graphing Calculator Activity
Student Edition Pages 550–555

Graphing Rational Functions

A graphing calculator can display graphs of rational functions on its screen. When graphing rational functions, you may need to use special viewing window parameters. Be aware of the asymptotes, since they are important in understanding the behavior of the function.

The graph of $y = \frac{x+1}{x+2}$ is shown at the right as it would be displayed on the screen of a TI-82 graphing calculator. (On certain calculators, including the TI-82, the vertical asymptote will also be graphed if the calculator is in the "connected" mode. Press MODE and change from "connected" to "Dot" to eliminate the graph of the vertical asymptote.)

1. Which of the following are correct ways to enter the expression on the right side of the equation $y = \frac{x+1}{x+2}$ to display its graph?

   $(x + 1)/x + 2$ $(x + 1) * (x + 2)^{-1}$

   $x + 1/x + 2$ $x + 1/(x + 2)$

   $(x + 1)/(x + 2)$ and $(x + 1) * (x + 2)^{-1}$ $x + 1/(x + 2)^{-1}$

Graph each equation on a graphing calculator. Then sketch the graph shown on the screen, indicating the x-axis scale and y-axis scale. See students' sketches.

2. $y = \frac{8}{x}$ 3. $y = \frac{3}{x-1}$

4. $y = \frac{2}{(x+3)(x-2)}$ 5. $y = \frac{x-1}{x^3}$

6. $y = \frac{2x^2}{x^2+6}$ 7. $y = \frac{x^2-7}{(x-1)^2(x+6)}$

Use the TRACE feature on a graphing calculator to determine the value each function approaches as the value of |x| continues to increase.

8. $f(x) = \frac{3}{x+1}$ 9. $g(x) = \frac{2x+1}{x-3}$
   -1 3

10. $f(x) = \frac{33}{x}$ 11. $q(x) = \frac{x+3}{(x+1)^2}$
    0 -1

12. $p(x) = \frac{x}{x^2-1}$ 13. $f(x) = \frac{3x^2+5}{4x^2}$
    1 and -1 0

TECH PREP

Tech Prep Applications Masters, pp. 17, 18

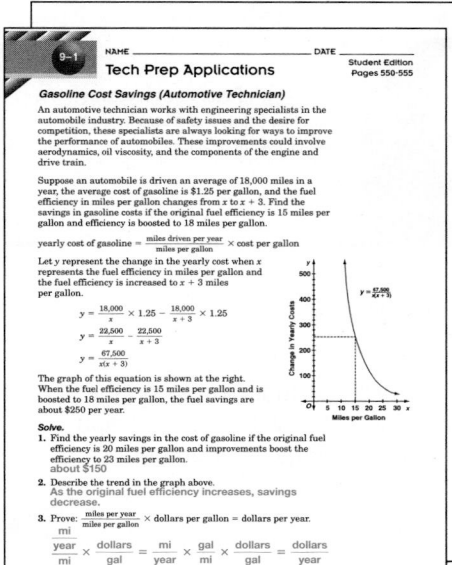

9-1 NAME _____ DATE _____
Tech Prep Applications
Student Edition Pages 550–555

Gasoline Cost Savings (Automotive Technician)

An automotive technician works with engineering specialists in the automobile industry. Because of safety issues and the desire for competition, these specialists are always looking for ways to improve the performance of automobiles. These improvements could involve aerodynamics, oil viscosity, and the components of the engine and drive train.

Suppose an automobile is driven an average of 18,000 miles in a year, the average cost of gasoline is $1.25 per gallon, and the fuel efficiency in miles per gallon changes from x to $x + 3$. Find the savings in gasoline costs if the original fuel efficiency is 15 miles per gallon and efficiency is boosted to 18 miles per gallon.

yearly cost of gasoline = $\frac{\text{miles driven per year}}{\text{miles per gallon}} \times$ cost per gallon

Let y represent the change in the yearly cost when x represents the fuel efficiency in miles per gallon and the fuel efficiency is increased to $x + 3$ miles per gallon.

$y = \frac{18,000}{x} \times 1.25 - \frac{18,000}{x+3} \times 1.25$

$y = \frac{22,500}{x} - \frac{22,500}{x+3}$

$y = \frac{67,500}{x(x+3)}$

The graph of this equation is shown at the right. When the fuel efficiency is 15 miles per gallon and is boosted to 18 miles per gallon, the fuel savings are about $250 per year.

$y = \frac{67,500}{x(x+3)}$

Solve.
1. Find the yearly savings in the cost of gasoline if the original fuel efficiency is 20 miles per gallon and improvements boost the efficiency to 23 miles per gallon.
   about $150

2. Describe the trend in the graph above.
   As the original fuel efficiency increases, savings decrease.

3. Prove: $\frac{\text{miles per year}}{\text{miles per gallon}} \times$ dollars per gallon = dollars per year.

   $\frac{\text{mi}}{\frac{\text{year}}{\text{mi}}} \times \frac{\text{dollars}}{\text{gal}} = \frac{\text{mi}}{\text{year}} \times \frac{\text{gal}}{\text{mi}} \times \frac{\text{dollars}}{\text{gal}} = \frac{\text{dollars}}{\text{year}}$

CONNECTIONS

Science and Math Lab Manual, pp. 95–98

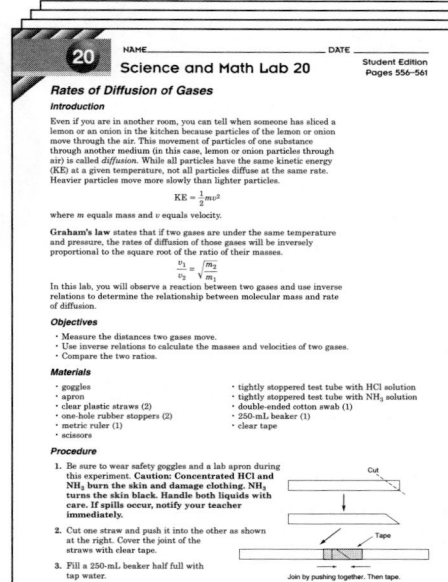

20 NAME _____ DATE _____
Science and Math Lab 20
Student Edition Pages 556–561

Rates of Diffusion of Gases

Introduction

Even if you are in another room, you can tell when someone has sliced a lemon or an onion in the kitchen because particles of the lemon or onion move through the air. This movement of particles of one substance through another medium (in this case, lemon or onion particles through air) is called *diffusion*. While all particles have the same kinetic energy (KE) at a given temperature, not all particles diffuse at the same rate. Heavier particles move more slowly than lighter particles.

$$KE = \frac{1}{2}mv^2$$

where m equals mass and v equals velocity.

Graham's law states that if two gases are under the same temperature and pressure, the rates of diffusion of those gases will be inversely proportional to the square root of the ratio of their masses.

$$\frac{v_1}{v_2} = \sqrt{\frac{m_2}{m_1}}$$

In this lab, you will observe a reaction between two gases and use inverse relations to determine the relationship between molecular mass and rate of diffusion.

Objectives
· Measure the distances two gases move.
· Use inverse relations to calculate the masses and velocities of two gases.
· Compare the two ratios.

Materials
· goggles
· apron
· clear plastic straws (2)
· one-hole rubber stoppers (2)
· metric ruler (1)
· scissors
· tightly stoppered test tube with HCl solution
· tightly stoppered test tube with NH_3 solution
· double-ended cotton swab (1)
· 250-mL beaker (1)
· clear tape

Procedure

1. Be sure to wear safety goggles and a lab apron during this experiment. **Caution:** Concentrated HCl and NH_3 burn the skin and damage clothing. NH_3 turns the skin black. Handle both liquids with care. If spills occur, notify your teacher immediately.

2. Cut one straw and push it into the other as shown at the right. Cover the joint of the straws with clear tape. Join by pushing together. Then tape.

3. Fill a 250-mL beaker half full with tap water.

PROBLEM SOLVING

Problem of the Week Cards, 22, 23

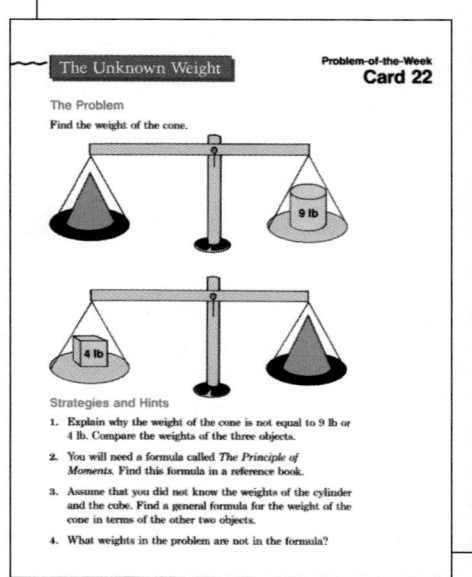

The Unknown Weight
Problem-of-the-Week Card 22

The Problem

Find the weight of the cone.

Strategies and Hints

1. Explain why the weight of the cone is not equal to 9 lb or 4 lb. Compare the weights of the three objects.

2. You will need a formula called *The Principle of Moments*. Find this formula in a reference book.

3. Assume that you did not know the weights of the cylinder and the cube. Find a general formula for the weight of the cone in terms of the other two objects.

4. What weights in the problem are not in the formula?

MAKING MATHEMATICS RELEVANT

This two-page introduction to the chapter provides students with an opportunity to explore contemporary topics and their applications to mathematics.

Background Information

Recycling Why is it necessary to recycle plastic bottles? Plastic is made from oil, and oil is a nonrenewable resource. A nonrenewable resource is one that cannot be replaced, such as metals, minerals, oil, and soil. Wood, by contrast, is a renewable resource, since it is easily replaced by planting more trees. Is Earth warming because of human pollution? There have been warming trends in Earth's history. The evidence is not yet conclusive, but most scientists now believe that the current warming trend is caused by humans.

CHAPTER 9

Exploring Rational Expressions

Objectives

In this chapter, you will:

- graph rational functions,
- solve problems involving direct, inverse, and joint variation,
- simplify rational expressions,
- solve rational equations, and
- solve problems by organizing data.

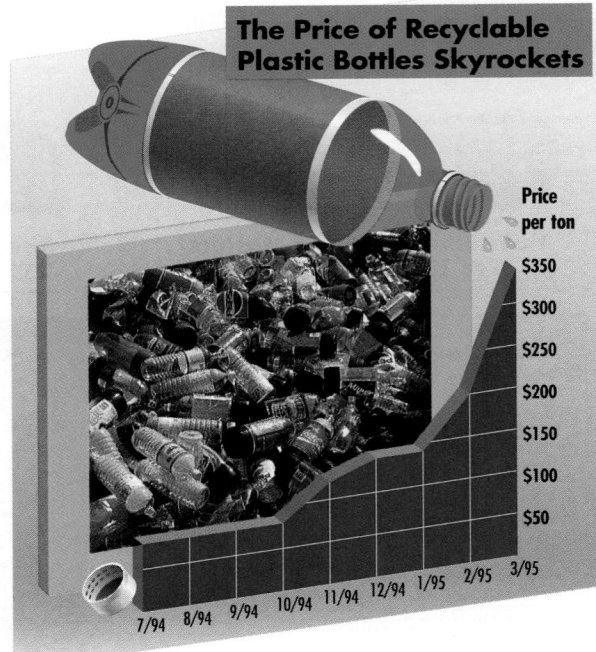

The Price of Recyclable Plastic Bottles Skyrockets

Price per ton: $350, $300, $250, $200, $150, $100, $50

7/94 8/94 9/94 10/94 11/94 12/94 1/95 2/95 3/95

Source: *Oakland Press*, 1995

What can one teenager do about the environment? You can clean your personal environment, your room. You can participate in a local effort to clean a neighborhood. Or you could go national and get everyone's help to better our environment.

TIME Line

180 B.C. Hypicle's *De ascensionibus*, a work on astronomy, introduces the 360-degree circle to Greek mathematics.

1878 Cuban poet, essayist, and patriot José Martí writes his collection of poems *Versos Libres (Free Verses)*.

190 B.C. | 185 | 180 | 175 | 170 | A.D. 1300 | 1400 | 1500 | 1600 | 1700 | 1800 | 1900 | 1930

A.D. 1527 Pascal's triangle appears for the first time in Europe in a book by German astronomer Peter Apian.

TIME Line

Extensive collections of photographs from the *Apollo 11* mission exist. Many of these can be found in library books about the moon. Students might want to do a class presentation on these photographs.

interNET CONNECTION

The WWW Virtual Library on the environment covers oceanography, forestry, ecology, environmental law, and energy.

World Wide Web
http://ecosys.drdr.virginia.edu/Environmental.html

Chapter Project

Form small groups and have some members research different environment issues such as landfills, the rain forest, pollution, or endangered species. Other members could make a list of ways that people can conserve energy and make a difference in helping the environment in everyday life, such as obeying the speed limit and turning off the water while brushing their teeth. Research recycling programs that are available in your community and find out how to participate in these programs. Create charts, graphs, or posters to visually display the data you collect and present your findings to the class.

When **Melissa Poe** was 9, she became concerned about pollution and the environment and wrote a letter to the President. She then started a club at her school in Nashville, Tennessee, to help protect the environment. At first her club had only six members. Now Poe is 16 and Kids For A Clean Environment (Kids F.A.C.E.®) has over 200,000 members worldwide. They publish a newsletter and created the Kid's Earth Flag, which was unveiled on Earth Day in 1995. It is a banner made of 20,000 cloth squares designed by kids from all over the world.

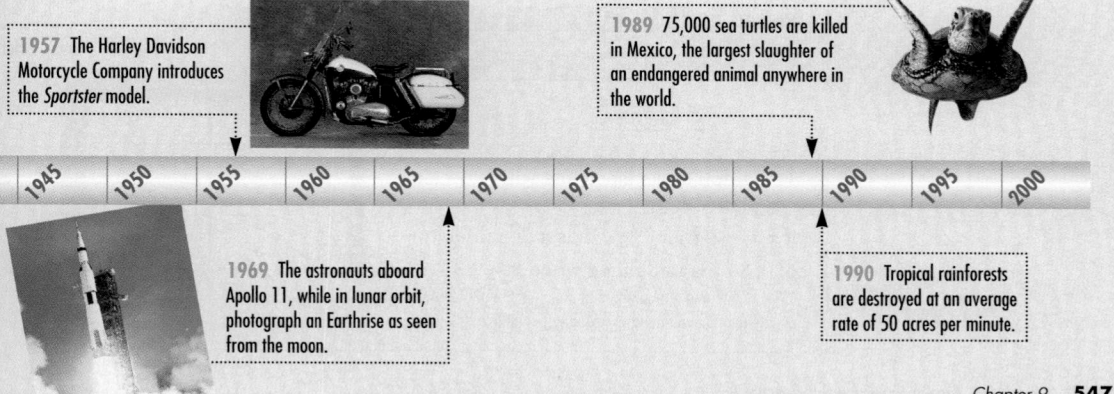

1957 The Harley Davidson Motorcycle Company introduces the *Sportster* model.

1989 75,000 sea turtles are killed in Mexico, the largest slaughter of an endangered animal anywhere in the world.

1969 The astronauts aboard Apollo 11, while in lunar orbit, photograph an Earthrise as seen from the moon.

1990 Tropical rainforests are destroyed at an average rate of 50 acres per minute.

Chapter 9 **547**

Alternative Chapter Projects

Two other chapter projects are included in the *Investigations and Projects Masters.* In Chapter 9 Project A, pp. 57–58, students extend the topic in the chapter opener. In Chapter 9 Project B, pp. 59–60, students schedule and estimate costs necessary in constructing a simple house or building.

Kids F.A.C.E.® has worked closely with two other organizations: CAPE—Children's Alliance for the Protection of the Environment, and YES—Youth Environmental Summit. Among the many activities they organize is tree planting.

Chapter Project

Cooperative Learning Students might call their local garbage collection department and inquire about where their trash goes. Do they use a landfill? Do they incinerate the trash? What, if anything, do they recycle?

Investigations and Projects Masters, p. 57

9 NAME_____ DATE_____

Chapter 9 Project A
Student Edition
Pages 548–584

Data on the Environment

1. Work in a small group to select a research topic on the environment. Possible topics include pollution, recycling, endangered species, and energy conservation.

2. Once you have chosen your topic, brainstorm a list of questions about it. The following questions can help you get started.

 • How is air pollution measured? How has air pollution in your city, state, or the whole United States changed over the past 50 years?

 • How many pounds of newspaper are recycled each year in your town? your state? the entire United States? What happens to recycled newspaper?

 • How has the number of endangered species changed over the past few years? How have the numbers of a particular endangered species changed over the past few years?

 • What is the savings in energy cost for one year of using a 60-watt bulb rather than a 100-watt bulb?

3. Gather information about your topic. Use the local and school library. Interview or write people in your area who can answer your questions.

4. Survey other students to find out how much they know about your topic. First, your group will need to write a survey question. For example, if you gathered data on endangered species, you might ask the question, "How many endangered species do you think there are?" Survey at least 20 students.

5. Decide how you want to present the information you gathered from your research and the results of your student survey. For example, you might decide to write an article for the school newspaper, to create a documentary for radio or television, or to design an interactive museum exhibit.

NCTM Standards: 1–6, 13

Objective
Use a graphing calculator to explore graphs of rational functions.

Recommended Time
25 minutes

Instructional Resources
Graphing Calculator Masters, pp. 49 and 50

These masters provide keystroking instruction for this lesson for the TI-81 and Casio graphing calculators.

1 FOCUS

Motivating the Lesson
Show students examples of graphs showing rational functions. Then ask students to find a way to trace the graphs without lifting up their pencils or pens. Explain this as the "pencil test" for continuity.

2 TEACH

Teaching Tip The graphing calculator is valuable for finding the general features of functions. However, for finding exact points of discontinuity, analytical methods often are necessary.

3 PRACTICE/APPLY

Assignment Guide
Core: 1–10
Enriched: 1–10

Additional Answers

1.
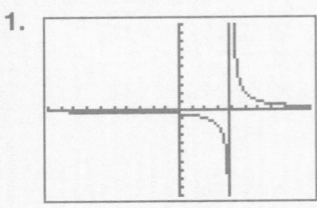

2.
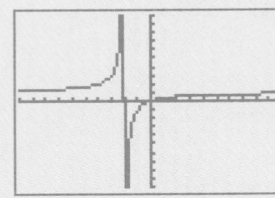

3.
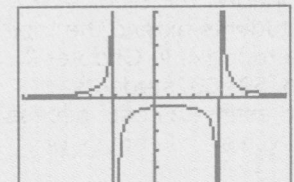

9-1A Graphing Technology
Rational Functions

A Preview of Lesson 9–1

A rational function is of the form $f(x) = \frac{p(x)}{q(x)}$, where $p(x)$ and $q(x)$ are polynomial functions and $q(x) \neq 0$. A graphing calculator is a good tool for exploring graphs of rational functions.

Graphs of rational functions may have breaks in **continuity**. This means that, unlike polynomial functions, which can be traced with a pencil that never leaves the paper, a rational function may not be traceable. Breaks in continuity can occur where there is a vertical asymptote or **point discontinuity**. Point discontinuity is like a hole in the graph. Vertical asymptotes and points of discontinuity occur for values of x that make the denominator of a rational function zero.

Example   **Graph $y = \frac{1}{x}$ in the standard viewing window.** *This is sometimes called the* <u>inverse function</u>.

The inverse function is often the parent function when examining families of rational functions.

Enter:  6

There is a break in continuity at $x = 0$. Looking at the equation, we can see that when $x = 0$, the function is undefined. In this case, the graph has a vertical asymptote at $x = 0$. *Sometimes graphing calculators "graph" this line. This is because the calculator connects all points plotted. To eliminate the graph of the asymptote, change the MODE setting from "Connected" to "Dot."*

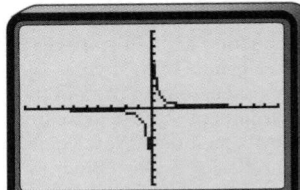

Example   **Graph $y = \frac{x^2 - 9}{x + 3}$ in the window $[-5, 4.4]$ by $[-7, 2]$ with scale factors of 1. Use the "Dot" mode.**

Enter: Y= (X,T,θ x² − 9
) ÷ (X,T,θ + 3
) GRAPH

The graph looks like a line with a break in continuity at $x = -3$. This occurs because if $x = -3$, then $\frac{x^2 - 9}{x + 3}$ has a denominator of 0. So y is undefined when $x = -3$. *If you TRACE along the graph to $x = -3$, you will see that there is no corresponding y value.*

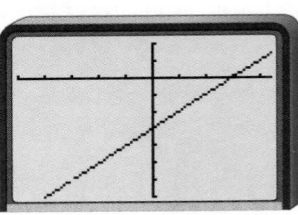

Recall that a complete graph of a function shows all of the important features of the graph, including the end behavior. The end behavior of some rational functions shows that graphs can have horizontal asymptotes.

Example ❸ Graph $y = \frac{4x + 2}{x - 1}$ in the standard viewing window. Then find the equation for the horizontal asymptote.

TECHNOLOGY
Tips

The reason you saw the break in continuity in Example 2 was because the range of the x-axis in the viewing window was a multiple of 94, the number of pixels across the screen. If you graph the function in another viewing window, you might not be able to see the break in continuity.

Enter: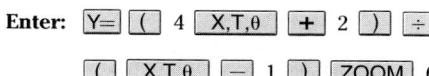

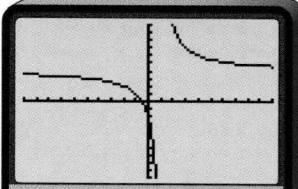

Trace along the graph and observe the y values as x grows larger and as x grows smaller. The y values approach 4. Thus, the equation for the horizontal asymptote is $y = 4$.

What is an equation of the horizontal asymptote for the graph in Example 1?

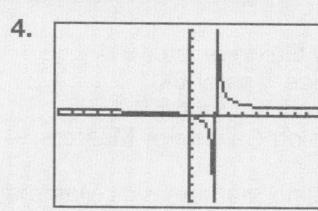

EXERCISES

Use a graphing calculator to graph each function so that a complete graph is shown. Sketch the graph on a sheet of paper. Write the equations of any vertical asymptotes or the x-coordinates of any points of discontinuity. 1–6. See margin for graphs.

1. $f(x) = \frac{2}{x - 4}$ $x = 4$ **2.** $g(x) = \frac{x}{x + 2}$ $x = -2$

3. $h(x) = \frac{8}{(x + 3)(x - 5)}$ $x = -3, 5$ **4.** $p(x) = \frac{2x}{3x - 6}$ $x = 2$

5. $q(x) = \frac{x^2 - 16}{x - 4}$ $x = 4$ **6.** $m(x) = \frac{-(2x + 7)}{(x + 7)(x + 2)}$ $x = -7, -2$

7–10. See margin for graphs.
Use a graphing calculator to graph each function so that a complete graph is shown. Sketch the graph on a sheet of paper. Trace the graph to determine the equations for any horizontal asymptotes.

7. $f(x) = \frac{7}{x}$ $y = 0$ **8.** $j(x) = \frac{x^2 - 3x + 2}{x^2 + x - 6}$ $y = 1$

9. $c(x) = \frac{8x - 5}{2x}$ $y = 4$ **10.** $d(x) = \frac{x - 9}{9 + 2x}$ $y = \frac{1}{2}$

Using Technology
This lesson offers an excellent opportunity for using technology in your algebra classroom. For more information on using technology, see *Graphing Calculators in the Mathematics Classroom,* one of the titles in the Glencoe Mathematics Professional Series.

4 ASSESS

Observing students working with technology is an excellent method of assessment.

Additional Answers

4.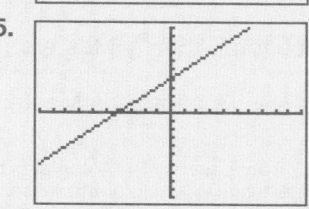

5.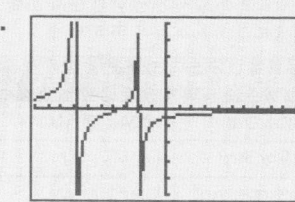

6.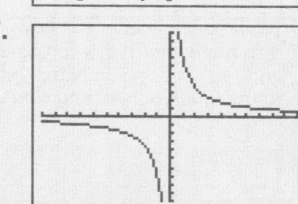

7.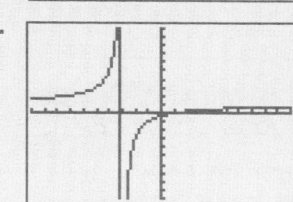

8.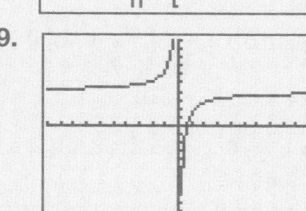

9.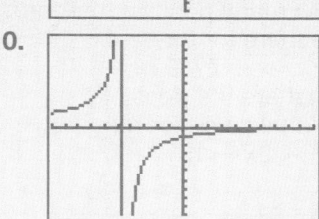

10.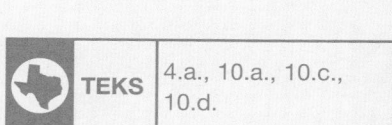

TEKS 4.a., 10.a., 10.c., 10.d.

Graphing Rational Functions

NCTM Standards: 1–6, 13

Instructional Resources

- Study Guide Master 9-1
- Practice Master 9-1
- Enrichment Master 9-1
- Graphing Calculator Masters, p. 9
- Modeling Mathematics Masters, p. 69
- Multicultural Activity Masters, p. 17
- Tech Prep Applications Masters, p. 17

 Transparency 9-1A contains the 5-Minute Check for this lesson; **Transparency 9-1B** contains a teaching aid for this lesson.

Recommended Pacing	
Standard Pacing	Day 2 of 10
Honors Pacing	Day 2 of 9
Block Scheduling*	Day 1 of 4

 *For more information on pacing and possible lesson plans, refer to the *Block Scheduling Booklet*.

1 FOCUS

 5-Minute Check
(over Chapter 8)

1. Find $f(-3)$ if $f(x) = 3x^2 + 2x - 6$. **15**
2. Find $2[p(x)] + 3[p(x + 1)]$ if $p(x) = 2x^2 + 3x + 7$. **$10x^2 + 27x + 50$**
3. How many roots does $f(x) = 5x^6 + 4x^5 - x^3 + x^2 - 6$ have? **6**
4. How many positive real zeros are there for $f(x) = 4x^3 - 2x^2 - x + 7$? **0 or 2**
5. What are the possible rational zeros for $f(x) = x^3 + 9x^2 - 3x + 15$? **$\pm1, \pm3, \pm5, \pm15$**

 **TEKS** 1.a., 4.a., 10.a., 10.b., 10.c., 10.e.

What YOU'LL LEARN
- To graph rational functions.

Why IT'S IMPORTANT
You can graph rational functions to solve problems involving medicine and auto safety.

 **F Y I**

Maria Gaetana Agnesi, born in Milan, Italy, in 1718, mastered Greek, Latin, Hebrew, and several modern languages by the age of 9. At around this age, she gave a speech in Latin defending higher education for women.

x	f(x)
−100	−0.0192
−10	−0.1429
0	−0.50
3	−2
3.5	−4
3.9	−20
4	**undefined**
4.1	20
4.5	4
5	2
10	0.3333
100	0.0208

 **F Y I**

In 1749, Maria Gaetana Agnesi was made an honorary lecturer at the University of Bologna as a researcher. But after her father's death in 1752, she devoted her life to charitable work and religious studies.

CONNECTION
Mathematics History

Mathematician Maria Gaetana Agnesi was one of the greatest women scholars of all time. In the analytic geometry section of her book *Analytical Institutions*, Agnesi discussed the characteristics of the equation $x^2 y = a^2 (a - y)$, called the "curve of Agnesi." The equation can be expressed as $y = \frac{a^3}{x^2 + a^2}$.

Because the function described above is the *ratio* of two polynomial expressions, a^3 and $x^2 + a^2$, it is called a **rational function.** A rational function is a function of the form $f(x) = \frac{p(x)}{q(x)}$, where $p(x)$ and $q(x)$ are polynomial functions and $q(x) \neq 0$. Here are other examples of rational functions.

$$f(x) = \frac{x}{x - 1} \qquad g(x) = \frac{3}{x - 3} \qquad h(x) = \frac{x + 1}{(x + 2)(x - 5)}$$

Because rational functions are expressed in the form of a fraction, the denominator of a rational function cannot be zero, since division by zero is not defined. *In the examples above, the functions are not defined at $x = 1$, $x = 3$, and $x = -2$ and $x = 5$, respectively.*

When graphing a rational function, determine when the denominator is 0, and remember to exclude those values from the domain. Sometimes a dashed line is drawn at those locations to show that a function of the form $f(x) = \frac{p(x)}{q(x)}$ approaches the values at which $q(x) = 0$, but neither touches nor intersects it.

Look at the graph of $f(x) = \frac{2}{x - 4}$ shown below. Notice that the graph of $f(x)$ approaches the graph of $x = 4$, but never touches or intersects it.

The lines that the graph of a rational function approaches are called **asymptotes.** If a function is not defined when $x = a$, then either there is a line with the equation $x = a$ that is a vertical asymptote or there is a "hole" in the graph at $x = a$. As shown at the right, the graph of $x = 4$ is a vertical asymptote. If the value of a function approaches a number b as the value of $|x|$ increases, the line with equation $f(x) = b$ is a horizontal asymptote. In the graph at the right, as $|x|$ increases, the function approaches 0. So, the graph of $f(x) = 0$ is a horizontal asymptote.

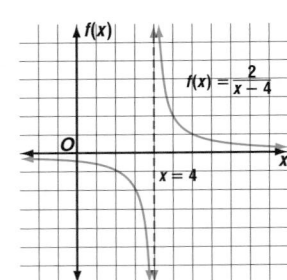

Example ① Graph $f(x) = \frac{x}{x+1}$. State the domain and range.

If $x = -1$, then $f(x)$ is undefined. Thus, the domain for this function includes all real numbers except -1. By plotting points, we see that this graph has a vertical asymptote with the equation $x = -1$. Study the pattern of values of $f(x)$ as the value of $|x|$ increases to determine the equation of the horizontal asymptote.

LOOK BACK

You can refer to Lesson 7-5 to review asymptotes of hyperbolas.

Finding the x- and y-intercepts is often useful when graphing rational functions.

x	f(x)
0	0
5	0.833
50	0.98
100	0.99
1000	0.999
−0.5	−1
−1.5	3
−5	1.25
−50	1.02
−100	1.0101
−1000	1.001

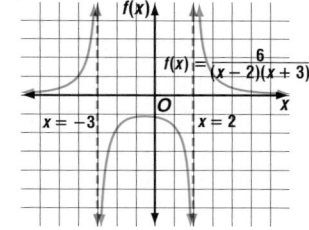

As the value of $|x|$ increases, it appears that the value of the function gets closer and closer to 1. The line with the equation $f(x) = 1$ is a horizontal asymptote of the function, and the range for this function includes all real numbers except 1.

To graph the function, plot points on either side of each asymptote until a pattern is visible. Then sketch the graph.

Using a calculator can help you generate a table of values that pinpoint horizontal asymptotes more easily.

Example ② Graph $f(x) = \frac{6}{(x-2)(x+3)}$.

The vertical asymptotes are the lines whose equations are $x = 2$ and $x = -3$. Use a calculator to generate a table of values for $f(x)$. Be sure to generate values near both sides of the asymptotes. Let's look at $x = 10$.

Enter: 6 ((10 − 2) × (10

+ 3)) = *0.057692307*

The same pattern of keystrokes can be used to find other values of $f(x)$ that approach those of the horizontal asymptote.

$f(10) = 0.057692307$

$f(100) = 0.000594412$

$f(1000) = 0.000005994$

$f(-10) = 0.071428571$

$f(-100) = 0.000606428$

$f(-1000) = 0.000006006$

As $|x|$ increases, it appears that the value of the function approaches, but never quite reaches, 0. An equation of the horizontal asymptote is $f(x) = 0$. Plot points on either side of each asymptote. Then sketch the graph.

GLENCOE *Technology*

 Interactive Mathematics Tools Software

This multimedia software provides an interactive lesson that uses Ohm's Law, $I = \frac{V}{R}$, to observe graphs of rational functions. A **Computer Journal** gives students an opportunity to write about what they have learned.

For Windows & Macintosh

Motivating the Lesson

Hands-On Activity Students can perform an experiment that illustrates inverse variation using a simple rational function. Students may do this in pairs. Darken the room. One student will aim a flashlight at the second student. They should vary the distance between them and make a rough graph with distance along the x-axis and apparent brightness along the y-axis.

2 TEACH

Teaching Tip Have students determine and graph the asymptotes of a function before plotting points.

In-Class Examples

For Example 1

Graph $f(x) = \frac{(x-1)}{x}$.

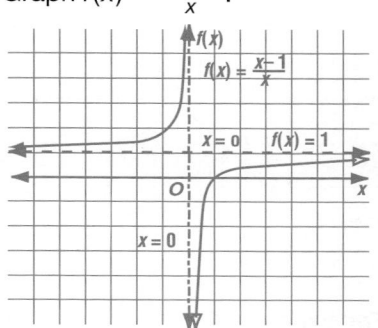

For Example 2

Graph $f(x) = \frac{-3}{x(x-3)}$.

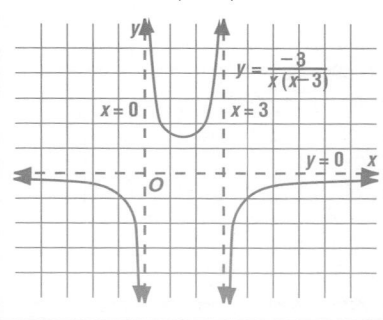

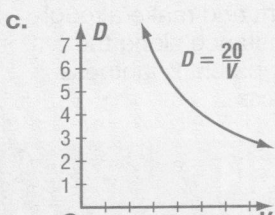

MODELING MATHEMATICS This modeling activity acquaints students with an example of a rational function in physics. Encourage students to speculate about the meaning of D if $V = 0$.

Answer for Modeling Mathematics

c.

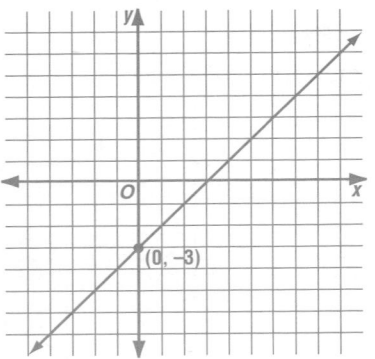

$D = \frac{20}{V}$

In-Class Examples

For Example 3

Graph $y = \frac{x^2 - 9}{x + 3}$.

(0, –3)

For Example 4

Graph $y = \frac{-2}{(x + 1)^2}$.

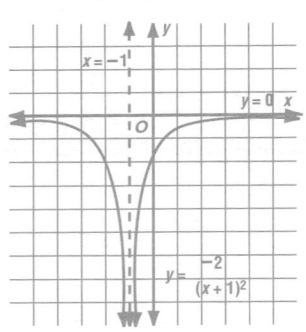

$x = -1$

$y = 0$

$y = \frac{-2}{(x+1)^2}$

Many real-life characteristics can be described by using rational functions.

MODELING MATHEMATICS

Rational Functions

Materials: ⚖️ balances 🥤 metric measuring cups

different liquids such as water, cooking oil, alcohol, sugar water, and salt water

c. See margin for sample graph.

The density of a material can be expressed as $D = \frac{m}{V}$, where m is the mass of the material in grams and V is the volume in cubic centimeters. By finding the volume and density of 20 grams of each liquid, you can sketch a graph of the function $D = \frac{20}{V}$.

b. Use the rational function $D = \frac{m}{V}$ to find the density of each liquid.

c. Graph the data by plotting the points (volume, density) on a graph. Then connect the points.

d. From the graph, find the asymptotes. $x = 0, y = 0$

Your Turn

a. Use a balance and metric measuring cups to find the volume of 20 grams of different liquids, such as water, cooking oil, alcohol, sugar water, and salt water. **a–b. See students' work.**

As you have learned, graphs of rational functions may have point discontinuity rather than vertical asymptotes. The graphs of these functions appear to have "holes." These holes are usually shown as circles on the graph.

Example **Graph** $g(x) = \frac{x^2 - 25}{x - 5}$.

x	g(x)
−1	4
0	5
1	6
2	7
3	8
4	9
5	undefined
6	11
7	12

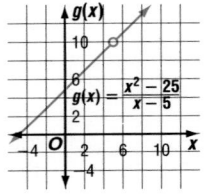

$g(x) = \frac{x^2 - 25}{x - 5}$

The graph looks like a line with a hole at (5, 10). Remember that the denominator cannot be zero, so $x - 5 \neq 0$, or $x \neq 5$. The rest of the graph looks like the line whose equation is $g(x) = x + 5$ because $\frac{x^2 - 25}{x - 5}$ simplifies to $x + 5$ when $x \neq 5$.

As you saw in Example 3, not all rational functions have graphs that are similar in appearance. Some contain no negative values for $f(x)$.

552 Chapter 9 Exploring Rational Expressions

Additional Answers

6.

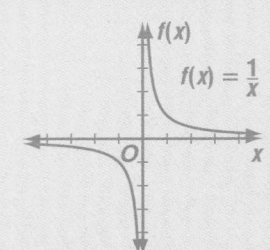

$f(x) = \frac{1}{x}$

7.

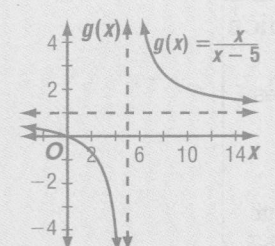

$g(x) = \frac{x}{x - 5}$

8.

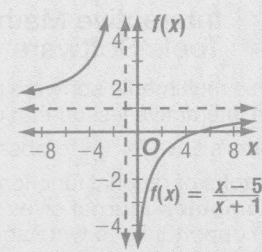

$f(x) = \frac{x - 5}{x + 1}$

Example  **4**

CONNECTION

Mathematics History

Refer to the "curve of Agnesi" in the application at the beginning of the lesson. This bell-shaped curve was discovered by Fermat nearly a hundred years before Agnesi. Graph $f(x) = \dfrac{a^3}{x^2 + a^2}$ if $a = 4$.

$$f(x) = \frac{a^3}{x^2 + a^2}$$

$$= \frac{(4)^3}{x^2 + (4)^2} \text{ or } \frac{64}{x^2 + 16} \quad \textit{Substitute 4 for x.}$$

Since $x^2 + 16$ can never equal 0, the graph of the function has no vertical asymptotes. Use a calculator to estimate the location of the horizontal asymptote.

x	f(x)
−500	0.0003
−50	0.0254
−5	1.5610
0	4
5	1.5610
50	0.0254
500	0.0003

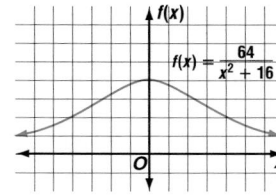

The pattern of values suggests that the equation of the horizontal asymptote will be $f(x) = 0$.

CHECK FOR UNDERSTANDING

Communicating Mathematics

1a. D: all real numbers except 3; R: all real numbers except 0

2. The graph of the first function has a vertical asymptote at $x = -2$. The graph of the second function has point discontinuity at $x = -2$.

Study the lesson. Then complete the following.

1. Consider $f(x) = \dfrac{1}{x-3}$.   **c.** $y = 0$; See students' work for table.
   a. **State** the domain and range of the function.
   b. **Write** an equation of the vertical asymptote for $f(x)$. $x = 3$
   c. **Write** an equation for the horizontal asymptote of the graph of $f(x)$. Generate a table of values to support your answer.

2. **Describe** the difference between the graphs of $y = \dfrac{x-4}{x+2}$ and $y = \dfrac{x^2-4}{x+2}$.

3. **Write** equations for the vertical and horizontal asymptotes of the graph at the right. $x = 2, f(x) = 0$

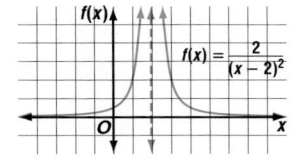

Guided Practice

4. $x = 2, y = 0$

5. $x = 1, x = -3, y = 0$

State the equations of the vertical and horizontal asymptotes for each rational function.

4. $f(x) = \dfrac{1}{x-2}$

5. $f(x) = \dfrac{2}{(x-1)(x+3)}$

Graph each rational function.   6–11. See margin.

6. $f(x) = \dfrac{1}{x}$

7. $g(x) = \dfrac{x}{x-5}$

8. $f(x) = \dfrac{x-5}{x+1}$

9. $g(x) = \dfrac{x-1}{x-4}$

10. $f(x) = \dfrac{1}{(x+2)^2}$

11. $h(x) = \dfrac{8}{(x-1)(x+3)}$

Lesson 9-1   Graphing Rational Functions   **553**

Reteaching

Using Discussion Have students discuss the advantages and disadvantages of three methods of studying rational functions: (1) a table of values, (2) plotting points with paper and pencil, and (3) the graphing calculator.

Additional Answer

11.

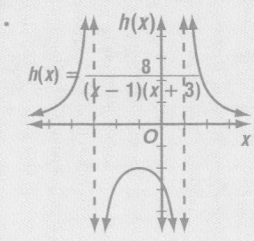

Check for Understanding

Exercises 1–12 are designed to help you assess your students' understanding through reading, writing, speaking, and modeling. You should work through Exercises 1–3 with your students and then monitor their work on Exercises 4–12.

Additional Answers

9.

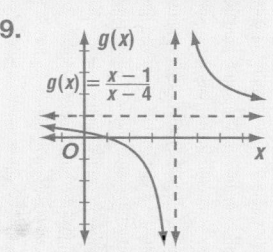

10.

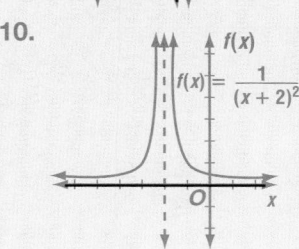

Study Guide Masters, p. 64

 9-1

NAME_____ DATE_____

Study Guide

Student Edition
Pages 550–555

Graphing Rational Functions

A rational function is an equation of the form $f(x) = \dfrac{p(x)}{q(x)}$ where $p(x)$ and $q(x)$ are polynomial functions and $q(x) \neq 0$. Functions such as $f(x) = \dfrac{x}{x-2}$ and $f(x) = \dfrac{3}{(x-4)(x-2)}$ are examples of rational functions.

The graph of a rational function has two or more branches. The branches of the graph approach lines called **asymptotes**. First graph the asymptotes. Then plot the points necessary to finish the graph.

Vertical Asymptote	**Horizontal Asymptote**
The line with the equation $x = a$, if the rational function is undefined when x is a.	The line with the equation $y = b$, if the value of the function approaches b as the value of $|x|$ increases.

Example: Graph $f(x) = \dfrac{x-1}{x}$.

The line with the equation $x = 0$ is a **vertical asymptote** because $f(x)$ is undefined when $x = 0$. As the value of $|x|$ increases, the value of the function approaches 1, as the table shows. The line with equation $y = 1$ is a **horizontal asymptote**.

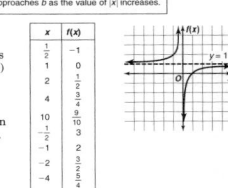

Graph each rational function.

1. $f(x) = \dfrac{3}{x+1}$

2. $f(x) = \dfrac{2}{x}$

3. $f(x) = \dfrac{2x+1}{x-3}$

4. $f(x) = \dfrac{2}{(x+3)^2}$

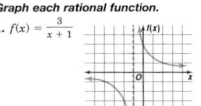

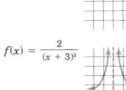

Chapter 9   **553**

Assignment Guide

Core: 13–33 odd, 34, 35, 37–43
Enriched: 14–32 even, 34–43

For **Extra Practice,** see p. 897.

The red A, B, and C flags, printed only in the Teacher's Wraparound Edition, indicate the level of difficulty of the exercises.

Additional Answers

12a.

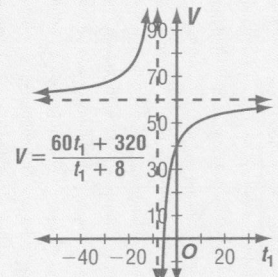

$$V = \frac{60t_1 + 320}{t_1 + 8}$$

35b. The graph has a vertical asymptote at $y = -12$ and a horizontal asymptote at $C = 1$.

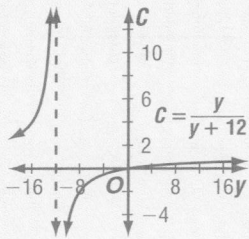

$$C = \frac{y}{y + 12}$$

Practice Masters, p. 64

NAME_____ DATE_____
Practice
Student Edition
Pages 550–555

Graphing Rational Functions
Graph each rational function.

1. $y = \frac{-4}{x-2}$

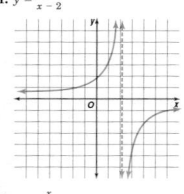

2. $y = \frac{3}{(x+1)(x-1)}$

3. $y = \frac{x}{x+3}$

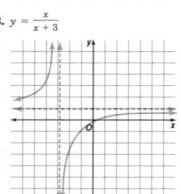

4. $y = \frac{-5}{x+1}$

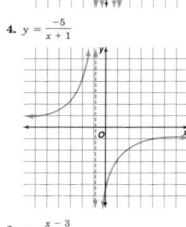

5. $y = \frac{3x}{(x+3)^2}$

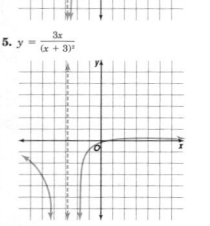

6. $y = \frac{x-3}{x-2}$

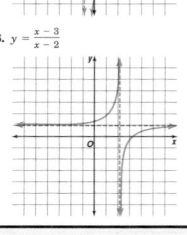

---

12. **Transportation** A train travels at one velocity V_1 for a given amount of time t_1 and then another velocity V_2 for a different amount of time t_2. The average velocity is given by the formula $V = \frac{V_1 t_1 + V_2 t_2}{t_1 + t_2}$.   **a. See margin.**

   a. Let t_1 be the independent variable and let V be the dependent variable. Draw the graph if $V_1 = 60$ mph, $V_2 = 40$ mph, and $t_2 = 8$ hours.

   b. Find V when $t_1 = 9$ hours.   **about 50.59 mph**

EXERCISES

Practice

State the equations of the vertical and horizontal asymptotes for each rational function.

13. $f(x) = \frac{x}{x-4}$

14. $g(x) = \frac{6}{(x-6)^2}$

15. $f(x) = \frac{4}{(x-1)(x+5)}$

16. $f(x) = \frac{1}{3x}$

17. $h(x) = \frac{x-1}{x-3}$

18. $t(x) = \frac{x}{x-7}$

Graph each rational function.   **19–33. See Solutions Manual.**

19. $f(x) = \frac{3}{x}$

20. $f(x) = \frac{1}{x+2}$

21. $f(x) = \frac{x}{x-3}$

22. $f(x) = \frac{x+4}{x-1}$

23. $f(x) = \frac{x-1}{x-3}$

24. $f(x) = \frac{-5}{x+1}$

25. $f(x) = \frac{x^2-36}{x+6}$

26. $f(x) = \frac{-3}{(x-2)^2}$

27. $f(x) = \frac{5x}{x+1}$

28. $f(x) = \frac{x^2-1}{x-1}$

29. $f(x) = \frac{1}{(x+3)^2}$

30. $f(x) = \frac{3}{(x-1)(x+5)}$

31. $f(x) = \frac{-1}{(x+2)(x-3)}$

32. $f(x) = \frac{x}{x^2-1}$

33. $f(x) = \frac{x-1}{x^2-4}$

Critical Thinking

34. Compare and contrast each family of graphs.   **a–d. See Solutions Manual.**

   a. $y = \frac{1}{x}$ and $y - 7 = \frac{1}{x}$ **b.** $y = \frac{1}{x}$ and $y = 4\left(\frac{1}{x}\right)$ **c.** $y = \frac{1}{x}$ and $y = \frac{1}{x+5}$

   d. Without making a table of values, use what you observed in parts a–c to sketch a graph of $y - 7 = 4\left(\frac{1}{x+5}\right)$.

Applications and Problem Solving

35. **Medications** For certain medicines, health care professionals may use Young's Rule, $C = \frac{y}{y+12} \cdot D$, to estimate the proper dosage for a child when the adult dosage is known.

   a. If C represents the child's dose, D represents the adult dose, and y represents the child's age in years, use Young's Rule to estimate the dosage of amoxicillin for an eight-year-old child if the adult dosage is 250 mg.   **100 mg**

   b. Draw and describe the graph of $C = \frac{y}{y+12}$. Note its shape, asymptotes, domain, and range.   **See margin.**

36. **Auto Safety** When a car has a front-end collision, the objects in the car (including passengers) keep moving forward until the impact occurs. After impact, objects are repelled. Seat belts and airbags limit how far you are jolted forward. The formula for the velocity you are thrown backward is $V_f = \frac{m_1 - m_2}{m_1 + m_2} v_i$, where m_1 and m_2 are the masses of the two objects meeting and v_i is the initial velocity.

   a. Let m_1 be the independent variable and let V_f be the dependent variable. Graph the function if $m_2 = 7$ kg and $v_i = 5$ m/s.   **See margin.**

   b. Find the value of V_f when the value of m_1 is 5 kg. $V_f \approx -0.83$ m/s

Additional Answer

36a.

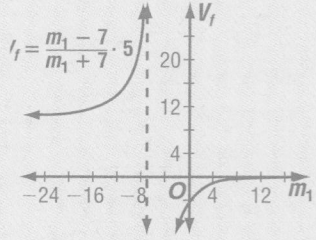

$$t_f = \frac{m_1 - 7}{m_1 + 7} \cdot 5$$

Tech Prep

Automotive Technician Students who are interested in automotive safety may want to do further research on the information given in Exercise 36 and explore the potential growth of this career. For more information on tech prep, see the *Teacher's Handbook*.

37. Determine whether $f(x) = x$ and $g(x) = -x$ are inverse functions. (Lesson 8–8) **no**

38. Approximate the real zeros of $g(x) = x^4 - 9x^3 + 25x^2 - 24x + 6$ to the nearest tenth. (Lesson 8–3) **0.4, 1.3, 2.6, 4.7**

$39.\ \dfrac{y^2}{34} - \dfrac{x^2}{6} = 1$

39. Write an equation for $6y^2 - 34x^2 = 204$ in standard form. (Lesson 7–5)

40. Statistics The lifetimes of 10,000 light bulbs are normally distributed. The mean lifetime is 300 days, and the standard deviation is 40 days. (Lesson 6–9)

   a. How many light bulbs will last between 260 and 340 days? **6800**

   b. How many light bulbs will last between 220 and 380 days? **9500**

   c. How many light bulbs will last less than 300 days? **5000**

   d. How many light bulbs will last more than 300 days? **5000**

   e. How many light bulbs will last more than 380 days? **250**

   f. How many light bulbs will last less than 180 days? **50**

41. Find the value of the discriminant and describe the nature of the roots of $x^2 - 10x + 25 = 0$. Then solve the equation. (Lesson 6–4) **0; 1 R, Q; 5**

$42.\ \left(\dfrac{3}{4}, -\dfrac{2}{3}, \dfrac{1}{2}\right)$

42. Solve the system of equations using augmented matrices. (Lesson 4–7)

$$8x - 3y - 4z = 6$$
$$4x + 9y - 2z = -4$$
$$6x + 12y + 5z = -1$$

43. Find the x- and y-intercepts of $3x - 2y = 12$. (Lesson 2–3) **x: 4; y: −6**

Closing Activity
Speaking Have students explain what an asymptote is.

WORKING ON THE

Refer to the Investigation on pages 474–475.

Suppose the gas station owner also told you that the tank is buried $2\frac{1}{2}$ feet below the surface. It has a diameter of $5\frac{3}{4}$ feet and a length of $9\frac{1}{8}$ feet.

1 What is the volume of the tank in cubic feet?

2 Research to find how many gallons are in a cubic foot. What is the volume of the tank in gallons?

3 Where on the dipstick would the marking be showing that the tank was one-half full? How did you arrive at this marking?

4 Using the data from your two experiments and the table of data from the Investigation in Lesson 8–8, describe the scale of the dipstick. How do you use the stick to determine the gallons of gasoline left in the tank?

Add the results of your work to your Investigation Folder.

Extension

Connections Have students use physics and chemistry books to find other rational functions. Determine and graph asymptotes for each. Use theoretical data to graph the functions.

In·ves·ti·ga·tion

Working on the Investigation
The Investigation on pages 474–475 is designed to be a long-term project that is completed over several days or weeks. Encourage students to keep their materials in their Investigation Folder as they work on the Investigation.

Enrichment Masters, p. 64

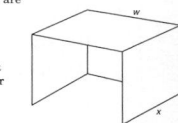

9-1 NAME_____ DATE_____
Enrichment Student Edition Pages 552–557

Finding Maximum or Minimum Values
Many problems require finding a maximum or minimum value. Such problems can often be solved by first writing a system of equations, and then writing a function of one variable. By graphing or making a table of values for the function, the maximum or minimum value can be found. Diagrams are often helpful for writing the initial system equations.

Example: A road salt storage shed is to be built with two square sides, a back, and a top. The shed is to be constructed of 900 square feet of corrugated steel. Find the dimensions for which the volume will be a maximum.

Let x represent the height and depth. Let w represent the width. Since the surface area is to be 900 square feet, $2x^2 + 2xw = 900$. Therefore, $w = \frac{450 - x^2}{x}$. The volume is given by $V = x^2w$. Substituting for w, $V = 450x - x^3$. By making a graph on a table of values for $V(x)$, you can show that there is a relative maximum which occurs when x is about 12.2 feet. The value of w will be about 24.5 feet.

Solve each problem.

1. A store owner wants to construct a 1000-square-foot rectangular display enclosure in the store's parking lot. Three sides are to be chainlink fencing which costs $9.00 per running foot. The fourth side is to be a brick wall which costs $18.75 per running foot. Find the dimensions that will minimize the cost. **length = 39.2 feet; width = 25.5 feet**

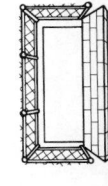

2. Gloria wants to make a rectangular patio along the back of her house. She plans to surround the patio on three sides with one foot square flagstones. She has 118 flagstones. Find the maximum area of the patio not including the area of the flagstones. **1740.5 square feet**

NCTM Standards: 1–6, 13

Instructional Resources

- Study Guide Master 9-2
- Practice Master 9-2
- Enrichment Master 9-2
- Assessment and Evaluation Masters, p. 240
- Multicultural Activity Masters, p. 18
- Science and Math Lab Manual, pp. 95–98
- Tech Prep Applications Masters, p. 18

 Transparency 9-2A contains the 5-Minute Check for this lesson; **Transparency 9-2B** contains a teaching aid for this lesson.

Recommended Pacing

Standard Pacing	Days 3 & 4 of 10
Honors Pacing	Day 3 of 9
Block Scheduling*	Day 2 of 4 (along with Lesson 9-3)

 *For more information on pacing and possible lesson plans, refer to the *Block Scheduling Booklet*.

1 FOCUS

 5-Minute Check
(over Lesson 9-1)

For Exercises 1–4, use
$f(x) = \dfrac{4}{(x + 2)(x - 3)}.$

1. How many asymptotes are there? **3**
2. Write equations for any vertical asymptotes.
   $x = -2, x = 3$
3. Write equations for any horizontal asymptotes. $y = 0$
4. Graph the equation.

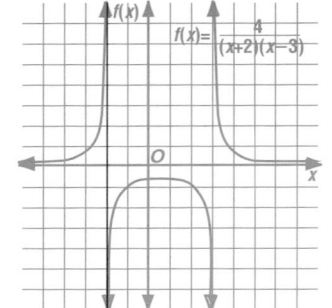

What YOU'LL LEARN

- To solve problems involving direct, inverse, and joint variation.

Why IT'S IMPORTANT

You can use direct, inverse, and joint variation to solve problems involving swimming and energy conservation.

F Y I

The record snowfall for a single snowstorm is 189 inches at Mt. Shasta, California in 1959.

LOOK BACK

You can refer to Lesson 2-4 to review the slope-intercept form of a linear equation.

9-2 Direct, Inverse, and Joint Variation

APPLICATION
Meteorology

Many areas of Northern California depend on the snowpack of the Sierra Nevada mountain range for their water supply. The volume of water produced from melting snow varies directly with the volume of snow. Meteorologists have determined that 250 cm³ of snow will melt to 28 cm³ of water. How much water does 900 cm³ of melting snow produce?

The relationship between the volume of the snowpack and the volume of water it produces can be expressed with the equation $y = kx$, where y represents the water produced from x, the amount of the snowpack. The k in this equation is called the **constant of variation.**

To find the value of k, substitute corresponding volumes of snowpack and water in the equation and solve for k.

$$y = kx$$
$$28 = k(250) \quad \text{Replace } y \text{ with 28 and } x \text{ with 250.}$$
$$\frac{28}{250} = k \quad \text{Divide each side by 250. } \textbf{Estimate: } \frac{25}{250} = 0.1$$
$$0.112 = k$$

So the relationship between the amount of snowpack and the amount of water it melts to is $y = 0.112x$. Use this equation to find the amount of water produced from 900 cm³ of snow.

$$y = kx$$
$$= 0.112(900) \quad \text{Replace } k \text{ with 0.112 and } x \text{ with 900.}$$
$$= 100.8 \quad \textbf{Estimate: } (0.1)900 = 90$$

Snowpack measuring 900 cm³ will produce 100.8 cm³ of water.

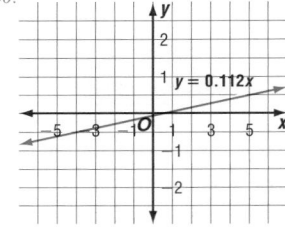

The relationship described above is an example of a **direct variation.** This means that y is a multiple of x. Note that the graph of a direct variation is a line through the origin. An equation of a direct variation is a special case of an equation written in slope-intercept form, $y = mx + b$. When $m = k$ and $b = 0$, $y = mx + b$ becomes $y = kx$. So the slope of a direct variation equation is its constant.

556 Chapter 9 Exploring Rational Expressions

F Y I

Snow covers, permanently or temporarily, about 23% of Earth's surface.

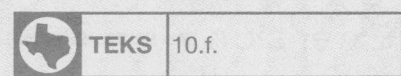
TEKS 10.f.

To express a direct variation, we say that *y varies directly as x*. In other words, as *x* increases, *y* increases or decreases at a constant rate.

Direct Variation	*y* varies directly as *x* if there is some nonzero constant *k* such that $y = kx$. *k* is called the *constant of variation*.

If you know that *y* varies directly as *x* and one set of values, you can use a proportion to find the other set of corresponding values.

$$y_1 = kx_1 \text{ and } y_2 = kx_2$$

$$\frac{y_1}{x_1} = k \qquad \frac{y_2}{x_2} = k$$

Therefore, $\frac{y_1}{x_1} = \frac{y_2}{x_2}$.

Using the properties of equality, you can find many other proportions that relate these same *x* and *y* values.

Example **If *y* varies directly as *x* and *y* = 9 when *x* is −15, find *y* when *x* = 21.**

Use a proportion that relates the values.

$$\frac{y_1}{x_1} = \frac{y_2}{x_2}$$

$$\frac{9}{-15} = \frac{y_2}{21} \qquad \textit{Substitute the known values.}$$

$$-15y_2 = (9)(21) \qquad \textit{Cross multiply.}$$

$$y_2 = -12.6 \qquad \textit{Divide each side by 15.}$$

When *x* = 21, the value of *y* is −12.6.

Many quantities are **inversely proportional** or are said to *vary inversely* with each other. For example, speed and time vary inversely with each other. When you travel to a particular location, as your speed increases, the time it takes to arrive at that location decreases.

Inverse Variation	*y* varies inversely as *x* if there is some nonzero constant *k* such that $xy = k$ or $y = \frac{k}{x}$.

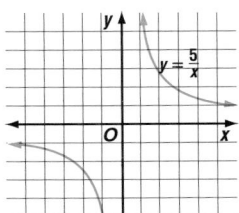

Suppose *y* varies inversely as *x* such that $xy = 5$ or $y = \frac{5}{x}$. The graph of this equation is shown at the left. Notice that in this case, *k* is a positive value, 5, so as the values of *x* increase, the values of *y* decrease.

Just as with direct variation, a proportion can be used with indirect variation to solve problems where some quantities are known. The following proportion is only one of several that can be formed.

$$x_1y_1 = k \text{ and } x_2y_2 = k$$

$$x_1y_1 = x_2y_2 \qquad \textit{Substitution property of equality}$$

$$\frac{x_1}{y_2} = \frac{x_2}{y_1} \qquad \textit{Divide each side by } y_1y_2.$$

Lesson 9–2 *Direct, Inverse, and Joint Variation* **557**

Motivating the Lesson
Hands-On Activity Measure the circumference of an inflated balloon. Immerse the balloon in a container of warm water for a few minutes and again measure the circumference. Repeat, using ice water. Have students look at the data. Ask how the last two measurements are related to the initial circumference.

2 TEACH

In-Class Example

For Example 1
If *y* varies directly as *x* and *y* = 6 when *x* = 11, find *y* when *x* = 3. $\frac{18}{11}$

Teaching Tip Be sure students do not consider an equation to represent an inverse variation simply because both variables are on the same side of the equals sign.

 Alternative Teaching Strategies

Student Diversity Use concrete illustrations to review the ideas of direct and inverse variation. Think of direct variation in this way: Lift a weight with your arm. As your arm goes up, the weight goes up. Think of inverse variation in this way: Lift an object with a lever. As your arm goes down, the object goes up.

For Example 2
If y varies inversely as x and $y = 10$ when $x = 20$, find x when $y = 16$. **12.5**

For Example 3
The volume V of a cone varies jointly as the square of the radius of the base r^2 and the height h. Find the equation of joint variation if $V = 285$, $r = 4$, and $h = 17$. $V = 1.05r^2h$
(Note: $1.05 \approx \frac{\pi}{3}$)

Teaching Tip Be sure students understand why joint variation is considered direct variation even though two of the variables are multiplied by each other.

Example **2**   If y varies inversely as x and $y = 4$ when $x = 12$, find y when $x = 5$.

$$\frac{x_1}{y_2} = \frac{x_2}{y_1}$$

$$\frac{12}{y_2} = \frac{5}{4} \qquad \text{\textit{Substitute the known values.}}$$

$$5y_2 = 48 \qquad \text{\textit{Cross multiply.}}$$

$$y_2 = \frac{48}{5} \text{ or } 9.6 \qquad \text{\textit{Divide each side by 5.}}$$

When $x = 5$, the value of y is $\frac{48}{5}$ or 9.6.

Another type of variation is **joint variation.** This type of variation occurs when one quantity varies directly as the product of two or more other quantities.

Joint Variation	y varies jointly as x and z if there is some number k such that $y = kxz$, where $x \neq 0$ and $z \neq 0$.

Example **3**   The area A of a trapezoid varies jointly as the height h and the sum of its bases b_1 and b_2. Find the equation of joint variation if $A = 48$ in^3, $h = 8$ in., $b_1 = 5$ in., and $b_2 = 7$ in.

Geometry

Explore   Read the problem and use the known values of A, h, b_1, and b_2 to find the equation of joint variation.

Plan   The area varies jointly as the height and the sum of its bases.

$$A \qquad = k \cdot \qquad h \qquad \cdot \qquad (b_1 + b_2)$$

Solve
$$A = kh(b_1 + b_2)$$
$$48 = k(8)(5 + 7) \qquad \text{\textit{Substitute the known values.}}$$
$$48 = k(8)(12)$$
$$48 = 96k$$
$$0.5 = k \qquad \text{\textit{Solve for k.}}$$

The equation for the area of a trapezoid is $A = 0.5h(b_1 + b_2)$.

Examine
$$A = 0.5h(b_1 + b_2)$$
$$48 \stackrel{?}{=} 0.5(8)(5 + 7) \qquad A = 48, h = 8, b_1 = 5, \text{ and } b_2 = 7$$
$$48 \stackrel{?}{=} 0.5(8)(12)$$
$$48 = 48 \checkmark$$

Thus, the equation is correct.

Alternative Teaching Strategies

Reading Algebra *Inverted* means "to be turned upside-down." In an inverse variation $y = \frac{k}{x}$, x and y are upside-down in relation to each other.

Communicating Mathematics

1. x increases if $k > 0$ and decreases if $k < 0$.

2. k is constant and never varies.

3. Direct; as the value of x increases, the value of y increases.

Study the lesson. Then complete the following.

1. **Describe** what happens when the value of y increases if y varies directly as x.

2. **Explain** how k is different from y and x in the equation $y = kx$.

3. **State** whether the graph at the right represents a direct or inverse variation. Explain.

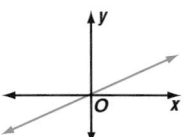

4. **Describe** two quantities in real life that vary directly with each other and two quantities that vary inversely with each other. **See margin for sample answer.**

Guided Practice

8. $y = \frac{50}{x}$; 25
9. $y = 5x$, 60
11a. $I = \frac{k}{d^2}$
11c. The sound will be heard $\frac{1}{4}$ as intensely.

State whether each equation represents a _direct_, _inverse_, or _joint_ variation. Then name the constant of variation.

5. $xy = -5$ inverse, -5 6. $y = 2xz$ joint, 2 7. $\frac{x}{y} = 3$ direct, $\frac{1}{3}$

Write an equation for each statement. Then solve the equation.

8. If y varies inversely as x and $y = 5$ when $x = 10$, find y when $x = 2$.

9. If y varies directly as x and $y = 15$ when $x = 3$, find y when $x = 12$.

10. If y varies jointly as x and z and $y = 80$ when $x = 5$ and $z = 8$, find y when $x = 16$ and $z = 2$. $y = 2xz$; 64

11. **Architecture** Architects have to consider how sound travels when designing large buildings such as theaters, auditoriums, or museums. Sound intensity I is inversely proportional to the square of the distance from the sound source d.
   a. Write an equation that represents this situation.
   b. If d is the independent variable and I is the dependent variable, graph the equation from part a when $k = 16$. **See margin.**
   c. If a person in a theater moves to a seat twice as far from the speakers, compare the new sound intensity to that of the original.

Practice

 A

State whether each equation represents a _direct_, _inverse_, or _joint_ variation. Then name the constant of variation. 17. direct, $-\frac{4}{3}$

12. $\frac{x}{5} = y$ direct, $\frac{1}{5}$ 13. $\frac{x}{y} = -7$ direct, $-\frac{1}{7}$ 14. $x = 4y$ direct, $\frac{1}{4}$

15. $x = \frac{1}{y}$ inverse, 1 16. $A = \frac{1}{2}bh$ joint, $\frac{1}{2}$ 17. $\frac{2}{3}a = -\frac{1}{2}b$

Write an equation for each statement. Then solve the equation.

18. $y = 4x$, 64
19. $rt = -54$, 4.91 B
20. $y = \frac{x}{12}$, 0.83
21. $xy = 50$, 1.25

18. If y varies directly as x and $y = 12$ when $x = 3$, find y when $x = 16$.

19. If r varies inversely as t and $r = 18$ when $t = -3$, find r when $t = -11$.

20. If y varies directly as x and $x = 6$ when $y = 0.5$, find y when $x = 10$.

21. If y varies inversely as x and $y = 2$ when $x = 25$, find x when $y = 40$.

Lesson 9-2 Direct, Inverse, and Joint Variation **559**

Reteaching

Using Alternative Methods Write variation equations. Name the type of variation represented.

1. Some points in a football game are based on the number of touchdowns scored. $p = 6t$; direct

2. Refreshment receipts are based on the number of stands open, the attendance, and a price of 50¢ per item. $r = 0.50na$; joint

3. The faster the wind blows, the lower attendance is. $as = k$; inverse

---

Check for Understanding

Exercises 1–11 are designed to help you assess your students' understanding through reading, writing, speaking, and modeling. You should work through Exercises 1–4 with your students and then monitor their work on Exercises 5–11.

Assignment Guide

Core: 13–35 odd, 36–42
Enriched: 12–28 even, 29–42

For **Extra Practice,** see p. 897.

The red A, B, and C flags, printed only in the Teacher's Wraparound Edition, indicate the level of difficulty of the exercises.

Additional Answers

4. Sample answer: direct variation, wages and hours worked; inverse variation, distance traveled and amount of gas in a car.

11b.

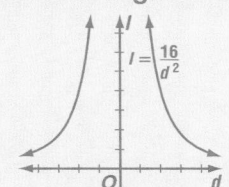

Study Guide Masters, p. 65

9-2 NAME_____ DATE_____
Study Guide Student Edition Pages 556–561

Direct, Inverse, and Joint Variation
Variables can be related by **direct**, **inverse**, and **joint variation**.

Direct Variation	Inverse Variation	Joint Variation
y varies directly as x if there is some constant k such that $y = kx$.	y varies inversely as x if there is some constant k such that $xy = k$.	y varies jointly as x and z if there is some number k such that $y = kxz$, where $x \neq 0$ and $z \neq 0$.

Examples:

If y varies directly as x and $y = 16$ when $x = 4$, find x when $y = 20$.
$\frac{y_1}{x_1} = \frac{y_2}{x_2}$
$\frac{16}{4} = \frac{20}{x_2}$
$16x_2 = (20)(4)$
$x_2 = 5$
The value of x is 5 when y is 20.

If y varies inversely as x and $y = 5$ when $x = 16$, find y when $x = 20$.
$\frac{x_1}{y_2} = \frac{x_2}{y_1}$
$\frac{16}{y_2} = \frac{20}{5}$
$80 = 20y_2$
$y_2 = 4$
The value of y is 4 when x is 20.

If y varies jointly as x and z and $y = 10$ when $x = 2$ and $z = 4$, find y when $x = 4$ and $z = 3$.
$\frac{y_1}{y_2} = \frac{x_2 z_2}{x_1 z_1}$
$\frac{10}{y} = \frac{2 \cdot 4}{4 \cdot 3}$
$120 = 8y$
$y = 15$
The value of y is 15 when $x = 4$ and $z = 3$.

Write an equation for each statement. Then solve the equation.

1. Find y when $x = 15$, if y varies inversely as x and $x = 10$ when $y = 12$. $\frac{15}{12} = \frac{10}{y}$; 8

2. Find y when $x = 8$, if x varies directly as y and $y = 9$, when $x = 6$. $\frac{y}{8} = \frac{9}{6}$; 12

3. Find y when $x = 5$ and $z = 3$, if y varies jointly as $x = 3$ and $z = 2$ when $y = 18$. $\frac{y}{18} = \frac{5 \cdot 3}{3 \cdot 2}$; 45

4. Find x when $y = 9$, if y varies directly as x and $x = 15$ when $y = 5$. $\frac{9}{x} = \frac{5}{15}$; 27

5. Find y when $x = 6$ and $z = 8$, if y varies jointly as $x = 4$ and $z = 2$ when $y = 6$. $\frac{y}{6} = \frac{6 \cdot 8}{4 \cdot 2}$; 36

6. Find x when $y = 27$, if y varies inversely as x and $x = 9$ when $y = 45$. $\frac{x}{45} = \frac{9}{27}$; 15

7. Find x when $y = 1000$, if y varies directly as x and $y = 50$ when $x = 200$. $\frac{1000}{x} = \frac{50}{200}$; 4000

8. Find x when $y = 76$, if y varies inversely as x and $y = 100$ when $x = 38$. $\frac{76}{100} = \frac{38}{y}$; 50

Additional Answer

31d. See students' work for table.

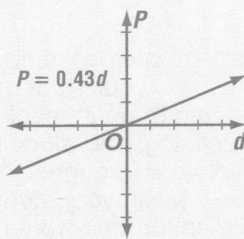

$P = 0.43d$

22. Suppose y varies jointly as x and z. Find y when $x = 8$ and $z = 3$, if $y = 16$ when $z = 2$ and $x = 5$.   **38.4**

23. Geometry   The area of a parallelogram varies jointly as its base and height. Parallelogram *DUCK* has a base of 15 meters, a height of 12 meters, and an area of 180 square meters. Find the height of parallelogram *DOVE* if its area is 1615 square meters and its base is 42.5 meters.   **38 meters**

24. $A = \frac{1}{2}bh$

24. Geometry   The area of a triangle varies jointly as the base and height. Find the equation of joint variation if $A = 100$, $b = 25$, and $h = 8$.

25. $\frac{22}{5}$

25. If y varies directly as x and $y = 1$ when $x = 5$, find y when $x = 22$.

26. If y varies inversely as x and $x = 14$ when $y = 7$, find x when $y = 2$.   **49**

27. If y varies directly as x and $y = \frac{2}{5}$ when $x = \frac{1}{20}$, find y when $x = \frac{1}{2}$.   **4**

28. If y varies inversely as x and $y = \frac{1}{8}$ when $x = 16$, find y when $x = \frac{2}{3}$.   **3**

29a. directly

Critical Thinking

29. a. How does the circumference of a circle vary with respect to its radius?

  b. What is the constant of variation? 2π

30. a. How does the volume of a sphere vary with respect to the cube of its radius?   **directly**

30b. $\frac{4}{3}\pi$

  b. What is the constant of variation?

Applications and Problem Solving

31. Swimming   When a person swims underwater, the pressure in his or her ears varies directly with the depth at which he or she is swimming. At 10 feet, the pressure is about 4.3 pounds per square inch (psi).

  a. Find an equation of direct variation that represents this situation. $P = 0.43d$

  b. Find the pressure if the depth is 60 feet.

  c. It is unsafe for amateur divers to swim where the water pressure is more than 65 psi. How deep can an amateur diver safely swim?

  d. Make a table showing the number of pounds of pressure at various depths of water. Use the data to sketch a graph of pressure versus depth.   **See margin.**

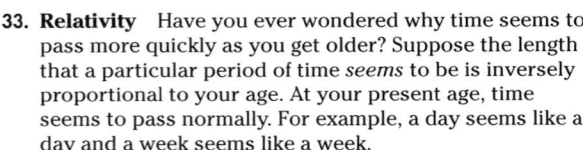

31b. 25.8 psi
31c. about 150 ft
32. approximately 5000 pounds
33a. like one third of a month

32. Aeronautics   The LEM (Lunar Exploration Module) used by astronauts to explore the moon's surface during the Apollo space missions weighs about 30,000 pounds on Earth. On the moon, there is less gravity so it weighs less, meaning that less fuel is needed to lift off from the moon's surface. The force of gravity on Earth is about 6 times as much as that on the moon. How much does the LEM weigh on the moon?

33. Relativity   Have you ever wondered why time seems to pass more quickly as you get older? Suppose the length that a particular period of time *seems* to be is inversely proportional to your age. At your present age, time seems to pass normally. For example, a day seems like a day and a week seems like a week.

  a. How long will a month seem to be when you are three times as old as you are now?

  b. How long did a week seem to be when you were a fifth as old as you are now?   **like 5 weeks**

  c. Winona, who is 30 years old, says to her 5-year-old, "You have to wait 10 more minutes before going swimming." In terms of the mother's time scale, how long does 10 minutes seem to her child?   **like 1 hour**

Practice Masters, p. 65

NAME_____ DATE_____

9-2   **Practice**   Student Edition Pages 556–561

Direct, Inverse, and Joint Variation

Write an equation for each statement. Then solve the equation.

1. Find y when $x = 6$, if y varies directly as x and $y = 8$ when $x = 2$.
$\frac{y}{6} = \frac{8}{2}$; 24

2. Find y when $x = 1.5$, if y varies directly as x and $y = -16$ when $x = 6$.
$\frac{y}{1.5} = \frac{-16}{6}$; -4

3. Find y when $x = 4$, if y varies directly as x and $y = 7$ when $x = 1.5$.
$\frac{y}{4} = \frac{7}{1.5}$; $\frac{56}{3}$

4. Find y when $x = 5$, if y varies directly as x and $y = 5$ when $x = 3.5$.
$\frac{y}{5} = \frac{5}{3.5}$; $\frac{50}{7}$

5. Find x when $y = 3$, if y varies inversely as x and $x = 4$, when $y = 16$.
$\frac{x}{16} = \frac{4}{3}$; $\frac{64}{3}$

6. Find x when $y = 5$, if y varies inversely as x and $x = 6$ when $y = -18$.
$\frac{x}{-18} = \frac{6}{5}$; -21.6

7. Find y when $x = 2\frac{1}{2}$, if y varies inversely as x and $x = 5$ when $y = 3$.
$\frac{2.5}{3} = \frac{5}{y}$; 6

8. Find y when $x = 10$, if y varies inversely as x and $x = 7.5$ when $y = 6$.
$\frac{10}{6} = \frac{7.5}{y}$; 4.5

9. Find y when $x = 4$ and $z = 15$, if y varies jointly as x and z and $y = 5$ when $z = 8$ and $x = 10$.
$y = \frac{1}{16} \cdot 4 \cdot 15$; $\frac{15}{4}$

10. Find y when $x = 12$ and $z = 2$, if y varies jointly as x and z and $y = 24$ when $z = 2$ and $x = 1$.
$y = 12 \cdot 12 \cdot 2$; 288

11. Find y when $x = 6$ and $z = 8$, if y varies jointly as x and z and $y = 60$ when $x = 3$ and $z = 4$.
$y = 5 \cdot 6 \cdot 8$; 240

12. Find y when $x = 4$ and $z = -1$, if y varies jointly as x and z and $y = 12$ when $x = -2$ and $z = 3$.
$y = -2 \cdot 4 \cdot -1$; 8

Classroom Vignette

"To find the constant of variation, I have students use a computer-generated program such as the Geometer Sketchpad to study topics such as the area of a triangle. The students never forget what they can see."

Noreen Allen
George Washington High School
Charleston, West Virginia

34a. 0.02, $C = \dfrac{0.02P_1P_2}{d^2}$

34. **Telecommunications** It has been found that the average number of daily phone calls C between two cities is directly proportional to the product of the populations P_1 and P_2 of two cities and inversely proportional to the square of the distance d between the cities. That is, $C = \dfrac{kP_1P_2}{d^2}$.

a. The distance between San Antonio and New Orleans is about 575 miles. If the average number of daily phone calls between the cities is 29,000, find the value of k and write the equation of variation.

City	Population (1992)
Chicago	2,768,000
Memphis	610,000
New Orleans	490,000
San Antonio	966,000

b. Memphis is about 399 miles from New Orleans. Find the average number of daily phone calls between them. **37,550 calls**

c. The average number of daily phone calls between Memphis and Chicago is 112,451. Find the distance between Memphis and Chicago. **548 miles**

d. Could you use this formula to find the populations or the average number of phone calls between two adjoining cities? Explain. **No, $d \neq 0$.**

35. **Energy Conservation** Many homes lose a significant amount of heat through their windows. The heat loss of a glass window varies jointly as the area of the window and the difference between the outside and inside temperatures. A window 3 feet wide by 5 feet long loses 500 BTU per hour when the temperature outside is $10°$ cooler than the temperature inside. Find the heat loss through the same window if the difference between the outside and inside temperatures is $30°$. **1500 BTU/h**

Mixed Review

36. Graph $f(x) = \dfrac{x}{x+1}$. (Lesson 9–1) **See margin.**

37. Find $g[h(x)]$ and $h[g(x)]$ for $g(x) = -x$ and $h(x) = -x$. (Lesson 8–7) **x, x**

38. Use synthetic substitution to find $f(2)$ and $f(-1)$ for $f(x) = 3x^4 + 8x^2 - 1$. (Lesson 8–2) **79, 10**

39. $\dfrac{(x+2)^2}{16} + \dfrac{(y-3)^2}{36} = 1$

39. Write an equation for the ellipse described below. (Lesson 7–4) The major axis is 12 units long and parallel to the y-axis. The minor axis is 8 units long and the center is at $(-2, 3)$.

40. Solve $d^2 \geq 3d + 28$. (Lesson 6–7) **$\{d \mid d \leq -4 \text{ or } d \geq 7\}$**

41. **Travel** The cruise ship *The Silver Dollar* has been rented to take 100 passengers to the Green Mountain Resort. The fare is $5 per person. The owner of the cruise ship has agreed to reduce the fare by 2¢ for each person taking the cruise for every passenger over 100 passengers in the group. How many passengers will produce a maximum profit for the owner? (Lesson 6–3) **175 passengers**

42. **Manufacturing** A manufacturer of boat motors has specifications for parts with given tolerance limits. If a part is to be 3.2 inches wide with a tolerance of 0.01 inches, this means that it must be at least 3.19 inches wide or at most 3.21 inches wide. This tolerance limit can be expressed by the absolute value inequality $|w - 3.2| \leq 0.01$, where w represents the width of the part. (Lesson 1–7) **b. 0.03 cm**

a. Find the maximum and minimum acceptable dimensions of a part that is supposed to be 7.32 centimeters long with a tolerance of 0.002 centimeter. **max, 7.322 cm; min, 7.318 cm**

b. Find the tolerance if a part must satisfy the inequality $5.18 \leq w \leq 5.24$.

Lesson 9–2 Direct, Inverse, and Joint Variation **561**

Extension

Reasoning A gas is kept at a constant temperature. As the volume occupied by the gas decreases from 60 ft³ to 40 ft³, the pressure increases by 2.5 pounds. If the pressure on the gas increases by another 2.5 pounds, what is the volume now occupied by the gas? **30 ft³**

Tech Prep

Telecommunications Technician Students who are interested in telecommunications may wish to do further research on the information provided in Exercise 34 and explore the potential growth of this career. For more information on tech prep, see the *Teacher's Handbook*.

4 ASSESS

Closing Activity

Writing Have each student write an application for each of direct, inverse, and joint variations.

Chapter 9, Quiz A (Lessons 9-1 and 9-2), is available in the *Assessment and Evaluation Masters,* p. 240.

Additional Answer

36.

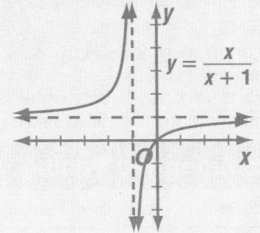

$y = \dfrac{x}{x+1}$

Enrichment Masters, p. 65

NAME_____ DATE_____

Student Edition Pages 558–56

9-2 Enrichment

Reading Algebra

In mathematics, the term *group* has a special meaning. The following numbered sentences discuss the idea of group and one interesting example of a group.

01 To be a group, a set of elements and a binary operation must satisfy four conditions: the set must be closed under the operation, the operation must be associative, there must be an identity element, and every element must have an inverse.

02 The following six functions form a group under the operation of composition of functions: $f_1(x) = x$, $f_2(x) = \dfrac{1}{x}$, $f_3(x) = 1 - x$, $f_4(x) = \dfrac{(x-1)}{x}$, $f_5(x) = \dfrac{x}{(x-1)}$, and $f_6(x) = \dfrac{1}{(1-x)}$.

03 This group is an example of a noncommutative group. For example, $f_3 \circ f_2 = f_4$, but $f_2 \circ f_3 = f_6$.

04 Some experimentation with this group will show that the identity element is f_1.

05 Every element is its own inverse except for f_4 and f_6, each of which is the inverse of the other.

Use the paragraph to answer these questions.

1. Explain what it means to say that a set is *closed* under an operation. Is the set of positive integers closed under subtraction? Performing the operation on any two elements of the set results in an element of the same set. No, 3 and 4 are positive integers but $3 - 4$ is not.

2. Subtraction is a noncommutative operation for the set of integers. Write an informal definition of noncommutative. The order in which the elements are used with the operation can affect the result.

3. For the set of integers, what is the identity element for the operation of multiplication? Justify your answer. 1, because, for every integer a, $a \cdot 1 = a$ and $1 \cdot a = a$.

4. Explain how the following statement relates to sentence 05: $(f_4 \cdot f_6)(x) = f_6[f_4(x)] = f_6\left(\dfrac{x-1}{x}\right) = \dfrac{1}{1 - \frac{(x-1)}{x}} = x = f_1(x)$.

It shows that f_4 is the inverse of f_6.

Multiplying and Dividing Rational Expressions

NCTM Standards: 1–5, 7

Instructional Resources

- Study Guide Master 9-3
- Practice Master 9-3
- Enrichment Master 9-3
- Assessment and Evaluation Masters, pp. 239–240
- Real-World Applications, 25

 Transparency 9-3A contains the 5-Minute Check for this lesson; **Transparency 9-3B** contains a teaching aid for this lesson.

Recommended Pacing

Standard Pacing	Day 5 of 10
Honors Pacing	Day 4 of 9
Block Scheduling*	Day 2 of 4 (along with Lesson 9-2)

 *For more information on pacing and possible lesson plans, refer to the *Block Scheduling Booklet*.

1 FOCUS

5-Minute Check
(over Lesson 9-2)

State whether each equation represents a *direct, inverse,* or *joint* variation.

1. $\frac{n_1}{x_2} = \frac{n_2}{x_1}$ inverse

2. $\frac{a_1}{c_1} = \frac{a_2}{c_2}$ direct

3. $V = \pi r^2 h$ joint

4. If y varies directly as x and $x = 3$ when $y = -2$, find x when $y = 7$. −10.5

5. If y varies inversely as x and $y = 16$ when $x = 2$, find y when $x = 6$. $5\frac{1}{3}$

Motivating the Lesson

Situational Problem Show students a sticker that gives the city and highway mileage rates for a new car. A consumer report comparing mileage ratings for different cars could also be used. Ask students how they think the rates were determined and why they differ.

562 *Chapter 9*

What YOU'LL LEARN

- To simplify rational expressions, and
- to simplify complex fractions.

Why IT'S IMPORTANT

You can use rational expressions to solve problems involving geometry.

LOOK BACK

You can refer to Lesson 5-4 to review finding the GCF.

 INTEGRATION

Geometry

The bases of two parallelograms are also the adjacent sides of rectangle N. Parallelogram L has an area of $2x^2 - 13x + 20$ square meters and a height of $3x + 1$ meters. Parallelogram M has an area of $3x^2 + 10x + 3$ square meters and a height of $x - 4$ meters. Find the area of rectangle N. *This problem will be solved in Example 5.*

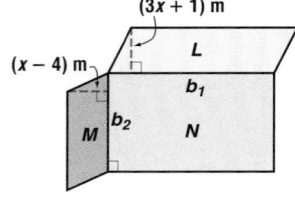

Because variables in algebra represent real numbers, operations with rational numbers and **rational algebraic expressions** are very similar. A rational number can be expressed as the quotient of two integers. A rational algebraic expression can be expressed as the quotient of two polynomials. In either case, the denominator can never be 0.

rational numbers		*rational algebraic expressions*	
$\frac{3}{7}$, $\frac{175}{100}$, $\frac{-7}{11}$		$\frac{7}{2x}$, $\frac{x+3}{x-5}$, $\frac{x+5}{x^2+4x-5}$	

To write a fraction in simplest form, you divide both the numerator and denominator by their greatest common factor (GCF). To simplify a rational algebraic expression, you use similar properties.

Example 1
a. **Simplify** $\frac{2x(x+1)}{(x+1)(x^2-4)}$.

b. **Under what conditions is this expression undefined?**

a. Look for common factors.

$$\frac{2x(x+1)}{(x+1)(x^2-4)} = \frac{2x}{x^2-4} \cdot \frac{\overset{1}{\cancel{x+1}}}{\underset{1}{\cancel{x+1}}}$$ *How is this similar to simplifying $\frac{4}{6}$?*

$$= \frac{2x}{x^2-4}$$ $\frac{x+1}{x+1} = 1$

TECHNOLOGY *Tips*

Verify this result by using a graphing calculator to graph the related equation. Press ZOOM 4 to see the point of discontinuity.

b. To find when the expression is undefined, completely factor the original denominator.

$$\frac{2x(x+1)}{(x+1)(x^2-4)} = \frac{2x(x+1)}{(x+1)(x-2)(x+2)}$$

The values that would make the denominator equal 0 are -1, 2, and -2. So, the expression is undefined when $x = -1$, $x = 2$, or $x = -2$.

Sometimes you can factor out -1 in the numerator or denominator to help simplify rational expressions.

Example **Simplify** $\frac{3a^3 - a^4}{2a^3 - 6a^2}$.

$$\frac{3a^3 - a^4}{2a^3 - 6a^2} = \frac{a^3(3 - a)}{2a^2(a - 3)}$$ *Factor the numerator and the denominator.*

$$= \frac{\overset{a}{\cancel{a^3}}(-1)(a \cancel{- 3})}{2a^2(a \cancel{- 3})}$$ $3 - a = -1(-3 + a)$ or $-1(a - 3)$

$$= \frac{(-1)a}{2}$$

$$= -\frac{a}{2}$$ *For what values is the original expression undefined?*

Remember that to multiply two fractions, you first multiply the numerators and then multiply the denominators. To divide two fractions, you multiply by the multiplicative inverse, or reciprocal, of the divisor.

Multiplication	**Division**
$\frac{3}{4} \cdot \frac{2}{15} = \frac{\overset{1}{\cancel{3}} \cdot \overset{1}{\cancel{2}}}{2 \cdot 2 \cdot 3 \cdot 5}$	$\frac{3}{5} \div \frac{9}{10} = \frac{3}{5} \cdot \frac{10}{9}$
$= \frac{1}{2 \cdot 5}$ or $\frac{1}{10}$	$= \frac{\overset{1}{\cancel{3}} \cdot 2 \cdot \overset{1}{\cancel{5}}}{\cancel{5} \cdot 3 \cdot \cancel{3}}$ or $\frac{2}{3}$

The same procedures are used for multiplying and dividing rational expressions. These can be generalized by the following rules.

Multiplying and Dividing Rational Expressions	For all rational expressions $\frac{a}{b}$ and $\frac{c}{d}$, $\frac{a}{b} \cdot \frac{c}{d} = \frac{ac}{bd}$, if $b \neq 0$ and $d \neq 0$, and $\frac{a}{b} \div \frac{c}{d} = \frac{a}{b} \cdot \frac{d}{c} = \frac{ad}{bc}$, if $b \neq 0$, $c \neq 0$, and $d \neq 0$.

The following examples show how these rules are used with rational expressions.

Example **Simplify each expression.**

a. $\frac{2a^2}{5b^2c} \cdot \frac{3bc^2}{8a^3}$

$$\frac{2a^2}{5b^2c} \cdot \frac{3bc^2}{8a^3} = \frac{\overset{1}{\cancel{2}} \cdot \overset{1}{\cancel{a}} \cdot \overset{1}{\cancel{a}} \cdot 3 \cdot \overset{1}{\cancel{b}} \cdot \overset{1}{\cancel{c}} \cdot c}{5 \cdot b \cdot \underset{1}{\cancel{b}} \cdot \underset{1}{\cancel{c}} \cdot \underset{4}{8} \cdot \underset{1}{\cancel{a}} \cdot \underset{1}{\cancel{a}} \cdot a}$$

$$= \frac{3 \cdot c}{5 \cdot b \cdot 4 \cdot a}$$ or $\frac{3c}{20ab}$

In-Class Examples

For Example 1

Simplify $\frac{2a^2(a^2 + 4)(b - 3)}{8ab^2(a - 2)(a^2 + 4)}$. Under what conditions is the expression undefined?

$\frac{a(b - 3)}{4b^2(a - 2)}$; $a = 0$ or 2, $b = 0$

For Example 2

Simplify $\frac{y^3 - ay^2}{y^2 - ay} \cdot y$

For Example 3
Simplify each expression.

a. $\frac{7a}{9b} \cdot \frac{63b^3}{35a^2}$ $\frac{7b^2}{5a}$

b. $\frac{14c^2d}{9m^3n^2} \div \frac{35cd^3}{24mn}$ $\frac{16c}{15d^2m^2n}$

Teaching Tip You may want to show *why* dividing is the same as multiplying by the multiplicative inverse.

$\frac{a}{b} \div \frac{c}{d}$ can be written as $\frac{\frac{a}{b}}{\frac{c}{d}}$.

Now multiply by 1 in the

form $\frac{\frac{d}{c}}{\frac{d}{c}}$.

$\frac{\frac{a}{b}}{\frac{c}{d}} \cdot \frac{\frac{d}{c}}{\frac{d}{c}} = \frac{\frac{a}{b} \cdot \frac{d}{c}}{1} = \frac{a}{b} \cdot \frac{d}{c}$

Cooperative Learning

Trade-A-Problem You may wish to have students work in cooperative groups of four. Have one student name a rational algebraic expression. Have another student name another expression, using the same variable(s). Have the third student multiply the two expressions, and the fourth student divide them. Discuss procedures and solutions. Rotate and repeat. For more information on the trade-a-problem strategy, see *Cooperative Learning in the Mathematics Classroom,* one of the titles in the Glencoe Mathematics Professional Series, pages 25–26.

In-Class Examples

For Example 4

Find $\frac{y+2}{y^2+5y} \div \frac{y(y-2)}{y^2-25}$.

Write the answer in simplest form.

$\frac{(y+2)(x-5)}{y^2(y-2)}$

For Example 5

A rectangular box has one side with an area of $(2x^2 + 7x - 15)$ square inches. The adjacent side has an area of $(3x^2 + 17x + 10)$ square inches. The height of the box is $(x + 5)$ inches. Find the area of the bottom of the box.

$(6x^2 - 5x - 6)$ in^2

b. $\frac{8x^2y}{15a^2b} \div \frac{2xy^2}{5ab^4}$

$\frac{8x^2y}{15a^2b} \div \frac{2xy^2}{5ab^4} = \frac{8x^2y}{15a^2b} \cdot \frac{5ab^4}{2xy^2}$ *Multiply by the reciprocal of the divisor.*

$= \frac{\overset{4}{\cancel{8}} \cdot \overset{1}{\cancel{5}} \cdot \overset{x}{\cancel{x^2}} \cdot y \cdot \overset{1}{\cancel{a}} \cdot \overset{b^3}{\cancel{b^4}}}{\underset{3}{\cancel{15}} \cdot \underset{1}{\cancel{2}} \cdot \underset{1}{\cancel{x}} \cdot \underset{y}{\cancel{y^2}} \cdot \underset{a}{\cancel{a^2}} \cdot \underset{1}{\cancel{b}}}$ *Factor and divide.*

$= \frac{4b^3x}{3ay}$

You follow these same steps when the rational expressions contain numerators and denominators that are polynomials with two or more terms.

Example **Find** $\frac{x^2+2x-8}{x^2+4x+3} \div \frac{x-2}{3x+3}$. **Write the answer in simplest form.**

$\frac{x^2+2x-8}{x^2+4x+3} \div \frac{x-2}{3x+3} = \frac{x^2+2x-8}{x^2+4x+3} \cdot \frac{3x+3}{x-2}$

$= \frac{(x+4)\overset{1}{\cancel{(x-2)}}}{(x+3)\underset{1}{\cancel{(x+1)}}} \cdot \frac{3\overset{1}{\cancel{(x+1)}}}{\underset{1}{\cancel{(x-2)}}}$

$= \frac{3(x+4)}{(x+3)} \text{ or } \frac{3x+12}{x+3}$

Example  **Refer to the application at the beginning of the lesson. Find the area of rectangle N.**

INTEGRATION

Geometry

The area of a parallelogram is found by using the formula $A = bh$. Since you know the area and height of each parallelogram, you can find the base measures, b_1 and b_2, by dividing the area by the height.

$b_1 = \frac{2x^2 - 13x + 20}{3x+1}$ $b_2 = \frac{3x^2 + 10x + 3}{x-4}$

$= \frac{(x-4)(2x-5)}{(3x+1)}$ $= \frac{(3x+1)(x+3)}{(x-4)}$ *For what values are these expressions undefined?*

The area of the rectangle is found by $A = bh$. In this case, b and h are the measures of the bases of the parallelograms. The area of rectangle N can be found by multiplying the bases b_1 and b_2.

$A = b_1 \cdot b_2$

$= \frac{(x-4)(2x-5)}{(3x+1)} \cdot \frac{(3x+1)(x+3)}{(x-4)}$

$= (2x-5)(x+3)$

$= 2x^2 + x - 15$

The area of rectangle N is $2x^2 + x - 15$ square meters.

Alternative Learning Styles

Visual Multiplication and division of rational functions can be verified using a graphing calculator. If you are multiplying $f(x)$ and $g(x)$, first graph $y = f(x) \cdot g(x)$; then graph the resulting product. If both graphs look the same, the answer is verified.

A **complex fraction** is a rational expression whose numerator and/or denominator contains a rational expression. The expressions below are complex fractions.

$$\frac{\frac{z+4t}{w}}{6z} \qquad \frac{\frac{8}{x}}{\frac{x}{3-y}} \qquad \frac{\frac{1}{x}+3}{\frac{2}{x}+5} \qquad \frac{\frac{x^2-4}{2}}{\frac{2-x}{5}}$$

Remember that a fraction is nothing more than a way to express a division problem. That is, $1 \div 3$ can be expressed as $\frac{1}{3}$. So to simplify any complex fraction, rewrite it as a division expression and use the rules for division.

Example **Simplify** $\dfrac{\frac{5a^2-20}{2a+2}}{\frac{10a-20}{4a}}$.

Rewrite the complex fraction as a division expression.

$$\frac{\frac{5a^2-20}{2a+2}}{\frac{10a-20}{4a}} = \frac{5a^2-20}{2a+2} \div \frac{10a-20}{4a}$$

$$= \frac{5a^2-20}{2a+2} \cdot \frac{4a}{10a-20}$$

$$= \frac{\overset{1}{5}(a+2)\overset{1}{(a-2)}}{\underset{1}{2}(a+1)} \cdot \frac{\overset{1}{\cancel{4}a}}{\underset{1}{\cancel{10}}(a-2)}$$

$$= \frac{a(a+2)}{a+1}$$

CHECK FOR UNDERSTANDING

Communicating Mathematics

Study the lesson. Then complete the following.

1. Suppose the numerator of a rational expression is a polynomial and the denominator of a rational expression is a different polynomial. Will factoring the polynomials necessarily provide a way to simplify the expression? Explain your answer.   See margin.

2. **Explain** under what conditions a rational polynomial expression is not defined.   When the denominator equals 0.

3. **State** the multiplicative inverse of $\frac{9a}{13b}$. $\frac{13b}{9a}$

4. **State** the greatest common factor of $ab - bc$ and $3xy + 4tr$.   1

Guided Practice

Find the GCF of the numerator and denominator for each expression. Then simplify the expression.

5. $\frac{30xy}{12x^2}$ $6x, \frac{5y}{2x}$

6. $\frac{-3xy^4}{21x^2y^2}$ $3xy^2, \frac{-y^2}{7x}$

7. $\frac{c+5}{2c+10}$ $c+5, \frac{1}{2}$

Lesson 9–3 Multiplying and Dividing Rational Expressions   **565**

Teaching Tip Be sure students understand the difference between complex numbers and complex fractions.

In-Class Example

For Example 6

Simplify $\dfrac{\frac{8x^2-72}{5x+10}}{\frac{4x-12}{5x}} \cdot \dfrac{2x(x+3)}{(x+2)}$

Teaching Tip Another way of simplifying the complex fraction in Example 6 is to multiply the numerator and denominator of the complex fraction by the LCM of the denominators of the separate fractions

3 PRACTICE/APPLY

Check for Understanding
Exercises 1–16 are designed to help you assess your students' understanding through reading, writing, speaking, and modeling. You should work through Exercises 1–4 with your students and then monitor their work on Exercises 5–16.

Error Analysis
Students sometimes cancel matching expressions that are not factors.

For example:

$$\frac{2x + \overset{1}{\cancel{5}}}{\underset{3}{\cancel{15}}} = \frac{2x+1}{3}$$

Point out that only *factors* can be cancelled (divided out) and that 5 is not a factor of $2x + 5$.

Additional Answer

1. No. For example,
$$\frac{x^2-4}{2x^2+12x+18} = \frac{(x-2)(x+2)}{2(x+3)(x+3)}.$$
There are no common factors, so the expression is in simplest form.

Reteaching

Using Properties Compare multiplying and dividing rational expressions to multiplying and dividing fractions.

$$\frac{3}{4} \times \frac{5}{6} = \frac{3 \times 5}{4 \times 6}$$

$$= \frac{15}{24} \text{ or } \frac{5}{8}$$

$$\frac{7}{8} \div \frac{7}{12} = \frac{\overset{1}{\cancel{7}}}{\underset{2}{\cancel{8}}} \times \frac{\overset{3}{\cancel{12}}}{\underset{1}{\cancel{7}}}$$

$$= \frac{3}{2} \text{ or } 1\frac{1}{2}$$

Simplify each expression.

8. $\dfrac{m^3}{3n} \div \left(-\dfrac{m^4}{9n^2}\right)$ $-\dfrac{3n}{m}$

9. $\dfrac{3ab}{4ac} \cdot \dfrac{6a^2}{3b^2}$ $\dfrac{3a^2}{2bc}$

10. $-\dfrac{-3}{5a} \div \left(-\dfrac{9}{15ab}\right)$ $-b$

11. $\left(\dfrac{3a^2}{a+2}\right)\left(\dfrac{a+2}{a^2}\right)$ 3

12. $\dfrac{5}{m-3} \div \dfrac{10}{m-3}$ $\dfrac{1}{2}$

13. $\left(\dfrac{4a+4}{3}\right)\left(\dfrac{1}{a+1}\right)$ $\dfrac{4}{3}$

14. $\dfrac{w^2-11w+24}{w^2-18w+80} \cdot \dfrac{w^2-15w+50}{w^2-9w+20}$ $\dfrac{w-3}{w-4}$

15. $\dfrac{\frac{2y}{y^2-4}}{\frac{3}{y^2-4y+4}}$ $\dfrac{2y(y-2)}{3(y+2)}$

16. **Geometry** The area of a triangle can be expressed as $4x^2 - 2x - 6$ square meters. The height of the triangle is $x + 1$ meters. Find the length of the base of the triangle. $(8x - 12)$ meters

EXERCISES

Practice **Simplify each expression.**

A
17. $\dfrac{45xy^3}{20y^7}$ $\dfrac{9x}{4y^4}$
18. $\dfrac{(-3x^2y)^3}{9x^2y^2}$ $-3x^4y$
19. $\dfrac{5x-5}{x^2-1}$ $\dfrac{5}{x+1}$

22. $\dfrac{3h}{(h+1)(h-2)}$

20. $\dfrac{p^3}{2q} \div \dfrac{-p^2}{4q}$ $-2p$
21. $\dfrac{y^2}{x+2} \div \dfrac{y}{x+2}$ y
22. $\dfrac{3h}{h+1}\left(\dfrac{1}{h-2}\right)$

25. $\dfrac{xz}{8y}$

23. $\dfrac{2a^2}{5b^2c} \cdot \dfrac{3bc^2}{8a^2}$ $\dfrac{3c}{20b}$
24. $\dfrac{35}{16x^2} \div \dfrac{21}{4x}$ $\dfrac{5}{12x}$
25. $\dfrac{2x^3y}{z^5} \div \left(-\dfrac{4xy}{z^3}\right)^2$

26. $\dfrac{(ab)^2}{c} \cdot \dfrac{cx^2}{xa^3b}$ $\dfrac{bx}{a}$
27. $\left(\dfrac{2x}{y}\right)^2 \cdot \dfrac{5}{6x}$ $\dfrac{10x}{3y^2}$
28. $\dfrac{t+3}{t-1} \cdot \dfrac{t-1}{t}$ $\dfrac{t+3}{t}$

31. $\dfrac{4}{15xyz^2}$

29. $\dfrac{(xy)}{a^3} \div \dfrac{x^2y^3}{(ab)^3}$ $\dfrac{b^3}{xy^2}$
30. $\dfrac{4a^3b}{7c^2d^3} \cdot \dfrac{21c^3d}{16abc^2}$ $\dfrac{3a^2}{4cd^2}$
31. $\dfrac{9x^2y^3}{(5xyz)^2} \div \dfrac{(3xy)^3}{20x^2y}$

B
32. $\dfrac{3x+6}{7x-7} \cdot \dfrac{14x-14}{5x+10}$ $\dfrac{6}{5}$
33. $\dfrac{3x^2-3}{2x^2+8x+6} \div \dfrac{5x^2-10x+5}{4x+12}$ $\dfrac{6}{5(x-1)}$

34. $\dfrac{4x^2-4}{9(x+1)^2} \cdot \dfrac{3x+3}{2x-2}$ $\dfrac{2}{3}$
35. $\dfrac{12x+6}{21x^2-21} \div \dfrac{6x^2+9x+3}{7x^3-7x^2}$ $\dfrac{2x^2}{3(x+1)^2}$

37. $\dfrac{5(x-3)}{2(x+1)}$

36. $\dfrac{12x^2+6x-6}{4(x+1)^2} \div \dfrac{6x-3}{2x+10}$ $\dfrac{x+5}{x+1}$
37. $\dfrac{5x^2+10x-75}{4x^2-24x-28} \cdot \dfrac{2x^2-10x-28}{x^2+7x+10}$

38. $\dfrac{2x+y}{2x-y}$

39. $\dfrac{3(m+n)}{m^2+n^2}$

40. $y+1$

C
38. $\dfrac{\frac{x+y}{2x-y}}{\frac{x+y}{2x+y}}$
39. $\dfrac{\frac{m+n}{5}}{\frac{m^2+n^2}{15}}$
40. $\dfrac{\frac{6y^2-6}{8y^2+8y}}{\frac{3y-3}{4y^2+4y}}$
41. $\dfrac{\frac{5x^2-5x-30}{45-15x}}{\frac{6+x-x^2}{4x-12}}$ $\dfrac{4}{3}$

Critical Thinking
42. Simplify $\dfrac{x^{-1}+y^{-1}}{x^{-1}-y^{-1}} \cdot \dfrac{y+x}{y-x}$

Assignment Guide
Core: 17–41 odd, 42, 43, 45–52
Enriched: 18–40 even, 42–52
All: Self Test, 1–10

For **Extra Practice,** see p. 897.

The red A, B, and C flags, printed only in the Teacher's Wraparound Edition, indicate the level of difficulty of the exercises.

Study Guide Masters, p. 66

 9-3

NAME_____ DATE_____
Student Edition Pages 562–568
Study Guide

Multiplying and Dividing Rational Expressions

To simplify a rational algebraic expression, divide both numerator and denominator by their GCF. Multiply rational expressions by multiplying the numerators and denominators. Dividing by a rational expression is the same as multiplying by its multiplicative inverse.

Multiplying Rational Expressions	Dividing Rational Expressions
For all rational expressions, $\frac{a}{b}$ and $\frac{c}{d}$, $b \neq 0$, and $d \neq 0$, $\frac{a}{b} \cdot \frac{c}{d} = \frac{ac}{bd}$	For all rational expressions, $\frac{a}{b}$ and $\frac{c}{d}$, $b \neq 0$, $c \neq 0$, and $d \neq 0$, $\frac{a}{b} \div \frac{c}{d} = \frac{a}{b} \cdot \frac{d}{c}$

A complex rational expression, also called a **complex fraction**, is an expression whose numerator or denominator, or both, contain rational expressions. To simplify a complex fraction, treat it as a division problem. Remember, all rational expressions must be reduced as much as possible.

Examples: Simplify each expression.

$\dfrac{x^2-9}{x^2+x-12} \cdot \dfrac{x+2}{x+3} = \dfrac{(x+3)(x-3)}{(x+4)(x-3)} \cdot \dfrac{x+2}{x+3}$
$= \dfrac{(x+3)(x-3)(x+2)}{(x+4)(x-3)(x+3)}$
$= \dfrac{x+2}{x+4}$

Simplify each expression.

1. $\dfrac{c(c-3)}{c^2-25} \cdot \dfrac{c^2+4c-5}{c^2-4c+3}$ $\dfrac{c}{c-5}$

2. $\dfrac{(m-3)^2}{m^2-6m+9} \cdot \dfrac{m^2-9m}{m^3-9}$ m

3. $\dfrac{x^2y^2z^3}{x^2-4} \div \dfrac{x^2y^4z}{x+2}$ $\dfrac{z^2}{(x-2)x^2y^2}$

4. $\dfrac{1}{x+3} \div \dfrac{2x}{(x+2)(x+3)}$ $\dfrac{x+2}{2x}$

5. $\dfrac{c^2+3c^2}{(c+5)^2} \cdot \dfrac{c^2-25}{c^2}$ $\dfrac{(c+3)(c-5)}{c+5}$

6. $\dfrac{\frac{x^2-4}{x+3}}{\frac{x^2-4x+4}{x^2+3x}}$ $\dfrac{x(x+2)}{x-2}$

7. $\dfrac{\frac{b^2-100}{b^2}}{\frac{3b^2-31b+10}{2b}}$ $\dfrac{2b+20}{b^2(3b-1)}$

8. $\dfrac{\frac{2x^2+9x+9}{x+1}}{\frac{10x^2+19x+6}{5x^2+7x+2}}$ $x+3$

9. $\dfrac{\frac{x^2y^2z}{a^3b^2}}{\frac{a^2b^3y}{b^2}}$ $\dfrac{xyz}{a^5}$

Applications and Problem Solving

43. Geometry The bases of two parallelograms are also the adjacent sides of a rectangle C. Parallelogram A has an area of $12x^2 + 2x - 2$ square feet and height of $2x - 5$ feet. Parallelogram B has an area of $2x^2 - 3x - 5$ square feet and height of $3x - 1$ feet. Find the area of rectangle C.   **$4x^2 + 6x + 2$ square feet**

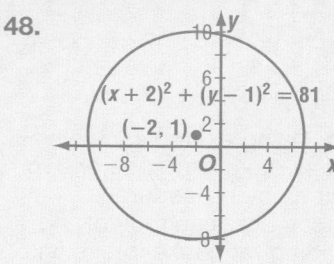

(2x − 5) ft

(3x − 1) ft

A

B b_2 b_1 C

44. 5, 12, 13 inches

44. Geometry The lengths of the sides of a right triangle can be expressed as $x + 2$ in., $x + 9$ in., and $x + 10$ in. Find the lengths of the sides.

Mixed Review

45. $21\frac{1}{3}$ m^3

45. Chemistry Boyle's Law states that the volume of a gas V varies inversely with applied pressure P. This is shown by the formula $P_1V_1 = P_2V_2$. Suppose a helium-filled balloon has a volume of 16 m^3 at sea level. The pressure at sea level is 1 atmosphere. The balloon rises to a point in the air where the pressure is 0.75 atmosphere. What is its volume?   (Lesson 9–2)

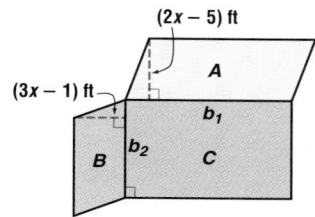

46. Solve $x^4 + 5x^3 + 6x^2 = 0$.   (Lesson 8–6)   **0, 0, −3, −2**

47. Find $f(x + h)$ for $f(x) = x^2 - \frac{1}{2}x$.
(Lesson 8–1) $x^2 + 2xh + h^2 - \frac{1}{2}x - \frac{1}{2}h$

48. (−2, 1), 9; See margin for graph.

48. Find the coordinates of the center and the radius of the circle whose equation is $(x + 2)^2 + (y - 1)^2 = 81$. Then draw the graph.   (Lesson 7–3)

49. Statistics Corporate Car Leasing leases cars to companies for use by their employees. The miles per gallon ratios for the cars leased to three of their clients are listed below.   (Lesson 6–8)

Boxes to Go: 22, 14, 33, 11, 25, 11, 22, 14, 36, 35, 28, 20, 36, 15, 21, 12, 22, 10

Fitright Shoes: 32, 16, 22, 24, 23, 13, 23, 31, 15, 21, 24, 27, 30, 21, 12, 24

TLC, Ltd.:   23, 28, 16, 30, 12, 22, 11, 33, 25, 28, 21, 25, 16, 30, 12, 29, 18, 24, 13, 25

a. Find the standard deviation for the Boxes to Go data.   **8.8**
b. Find the standard deviation for the Fitright Shoes data.   **5.9**
c. Find the standard deviation for the TLC, Ltd. data.   **6.7**
d. Which of the companies had the least variation?   **Fitright Shoes**

50. City Planning In the Winston Woods Park, a rectangular playground was planned that was to be 30 meters long by 20 meters wide. When the neighborhood association received a government grant for the playground, they decided to double the area of the playground by adding strips of the same width to one side and one end of the playground.   (Lesson 6–2)

a. How wide will the strips have to be?   **10 m**
b. What are the new dimensions of the playground?   **40 m by 30 m**

Extension

Problem Solving

Simplify $\dfrac{\dfrac{9x^2 - 12x + 4}{6x^2 - 13x + 6}}{\dfrac{6x^2 + 13x + 6}{4x^2 - 9}} \div \dfrac{\dfrac{9x^2 - 4}{6x^2 - 5x - 6}}{\dfrac{6x^2 + 5x - 6}{4x^2 - 12x + 9}}$.

$\dfrac{(3x - 2)(2x + 3)}{(2x - 3)(3x + 2)} = \dfrac{6x^2 + 5x - 6}{6x^2 - 5x - 6}$

Additional Answer

48.

$(x + 2)^2 + (y - 1)^2 = 81$
$(-2, 1)$

Practice Masters, p. 66

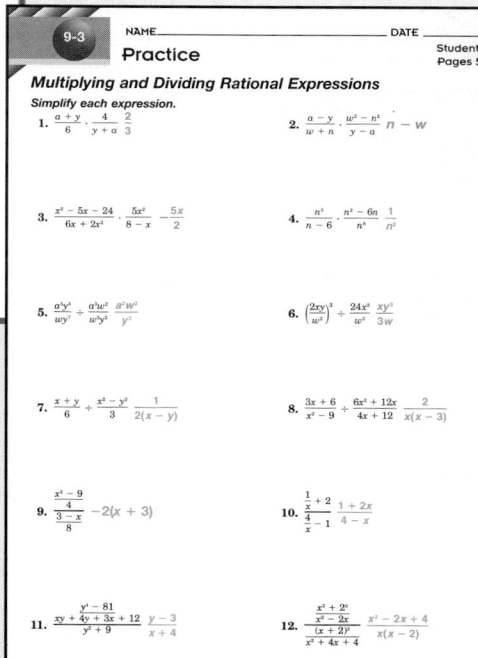

9-3   NAME_____ DATE_____
Practice   Student Edition
                            Pages 562–568

Multiplying and Dividing Rational Expressions
Simplify each expression.

1. $\frac{a+y}{6} \cdot \frac{4}{y+a} \cdot \frac{2}{3}$ 2. $\frac{a-y}{w+n} \cdot \frac{w^2 - n^2}{y-a}$ $n - w$

3. $\frac{x^2 - 5x - 24}{6x + 2x^2} \cdot \frac{5x^2}{8-x} \cdot \frac{5x}{2}$ 4. $\frac{n^5}{n-6} \cdot \frac{n^2 - 6n}{n^4}$ $\frac{1}{n^2}$

5. $\frac{a^2y^3}{wy^3} \div \frac{a^3w^2}{w^3y^2} \cdot \frac{a^3w^2}{y^3}$ 6. $\left(\frac{2xy}{w^2}\right)^3 \div \frac{24x^2}{w^3} \cdot \frac{xy^3}{3w}$

7. $\frac{x+y}{6} \div \frac{x^2 - y^2}{3} \cdot \frac{1}{2(x-y)}$ 8. $\frac{3x+6}{x^2-9} \div \frac{6x^2+12x}{4x+12} \cdot \frac{2}{x(x-3)}$

9. $\frac{\frac{x^2-9}{4}}{\frac{3-x}{8}}$ $-2(x+3)$ 10. $\frac{\frac{1}{x}+2}{\frac{4}{x}-1} \cdot \frac{1+2x}{4-x}$

11. $\frac{\frac{y^4-81}{xy+4y+3x+12}}{\frac{y-3}{y^2+9}} \cdot \frac{y-3}{x+4}$ 12. $\frac{\frac{x^3+2^3}{x^3-2x}}{\frac{(x+2)^2}{x^2+4x+4}} \cdot \frac{x^2 - 2x + 4}{x(x-2)}$

Closing Activity

Writing Using examples, have students write a sentence or two explaining any procedural differences between multiplying and dividing rational expressions.

Chapter 9, Quiz B (Lesson 9-3), is available in the *Assessment and Evaluation Masters*, p. 240.

Mid-Chapter Test (Lessons 9-1 through 9-3) is available in the *Assessment and Evaluation Masters*, p. 239.

SELF TEST

The Self Test provides students with a brief review of the concepts and skills in Lessons 9-1 through 9-3. Lesson numbers are given to the right of exercises or instruction lines so students can review concepts not yet mastered.

Enrichment Masters, p. 66

9-3

NAME_____ DATE_____

Enrichment

Student Edition
Pages 565–570

Expansions of Rational Expressions

Many rational expressions can be transformed into a **power series.** A power series is an infinite series of the form $A + Bx + Cx^2 + Dx^3 + \cdots$. The rational expression and the power series normally can be said to have the same values only for certain values of x. For example, the following equation holds only for values of x such that $-1 < x < 1$.

$$\frac{1}{1-x} = 1 + x + x^2 + x^3 + \cdots \text{ for } -1 < x < 1$$

Example: Expand $\frac{2+3x}{1+x+x^2}$ in ascending powers of x.

Assume that the expression equals a series of the form $A + Bx + Cx^2 + Dx^3 + \cdots$. Then multiply both sides of the equation by the denominator $1 + x + x^2$.

$$\frac{2+3x}{1+x+x^2} = A + Bx + Cx^2 + Dx^3 + \cdots$$
$$2 + 3x = (1 + x + x^2)(A + Bx + Cx^2 + Dx^3 + \cdots)$$
$$2 + 3x = A + Bx + Cx^2 + Dx^3 + \cdots$$
$$\qquad\quad + Ax + Bx^2 + Cx^3 + \cdots$$
$$\qquad\qquad\quad + Ax^2 + Bx^3 + \cdots$$
$$2 + 3x = A + (B + A)x + (C + B + A)x^2 + (D + C + B)x^3 + \cdots$$

Now, match the coefficients of the polynomials.

$2 = A$
$3 = B + A$
$0 = C + B + A$
$0 = D + C + B + A$

Finally, solve for A, B, C, and D and write the expansion.

$A = 2, B = 1, C = -3,$ and $D = 0$

Therefore, $\frac{2+3x}{1+x+x^2} = 2 + x - 3x^2 + \cdots$

Expand each rational expression to four terms.

1. $\dfrac{1-x}{1+x+x^2}$

   $1 - 2x + x^2 + x^3 + \cdots$

2. $\dfrac{2}{1-x}$

   $2 + x + x^2 + x^3 + \cdots$

3. $\dfrac{1}{1+x}$

   $1 - x + x^2 - x^3 + \cdots$

---

51. Evaluate the determinant of $\begin{bmatrix} 2 & -1 & -6 \\ 5 & 0 & 3 \\ -3 & 2 & 11 \end{bmatrix}$. (Lesson 4–4) **−8**

52. **Banking** Donna Bowers has a total of $4000 in her savings account and in a certificate of deposit (CD). Her savings account earns 6.5% interest annually. The CD pays 8% if the money is invested for five years. How much does she have in each investment if her interest earnings for the year will be $297.50? (Lesson 3–3) **$2500, CD; $1500, savings**

SELF TEST

State the equations of the vertical and horizontal asymptotes for the rational functions whose graphs are shown below. (Lesson 9–1)

1.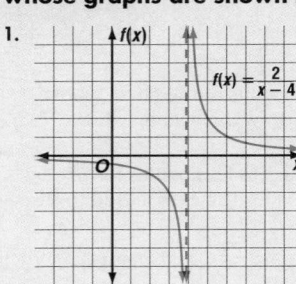

   $f(x) = \dfrac{2}{x-4}$

   $x = 4, \ y = 0$

2.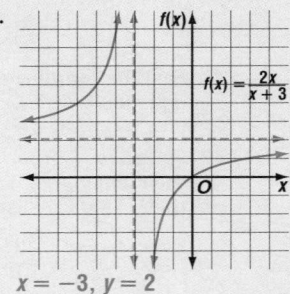

   $f(x) = \dfrac{2x}{x+3}$

   $x = -3, \ y = 2$

Graph each rational function. (Lesson 9–1) **3–4. See margin for graphs.**

3. $f(x) = \dfrac{3}{x+2}$

4. $f(x) = \dfrac{-2}{x^2 - 6x + 9}$

Solve. (Lesson 9–2)

5. If x varies directly as y and $y = \frac{1}{5}$ when $x = 11$, find x when $y = \frac{2}{5}$. **22**

6. If n varies inversely as m and $m = -8$ when $n = -2$, find m when $n = \frac{2}{3}$. **24**

7. **Diamonds** A jewelry store is having a sale on diamonds. A $\frac{1}{2}$-carat diamond is $640, and a $1\frac{1}{2}$-carat diamond is $1920. How much do you think a 2-carat diamond will cost? (Lesson 9–2) **$2560**

Simplify each expression. (Lesson 9–3) **10. $(w + 4)(3w + 4)$**

8. $\dfrac{4xy}{2yz} \cdot \dfrac{11x^2y}{5y^2}$ $\dfrac{22x^3}{5yz}$

9. $\dfrac{48}{6a + 42} \cdot \dfrac{7a + 49}{16}$ $\dfrac{7}{2}$

10. $\dfrac{w^2 + 5w + 4}{6} \div \dfrac{w + 1}{18w + 24}$

568 Chapter 9 Exploring Rational Expressions

Answers for the Self Test

3.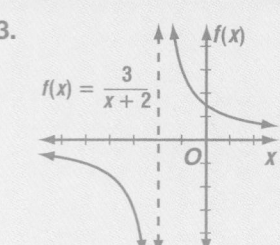

   $f(x) = \dfrac{3}{x + 2}$

4.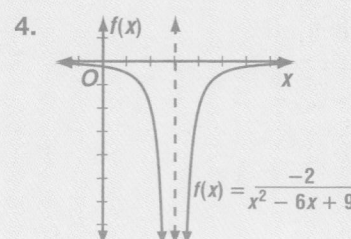

   $f(x) = \dfrac{-2}{x^2 - 6x + 9}$

Adding and Subtracting Rational Expressions

What YOU'LL LEARN

- To find the least common denominator of two or more algebraic expressions, and
- to add and subtract rational expressions.

Why IT'S IMPORTANT

You can use rational expressions to solve problems involving electricity and phgotography.

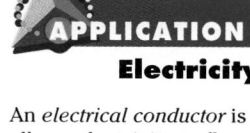

APPLICATION
Electricity

An *electrical conductor* is any piece of material that allows electricity to flow through it. Resistance is measured in units called *ohms*. A resistor is an electrical conductor that is manufactured to have a certain resistance. If two resistors are connected in *parallel*, then the resistance of the combination R is given by the formula $\frac{1}{R} = \frac{1}{R_1} + \frac{1}{R_2}$, where R_1 and R_2 are the resistances of the resistors. What is the effective resistance of a 30-ohm resistor and a 20-ohm resistor that are connected in parallel?

You will solve this problem in Exercise 42.

Parallel
R_1
flow
R_2
$\frac{1}{R} = \frac{1}{R_1} + \frac{1}{R_2}$

This formula involves the addition of two rational expressions. Remember from arithmetic that to add (or subtract) fractions, they must first be written as equivalent fractions with a common denominator. The least common denominator (LCD) is usually used. The LCD is the least common multiple (LCM) of the denominators.

Electricity-Producing Countries (billion kw/hr)

1. U.S., 3079.09
2. Russia, 1068.00
3. Japan, 888.09
4. China, 677.55
5. Germany, 573.75

Specific Case

$$\frac{4}{5} + \frac{3}{7} = \frac{4 \cdot 7}{5 \cdot 7} + \frac{3 \cdot 5}{7 \cdot 5}$$ *Find equivalent fractions that have a common denominator.*

$$= \frac{28}{35} + \frac{15}{35}$$

$$= \frac{43}{35}$$ *Add the numerators.*

General Case

$$\frac{a}{c} + \frac{b}{d} = \frac{a \cdot d}{c \cdot d} + \frac{b \cdot c}{c \cdot d}$$

$$= \frac{ad}{cd} + \frac{bc}{cd}$$

$$= \frac{ad + bc}{cd}$$

You can use this method to add and subtract rational expressions as well.

Example **1** Simplify $\frac{2x}{5ab^3} + \frac{4y}{3a^2b^2}$.

$$\frac{2x}{5ab^3} + \frac{4y}{3a^2b^2} = \frac{2x(3a)}{5ab^3(3a)} + \frac{4y(5b)}{3a^2b^2(5b)}$$ *The LCD is $15a^2b^3$. Find equivalent fractions that have this denominator.*

$$= \frac{6ax}{15a^2b^3} + \frac{20by}{15a^2b^3}$$ *Simplify each numerator and denominator.*

$$= \frac{6ax + 20by}{15a^2b^3}$$ *Add the numerators.*

The amount of electricity produced per capita for each country is as follows.

U.S.	12,000 kw/hr
Russia	6700 kw/hr
Japan	7000 kw/hr
China	560 kw/hr
Germany	7000 kw/hr

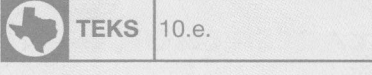

TEKS 10.e.

NCTM Standards: 1–5

Instructional Resources

- Study Guide Master 9-4
- Practice Master 9-4
- Enrichment Master 9-4
- Assessment and Evaluation Masters, p. 241

Transparency 9-4A contains the 5-Minute Check for this lesson; **Transparency 9-4B** contains a teaching aid for this lesson.

Recommended Pacing

Standard Pacing	Day 6 of 10
Honors Pacing	Day 5 of 9
Block Scheduling*	Day 3 of 4 (along with Lesson 9-5)

*For more information on pacing and possible lesson plans, refer to the *Block Scheduling Booklet*.

1 FOCUS

5-Minute Check
(over Lesson 9-3)

Simplify each expression.

1. $\frac{x^2 + 10x + 25}{x^2 + 2x - 15}$ $\frac{x + 5}{x - 3}$

2. $\frac{16ab^3}{25(4 - c)} \cdot \frac{5(c - 4)}{12a^2c^2}$ $\frac{-4b^3}{15ac^2}$

3. $\frac{x^2 - 16}{x^2 + 4x + 4} \cdot \frac{x + 2}{x - 4}$ $\frac{x + 4}{x + 2}$

4. $\frac{\frac{4 - y}{27}}{\frac{8 + y}{3}}$ $\frac{4 - y}{9(8 + y)}$

Motivating the Lesson

Situational Problem Show students several related objects. For example, 12 coins, consisting of 6 pennies, 4 dimes, and 2 nickels may be used. Ask questions about the objects. Sample: What fraction of the coins is made up of (a) dimes? $\frac{1}{3}$ (b) pennies? $\frac{1}{2}$ If you remove all the pennies and all the dimes, what fraction of the group have you removed altogether? $\frac{10}{12}$ or $\frac{5}{6}$

Teaching Tip Emphasize that students can use any common denominator, but the LCD requires the least simplification of the solution.

In-Class Examples

For Example 1

Simplify $\dfrac{9}{10a} + \dfrac{4a}{5b}$. $\dfrac{9b + 8a^2}{10ab}$

For Example 2

Simplify $\dfrac{1}{4a^2 - 4a + 1} + \dfrac{1 - a}{1 - 2a}$.

$\dfrac{2a^2 - 3a + 1}{(2a - 1)^2}$

For Example 3

Simplify $\dfrac{x + 2}{x - 1} - \dfrac{x - 3}{x + 1}$.

$\dfrac{7x - 1}{(x + 1)(x - 1)}$

Teaching Tip Be sure students understand that when both numerator and denominator are multiplied by the same number, the rational expression does not change in value, just in form.

Sometimes the common denominator is not easily recognized, especially when working with algebraic rational expressions. Just as in arithmetic, the LCD for two algebraic expressions must contain each factor of each denominator raised to the highest power that occurs in either denominator. You can find the LCD of more complicated fractions by factoring first, as in Example 2.

Example 2  Simplify $\dfrac{x}{x^2 + 5x + 6} - \dfrac{2}{x^2 + 4x + 4}$.

$$\dfrac{x}{x^2 + 5x + 6} - \dfrac{2}{x^2 + 4x + 4} = \dfrac{x}{(x + 2)(x + 3)} - \dfrac{2}{(x + 2)(x + 2)}$$

Factor the denominators. The LCD is $(x + 2)^2 (x + 3)$.

$$= \dfrac{x(x + 2)}{(x + 2)(x + 3)(x + 2)} - \dfrac{2(x + 3)}{(x + 2)(x + 2)(x + 3)}$$

$$= \dfrac{x^2 + 2x - 2x - 6}{(x + 2)^2(x + 3)}$$

$$= \dfrac{x^2 - 6}{(x + 2)^2(x + 3)}$$

CAREER CHOICES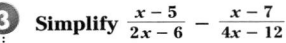

An **electrician** installs and maintains electrical systems for both residential and commercial customers. Electricians complete a 4-year apprenticeship program. The study of mathematics, science, mechanical drawing, and electronics is very helpful.

For more information, contact:
National Electrical
   Contractors Associations
   (NECA)
3 Bethesda Metro Center, #1100
Bethesda, MD 20814

In Example 2, you saw that the numerator was expressed as a binomial but the denominator was left as a product of factors. When you simplify the numerator, you sometimes discover that the polynomial contains a factor common to the denominator. Thus the rational expression can be further simplified.

Example 3 Simplify $\dfrac{x - 5}{2x - 6} - \dfrac{x - 7}{4x - 12}$.

$$\dfrac{x - 5}{2x - 6} - \dfrac{x - 7}{4x - 12} = \dfrac{x - 5}{2(x - 3)} - \dfrac{x - 7}{4(x - 3)}$$

Factor the denominators.

$$= \dfrac{(2)(x - 5) - (x - 7)}{4(x - 3)}$$

Since 2 is a factor of 4, it is not necessary to include an extra factor of 2 in the LCD. The LCD is $4(x - 3)$.

$$= \dfrac{2x - 10 - x + 7}{4(x - 3)}$$

Combine like terms in the numerator.

$$= \dfrac{x - 3}{4(x - 3)} \text{ or } \dfrac{1}{4}$$

Simplify, since $x - 3$ is a factor of the numerator and denominator.

The *Mathematics Exploration Toolkit (MET)* can be used to simplify rational expressions.

CAREER CHOICES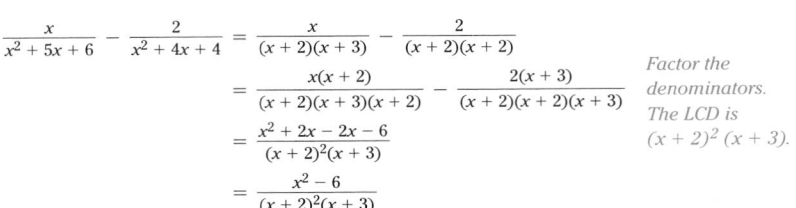

There are also related 2-year degree programs available at many community colleges. Electro-mechanical engineering technology and electronic engineering technology degrees are among these.

The CALC commands listed below are helpful when simplifying rational expressions.

SIMPLIFY (simp)   FACTOR (fac)   REDUCE (red)

Use the SIMPLIFY command to combine rational expressions. Once combined, use the FACTOR command to factor the numerator and denominator. In this form, the REDUCE command can be used to divide out any factors common to the numerator and denominator.

Simplify $\dfrac{y^2 - 4}{y^2} \div \dfrac{y + 2}{y}$.

Enter: $((y^{\wedge}2 - 4)/y^{\wedge}2)/((y + 2)/y)$

$\dfrac{y^2 - 4}{y^2} \div \dfrac{y + 2}{y}$

simp

$\dfrac{y^2 - 4}{y^2} \cdot \dfrac{y}{y + 2}$

fac

$\dfrac{y^3 - 4y}{y^3 + 2y^2}$

fac

$\dfrac{y(y - 2)(y + 2)}{yy(y + 2)}$

red

$\dfrac{y - 2}{y}$

Your Turn   b–c. See margin.
Use CALC commands to simplify each rational expression.

a. $\dfrac{x^3 - 2x^2}{x^4 - x^2} \quad \dfrac{x - 2}{(x + 1)(x - 1)}$

b. $\dfrac{8}{2y - 16} - \dfrac{y}{8 - y}$

c. $\dfrac{2y^2 - y - 1}{y^2 - 1} \cdot \dfrac{y + 1}{2y^2 + y}$

d. $\dfrac{2a}{3a - 15} + \dfrac{-16a + 20}{3a^2 - 12a - 15} \quad \dfrac{2(a - 2)}{3(a + 1)}$

e. $\dfrac{x}{x - 1} - \dfrac{x - 1}{x} - \dfrac{1}{x^2 - x} \quad \dfrac{2}{x}$

Sometimes simplifying complex fractions involves adding or subtracting rational expressions. One way to simplify a complex fraction is to simplify the numerator and the denominator separately and then simplify the resulting expressions.

Example **4**   **Simplify** $\dfrac{x + \frac{x}{3}}{x - \frac{x}{6}}$.

$\dfrac{x + \frac{x}{3}}{x - \frac{x}{6}} = \dfrac{\frac{3x}{3} + \frac{x}{3}}{\frac{6x}{6} - \frac{x}{6}}$ *The LCD of the numerator is 3.*
                                           The LCD of the denominator is 6.

$= \dfrac{\frac{4x}{3}}{\frac{5x}{6}}$ *Simplify the numerator and denominator.*

$= \dfrac{4x}{3} \div \dfrac{5x}{6}$ *Write the complex fraction as a division problem.*

$= \dfrac{4x}{3} \cdot \dfrac{6}{5x}$

$= \dfrac{4}{1} \cdot \dfrac{2}{5}$ or $\dfrac{8}{5}$

This Exploration introduces students to a software package that carries out the details of simplifying, factoring, and reducing when working with rational expressions. Some students may think it does all the work for them. In fact, it forces them to think carefully about when and why to apply each process and the goal they are aiming for in trying to solve the problem.

Answers for the Exploration

b. $\dfrac{y + 4}{y - 8}$

c. $\dfrac{1}{y}$

In-Class Example

For Example 4

Simplify $\dfrac{\frac{2x}{y} + 1 - \frac{y}{x}}{\frac{2x}{y} + \frac{y}{x} - 3} \cdot \dfrac{x + y}{x - y}$

Teaching Tip Be sure students realize that the LCD is found in addition and subtraction problems so that parts of equal size can be added or subtracted. This is not needed for multiplication or division. Be sure students understand that they do not find a common denominator to multiply or divide.

In-Class Example

For Example 5
Bill has a camera with a focal length of 15 cm. When the lens is 20 cm from the film, the camera is focused to take a picture of his wife. How far from the lens is his wife? **60 cm**

fabulous

FIRSTS

Types of photographic materials and techniques have grown dramatically. Among these are aerial, satellite, space, underwater, close-up, stereoscopic, infrared, ultraviolet, radiography, and nuclear-track recording.

3 PRACTICE/APPLY

Check for Understanding

Exercises 1–13 are designed to help you assess your students' understanding through reading, writing, speaking, and modeling. You should work through Exercises 1–4 with your students and then monitor their work on Exercises 5–13.

Additional Answer

4. Sample answer: One way to find the LCD is to factor each rational expression. The LCD must contain each factor of each denominator raised to the highest power that occurs in either denominator. It is necessary to find the LCD when adding or subtracting rational expressions.

Example ⑤

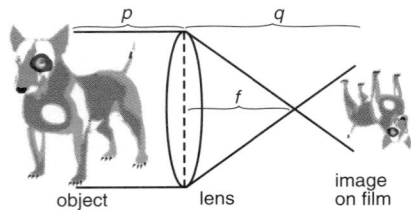

APPLICATION
Photography

To take sharp, clear pictures, a photographer must focus the camera precisely. The distance from the object to the lens p and the distance from the lens to the film q must be accurately calculated to ensure a sharp image. The focal length of the lens is f. These measurements are shown in the diagram below.

object   lens   image on film

The formula that relates these measures is $\frac{1}{p} + \frac{1}{q} = \frac{1}{f}$. Katanya has a camera with a focal length of 10 cm. If the lens is 12 cm from the film, how far should the dog be from the lens so that the picture will be in focus?

$$\frac{1}{p} + \frac{1}{q} = \frac{1}{f}$$

$$\frac{1}{p} = \frac{1}{f} - \frac{1}{q} \qquad \textit{Subtract } \tfrac{1}{q} \textit{ from each side.}$$

$$\frac{1}{p} = \frac{1}{10} - \frac{1}{12} \qquad f = 10 \textit{ and } q = 12$$

$$= \frac{1 \cdot 6}{10 \cdot 6} - \frac{1 \cdot 5}{12 \cdot 5} \qquad \textit{Find equivalent fractions that have a common denominator.}$$

$$= \frac{6}{60} - \frac{5}{60}$$

$$= \frac{1}{60} \qquad \textit{Subtract.}$$

In this case, because $\frac{1}{p} = \frac{1}{60}$, $p = 60$. Therefore, Katanya's dog should be 60 cm from the lens.

fabulous

FIRSTS

James Conway Farley (1854–1910)

James Conway Farley of Richmond, Virginia, was the first African American to gain recognition as a photographer. Of the many photographs he made, only one remains that is attributed to him.

CHECK FOR UNDERSTANDING

Practice — **Study the lesson. Then complete the following.**

1. **Find** each of the following for $x^2 + 5x + 6$ and $x^2 + x - 2$.
   a. the LCM $(x + 2)(x + 3)(x - 1)$ b. the GCF $(x + 2)$

2. **Write** $\frac{3y - 4}{5}$ as the difference of two fractions. $\frac{3y}{5} - \frac{4}{5}$

3. **You Decide**   Christine says that the sum of $\frac{a}{x}$ and $\frac{a}{b}$ is $\frac{a}{x + b}$ because the numerators are the same. André says "No way—it doesn't work that way." Christine asks "Why not?" What should André's answer be?   The denominators have to be the same to add the numerators.

 *MATH JOURNAL*

4. **Assess Yourself**   Explain how to find the LCD of two rational algebraic expressions and explain when it is necessary to find the LCD.   See margin.

572   Chapter 9   Exploring Rational Expressions

Reteaching

Using Problem Solving Compare adding and subtracting rational expressions to adding and subtracting fractions.

$$\frac{1}{15} + \frac{5}{6} = \frac{2}{30} + \frac{25}{30}$$
$$= \frac{27}{30}$$

The LCD is 30.

Alternative Learning Styles

Kinesthetic Perform an experiment similar to the problem in Example 5 with a lit candle and a simple convex lens. Measure the length of the lit candle and project the image through the lens onto a piece of paper. Measure the size of the projected image. Calculate the focal length of the lens.

Guided Practice

Find the LCD for each pair of denominators.

5. $10x^2, 35xy^2$ $70x^2y^2$

6. $x(x-2), x^2-4$ $x(x-2)(x+2)$

Simplify each expression.

7. $\dfrac{6}{ab} + \dfrac{8}{a}$ $\dfrac{6+8b}{ab}$

8. $\dfrac{2}{x^2y} - \dfrac{1}{xy}$ $\dfrac{2-x}{x^2y}$

10. $\dfrac{13}{y-8}$

9. $\dfrac{1}{(x+1)} + 2$ $\dfrac{2x+3}{x+1}$

10. $\dfrac{7}{y-8} - \dfrac{6}{8-y}$

11. $\dfrac{6}{x^2+4x+4} + \dfrac{5}{x+2}$ $\dfrac{5x+16}{(x+2)^2}$

12. $\dfrac{x}{x-y} + \dfrac{y}{y^2-x^2} + \dfrac{2x}{x+y}$ $\dfrac{3x^2-xy-y}{(x-y)(x+y)}$

13. **Photography** Refer to the lens formula in Example 5. Write the expression $\dfrac{1}{p} + \dfrac{1}{q}$ as a single rational expression.

$\dfrac{q+p}{pq}$

EXERCISES

Practice

Find the LCD for each pair of denominators.

14. $12y^2, 6x^2$ $12x^2y^2$

15. $4w-12, 2w-6$ $4w-12$

17. $x^2(x-y)(x+y)$

16. $36x^2y, 20xyz$ $180x^2yz$

17. $x^2-y^2, x^2(x+y)$

18. $(x+2)(x+1)(x-1)$

18. $(x+2)(x+1), x^2-1$

19. $2(x-5)(x+3)$

19. $2x-10, 2x^2-4x-30$

Simplify each expression.

20. $\dfrac{3m+2}{m+n} + \dfrac{4}{2m+2n}$ $\dfrac{3m+4}{m+n}$

21. $5 + \dfrac{x-3}{x+2}$ $\dfrac{6x+7}{x+2}$

29. $\dfrac{3m-10}{(m-5)(m+4)}$

22. $\dfrac{5}{3a} - \dfrac{2}{7a} - \dfrac{1}{2a}$ $\dfrac{37}{42a}$

23. $\dfrac{y}{y-4} - \dfrac{3}{4-y}$ $\dfrac{y+3}{y-4}$

30. $\dfrac{7x+38}{2(x-7)(x+4)}$

24. $\dfrac{m}{m^2-4} + \dfrac{2}{3m+6}$ $\dfrac{5m-4}{3(m+2)(m-2)}$

25. $y-3 + \dfrac{1}{y-3}$ $\dfrac{y^2-6y+10}{y-3}$

31. $\dfrac{-4x^2-5x-2}{(x+1)^2}$

26. $x+1+ \dfrac{1}{x+1}$ $\dfrac{x^2+2x+2}{x+1}$

27. $\dfrac{x}{x+3} - \dfrac{6x}{x^2-9}$ $\dfrac{x(x-9)}{(x+3)(x-3)}$

32. $\dfrac{-4x+15}{(x-4)(x-5)(x-5)}$

28. $\dfrac{5}{x+3} - \dfrac{2}{x-2}$ $\dfrac{3x-16}{(x+3)(x-2)}$

29. $\dfrac{m}{m^2-m-20} + \dfrac{2}{m+4}$

33. $\dfrac{-12x+21xy-4y}{6x^2y}$

30. $\dfrac{5}{x^2-3x-28} + \dfrac{7}{2x-14}$

31. $\dfrac{x}{x^2+2x+1} - \dfrac{x+2}{x+1} - \dfrac{3x}{x+1}$

35. $\dfrac{4x^2-2x-14}{x^2-4}$

32. $\dfrac{1}{x^2-9x+20} - \dfrac{5}{x^2-10x+25}$

33. $-\dfrac{18}{9xy} + \dfrac{7}{2x} - \dfrac{2}{3x^2}$

36. $\dfrac{-8x+20}{(x-4)(x+4)(x-2)}$

34. $\dfrac{m^2+n^2}{m^2-n^2} + \dfrac{m}{n-m} + \dfrac{n}{m+n}$ 0

35. $3 + \dfrac{x}{x+2} - \dfrac{2}{x^2-4}$

37. $\dfrac{2x^2+x-4}{(x-1)(x-2)}$

36. $\dfrac{x-4}{x^2+2x-8} - \dfrac{x+2}{x^2-16}$

37. $\dfrac{x+1}{x-1} + \dfrac{x+2}{x-2} + \dfrac{x}{x^2-3x+2}$

38. $\dfrac{(x+y)\left(\dfrac{1}{x}-\dfrac{1}{y}\right)}{(x-y)\left(\dfrac{1}{x}+\dfrac{1}{y}\right)}$ -1

39. $\dfrac{\dfrac{1}{x+2}+\dfrac{1}{x-5}}{\dfrac{2x^2-x-3}{x^2-3x-10}}$ $\dfrac{1}{x+1}$

Lesson 9-4 Adding and Subtracting Rational Expressions **573**

Assignment Guide

Core: 15–43 odd, 44–51
Enriched: 14–40 even, 41–51

For **Extra Practice,** see p. 898.

The red A, B, and C flags, printed only in the Teacher's Wraparound Edition, indicate the level of difficulty of the exercises.

Study Guide Masters, p. 67

Using the Programming Exercises The program given in Exercise 40 is for use with a TI-82 graphing calculator. For other programmable calculators, have students consult their owner's manual for commands similar to those presented here.

4 ASSESS

Closing Activity

Speaking Have students verbalize how to find the LCD of two algebraic expressions.

Chapter 9, Quiz C (Lesson 9-4), is available in the *Assessment and Evaluation Masters*, p. 241.

Additional Answer

43a.

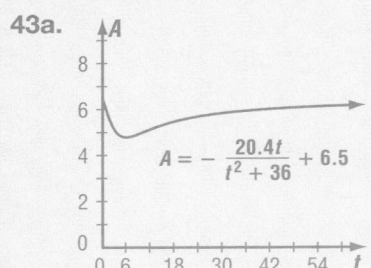

$$A = -\frac{20.4t}{t^2 + 36} + 6.5$$

Practice Masters, p. 67

9-4

NAME_____ DATE _____

Student Edition
Pages 569–575

Practice

Adding and Subtracting Rational Expressions

Simplify each expression.

1. $\frac{5}{6ab} - \frac{7}{8a}$

$\frac{20 - 21b}{24ab}$

2. $2x - 5 - \frac{x - 8}{x + 4}$

$\frac{2(x + 3)(x - 2)}{x + 4}$

3. $\frac{4}{a - 3} + \frac{9}{a - 5}$

$\frac{13a - 47}{(a - 3)(a - 5)}$

4. $\frac{16}{x^2 - 16} + \frac{2}{x + 4}$

$\frac{2}{x - 4}$

5. $\frac{5}{2x - 12} - \frac{20}{x^2 - 4x - 12}$

$\frac{5}{2(x + 2)}$

6. $\frac{2 - 5m}{m - 9} + \frac{4m - 5}{9 - m}$

$\frac{7 - 9m}{m - 9}$

7. $\frac{2p - 3}{p^2 - 5p + 6} - \frac{5}{p^2 - 9}$

$\frac{2p^2 - 2p + 1}{(p - 2)(p + 3)(p - 3)}$

8. $\frac{1}{5n} - \frac{3}{4} + \frac{7}{10n}$

$\frac{3(6 - 5n)}{20n}$

9. $\frac{\frac{r + 6}{r} + \frac{1}{r + 2}}{\frac{r^2 + 4r + 3}{r^2 + r}}$

$\frac{r + 4}{r + 2}$

10. $\frac{\frac{n + 5}{n + 9} - \frac{12}{n + 1}}{\frac{n + 9}{n + 1} - \frac{5}{n}}$

$\frac{n(n + 7)}{n + 5}$

11. $\frac{\frac{2}{x - y} + \frac{1}{x + y}}{\frac{1}{x - y}}$

$\frac{3x + y}{x + y}$

12. $\frac{x - \frac{5x}{x + 2}}{x - 3}$

$\frac{x^2}{x + 2}$

Programming

40. The graphing calculator program at the right computes the GCF and LCM for a pair of positive integers.

Use the program to find the GCF and LCM for each pair of integers.

a. 41, 3   1; 123
b. 1078, 1547   7; 238,238
c. 199, 24   1; 4776
d. 187, 221   17; 2431
e. 182, 1690   26; 11,830
f. 766, 424   2; 162,392

```
PROGRAM: GCFLCM
:Input "INTEGER" , A
:Input "INTEGER" , B
:A→E
:B→F
:Lbl R
:If A=B
:Goto 5
:If A<B
:Goto 4
:A-B→A
:Goto R
:Lbl 4
:B-A→B
:Goto R
:Lbl 5
:Disp "GCF IS" , A
:Disp "LCM IS" , E*F / A
```

Critical Thinking

41. Show that the product of two numbers equals the product of their LCM and GCF.   Sample answer: 2, 4; LCM = 4, GCF = 2; 4 × 2 = 8

Applications and Problem Solving

42. **Electricity** Refer to the application at the beginning of the lesson. Use the formula $\frac{1}{R} = \frac{1}{R_1} + \frac{1}{R_2}$ to find the effective resistance of a 30-ohm resistor and a 20-ohm resistor that are connected in parallel.   12 ohms

43. **Biology** After a person eats something that contains sugar, the pH or acid level *A* of their mouth can be determined by the formula $A = -\frac{20.4t}{t^2 + 36} + 6.5$, where *t* is the number of minutes that have elapsed since the food was eaten.

43a. See margin.

a. Sketch a graph of the equation.
b. Estimate the acid level after 30 minutes.   5.8

43c. It quickly drops below normal and then slowly rises back to normal.

c. If normal pH is 6.5, use the graph to describe what happens to the pH level after the first hour.
d. As the pH level decreases, the acidity level increases. After eating sugar, when is the acidity level the highest?   after 6 minutes

45. $-\frac{1}{2}, \frac{3}{2}, \frac{7}{2}$

Mixed Review

44. Simplify $-\frac{x^2 - y^2}{x + y} \cdot \frac{1}{x - y}$.   (Lesson 9–3) -1

45. Find all the zeros of $f(x) = 8x^3 - 36x^2 + 22x + 21$.   (Lesson 8–5)

574   Chapter 9   *Exploring Rational Expressions*

Extension

Reasoning Simplify the following.

$$\frac{\frac{4}{x - 4} - \frac{1}{x + 2}}{\frac{3x^2 + 24x + 48}{2x^2 - 4x - 16}} + \frac{\frac{x - 4}{x - 4} + \frac{x - 5}{x + 4}}{\frac{x - 3}{x - 3} + \frac{x - 3}{x + 2}} \quad 1$$

46a. circle

46b. hyperbole

46c. ellipse

46. Astronomy In the early 1600s, Johann Kepler studied the orbits of the planets and determined that they are elliptical. It is now known that orbits can take the shape of any of the conic sections. The equations of different orbits are given below. State the shape of each orbit. (Lesson 7–6)

a. $x^2 + y^2 = 75{,}000$ b. $x^2 + 5x = y^2 - 6y - 1$ c. $x^2 + y^2 - 4x = 9$

47. $y = -\frac{1}{6}(x - 11)^2 + \frac{1}{2}$

47. Write an equation of a parabola with focus at $(11, -1)$ and whose directrix is $y = 2$. (Lesson 7–2)

48. Write an equation of the parabola shown at the right. (Lesson 6–6) $y = 3(x - 1)^2$

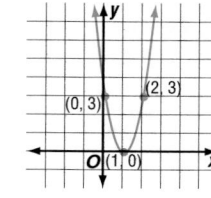

49. Solve $(x - 1)^2 - 4 = 0$ by graphing. (Lesson 6–1)
$-1, 3$; See margin for graph.

50. yes; $h = 88$

50. Fire Fighting The Woodsville City Fire Department is planning to buy some new hoses. These hoses must be powerful enough to propel water at least 75 feet into the air. The ad for the hose they are considering says that the water flows from the hose at a velocity as high as 72 feet per second. Use the formula $v = \sqrt{2gh}$, where v is the velocity of the water, g is the acceleration due to gravity (32 ft/s²), and h is the maximum height of the water flow, to determine whether this hose will be suitable. (Lesson 5–8)

51. Solve $\frac{5}{6}x - 15 = 20y$ for x. (Lesson 2–2) $x = 24y + 18$

Additional Answer

49.

$f(x) = (x - 1)^2 - 4$

WORKING ON THE In·ves·ti·ga·tion

Refer to the Investigation on pages 474–475.

When you found the percent of the tank that is full and the percent of the dipstick that is wet, you used ratios. Ratios in a general algebraic form are rational expressions.

1 Use your data to write a rational expression for finding the ratio for the percent of the tank that is full. Verify your expression.

2 Use your data to write a rational expression for finding the ratio for the percent of the dipstick that is wet. Verify your expression.

3 Determine how you calculated the percent of change in volume. Express this calculation as a rational expression.

4 Use the data from the table in Lesson 8–8 to verify your rational expression. Can this expression be used for any set of data regardless of the dimensions of the tank? Explain.

Add the results of your work to your Investigation Folder.

Lesson 9–4 Adding and Subtracting Rational Expressions **575**

In·ves·ti·ga·tion

Working on the Investigation

The Investigation on pages 474–475 is designed to be a long-term project that is completed over several days or weeks. Encourage students to keep their materials in their Investigation Folder as they work on the Investigation.

Enrichment Masters, p. 67

9-4 NAME _____ DATE _____
Enrichment Student Edition Pages 572–578

Partial Fractions

It is sometimes an advantage to rewrite a rational expression as the sum of two or more fractions. For example, you might do this in a calculus course while carrying out a procedure called integration.

You can resolve a rational expression into partial fractions if two conditions are met:

(1) The degree of the numerator must be less than the degree of the denominator; and
(2) The factors of the denominator must be known.

Example: Resolve $\frac{3}{x^3 + 1}$ into partial fractions.

The denominator has two factors, a linear factor, $x + 1$, and a quadratic factor, $x^2 - x + 1$. Start by writing the following equation. Notice that the degree of the numerators of each partial fraction is less than its denominator.

$\frac{3}{x^3 + 1} = \frac{A}{x + 1} + \frac{Bx + C}{x^2 - x + 1}$

Now, multiply both sides of the equation by $x^3 + 1$ to clear the fractions and finish the problem by solving for the coefficients A, B, and C.

$\frac{3}{x^3 + 1} = \frac{A}{x + 1} + \frac{Bx + C}{x^2 - x + 1}$
$3 = A(x^2 - x + 1) + (x + 1)(Bx + C)$
$3 = Ax^2 - Ax + A + Bx^2 + Cx + Bx + C$
$3 = (A + B)x^2 + (B + C - A)x + (A + C)$

Equating each term,
$0x^2 = (A + B)x^2$
$0x = (B + C - A)x$
$3 = (A + C)$

Therefore, $A = 1, B = -1, C = 2$, and
$\frac{3}{x^3 + 1} = \frac{1}{x + 1} + \frac{-x + 2}{x^2 - x + 1}$.

Resolve each rational expression into partial fractions.

1. $\frac{5x - 3}{x^2 - 2x - 3} = \frac{A}{x + 1} + \frac{B}{x - 3}$ $A = 2, B = 3$
2. $\frac{6x + 7}{(x + 2)^2} = \frac{A}{x + 2} + \frac{B}{(x + 2)^2}$ $A = 6, B = -5$
3. $\frac{4x^3 - x^2 - 3x - 2}{x^2(x + 1)^2} = \frac{A}{x} + \frac{B}{x^2} + \frac{C}{x + 1} + \frac{D}{(x + 1)^2}$ $A = 1, B = -2, C = 3, D = -4$

Chapter 9 **575**

Instructional Resources

- Study Guide Master 9-5
- Practice Master 9-5
- Enrichment Master 9-5
- Assessment and Evaluation Masters, p. 241
- Real-World Applications, 26

Transparency 9-5A contains the 5-Minute Check for this lesson; **Transparency 9-5B** contains a teaching aid for this lesson.

Recommended Pacing	
Standard Pacing	Days 7 & 8 of 10
Honors Pacing	Days 6 & 7 of 9
Block Scheduling*	Day 3 of 4 (along with Lesson 9-4)

*For more information on pacing and possible lesson plans, refer to the *Block Scheduling Booklet*.

1 FOCUS

5-Minute Check
(over Lesson 9-4)

Use the terms $\frac{2y}{y-3}$ and $\frac{3y-1}{y^2+2y-15}$ to answer Exercises 1–3.

1. What is the LCD?
$y^2 + 2y - 15$

2. What is the sum if the terms are added? $\frac{2y^2 + 13y - 1}{(y-3)(y+5)}$

3. What is the difference if the second term is subtracted from the first? $\frac{2y^2 + 7y + 1}{(y-3)(y+5)}$

4. Simplify $\frac{x - \frac{1}{x^2}}{x - \frac{1}{x}} \cdot \frac{x^2 + y + 1}{x(x+1)}$

Motivating the Lesson

Questioning Paddling a canoe upstream goes more slowly than paddling a canoe downstream with the same effort. Encourage students to think of similar examples.

9-5

Solving Rational Equations and Inequalities

What YOU'LL LEARN

- To solve rational equations and inequalities.

Why IT'S IMPORTANT

You can use rational equations and inequalities to solve problems involving art, cycling, and engineering.

fabulous FIRSTS

Miguel Indurain (1964–)

Spain's Miguel Indurain became the first person in the history of the Tour de France bicycle race to win five times in a row. He received his fifth victory in the summer of 1995.

APPLICATION
Cycling

Ken Hiroshi has started bicycling because his doctor told him it was great exercise. One thing his doctor suggested was that Ken find his normal bicycling speed, because for cycling to be an ideal exercise, you can't go too fast or too slow. Ken is having difficulty measuring his speed, because he always has to take wind into consideration. On a particular day, the wind added 3 km/hr to his rate when he was cycling with the wind, and subtracted 3 km/hr from his rate on his return trip. Ken discovered that in the same amount of time he could cycle 36 km with the wind, he could go only 24 km against the wind. What is his normal bicycling speed with no wind at all?

Recall that the formula that relates rate, time, and distance is $r \cdot t = d$. If r is Ken's rate with no wind, then his rate with the wind is $r + 3$ and his rate against the wind is $r - 3$. If t is his time for the trip each way, then using rate $\times$ time = distance, $(r - 3)t = 24$ and $(r + 3)t = 36$.

Solve each equation for t.

$$(r - 3)t = 24 \qquad\qquad (r + 3)t = 36$$
$$t = \frac{24}{r - 3} \qquad\qquad\qquad t = \frac{36}{r + 3}$$

The two expressions equal to t are equal to each other.

$$\frac{24}{r - 3} = \frac{36}{r + 3}$$

An equation that contains one or more rational expressions is called a **rational equation**. It is easiest to solve a rational equation if the fractions are eliminated. This can be done by multiplying each side of the equation by the least common denominator (LCD). Remember that when you multiply each side by the LCD, each term on each side must be multiplied by the LCD.

To solve $\frac{24}{r - 3} = \frac{36}{r + 3}$, multiply each side by the least common denominator $(r - 3)(r + 3)$.

$$\frac{24}{(r - 3)}(r - 3)(r + 3) = \frac{36}{(r + 3)}(r - 3)(r + 3)$$
$$24(r + 3) = 36(r - 3)$$
$$24r + 72 = 36r - 108$$
$$-12r = -180$$
$$r = 15$$

Without the wind, Ken would travel at a rate of 15 kilometers per hour.

fabulous FIRSTS

The first recorded bicycle race was on May 31, 1868. It was won by James Moore, an Englishman.

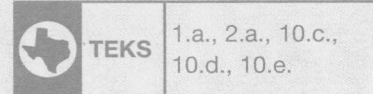

TEKS 1.a., 2.a., 10.c., 10.d., 10.e.

Since rate and time can only be positive, the values of the domain and range must both be greater than zero. Thus, only values in the first quadrant make sense.

Check by graphing $t = \dfrac{24}{r-3}$ and $t = \dfrac{36}{r+3}$ on the same coordinate axes. The intersection point is at (15, 2).

Remember, when you solve an equation by multiplying each side by a polynomial, you must make sure that you are not multiplying by 0. Even a false equation such as $3 = 2$ becomes true if you multiply each side by 0; the equation $0 \cdot 3 = 0 \cdot 2$ is true because both sides equal 0. This is the reason why checking your solutions in the *original* equation is so important.

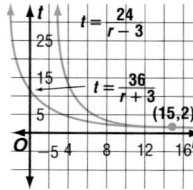

Example 1 Solve each equation. Check the solution.

a. $\dfrac{x+1}{3(x-2)} = \dfrac{5x}{6} + \dfrac{1}{x-2}$

$$\dfrac{x+1}{3(x-2)} = \dfrac{5x}{6} + \dfrac{1}{x-2} \qquad \textit{The LCD is } 6(x-2).$$

$$6(x-2)\,\dfrac{x+1}{3(x-2)} = 6(x-2)\left(\dfrac{5x}{6} + \dfrac{1}{x-2}\right)$$

$$6(x-2)\,\dfrac{x+1}{3(x-2)} = 6(x-2)\left(\dfrac{5x}{6}\right) + 6(x-2)\,\dfrac{1}{x-2}$$

$$2(x+1) = (x-2)(5x) + 6$$

$$2x + 2 = 5x^2 - 10x + 6$$

$$5x^2 - 12x + 4 = 0$$

$$(5x - 2)(x - 2) = 0$$

$$x = \dfrac{2}{5} \text{ or } x = 2$$

Check: Let $x = \dfrac{2}{5}$.

$$\dfrac{\frac{2}{5}+1}{3\left(\frac{2}{5}-2\right)} \overset{?}{=} \dfrac{5\left(\frac{2}{5}\right)}{6} + \dfrac{1}{\frac{2}{5}-2}$$

$$\dfrac{\frac{7}{5}}{3\left(-\frac{8}{5}\right)} \overset{?}{=} \dfrac{2}{6} + \dfrac{1}{-\frac{8}{5}}$$

$$\dfrac{\frac{7}{5}}{-\frac{24}{5}} \overset{?}{=} \dfrac{2}{6} + \left(-\dfrac{5}{8}\right)$$

$$\left(\dfrac{7}{5}\right)\left(-\dfrac{5}{24}\right) \overset{?}{=} \dfrac{8}{24} + \left(-\dfrac{15}{24}\right)$$

$$-\dfrac{7}{24} = -\dfrac{7}{24} \quad \checkmark$$

The solution is $\dfrac{2}{5}$.

Let $x = 2$.

$$\dfrac{2+1}{3(2-2)} \overset{?}{=} \dfrac{5(2)}{6} + \dfrac{1}{2-2}$$

$$\dfrac{3}{3(0)} \overset{?}{=} \dfrac{10}{6} + \dfrac{1}{0}$$

When you check the value 2, you get a zero in the denominator. So, 2 must be eliminated as a solution.

b. $\dfrac{r+2}{2r+1} = \dfrac{r}{3} + \dfrac{3}{4r+2}$

$$\dfrac{r+2}{2r+1} = \dfrac{r}{3} + \dfrac{3}{4r+2} \qquad \textit{The LCD is } 6(2r+1).$$

$$6(2r+1)\left(\dfrac{r+2}{2r+1}\right) = 6(2r+1)\left(\dfrac{r}{3} + \dfrac{3}{2(2r+1)}\right)$$

$$6(2r+1)\left(\dfrac{r+2}{2r+1}\right) = 6(2r+1)\left(\dfrac{r}{3}\right) + 6(2r+1)\left(\dfrac{3}{2(2r+1)}\right)$$

(continued on the next page)

Lesson 9–5 Solving Rational Equations and Inequalities **577**

2 TEACH

In-Class Examples

For Example 1
Solve each equation. Check the solution.

a. $\dfrac{7}{r+2} = \dfrac{6}{r-5}$ 47

b. $\dfrac{x}{x+2} - \dfrac{x+2}{x-2} = \dfrac{x+3}{x-2}$.
  -1 or -10

Teaching Tip Ask students to look at Example 1b and name the values of r that would automatically be excluded as a solution. $-\dfrac{1}{2}$

Cooperative Learning

Think-Pair-Share Have students work with a partner. Have each pair write a rational equation and take turns verbalizing each step needed to solve the equation and check the solution. Discuss any steps that are not commonly agreed upon. For more information on the think-pair-share strategy, see *Cooperative Learning in the Mathematics Classroom,* one of the titles in the Glencoe Mathematics Professional Series, pages 24–25.

For Example 2

Solve $\dfrac{3}{y+2} + \dfrac{7}{15} \geq \dfrac{23}{3y+6}$.

$y \geq 8$

$$6(r+2) = 2(2r+1)(r) + (3)(3)$$
$$6r + 12 = 4r^2 + 2r + 9$$
$$4r^2 - 4r - 3 = 0$$
$$(2r-3)(2r+1) = 0$$
$$r = \frac{3}{2} \text{ or } r = -\frac{1}{2}$$

Check: $\dfrac{r+2}{2r+1} = \dfrac{r}{3} + \dfrac{3}{4r+2}$

$$\dfrac{\frac{3}{2}+2}{2\left(\frac{3}{2}\right)+1} = \dfrac{\frac{3}{2}}{3} + \dfrac{3}{4\left(\frac{3}{2}\right)+2}$$

$$\dfrac{\frac{7}{2}}{4} \stackrel{?}{=} \dfrac{1}{2} + \dfrac{3}{8}$$

$$\dfrac{7}{8} \stackrel{?}{=} \dfrac{4}{8} + \dfrac{3}{8}$$

$$\dfrac{7}{8} = \dfrac{7}{8} \checkmark$$

When you check the value $-\dfrac{1}{2}$, you get a zero in the denominator. So, $-\dfrac{1}{2}$ must be eliminated as a solution.

The solution is $\dfrac{3}{2}$.

You can use what you now know about solving rational equations to solve *rational inequalities*.

Example **Solve** $\dfrac{x-2}{x} < \dfrac{x-4}{x-6}$.

$$\dfrac{x-2}{x} < \dfrac{x-4}{x-6}$$

$$x(x-6)\dfrac{x-2}{x} < x(x-6)\dfrac{x-4}{x-6} \qquad \textit{The LCD is } x(x-6).$$

$$x(x-6)\dfrac{x-2}{x} < x(x-6)\dfrac{x-4}{x-6}$$

$$(x-6)(x-2) < x(x-4)$$

$$x^2 - 8x + 12 < x^2 - 4x$$

$$-4x < -12$$

$$x > 3$$

It appears that $x > 3$. Test values on each part of the number line below to check the result.

Try $x = 1$.

$$\dfrac{x-2}{x} < \dfrac{x-4}{x-6}$$

$$\dfrac{1-2}{1} < \dfrac{1-4}{1-6}$$

$$-1 < \dfrac{3}{5} \checkmark$$

true

Try $x = 5$.

$$\dfrac{x-2}{x} < \dfrac{x-4}{x-6}$$

$$\dfrac{5-2}{5} < \dfrac{5-4}{5-6}$$

$$\dfrac{3}{5} \not< -1$$

false

So, $x < 3$, but $x \neq 0$ or 6. *Why?*

GLENCOE *Technology*

● **CD-ROM Interaction**

A multimedia simulation connects solving rational equations with the operation of a camera. A blackline master activity with teacher's notes provides a follow-up to the CD-ROM simulation.

For Windows & Macintosh

To solve rational inequalities, complete the following steps.

1. Solve the inequality.
2. Test values to find the solution.
3. State the excluded values.

Some real-world problems can be solved with rational equations.

Example ③

APPLICATION

Engineering

F Y I

Drilling tunnels from both ends requires great accuracy; if one of the machines goes 1° off course, after 1.5 miles it would miss the other half of the tunnel by over a quarter of a mile.

GLOBAL CONNECTIONS

The English Channel Tunnel, which runs between England and France, was completed in 1994 after more than 6 years and $15 billion. During its construction, 15,000 workers used a total of 11 tunnel-boring machines. Twenty-four of the tunnel's 31 miles run at an average depth of 131 feet beneath the channel seabed, making it the world's longest underwater tunnel.

onstruction of the English Channel Tunnel

Most tunnels are drilled using tunnel-boring machines that begin at both ends of the tunnel. Suppose a new underwater tunnel is being built and one tunnel-boring machine alone can finish the tunnel in 4 years. A different type of machine can tunnel to the other side in 3 years. If both machines start at opposite ends and work at the same time, when will the tunnel be finished?

Explore In one year, machine A can complete $\frac{1}{4}$ of the tunnel. In 2 years, it can complete $\frac{1}{4} \cdot 2$ or $\frac{2}{4}$ of the tunnel. In t years, it can complete $\frac{1}{4} \cdot t$ or $\frac{t}{4}$ of the tunnel.

In one year, machine B can complete $\frac{1}{3}$ of the tunnel. Using the same pattern as above, in t years it can complete $\frac{1}{3} \cdot t$ or $\frac{t}{3}$ of the tunnel.

Plan In t years, machine A can complete $\frac{t}{4}$ of the tunnel and, in that same time, machine B can complete $\frac{t}{3}$ of the tunnel. Together, they can complete the entire tunnel.

$$\overbrace{\frac{t}{4}}^{\text{machine A}} \quad + \quad \overbrace{\frac{t}{3}}^{\text{machine B}} \quad = \quad \overbrace{1}^{\text{entire tunnel}}$$

Solve
$$\frac{t}{4} + \frac{t}{3} = 1$$
$$12\left(\frac{t}{4} + \frac{t}{3}\right) = 12(1) \qquad \textit{Multiply by the LCD.}$$
$$3t + 4t = 12 \qquad \textit{Distributive property}$$
$$7t = 12 \qquad \textit{Combine like terms.}$$
$$t = \frac{12}{7} \text{ or } 1\frac{5}{7} \qquad \textit{Divide each side by 7.}$$

The tunnel can be completed in $1\frac{5}{7}$ years or about 1 year 9 months.

Examine Machine A digs through $\frac{1}{4}t$ or $\frac{1}{4}\left(\frac{12}{7}\right)$ of the tunnel: $\frac{1}{4}\left(\frac{12}{7}\right) = \frac{3}{7}$.

Machine B digs through $\frac{1}{3}t$ or $\frac{1}{3}\left(\frac{12}{7}\right)$ of the tunnel: $\frac{1}{3}\left(\frac{12}{7}\right) = \frac{4}{7}$.

Since $\frac{3}{7} + \frac{4}{7} = \frac{7}{7}$ or 1, the solution checks.

In-Class Example

For Example 3
Solve.

a. $\frac{t}{2} + \frac{t}{5} = 1 \quad \frac{10}{7}$

b. $\frac{t}{3} + \frac{t}{8} = 1 \quad \frac{24}{11}$

GLOBAL CONNECTIONS

The following table describes the five longest tunnels in the world.

Tunnel	Location	Length (miles)
Seikan	Japan	33.5
English Channel Tunnel	UK-France	31.1
Oshimizu	Japan	13.80
Simplon	Italy-Switzerland	12.3
Shin-Kanmon	Japan	11.6

F Y I

Students can verify this with a very simple calculation: 1° is $\frac{1}{360}$ of the circumference of a circle. A circle with a radius of 15 miles has a circumference of 30π miles. So a 1° arc of this circumference is $\frac{30\pi}{360} = \frac{\pi}{12} \approx \frac{1}{4}$ of a mile.

In-Class Example

For Example 4

A cyclist travels 8 km in the same time that a walker travels 3 km. The speed of the cyclist is 8 km more than the speed of the walker. Find the speed of the cyclist and the speed of the walker.

cyclist = 12.8 km/hr
walker = 4.8 km/hr

Sometimes it is helpful to **organize the data** that is given in a problem. One way of doing this is by making a drawing. In this way you can evaluate how to write an equation that helps you solve the problem.

Example

PROBLEM SOLVING
Organize Data

A car travels 300 km in the same time that a freight train travels 200 km. The speed of the car is 20 km/h more than the speed of the train. Find the speed of the car and the speed of the train.

Draw a diagram to display the information that you know.

time = t
20 km/h faster
300 km

time = t
200 km

Remember that $d = rt$. Since both vehicles travel the same amount of time, rewrite the formula in terms of t. That is, $\frac{d}{r} = t$. Then you can equate the formulas for the two vehicles in terms of t. Let r represent the speed of the train. So $r + 20$ represents the speed of the car.

$$\underbrace{car's\ time}_{} = \underbrace{train's\ time}_{}$$

$$\frac{distance}{rate} = \frac{300}{r + 20} \qquad \frac{distance}{rate} = \frac{200}{r} \qquad \text{Both vehicles travel the same time.}$$

$$\frac{300}{r + 20} = \frac{200}{r}$$

$$r(r + 20)\left(\frac{300}{r + 20}\right) = r(r + 20)\left(\frac{200}{r}\right) \qquad \text{Multiply each side by the LCD, } r(r + 20).$$

$$300r = 200r + 4000$$

$$100r = 4000 \qquad \text{Subtract 200r from each side.}$$

$$r = 40 \qquad \text{Divide by 100.}$$

So, the speed of the freight train is 40 km/h, and the speed of the car is 40 + 20 or 60 km/h.

 Alternative Learning Styles

Auditory Explain to students the concept of LCD. The LCD of two integers is usually greater than the two integers. For rational expressions, the situation is different. The LCD need not be greater, depending on the values for the variables. But it is still a common multiple. In fact, it is the common multiple with the least number of factors. After students listen to your explanation, have them express this concept in their own words.

Communicating Mathematics

Study the lesson. Then complete the following. 1. See margin.

1. **Explain** why the equation $x + \frac{1}{x-1} = 1 + \frac{1}{x-1}$ has no solution.

2. **Explain** why it is necessary to test values when solving rational inequalities. **because you multiply by quantities that may be positive or negative**

3. **a. State** what you would multiply each side of $\frac{x}{x-3} + \frac{x}{3} = 1$ by in order to solve the equation. $(x-3)(3)$

   b. What value(s) of x cannot be a solution? $x \neq 3$

4. **You Decide** Rick solved the rational equation $\frac{(x+3)^2}{5} = x + 3$ and told his friend Janine that the solution was 2. Janine said "You're right, Rick, but there's another solution to the equation." "That's impossible," said Rick, showing her his solution. Look at Rick's solution at the right. Who is correct? Explain. **See margin.**

   $$\frac{(x+3)^2}{5} = x + 3$$
   $$\frac{(x+3)^2}{5(x+3)} = 1$$
   $$\frac{(x+3)}{5} = 1$$
   $$(x+3) = 5$$
   $$x = 2$$

 MATH JOURNAL

5. Describe other methods you could use to organize data to make it easier to solve problems. **Sample answer: Use graphs or tables.**

Guided Practice

Find the LCD for each equation. State what values should be excluded as possible solutions. Then solve the equation and check your solution.

6. $5(y+4)$; -4; about 0.35, about -3.45

6. $\frac{2}{y+4} + y = \frac{1}{5}$

7. $(m-4)(m-2)$; 4, 2; 6

7. $\frac{1}{m-4} = \frac{2}{m-2}$

Solve each equation or inequality. Check your solutions.

8. $\frac{y}{y+1} = \frac{2}{3}$ 2

9. $\frac{x}{3} - \frac{2}{5} = 1$ $\frac{21}{5}$

10. $b^2 + \frac{17b}{6} = \frac{1}{2}$ $-3, \frac{1}{6}$

11. $\frac{2x}{3} - \frac{x+3}{6} > 2$ $x > 5$

12. $2\frac{2}{9}$ days

12. **Construction** The Delaware Demolition Company wants to build a brick wall to hide the area where they store wrecked cars from public view. One bricklayer can build this wall in 5 days. Another bricklayer can do the job in 4 days. If the company hires both of them to work together, how long will it take them to finish the wall?

Reteaching ▬▬▬▬▬

Using Alternative Methods When each side of a given equation is a fraction, show students the following shortcut—cross-multiplication.

$$\frac{5}{y+3} \times \frac{3}{y-1}$$
$$5(y-1) = 3(y+3)$$
$$5y - 5 = 3y + 9$$
$$2y = 14$$
$$y = 17$$

---

3 PRACTICE/APPLY

Check for Understanding
Exercises 1–12 are designed to help you assess your students' understanding through reading, writing, speaking, and modeling. You should work through Exercises 1–5 with your students and then monitor their work on Exercises 6–12.

Error Analysis
Students sometimes lose a solution to an equation when they divide each side of the equation by an expression that involves a variable. For example, if $x^2 = x$ is divided on each side by x, you obtain $x = 1$. The solution $x = 0$ is lost. To avoid this problem, students should check any numbers that make the divisor zero.

Additional Answers

1. If you subtract $\frac{1}{x-1}$ from each side, you get $x = 1$. But $x \neq 1$ because it gives 0 in the denominator.

4. Janine is correct; another solution is -3. To avoid losing a solution to an equation when you divide each side by an expression that involves a variable, check any numbers that make the divisor zero.

Study Guide Masters, p. 68

9-5 NAME_____ DATE _____
Study Guide Student Edition Pages 576–583

Solving Rational Equations

An equation that consists of one or more rational expressions is called a **rational equation**. One method of solving a rational equation is to multiply each side of the equation by the least common denominator (LCD) of *all* the denominators. Remember that a rational expression is undefined when the denominator is zero. Be sure to watch for solutions that would produce a denominator of zero. These solutions must be excluded from the final solution set.

Example: Solve $\frac{9}{10} + \frac{2}{x+1} = \frac{2}{5}$

$$\frac{9}{10} + \frac{2}{x+1} = \frac{2}{5}$$
$$10(x+1)\left(\frac{9}{10} + \frac{2}{x+1}\right) = \left(\frac{2}{5}\right)(10)(x+1)$$
$$9(x+1) + 20 = 4(x+1)$$
$$9x + 9 + 20 = 4x + 4$$
$$x = -25$$
$$5x = -5$$

Multiply each side by 10(x + 1), the LCD for all three denominators.

Check: $\frac{9}{10} + \frac{2}{x+1} = \frac{2}{5}$
$\frac{9}{10} + \frac{2}{-5+1} \stackrel{?}{=} \frac{2}{5}$
$\frac{9}{10} + \left(-\frac{1}{2}\right) \stackrel{?}{=} \frac{2}{5}$
$\frac{2}{5} = \frac{2}{5}$ ✓

The solution is -5.

Solve each equation. Check your solutions.

1. $\frac{2y}{3} - \frac{y+3}{6} = 2$ 5

2. $\frac{4t-3}{5} - \frac{4-2t}{3} = 1$ 2

3. $\frac{2x+1}{3} - \frac{x-5}{4} = \frac{1}{2}$ $-\frac{13}{5}$

4. $\frac{3m+2}{5m} + \frac{2m-1}{2m} = 4$ $-\frac{1}{24}$

5. $\frac{4}{x-1} = \frac{x+1}{12}$ ± 7

6. $\frac{x}{x-2} + \frac{4}{x-2} = 10$ $\frac{8}{3}$

7. $\frac{3}{4} - \frac{3m}{4m+6} = 8$ $-\frac{87}{64}$

8. $\frac{10}{m^2-1} + \frac{2m-5}{m-1} = \frac{2m+5}{m+1}$ $\frac{5}{3}$

Assignment Guide

Core: 13–37 odd, 38–44
Enriched: 14–30 even, 31–44

For **Extra Practice,** see p. 898.

The red A, B, and C flags, printed only in the Teacher's Wraparound Edition, indicate the level of difficulty of the exercises.

17. $(a-6)(a-2)$;
6, 2; 6.94, 1.73

19. 2   20. $z < 5$

22. 4, −1

23. −12, 1

24. $-\frac{11}{16} \le y \le 2$

Practice Masters, p. 68

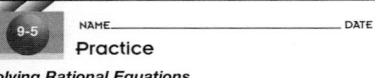

9-5   NAME_____ DATE _____
Practice   Student Edition
Pages 576–583

Solving Rational Equations
Solve each equation. Check your solutions.

1. $\frac{12}{x} + \frac{3}{4} = \frac{3}{2}$ 16
2. $\frac{x^2}{8} - 4 = \frac{x}{2}$ −4, 8

3. $\frac{x+10}{x^2-2} = \frac{4}{x} - \frac{2}{3}$, 4
4. $\frac{x}{x+2} + x = \frac{5x+8}{x+2}$ 4

5. $\frac{5}{x-5} = \frac{x}{x-5} - 1$ all reals except 5
6. $\frac{1}{3x-2} + \frac{5}{x} = 0$ $\frac{5}{8}$

7. $\frac{6}{x-1} = \frac{4}{x-2} + \frac{2}{x+1}$ ∅
8. $\frac{x+1}{x-3} = 4 - \frac{12}{x^2-2x-3}$ $-\frac{5}{3}$, 5

9. $\frac{1}{x-1} = \frac{2}{x+1} - \frac{1}{x+3}$ ∅
10. $\frac{1}{x+2} + \frac{1}{x-2} = \frac{3}{x+1}$ $1 \pm \sqrt{13}$

Solve.

1. The view of the rectangular box at the right shows three faces of the box. The areas of two of the faces are 30 cm² and 48 cm². The volume of the box is 240 cm³. What is the area of the third face?   40 cm²

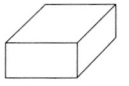

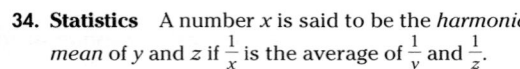

EXERCISES

Practice

Find the LCD for each equation. State what values should be excluded as possible solutions. Then solve the equation and check your solution.

13. $\frac{x+2}{2} - \frac{3}{4} = x$ 4; none; $\frac{1}{2}$

14. $\frac{1}{a} + \frac{1}{2} = \frac{2}{a}$ $2a$; 0; 2

15. $\frac{6}{m} = \frac{9}{m^2}$ m^2; 0; $\frac{3}{2}$

16. $\frac{x}{x-3} + \frac{1}{3} = 1$ $3(x-3)$; 3; −6

17. $\frac{3}{a-6} - \frac{1}{a-2} = 3$

18. $\frac{3y}{2+y} - \frac{5}{7} = 4$ $7(2+y)$; −2; $-\frac{11}{2}$

Solve each equation or inequality. Check your solutions.

19. $\frac{x+1}{3} + \frac{x-1}{3} = \frac{4}{3}$

20. $\frac{5+7z}{8} - \frac{15+3z}{10} < 2$

21. $y + 5 \le \frac{6}{y}$ $y \le -6$

22. $\frac{1}{t-1} + \frac{1}{t+2} = \frac{1}{2}$

23. $\frac{1}{m+2} - \frac{1}{3-m} = -\frac{1}{6}$

24. $\frac{1}{2y+1} + \frac{1}{y+1} \ge \frac{8}{15}$

25. $\frac{1}{9} + \frac{1}{2a} = \frac{1}{a^2}$ $-6, \frac{3}{2}$

26. $\frac{1}{1-x} = 1 - \frac{x}{x-1}$ $\{x \mid x \ne 1\}$

27. $\frac{3}{x^2+3x} + \frac{x+2}{x+3} = \frac{1}{x}$ −1

28. $\frac{6}{y^2+2y} - \frac{y+1}{y+2} = \frac{2}{y}$ $\frac{-3 \pm \sqrt{17}}{2}$

29. $\frac{1}{x+4} = \frac{2}{x^2+3x-4} - \frac{1}{1-x}$ ∅

30. $\frac{3}{b^2+5b+6} + \frac{b-1}{b+2} = \frac{7}{b+3}$ 7

Critical Thinking

31. Solve for a if $\frac{1}{a} - \frac{1}{b} = c$. $\frac{b}{bc+1}$

32. Find the values of A and B, if $\frac{A}{z+2} + \frac{B}{2z-3} = \frac{5z-11}{2z^2+z-6}$. $A = 3, B = -1$

Applications and Problem Solving

33a. $\frac{x+11}{x+20} \ge 0.70$

33c. Selena needs at least 10 consecutive free throws.

35. 58.75 mph

33. **Basketball**   Selena has scored 11 free throws in 20 attempts. Her coach has told her that she needs to bring her free-throw average (number of free throws made ÷ number of attempts) up to at least 70% or the coach will assign someone else to play her position. Selena wants to increase her average as quickly as possible.

a. Write an inequality to determine the number of consecutive free throws Selena must score to bring her average up to 0.70.

b. Solve the inequality. $x \ge 10$

c. Interpret your answer in terms of Selena's problem.

34. **Statistics**   A number x is said to be the *harmonic mean* of y and z if $\frac{1}{x}$ is the average of $\frac{1}{y}$ and $\frac{1}{z}$.

a. Find y if $x = 8$ and $z = 20$.   5

b. Find x if $y = 5$ and $z = 8$.   6.15

35. **Organize Data**   During one fourth of the time it took her to travel from Denver to Cheyenne, Alicia drove in a snowstorm at an average speed of 40 mph. She drove the rest of the time at an average speed of 65 mph. What was her average speed for the entire trip?

36. **Art**   Restoring a masterpiece is a long process. In the restoration of Leonardo da Vinci's 500-year-old *Last Supper*, it took a week to clean an area the size of a postage stamp. Suppose an artist works 12 weeks on restoring a painting. A second artist joins him and together they finish the restoration in 8 more weeks. If the second artist could have restored the painting alone in 24 weeks, how long would it have taken the first artist to restore the entire painting alone?   30 weeks

37. **Number Theory**   The ratio of 8 less than a number to 28 more than that number is 2 to 5. What is the number?   32

Extension

Problem Solving   Name all the excluded values of a for

$$\frac{a+2+\frac{2}{a+5}}{a+6+\frac{6}{a+1}} = \frac{a+5+\frac{3}{a+1}}{a-1-\frac{3}{a+1}}.$$

Then solve the equation.
−5, −1, −4, −3, −2, 2; $-\frac{11}{5}$

Mixed Review

38. Simplify $\dfrac{3}{a-2} + \dfrac{2}{a-3}$. (Lesson 9–4) $\dfrac{5a-13}{(a-2)(a-3)}$

39. State the number of positive real zeros, negative real zeros, and imaginary zeros for $f(x) = x^3 + 1$. (Lesson 8–4) **0; 1; 2**

40. Solve the system of equations. (Lesson 7–7) **(−4, −3), (−3, −4)**

$$x + y + 7 = 0$$
$$x^2 + y^2 = 25$$

41. $\sqrt{4.58}$ units

41. Geometry Find the distance between the points at $(-0.5, 1)$ and $(-2.2, -0.3)$. (Lesson 7–1)

42. $2x^2 - 7x + 3 = 0$

42. Write a quadratic equation that has 3 and $\frac{1}{2}$ as roots. (Lesson 6–5)

43. Environment The Natural Ideas store needs to order cube-shaped boxes to package commemorative globes designed for the 30th anniversary of Earth Day on April 22, 2000. The globes were made by school children in the community. The formula for the radius r of a sphere is $r = \sqrt[3]{\dfrac{3V}{4\pi}}$, where V is the volume. If the volume of each globe is 175 in³, what is the minimum size (to the nearest inch) that the boxes can be inside to fit around the globe? (Lesson 5–6) **about 7 in. × 7 in. × 7 in.**

44. Solve $4x + 3 < -9$ or $7 < 2x - 11$. (Lesson 1–7) $\{x \mid x < -3 \text{ or } x > 9\}$

Mathematics and SOCIETY

Prime Factoring

The excerpt below appeared in an article in *Science News* on May 7, 1994.

IT'S EASY TO MULTIPLY TWO LARGE PRIME numbers to obtain a larger number as the answer. But the reverse process—factoring a large number to determine its components—presents a formidable challenge. The problem appears so hard that the difficulty of factoring underlies the so-called RSA method of encrypting digital information. Last week, an international team of computer scientists, mathemati-cians, and other experts succeeded in finding the factors of a 129-digit number suggested 17 years ago as a test of the security of the RSA cryptographic scheme. This feat and other work now complicate encoding schemes used for national and commercial security. The effort required the use of more than 600 computers scattered throughout the world. ■

1. See students' work.

2. Sample answer: advances in computer processing power

3. See students' work.

1. If you were in charge of security for a company and you found out about the work described above, how do you think you would feel? Why?

2. Since 1977, what developments have occurred to enable the huge task of factoring RSA-129 to be performed?

3. What do you think about using a direct challenge in order to get a large problem solved? Can you think of an example from your own knowledge or experience where a challenge was used to inspire action?

Lesson 9–5 Solving Rational Equations and Inequalities **583**

Mathematics and SOCIETY

The word *cryptography* is derived from two ancient Greek words: *cryptos*, meaning "hidden," and *graphia*, meaning "writing." It was employed by Greek and Persian rulers 2500 years ago. Have students try to develop encoding systems using numbers or non-numeral systems. They can write secret messages to each other and decode them.

---

4 ASSESS

Closing Activity

Modeling Mark off 100 meters on the pavement outside. Have a runner and a walker begin the 100-meter course. Time the runner when he or she is finished. Have the walker stop at the same time and measure the distance he or she walked. Fit the results into an equation of the form found in Example 4.

Chapter 9, Quiz D (Lesson 9-5), is available in the *Assessment and Evaluation Masters,* p. 241.

Enrichment Masters, p. 68

9-5 NAME_____ DATE_____
Enrichment Student Edition Pages 579–586

Limits

Sequences of numbers with a rational expression for the general term often approach some number as a finite limit. For example, the reciprocals of the positive integers approach 0 as n gets larger and larger. This is written using the notation shown below. The symbol ∞ stands for infinity and $n \to \infty$ means that n is getting larger and larger, or "n goes to infinity."

$$1, \frac{1}{2}, \frac{1}{3}, \frac{1}{4}, \cdots, \frac{1}{n}, \cdots \qquad \lim_{n \to \infty} \frac{1}{n} = 0$$

Example: Find $\lim\limits_{n \to \infty} \dfrac{n^2}{(n+1)^2}$.

It is not immediately apparent whether the sequence approaches a limit or not. But notice what happens if we divide the numerator and denominator of the general term by n^2.

$$\frac{n^2}{(n+1)^2} = \frac{n^2}{n^2 + 2n + 1}$$

$$= \frac{\frac{n^2}{n^2}}{\frac{n^2}{n^2} + \frac{2n}{n^2} + \frac{1}{n^2}}$$

$$= \frac{1}{1 + \frac{2}{n} + \frac{1}{n^2}}$$

The two fractions in the denominator will approach a limit of 0 as n gets very large, so the entire expression approaches a limit of 1.

Find the following limits.

1. $\lim\limits_{n \to \infty} \dfrac{n^2 + 5n}{n^4 - 6}$ 0

2. $\lim\limits_{n \to \infty} \dfrac{1-n}{n^2}$ 0

3. $\lim\limits_{n \to \infty} \dfrac{2(n+1)+1}{2n+1}$ 1

4. $\lim\limits_{n \to \infty} \dfrac{2n+1}{1-3n}$ $-\dfrac{2}{3}$

Chapter 9 **583**

In·ves·ti·ga·tion
TEACHER NOTES

Closing the Investigation

This activity provides students an opportunity to bring their work on the Investigation to a close. For each Investigation, students should present their findings to the class. Here are some ways students can display their work.

- Conduct and report on an interview or survey.
- Write a letter, proposal, or report.
- Write an article for the school or local paper.
- Make a display, including graphs and/or charts.
- Plan an activity.

Assessment

To assess students' understanding of the concepts and topics explored in this Investigation and its follow-up activities, you may wish to examine students' Investigation Folders.

The scoring guide provided in the *Investigations and Projects Masters,* p. 15, provides a means for you to score students' work on the Investigation.

Investigations and Projects Masters, p. 15

Level	Specific Criteria
Scoring Guide **Chapters 8 and 9** Investigation	
Superior	· Shows thorough understanding of how a dipstick can be used to measure volume. Understands the concepts of *measurement scales, ratios, percents, volume, rational expressions,* and *inverse relations.* · Uses appropriate strategies to solve problems. · Computations are correct. · Written explanations are exemplary. · Charts, graphs, and report are appropriate and sensible. · Goes beyond the requirements of some or all problems.
Satisfactory, with Minor Flaws	· Shows understanding of how a dipstick can be used to measure volume. Understands the concepts of *measurement scales, ratios, percents, volume, rational expressions,* and *inverse relations.* · Uses appropriate strategies to solve problems. · Computations are mostly correct. · Written explanations are effective. · Charts, graphs, and report are appropriate and sensible. · Satisfies all requirements of problems.
Nearly Satisfactory, with Obvious Flaws	· Shows basic understanding of how a dipstick can be used to measure volume. Exhibits competency with most of the concepts of *measurement scales, ratios, percents, volume, rational expressions,* and *inverse relations.* · May not use appropriate strategies to solve problems. · Computations are mostly correct. · Written explanations are satisfactory. · Charts, graphs, and report are appropriate and sensible. · Satisfies most requirements of problems.
Unsatisfactory	· Shows little or no understanding of how a dipstick can be used to measure volume. Shows little or no understanding of the concepts of *measurement scales, ratios, percents, volume, rational expressions,* and *inverse relations.* · May not use appropriate strategies to solve problems. · Computations are incorrect. · Written explanations are not satisfactory. · Charts, graphs, and report are not appropriate or sensible. · Does not satisfy requirements of problems.

Fill It Up!

Refer to the Investigation on pages 474–475.

Gasoline stations usually have several tanks buried beneath the concrete surface. These tanks contain different octanes of gasoline. The tanks may differ in size depending on the demand for each octane of gasoline. In many areas, these tanks are refilled on a weekly basis.

The national average consumption of gasoline is 687 gallons of fuel per year per vehicle. The price of gasoline rises and falls with the global demand for barrels of crude oil. With the exception of the gasoline shortages in the 1970s, gasoline has been in abundance since 1950. However, the price of gasoline has risen with the price of crude oil.

PORTFOLIO ASSESSMENT

You may want to keep your work on this Investigation in your portfolio.

Analyze

You have conducted experiments and organized your data in various ways. It is now time to analyze your findings and state your conclusions.

1 Look over the data and graphs that you made from the two experiments. What generalizations can you make about these experiments that can be applied to any cylindrical tank?

2 Use your graphs and data to determine a general formula for finding the scale markings on a dipstick for a tank one-half full, one-fourth full, one-eighth full, five-eighths full, and three-fourths full given any cylindrical tank with radius r and height h.

3 Explain and justify your calculations and formula. Use a specific case as an example that your general process and formula work.

4 Draw scatter plots of the three sets of data. Let the vertical axis represent the dipstick reading in feet and let the horizontal axis represent the volume of the tank as percent full. Describe patterns in the data.

Write

Your superior has received several calls similar to the one you received from the franchise owner. He has asked you for a summary of your findings and your report to the franchise owner.

5 Summarize the procedure you used to investigate the problem of designing the scale of a dipstick in a cylindrical tank. Explain your findings from the experiments you conducted.

VOCABULARY

After completing this chapter, you should be able to define each term, property, or phrase and give an example or two of each.

Algebra
asymptotes   (p. 550)
complex fraction   (p. 565)
constant of variation   (p. 556)
continuity   (p. 548)
direct variation   (p. 556)
dividing rational expressions   (p. 563)
inversely proportional   (p. 557)
inverse variation   (p. 557)
joint variation   (p. 558)

multiplying rational expressions   (p. 563)
point discontinuity   (p. 548)
rational algebraic expressions   (p. 562)
rational equation   (p. 576)
rational function   (p. 550)
rational inequalities   (p. 578)

Problem Solving
organize data   (p. 580)

UNDERSTANDING AND USING THE VOCABULARY

State whether each sentence is *true* or *false*. If false, replace the underlined word or number to make a true sentence.

1. The equation $y = \dfrac{x^2 - 1}{x + 1}$ has a(n) <u>asymptote</u> at $x = -1$.   **false, point discontinuity**

2. The complex fraction $\dfrac{\frac{4}{5}}{\frac{2}{3}}$ can be reduced to $\dfrac{6}{5}$.   **true**

3. The equation $y = 3x$ is an example of <u>direct</u> variation.   **true**

4. The equation $y = \dfrac{x^2}{x + 1}$ is a(n) <u>polynomial</u> equation.   **false, rational**

5. The graph of $y = \dfrac{4}{x - 4}$ has a(n) <u>variation</u> at $x = 4$.   **false, asymptote**

6. The equation $b = \dfrac{2}{a}$ is a(n) <u>inverse</u> variation.   **true**

7. On the graph of $y = \dfrac{x - 5}{x + 2}$, there is a break in continuity at <u>$x = 2$</u>.   **false, $x = -2$**

8. The formula for the area of a triangle, $A = \dfrac{1}{2}bh$, is a(n) <u>inverse</u> variation.   **false, joint**

The Chapter Highlights begins with a listing of the new terms, properties, and phrases that were introduced in this chapter. Have students define each term and provide an example or two of it, if appropriate.

Assessment and Evaluation Masters, pp. 227–228

9 NAME_____ DATE _____
Chapter 9, Form 1B

Write the letter for the correct answer in the blank at the right of each problem.

1. What is the simplest form of $\dfrac{(3xy^3)^2}{9x^4y}$?   1. ___D___
A. $\dfrac{2y^5}{3x^2}$ B. $\dfrac{y^4}{3x^3}$ C. $\dfrac{x}{y^5}$ D. $\dfrac{y^6}{x^2}$

2. Simplify $\left(\dfrac{2a}{b}\right)^3 \cdot \left(\dfrac{b^2}{8}\right)$.   2. ___A___
A. $\dfrac{a^3}{b}$ B. $\dfrac{b}{a^3}$ C. $\dfrac{3a^3}{4b}$ D. $\dfrac{4b}{3a^3}$

3. Simplify $\dfrac{x^2 + 5x + 4}{x^2 + 2x + 1} \cdot \dfrac{2x + 2}{x + 4}$.   3. ___B___
A. $\dfrac{1}{2}$ B. 2 C. $\dfrac{(x+4)^2}{2(x+1)^2}$ D. $\dfrac{x+4}{2(x+1)}$

4. Which of the following is an equation of a verticle asymptote for the graph of $f(x) = \dfrac{x^2 + 5x + 6}{x - 1}$?   4. ___A___
A. $x = 1$ B. $x = -2$ C. $x = -2$ or $x = -3$ D. $y = 1$

5. Which of the following is the x-coordinate of a break in the graph of $f(x) = \dfrac{x + 5}{x^2 + 6x + 5}$?   5. ___B___
A. 5   B. -5 C. 1   D. -1

6. Simplify $\dfrac{x^2 - 9}{x^2 - 5x + 6} \div \dfrac{x^2 + 5x + 6}{x^2 - 4}$.   6. ___D___
A. $\dfrac{(x+3)^2}{(x-2)^2}$ B. -1 C. $\dfrac{x+2}{x-2}$ D. 1

7. Two fractions have denominators of $x^2 + 6x + 9$ and $x^2 - 9$. What is the least common denominator?   7. ___D___
A. $x^2 - 9$ B. $x^2 + 6x + 9$ C. $2x^2 + 6x$ D. $(x + 3)^2(x - 3)$

8. Simplify $\dfrac{y}{9y^2 - 9} + \dfrac{4}{y^2 + 2y + 1}$.   8. ___A___
A. $\dfrac{y^2 + 37y - 36}{9(y+1)^2(y-1)}$ B. $\dfrac{y+4}{10y^2 + 2y - 8}$ C. $\dfrac{y+4}{9(y+1)^2(y-1)}$ D. $\dfrac{y^2 + 38y - 35}{9(y-1)(y+1)^2}$

9. The volume (V) of a box varies jointly as the length (ℓ), width (w), and height (h). Find h if $V = 512\text{m}^3$, $\ell = 8\text{m}$, and $w = 4\text{m}$.   9. ___C___
A. 160m   B. 1.6m   C. 16m   D. 8m

10. Simplify $\dfrac{6n}{n^2 - 9} - \dfrac{3}{n + 3}$.   10. ___B___
A. $\dfrac{3}{n + 3}$ B. $\dfrac{3}{n - 3}$ C. $\dfrac{6n - 3}{n^2 - n + 12}$ D. $\dfrac{6n - 3}{n^2 - 9}$

11. Which of the following is an equation of the horizontal asymptote for the graph of $f(x) = \dfrac{2x + 3}{x - 1}$?   11. ___A___
A. $y = 2$ B. $y = 0$ C. $x = 1$ D. $y = 1$

---

9 NAME_____ DATE _____
Chapter 9 Test, Form 1B (Continued)

12. Simplify $\dfrac{1 + \frac{3}{x}}{1 + \frac{4}{x} + \frac{3}{x^2}}$.   12. ___D___
A. $\dfrac{(x+3)^2(x+1)}{x^3}$ B. $\dfrac{x+1}{x}$ C. $\dfrac{x+3}{x+7}$ D. $\dfrac{x}{x+1}$

13. What is the solution set of $7x + 29 = -\dfrac{30}{x}$?   13. ___C___
A. $\left\{-\dfrac{6}{7}, 5\right\}$ B. $\left\{\dfrac{6}{7}, -5\right\}$ C. $\left\{-\dfrac{15}{7}, -2\right\}$ D. $\varnothing$

14. What is the solution set of $\dfrac{n}{n - 4} + n = \dfrac{12 - 4n}{n - 4}$?   14. ___A___
A. $\{-4, 3\}$ B. $\{4, -3\}$ C. $\{-4\}$ D. $\{3\}$

15. Two numbers are in the ratio of 7 to 10. If 24 is added to each number, the resulting numbers are in the ratio of 1 to 2. Find the smaller of the two original numbers.   15. ___D___
A. -6 B. -42 C. 42   D. -60

16. If y varies inversely as x and $y = \dfrac{2}{3}$ when $x = -10$, what is y when $x = 15$?   16. ___B___
A. $\dfrac{4}{9}$ B. $-\dfrac{4}{9}$ C. -1 D. -100

17. If y varies directly as x and $y = 4$ when $x = -2$, what is y when $x = 30$?   17. ___C___
A. $-\dfrac{14}{15}$ B. 210   C. -210 D. $\dfrac{14}{15}$

18. Which equation represents the graph shown?   18. ___A___
A. $y = \dfrac{3}{x + 2}$ B. $y = \dfrac{3}{x - 2}$
C. $y = \dfrac{x}{x + 2}$ D. $y = \dfrac{x}{x - 2}$

19. If y varies jointly as x and z and $y = 60$, when $x = 10$ and $z = -3$, find y when $x = 8$ and $z = 15$.   19. ___A___
A. -240 B. 15   C. 240   D. -15

20. Tomas can do a job in 4 hours. Julia can do the same job in 3 hours. How many hours will it take the two of them to do the job if they work together?   20. ___B___
A. $\dfrac{7}{12}$ B. $\dfrac{12}{7}$ C. $\dfrac{1}{7}$ D. 7

Bonus A ship's propeller has blades that are ℓ feet long and that rotate at n revolutions per minute to produce a force of F tons. F varies jointly as the fourth power of ℓ and the square of n: $F = k\ell^4 n^2$. If ℓ is halved, what happens to F?   Bonus ___D___
A. halved   B. doubled   C. multiplied by 16   D. multiplied by $\dfrac{1}{16}$

Instructional Resources

Three multiple-choice tests and three free-response tests are provided in the *Assessment and Evaluation Masters.* Forms 1A and 2A are for honors pacing, and Forms 1B, 1C, 2B, and 2C are for average pacing. Chapter 9 Test, Form 1B is shown at the right. Chapter 9 Test, Form 2B is shown on the next page.

Skills and Concepts Encourage students to refer to the objectives and examples on the left as they complete the review exercises on the right.

Assessment and Evaluation Masters, pp. 233–234

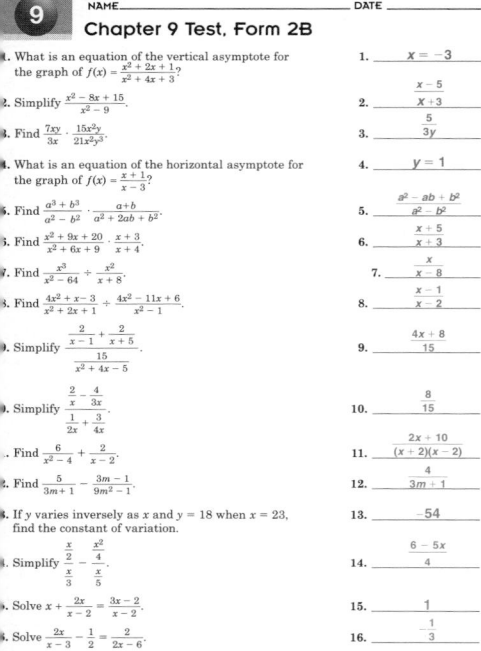

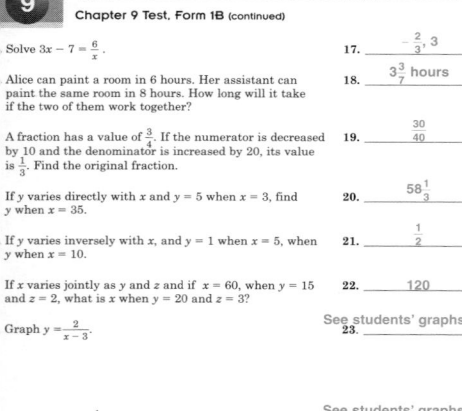

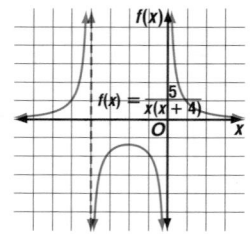

● **SKILLS AND CONCEPTS** ●

OBJECTIVES AND EXAMPLES

Upon completing this chapter, you should be able to:

● graph rational functions (Lesson 9–1)

Graph $f(x) = \dfrac{5}{x(x+4)}$.

REVIEW EXERCISES

Use these exercises to review and prepare for the chapter test.
9–13. See margin for graphs.
State the equations of the vertical and horizontal asymptotes for each rational function. Then graph each rational function.

9. $f(x) = \dfrac{4}{x-2}$ $x = 2; y = 0$

10. $f(x) = \dfrac{x}{x+3}$ $x = -3; y = 1$

11. $f(x) = \dfrac{2}{x}$ $x = 0; y = 0$

12. $f(x) = \dfrac{x-4}{x+3}$ $x = -3; y = 1$

13. $f(x) = \dfrac{5}{(x+1)(x-3)}$ $x = 3, x = -1; y = 0$

● solve problems involving direct, inverse, and joint variation (Lesson 9–2)

direct: $y = kx$
inverse: $xy = k$
joint: $y = kxz$

If y varies inversely as x and $x = 14$ when $y = -6$, find x when $y = -11$.

$$\dfrac{x_1}{y_2} = \dfrac{x_2}{y_1}$$

$$\dfrac{14}{-11} = \dfrac{x_2}{-6}$$

$$-11x_2 = -84$$

$$x_2 = \dfrac{84}{11} \text{ or } 7.\overline{63}$$

The value of x when $y = -11$ is $\dfrac{84}{11}$ or $7.\overline{63}$.

Write an equation for each statement. Then solve the equation. 14. $y = 3x\,; -\dfrac{5}{3}$

14. If y varies directly as x and $y = 21$ when $x = 7$, find x when $y = -5$.

15. If y varies inversely as x and $y = 9$ when $x = 2.5$, find y when $x = -0.6$.
    15. $xy = 22.5; -37.5$

16. If y varies inversely as x and $x = 28$ when $y = 18$, find x when $y = 63$. $xy = 504; 8$

17. If y varies directly as x and $x = 28$ when $y = 18$, find x when $y = 63$.
    17. $y = \dfrac{9}{14}x; 98$

18. If y varies jointly as x and z and $x = 2$ and $z = 4$ when $y = 16$, find y when $x = 5$ and $z = 8$. $y = 2xz; 80$

19. If y varies jointly as x and z and $x = 4$ and $z = 2$ when $y = 25$, find x when $y = 12$ and $z = 20$. $y = \dfrac{25}{8}xz; 0.192$

GLENCOE *Technology*

◎ **Test and Review Software**

You may use this software, a combination of an item generator and item bank, to create your own tests or worksheets. Types of items include free response, multiple choice, short answer, and open ended.

For IBM & Macintosh

Additional Answers

OBJECTIVES AND EXAMPLES

REVIEW EXERCISES

• simplify rational expressions (Lesson 9–3)

$$\frac{3x}{2y} \cdot \frac{8y^3}{6x^2} = \frac{\overset{1}{3} \cdot \overset{1}{x} \cdot \overset{4}{8} \cdot \overset{y^2}{y^3}}{\underset{1}{2} \cdot \underset{1}{y} \cdot \underset{2}{6} \cdot \underset{x}{x^2}}$$

$$= \frac{2y^2}{x}$$

$$\frac{x^2 - 4}{x^2 - 9} \div \frac{x + 2}{x - 3} = \frac{x^2 - 4}{x^2 - 9} \cdot \frac{x - 3}{x + 2}$$

$$= \frac{\overset{1}{(x+2)}(x-2)\overset{1}{(x-3)}}{(x+3)\underset{1}{(x-3)}\underset{1}{(x+2)}}$$

$$= \frac{x - 2}{x + 3}$$

Simplify each expression.

20. $\frac{-4ab}{21c} \cdot \frac{14c^2}{22a^2}$ $\frac{-4bc}{33a}$

21. $\frac{y - 2}{a - 3} \cdot (a - 3)$ $y - 2$

22. $\frac{a^2 - b^2}{6b} \div \frac{a + b}{36b^2}$ $6b(a - b)$

23. $\frac{5x(x + y)}{a} \div \frac{25x^3(x + y)}{a^2}$ $\frac{a}{5x^2}$

24. $\frac{y^2 - y - 12}{y + 2} \div \frac{y - 4}{y^2 - 4y - 12}$ $(y + 3)(y - 6)$

25. $\frac{x^2 + 3x - 10}{x^2 + 8x + 15} \cdot \frac{x^2 + 5x + 6}{x^2 + 4x + 4}$ $\frac{x - 2}{x + 2}$

• Simplify complex fractions (Lesson 9–3)

$$\frac{\dfrac{p^2 + 7p}{3p}}{\dfrac{49 - p^2}{3p - 21}} = \frac{p^2 + 7p}{3p} \div \frac{49 - p^2}{3p - 21}$$

$$= \frac{p^2 + 7p}{3p} \cdot \frac{3p - 21}{49 - p^2}$$

$$= \frac{\overset{1}{p}\overset{1}{(p + 7)}}{\underset{1}{3p}} \cdot \frac{\overset{1}{3}\overset{1}{(p - 7)}}{-(p + 7)(p - 7)}$$

$$= -1$$

Simplify each expression.

26. $\dfrac{\dfrac{1}{x}}{\dfrac{2x}{17}}$ $\dfrac{17}{2x^2}$

27. $\dfrac{\dfrac{1}{n^2 - 6n + 9}}{\dfrac{n + 3}{2n^2 - 18}}$ $\dfrac{2}{n - 3}$

28. $\dfrac{\dfrac{x^2 + 7x + 10}{x + 2}}{\dfrac{x^2 + 2x - 15}{x + 2}}$ $\dfrac{x + 2}{x - 3}$

• add and subtract rational expressions
(Lesson 9–4)

$$\frac{14}{x + y} - \frac{9x}{x^2 - y^2} = \frac{14}{x + y} - \frac{9x}{(x + y)(x - y)}$$

$$= \frac{14(x - y) - 9x}{(x + y)(x - y)}$$

$$= \frac{14x - 14y - 9x}{(x + y)(x - y)}$$

$$= \frac{5x - 14y}{(x + y)(x - y)}$$

Simplify each expression.

29. $\frac{-9}{4a} + \frac{7}{3b}$ $\frac{28a - 27b}{12ab}$

30. $\frac{x + 2}{x - 5} + 6$ $\frac{7(x - 4)}{x - 5}$

31. $\frac{x - 1}{x^2 - 1} + \frac{2}{5x + 5}$ $\frac{7}{5(x + 1)}$

32. $\frac{7}{y} - \frac{2}{3y}$ $\frac{19}{3y}$

33. $\frac{7}{y - 2} - \frac{11}{2 - y}$ $\frac{18}{y - 2}$

34. $\frac{3}{4b} - \frac{2}{5b} - \frac{1}{2b}$ $-\frac{3}{20b}$

35. $\frac{m + 3}{m^2 - 6m + 9} - \frac{8m - 24}{9 - m^2}$ $\frac{3(3m^2 - 14m + 27)}{(m + 3)(m - 3)^2}$

9.
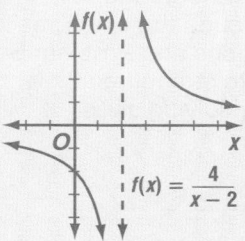
$f(x) = \frac{4}{x - 2}$

10.
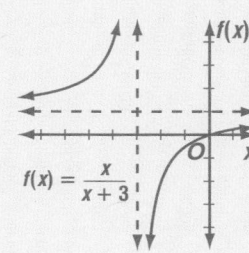
$f(x) = \frac{x}{x + 3}$

11.
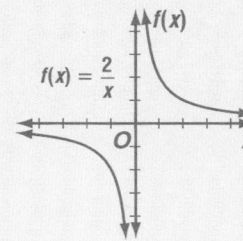
$f(x) = \frac{2}{x}$

12.
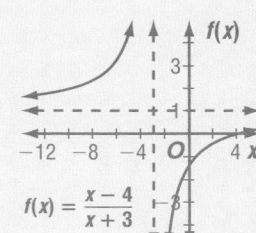
$f(x) = \frac{x - 4}{x + 3}$

13.
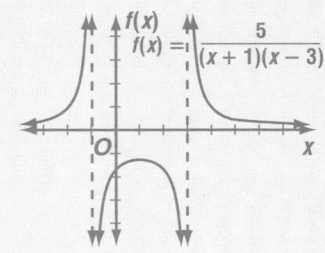
$f(x) = \frac{5}{(x + 1)(x - 3)}$

Applications and Problem Solving Encourage students to work through the exercises in the Applications and Problem Solving section to strengthen their problem-solving skills.

OBJECTIVES AND EXAMPLES

• solve rational equations (Lesson 9–5)

Solve $\frac{1}{x-1} + \frac{2}{x} = 0$.

The LCD for the two denominators is $x(x - 1)$.
Multiply each side of the equation by the LCD.

$$\frac{1}{x-1} + \frac{2}{x} = 0$$

$$x(x-1)\left(\frac{1}{x-1} + \frac{2}{x}\right) = x(x-1)(0)$$

$$x(x-1)\left(\frac{1}{x-1}\right) + x(x-1)\left(\frac{2}{x}\right) = x(x-1)(0)$$

$$1(x) + 2(x-1) = 0$$

$$x + 2x - 2 = 0$$

$$3x - 2 = 0$$

$$3x = 2$$

$$x = \frac{2}{3}$$

REVIEW EXERCISES

Solve each equation. Check your solutions.

36. $\frac{3}{y} + \frac{7}{y} = 9$ $\frac{10}{9}$

37. $1 + \frac{5}{y-1} = \frac{7}{6}$ **31**

38. $\frac{3x+2}{4} = \frac{9}{4} - \frac{3-2x}{6}$ **3**

39. $\frac{1}{r^2-1} = \frac{2}{r^2+r-2}$ **0**

40. $\frac{x}{x^2-1} + \frac{2}{x+1} = 1 + \frac{1}{2x-2}$ $\frac{3}{2}$

APPLICATIONS AND PROBLEM SOLVING

41. **Physics** The current I in an electrical circuit varies inversely with the resistance R in the circuit. (Lesson 9–2)

    a. Use the table below to write an equation relating the current and the resistance.
    $$I = \frac{6}{R}$$

I (amperes)	0.5	1.0	1.5	2.0	2.5	3.0	5.0
R (ohms)	12	6.0	4.0	3.0	2.4	2.0	1.2

    b. What is the constant of variation?   **6**

42. **Number Theory** The denominator of a fraction is 1 less than twice the numerator. If 7 is added to both the numerator and denominator, the resulting fraction has a value of $\frac{7}{10}$. Find the original fraction.
    (Lesson 9–5) $\frac{7}{13}$

43. **Auto Mechanics** When air is pumped into a tire, the pressure required varies inversely as the volume of the air. If the pressure is 30 lb/in^2 when the volume is 140 in^3, find the pressure when the volume is 100 in^3. (Lesson 9–2)
    42 lb/in^2

A practice test for Chapter 9 is provided on page 920.

ALTERNATIVE ASSESSMENT

COOPERATIVE LEARNING PROJECT

Saving for College   In this chapter, you explored rational functions. You graphed rational functions, simplified rational expressions, and solved rational equations. These equations were helpful in solving application problems.

In this project, you will organize a painting job. College Craft is the name of a painting company that uses college students to do its painting in the summer. The following list shows the students that Frank Anstine, the manager, knows will be returning this summer to paint, their experience, and their hourly rate of pay.

> José - 3 years experience - $12.00
> Brittany - 1 year experience - $8.00
> John - 1 year experience - $8.00

He also has two new students joining the company. They don't have any experience, and he will pay each of them $6.00/hour.

Mr. Anstine has received a job that will involve painting the outside of a house, including the trim. This job will take approximately 45 hours of time for one person to do it. Of this time, 15 hours would be in trim work. Brittany and José are the two best trim painters of the experienced students. Who should Mr. Anstine put on the paint and trim jobs in order to get the best work but at a low cost to him? He uses several students for each job in order to get the job done in less days.

Follow these steps to accomplish your task.

- Organize the data that you have.
- Determine a rational model to describe the amount of time it will take for various combinations of students to work.
- Determine what each of these combinations will cost Frank to pay the workers.
- Determine what needs to be changed in your model when changing the worker combinations.
- Use graphs to help show your conclusion.
- Write a paragraph describing the problem and your solution.

THINKING CRITICALLY

- Explain why, in the definition of joint variation, there is the restriction that $x \neq 0$ and $z \neq 0$.
- Are $\frac{1}{4x} = \frac{1}{7x}$ and $4x = 7x$ equivalent equations? Explain your answer. What happens when you multiply each side of the first equation by the LCD?

PORTFOLIO

Write an application problem for each of the three types of variations: direct, inverse, and joint. Solve each problem and then describe why your problems apply to each of the variations and what your answers mean in reference to the problems. Place this in your portfolio.

SELF EVALUATION

Comparing various methods and outcomes can help when making a decision about a problem. To compare is to examine the qualities of two or more things in order to discover similarities or differences.

Assess yourself. Do you use comparison when determining a strategy to use? Do you compare time, efficiency, and completeness of a method when determining how to solve a problem? Give an example of two different methods that can be used on a certain math and/or daily life problem. Write an explanation of the comparison of the two methods and which one would be best to use for that specific problem.

Chapter 9   Study Guide and Assessment **589**

Assessment and Evaluation Masters, pp. 238, 249

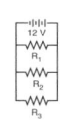

9   NAME_____ DATE_____

Chapter 9 Performance Assessment

Instructions: *Demonstrate your knowledge by giving a clear, concise solution to each problem. Be sure to include all relevant drawings and justify your answers. You may show your solution in more than one way or investigate beyond the requirements of the problem.*

1. When several electrical devices are connected together in series, the resistance R of the combination is equal to the sum of the resistances of the individuals.

$$R_n = R_1 + R_2 + R_3$$

   When resistors are connected together in parallel, the reciprocal of the resistance R of the combination is given by the sum of the reciprocals of the individual resistance.

$$\frac{1}{R_n} = \frac{1}{R_1} + \frac{1}{R_2} + \frac{1}{R_3}$$

   a. Find the resistance of the electrical circuit below if $R_1 = 2$, $R_2 = \frac{4}{x-1}$, $R_3 = \frac{3}{x}$, and $R_4 = \frac{4-8x}{x^2-x}$. Show your work.

   b. Find the resistance of the circuit at the right if $R_1 = \frac{x-y}{x}$, $R_2 = \frac{y^2-x^2}{2y^2}$, and $R_3 = \frac{x+y}{2x}$. Show your work.

   c. Draw an electrical circuit. Assign resistances to each resistor in terms of x. Then find the resistance of the circuit.

2. The average age of a group of newscasters and weather reporters is 40 years. If the average age of the newscasters is 54 years and the average age of the weather reporters is 32 years, what is the ratio of the number of newscasters to weather reporters? Explain your reasoning.

Scoring Guide
Chapter 9
Performance Assessment

Level	Specific Criteria
3 Superior	· Shows thorough understanding of the concepts of *simplifying rational expressions* and *solving rational equations*. · Uses appropriate strategies to solve problems. · Computations are correct. · Written explanations are exemplary. · Diagrams are accurate and appropriate. · Goes beyond requirements of problem.
2 Satisfactory, with Minor Flaws	· Shows understanding of the concepts of *simplifying rational expressions* and *solving rational equations*. · Uses appropriate strategies to solve problems. · Computations are mostly correct. · Written explanations are effective. · Diagrams are mostly accurate and appropriate. · Satisfies most requirements of problem.
1 Nearly Satisfactory, with Serious Flaws	· Shows understanding of most of the concepts of *simplifying rational expressions* and *solving rational equations*. · May not use appropriate strategies to solve problems. · Computations are mostly correct. · Written explanations are satisfactory. · Diagrams are mostly accurate and appropriate. · Satisfies most requirements of problem.
0 Unsatisfactory	· Shows little or no understanding of the concepts of *simplifying rational expressions* and *solving rational equations*. · May not use appropriate strategies to solve problems. · Computations are incorrect. · Written explanations are not satisfactory. · Diagrams are not accurate or appropriate. · Does not satisfy requirements of problem.

Alternative Assessment

The Alternative Assessment section provides students with the opportunity to assess their own work by thinking critically, working with others, keeping a portfolio, and honestly evaluating their own progress. For more information on alternative forms of assessment, see *Alternative Assessment in the Mathematics Classroom,* one of the titles in the Glencoe Mathematics Professional Series.

Performance Assessment

Performance Assessment tasks for this chapter are included in the *Assessment and Evaluation Masters.* A scoring guide is also provided.

NCTM Standards: 1–6

This Investigation is designed to be completed over several days or weeks. It may be considered optional. You may want to assign the Investigation and the follow-up activities to be completed at the same time.

Objective

Conduct experiments and analyze the data to formulate a report about the specifications and equipment needed to produce bungee jumping equipment.

Mathematical Overview

This Investigation will use the following mathematical skills and concepts from Chapters 10 and 11.

- making charts and graphs
- solving and evaluating equations using logarithms
- finding the nth term of an arithmetic sequence
- finding arithmetic means

Recommended Time

Part	Pages	Time
Investigation	590–591	1 class period
Working on the Investigation	616, 630, 655, 682	20 minutes each
Closing the Investigation	702	1 class period

Instructional Resources

Investigations and Projects Masters, pp. 17–20

A recording sheet, teacher notes, and scoring guide are provided for each Investigation in the *Investigations and Projects Masters.*

1 MOTIVATION

This Investigation uses common materials to investigate the specifications needed to produce bungee jumping equipment. Ask students if they have seen people bungee jumping. Discuss the importance of wearing and using the right equipment for this sport.

LONG-TERM PROJECT

In·ves·ti·ga·tion

MATERIALS NEEDED

centimeter ruler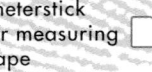

goggles

masking tape

meterstick or measuring tape

washers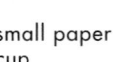

packaging tape

paper clip

rubber bands (3 different sizes)

small paper cup

wooden dowels

Have you ever considered bungee jumping? Modern bungee jumping dates back to April Fool's Day 1979 when members of the Oxford Dangerous Sports Club of Britain jumped off the 245-foot Clifton Bridge in Bristol, England, with bungee cords attached to their ankles. They were wearing tuxedos and top hats in honor of the occasion.

Suppose you work for a sporting goods manufacturer. Your company has decided to produce bungee jumping equipment. They believe the sport will "take off." You will lead a team of engineers who will investigate the specifications and equipment needed to produce bungee jumping equipment. You have been asked to create a detailed report of your findings. You will need to conduct research experiments before beginning the design process.

You decide that you need to conduct a number of experiments on the elasticity of the bungee. In the first experiment you will shoot a rubber band bungee and measure how far it will fly when stretched various lengths. You will also explore the maximum spring potential of the bungee. Realizing that the weight of a person is also a factor, you will experiment with weight and the springiness of the materials used.

In this Investigation, you will conduct research experiments and then analyze the data to formulate a detailed report. Your design team consists of three people. For the protection of everyone in the classroom, each person must wear protective goggles or eyeglasses during the experiments.

Make an Investigation Folder in which you can store all of your work on this Investigation for future use.

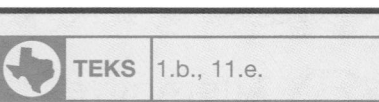

Cooperative Learning

This Investigation offers an excellent opportunity for using cooperative learning groups. For more information on cooperative learning strategies and group management, see *Cooperative Learning in the Mathematics Classroom,* one of the titles in the Glencoe Mathematics Professional Series.

TEKS | 1.b., 11.e.

DISTANCE STRETCHED (NEAREST CENTIMETER)	DISTANCE SHOT (NEAREST TENTH OF A METER)	DIFFERENCE FROM PREVIOUS SHOT
(natural state)	0	0.0

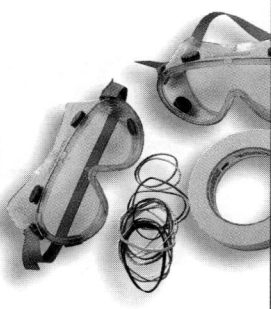

SETUP

1 Make three copies of the table. Select three rubber bands of different sizes.

2 Use masking tape to mark a starting line for your group on the floor. Mark a parallel line five meters away.

3 Select one rubber band for the first set of experiments. Measure the length of the rubber band in centimeters in its natural state (not stretched). Record this length in the first row of column 1.

4 Place one end of the rubber band over the end of a centimeter ruler. Hold the ruler chest-high, parallel to the floor, with the shooting edge directly above the starting line marked on the floor. Pull back the rubber band to a little past its natural state. For example, if a rubber band measures 5 centimeters in its natural state, then pull the rubber band so it stretches to 6 centimeters.

DATA COLLECTION

5 Use the table to record the length to which the rubber band was stretched. Measure how far the rubber band flew by measuring the distance from the starting line to the spot where the rubber band landed. Use a meterstick or measuring tape to measure the distance shot to the nearest tenth of a meter. Record this distance in column 2. Note that the first measurement will be in centimeters and the second in meters.

6 Shoot the rubber band again, increasing the distance the rubber band is stretched by 1 centimeter and measuring the distance the rubber band travels. Record the measurements in columns 1 and 2 of your table.

7 Continue to shoot the rubber band, increasing the distance it is stretched by 1 centimeter for each trial, until the rubber band will no longer stretch or it breaks. Record the distances in column 2. *Column 3 will be used later in the Investigation.*

8 Repeat this experiment using the other two rubber bands. Record the data in your other two tables.

You will continue working on this Investigation throughout Chapters 10 and 11.

Be sure to keep your tables, graphs, and other materials in your Investigation Folder.

Boing!! Investigation

Working on the Investigation
Lesson 10–3, p. 616
• • • • • • • • • • • • • • •
Working on the Investigation
Lesson 10–6, p. 630
• • • • • • • • • • • • • • •
Working on the Investigation
Lesson 11–1, p. 655
• • • • • • • • • • • • • • •
Working on the Investigation
Lesson 11–5, p. 682
• • • • • • • • • • • • • • •
Closing the Investigation
End of Chapter 11, p. 702
• • • • • • • • • • • • • • •

Investigation: Boing!! **591**

2 SETUP

You may have a student read the first two paragraphs of the Investigation to provide information about bungee jumping. You may then read the next three paragraphs, which introduce the activity. Discuss the activity with students. Then separate the class into groups of four.

3 MANAGEMENT

Each group member should be responsible for a specific task.

Recorder Collects data.
Measurer 1 Sets and measures the distances to shoot the rubber bands.
Measurer 2 Selects rubber bands and measures lengths of rubber bands.
Calculator Finds the difference from previous shots.

At the end of the activity, each member should turn in his or her respective equipment.

Sample Answers

Answers will vary as they are based on the distance chosen by each group.

Investigations and Projects Masters, p. 20

10, 11 NAME_____ DATE_____
Investigation, Chapters 10 and 11 Student Edition Pages 590–591, 616, 630, 655, 682, 702

Boing!

Use this section to draw your scatter plots and record your calculations from Working on the Investigation from Lesson 11-5.

First Experiment

Second Experiment

Equation relating the weight of the cup and the length the rubber band stretches:

Equation relating the weight of the cup and the length the rubber band stretches:

Third Experiment

Equation relating the weight of the cup and the length the rubber band stretches:

Please keep this page and any other research in your Investigation folder.

Exploring Exponential and Logarithmic Functions

PREVIEWING THE CHAPTER

This chapter begins with the use of graphing technology to graph exponential functions. Curve fitting using graphing technology is integrated to help students find an equation that describes data from real-world situations. Then students apply their knowledge of integers used as exponents to simplify expressions and solve equations where real numbers are used as exponents. Next, students learn to differentiate between exponential and logarithmic equations. They derive the properties of logarithms from the properties of exponents. Students are introduced to common and natural logarithms to solve equations with variable exponents.

Lesson (Pages)	Lesson Objectives	NCTM Standards	State/Local Objectives
10-1A (594–595)	Use a graphing calculator to draw graphs of exponential functions.	1–6	1.a., 4.b., 11.a., 11.b., 11.c., 11.d.
10-1 (596–602)	Simplify expressions and solve equations and inequalities involving real exponents.	1–6	1.a., 2.a., 4.a., 4.b., 11.b., 11.c., 11.d., 11.e.
10-1B (603–604)	Use a graphing calculator to fit a curve to a scatter plot of real-world data.	1–6, 10	1.b., 11.e.
10-2 (605–610)	Write exponential equations in logarithmic form and vice versa. Evaluate logarithmic expressions. Solve equations and inequalities involving logarithmic functions.	1–6	2.a., 4.a., 4.c., 11.a., 11.b., 11.c., 11.d., 11.e.
10-3 (611–616)	Simplify and evaluate expressions using properties of logarithms. Solve equations involving logarithms.	1–6	2.a., 11.c., 11.d., 11.e.
10-4 (617–621)	Identify the characteristic and the mantissa of a logarithm. Find common logarithms and antilogarithms.	1–6	
10-5 (622–625)	Find natural logarithms of numbers.	1–6	
10-6 (626–630)	Solve equations with variable exponents by using logarithms. Evaluate expressions involving logarithms with different bases. Solve problems by using estimation.	1–6	2.a., 11.c., 11.d., 11.e.
10-7 (631–636)	Use logarithms to solve problems involving growth and decay.	1–6	11.c., 11.d., 11.e.

A complete, 1-page lesson plan is provided for each lesson in the *Lesson Planning Guide*. Answer keys for each lesson are available in the *Answer Key Masters*.

You may want to refer to the **Course Planning Calendar** on page T12 for detailed information on pacing.
PACING: Standard—12 days; **Honors**—11 days; **Block**—5 days

LESSON PLANNING CHART

| Lesson (Pages) | Materials/ Manipulatives | Extra Practice (Student Edition) | BLACKLINE MASTERS | | | | | | | | | Real-World Applications | Interactive Mathematics Tools Software | Teaching Transparencies |
			Study Guide	Practice	Enrichment	Assessment and Evaluation	Modeling Mathematics	Multicultural Activity	Tech Prep Applications	Graphing Calculator	Science and Math Lab Manual			
10-1A (594–595)	graphing calculator									pp. 51, 52				
10-1 (596–602)	graphing calculator	p. 898	p. 69	p. 69	p. 69		pp. 52–54	p. 19						10-1A 10-1B
10-1B (603–604)	graphing calculator									pp. 53, 54				
10-2 (605–610)		p. 899	p. 70	p. 70	p. 70	p. 268				p. 10		27	10-2	10-2A 10-2B
10-3 (611–616)		p. 899	p. 71	p. 71	p. 71									10-3A 10-3B
10-4 (617–621)	calculator	p. 899	p. 72	p. 72	p. 72	pp. 267, 268						28		10-4A 10-4B
10-5 (622–625)	scientific calculator	p. 900	p. 73	p. 73	p. 73						pp. 99–104			10-5A 10-5B
10-6 (626–630)		p. 900	p. 74	p. 74	p. 74	p. 269	p. 70		p. 19				10-6	10-6A 10-6B
10-7 (631–636)	calculator graphing calculator	p. 900	p. 75	p. 75	p. 75	p. 269		p. 20	p. 20				10-7	10-7A 10-7B
Study Guide/ Assessment (637–641)						pp. 253 –266, 270 –272								

ORGANIZING THE CHAPTER

OTHER CHAPTER RESOURCES

Student Edition
Investigation, pp. 590–591
Chapter Opener, pp. 592–593
Mathematics and Society, p. 610
Working on the Investigation,
pp. 616, 630

Teacher's Classroom Resources
Investigations and Projects Masters,
pp. 61–64

Technology
Teacher's Guide for Software
Resources
Test and Review Software (IBM
and Macintosh)
CD-ROM Interactions (Windows
and Macintosh)

Professional Publications
Block Scheduling Booklet
Glencoe Mathematics Professional
Series

OUTSIDE RESOURCES

Books/Periodicals
Kelly, Brendan, *Exploring Functions with the TI-82
Graphics Calculator*
Shell Centre for Mathematical Education, *The
Language of Functions and Graphs*

Software
Algebra II, Part I, IBM

Videos/CD-ROMs
*Using Graphing Calculators in Mathematics
Education*, NASCO

See the *Teacher's Guide for Software Resources* for software addresses.

ASSESSMENT RESOURCES

Student Edition
Math Journal, pp. 614, 619
Mixed Review, pp. 602, 609,
616, 621, 625, 629, 636
Self Test, p. 621
Chapter Highlights, p. 637
Chapter Study Guide and
Assessment, pp. 638–640
Alternative Assessment, p. 641
Portfolio, p. 641

College Entrance Exam Practice,
pp. 642–643

Teacher's Wraparound Edition
5-Minute Check, pp. 596, 605,
611, 617, 622, 626, 631
Check for Understanding, pp. 599,
608, 614, 619, 624, 628, 633
Closing Activity, pp. 602, 610,
616, 621, 625, 630, 636
Cooperative Learning, pp. 606,
623

Assessment and Evaluation Masters
Multiple-Choice Tests, Forms 1A
(Honors), 1B (Average), 1C
(Basic), pp. 253–258
Free-Response Tests, Forms 2A
(Honors), 2B (Average), 2C
(Basic), pp. 259–264
Calculator-Based Test, p. 265
Performance Assessment, p. 266
Mid-Chapter Test, p. 267
Quizzes A–D, pp. 268–269
Standardized Test Practice, p. 270
Cumulative Review, pp. 271–272

ENHANCING THE CHAPTER

Examples of some of the materials for enhancing Chapter 10 are shown below.

DIVERSITY

Multicultural Activity Masters, pp. 19, 20

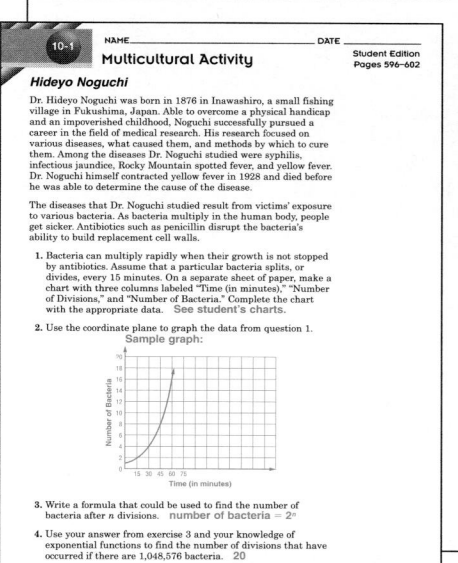

APPLICATIONS

Real-World Applications, 27, 28

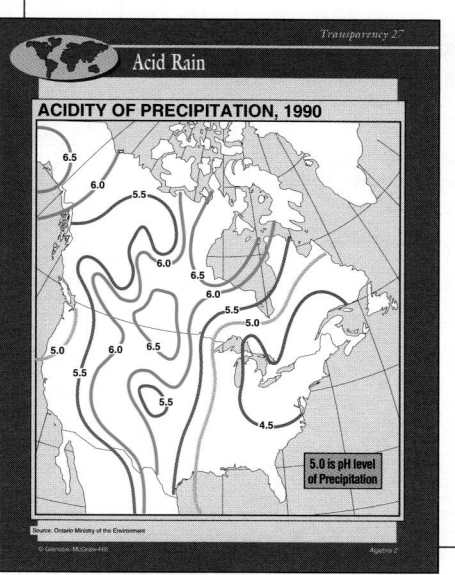

TECHNOLOGY

Graphing Calculator Masters, p. 10

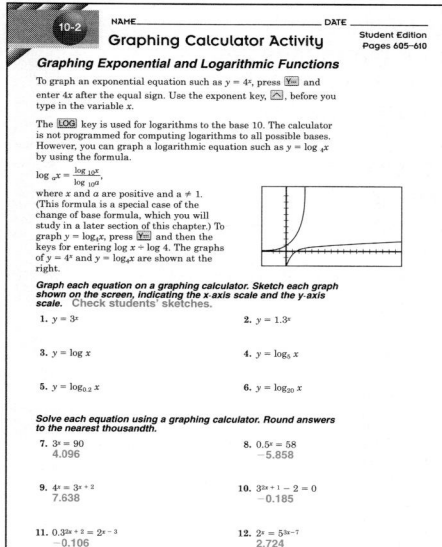

TECH PREP

Tech Prep Applications Masters, pp. 19, 20

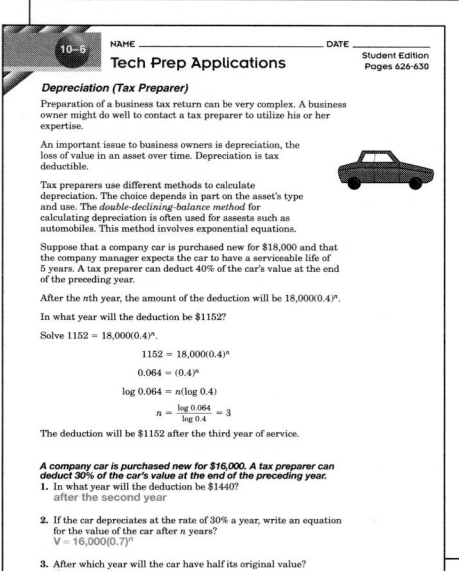

CONNECTIONS

Science and Math Lab Manual, pp. 99–104

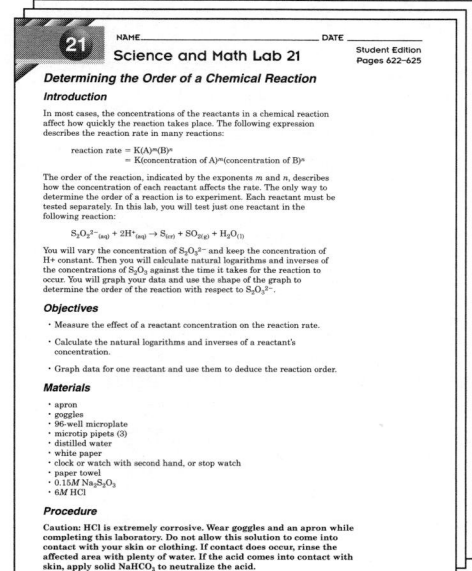

PROBLEM SOLVING

Problem of the Week Cards, 24, 25, 26

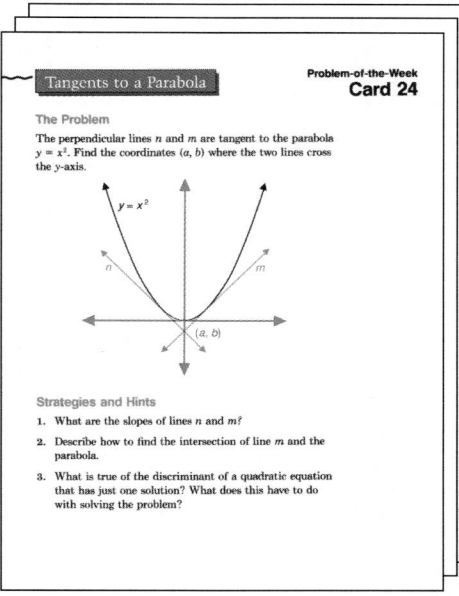

MAKING MATHEMATICS RELEVANT

This two-page introduction to the chapter provides students with an opportunity to explore contemporary topics and their applications to mathematics.

Background Information

AIDS Awareness AIDS is caused by a virus called HIV. Other diseases caused by viruses include the flu, colds, polio, chicken pox, measles, and mumps. HIV is contagious, but is not easily transmitted. You cannot contract it from mosquitoes, shaking hands, or being near someone infected with HIV. You can contract it through sexual contact with someone who has it. Drug users can also get it if they use a needle used by someone infected with HIV. Also, a pregnant woman can pass it on to her unborn child.

CHAPTER 10

Exploring Exponential and Logarithmic Functions

Objectives

In this chapter, you will:

- simplify expressions and solve equations involving real exponents,
- write exponential equations in logarithmic form and vice versa,
- evaluate expressions and solve equations involving logarithms,
- find common and natural logarithms and antilogarithms, and
- solve equations with variable exponents by using logarithms.

AIDS Cases Worldwide

Numbers in Millions

Source: *Weekly Epidemiological Record*

Many teenagers think they are immortal. When the news mentions tragedy, whether violence involving guns, traffic fatalities, or death from AIDS, many teens believe it will never happen to them. The best remedy for this "live forever" attitude is knowledge. Information about firearm safety, teen driving statistics, and the AIDS epidemic is vital for your own personal safety.

TIME Line

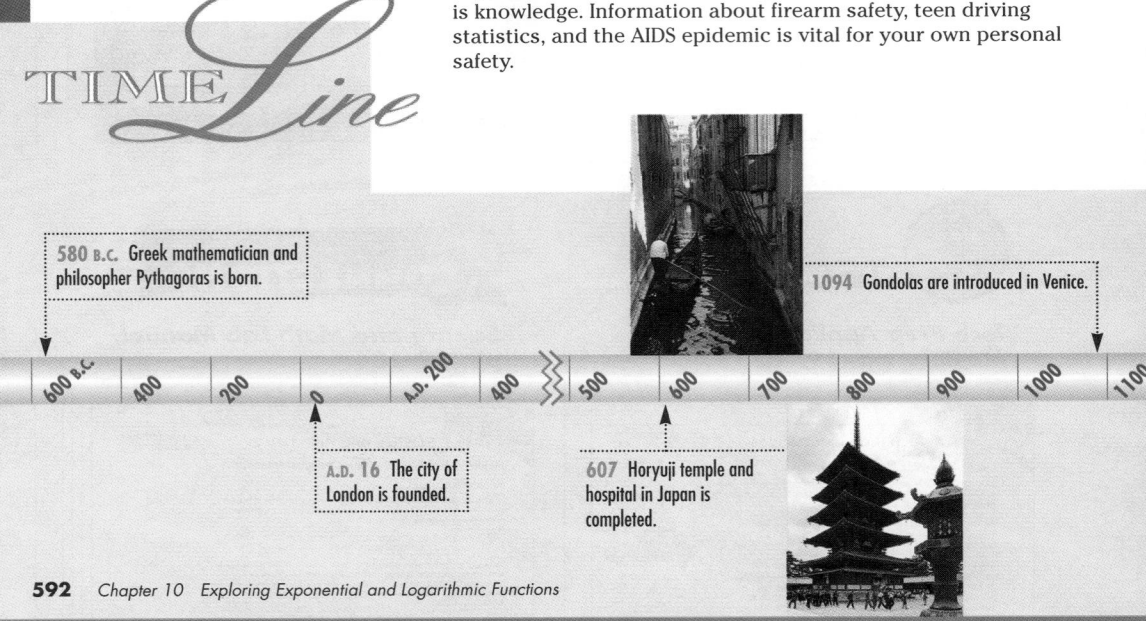

580 B.C. Greek mathematician and philosopher Pythagoras is born.

1094 Gondolas are introduced in Venice.

A.D. 16 The city of London is founded.

607 Horyuji temple and hospital in Japan is completed.

592   Chapter 10   Exploring Exponential and Logarithmic Functions

TIME Line

Students might find it interesting to report on Pythagoras of Samos. Not only is he responsible for the Pythagorean theorem, but he also founded a mystical cult which held that the whole universe is explainable in terms of numbers. Certain numbers were believed to have spiritual significance.

interNET CONNECTION

"To children struggling with AIDS we give love, friends, memories, laughter, hope, hugs, high-five's, acceptance, . . ."

World Wide Web
http://www.digital.com/cust/camp

ChapterProject

Research the number of AIDS cases in the United States for each year since 1980.

- Draw a graph for these data.
- Use the coordinates of two points on your graph to write an exponential equation to model the growth in the number of AIDS cases.

- Use your equation to predict the number of AIDS cases in the United States in the year 2010.
- Write a paper about the research being done concerning AIDS. Are there any prospects for a cure for this disease? What can be done to slow the growth in the number of cases each year?

Neil Willenson is a 25-year-old political activist from Wisconsin who wanted to do something to help children with AIDS. He read Ryan White's book about his struggle with AIDS, and this encouraged him to start a summer camp for young children with the disease. He began raising funds. In 1993, Camp Heartland opened and 74 children had a free summer camp experience.

Since then, over a million dollars in private donations have helped hundreds of children with HIV or AIDS have fun at summer camp. Neil was awarded the $25,000 Arthur Ashe Award which he donated to Camp Heartland. He believes "kids need a safe haven where they can go and feel 100% accepted."

Let Neil Willenson speak for himself. "This disease, more than any other, is absolutely preventable: AIDS education and awareness needs to be mandatory in every school. Children are not idiots. They need to know how the disease is transmitted. AIDS education should be age-appropriate, but it should start at kindergarten and be discussed over and over."

ChapterProject

Cooperative Learning Charts and tables should be prepared to display the statistical data for the entire class. Students might want to use computer software to prepare charts, print them on transparencies, and use these as overheads during a class presentation.

1494 The first algebra book is printed.

1889 American Indian Susan La Flesche Picotte becomes a medical doctor.

1605 Spanish writer Miguel de Cervantes publishes his novel *Don Quixote.*

1993 The movie *Jurassic Park* is released.

Chapter 10 **593**

Alternative Chapter Projects

Two other chapter projects are included in the *Investigations and Projects Masters.* In Chapter 10 Project A, pp. 61–62, students extend the topic in the chapter opener. In Chapter 10 Project B, pp. 63–64, students plan the start-up of a small business.

Investigations and Projects Masters, p. 61

10 NAME_____ DATE_____
Chapter 10 Project A
Student Edition
Pages 594–636

Epidemic Proportions

1. Epidemics have always posed a threat to humans. For this project, you will work with a small group to research the Black Death, an epidemic of the disease called plague that ravaged Europe in the 1300s. As you complete your research, answer the following questions.

 • What are the kinds and characteristics of plague? How is it transmitted?

 • How did the Black Death come to Europe and spread between the years 1347 and 1351?

 • How many Europeans are estimated to have died from the plague during those years? What proportion of the population of Europe at that time does this number represent?

 • What preventative measures and treatments exist today for plague?

2. Although isolated cases of plague still crop up from time to time, other infectious diseases are of much greater concern today. Besides AIDS, which has now reached epidemic proportions, diseases such as Ebola, dengue, and hanta virus have made destructive appearances. Research one or more of these diseases. What do scientists think is causing outbreaks? What is being done to combat them? How prevalent are these diseases throughout the world today?

3. Make maps, charts, and graphs to organize and explain the data you collected in exercises 1 and 2.

4. With your group, decide the best way to present the information you have gathered. Possibilities include a multimedia encyclopedia article or a museum exhibit. Include the maps, charts, and graphs you created in exercise 3. Be sure to show how exponential equations can be used to model the spread of epidemics.

10-1A Graphing Technology
Exponential and Logarithmic Functions

A Preview of Lesson 10-1

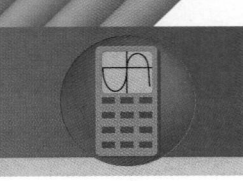

NCTM Standards: 1–6

Objective

Use a graphing calculator to draw graphs of exponential functions.

Recommended Time

25 minutes

Instructional Resources

Graphing Calculator Masters, pp. 51 and 52

These masters provide keystroking instruction for this lesson for the TI-81 and Casio graphing calculators.

1 FOCUS

Motivating the Lesson

Use paint and a piece of paper to illustrate the concept of axis of symmetry. Put paint on one side of a piece of paper. Then fold the paper in half and spread out the paint by pressing on the paper. Where the paper was folded is the axis of symmetry. Unfold the paper and the two sides will have the same design on them. Relate this to the axis of symmetry in graphing.

2 TEACH

Teaching Tip Logarithmic and exponential functions are inverses of each other because the x and y values are interchanged.

Teaching Tip Emphasize to students that the line of symmetry in Example 1 is the graph of $x = 0$, and the line of symmetry in Example 2 is the graph of $y = x$.

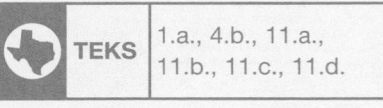

| TEKS | 1.a., 4.b., 11.a., 11.b., 11.c., 11.d. |

You can draw graphs of exponential and logarithmic functions with a graphing calculator. An **exponential function** is a function of the form $y = a^x$, where $a > 0$ and $a \neq 1$. A **logarithmic function** is a function of the form $x = a^y$, where $a > 0$ and $a \neq 1$. It is denoted $y = \log_a x$ and is the inverse of the exponential function $y = a^x$.

Example ❶ Graph $y = 2^x$ and $y = \left(\frac{1}{2}\right)^x$ in the standard viewing window. Then describe any similarities and differences.

Enter: [Y=] 2 [∧] [X,T,θ] [ENTER]
[(] 1 [÷] 2 [)] [∧] [X,T,θ]
[ZOOM] 6

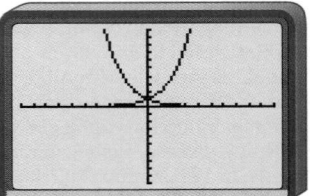

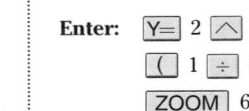

Tips

Remember to clear the *Y* = list before entering a new equation.

The two graphs are reflections of each other with the *y*-axis serving as the axis of symmetry. Both graphs pass through the point $(0, 1)$, and both have the *x*-axis as a horizontal asymptote.

The TI-82 has $y = \log_{10} x$ as a built-in function. Enter [Y=] [LOG] [X,T,θ] [GRAPH] to view this graph.

To graph logarithmic functions with bases other than 10, you must use the **change of base formula**, $\log_a x = \dfrac{\log_{10} x}{\log_{10} a}$. *You will use the change of base formula in Lesson 10-6.*

Example ❷ Graph $y = 2^x$ and $y = \log_2 x$ in the standard viewing window. Then describe any similarities and differences.

Use the change of base formula to graph $y = \log_2 x$.

$$\log_2 x = \frac{\log_{10} x}{\log_{10} 2}$$

Enter: [Y=] 2 [∧] [X,T,θ] [ENTER]
[LOG] [X,T,θ] [÷] [LOG] 2
[ZOOM] 6

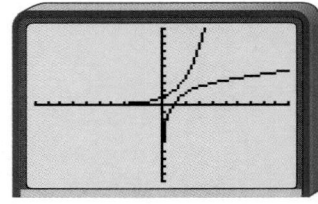

Since these two functions are inverses, the domain of $y = 2^x$, real numbers, is the range of $y = \log_2 x$, and the range of $y = 2^x$, positive real numbers, is the domain of $y = \log_2 x$.

The graphs are reflections of each other over the line $y = x$. TRACE each function and examine the points carefully. For any point on the graph of $y = \log_2 x$, there is a point on the graph of $y = 2^x$ whose coordinates are reversed. For example, $(1, 0)$, $(4, 2)$, and $(8, 3)$ are points on the graphs of $y = \log_2 x$, and $(0, 1)$, $(2, 4)$, and $(3, 8)$ are points on the graph of $y = 2^x$.

594 Chapter 10 *Exploring Exponential and Logarithmic Functions*

LOOK BACK

You can refer to Lesson 6-1A for information on solving solutions by finding the x-intercepts.

There are two methods that can be used with a graphing calculator to find a solution to exponential equations.

Method 1: Graph each side of the equation as a separate function and estimate the point at which they intersect.

Method 2: Rewrite the equation so that one side equals zero. Graph the related function and find the x-intercept.

Example ③ **Find the solution of $3^x = 2^{5x-1}$ to the nearest hundredth. Use the viewing window $[-3, 3]$ by $[-3, 3]$.**

Use the second method to solve the equation.
Rewrite the equation as $3^x - 2^{5x-1} = 0$. Graph the related function $y = 3^x - 2^{5x-1}$.

Enter:

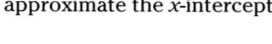

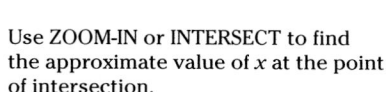

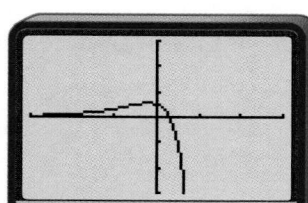

Now use ZOOM-IN or ROOT to approximate the x-intercept.

The solution is about 0.29.

Check this solution using the first method.

Enter: Y= 3 ∧ X,T,θ ENTER

Y= 2 ∧ (5 X,T,θ −

1) GRAPH

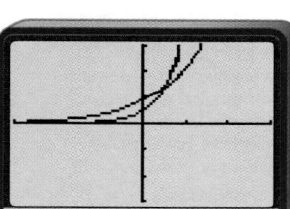

Use ZOOM-IN or INTERSECT to find the approximate value of x at the point of intersection.

The solution of 0.29 is correct.

EXERCISES

Use a graphing calculator to obtain a complete graph of each function. Then sketch the graph on a sheet of paper. 1–6. See margin.

1. $y = 10^x$

2. $y = 3.5^x$

3. $y = 0.1^x$

4. $y = 0.05^x$

5. $y = \log_4 x$

6. $y = \log_{0.3} x$

Solve each equation graphically. Round solutions to the nearest hundredth.

7. $4^x = 8$ 1.50

8. $3.2^x = 52.5$ 3.41

9. $2.1^{x-5} = 9.7$ 8.06

10. $0.65^{x+3} = 3^{2x-1}$ −0.07

11. $2^x = x^2$ −0.77, 2, 4

12. $1.5^x = 2500$ 19.30

13. $\log_{10} x = 0.23$ 1.70

14. $\log_2 (x + 2) = \log_{0.5} 2$ −1.50

15. $\log_9 (x + 4) = \log_2 x$ 1.73

16. $3^{4x-7} = 4^{2x+3}$ 7.30

Using Technology

This lesson offers an excellent opportunity for using technology in your algebra classroom. For more information on using technology, see *Graphing Calculators in the Mathematics Classroom*, one of the titles in the Glencoe Mathematics Professional Series.

Additional Answer

6.

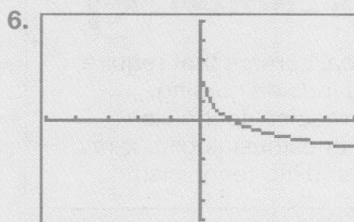

3 PRACTICE/APPLY

Assignment Guide

Core: 1–16
Enriched: 1–16

4 ASSESS

Observing students working with technology is an excellent method of assessment.

Additional Answers

1.

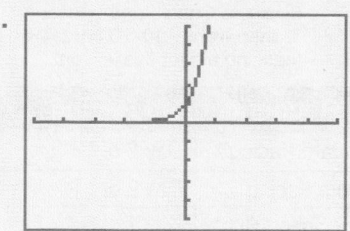

2.

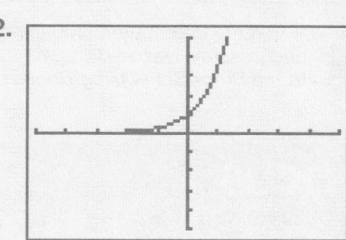

3.

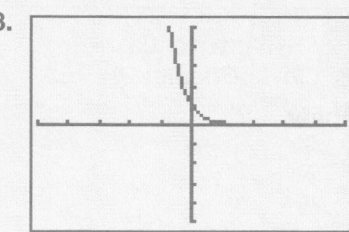

4.

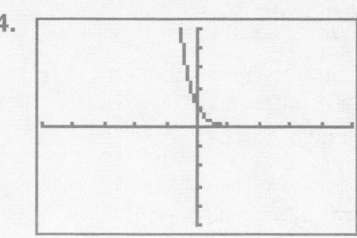

5.

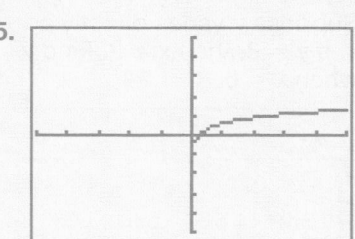

Real Exponents and Exponential Functions

NCTM Standards: 1–6

Instructional Resources

- Study Guide Master 10-1
- Practice Master 10-1
- Enrichment Master 10-1
- Modeling Mathematics Masters, pp. 52–54
- Multicultural Activity Masters, p. 19

Transparency 10-1A contains the 5-Minute Check for this lesson; **Transparency 10-1B** contains a teaching aid for this lesson.

Recommended Pacing	
Standard Pacing	Day 2 of 12
Honors Pacing	Day 2 of 11
Block Scheduling*	Day 1 of 5

*For more information on pacing and possible lesson plans, refer to the *Block Scheduling Booklet*.

1 FOCUS

5-Minute Check
(over Chapter 9)

Simplify.

1. $\dfrac{x-3}{x+2} - \dfrac{x+1}{x-2}$

   $\dfrac{-4(2x-1)}{(x+2)(x-2)}$

2. $\dfrac{b-1}{b} + \dfrac{b}{b+1}$

   $\dfrac{2b^2-1}{b(b+1)}$

3. $\dfrac{x^2-y^2}{8x} \div \dfrac{x+y}{64x^2}$

   $8x(x-y)$

4. Solve $\dfrac{2}{y} - \dfrac{4}{y} = 10$. $-\dfrac{1}{5}$

5. Suppose y varies directly as x. If $y = 8$, then $x = 2$. Find y when $x = 6$. $y = 24$

TEKS 1.a., 2.a., 4.a., 4.b., 11.b., 11.c., 11.d., 11.e.

What YOU'LL LEARN

- To simplify expressions and solve equations and inequalities involving real exponents.

Why IT'S IMPORTANT

You can use exponential functions to solve problems involving disease control and animal behavior.

CAREER CHOICES

A **physician** diagnoses illnesses and prescribes and administers treatment for their patients. They counsel patients about preventive health care.

An undergraduate degree, completion of a 4-year medical school degree, and graduate medical education are required to be a licensed physician.

For more information, contact:
American Medical Association
515 N. State St.
Chicago, IL 60610

Disease Control

In the movie *Outbreak*, a dreadful disease is predicted to spread across the United States in just a matter of days. How could a disease spread so quickly?

Suppose that every 8 hours, a sick person infects 2 people before the disease is diagnosed and he or she is quarantined. Consider each 8 hours as one time period. At the beginning, one individual is infected. During the first time period, this person infects 2 people. During the second time period, the first person is quarantined, but the 2 people he or she infected each infect 2 more people. During the third time period, the 2 people are quarantined, and the 4 people they infected are each responsible for infecting 2 more people. During the third time period, 4×2 or 8 people are infected.

This pattern can be summarized in the table at the right. The number of people infected during a time period y can be expressed as a function of time where x is the number of 8-hour periods. This function, $y = 2^x$, is an **exponential function**.

During the end of the 21st time period (the end of the first week), 2^{21} or 2,097,152 new people will be infected!

Time Period	Number Infected	Pattern
0	1	2^0
1	$1 \times 2 = 2$	2^1
2	$2 \times 2 = 4$	2^2
3	$4 \times 2 = 8$	2^3
4	$8 \times 2 = 16$	2^4
.	.	.
.	.	.
.	.	.
x	y	2^x

Let's take a close look at the graph of $y = 2^x$. Make a table of values to help draw the curve. *Note that negative values of x have no meaning in the example above.*

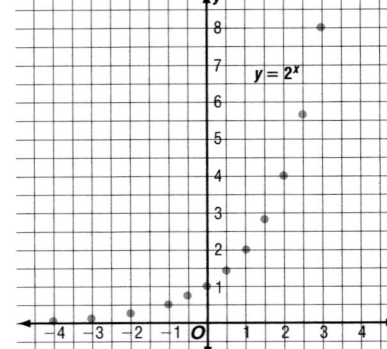

x	2^x or y	y
-4	$2^{-4} = \frac{1}{16}$	0.06
-3	$2^{-3} = \frac{1}{8}$	0.13
-2	$2^{-2} = \frac{1}{4}$	0.25
-1	$2^{-1} = \frac{1}{2}$	0.50
$-\frac{1}{2}$	$2^{-\frac{1}{2}} = \frac{1}{2}\sqrt{2}$	0.71
0	$2^0 = 1$	1

x	2^x or y	y
$\frac{1}{2}$	$2^{\frac{1}{2}} = \sqrt{2}$	1.41
1	$2^1 = 2$	2
$\frac{3}{2}$	$2^{\frac{3}{2}} = 2\sqrt{2}$	2.83
2	$2^2 = 4$	4
$\frac{5}{2}$	$2^{\frac{5}{2}} = 4\sqrt{2}$	5.66
3	$2^3 = 8$	8

CAREER CHOICES

Other medical careers that require less training include nursing, emergency medical technician, paramedic, anesthesiologist, x-ray technician, and lab technician.

F Y I

In the 14th century when the plague, or Black Death, struck Europe, nearly one fourth of the total population died from the great epidemic.

Since 2^x has not been defined when x is irrational, there are "holes" in the graph of $y = 2^x$. We can expand the domain of $y = 2^x$ to include irrational numbers. The domain will then include all real numbers. Draw the graph of $y = 2^x$ with no "holes" in the graph. The set of points on the graph is complete, or *continuous*, and the graph is a smooth curve. You can use the graph of $y = 2^x$ to estimate the value of 2^x when x is any real number.

Use the graph to estimate the value of $2^{\sqrt{3}}$, which is the value of y when $x = \sqrt{3}$.

$1.7 < \sqrt{3} < 1.8$ since $\sqrt{3} \approx 1.732$.

From the graph, the value of y is approximately 3.3.

Use a calculator to check this answer.

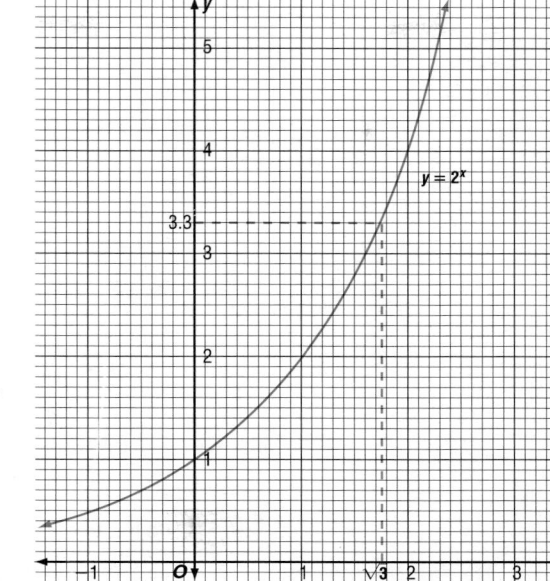

Enter: 2 $\boxed{y^x}$ 3 $\boxed{\sqrt{x}}$

   $\boxed{=}$ *3.32199709*

The calculator verifies the estimation from the graph.

$2^{\sqrt{3}} \approx 3.3$

All properties of rational exponents apply to real exponents.

Example Simplify each expression.

  a. $7^{\sqrt{2}} \cdot 7^{\sqrt{3}}$

  $7^{\sqrt{2}} \cdot 7^{\sqrt{3}} = 7^{\sqrt{2} + \sqrt{3}}$ *Product of powers property*
  You can use your calculator to verify the result.

  b. $\left(8^{\sqrt{3}}\right)^{\sqrt{5}}$

  $\left(8^{\sqrt{3}}\right)^{\sqrt{5}} = 8^{\sqrt{3} \cdot \sqrt{5}}$ *Power of a power property*

  $= 8^{\sqrt{15}}$

In general, an exponential function can be written in the form $y = ab^x$.

Definition of Exponential Function	An equation of the form $y = a \cdot b^x$, where $a \neq 0$, $b > 0$, and $b \neq 1$, is called an exponential function with base b.

Motivating the Lesson
Situational Problem Show students a copy of a family tree. Ask students how many parents, grandparents, and great grandparents a person has. Ask students to consider their answers to the previous questions and to think of a way to determine how many ancestors a person would have a certain number of generations ago.

F Y I

The plague, most likely a mixture of bubonic and pneumonic plagues, caused a severe shortage in manual labor. Many farmers had to pay for labor, which increased the standard of living for artisans and peasants.

2 TEACH

In-Class Example

For Example 1
Simplify each expression.
a. $8^{\sqrt{6}} \cdot 4^{\sqrt{54}}$ $2^{9\sqrt{6}}$

b. $\left(27^{\sqrt{5}}\right)^{\sqrt{2}}$ $27^{\sqrt{10}}$

Teaching Tip Explain to students that a function $y = f(x)$ is an increasing function if y increases as x increases. Also, a function $y = f(x)$ is a decreasing function if y decreases as x increases.

Alternative Teaching Strategies

Student Diversity Review the basic rules for working with exponents. Give illustrations for each.

In-Class Example

For Example 2
Predict the rabbit population in Australia for 1995, presuming no action was taken to curb their increase.
$65,000(6.20)^{130}$; On a calculator, this is an overflow value.

A family of exponential functions is graphed at the right. Notice that $a = 1$ in each case.

$y = 7^x$ *When $b > 1$, the value of y increases as the value of x increases.*

$y = 2^x$

$y = \left(\frac{3}{4}\right)^x$ *When $0 < b < 1$, the value of y increases as the value of x decreases.*

$y = \left(\frac{1}{2}\right)^x$

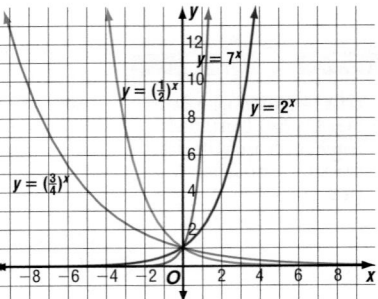

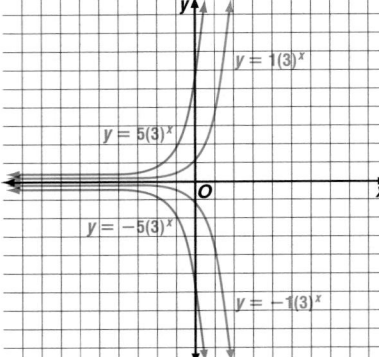

Another family of exponential functions is graphed at the left. Study this family of graphs.

$y = 1(3)^x$
$y = 5(3)^x$ *Notice that the y-intercept*
$y = -1(3)^x$ *of each graph equals the*
$y = -5(3)^x$ *value of a.*

The graph of $y = a \cdot b^x$ is the reflection of $y = -a \cdot b^x$ across the x-axis.

Exponential functions are frequently used to model population growth.

Example ❷

APPLICATION
Animal Control

During the nineteenth century, rabbits were brought to Australia. Since the rabbits had no natural enemies on that continent, their population increased rapidly. Suppose there were 65,000 rabbits in Australia in 1865 and 2,500,000 rabbits in 1867.

a. Write an exponential equation that could be used to model the rabbit population in Australia. Write the equation in terms of the number of years elapsed since 1865.

b. Estimate the Australian rabbit population in 1872.

a. For the year 1865, the time t equals 0, and the initial population p equals 65,000. Substitute these values in the standard exponential equation to find the value of a.

$p = ab^t$
$65{,}000 = ab^0$ *Replace p with 65,000 and t with 0.*
$65{,}000 = a(1)$ $b^0 = 1$
$65{,}000 = a$

For the year 1867, the time t equals 2, and the population p equals 2,500,000. Substitute these values in the standard exponential equation to find the value of b.

$p = ab^t$
$2{,}500{,}000 = 65{,}000b^2$ *Replace p with 2,500,000, a with 65,000, and t with 2.*
$38.46 \approx b^2$ *Division property of equality*
$6.20 \approx b$

The equation that models the rabbit population is $p = 65{,}000(6.20)^t$.

598   Chapter 10   Exploring Exponential and Logarithmic Functions

Alternative Learning Styles

Visual Have students graph several exponential functions on semilog paper. The vertical scale is adjusted so that graphs of exponential functions are straight lines. Point out to students that only when the x-scale and the y-scale are the same can you categorize the function based on its shape.

b. For the year 1872, the time t equals 7.

$$p = 65{,}000(6.20)^t$$
$$= 65{,}000(6.20)^7$$
$$\approx 22{,}890{,}495{,}000$$

According to the equation, the rabbit population was about 22,890,495,000 in 1872.

The following property is very useful when solving equations involving exponential functions.

Property of Equality for Exponential Functions	Suppose b is a positive number other than 1. Then $b^{x_1} = b^{x_2}$ if and only if $x_1 = x_2$.

This property also holds for inequalities.

Example ③ **a.** Solve $64 = 2^{3n + 1}$.

$$64 = 2^{3n + 1}$$
$$2^6 = 2^{3n + 1}$$
$$6 = 3n + 1$$
$$\frac{5}{3} = n$$

The solution is $\frac{5}{3}$.

Check: $64 = 2^{3n + 1}$
$$64 \stackrel{?}{=} 2^{3\left(\frac{5}{3}\right) + 1}$$
$$64 \stackrel{?}{=} 2^{5 + 1}$$
$$64 \stackrel{?}{=} 2^6$$
$$64 = 64 \checkmark$$

b. Solve $6^{2n-1} > \frac{1}{216}$.

$$6^{2n-1} > \frac{1}{216}$$
$$6^{2n-1} > 6^{-3}$$
$$2n-1 > -3$$
$$n > -1$$

The solution is $n > -1$.

Check: Try $n = 0$.
$$6^{2n - 1} > \frac{1}{216}$$
$$6^{2(0) - 1} \stackrel{?}{>} \frac{1}{216}$$
$$\frac{1}{6} > \frac{1}{216} \checkmark$$

CHECK FOR UNDERSTANDING

Communicating Mathematics

Study the lesson. Then complete the following.

1. **You Decide** Todd says that $y = x^2$ is an exponential function. Juan disagrees. Who is correct? Explain.   **See margin.**

2. **Describe** the domains and ranges of functions of the form $y = a \cdot b^x$ when:
   a. $a = 1, b > 0.$ **b.** $a > 1, b > 0.$ **c.** $a < 1, b > 0.$

3. **Compare** the graphs of $y = 2^{-x}$, $y = \left(\frac{1}{2}\right)^x$, and $y = (0.5)^x$.

4. **Name** the y-intercepts for the graph of $y = b^x$, where b is any real number.

5. **Explain** why 1 is excluded as a value for a in the property of equality for exponential functions. $1^{x_1} = 1^{x_2}$ for any x_1 and x_2.

6. **Explain** how you could use a calculator to determine which of the following values is the best approximation for the value of x in the equation $3 = 2.3^x$. Give the best approximation.   **See margin.**
   a. 1.2 **b.** 1.3 **c.** 1.4 **d.** 1.5

2a. D: x is a real number; R: $y > 0$

2b. D: x is a real number; R: $y > 0$

2c. D: x is a real number; R: $y < 0$

3. They are the same.

4. 1

Lesson 10–1   Real Exponents and Exponential Functions **599**

In-Class Example

For Example 3
Solve each equation or inequality.

a. $3^4 = 27^{m - 1}$ $\frac{7}{3}$

b. $16^{2n + 1} \leq \frac{1}{32}$ $n \leq -\frac{9}{8}$

c. $\left(\frac{1}{25}\right)^{2n} = 5^{n - 5}$ 1

3 PRACTICE/APPLY

Check for Understanding
Exercises 1–17 are designed to help you assess your students' understanding through reading, writing, speaking, and modeling. You should work through Exercises 1–6 with your students and then monitor their work on Exercises 7–17.

Error Analysis
Students will need to remember the rules for radical exponents and negative exponents. A quick review will help to alleviate problems from the beginning.

Additional Answers

1. Juan; If the equation is an exponential function, the exponent must be a variable.
6. Sample answer: Find 2.3^x for each possible value of x to determine which expression is about 3; b.

Reteaching

Using Modeling Have students use graphing calculators to plot a graph of the equations $y = 3^x$, $y = \left(\frac{1}{3}\right)^x$, and $y = 5^x$. Using this graph, students can compare and contrast the relationships and then deduce where the graphs of $y = \left(\frac{1}{5}\right)^x$, $y = 7^x$, and $y = \left(\frac{1}{4}\right)^x$ would lie.

Assignment Guide

Core: 19–51 odd, 52, 53, 55, 57–68

Enriched: 18–50 even, 52–68

For **Extra Practice,** see p. 898.

The red A, B, and C flags, printed only in the Teacher's Wraparound Edition, indicate the level of difficulty of the exercises.

Additional Answer

48.

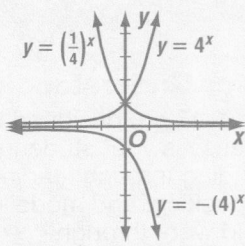

$$y = \left(\tfrac{1}{4}\right)^x \qquad y = 4^x$$

$$y = -(4)^x$$

The graph of $y = -(4)^x$ is the reflection of the graph of $y = 4^x$ over the x-axis. The graph of $y = \left(\tfrac{1}{4}\right)^x$ is the reflection of the graph of $y = 4^x$ over the y-axis.

Study Guide Masters, p. 69

NAME _____ DATE _____

Student Edition
Pages 596–602

Study Guide

Real Exponents and Exponential Functions

Refer to the following definitions and example when working with real exponents. All the properties of rational exponents that you know apply to real exponents as well. Recall that $a^m \cdot a^n = a^{m+n}$, $(a^m)^n = a^{mn}$, and $a^m \div a^n = a^{m-n}$ (when $a \neq 0$).

Definition of Exponential Function
An equation of the form $y = a \cdot b^x$, where $a \neq 0$, $b > 0$, and $b \neq 1$, is called an exponential function with base b.

Property of Equality for Exponential Functions	
Definition	**Example**
Suppose b is a positive number other than 1. Then $b^{x_1} = b^{x_2}$ if and only if $x_1 = x_2$.	Solve $2^n = 2^{3n-1}$ for n. $2^n = 2^{3n-1}$ $5 = 3n - 1$ Property of Equality $6 = 3n$ for Exponential Functions $2 = n$

Simplify each expression.

1. $(3^{\sqrt{2}})^{\sqrt{2}}$ 9
2. $8^{\sqrt{3}} \div 2^{\sqrt{3}}$ $4^{\sqrt{3}}$
3. $(m^{\sqrt{3}})^{\sqrt{7}}$ m^{14}

4. $(x^{\sqrt{2}}y^{\sqrt{7}})^{\sqrt{2}}$ x^2y^6
5. $25^{\sqrt{2}} \cdot 125^{\sqrt{2}}$ $5^{5\sqrt{2}}$ or $3125^{\sqrt{2}}$
6. $(c^{\sqrt{6}})^{\sqrt{42}}$ $c^{3\sqrt{42}}$

Solve each equation.

7. $2^{x+1} = 2^{2x+3}$ -2
8. $4^{x+1} = 8^{2x+3}$ $-\tfrac{7}{4}$
9. $3^{3x-1} = \tfrac{1}{9}$ $-\tfrac{1}{2}$

10. $2^{2x+1} = 4^{2x+2}$ $-\tfrac{3}{2}$
11. $6^x = 6^{6x+1}$ $-\tfrac{1}{5}$
12. $8^{2x} = 16^{x-3}$ -6

600   *Chapter 10*

Use the graph of $y = 2^x$ on page 597 or a calculator to approximate each expression to the nearest tenth.

7. $2^{\sqrt{5}}$ 4.7
8. $4^{0.6}$ 2.3

Use the rule of exponents to simplify each expression.

9. $5^{\sqrt{2}} \cdot 5^{3\sqrt{2}}$ $5^{4\sqrt{2}}$
10. $\left(3^{\sqrt{5}}\right)^{\sqrt{5}}$ 3^5 or 243
11. $27^{\sqrt{5}} \div 3^{\sqrt{5}}$ $3^{2\sqrt{5}}$

Find the value of a if the graph of an exponential function of the form $y = a \cdot 2^x$ passes through the given point.

12. $A(2, 12)$ 3
13. $B(3, -16)$ -2

Solve each equation or inequality.

14. $3^n = 81$ 4
15. $2^{2n} \leq \tfrac{1}{16}$ $n \leq -2$
16. $\left(\tfrac{1}{7}\right)^{b-3} = 343$ 0

17. **Biology** Mitosis is a process of cell duplication in which one cell divides into two. The *Escherichia coli* is one of the fastest growing bacteria. It can reproduce itself in 15 minutes. If you begin with one *Escherichia coli* cell, how many cells will there be in one hour?   **16 cells**

Escherichia coli

EXERCISES

Practice

Use the graph of $y = 2^x$ on page 597 or a calculator to evaluate each expression to the nearest tenth.

18. $2^{1.7}$ 3.2
19. $2^{-0.5}$ 0.7
20. $2^{\sqrt{2}}$ 2.7
21. $2^{-1.1}$ 0.5
22. $16^{0.4}$ 3.0
23. $8^{-0.3}$ 0.5

Simplify each expression.

24. $\left(2^{\sqrt{2}}\right)^{\sqrt{8}}$ 2^4 or 16
25. $4^{\sqrt{2}} \cdot 4^{2\sqrt{2}}$ $4^{3\sqrt{2}}$
26. $7^{3\sqrt{2}} \div 7^{\sqrt{2}}$ $7^{2\sqrt{2}}$

27. $\left(y^{\sqrt{3}}\right)^{\sqrt{12}}$ y^6
28. $5^{\sqrt{3}} \cdot 5^{\sqrt{27}}$ $5^{4\sqrt{3}}$
29. $64^{\sqrt{7}} \div 2^{\sqrt{7}}$ $2^{5\sqrt{7}}$

30. $2\left(3^{\sqrt{2}}\right)\left(3^{-\sqrt{2}}\right)$ 2
31. $\left(a^{\sqrt{5}}\right)^{\sqrt{20}}$ a^{10}
32. $\left(m^{\sqrt{3}} + n^{\sqrt{2}}\right)^2$

32. $m^{2\sqrt{3}} + 2m^{\sqrt{3}}n^{\sqrt{2}} + n^{2\sqrt{2}}$

Find the value of a if the graph of an exponential function of the form $y = a \cdot 3^x$ passes through the given point.

33. $C(2, 36)$ 4
34. $D(-1, 15)$ 45
35. $E(4, -81)$ -1
36. $F(-2, -2)$ -18
37. $G(5, 27)$ $\tfrac{1}{9}$
38. $H\left(-3, \tfrac{1}{9}\right)$ 3

Solve each equation or inequality.

39. $3^{4x} = 3^{3-x}$ $\tfrac{3}{5}$
40. $5^{n-3} \geq \tfrac{1}{25}$ $n \geq 1$
41. $\tfrac{1}{32} = 2^{1-m}$ 6

42. $9^{2p} = 27^{p-1}$ -3
43. $16^n > 8^{n+1}$ $n < -3$
44. $\left(\tfrac{1}{9}\right)^m = 81^{m+4}$ $-\tfrac{8}{3}$

45. 12

46. 10

45. $2^x \cdot 4^{x+5} = 4^{2x-1}$
46. $2^{5x} \cdot 16^{1-x} = 4^{x-3}$
47. $25^x = 5^{x^2-15}$ $-3, 5$

48. On the same coordinate plane, graph $y = 4^x$, $y = -(4)^x$, and $y = \left(\tfrac{1}{4}\right)^x$. Compare the graphs.   See margin.

Use a graphing calculator to graph each of the following.

49. $y = 2.1^x$ **50.** $y = 0.5(2.1)^x$ **51.** $y = -0.2(2.1)^x$

49–51. See margin.

**Critical
Thinking**

52. Using a calculator, approximate to the nearest tenth the value of x when $y = 2$ in the expression $y = 2.3^x$.   **0.8**

**Applications and
Problem Solving**

53. Look for a Pattern A large piece of paper is cut in half, and one of the resulting pieces is placed on top of the other. Then the pieces in the stack are cut in half and placed on top of each other. Suppose this procedure is repeated several times.

  a. How many pieces will be in the stack after the first cut? after the second cut? after the third cut? after the fourth cut? **2, 4, 8, 16**

  b. Use the pattern in step a to write an equation for the number of pieces in the stack after x cuts. $y = 2^x$

  c. The thickness of ordinary paper is about 0.003 inch. Write an equation for the thickness of the stack of paper after x cuts. $y = 0.003(2)^x$

53d. about 3,221,225.47 in.

  d. How thick will the stack of paper be after 30 cuts?

54. Animal Behavior Studies show an animal will defend an area in square yards that is directly proportional to the 1.31 power of the animal's weight in pounds.

  a. If a 45-pound beaver will defend 170 square yards, write an equation for the area a defended by a beaver weighing w pounds. $a = 1.16w^{1.31}$

  b. Thousands of years ago, some beavers grew to be 11 feet long and weighed 430 pounds. Use your equation in step a to determine the area defended by these animals. **about 3268 square yards**

55. Atmospheric Pressure Atmospheric pressure decreases at higher altitudes. In the equation $P = 14.7(10)^{-0.02h}$, P represents the atmospheric pressure in pounds per square inch, and h represents the altitude above sea level in miles.

  a. The elevation of Boston, Massachusetts, is about sea level. Find the atmospheric pressure in Boston. **about 14.7 psi**

  b. The elevation of Denver, Colorado, is about 1 mile. Find the atmospheric pressure in Denver. **about 14.0 psi**

  c. The highest mountain in the world is Mt. Everest in Nepal, which is about 5.5 miles above sea level. Find the atmospheric pressure at the top of this mountain. **about 11.4 psi**

55d. about 16.0 psi

  d. About 6 million years ago, the Mediterranean Sea dried up. The bottom of the valley formed by this dry sea was about 1.9 miles below sea level. Find the atmospheric pressure at the bottom of this valley.

  e. Graph the equation for the atmospheric pressure. Explain the meaning of the points on the graph that have negative values for h. **See margin.**

Additional Answers

49.

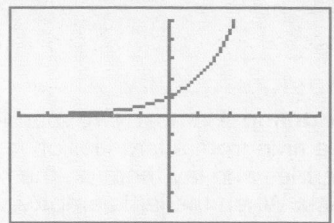

50.

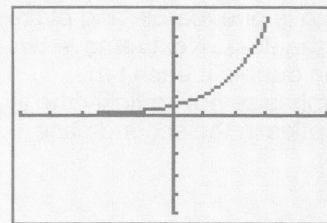

51.

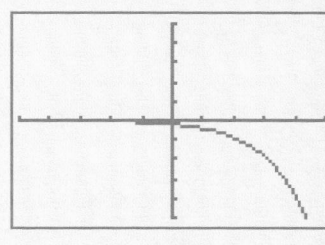

55e.

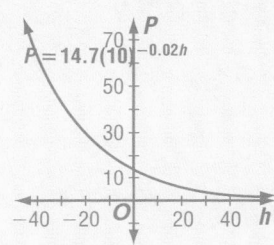

**They represent the
atmospheric pressure for
places below sea level.**

Practice Masters, p. 69

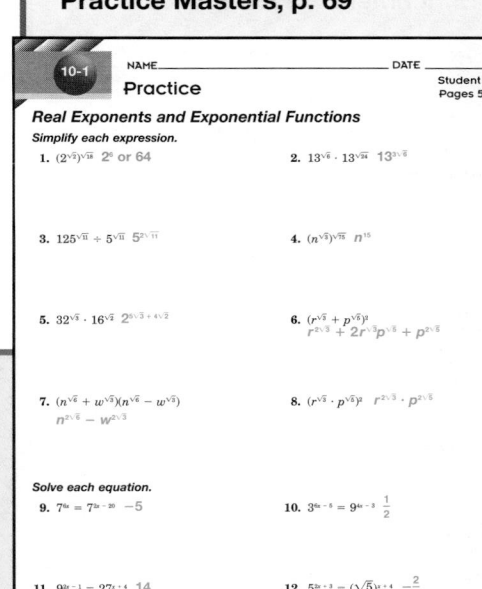

Closing Activity

Modeling Remove two marbles at a time from a large jar of marbles and lay them on the desk. When the jar is empty, return the marbles to the jar. Now remove one marble and place it on the desk. Next remove two, then double it each time. Emphasize how quickly the jar empties in the second case.

Enrichment Masters, p. 69

NAME_____ DATE_____

10-1
Enrichment

Student Edition
Pages 596–602

Finding Solutions of $x^y = y^x$

Perhaps you have noticed that if x and y are interchanged in equations such as $x = y$ and $xy = 1$, the resulting equation is equivalent to the original equation. The same is true of the equation $x^y = y^x$. However, finding solutions of $x^y = y^x$ and drawing its graph is not a simple process.

Solve each problem. Assume that x and y are positive real numbers.

1. If $a > 0$, will (a, a) be a solution of $x^y = y^x$? Justify your answer.
   yes, since $a^a = a^a$ must be true (reflexive prop. of equality)

2. If $c > 0$, $d > 0$, and (c, d) is a solution of $x^y = y^x$, will (d, c) also be a solution? Justify your answer. yes; Replacing x with d, y with c gives $d^c = c^d$; but if (c, d) is a solution, $c^d = d^c$. So, by the symmetric property of equality, $d^c = c^d$ is true.

3. Use 2 as a value for y in $x^y = y^x$. The equation becomes $x^2 = 2^x$.

   a. Find equations for two functions, $f(x)$ and $g(x)$ that you could graph to find the solutions of $x^2 = 2^x$. Then graph the functions on a separate sheet of graph paper. $f(x) = x^2$, $g(x) = 2^x$ See students' graphs.

   b. Use the graph you drew for Part a to state two solutions for $x^2 = 2^x$. Then use these solutions to state two solutions for $x^y = y^x$. 2, 4; (2, 2), (4, 2)

4. In this exercise, a graphing calculator will be very helpful. Use the technique of Exercise 3 to complete the tables below. Then graph $x^y = y^x$ for positive values of x and y. If there are asymptotes, show them in your diagram using dotted lines. Note that in the table, some values of y call for one value of x, others call for two.

x	y
1	1
2	2
3	3
4	4
1	1
2	2
4	2
3	3
2.5	3

x	y
4	4
2	4
5	5
1.8	5
8	8
1.5	8

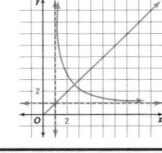

56. **City Planning** The school board in Orlando, Florida, needs to project the population growth for the remainder of the century to plan for the construction of new schools. One of the formulas the board can use is $P = 164{,}693(2.7)^{0.007t}$, where t represents the number of years since 1990 and 164,693 was the population of Orlando according to the 1990 census. Use a calculator to determine how large the population will be in the year 2000. **about 176,552**

57. **Forestry** The diameter of the base of a tree trunk in centimeters varies directly with the $\frac{3}{2}$ power of its height in meters.

57a. $d = 1.30h^{\frac{3}{2}}$

a. A young sequoia tree is 6 meters tall, and the diameter of its base is 19.1 centimeters. Use this information to write an equation for the diameter d of the base of a sequoia tree if its height is h meters high.

b. One of the oldest living things on Earth is the General Sherman Tree in Sequoia National Park in California. This sequoia is between 2200 and 2500 years old. If it is about 83.8 meters high, find the diameter at its base. **about 997 cm**

Mixed Review

58. Solve $\frac{6}{a - 7} = \frac{a - 49}{a^2 - 7a} + \frac{1}{a}$. (Lesson 9–5) **−14**

59. State the number of positive real zeros, negative real zeros, and imaginary zeros for $f(x) = -x^4 - x^2 - x - 1$. (Lesson 8–4) **0; 2 or 0; 2 or 4**

60. $x = \frac{1}{20}y^2 - 5$

60. **Communication** A microphone is placed at the focus of a parabolic reflector to collect sounds for the television broadcast of a football game. The focus of the parabola that is the cross section of the reflector is 5 inches from the vertex. The latus rectum is 20 inches long. Assuming that the focus is at the origin and the parabola opens to the right, write the equation of the cross section. (Lesson 7–2)

61. **Cartography** Edison is located at (9, 3) on the road map. Kettering is located at (12, 5) on the same map. Each side of a grid on the map represents 10 miles. Use the distance formula to approximate the distance between Edison and Kettering. (Lesson 7–1) **36 mi**

62. Solve $x^2 + 14x - 12 = 0$ by completing the square. (Lesson 6–3) **$-7 \pm \sqrt{61}$**

63. $\frac{3 + 4i}{25}$

63. Find the multiplicative inverse of $3 - 4i$. (Lesson 5–10)

64. Simplify $\frac{(3 + \sqrt{5})}{(1 + \sqrt{2})}$. (Lesson 5–6) **$-3 + 3\sqrt{2} - \sqrt{5} + \sqrt{10}$**

65. If $A = \begin{bmatrix} -2 & 3 \\ 1 & 10 \\ 0 & -6 \end{bmatrix}$ and $B = \begin{bmatrix} 9 & 3 \\ 1 & 4 \end{bmatrix}$, find AB. (Lesson 4–3) $\begin{bmatrix} -15 & 6 \\ 19 & 43 \\ -6 & -24 \end{bmatrix}$

66. Solve the system of equations. (Lesson 3–7) **(5, 3, 7)**

$$r + s + t = 15$$
$$r + t = 12$$
$$s + t = 10$$

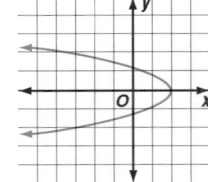

67. Use the vertical line test to determine whether the relation graphed at the right is a function. (Lesson 2–1) **no**

68. associative property of addition

68. State the property illustrated by the following equation. $4 + (a + r) = (4 + a) + r$ (Lesson 1–2)

Extension

Reasoning Suppose $a < b$ and $x > 0$. For which values of x is $x^a < x^b$? **$x > 1$**

10–1B Graphing Technology
Curve Fitting with Real-World Data

An Extension of Lesson 10–1

As we have seen in earlier chapters, we are often confronted with data for which we need to find an equation that best describes the information.

Example ●

In 1985, Kayla received $30.00 from her grandparents for her fifth birthday. Her mother deposited it into a bank account for her. Both Kayla and her mother forgot about the money and made no further deposits or withdrawals. The table to the right shows the account balance for several years.

Elapsed Time (years)	Balance
0	$30.00
5	$41.10
10	$56.31
15	$77.16
20	$105.71
25	$144.83
30	$198.43

a. Use a graphing calculator to enter the data and draw a scatter plot that shows how the account balance is related to time.
b. If Kayla discovers the account with the birthday money on her 50th birthday, how much will she have in the account?

LOOK BACK

You can refer to Lessons 2-5B and 8-3B for information on entering data and graphing scatter plots on the graphing calculator.

a. Enter the elapsed time data into the L1 list on the STAT menu and enter the balance data into the L2 list. Be sure to clear the Y= list. Press [2nd] [STAT PLOT] and select plot 1. Make sure that plot 1 is on, scatter plot is chosen, the *x* list is L1, and the *y* list is L2. Use the viewing window [0, 35] with a scale factor of 5 by [0, 300] with a scale factor of 20. Press [GRAPH] .

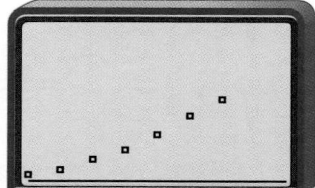

We see from the data that the equation that best fits the data must be a curve. This means the equation is probably polynomial or exponential. Let's try an exponential model. To determine the exponential equation that best fits the data, use the exponential regression feature of the calculator.

Enter: [STAT] [▶] [ALPHA] A [2nd] L1 [,] [2nd] L2 [ENTER]

The equation is $y = 29.99908551(1.065001351)^x$.

The calculator also reports an *r*-value of 0.999999998. Recall that this number is a correlation coefficient that indicates how well the equation fits the data. A perfect fit would be $r = 1$. Therefore, we can conclude that this equation is indeed a good fit for the data.

(continued on the next page)

NCTM Standards: 1–6, 10

Objective
Use a graphing calculator to fit a curve to a scatter plot of real-world data.

Recommended Time
25 minutes

Instructional Resources
Graphing Calculator Masters, pp. 53 and 54

These masters provide keystroking instruction for this lesson for the TI-81 and Casio graphing calculators.

1 FOCUS

Motivating the Lesson
This lesson expands on what students did in Lesson 10-1A. Have students discuss what the line on a graph represents. Why doesn't real-world data conform exactly to the graph of an equation? Why is it okay to approximate with a best-fit curve?

2 TEACH

Teaching Tip Point out to students that predictions are more accurate the closer an *r* value is to 1.0.

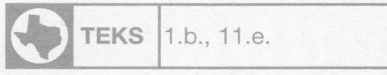

TEKS | 1.b., 11.e.

4 ASSESS

Observing students working with technology is an excellent method of assessment.

Additional Answers

1.
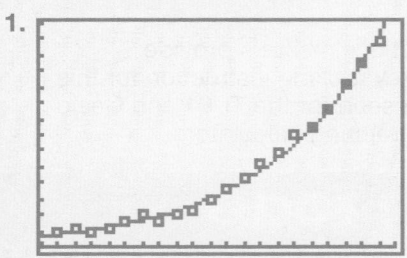

2. $y = (1.159105 \times 10^{-11})$ $(1.014951462)^x$; $r = 0.9901350318$
The best-fit line rises at an exponential rate and closely fits the plotted data.

4. A quadratic equation might be a good model for this example because the shape is close to a portion of the parabola.

5. Louisiana Purchase

To check this equation visually, overlap the graph of the equation with the scatter plot.

Enter: [Y=] [VARS] 5

[▶] [▶] 7

[GRAPH]

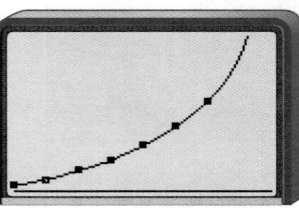

b. On Kayla's 50th birthday, the money will have been in the account for $50 - 5$ or 45 years. From the graphics screen, enter [2nd] [CALC] 1 45 [ENTER].
(Be sure your viewing window is large enough to include $x = 45$.) The calculator returns a y-value of 510.34651. Kayla will have $510.35 in the account when she is 50 years old.

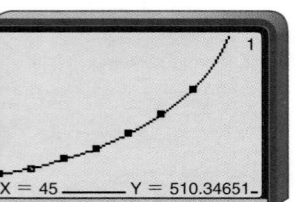
X = 45 ___ Y = 510.34651

EXERCISES

According to the World Almanac, the population per square mile in the United States has changed dramatically over a period of years.

Year	People per Square Mile	Year	People per Square Mile
1790	4.5	1890	17.8
1800	6.1	1900	21.5
1810	4.3	1910	26.0
1820	5.5	1920	29.9
1830	7.4	1930	34.7
1840	9.8	1940	37.2
1850	7.9	1950	42.6
1860	10.6	1960	50.6
1870	10.9	1970	57.5
1880	14.2	1980	64.0

1. Use a graphing calculator to draw a scatter plot of the data. Then calculate and graph the curve of best fit that shows how the year is related to the number of people per square mile. Use ExpReg for this example.   See margin.

2. Write the equation of best fit. Write a sentence that describes the fit of the graph to the data.   See margin.

3. Based on the graph, estimate the population density for 2000. Check this using the CALC value.   about 90.088

4. Do you think there are any other types of equations that would be good models for this data? Why or why not?   See margin.

5. **History**   What event occurred between 1800 and 1810 that would account for the sudden big decrease in population per square mile?

Using Technology

This lesson offers an excellent opportunity for using technology in your algebra classroom. For more information on using technology, see *Graphing Calculators in the Mathematics Classroom*, one of the titles in the Glencoe Mathematics Professional Series.

10-2

Logarithms and Logarithmic Functions

What YOU'LL LEARN

- To write exponential equations in logarithmic form and vice versa,
- to evaluate logarithmic expressions, and
- to solve equations and inequalities involving logarithmic functions.

Why IT'S IMPORTANT

You can use logarithmic functions to solve problems involving chemistry and geology.

GLOBAL CONNECTIONS

The history of seismology goes back to China and the earliest known seismograph was invented by Zhang Heng in A.D. 132. It was a large brass vessel with a heavy pendulum and several arms which tripped when an earthquake tremor was felt. This helped determine the direction of the quake.

APPLICATION
Geology

Logarithms are exponents. They were once used to simplify calculations, but the advent of calculators and computers caused calculation with logarithms to be used less and less.

An example of logarithms at work is the Richter scale. The Richter scale is used to measure the strength of an earthquake. It is a logarithmic scale based on the powers of ten. The table below gives the effects of earthquakes of various intensities.

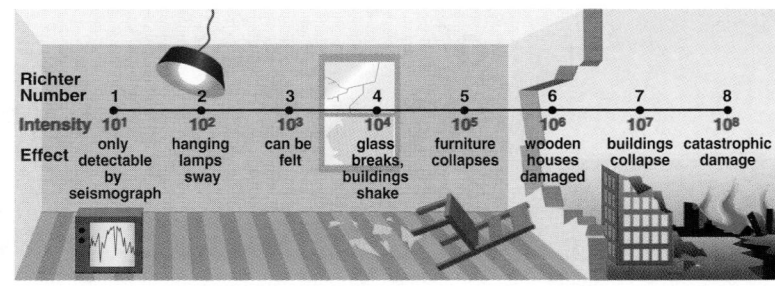

Richter Number	1	2	3	4	5	6	7	8
Intensity	10^1	10^2	10^3	10^4	10^5	10^6	10^7	10^8
Effect	only detectable by seismograph	hanging lamps sway	can be felt	glass breaks, buildings shake	furniture collapses	wooden houses damaged	buildings collapse	catastrophic damage

The 1906 San Francisco earthquake measured 8.3 on the Richter scale. The Loma Prieta earthquake that interrupted the 1989 World Series in San Francisco measured 7.1. *We will compare the magnitudes of these two famous earthquakes in Example 2.*

The tables below show two related exponential equations. You will recognize the equation in the table on the left as an exponential function.

Given the exponent, x, compute the power of 2 as y.

x	$2^x = y$	y
-1	$2^{-1} = y$	?
2	$2^2 = y$	?
3	$2^3 = y$	?
6	$2^6 = y$	?

Given x as the power of 2, compute the exponent, y.

y	$2^y = x$	x
?	$2^y = \frac{1}{2}$	$\frac{1}{2}$
?	$2^y = 4$	4
?	$2^y = 8$	8
?	$2^y = 64$	64

In the relation shown in the table on the right, $2^y = x$, the exponent y is called the **logarithm**, base 2, of x. This relation is written $\log_2 x = y$ and is read "the log base 2 of x is equal to y." The logarithm corresponds to the exponent. Study the diagram below.

Exponential Equation   **Logarithmic Equation**

$$n = b^p \qquad\qquad p = \log_b n$$

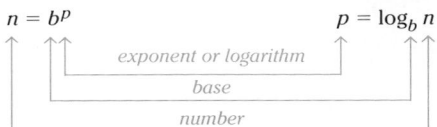

exponent or logarithm
base
number

Lesson 10–2 Logarithms and Logarithmic Functions **605**

GLOBAL CONNECTIONS

An earthquake registering 4.5 on the Richter scale is detectable within 20 miles of the epicenter and may cause slight damage. The effects of an earthquake are strongly dependent upon the type of earth in the area. Loose shale or dirt can seem fluid when shaken strongly.

10-2 LESSON NOTES

NCTM Standards: 1–6

Instructional Resources

- Study Guide Master 10-2
- Practice Master 10-2
- Enrichment Master 10-2
- Assessment and Evaluation Masters, p. 268
- Graphing Calculator Masters, p. 10
- Real-World Applications, 27

 Transparency 10-2A contains the 5-Minute Check for this lesson; **Transparency 10-2B** contains a teaching aid for this lesson.

Recommended Pacing	
Standard Pacing	Day 4 of 12
Honors Pacing	Day 4 of 11
Block Scheduling*	Day 2 of 5 (along with Lesson 10-3)

 *For more information on pacing and possible lesson plans, refer to the *Block Scheduling Booklet*.

1 FOCUS

 5-Minute Check
(over Lesson 10-1)

Simplify.

1. $\left(2^{\sqrt{5}}\right)^{\sqrt{5}}$ 2^5
2. $2^{\sqrt{2}} \cdot 16^{\sqrt{32}}$ $2^{17\sqrt{2}}$
3. $\dfrac{49^{\sqrt{2}}}{7^{\sqrt{12}}}$ $7^{2\sqrt{2}-2\sqrt{3}}$

Solve.

4. $\left(\sqrt{2}\right)^{n+1} = 8^{n-1}$ $\dfrac{7}{5}$
5. $36^{3p-1} = 6^{4p+2}$ 2

 **TEKS** 2.a., 4.a., 4.c., 11.a., 11.b., 11.c., 11.d., 11.e.

Chapter 10 **605**

Situational Problem Present the following problem. A large organization has 2500 members. To announce unscheduled meetings, the president calls 5 members, each of these calls 5 members, and so on until all members are called. Assuming the president is level 1, how many levels of calls must be made? Have students discuss problems that would arise if they were to use a diagram to solve.

2 TEACH

Teaching Tip Have students make flash cards with an exponential equation on one side and its corresponding logarithmic equation on the other side. Have students work in pairs and use the cards to reinforce the relationship of the two equations.

Teaching Tip Have students review the definition of inverse functions.

In-Class Examples

For Example 1
Solve each equation.

a. $\log_7 \frac{1}{49} = y$ -2

b. $\log_{\frac{1}{3}} 27 = y$ -3

c. $\log_6 x = 2$ 36

For Example 2
A telephone network takes 12 minutes per set of calls and a total of an hour to reach everyone. If 243 calls are made in the last round, how many people will each person call?
3 people

	Suppose $b > 0$ and $b \neq 1$. For $n > 0$, there is a number p such that
Definition of Logarithm	$\log_b n = p$ if and only if $b^p = n$.

The chart below shows some equivalent exponential and logarithmic equations.

Exponential Equation	Logarithmic Equation
$5^2 = 25$	$\log_5 25 = 2$
$10^5 = 100{,}000$	$\log_{10} 100{,}000 = 5$
$8^0 = 1$	$\log_8 1 = 0$
$2^{-4} = \frac{1}{16}$	$\log_2 \frac{1}{16} = -4$
$9^{\frac{1}{2}} = 3$	$\log_9 3 = \frac{1}{2}$

You can find the value of a variable in a logarithmic equation $\log_b x = y$ when values for two of the variables are known.

Example Solve each equation.

a. $\log_9 x = \frac{3}{2}$

$\log_9 x = \frac{3}{2}$

$9^{\frac{3}{2}} = x$ *Definition of logarithm*

$(3^2)^{\frac{3}{2}} = x$

$3^3 = x$ *Power of a power*

$27 = x$

b. $\log_4 256 = y$

$\log_4 256 = y$

$4^y = 256$ *Definition of logarithm*

$(2^2)^y = 2^8$

$2^{2y} = 2^8$ *Power of a power*

$2y = 8$ *Property of equality for exponential functions*

$y = 4$

Example  Refer to the application at the beginning of the lesson. Compare the magnitude of the 1906 quake to the 1989 quake.

APPLICATION
Geology

Let x represent the measure of the 1906 quake and let y represent the measure of the 1989 quake.

Quake	Richter Value as Exponents	Richter Value as Logarithms
1906	$10^{8.3} = x$	$8.3 = \log_{10} x$
1989	$10^{7.1} = y$	$7.1 = \log_{10} y$

Use the Richter values as exponents to find the ratio of the magnitude of the 1906 quake to the 1989 quake.

$\dfrac{x}{y} = \dfrac{10^{8.3}}{10^{7.1}}$

$= 10^{1.2}$ *Division of powers*

≈ 15.8

Therefore, the intensity of the 1906 earthquake was approximately 16 times greater than that of the 1989 quake.

 Cooperative Learning

Co-op Co-op Provide each group with a "superball." Have students assume the ball rebounds to 90% of its previous height on each bounce. Have students use the ball and logarithms to model the number of bounces it takes for the ball to rebound to a given height if the ball is initially dropped from 8 feet.
$h = 8 - 0.9^n; \; n = \log_{0.9}(8 - h)$

For more information on the co-op co-op strategy, see *Cooperative Learning in the Mathematics Classroom,* one of the titles in the Glencoe Mathematics Professional Series, page 30.

Let's look at the graphs of an exponential function and its corresponding logarithmic function. In fact, you can use a table of values for $y = 2^x$ to make a table of values for $x = 2^y$.

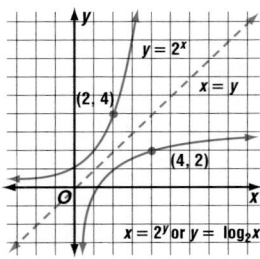

$x = y$

$(2, 4)$

$(4, 2)$

$y = 2^x$

$x = 2^y$ or $y = \log_2 x$

$y = 2^x$

x	y
−3	$\frac{1}{8}$
−2	$\frac{1}{4}$
−1	$\frac{1}{2}$
0	1
1	2
2	4
3	8

$x = 2^y$ or $y = \log_2 x$

x	y
$\frac{1}{8}$	−3
$\frac{1}{4}$	−2
$\frac{1}{2}$	−1
1	0
2	1
4	2
8	3

For every point (a, b) on the graph of $y = 2^x$, there is a point on the graph of $y = \log_2 x$ with coordinates (b, a).

The x and y values are reversed.

Notice that the graphs are reflections of each other over the line $y = x$. The fact that x and y switch places is apparent in the domains and ranges.

LOOK BACK

You can refer to Lesson 8-8 for information on inverse functions.

	For $y = 2^x$	**For $x = 2^y$ or $y = \log_2 x$**
Domain	all real numbers	positive real numbers
Range	positive real numbers	all real numbers

The relations are inverses of each other. Using the vertical line test, you can see that no vertical line can intersect the graph of $y = \log_2 x$ in more than one place, so $y = \log_2 x$ is a function, called a **logarithmic function**.

Definition of Logarithmic Function	An equation of the form $y = \log_b x$, where $b > 0$ and $b \neq 1$, is called a logarithmic function.

LOOK BACK

You can refer to Lesson 8-7 for information on composition of functions.

Since the exponential function $y = b^x$ and the logarithmic function $y = \log_b x$ are inverses of each other, their composites are the identity function. Let $f(x) = \log_b x$ and $g(x) = b^x$. For $f(x)$ and $g(x)$ to be inverses, it must be true that $f(g(x)) = x$ and $g(f(x)) = x$.

$$f(g(x)) = x \qquad\qquad g(f(x)) = x$$
$$f(b^x) = x \qquad\qquad g(\log_b x) = x$$
$$\log_b b^x = x \qquad\qquad b^{\log_b x} = x$$

Example ③ Evaluate each expression.

a. $\log_5 5^3$ b. $6^{\log_6(2x+5)}$

$\log_5 5^3 = 3$ $\log_b b^x = x$ $6^{\log_6(2x+5)} = 2x + 5$ $b^{\log_b x} = x$

A property similar to the property for exponential functions applies to the logarithmic functions.

Lesson 10-2 Logarithms and Logarithmic Functions **607**

In-Class Example

For Example 3
Evaluate each expression.

a. $\log_5 5^8$ 8
b. $3^{\log_3 (x^2 - 3)}$ $x^2 - 3$

GLENCOE *Technology*

Interactive Mathematics Tools Software

This multimedia software provides an interactive lesson by helping students discover the rules for finding the inverse of logarithmic and exponential functions. A **Computer Journal** gives students an opportunity to write about what they have learned.

For Windows & Macintosh

608 Chapter 10

In-Class Example

For Example 4
Solve each equation.

a. $\log_7 (2x + 1) = \log_7 (3x - 5)$ 6

b. $\log_8 (x^2 - 14) = \log_8 (5x)$
7 or −2
The only solution is 7 since $\log_8 (5 \cdot -2)$ is not defined.

Teaching Tip For Example 4, remind students to confirm that the base is the same on both sides of the equals sign before working the problems.

3 PRACTICE/APPLY

Check for Understanding

Exercises 1–21 are designed to help you assess your students' understanding through reading, writing, speaking, and modeling. You should work through Exercises 1–5 with your students and then monitor their work on Exercises 6–21.

Study Guide Masters, p. 70

NAME_____ DATE _____

Student Edition
Pages 605–610

Study Guide

10-2

Logarithms and Logarithmic Functions

Logarithmic functions are the inverses of exponential functions.

Exponential Equation	Logarithmic Equation
$n = b^p$	$p = \log_b n$

Definition of Logarithms

Definition	Example
Suppose $b > 0$ and $b \ne 1$. For $n > 0$, there is a number p such that $\log_b n = p$ if and only if $b^p = n$.	Solve $\log_2 x = 3$ for x. $\log_2 x = 3$ $2^3 = x$ Definition of Logarithms $x = 8$

You can use the Property of Logarithmic Functions to solve exponential functions involving logarithms.

Property of Equality for Logarithmic Functions

Definition	Example
Suppose $b > 0$ and $b \ne 1$. Then $\log_b x_1 = \log_b x_2$ if and only if $x_1 = x_2$.	Solve $\log_2(2x - 4) = \log_2(7x + 1)$. $\log_2(2x - 4) = \log_2(7x + 1)$ $2x - 4 = 7x + 1$ Property of Equality for $-5x = 5$ Logarithmic Functions $x = -1$

Evaluate each expression.

1. $\log_4 64$ 3
2. $\log_2 64$ 6
3. $\log_{10} 100{,}000$ 5
4. $\log_5 625$ 4
5. $\log_3 27$ 3
6. $\log_{11} 121$ 2

Solve each equation.

7. $\log_5 m = 4$ 625
8. $\log_2 32 = 3x$ $\frac{5}{3}$
9. $\log_3 2c = -2$ $\frac{1}{18}$
10. $\log_7(3x - 1) = \log_7(2x + 3)$ 4
11. $\log_3(x^2 - 6) = \log_3(2x + 2)$ 4, −2

Property of Equality for Logarithmic Functions	Suppose $b > 0$ and $b \ne 1$. Then $\log_b x_1 = \log_b x_2$ if and only if $x_1 = x_2$.

This property also holds for inequalities.

Example 4 **Solve each equation or inequality.**

a. $\log_{10} (t^2 - 6) = \log_{10} t$

$\log_{10} (t^2 - 6) = \log_{10} t$

$t^2 - 6 = t$ *Property of equality for logarithmic functions*

$t^2 - t - 6 = 0$

$(t - 3)(t + 2) = 0$

$t = 3 \quad \text{or} \quad t = -2$ *Zero product property*

Eliminate −2, because $\log_b x$ is defined only if $x > 0$. Thus, the solution is 3.

b. $\log_3 (3x - 5) \ge \log_3 (x + 7)$

$\log_3 (3x - 5) \ge \log_3 (x + 7)$

$3x - 5 \ge x + 7$

$2x \ge 12$

$x \ge 6$

CHECK FOR UNDERSTANDING

Communicating Mathematics

1. the logarithm base 2 of x

MODELING MATHEMATICS

Study the lesson. Then complete the following.

1. **Give** another name for the exponent y in the equation $2^y = x$.

2. **Write** an example of a logarithmic function. **Sample answer:** $y = \log_2 x$

3. **Describe** the domain of $y = 2^x$. all real numbers

4. **Describe** the range of $y = \log_2 x$. all real numbers

5. **Draw** a graph of $y = 3^x$. Place a geomirror along the line represented by the equation $y = x$. Use the reflection seen in the geomirror to draw the graph of $y = \log_3 x$. See margin.

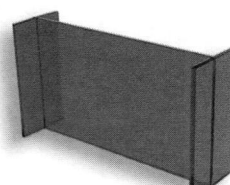

Guided Practice

8. $\log_4 \frac{1}{16} = -2$

9. $5^3 = 125$

10. $8^{\frac{2}{3}} = 4$

11. $10^{-3} = 0.001$

Write each equation in logarithmic form.

6. $3^3 = 27$ $\log_3 27 = 3$
7. $2^5 = 32$ $\log_2 32 = 5$
8. $4^{-2} = \frac{1}{16}$

Write each equation in exponential form.

9. $\log_5 125 = 3$
10. $\log_8 4 = \frac{2}{3}$
11. $\log_{10} 0.001 = -3$

Evaluate each expression.

12. $\log_3 \frac{1}{27}$ −3
13. $\log_{16} 4$ $\frac{1}{2}$
14. $5^{\log_5 25}$ 25

Solve each equation or inequality.

15. $\log_7 y = -2$ $\frac{1}{49}$
16. $\log_b 64 = 3$ 4
17. $\log_{\frac{1}{3}} 27 = x$ −3
18. $\log_5 (2x - 3) > \log_5 (x + 2)$ $x > 5$
19. $\log_{10} (x^2 + 36) = \log_{10} 100$ ±8
20. $\log_3 3^{(2x - 1)} = 7$ 4

21. **Geology** How much stronger is an earthquake with a Richter scale rating of 7 than an aftershock with a rating of 4? 10^3 or 1000 times stronger

608 Chapter 10 *Exploring Exponential and Logarithmic Functions*

Reteaching

Using Discussion Have students graph the exponential equation $y = 4^x$ and the logarithmic equation $y = \log_4 x$ which is really $4^y = x$. Compare and contrast these graphs and discuss.

Additional Answer

5.

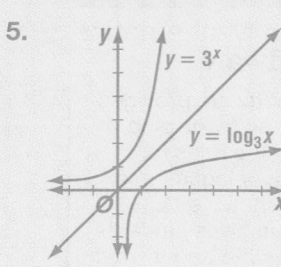

Practice

Evaluate each expression.

22. $\log_{10} 1000$ **3**   **23.** $\log_5 25$ **2**   **24.** $\log_{14} 196$ **2**

25. $\log_3 \frac{1}{81}$ **−4**   **26.** $\log_2 \frac{1}{128}$ **−7**   **27.** $\log_{36} 6$ $\frac{1}{2}$

28. $\log_8 8^4$ **4**   **29.** $3^{\log_3 243}$ **243**   **30.** $7^{\log_7(x+3)}$ $x + 3$

Solve each equation or inequality.

31. $\log_2 x = 5$ **32**   **32.** $\log_3 27 = y$ **3**   **33.** $\log_b 9 = 2$ **3**

34. $\log_5 \sqrt{5} = y$ $\frac{1}{2}$ **35.** $\log_{25} x = \frac{3}{2}$ **125**   **36.** $\log_b 0.01 = -2$ **10**

37. $\log_{\frac{1}{10}} x = -3$ **1000**   **38.** $\log_{3x} 125 = 3$ $\frac{5}{3}$ **39.** $\log_{x+2} 16 = 2$ **2**

41. $x < \frac{1}{2}$

40. $\log_8 (3x - 1) = \log_8 (2x^2)$ $\frac{1}{2}, 1$ **41.** $\log_2 (4x + 10) - \log_2 (x + 1) < 3$

42. $\log_{10} (x^2 + 16) = \log_{10} 80$ ± 8 **43.** $4^{\log_4(x-1)} = -0.5$ **0.5**

44. $\log_2 2^{(3x+2)} = 14$ **4**   **45.** $3^{\log_3 10} = x$ **10**

46. $\log_{10} (\log_8 8) = x$ **0**   **47.** $\log_4 (\log_2 16) = y$ **1**

Graph each pair of equations on the same axes.   48–49. See margin.

48. $y = \log_5 x$ and $y = 5^x$ **49.** $y = \log_{\frac{1}{3}} x$ and $y = \left(\frac{1}{3}\right)^x$

50. The graphs are reflections of each other along the line $x = y$.

50. Study the graphs in Exercises 48 and 49. What is the relationship of each pair of graphs?

51. Graph $y = \log_{10} x$, $y = \log_5 x$, $y = \log_{\frac{1}{3}} x$ and $y = \log_{\frac{1}{2}} x$ on the same set of axes. Assume that the parent graph is the graph of $y = \log_{10} x$. Describe this family of graphs in terms of the parent graph.   **See Solutions Manual.**

Show that each statement is true.   52–55. See Solutions Manual.

52. $\log_4 4 + \log_4 16 = \log_4 64$ **53.** $\log_4 16 = 2 \log_4 4$

54. $\log_2 8 \cdot \log_8 2 = 1$ **55.** $\log_{10} [\log_3 (\log_4 64)] = 0$

Critical Thinking

56. If $x = \log_{10} 2460$, the value of x is between two consecutive integers. Name these integers and explain how you determined the values.

Applications and Problem Solving

56. 3 and 4; 2460 is between 1000 or 10^3 and 10,000 or 10^4

57. about 1.26 times greater

58. about 630 times more acidic

59. $11^{4\sqrt{5}}$

57. Geology   The Seattle quake of April 29, 1965, measured 7.0 on the Richter scale. The San Francisco quake of 1989 measured 7.1. How many times more severe was the San Francisco quake than the Seattle quake?

58. Chemistry   The pH of a solution is a measure of its acidity and is written as a logarithm to the base 10. A low pH indicates an acidic solution, and a high pH indicates a basic solution. Neutral water has a pH of 7. Acid rain has a pH of 4.2. How many more times acidic is the acid rain than neutral water?

Mixed Review

59. Simplify $11^{\sqrt{5}} \cdot 11^{\sqrt{45}}$.   (Lesson 10–1)

60. Physics   The volume of any gas varies inversely with its pressure as long as the temperature remains constant. If a helium-filled balloon has a volume of 3.4 cubic decimeters at a pressure of 120 kilopascals, what is its volume at 101.3 kilopascals?   (Lesson 9–2)   about 4.03 dm³

Lesson 10–2   Logarithms and Logarithmic Functions   **609**

Tech Prep

Geologist   Students who are interested in geology may wish to do further research on the data given in Exercise 57 and explore the potential growth of this career. For more information on tech prep, see the *Teacher's Handbook.*

Extension

Connections   Have students research radiocarbon dating. Have them write a short report on the subject, relating their findings to exponential functions and logarithms.

Assignment Guide

Core: 23–55 odd, 56, 57, 59–69
Enriched: 22–54 even, 56–69

For **Extra Practice,** see p. 899.

The red A, B, and C flags, printed only in the Teacher's Wraparound Edition, indicate the level of difficulty of the exercises.

Additional Answers

48.

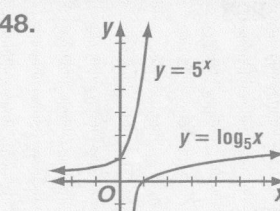

$y = 5^x$

$y = \log_5 x$

49.

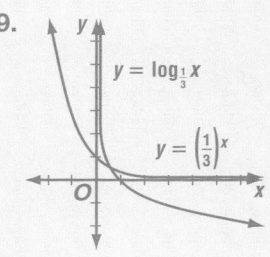

$y = \log_{\frac{1}{3}} x$

$y = \left(\frac{1}{3}\right)^x$

Practice Masters, p. 70

10-2   NAME_____   DATE_____

Practice   Student Edition Pages 605–610

Logarithms and Logarithmic Functions

Write each equation in logarithmic form.

1. $5^3 = 125$ $\log_5 125 = 3$ **2.** $27^{\frac{4}{3}} = 81$ $\log_{27} 81 = \frac{4}{3}$

Write each equation in exponential form.

3. $\log_{10} 0.00001 = -5$ $10^{-5} = 0.00001$ **4.** $\log_{\frac{2}{3}} \frac{\sqrt{6}}{3} = -\frac{1}{2}$ $\left(\frac{3}{2}\right)^{-\frac{1}{2}} = \frac{\sqrt{6}}{3}$

Evaluate each expression.

5. $\log_3 81$ 4   **6.** $\log_{10} 0.0001$ −4

7. $\log_2 \frac{1}{16}$ −4   **8.** $\log_{\frac{1}{3}} 27$ −3

9. $\log_9 1$ 0   **10.** $\log_8 4$ $\frac{2}{3}$

Solve each equation.

11. $\log_4 x = \frac{3}{2}$ 8   **12.** $\log_7 16 = -4$ $\frac{1}{2}$

13. $\log_9 \frac{1}{8} = -3$ 2   **14.** $\log_7 n = -\frac{1}{2}$ $\frac{\sqrt{7}}{7}$

15. $\log_{\sqrt{5}} y = \frac{4}{3}$ $5^{\frac{2}{3}}$ or $\sqrt[3]{25}$ **16.** $\log_8 \sqrt[4]{9} = \frac{1}{6}$ 81

17. $\log_5(3x + 7) = \log_5(7x + 4)$ $\frac{3}{4}$ **18.** $\log_7(8x + 20) = \log_7(x + 6)$ −2

19. $\log_2(9x - 1) = \log_2(4x - 16)$ no solution   **20.** $\log_{10}(x - 9) = \log_{10}(3x - 13)$ no solution

21. $\log_6(x^2 - 30) = \log_6 6$ ± 6 **22.** $\log_8(x^2 + 6) = \log_8 5x$ 2, 3

Closing Activity

Speaking Have students define number, base, and logarithm as they apply to exponential and logarithmic equations.

Chapter 10, Quiz A (Lessons 10-1 and 10-2), is available in the *Assessment and Evaluation Masters*, p. 268.

Additional Answers

61. $f \circ g$ does not exist; $g \circ f = \{(2, 5), (-1, -1), (3, 2)\}$

67.

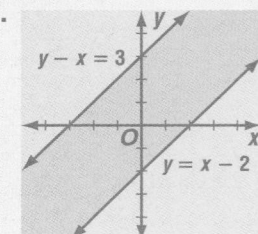

$y - x = 3$
$y = x - 2$

Enrichment Masters, p. 70

NAME_____ DATE_____
Student Edition
Enrichment Pages 605–610

Musical Relationships

The frequencies of notes in a musical scale that are one octave apart are related by an exponential equation. For the eight C notes on a piano, the equation is $C_n = C_1 2^{n-1}$, where C_n represents the frequency of note C_n.

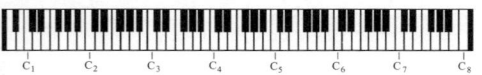

$C_1 \quad C_2 \quad C_3 \quad C_4 \quad C_5 \quad C_6 \quad C_7 \quad C_8$

1. Find the relationship between C_1 and C_2. $C_2 = 2C_1$

2. Find the relationship between C_1 and C_4. $C_4 = 8C_1$

The frequencies of consecutive notes are related by a common ratio r. The general equation is $f_n = f_1 r^{n-1}$.

3. If the frequency of middle C is 261.6 cycles per second and the frequency of the next higher C is 523.2 cycles per second, find the common ratio r. (*Hint:* The two C's are 12 notes apart.) Write the answer as a radical expression. $r = \sqrt[12]{2}$

C♯ D♯   F♯ G♯ A♯

4. Substitute decimal values for r and f_1 to find a specific equation for f_n. $f_n = 261.1(1.05946)^{n-1}$

C₁ D E F G A B C₂

5. Find the frequency of F♯ above middle C. $f_7 = 261.6(1.05946)^7 \approx 369.95$

6. The frets on a guitar are spaced so that the sound made by pressing a string against one fret has about 1.0595 times the wavelength of the sound made by using the next fret. The general equation is $w_n = w_0(1.0595)^n$. Describe the arrangement of the frets on a guitar. The frets are spaced in a logarithmic scale.

---

62. $\dfrac{(x-3)^2}{4} - \dfrac{(y+5)^2}{9} = 1$

61. If $f = \{(2, 1), (-1, 6), (3, 2)\}$ and $g = \{(2, 2), (6, -1), (1, 5)\}$, express $f \circ g$ and $g \circ f$, if they exist, as sets of ordered pairs. (Lesson 8–7) **See margin.**

62. Write the equation of the hyperbola in the graph at the right. (Lesson 7–5)

(3, −5)

63. Write a quadratic equation that has roots 6 and −6. (Lesson 6–5) $x^2 - 36 = 0$

64. Solve $x^2 + 6x = -9$ by factoring. (Lesson 6–2) **−3**

65. Physics Find the time t (in seconds) that it takes for a free-falling object to fall a distance s of 200 feet. Use the formula $t = \frac{1}{4}\sqrt{s}$. (Lesson 5–6) **about 3.54 s**

66. Evaluate the determinant of $\begin{bmatrix} 6 & 5 & -2 \\ -3 & 0 & 6 \\ 1 & 4 & 2 \end{bmatrix}$ (Lesson 4–4) **−60**

67. Solve the system of inequalities by graphing. (Lesson 3–4) **See margin.**
$y - x \leq 3$
$y \geq x - 2$

68. Find the y-intercept and the x-intercept of the graph of $3x + 5y = 30$. (Lesson 2–3) **6; 10**

69. Solve $8x + 5 < 7x - 3$. (Lesson 1–6) **$x < -8$**

Mathematics and SOCIETY

Earthquake!

The excerpt below appeared in an article in *Science News* on October 15, 1994.

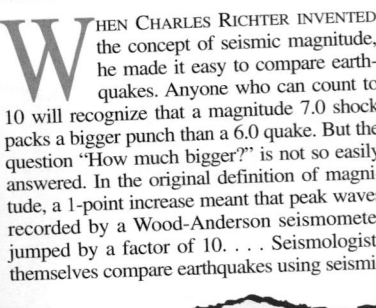

WHEN CHARLES RICHTER INVENTED the concept of seismic magnitude, he made it easy to compare earthquakes. Anyone who can count to 10 will recognize that a magnitude 7.0 shock packs a bigger punch than a 6.0 quake. But the question "How much bigger?" is not so easily answered. In the original definition of magnitude, a 1-point increase meant that peak waves recorded by a Wood-Anderson seismometer jumped by a factor of 10. . . . Seismologists themselves compare earthquakes using seismic moments. . . . But moments are expressed in unwieldy numbers, such as 2×10^{27} newton meters—clearly not an appealing figure for the public. Pat Jorgenson, a USGS spokeswoman in Menlo Park, Calif., says she would prefer to discuss quakes in terms of something people can comprehend. . . . In that vein, a magnitude 1.0 earthquake would equal roughly 6 ounces of TNT. For a magnitude 5.0, think of 1000 tons of TNT. . . . The largest recorded earthquake, of moment magnitude 9.5, in Chile in 1960, equaled about 3 billion tons of TNT. ■

1. Between one-unit intervals on the Richter scale, the magnitude of earthquake strength increases by a factor of 10. What is the mathematical name for this type of scale? **logarithmic with base 10**

2. The largest earthquakes can be several billion times stronger than the smallest. What problems might arise if you tried to design a simpler, more understandable measuring scale? **See margin.**

3. See students' work. **3.** Choose or invent your own unit of measurement to measure quakes.

Mathematics and SOCIETY

Born in Ohio in 1900, Charles Richter moved to Los Angeles in 1916. In 1935 he developed the Richter scale in collaboration with German-born Beno Guttenberg. Richter mapped out earthquake-prone areas of the U.S., but surprisingly, he never believed the scale could be used for prediction.

Answer for Mathematics and Society

2. Sample answer: Problems arise trying to devise a scale that is simpler and easier to understand and yet can take into account the huge differences in magnitude that need to be measured.

Properties of Logarithms

What YOU'LL LEARN

- To simplify and evaluate expressions using properties of logarithms, and
- to solve equations involving logarithms.

Why IT'S IMPORTANT

You can use logarithms to solve problems involving biology and medicine.

CONNECTION
Chemistry

The levels of the acidity of the foods we eat is a concern to some health-conscious consumers. Most of the foods that we consume tend to be more acidic than basic. The pH scale measures acidity; a low pH indicates an acidic solution, and a high pH indicates a basic solution. It is another example of a logarithmic scale based on powers of ten.

pH Levels of Product	Common Products pH Level
Lemon juice	2.1
Sauerkraut	3.5
Tomatoes	4.2
Black coffee	5.0
Milk	6.4
Pure water	7.0
Eggs	7.8
Milk of magnesia	10.0

Black coffee has a pH of 5, while neutral water has a pH of 7. Black coffee is one hundred times more acidic than neutral water, since $10^{7-5} = 10^2$ or 100.

Since logarithms are exponents, the properties of logarithms can be derived from the properties of exponents that you already know. Recall that the product of powers is found by adding exponents.

$$\log_2 (8 \cdot 32) = \log_2 (2^3 \cdot 2^5) \qquad \log_2 8 + \log_2 32 = \log_2 2^3 + \log_2 2^5$$
$$= \log_2 (2^{3+5}) \qquad\qquad\qquad = 3 + 5$$
$$= 3 + 5$$

So, $\log_2 (8 \cdot 32) = \log_2 8 + \log_2 32$. This example indicates that the logarithm of a product is the sum of the logarithms of the factors.

Product Property of Logarithms	**For all positive numbers m, n, and b, where $b \neq 1$, $\log_b mn = \log_b m + \log_b n$.**

To prove this property, let $b^x = m$ and $b^y = n$.

Then $\log_b m = x$ and $\log_b n = y$.

$$b^x b^y = mn$$
$$b^{x+y} = mn \qquad \textit{Multiplying powers}$$
$$\log_b b^{x+y} = \log_b mn \qquad \textit{Property of equality for logarithmic functions}$$
$$x + y = \log_b mn \qquad \textit{Definition of inverse functions}$$
$$\log_b m + \log_b n = \log_b mn \qquad \textit{Replace x with } \log_b m \textit{ and y with } \log_b n.$$

Example ① Given $\log_3 5 \approx 1.4650$, find each logarithm.
  a. $\log_3 45$ b. $\log_3 25$

$$\log_3 45 = \log_3 (3^2 \cdot 5) \qquad\qquad \log_3 25 = \log_3 (5 \cdot 5)$$
$$= \log_3 3^2 + \log_3 5 \qquad\qquad\quad = \log_3 5 + \log_3 5$$
$$\approx 2 + 1.4650 \text{ or } 3.4650 \qquad\qquad \approx 1.4650 + 1.4650 \text{ or } 2.9300$$

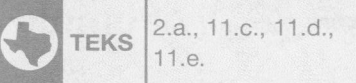
TEKS   2.a., 11.c., 11.d., 11.e.

Instructional Resources

- Study Guide Master 10-3
- Practice Master 10-3
- Enrichment Master 10-3

 Transparency 10-3A contains the 5-Minute Check for this lesson; **Transparency 10-3B** contains a teaching aid for this lesson.

Recommended Pacing	
Standard Pacing	Day 5 of 12
Honors Pacing	Day 5 of 11
Block Scheduling*	Day 2 of 5 (along with Lesson 10-2)

 *For more information on pacing and possible lesson plans, refer to the *Block Scheduling Booklet.*

1 FOCUS

5-Minute Check
(over Lesson 10-2)

Evaluate.

1. $\log_5 x = 3$ **125**

2. $\log_a \frac{1}{9} = -2$ **3**

3. Write $\log_4 64 = 3$ in exponential form. $4^3 = 64$

Solve.

4. $\log_5 (4x) = \log_5 (x^2 - 5)$ **5**

5. $\log_6 (4x + 7) = \log_6 (6x - 9)$ **8**

Motivating the Lesson

Hands-On Activity Provide samples of lemon juice, sauerkraut, tomato juice, milk, and water. Ask a student to volunteer to take a blindfold taste test. Samples will be given to the student at random. The volunteer is to rank the samples' acidity. He or she should also try to say how much more acidic a sample is than the one ranked below it.

In-Class Examples

For Example 1
Given $\log_{12} 8 \approx 0.8368$ and $\log_{12} 10 \approx 0.9226$, find each logarithm.

a. $\log_{12} 80$ **1.7634**
b. $\log_{12} 96$ **1.8368**

For Example 2
Given $\log_{16} 3 \approx 0.3962$ and $\log_{16} 20 \approx 1.0805$, find each logarithm.

a. $\log_{16} \frac{5}{64}$ **−0.9195**

b. $\log_{16} \frac{3}{16}$ **−0.6038**

For Example 3
Find the amount of hydrogen in a liter of acid rain that has a pH of 7. 10^{-7}

Teaching Tip As background for Example 3, tell students that all rain is slightly acidic. Neutral water dissolves nitrogen and carbon oxides in the air, forming weak acids. These weak acids do not harm the environment.

To find the quotient of powers, you subtract the exponents.

$$\log_2 \frac{32}{8} = \log_2 \frac{2^5}{2^3} \qquad\qquad \log_2 32 - \log_2 8 = \log_2 2^5 - \log_2 2^3$$
$$= \log_2 (2^{5-3}) \qquad\qquad\qquad\qquad\qquad = 5 - 3$$
$$= 5 - 3 \qquad\qquad\qquad\qquad\qquad\qquad = 2$$
$$= 2$$

So, $\log_2 \frac{32}{8} = \log_2 32 - \log_2 8$. This example indicates that the logarithm of a quotient can be found by subtracting the logarithm of the denominator from the logarithm of the numerator.

Quotient Property of Logarithms	**For all positive numbers m, n, and b, where $b \neq 1$, $\log_b \frac{m}{n} = \log_b m - \log_b n$.**

To prove this property, let $b^x = m$ and $b^y = n$.
Then $\log_b m = x$ and $\log_b n = y$.

$$\frac{b^x}{b^y} = \frac{m}{n}$$
$$b^{x-y} = \frac{m}{n} \qquad \textit{Division of powers}$$
$$\log_b b^{x-y} = \log_b \frac{m}{n} \qquad \textit{Property of equality for logarithmic functions}$$
$$x - y = \log_b \frac{m}{n} \qquad \textit{Definition of inverse functions}$$
$$\log_b m - \log_b n = \log_b \frac{m}{n} \qquad \textit{Replace x with } \log_b m \textit{ and y with } \log_b n.$$

Example **2** Given $\log_4 5 \approx 1.1610$ and $\log_4 15 \approx 1.9534$, find each logarithm.

a. $\log_4 \frac{5}{16}$ **b.** $\log_4 3$

$$\log_4 \frac{5}{16} = \log_4 \frac{5}{4^2} \qquad\qquad \log_4 3 = \log_4 \frac{15}{5}$$
$$= \log_4 5 - \log_4 4^2 \qquad\qquad = \log_4 15 - \log_4 5$$
$$\approx 1.1610 - 2 \quad \text{or} \quad -0.8390 \qquad \approx 1.9534 - 1.1610 \quad \text{or} \quad 0.7924$$

Example **3**

Chemistry

The pH of a substance is the concentration of hydrogen ions, $[H^+]$, measured in moles of hydrogen per liter of substance. It is given by the formula $pH = \log_{10} \frac{1}{[H^+]}$. Find the amount of hydrogen in a liter of acid rain that has a pH of 4.2.

Explore   Read the problem. You know the formula for finding pH and the pH of the rain. You want to find the amount of hydrogen in a liter of this rain.

Plan   Write the equation. Then, solve for $[H+]$.

 Alternative Learning Styles

Kinesthetic Provide students with some pH paper that has a comparison pH chart and several different liquids, such as distilled water, tap water, pond water, and dilute solutions of baking soda and vinegar.

Have students determine the pH for each liquid. From the pH values, have students determine how much more acidic the lowest pH is than the highest pH.

Solve $\quad$ pH $= \log_{10} \frac{1}{[H+]}$ $\qquad$ *Replace pH with 4.2.*

$$4.2 = \log_{10} \frac{1}{[H+]}$$

$$4.2 = \log_{10} 1 - \log_{10} [H+] \quad \text{\textit{Quotient property of logarithms}}$$

$$4.2 = 0 - \log_{10} [H+] \quad \text{\textit{log}}_{10} \text{\textit{1} = 0}$$

$$4.2 = -\log_{10} [H+]$$

$$-4.2 = \log_{10} [H+]$$

$$10^{-4.2} = [H+] \qquad \text{\textit{Definition of logarithm}}$$

There are $10^{-4.2}$, or about 0.000063, moles of hydrogen in a liter of this rain.

Examine $\quad$ Check the solution.

$$4.2 \overset{?}{=} \log_{10} \frac{1}{10^{-4.2}}$$

$$4.2 \overset{?}{=} \log_{10} 1 - \log_{10} 10^{-4.2}$$

$$4.2 \overset{?}{=} 0 - (-4.2)$$

$$4.2 = 4.2 \quad \checkmark$$

The power of a power is found by multiplying the two exponents.

$$
\begin{aligned}
\log_3 9^4 &= \log_3 (3^2)^4 & \qquad 4 \log_3 9 &= (\log_3 9) \cdot 4 \\
&= \log_3 3^{2 \cdot 4} & &= (\log_3 3^2) \cdot 4 \\
&= 2 \cdot 4 & &= 2 \cdot 4
\end{aligned}
$$

So, $\log_3 9^4 = 4 \log_3 9$. This example indicates that the logarithm of a power is the product of the logarithm and the exponent.

Power Property of Logarithms	**For any real number p and positive numbers m and b, where $b \neq 1$,** $$\log_b m^p = p \cdot \log_b m.$$

You will prove this property in Exercise 3.

Example 4 illustrates how to use the properties of logarithms to solve equations involving logarithms.

Example  **Solve each equation.**

a. $2 \log_3 6 - \frac{1}{4} \log_3 16 = \log_3 x$

$$2 \log_3 6 - \frac{1}{4} \log_3 16 = \log_3 x$$

$$\log_3 6^2 - \log_3 16^{\frac{1}{4}} = \log_3 x \quad \text{\textit{Power property of logarithms}}$$

$$\log_3 36 - \log_3 2 = \log_3 x$$

$$\log_3 \frac{36}{2} = \log_3 x \quad \text{\textit{Quotient property of logarithms}}$$

$$\log_3 18 = \log_3 x$$

$$18 = x \quad \text{\textit{Property of equality for logarithmic functions}}$$

The solution is 18.

In-Class Example

For Example 4
Solve each equation.

a. $4 \log_8 x = \log_8 81$
 ± 3
 The only solution is 3 since $4 \log_8 (-3)$ is not defined.

b. $\log_5 (y - 12) + \log_5 (y + 12) = 2$
 ± 13
 The only solution is 13 since $\log_5 (-13 - 12)$ and $\log_5 (-13 + 12)$ are not defined.

Check for Understanding

Exercises 1–16 are designed to help you assess your students' understanding through reading, writing, speaking, and modeling. You should work through Exercises 1–4 with your students and then monitor their work on Exercises 5–16.

Additional Answers

1. The pH of a solution indicates its acidity. The pH level is actually an exponent to the power of 10, so it is a logarithm to the base 10.

3. Sample answer: Let $b^x = m$, then $\log_b m = x$.

$$(b^x)^p = m^p$$
$$b^{xp} = m^p \qquad \text{Multiplying exponents}$$
$$\log_b b^{xp} = \log_b m^p \qquad \text{Property of equality for logarithmic functions}$$
$$xp = \log_b m^p \qquad \text{Definition of inverse functions}$$
$$p \log_b m = \log_b m^p \qquad \text{Substitution property}$$

Study Guide Masters, p. 71

10-3

NAME_____ DATE _____

Student Edition
Pages 611–616

Study Guide

Properties of Logarithms

Logarithms are exponents. Thus, the properties of logarithms can be derived from the properties of exponents.

Properties of Logarithms	
For all positive numbers m, n, and b, where $b \neq 1$.	
Property	**Example**
Product Property $\log_b mn = \log_b m + \log_b n$	Given $\log_5 5 = 1.465$, find $\log_5 25$. $\log_5 25 = \log_5 (5 \cdot 5)$ $= \log_5 5 + \log_5 5$ $= 1.465 + 1.465$ or 2.930
Quotient Property $\log_b \frac{m}{n} = \log_b m - \log_b n$	Given $\log_5 2 = 0.3869$ and $\log_5 20 = 1.6720$, find $\log_5 0.1$. $\log_5 0.1 = \log_5 \left(\frac{2}{20}\right)$ $= \log_5 2 - \log_5 20$ $= 0.3869 - 1.6720$ or -1.2851
Power Property $\log_b m^p = p \cdot \log_b m$	Solve $2 \log_4 x - \log_4 8 = \log_4 8$. $2 \log_4 x - \log_4 8 = \log_4 8$ $2 \log_4 x = \log_4 8 + \log_4 8$ $2 \log_4 x = \log_4 (8 \cdot 8)$ $2 \log_4 x = \log_4 64$ $\log_4 x^2 = \log_4 64$ $x^2 = 64$ $x = \pm 8$

Use $\log_{12} 3 = 0.4421$ and $\log_{12} 7 = 0.7831$ to evaluate each expression.

1. $\log_{12} 21$ 1.2252
2. $\log_{12} \frac{7}{3}$ 0.3410
3. $\log_{12} 49$ 1.5662
4. $\log_{12} 36$ 1.4421
5. $\log_{12} 48$ 1.5579
6. $\log_{12} \frac{36}{49}$ 0.1241

Solve each equation.

7. $\log_5 4 - \log_5 (x + 3) = \log_5 8$ $-\frac{5}{2}$
8. $\log_{10}(x + 3) - \log_{10}(2x - 1) = \log_{10} 2$ $\frac{5}{3}$
9. $\log_5 (c + 3) - \log_5 (4c - 1) = \log_5 5$ $\frac{8}{19}$
10. $\log_2 x - 3 \log_2 5 = 2 \log_2 10$ 12,500

614 Chapter 10

---

b. $\log_{10} z + \log_{10} (z + 3) = 1$

$$\log_{10} z + \log_{10} (z + 3) = 1$$
$$\log_{10} z(z + 3) = 1 \qquad \textit{Product property of logarithms}$$
$$z(z + 3) = 10^1 \qquad \textit{Definition of logarithm}$$
$$z^2 + 3z - 10 = 0$$
$$(z + 5)(z - 2) = 0$$
$$z + 5 = 0 \quad \text{or} \quad z - 2 = 0 \qquad \textit{Zero product property}$$
$$z = -5 \qquad\qquad z = 2$$

Check: $\log_{10} z + \log_{10} (z + 3) = 1$
$\log_{10} (-5) + \log_{10} (-5 + 3) \overset{?}{=} 1$
$\log_{10} (-5) + \log_{10}(-2) \overset{?}{=} 1$
Both $\log_{10} (-5)$ and $\log_{10} (-2)$ are undefined, so -5 is not a solution.

$\log_{10} z + \log_{10} (z + 3) = 1$
$\log_{10} 2 + \log_{10} (2 + 3) \overset{?}{=} 1$
$\log_{10} 2 + \log_{10} 5 \overset{?}{=} 1$
$\log_{10} (2 \cdot 5) \overset{?}{=} 1$
$\log_{10} 10 \overset{?}{=} 1$
$1 = 1 \checkmark$

The only solution is 2.

CHECK FOR UNDERSTANDING

Communicating Mathematics

Study the lesson. Then complete the following.

1. **Describe** what the pH of a solution indicates and how it is related to logarithms. See margin.

2. **Name** the properties that serve as guidelines to derive the properties of logarithms. properties of exponents

3. **Prove** the power property of logarithms. See margin.

MATH JOURNAL

4. **Assess Yourself** List three properties of exponents and their related properties of logarithms. Do you find the properties of exponents or the properties of logarithms easier to understand? Do you have difficulty understanding or applying any of these properties? See margin.

5. $2 \log_4 x + \log_4 y$ 6. $3 \log_3 x + 3 \log_3 y$

Guided Practice

Express each logarithm as the sum or difference of simpler logarithmic expressions.

5. $\log_4 x^2 y$
6. $\log_3 (xy)^3$
7. $\log_5 \frac{ac}{b}$
8. $\log_2 r^{\frac{1}{3}} t$

7. $\log_5 a + \log_5 c - \log_5 b$ 8. $\frac{1}{3} \log_2 r + \log_2 t$

Use $\log_2 3 \approx 1.585$ and $\log_2 7 \approx 2.807$ to evaluate each expression.

9. $\log_2 \frac{7}{3}$ 1.222
10. $\log_2 36$ 5.170
11. $\log_2 0.75$ -0.415

Solve each equation.   14. 14   16. about 25,119 times more acidic

12. $\log_2 5 + \log_2 x = \log_2 15$ 3
13. $\log_5 16 - \log_5 2t = \log_5 2$ 4
14. $\log_{10} 7 + \log_{10} (n - 2) = \log_{10} 6n$
15. $\log_2 (y + 2) - 1 = \log_2 (y - 2)$ 6

16. **Chemistry** If the pH level of tomato juice is 4.1 and pH level of baking soda is 8.5, how much more acidic is tomato juice than baking soda?

Reteaching ▬▬▬

Logical Thinking Give students equations that have been solved in an incorrect manner involving the properties of logarithms. Have them identify and explain the mistakes and solve correctly.

Additional Answer

4. multiplying exponents → product property of logarithms
dividing exponents → quotient property of logarithms
power of powers → power property of logarithms
See students' work.

Practice

Use $\log_3 2 \approx 0.6310$ and $\log_3 7 \approx 1.7712$ to evaluate each expression.

17. $\log_3 4$ 1.262
18. $\log_3 49$ 3.5424
19. $\log_3 \frac{7}{2}$ 1.1402

20. $\log_3 18$ 2.6310
21. $\log_3 \frac{2}{3}$ −0.3690
22. $\log_3 54$ 3.6310

23. $\log_3 108$ 4.2620
24. $\log_3 \frac{18}{49}$ −0.9114
25. $\log_3 \frac{7}{9}$ −0.2288

Solve each equation.

26. $\log_3 2 + \log_3 7 = \log_3 x$ 14
27. $\log_5 42 - \log_5 6 = \log_5 k$ 7

29. 14

28. $\log_5 m = \frac{1}{3}\log_5 125$ 5
29. $\log_{10} y = \frac{1}{4}\log_{10} 16 + \frac{1}{2}\log_{10} 49$

30. $\log_9 5 + \log_9 (n + 1) = \log_9 6n$ 5
31. $3\log_5 x - \log_5 4 = \log_5 16$ 4

32. $2\log_3 y + \log_3 0.1 = \log_3 5 + \log_3 2$ 10

33. $\log_{10} a + \log_{10} (a + 21) = 2$ 4

34. $\log_6 48 - \log_6 \frac{16}{5} + \log_6 5 = \log_6 5x$ 15

35. $\log_3 64 - \log_3 \frac{8}{3} + \log_3 2 = \log_3 4r$ 12

36. $\log_6 (b^2 + 2) + \log_6 2 = 2$ ±4

37. $\log_3 (5z + 5) - \log_3 (z^2 - 1) = 0$ 6

Solve for a.

38. $\frac{y}{3} + 1$

41. $\frac{1}{2}(n + 1)$

42. $\log_b \left[\dfrac{x^2\sqrt[3]{x+2}}{(x-3)^4}\right]$

43. $\log_b \dfrac{x}{y^3}$

44. $y = \dfrac{a}{bc}$

38. $\log_n a = \log_n (y + 3) - \log_n 3$
39. $\log_b 2a - \log_b x^3 = \log_b x$ $\frac{x^4}{2}$

40. $\log_x a^2 + 5\log_x y = \log_x a$ $\frac{1}{y^5}$
41. $\log_b 4 + 2\log_b a = 2\log_b (n + 1)$

Write each expression as one logarithm.

42. $2\log_b x + \frac{1}{3}\log_b (x + 2) - 4\log_b (x - 3)$

43. $\log_b (xy^2) + 2\log_b \frac{x}{y} - 3\log_b \left(yx^{\frac{2}{3}}\right)$

Critical Thinking

44. If $\log_m y = \log_m a - \log_m b - \log_m c$, express y in terms of a, b, and c.

Applications and Problem Solving

45. Medicine The pH of a person's blood can be found by using the Henderson-Hasselbach formula. The formula is $pH = 6.1 + \log_{10} \frac{B}{C}$, where B represents the concentration of bicarbonate, which is a base, and C represents the concentration of carbonic acid, which is an acid. Most people have a blood pH of about 7.4.

  a. Use a property of logarithms to write the equation without a fraction.
    $pH = 6.1 + \log_{10} B - \log_{10} C$

  b. A pH of 7 is neutral, and pH numbers less than 7 represent acidic solutions. pH levels greater than 7 represent basic solutions. Is blood normally an acid, a base, or a neutral?
    a very weak base

  c. Use a scientific calculator to find the pH of a person's blood if the concentration of bicarbonate is 25 and concentration of carbonic acid is 2.   7.197

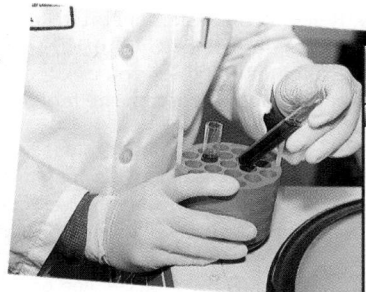

Lesson 10-3 Properties of Logarithms   **615**

Susan McKinney Steward (1848–1918)

Susan McKinney Steward was the first black woman to be formally certified as a medical doctor. She helped to establish the Women's Hospital and Dispensary in Brooklyn.

Assignment Guide

Core: 17–43 odd, 44, 45, 47–54
Enriched: 18–42 even, 44–54

For **Extra Practice,** see p. 899.

The red A, B, and C flags, printed only in the Teacher's Wraparound Edition, indicate the level of difficulty of the exercises.

fabulous FIRSTS

The first incorporated hospital in America was the Pennsylvania Hospital in Philadelphia, which obtained a charter from the crown in 1751.

Practice Masters, p. 71

| 10-3 | NAME_____ DATE_____ |

Practice   Student Editi
Pages 611–

Properties of Logarithms

Evaluate each expression.

1. $n^{\log_n 3}$ 3
2. $14^{\log_{14} 6}$ 6

Use $\log_{10} 5 = 0.6990$ and $\log_{10} 7 = 0.8451$ to evaluate each expression.

3. $\log_{10} 35$ 1.5441
4. $\log_{10} \frac{7}{5}$ 0.1461

5. $\log_{10} 25$ 1.3980
6. $\log_{10} 490$ 2.6902

7. $\log_{10} \left(1\frac{2}{5}\right)$ 0.1549
8. $\log_{10} 0.05$ −1.3010

Solve each equation.

9. $\log_6 x + \log_6 9 = \log_6 54$ 6
10. $\log_8 48 - \log_8 w = \log_8 4$ 12

11. $\log_7 n = \frac{2}{3}\log_7 8$ 4
12. $\log_3 y = \frac{1}{4}\log_3 16 + \frac{1}{3}\log_3 64$ 8

13. $\log_9 (3u + 14) - \log_9 5 = \log_9 2u$ 2
14. $\log_7 x + \log_7 x - \log_7 3 = \log_7 12$ 6

15. $4\log_2 x + \log_2 5 = \log_2 405$ 3
16. $\log_6 (2x - 5) + 1 = \log_6 (7x + 10)$ 8

17. $\log_{10} (9x + 5) - \log_{10} (x^2 - 1) = \frac{1}{2}$ 3
18. $\log_8 (n - 3) + \log_8 (n + 4) = 1$ 4

19. $\log_6 (3m + 7) - \log_6 (m + 4) = 2\log_6 6 - 3\log_6 3$ −1

20. $\log_4 (2x + 8) - \log_4 (2x^2 + 21x + 61) = -3$ $\frac{1}{2}$, −3

Closing Activity

Speaking Have students explain why $\log_5 8^2$ is equivalent to $2 \log_5 8$.

46a. $\log_{10}\left(\dfrac{C_2}{C_1}\right)^{1.4}$

48. $\dfrac{x+2}{x+4}$

46. Biology The formula for the energy needed to transport a substance from the outside of a living cell to the inside of that cell is $E = 1.4(\log_{10} C_2 - \log_{10} C_1)$, where E represents the energy in kilocalories per gram molecule, C_1 represents the concentration outside the cell, and C_2 represents the concentration inside the cell.

  a. Use the properties of logarithms to write the value of E as one logarithm.

  b. If the concentration inside the cell is three times the concentration outside the cell, find the energy for a substance to travel from the outside to the inside.   **about 0.668 kilocalories per gram**

Mixed Review

47. Solve $\log_3 243 = y$.   (Lesson 10–2)   **5**

48. Find $\dfrac{x+2}{x+3} \div \dfrac{x^2+x-12}{x^2-9}$. Write the answer in simplest form.   (Lesson 9–3)

49. Find $p(a+1)$ if $p(x) = 4x - x^2 - 4$.   (Lesson 8–1) $-a^2 + 2a - 1$

50. Geometry Find the coordinates of the midpoint of $\overline{AB}$ with $A(5, 5)$ and $B(6, -7)$.   (Lesson 7–1)   **(5.5, −1)**

51. State whether $x^2 + 8x + 64$ is a perfect square.   (Lesson 6–3)   **no**

52. Energy A circular cell must deliver 18 watts of energy. If each square centimeter of the cell that is in sunlight produces 0.01 watt of energy, how long must the radius of the cell be?   (Lesson 5–8)   **about 23.94 cm**

53. Factor $x^3 + 2x^2 - 35x$.   (Lesson 5–4) $x(x+7)(x-5)$

54. Solve the system of equations.   (Lesson 3–2)   **(−2, 2)**

$$2x + 3y = 2$$
$$3x - 4y = -14$$

WORKING ON THE

Refer to the Investigation on pages 590–591.

Refer to the data generated from your shooting experiments with the three rubber bands. Examine the tables you created. Explain any patterns you notice from the tables.

1 Create a coordinate plane with the horizontal axis representing the length the rubber band was stretched and the vertical axis representing the distance the rubber band flew for each rubber band. Graph the data for each rubber band. Draw a best-fit line or curve.

2 Describe the shape of each of the graphs. Are any of the graphs functions? If they are functions, describe the type of function you think each one is and justify your answer.

3 Refer to the third column of each table. Compute the difference between the distance each shot flew and the distance the previous shot flew. What pattern, if any, do you notice? What is the relationship between the data in the second column and the data in the third column?

4 Compare the graphs of the three rubber bands. Are the graphs the same? Explain. If there are differences, describe them.

Add the results of your work to your Investigation Folder.

Enrichment Masters, p. 71

NAME_____ DATE _____

10-3   Enrichment

Student Edition
Pages 611–616

Spirals

Consider an angle in standard position with its vertex at a point O called the pole. Its initial side is on a coordinatized axis called the polar axis. A point P on the terminal side of the angle is named by the polar coordinates (r, θ), where r is the directed distance of the point from O and θ is the measure of the angle. Graphs in this system may be drawn on polar coordinate paper such as the kind shown below.

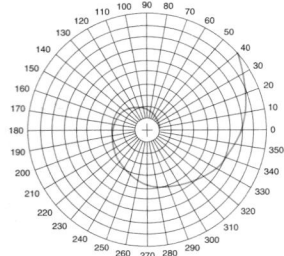

1. Use a calculator to complete the table for $\log_r r = \dfrac{\theta}{120}$. (*Hint:* To find θ on a calculator, press 120 $\times$ r LOG $\div$ 2 LOG .)

r	1	2	3	4	5	6	7	8
θ	0°	120°	190°	240°	279°	310°	337°	360°

2. Plot the points found in Exercise 1 on the grid above and connect to form a smooth curve.

This type of spiral is called a logarithmic spiral because the angle measures are proportional to the logarithms of the radii.

Extension

Problem Solving Solve

$$\frac{1}{2}\log_b(x+2) + \frac{1}{2}\log_b(x-22) = \frac{2}{3}\log_b 27.$$ **25**

In·ves·ti·ga·tion

Working on the Investigation

The Investigation on pages 590–591 is designed to be a long-term project that is completed over several days or weeks. Encourage students to keep their materials in their Investigation Folder as they work on the Investigation.

Common Logarithms

What YOU'LL LEARN

- To identify the characteristic and the mantissa of a logarithm, and
- to find common logarithms and antilogarithms.

Why IT'S IMPORTANT

You can use common logarithms to solve problems involving astronomy and acoustics.

APPLICATION
Acoustics

One of the more useful logarithms is base 10, because our number system is base 10. Base 10 logarithms are called **common logarithms.** These are usually written without the subscript 10, so $\log_{10} x$ is written as $\log x$.

Common logarithms are used in the measure of sound. The loudness L, in decibels, of a particular sound is defined as $L = 10 \log \frac{I}{I_0}$, where I is the intensity of the sound and I_0 is the minimum intensity of sound detectable by the human ear. Soft recorded music is about 4000 times the minimum intensity of sound detectable by the human ear. Use the definition of logarithms to find the loudness in decibels.

$$L = 10 \log \frac{I}{I_0}$$
$$= 10 \log \frac{4000\, I_0}{I_0} \quad \textit{Substitution}$$
$$= 10 \log 4000$$
$$\approx 10(3.602)$$
$$\approx 36$$

Soft recorded music is about 36 decibels. Other common sounds and their approximate decibels levels are listed in the chart below.

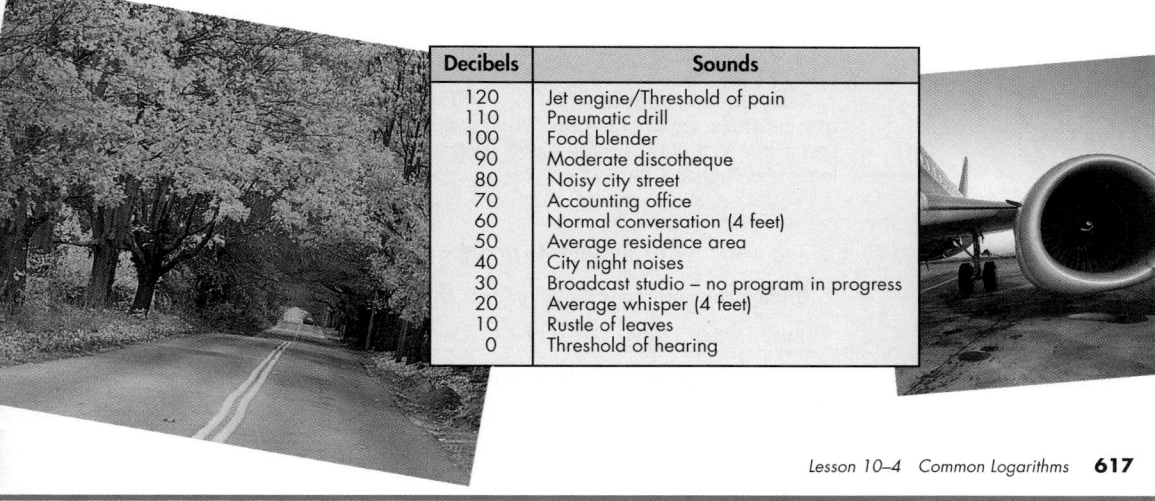

Decibels	Sounds
120	Jet engine/Threshold of pain
110	Pneumatic drill
100	Food blender
90	Moderate discotheque
80	Noisy city street
70	Accounting office
60	Normal conversation (4 feet)
50	Average residence area
40	City night noises
30	Broadcast studio – no program in progress
20	Average whisper (4 feet)
10	Rustle of leaves
0	Threshold of hearing

NCTM Standards: 1–6

Instructional Resources

- Study Guide Master 10-4
- Practice Master 10-4
- Enrichment Master 10-4
- Assessment and Evaluation Masters, pp. 267–268
- Real-World Applications, 28

Transparency 10-4A contains the 5-Minute Check for this lesson; **Transparency 10-4B** contains a teaching aid for this lesson.

Recommended Pacing	
Standard Pacing	Day 6 of 12
Honors Pacing	Day 6 of 11
Block Scheduling*	Day 3 of 5 (along with Lesson 10-5)

*For more information on pacing and possible lesson plans, refer to the *Block Scheduling Booklet.*

1 FOCUS

5-Minute Check
(over Lesson 10-3)

Given $\log_{16} 3 \approx 0.3962$ and $\log_{16} 20 \approx 1.0805$, find each logarithm.

1. $\log_{16} \frac{9}{16}$ −0.2076

2. $\log_{16} \frac{81}{48}$ 0.1886

Solve.

3. $\log_4 48 - \log_4 x = \log_4 6$ 8

4. $2 \log_7 3 + 3 \log_7 2 = \log_7 x$ 72

5. $\log_4 (x + 2) + \log_4 (x - 4) = 2$ 6

Classroom Vignette

"Prior to the invention of hand-held calculators, computations involving powers and roots of numbers were especially well-suited to the use of logarithms. Of course, such methods are now obsolete. But to give students a historical perspective, I demonstrate how logarithms were once used to compute examples like $3(53.2)^2 (2.79)^4$ and $\sqrt[3]{488} \times (1.19)^2$."

Scott Hendrickson
American Fork High School
American Fork, Utah

Motivating the Lesson

Hands-On Activity Borrow a decibel meter from the science department. Have a student whisper into the meter. Ask a second student to try to speak into the meter twice as loud. Ask a third student to try to speak twice as loud as the student before. Continue this, having students use objects in the room to create even louder sounds.

2 TEACH

Teaching Tip For Example 1, you may want to use a calculator to reinforce the relationship between a number expressed in scientific notation and the characteristic of the logarithm of the number. Have students find the logarithms of 5.94, 59.4, 594, and 5940 and compare the characteristics.

In-Class Examples

For Example 1

a. If log 3.87 ≈ 0.5877, find the value of log 38.7. **1.5877**

b. If log 7.53 ≈ 0.8768, find the value of log 7530. **3.8768**

For Example 2
Use a scientific calculator to find each logarithm. Write the result with a positive mantissa.

a. log 2.6 **0.4150**

b. log 0.00041 **6.6128 − 10**

For Example 3
Use a scientific calculator to find the antilogarithm of each logarithm.

a. 0.1790 **1.51**

b. 0.7210 − 3 **0.00526**

Expressing a number in scientific notation is helpful when working with common logarithms.

Example If log 1.2 ≈ 0.0792, find each of the following.
  a. log 120   **b.** log 0.12

F Y I

A Scottish lord by the name of John Napier is credited with the invention of logarithms. He started his work with logarithms in 1594, and first published a table of logarithms in 1614.

$$\begin{aligned} \log 120 &= \log (1.2 \times 10^2) \\ &= \log 1.2 + \log 10^2 \\ &\approx 0.0792 + 2 \text{ or } 2.0792 \end{aligned}$$

$$\begin{aligned} \log 0.12 &= \log (1.2 \times 10^{-1}) \\ &= \log 1.2 + \log 10^{-1} \\ &\approx 0.0972 + (-1) \end{aligned}$$

Look closely at the results of Example 1. Notice that log 120 and log 0.12 have the same decimal part, or **mantissa,** 0.0792, but different integer parts, 2 and −1. The integer part of the common logarithm of a number is called its **characteristic** and indicates the magnitude of the number. The characteristic is the exponent of 10 when the original number is expressed in scientific notation.

$$\log (1.2 \times 10^2) = \log 1.2 + \log 10^2$$
$$= 0.0792 + 2$$

mantissa   characteristic

The mantissa is usually expressed as a positive number. To avoid negative mantissas, we rewrite the negative mantissa as the difference of a positive number and an integer, usually 10.

Example Use a scientific calculator to find log 0.0038. Write the result with a positive mantissa.

The ⎡LOG⎤ key is used to find common logarithms.

Enter: .0038 ⎡LOG⎤   −2.420216403

The value of log 0.0038 is approximately −2.4202.

To write the logarithm with a positive mantissa, add and subtract 10.

(−2.4202 + 10) − 10 = 7.5798 − 10   *10 − 10 = 0 and a + 0 = a.*

The characteristic of the logarithm is 7 − 10 or −3. Thus, the mantissa is 0.5798.

Sometimes an application of logarithms requires that you use the inverse of logarithms, exponentiation. When you are given the logarithm of a number and asked to find the number, you are finding the **antilogarithm.** That is, if log x = a, then x = antilog a.

Example Use a scientific calculator to find the antilogarithm of 3.073.

To find the antilogarithm on your calculator, use the ⎡10ˣ⎤ key.

Enter: 3.073 ⎡2nd⎤ ⎡10ˣ⎤   1183.041556

The antilogarithm of 3.073 is approximately 1183.
This means that $10^{3.073} \approx 1183$.

F Y I

John Napier also is credited with the design of weapons. He designed mirrors that burned, a piece of artillery, and a chariot with small holes through which the charioteers could shoot at the enemy.

Alternative Learning Styles

Auditory Encourage students to discuss the real-world examples of logarithms and exponents studied in the first four lessons. Encourage them to notice the similarities and think up other real-world examples.

Example ④

APPLICATION

Acoustics

On June 15, 1995, Ted Nugent with Bad Company played at the Polaris Amphitheater in Columbus, Ohio. Several miles away, the intensity of the music at the concert registered 66.6 decibels. How many times the minimum intensity of sound detectable by the human ear was this sound, if I_0 is defined to be 1?

Use the formula $L = 10 \log \dfrac{I}{I_0}$

given at the beginning of the lesson.

$$L = 10 \log \dfrac{I}{I_0}$$
$$66.6 = 10 \log \dfrac{I}{I_0}$$
$$6.66 = \log I$$
$$\text{antilog } 6.66 = \text{antilog } (\log I)$$
$$10^{6.66} = I$$
$$4{,}570{,}882 \approx I$$

The sound several miles away from the rock concert was approximately 4,570,000 times the minimum intensity of sound detectable by the human ear.

CHECK FOR UNDERSTANDING

Communicating Mathematics

Study the lesson. Then complete the following.

1. **Describe** the function you are performing when you take the antilogarithm of a value, such as x.   raising 10 to this power: antilog $x = 10^x$

2. **Name** the base used by the calculator [LOG] key. What are these logarithms called?   10; common logarithms

3. When a number is expressed in scientific notation, its exponent of 10 corresponds to what part of its common logarithm?   characteristic

MATH JOURNAL

4. The word logarithm is actually a contraction of "logical arithmetic."

  a. **Explain** why using logarithms was once considered a logical way to multiply or divide some numbers.   See margin.

  b. **Explain** why logarithms are no longer used to multiply or divide numbers.   See margin.

  c. **Name** some uses for common logarithms today.   Sample answers: Richter scale, pH levels, decibel levels

Guided Practice

If log 875 = 2.9420, find each number.

5. characteristic of log 875   2   6. log 8.75   0.9420

Use a scientific calculator to find the logarithm for each number rounded to four decimal places. Then state the mantissa and characteristic.

7. 13.7   1.1367; 0.1367; 1   8. 0.056   −1.2518; 0.7482; −2

Use a scientific calculator to find the antilogarithm of each logarithm rounded to four decimal places.

9. 0.4573   2.8662   10. −2.1477   0.0071

Lesson 10-4   Common Logarithms   **619**

In-Class Example

For Example 4
If the sound at a concert reached 115 decibels, would the listeners be in danger of causing damage to their ears?
No, the intensity of the music was 0.3162 $\dfrac{W}{m^2}$, which is less than 1.

3 PRACTICE/APPLY

Check for Understanding
Exercises 1–11 are designed to help you assess your students' understanding through reading, writing, speaking, and modeling. You should work through Exercises 1–4 with your students and then monitor their work on Exercises 5–11.

Error Analysis
When taking the log of an expression, take the log of the whole expression, not the separate parts.
Example:

$$\log \dfrac{4 \cdot 8}{3 \cdot 1} \neq \dfrac{\log 4 \cdot \log 8}{\log 3 \cdot \log 1}$$

correct   incorrect

Study Guide Masters, p. 72

10-4   NAME_____   DATE_____
Study Guide   Student Edition Pages 617–621

Common Logarithms
Logarithms to base 10 are called **common logarithms.** Every logarithm has two parts, the **mantissa** and the **characteristic.** Logarithms depend on the use of scientific notation. The mantissa is the logarithm of a number between 1 and 10. The characteristic is the power of ten that is used when the number is expressed in scientific notation.

A scientific calculator can be used to find common logarithms. Use the [LOG] key.	**Example:** Find log 273. ENTER: 273 [LOG] 2.4361626 The value of log 273 is approximately 2.4362.
In some cases, the calculator will display a negative number. To avoid a negative mantissa, you can add and subtract 10, in effect adding 0.	**Example:** Find log 0.0034. ENTER: 0.0034 [LOG] −2.4685211 The value of log 0.0034 is approximately −2.4685. −2.4685 + 10 − 10 = 7.5315 − 10
Sometimes a logarithm is given and you must find the number. The number is called the **antilogarithm.** If log $x = a$, then $x =$ antilog a. You can use the [INV] and [LOG] keys to find the antilog of a logarithm.	**Example:** If log $x = 3.6355$, find x. ENTER: 3.6355 [INV] [LOG] 4320.161676 The value of x is approximately 4320.

Use a scientific calculator to find the logarithm for each number rounded to four decimal places. Then state the characteristic and the mantissa.

1. 286.1   2. 0.0048   3. 72.68
   2.4565; 2; 0.4565   −2.3188; −3; 0.6812   1.8613; 1; 0.8613

4. 0.496   5. 6.15   6. 0.0000008
   −0.3045; −1; 0.6955   0.7889; 0; 0.7889   −6.0969; −7; 0.9031

Use a scientific calculator to find the antilogarithm of each logarithm rounded to four decimal places.

7. 2.162   8. −1.42   9. 3.493
   145.2112   0.0380   3111.7163

10. −2.353   11. 0.681   12. 4.111
    0.0044   4.7973   12,912.1927

Reteaching ▬▬▬

Using Alternative Methods Have students write the mathematical meaning of "Find the log of 2.87."
log 2.87 = x means $10^x = 2.87$
Find x, accurate to four decimal places, and state the characteristic and mantissa. $x = 0.2579$, characteristic is 0, and mantissa is .4579

Additional Answers

4a. Adding or subtracting logarithms and then finding the antilogarithm of the sum or difference was easier than multiplying or dividing some numbers.

4b. Multiplication and division can be accomplished more quickly with a calculator than with logarithms.

Assignment Guide

Core: 13–29 odd, 30, 31, 33–38
Enriched: 12–28 even, 30–38
All: Self Test, 1–10

For **Extra Practice,** see p. 899.

The red A, B, and C flags, printed only in the Teacher's Wraparound Edition, indicate the level of difficulty of the exercises.

Additional Answer

30. Since calculators use logarithms, finding $(-3)^3$ would proceed as follows.
$$x = (-3)^3$$
$$\log x = \log (-3)^3$$
$$\log x = 3 \log (-3)$$
Since the logarithm of -3 is undefined, the calculator sends an error message.

Practice Masters, p. 72

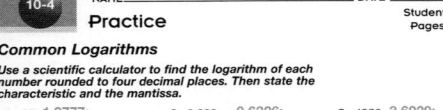

10-4	NAME_____ DATE_____

Practice

Student Edition
Pages 617–621

Common Logarithms

Use a scientific calculator to find the logarithm of each number rounded to four decimal places. Then state the characteristic and the mantissa.

1. 95 1.9777; 1; 0.9777
2. 0.233 −0.6326; −1; 0.3674
3. 4920 3.6920; 3; 0.6920
4. 30,700 4.4871; 4; 0.4871
5. 211.3 2.3249; 2; 0.3249
6. 4.321 0.6356; 0; 0.6356
7. 8.125 0.9098; 0; 0.9098
8. 17.654 1.2468; 1; 0.2468
9. 0.0004764 −3.3220; −4; 0.6780
10. 1.8519 0.2676; 0; 0.2676
11. 6.437 × 10⁻⁹ −8.1913; −9; 0.8086
12. 0.0125 −1.9031; −2; 0.0969

Use a scientific calculator to find the antilogarithm of each logarithm rounded to four decimal places.

13. 2.63 426.5795
14. −0.4089 0.3900
15. 2.9484 887.9735
16. −2.2168 0.0061
17. 3.6940 4943.1069
18. 0.6456 − 3 0.0044
19. 4.8503 70,843.4985
20. 0.6164 − 2 0.0413
21. 5.3 199,526.2315
22. 2.384 242.1029
23. −1.55 0.0282
24. −3.2479 0.0006

11. **Astronomy** The *parallax* of a star is the difference in direction of the star as seen from two widely separate points. The brightness of a star as observed from Earth is its apparent magnitude. Interstellar space is measured in parsecs. One parsec is about 19.2 trillion miles. The absolute magnitude of a star is the magnitude that a star would have if it were 10 parsecs from Earth. For stars more than 30 parsecs from Earth, the formula relating the parallax p, the absolute magnitude M, and the apparent magnitude m is $M = m + 5 + 5 \log p$. The star M35 in the constellation Gemini has an apparent magnitude of 5.3 and a parallax of about 0.018. Find the absolute magnitude of star M35.   about 1.58

EXERCISES

Practice

A

If log 6500 = 3.8129, find each number.

12. mantissa of log 6500 0.8129
13. characteristic of log 6500 3
14. antilog 3.8129 6500
15. log 6.5 0.8129
16. $10^{3.8129}$ 6500
17. mantissa of log 0.065 0.8129

B

Use a scientific calculator to find the logarithm for each number rounded to four decimal places. Then state the mantissa and characteristic.

18. 64.7
19. 900.4
20. 0.047
21. 6.377
22. 0.0035
23. 0.0007

18. 1.8109; 0.8109; 1
19. 2.9544; 0.9544; 2
20. −1.3279; 0.6721; −2
21. 0.8046; 0.8046; 0
22. −2.4559; 0.5441; −3
23. −3.1549; 0.8451; −4

Use a scientific calculator to find the antilogarithm for each logarithm rounded to four decimal places.

24. 0.3142 2.0616
25. 2.1495 141.0912
26. −0.2615 0.5476

C

27. −1.8143 0.0153
28. 0.5734 − 3 0.0037
29. 7.1394 − 10 0.0014

Critical Thinking

30. Try to find $(-3)^3$ on your calculator. Some calculators will say "*ERROR*," even though $(-3)^3 = -27$. Can you think of a reason why they might do this? Explain. See margin.

Application and Problem Solving

31. **Acoustics** Mary Esperanza had a new muffler installed on her car. As a result, the noise level of the engine of her car dropped from 85 decibels to 73 decibels.   a. about 316,227,766 times
   a. How many times the minimum intensity of sound detectable by the human ear was the car with the old muffler if I_0 is defined to be 1?
   b. How many times the minimum intensity of sound detectable by the human ear is the car with the new muffler? about 19,952,623 times
   c. Find the percent of decrease of the intensity of the sound with the new muffler. about 93.7%

32. **Geology** As you know, the Richter scale is a logarithmic scale. An earthquake that measures 6 on the Richter scale is 10^6 times as intense as the weakest earthquake perceptible by a seismograph.

32a. about 199,526 times

   a. How much more intense is an earthquake that measures 5.3 on the Richter scale than the weakest perceptible earthquake?
   b. How much more intense was the San Francisco earthquake of 1989, a 7.1 on the Richter scale, than its strongest aftershock, a 4.3 on the Richter scale? about 631 times

 **Tech Prep**

Noise Control Engineer Students who are interested in noise control may wish to do further research on the information provided in Exercise 31 and explore the potential growth of this career. For more information on tech prep, see the *Teacher's Handbook*.

33. Solve $2 \log_6 3 + 3 \log_6 2 = \log_6 x$.
(Lesson 10–3) **72**

34. Determine whether $f(x) = \dfrac{x-1}{2}$ and
$g(x) = 2x + 1$ are inverse functions.
(Lesson 8–8) **yes**

35. Write the equation of the parabola
shown at the right. (Lesson 6–6)
$y = 3(x - 4)^2 - 1$

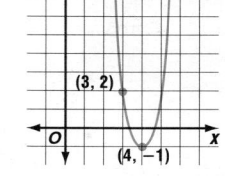

36. Astronomy When a solar flare occurs on the sun, it sends out light waves
that travel through space at a speed of 1.08×10^9 kilometers per hour. If a
satellite in space detects the flare 2 hours after its occurrence, how far is
the satellite from the sun? (Lesson 5–1) **2.16×10^9 km**

37. Find $3 \begin{bmatrix} 4 \\ 1 \\ 7 \end{bmatrix} + 2 \begin{bmatrix} 3 \\ -2 \\ 6 \end{bmatrix} - 5 \begin{bmatrix} -2 \\ 3 \\ 6 \end{bmatrix}$. (Lesson 4–2) $\begin{bmatrix} 28 \\ -16 \\ 3 \end{bmatrix}$

38. Manufacturing Denim Duds makes denim jackets and jeans. Each
garment must be cut from a pattern and sewn. There are 40 worker-hours
per day available for cutting and 52 worker-hours per day for sewing. The
chart below shows the number of hours for each operation needed to
make both garments, as well as the profit on the garment.

Garment	Cutting Hours	Sewing Hours	Profit
jacket	1	4	$14
jeans	2	2	$8

How many of each garment should the company make to maximize profit?
(Lesson 3–6) **4 pair jeans, 18 jackets**

SELF TEST

Solve each equation. (Lesson 10–1)

1. $5^{3y+4} = 5^y$ **-2**

2. $2^{x+3} = \dfrac{1}{16}$ **-7**

Evaluate each expression. (Lesson 10–2)

3. $\log_{10} 10{,}000$ **4**

4. $\log_3 \dfrac{1}{243}$ **-5**

5. $\log_{25} 5$ **$\dfrac{1}{2}$**

6. Seismology The earthquake that occurred in southern Peru in 1991 registered a 5.6 on the Richter
scale. In 1990, an earthquake occurred in northern Peru that registered a 6.4 on the Richter scale.
How much more intense was the 1990 earthquake in northern Peru that the 1991 earthquake in
southern Peru? (Lesson 10–2) **about 6.3 times more intense**

Solve each equation. (Lesson 10–3)

7. $2 \log_6 4 - \dfrac{1}{3} \log_6 8 = \log_6 y$ **8**

8. $\log_2 (9t + 5) - \log_2 (t^2 - 1) = 2$ **3**

**Use a scientific calculator to find the logarithm for each number rounded to four decimal
places. Then state the mantissa and the characteristic.** (Lesson 10–4)

9. 600.6 **2.7786; 0.7786; 2**

10. 0.189 **-0.7235; 0.2765; -1**

Lesson 10–4 Common Logarithms **621**

Extension

Communication Have each student
work with a partner to explain to each
other how to solve $(x - 3) \log x \geq 0$.
Then solve the inequality. **$0 < x \leq 1$ or
$x \geq 3$**

SELF TEST

The Self Test provides students with
a brief review of the concepts and
skills in Lessons 10-1 through 10-4.
Lesson numbers are given to the
right of exercises or instruction lines
so students can review concepts not
yet mastered.

4 ASSESS

Closing Activity

Writing Have students explain
the difference between logarithms
and antilogarithms.

**Chapter 10, Quiz B (Lessons
10-3 and 10-4),** is available in the
*Assessment and Evaluation
Masters,* p. 268.

**Mid-Chapter Test (Lessons 10-1
through 10-4)** is available in the
*Assessment and Evaluation
Masters,* p. 267.

Enrichment Masters, p. 72

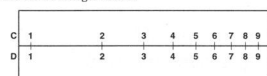
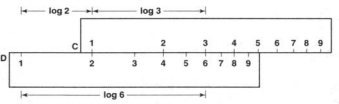
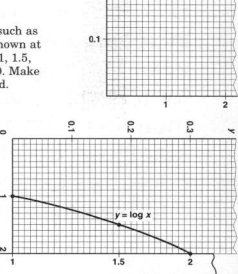

10-4 NAME_____ DATE_____
Student Edition
Pages 617–621
Enrichment

The Slide Rule

Before the invention of electronic calculators, computations were
often performed on a slide rule. A slide rule is based on the idea of
logarithms. It has two movable rods labeled with C and D scales.
Each of the scales is logarithmic.

To multiply 2×3 on a slide rule, move the C rod to the right as
shown below. You can find 2×3 by adding log 2 to log 3, and the
slide rule adds the lengths for you. The distance you get is 0.778,
or the logarithm of 6.

1-2 See students' work.

Follow the steps to make a slide rule.

1. Use graph paper that has small squares, such as
10 squares to the inch. Using the scales shown at
the right, plot the curve $y = \log x$ for $x = 1, 1.5$,
and the whole numbers from 2 through 10. Make
an obvious heavy dot for each point plotted.

2. You will need two strips of cardboard. A
5-by-7 index card, cut in half the long
way, will work fine. Turn the graph you
made in Exercise 1 sideways and use it
to mark a logarithmic scale on each of
the two strips. The figure shows the
mark for 2 being drawn.

3. Explain how to use a slide rule to
divide 8 by 2. Line up the 2 on
the C scale with the 8 on the
D scale. The quotient is the
number on the D scale below
the 1 on the C scale.

NCTM Standards: 1–6

Instructional Resources

- Study Guide Master 10-5
- Practice Master 10-5
- Enrichment Master 10-5
- Science and Math Lab Manual, pp. 99–104

Transparency 10-5A contains the 5-Minute Check for this lesson; **Transparency 10-5B** contains a teaching aid for this lesson.

Recommended Pacing	
Standard Pacing	Day 7 of 12
Honors Pacing	Day 7 of 11
Block Scheduling*	Day 3 of 5 (along with Lesson 10-4)

*For more information on pacing and possible lesson plans, refer to the *Block Scheduling Booklet*.

1 FOCUS

5-Minute Check
(over Lesson 10-4)

Find the logarithm of each number.

1. 58.2 **1.7649**
2. 0.3 **9.4771 − 10**

Find the antilogarithm of each number.

3. 0.6304 **4.27**
4. 0.3194 − 2 **0.02087**
5. Use logarithms to find 150^3.
   3,375,000

Motivating the Lesson

Questioning Point out to students that the number of stamps issued each year by the U.S. Postal Service has been increasing since 1948. Ask them what factors may be responsible for this increase. Collectors create more demand for new types of stamps to collect. Ask why non-collectors care what stamps go on their envelopes.

10-5

Natural Logarithms

What YOU'LL LEARN

- To find natural logarithms of numbers.

Why IT'S IMPORTANT

You can use natural logarithms to solve problems involving sales and physics.

First Countries/Cities to Issue Stamps

1. United Kingdom, May, 1840
2. New York City, Feb., 1842
3. Zurich, Switzerland, March, 1843
4. Brazil, Aug., 1843
5. Geneva, Switzerland, Oct., 1843

APPLICATION
Postal Service

In 1989, the *Scott Postage Stamp Catalog* listed more than 2400 different postage stamps. As indicated in the graph at the right, the United States Post Office took 77 years to issue its first 600 stamps, 37 years to issue the next 600, approximately half as long to issue the third 600, and so on.

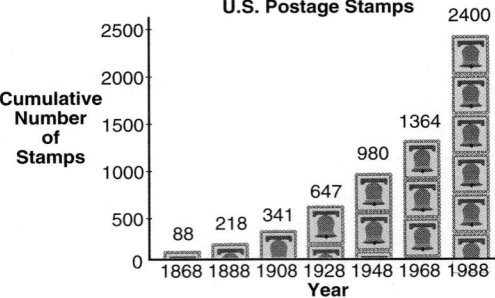

These figures suggest that the time needed to issue a fixed number of stamps has been decreasing exponentially. In fact, the number of stamps issued is growing exponentially and is approximately modeled by the formula $S = 83e^{0.024t}$, where S represents the cumulative number of stamps issued, t represents the number of years since 1848, and e is a special irrational number.

In 1998, 150 years after the first stamp was issued, about how many different U.S. postage stamps will have been issued? *This problem will be solved in Example 3.*

The number e used in this **exponential growth** problem is used extensively in science and mathematics. It is an irrational number whose value is approximately 2.718. e is the base for the **natural logarithms,** which are abbreviated ln. The natural logarithm of e is 1. All properties of logarithms that you have learned apply to the natural logarithms as well. The key marked LN on your calculator is the natural logarithm key.

Example ❶ **Use a scientific calculator to find ln 3.925.**

Enter: 3.925 LN *1.367366351*

The natural logarithm of 3.925 is approximately 1.3674.

You can take antilogarithms of natural logarithms as well. The symbol for the antilogarithm of x is antiln x.

Example ❷ **a. Find x if ln $x \approx 3.4825$**

$\ln x \approx 3.4825$

$x \approx$ antiln 3.4825

Enter: 3.4825 2nd e^x *32.5409729*

So x is approximately 32.5410.

b. Find e if ln $e = 1$.

$\ln e = 1$

$e =$ antiln 1

Enter: 1 2nd e^x *2.718281828*

So e is approximately 2.7183.

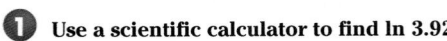

During 1994, the U.S. Postal Service issued over 140 varieties of stamps. This included 94 commemoratives, 9 definitives, and 10 special issues.

Equations involving e are easier to solve using natural logarithms, rather than using common logarithms, since $\ln e = 1$.

Example ③

APPLICATION
Postal Service

TECHNOLOGY
Tips
If your scientific calculator has no e^x key, use the INV key and then the LN key.

Use the formula $S = 83e^{0.024t}$ and natural logarithms to determine about how many different U.S. postage stamps will have been issued from 1848 to 1998.

$t = 1998 - 1848$ or 150 years

$$S = 83e^{0.024t}$$
$$S = 83e^{0.024(150)} \qquad t = 150$$
$$S = 83e^{3.6} \qquad \textit{Simplify.}$$
$$\ln S = \ln(83e^{3.6}) \qquad \textit{Take the natural logarithm of each side.}$$
$$\ln S = \ln 83 + 3.6 \ln e \qquad \textit{Power and product properties of logarithms}$$
$$\ln S = \ln 83 + 3.6 \qquad \textit{Since e is the base for natural logarithms,} \; \ln e = 1.$$
$$\ln S \approx 8.018841$$
$$\text{antiln}\,(\ln S) \approx \text{antiln}\, 8.018841 \qquad \textit{Take the antilogarithm of each side.}$$
$$S \approx 3038$$

So, approximately 3038 stamps will have been issued by 1998.

When interest is compounded *continuously*, the amount of money A in an account after t years is found using the formula $A = Pe^{rt}$, where P represents the amount of the principal and r represents the annual interest rate.

Example ④

APPLICATION
Finance

Mr. and Mrs. Franco are planning to take a cruise for their twenty-fifth wedding anniversary. They have six years to save $3500 for the cruise. If the six-year certificate of deposit they buy now pays 8% interest compounded continuously, how much should they invest now in order to have $3500 for the cruise?

$$A = Pe^{rt}$$
$$3500 = Pe^{(0.08)(6)} \qquad \textit{Replace A with 3500, r with 0.08, and t with 6.}$$
$$3500 = Pe^{0.48} \qquad \textit{Simplify.}$$
$$\ln 3500 = \ln(Pe^{0.48}) \qquad \textit{Take the natural logarithm of each side.}$$
$$\ln 3500 = \ln P + (0.48)\ln e \qquad \textit{Power and product properties of logarithms}$$
$$\ln 3500 = \ln P + 0.48 \qquad \textit{Since e is the base for natural logarithms,} \; \ln e = 1.$$
$$7.680518 \approx \ln P$$
$$\text{antiln}\, 7.680518 \approx \text{antiln}\,(\ln P) \qquad \textit{Take the antilogarithm of each side.}$$
$$2165.74 \approx P$$

Mr. and Mrs. Franco should invest $2165.74 to earn enough for the trip.

CHECK FOR UNDERSTANDING

Communicating Mathematics

Study the lesson. Then complete the following.

1. **Name** the base of natural logarithms. the number e

2. **Describe** a situation for which you should choose to use natural logarithms instead of common logarithms to solve a problem. See margin.

3. **Describe** a situation that could be represented by the equation $A = 2500e^{0.08t}$. See margin.

Lesson 10–5 Natural Logarithms **623**

Cooperative Learning

Co-op Co-op Have teams of students research different applications of logarithms and natural logarithms. Presentations to the class should include sample graphs. For more information on the co-op co-op strategy, see *Cooperative Learning in the Mathematics Classroom*, one of the titles in the Glencoe Mathematics Professional Series, page 32.

Additional Answers

2. Natural logarithms are used when the base of the exponent is e.

3. Sample answer: $2500 is invested at 8% annual interest.

---

2 TEACH

In-Class Examples

For Example 1
Use a scientific calculator to find each natural logarithm.

a. Find $\ln 2.68$. ≈ 0.9858
b. Find $\ln 0.045$. ≈ -3.101

For Example 2

a. Find x if $\ln x \approx 0.75$.
$x \approx 2.117$
b. Find x if $\ln x \approx 5.4$.
$x \approx 221.41$

For Example 3
Suppose $250 is deposited in a savings account. The interest rate is 10% compounded continuously. When will the original deposit be doubled?
$500 = 250e^{0.10t}$ $t \approx 6.93$
approximately 6.93 years

For Example 4
If the Francos find a six-year certificate of deposit that pays 9.9% interest compounded continuously, how much should they invest? $1932.40

Teaching Tip The natural logarithm of x is sometimes denoted $\log_e x$, but more often $\ln x$.

Study Guide Masters, p. 73

10-5
NAME_____ DATE_____
Study Guide
Student Edition
Pages 622–625

Natural Logarithms

The number e is used extensively in science and mathematics. It is an irrational number whose value is approximately 2.718. e is the base for the **natural logarithms**. All the properties of common logarithms apply also to natural logarithms. You can use a scientific calculator to compute with natural logarithms. The key marked LN is the natural logarithm key.

Example: Find $\ln 2.856$ using a calculator.
ENTER: 2.856 LN 1.0494220
The natural logarithm of 2.856 is approximately 1.0494.

You can also find the antilogarithms of natural logarithms.

Example: Find x if $\ln x = 2.874$.
ENTER: 2.874 2nd e^x 748.169500
So x is about 748.

Use a scientific calculator to find each value, rounded to four decimal places.

1. $\ln 732$ 6.5958	2. $\ln 1685$ 7.4295	3. $\ln 84,350$ 11.3427
4. $\ln 0.735$ -0.3079	5. $\ln 100$ 4.6051	6. $\ln 0.0824$ -2.4962
7. $\ln 2.388$ 0.8705	8. $\ln 128,245$ 11.7617	9. $\ln 0.00614$ -5.0929
10. antiln 1.3475 3.8478	11. antiln 2.3862 10.8721	12. antiln 0.5384 1.7133
13. antiln 0.0813 1.0847	14. antiln 4.3165 74.9259	15. antiln 2.4 11.0232
16. antiln 3.111 22.4435	17. antiln 0.113 1.1196	18. antiln 10 22026.4658

Check for Understanding

Exercises 1–10 are designed to help you assess your students' understanding through reading, writing, speaking, and modeling. You should work through Exercises 1–3 with your students and then monitor their work on Exercises 4–10.

Assignment Guide

Core: 11–35 odd, 37–43
Enriched: 12–32 even, 33–43

For **Extra Practice,** see p. 900.

The red A, B, and C flags, printed only in the Teacher's Wraparound Edition, indicate the level of difficulty of the exercises.

Additional Answer

29.

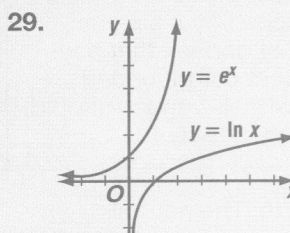

Practice Masters, p. 73

Guided Practice

Use a scientific calculator to find each value rounded to four decimal places. **9. 0.2066**

4. ln 3.12 **1.1378**   5. ln 0.045 **−3.1011**   6. ln 0.772 **−0.2588**
7. antiln 0.2594 **1.2961** 8. antiln 2.0175 **7.5195** 9. antiln −1.5771

10. **Finance** Atepa's grandparents opened a savings account for her when she was born. They placed $1000 in an account that paid $6\frac{1}{2}$% interest compounded continuously. Atepa is now 16 years old and would like to buy a used car that costs $2500. Does she have enough money in her account to buy the car? Explain.   **Yes; she has $2829.22 in her account.**

EXERCISES

Practice

Use a scientific calculator to find each value rounded to four decimal places.

22. 13.5299
23. 0.8940
24. 0.0104
26. 0.1349

A
11. ln 7.95 **2.0732**   12. ln 1.34 **0.2927**   13. ln 57.3 **4.0483**
14. ln 0.958 **−0.0429**   15. ln 2.7183 **1.000**   16. ln 10,000 **9.2103**
17. ln 0.005 **−5.2983**   18. ln 1.002 **0.0020**   19. ln 0.01 **−4.6052**

B
20. antiln 0.782 **2.1858** 21. antiln 0 **1.0000**   22. antiln 2.6049
23. antiln −0.112   24. antiln −4.567   25. antiln 1.005 **2.7319**
26. antiln −2.003   27. antiln 1.55 **4.7115**   28. antiln −1.679 **0.1866**

Graph each pair of equations on the same axis.   **29–32. See margin.**

C
29. $y = \ln x$ and $y = e^x$ 30. $y = \log x$ and $y = \ln x$
31. Compare and contrast the graphs in Exercise 29.
32. Compare and contrast the graphs in Exercise 30.

Critical Thinking

33. The great Swiss mathematician Leonhard Euler, for whom the number e is named, defined e as the sum of the series $1 + \frac{1}{1} + \frac{1}{1 \cdot 2} + \frac{1}{1 \cdot 2 \cdot 3} + \frac{1}{1 \cdot 2 \cdot 3 \cdot 4} + \dots$.
    a. Calculate the value of e using six terms in the series.   **about 2.7167**
    b. Calculate the value of e using eight terms in the series.   **about 2.7183**
    c. Which value is more accurate?   **the second one**
    d. Find the percent of the change in the values.   **about 0.06%**

Applications and Problem Solving

35a. about 1,587,209,679 drives

34. **Finance** Kang is saving money to go on a trip to Europe after his college graduation. He will finish college five years from now. If the five-year certificate of deposit he buys pays 7.25% interest compounded continuously, how much should he invest now in order to have $3000 for the trip?   **about $2088**

35. **Sales** The sales of CD-ROM drives have been increasing since 1984. Suppose the number of CD-ROM drives sold S in a given year is approximated by the formula $S = 75,000e^{0.83t}$, where t is the number of years since 1988.

    a. Estimate the number of these drives that will be sold in the year 2000.
    b. Draw a graph of $S = 75,000e^{0.83t}$. How does your graph compare to the graph at the right?   **See Solutions Manual.**

CD-ROM Drive Sales

4.8 million
1.5 million
75,000   240,000
1988   1990   1992   1993

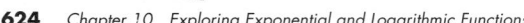

Reteaching

Decision Making Have students discuss the question, "If the natural logarithm of 3 is approximately 1.0986, then how would we use that information to write an antilogarithm statement?"   **The antilogarithm of 1.0986 is approximately 3.**

Additional Answer

30.

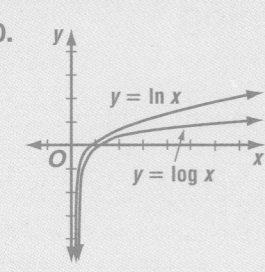

36. Physics The intensity of light decreases as it passes through sea water. The equation $\ln \frac{I_0}{I} = 0.014d$ relates the intensity of light I at the depth of d centimeters with the intensity of light I_0 in the atmosphere. Find the depth of the water where the intensity of the light is half the intensity of the light in the atmosphere. **about 49.5 cm**

Mixed Review

37. Use a calculator to find each value, rounded to four decimal places. (Lesson 10–4)

37a. 1.8882

37b. −2.2518

37c. 3603.2965

37d. 0.0006

  a. log 77.3   **b.** log 0.0056   **c.** antilog 3.5567   **d.** antilog (6.7891 − 10)

38. Simplify $\dfrac{\frac{x^2}{x^2 - 25y^2}}{\frac{x}{5y - x}}$. (Lesson 9–3) $\dfrac{-x}{x + 5y}$

39. Use the graph of the polynomial function $f(x) = x^5 + x^4 - x - 1$ at the right to determine at least one of the binomial factors of the polynomial. Then find all factors of the polynomial. (Lesson 8–2) $(x + 1)^2(x - 1)(x^2 + 1)$

40. Manufacturing The weights of boxes of cereal filled by a machine are normally distributed. The mean weight is 510 grams with a standard deviation of 4 grams. (Lesson 6–9)

  a. Of 1000 boxes, how many weigh at least 510 grams? **500 boxes**

40b. 815 boxes

40c. 5 boxes

  b. Of 1000 boxes, how many weigh between 502 and 514 grams?

  c. A machine at the end of the production line checks the weight of the boxes before they are shipped to the stores. If a box weighs more than 522 grams, it is sent back to the beginning of the line to be emptied and reused. Of 1000 boxes, how many will be sent back for this reason?

  d. The machine that checks the weight of the boxes sends back boxes that weigh less than 502 grams. Of 1000 boxes, how many will be sent back for this reason? **25 boxes**

41. Photography Shina Murakami is a professional photographer. She has a photograph that is 4 inches wide and 6 inches long. She wishes to make a print of the photograph for a competition. The area of the new print is to be five times the area of the original. If Ms. Murakami is going to add the same amount to the length and the width of the photograph, what will the dimensions of the new print be? (Lesson 6–4) **10 in. by 12 in.**

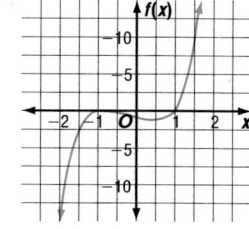

42. Solve $\begin{vmatrix} x & 5 & 2 \\ -6 & 4 & 1 \\ 3 & 1 & x \end{vmatrix} = x^2 + 22x - 1$. (Lesson 4–4) $\frac{5}{3}, -4$

43. Graph the system of inequalities. Name the coordinates of the vertices of the polygon formed. Find the maximum and minimum values of the function. (Lesson 3–5) **See margin for graph.**

  $x \geq 0$ **vertices: (0, 0), (0, 3), (2, 0), (1.5, 1.5)**

  $y \geq 0$ **max: f(0, 3) = 12**

  $y \leq 3 - x$ **min: f(0, 0) = 0**

  $3x + y \leq 6$

  $f(x, y) = 2x + 4y$

Extension

Connections Have students research several radioactive elements and name the half-life for each. Using the formula $y = ne^{kt}$ (amount of radioactive substance present after t years), and assuming 100 g of each element is present initially, $n = 100$, have students determine k (constant) for each of the elements.

---

4 ASSESS

Closing Activity

Writing Have students compare and contrast natural and common logarithms.

Additional Answers

31. The graphs of $y = \ln x$ and $y = e^x$ are reflections of each other along the line $x = y$.

32. Both graphs pass through (1, 0). Where $y > 0$, the rise of the graph of $y = \ln x$ is steeper than the rise of the graph of $y = \log x$. Where $y < 0$, the rise of the graph of $y = \log x$ is steeper than the rise of the graph of $y = \ln x$.

43.

(0, 3)   (1.5, 1.5)   (2, 0)

Enrichment Masters, p. 73

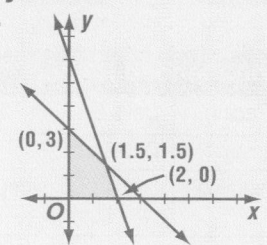

Instructional Resources

- Study Guide Master 10-6
- Practice Master 10-6
- Enrichment Master 10-6
- Assessment and Evaluation Masters, p. 269
- Modeling Mathematics Masters, p. 70
- Tech Prep Applications Masters, p. 19

 Transparency 10-6A contains the 5-Minute Check for this lesson; **Transparency 10-6B** contains a teaching aid for this lesson.

Recommended Pacing	
Standard Pacing	Days 8 & 9 of 12
Honors Pacing	Day 8 of 11
Block Scheduling*	Day 4 of 5 (along with Lesson 10-7)

 *For more information on pacing and possible lesson plans, refer to the *Block Scheduling Booklet*.

1 FOCUS

 ### 5-Minute Check
(over Lesson 10-5)

1. Find ln 5.46. **1.697**
2. Find ln 0.083. **−2.49**
3. Find x if ln $x = 3.7$.
   x **40.45**
4. Find x if ln $x = 0.62$.
   x **1.86**
5. Shana invests a sum of money at 8% interest compounded continuously. How much must she invest now to have a total of $10,000 in five years? **$6703.20**

 **TEKS** 2.a., 11.c., 11.d., 11.e.

Solving Exponential Equations

What YOU'LL LEARN

- To solve equations with variable exponents by using logarithms,
- to evaluate expressions involving logarithms with different bases, and
- to solve problems by using estimation.

Why IT'S IMPORTANT

You can use exponential equations to solve problems involving sports and demographics.

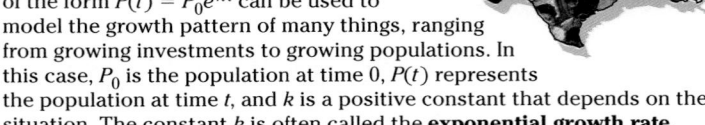

APPLICATION
Demographics

The population of the United States is continually growing. In 1992, the population in the United States was 249 million, and the exponential growth rate was 0.9% per year. An equation of the form $P(t) = P_0 e^{kt}$ can be used to model the growth pattern of many things, ranging from growing investments to growing populations. In this case, P_0 is the population at time 0, $P(t)$ represents the population at time t, and k is a positive constant that depends on the situation. The constant k is often called the **exponential growth rate.**

Equations of the type described above are called **exponential equations.** Exponential equations are equations in which the variables appear as exponents. These equations can be solved using the property of equality for logarithmic functions. **Use estimation** to make sure you're on the right track.

Example

PROBLEM SOLVING
Use Estimation

Suppose $6^x = 42$.
a. **Estimate the value of x.**
b. **Solve the equation.**

a. Since $6^2 = 36$ and $6^3 = 216$, the value of x is between 2 and 3. The value of x should be much closer to 2 than 3.

b. $6^x = 42$

   $\log 6^x = \log 42$ *Property of equality for logarithmic functions*

   $x \log 6 = \log 42$ *Power property of logarithms*

   $x = \dfrac{\log 42}{\log 6}$ *Divide each side by log 6.*

   $x \approx \dfrac{1.6232}{0.7782}$

   $x \approx 2.086$

The solution is approximately 2.086, which is consistent with the estimate.

Check: Use a scientific calculator to find the value of $6^{2.086}$.

Enter: 6 [x^y] 2.086 [=] 41.99750672

The answer is reasonable.

Example Refer to the application at the beginning of the lesson. How many years after 1992 will it take for the U.S. population to reach 300 million if the exponential growth rate remains at 0.9%?

APPLICATION
Demographics

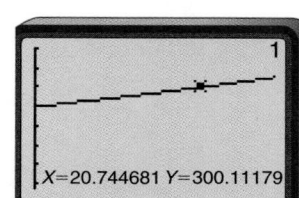

$$P(t) = P_0 e^{kt}$$

$$300 = 249e^{0.009t} \qquad \textit{P}_0 = 249, \; k = 0.009, \text{ and } P(t) = 300$$

$$\frac{300}{249} = e^{0.009t} \qquad \textit{Divide each side by 249.}$$

$$\ln \frac{300}{249} = \ln e^{0.009t} \qquad \textit{Take the natural logarithm of each side.}$$

$$\ln \frac{300}{249} = 0.009t \qquad \textit{Definition of natural logarithm}$$

$$\ln 300 - \ln 249 = 0.009t \qquad \textit{Quotient property of logarithms}$$

$$5.7038 - 5.5175 \approx 0.009t$$

$$0.1863 \approx 0.009t$$

$$20.7 \approx t$$

The population in the United States will reach 300,000,000 about 21 years after 1992, or in 2013.

Check: Use a graphing calculator to graph the equation $y = 249e^{0.009x}$. Use TRACE to find the value of x when $y = 300$.

The value of x is about 20.7. The answer is correct.

X=20.744681 Y=300.11179

In some equations, variables are found in more than one exponent.

Example ③ Solve $8^{2x-5} = 5^{x+1}$.

$$8^{2x-5} = 5^{x+1}$$

$$\log 8^{2x-5} = \log 5^{x+1} \qquad \textit{Property of equality for logarithmic functions}$$

$$(2x - 5) \log 8 = (x + 1) \log 5 \qquad \textit{Power property of logarithms}$$

$$2x \log 8 - 5 \log 8 = x \log 5 + \log 5 \qquad \textit{Distributive property}$$

$$2x \log 8 - x \log 5 = \log 5 + 5 \log 8$$

$$x(2 \log 8 - \log 5) = \log 5 + 5 \log 8 \qquad \textit{Distributive property}$$

$$x = \frac{\log 5 + 5 \log 8}{2 \log 8 - \log 5}$$

$$x \approx \frac{0.6990 + 5(0.9031)}{2(0.9031) - 0.6990}$$

$$x \approx 4.7095$$

The solution is approximately 4.7095. *Check this result.*

Questioning Have students survey the local banks and determine how often interest is compounded on different interest-bearing accounts. Ask students if they know how this affects how much they earn. Compare effective annual yields based on how frequently the investment is compounded.

2 TEACH

Teaching Tip In Example 1, remind students that $\frac{\log 42}{\log 6} \neq \log (42 - 6)$.

Teaching Tip Due to rounding, answers to many exercises may vary.

In-Class Examples

For Example 1
Suppose $7^x = 20$.

a. Estimate the value of x.
The value of x is between 1 and 2.

b. Solve the equation.
≈ 1.5395

For Example 2
How long would it take to triple an investment of $500 at 8% interest compounded quarterly?
$A = P\left(1 + \frac{r}{n}\right)^{nt}$
about 13.9 years

For Example 3
Solve $10^{x+2} = 100^{2x-1}$.
≈ 1.33

Alternative Teaching Strategies

Reading Algebra Point out that in the popular press, *exponential* refers to extremely fast growth rates. Remind students that, in mathematics, exponential growth rates can be quite slow, especially in the short run.

In-Class Example

For Example 4

Express $\log_{11} 63$ in terms of common logarithms. Then approximate its value to three decimal places.

Let $x = \log_{11} 63$.

Then $11^x = 63$

$\log 11^x = \log 63$

$x \log 11 = \log 63$

$x = \dfrac{\log 63}{\log 11}$

$x \approx 1.7278$

3 PRACTICE/APPLY

Check for Understanding

Exercises 1–12 are designed to help you assess your students' understanding through reading, writing, speaking, and modeling. You should work through Exercises 1–3 with your students and then monitor their work on Exercises 4–12.

Error Analysis

Show students that the logarithm of a number is a number in itself. Therefore, when dividing logs, the log must stay with the number.

So, $\dfrac{\log 10}{\log 5} \neq \log 2$.

Study Guide Masters, p. 74

It is possible to evaluate expressions involving logarithms with different bases. Since calculators are usually not programmed with all possible bases for logarithms, the **change of base formula** can be very helpful.

Change of Base Formula	For all positive numbers a, b, and n, where $a \neq 1$ and $b \neq 1$, $$\log_a n = \frac{\log_b n}{\log_b a}.$$

Example **4** Express each logarithm in terms of common logarithms. Then approximate its value to three decimal places.

a. $\log_8 77$

$\log_a n = \dfrac{\log_b n}{\log_b a}$ *Change of base formula*

$\log_8 77 = \dfrac{\log 77}{\log 8}$ $a = 8, n = 77, b = 10$

≈ 2.0889

The value of $\log_8 77$ is approximately 2.089.

b. $\log_{16} 64$

$\log_a n = \dfrac{\log_b n}{\log_b a}$ *Change of base formula*

$\log_{16} 64 = \dfrac{\log 64}{\log 16}$ $a = 16, n = 64, b = 10$

$= 1.5$

The value of $\log_{16} 64$ is 1.5.   *Why is this an exact value?*

CHECK FOR UNDERSTANDING

Communicating Mathematics

Study the lesson. Then complete the following.   1–3. See margin.

1. **You Decide**   Karen sees the exponent in the equation $36 = x^5$ and decides to use logarithms to solve the equation. Tisha tells her that this is not an exponential equation and she does not need logarithms to solve the equation. Who is correct? Explain.

2. **Describe** a situation when you might use the change of base formula.

3. Could you use the change of base formula to express a logarithm in terms of natural logarithms? Explain.

Guided Practice

Find the value of each logarithm to three decimal places.

4. $\log_4 22$ **2.230**

5. $\log_{12} 95$ **1.833**

Use logarithms to solve each equation. Round to three decimal places.

6. $5^x = 52$ **2.455**

7. $8^{2a} = 124$ **1.159**

8. $2.1^{t-5} = 9.32$ **8.009**

9. $y = \log_4 125$ **3.483**

10. $2^{2x+3} = 3^{3x}$ **1.089**

11. $2^n = \sqrt{3^{n-2}}$ **−7.638**

12. **Finance**   If $1500 is placed in an account that pays 6.5% interest compounded continuously, how long will it take for the money in the account to double? Use the formula $A = Pe^{rt}$.   **about 10.7 years**

628   Chapter 10   Exploring Exponential and Logarithmic Functions

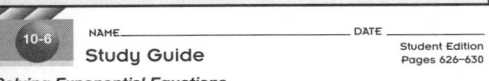

NAME _____   **DATE** _____

Student Edition Pages 626–630

Study Guide   10-6

Solving Exponential Equations

An equation with a variable in an exponent is called an **exponential equation**. Such an equation can be solved by using the Property of Equality for Logarithmic Functions.	**Example:** Solve $3^x = 16$. $3^x = 16$ $\log 3^x = \log 16$ $x \log 3 = \log 16$ $x = \dfrac{\log 16}{\log 3}$ $x = \dfrac{1.2041}{0.4771}$ $x = 2.5238$
The Change of Base Formula can be used to find logarithms with bases other than 10. The computations can be done using a calculator. **Change of Base Formula** For all positive numbers a, b, and n, where $a \neq 1$ and $b \neq 1$, then $\log_a n = \dfrac{\log_b n}{\log_b a}$.	**Example:** Express $\log_7 35$ in terms of common logarithms. Then find its value. $\log_7 35 = \dfrac{\log 35}{\log 7}$ $= \dfrac{1.5441}{0.4771}$ $= 3.2364$

Approximate the value of each logarithm to three decimal places.

1. $\log_5 4$ 2.000

2. $\log_6 75$ 2.683

3. $\log_{11} 67$ 16.026

4. $\log_{12} 2$ 0.279

5. $\log_{14} 126$ 1.833

6. $\log_7 896$ 3.493

Use logarithms to solve each equation.

7. $4^x = 80$ 3.1611

8. $5^x = 10$ 1.4306

9. $5^x = 18.5$ 1.8127

10. $1.3^{3x} = 78$ 8.3028

11. $6^{x-1} = 8$ 0.0535

12. $2^x = 5^{x-2}$ 3.5132

Reteaching ━━━━━

Using Substeps Have students work through the following problem. At each step, have a student explain the rule or reasoning used.

$3^{x^2+4x} = \dfrac{1}{27}$ $-3, -1$

Additional Answers

1. Tisha; in exponential equations, the unknown is an exponent. To solve $36 = x^5$, Karen must find $36^{\frac{1}{5}}$.

2. when finding logarithms of different bases on the calculator

3. Yes; use the change of base formula using $a = e$, $b = 10$, and $n =$ the number.

Practice

Find the value of each logarithm to three decimal places.

13. $\log_5 16$ **1.723**
14. $\log_6 82$ **2.459**
15. $\log_3 125$ **4.395**
16. $\log_2 100$ **6.644**
17. $\log_{12} 25$ **1.295**
18. $\log_4 48$ **2.792**

Use logarithms to solve each equation. Round to three decimal places.

B

19. $9^b = 45$ **1.732**
20. $2^x = 30$ **4.907**
21. $5^p = 34$ **2.191**
22. $3.1^{a-3} = 9.42$ **4.982**
23. $6^{x+2} = 17.2$ **−0.412**
24. $8.2^{n-3} = 42.5$ **4.782**
25. $x = \log_5 61.4$ **2.558**
26. $8^{y-2} = 7.28$ **2.955**
27. $t = \log_8 200$ **2.548**
28. $5^{s+2} = 15.3$ **−0.305**
29. $9^{z-4} = 6.28$ **4.836**
30. $7.6^{a-2} = 41.7$ **3.839**
31. $3.5^{3x+1} = 65.4$
32. $20^{x^2} = 70$ **±1.191**
33. $8^{x^2-2} = 32$ **±1.915**
34. $5.8^{x^2-3} = 82.9$
35. $9^a = 2^a$ **0**
36. $5^{x-1} = 3^x$ **3.151**

C
37. $7^{t-2} = 5t$ **11.567**
38. $16^{d-4} = 3^{3-d}$ **3.716**
39. $8^{x-2} = 5^x$ **8.849**
40. $5^{3y} = 8^{y-1}$ **−0.756**
41. $5^{5a-2} = 2^{2a+1}$
42. $8^{2y} = 52^{4y+3}$ **−1.018**
43. $40^{3x} = 5^{2x+1}$ **0.205**
44. $4^n = \sqrt{5^{n-2}}$
45. $\sqrt[3]{2^{x-1}} = 8^{x-2}$

31. 0.779
34. ±2.348
41. 0.587
44. −2.767
45. 2.125

Critical Thinking

46. Let x be any real number and let a, b, and n be positive real numbers with $a \neq 1$ and $b \neq 1$. Show that if $x = \log_a n$, then $x = \dfrac{\log_b n}{\log_b a}$. **See margin.**

Applications and Problem Solving

47. **Demographics** The population of Antlers, Oklahoma, is about 2500. Suppose it is growing at an exponential rate of 3%. Use the formula $P(t) = P_0 e^{kt}$ to determine approximately how long it will take the town's population to double. **about 23 years**

48. **Olympics** Since the modern Olympics began in 1896 with 42 events, the number of events has continued to grow. Suppose the exponential growth rate of the number of events is 1.9%.

48a. 111.6 years or by the 2008 Summer Olympics

   a. Use the formula $E = 42e^{kt}$, where E is the number of events, k is the exponential growth rate, and t is the time in years since 1896, to determine how long after the first modern Olympics we can expect there to be 350 Summer Olympic events.

   b. Draw the graph of $E = 42e^{0.019t}$. How does your graph compare to the chart above? **See margin.**

Summer Olympics Events

Year	City	Number
1968	Mexico City	172
1972	Munich	196
1976	Montreal	199
1980	Moscow	200
1984	Los Angeles	223
1988	Seoul	237
1992	Barcelona	257
1996	Atlanta	271

Source: Atlanta Committee for the Olympic Games

Mixed Review

49. Use a calculator to find antiln −6.083, rounded to four decimal places. (Lesson 10–5) **0.0023**

50. **Construction** A painter works on a job for 10 days and is then joined by an associate. Together they finish the job in 6 more days. The associate could have done the job in 30 days. How long would it have taken the painter to do the job alone? (Lesson 9–5) **20 days**

51. Solve $b^4 - 5b^2 + 4 = 0$. (Lesson 8–6) **±2, ±1**

52. State whether the graph of $4y^2 - x^2 - 24y + 6x = 11$ is a parabola, a circle, an ellipse, or a hyperbola. (Lesson 7–6) **hyperbola**

GLENCOE *Technology*

Interactive Mathematics Tools Software

This multimedia software provides an interactive lesson by having students consider several cases of automobile sales to determine the best deal, by using an exponential formula. A **Computer Journal** gives students an opportunity to write about what they have learned.

For Windows & Macintosh

Assignment Guide

Core: 13–45 odd, 46, 47, 49–57
Enriched: 14–44 even, 46–57

For **Extra Practice,** see p. 900.

The red A, B, and C flags, printed only in the Teacher's Wraparound Edition, indicate the level of difficulty of the exercises.

Additional Answers

46.
$$x = \log_a n$$
$$a^x = a^{\log_a n}$$
$$a^x = n$$
$$\log_b a^x = \log_b n$$
$$x \log_b a = \log_b n$$
$$x = \frac{\log_b n}{\log_b a}$$

48b.

$$E = 42e^{0.019t}$$

Sample answer: Both show that the number of events is increasing more and more at each Olympics.

Practice Masters, p. 74

10-6   NAME_____ DATE _____
       Practice   Student Edition
                               Pages 626–630

Solving Exponential Equations
Use logarithms to solve each equation.

1. $3.5^t = 47.9$ **3.0885**
2. $8.2^r = 64.5$ **1.9802**
3. $7.2^{k-4} = 8.21$ **5.0665**
4. $2^{k-1} = 7.31$ **1.8699**
5. $y = \log_t 78.5$ **3.9715**
6. $k = \log_t 91.8$ **3.2602**
7. $4^b = 9^{r-1}$ **−3.8188**
8. $7^{3k} = 12^{k+2}$ **1.4823**
9. $17c^{\frac{3}{5}} = 44$ **4.1640**
10. $7x^{\frac{2}{3}} = 111$ **11.6645**
11. $5^{2x-3} = 72$ **±2.3785**
12. $\sqrt[3]{3^{x+5}} = 7^x$ **1.6208**

Solve.

13. Jim wants to paint the walls of a room that is 15 feet wide and 20 feet long. The ceiling is 8 feet high. How many gallons of paint will he need if each gallon covers 350 square feet and he wants to give the room two coats of paint? **4 gallons**

Closing Activity

Speaking Have students, in their own words, explain how to change a logarithm from one base to another.

Chapter 10, Quiz C (Lessons 10-5 and 10-6), is available in the *Assessment and Evaluation Masters,* p. 269.

Additional Answer

56. $\begin{bmatrix} 6 & 5 \\ 3 & -1 \end{bmatrix} \cdot \begin{bmatrix} x \\ y \end{bmatrix} = \begin{bmatrix} 8 \\ 7 \end{bmatrix}$

Enrichment Masters, p. 74

NAME_____ DATE_____

Enrichment

Student Edition
Pages 626–630

Effective Annual Yield

When interest is compounded more than once per year, the effective annual yield is higher than the annual interest rate. The effective annual yield, E, is the interest rate that would give the same amount of interest if the interest were compounded once per year. If P dollars are invested for one year, the value of the investment at the end of the year is $A = P(1 + E)$. If P dollars are invested for one year at a nominal rate r compounded n times per year, the value of the investment at the end of the year is $A = P\left(1 + \frac{r}{n}\right)^n$. Setting the amounts equal and solving for E will produce a formula for the effective annual yield.

$$P(1 + E) = P\left(1 + \frac{r}{n}\right)^n$$
$$1 + E = \left(1 + \frac{r}{n}\right)^n$$
$$E = \left(1 + \frac{r}{n}\right)^n - 1$$

If compounding is continuous, the value of the investment at the end of one year is $A = Pe^r$. Again set the amounts equal and solve for E. A formula for the effective annual yield under continuous compounding is obtained.

$$P(1 + E) = Pe^r$$
$$1 + E = e^r$$
$$E = e^r - 1$$

Examples:

Find the effective annual yield of an investment made at 7.5% compounded monthly.

$r = 0.075$
$n = 12$
$E = \left(1 + \frac{0.075}{12}\right)^{12} - 1 \approx 7.76\%$

Find the effective annual yield of an investment made at 6.25% compounded continuously.

$r = 0.0625$
$E = e^{0.0625} - 1 \approx 6.45\%$

Find the effective annual yield for each investment.

1. 10% compounded quarterly
   10.38%
2. 8.5% compounded monthly
   8.84%
3. 9.25% compounded continuously
   9.69%
4. 7.75% compounded continuously
   8.06%
5. 6.5% compounded daily (assume a 365-day year)
   6.72%
6. Which investment yields more interest—9% compounded continuously or 9.2% compounded quarterly? **9.2% quarterly**

---

53. Solve $(x + 2)(x + 9) > 0$. (Lesson 6–7) $\{x \mid x > -2 \text{ or } x < -9\}$

54. **Art** Morgan needs to paint a landscape for art class. She has 6 feet of framing material to frame the finished painting. What should the dimensions of her canvas be for the painting to have the maximum area? (Lesson 6–1) **1.5 ft by 1.5 ft**

55. Find the values of x and y for which the sentence $2x + 5yi = 4 + 15i$ is true. (Lesson 5–9) $x = 2, y = 3$

56. Write the system of equations as a matrix equation. Then solve the system.
$6x + 5y = 8$ (Lesson 4–6)
$3x - y = 7$ $\left(\frac{43}{21}, -\frac{6}{7}\right)$; **See margin for matrix equation.**

57. Write an equation in standard form for the line that passes through the point at (4, 6) and is perpendicular to the line whose equation is
$y = \frac{2}{3}x + 5$. (Lesson 2–4) $3x + 2y = 24$

WORKING ON THE In·ves·ti·ga·tion

Refer to the Investigation on pages 590–591.

Your manager has asked you to explore the maximum spring potential of the bungee. She is interested in finding the longest distance a jumper would bounce back for any length. She believes that the new bungee product would dominate the market if the spring was greater than that of other bungee equipment. The jumper would therefore experience a greater bounce at the end of his or her drop.

You need to analyze the spring of the rubber bands you tested. Define the *elastic potential* as the ratio of the distance bounced to the length of the stretch. In this manner, you can find the point at which the rubber band has the greatest spring in relationship to the amount it is stretched.

1 Examine one of your graphs. How can the elastic potential be illustrated on that graph using your definition? Is there a numerical value that describes the elastic potential? Explain.

2 Draw new graphs for all three rubber bands using the ratio on the vertical axis instead of the distance bounced. Connect the points in order with line segments. Determine the slope of each segment. Record the slope. Describe the slope in terms of a ratio. What does the ratio indicate?

3 What is the maximum elastic potential for each of the rubber bands? At the maximum elastic potential, what is the distance stretched and the resulting shot distance for each rubber band?

4 Now make three graphs with the horizontal axis representing the distance stretched and the vertical axis representing the elastic potential. Are the graphs logarithmic or exponential in shape? Do each of the graphs verify your predictions for the maximum elastic potentials?

5 Make a recommendation regarding the spring of the rubber bands. Indicate the optimum stretch length for each rubber band you tested. Justify your recommendation.

Add the results of your work to your Investigation Folder.

630 Chapter 10 *Exploring Exponential and Logarithmic Functions*

Extension

Problem Solving Solve $x^{\log x} = \frac{x^3}{100}$.

10 or 100

In·ves·ti·ga·tion

Working on the Investigation

The Investigation on pages 590–591 is designed to be a long-term project that is completed over several days or weeks. Encourage students to keep their materials in their Investigation Folder as they work on the Investigation.

NCTM Standards: 1–6

Instructional Resources

- Study Guide Master 10-7
- Practice Master 10-7
- Enrichment Master 10-7
- Assessment and Evaluation Masters, p. 269
- Multicultural Activity Masters, p. 20
- Tech Prep Applications Masters, p. 20

Transparency 10-7A contains the 5-Minute Check for this lesson; **Transparency 10-7B** contains a teaching aid for this lesson.

Recommended Pacing	
Standard Pacing	Day 10 of 12
Honors Pacing	Day 9 of 11
Block Scheduling*	Day 4 of 5 (along with Lesson 10-6)

*For more information on pacing and possible lesson plans, refer to the *Block Scheduling Booklet*.

What YOU'LL LEARN

- To use logarithms to solve problems involving growth and decay.

Why IT'S IMPORTANT

You can solve growth and decay problems to learn more about paleontology and communication.

APPLICATION
Paleontology

Paleontologists study life of past geological periods by studying fossil remains. They use carbon-14 (C^{14}) to estimate the age of fossils. Carbon-14 decays with time. In 5760 years, just half of the mass of this substance will remain. This period is called its *half-life*. To find the age of a fossil with just $\frac{1}{5}$ of the carbon-14 remaining, paleontologists must use the decay formula for this substance.

The **general formula for growth and decay** is $y = ne^{kt}$, where y is the final amount, n is the initial amount, k is a constant, and t is the time. To determine the decay formula for carbon-14, assume that the initial amount n is represented by 2 units. Then, after 5760 years, the final amount y must be 1 unit. Substitute these values into the general formula and solve for the constant k.

$$y = ne^{kt} \qquad \textit{General formula for growth and decay}$$
$$1 = 2e^{k(5760)} \qquad \textit{y = 1, n = 2, t = 5760}$$
$$0.5 = e^{5760k}$$
$$\ln 0.5 = \ln e^{5760k} \qquad \textit{Take the natural logarithm of each side.}$$
$$\ln 0.5 = 5760k \ln e \qquad \textit{Power property of logarithms}$$
$$\ln 0.5 = 5760k \qquad \textit{ln e = 1}$$
$$\frac{\ln 0.5}{5760} = k$$
$$-0.00012 \approx k$$

The equation for the decay of carbon-14 is $y = ne^{-0.00012t}$, where t is given in years.

Now use this formula to determine the age of a fossil that has $\frac{1}{5}$ of its carbon-14 remaining. Assume that the initial amount is 5 units and the final amount is 1 unit. Then, solve the equation for t.

$$y = ne^{-0.00012t} \qquad \textit{Formula for the decay of carbon-14}$$
$$1 = 5e^{-0.00012t} \qquad \textit{y = 1, n = 5}$$
$$0.2 = e^{-0.00012t}$$
$$\ln 0.2 = \ln e^{-0.00012t} \qquad \textit{Take the natural logarithm of each side.}$$
$$\ln 0.2 = -0.00012t \ln e \qquad \textit{Power property of logarithm}$$
$$\ln 0.2 = -0.00012t \qquad \textit{ln e = 1}$$
$$\frac{\ln 0.2}{-0.00012} = t$$
$$13,412 \approx t$$

The fossil is about 13,400 years old.

The general formula for growth and decay also describes materials that grow exponentially. In this case, the value of k will be positive.

Lesson 10–7 Growth and Decay **631**

fabulous
FIRSTS

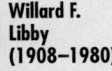

Willard F. Libby (1908–1980)

W.F. Libby of the University of Chicago won the Nobel Prize for Chemistry in 1960 for his method to use carbon-14 for age determination in archaeology. In 1947, he was the first scientist to explain the formation of carbon-14 in the atmosphere and develop a radioactive test to date organic deposits.

1 FOCUS

5-Minute Check *(over Lesson 10-6)*

Express x in terms of common logarithms.

1. $7^x = \sqrt{11}$ $\dfrac{\log 11}{2 \log 7}$

2. $3^x = 4\sqrt{5}$ $\dfrac{\log 4}{\log 3} + \dfrac{\log 5}{2 \log 3}$

Solve each equation using logarithms.

3. $x = \log_{16} 232 \approx 1.964$
4. $7^{2x} = 74 \approx 1.106$
5. $32^{2y} = 5^{4y+1} \approx 3.2598$

fabulous
FIRSTS

There are six categories of Nobel Prizes: physics, chemistry, literature, physiology or medicine, peace, and economic science. They are not dependent upon nationality, race, creed, ideology, or political backing. If there is not a worthy candidate, the award is not given that year.

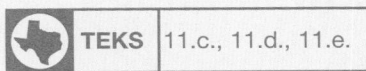

TEKS | 11.c., 11.d., 11.e.

Motivating the Lesson

Questioning Elicit student responses to the following question. Now that you have determined and used logarithms, in what situations would they be useful in solving problems? **Determining rate of return on certificates of deposit or interest-bearing bank accounts; studying anything with exponential growth, such as population; determining age of fossils; and many others.**

2 TEACH

In-Class Examples

For Example 1
For a certain radioactive element, k is -0.377 when t is measured in days. How long will it take 500 grams of the element to reduce to 200 grams? **There will be 200 grams of the element after approximately 2.4 days.**

For Example 2
The Jamesons bought a new house 5 years ago for $65,000. The house is now worth $117,000. Assuming a steady rate of growth, what was the yearly rate of appreciation? **The rate of appreciation was approximately 12.5%.**

Teaching Tip Remind students of the differences between common and natural logarithms, when each is used, and how the value of each is determined.

Example **1**

CONNECTION
Biology

Bacteria usually reproduce by a process known as *binary fission*. In this type of reproduction, one bacterium divides, forming two bacteria. Under ideal conditions, some bacteria can reproduce every 20 minutes. Find the constant k for the growth of these types of bacteria under ideal conditions and write the growth equation.

$$y = ne^{kt}$$
$$2 = 1e^{k(20)} \quad \text{One bacterium can produce two in 20 minutes.}$$
$$2 = e^{20k}$$
$$\ln 2 = \ln e^{20k} \quad \text{Take the natural logarithm of each side.}$$
$$\ln 2 = 20k \ln e \quad \text{Power property of logarithms}$$
$$\ln 2 = 20k \quad \text{ln } e = 1$$
$$\frac{\ln 2}{20} = k$$
$$0.0347 \approx k$$

The value of the constant for the bacteria is approximately 0.0347. The growth equation is $y = ne^{0.0347t}$, where t is given in minutes.

Certain assets, such as cars, houses, and business equipment, appreciate or depreciate, that is, increase or decrease in value, with time. The formula $V_n = P(1 + r)^n$, where V_n is the new value, P is the initial value, r is the fixed rate of appreciation or depreciation, and n is the number of years, can be used to compute the value of an asset. The value of r for a depreciating asset will be negative, and the value of r for an appreciating asset will be positive.

Example **2**

APPLICATION
Agriculture

The Thomas family includes several generations of farmers. They have an opportunity to buy 50 acres adjacent to their farm for $800 per acre. In the past, the price of farmland has gone up 3% a year. If this continues, how long will it be before the land is worth $1000 per acre?

Explore   Read the problem. The problem gives the value of the land now and the annual percent of increase in the price of land. It asks you to find when the land will be worth $1000 an acre.

Plan   Substitute 1000 for V_n, 800 for P, and 0.03 for r in the formula $V_n = P(1 + r)^n$. Then, use logarithms to solve for n.

Solve
$$V_n = P(1 + r)^n$$
$$1000 = 800(1 + 0.03)^n \quad V_n = 1000, P = 800, r = 0.03$$
$$1.25 = 1.03^n$$
$$\log 1.25 = \log 1.03^n \quad \text{Take the common logarithm of each side.}$$
$$\log 1.25 = n \log 1.03 \quad \text{Product property of logarithms}$$
$$\frac{\log 1.25}{\log 1.03} = n$$
$$7.549 \approx n$$

The value of the land will be $1000 per acre in about $7\frac{1}{2}$ years.

Examine   Use the formula to find the value of the land in 7.5 years.
$$V_n = P(1 + r)^n$$
$$= 800(1 + 0.03)^{7.5} \quad P = 800, r = 0.03, n = 7.5$$
$$\approx 999 \quad \text{Use a calculator to evaluate the expression.}$$

The value of the V_n is about 1000, so the answer seems reasonable.

GLENCOE Technology

Interactive Mathematics Tools Software

This multimedia software provides an interactive lesson that uses the formula $A = p\left(1 + \frac{r}{t}\right)^{nt}$ to observe how changes in each variable affect the amount in an account. A **Computer Journal** gives students an opportunity to write about what they have learned.

For Windows & Macintosh

GLENCOE Technology

CD-ROM Interaction

A multimedia simulation ties sampling, curve fitting, and exponential growth with research on the feasibility of plankton farming. A blackline master activity with teacher's notes provides a follow-up to the CD-ROM simulation.

For Windows & Macintosh

Logarithms can be used to solve problems involving an exponential function $y = ab^x$.

Example ③

APPLICATION
Broadcasting

The FM frequencies of radio transmissions range from 88 to 108 megahertz. However, these frequencies are not marked uniformly along the display of a radio receiver. Assume that the frequencies are an exponential function of the distance from the left end of the display. Write an equation for the FM frequencies along a display that is 15 centimeters long.

Let x represent the distance from the left end, and let y represent the frequency. Since 88 megahertz is 0 centimeters from the left end and 108 megahertz is 15 centimeters from the left end, the ordered pairs (0, 88) and (15, 108) are solutions to the function $y = ab^x$. Use (0, 88) to solve for a.

$y = ab^x$
$88 = ab^0$ $x = 0, y = 88$
$88 = a(1)$ $b^0 = 1$
$88 = a$

Then use (15, 108) to solve for b.

$y = ab^x$
$108 = 88b^{15}$ $a = 88, x = 15, and\ y = 108$
$\log 108 = \log(88b^{15})$ Take the common logarithm of each side.
$\log 108 = \log 88 + \log b^{15}$ Product property of logarithms
$\log 108 = \log 88 + 15 \log b$ Power properties of logarithms
$\log 108 - \log 88 = 15 \log b$
$\frac{\log 108 - \log 88}{15} = \log b$
$0.0059 \approx \log b$
$\text{antilog}\ 0.0059 \approx \text{antilog}\ (\log b)$ Take the antilogarithm of each side.
$1.0137 \approx b$

The relationship of the frequencies and the distance from the left side of the display is approximated by the equation $y = 88(1.0137)^x$, where y is the frequency in megahertz and x is the distance in centimeters.

CHECK FOR UNDERSTANDING

Communicating Mathematics

Study the lesson. Then complete the following.   1–2. See margin.

1. **Describe** a situation in which the constant k in the formula for growth and decay is positive and one in which k is negative. Describe the situation if the value of k is zero.

2. **Explain** why the natural logarithm was used in Example 1 and the common logarithm was used in Examples 2 and 3. Could you solve Example 1 using common logarithms? Could you solve Examples 2 and 3 by using natural logarithms? Explain.

Guided Practice

3. **Broadcasting**   Refer to Example 3.
   a. Find the FM frequency that corresponds to the point that is 3.5 centimeters from the left side of the display.   **about 92.3 megahertz**
   b. Find the location on the radio display that corresponds to the FM frequency of 100 megahertz.   **about 9.4 cm from the left side**

Lesson 10-7 Growth and Decay   **633**

Reteaching ▬▬▬▬▬

Using Data   Have the class work through the following problem aloud. The population of Fargo, Ohio, can be modeled by the equation $y = ce^{kt}$ where c and k are constants and t is the time in years. If Fargo had 3000 residents in 1960 and 4200 in 1970, what was its population in 1980?
5880 in 1980

In-Class Example

For Example 3
Assume $100 is deposited in a savings account. The interest rate is 6% compounded continuously. When will the money be double the original amount?
In approximately 11.55 years

Teaching Tip You may also want students to identify the appropriate formula for solving each exercise.

3 PRACTICE/APPLY

Check for Understanding
Exercises 1–5 are designed to help you assess your students' understanding through reading, writing, speaking, and modeling. You should work through Exercises 1–2 with your students and then monitor their work on Exercises 3–5.

Additional Answers

1. Sample answer: The constant is positive when growth is depicted such as in the case of bacterial growth. The constant is negative when decay is depicted such as in radioactive decay. If k is zero, then the population is not growing or decaying and the function is a constant function.

2. Example 1 is dealing with e, and Examples 2 and 3 are dealing with base 10 numbers; yes; yes; you can take the logarithm of each side of an equation as long as you use the same base on both sides. Therefore, you can use natural logarithms or common logarithms in any problem.

Assignment Guide

Core: 7–15 odd, 16–21
Enriched: 6–14 even, 15–21

For **Extra Practice,** see p. 900.

The red A, B, and C flags, printed only in the Teacher's Wraparound Edition, indicate the level of difficulty of the exercises.

Additional Answers

9c. Sample answer: If the economy of a city is doing well, more people than expected may move into the area. If the economy is not doing well, people may lose their jobs and move out of the area.

11. No; the bone is only about 19,000 years old, and dinosaurs died out 63,000,000 years ago.

Study Guide Masters, p. 75

NAME_____ DATE_____
Student Edition
Pages 631–636

Study Guide

10-7

Growth and Decay

Many problems can be solved by applying the following formulas:

Growth and Decay Formula	$y = ne^{kt}$	y is the final amount, n is the initial amount, k is a constant, and t represents time.
Continuously Compounded Interest	$A = Pe^{rt}$	P is the initial investment, r is the annual interest rate, and t is the time in years.
Value of Equipment and Assets in Business	$V_n = P(1 + r)^n$	V_n is the new value, P is the initial value, r is the fixed rate of appreciation or depreciation, and n is the number of years.

Example: Find how long it will take money to double if it is invested at 8% annual interest, compounded continuously.

$A = Pe^{rt}$ — Substitute 2 for A, 1 for P since the amount is doubled. $r = 0.08$
$2 = 1e^{0.08t}$
$\ln 2 = \ln e^{0.08t}$ — Take the natural log of each side.
$\ln 2 = 0.08t(\ln e)$ — Power Property of Logarithms
$\ln 2 = 0.08t$
$\frac{\ln 2}{0.08} = t$
$8.6643 = t$

The money will double in approximately 8.66 years.

Solve.

1. Carl plans to invest $500 at 8.25% interest, compounded continously. How long will it take for his money to triple?
13.316 years

2. A certain strain of bacteria grows from 40 to 326 in 120 minutes. Find k for the growth formula.
0.0175

3. A $40,000 car depreciates at a constant rate of 12% per year. In how many years will the car be worth $12,000?
9.42 years

4. **Business** Zeller Industries bought a computer for $4600. It is expected to depreciate at a steady rate of 20% a year. When will the value have depreciated to $2000? **about 3.7 years**

5. **Chemistry** The half life of radium (Ra^{226}) is 1620 years.
   a. Find the constant k in the formula $y = ne^{kt}$ for radium (Ra^{226}) when t is given in years. **about -0.00043**
   b. Write the equation for the decay of radium (Ra^{226}) $y = ne^{-0.00043t}$
   c. Suppose a 20-gram sample of radium (Ra^{226}) is sealed in a box. Find the mass of the radium after 5000 years. **about 2.33 grams**
   d. When will a sample of radium (Ra^{226}) be one fourth of its original mass?
   e. When will a 20-gram sample of radium (Ra^{226}) be completely gone? Explain.

5d. in about 3224 years
5e. Never; the amount left will always be half of the amount that existed 1620 years ago.

EXERCISES

Applications and Problem Solving

6. about $100,367

8a. about $y = 535(1.0803)^x$

9b. about 674,190 people

6. **Real Estate** Mr. and Mrs. Sawyer bought a condominium for $75,000. Assuming that its value will appreciate 6% a year, how much will the condo be worth in five years when the Sawyers are ready to move?

7. **Medicine** Radioactive iodine is used to determine the health of the thyroid gland. It decays according to the equation $y = ne^{-0.0856t}$, where t is in days. Find the half-life of this substance. **about 8.1 days**

8. **Broadcasting** The AM frequencies of radio transmissions range from 535 to 1705 kilohertz. Assume that the frequencies are an exponential function of the distance from the left of the display on a radio.
   a. Write an equation for the AM frequencies along a display that is 15 centimeters long.
   b. Find the AM frequency that corresponds to the point that is 4.5 centimeters from the left side of the display. **about 757 kilohertz**
   c. Find the location on the radio display that corresponds to the AM frequency of 1000 kilohertz. **about 8.1 cm from the left side**

9. **Population Growth** The city of Knoxville, Tennessee, grew from a population of 546,488 in 1980 to a population of 585,960 in 1990.
   a. Use this information to write a growth equation for Knoxville, where t is the number of years after 1980. **about $y = 546,488e^{0.0070t}$**
   b. Use your equation to predict the population of Knoxville in 2010.
   c. What factors might affect the population growth of a city such as Knoxville? **See margin.**

10. **Space Travel** A radioisotope is used as a power source for a satellite. The power output is given by the equation $P = 50e^{-\frac{t}{250}}$, where P is the power in watts and t is the time in days.
    a. Find the power available after 100 days. **about 33.5 watts**
    b. Ten watts of power are required to operate the equipment in the satellite. How long can the satellite continue to operate? **about 402 days**

11. **Paleontology** A paleontologist finds a bone that might be a dinosaur bone. In the laboratory, she finds that the radiocarbon found in this bone is $\frac{1}{10}$ of that found in living bone tissue. Could this bone have belonged to a dinosaur? Explain. (*Hint:* The dinosaurs lived from 220 million years ago to 63 million years ago.) **See margin.**

12. Real Estate The Diaz family bought a new house 10 years ago for $80,000. The house is now worth $140,000. Assuming a steady rate of growth, what was the yearly rate of appreciation? about 5.75%

13. Cooking The amount of time needed to cook scrambled eggs in the microwave depends on the number of eggs being cooked. The chart at the right shows the suggested times for cooking eggs in a certain microwave.
a. about $t = 1.0208n^{0.7776}$

Number of Eggs	Cooking Time (min)
2	$1\frac{3}{4}$
4	3

a. Assume that the number of minutes is a function of some power of the number of eggs. Write a general equation of the form $t = an^b$, where t is the time in minutes, n is the number of eggs, and a and b are constants. (*Hint:* Use a system of equations to solve for the constants.)

b. Find the amount of time needed to cook 3 eggs and to cook 5 eggs.
about 2.4 min; about 3.6 min

14. Communication A rumor can spread very quickly. The number of people H who have heard a rumor can be approximated by the equation $H = \dfrac{P}{1 + (P - S)e^{-0.4t}}$ where P is the total population, S is the number of people who start the rumor, and t is the time in minutes. During lunch period, two students decide to start a rumor that the principal will let the students out of school one hour early that day. If there are 1600 students in the school, how much time will pass before half of the students have heard the rumor? about 18.4 min

Programming

15. The graphing calculator program at the right uses the formula
$$S = R\left[\dfrac{(1+I)^N - 1}{I}\right]$$ to find how many payments are needed to accumulate a given amount of money when payments are made at regular intervals and interest is compounded at the end of each payment period. In the formula, S represents the money accumulated after the last payment, R represents the amount of each payment, I represents the interest rate per payment period (represented as a decimal), and N represents the number of payments per year. In the program, Y represents the number of payments per year, and A represents the annual interest rate.

```
PROGRAM: PAYMENTS
: Prompt S, R, A, Y
: A/Y→I
: log(SI/R+1)/(log(1+I))→N
: If N=int (N+1)
: Then
: Goto 1
: End
: int(N+1)→N
: Lbl 1
: Disp "PAYMENTS NEEDED:",N
```

Use the program to determine the number of payments needed to accumulate the indicated amount of money, given the amount of each payment, the annual interest rate, and the number of payments each year.

a. $4000, $300, 9%, 2   11
b. $7500, $400, 8.5%, 4   16
c. $8995, $156, 9.25%, 12   48
d. $14,600, $195, 8.75%, 12   60
e. $96,000, $850, 9.65%, 12   81
f. $90,000, $425, 9.65%, 26   157

Critical Thinking

16. Compare the formulas for exponential growth, $y = ne^{kt}$, and for continuously compounded interest, $A = Pe^{rt}$. Explain how the formulas are related. See margin.

Using the Programming Exercises The program given in Exercise 15 is for use with a TI-82 graphing calculator. For other programmable calculators, have students consult their owner's manual for commands similar to those presented here.

Additional Answer

16. The compound interest formula is actually a special case of the growth rate.

Practice Masters, p. 75

10-7

NAME _____ DATE _____

Practice

Student Edition
Pages 631–63

Growth and Decay

Solve.

1. Suppose $500 is invested at 6% annual interest compounded twice a year. When will the investment be worth $1000?
11.72 years

2. Suppose $500 is invested at 6% annual interest compounded continuously. When will the investment be worth $1000?
11.55 years

3. An organism of a certain type can grow from 30 to 195 organisms in 5 hours. Find k for the growth formula.
0.3744

4. For a certain strain of bacteria, k is 0.825 when t is measured in days. How long will it take 20 bacteria to increase to 2000?
5.582 days

5. An investment service promises to triple your money in 12 years. Assuming continuous compounding of interest, what rate of interest is needed?
9.155%

6. A substance decomposes radioactively. Its half-life is 32 years. Find the constant k in the decay formula.
−0.02166

7. A piece of machinery valued at $250,000 depreciates at 12% per year by the fixed rate method. After how many years will the value have depreciated to $100,000?
7.168 years

8. Dave bought a new car 8 years ago for $8400. To buy a new car comparably equipped now would cost $12,500. Assuming a steady rate of increase, what was the yearly rate of inflation in car prices over the 8-year period?
5.09%

Closing Activity

Modeling Take a large piece of paper. Fold it in half and record the number of regions in the paper. Fold it in half again, record, and continue this process until the paper is too small to fold again.

Chapter 10, Quiz D (Lesson 10-7), is available in the *Assessment and Evaluation Masters*, p. 269.

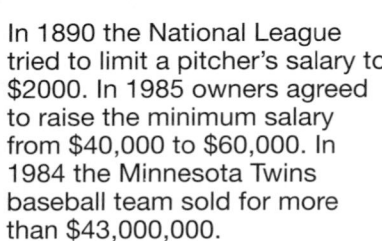

F Y I

In 1890 the National League tried to limit a pitcher's salary to $2000. In 1985 owners agreed to raise the minimum salary from $40,000 to $60,000. In 1984 the Minnesota Twins baseball team sold for more than $43,000,000.

Enrichment Masters, p. 75

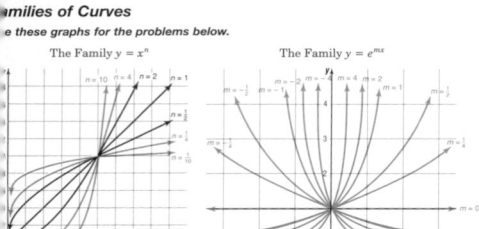

10-7 NAME_____ DATE_____
Student Edition
Pages 631-636
Enrichment

milies of Curves
e these graphs for the problems below.

The Family $y = x^n$ The Family $y = e^{mx}$

Use the graph on the left to describe the relationship among the curves $y = x^{\frac{1}{2}}, y = x^1$, and $y = x^2$. For $n = \frac{1}{2}$ and $n = 2$, the graphs are reflections of one another in the line with equation $y = x^1$.

Graph $y = x^n$ for $n = \frac{1}{10}, \frac{1}{4}$, 4, and 10 on the grid with $y = x^{\frac{1}{2}}$, $y = x^1$, and $y = x^2$. See students' graphs.

Which two regions in the first quadrant contain no points of the graphs of the family for $y = x^n$?
$\{(x, y)|x \geq 1$ and $0 < y \leq 1\}$ and $\{(x, y)|0 < x \leq 1$ and $y \geq 1\}$

On the right grid, graph the members of the family $y = e^{mx}$ for which $m = 1$ and $m = -1$. See students' graphs.

Describe the relationship among these two curves and the y-axis. the graphs for $m = 1$ and $m = -1$ are reflections in the y-axis.

Graph $y = e^{mx}$ for $m = 0, \pm\frac{1}{4}, \pm\frac{1}{2}, \pm2$, and ±4. See students' graphs.

Mixed Review

17. Solve $7^{x-2} = 5^{3-x}$. (Lesson 10-6) **about 2.45**

18. Find the equation for the ellipse shown at the right. Then give the coordinates of the foci. (Lesson 7-4)
$\frac{x^2}{4} + \frac{y^2}{16} = 1; (0, \pm2\sqrt{3})$

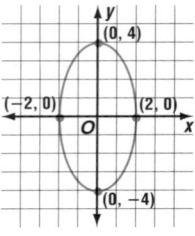

19. Physics The distance s an object travels can be computed when the initial speed v_i, time elapsed t, and the rate of constant acceleration a is known. The formula that relates these factors is $s = v_i t + \frac{1}{2}at^2$. Michael drives a red sports car on a race track at an initial velocity of 24 ft/s and begins to accelerate at a constant rate of 8 ft/s². (Lesson 6-3)
  a. How long will it take him to travel a distance of 100 feet? **about 2.8 s**
  b. How long will it take him to travel a distance of 200 feet? **about 4.7 s**
  c. How long will it take him to travel a distance of 300 feet? **about 6.2 s**
  d. Study your answers to parts a–c. As the distance doubles, does the amount of time double? Explain your answer. **No, the formula is not a direct variation.**

F Y I

The baseball stadium with largest seating capacity is Mile High Stadium, home of the Colorado Rockies. Wrigley Field, home of the Chicago Cubs, has the smallest seating capacity of the major league fields.

20. Baseball The seating capacities of the major league baseball stadiums are listed below. (Lesson 4-8)

34,142	38,710	40,625	42,400	43,739	44,702	47,313	48,000
48,041	49,292	50,516	52,003	52,416	52,952	53,192	54,816
55,601	55,883	56,000	56,227	57,545	58,727	59,002	59,702
62,000	62,382	64,593	76,100				

  a. Find the range of the data. **41,958**
  b. Find the quartiles of the data. **47,656.5, 53,072, 58,136**
  c. Find the interquartile range of the data. **10,479.5**
  d. Find any outliers in the data. **76,100**
  e. Draw a box-and-whisker plot for the data. **See margin.**

21. 128 cm²

21. Geometry The formula for the area of a trapezoid is $A = \frac{h}{2}(b_1 + b_2)$, where A represents the measure of the area, h represents the measure of the altitude, and b_1 and b_2 represent the measures of the bases. Find the measure of the area of the trapezoid whose height is 8 centimeters and whose bases measure 12 centimeters and 20 centimeters. (Lesson 1-2)

Extension ▬▬▬▬

Connections Have students solve the following problem. In 4 years, an investment of $750 grew to $1050. When will the investment be tripled, assuming continuous compounding?
13.06 years

Additional Answer

20e.

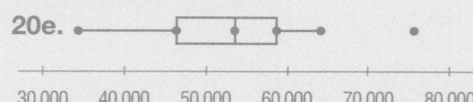

Using the
CHAPTER HIGHLIGHTS

The Chapter Highlights begins with a listing of the new terms, properties, and phrases that were introduced in this chapter. Have students define each term and provide an example or two of it, if appropriate.

VOCABULARY

After completing this chapter, you should be able to define each term, property, or phrase and give an example or two of each.

Algebra

antilogarithm (p. 618)

change of base formula (pp. 594, 628)

characteristic (p. 618)

common logarithms (p. 617)

exponential equations (p. 626)

exponential function (pp. 594, 596)

exponential growth (p. 622)

exponential growth rate (p. 626)

general formula for growth and decay (p. 631)

logarithm (p. 605)

logarithmic function (pp. 594, 607)

mantissa (p. 618)

natural logarithms (p. 622)

power property of logarithms (p. 613)

product property of logarithms (p. 611)

property of equality for exponential functions (p. 599)

property of equality for logarithmic functions (p. 608)

quotient property of logarithms (p. 612)

Problem Solving

use estimation (p. 626)

Assessment and Evaluation Masters, pp. 255–256

10 NAME_____ DATE_____
Chapter 10 Test, Form 1B

Write the letter for the correct answer in the blank at the right of each problem.

1. What is the simplest form of $16^{\sqrt{2}} \cdot 4^{\sqrt{2}}$?
   A. 400   B. 40   C. $2^{6\sqrt{2}}$ D. 4^6 1. ___C___

2. What is the solution of $\left(\frac{1}{5}\right)^x = 5^{x+6}$?
   A. -7 B. -3 C. 3   D. 0   2. ___B___

3. What is the approximate solution of $3^{x-1} = 4.2$?
   A. 1.15   B. 2.31   C. 1.31   D. 0.31   3. ___B___

4. What is $\log_{10} 0.001 = -3$ in exponential form?
   A. $0.001^{-3} = 10$ B. $-3^{10} = 0.001$ C. $10^{-3} = 0.001$ D. $10^{0.001} = 3$ 4. ___C___

5. Find ln 150 rounded to four decimal places.
   A. 2.1761   B. 5   C. 5.0106   D. 0.0106   5. ___C___

6. What is the solution set of $\log_x 25 = 2$?
   A. $\{-5, 5\}$ B. $\{12.5\}$ C. $\{5\}$ D. $\{625\}$ 6. ___C___

7. Find the value of a if an exponential function of the form $y = a \cdot 2^x$ passes through the point $(2, 20)$.
   A. 5   B. -5 C. $\frac{1}{5}$ D. 80   7. ___A___

8. Evaluate $4^{1.4}$ to the nearest tenth.
   A. 0.35   B. 0.1   C. 5.6   D. 7.0   8. ___D___

9. What is the value of $9^{\log_9 4}$?
   A. 81   B. 36   C. 9   D. 4   9. ___D___

10. What is the solution set of $\log_5 x^2 = \log_5 (6x + 27)$?
    A. Ø   B. $\{9\}$ C. $\{-4.5\}$ D. $\{9, -3\}$ 10. ___D___

11. If $\log_5 6 = 1.1133$ and $\log_5 2 = 0.4307$, what is the value of $\log_5 12$?
    A. 0.6826   B. 1.5440   C. 0.4794   D. 1.2918   11. ___B___

12. A bacteria can triple in population every hour. Which equation represents this situation?
    A. $y = 3e^x$ B. $3 = e^k$ C. $1 = e^{3k}$ D. $y = e^{3x}$ 12. ___B___

13. What is the solution set of $3 \log_5 x = 4 \log_5 2 - \frac{1}{2} \log_5 4$?
    A. $\{5\}$ B. $\{4\}$ C. $\{2\}$ D. Ø   13. ___C___

10 NAME_____ DATE_____
Chapter 10 Test, Form 1B (continued)

14. What is the solution set of $\log_3 (a - 2) + \log_3 (a - 2) = 2$?
    A. $\{3\}$ B. $\{2\}$ C. $\{5\}$ D. $\{-1, 5\}$ 14. ___C___

15. If $\log w = 7$ and $\log n = 4$, what is the value of wn?
    A. 3   B. 4   C. 1.75   D. 11   15. ___D___

16. If $\log 0.008 = -2.0969$, what is the mantissa of $\log 0.008$?
    A. 0.0969   B. -3 C. -2 D. 0.9031   16. ___D___

17. If $\log 8000 = 3.9031$, what is the characteristic of $\log 8000$?
    A. 0.0969   B. 3   C. 4   D. 0.9031   17. ___B___

18. What is the common logarithm of 589,000?
    A. 0.7701   B. 5   C. 5.7701   D. 6.3784   18. ___C___

19. What is the antilogarithm of $0.6875 - 2$?
    A. 0.2691   B. 3.870   C. 4.869   D. 0.0487   19. ___D___

20. What is the value of ln 0.045, accurate to four decimal places?
    A. -3.1011 B. -1.3468 C. 0.6532   D. 0.8989   20. ___A___

21. What is the value of antiln 2.875, accurate to four significant digits?
    A. 0.4586   B. 749.9   C. 1.056   D. 17.72   21. ___D___

22. What is the approximate value of $\log_4 9$?
    A. 1.585   B. 0.6309   C. 0.9542   D. 1.6021   22. ___A___

23. What is the approximate solution of $7^x = 3^{x+1}$?
    A. 6   B. 1.297   C. 1.771   D. 2   23. ___B___

24. A certain strain of bacteria can grow from 200 to 900 in 3 hours. What is the approximate value of k for the growth formula $y = ne^{kt}$?
    A. 4.5   B. 1.369   C. 1.5   D. 0.5014   24. ___D___

25. Assume $150 is deposited in a savings account. If the interest rate is 5.5% compounded continuously, after how many years will the amount of money in the account be doubled? Use $A = Pe^{rt}$.
    A. 4.61 years   B. 6.3 years   C. 12.6 years   D. 18.2 years   25. ___C___

Bonus What is the solution set of the equation $\log (x + 2) = \log x + 2$?
    A. $\{98\}$ B. $\{8\}$ C. $\{-2\}$ D. $\left\{\frac{2}{99}\right\}$ Bonus ___D___

UNDERSTANDING AND USING THE VOCABULARY

Choose the letter that best answers each question.

1. To solve $\log_8 (2y + 3) = \log_8 (y - 4)$, what property would you use?   **h**

2. What do the following have in common?   **d**
   log 6500 and log 6.5

3. What kind of function is $y = \frac{1}{2}(5)^x$?   **b**

4. Name the property shown in each example.
   a. $3 \log_2 5 = \log_2 5^3$ **e**
   b. $\log_4 2x = \log_4 2 + \log_4 x$ **f**
   c. $\log_3 \frac{4}{5} = \log_3 4 - \log_3 5$ **i**

5. What do the following have in common?   **a**
   log 0.28 and log $\frac{3}{4}$

6. What kind of function is $y = \log_2 x$?   **c**

7. To solve $9^{2p} = 27^{p-1}$, what property would you use?   **g**

a. characteristic

b. exponential function

c. logarithmic function

d. mantissa

e. power property of logarithms

f. product property of logarithms

g. property of equality for exponential functions

h. property of equality for logarithmic functions

i. quotient property of logarithms

Instructional Resources

Three multiple-choice tests and three free-response tests are provided in the *Assessment and Evaluation Masters*. Forms 1A and 2A are for honors pacing, and Forms 1B, 1C, 2B, and 2C are for average pacing. Chapter 10 Test, Form 1B is shown at the right. Chapter 10 Test, Form 2B is shown on the next page.

Skills and Concepts Encourage students to refer to the objectives and examples on the left as they complete the review exercises on the right.

Assessment and Evaluation Masters, pp. 261–262

10 NAME_____ DATE _____

Chapter 10 Test, Form 2B

1. Simplify $7^{\sqrt{5}} \cdot 7^{\sqrt{8}}$.　　1. ____$7^{\sqrt{5}+2\sqrt{2}}$____

2. Simplify $(x^{\sqrt{3}})^{\sqrt{3}}$.　　2. ____$x^3$____

3. Solve the equation $\frac{1}{6} = 6^{a+4}$.　　3. ____-5____

4. Approximate $1.2^{1.3}$ to the nearest tenth.　　4. ____1.3____

5. Write $\log_6 36 = 2$ in exponential form.　　5. ____$6^2 = 36$____

6. Find antiln 2.3694. Round your answer to three decimal places.　　6. ____10.691____

7. Evaluate $\log_7 7^6$.　　7. ____6____

8. Evaluate $5^{\log_5 3}$.　　8. ____3____

Solve each equation.

9. $5^{x-2} = 16$　　9. ____3.72____

10. $\log_8 y = 3$　　10. ____512____

11. $\log_6 (5 - 3a) = \log_6 (a^2 - 5)$　　11. ____-5____

12. $\log_3 (x + 3) + \log_3 (x - 2) = \log_3 14$　　12. ____4____

13. $\log_2 (2x + 6) - \log_2 x = 3$　　13. ____1____

14. $\log_5 x = \frac{1}{2}\log_5 25$　　14. ____5____

15. If $\log_7 3 = a$ and $\log_7 5 = b$, express $\log_7 \frac{3}{5}$ in terms of a and b.　　15. ____$a - b$____

10 NAME_____ DATE _____

Chapter 10 Test, Form 2B (continued)

16. Find log 0.0715. Round your answer to four decimal places.　　16. ____-1.1457____

17. Find antilog 2.903. Round your answer to the nearest whole number.　　17. ____800____

18. What is the characteristic of log 2078?　　18. ____3____

19. What is the mantissa of log 7.68?　　19. ____0.8854____

20. Find ln 39.4. Round your answer to four decimal places.　　20. ____3.6738____

21. Find antiln 0.144. Round your answer to three decimal places.　　21. ____1.155____

22. Use logarithms to solve the equation $4^x = 28$. Round your answer to four decimal places.　　22. ____2.4037____

23. Use logarithms to solve the equation $2^y = 5^{y-2}$. Round your answer to four decimal places.　　23. ____3.5129____

24. Assume $150 is deposited in a savings account. If the interest rate is 6.5% compounded continuously, after how many years will the investment be worth $450? Use the formula $A = Pe^{rt}$. Round your answer to the nearest tenth of a year.　　24. ____16.9 years____

25. In 5 years, radioactivity reduces the mass of a 100-gram sample of an element to 80 grams. For this element, find the approximate value of the constant k in $y = ne^{kt}$.　　25. ____-0.0446____

Bonus Evaluate 3^{500}. Write the answer in scientific notation with three significant digits.　　Bonus ____3.64×10^{238}____

SKILLS AND CONCEPTS

OBJECTIVES AND EXAMPLES	REVIEW EXERCISES

Upon completing this chapter, you should be able to:

Use these exercises to review and prepare for the chapter test.

• simplify expressions and solve equations involving real exponents (Lesson 10–1)

Simplify $16^{\sqrt{12}} \div 8^{\sqrt{3}}$.

$$16^{\sqrt{12}} \div 8^{\sqrt{3}} = (2^4)^{\sqrt{12}} \div (2^3)^{\sqrt{3}}$$
$$= 2^{8\sqrt{3}} \div 2^{3\sqrt{3}}$$
$$= 2^{8\sqrt{3} - 3\sqrt{3}}$$
$$= 2^{5\sqrt{3}}$$

Simplify each expression. 11. $8^{3\sqrt{3}}$

8. $3^{\sqrt{2}} \cdot 3^{\sqrt{2}}$　$3^{2\sqrt{2}}$　　9. $\left(x^{\sqrt{5}}\right)^{\sqrt{20}}$　x^{10}

10. $\frac{49^{\sqrt{2}}}{7^{\sqrt{12}}}$　$7^{2\sqrt{2}-2\sqrt{3}}$　　11. $\left(8^{\sqrt{3}}\right)\left(8^{-2\sqrt{3}}\right)\left(8^{4\sqrt{3}}\right)$

Solve each equation.

12. $2^{6x} = 4^{5x+2}$　-1　　13. $49^{3p+1} = 7^{2p-5}$　$-\frac{7}{4}$

14. $9^{x^2} = 27^{x^2-2}$　$\pm\sqrt{6}$　　15. $9^x = \frac{1}{81}$　-2

• write exponential equations in logarithmic form and vice versa (Lesson 10–2)

Write $3^3 = 27$ in logarithmic form.

$$3^3 = 27$$
$$3 = \log_3 27$$

Write $\log_4 64 = 3$ in exponential form.

$$\log_4 64 = 3$$
$$64 = 4^3$$

Write each equation in logarithmic form.

16. $7^3 = 343$　　17. $5^{-2} = \frac{1}{25}$

16. $\log_7 343 = 3$　　17. $\log_5 \frac{1}{25} = -2$

18. $4^0 = 1$　$\log_4 1 = 0$　　19. $4^{\frac{3}{2}} = 8$　$\log_4 8 = \frac{3}{2}$

Write each equation in exponential form.

20. $\log_4 64 = 3$　$4^3 = 64$　21. $\log_8 2 = \frac{1}{3}$　$8^{\frac{1}{3}} = 2$

22. $\log_6 \frac{1}{36} = -2$　　23. $\log_6 1 = 0$　$6^0 = 1$

22. $6^{-2} = \frac{1}{36}$

• evaluate logarithmic expressions (Lesson 10–2)

Evaluate $\log_3 3^5$.

$$\log_3 3^5 = x$$
$$3^x = 3^5$$
$$x = 5$$

Evaluate each expression.

24. $6^{\log_6 7}$　7

25. $\log_{10} 10^{-3}$　-3

26. $\log_{64} 8$　$\frac{1}{2}$

27. $\log_{12} 144$　2

• solve equations involving logarithmic functions (Lesson 10–2)

Solve $\log_b 16 = 4$.

$$\log_b 16 = 4$$
$$b^4 = 16$$
$$b^4 = 2^4$$
$$b = 2$$

Solve $\log_3 10 = \log_3 (2x)$.

$$\log_3 10 = \log_3 (2x)$$
$$10 = 2x$$
$$5 = x$$

Solve each equation.

28. $\log_b 9 = 2$　3　　29. $\log_4 x = \frac{1}{2}$　2

30. $\log_3 x = -3$　$\frac{1}{27}$　　31. $\log_7 2401 = x$　4

32. $\log_7 (x^2 + x) = \log_7 12$　$-4, 3$

33. $\log_6 12 = \log_6 (5x - 3)$　3

34. $\log_8 (3y - 1) = \log_8 (y + 4)$　2.5

35. $\log_2 (x^2 + 6x) = \log_2 (x - 4)$　no solution

638 Chapter 10 Study Guide and Assessment

GLENCOE Technology

◉ **Test and Review Software**

You may use this software, a combination of an item generator and item bank, to create your own tests or worksheets. Types of items include free response, multiple choice, short answer, and open ended.

For IBM & Macintosh

OBJECTIVES AND EXAMPLES

• simplify and evaluate expressions using properties of logarithms (Lesson 10–3)

Use $\log_{12} 9 \approx 0.884$ and $\log_{12} 18 \approx 1.163$ to evaluate $\log_{12} 2$.

$$\log_{12} 2 = \log_{12}\left(\frac{18}{9}\right)$$
$$= \log_{12} 18 - \log_{12} 9$$
$$\approx 1.163 - 0.884$$
$$\approx 0.279$$

• solve equations involving logarithms (Lesson 10–3)

Solve $2\log_5 6 - \frac{1}{3}\log_5 27 = \log_5 x$.

$$2\log_5 6 - \frac{1}{3}\log_5 27 = \log_5 x$$
$$\log_5 6^2 - \log_5 27^{\frac{1}{3}} = \log_5 x$$
$$\log_5 36 - \log_5 3 = \log_5 x$$
$$\log_5 \frac{36}{3} = \log_5 x$$
$$\log_5 12 = \log_5 x$$
$$12 = x$$

• find common logarithms and antilogarithms (Lesson 10–4)

Use a scientific calculator to find the logarithm of 56.4.

Use the **LOG** key.

Enter: 56.4 **LOG** *1.751279104*

Use a scientific calculator to find the antilogarithm of 2.738.

Use the **10ˣ** key.

Enter: 2.738 **2nd** **10ˣ** *547.0159629*

• find natural logarithms of numbers (Lesson 10–5)

Use a scientific calculator to find the natural logarithm of 56.4.

Use the **LN** key.

Enter: 56.4 **LN** *4.032469158*

Use a scientific calculator to find the natural antilogarithm of 2.738.

Use the **eˣ** key.

Enter: 2.738 **2nd** **eˣ** *15.45604208*

REVIEW EXERCISES

Use $\log_9 7 \approx 0.8856$ and $\log_9 4 \approx 0.6309$ to evaluate each expression.

36. $\log_9 28$ **1.5165**
37. $\log_9 49$ **1.7712**
38. $\log_9 144$ **2.2618**
39. $\log_9 15.75$ **1.2547**

Solve each equation.

40. $\log_3 x - \log_3 4 = \log_3 12$ **48**
41. $\log_2 y = \frac{1}{3}\log_2 27$ **3**
42. $\log_5 7 + \frac{1}{2}\log_5 4 = \log_5 x$ **14**
43. $2\log_2 x - \log_2(x + 3) = 2$ **6**
44. $\log_7 m = \frac{1}{3}\log_7 64 + \frac{1}{2}\log_7 121$ **44**

Use a scientific calculator to find the logarithm for each number rounded to four decimal places.

45. 46.56   **1.6680**   46. 678.1   **2.8313**
47. 0.00468   **−2.3298**   48. 0.183   **−0.7375**

Use a scientific calculator to find the antilogarithm for each number rounded to four decimal places.

49. 2.75   **562.3413**   50. 1.999   **99.7700**
51. −0.567   **0.2710**   52. −3.47   **0.0003**

Use a scientific calculator to find each value rounded to four decimal places.

53. $\ln 2.3$ **0.8329**   54. $\ln 9.25$ **2.2246**
55. $\ln 50$ **3.9120**   56. $\ln 0.05$ **−2.9957**
57. antiln 1.9755   **7.2102**   58. antiln 2.246   **9.4499**
59. antiln −0.489   60. antiln −4.5   **0.0111**
    0.6132

Applications and Problem Solving Encourage students to work through the exercises in the Applications and Problem Solving section to strengthen their problem-solving skills.

| OBJECTIVES AND EXAMPLES | REVIEW EXERCISES |

● evaluate expressions involving logarithms with different bases   (Lesson 10–6)

Approximate the value of $\log_8 72$ to three decimal places.

$$\log_a n = \frac{\log_b n}{\log_b a}$$

$$\log_8 72 = \frac{\log 72}{\log 8}$$

$$= \frac{1.8573}{0.9031}$$

$$\approx 2.057$$

Approximate the value of each logarithm to three decimal places.

61. $\log_5 15$ **1.683**

62. $\log_4 100$ **3.322**

63. $\log_{12} 15$ **1.090**

64. $\log_2 36$ **5.170**

65. $\log_9 108$ **2.131**

66. $\log_{11} 104$ **1.937**

● solve equations with variable exponents by using logarithms   (Lesson 10–6)

Solve $3^{x-4} = 5^{x-1}$.

$$3^{x-4} = 5^{x-1}$$

$$\log 3^{x-4} = \log 5^{x-1}$$

$$(x-4)\log 3 = (x-1)\log 5$$

$$x \log 3 - 4 \log 3 = x \log 5 - \log 5$$

$$x \log 3 - x \log 5 = 4 \log 3 - \log 5$$

$$x (\log 3 - \log 5) = 4 \log 3 - \log 5$$

$$x = \frac{4 \log 3 - \log 5}{\log 3 - \log 5}$$

$$x \approx -5.4520$$

Use logarithms to solve each equation.

67. $2^x = 53$ **5.7286**

68. $\log_4 11.2 = x$ **1.7427**

69. $2.3^{x^2} = 66.6$ **±2.2452**

70. $3^{4x-7} = 4^{2x+3}$ **7.3059**

71. $6^{3y} = 8^{y-3}$ **−1.8928**

72. $x = \log_{20} 1000$ **2.3059**

73. $12^{x-4} = 4^{2-x}$ **3.2838**

74. $2.1^{x-5} = 9.32$ **8.0086**

APPLICATIONS AND PROBLEM SOLVING

75. **Atmospheric Pressure**   Atmosphere pressure can be determined by using the equation $P = 14.7(10)^{-0.02h}$, where P is the atmospheric pressure in pounds per square inch and h is the altitude above sea level in miles. Find the atmospheric pressure at an altitude of 3 miles above sea level.   (Lesson 10–1)   **about 12.8 psi**

76. **Finance**   Mr. and Mrs. Grauser invested $500 at 6.5% compounded continuously.   (Lesson 10–5)

   a. Find the value of the investment after 7 years.   **$788.09**

   b. When will the Grausers' investment triple?   **76b. 16.9 years**

77. **Biology**   For a certain strain of bacteria, k is 0.872 when t is measured in days. How long will it take 9 bacteria to increase to 738 bacteria?   (Lesson 10–7)   **5.05 days**

78. **Chemistry**   Radium-226 decomposes radioactively. Its half-life, the time it takes for half of the sample to decompose, is 1800 years. Find the constant k in the decay formula for this compound.   (Lesson 10–7)   **about −0.000385**

A practice test for Chapter 10 is provided on page 921.

ALTERNATIVE ASSESSMENT

COOPERATIVE LEARNING PROJECT

Buying a House   Exponential equations in the form of formulas enable people to make major financial decisions.

In this project, you will develop a report for a married couple that is buying their first house. Jenna and Jarod had a meeting with a mortgage banker. He told them that the rule of thumb for borrowing money for a mortgage is that their monthly payment should be no more than 28% of their gross monthly income. Jenna makes $35,000 a year as a nurse, and Jarod makes $25,000 a year as a teacher. They are thinking about waiting at least three more years to start a family. At that time, Jenna hopes to take a year off work and then resume her work part-time.

Use the monthly payment formula

$$MP = P\left[\frac{\frac{r}{12}\left(1 + \frac{r}{12}\right)^{12T}}{\left(1 + \frac{r}{12}\right)^{12T-1}}\right], \text{ where } P = \text{amount of}$$

mortgage, r = interest rate, and T = term of mortgage in years, to write a report for Jenna and Jarod about whether to use a 15-year or 30-year mortgage and how much they should plan on borrowing, after putting 20% down, based on their salaries, jobs, future plans, and term of the mortgage.

Consider these ideas while accomplishing your task.

- Calculate how much their monthly payment should be based on the rule of thumb and their circumstances.
- Analyze what calculations will be needed.

- Prepare a spreadsheet or chart to organize the various calculations.
- Determine the price range of a house for them considering a 15-year mortgage.
- Determine the price range of a house for them considering a 30-year mortgage.
- Write a report explaining all of their options.
- Give a recommendation and explain why.

THINKING CRITICALLY

- Show algebraically and graphically that $f(x) = \log_b x$ and $g(x) = b^x$ are inverse functions.
- On some calculators, $\log x$ and 10^x are on the same key position. Why is this? Give examples of other functions that share this relationship.

PORTFOLIO

Evaluating what you don't understand about a concept is important in achieving a comprehensive understanding of that subject. Think about the concept you found most difficult to understand in this chapter. Write about why you found that concept difficult to understand and explain how you managed to understand it. What methods did you use in order to gain understanding and did they work? Place this in your portfolio.

SELF EVALUATION

When searching for an error, you can use three categories to organize your search. These categories are misunderstanding, misapplied strategy, and miscalculation. When misunderstanding is the cause for the error, it is due to a failure to comprehend the overall concept of the problem. When a misapplied strategy is the cause for the error, it comes from using the wrong format. When miscalculation is the cause for the error, it is due to errors in calculating or checking.

Assess yourself. Do you categorize your errors? When looking for the reason for an error, do you go through a checklist to determine the error or do you randomly search for the problem? Give three error categories that could be used in your daily life and explain what each one means.

Assessment and Evaluation Masters, pp. 266, 277

10   NAME_____   DATE_____

Chapter 10 Performance Assessment

Instructions: Demonstrate your knowledge by giving a clear, concise solution to each problem. Be sure to include all relevant drawings and justify your answers. You may show your solution in more than one way or investigate beyond the requirements of the problem.

1. According to a commonly used rule, the Rule of 72, an estimation of the number of years it will take to double an investment invested at $n\%$ is given by $72 \div n$.

   a. Estimate the number of years it would require for $4000 invested at 8% to be worth $8000.

   b. Find the number of years it would take for a savings account of $4000 to double if invested at 8% compounded annually.

   c. How long will it take a $4000 savings account to double when invested at 8% compounded continuously?

   d. Is the Rule of 72 a better estimate for the time required to double an investment deposited at a fixed rate when compounded annually or continuously?

   e. Find a more accurate rule for estimating the time required to double money invested at a constant rate compounded continuously.

2. a. Explain the meaning of x in the equation $\log_2 65 = x$.

   b. Estimate the value of x in part a. Justify your answer.

   c. Solve the equation $\log_3 (x - 2) + \log_3 (2x + 1) = 1$. Show your work and justify each step.

Scoring Guide
Chapter 10
Performance Assessment

Level	Specific Criteria
3 Superior	• Shows thorough understanding of the concepts *solving equations involving logarithmic and exponential functions* and *using estimation to solve problems*. • Uses appropriate strategies to solve problems. • Computations are correct. • Written explanations are exemplary. • Goes beyond requirements of problem.
2 Satisfactory, with Minor Flaws	• Shows understanding of the concepts *solving equations involving logarithmic and exponential functions* and *using estimation to solve problems*. • Uses appropriate strategies to solve problems. • Computations are mostly correct. • Written explanations are effective. • Satisfies all requirements of problem.
1 Nearly Satisfactory, with Serious Flaws	• Shows understanding of most of the concepts *solving equations involving logarithmic and exponential functions* and *using estimation to solve problems*. • May not use appropriate strategies to solve problems. • Computations are mostly correct. • Written explanations are satisfactory. • Satisfies most requirements of problem.
0 Unsatisfactory	• Shows little or no understanding of the concepts *solving equations involving logarithmic and exponential functions* and *using estimation to solve problems*. • May not use appropriate strategies to solve problems. • Computations are incorrect. • Written explanations are not satisfactory. • Does not satisfy requirements of problem.

 **Alternative Assessment**

The Alternative Assessment section provides students with the opportunity to assess their own work by thinking critically, working with others, keeping a portfolio, and honestly evaluating their own progress. For more information on alternative forms of assessment, see *Alternative Assessment in the Mathematics*

Classroom, one of the titles in the Glencoe Mathematics Professional Series.

 **Performance Assessment**

Performance Assessment tasks for this chapter are included in the *Assessment and Evaluation Masters.* A scoring guide is also provided.

Using the COLLEGE ENTRANCE EXAM PRACTICE

These two pages review the skills and concepts presented in Chapters 1–10. This review is formatted to reflect new trends in college entrance testing.

A more traditional cumulative review, shown below, is provided in the *Assessment and Evaluation Masters*, pp. 271–272.

Assessment and Evaluation Masters, pp. 271–272

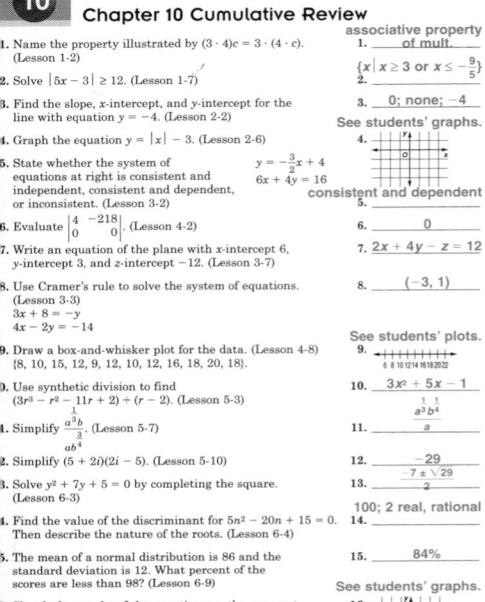

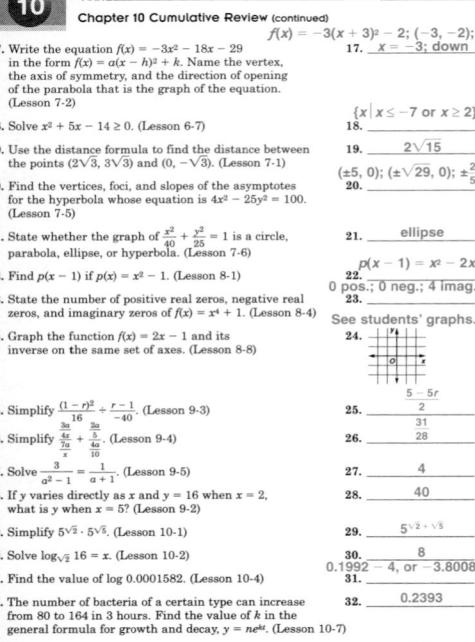

COLLEGE ENTRANCE EXAM PRACTICE

CHAPTERS 1–10

SECTION ONE: MULTIPLE CHOICE

There are eight multiple-choice questions in this section. After working each problem, write the letter of the correct answer on your paper.

1. Which is a quadratic equation? **C**

  A. $x^3 + 2x + 3 = 0$

  B. $3x - 7 = 0$

  C. $2x^2 - 9x + 7 = 0$

  D. $5x^2 + 3xy - 1 = 0$

2. Geometry A mathematics professor called the hardware store to order fencing to outline his pentagon-shaped garden. He gave the store manager the measures of each side as $\frac{1}{x}$, $\frac{2}{x-2}$, $\frac{3}{x}$, $\frac{4}{x-2}$, and $\frac{x}{x-2}$. The manager panicked until he found an algebra student to help him out. What was the perimeter of the professor's garden? **B**

  A. $\frac{9+x}{x(x-2)}$ **B.** $\frac{x^2 + 10x - 8}{x(x-2)}$

  C. $\frac{x^2 + 9x - 6}{x}$ **D.** $\frac{x+2}{x-2}$

3. Find the second row of **C**
$$\begin{bmatrix} 0 & 9 \\ 4 & 3 \\ -2 & 7 \end{bmatrix} \cdot \begin{bmatrix} 2 & -1 & -2 \\ 0 & 8 & -5 \end{bmatrix}.$$

  A. $[0 \;\; 72 \;\; -45]$ **B.** $[-4 \;\; 58 \;\; -31]$

  C. $[8 \;\; 20 \;\; -23]$ **D.** $[72 \;\; 20 \;\; 58]$

4. Geometry Find the area of the figure below. **B**

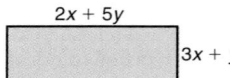

  A. $(5x^2 + 10xy + 5y^2)$ square units

  B. $(6x^2 + 17xy + 5y^2)$ square units

  C. $(21x^2y^2)$ square units

  D. $(11x^2 + 17xy + y^2)$ square units

5. Sally's office has a system to let people know when the department will have a meeting. Sally calls three people, then those three people each call three other people, and so on, until the whole department is notified. If it takes 10 minutes for a person to call three people and the whole department is notified within 30 minutes, how many people will be notified in the last round? **D**

  A. 3 people   **B.** 30 people

  C. 9 people   **D.** 27 people

6. Choose the graph of $\frac{x^2}{25} + \frac{y^2}{16} = 1$. **B**

  A. 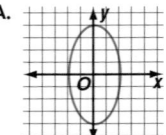   **B.**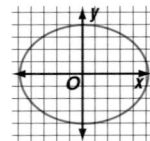

  C. 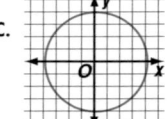   **D.**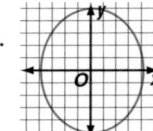

7. In planning a trip, the distance you travel varies jointly as the time and rate of speed. LaDonna Metcalf must travel 396 miles in 8 hours to meet a client. She travels 6 hours at 55 mph. She stops for a half an hour to rest and eat lunch. What is the minimum speed at which she must travel to meet her appointment? **C**

  A. 66 mph   **B.** 99 mph

  C. 44 mph   **D.** 50 mph

8. Geometry The perimeter of Mr. Baxter's back yard is 152 feet. He plans to use wood fencing along one length of the yard, and wire fencing along the other three boundaries. If the length exceeds twice the width by 7 feet, how much wood fencing will Mr. Baxter require? **A**

  A. 53 feet   **B.** 23 feet

  C. 99 feet   **D.** 138 feet

Standardized Test Practice Questions are also provided in the *Assessment and Evaluation Masters*, p. 270.

SECTION TWO: SHORT ANSWER

This section contains ten questions for which you will provide short answers. Write your answer on your paper.

9. Show that $\log_3 27 + \log_3 3 = \log_3 81$.

$$3 + 1 = 4$$

10. The graphs of $2y + x = 6$ and $y = 2x + 3$ contain two sides of a rectangle. If one vertex of the rectangle has coordinates $(8, 4)$, draw the rectangle. **See Solutions Manual.**

11. Solve $6t^2 + 28t - 10 = 0$. Then find the sum and product of the roots to check the solution.

$$-5, \frac{1}{3}; -\frac{14}{3}, -\frac{5}{3}$$

12. After conducting a survey on raising taxes for schools in Northridge, a statistician said the number of women in favor of the tax levy could be expressed by $\dfrac{3 + 10t^2 - 17t}{5t^2 + 4t - 1}$. The number of men in favor of the levy can be expressed by $\dfrac{4t^2 - 9}{3 + 5t + 2t^2}$. Find the ratio of women to men in simplest form. **1**

13. Graph the system of equations below and state its solution and the type of system it represents (consistent and independent, consistent and dependent, or inconsistent).

$$2x - 7 = 3y$$
$$x - y = 5 \qquad \textbf{(8, 3); consistent, independent}$$

14. Physics The formula for finding centripetal force F_c, the inward force that must be applied to keep an object moving in a circle, is $F_c = \dfrac{mv^2}{r}$. In this equation, m represents the mass of the object, v represents the velocity, and r represents the radius of the circular path. Solve the formula for the velocity and write the result in simplified form.

$$v = \frac{\sqrt{F_c rm}}{m}$$

15. Find the value of the discriminant of the equation $2x^2 + x - 3 = 0$ and then describe the nature of its roots. **25; 2 rational roots**

16. Solve the system of equations.
$$3x + 4y = -7$$
$$2x + y = -3 \qquad \textbf{(–1, –1)}$$

17. Luis' grandfather invested $150 at 5% interest compounded quarterly. When the account was recently given to Luis, it contained $6230. How long ago did Luis' grandfather invest the $150? **75 years ago**

18. Solve $\log_4 (x + 3) + \log_4 (x - 3) = 2$. **5**

SECTION THREE: COMPARISON

This section contains five comparison problems which involve comparing two quantities, one in column A and one in column B. In certain questions, information related to one or both quantities is centered above them. All variables used represent real numbers.

Compare quantities A and B below.

- Write A if quantity A is greater.
- Write B if quantity B is greater.
- Write C if the two quantities are equal.
- Write D if there is not enough information to determine the relationship.

19. D   **20.** B   **21.** C   **22.** A   **23.** B

Column A	Column B
$x^2 = 100$ $y^2 = 36$	
19. x	y
20. antiln 0.288	x, if $2000 = 5^{0.045x}$
$f(x) = x + 4$ $g(x) = x + 9$	
21. $f[g(x)]$	$g[f(x)]$
22. $\dfrac{1}{3}$	$\dfrac{1}{3\sqrt{3}}$
23. y, if $\dfrac{2y - 5}{6} - \dfrac{y - 5}{4} = \dfrac{3}{4}$	x, if $\dfrac{x - 4}{x - 2} = \dfrac{x - 2}{x + 2} + \dfrac{1}{x - 2}$

11

Investigating Sequences and Series

PREVIEWING THE CHAPTER

This chapter begins with arithmetic sequences and presents a formula for a general *n*th term of a sequence. Arithmetic series are defined, and students find sums and specific terms in an arithmetic series. Geometric sequences and series are introduced in a similar manner. Then students study infinite geometric series and use a formula to find their sums. Students look for a pattern in a series of numbers to find the next number and other numbers in sequences and series. Students apply this knowledge to investigate special sequences and fractals and to iterate functions. The chapter concludes with the binomial theorem. Students expand powers of binomials using Pascal's triangle as well as the theorem and find specific terms of the binomial expansion.

Lesson (Pages)	Lesson Objectives	NCTM Standards	State/Local Objectives
11-1A (646–647)	Use a graphing calculator to investigate sequences.	1–5, 12	1.b.
11-1 (648–655)	Find the next term in a sequence by looking for a pattern. Find the *n*th term of an arithmetic sequence. Find the position of a given term in an arithmetic sequence. Find arithmetic means.	1–5, 8, 12	1.a.
11-2 (656–661)	Find sums of arithmetic series. Find specific terms in an arithmetic series. Use sigma notation to express sums.	1–5, 12	
11-3 (662–669)	Find the *n*th term of a geometric sequence. Find the position of a given term in a geometric sequence. Find geometric means.	1–5, 8, 12	1.b., 11.e.
11-4 (670–675)	Find sums of geometric series. Find specific terms in a geometric series. Use sigma notation to express sums.	1–5, 12	
11-5 (676–682)	Find sums of infinite geometric series.	1–5, 8, 12–13	
11-6 (683–687)	Recognize and use special sequences. Iterate functions.	1–6, 12	
11-7 (688–694)	Define and draw fractals. Write a recursive formula for the perimeter or area of a fractal.	1–5, 7, 12–13	
11-8 (695–701)	Expand powers of binomials by using Pascal's triangle and the binomial theorem. Find specific terms of binomial expansions.	1–5, 11–12	

A complete, 1-page lesson plan is provided for each lesson in the *Lesson Planning Guide*. Answer keys for each lesson are available in the *Answer Key Masters.*

You may want to refer to the **Course Planning Calendar** on page T12 for detailed information on pacing.
PACING: Standard—14 days; **Honors**—11 days; **Block**—7 days

LESSON PLANNING CHART

| Lesson (Pages) | Materials/ Manipulatives | Extra Practice (Student Edition) | BLACKLINE MASTERS | | | | | | | | | Real-World Applications | Interactive Mathematics Tools Software | Teaching Transparencies |
			Study Guide	Practice	Enrichment	Assessment and Evaluation	Modeling Mathematics	Multicultural Activity	Tech Prep Applications	Graphing Calculator	Science and Math Lab Manual			
11-1A (646–647)	graphing calculator									pp. 55, 56				
11-1 (648–655)	isometric dot paper graphing calculator	p. 901	p. 76	p. 76	p. 76		p. 71	p. 21		p. 11		29	11-1	11-1A 11-1B
11-2 (656–661)	graphing calculator	p. 901	p. 77	p. 77	p. 77	p. 296					pp.105 –110			11-2A 11-2B
11-3 (662–669)	graphing calculator	p. 901	p. 78	p. 78	p. 78				p. 21				11-3	11-3A 11-3B
11-4 (670–675)	ruler* colored pencils graphing calculator	p. 902	p. 79	p. 79	p. 79	pp. 295, 296			p. 22	p. 22				11-4A 11-4B
11-5 (676–682)		p. 902	p. 80	p. 80	p. 80									11-5A 11-5B
11-6 (683–687)	penny, nickel, and dime	p. 902	p. 81	p. 81	p. 81	p. 297								11-6A 11-6B
11-7 (688–694)	isometric dot paper graphing calculator	p. 903	p. 82	p. 82	p. 82									11-7A 11-7B
11-8 (695–701)	graphing calculator	p. 903	p. 83	p. 83	p. 83	p. 297						30	11-8.1 11-8.2	11-8A 11-8B
Study Guide/ Assessment (703–707)						pp. 281 –294, 298 –300								

*Included in Glencoe's Student Manipulative Kit and Overhead Manipulative Resources.

ORGANIZING THE CHAPTER

OTHER CHAPTER RESOURCES

Student Edition
Chapter Opener, pp. 644–645
Mathematics and Society, p. 694
Working on the Investigation,
   pp. 655, 682
Closing the Investigation, p. 702

Teacher's Classroom Resources
Investigations and Projects Masters,
   pp. 65–68

Technology
Teacher's Guide for Software
   Resources
Test and Review Software (IBM
   and Macintosh)
CD-ROM Interactions (Windows
   and Macintosh)

Professional Publications
Block Scheduling Booklet
Glencoe Mathematics Professional
   Series

OUTSIDE RESOURCES

Books/Periodicals
Gleick, James, *Chaos: Making a New Science*,
   Viking Penguin

Software
Exploring Chaos, Apple II, MECC

Videos/CD-ROMs
Nothing but Zooms, Art Matrix

See the *Teacher's Guide for Software Resources* for software addresses.

ASSESSMENT RESOURCES

Student Edition
Math Journal, pp. 666, 680
Mixed Review, pp. 654, 661,
   669, 675, 681, 687, 694, 701
Self Test, p. 675
Chapter Highlights, p. 703
Chapter Study Guide and
   Assessment, pp. 704–706
Alternative Assessment, p. 707
   Portfolio, p. 707

College Entrance Exam Practice,
   pp. 708–709

Teacher's Wraparound Edition
5-Minute Check, pp. 648, 656,
   662, 670, 676, 683, 688, 695
Check for Understanding, pp. 651,
   659, 666, 673, 679, 686, 692,
   699
Closing Activity, pp. 655, 661,
   669, 675, 682, 687, 694, 701
Cooperative Learning, pp. 663, 671

Assessment and Evaluation Masters
Multiple-Choice Tests, Forms 1A
   (Honors), 1B (Average), 1C
   (Basic), pp. 281–286
Free-Response Tests, Forms 2A
   (Honors), 2B (Average), 2C
   (Basic), pp. 287–292
Calculator-Based Test, p. 293
Performance Assessment, p. 294
Mid-Chapter Test, p. 295
Quizzes A–D, pp. 296–297
Standardized Test Practice, p. 298
Cumulative Review, pp. 299–300

ENHANCING THE CHAPTER

Examples of some of the materials for enhancing Chapter 11 are shown below.

DIVERSITY

Multicultural Activity Masters, pp. 21, 22

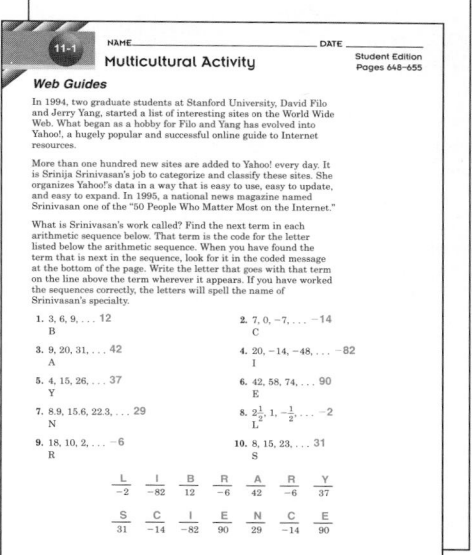

APPLICATIONS

Real-World Applications, 29, 30

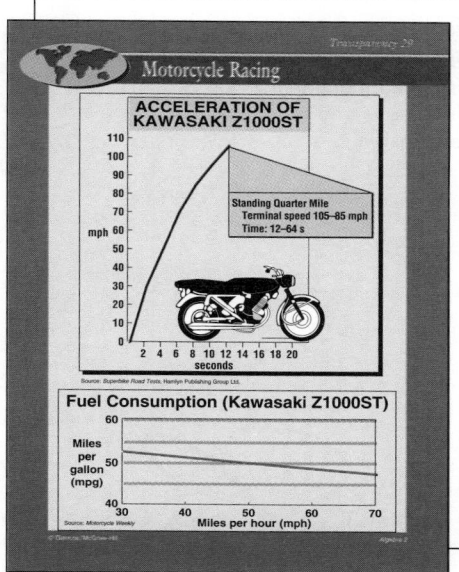

TECHNOLOGY

Graphing Calculator Masters, p. 11

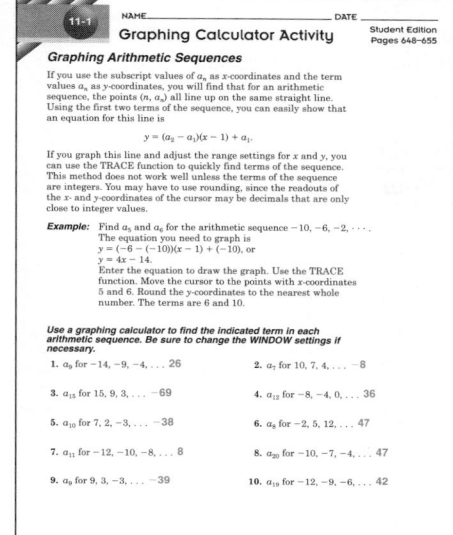

TECH PREP

Tech Prep Applications Masters, pp. 21, 22

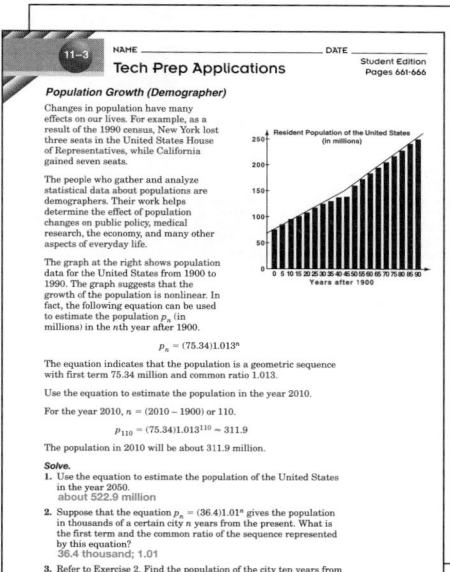

CONNECTIONS

Science and Math Lab Manual, pp. 105–110

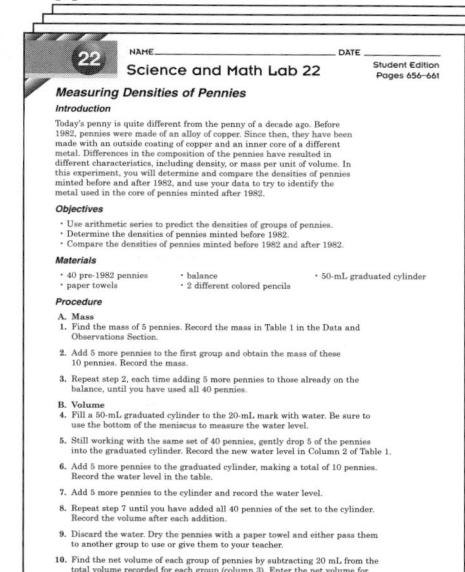

PROBLEM SOLVING

Problem of the Week Cards, 27, 28, 29

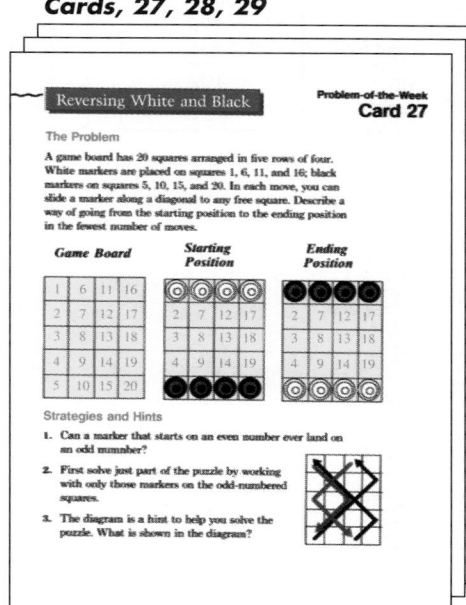

MAKING MATHEMATICS RELEVANT

This two-page introduction to the chapter provides students with an opportunity to explore contemporary topics and their applications to mathematics.

Background Information

SAT Scores In the table below are the steadily declining SAT verbal scores from 1971 through 1994. It might be valuable to research the verbal SAT scores for your own school and state. Generate a discussion in class about the possible causes for this decline.

Average Verbal SAT Scores	
Year	**Score**
1971	455
1972	453
1973	446
1974	444
1975	434
1976	431
1977	429
1978	429
1979	427
1980	424
1981	424
1982	426
1983	425
1984	426
1985	431
1986	431
1987	430
1988	428
1989	427
1990	424
1991	422
1992	423
1993	424
1994	423

Investigating Sequences and Series

Objectives

In this chapter, you will:

- find the next number in a sequence by looking for a pattern,
- find terms in arithmetic and geometric sequences,
- find sums of arithmetic and geometric series, and
- use the binomial theorem to find terms of a binomial expansion.

Newspaper Circulation Declines

Percent change since March 31, 1994		Six months circulation ended March 31, 1995
−7.03%	Newsday	669,739
−5.18%	San Francisco Chronicle	499,526
−5.00%	New York Daily News	725,599
−4.34%	Chicago Sun-Times	500,969
−4.18%	Los Angeles Times	1,058,498
−3.39%	Detroit Free Press	531,825
−2.83%	Newark Star-Ledger	450,316
−2.29%	Miami Herald	397,943
−1.38%	New York Times	1,170,869
−0.87%	Chicago Tribune	691,283
−0.55%	Houston Chronicle	413,717

Source: Audit Bureau of Circulations

In 1993, the U.S. Department of Education organized the most comprehensive study of literacy ever done of Americans. The results were shocking, indicating that half of all adults have serious deficiencies in their ability to function and make practical use of the basic skills of reading, writing, and arithmetic.

TIME *Line*

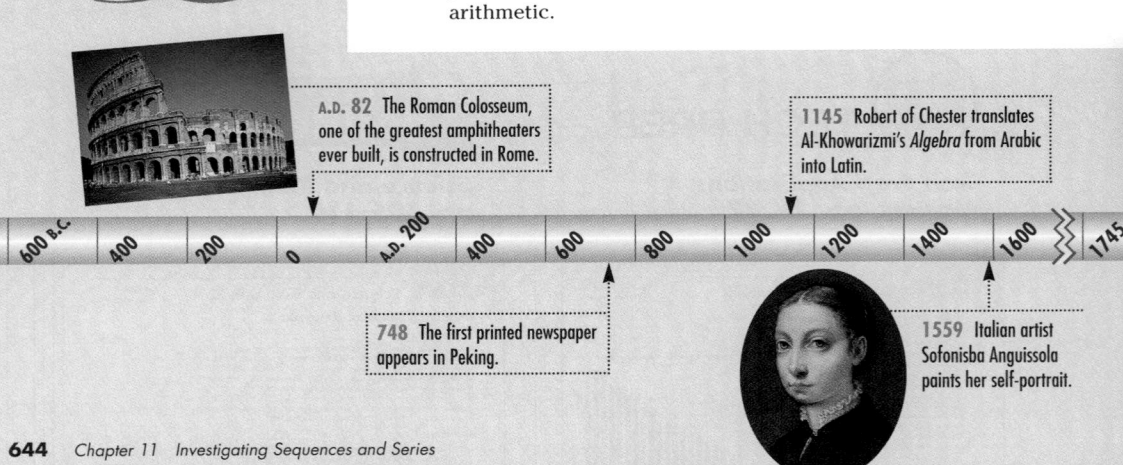

A.D. 82 The Roman Colosseum, one of the greatest amphitheaters ever built, is constructed in Rome.

1145 Robert of Chester translates Al-Khowarizmi's *Algebra* from Arabic into Latin.

748 The first printed newspaper appears in Peking.

1559 Italian artist Sofonisba Anguissola paints her self-portrait.

TIME *Line*

Students might find it interesting to write a report on the Al-Khowarizmi's early work on algebra. A Persian mathematician, he was a scholar of varied talents and interests.

*inter*NET CONNECTION

Check out the National Education Goals that we hope to attain by the year 2000. Explore further for challenges we face and ways to overcome them.

World Wide Web
http://www.ed.gov/pubs/
PrisonersOfTime/Goals.html

Chapter Project

In small groups, research different volunteer programs in your community that help promote literacy and an appreciation for reading. There may be programs at the library, at colleges or universities in your area, or sponsored by youth groups. Develop a volunteer project or club at your school that would encourage learning in various age groups such as senior citizens or children in elementary school. Make an outline listing the types of services that you could provide to encourage literacy and write a report that includes the time, materials, such as books and magazines, and volunteers needed for the project.

One method of combating America's literacy problem is to demonstrate a passion for reading. **Lynnea Fajardo,** a student at Red Mountain High School in Mesa, Arizona, is a literacy volunteer. She is president of her school's RIF (Reading Is Fundamental) Club, and volunteers her free time promoting literacy by distributing free books to students, libraries, hospitals, and other locations in her community. The RIF Club participates in reading projects, creates open reading corners, and with a program called Reading Buddies, is spreading the love of books to elementary students.

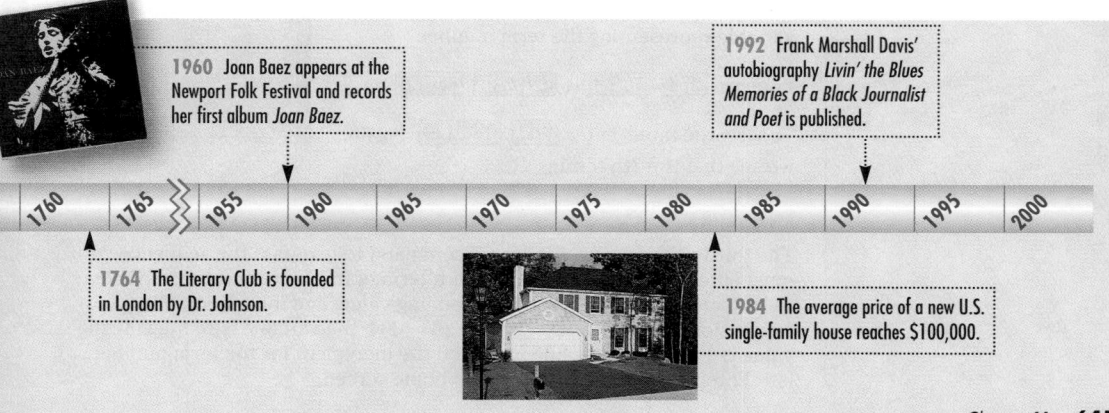

1960 Joan Baez appears at the Newport Folk Festival and records her first album *Joan Baez*.

1992 Frank Marshall Davis' autobiography *Livin' the Blues Memories of a Black Journalist and Poet* is published.

1764 The Literary Club is founded in London by Dr. Johnson.

1984 The average price of a new U.S. single-family house reaches $100,000.

1760 1765 1955 1960 1965 1970 1975 1980 1985 1990 1995 2000

Chapter 11 **645**

Alternative Chapter Projects

Two other chapter projects are included in the *Investigations and Projects Masters.* In Chapter 11 Project A, pp. 65–66, students extend the topic in the chapter opener. In Chapter 11 Project B, pp. 67–68, students prepare a consumer's guide on over-the-counter medications.

RIF was recognized by President George Bush as his 432nd Point of Light. More than 600 students have participated in Read-A-Thons organized by RIF, and more than 40,000 books have been distributed by libraries, hospitals, and other community organizations.

Chapter Project

Cooperative Learning Each member of the research team can investigate a different volunteer program. Have them compare the results when they return. What group does each program target? What kind of people volunteer for each service? What methods do they use?

Investigations and Projects Masters, p. 65

11 NAME _____ DATE _____
Chapter 11 Project A Student Edition Pages 646–702

Learning and Earning

1. How many of today's students like to read in their spare time? For this project, you will work with a partner to survey at least 25 randomly selected students about their reading habits. You can either ask your survey questions directly or hand out copies of questionnaires for students to complete. Here are some ideas for questions you might want to ask.

   • How do you like reading? (Give five possible answers ranging from "Very much" to "Not at all.")

   • Outside of school, what kinds of materials do you read? (Provide several suggestions, such as magazines, novels, and newspapers.)

   • Do you read in the summer and during vacations?

2. Some organizations encourage young people to read by paying them for each book they finish. Find out more about reading-for-payment programs, including the reasons for starting them and the amounts students can earn. If necessary, ask the librarian at your school or public library to help you search newspapers and magazines for this information.

3. Interview teachers and parents to find out how they feel about paying young people to read. Determine the percentages of adults who approve and disapprove of such programs.

4. Make charts and graphs to organize and explain the data you collected in exercises 1, 2, and 3.

5. Write an article for your community or school newspaper that summarizes the results of your survey and interviews. Include the charts and graphs you created. Explain how arithmetic sequences can be used to find out how much money a student could make by reading the nth book in a sample reading-for-payment program.

NCTM Standards: 1–5, 12

Objective
Use a graphing calculator to investigate sequences.

Recommended Time
25 minutes

Instructional Resources
Graphing Calculator Masters, pp. 55 and 56

These masters provide keystroking instruction for this lesson for the TI-81 and Casio graphing calculators.

1 FOCUS

Motivating the Lesson
Graphing calculators can be used to investigate sequences. They can be used with either numerical or graphical techniques.

2 TEACH

Teaching Tip Many types of calculators allow students to quickly generate arithmetic sequences. This saves the students tedious computational work.

Teaching Tip Most scientific calculators display only one term of a sequence at a time, while graphing calculators typically display quite a few terms at a time, in table format.

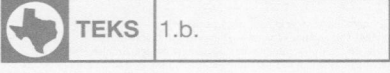
TEKS | 1.b.

11–1A Graphing Technology
Arithmetic Sequences
A Preview of Lesson 11–1

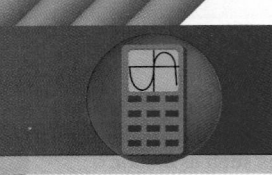

Graphing calculators have several features that allow us to investigate sequences. Both numerical and graphical techniques can be used. In Example 1, numerical techniques are used to find the desired term.

Example **1** **Find the 5th term of the arithmetic sequence 17, 21, 25, ...**

Method 1
Begin by storing the first term of the sequence as x.

Enter: 17 [STO▶] [X,T,θ] [ENTER]

Now, to generate the second term, store $17 + 4$ as x.

Enter: [X,T,θ] [+] 4 [STO▶] [X,T,θ]
[ENTER]

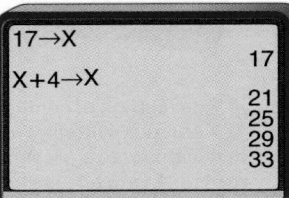

Continue to press [ENTER] to generate successive terms of the sequence.

Remember, whatever the current value for x, [ENTER] computes $x + 4$. The 5th term is 33.

Method 2
First determine the formula for the nth term of the sequence. Then use the table feature of the calculator to generate values. The first term of the sequence is 17, and the common difference is 4. So the formula for the nth term is $a_n = 17 + (n - 1)4$.

Enter this formula into the calculator as $Y_1 = 17 + (x - 1)4$.

Enter: [Y=] 17 [+] [(] [X,T,θ] [−] 1 [)] 4

Now set up the table with the independent variable representing the term number.

Enter: [2nd] [TblSet] 1 [ENTER] 1 [ENTER]

To view the table, enter [2nd] [TABLE]. Again, we see that the 7th term is 41.

X	Y₁
1	17
2	21
3	25
4	29
5	33
6	37
7	41
X=1	

Method 3
The third method uses the "seq(" command to generate the sequence. You must enter the expression for the nth term of the sequence, the variable to be incremented, starting value, ending value, and increment. The expression for the nth term is $17 + (N - 1)4$, the variable is N, the starting value is 1, the ending value is 10, and the increment for the term number is 1. Enter the information from the home screen.

You will learn how to find the formula for sequences in Lessons 11–1 and 11–3.

646 *Chapter 11 Investigating Sequences and Series*

Enter: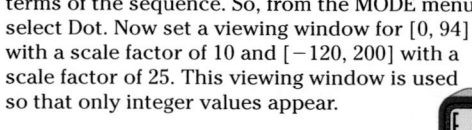

The calculator generates a list of values for the first 10 terms of the sequence.

Use the right arrow key to see the first seven terms. The seventh term is 41.

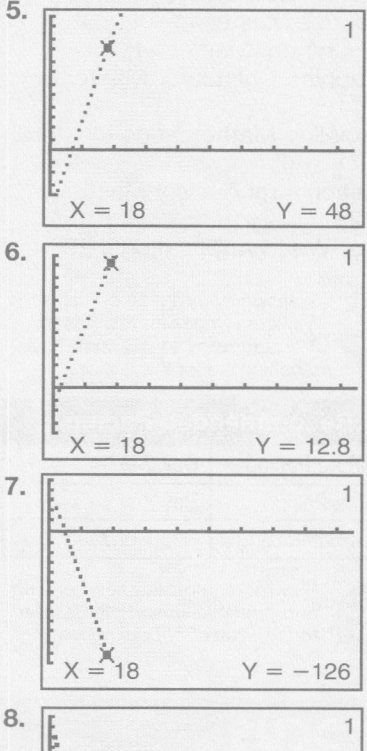

You can use a graphing calculator to generate the graph of a sequence. The graph will be a series of plotted points. The x-coordinates represent the term numbers, and the y-coordinates represent the values of the terms. You can then find the terms of a sequence by using the graph.

Example ② **Use graphing to find the 5th and 25th terms of the sequence**
$-112, -101, -90, -79, ...$

Use the Edit option on the STAT menu feature to enter the term numbers 1, 2, 3, 4 into L1 and the value of the terms $-112, -101, -90, -79$ into L2.

We want to plot only those points that represent terms of the sequence. So, from the MODE menu, select Dot. Now set a viewing window for [0, 94] with a scale factor of 10 and [−120, 200] with a scale factor of 25. This viewing window is used so that only integer values appear.

> **TECHNOLOGY Tips**
>
> You can also graph the line containing the terms of an arithmetic sequence by entering the formula for the nth term as Y1 and then pressing GRAPH.

Enter: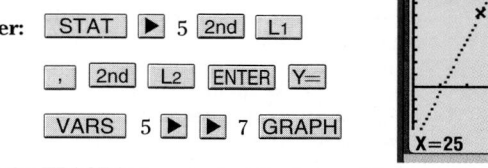

Use the TRACE feature to find the terms. The 5th term is −68, and the 25th term is 152.

EXERCISES

Find the 11th term of each sequence by using a numerical technique.

1. 47, 54, 61, 68, 75, 82, ...   **117**
2. 4.5, 3.75, 3, 2.25, 1.5, ...   **−3**
3. 2.132, 3.13, 4.128, 5.126, ...   **12.112**
4. −57, −59.5, −62, −64.5, −67, ...

Find the 18th term of each sequence by graphing.   **5–8. See margin for graphs.**

5. −20, −16, −12, −8, −4, ...   **48**
6. −0.8, 0, 0.8, 1.6, 2.4, ...   **12.8**
7. 27, 18, 9, 0, −9, ...   **−126**
8. $3, \frac{13}{5}, \frac{11}{5}, \frac{9}{5}, ...$ **−3.8**

9. Use a graphing calculator to find the missing terms in the sequence 148, 146.83, 145.66, _?_, _?_, _?_, 140.98.   **144.49, 143.32, 142.15**

10. 115 is the _?_ th term of the sequence 17, 20.5, 24, 27.5, ...   **29**

4. −82

Using Technology

This lesson offers an excellent opportunity for using technology in your algebra classroom. For more information on using technology, see *Graphing Calculators in the Mathematics Classroom,* one of the titles in the Glencoe Mathematics Professional Series.

3 PRACTICE/APPLY

Assignment Guide

Core: 1–10
Enriched: 1–10

Additional Answers

5.
6.
7.
8.

4 ASSESS

Observing students working with technology is an excellent method of assessment.

Instructional Resources

- Study Guide Master 11-1
- Practice Master 11-1
- Enrichment Master 11-1
- Graphing Calculator Masters, p. 11
- Modeling Mathematics Masters, p. 71
- Multicultural Activity Masters, p. 21
- Real-World Applications, 29

 Transparency 11-1A contains the 5-Minute Check for this lesson; **Transparency 11-1B** contains a teaching aid for this lesson.

Recommended Pacing	
Standard Pacing	Day 2 of 14
Honors Pacing	Day 2 of 11
Block Scheduling*	Day 1 of 7

 *For more information on pacing and possible lesson plans, refer to the *Block Scheduling Booklet.*

1 FOCUS

 5-Minute Check
(over Chapter 10)

1. Write $5^3 = 125$ in logarithmic form. $\log_5 125 = 3$
2. Solve $\log_2 (3x - 2) = \log_2 (2x + 6)$. $x = 8$
3. Solve $\log_7 (m - 5) = 1$. $m = 12$
4. Find the antilogarithm of $0.4409 - 2$. 0.0276
5. Solve $8^{x-2} = 5^x$ by using logarithms. 8.8486

 TEKS | 1.a.

11-1 Arithmetic Sequences

What YOU'LL LEARN

- To find the next term in a sequence by looking for a pattern,
- to find the *n*th term of an arithmetic sequence,
- to find the position of a given term in an arithmetic sequence, and
- to find arithmetic means.

Why IT'S IMPORTANT

You can use arithmetic sequences to solve problems involving antiques and broadcasting.

All Time Most Popular Commemorative Stamps
1. Elvis, 1993
2. Wildflowers, 1992
3. Rock and Roll, 1993
4. Moon Landing, 1994
5. Summer Olympics, 1992

APPLICATION
Broadcasting

In radio broadcasting, autumn is one of the most critical periods for ratings. Radio stations try to pull in as many listeners as they can by using a variety of gimmicks. In the fall of 1995, radio station WBNS 97.1 had a contest in which listeners had a chance to win $1000 every hour. In order to win, listeners needed to call in and correctly answer a contest question. The contest started with $1000, and $97 was added for the next caller each time the previous caller answered the question incorrectly. Suppose you were the 18th caller and the first to answer the question correctly. How much money would you win? *This problem will be solved in Example 3.*

We can use a table to show the amount of prize money available after each caller answers incorrectly.

Number of Callers	1	2	3	4	5	6	7	8
Prize Money	$1000	$1097	$1194	$1291	$1388	$1485	$1582	$1679

The graph shows the information from the table. This graph represents a *discrete* function. That is, the domain is made up of distinct values and there is no continuity between those values. The range is the set of numbers representing the amount of prize money. This set of numbers is an example of a **sequence.** Each number in a sequence is called a **term.** The first term is symbolized by a_1, the second term by a_2, and so on to a_n, the *n*th term. *What kind of figure would you have if the points on the graph were connected?*

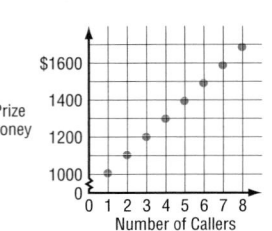

You can find the next term in a sequence by looking for a pattern. One way to do this is to find the difference of consecutive terms.

Example ① **PROBLEM SOLVING**
Look for a Pattern

The table at the right shows the cost of mailing letters first class in the U.S. in 1995. If the cost continues to increase at the same rate for each ounce, find how much it costs to mail letters that weigh 6, 7, and 8 ounces.

Weight Not Exceeding (ounces)	Cost
1	$0.32
2	0.55
3	0.78
4	1.01
5	1.24

Find the difference of consecutive terms.

0.32, 0.55, 0.78, 1.01, 1.24, ?, ?, ?, ...
     +0.23 +0.23 +0.23 +0.23 +0.23 +0.23 +0.23

The difference between each term is 0.23. The next three terms are $1.24 + 0.23$ or 1.47, $1.47 + 0.23$ or 1.70, and $1.70 + 0.23$ or 1.93. So, it costs $1.47, $1.70, and $1.93 to mail letters that weigh 6, 7, and 8 ounces, respectively.

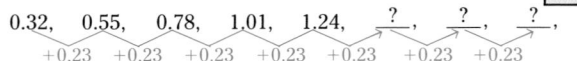

The first adhesive postage stamp went on sale on July 1, 1847. The use of postage stamps was not required by law until January 1, 1856.

The sequence shown in the table in Example 1 contains five terms. Therefore, $a_1 = 0.32$ and $a_5 = 1.24$. Each term of the sequence can be found by adding 0.23 to the previous term. A sequence of this type is called an **arithmetic sequence**. The number added to find the next term of an arithmetic sequence is called the **common difference** and is symbolized by the variable d.

Definition of Arithmetic Sequence	An arithmetic sequence is a sequence in which each term after the first is found by adding a constant, called the common difference d, to the previous term.

To find the next terms in a sequence that you know is arithmetic, you do not need to look for a pattern. Instead, find the common difference by subtracting any term from its succeeding term. Then add the common difference to the last term you are given to find successive terms.

Example **Find the next four terms of the arithmetic sequence 91, 83, 75, ...**

Find the common difference d by subtracting two consecutive terms.

$83 - 91 = -8$ and $75 - 83 = -8$ So, $d = -8$.

Now add -8 to the last term of the sequence, and then continue adding until the next four terms are found.

$$75 + (-8) = 67$$
$$67 + (-8) = 59$$
$$59 + (-8) = 51$$
$$51 + (-8) = 43$$

Therefore, the next four terms of the sequence are 67, 59, 51, and 43.

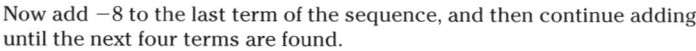

There is a pattern in the way terms of an arithmetic sequence are formed. It is possible to develop a formula that expresses each term of an arithmetic sequence in terms of the first term a_1 and the common difference d. Let's use the terms of the sequence in Example 2.

Sequence	numerical	91	83	75	67	...	
	symbols	a_1	a_2	a_3	a_4	...	a_n
Expressed in Terms of d and the First Term	numerical	$91 + 0(-8)$	$91 + 1(-8)$	$91 + 2(-8)$	$91 + 3(-8)$	...	$91 + (n-1)(-8)$
	symbols	$a_1 + 0 \cdot d$	$a_1 + 1 \cdot d$	$a_1 + 2 \cdot d$	$a_1 + 3 \cdot d$	...	$a_1 + (n-1)d$

The following formula generalizes this pattern for any sequence.

Formula for the nth Term of an Arithmetic Sequence	The nth term a_n of an arithmetic sequence with first term a_1 and common difference d is given by $$a_n = a_1 + (n-1)d,$$ where n is a positive integer.

Lesson 11–1 Arithmetic Sequences **649**

2 TEACH

In-Class Examples

For Example 1
Find the next four terms of each arithmetic sequence.

a. 26, 21, 16, ... **11, 6, 1, −4**
b. $\frac{1}{2}, 1\frac{1}{8}, 1\frac{3}{4}, ...$ $2\frac{3}{8}, 3, 3\frac{5}{8}, 4\frac{1}{4}$

For Example 2
Find the next four terms of each arithmetic sequence.

a. 34, 40, 46, ... **52, 58, 64, 70**
b. 62, 57, 52, ... **47, 42, 37, 32**

Teaching Tip Note that some sequences are infinite, such as this one, and some, such as that in the application, are not. The application sequence is limited by the speed limitations of the car and track.

GLENCOE *Technology*

Interactive Mathematics Tools Software

This multimedia software provides an interactive lesson in which students determine the next number in an arithmetic sequence. A **Computer Journal** gives students an opportunity to write about what they have learned.
For Windows & Macintosh

In-Class Examples

For Example 3
Suppose a race car driver increases her speed at a constant rate. What will her speed be after 20 seconds if her initial speed is 65 mph and her rate of acceleration is 4.8 mph? **156.2 mph**

For Example 4
a. Find the six arithmetic means between 12 and 47.
17, 22, 27, 32, 37, 42
b. Find the missing terms of the sequence __, 17, __, __, __, -7. **23, 11, 5, -1**

fabulous
FIRSTS

In 1906 Massachusetts was the location of the first known radio program in the United States. Regular broadcasts began in 1920.

Example  **3** Refer to the application at the beginning of the lesson. How much money would you win if you were the 18th caller and you answered the contest question correctly?

APPLICATION
Broadcasting

If $a_1 = 1000$ and $d = 97$, a_{18} represents the cash the 18th caller will win. So, $n = 18$.

Find a_{18} using $a_n = a_1 + (n - 1)d$.

$a_n = a_1 + (n - 1)d$

$a_{18} = 1000 + (18 - 1)97$ *Substitute the known values.*

$a_{18} = 1000 + 1649$ or 2649 *Simplify.*

If you were the 18th caller and you answered the question correctly, you would win $2649.

fabulous
FIRSTS

Jack L. Cooper (1889–   )

African-American radio pioneer Jack Cooper was the first to originate a community news broadcast about African Americans in Chicago during the 1920s. He was also the first to play popular African-American music.

Sometimes you may know two terms of a sequence, but they are not consecutive terms of that sequence. The terms between any two nonconsecutive terms of an arithmetic sequence are called **arithmetic means**. In the sequence below, 32, 41, and 50 are the three arithmetic means between 23 and 59.

$$14, 23, 32, 41, 50, 59, 68, 77$$

Example **4** a. Find the four arithmetic means between 18 and 78.
b. Graph the sequence using the *x*-axis for the number of the term and the *y*-axis for the term itself.

a. You can use the *n*th term formula to find the common difference. In the sequence 18, _?_ , _?_ , _?_ , _?_ , 78, 18 is a_1 and 78 is a_6.

$a_n = a_1 + (n - 1)d$

$a_6 = 18 + (6 - 1)d$ *$a_1 = 18$ and $n = 6$*

$78 = 18 + 5d$ *$a_6 = 78$*

$60 = 5d$ *Subtract 18 from each side.*

$12 = d$ *Divide each side by 5.*

Now use the value of *d* to find the four arithmetic means.

$18 + 12 = 30 \qquad 30 + 12 = 42 \qquad 42 + 12 = 54 \qquad 54 + 12 = 66$

The arithmetic means are 30, 42, 54, and 66.

b.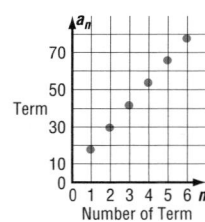

 Alternative Teaching Strategies

Student Diversity Have students list situations in which arithmetic sequences are used and write a sample sequence for each situation. For example, the sequence for money earned after each hour worked would be $4.25, $8.50, $12.75, ... if a person makes $4.25 per hour. The score for a team in a football game would be 0, 3, 6, 9, 12, ... if only field goals were scored.

You can write a linear equation for the nth term of an arithmetic sequence.

Example **5** **Write an equation for the nth term of the arithmetic sequence 6, 13, 20, 27, ...**

In this sequence, $a_1 = 6$ and $d = 7$. Use the nth term formula to write the equation.

$$a_n = a_1 + (n - 1)d$$
$$a_n = 6 + (n - 1)7 \quad \textit{Substitute the known values.}$$
$$a_n = 6 + 7n - 7$$
$$a_n = 7n - 1 \quad \textit{Simplify.}$$

The equation is $a_n = 7n - 1$. The graph of the line given by this equation contains the terms of the arithmetic sequence. *Compare the slope of the line described by this equation and the value of the common difference.*

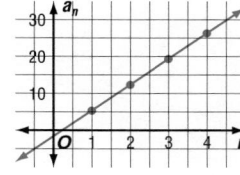

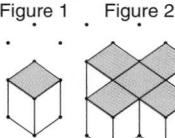 **MODELING**
MATHEMATICS

Arithmetic Sequences

Materials: isometric dot paper

Look at the figures below. The length of the side of each cube is 1 centimeter. Copy the figures on isometric dot paper. Be sure to draw correctly.

Figure 1   Figure 2   Figure 3

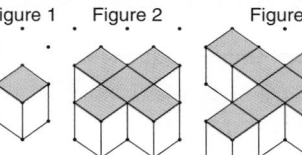

b. $1 \text{ cm}^3, 5 \text{ cm}^3, 9 \text{ cm}^3, 13 \text{ cm}^3$

Your Turn

a. Based on the pattern, draw Figure 4 on the dot paper. **See margin.**
b. Find the volumes of the four figures.
c. Suppose the number of cubes in the pattern continues. Write an equation to represent the volume of Figure n. $a_n = 4n - 3$
d. What would the volume of Figure 12 be? 45 cm^3

CHECK FOR UNDERSTANDING

Communicating Mathematics

2. No, 10.5 is not in the domain of this function.

3a. $-4, -2, 0, 2, 4$

3b. The domain is made up of distinct values.

3d. 2; The slope is the common difference of the sequence.

Study the lesson. Then complete the following.

1. **Explain** how to determine whether a list of numbers is an arithmetic sequence. **See margin.**

2. **Explain** whether 24 is a term in the sequence represented by $a_n = 5 + (n - 1)2$.

3. Refer to the graph of the arithmetic sequence at the right.
   a. Write the first five terms of the sequence.
   b. Explain why the points are not connected.
   c. What is the equation of the line that passes through these points? $a_n = 2n - 6$
   d. State the slope of the line in part c and explain how it relates to the nature of the sequence.

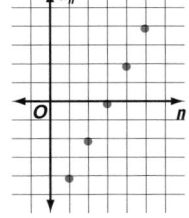

Lesson 11–1 Arithmetic Sequences **651**

Reteaching ▬▬▬▬

Using Alternative Methods Have students find either the arithmetic mean, the difference, or a missing term for various problems. Then, match the number that they find with its corresponding letter of the alphabet and find the "word" that it spells.

 MODELING
MATHEMATICS This modeling activity gives students a hands-on experience of repeating a process. The basic idea of a sequence is the repeating of a process.

Answer for Modeling Mathematics

a.

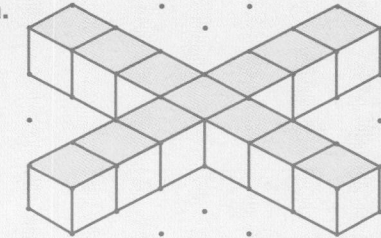

3 PRACTICE/APPLY

Check for Understanding
Exercises 1–15 are designed to help you assess your students' understanding through reading, writing, speaking, and modeling. You should work through Exercises 1–4 with your students and then monitor their work on Exercises 5–15.

Additional Answer

1. Consider three consecutive terms of the sequence and find whether the same number is added to each term to get the next.

For **Extra Practice,** see p. 901.

The red A, B, and C flags, printed only in the Teacher's Wraparound Edition, indicate the level of difficulty of the exercises.

Additional Answers

4. Janice is correct; $n = -16$ is not in the domain since it is not a positive integer.

13b.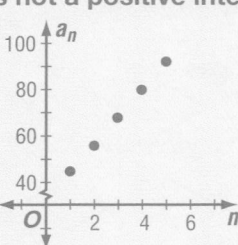

37.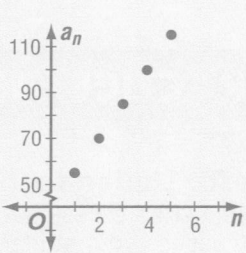

38.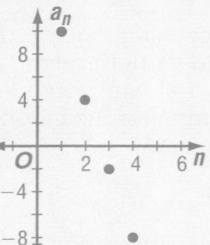

39.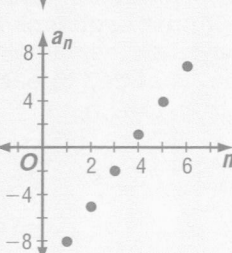

40.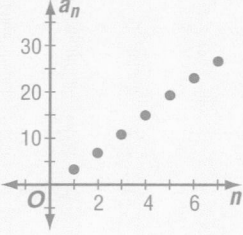

---

4. **You Decide**   Andrea says that 220 is a term of the sequence $a_n = 16 - (n - 1)12$. Janice says that this is impossible. Who is correct? Explain.   **See margin.**

Guided Practice

Find the next four terms of each arithmetic sequence.

5. 12, 16, 20, ...   **24, 28, 32, 36**   6. 3, 1, −1, ...   **−3, −5, −7, −9**

Find the first five terms of each arithmetic sequence described.

7. $a_1 = 5, d = 3$ **5, 8, 11, 14, 17**   8. $a_1 = 14, d = -2$ **14, 12, 10, 8, 6**

Find the nth term of each arithmetic sequence.

9. $a_1 = 3, d = -5, n = 24$ **−112**   10. $a_1 = -5, d = 7, n = 13$ **79**

11. Complete: 68 is the $\underline{\ ?\ }$th term of −2, 3, 8, ...   **15**

12. Find a_{13} for the arithmetic sequence −17, −12, −7, ...   **43**

13. **a.** Find the three arithmetic means between 44 and 92.   **56, 68, 80**
     b. Graph the sequence using the x-axis for the number of the term and the y-axis for the term itself.   **See margin.**

14. Write an equation for the nth term of the arithmetic sequence −26, −15, −4, 7, ... $a_n = 11n - 37$

15. **Consumerism**   Jamila bought a snowboard priced at $545. She put $145 down and made equal monthly payments. At the end of every month, she was given a statement of the balance owed. For the first four months, the balances were $361, $322, $283, and $244. If she paid the same amount each month, what was her balance at the end of 8 months?   **$88**

EXERCISES

Practice

A

Find the next four terms of each arithmetic sequence.

16. 9, 16, 23, ...   **30, 37, 44, 51**   17. 31, 24, 17, ...   **10, 3, −4, −11**

18. $\frac{1}{4}, \frac{3}{4}, \frac{5}{4}, ...$ $\frac{7}{4}, \frac{9}{4}, \frac{11}{4}, \frac{13}{4}$ 19. −7.8, −3.8, 0.2, ...

19. 4.2, 8.2, 12.2, 16.2

Find the first five terms of each arithmetic sequence described.

20. $a_1 = 12, d = -3$ **12, 9, 6, 3, 0**   21. $a_1 = 41, d = 5$ **41, 46, 51, 56, 61**

22. $a_1 = \frac{4}{3}, d = -\frac{1}{3}$ $\frac{4}{3}, 1, \frac{2}{3}, \frac{1}{3}, 0$ 23. $a_1 = \frac{5}{8}, d = \frac{3}{8}$ $\frac{5}{8}, 1, \frac{11}{8}, \frac{14}{8}, \frac{17}{8}$

Find the nth term of each arithmetic sequence.

24. $a_1 = 3, d = 7, n = 14$ **94**   25. $a_1 = -4, d = -9, n = 20$ **−175**

26. $a_1 = 5, d = \frac{1}{3}, n = 12$ $8\frac{2}{3}$ 27. $a_1 = \frac{5}{2}, d = -\frac{3}{2}, n = 11$ $-12\frac{1}{2}$

B   28. $a_1 = 35, d = 3, n = 101$ **335**   29. $a_1 = 20, d = 4, n = 81$ **340**

Complete each statement.

30. 170 is the $\underline{\ ?\ }$th term of −4, 2, 8, ...   **30**

31. 124 is the $\underline{\ ?\ }$th term of −2, 5, 12, ...   **19**

32. −14 is the $\underline{\ ?\ }$nd term of $2\frac{1}{5}, 2, 1\frac{4}{5}, ...$ **82**

Find the indicated term in each arithmetic sequence.

33. a_{12} for −17, −13, −9, ...   **27**   34. a_{21} for 121, 118, 115, ...   **61**

35. a_{43} for 5, 9, 13, 17, ...   **173**   36. a_{12} for 8, 3, −2, ...   **−47**

Find the arithmetic means in each sequence. Then graph each sequence using the x-axis for the number of the term and the y-axis for the term itself.

37–40. See margin for graphs.

37. 70, 85, 100
39. −8, −2, 1, 7
40. 7, 11, 15, 19, 23

37. 55, ?, ?, ?, 115

38. 10, ?, ?, −8   4, −2

39. ?, −5, ?, ?, 4, ?

40. 3, ?, ?, ?, ?, ?, 27

Find the values of y that make each sequence arithmetic.

41. −4, 2, 8, 3y + 5, ...   3

42. 5, 9, 2y − 1, ...   7

43. y + 2, 6, y, ...   5

44. y + 8, 4y + 6, 3y, ...   −1

Write an equation for the nth term of each arithmetic sequence.

45. 7, 16, 25, 34, ... $a_n = 9n − 2$

46. 18, 11, 4, −3, ... $a_n = −7n + 25$

47. a. The first term of an arithmetic sequence is 7, and each term is 4 more than the previous term. Find the value of the eighth term.   35
   b. Write a formula for the nth term of this sequence. $a_n = 4n + 3$

48a. See margin for drawings.
48b. yes; $a_n = 4n − 3$

48. The first three pentagonal numbers are shown below.
   a. Make drawings to find the next three pentagonal numbers.   13, 17, 21
   b. Do the pentagonal numbers form an arithmetic sequence? Write an equation representing the nth pentagonal number.
   c. What is the common difference?   4
   d. Justify whether 397 is a pentagonal number.   Yes, it's the 100th term.

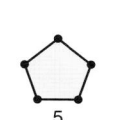
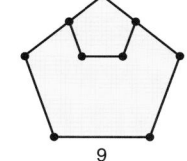

1   5   9

49. The fifth term of an arithmetic sequence is 19, and the 11th term is 43. Find the first term and the 87th term   3, 347

50. Find three numbers that have a sum of 36, a product of 276, and form an arithmetic sequence.   1, 12, 23

51–54. See margin for graphs.

Graphing Calculator

Use a graphing calculator to find the 12th term of each sequence. Then graph the sequence. Sketch the graph on grid paper.

51. −31, −24, −17, −10, ...   46

52. 317, 313, 309, 305, ...   273

53. −16, −13, −10, −7, ...   17

54. 23, 29, 35, 41, 47, ...   89

Critical Thinking

55. Use an arithmetic sequence to find how many multiples of 7 are between 36 and 391.   50

56. The first three terms of an arithmetic sequence are u, v, and w. Express w in terms of u and v. Justify your answer. $w = (v − u) + v$ or $2v − u$

Applications and Problem Solving

57. Geology Geologists have calculated that the continents of Europe and America are drifting apart at an average of 12 miles every 1 million years. That's an average of 0.75 inch a year. If the continents continue to drift apart at the same rate, how many inches will they drift in 50 years? (*Hint:* $a_1 = 0.75$.)   37.5 in.

Additional Answer

48a.

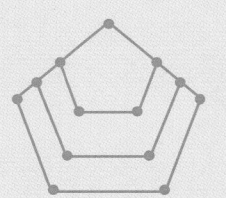
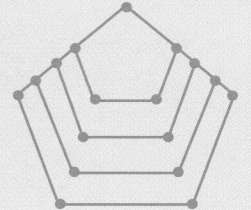
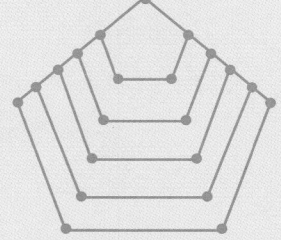

Additional Answers

51.

X = 12   Y = 46

52.

X = 12   Y = 273

53.

X = 12   Y = 17

54.

X = 12   Y = 89

Study Guide Masters, p. 76

NAME_____ DATE_____

11-1   **Study Guide**   Student Editio Pages 648–65

Arithmetic Sequences

A set of numbers in a specific order is called a **sequence**. Each number in a sequence is called a **term.** The first term is symbolized by a_1 and the second term by a_2, so that, in general, a_n represents the nth term. An **arithmetic sequence** is a sequence in which each term, after the first, is found by adding a constant, called the *common difference,* to the previous term.

nth Term of an Arithmetic Sequence
The nth term, a_n, of an arithmetic sequence with first term a_1 and common difference d is given by the formula $a_n = a_1 + (n − 1)d$, where n is a positive integer.

Example: Find the tenth term, a_{10}, of the arithmetic sequence with $a_1 = 7$ and $d = 3$.

$a_n = a_1 + (n − 1)d$
$a_{10} = 7 + (10 − 1)3$
$= 7 + 27$
$= 34$

The tenth term is 34.

Find the indicated term in each arithmetic sequence.

1. a_{14} for $a_1 = 4$, $d = 6$ 82

2. a_{12} for $a_1 = −4$, $d = −2$ −26

3. a_{15} for $a_1 = 5$, $d = −3$ −37

4. a_{10} for 0, −3, −6, −9, ...   −27

5. a_{12} for 4, 10, 16, 22, ···   70

6. a_{21} for 10, 6, 2, −2, ···   −70

Find the missing terms in each arithmetic sequence.

7. 5, 3, 1, −1, −3

8. −7, −5, −3, −1, 1

9. 24, 33, 42, 51, 60

10. 18, 13, 8, 3, −2

11. 17, 10, 3, −4, −11

12. 12, 10, 8, 6, 4, 2

Additional Answer

59a.

The bottom right box is divided into 4 parts.

58. Physics People used to believe that the heavier an object was, the faster it would fall. Galileo proved that this was incorrect. He dropped two different weights simultaneously from the Leaning Tower of Pisa, and they both hit the ground at the same instant. When an object is dropped from a tall building, no matter how much it weighs, it falls 16 feet in the first second, 48 feet in the second second, and 80 feet in the third second. How many feet would a falling object fall in the tenth second? **304 ft**

59. Look for a Pattern Look at the figures below.

Figure 1   Figure 2   Figure 3

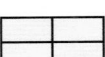 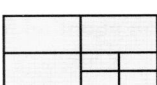 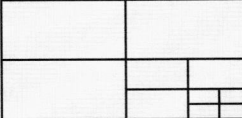

59a. See margin.

  a. Describe the pattern and draw what you think Figure 4 should look like.
  b. How many rectangles are in Figure 1? (*Hint:* There are more than 5.) **9**
  c. How many rectangles are there in Figures 2 and 3? **19, 29**
  d. How many rectangles would there be in Figure 50? **499**
  e. How many rectangles would there be in Figure n? **$10n - 1$**

60. Antiques In 1996, Belkis received a collection of 574 baseball cards that was started by her grandfather in 1938. Each year, her grandfather added the same number of cards to his collection. When Belkis' father received the collection in 1964, there were 254 cards. Belkis' father continued to add the same number of cards to the collection each year. Suppose 1938 is year 1 and 1964 is year 26.

60a. 4 cards

  a. How many baseball cards did Belkis' grandfather start out with?
  b. How many cards were added to the collection each year? **10 cards**
  c. If Belkis continues to add the same number of cards to the collection each year, how many cards will she have in 2010? **714 cards**

Mixed Review

61. about 1.3863

61. Biology The general formula for growth is $y = ne^{kt}$, where y is the final amount, n is the initial amount, k is a constant, and t is the time. A culture of a certain bacteria will grow from 500 to 4000 bacteria in 90 minutes. Find the constant k for this bacteria if t is in hours. (Lesson 10–7)

62. Solve $\log_3 729 = x$. (Lesson 10–2) **6**

63. Simplify $\dfrac{y^2 - y}{y^2 - y^2} + \dfrac{y^2 - 2y + 1}{1 - y}$. (Lesson 9–4) $\dfrac{y^3 - w^2y - y + w^2}{w^2 - y^2}$

64. If $f(x) = 3x$ and $g(x) = x - 1$, find $f[g(x)]$. (Lesson 8–7) **$3x - 3$**

65. State whether the graph of $x = (y + 4)^2 - 6$ is a parabola, a circle, an ellipse, or a hyperbola. (Lesson 7–6) **parabola**

66. $13\sqrt{2} + \sqrt{65} + \sqrt{197}$ units

66. Geometry Find the perimeter of a quadrilateral with vertices at $(4, 5)$, $(-4, 6)$, $(-5, -8)$, and $(6, 3)$. (Lesson 7–1)

Practice Masters, p. 76

11-1

NAME_____ DATE_____

Practice

Student Edition
Pages 648–654

Arithmetic Sequences

Find the nth term of each arithmetic sequence.

1. $a_1 = -5, d = 4, n = 9$
27

2. $a_1 = 13, d = -\frac{5}{2}, n = 29$
−57

3. $a_1 = 3, d = -4, n = 6$
−17

4. $a_1 = -5, d = \frac{1}{2}, n = 10$
$-\frac{1}{2}$

Complete each statement.

5. 97 is the ___?___ th term of −3, 1, 5, 9, ⋯.   26

6. −10 is the ___?___ th term of 14, 12.5, 11, 9.5, ⋯.   17

Find the indicated term in each arithmetic sequence.

7. a_{15} for −3, 3, 9, ⋯
81

8. a_{19} for 17, 12, 7, ⋯
−73

9. a_{26} for 1, $\frac{7}{3}$, $\frac{11}{3}$, ⋯
$\frac{103}{3}$

10. a_{26} for 17, $16\frac{2}{3}$, $16\frac{1}{3}$, ⋯
$\frac{17}{3}$

Find the missing terms in each arithmetic sequence.

11. 3, _____, _____, 20
$8\frac{2}{3}$, $14\frac{1}{3}$

12. _____, −10, _____, _____, _____, 14
−16, −4, 2, 8

13. 5, _____, _____, 27
$12\frac{1}{3}$, $19\frac{2}{3}$

14. _____, 4, _____, _____, _____, 29
$-2\frac{1}{4}$, $10\frac{1}{4}$, $16\frac{1}{2}$, $22\frac{3}{4}$

15. How many multiples of 11 are there between 13 and 384?
33

67. Name the vertex, axis of symmetry, and direction of opening for the graph of $f(x) = -4(x - 9)^2$. (Lesson 6–6) **(9, 0); $x = 9$; downward**

68. Solve $\sqrt[3]{x + 5} + 6 = 4$ (Lesson 5–8) **−13**

69. If $A = \begin{bmatrix} -3 & 5 \\ 1 & -4 \end{bmatrix}$, find A^{-1}. (Lesson 4–5) **$\frac{1}{7}\begin{bmatrix} -4 & -5 \\ -1 & -3 \end{bmatrix}$**

70. Determine the slope of the line that passes through $(1, -3)$ and $(0, -5)$. (Lesson 2–3) **2**

71. Solve $4 + |2x| > 0$. (Lesson 1–7) **all reals**

---

4 ASSESS

Closing Activity

Speaking Have students use examples to explain how to determine arithmetic means.

WORKING ON THE
In·ves·ti·ga·tion

Refer to the Investigation on pages 590–591.

The weight of a jumper has an effect on the stretching of the bungee. You decide to create an experiment to measure the degree of stretch in relation to weight. You will need three rubber bands of different sizes, a small paper cup, a paper clip, 50 or more washers, a centimeter ruler, a wooden dowel rod, and tape.

1 Straighten the paper clip and use it to punch two small holes on opposite sides of the cup about a centimeter below the rim of the cup. Loop one of the rubber bands inside the cup and slide the paper clip through the two holes and through the loop of the rubber band, so that the cup could be held by the rubber band like a bucket on a rope.

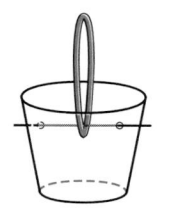

2 Tape a wooden dowel to the top of the table so that about 5 inches of the dowel hangs over the edge of the table. Slide the free end of the

rubber band over the dowel so that the cup hangs from the dowel. Make a table with columns labeled *length of rubber band* and *number of washers*. Measure the distance from the top of the cup to the base of the dowel. Record this as your initial length with zero washers.

3 Put five washers in the bottom of the cup. Measure the length of the rubber band again from the top of the cup to the base of the dowel. Record the length and number of washers.

4 Continue adding washers, five at a time, and measuring the length of the rubber band. Record the data as you add each set of washers.

5 Study the numbers in your table. What patterns do you observe? Are you able to continue adding washers until you reach the length that matches the maximum elastic potential that you found earlier?

Add the results of your work to your Investigation Folder.

Lesson 11-1 Arithmetic Sequences **655**

Enrichment Masters, p. 76

Extension

Reasoning Have students state a rule that defines a sequence with the first four terms as follows: 1, 0, 1, 0, ...
$$a_n = \frac{1 + (-1)^{n-1}}{2}$$

In·ves·ti·ga·tion

Working on the Investigation

The Investigation on pages 590–591 is designed to be a long-term project that is completed over several days or weeks. Encourage students to keep their materials in their Investigation Folder as they work on the Investigation.

11-1 NAME_____ DATE_____
Enrichment Student Edition Pages 648–654

Fibonacci Sequence

Leonardo Fibonacci first discovered the sequence of numbers named for him while studying rabbits. He wanted to know how many pairs of rabbits would be produced in n months, starting with a single pair of newborn rabbits. He made the following assumptions.

1. Newborn rabbits become adults in one month.
2. Each pair of rabbits produces one pair each month.
3. No rabbits die.

Let F_n represent the number of pairs of rabbits at the end of n months. If you begin with one pair of newborn rabbits, $F_0 = F_1 = 1$. This pair of rabbits would produce one pair at the end of the second month, so $F_2 = 1 + 1$, or 2. At the end of the third month, the first pair of rabbits would produce another pair. Thus, $F_3 = 2 + 1$, or 3.

The chart below shows the number of rabbits each month for several months.

Month	Adult Pairs	Newborn Pairs	Total
F_0	0	1	1
F_1	1	0	1
F_2	1	1	2
F_3	2	1	3
F_4	3	2	5
F_5	5	3	8

Solve.

1. Starting with a single pair of newborn rabbits, how many rabbits would there be at the end of 12 months? 233

2. Write the first 10 terms of the sequence for which $F_0 = 3$, $F_1 = 4$, and $F_n = F_{n-2} + F_{n-1}$.
3, 4, 7, 11, 18, 29, 47, 76, 123, 199, 322

3. Write the first 10 terms of the sequence for which $F_0 = 1$, $F_1 = 5$, $F_n = F_{n-2} + F_{n-1}$.
1, 5, 6, 11, 17, 28, 45, 73, 118, 191, 309

Chapter 11 **655**

Instructional Resources

• Study Guide Master 11-2
• Practice Master 11-2
• Enrichment Master 11-2
• Assessment and Evaluation Masters, p. 296
• Science and Math Lab Manual, pp. 105–110

 Transparency 11-2A contains the 5-Minute Check for this lesson; **Transparency 11-2B** contains a teaching aid for this lesson.

Recommended Pacing

Standard Pacing	Days 3 & 4 of 14
Honors Pacing	Day 3 of 11
Block Scheduling*	Day 2 of 7

 *For more information on pacing and possible lesson plans, refer to the *Block Scheduling Booklet*.

1 FOCUS

 ### 5-Minute Check
(over Lesson 11-1)

Find the *n*th term of each arithmetic sequence.

1. $a_1 = 7, d = 3, n = 14$
   $a_n = 46$
2. $a_1 = 20, d = 4, n = 100$
   $a_n = 416$
3. Find the 12th term of the sequence $-17, -13, -9, \ldots$.
   $a_{12} = 27$
4. Which term of the sequence $-2, 5, 12, \ldots$ is 124? **19**
5. Find the missing terms of the sequence 55, __, __, __, 115.
   70, 85, 100

What YOU'LL LEARN

• To find sums of arithmetic series,
• to find specific terms in an arithmetic series, and
• to use sigma notation to express sums.

Why IT'S IMPORTANT

You can use arithmetic series to solve problems involving construction and entertainment.

F Y I

Kwanzaa means "first fruits" in Kiswahili. The seven candles represent purpose, self-determination, unity, creativity, collective work and responsibility, cooperative economics, and faith.

Arithmetic Series

APPLICATION
World Cultures

Kwanzaa is an African-American harvest festival celebrating the new year. During the festival, a special ritual is performed involving the lighting of seven candles which are called the *mushumaa saba*. Each of these candles symbolizes a different human quality. On the first night, one of the candles is lit and then blown out. On the second night, a new candle and the candle from the previous night are lit and then blown out. For seven nights, this pattern of lighting a new candle and relighting all the candles from the previous nights continues. What is the total number of lightings during this festival?

One candle is lit on the first night, two candles are lit on the second night, and so forth. These lightings can be represented by the sequence 1, 2, 3, 4, 5, 6, 7.

The total would be the sum of the terms in the sequence.

first night		*second night*		*third night*		*fourth night*		*fifth night*		*sixth night*		*seventh night*		
1	+	2	+	3	+	4	+	5	+	6	+	7	=	28

The indicated sum of the terms of a sequence is called a **series.** The series shown above is an **arithmetic series.**

The lists below show examples of arithmetic sequences and their corresponding arithmetic series.

Arithmetic Sequences	**Arithmetic Series**
4, 7, 10, 13, 16	4 + 7 + 10 + 13 + 16
$-10, -4, 2$	$-10 + (-4) + 2$
$\frac{2}{7}, \frac{6}{7}, \frac{10}{7}, \frac{14}{7}$	$\frac{2}{7} + \frac{6}{7} + \frac{10}{7} + \frac{14}{7}$

The symbol S_n is used to represent the sum of the first n terms of a series. For example, S_3 means the sum of the first three terms of a series. In the series $4 + 7 + 10 + 13 + 16$, S_3 would be $4 + 7 + 10$ or 21.

If a series has a large number of terms, it is not convenient to list all the terms and then find their sum. To develop a general formula for the sum of any arithmetic series, let's consider the series of candle lightings.

$$S_7 = 1 + 2 + 3 + 4 + 5 + 6 + 7$$

F Y I

The earliest recorded New Year's festival dates to about 2000 B.C. in Mesopotamia. This festival occurred at the new moon nearest the spring equinox.

Suppose we write S_7 in two different orders and find the sum.

$$
\begin{array}{r}
S_7 = 1 + 2 + 3 + 4 + 5 + 6 + 7 \\
+ \quad S_7 = 7 + 6 + 5 + 4 + 3 + 2 + 1 \\
\hline
2 \cdot S_7 = \underbrace{8 + 8 + 8 + 8 + 8 + 8 + 8}_{7 \text{ sums of } 8}
\end{array}
$$

$$2 \cdot S_7 = 7(8)$$
$$S_7 = \frac{7}{2}(8) \quad \textit{Divide each side by 2.}$$

Now let's analyze what these numbers represent in terms of S_n. In the equation $S_7 = \frac{7}{2}(8)$, 7 represents n and 8 represents the sum of the first and last terms, $a_1 + a_n$. Thus, we can replace the equation with the formula $S_n = \frac{n}{2}(a_1 + a_n)$. This formula can be used to find the sum of any arithmetic series.

Sum of an Arithmetic Series	The sum S_n of the first n terms of an arithmetic series is given by $S_n = \frac{n}{2}(a_1 + a_n)$, where n is a positive integer.

Example Find the sum of the first 50 positive even integers.

$$S_n = \frac{n}{2}(a_1 + a_n)$$
$$S_{50} = \frac{50}{2}(2 + 100) \quad a_1 = 2, n = 50, \text{ and } a_n = a_{50} = 100$$
$$= 25(102) \text{ or } 2550$$

The sum of the first 50 positive even integers is 2550. *Check this result.*

In Lesson 11-1, you learned that in an arithmetic sequence, $a_n = a_1 + (n-1)d$. Using this formula and substitution gives us another version of the formula for the sum of an arithmetic sequence.

$$S_n = \frac{n}{2}(a_1 + a_n)$$
$$= \frac{n}{2}\{a_1 + [a_1 + (n-1)d]\} \quad \textit{Substitute } a_1 + (n-1)d \textit{ for } a_n.$$
$$= \frac{n}{2}[2a_1 + (n-1)d] \quad \textit{Combine like terms.}$$

You can use this formula when you do not know the value of the last term.

Example Find the sum of the first 40 terms of an arithmetic series in which $a_1 = 70$ and $d = -21$.
The series is $70 + 49 + 28 + 7 + \dots$.

$$S_n = \frac{n}{2}[2a_1 + (n-1)d] \quad \textit{Use the formula for } S_n.$$
$$= \frac{40}{2}[2(70) + (40-1)(-21)] \quad \textit{Substitute the known values.}$$
$$= -13,580$$

Lesson 11-2 Arithmetic Series **657**

Chapter 11 **657**

Motivating the Lesson
Hands-On Activity Show students an empty jar and a container of pennies. Ask students if they were to place pennies in the jar according to an arithmetic sequence (give examples such as 1 one day, 3 the next, then 5, ...), if there would be a way, other than counting the pennies, to determine the total number added after a certain number of days.

2 TEACH

In-Class Examples

For Example 1
Find the sum of each described series.

a. first 50 positive integers 1275
b. first 10 odd integers 100

For Example 2
Find the sum of each described series.

a. first 60 terms in which $a_1 = 15$ and $d = 80$ 142,500
b. first 15 odd integers 225

 Alternative Learning Styles

Kinesthetic Using coins, counters, or tiles, have students work in cooperative groups to model several arithmetic series. For each series, have students find the sum by using a sum formula and then check the results by counting.

In-Class Examples

For Example 3
A supermarket display consists of six rows of stacked boxes. Each row has three fewer boxes than the one below it. The top row has 35 boxes. How many boxes are in the display?
255 boxes

For Example 4
Find the first three terms of the arithmetic series in which $a_1 = 5$, $a_n = 100$, and $S_n = 1050$.
5, 10, 15

Teaching Tip Explain to students that this notation is called sigma notation because the Greek letter sigma (Σ) is used.

Example ③

CONNECTION
Physics

Refer to Exercise 58 in Lesson 11–1. A free-falling object falls 16 feet in the first second, 48 feet in the second second, 80 feet in the third second, and so on. How many feet would a free-falling object fall in 20 seconds if air resistance is ignored?

To find the total distance fallen by an object, add the first 20 terms of the sequence 16, 48, 80, ...

$$S_n = \frac{n}{2}[2a_1 + (n-1)d]$$
$$= \frac{20}{2}[2(16) + (20-1)32] \quad n = 20,\ a_1 = 16,\ d = 32$$
$$= 10(32 + 608)$$
$$= 6400$$

A free-falling object would fall 6400 feet in 20 seconds.

It is sometimes necessary to use both the sum formula and the nth term formula to solve a problem. You must analyze the information you are given and then decide which formula to use first.

Example ④

Find the first three terms of an arithmetic series in which $a_1 = 13$, $a_n = 157$, and $S_n = 1445$.

Step 1 Use $S_n = \frac{n}{2}(a_1 + a_n)$ first to find n since a_1, a_n, and S_n are known.

$$S_n = \frac{n}{2}(a_1 + a_n)$$
$$1445 = \frac{n}{2}(13 + 157)$$
$$1445 = 85n$$
$$n = 17$$

Step 2 Find d.

$$a_n = a_1 + (n-1)d$$
$$157 = 13 + (17-1)d$$
$$144 = 16d$$
$$d = 9$$

Step 3 Determine a_2 and a_3.
$$a_2 = 13 + 9 \text{ or } 22 \qquad a_3 = 22 + 9 \text{ or } 31$$
The first three terms are 13, 22, and 31.

Writing out a series is often time-consuming and lengthy. To simplify this, mathematicians use a more concise notation called **sigma** or **summation notation.** $2 + 4 + 6 + 8 + ... + 20$ can be expressed as $\sum\limits_{n=1}^{10} 2n$. This expression is read *the sum of 2n as n increases from 1 to 10.*

last value of n ⟍
$$\sum_{n=1}^{10} 2n$$
first value of n ⟋ ⟍ *formula for the related sequence*

When using sigma notation, the variable defined below the Σ (sigma) is called the **index of summation.** The upper number is the *upper limit* of the index. To generate the terms of the series, successively replace the index of summation with consecutive integers as values of n. In this series, the values of n are 1, 2, 3, and so on, through 10.

Example **5** Write the terms of $\sum_{k=3}^{7} (2k + 5)$ and find the sum.

Method 1	Method 2
Replace k with 3 and then with 4, 5, 6, and 7 to find the terms.	Use $S_n = \frac{n}{2}(a_1 + a_n)$.
$\sum_{k=3}^{7} (2k + 5) = [2(3) + 5] + [2(4) + 5] +$ $\qquad [2(5) + 5] + [2(6) + 5] +$ $\qquad [2(7) + 5]$ $\qquad = 11 + 13 + 15 + 17 + 19$ $\qquad = 75$	$n = 5, a_1 = 11$ $a_n = a_5 = 2(7) + 5$ or 19 $S_n = \frac{5}{2}(11 + 19)$ $\qquad = 75$

The sum of the series is 75.

You can use the sum and sequence functions on a graphing calculator to find the sum of an arithmetic series.

EXPLORATION

GRAPHING CALCULATORS

To find the sum of $\sum_{n=3}^{12} (4n + 1)$, enter the following.

Enter: [2nd] [LIST] [▶] 5   *Retrieves the sum function.*

        [2nd] [LIST] 5   *Retrieves the sequence function.*

After the "sum seq(" prompt, enter the expression, variable, first value of n, last value of n, and step size, or $(4n + 1, n, 3, 12, 1)$.   *Step size will always be 1.*

Enter: 4 [ALPHA] [N] [+] 1 [,] [ALPHA] [N] [,] 3 [,] 12 [,] 1

        [)] [ENTER] *310*

The sum of the series is 310.

Your Turn

Use a graphing calculator to find the sum of each series.

a. $\sum_{n=1}^{20} (4 + 3n)$ **710**   **b.** $\sum_{k=3}^{9} (5k + 4)$ **238**   **c.** $\sum_{t=2}^{35} (4t - 17)$ **1938**

Just as a polynomial can be expressed in more than one form, the summation of a series can be expressed in different ways. The summation of the series in Example 5 is expressed as $\sum_{k=3}^{7} (2k + 5)$. It can also be expressed as $\sum_{k=3}^{7} [7 + 2(k - 1)]$ or $\sum_{k=6}^{10} (2k - 1)$.   *Why?*

CHECK FOR UNDERSTANDING

Communicating Mathematics

Study the lesson. Then complete the following.

1. **Define** the term *indicated sum*.

2. **Explain** the purpose of the index of summation.

3. **Explain** when it is necessary to use both versions of the sum formula to solve a problem.

Lesson 11–2 Arithmetic Series   **659**

1. The sum of a specified group of terms of a sequence.

2. It tells which terms to add and how many.

3. Sample answer: To find terms of a series when the sum is known, but not the last term.

Reteaching

Translating Expressions Sam's parents decided when he was born to put $100 times his age away for him at every birthday through his 18th birthday as a way to save for college. How much money will they have saved after his 18th birthday, without taking into account the interest earned? How much do you think would be saved if they put away $200 times his age every birthday? Check your answer. Discuss. **$17,100; $34,200**

In-Class Example

For Example 5
Write the terms of each series and find the sum.

a. $\sum_{n=1}^{6} (3n + 7)$

    $10 + 13 + 16 + 19 + 22 + 25 = 105$

b. $\sum_{i=1}^{4} (3i - 6)$

    $-3 + 0 + 3 + 6 = 6$

EXPLORATION

In this activity, students learn to use the sequence functions on a graphing calculator. The series of keystrokes is quite long. Students need to verify the keystrokes before pushing [ENTER].

---

3 PRACTICE/APPLY

Check for Understanding

Exercises 1–15 are designed to help you assess your students' understanding through reading, writing, speaking, and modeling. You should work through Exercises 1–3 with your students and then monitor their work on Exercises 4–15.

Study Guide Masters, p. 77

NAME_____ DATE_____

11-2
Study Guide   Student Edition
                   Pages 655–66

Arithmetic Series

The indicated sum of the terms of a sequence is called a **series**. The symbol S_n is used to represent the sum of the first n terms of a series. Since $a_n = a_1 + (n - 1)d$, substitute this into the formula $S_n = \frac{n}{2}(a_1 + a_n)$ and get another formula for S_n,

$S_n = \frac{n}{2}[2a_1 + (n - 1)d]$.

> **Sum of an Arithmetic Series**
> The sum, S_n of the first n terms of an arithmetic series is given by the following formula.
> $S_n = \frac{n}{2}(a_1 + a_n)$

Example: Find the sum of the first 20 terms of an arithmetic series where $a_1 = 10$ and $d = 3$.
    $S_n = \frac{n}{2}[2a_1 + (n - 1)d]$
    $S_{20} = \frac{20}{2}[2(10) + (20 - 1)3]$
    $= 770$

Sigma notation can also be used to express an arithmetic series.

Example: Find $\sum_{k=1}^{4} (2k - 3)$.
   $\sum_{k=1}^{4} (2k - 3) = \frac{2(1) - 3}{-1} + \frac{2(2) - 3}{1} + \frac{2(3) - 3}{3} + \frac{2(4) - 3}{5}$
      $= 8$

Find S_n for each arithmetic series described.

1. $a_1 = 12, a_n = 100, n = 12$ **2.** $a_1 = 50, a_n = -50, n = 15$
   672   -300

3. $a_1 = 42, n = 6, d = 6$ **4.** $a_1 = 4, n = 20, d = 2\frac{1}{2}$
   126                               $55\frac{1}{2}$

5. $8 + 6 + 4 + \cdots + -10$ **6.** $3 + 6 + 9 + \cdots + 99$
   -10 1683

7. $\sum_{n=1}^{20} (2n + 1)$ **8.** $\sum_{x=5}^{25} x - 1$
   340   294

9. the first 50 positive odd integers   **10.** the first 100 positive multiples of 5
   2500   25,250

Find the first three terms of each arithmetic series.

11. $a_1 = 7, a_n = 83, S_n = 900$ **12.** $a_1 = 5, a_n = 200, S_n = 4100$
   7, 11, 15   5, 10, 15

Chapter 11   **659**

Assignment Guide

Core: 17–41 odd, 42, 43, 45–52
Enriched: 16–40 even, 42–52

For **Extra Practice,** see p. 901.

The red A, B, and C flags, printed only in the Teacher's Wraparound Edition, indicate the level of difficulty of the exercises.

Guided Practice

State the first term, the common difference, the last term, and the number of terms for each arithmetic series.

4. 7, −6, −11, 4

5. 6, 1.4, 11.6, 5

4. $7 + 1 + (-5) + (-11)$

5. $6 + 7.4 + 8.8 + 10.2 + 11.6$

6. $a_1 + 35 + 38 + 41 + 44$
32, 3, 44, 5

7. $a_1 + 12 - 6 - 24 - 42 - 60 + a_7$
30, −18, −78, 7

Find S_n for each arithmetic series described.

8. $a_1 = 4, a_n = 100, n = 25$ 1300

9. $a_1 = 40, n = 20, d = -3$ 230

10. $a_1 = 132, d = -4, a_n = 52$ 1932

11. $d = 5, n = 16, a_n = 72$ 552

Find the sum of each arithmetic series.

12. $5 + 11 + 17 + ... + 95$ 800

13. $38 + 35 + 32 + ... + 2$ 260

14. $2 + 4 + 6 + 8 + 10 + 12 + 14; 56$

14. Write the terms of $\sum_{n=1}^{7} 2n$ and find the sum.

15. **a.** Compute the sum of the first 1000 positive even integers.   1,001,000
b. Compute the sum of the multiples of 3 from 3 to 999.   166,833

EXERCISES

Practice

Find S_n for each arithmetic series described.

16. $a_1 = 7, a_n = 79, n = 8$ 344

17. $a_1 = 58, a_n = -7, n = 26$ 663

18. $a_1 = 43, n = 19, a_n = 115$ 1501

19. $a_1 = 76, n = 21, a_n = 176$ 2646

20. $a_1 = 7, d = -2, n = 9$ −9

21. $a_1 = 3, a_n = -38, n = 8$ −140

22. $a_1 = 5, d = \frac{1}{2}, n = 13$ 104

23. $a_1 = 12, d = \frac{1}{3}, n = 13$ 182

B

24. $a_1 = 91, d = -4, a_n = 15$ 1060

25. $d = 7, n = 18, a_n = 72$ 225

26. $d = -3, n = 21, a_n = -64$ −714

27. $a_1 = -2, d = \frac{1}{3}, a_n = 9$ 119

32. $13 + 15 + 17 + 19 + 21 + 23; 108$

33. $92 + 97 + 102 + 107 + 112; 510$

34. $-21 - 30 - 39 - 48 - 57; -195$

35. 17, 26, 35

36. 13, 18, 23

37. −12, −9, −6

38. −13, −8, −3

39. $\sum_{n=1}^{12} \frac{1}{5}n; \frac{78}{5}$

Find the sum of each arithmetic series.

28. $6 + 13 + 20 + 27 + ... + 97$ 721

29. $7 + 14 + 21 + 28 + ... + 98$ 735

30. $34 + 30 + 26 + ... + 2$ 162

31. $16 + 10 + 4 + ... + (-50)$ −204

Write the terms of each arithmetic series and find the sum.

32. $\sum_{n=1}^{6} (2n + 11)$

33. $\sum_{t=19}^{23} (5t - 3)$

34. $\sum_{k=7}^{11} (42 - 9k)$

Find the first three terms of each arithmetic series.

C

35. $a_1 = 17, a_n = 197, S_n = 2247$

36. $n = 19, a_n = 103, S_n = 1102$

37. $n = 31, a_n = 78, S_n = 1023$

38. $a_1 = -13, a_n = 427, S_n = 18,423$

39. Write the series $\frac{1}{5} + \frac{2}{5} + \frac{3}{5} + ... + \frac{12}{5}$ in summation notation and find the sum.

Graphing Calculator

Use a graphing calculator to find the sum of each arithmetic series.

40. $\sum_{n=21}^{75} (2n + 5)$ 5555

41. $\sum_{n=10}^{50} (3n - 1)$ 3649

Practice Masters, p. 77

11-2   NAME _____ DATE _____
Practice   Student Edition
Pages 655–660

Arithmetic Series

Find S_n for each arithmetic series described.

1. $a_1 = 16, a_n = 98, n = 13$ 741

2. $a_1 = 13, d = -6, n = 21$ −987

3. $d = -\frac{2}{3}, n = 16, a_n = 44$ 784

4. $a_1 = -121, d = 3, a_n = 5$ −2494

Find the sum of each arithmetic series.

5. $5 + 7 + 9 + ... + 27$ 192

6. $-4 + 1 + 6 + ... + 91$ 870

7. $13 + 20 + 27 + ... + 272$ 5415

8. $89 + 86 + 83 + ... + 20$ 1308

9. $\sum_{k=3}^{6} (5k - 10)$ 105

10. $\sum_{p=4}^{10} (2p + 1)$ 105

11. $\sum_{n=1}^{6} (3n + 5)$ 93

12. $\sum_{j=1}^{5} (9 - 4j)$ −15

Find the first three terms of each arithmetic series.

13. $a_1 = 14, a_n = -85, S_n = -1207$ 14, 11, 8

14. $n = 16, a_n = 15, S_n = -120$ −30, −27, −24

Solve.

15. A display in a grocery store has 1 can on the top row, 2 cans on the 2nd row, 3 cans on the 3rd row, and so on. How many cans are needed to make 25 rows?   325

42. a. Evaluate $\sum_{a=3}^{6}(a-2)^2$ and $\sum_{a=1}^{4}a^2$. **30, 30**

   b. What do you notice? **They describe the same series.**

   c. Why does this work? **The summation of a series can be expressed in different ways.**

43. Construction A company responsible for laying the foundation of a new high-rise office building must pay $5000 a day for the first five days that the completion of the foundation is late. On the sixth day and each day thereafter, the penalty is increased by $200 a day. If the company was penalized $65,600, how many days late were they in laying the foundation? **12 days**

44. Entertainment As of March, 1994, Andrew Lloyd Webber's musical *Phantom of the Opera* had been performed on Broadway 2576 times. Some theaters that present the musical have seats with limited viewing. For example, not everyone who attended the show at the Ohio Theatre in 1995 could see the famous scene where the chandelier comes crashing to the stage. Suppose only the people in the first 24 rows had 100% visibility. In this section there are 20 seats in the first row, and each subsequent row has one more seat than the row in front of it. How many seats are there in the Ohio Theater where people can see the whole show? **756 seats**

45. Aeronautics A rocket rises 20 feet in the first second, 60 feet in the second second, and 100 feet in the third second. If it continues at this rate, how many feet will it rise in the 20th second? (Lesson 11–1) **780 ft**

46. Solve $4.3^{3x+1} = 78.5$. (Lesson 10–6) **about 0.6638**

47. Use a calculator to find the natural logarithm of 0.056, rounded to four decimal places. (Lesson 10–5) **−2.8824**

48. Construction Mike Welch can paint his house in 15 hours. His friend Joe can paint the house in 20 hours. If they work together, how long will it take them to paint the house? (Lesson 9–5) $8\frac{4}{7}$ **hours**

49. Determine whether the graph at the right represents an odd-degree function or an even-degree function. Then state how many real zeros the function has. (Lesson 8–1) **even; 2**

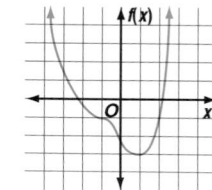

50. Solve the system of equations. (Lesson 7–7)
$$x - y = -2$$
$$\frac{(x-2)^2}{16} + \frac{y^2}{16} = 1 \quad (-2, 0), (2, 4)$$

51. $f(x) = x^2 + 4x - 2;$
$x^2; 4x; -2$

51. Write $f(x) = (x+2)^2 - 6$ in quadratic form. Identify the quadratic term, the linear term, and the constant term. (Lesson 6–1)

52. Statistics The U.S. Department of Agriculture recommends two to four servings of fruit daily. Fruit is a good source of fiber as well as vitamins and minerals. The chart at the right displays the fiber content for one serving size of each fruit listed. (Lesson 4–8)

   a. Find the range of the data. **3.4**

   b. Find the quartiles of the data. **0.6, 0.8, 1.5**

   c. Find the interquartile range of the data. **0.9**

   d. Name any outliers in the data. **3.7**

   e. Make a box-and-whisker plot of the data. **See margin.**

The Pick of the Crop	Fruit	Fiber (gm)
	Apple	1.0
	Apricots	1.0
	Banana	0.6
	Blueberries	2.0
	Cantaloupe	0.6
	Grapefruit	0.3
	Kiwi	0.8
	Orange	0.6
	Peach	0.6
	Pear	2.3
	Raspberries	3.7
	Strawberries	0.8
	Watermelon	0.5

Source: *Vitality,* Sept. 1995

Extension

Problem Solving The Cortez family moved to a new house six years ago. The value of the house increased 5 percent of the original price the first year, 10 percent the second year, 15 percent the third year, and so on for six years. If the value of the house today is $123,000, how much did the Cortez family pay for the house?
$60,000

---

4 ASSESS

Closing Activity

Modeling Using small objects such as beans, paper clips, and so on, have students model an arithmetic series.

Chapter 11, Quiz A (Lessons 11-1 and 11-2), is available in the *Assessment and Evaluation Masters,* p. 296.

Additional Answer

52e.

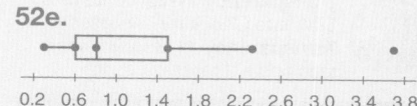

Enrichment Masters, p. 77

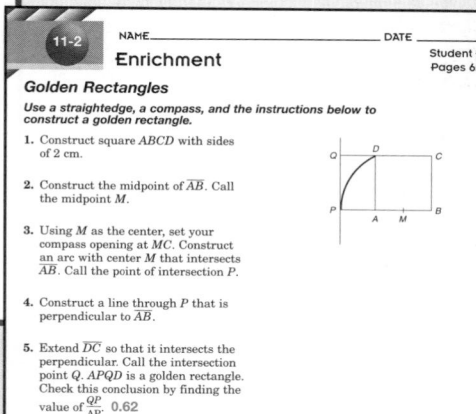

11-2 NAME_____ DATE_____
Enrichment
Student Edition
Pages 655–660

Golden Rectangles

Use a straightedge, a compass, and the instructions below to construct a golden rectangle.

1. Construct square *ABCD* with sides of 2 cm.

2. Construct the midpoint of $\overline{AB}$. Call the midpoint *M*.

3. Using *M* as the center, set your compass opening at *MC*. Construct an arc with center *M* that intersects $\overline{AB}$. Call the point of intersection *P*.

4. Construct a line through *P* that is perpendicular to $\overline{AB}$.

5. Extend $\overline{DC}$ so that it intersects the perpendicular. Call the intersection point *Q*. *APQD* is a golden rectangle. Check this conclusion by finding the value of $\frac{QP}{AP}$. 0.62

A figure consisting of similar golden rectangles is shown below. Use a compass and the instructions below to draw quarter-circle arcs that form a spiral like that found in the shell of a chambered nautilus.

6. Using *A* as a center, draw an arc that passes through *B* and *C*.

7. Using *D* as a center, draw an arc that passes through *C* and *E*.

8. Using *F* as a center, draw an arc that passes through *E* and *G*.

9. Continue drawing arcs, using *H*, *K*, and *M* as the centers.

NCTM Standards: 1–5, 8, 12

Instructional Resources

- Study Guide Master 11-3
- Practice Master 11-3
- Enrichment Master 11-3
- Tech Prep Applications Masters, p. 21

Transparency 11-3A contains the 5-Minute Check for this lesson; **Transparency 11-3B** contains a teaching aid for this lesson.

Recommended Pacing	
Standard Pacing	Day 5 of 14
Honors Pacing	Day 4 of 11
Block Scheduling*	Day 3 of 7 (along with Lesson 11-4)

*For more information on pacing and possible lesson plans, refer to the *Block Scheduling Booklet*.

1 FOCUS

5-Minute Check
(over Lesson 11-2)

Find the sum S_n for each arithmetic series described.

1. $a_1 = 4$, $a_n = -16$, and $n = 5$.
   $S_5 = -30$
2. $a_1 = 3$, $a_n = 33$, and $n = 6$.
   $S_6 = 108$
3. Find the sum of the even integers from 2 through 1000. 250,500
4. Find the sum of the series $-4 + (-1) + 2 + 5 + \ldots + 53$.
   $S = 490$
5. Find the sum of the series $\sum_{k=0}^{5} (5k - 7)$. $S = 33$

Motivating the Lesson

Situational Problem Show students a picture of some bacteria growing in a petri dish. Ask students if they can name the number of organisms produced by 6 initial organisms reproducing one time. Ask how many would be produced by each of these new organisms reproducing.

662 *Chapter 11*

11-3

Geometric Sequences

What YOU'LL LEARN

- To find the *n*th term of a geometric sequence,
- to find the position of a given term in a geometric sequence, and
- to find geometric means.

Why IT'S IMPORTANT

You can use geometric sequences to solve problems involving literature and animation.

APPLICATION
Animation

Animation is the process of using drawings in a sequential manner to simulate movement. A full-feature film requires hundreds of thousands of hand-painted scenes called *cels*. In 1994, Disney's *The Lion King* used a combination of painted cels and computer graphics to minimize the number of cels needed for the picture. For example, one set of cels was produced to picture a wildebeest running over a hillside. The computer technicians took those cels, duplicated them electronically, and produced the effect of a herd of hundreds of wildebeests running over the same hillside.

To produce a vanishing effect in an animation film, the character's image is reduced 50% with each consecutive cel. Suppose the original area of a character's image is defined as 1 (representing 100%) and the vanishing effect is applied over 8 cels of film. What happens to the area of the character with each successive reduction?

Number of Reductions	0	1	2	3	4	5	6	7	8
Area of Image	1	$\frac{1}{2}$	$\frac{1}{4}$	$\frac{1}{8}$	$\frac{1}{16}$	$\frac{1}{32}$	$\frac{1}{64}$	$\frac{1}{128}$	$\frac{1}{256}$
Percent of Original	100	50	25	12.5	6.25	3.125	1.5625	0.78125	0.390625

Pattern $\times\frac{1}{2}$ $\times\frac{1}{2}$ $\times\frac{1}{2}$ $\times\frac{1}{2}$ $\times\frac{1}{2}$ $\times\frac{1}{2}$ $\times\frac{1}{2}$ $\times\frac{1}{2}$

FYI

In 1995, Disney released *Toy Story*, which was the first completely computer-animated film.

Let's graph the function represented by the number of reductions and the percent of the original. Notice that these points follow the same pattern as the exponential function $y = \left(\frac{1}{2}\right)^x$, except that this graph is discrete.

Notice that with each successive reduction the image is one-half the size of the previous image. Each term of the sequence is found by multiplying the previous term by $\frac{1}{2}$. This is an example of a **geometric sequence**. The number by which each term is multiplied is called the **common ratio** and is symbolized by the variable *r*.

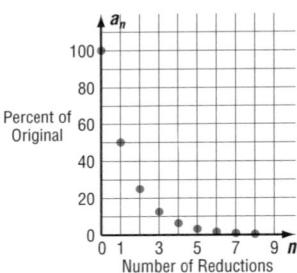

Definition of Geometric Sequence	A geometric sequence is one in which each term after the first is found by multiplying the previous term by a constant called the common ratio, *r*.

FYI

The world's first full-length animated film was *The Adventures of Prince Achmed*. It was developed by a German artist in 1926.

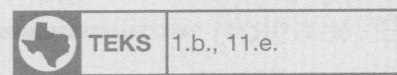

TEKS 1.b., 11.e.

As with arithmetic sequences, you can name the terms of a geometric sequence using a_1, a_2, a_3, and so on. Suppose the nth term is defined as a_n. Then its previous term is a_{n-1}. So, $a_n = r(a_{n-1})$. Thus, $r = \dfrac{a_n}{a_{n-1}}$. That is, the common ratio is found by dividing any term by its previous term. This can be used to find any term in a geometric sequence.

Example **Find the next two terms of the geometric sequence 3, 12, 48, ...**

First find the common ratio. Let 3 be a_{n-1} and let 12 be a_n.

$$r = \frac{a_n}{a_{n-1}}$$
$$= \frac{12}{3} \text{ or } 4 \qquad \text{The common ratio is 4.}$$

The fourth term is $a_4 = r \cdot a_3$, so $a_4 = 4(48)$ or 192.

The fifth term is $a_5 = r \cdot a_4$, so $a_5 = 4(192)$ or 768.

The next two terms of the sequence are 192 and 768.

CAREER CHOICES

A **computer scientist** develops and designs the hardware, the processor chips, and video cards that display the computer graphics for computer animation.

Computer scientists have a background in mathematics, science and engineering, and usually a degree in computer science.

For more information, contact:

Association for Computer Machinery
1515 Broadway
New York, NY 10036

We have seen that each term of a geometric sequence can be expressed in terms of r and its previous term. However, it is also possible to develop a formula that expresses each term of a geometric sequence in terms of r and the first term a_1. Study the patterns shown in the table below for the sequence 3, 12, 48, 192, ...

Sequence	numerical	3	12	48	192	. . .	
	symbols	a_1	a_2	a_3	a_4	. . .	a_n
Expressed in Terms of r and the Previous Term	numerical	3	3(4)	12(4)	48(4)	. . .	
	symbols	a_1	$a_1 \cdot r$	$a_2 \cdot r$	$a_3 \cdot r$	. . .	$a_{n-1} \cdot r$
Expressed in Terms of r and the First Term	numerical	3 $3(4^0)$	3(4) $3(4^1)$	3(16) $3(4^2)$	3(64) $3(4^3)$	. . .	
	symbols	$a_1 \cdot r^0$	$a_1 \cdot r^1$	$a_1 \cdot r^2$	$a_1 \cdot r^3$	. . .	$a_1 \cdot r^{n-1}$

The three values in the last column of the table all describe the nth term of a geometric sequence. This leads us to the following formula for finding any term of a geometric sequence.

Formula for the nth term of a Geometric Sequence	The nth term a_n of a geometric sequence with first term a_1 and common ratio r is given by either formula. $$a_n = a_{n-1} \cdot r \qquad \text{or} \qquad a_n = a_1 \cdot r^{n-1}$$

Since a_n can represent any term of the sequence, you can use these formulas to find the value of any term in a geometric sequence.

2 TEACH

In-Class Example

For Example 1
Find the next two terms of each geometric sequence.
a. 4, 16, 64, ... 256, 1024
b. 81, 27, 9, ... 3, 1

Teaching Tip Be sure students understand the importance of using consecutive terms to find the common ratio, not just any two terms.

CAREER CHOICES

Computer science was established as a discipline in the 1960s. It has been redefined many times since then. Because of the constant advances and developments in technology, a computer scientist needs to change with the times and keep up with advances.

 Cooperative Learning

Trade-A-Problem Using groups of four students each, have one student write the first few terms of a geometric sequence. Have other students, in turn, name a_1, r, and a value for n. Have students collectively determine a value for a_n.

For more information on the trade-a-problem strategy, see *Cooperative Learning in the Mathematics Classroom,* one of the titles in the Glencoe Mathematics Professional Series, pages 25–26.

In-Class Examples

For Example 2
Write the first six terms of each geometric sequence described.

a. $a_1 = 4$ and $r = 3$
 4, 12, 36, 108, 324, 972

b. $a_1 = 125$ and $r = -\frac{2}{5}$
 125, −50, 20, −8, $\frac{16}{5}$, −$\frac{32}{25}$

For Example 3
Find the nth term of each described geometric sequence.

a. $a_4 = 10$, $n = 5$, $r = \frac{1}{2}$ 5

b. $a_6 = 5$, $n = 9$, $r = 3$ 135

For Example 4
The illustration below shows a sequence of squares. What would be the dimensions of the next two squares in the sequence?
Side = 27 for the fourth square, and side = 81 for the fifth square.

  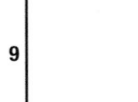

Example **Write the first six terms of a geometric sequence in which $a_1 = 3$ and $r = 2$.**

Method 1: Use $a_n = a_{n-1} \cdot r$.

$a_1 = 3$
$a_2 = 3 \times 2$ or 6
$a_3 = 6 \times 2$ or 12
$a_4 = 12 \times 2$ or 24
$a_5 = 24 \times 2$ or 48
$a_6 = 48 \times 2$ or 96

Method 2: Use $a_n = a_1 \cdot r^{n-1}$.

$a_1 = 3 \cdot 2^{1-1}$ or 3
$a_2 = 3 \cdot 2^{2-1}$ or 6
$a_3 = 3 \cdot 2^{3-1}$ or 12
$a_4 = 3 \cdot 2^{4-1}$ or 24
$a_5 = 3 \cdot 2^{5-1}$ or 48
$a_6 = 3 \cdot 2^{6-1}$ or 96

You can also use the formula for the nth term to find a given term when you know the common ratio and one term of the geometric sequence, but not the first term of the sequence.

Example **Find the ninth term of a geometric sequence in which $a_3 = 63$ and $r = -3$.**

Method 1

Start with the third term and use the common ratio to find the ninth term.

$a_3 = 63$
$a_4 = 63 \cdot (-3)$ or -189
$a_5 = -189 \cdot (-3)$ or 567
$a_6 = 567 \cdot (-3)$ or -1701
$a_7 = -1701 \cdot (-3)$ or 5103
$a_8 = 5103 \cdot (-3)$ or $-15{,}309$
$a_9 = -15{,}309 \cdot (-3)$ or 45,927

Method 2

First find the value of a_1.
$a_3 = a_1 \cdot r^{3-1}$
$63 = a_1 \cdot (-3)^2$
$\frac{63}{9} = a_1$
$7 = a_1$

Use the formula $a_n = a_1 \cdot r^{n-1}$ to find a_9.
$a_9 = a_1 \cdot r^{9-1}$
$\quad = 7 \cdot (-3)^8$ or 45,927

The ninth term of the sequence is 45,927.

Geometric sequences can be modeled in ways other than lists of numbers.

Example **The illustration below shows a sequence of 30°-60°-90° triangles. Draw the next triangle in the sequence.**

INTEGRATION
Geometry

Notice that the measure of each side of the triangle is twice the measure of the corresponding side in the previous triangle. Thus, the measures form a geometric sequence and $r = 2$.

Multiply each side of the last triangle by 2 to find the measures of the sides of the fourth triangle and draw the triangle.
$8 \cdot 2 = 16$
$4 \cdot 2 = 8$
$4\sqrt{3} \cdot 2 = 8\sqrt{3}$

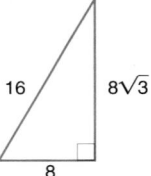

GLENCOE *Technology*

Interactive Mathematics Tools Software

This multimedia software provides an interactive lesson in which students determine the next number in a geometric sequence. A **Computer Journal** gives students an opportunity to write about what they have learned.

For Windows & Macintosh

In Lesson 11–1A, you learned to use a graphing calculator to find and graph the terms of an arithmetic sequence. You can use the same skills with geometric sequences.

TECHNOLOGY Tips

You can also view the full list created by the seq(command by using the left and right arrow keys to scroll through the values immediately after pressing ENTER .

LOOK BACK

You can refer to Lesson 2-5B for more information on graphing scatter plots on a graphing calculator.

1, −2, 4, −8, 16, −32, 64, −128, 256, −512; See margin for graph.

EXPLORATION
GRAPHING CALCULATORS

Use a graphing calculator to find the first 12 terms of a geometric sequence in which $a_1 = 4$ and $r = 0.5$. Then graph the sequence.

First clear the L1, L2, and Y= lists. Use the seq(command to enter the values of n into L1. Be sure to enter the information from the home screen.

Enter: 2nd LIST 5 ALPHA N , ALPHA N , 1 , 12 ,
1) STO▶ 2nd L1 ENTER   {1 2 3 4 5 6 7 ...

Use the general formula with the seq(command to calculate the terms of the sequence and enter them into L2.

Enter: 2nd LIST 5 4 × .5 ∧ (ALPHA N − 1)
, ALPHA N , 1 , 12 , 1) STO▶ 2nd L2
ENTER   {4 2 1 .5 .25 ...

Press STAT 1 to view the lists containing the sequence terms. Take note of the range of values in list L2 so that you can set the proper window for graphing the sequence.

After entering the WINDOW settings, press 2nd STAT PLOT 1. Make sure the plot is turned on, the scatter plot is selected, L1 is the Xlist, and L2 is the Ylist. Then press GRAPH .

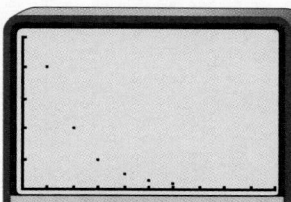

Your Turn

Find the first ten terms of a geometric sequence in which $a_1 = 1$ and $r = -2$. Then graph the sequence.

EXPLORATION

In this activity, students will become familiar with the features of a graphing calculator needed to graph a sequence. Point out that a scatter plot is used instead of curve-fitting because a sequence is not a smooth function, but simply isolated points.

Answer for the Exploration

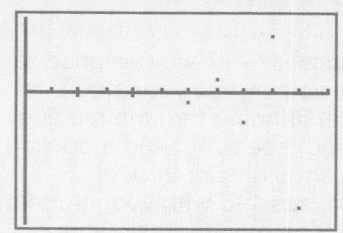

In Lesson 11–1, you learned that the missing terms between two nonconsecutive terms in an arithmetic sequence were called *arithmetic means*. Likewise, the missing term(s) between two nonconsecutive terms in a geometric sequence are called **geometric means**. In the sequence 3, 12, 48, 192, 768, ..., the three geometric means between 3 and 768 are 12, 48, and 192. You can use the common ratio to find the geometric means in a given sequence.

In-Class Example

For Example 5

Find the missing geometric means for the sequence $\underline{\quad}, \underline{\quad}, 25, \underline{\quad}, \underline{\quad}, \underline{\quad}, \underline{\quad}, \dfrac{32}{125}$.

$\dfrac{625}{4}, \dfrac{125}{2}, 10, 4, \dfrac{8}{5}, \dfrac{16}{25}$

3 PRACTICE/APPLY

Check for Understanding

Exercises 1–17 are designed to help you assess your students' understanding through reading, writing, speaking, and modeling. You should work through Exercises 1–5 with your students and then monitor their work on Exercises 6–17.

Error Analysis

When students are finding a geometric mean, have them check their answers by dividing some of the terms to see if they get the same r each time.

Additional Answers

1. Each successive term of a geometric sequence is found by multiplying the previous term by a number instead of adding a number to the previous term as in an arithmetic sequence.
2. The common ratio is the factor relating two consecutive terms of a geometric sequence.
3. Find the ratio between each pair of terms. If all pairs have the same ratio, the sequence is a geometric sequence.
4. Sample answer: Let $a_1 = 324$, so 12 would be a_4. Use the general formula for the nth term of a geometric sequence to find the value of r and then use that value to find the missing terms: 108 and 36.

Example 5

a. Find the three geometric means between 3.4 and 2125.
b. Graph the sequence using the x-axis for the number of the term and the y-axis for the term itself.

a. You can use the nth term formula to find the value of r. In the sequence 3.4, $\underline{?}$, $\underline{?}$, $\underline{?}$, 2125, 3.4 is a_1 and 2125 is a_5.

$a_n = a_1 \cdot r^{n-1}$
$a_5 = a_1 \cdot r^{5-1}$ $n = 5$
$2125 = 3.4 \cdot r^4$ $a_5 = 2125$ and $a_1 = 3.4$
$625 = r^4$ *Divide each side by 3.4.*
$\pm 5 = r$ *Take the fourth root of each side.*

There are two possible common ratios, so there are two possible sets of geometric means. Use each value of r to find the missing terms.

$r = 5$	$r = -5$
$a_1 = 3.4 \,(5)$ or 17	$a_1 = 3.4 \,(-5)$ or -17
$a_2 = 17(5)$ or 85	$a_2 = -17(-5)$ or 85
$a_3 = 85(5)$ or 425	$a_3 = 85(-5)$ or -425

Check: Will each value of r give you the correct 5th term?
$425(5) = 2125$ ✓ $-425(-5) = 2125$ ✓

The geometric means are 17, 85, and 425 or $-17, 85,$ and -425.

b.
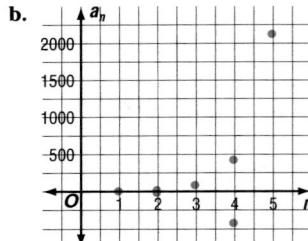

CHECK FOR UNDERSTANDING

Communicating Mathematics

5. No, if r is negative, the points do not fall into this pattern.

Math Journal

Study the lesson. Then complete the following.   1–4. See margin.

1. **Explain** how a geometric sequence differs from an arithmetic sequence.
2. **Define** common ratio.
3. **Explain** how you know if a list of numbers forms a geometric sequence.
4. **Explain** how you would find the two geometric means between 324 and 12.
5. **Assess Yourself** The points of the graph of the geometric sequence in the Exploration are part of the graph of an exponential function. Do you think this statement holds true for the graphs of all geometric sequences? Explain. Give an example to support your answer.

666   Chapter 11   *Investigating Sequences and Series*

Reteaching

Using Problem Solving Have each student in each row of the class make up problems given a task. For example: Row 1: Students make up their own geometric sequence, giving the first three terms and asking for the fourth term.

Row 2: Students make up their own geometric sequence, giving the first and nth term and asking for the geometric mean, and so on. Have students exchange problems and solve.

Guided Practice

Determine whether each sequence is geometric. If so, find the common ratio.

6. $5, 20, 80, 320$ **yes, 4**

7. $3, -15, 75, -375$ **yes, −5**

8. $5, 20, 35, 50$ **no**

9. $\frac{2}{3}, \frac{4}{9}, \frac{8}{27}, \frac{16}{81}$ **yes, $\frac{2}{3}$**

Find the next two terms of each geometric sequence.

10. $20, 30, 45, \ldots$ **67.5, 101.25**

11. $-\frac{1}{4}, \frac{1}{2}, -1$ **2, −4**

12. Find the first five terms of the geometric sequence in which $a_1 = -2$ and $r = 3$.   **−2, −6, −18, −54, −162**

Find the nth term of each geometric sequence.

13. $a_1 = 7, n = 4, r = 2$ **56**

14. $a_3 = 32, n = 6, r = -0.5$ **−4**

16a. 2, 4

15. Find a_9 for the geometric sequence $60, 30, 15, \ldots$ $\frac{15}{64}$

16. **a.** Find the two geometric means between 1 and 8.

   b. Graph the sequence using the x-axis for the number of the term and the y-axis for the term itself.   **See Solutions Manual.**

F Y I

During 1812–1822, Jakob and Wilhelm Grimm published three volumes of folk stories that they had gathered from the people in their village of Kassel, Germany. Today, the collection of over 210 tales is known as *Grimm's Fairy Tales*.

17. **Literature**   In one of Grimm's Fairy Tales, Rumpelstiltskin has the ability to spin straw into gold. Suppose on the first day, he spun 5 pieces of straw into gold, and each day thereafter he spun twice as much. How many pieces of straw would he have spun into gold by the end of a week?   **635**

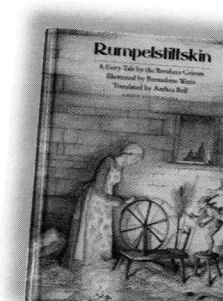

EXERCISES

Practice

A

Find the next two terms of each geometric sequence.   **20. 54, 81**

18. $405, 135, 45, \ldots$ **15, 5**

19. $81, 108, 144, \ldots$

20. $16, 24, 36, \ldots$

21. $162, 108, 72, \ldots$

22. $\frac{4}{27}, -\frac{4}{9}, \frac{4}{3}, \ldots$ **−4, 12**

23. $64, -16, 4, \ldots$

19. **192, 256**

21. **48, 32**

23. **−1, $\frac{1}{4}$**

24. **2, −6, 18, −54, 162**

25. **243, 81, 27, 9, 3**

26. **576, −288, 144, −72, 36**

Find the first five terms of each geometric sequence described.

24. $a_1 = 2, \ r = -3$

25. $a_1 = 243, r = \frac{1}{3}$

26. $a_1 = 576, r = -0.5$

Find the nth term of each geometric sequence.

27. $a_1 = \frac{1}{3}, n = 8, r = 3$ **729**

28. $a_1 = \frac{1}{64}, n = 9, r = 4$ **1024**

29. $a_1 = 16{,}807, n = 6, r = \frac{3}{7}$ **243**

30. $a_1 = 4096, n = 8, r = \frac{1}{4}$ $\frac{1}{4}$

B

31. $a_4 = 16, n = 8, r = 0.5$ **1**

32. $a_6 = 3, n = 12, r = 2$ **192**

Find the indicated term in each geometric sequence.

33. a_9 for $\frac{1}{5}, 1, 5, \ldots$ **78,125**

34. a_7 for $\frac{1}{32}, \frac{1}{16}, \frac{1}{8}, \ldots$ **2**

35. a_8 for $4, -12, 36, \ldots$ **−8748**

36. a_6 for $540, 90, 15, \ldots$ $\frac{5}{72}$

37. **±18, 36, ±72**

38. **±12, 36, ±108**

39. **16, 8, 4, 2**

40. **3, 6, 24, 48**

Find the geometric means in each sequence. Then graph each sequence using the x-axis for the number of the term and the y-axis for the term itself.   **37–40. See margin for graphs.**

37. $9, \underline{\ ?\ }, \underline{\ ?\ }, \underline{\ ?\ }, 144$

38. $4, \underline{\ ?\ }, \underline{\ ?\ }, \underline{\ ?\ }, 324$

39. $32, \underline{\ ?\ }, \underline{\ ?\ }, \underline{\ ?\ }, \underline{\ ?\ }, 1$

40. $\underline{\ ?\ }, \underline{\ ?\ }, 12, \underline{\ ?\ }, \underline{\ ?\ }, 96$

Lesson 11–3   Geometric Sequences   **667**

Additional Answers

39.

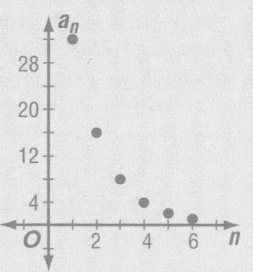

40.

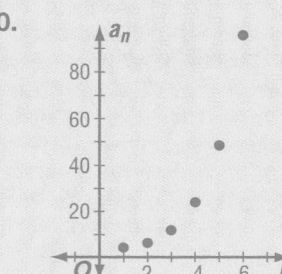

Assignment Guide

Core: 19–57 odd, 58–67
Enriched: 18–50 even, 52–67

For **Extra Practice,** see p. 901.

The red A, B, and C flags, printed only in the Teacher's Wraparound Edition, indicate the level of difficulty of the exercises.

F Y I

The Brothers Grimm studied law before circumstances turned them to folklore. *Grimm's Fairy Tales* is translated into 70 languages and is considered the earliest "scientific" collection of folktales.

Additional Answers

37.

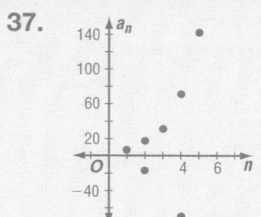

38.

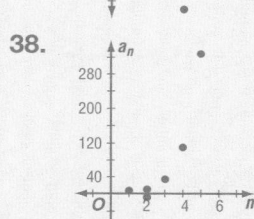

Study Guide Masters, p. 78

11-3   NAME_____ DATE_____

Study Guide   Student Edition Pages 661–666

Geometric Sequences

A **geometric sequence** is a sequence in which each term after the first can be found by multiplying the preceding term by a constant, called the **common ratio**. The common ratio, r, can be found by dividing any term by the preceding term. The terms between any two nonconsecutive terms of a geometric sequence are called **geometric means**.

nth Term of the Geometric Sequence

The nth term, a_n, of a geometric sequence with first term a_1 and common ratio r is given by either of the following formulas.

$a_n = a_{n-1} r$ or $a_n = a_1 r^{n-1}$

Example: Write the first four terms of a geometric sequence in which $a_1 = 3$ and $r = 2$. Find each term using the formula $a_n = a_1 r^{n-1}$.

a_1	a_2	a_3	a_4
3	$3 \cdot 2$	$3 \cdot 2^2$	$3 \cdot 2^3$
3	6	12	24

The first four terms are 3, 6, 12, and 24.

Find the nth term of each geometric sequence.

1. $a_1 = -10, r = 4, n = 2$
   −40

2. $a_1 = 4, r = 3, n = 9$
   26,244

3. $a_1 = -14, r = -\frac{1}{2}, n = 5$
   $-\frac{7}{8}$

4. $a_1 = -6, r = -\frac{1}{2}, n = 8$
   $\frac{3}{64}$

5. $a_1 = 9, r = -3, n = 7$
   729

6. $a_1 = 16, r = 2, n = 10$
   1024

7. $a_1 = -1, r = -1, n = 100$
   −1

8. $a_3 = \frac{3}{8}, r = \frac{1}{2}, n = 6$
   $\frac{3}{64}$

9. $a_4 = \frac{1}{81}, r = \frac{1}{3}, n = 5$
   $\frac{1}{243}$

10. $a_1 = 8, r = \frac{2}{3}, n = 5$
   $\frac{128}{81}$

11. $a_5 = \frac{1}{10}, r = \frac{1}{10}, n = 6$
   $\frac{1}{10{,}000}$

12. $a_4 = -54, r = -3, n = 6$
   −486

Chapter 11   **667**

Additional Answers

49. 2, 4, 8, 16, 32

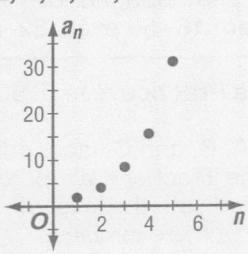

50. 12, 6, 3, 1.5, 0.75, 0.375, 0.1875, 0.09375, 0.046875, 0.0234375

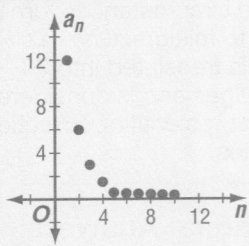

51. 243, 81, 27, 9, 3, 1, $\frac{1}{3}$, $\frac{1}{9}$

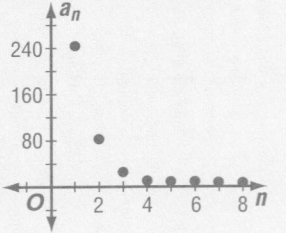

Practice Masters, p. 78

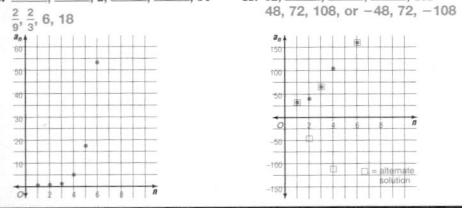

NAME_____ DATE _____

11-3   **Practice**   Student Edition
Pages 661–666

Geometric Sequences
Find the first four terms of each geometric sequence.

1. $a_1 = -6, r = -\frac{2}{3}$
$-6, 4, -\frac{8}{3}, \frac{16}{9}$

2. $a_1 = 2, r = \sqrt{3}$
$2, 2\sqrt{3}, 6, 6\sqrt{3}$

3. $a_1 = -\frac{5}{2}, r = 2$
$-\frac{5}{2}, -5, -10, -20$

4. $a_1 = \sqrt{2}, r = \sqrt{3}$
$\sqrt{2}, \sqrt{6}, 3\sqrt{2}, 3\sqrt{6}$

Find the nth term of each geometric sequence.

5. $a_1 = 5, n = 4, r = 3$ 135

6. $a_4 = 20, n = 6, r = -3$ 180

7. $a_1 = -4, n = 6, r = -2$ 128

8. $a_5 = 8, n = 12, r = \frac{1}{2}$ $\frac{1}{8}$

Solve.
9. Each foot of water screens out 60% of the light above. What percent of the light remains after passing through 5 feet of water? 1.024%

Find the geometric means in each sequence. Then graph each sequence, using the x-axis for the number of the term and the y-axis for the term itself.

10. $\frac{2}{9}, \frac{2}{3}, \_\_\_, 2, \_\_\_, \_\_\_, 54$
$\frac{2}{3}, 6, 18$

11. 32, $\_\_\_, \_\_\_, \_\_\_, 162$
48, 72, 108, or −48, 72, −108

Find the value(s) of y that makes each sequence geometric.

41. 2, 8, 32, $5y + 3$, ... 25

42. 3, 6, $2y + 18$, ... −3

43. $y + 1, y, y - 4,$ ... $-\frac{4}{3}$

44. $y + 1, 2y - 1, 4y - 3,$ ... $\frac{4}{5}$

Write the formula for the nth term for each graphed sequence.

45.

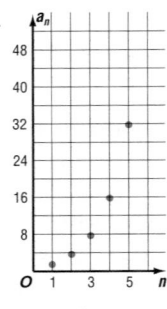

$a_n = 2^n$

46.

$a_n = 36\left(\frac{1}{3}\right)^{n-1}$

47.

$a_n = \frac{4}{25}(-5)^{n-1}$

48. The first term of a geometric sequence is 0.6, and each term is 4 times the previous term.

a. Find the value of the seventh term. 2457.6

b. Write a formula for the nth term of this sequence. $a_n = 0.6(4)^{n-1}$

Graphing Calculator

Use a graphing calculator to list the first n terms of each geometric sequence described. Then graph the sequence. Sketch the graph on grid paper. 49–51. See margin.

49. $a_1 = 2, n = 5, r = 2$

50. $a_1 = 12, n = 10, r = 0.5$

51. $a_1 = 243, n = 8, r = \frac{1}{3}$

Critical Thinking

52. $c = \frac{b^2}{a}$
53. See margin.

52. The first three terms of a geometric sequence are a, b, and c. Express c in terms of a and b. Justify your answer.

53. Write an argument to show that $a_n = a_{n-1}r$ and $a_n = a_1 r^{n-1}$ are equivalent.

54. If each term of a geometric sequence is multiplied by the same real number, is the resulting sequence geometric? Explain. **Yes, both sequences have the same value of r.**

Applications and Problem Solving

55. Ice Sculpture In many states where snow and ice are abundant in the winter months, art students at various universities have ice sculpting contests. They use chain saws, axes, and chisels to create their masterpieces. The events are held outdoors when the temperature is cold enough to prevent rapid thawing. Suppose a warm front passes through during the contest and a 1000-pound sculpture begins to melt. It loses one-fifth of its weight per hour. How much of the sculpture will be left after 6 hours? 262.144 lb

Additional Answer

53. Sample answer: In a geometric sequence, each subsequent term can be found by multiplying the preceding term by r. So the nth term of a sequence a_n would equal $a_{n-1}r$. Each term of the sequence can be expressed in terms of the first term. The second term is $a_1 \cdot r$, the third term is $a_1 \cdot r \cdot r$ or $a_1 r^2$, the fourth term is $a_1 \cdot r \cdot r \cdot r$ or $a_1 r^3$, and so on. Notice each term is a product of a_1 and $n-1$ factors of r. So the nth term would be $a_1 r^{n-1}$. Since $a_{n-1}r$ and $a_1 r^{n-1}$ both describe the nth term, they are equivalent.

56. Medicine   Iodine-131 is used medically to study the activity of the thyroid gland. Iodine-131 has a *half-life* of about 8 days. This means that approximately every 8 days, half of the mass of the iodine decays into another element. If a container held a mass of 64 milligrams of iodine-131, how much is left after 40 days?   **2 mg**

57. Aquatic Farming   In Spain, blue mussels are grown in farms that have produced up to 250,000 pounds of pure seafood per acre per year. This compares with using land to grow cattle at a rate of 100 pounds of beef per acre per year. The farms consist of parallel ropes, called *long lines*, that float on the surface of the ocean. From these long lines, ropes are suspended vertically upon which the mussels grow.

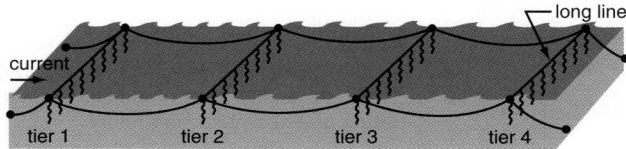

As the water flows through the mussels, they filter out available food particles. If there are equal numbers of mussels in each tier, the concentration of food particles in the water should decrease by the same percent as the water moves from tier to tier.

a. Suppose that the food concentration entering the first tier is 320 mg/L and 99% of the food particles that enter each tier remains as the water leaves the tier. What is the concentration of food entering the 5th tier?   **307 mg/L**

b. After how many tiers will the concentration of the food particles be less than 75% of the original concentration?   **29 tiers**

57c. at most 47 tiers

c. Assuming there must be at least 200 mg/L of food for a mussel to survive, what is the maximum number of tiers possible in this farm?

Mixed Review

58. Find S_n for an arithmetic series in which $a_1 = 11$, $a_n = 44$, and $n = 23$. (Lesson 11–2)   **632.5**

59. Solve $\log_5 4 + \log_5 x = \log_5 36$. (Lesson 10–3)   **9**

60. Real Estate   Budget Realty charges a commission of $4800 on the sale of a $90,000 home. At that rate, how much commission would be charged on the sale of a $219,000 home? (Lesson 9–2)   **$11,680**

61. Solve $x - 7\sqrt{x} - 8 = 0$. (Lesson 8–6)   **64**

62. Graph $f(x) = x^4 - 8x^2 + 10$. (Lesson 8–3)   **See margin.**

63. $x = \frac{1}{18}(y + 7)^2 + \frac{5}{2}$

63. Write an equation of the parabola with a focus at $(7, -7)$ and $x = -2$ as the equation of its directrix. (Lesson 7–2)

64. Solve $(x - 7)(x + 2) > 0$. (Lesson 6–7) $\{x \mid x < -2 \text{ or } x > 7\}$

65. Simplify $(5 + i)(2 - 3i)$. (Lesson 5–9) $13 - 13i$

66. Factor $3y^2 + 5y + 2$. (Lesson 5–4) $(3y + 2)(y + 1)$

67. O'Hare, 31.2 million; Heathrow, 24 million

67. Airports   According to the Airports Council International, the busiest airport in the world is Chicago's O'Hare Airport, and the second busiest is London's Heathrow Airport. Together they handled 55.2 million passengers in the first six months of 1994. If O'Hare handled 7.2 million more than Heathrow, how many were handled by each airport? (Lesson 3–2)

Extension

Connections Suppose the height of a plant is measured in meters every four weeks and the results are expressed as the geometric sequence 1, 1.04, 1.0816, ... How tall was the plant when first measured? What is the value of *r*? Approximately how tall will the plant be after 10 months?
1 meter, 1.04, 1.4802 meters

Tech Prep

Medical Technician Students who are interested in medicine may wish to do further research on the data given in Exercise 56 and explore the potential growth of this career. For more information on tech prep, see the *Teacher's Handbook.*

4 ASSESS

Closing Activity

Speaking Have students use examples to explain why either formula for a_n can be used to determine its value.

Additional Answer

62.

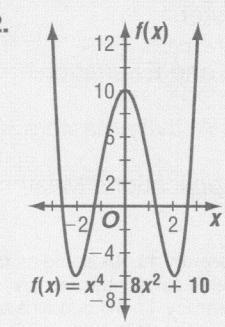

$f(x) = x^4 - 8x^2 + 10$

Enrichment Masters, p. 78

11-3   NAME _____   DATE _____
Enrichment   Student Edition
Pages 661–666

Half the Distance

Suppose you are 200 feet from a fixed point, P. Suppose that you are able to move to the halfway point in one minute, to the next halfway point one minute after that, and so on.

An interesting sequence results from this problem. According to the problem, you never actually reach the point P, but you do get arbitrarily close to it.

You can compute how long it will take to get within some specified small distance of the point. On a calculator, you enter the distance to be covered and then count the number of successive divisions by 2 necessary to get within the desired distance.

Example: How many minutes are needed to get within 0.1 feet of a point 200 feet away?

ENTER: 200 $\boxed{\div}$ 2 $\boxed{=}$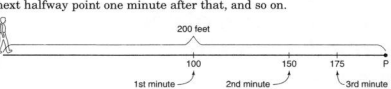

Result: 0.0976562
　Count the number of times pressing $\boxed{=}$.
　The time needed is 11 minutes.

Use the method illustrated above to solve each problem.

1. If it is about 2500 miles from Los Angeles to New York, how many minutes would it take to get within 0.1 mile of New York? How far from New York are you at that time? **15 minutes, 0.0762934 mile**

2. If it is 25,000 miles around Earth, how many minutes would it take to get within 0.5 mile of the full distance around Earth? How far short would you be? **16 minutes; 0.3814697 mile**

3. If it is about 250,000 miles from Earth to the Moon, how many minutes would it take to get within 0.5 mile of the Moon? How far from the surface of the Moon would you be? **19 minutes, 0.4768372 mile**

4. If it is about 30,000,000 feet from Honolulu to Miami, how many minutes would it take to get to within 1 foot of Miami? How far from Miami would you be at that time? **25 minutes, 0.8940697 foot**

5. If it is about 93,000,000 miles to the sun, how many minutes would it take to get within 500 miles of the sun? How far from the sun would you be at that time? **18 minutes, 354.766846 miles**

Instructional Resources

- Study Guide Master 11-4
- Practice Master 11-4
- Enrichment Master 11-4
- Assessment and Evaluation Masters, pp. 295–296
- Multicultural Activity Masters, p. 22
- Tech Prep Applications Masters, p. 22

 Transparency 11-4A contains the 5-Minute Check for this lesson; **Transparency 11-4B** contains a teaching aid for this lesson.

Recommended Pacing	
Standard Pacing	Days 6 & 7 of 14
Honors Pacing	Day 5 of 11
Block Scheduling*	Day 3 of 7 (along with Lesson 11-3)

 *For more information on pacing and possible lesson plans, refer to the *Block Scheduling Booklet*.

1 FOCUS

 ### 5-Minute Check
(over Lesson 11-3)

1. Find the next two terms of the geometric sequence 3, −12, 48, …. **−192, 768**

Find the *n*th term of each described geometric sequence.

2. $a_1 = -2$, $n = 5$, and $r = 3$
   $a_5 = -162$
3. $a_1 = -5$, $n = 4$, and $r = 2$
   $a_4 = -40$
4. Find the missing geometric means of the sequence 40, __, __, 135. **60, 90**
5. A certain model automobile depreciates 20% of its value each year. If it costs $16,800 new, what is its value at the end of eight years? **$2818.57**

11-4

Geometric Series

 **APPLICATION**
Genealogy

What YOU'LL LEARN

- To find sums of geometric series,
- to find specific terms in a geometric series, and
- to use sigma notation to express sums.

Why IT'S IMPORTANT

You can use geometric series to solve problems involving aviation and genealogy.

Shantal is researching her ancestry. She has decided to create a family tree. To help her organize her research, Shantal wanted to figure out how many people she would be researching as she went back from generation to generation. She started her research by asking family members about her grandparents, great-grandparents, and great-great-grandparents. Let's use a diagram to help Shantal calculate her parental lineage for four generations. Let F represent father and M represent mother.

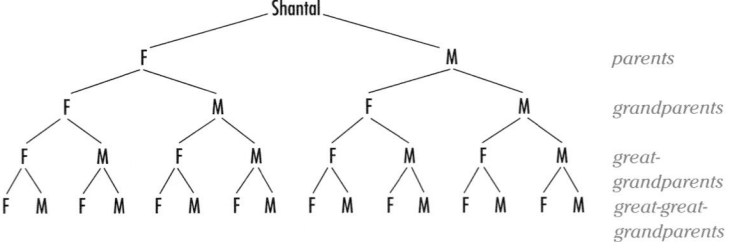

The total is given by the equation below.

$$\underbrace{2}_{\text{parents}} + \underbrace{4}_{\text{grandparents}} + \underbrace{8}_{\text{great-grandparents}} + \underbrace{16}_{\text{great-great-grandparents}} = 30$$

What would be the number of people in her parental family tree if she went back 8 previous generations?

Notice that 2, 4, 8, and 16 form a geometric sequence in which $a_1 = 2$ and $r = 2$. The indicated sum of the terms of a geometric sequence is called a **geometric series.** The lists below show examples of geometric sequences and their corresponding geometric series.

Geometric Sequences	Geometric Series
1, 3, 9, 27, 81	$1 + 3 + 9 + 27 + 81$
5, −10, 20	$5 + (-10) + 20$
$4, 1, \frac{1}{4}, \frac{1}{16}$	$4 + 1 + \frac{1}{4} + \frac{1}{16}$

You can develop a formula for finding the sum of a geometric series. Let's explore this formula using the sequence above for 8 terms. As with arithmetic series, S_n represents the sum of n terms.

$$S_8 = 2 + 4 + 8 + 16 + 32 + 64 + 128 + 256 \quad \textit{Now multiply each side by 2.}$$
$$(-)\ 2S_8 = \quad\ \ 4 + 8 + 16 + 32 + 64 + 128 + 256 + 512 \quad \textit{Align the terms.}$$
$$(1-2)S_8 = 2 + 0 + 0 + \ 0 + \ 0 + \ 0 + \ \ 0 + \ \ 0 - 512 \quad \textit{Subtract the two equations.}$$
$$S_8 = \frac{2 - 512}{1 - 2} \text{ or } 510$$

There are 510 people in Shantal's parental family tree for 8 previous generations.

Now let's analyze what these numbers represent in terms of S_n. In the equation $S_8 = \frac{2 - 512}{1 - 2}$, the 2 in the numerator represents a_1, 512 represents a_9, and the 2 in the denominator represents r. Thus, we can replace the equation with the formula $S_8 = \frac{a_1 - a_9}{1 - r}$. Since a_9 can also be written as $a_1 r^8$, this expression could also be written as $\frac{a_1 - a_1 r^8}{1 - r}$. These rational expressions can be used to find the sum of any geometric series.

Sum of a Geometric Series	**The sum S_n of the first n terms of a geometric series is given by** $$S_n = \frac{a_1 - a_1 r^n}{1 - r} \text{ or } S_n = \frac{a_1(1 - r^n)}{1 - r}, \text{ where } r \neq 1.$$

The formula for the sum of a geometric series restricts the value of r so that division by 0 does not occur. An example of a geometric series in which $r = 1$ is 3, 3, 3, ... To find the sum of n 3s, you would find the product of 3 and n or $3n$. In general terms, the sum of a geometric series in which $r = 1$ would be $n \cdot a_1$.

Example 1

Find the sum of the first six terms of the geometric series for which $a_1 = 5$ and $r = -2$.

$$S_n = \frac{a_1 - a_1 r^n}{1 - r}$$

$$= \frac{5 - 5(-2)^6}{1 - (-2)} \qquad a_1 = 5, r = -2, \text{ and } n = 6$$

$$= \frac{-315}{3} \text{ or } -105$$

The sum of the first six terms of the series is -105. *Check this result.*

Geometric series can be used to explain natural phenomena.

Example 2

APPLICATION

Aviation

As a hot-air balloon rises from Earth's surface, the air in the balloon cools. If the air is not reheated, the balloon rises more slowly with each minute of flight. Suppose that after 1 minute, a hot-air balloon rises 120 feet. In each succeeding minute, the balloon rises only 60% as far as it rose in the previous minute. How far will the balloon rise in 8 minutes?

The change in height after each minute is a geometric series in which $a_1 = 120$, $n = 8$, and $r = 0.6$. Use the formula for the sum of a geometric series.

$$S_n = \frac{a_1(1 - r^n)}{1 - r}$$

$$= \frac{120(1 - 0.6^8)}{1 - 0.6}$$

$$\approx 294.961152 \quad \textit{Use a calculator.}$$

The balloon will rise about 295 feet in 8 minutes.

Motivating the Lesson
Situational Problem Refer to Motivating the Lesson on p. 662. Ask students how they would know how many organisms were present after a given number of divisions.

2 TEACH

In-Class Examples

For Example 1
Find the sum of each described geometric series.
a. $a_1 = 16$, $r = \frac{1}{2}$, and $n = 7$
$\frac{127}{4}$ or 31.75

b. $a_1 = 4$, $r = -\frac{1}{2}$, and $n = 8$
$\frac{85}{32}$ or 2.656

For Example 2
How far will the balloon rise in 10 minutes?
about 298.186 feet

Teaching Tip Students associate addition with arithmetic sequences and multiplication with geometric sequences and may be confused when addition is used to find a geometric series. Emphasize that multiplication is used to find the terms of the geometric sequence but, by definition, a series of either type uses addition.

Cooperative Learning

Think-Pair-Share Using counters of one color to represent single digits and counters of another color to represent multiples of 10, have students model a sum for a given number of terms of a geometric series. Students should work with a partner. Have students use the formula to check the modeled sum. For more information on the think-pair-share strategy, see *Cooperative Learning in the Mathematics Classroom,* one of the titles in the Glencoe Mathematics Professional Series, pages 24–25.

In-Class Examples

For Example 3
Find the sum of a geometric series for which $a_1 = 4$, $a_n = 256$, and $r = 4$. $S_n = 340$

For Example 4
In a certain geometric series, $S_8 = 13,120$ and $r = 3$. Find a_1 for the series. $a_1 = 4$

 MODELING MATHEMATICS In this activity, students are given a visual model of a series. In particular, they will see that the series cannot be greater than the area of the original triangle.

Answers for Modeling Mathematics

a. $\frac{1}{4} + 3\left(\frac{1}{16}\right) + 9\left(\frac{1}{64}\right) = \frac{37}{64}$

b. $\frac{1}{4} + \frac{3}{16} + \frac{9}{64} + \frac{27}{256} + \frac{81}{1024} + \frac{243}{4096} = \frac{3367}{4096} \approx 0.8220214844$

How can you find the sum of a geometric series if you know the last term of the series but not how many terms there are in the series? Remember the general formula of the nth term of a geometric sequence, $a_n = a_1 r^{n-1}$. We need to find an equivalent expression that involves r^n.

$$a_n = a_1 r^{n-1}$$
$$a_n \cdot r = a_1 r^{n-1} \cdot r \quad \text{Multiply each side by } r.$$
$$a_n \cdot r = a_1 r^n \qquad r^{n-1}r^1 = r^{n-1+1} \text{ or } r^n$$

Now we can substitute $a_n \cdot r$ for $a_1 r^n$ in the formula for the sum of a geometric series. The formula becomes $S_n = \frac{a_1 - a_n r}{1 - r}$.

Example ③ **Find the sum of a geometric series for which $a_1 = 729$, $a_n = -3$, and $r = -\frac{1}{3}$.**

Since we do not know the value of n, use the alternate formula.

$$S_n = \frac{a_1 - a_n r}{1 - r}$$
$$= \frac{729 - (-3)\left(-\frac{1}{3}\right)}{1 - \left(-\frac{1}{3}\right)} \quad a_1 = 729,\ a_n = -3,\ \text{and } r = -\frac{1}{3}$$
$$= \frac{728}{\frac{4}{3}} \text{ or } 546$$

TECHNOLOGY Tips

You can use a graphing calculator to generate the terms of a geometric series. Store the first term as x. Then generate the second term by storing x times the common ratio.

Continue to press ENTER to generate successive terms of the series.

You can also use the formula for the sum of a geometric series to find a given term of the series.

Example ④ **Find a_1 in a geometric series for which $S_7 = 70,933$ and $r = 4$.**

$$S_n = \frac{a_1(1 - r^n)}{1 - r}$$
$$70,993 = \frac{a_1(1 - 4^7)}{1 - 4} \quad S_n = 70,993 \text{ and } r = 4$$
$$70,993 = \frac{-16,383a_1}{-3}$$
$$70,993 = 5461a_1$$
$$13 = a_1$$

MODELING MATHEMATICS — Geometric Series

Materials:  ruler ✏ colored pencil

You can use area to model a geometric series.

a. Draw a large equilateral triangle on your paper.

b. Find the midpoint of each side of the triangle and connect the midpoints to form four congruent triangles.

c. Color the center triangle. If the area of the original triangle is 1, what is the area of the colored triangle? $\frac{1}{4}$

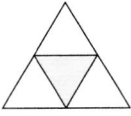

d. Find the midpoints of each side of each uncolored triangle. Connect those midpoints to form congruent triangles and color in each center triangle.

e. Find the total area of the colored triangles. e. $\frac{1}{4} + 3\left(\frac{1}{16}\right)$ or $\frac{7}{16}$ sq units

Your Turn   a–b. See margin.

a. Repeat the process again for each uncolored triangle. What is the resulting shaded area?

b. Write a series for six repetitions of this process.

In Lesson 11–2, you learned that you can write the sum of an arithmetic series by using sigma notation and the general form for an arithmetic sequence. You can also use sigma notation to write the sum of a geometric series.

Example ⑤ Write the terms of $\sum_{n=1}^{5} 4(3)^{n-1}$ and find the sum.

There are two ways in which you can find the sum.

Method 1

$$\sum_{n=1}^{5} 4(3)^{n-1} = 4(3^{1-1}) + 4(3^{2-1}) + 4(3^{3-1}) + \\ 4(3^{4-1}) + 4(3^{5-1})$$
$$= 4(1) + 4(3) + 4(9) + 4(27) + 4(81)$$
$$= 4 + 12 + 36 + 108 + 324$$
$$= 484$$

Method 2

Use $S_n = \dfrac{a_1(1-r^n)}{1-r}$

$a_1 = 4, r = 3, n = 5$

$$S_n = \dfrac{4(1-3^5)}{1-3}$$
$$= 484$$

The sum of the series is 484.

CHECK FOR UNDERSTANDING

Communicating Mathematics

3. $a_1 = 1, r = -3,$ and $n = 6; \sum_{n=1}^{6}(-3)^{n-1}$

MODELING MATHEMATICS

Guided Practice

15. $81 + 27 + 9 + 3 + 1 + \frac{1}{3} + \frac{1}{9}; 121\frac{4}{9}$

Study the lesson. Then complete the following. 1–2. See margin.

1. **Explain** how a geometric series is similar to an arithmetic series.

2. **Determine** which form of the formula for the sum of a geometric series is most appropriate to use for each series described.
   a. $r = -0.5, n = 5, a_1 = 48$ **b.** $a_n = 3, r = -0.5, a_1 = 48$ **c.** 5, 5, 5, ...

3. **Explain** how you would write $1 - 3 + 9 - 27 + 81 - 243$ in sigma notation.

4. Refer to the Modeling Mathematics activity. Suppose the triangle you started with was an isosceles triangle. In what ways, if any, would the series for the area of colored portion change? **no change**

5. 6, −3, −162, 4 6. 7, 0.5, 0.875, 4

State the first term, the common ratio, the last term, and the number of terms for each geometric series.

5. $6 + (-18) + 54 + (-162)$

6. $7 + 3.5 + 1.75 + 0.875$

7. $a_1 + 12 + 36 + 108 + 324$
   4, 3, 324, 5

8. $a_1 + 18 - 36 + 72 + a_5$
   −9, −2, −144, 5

Find S_n for each geometric series described. 10. 39,063

9. $a_1 = 12, r = -3, a_5 = 972$ **732**

10. $a_1 = 3, r = -5, a_n = 46,875$

11. $a_1 = 5, r = 2, n = 14$ **81,915**

12. $a_1 = 243, n = 5, r = -\frac{2}{3}$ **165**

Find the sum of each geometric series. 13. $147\frac{7}{9}$

13. $54 + 36 + 24 + 16 + ...$ to 6 terms

14. $3 - 6 + 12 + ...$ to 7 terms **129**

15. Write the terms of $\sum_{n=1}^{7} 81\left(\frac{1}{3}\right)^{n-1}$ and find the sum.

16. **Meteorology** The Brazos River begins at the junction of the Salt and Double Mountain Forks Rivers in Stonewall County, Texas, and empties into the Gulf of Mexico. A 5-day rainstorm caused the river to rise. After the first day, the river rose one inch. Each day, the rise in the river tripled. How much has the river risen after 5 days? **121 in. or about 10 ft**

Lesson 11–4 Geometric Series **673**

Reteaching

Using Cooperative Learning Have groups of students make up a geometric series and write it in sigma notation. Then have groups exchange problems and find the sum of the geometric series. Return to original groups to check answers.

In-Class Example

For Example 5
Write the terms of
$\sum_{s=5}^{8} \frac{1}{2}(3)^{2s-9}$ and find the sum.
$\dfrac{3}{2} + \dfrac{27}{2} + \dfrac{243}{2} + \dfrac{2187}{2} = 1230$

Check for Understanding

Exercises 1–16 are designed to help you assess your students' understanding through reading, writing, speaking, and modeling. You should work through Exercises 1–4 with your students and then monitor their work on Exercises 5–16.

Additional Answers

1. Both are the sums of the terms of a sequence.

2a. $S_n = \dfrac{a_1 - a_1 r^n}{1-r}$

2b. $S_n = \dfrac{a_1 - a_n r}{1-r}$

2c. $S_n = a_1 n$

Study Guide Masters, p. 79

NAME _____ DATE _____
Study Guide Student Edition Pages 667–673

Geometric Series
The indicated sum of the terms of a geometric sequence is called a **geometric series**.

> **Sum of a Geometric Series**
> The sum S_n of the first n terms of a geometric series is given by
> $S_n = \dfrac{a_1 - a_1 r^n}{1-r}$ or $S_n = \dfrac{a_1(1-r^n)}{1-r}$, where $r \ne 1$.

Example: Find the sum of the first seven terms of the geometric series for which $a_1 = 4$ and $r = -3$.
$S_n = \dfrac{a_1 - a_1 r^n}{1-r}$
$S_7 = \dfrac{4 - 4(-3)^7}{1-(-3)}$
$= 2188$
The sum of the first seven terms is 2188.

Sigma notation can also be used to express a geometric series.

Example: Write $\sum_{j=1}^{5} 2(3^j)$ in expanded form and find the sum.
$\sum_{j=1}^{5} 2(3^j) = 2(3^1) + 2(3^2) + 2(3^3) + 2(3^4) + 2(3^5)$
$= 6 + 18 + 54 + 162 + 486$
$= 726$

Find the sum of each geometric series.
1. $6 + 18 + 54 + \cdots$ to 6 terms **2184**
2. $10 + 5 + \frac{5}{2} + \cdots$ to 5 terms **$19\frac{3}{8}$**
3. $a_1 = 3, r = \frac{1}{3}, n = 4$ **$4\frac{4}{9}$**
4. $a_1 = 8, r = -2, n = 7$ **344**
5. $a_1 = 2, r = -3, a_5 = 162$ **122**
6. $a_1 = \frac{2}{3}, r = 6, a_4 = 864$ **$1036\frac{2}{3}$**

Write the terms of each geometric series and find the sum.
7. $\sum_{j=1}^{5} 3j$
   $3 \cdot 1 + 3 \cdot 2 + 3 \cdot 3 + 3 \cdot 4 = 30$
8. $\sum_{j=4}^{8} 2^j$
   $2^4 + 2^5 + 2^6 + 2^7 + 2^8 = 496$
Express each series in sigma notation and find the sum.
9. $1 + 3 + 9 + 27 + 81$ $\sum 3^{j-1} = 113$
10. $1 - 2 + 4 - 8 + 16 - 32$ $\sum (-2)^{j-1} = -21$

Assignment Guide

Core: 17–45 odd, 46, 47, 49–56
Enriched: 18–44 even, 46–56
All: Self Test, 1–11

For **Extra Practice,** see p. 902.

The red A, B, and C flags, printed only in the Teacher's Wraparound Edition, indicate the level of difficulty of the exercises.

Practice

A

Find S_n for each geometric series described.

17. $a_1 = 625, r = \frac{3}{5}, n = 5$ **1441**
18. $a_1 = 4, r = 0.5, n = 8$ **7.96875**
19. $a_1 = 5, r = 3, n = 12$ **1,328,600**
20. $a_1 = 2401, n = 5, r = -\frac{1}{7}$ **2101**
21. $a_1 = 4, n = 5, r = -3$ **244**
22. $a_1 = 625, n = 8, r = 0.4$ **1040.984**

B

23. $a_1 = 1296, a_5 = 1, r = -\frac{1}{6}$ **1111**
24. $a_1 = 3, a_8 = 384, r = 2$ **765**
25. $a_1 = 343, r = -\frac{1}{7}, a_4 = -1$ **300**
26. $a_1 = 64, a_{10} = -\frac{1}{8}, r = -\frac{1}{6}$ **$54\frac{47}{56}$**
27. $a_1 = 4, a_6 = 0.125, r = 0.5$ **7.875**
28. $a_2 = -36, a_5 = 972, n = 7$ **6564**
29. $a_2 = 250, a_3 = 100, n = 8$ **1040.984**
30. $a_3 = -36, a_6 = -972, n = 10$ **−118,096**

Find the sum of each geometric series.   32. 206,668   33. 2101

31. $12 + 12 + 12 + ...$ to 12 terms   **144**
32. $7 + 21 + 63 + ...$ to 10 terms
33. $2401 - 343 + 49 - ...$ to 5 terms
34. $\frac{1}{9} - \frac{1}{3} + 1 - ...$ to 6 terms   **$-\frac{182}{9}$**

Write the terms of each geometric series and find the sum.

35. $\sum_{n=1}^{9} 5(2)^{n-1}$
36. $\sum_{1}^{8} 64\left(\frac{3}{4}\right)^{n-1}$
37. $\sum_{n=1}^{6} 2(-3)^{n-1}$

Find a_1 for each geometric series described.

38. $S_n = -364, r = -3, n = 6$ **2**
39. $S_n = \frac{215}{64}, r = -\frac{1}{2}, n = 7$ **5**
40. $S_n = 315, a_n = 5, r = 0.5$ **160**
41. $S_n = 165, a_n = 48, r = -\frac{2}{3}$ **243**

C

Express each series in sigma notation and find the sum.

42. $75 + 15 + 3 + ...$ to 10 terms
43. $243 + 162 + 108 + 72 + ...$ to 12 terms

Graphing Calculator

Use a graphing calculator to find the sum of each geometric series.

44. $\sum_{n=1}^{10} \frac{1}{3}\left(\frac{4}{3}\right)^{n-1}$ **16.75772663**
45. $\sum_{n=1}^{20} 3(-2)^{n-1}$ **−1,048,575**

Critical Thinking

46a. A levels out to 93.75; B and C get increasingly larger; D gets closer to 8.

46b. B and C would continue to increase; A would be 93.75; D would be close to 8.

46c. If $r > 1$, sum gets larger and larger.
If $0 < r < 1$, the sum approaches a number.

46. Copy the table below and use a calculator to complete.

Sequence	Sum of First 5 Terms	Sum of First 10 Terms	Sum of First 15 Terms	Sum of First 20 Terms
A: $75 + 15 + 3 + ...$	93.72	93.7499904	93.75	93.75
B: $1 + 2 + 4 + 8 + ...$	31	1023	32,767	1,048,575
C: $a_1 = 25, r = 2$	775	25,575	819,175	26,214,375
D: $a_1 = 4, r = 0.5$	7.75	7.9921875	7.999755859	7.999992371

a. What pattern(s) do you notice as the number of terms included in the sum get larger?
b. Predict what type of number you would get in each case if the table were extended to the first 50 and first 100 terms.
c. Write a general statement about the sum of a geometric series as the number of terms included increases.

Left margin answer box:

35. $5 + 10 + 20 + 40 + 80 + 160 + 320 + 640 + 1280; 2555$

36. $64 + 48 + 36 + 27 + 20\frac{1}{4} + 15\frac{3}{16} + 11\frac{25}{64} + 8\frac{139}{256}; 230\frac{95}{256}$

37. $2 - 6 + 18 - 54 + 162 - 486; -364$

42. $\sum_{n=1}^{10} 75\left(\frac{1}{5}\right)^{n-1}, 93.75$

43. $\sum_{n=1}^{12} 243\left(\frac{2}{3}\right)^{n-1}, 723.38$

Practice Masters, p. 79

NAME _____   DATE _____

11-4   **Practice**
Student Edition
Pages 667–673

Geometric Series

Find the sum of each geometric series.

1. $160 + 80 + 40 + ..., n = 6$ 315
2. $a_1 = 5, r = -\frac{1}{2}, n = 7$ $\frac{215}{64}$
3. $a_5 = \frac{-3}{8}, a_3 = \frac{1}{4}, n = 5$ $\frac{58}{144}$
4. $a_1 = 8, a_5 = 2, n = 6$ 21 or 63

Express each series in sigma notation and find the sum.

5. $54 + 18 + 6 + 2 + \frac{2}{3} + \frac{2}{9}$ $\sum_{n=1}^{6} 54\left(\frac{1}{3}\right)^{n-1}$ $80\frac{8}{9}$
6. $16 - 24 + 36 - 54 + 81 - 121.5 + 182.25$ $\sum_{n=1}^{7} 16\left(-\frac{3}{2}\right)^{n-1}$

Find a_1 for each geometric series described.

7. $S_n = -55, r = -\frac{2}{3}, n = 5$ −81
8. $S_n = 2457, a_n = 3072, r = -4$ −3

Solve.

9. A pile driver drives a post 9 feet into the ground on its first hit. Each additional hit drives the post $\frac{2}{3}$ the distance of the prior hit. Find the total distance the post has been driven after 4 hits. $21\frac{2}{3}$ ft

10. In problem 9, what is the greatest distance the pole could be driven into the ground?   27 ft

11. Hugh Moore makes up a joke and tells it to his 5 closest friends on Sunday morning. Each of those friends tells his or her 5 closest friends on Monday morning, and so on. Assuming no duplication, how many people will have heard the joke by the end of Saturday?   97,655; 97,656 if Hugh is included

674   Chapter 11

Extension

Reasoning   Have students determine a set of requirements for n, a_1, and r that will result in a negative S_n. Using their requirements, have them name sample values for n, a_1, and r, and find S_n.
Sample answer: n is even, a_1 is positive, and $r \le -1$;
$n = 4, a_1 = 2$, and $r = -3; s_n = -40$

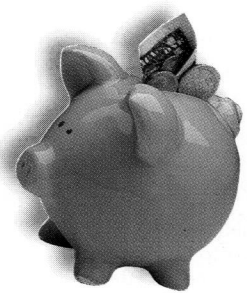

Applications and Problem Solving

47. Savings Yolanda read an article about a surefire plan to have enough money saved for a comfortable early retirement. According to the plan, on the first day she puts aside a penny. Each day thereafter, she contributes an amount that is double the previous day's amount.
  a. If Yolanda stays true to this plan, how much would she have set aside at the end of 10 days? 20 days? **$10.23, $10,485.75**
  b. Why is the surefire plan not a feasible one?

48. Landscaping Raheem is helping his father install a fence across their backyard. He uses a sledgehammer to drive pointed fence posts into the ground. On his first stroke, he drives the post 4 inches into the ground. The soil is denser the deeper he drives, so each stroke after the first, he can only drive the post 40% of the distance he did on the previous swing of the hammer. After 10 strokes, how far has he driven the post into the ground? **6.67 in.**

Mixed Review

49. Find the missing terms of the geometric sequence $\underline{\ ?\ }$, $\underline{\ ?\ }$, $\frac{3}{2}$, 9, 54. (Lesson 11–3)

47b. The amount you have to put away each day exceeds the funds available to anyone.

49. $\frac{1}{24}, \frac{1}{4}$

52. $0, -\frac{1}{3}, \frac{1}{2}, -\frac{1}{2}$

53. $\left(\frac{3}{2}, -4\right)$; about 6.2 units

50. Find the nth term of an arithmetic sequence in which $a_1 = -3$, $d = -9$, and $n = 11$. (Lesson 11–1) **−93**

51. Solve $6^x = 216$. (Lesson 10–1) **3**

52. Find all zeros of $g(x) = 12x^4 + 4x^3 - 3x^2 - x$. (Lesson 8–5)

53. Find the center and radius of the circle whose equation is $x^2 + y^2 - 3x + 8y = 20$. (Lesson 7–3)

54. Statistics Ramón is studying the effects of different fertilizers on tree growth. The heights in centimeters of the trees he planted last year are 49, 54, 61, 49, 54, 51, 56, and 58. Find the standard deviation of the heights. (Lesson 6–8) **4 cm**

55. Given $f(x, y) = 3x + 2y$, find $f(5, -2)$. (Lesson 3–5) **11**

56. Solve $|x - 15| < 45$. (Lesson 1–7) **{$x\,|\,-30 < x < 60$}**

SELF TEST

Find the nth term of each arithmetic sequence. (Lesson 11–1)

1. $a_1 = 7, d = 3, n = 14$ **46**

2. $a_1 = 2, d = \frac{1}{2}, n = 8$ **$\frac{11}{2}$**

Find the sum of each arithmetic series described. (Lesson 11–2)

3. $6 + 12 + 18 + \ldots + 96$ **816**

4. $\sum_{n=1}^{30} (2n - 1)$ **900**

5. 30, 36, 42; See margin for graph.
5. Find the missing arithmetic means in 24, $\underline{\ ?\ }$, $\underline{\ ?\ }$, $\underline{\ ?\ }$, 48. Then graph the sequence. (Lesson 11–1)

6. Consumerism A display of soup cans at Grocery Mart is stacked in the shape of a pyramid. There are 6 cans in the top row, 8 cans in the next row, 10 cans in the next row, and so on. The display contains 12 rows of cans. How many cans of soup are in the display? (Lesson 11–2) **204 cans**

Find the nth term of each geometric sequence. (Lesson 11–3)

7. $a_1 = 4, n = 3, r = 5$ **100**

8. $a_1 = 243, n = 5, r = -\frac{1}{3}$ **3**

9. Find the missing geometric means in 3, $\underline{\ ?\ }$, $\underline{\ ?\ }$, $\underline{\ ?\ }$, 48. Then graph the sequence. (Lesson 11–3)
±6, 12, ±24; See margin for graph.

Find the sum of each geometric series described. (Lesson 11–4)

10. $a_1 = 5, r = 3, n = 12$ **1,328,600**

11. $\sum_{n=1}^{6} 2(-3)^{n-1}$ **−364**

Lesson 11–4 Geometric Series **675**

Answers for the Self Test

5.

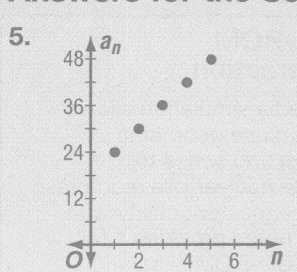

9.

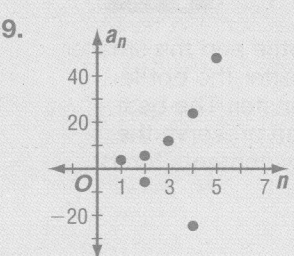

---

4 ASSESS

Closing Activity

Writing Have students compare and contrast arithmetic and geometric series.

Chapter 11, Quiz B (Lessons 11-3 and 11-4), is available in the *Assessment and Evaluation Masters*, p. 296.

Mid-Chapter Test (Lessons 11-1 through 11-4) is available in the *Assessment and Evaluation Masters*, p. 295.

SELF TEST

The Self Test provides students with a brief review of the concepts and skills in Lesson 11-1 through 11-4. Lesson numbers are given to the right of exercises or instruction lines so students can review concepts not yet mastered.

Enrichment Masters, p. 79

11-4 NAME_____ DATE_____

Enrichment Student Edition Pages 667–673

Annuities

An annuity is a fixed amount of money payable at given intervals. For example, suppose you wanted to set up a trust fund so that $30,000 could be withdrawn each year for 14 years before the money ran out. Assume the money can be invested at 9%.

You must find the amount of money that needs to be invested. Call this amount A. After the third payment, the amount left is

$$1.09[1.09A - 30,000(1 + 1.09)] - 30,000 = 1.09^2A - 30,000(1 + 1.09 + 1.09^2).$$

The results are summarized in the table below.

Payment Number	Number of Dollars Left After Payment
1	$A - 30,000$
2	$1.09A - 30,000(1 + 1.09)$
3	$1.09^2A - 30,000(1 + 1.09 + 1.09^2)$

1. Use the pattern shown in the table to find the number of dollars left after the fourth payment.
$1.09^3A - 30,000(1 + 1.09 + 1.09^2 + 1.09^3)$
2. Find the amount left after the tenth payment.

The amount left after the 14th payment is $1.09^{13}A - 30,000(1 + 1.09 + 1.09^2 + \cdots + 1.09^{13})$. However, there should be no money left after the 14th and final payment.

$$1.09^{13}A - 30,000(1 + 1.09 + 1.09^2 + \cdots + 1.09^{13}) = 0$$

Notice that $1 + 1.09 + 1.09^2 + \cdots + 1.09^{13}$ is a geometric series where $a_1 = 1, a_n = 1.09^{13}, n = 14$ and $r = 1.09$.

Using the formula for S_n,

$$1 + 1.09 + 1.09^2 + \cdots + 1.09^{13} = \frac{a_1 - a_n r^n}{1 - r} = \frac{1 - 1.09^{14}}{1 - 1.09} = \frac{1 - 1.09^{14}}{-0.09}.$$

3. Show that when you solve for A you get $A = \frac{30,000}{0.09}\left(\frac{1.09^{14} - 1}{1.09^{14}}\right)$.

$1.09^{13}A - 30,000\left(\frac{1 - 1.09^{14}}{-0.09}\right) = 0$ results in stated expression for A.

Therefore, to provide $30,000 for 14 years where the annual interest rate is 9%, you need $\frac{30,000}{0.09}\left(\frac{1.09^{14} - 1}{1.09^{14}}\right)$ dollars.

4. Use a calculator to find the value of A in problem 3. **$254,607**

In general, if you wish to provide P dollars for each of n years at an annual rate of r%, you need A dollars where

$$\left(1 + \frac{r}{100}\right)^{n-1}A - P\left[1 + \left(1 + \frac{r}{100}\right) + \left(1 + \frac{r}{100}\right)^2 + \cdots + \left(1 + \frac{r}{100}\right)^{n-1}\right] = 0.$$

You can solve this equation for A, given P, n, and r.

Chapter 11 **675**

NCTM Standards: 1–5, 8, 12–13

Instructional Resources

- Study Guide Master 11-5
- Practice Master 11-5
- Enrichment Master 11-5

 Transparency 11-5A contains the 5-Minute Check for this lesson; **Transparency 11-5B** contains a teaching aid for this lesson.

Recommended Pacing

Standard Pacing	Day 8 of 14
Honors Pacing	Day 6 of 11
Block Scheduling*	Day 4 of 7 (along with Lesson 11-6)

 *For more information on pacing and possible lesson plans, refer to the *Block Scheduling Booklet.*

1 FOCUS

 ### 5-Minute Check
(over Lesson 11-4)

1. For the given geometric series, state the first term, the common ratio, the last term, and the number of terms.
$a_1 + (-6) + 18 + (-54) + 162 + a_6$
$a_1 = 2, r = -3, a_6 = -486,$ **6 terms**

2. Find the sum of the geometric series with $a_1 = 81$, $r = \frac{1}{3}$, and $n = 7$. **$121\frac{4}{9}$**

3. Find the sum of the geometric series $2 + 4 + 8 + \dots$ to ten terms. **2046**

4. Find the sum of nine terms of the geometric series with $a_1 = -2$ and $r = -\frac{1}{4}$.
-1.600006

5. Use sigma notation to express the series $4 - 12 + 36 - 108 + 324$.
$$\sum_{n=1}^{5} 4(-3)^{n-1}$$

- To find sums of infinite geometric series.

Why IT'S IMPORTANT

You can use infinite geometric series to solve problems involving physics and ballooning.

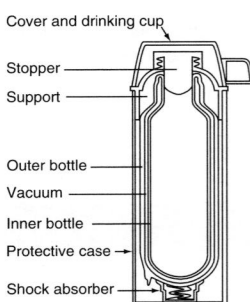

Cover and drinking cup
Stopper
Support
Outer bottle
Vacuum
Inner bottle
Protective case
Shock absorber

The word *thermos* is now used as a general term for a vacuum flask. It comes from the brand name Thermos®, which was the first manufacturer of vacuum flasks for public use in 1907.

 ## CONNECTION
Physics

Have you ever had hot cocoa get cold before you finished drinking it? It was a similar problem that led British chemist Sir James Dewar to develop the vacuum flask, commonly called the thermos bottle. A thermos bottle is a double-walled glass vessel with silver coating to reflect the radiation of heat into the bottle to keep the liquid hot or away from the bottle to preserve the cold. The space between the glass walls is a partial vacuum. Since it contains so little air, a good vacuum does not conduct heat or cold. In this manner, the flask can keep liquids at the proper temperature for several hours.

Pumps can be used to create a vacuum. Suppose a pump removes 25% of the air from a sealed 1-liter container on each stroke of its piston. A geometric series could be used to calculate the total amount of air being removed from the container. Since the goal is to remove all of the air and $r = 0.75$, this is an example of an **infinite geometric series.**

Stroke	Air Removed By Pump	Amount of Air Remaining
1	$\frac{1}{4}$	$\frac{3}{4}$
2	$\frac{1}{4}$ of $\frac{3}{4}$, or $\frac{1}{4}\left(\frac{3}{4}\right)$	$\frac{3}{4}$ of $\frac{3}{4}$, or $\left(\frac{3}{4}\right)^2$
3	$\frac{1}{4}$ of $\left(\frac{3}{4}\right)^2$, or $\frac{1}{4}\left(\frac{3}{4}\right)^2$	$\frac{3}{4}$ of $\left(\frac{3}{4}\right)^2$ or $\left(\frac{3}{4}\right)^3$
n	$\frac{1}{4}$ of $\left(\frac{3}{4}\right)^{n-1}$, or $\frac{1}{4}\left(\frac{3}{4}\right)^{n-1}$	$\frac{3}{4}$ of $\left(\frac{3}{4}\right)^{n-1}$, or $\left(\frac{3}{4}\right)^n$

The series representing the total amount of air removed can be written as $\sum_{n=1}^{\infty} \frac{1}{4}\left(\frac{3}{4}\right)^{n-1}$. The amount of air removed after n strokes, S_n, is called a **partial sum** of an infinite series, because it is the sum of a certain number of terms and not the entire series. A graph can help us see a pattern in the partial sums.

n	S_n
1	0.25
2	0.4375
3	0.578125
4	0.6835938
5	0.7626953
10	0.9436865
50	0.9999994
100	1

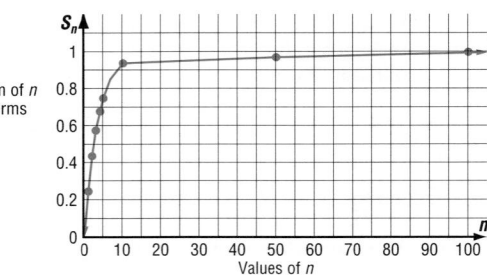

Sum of n Terms — Values of n

Notice that as n increases, the sum levels off and approaches a limit. This pattern is characteristic of infinite geometric series in which $|r| < 1$.

 The larger the bottle and the smaller the mouth, the better the bottle prevents heat transfer. The best vacuum bottle can preserve the temperature of its contents for 12 hours.

 ## GLENCOE Technology

CD-ROM Interaction

A multimedia simulation allows students to use geometric sequences and series to investigate nuclear pile reactors. A blackline master activity with teacher's notes provides a follow-up to the CD-ROM simulation.

For Windows & Macintosh

Let's look at the formula for the sum of a geometric series and determine how it can be used to find a formula for the sum of an infinite geometric series.

$$S_n = \frac{a_1 - a_1 r^n}{1 - r}$$

$$= \frac{a_1}{1 - r} - \frac{a_1 r^n}{1 - r} \qquad \textit{Rewrite as the difference of two rational expressions.}$$

$$= \frac{\frac{1}{4}}{1 - \frac{3}{4}} - \frac{\frac{1}{4}\left(\frac{3}{4}\right)^n}{1 - \frac{3}{4}} \qquad a_1 = \frac{1}{4} \text{ and } r = \frac{3}{4}$$

$$= \frac{\frac{1}{4}}{\frac{1}{4}} - \frac{\frac{1}{4}\left(\frac{3}{4}\right)^n}{\frac{1}{4}} \text{ or } 1 - \left(\frac{3}{4}\right)^n$$

As the value of n increases, the value of the second term decreases and approaches 0. Thus, the sum actually has the same value as the first term, 1. That is, gradually the pump is removing all of the air from the container, although at no point does it finish doing so. If the pump operated forever, it would remove all of the air. In fact, after as few as 50 strokes, it has removed nearly all of the air. The table on the previous page supports this conclusion. This suggests the following definition.

Sum of an Infinite Geometric Series	**The sum S of an infinite geometric series where $-1 < r < 1$ is given by** $$S = \frac{a_1}{1 - r}.$$

An infinite geometric series in which $|r| \geq 1$ does not have a sum. Consider the series $1 + 2 + 4 + 8 + 16 + \dots$. In this series, $a_1 = 1$ and $r = 2$. The table at the right shows some of the partial sums of this series. As the value of n increases, the sum becomes increasingly greater and has no limit. With each additional term of the series, the sum grows without bound. That is, the sum does not approach a particular value. *If $r < -1$, what happens to the sum?*

n	S_n
5	31
10	1023
15	32,767
20	1,048,575

Example ❶ **Find the sum of each infinite geometric series, if it exists.**

a. $\frac{2}{3} + \frac{4}{9} + \frac{8}{27} + \dots$

First find the value of r to determine if a sum exists.

$a_1 = \frac{2}{3}$ and $a_2 = \frac{4}{9}$, so $r = \frac{\frac{4}{9}}{\frac{2}{3}}$ or $\frac{2}{3}$. Since $\left|\frac{2}{3}\right| < 1$, a sum exists. Now use

the formula for the sum of an infinite geometric series.

$$S = \frac{a_1}{1 - r}$$

$$= \frac{\frac{2}{3}}{1 - \frac{2}{3}} \qquad a_1 = \frac{2}{3} \text{ and } r = \frac{2}{3}$$

$$= \frac{\frac{2}{3}}{\frac{1}{3}}$$

$$= \frac{2}{3} \cdot \frac{3}{1} \text{ or } 2$$

b. $1 - 3 + 9 - 27$

$a_1 = 1$ and $a_2 = -3$, so $r = \frac{-3}{1}$. Since $|-3| > 1$, no sum exists.

Alternative Teaching Strategies

Reading Algebra Share with students that the word *geometry* comes from the Greek word *geos,* which means "land," and *metrein,* which means "to measure." The word *infinite* comes from the Latin word *infinitus,* which means "unbounded." Have students look up the definition of the word *series* and describe in their own words what an infinite geometric series is.

Motivating the Lesson
Questioning Read aloud the Edgar Allen Poe short story, "The Pit and the Pendulum." Discuss pendulums and how they relate to geometric sequences and series.

2 TEACH

In-Class Example

For Example 1
Find the sum of each infinite geometric series, if it exists.

a. $8 + 4 + 2 + \dots$ **16**

b. $1 - \frac{1}{3} + \frac{1}{9} - \dots$ **$\frac{3}{4}$**

In-Class Examples

For Example 2
How far will a ball travel before it stops bouncing if it is dropped 24 feet and rebounds $\frac{3}{4}$ the height of the previous bounce?
96 feet

For Example 3
Express 0.23 as a rational number of the form $\frac{a}{b}$. $\frac{23}{99}$

Teaching Tip Explain to students that if the repeating decimal has two or more digits that repeat, this number of digits is the basis for the series. For example, if the decimal is 0.171717... , 0.17 is a_1, and r is 0.01. Watch for fractional values of r that are not less than 1.

If no further force is exerted on a pendulum when it is set in motion, the distance it swings back and forth becomes less and less. The total distance it swings is an example of an infinite geometric series.

Example 2

Physics

F Y I

If a pendulum can be modeled by an infinite geometric series, then theoretically, it should never stop swinging. In reality, the swing of the pendulum is affected by air friction, so that eventually it does stop moving.

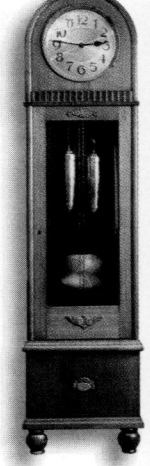

The spring in Juanita's old grandfather clock is broken. When you try to set the pendulum in motion by holding it against the wall of the clock and letting go, it follows a swing pattern of 25 cm, 20 cm, 16 cm, and so on until it comes to rest. What is the total distance the pendulum swings before coming to rest?

The swing pattern of the clock's pendulum forms the infinite series 25 + 20 + 16 + ... First determine if a sum exists.

$a_1 = 25$ and $a_2 = 20$, so $r = \frac{20}{25}$ or $\frac{4}{5}$. Since $\left|\frac{4}{5}\right| < 1$, a sum exists.

$$S = \frac{a_1}{1 - r}$$
$$= \frac{25}{1 - \frac{4}{5}}$$
$$= \frac{25}{\frac{1}{5}}$$
$$= 25 \cdot 5 \text{ or } 125$$

The distance traveled by the pendulum before it stops is 125 cm.

The sum of an infinite geometric series can be used to express a repeating decimal as a rational number in the form $\frac{a}{b}$. Remember that repeating decimals such as $0.\overline{2}$ and $0.\overline{47}$ represent 0.22222 ... and 0.4747474747 ... , respectively. Each of the expressions can be written as an infinite geometric series.

Example 3

Express $0.\overline{12}$ as a rational number of the form $\frac{a}{b}$.

Rewrite the repeating decimal as a sum.

$0.\overline{12} = 0.121212 ...$

$\quad\quad = 0.12 + 0.0012 + 0.000012 + ...$

$\quad\quad = \frac{12}{100} + \frac{12}{10,000} + \frac{12}{1,000,000} + ...$

In this series, $a_1 = \frac{12}{100}$ or 0.12, and each term is $\frac{1}{100}$ of the preceding term, so $r = \frac{1}{100}$ or 0.01. You can determine the sum of this series by using either the decimal or fractional values for a_1 and r.

Method 1

$S = \frac{a_1}{1 - r}$

$= \frac{\frac{12}{100}}{1 - \frac{1}{100}}$

$= \frac{\frac{12}{100}}{\frac{99}{100}}$

$= \frac{12}{100} \cdot \frac{100}{99}$

$= \frac{12}{99}$ or $\frac{4}{33}$

Method 2

Let $S = 0.121212 ....$

$100S = 12.121212 ...$ *Multiply each side by 100.*

$99S = 12$ *Subtract S from each side.*

$S = \frac{12}{99}$ or $\frac{4}{33}$ *Divide each side by 99.*

F Y I

For centuries, scientists have tried to invent a perpetual motion machine. However, because of the force of friction, which acts against motion, a perpetual motion machine has not been achieved.

In Lesson 11–4, we used sigma notation to write an expression for the partial sum S_n. You can also use sigma notation to write an expression for the sum of an infinite series. The mathematical symbol ∞, or *infinity*, means endless. Since there is no last term in an infinite series, we use the symbol ∞ in place of n as the upper limit of the sum to indicate that the sum goes on forever.

Example **4** **Evaluate** $\displaystyle\sum_{n=1}^{\infty} 35\left(-\frac{1}{4}\right)^{n-1}$.

Remember that sigma notation uses the general form of the nth term of the geometric series, or $a_1 r^{n-1}$. Thus, in this series, $a_1 = 35$ and $r = -\frac{1}{4}$. Use the formula for the sum of an infinite geometric series.

$$S = \frac{a_1}{1 - r}$$

$$= \frac{35}{1 - \left(-\frac{1}{4}\right)}$$

$$= \frac{35}{\frac{5}{4}}$$

$$= \frac{35}{1} \cdot \frac{4}{5} \text{ or } 28$$

Thus, $\displaystyle\sum_{n=1}^{\infty} 35\left(-\frac{1}{4}\right)^{n-1} = 28$.

CHECK FOR UNDERSTANDING

Communicating Mathematics

Study the lesson. Then complete the following.

1. **Write** the formula for the sum of an infinite geometric series. Then explain how this formula is derived from $S_n = \dfrac{a_1 - a_1 r^n}{1 - r}$. **See margin.**

2. **Determine** if the sum of an infinite series in which $r = \dfrac{11}{10}$ can be computed. Explain your answer. **No, because $|r| > 1$.**

3a. $S_n = \dfrac{3 - 3(0.8)^n}{1 - 0.8}$

3. **a. Substitute** the values $a_1 = 3$ and $r = 0.8$ into the formula for a partial sum of n terms.

   b. Describe the value of $(0.8)^n$ as n increases without bound. **It approaches 0.**

3c. The numerator approaches the value of 3.

   c. As n increases in $(0.8)^n$, what happens to the value of the numerator in S_n?

   d. As n increases without bound, what happens to the value of S_n? **It approaches 15.**

4. **Estimate** the sum S_n of the geometric series whose partial sums are graphed at the right. **25**

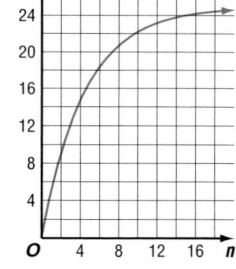

5. Trent; $r = \dfrac{3}{8} \div \dfrac{1}{2}$ or $\dfrac{6}{8}$.

5. **You Decide** Lynn and Trent disagreed on whether the geometric series $\dfrac{1}{2} + \dfrac{3}{8} + \dfrac{9}{24} + \dots$ had a sum. Lynn said the series had no sum since $r = \dfrac{1}{2} \div \dfrac{3}{8}$ or $\dfrac{8}{6}$ and $\left|\dfrac{8}{6}\right| > 1$. Trent still disagreed. Who is correct? Explain.

In-Class Example

For Example 4

Evaluate $\displaystyle\sum_{n=1}^{\infty} 9\left(\frac{1}{2}\right)^{n-1}$. $S = 18$

3 PRACTICE/APPLY

Check for Understanding
Exercises 1–16 are designed to help you assess your students' understanding through reading, writing, speaking, and modeling. You should work through Exercises 1–6 with your students and then monitor their work on Exercises 7–16.

Error Analysis
When r is fractional, watch that, when finding r, the division is in the correct order. When dividing fractions, remember to multiply by the reciprocal.
Example: $\dfrac{1}{2} + \dfrac{3}{3} + \dfrac{2}{9} + \dots$

$r =$	$r =$	$r =$
$\dfrac{1}{2} \div \dfrac{1}{3}$	$\dfrac{1}{3} \div \dfrac{1}{2}$	$\dfrac{1}{3} \div \dfrac{1}{2}$
no	$r = \dfrac{1}{3} \cdot \dfrac{2}{1}$	$r = \dfrac{1}{3} \cdot \dfrac{1}{2}$
	$r = \dfrac{2}{3}$	$r = \dfrac{1}{6}$
	yes	no

Additional Answer
1. $S_n = \dfrac{a_1 - a_1 r^n}{1 - r} = \dfrac{a_1}{1 - r} - \dfrac{a_1 r^n}{1 - r}$.
   For $|r| < 1$, as n approaches ∞, r^n approaches 0, so the second fraction approaches 0. Thus S_n for $n = \infty$ becomes $\dfrac{a_1}{1 - r}$.

Reteaching

Decision Making Give students some possible values of r and ask if the geometric series with that r could be an infinite one. Have them explain why or why not.

Assignment Guide

Core: 17–49 odd, 51–59
Enriched: 18–46 even, 47–59

For **Extra Practice,** see p. 902.

The red A, B, and C flags, printed only in the Teacher's Wraparound Edition, indicate the level of difficulty of the exercises.

MATH JOURNAL

6. Describe how you would write the sum of a given infinite geometric series in sigma notation. Include examples.   **See students' work.**

Guided Practice

Find a_1 and r for each series. Then find the sum, if it exists.

7. $36 + 24 + 16 + \ldots$ $36, \frac{2}{3}; 108$

8. $16 - 24 + 36 - \ldots$ $16, -\frac{3}{2};$ none

9. $6 - 4 + \frac{8}{3} - \ldots$ $6, -\frac{2}{3}; \frac{18}{5}$

10. $\frac{1}{4} + \frac{1}{6} + \frac{2}{9} + \ldots$ $\frac{1}{4}, \frac{2}{3}, \frac{3}{4}$

11. $16 + 24 + 36 + \ldots$ $16, \frac{3}{2};$ none

12. $\sum_{n=1}^{\infty} 40\left(\frac{3}{5}\right)^{n-1}$ $40, \frac{3}{5}; 100$

Express each decimal as a rational number of the form $\frac{a}{b}$.

13. $0.\overline{5}$ $\frac{5}{9}$

14. $0.\overline{37}$ $\frac{37}{99}$

15. $0.\overline{175}$ $\frac{175}{999}$

16. **Hot-Air Ballooning**   A hot-air balloon rises 80 feet in its first minute of flight. If in each succeeding minute the balloon rises only 90% as far as in the previous minute, what will be the balloon's maximum altitude?   **800 ft**

EXERCISES

Practice

 A

Find the sum of each infinite geometric series, if it exists.

17. $a_1 = 4, r = \frac{5}{7}$ 14

18. $a_1 = 12, r = -\frac{3}{5}$ 7.5

19. $a_1 = 18, r = 0.6$ 45

20. does not exist

20. $a_1 = 14, r = \frac{7}{3}$

21. $15 + 10 + \frac{20}{3} + \ldots$

22. $\frac{5}{3} + \frac{25}{3} + \frac{125}{3} + \ldots$

21. 45

22. does not exist

23. $1 + \frac{2}{3} + \frac{4}{9} + \ldots$ 3

24. $3 + 1.8 + 1.08 + \ldots$

25. $18 - 12 + 8 - \ldots$ $\frac{54}{5}$

24. 7.5

26. $12 - 18 + 25 - \ldots$

27. $\frac{5}{3} + \frac{10}{9} + \frac{20}{27} + \ldots$ 5

28. $\frac{3}{2} - \frac{3}{4} + \frac{3}{8} - \ldots$ 1

26. does not exist

B

29. $\sum_{n=1}^{\infty} 48\left(\frac{2}{3}\right)^{n-1}$ 144

30. $\sum_{n=1}^{\infty} \left(\frac{3}{8}\right)\left(\frac{3}{4}\right)^{n-1}$ $\frac{3}{2}$

31. $\sum_{n=1}^{\infty} -24\left(-\frac{3}{5}\right)^{n-1}$ -15

Express each decimal as a rational number of the form $\frac{a}{b}$.

32. $0.\overline{7}$ $\frac{7}{9}$

33. $0.\overline{1}$ $\frac{1}{9}$

34. $0.\overline{36}$ $\frac{4}{11}$

35. $0.\overline{82}$ $\frac{82}{99}$

36. $4.\overline{6}$ $\frac{14}{3}$

37. $0.4\overline{5}$ $\frac{41}{90}$

38. $0.2\overline{31}$ $\frac{229}{990}$

39. $0.\overline{99}$ 1

40. $\sum_{n=1}^{\infty} 10(-0.1)^{n-1}, \frac{100}{11}$

Write each infinite geometric series in sigma notation. Then find the sum, if it exists.

C

40. $10 - 1 + 0.1 + \ldots$

41. $3 + 27 + 243 + \ldots$

42. $1 - 0.5 + 0.25 - \ldots$

41. $\sum_{n=1}^{\infty} 3(9)^{n-1}$, does not exist

43. The sum of an infinite geometric series is 81, and its common ratio is $\frac{2}{3}$. Find the first three terms of the series.   **27, 18, 12**

44. The sum of an infinite geometric series is 125, and the value of r is 0.4. Find the first three terms of the series.   **75, 30, 12**

42. $\sum_{n=1}^{\infty} 1(-0.5)^{n-1}, \frac{2}{3}$

45. The common ratio of an infinite geometric series is $\frac{11}{16}$, and its sum is $76\frac{4}{5}$. Find the first four terms of the series. $24, 16\frac{1}{2}, 11\frac{11}{32}, 7\frac{409}{512}$

46. The first term of an infinite geometric series is -8, and its sum is $-13\frac{1}{3}$. Find the first four terms of the series. $-8, -3\frac{1}{5}, -1\frac{7}{25}, -\frac{64}{125}$

Study Guide Masters, p. 80

11-5

NAME_____ DATE _____

Student Edition
Pages 674–679

Study Guide

Infinite Geometric Series

An infinite geometric series is a geometric series in which the number of terms is unlimited. In an infinite geometric series for which $|r| < 1$, the values of the terms approach zero as n increases. The sum of the first n terms approaches a specific number, S, which is called the sum of the infinite geometric series.

Sum of an Infinite Geometric Series
The sum, S, of an infinite geometric series, where the common ratio is $-1 < r < 1$, is given by the following formula. $S = \frac{a_1}{1 - r}$

Example: Find the sum of the infinite geometric series

$20 - 10 + 5 - 2\frac{1}{2} + 1\frac{1}{4} + \ldots$

$a_2 = a_1 r$
$-10 = 20r$
$-\frac{1}{2} = r$

$S = \frac{20}{1 - \left(-\frac{1}{2}\right)}$ or $\frac{40}{3}$

The sum is $\frac{40}{3}$.

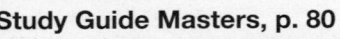
Find the sum of each infinite geometric series, if it exists.

1. $a_1 = -7, r = \frac{5}{8}$ $-18\frac{2}{3}$

2. $a_1 = 4, r = \frac{1}{2}$ 8

3. $\frac{2}{9} + \frac{5}{27} + \frac{25}{162} + \ldots$ $1\frac{1}{3}$

4. $15 + 10 + 6\frac{2}{3} + \ldots$ 45

5. $a_1 = 6, r = \frac{2}{5}$ 10

6. $18 - 9 + 4\frac{1}{2} - 2\frac{1}{4} + \ldots$ 12

7. $\frac{1}{10} + \frac{1}{20} + \frac{1}{40} + \ldots$ $\frac{1}{5}$

8. $6 - 12 + 24 - 48 + \ldots$ does not exist

Find the first four terms of each infinite geometric series described.

9. $S = -16, r = \frac{1}{4}$ $-12, -3, -\frac{3}{4}, -\frac{3}{16}$

10. $S = 48, r = -\frac{2}{3}$ $80, -\frac{160}{3}, \frac{320}{9}, -\frac{640}{27}$

11. $S = \frac{33}{4}, r = \frac{1}{3}$ $\frac{11}{2}, \frac{11}{6}, \frac{11}{18}, \frac{11}{54}$

12. $S = 5, r = \frac{1}{5}$ $4, \frac{4}{5}, \frac{4}{25}, \frac{4}{125}$

13. $S = \frac{20}{3}, r = -\frac{1}{2}$ $10, -5, \frac{5}{2}, -\frac{5}{4}$

14. $S = \frac{1}{12}, r = -\frac{1}{3}$ $\frac{1}{9}, -\frac{1}{27}, \frac{1}{81}, -\frac{1}{243}$

 Tech Prep

Child Care Aide   Students who are interested in child care may wish to do further research on the data given in Exercise 49 and explore the potential growth of this career. For more information on tech prep, see the *Teacher's Handbook.*

47. The infinite series discussed in this lesson are infinite geometric series. Is it possible to have infinite arithmetic series? If so, do these series have sums? Explain and give examples.   Yes, it is possible to have infinite arithmetic series, but a sum does not exist since the sum increases with each term, or decreases with each term if d is negative.

Applications and Problem Solving

48. Draw a Diagram   Some physics students were experimenting with the rebound effect of a rubber ball. They used a motion detector and a 10-foot clear glass tube to determine that when a ball was dropped from this height, it rebounds or bounces 6 feet. The motion detector also recorded that on each consecutive bounce of the ball, it rebounded in the same proportion as that of the first bounce.

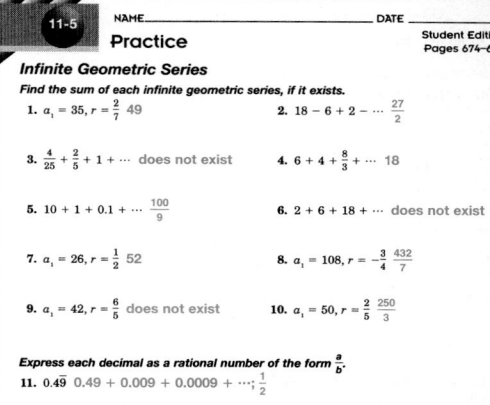

48b. $10 + 6 + 3.6 + 2.16 + ... = 25$
48c. $6 + 3.6 + 2.16 + ... = 15$

  a. Draw a diagram to illustrate the pattern of the vertical distances traveled by the ball until it stops bouncing.   See margin.

  b. Write an infinite geometric series to represent the total of the distances the ball travels in a downward motion. Then find the sum.

  c. Write an infinite geometric series to represent the total of the distances the ball travels upward. Then find the sum.

  d. How do the two series in parts c and d compare? $S_D = 10 + S_U$

  e. Find the total vertical distance traveled by the bouncing ball before it stops bouncing.   40 ft

49. Child's Play   Rebeca's little sister likes for her to push her in the swing at the park in their neighborhood. The other day, Rebeca pulled the swing back and let it go. She would have kept pushing, but she suddenly saw a friend at the other end of the park. The swing traveled a total distance of 10 feet before heading back the other way. Each swing afterwards was only 80% as long as the previous one. Find the total distance the swing traveled before it stopped.   50 ft

50. Geometry   The perimeter of square $ABCD$ at the right is 40 cm. If the midpoints of each side were connected, a smaller square would result. Suppose the process of connecting midpoints of sides of squares and drawing new squares were continued indefinitely.

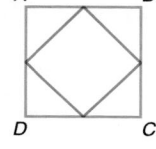

50a. $40 + 20\sqrt{2} + 20 + ...$

  a. Write an infinite geometric series to represent the sum of the perimeters of the squares formed by this process.

  b. Find the sum of all of the perimeters of all the squares formed.
  $\left(80 + 40\sqrt{2}\right)$ cm

Mixed Review

51. Use sigma notation to express $1 - 3 + 9 - 27 + 81 - 243$.   (Lesson 11–4)

51. $\displaystyle\sum_{n=1}^{6} (-3)^{n-1}$

52. Physics   A vacuum pump removes $\frac{1}{5}$ of the air from a sealed container on each stroke of its piston. What percent of the air remains after five strokes of the piston? (Lesson 11–3)   about 32.8%

53. Simplify $\dfrac{3y + 1}{2y - 10} + \dfrac{1}{y^2 - 2y - 15}$.   (Lesson 9–4) $\dfrac{3y^2 + 10y + 5}{2(y - 5)(y + 3)}$

54. $\dfrac{x^2}{208,802,500} + \dfrac{y^2}{144,802,500} = 1$

54. Astronomy   A satellite is in an elliptical orbit with the center of Earth at one focus. The major axis of the orbit is 28,900 miles long, and the center of Earth is 8000 miles from the center of the ellipse. Assuming that the center of the ellipse is the origin and the foci lie on the x-axis, write the equation of the path of the satellite.   (Lesson 7–4)

Additional Answer

48a.

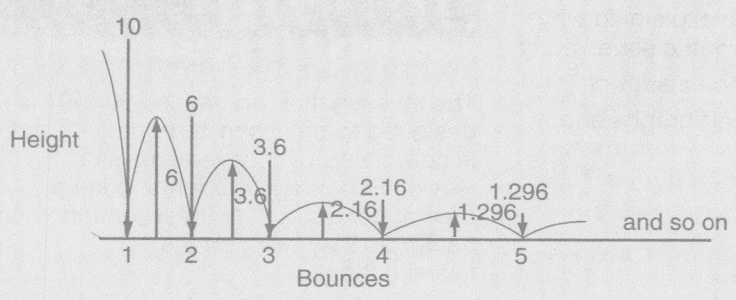

Practice Masters, p. 80

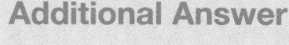

11-5   NAME_____   DATE_____
Practice   Student Edition
Pages 674–679

Infinite Geometric Series

Find the sum of each infinite geometric series, if it exists.
1. $a_1 = 35, r = \frac{2}{7}$ 49
2. $18 - 6 + 2 - \cdots$ $\frac{27}{2}$
3. $\frac{4}{25} + \frac{2}{5} + 1 + \cdots$ does not exist
4. $6 + 4 + \frac{8}{3} + \cdots$ 18
5. $10 + 1 + 0.1 + \cdots$ $\frac{100}{9}$
6. $2 + 6 + 18 + \cdots$ does not exist
7. $a_1 = 26, r = \frac{1}{2}$ 52
8. $a_1 = 108, r = -\frac{3}{4}$ $\frac{432}{7}$
9. $a_1 = 42, r = \frac{6}{5}$ does not exist
10. $a_1 = 50, r = \frac{2}{5}$ $\frac{250}{3}$

Express each decimal as a rational number of the form $\frac{a}{b}$.
11. $0.\overline{49}$ $0.49 + 0.009 + 0.0009 + \cdots; \frac{1}{2}$
12. $0.\overline{164}$ $0.164 + 0.000164 + 0.000000164 + \cdots; \frac{164}{999}$
13. $0.2\overline{8}$ $0.28 + 0.008 + 0.0008 + \cdots; \frac{13}{45}$
14. $0.6\overline{41}$ $0.641 + 0.00041 + 0.00000041 + \cdots; \frac{127}{198}$

Find the first three terms of each infinite geometric series.
15. $S = 64, r = -\frac{3}{4}$ $112 - 84 + 63$
16. $S = 625, r = \frac{1}{5}$ $500 + 100 + 20$
17. $S = 90, r = -\frac{1}{2}$ $135 - 67.5 + 33.75$
18. $S = 4, r = \frac{1}{3}$ $\frac{8}{3} + \frac{8}{9} + \frac{8}{27}$

Closing Activity

Speaking Have students explain why a sum can be found for some infinite geometric series and not for others.

55a. 340 items

55b. 475 items

55c. 495 items

55d. 170 items

55. Statistics Suppose 500 items are normally distributed. (Lesson 6–9)
a. How many items are within one standard deviation from the mean?
b. How many items are within two standard deviations from the mean?
c. How many items are within three standard deviations from the mean?
d. How many items are within one standard deviation less than the mean?
e. How many items are within two standard deviations greater than the mean? **237.5 items**

56. Geometry The area of rectangle $ABCD$ is represented by $6x^2 + 38x + 56$. Its width is represented by $2x + 8$. Find the length of rectangle $ABCD$. (Lesson 5–3) **$3x + 7$**

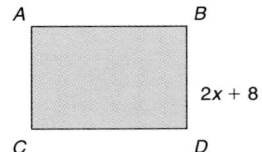

$2x + 8$

57. Solve the system of equations using augmented matrices. (Lesson 4–7)

$a + \frac{1}{2}b - 3c = 19$

$\frac{1}{2}a - b + 2c = -16$

$5a + 2b - 2c = 50$ **(4, 12, −3)**

58. Retailing A salesman receives $25 for every vacuum cleaner he sells. If he sells more than 10 vacuum cleaners a week, he will receive an additional $1.75 for each successive sale until he is paid a maximum of $46 per vacuum cleaner. How many must he sell to reach this maximum? (Lesson 3–5) **22**

59. Find the slope-intercept form of the equation of the line that has a slope of $\frac{3}{4}$ and passes through the point at (8, 2). (Lesson 2–4) **$y = \frac{3}{4}x - 4$**

WORKING ON THE Investigation

Refer to the Investigation on pages 590–591.

A scatter plot can help you analyze data and search for any patterns that may exist.

1 Draw a scatter plot for the data from the table in the Working on the Investigation feature in Lesson 11–1 on page 655. Then draw a best-fit line or curve. What do you notice about the graph? What relationship exists between the weight (number of washers) in the cup and the length of the rubber band? What type of a function does it portray?

2 Write an equation to relate the weight in the cup and the length the rubber band stretches.

3 What would you predict would happen in all aspects of the experiment if you continued to add washers?

4 Repeat the experiment with the other two rubber bands.

5 Create two separate scatter plots and best-fit lines or curves of the weights and the lengths of the other two rubber bands. Describe the graphs. Are the data points linear? How does the length compare as the weight in the cup gets heavier? Do each of the graphs illustrate a similar effect with more weight?

Add the results of your work to your Investigation Folder.

682   Chapter 11   Investigating Sequences and Series

Enrichment Masters, p. 80

NAME_____ DATE _____   Student Edition Pages 674–679

11-5 Enrichment

Convergence and Divergence

Convergence and divergence are terms that relate to the existence of a sum of an infinite series. If a sum exists, the series is convergent. If not, the series is divergent. Consider the series $12 + 3 + \frac{3}{4} + \frac{3}{16} + \cdots$. This is a geometric series with $r = \frac{1}{4}$. The sum is given by the formula $S = \frac{a_1}{1-r}$. Thus, the sum is $12 \div \frac{3}{4}$ or 16. This series is convergent since a sum exists. Notice that the first two terms have a sum of 15. As more terms are added, the sum comes closer (or converges) to 16.

Recall that a geometric series has a sum if and only if $-1 < r < 1$. Thus, a geometric series is convergent if r is between -1 and 1, and divergent if r has another value. An infinite arithmetic series cannot have a sum unless all of the terms are equal to zero.

Examples: (a) $2 + 5 + 8 + 11 + \cdots$ divergent
(b) $-2 + 4 + -8 + 16 + \cdots$ divergent
(c) $16 + 8 + 4 + 2 + \cdots$ convergent

Determine whether each series is convergent or divergent. If the series is convergent, find the sum.

1. $5 + 10 + 15 + 20 + \cdots$ divergent
2. $16 + 8 + 4 + 2 + \cdots$ convergent; 32
3. $1 + 0.1 + 0.01 + 0.001 + \cdots$ convergent; 1.11
4. $4 + 2 + 0 - 2 - \cdots$ divergent
5. $2 - 4 + 8 - 16 + \cdots$ divergent
6. $1 - \frac{1}{5} + \frac{1}{25} - \frac{1}{125} + \cdots$ convergent; $\frac{5}{6}$
7. $4 + 2.4 + 1.44 + 0.864 + \cdots$ convergent; 10
8. $\frac{1}{8} + \frac{1}{4} + \frac{1}{2} + 1 + \cdots$ divergent
9. $-\frac{5}{3} + \frac{10}{9} - \frac{20}{27} + \frac{40}{81} - \cdots$ convergent; -1
10. $48 + 12 + 3 + \frac{3}{4} + \cdots$ convergent; 64

Bonus: Is $1 + \frac{1}{2} + \frac{1}{3} + \frac{1}{4} + \frac{1}{5} + \cdots$ convergent or divergent? divergent

---

Extension

Communication Have each student write a short paragraph explaining why there is no infinite geometric series that has 6 as its first term and a sum of $\frac{3}{4}$. Have students share paragraphs and discuss any differences. **Paragraphs might include that r would need to be -7 to satisfy $S = \frac{a_1}{(1-r)}$, and this formula is true only for $-1 < r < 1$.**

Investigation

Working on the Investigation

The Investigation on pages 590–591 is designed to be a long-term project that is completed over several days or weeks. Encourage students to keep their materials in their Investigation Folder as they work on the Investigation.

Recursion and Special Sequences

What YOU'LL LEARN

- To recognize and use special sequences, and
- to iterate functions.

Why IT'S IMPORTANT

You can use recursion and special sequences to solve problems involving inflation and nature.

APPLICATION
Nature

The seeds in the center of a sunflower show an example of a pattern often found in nature. The number of counterclockwise spirals is 8, and the number of clockwise spirals is 13. These are two numbers in a famous pattern of numbers called the **Fibonacci sequence,** named after its discoverer, Leonardo Fibonacci, who presented it in 1201. The sequence is shown below.

$$1, 1, 2, 3, 5, 8, 13, 21, 34, 55, 89, 144, \ldots$$

Notice the pattern in this sequence. After the second number, each number in the sequence is the sum of the two numbers that precede it. That is, $2 = 1 + 1$, $3 = 2 + 1$, $5 = 3 + 2$, $8 = 5 + 3$, $13 = 8 + 5$, and so on.

first term	a_1		1
second term	a_2		1
third term	a_3	$a_1 + a_2$	$1 + 1 = 2$
fourth term	a_4	$a_2 + a_3$	$1 + 2 = 3$
fifth term	a_5	$a_3 + a_4$	$2 + 3 = 5$
$\vdots$	$\vdots$	$\vdots$	$\vdots$
nth term	a_n	$a_{n-2} + a_{n-1}$	

The formula $a_n = a_{n-2} + a_{n-1}$ is an example of a **recursive formula.** This means that each succeeding term is formulated from one or more previous terms.

Definition of Recursive Formula	**A recursive formula has two parts:** • the value(s) of the first term(s), and • a recursion equation that shows how to find each term from the term(s) before it.

$a_n = a_1 + (n - 1)d$ and $a_n = a_1 r^{n-1}$ are not recursive. These sequences are determined by the number of the term n rather than by the preceding term.

A recursive formula for a sequence describes how to find the nth term from the term(s) before it.

Sequence	Sequence Type	Recursive Formula
9, 13, 17, ...	arithmetic	$a_{n+1} = a_n + 4, a_1 = 9, n \geq 1$
7, 21, 63, ...	geometric	$a_{n+1} = a_n \cdot 3, a_1 = 7, n \geq 1$
1, 1, 2, 3, 5, 8, ...	Fibonacci	$a_n = a_{n-1} + a_{n-2}, a_1 = 1, a_2 = 1, n \geq 3$

Example ① **Find the first five terms of the sequence in which $a_1 = 5$ and $a_{n+1} = 2a_n + 3, n \geq 1$.**

$a_1 = 5$ and $a_{n+1} = 2a_n + 3$

$a_{1+1} = 2a_1 + 3 \qquad n = 1$
$\quad a_2 = 2(5) + 3$ or 13

$a_{2+1} = 2a_2 + 3 \qquad n = 2$
$\quad a_3 = 2(13) + 3$ or 29

$a_{3+1} = 2a_3 + 3 \qquad n = 3$
$\quad a_4 = 2(29) + 3$ or 61

$a_{4+1} = 2a_4 + 3 \qquad n = 4$
$\quad a_4 = 2(61) + 3$ or 125

The first five terms of the sequence are 5, 13, 29, 61, and 125.

Lesson 11-6 Recursion and Special Sequences **683**

1 FOCUS

5-Minute Check
(over Lesson 11-5)

1. Find the sum of the infinite geometric series $12 + 3 + \frac{3}{4} + \frac{3}{16} + \ldots$ **$S = 16$**

2. Find the sum of the infinite geometric series described by $a_1 = -2$ and $r = -\frac{1}{4}$. **$S = -\frac{8}{5}$**

3. Find a common fraction equivalent to the repeating decimal $0.\overline{25}$. **$\frac{25}{99}$**

4. Find the first three terms of the infinite geometric series with $S = 21$ and $r = \frac{1}{7}$. **$18 + \frac{18}{7} + \frac{18}{49}$**

5. A hot air balloon rises 120 feet in its first minute of flight. In each succeeding minute, it rises only 80% as high as in the previous minute. What will be its maximum altitude if it rises freely? **600 feet**

NCTM Standards: 1–6, 12

Instructional Resources

- Study Guide Master 11-6
- Practice Master 11-6
- Enrichment Master 11-6
- Assessment and Evaluation Masters, p. 297

Transparency 11-6A contains the 5-Minute Check for this lesson; **Transparency 11-6B** contains a teaching aid for this lesson.

Recommended Pacing

Standard Pacing	Days 9 & 10 of 14
Honors Pacing	Day 7 of 11
Block Scheduling*	Day 4 of 7 (along with Lesson 11-5)

*For more information on pacing and possible lesson plans, refer to the *Block Scheduling Booklet.*

Hands-On Activity Use the photograph of a sunflower to verify, by counting, the number of clockwise and counterclockwise spirals.

2 TEACH

In-Class Example

For Example 1
Find the first six terms of the sequence in which $a_1 = 3$ and $a_{n+1} = 2a_n - 1$, $n \geq 1$.
3, 5, 9, 17, 33, 65

 MODELING MATHEMATICS The Tower of Hanoi game provides students with hands-on experience of a challenging puzzle that requires recursive thinking. If students do not use the most efficient strategy, they will not get the same sequence.

Teaching Tip Emphasize to students that in recursion, the function operates on the preceding term. This means that there is no way to find the $n + 1$ term without computing terms 1 through n.

MODELING MATHEMATICS

Special Sequences

Materials: penny, nickel, and dime

The object of the game *Tower of Hanoi* is to move a stack of n coins from one position to another with the fewest moves, a_n. There are three positions and the following rules must be followed.

- You can only move one coin at a time.
- A coin must be placed on top of another coin, not underneath.
- A smaller coin may be placed on top of a larger coin, but not vice versa. For example, a nickel may not be placed on top of a dime.

Draw 3 circles on a sheet of paper, as shown below.

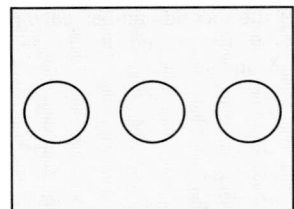

Your Turn

a. Place a dime on the first circle. What is the least number of moves that you can take to get it to the second circle? **1 move**

b. Place a dime and a penny on the first circle, with the dime on top. What is the least number of moves that you can take to get the stack to another circle? (Remember, a penny cannot be placed on top of a dime.) **3 moves**

c. Place a nickel, penny, and dime on the first circle. What is the least number of moves that you can take to get the stack to another circle? **7 moves**

d. The least number of moves a_n required to move a stack of n coins can be represented by the function $a_n = 2^n - 1$. Find the number of moves required to move a stack of 4 coins and a stack of 5 coins. **15, 31**

 LOOK BACK

Refer to Lesson 8–7B for an introduction to iteration.

Recall that iteration is a special type of recursion. Iteration is the process of composing a function with itself repeatedly. To understand the concept of iteration more clearly, use a calculator to find $\sqrt{2}$.

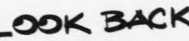 $\sqrt{2} \approx 1.414213562$

Then take the square root of that square root.

$\sqrt{1.414213562} = 1.189207115.$

Repeat the process three more times.

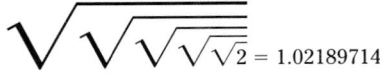 $\sqrt{\sqrt{\sqrt{\sqrt{\sqrt{2}}}}} = 1.021897149$

GLOBAL CONNECTIONS

The most popular board game on the African Continent is *mancala* and its hundreds of variations. This game of movement and capture using stones and cups is very mathematical in nature and has been played for centuries.

Each successive use of the square root function depends on the output of the previous root. In symbols, this can be represented by $f(f(f(f(f(x)))))$, where $f(f(x)) = f \circ f(x)$, the composition of functions. This example illustrates a recursion that composes a function with itself repeatedly. Note that all iterations are recursions, but not vice versa. For example, the Fibonacci sequence, which is a recursion, requires the input of two preceding terms. It is not the composition of a function to itself.

Iteration needs an initial value, x_0. To iterate a function $f(x)$, find the function value $f(x_0)$ of the initial value x_0. The value of $f(x_0)$ is x_1. The second iterate is the value of the function performed on the output, that is, $f(f(x_0))$ or $f(x_1)$.

 **Alternative Learning Styles**

Visual Have students work in small groups and play the Tower of Hanoi game repeatedly. As one student plays, the others should observe and try to describe the process step by step. They should arrive at the process through group discussion.

 **GLOBAL CONNECTIONS**

Books with mathematical games have been in production since the seventeenth century.

Example ② **Find the first three iterates x_1, x_2, x_3 of the function $f(x) = 3x + 1$ for an initial value of $x_0 = 1$.**

To find the first iterate x_1, find the value of the function for $x_0 = 1$.

$f(x_0) = f(1)$
$\qquad = 3(1) + 1$ or 4   So, $x_1 = 4$.

To find the second iterate x_2, substitute x_1 for x.

$f(x_1) = f(4)$
$\qquad = 3(4) + 1$ or 13   So, $x_2 = 13$.

Substitute x_2 for x to find the third iterate.

$f(x_2) = f(13)$
$\qquad = 3(13) + 1$ or 40   So, $x_3 = 40$.

The first three iterates of the function $f(x) = 3x + 1$ for an initial value of $x_0 = 1$ are 4, 13, and 40.

Iteration sequences may describe a wide variety of real-world situations. One use of iteration involves compound interest.

Example ③

APPLICATION

Savings

Haloke's parents started a savings account for her when she was born. They invested $500 in an account that pays 6% interest compounded annually. Find the balance of the account after each of the first three years.

Explore   We need to find an equation that describes the balance of the account after 3 years.

Plan   Let b_n represent the balance after each year. So $b_0 = 500$. The interest is found by multiplying the balance of the account after the $(n - 1)$st year by the annual interest rate, which is 6%.

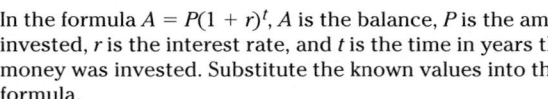

$$\underbrace{\text{new balance}}_{b_n} = \underbrace{\text{previous balance}}_{b_{n-1}} + \underbrace{\text{accumulated interest}}_{0.06 \cdot b_{n-1}}$$

Solve $b_1 = b_0 + 0.06b_0$
$\qquad = 500 + (0.06)(500)$
$\qquad = 530$ *balance after the first year*

$b_2 = b_1 + 0.06b_1$
$\qquad = 530 + 0.06(530)$
$\qquad = 561.80$ *balance after the second year*

$b_3 = b_2 + 0.06b_2$
$\qquad = 561.80 + 0.06(561.80)$
$\qquad = 595.51$ *balance after the third year*

Examine   In the formula $A = P(1 + r)^t$, A is the balance, P is the amount invested, r is the interest rate, and t is the time in years that the money was invested. Substitute the known values into the formula.

$A = P(1 + r)^t$
$\quad = 500(1 + 0.06)^3$ *$P = 500$, $r = 0.06$, and $t = 3$*
$\quad = 595.51$ ✓

Lesson 11–6 Recursion and Special Sequences   **685**

In-Class Examples

For Example 2
Find the first three iterates x_1, x_2, x_3 of the function $f(x) = 4x - 2$ for an initial value of $x_0 = 2$.
6, 22, 86

For Example 3
Find the balance of the account for the fourth and fifth years.
$631.24, $669.11

Study Guide Masters, p. 81

11-6   NAME_____ DATE_____

Study Guide   Student Edition Pages 680–685

Recursion and Special Sequences

A recursive sequence is a sequence in which each succeeding term is formulated from one or more previous terms. A **recursive formula** for a sequence describes how to find the nth term from the term(s) before it.

Parts of a Recursive Formula
1. the value of the first term(s)
2. a recursive equation that shows how to find each term from the term(s) before it

Example: Find the first six terms of the sequence where $f(0) = 4$ and $f(n + 1) = f(n) + 3$.
$f(0) = 4$
$f(1) = f(0) + 3 = 4 + 3 = 7$
$f(2) = f(1) + 3 = 7 + 3 = 10$
$f(3) = f(2) + 3 = 10 + 3 = 13$
$f(4) = f(3) + 3 = 13 + 3 = 16$
$f(5) = f(4) + 3 = 16 + 3 = 19$

A special type of recursion is **iteration**. Iteration is the process of composing a function with itself repeatedly.

Example: Find the first four iterates of $f(x) = 3x + 5$ for an initial value of $x_0 = 1$.
$f(x_1) = f(1) = 3(1) + 5 = 8$
$f(x_2) = f(8) = 3(8) + 5 = 29$
$f(x_3) = f(29) = 3(29) + 5 = 92$
$f(x_4) = f(92) = 3(92) + 5 = 281$

Find the first six terms of each sequence.

1. $f(0) = 1$; $f(2) = 1$; $f(n + 1) = f(n) + f(n - 1)$ where $n \geq 2$.
   1, 1, 2, 3, 5, 8
2. $f(1) = 1$; $f(n + 1) = \frac{1}{1 + f(n)}$
   $1, \frac{1}{2}, \frac{2}{3}, \frac{3}{5}, \frac{5}{8}, \frac{8}{13}$
3. $f(0) = 3$; $f(n + 1) = f(n) + 2n$
   3, 3, 5, 9, 15, 23
4. $f(0) = 5$; $f(n + 1) = f(n) + 2$
   5, 7, 9, 11, 13, 15
5. $f(0) = 1$; $f(n + 1) = (n + 1) \cdot f(n)$
   1, 1, 2, 6, 24, 120
6. $f(1) = 13$; $f(n + 1) = f(n) - n + 3$
   13, 15, 16, 16, 15, 13

Find the first three iterates of each function, using the given initial value.

7. $f(x) = x - 1$; $x_0 = 4$
   3, 2, 1
8. $f(x) = 2x^2 + 5$; $x_0 = -4$
   37, 2743, 1,548,103
9. $f(x) = x^2 - 3x$; $x_0 = 1$
   -2, 10, 70
10. $f(x) = 4x - 6$; $x_0 = -5$
   -26, -110, -446
11. $f(x) = x^2 + 2x + 1$; $x_0 = -2$
   1, 4, 25
12. $f(x) = 4x^2 - 9$; $x_0 = -1$
   -5, 91, 33,115

Check for Understanding

Exercises 1–10 are designed to help you assess your students' understanding through reading, writing, speaking, and modeling. You should work through Exercises 1–3 with your students and then monitor their work on Exercises 4–10.

Assignment Guide

Core: 11–31 odd, 33–37
Enriched: 12–28 even, 29–37

For **Extra Practice,** see p. 902.

The red A, B, and C flags, printed only in the Teacher's Wraparound Edition, indicate the level of difficulty of the exercises.

Additional Answer

2. Iteration is the composition of a function to itself. For $f(x) = 5x - 1$, the iterate is $f(f(x)) = 5(5x - 1) - 1$ or $f(f(x)) = 25x - 6$.

Practice Masters, p. 81

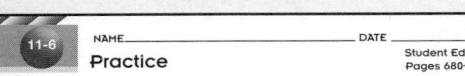

11-6 NAME_____ DATE_____
Practice   Student Edition
                                  Pages 680–685

Recursion and Special Sequences
Find the first six terms of each sequence.

1. $f(0) = 1; f(n + 1) = 4(n - 1)$
   where $n \geq 2$
   1, 1, 4, 4, 16, 16

2. $f(0) = 1; f(n + 1) = \frac{1}{2} + f(n)$
   $-1, -\frac{1}{2}, 0, \frac{1}{2}, 1, \frac{3}{2}$

3. $f(0) = 1; f(1) = 1;$
   $f(n + 1) = 24 + f(n - 1)(-5)$
   1, 1, 19, 19, −71, −71

4. $f(0) = 2; f(n + 1) = f(n) + n - 2$
   2, 1, 1, 2, 4, 7

5. $f(0) = 4; f(n + 1) = (n - 1) + f(n)$
   4, 3, 3, 4, 6, 9

6. $f(1) = 1; f(2) = 1; f(n + 1) =$
   $f(n) - f(n - 1)$ where $n \geq 2$
   1, 1, 0, −1, −1, 0

Find the first three iterates of each function, using the given initial value.

7. $f(x) = 8 + 3x; x_0 = 1$
   11, 41, 131

8. $f(x) = \frac{2}{2x - 1}; x_0 = -1$
   $-\frac{2}{3}, -\frac{6}{7}, -\frac{14}{19}$

9. $f(x) = 2x^2; x_0 = 5$
   50, 5000, 50,000,000

10. $f(x) = x(x + 1); x_0 = -5$
    20, 420, 176,820

11. $f(x) = \frac{x - 1}{x}; x_0 = 10$
    $\frac{9}{10}, -\frac{1}{9}, 10$

12. $f(x) = 10x + 2; x_0 = -1$
    −8, −72, −718

CHECK FOR UNDERSTANDING

Communicating Mathematics

1. $a_n = a_{n-1} + d$

Study the lesson. Then complete the following.

1. Which formula for the nth term of an arithmetic sequence is recursive: $a_n = a_1 + (n - 1)d$ or $a_n = a_{n-1} + d$? Explain how you know.

2. **Explain** how the composition of functions and iteration are related. Use the function $f(x) = 5x - 1$ as an illustration.   **See margin.**

3. Refer to the Modeling Mathematics activity. Write the function $a_n = 2^n - 1$ as a recursive function in terms of a_{n-1}. $a_n = 2a_{n-1} + 1$

Guided Practice

8. −22, −52, −112, −232, −472

9. −7.2, −22.4, −52.8, −113.6, −235.2

Find the first six terms of each sequence.

4. $a_1 = 12, a_{n+1} = a_n - 3$
   12, 9, 6, 3, 0, −3

5. $a_1 = 1, a_2 = 2, a_{n+2} = 4a_{n+1} - 3a_n$
   1, 2, 5, 14, 41, 122

Find the first three iterates of each function, using the given initial values.

6. $f(x) = 3x - 4, x_0 = 3$ 5, 11, 29

7. $f(x) = x^2 + 2, x_0 = -1$ 3, 11, 123

Find the first five iterates of $f(x) = 2x - 8$ for each initial value.

8. $x_0 = -7$

9. $x_0 = 0.4$

10. **Inflation**   If inflation is 3%, the cost $c(x)$ next year for a loaf of Italian bread can be found by the function $c(x) = x(1.03)^n$, where x is the cost this year and n is the number of years from now. If the cost this year is $1.80, what will the cost be ten years from now, if inflation continues at the same rate?   **about $2.42**

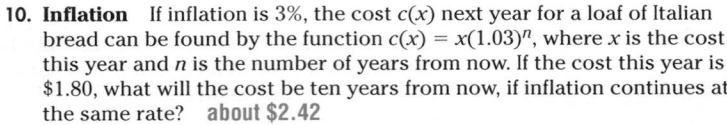

EXERCISES

Practice

11. 9, 14, 24, 44, 84, 164

13. 13, 18, 23, 28, 33, 38

14. 4, −3, 5, −1, 9, 7

15. 1, $\frac{1}{2}, \frac{1}{3}, \frac{1}{4}, \frac{1}{5}, \frac{1}{6}$

25. −3, −17, −73, −297, −1193

26. −1.6, −11.4, −50.6, −207.4, −834.6

29. 0.33, 0.333, 0.3333, ... ; The values approach $\frac{1}{3}$.

Find the first six terms of each sequence.   12. −6, −3, 0, 3, 6, 9

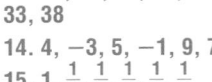 A

11. $a_1 = 9, a_{n+1} = 2a_n - 4$

12. $a_1 = -6, a_{n+1} = a_n + 3$

13. $a_1 = 13, a_{n+1} = a_n + 5$

14. $a_1 = 4, a_2 = -3, a_{n+2} = a_{n+1} + 2a_n$

15. $a_1 = 1, a_{n+1} = \frac{n}{n+1} \cdot a_n$

16. $a_1 = 6, a_{n+1} = a_n + (n + 3)$
    6, 10, 15, 21, 28, 36

Find the first three iterates of each function, using the given initial values.   17. 16, 142, 1276   19. −7, −16, −43   20. −3, 13, 333

 B

17. $f(x) = 9x - 2, x_0 = 2$

18. $f(x) = 4x - 3, x_0 = 2$ 5, 17, 65

19. $f(x) = 3x + 5, x_0 = -4$

20. $f(x) = 2x^2 - 5, x_0 = -1$

21. $f(x) = 3x^2 - 4, x_0 = 1$

22. $f(x) = x^2 + 3x + 1, x_0 = 1$

21. −1, −1, −1   22. 5, 41, 1805   24. −13, −57, −233, −937, −3753

Find the first five iterates of $f(x) = 4x - 5$ for each initial value.

 C

23. $x_0 = 6$ 19, 71, 279, 1111, 4439

24. $x_0 = -2$

25. $x_0 = \frac{1}{2}$

26. $x_0 = 0.85$

27. If $a_0 = 7$ and $a_{n+1} = a_n + 12$, find the value of a_5.   67

28. If $a_0 = 1$ and $a_{n+1} = -2.1$, then what is the value of a_4?   −2.1

Critical Thinking

29. Iterate the function $f(x) = 0.1x + 0.3$ several times with the initial value of $x_0 = 0.3$. Describe the pattern that emerges.

Reteaching

Using Models Summarize real-world examples of Fibonacci sequences. Many can be found in nature: leaf-growth patterns, spirals in pineapples, and population growth in animal and human populations.

30. Finance Aletha Johnson is taking out a mortgage loan for $120,000 to buy a new house. Her monthly payments are $942.55, and the function $B_n = B_{n-1}(1.0075) - 942.55$ describes the balance of the loan at the end of each month. Find the balance of the loan for the first eight months.
$119,957.45, $119,914.58, $119,871.39, $119,827.88, $119,784.03, $119,739.87, $119,695.36, $119,650.53

31. Look for a Pattern Look at the figures representing triangular numbers shown below.

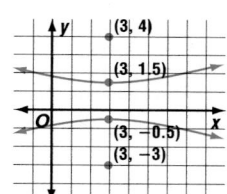

Figure 1   Figure 2   Figure 3   Figure 4   Figure 5

31b. $a_{n+1} = a_n + (n + 1)$

a. Write a sequence of the first five triangular numbers.   1, 3, 6, 10, 15

b. Write a recursive formula for the *n*th triangular number, a_n.

c. What is the 80th triangular number?   3240

32. Special Sequences The Lucas sequence was developed from the Fibonacci sequence. In the Lucas sequence, $L_1 = F_1$ and $L_n = F_{n+1} + F_{n-1}$ for $n \geq 2$. Find the first eight terms of the Lucas sequence.
1, 3, 4, 7, 11, 18, 29, 47

Mixed Review

33. Find the sum of the infinite series $9 + 6 + 4 + \ldots$.   (Lesson 11–5)   27

34. Physics The intensity of illumination on a surface varies inversely as the square of the distance from the light source. A surface is 12 meters from a light source. How far must the surface be from the source to receive twice as much illumination?   (Lesson 9–2) $6\sqrt{2}$ meters

35. $\dfrac{(y - 0.5)^2}{1} - \dfrac{(x - 3)^2}{11.25} = 1$

35. Write the equation of the hyperbola graphed at the right. (Lesson 7–5)

36. $\begin{bmatrix} 28 \\ -16 \\ 3 \end{bmatrix}$

36. Find $3\begin{bmatrix} 4 \\ 1 \\ 7 \end{bmatrix} + 2\begin{bmatrix} 3 \\ -2 \\ 6 \end{bmatrix} - 5\begin{bmatrix} -2 \\ 3 \\ 6 \end{bmatrix}$.   (Lesson 4–2)

37. Statistics The numbers of job-related injuries at a construction site for each month of 1995 are listed below.   (Lesson 1–3)

10	13	15	39	21	24
19	16	39	17	23	25

a. Make a line plot of the numbers of injuries.   a–b. See margin.

b. Make a stem-and-leaf plot of the number of injuries.

c. 20; 39; 21.75

c. Find the median, mode, and mean of the numbers of injuries.

Extension

Problem Solving When a cell divides, the number of cells is doubled. The number of cells can be written nonrecursively as $a_n = 2^n$. How would this be written recursively? $a_n = 2n$

---

4 ASSESS

Closing Activity

Writing Have students write a paragraph explaining the main concept underlying the definitions of recursion and iteration.

Chapter 11, Quiz C (Lessons 11-5 and 11-6), is available in the *Assessment and Evaluation Masters*, p. 297.

Additional Answers

37a.

Numbers of Job-Related Injuries

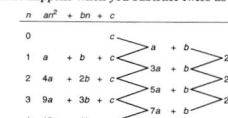

37b.

Stem	Leaf
1	0 3 5 6 7 9
2	1 3 4 5
3	9 9

$2|1 = 21$

Enrichment Masters, p. 81

11-6   NAME_____   DATE_____
Enrichment   Student Edition Pages 680–685

Quadratic Formulas for Sequences

An ordinary arithmetic sequence is formed using a rule such as $bn + c$. The first term is c, b is called the common difference, and n takes on the values 0, 1, 2, 3, and so on. The value of term $n + 1$ equals $b(n + 1) + c$ or $bn + b + c$. So, the value of a term is a function of the term number.

Some sequences use quadratic functions. A method called *finite differences* can be used to find the values of the terms. Notice what happens when you subtract twice as shown in this table.

n	$an^2 + bn + c$		
0	c		
1	$a + b + c$	$a + b$	$2a$
2	$4a + 2b + c$	$3a + b$	$2a$
3	$9a + 3b + c$	$5a + b$	$2a$
4	$16a + 4b + c$	$7a + b$	

A sequence that yields a common difference after two subtractions can be generated by a quadratic expression. For example, the sequence 1, 5, 12, 22, 35, ⋯ gives a common difference of 3 after two subtractions. Using the table above, you write and solve three equations to find the general rule. The equations are $1 = c$, $5 = a + b + c$, and $12 = 4a + 2b + c$.

Solve each problem.

1. Refer to the sequence in the example above. Solve the system of equations for a, b, and c and then find the quadratic expression for the sequence. Then write the next three terms.
$\frac{3}{2}n^2 + \frac{5}{2}n + 1$; 51, 70, 92

2. The number of line segments connecting n points forms the sequence 0, 0, 1, 3, 6, 10, ⋯, in which n is the number of points and the term value is the number of line segments. What is the common difference after the second subtraction? Find a quadratic expression for the term value.
$1; \frac{1}{2}n^2 - \frac{1}{2}n$

3. The maximum number of regions formed by n chords in a circle forms the sequence 1, 2, 4, 7, 11, 16, ⋯. (A chord is a line segment joining any two points on a circle.) Draw circles to illustrate the first four terms of the sequence. Then find a quadratic expression for the term value.

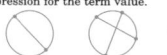

$\frac{1}{2}n^2 + \frac{1}{2}n + 1$

NCTM Standards: 1–5, 7, 12–13

Instructional Resources

- Study Guide Master 11-7
- Practice Master 11-7
- Enrichment Master 11-7

Transparency 11-7A contains the 5-Minute Check for this lesson; **Transparency 11-7B** contains a teaching aid for this lesson.

Recommended Pacing	
Standard Pacing	Day 11 of 14
Honors Pacing	Day 8 of 11
Block Scheduling*	Day 5 of 7

*For more information on pacing and possible lesson plans, refer to the *Block Scheduling Booklet*.

1 FOCUS

5-Minute Check
(over Lesson 11-6)

Find the first four terms of each sequence.

1. $a_1 = 2, a_{n+1} = 3a_n - 1$
2, 5, 14, 41

2. $a_1 = 10, a_{n+1} = 2a_n - 5$
10, 15, 25, 45

3. $a_1 = -1, a_{n+1} = 5a_n + 2$
−1, −3, −13, −63

Find the first three iterates x_1, x_2, x_3 of each function.

4. $f(x) = 4x + 2, x_0 = 1$
6, 26, 106

5. $f(x) = x^2 + 1, x_0 = 2$
5, 26, 677

Motivating the Lesson

Hands-On Activity Have students bring to class objects from nature that cannot be described simply in terms of conventional geometric figures: squares, rectangles, triangles, and other regular polygons.

Fractals

11-7

What YOU'LL LEARN

- To define and draw fractals, and
- to write a recursive formula for the perimeter or area of a fractal.

Why IT'S IMPORTANT

You can use fractals to solve problems involving geology and literature.

APPLICATION
Nature

Nature is filled with many intricate shapes. Euclidean geometry with its points, planes, and polygons cannot begin to describe the shapes we see from day to day. Clouds, leaves, wood, coastlines, rust, and broccoli are far too complicated for Euclidean geometry. Yet, patterns are imbedded in these shapes. In this century, a new branch of mathematics called **fractal geometry** is providing models of nature's designs. Some fractals that model natural patterns are shown below.

One of the most obvious fractal patterns occurs in a tree. Consider how the main trunk of the tree splits into large branches. The large branches of a tree split into smaller branches. Similarly, the smaller branches split into twigs, and so on.

MODELING MATHEMATICS

Fractal Trees

Materials:  isometric dot paper

In this activity, you will make a fractal tree and investigate some of its patterns.

Your Turn a–c. See students' work.

a. At the bottom center of your dot paper, draw a vertical line segment to represent the tree trunk. From the endpoint, draw two branches half as long. The angle between the branches should be 120°.

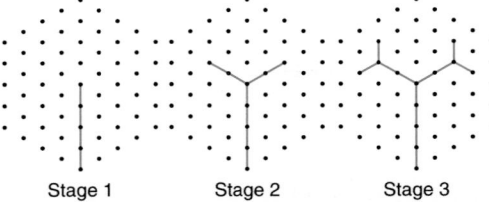

| Stage 1 | Stage 2 | Stage 3 |

e. infinite length

b. Continue drawing branches until they become too small to draw. The first three stages are shown.

c. Can you find small parts of the tree that look like the entire tree? If so, circle them on your drawing.

d. Suppose the length of the tree trunk is 1 unit. How many branches are $\frac{1}{2}$ unit? What is the total length of the branches that are $\frac{1}{2}$ unit long? Find the total lengths for branches that are $\frac{1}{4}, \frac{1}{8}$, and $\frac{1}{16}$ unit. 2, 1; 1; 1; 1

e. If you could continue to draw branches, what is the total length of the branches of the tree?

When small parts of a fractal tree are magnified, the detail is not lost. In fact, the magnified part looks the same as the entire structure. This characteristic is called **self-similarity**. Self-similar objects are those in which we can find replicas of the entire shape or object embedded over and over again inside the object in different sizes.

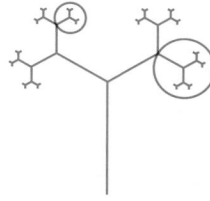

One of the characteristics of a fractal is that it exhibits self-similarity. Other characteristics can be described as follows.

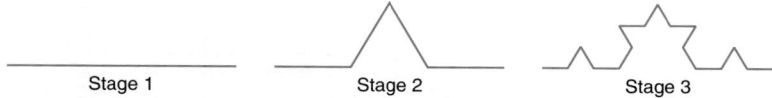

| Definition of Fractal | **A fractal is a geometric figure that has self-similarity, is created using a recursive process, and is infinite in structure.** |

The key to constructing a fractal lies in the replication of a pattern. Suppose you start with a rule that describes a pattern. At each stage in the process, you apply this rule to smaller and smaller parts of the figure. To construct a fractal, this iteration would be applied over and over, without end. In 1904, Swedish mathematician Helge von Koch used such a method to produce a classic fractal, now called the Koch curve.

To construct a Koch curve, start with a line segment. The iterative rule is to construct an equilateral triangle on the middle third of each segment, removing the base of the triangle.

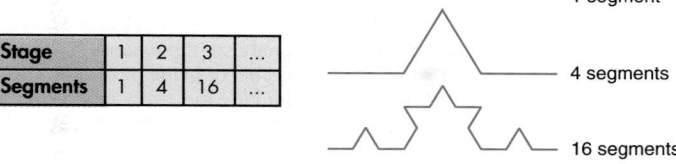

Stage 1   Stage 2   Stage 3

When a Koch curve is applied to an equilateral triangle, a Koch snowflake is produced.

Example **1** **Draw the first four stages of the Koch snowflake.**

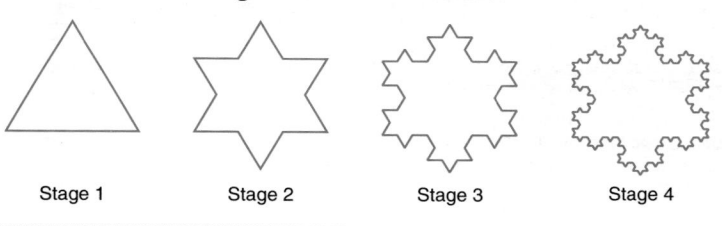

Stage 1   Stage 2   Stage 3   Stage 4

In addition to producing fascinating visual patterns, number patterns are also evident in fractals. These patterns can be described by recursive formulas. Consider the number of segments at each stage of the Koch snowflake. Let's begin by finding a pattern in the Koch curve shown at the right.

1 segment

4 segments

16 segments

Stage	1	2	3	...
Segments	1	4	16	...

Lesson 11–7 Fractals **689**

MODELING MATHEMATICS In this activity, students will construct a visual model of a tree with its branching structure.

In-Class Example

For Example 1
Draw the next two stages of the figure below.

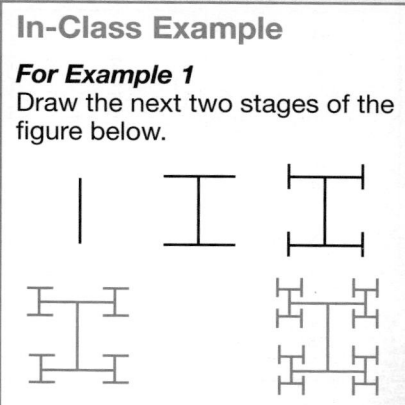

Teaching Tip Point out to students that the fractal structures generated in mathematics are idealized structures. Objects in the natural world that seem to have a fractal structure are not nearly so regular or symmetric.

In-Class Example

For Example 2

Find the total line length at each stage of the Koch snowflake and find a recursive formula that describes the line length.

Stage	Length
1	1
2	$1\frac{2}{3}$
3	$2\frac{1}{9}$
4	$2\frac{11}{27}$
5	$2\frac{49}{81}$

$$a_1 = 1$$
$$a_{n+1} = a_n + \left(\frac{2}{3}\right)^n$$

The word *fractal* was coined by the mathematician Benoit B. Mandelbrot in 1975.

Since the Koch snowflake is formed by applying the Koch curve to the three segments of an equilateral triangle, the number of segments in a Koch snowflake is as follows.

Stage	1	2	3	...
Segments	3×1 or 3	3×4 or 12	3×16 or 48	...

At each successive stage, one line segment is replaced by four smaller segments. Therefore, the pattern can be described by the recursive formula $a_1 = 3$ and $a_{n+1} = 4a_n$. It appears that the number of segments becomes infinite as the number of stages increases.

Example  **2**

INTEGRATION
Geometry

Refer to the Koch snowflake in Example 1.

a. If the length of each segment of the equilateral triangle in Stage 1 is 9 units, find a recursive formula that describes how the perimeter of the snowflake changes as the number of stages increases.

b. Find the perimeter of the Koch snowflake at Stage 5.

c. Describe in words how the perimeter of the Koch snowflake changes as the number of stages increases.

a. Remember that a Koch snowflake is formed by constructing an equilateral triangle on the middle third of each segment. First, determine the perimeter through Stage 3.

Stage (n)	1	2	3	...
Number of segments	3	12	48	...
Length of each segment	9	3	1	...
Perimeter (a_n)	27	36	48	...

As the number of stages increases, the perimeter increases by a factor of $\frac{4}{3}$. Therefore, a recursive formula for the perimeter is $a_1 = 27$, $a_{n+1} = \frac{4}{3}a_n$.

F Y I

If the original segment in a Koch snowflake were 1 inch long, the perimeter at Stage 50 would be 62.7 *miles!*

b. From the chart above, you know that $a_3 = 48$. Find a_4 and a_5.

$$a_4 = \frac{4}{3}a_3 \qquad\qquad a_5 = \frac{4}{3}a_4$$
$$= \left(\frac{4}{3}\right)48 \qquad\qquad = \left(\frac{4}{3}\right)64$$
$$= 64 \qquad\qquad = 85.3$$

The perimeter of the Koch snowflake at Stage 5 is about 85.3 units.

c. It appears that the perimeter of the Koch snowflake increases without bound. The common ratio or growth factor is $\frac{4}{3}$ and $\left|\frac{4}{3}\right| > 1$.

Fractal geometry is a branch of *chaos theory,* which is being used to study and make sense of natural phenomena traditionally thought to neither have patterns nor be capable of being described through mathematical modeling. Such phenomena include the study of weather patterns, earthquake occurrences, and fluctuations in the stock market. Let's see how chaos theory works by playing a chaos game.

First, draw an equilateral triangle on a piece of
paper. Label the vertices of the triangle T, R, and L
to represent top, right, and left. Choose any point
x_0 in the interior of the triangle as the starting point.
Roll a die to choose T, R, or L at random. Then plot
the point that is halfway to the vertex that has been
selected. Continue to roll a die to choose vertices
and plot points.

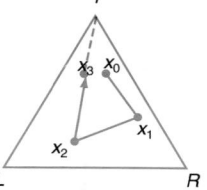

Do you see a pattern? Probably not! It seems unlikely that a random
succession of midpoints would produce anything but a lot of points. Even if
you could take the time to plot 500 such points, you may not see a pattern.
However, here is where a computer or graphing calculator is an invaluable
tool. In the following Exploration, you will program a graphing calculator to
play a chaos game.

The following program will generate 3000 points in a chaos game.

```
PROGRAM: SIERPINS
:FnOff                    :If 1/3<N and N≤2/3
:ClrDraw                  :Then
:PlotsOff                 :.5(.5+X)→X
:AxesOff                  :.5(1+Y)→Y
:0→Xmin: 1→Xmax           :End
:0→Ymin: 1→Ymax           :If 2/3<N
:rand→X: rand→Y           :Then
:For (K, 1, 3000)         :.5(1+X)→X
:rand→N                   :.5Y→Y
:If N≤1/3                 :End
:Then                     :Pt - On (X, Y)
:.5X→X                    :End
:.5Y→Y                    :StorePic  Pic6
:End
```

Your Turn   a. See students' work.

a. Describe the pattern produced by this chaos game.
b. Do you think this pattern might be a fractal? Explain your reasoning.

b. Yes, it has self-
similarity, is created
using recursive process,
and is infinite.

*Sierpinski's triangle is also
called* Sierpinski's gasket.

The picture generated in the Exploration above is a fractal called *Sierpinski's
triangle,* named after the Polish mathematician Waclaw Sierpinski, who
introduced it in 1916. Sierpinski's triangle can be constructed by using the
following recursive process.

1. Start with an equilateral triangle.

2. Connect the midpoint of the sides
   with line segments.

3. Remove the middle triangle.

4. Apply steps 1–3 to each of the
   remaining triangles repeatedly.

EXPLORATION

Students will enter and run a
program to generate Sierpinski's
triangle. Emphasize that the
If/Then groups are subdividing
line segments. This is the clue
that it could be a program for a
fractal.

In-Class Example

For Example 3

Find the values of a_2, a_3, a_4, and a_5 for the area of the Sierpinski triangle. **48, 36, 27, 20.25**

3 PRACTICE/APPLY

Check for Understanding

Exercises 1–6 are designed to help you assess your students' understanding through reading, writing, speaking, and modeling. You should work through Exercises 1–3 with your students and then monitor their work on Exercises 4–6.

Additional Answer

4.

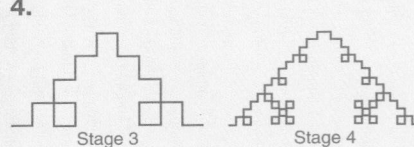

Stage 3   Stage 4

Study Guide Masters, p. 82

 11-7

NAME _____ DATE _____

Study Guide

Student Edition
Pages 686–691

Fractals

A fractal is a geometric figure that has self-similarity, is created using a recursive process, and is infinite in its structure. Fractal geometry provides models for many of nature's designs and patterns.

Example: Air bubbles in fluids are an example of fractals in science.

 a. Find the number of bubbles in the 6th stage if the recursive formula for the increase in the number of bubbles per stage is $a_1 = 1$, $a_{n+1} = 3a_n - 1$.

$a_1 = 1$
$a_2 = 3(1) - 1 = 2$
$a_3 = 3(2) - 1 = 5$
$a_4 = 3(5) - 1 = 14$
$a_5 = 3(14) - 1 = 41$
$a_6 = 3(41) - 1 = 122$

 b. Draw a diagram of the first four stages of this air bubble example.

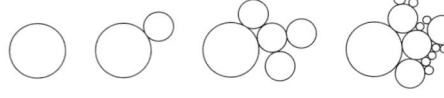

Draw the next stage of the fractal formed by replacing each segment with the pattern shown.

1.   2.

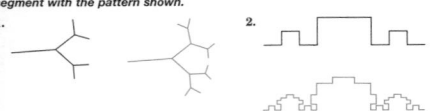

3. Tree branches are an example of fractal geometry. Find the number of branches at stage 5 if the recursive formula is $a_1 = 1$ and $a_{n+1} = 2a_n + 1$. $a_5 = 2(15) + 1 = 31$ branches

4. Describe an example of fractals found in the human body. Examples of fractals in the human body include the blood vessels: arteries, capillaries, and veins.

692 Chapter 11

Example **3** a. Draw the first four stages of Sierpinski's Triangle.
 b. If the area of the triangle at Stage 1 is 64 square units, find a recursive formula that describes how the area of the triangle changes as the number of stages increases.
 c. Describe in words how the area of the triangle changes as the number of stages increases.

 a.

Stage 1   Stage 2   Stage 3   Stage 4

 b. Make a table showing the area of each stage.

Stage	1	2	3	...
Area	64	48	36	...

As the number of stages increases, the area decreases by a factor of $\frac{3}{4}$. Therefore, a recursive formula is $a_1 = 64$, $a_{n+1} = \frac{3}{4}a_n$.

 c. It appears that the area remaining in the triangle approaches zero. The common ratio or growth factor is $\frac{3}{4}$ and $\left|\frac{3}{4}\right| < 1$.

CHECK FOR UNDERSTANDING

Communicating Mathematics

Study the lesson. Then complete the following.

1. **Explain** how a cloud or a tree can be considered a fractal. **See students' work.**

2. **Explain** how recursion is used in creating fractals. **A rule is applied to smaller and smaller parts.**

3. **Explain** how self-similarity is evident in a fern. **Small parts of the frond look like the entire frond.**

Guided Practice

4. The figure at the right shows the first two stages of a fractal formed by constructing a square on the middle third of the segment and removing the base of the square. Draw the next two stages. **See margin.**

Stage 1   Stage 2

5. Refer to Example 3. a. $a_1 = 1$, $a_{n+1} = 3a_n$
 a. Write a recursive formula that describes how the number of shaded triangles changes as the number of stages increases.
 b. Find the number of shaded triangles at Stage 5. **81**

6. **Botany** Botanists have found that the angle between the main branches of a tree and its trunk remain constant in each species. How is this finding related to fractal geometry? **Small parts look like the entire tree.**

692 Chapter 11 *Investigating Sequences and Series*

Reteaching

Using Alternative Methods Explore several ways of successively subdividing a square. Each leads to a different type of fractal pattern.

Practice

7–8. See margin.

Draw the next stage of a fractal formed by replacing each segment with the pattern shown.

7.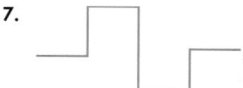

8.

9. A fractal is formed by trisecting the sides of a square, which forms 9 smaller squares, and then removing the middle square.

Stage 1   Stage 2

  a. Draw Stages 3 and 4.   **See margin.**

  b. Write a recursive formula that describes how the number of squares changes as the number of stages increases. $a_1 = 1, a_{n+1} = 8a_n$

  c. Find the number of squares at Stage 6.   **32,768**

9d. $a_1 = 81, a_{n+1} = \frac{8}{9}a_n$

  d. Suppose the area at Stage 1 is 81 square units. Write a recursive formula that describes how the area of the square carpet changes as the number of stages increases.

  e. Describe how the area of one of the squares changes as the number of stages increases.   **The area approaches zero.**

Critical Thinking

10. The perimeter of a Koch snowflake becomes infinite as the number of stages increases. Is the area of a Koch snowflake infinite or finite? Explain your reasoning.   **See margin.**

Applications and Problem Solving

11. Sample answer: Small changes produced unexpected results.

11. **Literature**   In *Jurassic Park*, mathematician Ian Malcolm uses chaos theory. Find a copy of the book or a book review and describe the role that chaos theory plays in the book.

12. Sample answer: Within each mountain range, you can see features of the whole range.

12. **Geology**   The photograph at the right shows the foothills of the Himalayas as seen from the Landsat-1 satellite. Describe the fractal self-similarity of the foothills.

13. See students' work.

13. **Art**   The photograph at the right shows Escher's studies of Sierpinski's triangle patterns on the twelfth century pulpit of the Ravello cathedral, designed by Nicola di Bartolomeo of Foggia. Create your own design using Sierpinski's triangle.

Extension

Connections Have students research the history of research in fractals. Mandelbrot's own books are an excellent source.

Additional Answer

10. Finite; the series of areas is an infinite series with $r = \frac{3}{4}$; therefore, it has a sum.

Assignment Guide

Core: 7, 9, 10, 11, 13, 14–18
Enriched: 8–10, 12, 14–18

For **Extra Practice,** see p. 903.

The red A, B, and C flags, printed only in the Teacher's Wraparound Edition, indicate the level of difficulty of the exercises.

Additional Answers

7.

8.

9a.

Stage 3   Stage 4

Practice Masters, p. 82

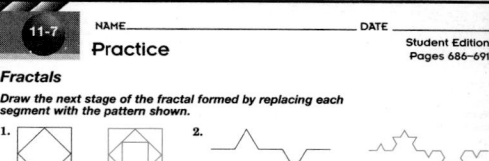

11-7   NAME_____   DATE_____
       Practice   Student Edition
                             Pages 686–691

Fractals

Draw the next stage of the fractal formed by replacing each segment with the pattern shown.

1.   2.

3. Refer to Sierpinski's Triangle on page 691 in the text.
  a. Draw the first four stages.

  b. If the perimeter of stage 1 is 24, find a recursive formula that describes how the perimeters of the shaded triangles change as the number of stages increase.
   $a_n = 24, a_{n+1} = \left(\frac{3}{2}\right)a_n$

  c. Find the perimeter of the shaded triangles in stage 7.
   $a_7 = \left(\frac{3}{2}\right)(182.25) = 273.375$

Closing Activity

Modeling Have students design and build a simple fractal from available materials. They could cut lengths of wood into smaller and smaller pieces with each cut and arrange them in systematic design.

Mixed Review

14. Find the first five terms of the sequence in which $a_1 = 3$, $a_{n+1} = 2a_n + 5$. (Lesson 11–6) **3, 11, 27, 59, 123**

15. Use a calculator to find the natural logarithm of 0.056, rounded to four decimal places. (Lesson 10–5) **−2.8824**

16. Electronics Sharon Weisman is an electrical engineer designing the electrical circuits for a new office building. There are three basic things to be considered in an electrical circuit: the flow of the electrical current I, the resistance to the flow Z called impedance, and electromotive force E called voltage. These quantities are related in the formula $E = I \cdot Z$. The current of the circuit Ms. Weisman is designing is to be $(35 - j40)$ amperes. Electrical engineers use the letter j to represent the imaginary unit. Find the impedance of the circuit if the voltage is to be $(430 - j330)$ volts. (Lesson 5–10) **(10 + j2) ohms**

17. Write $\begin{bmatrix} 5 & 1 \\ 2 & -3 \end{bmatrix} \cdot \begin{bmatrix} x \\ y \end{bmatrix} = \begin{bmatrix} 26 \\ 41 \end{bmatrix}$ as a system of linear equations. (Lesson 4–6)

17. $5x + y = 26$, $2x − 3y = 41$

18. Solve $|x - 7| = 12$. (Lesson 1–5) **−5, 19**

Mathematics *and* SOCIETY

Chaos on the Tilt-a-Whirl

The excerpt below appeared in an article in *Science News* on February 26, 1994.

MUCH OF THE FUN OF AN AMUSEMENT-park ride arises from its stomach-churning, mind-tingling unpredictability. The Tilt-a-Whirl, for example, spins its passengers in one direction, then another, sometimes hesitating between forays and sometimes swinging them abruptly from one motion to another. The rider never knows exactly what will come next. . . . Intrigued by the possibility that the motion of the Tilt-a-Whirl cars may represent an example of chaotic behavior, Richard L. Kautz of the National Institute of Standards and Technology . . . and Brett M. Huggard of Northern Arizona University . . . worked out a mathematical equation to describe the forces acting on each car. . . . Chaotic motion occurs at intermediate speeds, close to the 6.5 revolutions per minute at which the ride actually operates. . . . At intermediate speeds, the jumbled mixture of car rotations never repeats itself exactly, which gives the Tilt-a-Whirl its lively and unpredictable behavior. ■

1. Sample answer: to cause more rotation

1. Tilt-a-Whirl riders can often be seen throwing their weight from side to side at certain places in the ride cycle. Why might they be doing this?

2. Contrast the type of ride you experience on a Tilt-a-Whirl with that which you experience on a roller coaster or merry-go-round. What accounts for these differences? **See margin.**

3. In designing an amusement-park ride, what kinds of necessary information could a mathematical model provide? **See margin.**

Enrichment Masters, p. 82

11-7 NAME_____ DATE_____
Student Edition
Pages 686–691

Enrichment

Geometric Puzzlers

For the problems on this page, you will need to use the Pythagorean Theorem and the formulas for the area of a triangle and a trapezoid.

1. A rectangle measures 5 by 12 units. The upper left corner is cut off as shown in the diagram.

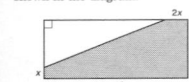

a. Find the area $A(x)$ of the shaded pentagon.
$A(x) = 60 - (5 - x)(6 - x)$

b. Find x and $2x$ so that $A(x)$ is a maximum. What happens to the cut-off triangle?
$x = 5$ and $2x = 10$; the triangle will not exist.

2. A triangle with sides of lengths a, a, and b is isosceles. Two triangles are cut off so that the remaining pentagon has five equal sides of length x. The value of x can be found using this equation.

$(2b - a)x^2 + (4a^2 - b^2)(2x - a) = 0$

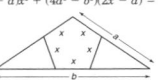

a. Find x when $a = 10$ and $b = 12$.
$x ≈ 4.46$

b. Can a be equal to $2b$?
Yes, but it would not be possible to have a pentagon of the type described.

3. The coordinates of the vertices of a triangle are $A(0, 0)$, $B(11, 0)$, and $C(0, 11)$. A line $x = k$ cuts the triangle into two equal pieces having equal area.

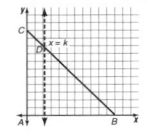

a. What are the coordinates of point D?
$(k, 11 - k)$

b. Write and solve an equation for finding the value of k.
$\frac{1}{2}k(11 + 11 - k) = 22$;
$k = 11 - \sqrt{77}$

4. Inside a square are five circles with the same radius.

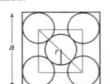

a. Connect the center of the top left circle to the center of the bottom right circle. Express this length in terms of r.
$4r$

b. Draw the square with vertices at the centers of the four outside circles. Express the diagonal of this square in terms of r and a.
$(a - 2r)\sqrt{2}$

Mathematics *and* SOCIETY

In Greek mythology, *chaos* was the void that existed before the creation of the universe. Chaos was viewed as an unformed mass that contained all the seeds of nature. After this period of history, *chaos* came to mean disorder and confusion. But modern chaos theory sees all disorder as having an underlying order.

Answers for Mathematics and Society

2. The roller coaster and merry-go-round produce motions that are cyclical, repetitive, and predictable. The motions of the Tilt-a-Whirl are not repetitive or predictable; they vary with each ride.

3. A mathematical model can provide information about speed and direction of motions; forces exerted on riders, cars, platforms, or supports; and design parameters for supports and restraints.

The Binomial Theorem

INTEGRATION
Probability

What YOU'LL LEARN

- To expand powers of binomials by using Pascal's triangle and the binomial theorem, and
- to find specific terms of binomial expansions.

Why IT'S IMPORTANT

You can use the binomial theorem to solve problems involving probability and games.

Carol Perez plays in a bowling league on Saturday mornings. Her scores are improving. At the present time, she averages 2 strikes per game (10 frames). Today, her team is playing the number one team, and Carol feels "up" for the competition. She wants to score 4 strikes in the first game. What is the probability that she will make 4 strikes in the first game? To answer this question, you need to understand the binomial theorem. *The approach and solution to this problem will be considered in Example 6.*

You have observed patterns in both geometric and arithmetic sequences. Observe some of the patterns that appear when $(a + b)^n$ is expanded for $n = 0, 1, 2, 3,$ and 4.

$$(a + b)^0 = 1a^0b^0$$
$$(a + b)^1 = 1a^1b^0 + 1a^0b^1$$
$$(a + b)^2 = 1a^2b^0 + 2a^1b^1 + 1a^0b^2$$
$$(a + b)^3 = 1a^3b^0 + 3a^2b^1 + 3a^1b^2 + 1a^0b^3$$
$$(a + b)^4 = 1a^4b^0 + 4a^3b^1 + 6a^2b^2 + 4a^1b^3 + 1a^0b^4$$

What is the pattern of the exponents of a and b in each row?

Here is a list of some of the patterns seen in the expansion of $(a + b)^n$.

1. The exponent of $(a + b)^n$, n, is the exponent of a in the first term and the exponent of b in the last term.

2. In successive terms, the exponent of a decreases by one. It is n in the first term and zero in the last term.

3. In successive terms, the exponent of b increases by one. It is zero in the first term and n in the last term.

4. The sum of the exponents in each term is n.

5. The coefficients are symmetric. They increase at the beginning and decrease at the end to the expansion.

The coefficients form a pattern that is often displayed in a triangular formation. This is known as **Pascal's triangle.** Notice that each row is formed by starting and ending with 1. Then each coefficient is the sum of the pair of coefficients above it in the previous row.

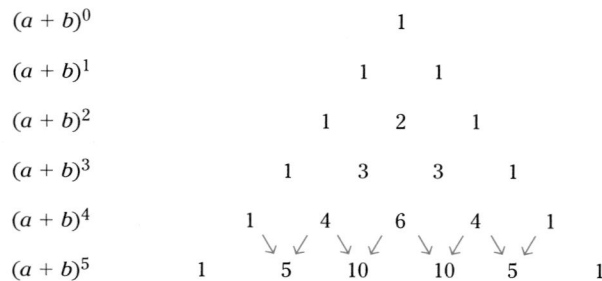

$$(a + b)^0 \qquad\qquad 1$$
$$(a + b)^1 \qquad\qquad 1 \quad 1$$
$$(a + b)^2 \qquad\qquad 1 \quad 2 \quad 1$$
$$(a + b)^3 \qquad\quad 1 \quad 3 \quad 3 \quad 1$$
$$(a + b)^4 \qquad 1 \quad 4 \quad 6 \quad 4 \quad 1$$
$$(a + b)^5 \quad 1 \quad 5 \quad 10 \quad 10 \quad 5 \quad 1$$

F Y I

Pascal's triangle is named for a French mathematician Blaise Pascal (1623–1662). However, this triangle appeared in a Chinese publication in A.D. 1303. A Persian mathematician, Omar Khayyam, appeared to have knowledge of the triangle about A.D. 1100. Also, an Italian mathematician, Niccolo Tartaglia, claimed he invented the triangle in 1556.

F Y I

Omar Khayyam was not only a brilliant mathematician, but a great poet. His *Rubaiyat* was translated and published by Edward Fitzgerald in 1859.

11-8 LESSON NOTES

NCTM Standards: 1–5, 11–12

Instructional Resources

- Study Guide Master 11-8
- Practice Master 11-8
- Enrichment Master 11-8
- Assessment and Evaluation Masters, p. 297
- Real-World Applications, 30

Transparency 11-8A contains the 5-Minute Check for this lesson; **Transparency 11-8B** contains a teaching aid for this lesson.

Recommended Pacing	
Standard Pacing	Day 12 of 14
Honors Pacing	Day 9 of 11
Block Scheduling*	Day 6 of 7

*For more information on pacing and possible lesson plans, refer to the *Block Scheduling Booklet.*

1 FOCUS

5-Minute Check
(over Lesson 11-7)

Draw the next stage of each fractal.

1.

2.

3.

Find the x_2, x_3, and x_4 terms of the following sequences.

4. $x_0 = 1, x_1 = 2$
   $x_n = x_{n-1} + x_{n-2}$
   3, 5, 8

5. $x_0 = 2, x_1 = 3$
   $x_n = 2x_{n-1} + 2x_{n-2}$
   10, 26, 72

Questioning Ask students to name a busy intersection near the school. Ask them if there is a way to predict the traffic pattern if there are points of interest in all directions that a car can go from that intersection.

2 TEACH

In-Class Examples

For Example 1
Use the pattern in Pascal's triangle to write each binomial in expanded form.

a. $(x + y)^5$ $x^5 + 5x^4y + 10x^3y^2 + 10x^2y^3 + 5xy^4 + y^5$

b. $(3r - 2s)^3$
$27r^3 - 54r^2s + 36rs^2 - 8s^3$

For Example 2
Use the binomial theorem to write each binomial in expanded form.

a. $(d - c)^4$ $d^4 - 4d^3c + 6d^2c^2 - 4dc^3 + c^4$

b. $(2a + b)^6$ $64a^6 + 192a^5b + 240a^4b^2 + 160a^3b^3 + 60a^2b^4 + 12ab^5 + b^6$

Teaching Tip Note that if b is negative, the theorem can still be used; just consider $(a - b)^n$ to be $[a + (-b)]^n$. Signs will alternate, being negative when the exponent of b is odd.

Example Use the pattern in Pascal's triangle to write $(x + y)^6$ in expanded form.

The next line of Pascal's triangle is listed below.

$$1 \quad 6 \quad 15 \quad 20 \quad 15 \quad 6 \quad 1 \quad \textit{(a + b)}^6 \textit{ has 7 terms.}$$

$$(a + b)^6 = 1x^6y^0 + 6x^5y^1 + 15x^4y^2 + 20x^3y^3 + 15x^2y^4 + 6x^1y^5 + 1x^0y^6$$

$$= x^6 + 6x^5y + 15x^4y^2 + 20x^3y^3 + 15x^2y^4 + 6xy^5 + y^6$$

Another way to show the coefficients is by writing them in terms of the previous coefficient, as you would in a sequence.

$(a + b)^0$					1	*Eliminate common factors that are shown in color.*
$(a + b)^1$				1	$\frac{1}{1}$	*The coefficients are symmetrical.*
$(a + b)^2$			1	$\frac{2}{1}$	$\frac{2 \cdot 1}{1 \cdot 2}$	
$(a + b)^3$		1	$\frac{3}{1}$	$\frac{3 \cdot 2}{1 \cdot 2}$	$\frac{3 \cdot 2 \cdot 1}{1 \cdot 2 \cdot 3}$	
$(a + b)^4$	1	$\frac{4}{1}$	$\frac{4 \cdot 3}{1 \cdot 2}$	$\frac{4 \cdot 3 \cdot 2}{1 \cdot 2 \cdot 3}$	$\frac{4 \cdot 3 \cdot 2 \cdot 1}{1 \cdot 2 \cdot 3 \cdot 4}$	

This pattern provides the coefficients of $(a + b)^n$ for any value of n where n is a nonnegative integer. This pattern is summarized in the **binomial theorem.**

The Binomial Theorem	**If n is a positive integer, then** $(a + b)^n = 1a^nb^0 + \frac{n}{1}a^{n-1}b^1 + \frac{n(n-1)}{1 \cdot 2}a^{n-2}b^2 + \ldots + 1a^0b^n.$

Example Use the binomial theorem to write $(a - b)^7$ in expanded form.

The expansion will have eight terms. Find the first four terms using the sequence $1, \frac{7}{1}, \frac{7 \cdot 6}{1 \cdot 2}, \frac{7 \cdot 6 \cdot 5}{1 \cdot 2 \cdot 3}$. Then use symmetry to find the remaining terms.

$$(a - b)^7 = a^7(-b)^0 + \frac{7}{1}a^6(-b)^1 + \frac{7 \cdot 6}{1 \cdot 2}a^5(-b)^2 + \frac{7 \cdot 6 \cdot 5}{1 \cdot 2 \cdot 3}a^4(-b)^3 + \ldots$$

$$= a^7 - 7a^6b^1 + 21a^5b^2 - 35a^4b^3 + \ldots$$

$$= a^7 - 7a^6b + 21a^5b^2 - 35a^4b^3 + 35a^3b^4 - 21a^2b^5 + 7ab^6 - b^7$$

Note that in terms having the same coefficients, the exponents are reversed, as in $21a^5b^2$ and $21a^2b^5$.

 Alternative Learning Styles

Auditory In discussing the binomial theorem with students, be sure they understand the pattern. You may want to show them the first several terms on the chalkboard and have them name the next four terms. Use discussion to emphasize relationships between the binomial theorem, factorials, and sigma notation.

 GLENCOE Technology

Interactive Mathematics Tools Software

This multimedia software provides an interactive lesson in which students find patterns in problems of different outcomes. A **Computer Journal** gives students an opportunity to write about what they have learned.

For Windows & Macintosh

By definition, 0! = 1.

The pattern in the factors of the coefficients in Example 2 are parts of special products called **factorials**. The product of $4 \cdot 3 \cdot 2 \cdot 1$ can be expressed as 4! and is read *4 factorial*. For all positive integer values of n,

$$n! = n(n-1)(n-2)(n-3) \ldots 2 \cdot 1.$$

Example ③ Evaluate $\dfrac{9!}{4!5!}$.

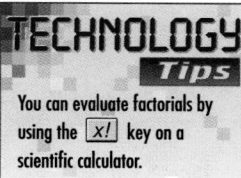
TECHNOLOGY
Tips
You can evaluate factorials by using the $\boxed{x!}$ key on a scientific calculator.

$$\frac{9!}{4!5!} = \frac{9 \cdot 8 \cdot 7 \cdot 6 \cdot \overset{1}{\cancel{5 \cdot 4 \cdot 3 \cdot 2 \cdot 1}}}{4 \cdot 3 \cdot 2 \cdot 1 \cdot \underset{1}{\cancel{5 \cdot 4 \cdot 3 \cdot 2 \cdot 1}}}$$

Note that $9! = 9 \cdot 8 \cdot 7 \cdot 6 \cdot 5!$.
So $\dfrac{9!}{4!5!} = \dfrac{9 \cdot 8 \cdot 7 \cdot 6 \cdot 5!}{4!5!}$ or $\dfrac{9 \cdot 8 \cdot 7 \cdot 6}{4 \cdot 3 \cdot 2 \cdot 1}$.

$$= \frac{9 \cdot 8 \cdot 7 \cdot 6}{4 \cdot 3 \cdot 2 \cdot 1} \text{ or } 126$$

EXPLORATION   GRAPHING CALCULATORS

You can use a graphing calculator to find the value of 6!. To do this, first press 6. Then press $\boxed{\text{MATH}}$ and highlight PRB. Four items will show on your screen. You want the factorial function, so use the direction keys to highlight 4. Press $\boxed{\text{ENTER}}$ and then $\boxed{\text{ENTER}}$ again. Your screen should show that 6! is equal to 720.

Your Turn

Use a graphing calculator to evaluate each expression.
a. 12!   479,001,600   **b.** 7!   5040   **c.** $\dfrac{10!}{5!}$ 30,240   **d.** $\dfrac{15!}{8!7!}$ 6435

In Example 2, notice that products like $\dfrac{7 \cdot 6 \cdot 5}{1 \cdot 2 \cdot 3}$ can be written as a quotient of factorials. In this case, $\dfrac{7 \cdot 6 \cdot 5}{1 \cdot 2 \cdot 3} = \dfrac{7!}{3!4!}$. Using this same method, we can rewrite the series that equals $(a+b)^7$ using factorials.

$$(a+b)^n = \frac{7!}{0!7!}a^7 + \frac{7!}{1!6!}a^6b^1 + \frac{7!}{2!5!}a^5b^2 + \frac{7!}{3!4!}a^4b^3 + \frac{7!}{4!3!}a^3b^4 +$$
$$\frac{7!}{5!2!}a^2b^5 + \frac{7!}{6!1!}a^1b^6 + \frac{7!}{7!0!}b^7$$

This same pattern can be used to write the series using sigma notation.

$$(a+b)^7 = \sum_{k=0}^{7} \frac{7!}{k!(7-k)!}a^{7-k}b^k$$

The binomial theorem can also be written both in factorial notation and in sigma notation.

$$(a+b)^n = \frac{n!}{0!(n-0)!}a^n + \frac{n!}{1!(n-1)!}a^{n-1}b^1 + \frac{n!}{2!(n-2)!}a^{n-2}b^2 + \ldots$$
$$= \sum_{k=0}^{n} \frac{n!}{k!(n-k)!}a^{n-k}b^k$$

Lesson 11–8   The Binomial Theorem **697**

EXPLORATION

This activity introduces students to the use of the factorial function on the graphing calculator.

GLENCOE *Technology*

Interactive Mathematics Tools Software

This multimedia software provides an interactive lesson by having students consider how changes in length of a loan, interest rate, and the amount and number of monthly payments affect the time it takes to pay off a loan. A **Computer Journal** gives students an opportunity to write about what they have learned.

For Windows & Macintosh

For Example 4
Express each binomial using sigma notation. Then expand and simplify each expression.

a. $(m - 7)^4$ $\displaystyle\sum_{k=0}^{4} \frac{4!}{k!(4-k)!} (m)^{4-k}$;

$m^4 - 28m^3 + 294m^2 - 1372m + 2401$

b. $(z - 1)^7$ $\displaystyle\sum_{k=0}^{7} \frac{7!}{k!(7-k)!} (z)^{7-k}$;

$\dfrac{z^7}{128} - \dfrac{7z^6}{64} + \dfrac{21z^5}{32} - \dfrac{35z^4}{16} + \dfrac{35z^3}{8} - \dfrac{21z^4}{4} + \dfrac{7z}{2} - 1$

For Example 5
Find the indicated term of each expression.

a. fifth term of $(r + s)^{10}$ $210r^6s^4$
b. seventh term of $(2r + s)^8$ $112r^2s^6$

For Example 6
Jim has a batting average of .260, which means he has a failure rate of .740. Write the binomial term for exactly 6 hits in the next 9 at bats. Compute the percent rate.

$\dfrac{9!}{3!(9-3)!} (.260)^6 (.740)^3$

The percent rate is approximately 1% for each hit.

Teaching Tip You may want to have students simplify each expression before solving. For example,

$\dfrac{10!}{8!} = \dfrac{10 \cdot 9 \cdot 8!}{8!} = 10 \cdot 9$ or 90.

3 PRACTICE/APPLY

Check for Understanding
Exercises 1–13 are designed to help you assess your students' understanding through reading, writing, speaking, and modeling. You should work through Exercises 1–4 with your students and then monitor their work on Exercises 5–13.

Error Analysis
When expanding a binomial, watch that students use the whole term of the binomial to expand.
Example:
$(4x - 2y)^3 =$
  $(4x)^3 + 3(4x)^2(-2y) + ...$
$(4x - 2y)^3 \neq$
  $4x^3 + 3 \cdot 4x^2 \cdot -2y + ...$

Example **4**   **Express $(3m + d)^5$ using sigma notation. Then expand and simplify the expression.**

$$(3m + d)^5 = \sum_{k=0}^{5} \frac{5!}{k!(5-k)!}(3m)^{5-k}d^k$$

$$= \frac{5!}{0!5!}(3m)^5d^0 + \frac{5!}{1!4!}(3m)^4d^1 + \frac{5!}{2!3!}(3m)^3d^2 + \frac{5!}{3!2!}(3m)^2d^3 +$$
$$\quad \frac{5!}{4!1!}(3m)^1d^4 + \frac{5!}{5!0!}(3m)^0d^5$$

$$= \frac{5\cdot4\cdot3\cdot2\cdot1}{1\cdot5\cdot4\cdot3\cdot2\cdot1}(3m)^5 + \frac{5\cdot4\cdot3\cdot2\cdot1}{1\cdot4\cdot3\cdot2\cdot1}(3m)^4d +$$
$$\quad \frac{5\cdot4\cdot3\cdot2\cdot1}{2\cdot1\cdot3\cdot2\cdot1}(3m)^3d^2 + \frac{5\cdot4\cdot3\cdot2\cdot1}{3\cdot2\cdot1\cdot2\cdot1}(3m)^2d^3 +$$
$$\quad \frac{5\cdot4\cdot3\cdot2\cdot1}{4\cdot3\cdot2\cdot1\cdot1}(3m)d^4 + \frac{5\cdot4\cdot3\cdot2\cdot1}{5\cdot4\cdot3\cdot2\cdot1\cdot1}d^5$$

$$= 243\,m^5 + 405m^4d + 270m^3d^2 + 90m^2d^3 + 15md^4 + d^5$$

Sometimes a particular term in the expansion of a binomial is needed. Note that in the sigma notation form of the binomial theorem, $k = 0$ for the first term, $k = 1$ for the second term, and so on. In general, the value of k is always one less that the number of the term you are seeking.

Example **5**   **Find the seventh term of $(p + q)^{11}$.**

First use the binomial theorem to write the general form of the expansion.

$$(p + q)^{11} = \sum_{k=0}^{11} \frac{11!}{k!(11-k)!} p^{11-k}q^k$$

In the seventh term, $k = 6$ since k starts at 0.

The seventh term, $\dfrac{11!}{6!(11-6)!}p^{11-6}q^6$, is $\dfrac{11\cdot10\cdot9\cdot8\cdot7}{5\cdot4\cdot3\cdot2\cdot1}p^5q^6$ or $462p^5q^6$.

The binomial theorem can also be used to compute probability.

Example **6**   **Refer to the probability question at the beginning of the lesson. What is the probability that Carol will get 4 strikes in the game?**

INTEGRATION
Probability

Let s represent the probability of getting a strike in a given frame, and let n represent the probability of not getting a strike in the frame. Since there are 10 frames in a game, we can use the binomial theorem to find any term in the expansion of $(s + n)^{10}$.

$$(s + n)^{10} = \sum_{k=0}^{10} \frac{10!}{k!(10-k)!} s^{10-k}n^k$$

To find the probability of 4 strikes, compute the term in which the exponent of s is 4. Since $10 - 6 = 4$, find the term in which $k = 6$, the seventh term.

$$\frac{10!}{6!4!} s^4n^6 \text{ or } 210s^4n^6$$

With an average of two strikes per game, the probability that Carol will get a strike in a given frame is 2 out of 10 or 0.2. The probability that Carol will not get a strike is 8 out of 10 or 0.8. Evaluate the expression for the seventh term if $s = 0.2$ and $n = 0.8$.

$$210s^4n^6 \quad \rightarrow \quad 210(0.2)^4(0.8)^6 \approx 0.088$$

The probability that Carol will make 4 strikes in the game is about 0.088 or 8.8%.

Reteaching

Using Data Have students find the decimal expansion of a given expression using a specified number of terms and an indicated accuracy.

Example:
$(1.05)^5$, 3 terms, hundredths
$(1.05)^5 = (1 + 0.05)^5$
$15 + 5 \cdot 1^4 \cdot (0.05) + \dfrac{5(4)}{1 \cdot 2} \cdot 1^3 \cdot (0.05)^2$

$(1.05)^5 \approx 1.28$

Additional Answers

1. For each coefficient, add the pair of coefficients above its location.

2. Neither; consecutive terms have neither a common difference nor a common ratio.

3a. Sample answer: The exponent of b is one less than the number of the term. The sum of the exponents must equal the degree of the expansion.

Communicating Mathematics

Study the lesson. Then complete the following.   1–3. See margin.

1. **Explain** how to form additional rows of Pascal's triangle.

2. Is the sequence pattern for the coefficients of $(a + b)^n$ an arithmetic sequence, a geometric sequence, or neither? Explain.

3. The sixth term of $(a + b)^8$ is $\frac{8!}{5!3!}a^3b^5$.
   a. **Explain** the relationship between the number of the term and the exponents.
   b. **Explain** the relationship among the exponents, the degree of the expansion, and the factorials.
   c. **Explain** how this expression relates to the general form for a term $\frac{n!}{k!(n-k)!}a^{n-k}b^k$.

4. **Name** three methods for computing the coefficients of a binomial expansion.   Sample answers: Pascal's triangle, binomial theorem, multiplication, factorials

Guided Practice

Use a calculator to evaluate each expression.

5. $8!$ 40,320
6. $\frac{13!}{9!}$ 17,160
7. $\frac{12!}{2!10!}$ 66

Expand each binomial.   8–10. See margin.

8. $(p + q)^5$
9. $(t + 2)^6$
10. $(x - y)^4$

Find the indicated term of each expansion.

12. 1,088,640a^6b^4

11. fourth term of $(a + b)^8$ $56a^5b^3$
12. fifth term of $(2a + 3b)^{10}$

13. **Geometry** Use the binomial theorem to write an expression for the volume of the cube at the right.
   $(8x^3 - 36x^2 + 54x - 27)$ cm^3

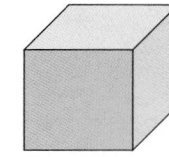

$(2x - 3)$ cm

Practice

A

Use a calculator to evaluate each expression.

14. $9!$ 362,880
15. $5!$ 120
16. $13!$ 6,227,020,800
17. $\frac{9!}{7!}$ 72
18. $\frac{7!}{4!}$ 210
19. $\frac{15!}{11!}$ 32,760
20. $\frac{12!}{8!4!}$ 495
21. $\frac{10!}{4!6!}$ 210
22. $\frac{14!}{5!9!}$ 2002

Expand each binomial.   23–31. See margin.

B

23. $(r + s)^7$
24. $(a - b)^3$
25. $(m - a)^5$
26. $(2a + b)^6$
27. $(2b - x)^4$
28. $(3x - 2y)^5$
29. $(3x + 2y)^4$
30. $\left(\frac{a}{2} + 2\right)^5$
31. $\left(3 + \frac{m}{3}\right)^5$

Find the indicated term of each expression.

35. 145,152x^6y^3

36. 1,088,640a^6b^4

32. fourth term of $(x + 2)^7$ $280x^4$
33. seventh term of $(x + y)^{12}$ $924x^6y^6$
34. sixth term of $(x - y)^9$ $-126x^4y^5$
35. fourth term of $(2x + 3y)^9$
36. fifth term of $(2a + 3b)^{10}$
37. fifth term of $\left(\frac{2}{5} + \frac{3}{5}\right)^{10}$ 0.111477

Additional Answers

23. $r^7 + 7r^6s + 21r^5s^2 + 35r^4s^3 + 35r^3s^4 + 21r^2s^5 + 7rs^6 + s^7$
24. $a^3 - 3a^2b + 3ab^2 - b^3$
25. $m^5 - 5m^4a + 10m^3a^2 - 10m^2a^3 + 5ma^4 - a^5$
26. $64a^6 + 192a^5b + 240a^4b^2 + 160a^3b^3 + 60a^2b^4 + 12ab^5 + b^6$
27. $16b^4 - 32b^3x + 24b^2x^2 - 8bx^3 + x^4$
28. $243x^5 - 810x^4y + 1080x^3y^2 - 720x^2y^3 + 240xy^4 - 32y^5$
29. $81x^4 + 216x^3y + 216x^2y^2 + 96xy^3 + 16y^4$
30. $\frac{a^5}{32} + \frac{5a^4}{8} + 5a^3 + 20a^2 + 40a + 32$
31. $243 + 135m + 30m^2 + \frac{10m^3}{3} + \frac{5m^4}{27} + \frac{m^5}{243}$

Assignment Guide

Core: 15–47 odd, 49–57
Enriched: 14–42 even, 43–57

For **Extra Practice,** see p. 903.

The red A, B, and C flags, printed only in the Teacher's Wraparound Edition, indicate the level of difficulty of the exercises.

Additional Answers

3b. Sample answer: The degree of expansion is used as factorial in the numerator. Factorials in the denominator are the exponents of the variables.

3c. Sample answer: n is the degree of expansion, k is one less than the number of the term, the sum of the exponents of a and b equals the degree of expansion, and in the denominator, k and $n - k$ are the exponents of the variables.

8. $p^5 + 5p^4q + 10p^3q^2 + 10p^2q^3 + 5pq^4 + q^5$

9. $t^6 + 12t^5 + 60t^4 + 160t^3 + 240t^2 + 192t + 64$

10. $x^4 - 4x^3y + 6x^2y^2 - 4xy^3 + y^4$

Study Guide Masters, p. 83

11-8   NAME_____   DATE_____
Study Guide   Student Edition Pages 692–697

The Binomial Theorem

The binomial expression $(a + b)$ can be raised to various powers. There are patterns to be found in the powers of $(a + b)$ listed below.

$(a + b)^0 = 1a^0b^0$
$(a + b)^1 = 1a^1b^0 + 1a^0b^1$
$(a + b)^2 = 1a^2b^0 + 2a^1b^1 + 1a^0b^2$
$(a + b)^3 = 1a^3b^0 + 3a^2b^1 + 3a^1b^2 + 1a^0b^3$
$(a + b)^4 = 1a^4b^0 + 4a^3b^1 + 6a^2b^2 + 4a^1b^3 + 1a^0b^4$.

Next look at just the numerical coefficients and the pattern becomes obvious. This is known as Pascal's Triangle. Each new row is formed by adding elements of the previous row in pairs. Each row begins and ends with one.

$(a + b)^0$ 1
$(a + b)^1$ 1   1
$(a + b)^2$ 1   2   1
$(a + b)^3$ 1   3   3   1
$(a + b)^4$ 1   4   6   4   1

The Binomial Theorem summarizes these patterns.

The Binomial Theorem	Definition of n Factorial
If n is a positive integer, then $(a + b)^n = 1a^nb^0 + \frac{n}{1}a^{n-1}b^1 + \frac{n(n-1)}{1 \cdot 2}a^{n-2}b^2 + \cdots + 1a^0b^n$.	If n is a positive integer, the expression $n!$ (n factorial) is defined as follows: $n! = n(n-1)(n-2) \cdots 1$

Use a calculator to evaluate each expression.

1. $\frac{12!}{3!5!}$ 665,280
2. $\frac{13!10!}{6!17!}$ $\frac{3}{34}$
3. $\frac{20!4!}{18!3!}$ 1520
4. $\frac{18!2!}{20!}$ $\frac{1}{190}$
5. $\frac{16!}{12!}$ 43,680
6. $\frac{12!}{6!6!}$ 924
7. $9!$ 362,880
8. $\frac{12!}{8!4!}$ 495

Expand each binomial.

9. $(m + t)^6$
   $m^6 + 6m^5t + 15m^4t^2 + 20m^3t^3 + 15m^2t^4 + 6mt^5 + t^6$
10. $(4m + 2y)^4$
   $256m^4 + 512m^3y + 384m^2y^2 + 128my^3 + 16y^4$
11. $(2 - q)^5$ $32 - 80q + 80q^2 - 40q^3 + 10q^4 - q^5$
12. $(x - y)^3$ $x^3 - 3x^2y + 3xy^2 - y^3$

Find the indicated term of each expression.

13. fourth term of $(2a + b)^6$ $40a^3b^3$
14. fifth term of $(y - 5)^6$ $9375y^2$

Using the Programming Exercises The program given in Exercise 42 is for use with a TI-82 graphing calculator. For other programmable calculators, have students consult their owner's manual for commands similar to those presented here.

Additional Answer

44d. Sample answer: For any row, the number of ball bearings in each section is proportional to the numbers in that row of Pascal's triangle.

Simplify.   40. $(n + 3)(n + 2)$ or $n^2 + 5n + 6$

38. $\dfrac{(k+1)!}{k!}$
$k + 1$

39. $\dfrac{(k+2)!(k+3)}{(k+3)!}$

40. $\dfrac{(n+3)!}{(n+1)!}$

41. $\dfrac{8!(n-4)!}{8 \cdot 6!(n-3)!}$
$\dfrac{7}{n-3}$

Programming

42. The program at the right generates the coefficients in Pascal's triangle from row 0 through row n for $(a + b)^n$. You must input the values of n and press enter to generate each new row.

Find the coefficients of the terms of each expansion.

a. $(a + b)^7$ 1, 7, 21, 35, 35, 21, 7, 1
b. $(x + y)^8$ 1, 8, 28, 56, 70, 56, 28, 8, 1
c. $(r + s)^{10}$ 1, 10, 45, 120, 210, 252, 210, 120, 45, 10, 1

```
PROGRAM:PASCAL
: Disp "ENTER THE
   VALUE OF N"
: Input Y
: For(N,0,Y)
: ClrHome
: Disp N
: Disp " "
: For (R,0,N)
: 1->C
: If N<N-R+1
: Goto 1
: For(X,N,N-R+1,-1)
: CX/(N-X+1)->C
: End
: Lbl 1
: Disp C
: End
: Pause
: End
```

Critical Thinking

43. Suppose $(a + b)$ is raised to some positive integer power and one term in the binomial series is $170{,}544a^{15}b^7$.

a. Which term of the series is $170{,}544a^{15}b^7$?   **eighth**
b. To what power was $(a + b)$ raised?   **22nd power**
c. What is the next term in the series? $319{,}770a^{14}b^8$

Applications and Problem Solving

44. **Games**   At the Centerville Centennial Celebration, the young children play various games. A diagram of one game is shown at the right. In this game, children drop ball bearings down a chute. A pattern of nails causes the ball bearings to take various paths down to the five sections at the bottom. At each nail, there is an equal chance for the ball bearing to go either way. Since the bearings have only two choices at each level, this is called a binomial distribution.   **d. See margin.**

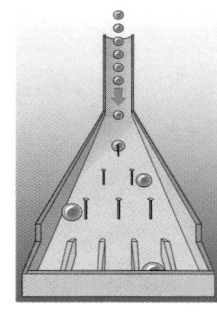

a. If 16 ball bearings are dropped through the chute, how many would you expect to end in each section?   1; 4; 6; 4; 1
b. If 64 ball bearings are dropped through the chute, how many would you expect to end in each section?   4; 16; 24; 16; 4
c. If another level of a nails are added to the game, describe the expected distribution of 64 ball bearings.   2; 10; 20; 20; 10; 2
d. Describe how this game is related with the Pascal's triangle.

700   Chapter 11   Investigating Sequences and Series

Practice Masters, p. 83

NAME_____   DATE_____

11-8   Practice   Student Edition Pages 692–697

The Binomial Theorem

Use a calculator to evaluate each expression.

1. 7! 5040
2. 6!4! 17,280
3. $\frac{8!}{6!2!}$ 28

4. $\frac{8!}{5!3!}$ 56
5. (3! − 2!)! 24
6. $\left(\frac{0! + 1! + 3!}{2!}\right)!$ 24

Expand each binomial.

7. $(x + 3)^4$ $x^4 + 12x^3 + 54x^2 + 108x + 81$
8. $(2m - y)^4$ $16m^4 − 32m^3y + 24m^2y^2 − 8my^3 + y^4$
9. $(2x - y)^5$ $32x^5 − 80x^4y + 80x^3y^2 − 40x^2y^3 + 10xy^4 − y^5$
10. $(r + 3)^5$ $r^5 + 15r^4 + 90r^3 + 270r^2 + 405r + 243$
11. $(n + v)^8$ $n^8 + 8n^7v + 28n^6v^2 + 56n^5v^3 + 70n^4v^4 + 56n^3v^5 + 28n^2v^6 + 8nv^7 + v^8$
12. $(x - y)^7$ $x^7 − 7x^6y + 21x^5y^2 − 35x^4y^3 + 35x^3y^4 − 21x^2y^5 + 7xy^6 − y^7$

Find the indicated term of each expression.

13. fourth term of $(x - 3y)^6$ $−540x^3y^3$
14. fifth term of $(2x - 1)^9$ $4032x^5$
15. seventh term of $(x + y)^{10}$ $210x^4y^6$
16. tenth term of $(2x + y)^{12}$ $1760x^3y^9$
17. Find the sixth element in the tenth row of Pascal's triangle.   126
18. Find the ninth element in the fourteenth row of Pascal's triangle.   1287

45. 1, 2, 4, 8, 16; 512

45. Look for a Pattern Find the sum of each of the first five rows of Pascal's triangle. Predict the sum of the tenth row of Pascal's triangle.

46. Football Steve Young is a quarterback with the San Francisco 49ers. In 1993, he had a pass completion rate of 0.68. What is the probability that he would complete exactly 3 out of his next 4 pass attempts? **about 40.2%**

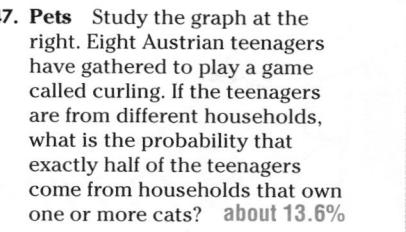

GLOBAL CONNECTIONS

Curling is a popular game in Canada and Austria. It is played on ice with 4 players on a team. Each team tries to slide curling stones toward a target circle. Players sweep the ice ahead of the path of the stones to alter the location at which the stone will stop.

47. Pets Study the graph at the right. Eight Austrian teenagers have gathered to play a game called curling. If the teenagers are from different households, what is the probability that exactly half of the teenagers come from households that own one or more cats? **about 13.6%**

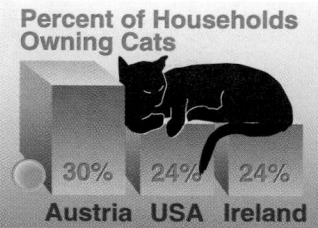

Percent of Households Owning Cats

30%   24%   24%
Austria USA Ireland

Source: The Gallup Organization

48. Employment A company has a large number of qualified job applicants for a specific job. Suppose 40% of the applicants are women and 60% are men. The company decides to hire 7 of the applicants and 5 of the applicants chosen are men.   **c. No, since 26.1% is greater than 5%.**

a. If the applicants were picked at random, what is the probability that the 5 out of the 7 would be men? **about 26.1%**

b. Do you think that the company is biased in its hiring practices? Explain.

c. Researchers who study possible bias in hiring practices frequently look for probabilities that are 5% or less. Would this situation cause a researcher to look into the hiring practices of the company? Explain.

48b. See students' work.

Curling

Mixed Review

49. Find the sum of the infinite series $\frac{1}{2} + \frac{1}{3} + \frac{2}{9} + \frac{4}{27} + \dots$ (Lesson 11–5) $\frac{3}{2}$

50. The third term of an arithmetic sequence is 14, and the ninth term is −1. Find the first four terms of the sequence.   (Lesson 11–1)   **19, 16.5, 14, 11.5**

51. Biology The number of a certain type of bacteria can increase from 80 to 164 in 3 hours. Find the approximate value of k in the growth formula $y = ne^{kt}$, where t is given in hours.   (Lesson 10–7)   **0.2393**

52. Solve $\log_3 243 = x$.   (Lesson 10–2)   **5**

53. Auto Mechanics When air is pumped into a tire, the pressure required varies inversely as the volume of the air. If the pressure is 30 lb/in^2 when the volume is 140 in^3, find the pressure when the volume is 100 in^3. (Lesson 9–2)   **42 lb/in^2**

54. $9x^2 - 24x + 22$

54. If $f(x) = x^2 + 6$ and $g(x) = 3x - 4$, find $[f \circ g](x)$.   (Lesson 8–7)

55. Is the graph of $x^2 + y^2 - 8x + 6y + 24 = 0$ a parabola, a circle, an ellipse, or a hyperbola?   (Lesson 7–6)   **circle**

56. Solve $5 - \sqrt{b + 2} = 0$.   (Lesson 5–8)   **23**

57. $y = \frac{2}{3}x + \frac{10}{3}$

57. Write an equation of the line that passes through the point at (4, 6) and is parallel to the line whose equation is $y = \frac{2}{3}x + 5$.   (Lesson 2–4)

Lesson 11–8   The Binomial Theorem **701**

Extension

Problem Solving Have students use an example and a calculator to verify the correctness of the binomial expansion. An example is to use the binomial expression $(0.3 + 0.7)^5$. Expand the expansion, then evaluate both the expression and the original expression to show that the evaluations are equal. In this case, both equal 1.

GLOBAL CONNECTIONS

In curling, the regulation size for a stone is no more than 44 pounds in weight with a circumference of no more than 36 inches.

---

4 ASSESS

Closing Activity

Speaking Have students explain how factorials are used in the expansion of a binomial using the binomial theorem.

Enrichment Masters, p. 83

11-8   NAME_____   DATE_____

Enrichment   Student Edition Pages 692–6

Patterns in Pascal's Triangle

You have learned that the coefficients in the expansion of $(x + y)^n$ yield a number pyramid called **Pascal's triangle.**

```
Row 1 ———→            1
Row 2 ———→           1 1
Row 3 ———→          1 2 1
Row 4 ———→         1 3 3 1
Row 5 ———→        1 4 6 4 1
Row 6 ———→       1 5 10 10 5 1
Row 7 ———→      1 6 15 20 15 6 1
```

As many rows can be added to the bottom of the pyramid as you please.

This activity explores some of the interesting properties of this famous number pyramid.

1. Pick a row of Pascal's triangle.
   a. What is the sum of all the numbers in all the rows *above* the row you picked? See students' work.
   b. What is the sum of all the numbers in the row you picked? See students' work.
   c. How are your answers for parts a and b related? The answer for Part b is 1 more than the answer for Part a.
   d. Repeat Parts a through c for at least three more rows of Pascal's triangle. What generalization seems to be true? It appears that the sum of the numbers in any row is 1 more than the sum of the numbers in all of the rows above it.
   e. See if you can prove your generalization. Sum of numbers in row $n = 2^n - 2^0 + 2^1 + 2^2 + \dots + 2^{n-1}$, which, by the formula for the sum of a geometric series, is $2^{n-1} - 1$.

2. Pick any row of Pascal's triangle that comes after the first.
   a. Starting at the left end of the row, add the first number, the third number, the fifth number, and so on. State the sum. See students' work.
   b. In the same row, add the second number, the fourth number, and so on. State the sum. See students' work.
   c. How do the sums in Parts a and b compare? The sums are equal.
   d. Repeat Parts a through c for at least three other rows of Pascal's triangle. What generalization seems to be true? In any row of Pascal's triangle after the first, the sum of the odd numbered terms is equal to the sum of the even numbered terms.

Chapter 11 **701**

Closing the Investigation

This activity provides students an opportunity to bring their work on the Investigation to a close. For each Investigation, students should present their findings to the class. Here are some ways students can display their work.

- Conduct and report on an interview or survey.
- Write a letter, proposal, or report.
- Write an article for the school or local paper.
- Make a display, including graphs and/or charts.
- Plan an activity.

Assessment

To assess students' understanding of the concepts and topics explored in the Investigation and its follow-up activities, you may wish to examine students' Investigation Folders.

The scoring guide provided in the *Investigations and Projects Masters,* p. 19, provides a means for you to score students' work on the Investigation.

Investigations and Projects Masters, p. 19

Scoring Guide
Chapters 10 and 11
Investigation

Level	Specific Criteria
3 Superior	• Shows thorough understanding of data collection, comparison and analysis, and determining functions. Exhibits a thorough understanding of concepts including *elastic potential, slope,* and *ratio.* • Uses appropriate strategies to solve problems. • Computations are correct. • Written explanations are exemplary. • Charts, graphs, and report are appropriate and sensible. • Goes beyond requirements of some or all problems.
2 Satisfactory, with Minor Flaws	• Shows understanding of data collection, comparison and analysis, and determining functions. Understands the concepts of *elastic potential, slope,* and *ratio.* • Uses appropriate strategies to solve problems. • Computations are mostly correct. • Written explanations are effective. • Charts, graphs, and report are appropriate and sensible. • Satisfies all requirements of problems.
1 Nearly Satisfactory, with Obvious Flaws	• Shows understanding of data collection, comparison and analysis, and determining functions. Has a basic understanding of the concepts of *elastic potential, slope,* and *ratio.* • May not use appropriate strategies to solve problems. • Computations are mostly correct. • Written explanations are satisfactory. • Charts, graphs, and report are mostly appropriate and sensible. • Satisfies most requirements of problems.
0 Unsatisfactory	• Does not always show understanding of data collection, comparison and analysis, and determining functions. Shows little or no understanding of the concepts of *elastic potential, slope,* and *ratio.* • May not use appropriate strategies to solve problems. • Computations are incorrect. • Written explanations are not satisfactory. • Charts, graphs, and report are not appropriate or sensible. • Does not satisfy requirements of problems.

Refer to the Investigation on pages 590–591.

Review the conclusions you have drawn from your experiments with the rubber bands and review the instructions given to you by your manager as you begin to close this Investigation.

Analyze

You have conducted experiments and organized your data in various ways. It is now time to analyze your findings and state your conclusions.

PORTFOLIO ASSESSMENT

You may want to keep your work on this Investigation in your portfolio.

1 Review your data and create a summary chart of the different experiments and how they relate to one another.

2 What information does this chart reflect? Does it give information about factors that would contribute to the performance of the bungee equipment? Explain.

3 What can you conclude about the weight of the falling object and the effect it will have on the length that the bungee is stretched? Do you think gravity will have any effect on this? Explain.

Write

The summary report to your manager should explain your process for investigating bungee jumping equipment and what you found from your investigations.

4 Explain the experiments you used to analyze bungee jumping. Use your graphs and charts to summarize your findings.

5 For each size rubber band, describe the optimum length that each rubber band should be stretched to get the most spring for the effort. Explain how you found the elastic potential for the rubber bands and which length rubber band has the greatest elastic potential.

6 Determine the weight required to stretch each rubber band to the length at which it reaches its greatest elastic potential. Explain your findings.

7 Using all of these factors and data, write a report to your manager.

- Explain the factors that contribute to a bungee providing an optimum spring.
- List specific size bungees, the weight that would allow the bungee to stretch to a desired length for the best spring and the elastic potential that would be achieved.
- Describe a general relationship between the size of the bungee and the weight of a person using the bungee.
- Describe how these factors relate to the elastic potential.
- Determine what effect repeated use of the bungee has on the bungee's elasticity and safety.
- Summarize the report with an overall recommendation to your manager.

VOCABULARY

After completing this chapter, you should be able to define each term, property, or phrase and give an example or two of each.

Discrete Mathematics

arithmetic means (p. 650)
arithmetic sequence (p. 649)
arithmetic series (p. 656)
binomial theorem (p. 696)
common difference (p. 649)
common ratio (p. 662)
factorials (p. 697)
Fibonacci sequence (p. 683)
formula for *n*th term of an arithmetic sequence (p. 649)
formula for *n*th term of a geometric sequence (p. 663)

geometric means (p. 665)
geometric sequence (p. 662)
geometric series (p. 670)
index of summation (p. 658)
infinite geometric series (p. 676)
partial sum (p. 676)
Pascal's triangle (p. 695)
recursive formula (p. 683)
sequence (p. 648)
series (p. 656)

sigma notation (p. 658)
sum of an arithmetic series (p. 657)
sum of an infinite geometric series (p. 677)
sum of a geometric series (p. 671)
summation notation (p. 658)
term (p. 648)

Geometry

fractal geometry (p. 688)
self-similarity (p. 689)

UNDERSTANDING AND USING THE VOCABULARY

Choose the correct letter that best completes each statement.

1. A(n) _____ of an infinite series is the sum of a certain number of terms, but not the entire series. **k**

2. If a sequence has a common ratio, then it is a(n) _____. **i**

3. Using _____, the series $2 + 5 + 8 + 11 + 14$ can be written as $\sum_{n=1}^{5} (3n - 1)$. **l**

4. Eleven and 17 are the two _____ between 5 and 23 in the sequence 5, 11, 17, 23. **a**

5. Using the _____, $(a - 2)^4$ can be expanded to $a^4 - 8a^3 + 24a^2 - 32a + 16$. **d**

6. The _____ of the sequence $3, 2, \frac{4}{3}, \frac{8}{9}, \frac{16}{27}$ is $\frac{2}{3}$. **f**

7. The sequence $\frac{1}{2}, 3, 5\frac{1}{2}, 8, 10\frac{1}{2}$, is a(n) _____, and $2\frac{1}{2}$ is the _____. **b, e**

8. In the 7th row of Pascal's triangle, the third term is _____. **m**

9. The _____ $11 + 16.5 + 22 + 27.5 + 33$ has a sum of 110. **c**

10. A(n) _____ is expressed as $n! = n(n - 1)(n - 2) \cdots 2 \cdot 1$. **g**

a. arithmetic means
b. arithmetic sequence
c. arithmetic series
d. binomial theorem
e. common difference
f. common ratio
g. factorial
h. geometric means
i. geometric sequence
j. geometric series
k. partial sum
l. sigma notation
m. 15
n. 20

Chapter 11 Highlights **703**

Instructional Resources

Three multiple-choice tests and three free-response tests are provided in the *Assessment and Evaluation Masters.* Forms 1A and 2A are for honors pacing, and Forms 1B, 1C, 2B, and 2C are for average pacing. Chapter 11 Test, Form 1B is shown at the right. Chapter 11 Test, Form 2B is shown on the next page.

Using the CHAPTER HIGHLIGHTS

The Chapter Highlights begins with a listing of the new terms, properties, and phrases that were introduced in this chapter. Have students define each term and provide an example or two of it, if appropriate.

Assessment and Evaluation Masters, pp. 283–284

---

11 NAME_____ DATE_____

Chapter 11 Test, Form 1B

Write the letter for the correct answer in the blank at the right of each problem.

1. What is the 8th term of the sequence $a_1 = -1$, $a_n = (-n + 1)a_{n-1}, n \geq 2$?
A. 600 B. −600 C. 720 D. −720 ___ **D**

2. What is the 7th term of the sequence $a_1 = 1$, $a_2 = 5$, $a_n = a_{n-2} + a_{n-1}, n \geq 3$?
A. 56 B. 63 C. 73 D. 75 ___ **C**

3. What is the 20th term of the arithmetic sequence in which $a_1 = 5$ and $d = 4$?
A. 81 B. 85 C. 96 D. 105 ___ **A**

4. Which term of the arithmetic sequence $-7, -2, 3, \ldots$ is 168?
A. 35th B. 36th C. 37th D. 38th ___ **B**

5. What are the arithmetic means of 6, ___, ___, 30?
A. 12, 24 B. 14, 22 C. 12, 18 D. 18, 18 ___ **B**

6. What is S_n for the arithmetic series in which $a_1 = 3$, $d = 0.5$, and $a_n = 8.5$?
A. 27 B. 54 C. 69.5 D. 69 ___ **D**

7. What is the 1st term of the arithmetic series in which $n = 6$, $a_n = 44$, and $S_n = 174$?
A. −58 B. 58 C. 14 D. −14 ___ **C**

8. What is the common ratio of the geometric sequence 4, 12, 36, 108, $\cdots$?
A. 3 B. $\frac{1}{3}$ C. 8 D. $\frac{1}{8}$ ___ **A**

9. What is the 6th term of the geometric sequence in which $a_1 = 4$ and $r = 3$?
A. 247 B. 972 C. 733 D. 2916 ___ **B**

10. What is the sum of the first 7 terms of the geometric series $1 + 2 + 4 + \cdots$?
A. 64 B. 255 C. 127 D. 256 ___ **C**

11. What is S_n for the geometric series in which $a_3 = 4$, $a_4 = -16$, and $n = 5$?
A. 205 B. $51\frac{1}{4}$ C. −205 D. $-51\frac{1}{4}$ ___ **B**

12. What is the 1st term of the geometric series in which $S_n = \frac{255}{4}$, $r = 2$, and $n = 8$?
A. $\frac{1}{8}$ B. $-\frac{1}{8}$ C. $\frac{1}{4}$ D. $-\frac{1}{4}$ ___ **C**

---

11 NAME_____ DATE_____

Chapter 11 Test, Form 1B *(continued)*

13. What is the sum of the infinite geometric sequence in which $a_1 = -10$ and $r = \frac{1}{5}$?
A. $\frac{25}{3}$ B. $-\frac{25}{3}$ C. $\frac{25}{2}$ D. $-\frac{25}{2}$ ___ **D**

14. What is the sum of the infinite geometric series $5 + 4 + \frac{16}{5} + \cdots$?
A. 20 B. 25 C. $\frac{1}{5}$ D. 16 ___ **B**

15. The figures at the right show the first two stages of a fractal formed by constructing a square on the middle third of each side of a square and then removing the base. Which of the following is Stage 3? ___ **D**
A. B. C. D.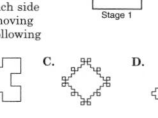

16. If $S = 24$ and $r = \frac{1}{6}$, what is the 1st term of the infinite geometric series?
A. $\frac{144}{7}$ B. $\frac{144}{5}$ C. 20 D. 4 ___ **C**

17. Evaluate $\sum_{n=1}^{24} (2n - 1)$.
A. 576 B. 1128 C. 1152 D. 1176 ___ **A**

18. Evaluate $\frac{10!}{6!4!}$.
A. 210 B. 420 C. 1260 D. 5040 ___ **A**

19. $125x^3 + 300x^2 + 240x + 64$ is the expansion of which expression?
A. $(4x + 5)^3$ B. $(5x + 4)^2$ C. $(3x + 4)^3$ D. $(5x + 4)^3$ ___ **D**

20. What is the 6th term of $(x - 2y)^{10}$?
A. $3360x^5y^5$ B. $13,440x^4y^6$ C. $-8064x^5y^5$ D. $3360x^6y^4$ ___ **C**

Bonus Use sigma notation to express the series $5 - 10 + 20 - 40 + 80$. Bonus ___ **B**
A. $\sum_{n=1}^{5} 5n(-1)^{n-1}$ B. $\sum_{n=0}^{4} 5(-2)^n$ C. $\sum_{n=1}^{5} 5n(-1)^{n+1}$ D. $\sum_{n=0}^{4} 5(2^n)$

Skills and Concepts Encourage students to refer to the objectives and examples on the left as they complete the review exercises on the right.

Assessment and Evaluation Masters, pp. 289–290

11 NAME_____ DATE_____

Chapter 11 Test, Form 2B

1. Find the first six terms of the sequence $a_1 = 4$, $a_2 = 4$, $a_n = a_{n-2} + a_{n-1}$, $n \geq 3$.

1. ___4, 4, 8, 12, 20, 32___

2. Find the first five terms of the arithmetic sequence in which $a_1 = 11$ and $d = 3.5$.

2. ___11, 14.5, 18, 21.5, 25___

3. Find the 31st term of the arithmetic sequence in which $a_1 = 6$ and $d = 7$.

3. ___216___

4. Find a_8 for the sequence $a_1 = -2$, $a_n = 3a_{n-1} + 6$.

4. ___2184___

5. Find arithmetic means of -8, ___, ___, ___, 12.

5. ___-3, 2, 7___

6. Which term of the arithmetic sequence -5, 3, 11, $\cdots$ is 131?

6. ___18th___

7. Write a recursive formula for the sequence 3, 9, 21, 45, $\cdots$.

7. ___$a_1 = 3$, $a_n = 2a_{n-1} + 3$___

8. Evaluate $\sum_{x=3}^{7} (2x - 4)$.

8. ___30___

9. What is S_n for the arithmetic series in which $a_1 = 5$, $a_n = 104$, and $n = 34$?

9. ___1853___

10. What is S_n for the arithmetic series in which $a_1 = 7$, $d = 11$, and $n = 20$?

10. ___2230___

11. Draw the next stage.

Stage 1   Stage 2

11.

12. Find the common ratio of the geometric sequence $\frac{2}{5}$, $\frac{6}{5}$, $\frac{18}{5}$, $\frac{54}{5}$, $\cdots$.

12. ___3___

11 NAME_____ DATE_____

Chapter 11 Test, Form 2B (continued)

13. Find the third term of $(x - 2y)^4$.

13. ___$24x^2y^2$___

14. Find the 5th term of the geometric sequence in which $a_1 = 40$ and $r = \frac{1}{2}$.

14. ___$\frac{5}{2}$___

15. Find the geometric means of 4, ___, ___, 108.

15. ___12, 36___

16. Find the sum of the geometric series in which $a_1 = 7$, $r = 2$, and $n = 5$.

16. ___217___

17. Find the sum of the geometric series in which $a_1 = 256$, $a_n = 81$, and $r = \frac{3}{4}$.

17. ___781___

18. Find a_1 for the geometric sequence in which $S_n = 105$, $r = -2$, and $n = 6$.

18. ___-5___

19. Find the sum of the infinite geometric series in which $a_1 = 9$ and $r = \frac{2}{3}$.

19. ___27___

20. Find a common fraction equivalent to the repeating decimal 0.41.

20. ___$\frac{41}{99}$___

21. Write $\frac{1}{2} + \frac{1}{4} + \frac{1}{8} + \cdots + \frac{1}{256}$ in sigma notation.

21. ___$\sum_{n=1}^{8} \frac{1}{2^n}$___

22. Expand $(3x + 2)^3$.

22. ___$27x^3 + 54x^2 + 36x + 8$___

23. Find the 3rd term of $(2x + 4)^4$.

23. ___$384x^2$___

24. A meeting room has 30 rows of seats. There are 10 seats in the first row, 12 in the second row, 14 in the third row, and so on. How many seats are in the meeting room?

24. ___1170___

25. Draw the next stage.

Stage 1   Stage 2

25.

Bonus Find all values of x and y for which 3, x, y is an arithmetic sequence and x, y, 8 is a geometric sequence.

Bonus ___$x = \frac{1}{2}$, $y = -2$ or $x = \frac{9}{2}$, $y = 6$___

SKILLS AND CONCEPTS

OBJECTIVES AND EXAMPLES	REVIEW EXERCISES

Upon completing this chapter, you should be able to:

Use these exercises to review and prepare for the chapter test.

• find the *n*th term of an arithmetic sequence (Lesson 11–1)

If $a_1 = -17$, $d = 4$, and $n = 12$, find a_{12}.

$a_n = a_1 + (n - 1)d$

$a_{12} = -17 + (12 - 1)4$

$a_{12} = -17 + 44$

$a_{12} = 27$

Find the *n*th term of each arithmetic sequence.

11. $a_1 = 6$, $d = 8$, $n = 5$ **38**
12. $a_1 = -5$, $d = 7$, $n = 22$ **142**
13. $a_1 = 5$, $d = -2$, $n = 9$ **-11**
14. $a_1 = -2$, $d = -3$, $n = 15$ **-44**
15. $a_1 = 4$, $d = 3$, $n = 32$ **97**
16. $a_1 = 8$, $d = -5$, $n = 10$ **-37**

• find the position of a given term in an arithmetic sequence (Lesson 11–1)

-3 is what term of the sequence 7, 5, 3, ... ?

$-3 = 7 + (n - 1)(-2)$

$-3 = 7 - 2n + 2$

$n = 6$

Complete each statement.

17. 72 is the __?__ th term of -5, 2, 9, ...   **12**
18. -37 is the __?__ th term of 1, -1, -3, -5, ...   **20**
19. 49 is the __?__ th term of 4, 9, 14, ...   **10**
20. $-\frac{17}{4}$ is the __?__ th term of $2\frac{1}{4}$, 2, $1\frac{3}{4}$, ...   **27**

• find arithmetic means (Lesson 11–1)

Find the two arithmetic means between 4 and 25.

$25 = 4 + (4 - 1)d$

$25 = 4 + 3d$

$7 = d$

Therefore, $4 + 7 = 11$ and $11 + 7 = 18$.

The arithmetic means are 11 and 18.

Find the arithmetic means in each sequence.

21. -7, __?__, __?__, __?__, 9   **-3, 1, 5**
22. 12, __?__, __?__, 4   **$\frac{28}{3}$, $\frac{20}{3}$**
23. __?__, 6, __?__, __?__, -3, __?__   **9, 3, 0, -6**
24. __?__, 49, __?__, __?__, 28   **56, 42, 35**

• find sums of arithmetic series (Lesson 11–2)

Find S_n for the arithmetic series described by $a_1 = 34$, $a_n = 2$, and $n = 9$.

$S_n = \frac{n}{2}(a_1 + a_n)$

$S_9 = \frac{9}{2}(34 + 2)$

$S_9 = \frac{9}{2}(36)$

$S_9 = 162$

29. 7, 10, 13, 16, 19, 22, 25, 28, 31, 34, 37, 40; **282**

Find S_n for each arithmetic series described.

25. $a_1 = 12$, $a_n = 117$, $n = 36$ **2322**
26. $4 + 10 + 16 + ... + 106$ **990**
27. $a_1 = 85$, $a_n = 25$, $n = 21$ **1155**
28. $10 + 4 + (-2) + ... + (-50)$ **-220**
29. Write the terms of the arithmetic series $\sum_{n=2}^{13} (3n + 1)$ and find the sum.
30. Find the first three terms of an arithmetic series if $a_1 = 3$, $a_n = 24$, and $S_n = 108$.   **3, 6, 9**

GLENCOE *Technology*

Test and Review Software

You may use this software, a combination of an item generator and item bank, to create your own tests or worksheets. Types of items include free response, multiple choice, short answer, and open ended.

For IBM & Macintosh

OBJECTIVES AND EXAMPLES	REVIEW EXERCISES

OBJECTIVES AND EXAMPLES

• find the nth term of a geometric sequence
(Lesson 11–3)

If $a_1 = 7$, $r = 3$, and $n = 5$, find a_5.

$a_n = a_1 r^{n-1}$

$a_5 = 7(3)^{5-1}$

$a_{12} = 7(81)$

$a_{12} = 567$

REVIEW EXERCISES

Find the indicated term in each geometric sequence.

31. a_6 for $\frac{2}{3}, \frac{4}{3}, \frac{8}{3}, \ldots$ $\frac{64}{3}$

32. a_n for $a_1 = 2$, $r = 2$, and $n = 5$ **32**

33. a_n for $a_1 = 7$, $r = 2$, and $n = 4$ **56**

34. a_n for $a_1 = 243$, $r = -\frac{1}{3}$, and $n = 5$ **3**

• find geometric means   (Lesson 11–3)

Find the two geometric means between 1 and 8.

$8 = 1r^{4-1}$

$8 = r^3$

$2 = r$

Therefore, $1(2) = 2$ and $2(2) = 4$.

The geometric means are 2 and 4.

Find the geometric means in each sequence.

35. $3, \underline{\ ?\ }, \underline{\ ?\ }, \underline{\ ?\ }, 48$±**6, 12, ±24**

36. $7.5, \underline{\ ?\ }, \underline{\ ?\ }, \underline{\ ?\ }, 120$±**15, 30, ±60**

37. $8, \underline{\ ?\ }, \underline{\ ?\ }, \underline{\ ?\ }, \underline{\ ?\ }, \frac{1}{4}$**4, 2, 1, $\frac{1}{2}$**

38. $5, \underline{\ ?\ }, \underline{\ ?\ }, \underline{\ ?\ }, 80$±**10, 20, ±40**

39. $-2, \underline{\ ?\ }, -98, \underline{\ ?\ }, \underline{\ ?\ }$±**14, ±686, −4802**

• find sums of geometric series   (Lesson 11–4)

Find S_n for the geometric series described by $a_1 = 7$, $r = 3$, and $n = 14$.

$S_n = \frac{a_1 - a_1 r^n}{1 - r}$

$S_{14} = \frac{7 - 7(3^{14})}{1 - 3}$

$= 16{,}740{,}388$

Find S_n for each geometric series described.

40. $a_1 = 12$, $r = 3$, $n = 5$ **1452**

41. $a_1 = 4$, $r = -\frac{1}{2}$, $n = 6$ $\frac{21}{8}$

42. $a_1 = 256$, $r = 0.75$, $n = 9$ **947.11**

43. $a_1 = 1$, $a_5 = \frac{1}{16}$, $r = -\frac{1}{2}$ $\frac{11}{16}$

44. $a_1 = 625$, $a_5 = 81$, $r = \frac{3}{5}$ **1441**

• find specific terms in a series   (Lesson 11–4)

Find a_1 if $S_5 = 2.75$ and $r = -2$.

$2.75 = \frac{a_1(1 - (-2)^5)}{1 - (-2)}$

$\frac{11}{4} = \frac{a_1(33)}{3}$

$33 = 132a_1$

$\frac{1}{4} = a_1$

Find a_1 for each geometric series described.

45. $S_n = 1031$, $r = \frac{2}{5}$, $n = 5$ **625**

46. $S_n = 30$, $r = -2$, $n = 4$ **−6**

47. $S_n = -61$, $r = -1$, $n = 5$ **−61**

48. $S_n = 244$, $r = -3$, $n = 5$ **4**

Applications and Problem Solving Encourage students to work through the exercises in the Applications and Problem Solving section to strengthen their problem-solving skills.

OBJECTIVES AND EXAMPLES	REVIEW EXERCISES

- find sums of infinite geometric series   (Lesson 11–5)

Find the sum of the infinite geometric series described by $a_1 = 18$ and $r = -\frac{2}{7}$.

$$S = \frac{a_1}{1-r}$$

$$S = \frac{18}{1-\left(-\frac{2}{7}\right)} = \frac{18}{\frac{9}{7}} \text{ or } 14$$

Find the sum of each infinite geometric series, it if exists.

49. $a_1 = 6$ and $r = \frac{11}{12}$ **72**

50. $\frac{1}{8} - \frac{3}{16} + \frac{9}{32} - \frac{27}{64} + \dots$ **does not exist**

51. $a_1 = -2$ and $r = -\frac{5}{8}$ $-\frac{16}{13}$

52. $10 - \frac{5}{2} + \frac{5}{8} + \dots$ **8**

- iterate functions   (Lesson 11–6)

Find the first three iterates of the function $f(x) = -5x - 1$ for an initial value of $x_0 = -1$.

$$f(x_0) = f(-1)$$
$$= -5(-1) - 1 \text{ or } 4 \qquad \text{So, } x_1 = 4.$$
$$f(x_1) = f(4)$$
$$= -5(4) - 1 \text{ or } -21 \qquad \text{So, } x_2 = -21.$$
$$f(x_2) = f(-21)$$
$$= -5(-21) - 1 \text{ or } 104 \qquad \text{So, } x_3 = 104.$$

The first three iterates are 4, -21, and 104.

Find the first three iterates of each function, using the given initial values.

53. $f(x) = -2x + 3, x_0 = 1$ **1, 1, 1**

54. $f(x) = 7x - 4, x_0 = 2$ **10, 66, 458**

55. $f(x) = x^2 - 6, x_0 = -1$ **−5, 19, 355**

56. $f(x) = -2x^2 - x + 5, x_0 = -2$ **−1, 4, −31**

- expand powers of binomials by using Pascal's triangle and the binomial theorem   (Lesson 11–8)

Use the binomial theorem to express $(a - 2b)^4$ in expanded form.

$$(a - 2b)^4 = a^4 + 4a^3(-2b) + \frac{4(3)}{1 \cdot 2} a^2(-2b)^2$$
$$+ \frac{4(3)(2)}{1 \cdot 2 \cdot 3} a(-2b)^3 + (-2b)^4$$
$$= a^4 - 8a^3b + 24a^2b^2 - 32ab^3 + 16b^4$$

Expand each binomial.

57. $(x + y)^3$ $x^3 + 3x^2y + 3xy^2 + y^3$

58. $(x - 2)^4$ $x^4 - 8x^3 + 24x^2 - 32x + 16$

59. $(3r + s)^5$ $243r^5 + 405r^4s + 270r^3s^2 + 90r^2s^3 + 15rs^4 + s^5$

Find the indicated term of each expression.

60. fourth term of $(x + 2y)^6$ $160x^3y^3$

61. second term of $(4x - 5)^{10}$ $-13,107,200x^9$

62. seventh term of $(x - y)^{15}$ $5005x^9y^6$

APPLICATIONS AND PROBLEM SOLVING

63. 43

63. Fine Arts   A layered sculpture is arranged so that there are 5 diamonds on the first layer, 7 diamonds on the second layer, 9 diamonds on the third layer, and so on. How many diamonds are there on the twentieth layer?   (Lesson 11–2)

A practice test for Chapter 11 is provided on page 922.

64. Fractals   A side of an equilateral triangle is 20 inches long. The midpoints of its sides are joined to form a smaller equilateral triangle. If this process is continued infinitely, find the sum of the perimeters of the triangles. (Lesson 11–7)   **120 in.**

ALTERNATIVE ASSESSMENT

COOPERATIVE LEARNING PROJECT

Peach Farming   In this project, you will analyze a planting situation for a tree farmer. A peach farmer in Georgia calculates that he can produce 54 boxes of peaches per tree if he plants 40 trees per acre. If he plants one more tree per acre, the yield drops one box per tree due to congestion. His farm is 160 acres.

Find the number of trees per acre he should plant in order to maximize the total production. What would his total production of boxes be if he would plant that number of trees per acre? Would it be more productive and cost efficient for him to plant 43 trees or 51 trees? Explain.

What type of sequence is the number of boxes of peaches per acre for successive numbers of trees? Write a recursive formula to describe it.

Incorporate these ideas in your project.

- Formulate a chart for your data.
- Look for patterns.
- Determine a maximization for total production.
- Look at all the avenues in tree farming and write a recommendation for the farmer.

THINKING CRITICALLY

In the Fibonacci sequence, each term after the second term is found by adding the two previous terms. Is this sequence an arithmetic sequence? Explain your answer.   **No, the same number is not added to each term.**

Use 1, 2, 3, ... as the basis to generate at least two different sequences. For each sequence generated, give a rule and the first six terms in the sequence. **Sample answers: 1, 2, 3, 4, 5, 6, ..., $a_n = n$, where $n \geq 1$; 1, 2, 3, 6, 11, 20, ..., $a_{n+1} = a_{n-2} + a_{n-1} + a_n$, where $n \geq 3$.**

PORTFOLIO

Throughout this course, you have been working in groups to solve problems. What roles do you play in the group?

- Are you a leader who takes charge?
- Do you help to keep your group on task?
- Do you ask questions?
- Do you just listen and copy down answers?
- In what ways are you a good group member?
- How could you do better?
- Did your group work well together? Why?

Place this in your portfolio.

SELF EVALUATION

The problem-solving strategy of looking for a pattern is an important skill that we all need to develop. However, expecting a pattern in a problem to automatically jump out does not often happen. Changing certain conditions in a problem situation and looking for a pattern to emerge is more likely to happen.

Assess yourself. Do you look for patterns? Do you change certain conditions in order to help you look for patterns? Think of a situation in mathematics and also in your daily life where looking for a pattern would be an appropriate strategy to use in order to help you solve the situation. Explain how it was helpful.

Chapter 11   Study Guide and Assessment   **707**

Assessment and Evaluation Masters, pp. 294, 305

NAME_____ DATE_____

11   **Chapter 11 Performance Assessment**

Instructions: *Demonstrate your knowledge by giving a clear, concise solution to each problem. Be sure to include all relevant drawings and justify your answers. You may show your solution in more than one way or investigate beyond the requirements of the problem.*

1. a. Explain in your own words what is meant by the term *arithmetic sequence.*

   b. Write an arithmetic sequence.

   c. Write the formula for the nth term of your arithmetic sequence. Then find the 30th term.

   d.. Explain how sequences and series are related.

   e. Find the sum of the first 30 terms of your sequence.

2. a. Explain in your own words what is meant by the term *geometric sequence.*

   b. Write a geometric sequence.

   c. Write the formula for the nth term of your geometric sequence. Then find the 10th term.

   d. Find the sum of the first 10 terms of your sequence.

3. Find $(a + b)^7$ in at least two ways. Show your work and explain each step.

4. Describe how you would find the difference between the sum of the first 50 odd natural numbers and the sum of the first 50 even natural numbers. Justify each step.

Scoring Guide
Chapter 11
Performance Assessment

Level	Specific Criteria
3 Superior	· Shows thorough understanding of the concepts *arithmetic and geometric sequences, arithmetic and geometric series,* and *the binomial theorem.* · Computations are correct. · Written explanations are exemplary. · Goes beyond requirements of problem.
2 Satisfactory, with Minor Flaws	· Shows understanding of the concepts *arithmetic and geometric sequences, arithmetic and geometric series,* and *the binomial theorem.* · Computations are mostly correct. · Written explanations are effective. · Satisfies all requirements of problem.
1 Nearly Satisfactory, with Serious Flaws	· Shows understanding of most of the concepts *arithmetic and geometric sequences, arithmetic and geometric series,* and *the binomial theorem.* · Computations are mostly correct. · Written explanations are satisfactory. · Satisfies most requirements of problem.
0 Unsatisfactory	· Shows little or no understanding of the concepts *arithmetic and geometric sequences, arithmetic and geometric series,* and *the binomial theorem.* · Computations are incorrect. · Written explanations are not satisfactory. · Does not satisfy requirements of problem.

 Alternative Assessment

The Alternative Assessment section provides students with the opportunity to assess their own work by thinking critically, working with others, keeping a portfolio, and honestly evaluating their own progress. For more information on alternative forms of assessment, see *Alternative Assessment in the Mathematics Classroom,* one of the titles in the Glencoe Mathematics Professional Series.

 Performance Assessment

Performance Assessment tasks for this chapter are included in the *Assessment and Evaluation Masters.* A scoring guide is also provided.

Using the COLLEGE ENTRANCE EXAM PRACTICE

These two pages review the skills and concepts presented in Chapters 1–11. This review is formatted to reflect new trends in college entrance testing.

A more traditional cumulative review is provided in the *Assessment and Evaluation Masters,* pp. 299–300.

Assessment and Evaluation Masters, pp. 299–300

11 NAME_____ DATE_____

Chapter 11 Cumulative Review

1. Name the property illustrated by $1 = 11^2 \times \frac{1}{11^2}$. (Lesson 1-6)
   1. __multiplicative inverse__

2. Solve $4 + |5 - x| \le 6$. (Lesson 1-7)
   2. __$\{x \mid 3 \le x \le 7\}$__

3. Find the slope, x-intercept, and y-intercept of the line with equation $y = \frac{1}{5}x$. (Lesson 2-2)
   3. __$\frac{1}{5}; 0; 0$__

4. Find the standard from of the equation of the line passing through (3, 5) and having a slope of 0. (Lesson 2-2)
   4. __$y = 5$__ See students' graphs.

5. Graph the system of inequalities. (Lesson 3-4) $x \ge 0, y \ge 0, y \le 4 - \frac{1}{2}x$
   5. __

6. Consider the pairs (x, y) in the solution set of the system $x \ge 0, y \ge 0, 2x + y \le 800, 2x + 3y \le 1200$. For what pair does $f(x, y) = 2x + 1.5y$ have its maximum value? (Lesson 3-5)
   6. __(300, 200)__

7. Solve the system of equations. (Lesson 3-7) $x + 3y + z = 3$; $3x - y + 2z = 15$; $2x + y - 2x = -5$
   7. __(2, −1, −4)__

8. Find the inverse of $\begin{bmatrix} 4 & -2 \\ 6 & -5 \end{bmatrix}$. (Lesson 4-4)
   8. __$-\frac{1}{8}\begin{bmatrix} -5 & 2 \\ -6 & 4 \end{bmatrix}$__

9. Simplify $\left(\frac{3}{2x^2}\right)^{-2}$. (Lesson 5-1)
   9. __$\frac{4x^4}{9}$__

10. Simplify $\sqrt{5}(4 - \sqrt{5})$. (Lesson 5-6)
    10. __$4\sqrt{5} - 5$__

11. Factor $4r^2 + 10r - 14$. (Lesson 6-4)
    11. __$2(2r + 7)(r - 1)$__

12. Solve $13 - \sqrt{3x + 7} = 6$. (Lesson 5-8)
    12. __$\frac{14}{3}$__

13. Use the quadratic formula to solve $x^2 - 3x - 7 = 0$. (Lesson 6-4)
    13. __$\frac{3 \pm \sqrt{37}}{2}$__

14. Find the sum and product of the roots of the equation $x^2 - 9x - 52 = 0$. Then solve the equation. (Lesson 6-5)
    14. __9; −52; −4, 13__

15. Find the value of a for which the point with coordinates $(-5, 2)$ is on the graph of $f(x) = ax^2$. (Lesson 6-6)
    15. __$\frac{2}{25}$__

16. Write the equation $f(x) = -2x^2 + 16x - 32$ in the form $f(x) = a(x - h)^2$. State the vertex, the axis of symmetry, and the direction of opening of the parabola which is its graph. (Lesson 6-6)
    16. __$f(x) = -2(x - 4)^2$; (4, 0); $x = 4$; down__

11 NAME_____ DATE_____

Chapter 11 Cumulative Review (continued)

17. If the mean of a set of data is 95, and the standard deviation is 8, what percent of the scores lie between 87 and 111? (Lesson 6-8)
    17. __81.5%__

18. State whether the graph of $y^2 = 8x$ is a parabola, circle, ellipse, or hyperbola. Then graph the equation. (Lesson 7-6)
    18. __parabola; see students' graphs.__

19. Find the center and radius of the circle with equation $(x - 3)^2 + y^2 = 40$. (Lesson 7-3)
    19. __(3, 0); $2\sqrt{10}$__

20. State the vertices, foci, and slopes of the asymptotes of the graph $\frac{x^2}{9} - \frac{y^2}{16} = 1$. Then graph the equation. (Lesson 7-5)
    20. __$(\pm 3, 0)$; $(\pm 5, 0)$; $\pm\frac{4}{3}$; see students' graphs.__

21. Find $p(1)$ if $p(x) = x^2 - 2x + 6$. (Lesson 8-1)
    21. __5__

22. Approximate to the nearest tenth the real zeros of the function $f(x) = x^3 - 3x^2 + 2x - 4$. (Lesson 8-3)
    22. __2.8__

23. Find $[f \circ g](x)$ if $f(x) = x^2 + 3x - 8$ and $g(x) = x^2 - 1$. (Lesson 8-8)
    23. __$x^4 + x^2 - 10$__

24. Simplify $\frac{(a - 1)^2}{(a + 1)^2} \cdot \frac{(a + 1)(a + 2)}{(a - 1)}$. (Lesson 9-3)
    24. __$\frac{(a - 1)(a + 2)}{a + 1}$__

25. Simplify $\frac{\frac{16m}{c^2 + 8c + 16}}{\frac{6m^3}{c^2 + 5c + 8}}$. (Lesson 9-3)
    25. __$\frac{8(c + 2)}{3m^2(c + 4)}$__

26. Find the standard deviation of the following data. {5, 7, 9, 15, 21} (Lesson 6-8)
    26. __5.85__

27. Write $\log_2 \frac{1}{32} = -5$ in exponential form. (Lesson 10-2)
    27. __$2^{-5} = \frac{1}{32}$__

28. Evaluate $5^{\log_5 16}$. (Lesson 10-2)
    28. __16__

29. Solve $\log_5 x + \log_5 (3x + 2) = \log_5 5 + 2 \log_5 x$. (Lesson 10-2)
    29. __1__

30. Find the sum of the arithmetic series for which $n = 8, a_1 = 1$, and $a_n = 13$. (Lesson 11-2)
    30. __56__

31. Find the first term of the geometric series for which $S_n = 105, r = 4$, and $n = 3$. (Lesson 11-4)
    31. __5__

32. Draw the next stage. (Lesson 11-7)
    32. __

33. Expand $(2x - y)^4$. (Lesson 11-8)
    33. __$16x^4 - 32x^3y + 24x^2y^2 - 8xy^3 + y^4$__

COLLEGE ENTRANCE EXAM PRACTICE

CHAPTERS 1–11

SECTION ONE: MULTIPLE CHOICE

There are ten multiple-choice questions in this section. After working each problem, write the letter of the correct answer on your paper.

1. Find the center and radius of the circle whose equation is $(x + 8)^2 + (y - 3)^2 = 25$.   **B**

   A. $(8, -3); 5$

   B. $(-8, 3); 5$

   C. $(3, 8); 5$

   D. $(-3, 8); 5$

2. Solve for x in the equation $\begin{vmatrix} x & 7 & 5 \\ 0 & 3 & 4 \\ 3 & 2 & -2 \end{vmatrix} = 11$.   **D**

   A. -6

   B. 84

   C. -28

   D. 2

3. Find the first three terms of the arithmetic series for which $a_1 = 6, a_n = 306$, and $S_n = 1716$.   **A**

   A. 6, 36, 66

   B. 6, 17, 28

   C. 6, 25, 44

   D. 6, 66, 726

4. Simplify $\left(4^{\sqrt{3}}\right)^{\sqrt{2}}$.   **C**

   A. $4^{\sqrt{5}}$

   B. 4096

   C. $4^{\sqrt{6}}$

   D. $4^{\sqrt{\frac{3}{2}}}$

5. Solve the system of equations.   **A**

   $3x - 2y + 2z = -2$

   $x - 3y + z = -2$

   $2x - y + 4z = 7$

   A. $(-2, 1, 3)$

   B. $(2, 7, -4)$

   C. $(1, 4, 3)$

   D. $\left(-2, \frac{1}{3}, -\frac{5}{3}\right)$

6. If $A_{4\times3}$ is multiplied by $B_{3\times5}$, what are the dimensions of the product?   **B**

   A. 3×3

   B. 4×5

   C. 5×4

   D. 4×3

7. The last term of an arithmetic sequence is 207, the common difference is 3, and the number of terms is 14. Choose the equation that would find the first term of the sequence.   **C**

   A. $x = 207 + (3 - 1)14$

   B. $14 = 207 + (x - 1)3$

   C. $207 = x + (14 - 1)3$

   D. $3 = 207 + (14 - 1)x$

8. Simplify $\dfrac{\frac{3x}{4x - 1}}{1 + \frac{3x}{x - 1}}$.   **B**

   A. 1

   B. $\dfrac{3x(x - 1)}{(4x - 1)^2}$

   C. $\dfrac{3x}{x - 1}$

   D. $\dfrac{1}{4x - 1}$

9. Which two radicals are like radicals?   **D**

   A. $\sqrt{5}$ and $\sqrt[3]{5}$

   B. $7\sqrt{x}$ and $\sqrt{7x}$

   C. $\sqrt{4x}$ and $\sqrt{4y}$

   D. $2\sqrt[3]{9}$ and $3\sqrt[3]{9}$

10. Simplify $(5ab^2)(a^3b)(-3c^2) + (7bc)(3ac)(a^3b)^2$.   **C**

    A. $6a^{11}b^6c^4$

    B. $2a^4b^3c^2 + 21a^7b^3c^2$

    C. $-15a^4b^3c^2 + 21a^7b^3c^2$

    D. $-15a^3b^2c^2 + 10a^6b^3c$

Standardized Test Practice Questions

Standardized Test Practice Questions are also provided in the *Assessment and Evaluation Masters,* p. 298.

SECTION TWO: SHORT ANSWER

This section contains ten questions for which you will provide short answers. Write your answer on your paper.

11. Jackie is in charge of building a set for the school play. She wants each rectangular window to have an area of 315 square inches. She also wants each window to be 6 inches taller than it is wide. What are the dimensions of the window?   **21 in. × 15 in.**

12. A piece of machinery valued at $75,000 depreciates at a steady rate of 8% yearly. When will the value be $15,000? Use $V_n = P(1 + r)^n$.   **19.3 years**

13. The volume of a rectangular box is 2475 cubic units. The length of the box is three units more than twice the width of the box. The height is two units less than the width. Find the dimensions of the box.   **9 × 11 × 25 units**

14. The teaching staff of Fairmeadow High School informs its members of school cancellation by telephone. The principal calls 2 teachers, each one of whom calls 2 other teachers, and so on. In order to inform the entire staff, 6 rounds of calls are made. Counting the principal, find how many people are on staff at Fairmeadow High School.   **127 people**

15. Find $(a^4 - 5a^3 - 13a^2 + 53a + 60) \div (a + 1)$ by using synthetic division. $a^3 - 6a^2 - 7a + 60$

16. A ball dropped 120 feet bounces $\frac{2}{3}$ of the height from which it fell on each bounce. How far will it travel before coming to rest?   **600 ft**

17. The hourly wages of eight employees of the Sequoia Insurance Company are $4.45, $5.50, $6.30, $11.00, $5.50, $17.20, $12.20, and $7.80. Find the median, mode, mean, and standard deviation of the wages of these employees.   **$7.05, $5.50, $8.74, $4.11**

18. Find the radius r of a sphere whose surface area S is 616 square inches. Use the formula $r = \frac{1}{2}\sqrt{\frac{S}{\pi}}$.   **7 inches**

19. The sum of Josh and Yuji's ages is 32. Twice Josh's age is 4 more than double Yuji's age. Find their ages.   **Josh, 17; Yuji, 15**

20. Television signals travel at the speed of light. If the speed of light is 3.00×10^5 kilometers per second, how long would it take for signals broadcasting from a television station to reach a house 36 kilometers away?   **1.2×10^{-4} or 0.00012 seconds**

21. C   22. B   23. A   24. D   25. C

SECTION THREE: COMPARISON

This section contains five comparison problems that involve comparing two quantities, one in column A and one in column B. In certain questions, information related to one or both quantities is centered above them. All variables used represent real numbers.

Compare quantities A and B below.

- Write A if quantity A is greater.
- Write B if quantity B is greater.
- Write C if the two quantities are equal.
- Write D if there is not enough information to determine the relationship.

Column A	Column B
$\dfrac{a}{b} = \dfrac{7}{3}$	
21. $12a$	$28b$
22. $5^{x+2} = 15.3$	$9^{x-4} = 6.28$
$x > 1$	
23. $\dfrac{2x^3 + 15x^2 + 22x - 15}{x + 3}$	$\dfrac{x^3 + 3x^2 - 7x + 1}{x - 1}$
$\dfrac{a + b}{a^{\frac{1}{2}} + b}$	
24. a	b
25. the inverse of $f(x) = \dfrac{5x + 2}{2}$	$\dfrac{x - 1}{2\sqrt{5}} \cdot \dfrac{4}{\sqrt{5}}$

Investigating Discrete Mathematics and Probability

PREVIEWING THE CHAPTER

In this chapter, students begin by using the fundamental counting principle, and the strategy of solving a simpler problem is introduced. Next, linear and circular permutations and combinations are examined, and formulas are derived to solve problems. Then, students find the probability that an event will occur when the events are independent or dependent and the probability that events A or B will occur with mutually exclusive or inclusive events. Next, students apply binomial experiments and simulation to solve various probability problems. The chapter concludes with students designing and conducting experiments, determining appropriate samples, and testing hypotheses.

Lesson (Pages)	Lesson Objectives	NCTM Standards	State/Local Objectives
12-1 (712–717)	Solve problems by using the fundamental counting principle. Solve problems by using the strategy of solving a simpler problem.	1–4, 12	
12-2 (718–725)	Solve problems involving linear and circular permutations.	1–4, 12	
12-3 (726–731)	Solve problems involving combinations.	1–4, 12	
12-4 (732–738)	Find the probability of an event. Determine the odds of success and failure of an event.	1–4, 11	
12-5 (739–745)	Find the probability of two or more independent or dependent events.	1–4, 11	
12-6 (746–751)	Find the probability of mutually exclusive or inclusive events.	1–4, 11	
12-7 (752–757)	Use binomial experiments to find probabilities. Use simulation to solve various probability problems.	1–4, 11–12	
12-8 (758–762)	Determine an unbiased sample. Find margins of sampling error. Test hypotheses by designing and conducting experiments.	1–4, 11–12	

ORGANIZING THE CHAPTER

A complete, 1-page lesson plan is provided for each lesson in the *Lesson Planning Guide*. Answer keys for each lesson are available in the *Answer Key Masters*.

You may want to refer to the **Course Planning Calendar** on page T12 for detailed information on pacing.
PACING: Standard—12 days; **Honors**—10 days; **Block**—6 days

LESSON PLANNING CHART

| Lesson (Pages) | Materials/ Manipulatives | Extra Practice (Student Edition) | Blackline Masters | | | | | | | | | Real-World Applications | Interactive Mathematics Tools Software | Teaching Transparencies |
			Study Guide	Practice	Enrichment	Assessment and Evaluation	Modeling Mathematics	Multicultural Activity	Tech Prep Applications	Graphing Calculator	Science and Math Lab Manual			
12-1 (712–717)		p. 903	p. 84	p. 84	p. 84									12-1A 12-1B
12-2 (718–725)	graphing calculator	p. 904	p. 85	p. 85	p. 85	p. 324						31		12-2A 12-2B
12-3 (726–731)	graphing calculator	p. 904	p. 86	p. 86	p. 86					p. 12				12-3A 12-3B
12-4 (732–738)		p. 904	p. 87	p. 87	p. 87	pp. 323, 324	p. 23				pp. 111–116		12-4	12-4A 12-4B
12-5 (739–745)		p. 905	p. 88	p. 88	p. 88		pp. 55–57		p. 23				12-5	12-5A 12-5B
12-6 (746–751)		p. 905	p. 89	p. 89	p. 89	p. 325								12-6A 12-6B
12-7 (752–757)	packages of candy	p. 905	p. 90	p. 90	p. 90		p. 72	p. 24	p. 24			32	12-7	12-7A 12-7B
12-8 (758–762)	meterstick stopwatch grid paper graphing calculator	p. 906	p. 91	p. 91	p. 91	p. 325								12-8A 12-8B
Study Guide/ Assessment (763–767)						pp. 309 –322, 326– 328								

ORGANIZING THE CHAPTER

OTHER CHAPTER RESOURCES

Student Edition
Chapter Opener, pp. 710–711
Mathematics and Society, p. 731

Teacher's Classroom Resources
Investigations and Projects Masters, pp. 69–72

Technology
Teacher's Guide for Software Resources
Test and Review Software (IBM and Macintosh)
CD-ROM Interactions (Windows and Macintosh)

Professional Publications
Block Scheduling Booklet
Glencoe Mathematics Professional Series

OUTSIDE RESOURCES

Books/Periodicals
The Art and Techniques of Simulation, Dale Seymour Publications
Exploring Surveys and Information from Samples, Dale Seymour Publications

Software
Algebra II Skills, Tom Snyder Publications
Probability Lab—MECC, NASCO

Videos/CD-ROMs
Algebra for Everyone, NCTM

See the *Teacher's Guide for Software Resources* for software addresses.

ASSESSMENT RESOURCES

Student Edition
Math Journal, pp. 715, 729, 735, 748
Mixed Review, pp. 717, 725, 731, 738, 745, 751, 757, 762
Self Test, p. 738
Chapter Highlights, p. 763
Chapter Study Guide and Assessment, pp. 764–766
Alternative Assessment, p. 767
Portfolio, p. 767

Teacher's Wraparound Edition
5-Minute Check, pp. 712, 718, 726, 732, 739, 746, 752, 758
Check for Understanding, pp. 714, 722, 728, 735, 742, 748, 755, 760
Closing Activity, pp. 717, 725, 731, 738, 745, 751, 757, 762
Cooperative Learning, pp. 714, 744

Assessment and Evaluation Masters
Multiple-Choice Tests, Forms 1A (Honors), 1B (Average), 1C (Basic), pp. 309–314
Free-Response Tests, Forms 2A (Honors), 2B (Average), 2C (Basic), pp. 315–320
Calculator-Based Test, p. 321
Performance Assessment, p. 322
Mid-Chapter Test, p. 323
Quizzes A–D, pp. 324–325
Standardized Test Practice, p. 326
Cumulative Review, pp. 327–328

ENHANCING THE CHAPTER

Examples of some of the materials for enhancing Chapter 12 are shown below.

DIVERSITY

Multicultural Activity Masters, pp. 23, 24

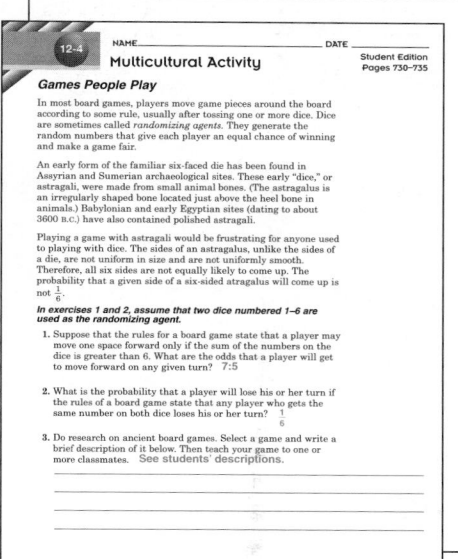

APPLICATIONS

Real-World Applications, 31, 32

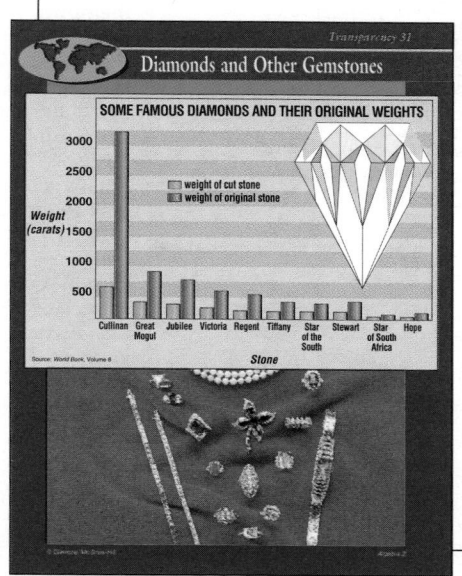

TECHNOLOGY

Graphing Calculator Masters, p. 12

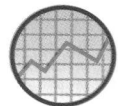

TECH PREP

Tech Prep Applications Masters, pp. 23, 24

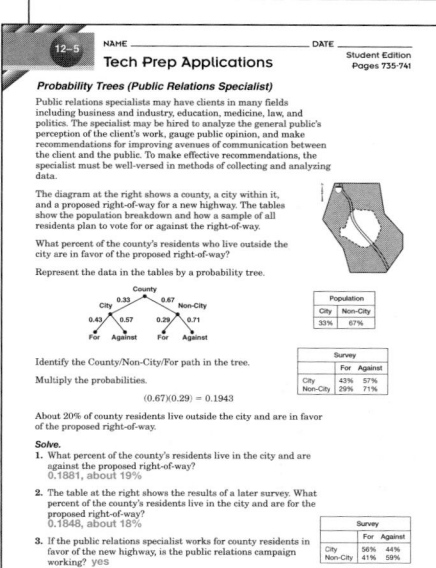

CONNECTIONS

Science and Math Lab Manual, pp. 111–116

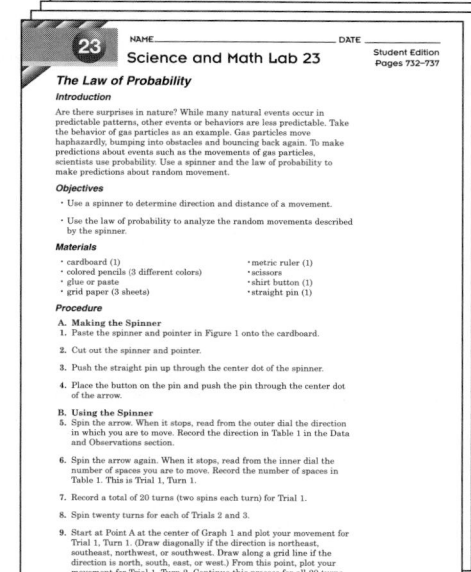

PROBLEM SOLVING

Problem of the Week Cards, 30, 31, 32

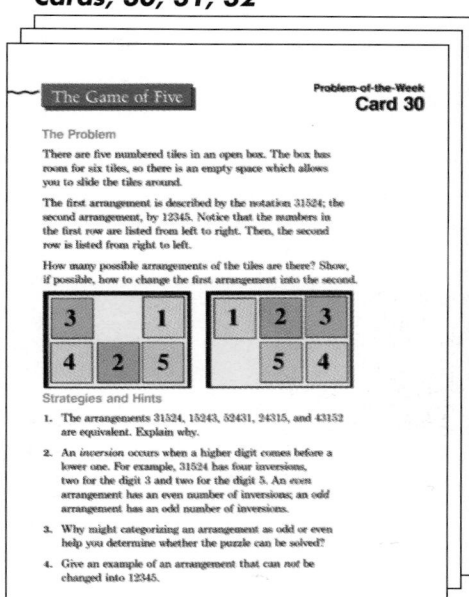

MAKING MATHEMATICS RELEVANT

This two-page introduction to the chapter provides students with an opportunity to explore contemporary topics and their applications to mathematics.

Background Information

Minimum Wage Those in favor of raising the minimum wage often argue that people cannot support themselves on the current minimum wage. Working 40 hours a week at $4.25 per hour yields $170 per week or $8840 per year. If the minimum wage is increased to $5.15 per hour, these figures are $206 per week or $10,712 per year. Would this income be enough to support a family? If not, what minimum wage would be sufficient?

CHAPTER 12

Investigating Discrete Mathematics and Probability

Objectives

In this chapter, you will:

- solve problems by solving simpler, related problems,
- solve problems involving permutations and combinations,
- find probabilities of events,
- determine the odds of success or failure of events, and
- use experiments and simulation to solve problems.

Most teenagers begin to earn money at minimum wage. Yet some enterprising teens have the courage and determination to start their own businesses. Have you ever thought about starting your own business? What are your interests? Is there a need for a certain service or business in your community?

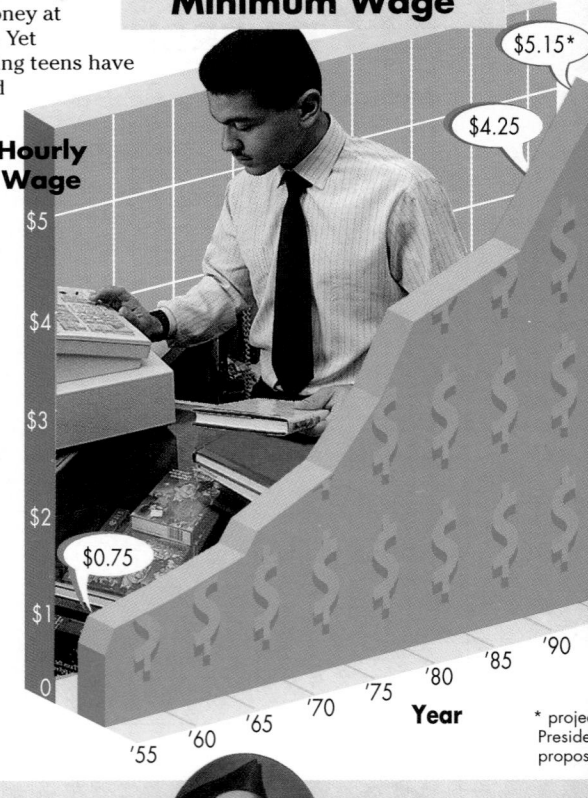

Minimum Wage

$5.15*

$4.25

Hourly Wage

$0.75

Year

'55 '60 '65 '70 '75 '80 '85 '90

* project Presider proposc

TIME Line

3500 B.C. Wheeled vehicles appear in Mesopotamia.

1733 English machinist and engineer John Kay invents the flying-shuttle loom for weaving.

A.D. 704 The Chinese begin printing with wood blocks.

TIME Line

Students might want to research one of the most important advances in modern mathematics—the computer proof of the Four-Color Conjecture. For centuries it was known that only four colors are required, but it eluded proof for as many centuries. The proof that the computer produced is in no way as elegant as proofs discovered by humans. But because it works, this has revolutionized mathematical research.

inter NET CONNECTION

Information on starting, financing, and expanding your business is available from the Small Business Administration on-line on the Web.

World Wide Web
http://www.sbaonline.sba.gov/

ChapterProject

In response to the riots in L.A. in 1992, a group of forty students in Tammy Bird's biology class at Crenshaw High School in Los Angeles decided to start an organic garden. The garden flourished, and the group donated some of the produce to needy families and sold the rest at a farmers' market.

The students formed a company called **"Food from the 'Hood"** and started a college scholarship fund. Local business leaders helped them develop and sell a salad dressing called "Straight out 'the Garden," now sold in over 2000 stores in 23 states. Expected profits this year could be $50,000, all going to the scholarship fund. As Terie Smith, 15, says, "We showed that a group of inner-city kids can and did make a difference."

Organize into cooperative groups of entrepreneurs. Your group should investigate various ways high school students could use their talents and expertise to start their own business. Use the research facilities of your library, information gathered from local business and community groups or government agencies, and decide what services or products are needed in your community. Decide what steps are needed to get started, if entrepreneurial training programs are available in your area, and the benefits of using them. List the advantages and disadvantages of running your own business and report on your findings.

1890 The book *Poems by Emily Dickinson* is published four years after her death.

1991 Kim Zmeskal becomes the first American woman to win an all-around world championship in gymnastics.

| 1780 | 1800 | 1820 | 1840 | 1860 | 1880 | 1900 | 1920 | 1940 | 1960 | 1980 | 2000 |

1799 Karl Friedrich Gauss proves the fundamental theorem of algebra.

1947 American opera singer Maria Callas achieves her first success singing the title role in *La Gioconda* in Verona, Italy.

1976 In the first major computer-assisted proof, it is shown that any map can be colored with four colors so that no two regions with the same color are adjacent.

Alternative Chapter Projects

Two other chapter projects are included in the *Investigations and Projects Masters*. In Chapter 12 Project A, pp. 69–70, students extend the topic in the chapter opener. In Chapter 12 Project B, pp. 71–72, students explore and research areas within environmental science.

Forty students at Crenshaw High School began with a simple goal: to plant life and hope among the ashes of the L.A. riots in 1992. It was a straight-forward biology project—to grow vegetables and flowering plants in a garden at their school. It blossomed into a successful business, teaching the students not just science, but accounting, marketing, and self-reliance.

ChapterProject

Cooperative Learning In cooperative groups, students can split up the research tasks as they investigate local businesses and then decide together what services or products are needed in the community. This activity allows students to closely examine the opportunities and problems involved in setting up and running one's own business.

Investigations and Projects Masters, p. 69

12-A	NAME_____ DATE_____
	Chapter 12 Project A Student Edition Pages 710–762

A Game Effort

1. Work with a partner. Brainstorm ideas for a new type of board game that you would like to manufacture and sell. You may want to use games you enjoy playing as models.

2. Make a sketch of the game board. Devise a set of rules for playing the game. Think about how players will move their game pieces, earn points, and determine a winner. Use your knowledge of probability to help you make the game fair and challenging.

3. List the items you would need to make your game. Find out about the cost of the items you listed.

4. If possible, interview one or more people who design board games and ask them to describe their job. Ask about any marketing strategies their company uses. During the interview, show them your ideas and the list you have made and ask them for any suggestions they have. If they suggest changes to your work, be sure you understand why before you make the changes. If an interview is not possible, use an online service or other resource to obtain information.

5. Write a report describing the final plan for your new game. Be sure to include information about how your knowledge of probability helped you design the game.

NCTM Standards: 1–4, 12

Instructional Resources

- Study Guide Master 12-1
- Practice Master 12-1
- Enrichment Master 12-1

 Transparency 12-1A contains the 5-Minute Check for this lesson; **Transparency 12-1B** contains a teaching aid for this lesson.

Recommended Pacing	
Standard Pacing	Day 1 of 12
Honors Pacing	Day 1 of 10
Block Scheduling*	Day 1 of 6 (along with Lesson 12-2)

 *For more information on pacing and possible lesson plans, refer to the *Block Scheduling Booklet.*

1 FOCUS

 5-Minute Check
(over Chapter 11)

1. Find the *n*th term of the arithmetic sequence if $a_1 = 3$, $d = 7$, and $n = 34$. $a_{34} = 234$
2. Find the three geometric means between 4 and 324. **12, 36, 108 or −12, 36, −108**
3. Find the sum of the infinite geometric series $\frac{1}{2} + \frac{1}{3} + \frac{2}{9} + \frac{4}{27} + \ldots$. **$\frac{3}{2}$**
4. Expand $(3a + b)^5$. **$243a^5 + 405a^4b + 270a^3b^2 + 90a^2b^3 + 15ab^4 + b^5$**
5. Find the fourth term of $(2m − 3)^6$. **$-4320m^3$**

Motivating the Lesson

Questioning Bring a menu to class. Tell students that you want to order a sandwich, a beverage, and one side order. Using the menu, have students give several possible orders. Ask students how they would know how many different orders are possible.

The Counting Principle

12-1

What YOU'LL LEARN

- To solve problems by using the fundamental counting principle, and
- to solve problems by using the strategy of solving a simpler problem.

Why IT'S IMPORTANT

You can use the counting principle to solve problems involving communication and linguistics.

APPLICATION
Telecommunications

Area codes were invented in the 1940s when the Bell Telephone Company realized they could not hire enough operators to handle all of the long-distance calls that were being made. At that time, Bell researchers developed a system of 3-digit codes that would automatically route calls to long distance. These area codes were used for North America, including Canada, the Caribbean, and Bermuda, but not Mexico.

With this system, the first digit could be any number from 2 through 9. Only 1 or 0 could be used as the middle digit. The last digit could be any number between 0 and 9. How many area code combinations were possible? *This problem will be solved in Example 2.*

Sometimes a problem is easier to solve if you first **solve a simpler problem.** After solving the simpler problem, you can use the concepts that you used to solve the original problem.

Example ① Suppose your state is adding a new area code. The first digit must be a 6 or 7, the second digit must be a 0 or 1, and the third digit can be a 3, 4 or 5. How many area codes are possible?

The Bell system predicted in the 1940s that there would be enough combinations to last until the year 2000. They were about 5 years off. In addition to now dialing 1 before the area code, starting in 1995, the middle digits of area codes can now be digits other than 1 or 0.

First Digit	Second Digit	Third Digit	Possible Area Codes
6	0	3	603
		4	604
		5	605
	1	3	613
		4	614
		5	615
7	0	3	703
		4	704
		5	705
	1	3	713
		4	714
		5	715

Thus, your state has a total of 12 choices for a new area code.

F Y I

If all restrictions on area-code numbers were lifted, allowing 0 through 9 for any of the three digits, how many area codes would be possible? **1000**

Choosing the three numbers for an area code are called **independent events** because one choice does not affect the others. The *tree diagram* shown in Example 1 illustrates all of the different choices your state has in choosing the final area code.

You can find this same total number of choices without drawing a diagram.

	First Digit	Second Digit	Third Digit
Choices	6 or 7	0 or 1	3, 4, or 5
Number of Choices	2	2	3

The total number of choices can be found by multiplying the number of choices for each decision. The total number of choices is $2 \cdot 2 \cdot 3$ or 12. This example illustrates the **fundamental counting principle**.

Fundamental Counting Principle	If event *M* can occur in *m* ways and is followed by an independent event *N* that can occur in *n* ways, then the event *M* followed by the event *N* can occur in $m \cdot n$ ways.

This principle can be extended to any number of events. You can use this principle and what you learned in Example 1 to find the total number of area code combinations referred to in the application at the beginning of the lesson.

Example 2   Using the Bell researchers' 3-digit system from the 1940s, how many total area code combinations were possible?

APPLICATION
Communication

Since each choice of digits is not affected by the previous choice, these are *independent events*.

	First Digit	Second Digit	Third Digit
Choices	2, 3, 4, 5, 6, 7, 8, 9	0, 1	0, 1, 2, 3, 4, 5, 6, 7, 8, 9
Number of Choices	8	2	10

The total number of combinations can be found by multiplying the number of choices for each digit. The total number of area code combinations is $8 \cdot 2 \cdot 10$ or 160.

Example 3   Justin works part-time delivering pizzas for a local restaurant. His manager provides him with a pager so she can contact him at any time, even while he is making deliveries. To activate the pager, a 7-digit pager number is assigned to it. If the prefix is 337, how many 7-digit numbers are available?

The first group of three digits in a telephone number is called a prefix.

Since each of the last four digits can be used any number of times, there are 10 choices for each. These are *independent events*.

Digit in Pager Number	4th	5th	6th	7th
Number of Choices	10	10	10	10

There are $10 \cdot 10 \cdot 10 \cdot 10$ or 10,000 possible pager numbers available.

Lesson 12–1   The Counting Principle   **713**

In-Class Examples

For Example 1
How many four-letter patterns can be formed using the letters *x, y,* and *z* if letters may be repeated?   81

For Example 2
How many four-letter patterns can be formed using the letters *A, B, C,* and *D* if each letter is used exactly once?   24

For Example 3
How many two-digit numbers can be formed from the digits 1, 2, 3, 4, and 5 if repetitions are allowed?   25

Teaching Tip Make sure students know how to read a tree diagram so they can identify the possibilities.

Teaching Tip Emphasize that the first step in solving a problem by using the fundamental counting principle is to decide whether the events are dependent or independent.

In-Class Examples

For Example 4
How many ways can 5 cars be parked along the street if the only red one must be in the middle? 24

For Example 5
How many ways can 5 different books be arranged on a shelf? 120

3 PRACTICE/APPLY

Check for Understanding

Exercises 1–11 are designed to help you assess your students' understanding through reading, writing, speaking, and modeling. You should work through Exercises 1–5 with your students and then monitor their work on Exercises 6–11.

Assignment Guide
Core: 13–27 odd, 28, 29, 31, 33–39
Enriched: 12–26 even, 28–39

For **Extra Practice,** see p. 903.

The red A, B, and C flags, printed only in the Teacher's Wraparound Edition, indicate the level of difficulty of the exercises.

Some applications involve **dependent events**. That is, the outcome of one event *does affect* the outcome of another event.

Example ❹

APPLICATION
Banking

Tara opened a savings account so she could deposit the money she earns from her paper route. She received an automatic teller machine card with her account. Tara needs to choose a 4-digit PIN (personal identification number) for her new card, but she may not use any digit more than once. From how many different 4-digit PINs can she choose?

After the first digit is chosen, it cannot be chosen again. So there are only nine choices for the second digit. After the second digit is chosen, there are only eight choices for the third digit and seven choices for the fourth digit. These are *dependent events*.

Digit in PIN	1st	2nd	3rd	4th
Number of Choices	10	9	8	7

Tara can choose $10 \cdot 9 \cdot 8 \cdot 7$ or 5040 different PIN numbers.

Example ❺ Solve the problem in the comic below.

PEANUTS®

PEANUTS reprinted by permission of United Feature Syndicate, Inc.

LOOK BACK
You can refer to Lesson 11-8 for information on factorials.

You can help Peppermint Patty overcome her math anxiety. Finding out how many ways nine different books can be arranged on a shelf is an example of a *dependent event*.

Books	1st	2nd	3rd	4th	5th	6th	7th	8th	9th
Number of Choices	9	8	7	6	5	4	3	2	1

There are $9 \cdot 8 \cdot 7 \cdot 6 \cdot 5 \cdot 4 \cdot 3 \cdot 2 \cdot 1$ or 362,880 ways the books can be arranged on a shelf. *Note that $9 \cdot 8 \cdot 7 \cdot 6 \cdot 5 \cdot 4 \cdot 3 \cdot 2 \cdot 1 = 9!$.*

714 Chapter 12 *Investigating Discrete Mathematics and Probability*

Cooperative Learning

Brainstorming Separate students into pairs to design yes/no survey questions about tastes in food. Collect the questions and administer the survey to the entire class. Compute the results and communicate them to the class. Point out to students that with the counting principle they can compute the number of possible answers to the survey. For more information on the brainstorming strategy, see *Cooperative Learning in the Mathematics Classroom,* one of the titles in the Glencoe Mathematics Professional Series, page 30.

Communicating Mathematics

Study the lesson. Then complete the following.   1–4. See margin.

1. **Explain** the fundamental counting principle in your own words.

2. **Describe** the difference between independent and dependent events. Give an example of each.

3. **Draw** a tree diagram to illustrate all the different choices when spinning both spinners at the same time.

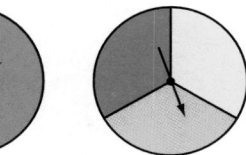

4. **Explain** the advantages of using a simpler problem to solve problems.

5. Now that the middle digit in an area code can be any number between 0 or 9, show how many area code combinations are possible.
$8 \cdot 10 \cdot 10$ or 800 possible area codes

Guided Practice

6–7. See Solutions Manual.

Draw a tree diagram to illustrate all of the possibilities.

6. the possibilities for boys and girls in a family with two children (*Hint:* Having a boy, then a girl is different from having a girl, then a boy.)

7. sweatshirts that come in sizes small, medium, and large and in the colors red, navy, and white

State whether the following events are *independent* or *dependent*.

8. choosing the color and size of a pair of shoes   independent

9. choosing the winner and loser of a chess game   dependent

Solve each problem.

10. **School**   At Dublin Coffman High School, Cecelia is taking six different classes. Assuming that each of these classes is offered each period, how many different schedules might she have?   720 schedules

11. **Tests**   Alberto's math quiz has eight true-false questions. How many different choices for giving answers to the eight questions are possible? 2^8 or 256 choices

EXERCISES

Practice

12–16. See Solutions Manual.

▶ A

Draw a tree diagram to illustrate all of the possibilities.

12. two pennies are tossed and a number cube is rolled

13. boys and girls in a family with three children

14. buying tennis, basketball, aerobic, running, or cross-country shoes in black, white, blue, or red

15. ordering a hamburger rare, medium, or well done with either ketchup, mayonnaise, cheese, onion, or tomato as your choice of topping

16. choosing a phone that comes in a wall or desk model in black, almond, or transparent that has a redial or hold button

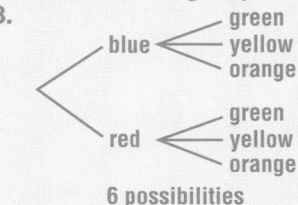

Lesson 12–1   The Counting Principle   **715**

Reteaching

Using Diagrams Have students draw tree diagrams for various counting problems. Have them discuss when using a tree diagram would or would not be beneficial.

Additional Answers

1. Sample answer: The fundamental counting principle allows you to determine the total number of ways independent events can happen in sequence given the number of choices for each event occurring.

2. With independent events, one choice for an event does not affect any of the possibilities for another event. Examples include rolling dice and picking a marble out of a sack, replacing the marble, and picking again. With dependent events, each choice is affected by the previous choice. Examples include choosing numbers in a lottery and selecting members of a team from a group.

3.
```
        green
blue  < yellow
        orange

        green
red   < yellow
        orange
```
6 possibilities

4. Sample answer: In solving a simpler problem, a pattern or shortcut may emerge that can be applied to the more difficult problem.

Study Guide Masters, p. 84

12-1   NAME_____ DATE_____
Study Guide   Student Edition Pages 708–713

The Counting Principle

If the outcome of one event does not affect the outcome of another event and vice versa, the events are called **independent** events. If their outcomes do affect one another, they are **dependent** events.

Fundamental Counting Principle
If event M can occur in m ways and is followed by event N that can occur in n ways, then the event M followed by the event N can occur in $m \cdot n$ ways.

Example: How many 3-digit numbers can be formed from the digits 1, 2, 3, 4, and 5 if each digit can be used repeatedly?

The use of a digit in one place-value position does not affect whether it may be used in another. There are 5 ways to choose a digit to occupy each of the three place-value positions. Therefore, by the fundamental counting principle, the total number of three-digit numbers possible is $5 \cdot 5 \cdot 5$, or 125.

Solve.

1. The letters A, B, C, and D are used to form four-letter passwords for entering a computer file. How many passwords are possible if letters can be repeated any number of times?
256

2. How many ways can the first five letters of the alphabet be arranged if each is used only once?
120

3. A restaurant serves 5 main dishes, 3 salads and 4 desserts. How many different meals could be ordered if each has a main dish, a salad, and a dessert?
60

4. How many different ways can 4 different books be arranged on the shelf?
24

5. How many 5-digit even numbers can be formed using the digits 4, 6, 7, 2, 8 if digits can be repeated any number of times?
2500

6. How many 4-digit positive even integers are there?
4500

7. How many license plate numbers consisting of three letters followed by three numbers are possible when repetition is allowed?
17,576,000

8. How many combinations are possible using the information in problem 7 if no repetition is allowed?
11,232,000

State whether the events are *independent* or *dependent*.

17. choosing a president, vice president, secretary, and treasurer for Student Council **dependent, if a person can hold only one office**

18. selecting a fiction book and a non-fiction book at the library **independent**

19. The letters A through Z are written on pieces of paper and placed in a jar. Four of them are selected one after the other without replacing any of the pieces of paper. **dependent**

20. Each of six people guess the total number of points in a basketball game. They write down the guess without telling what it is. **independent**

Solve each problem.

21. Suppose five points in a plane represent towns that are connected by roads. Starting at any one town, how many different routes are there so that you visit each town exactly once? **120 routes**

22. How many different batting orders does a baseball team of nine players have if the pitcher bats last? **40,320 orders**

23. The letters r, s, t, v, and w are to be used to form 5-letter passwords for an office security system. How many passwords can be formed if the letters can be used more than once in any password? **3125 passwords**

24. In Ohio, a standard license plate has three letters followed by three digits. The first letter cannot be I or O, and the last digit cannot be zero. How many possible plates are there? **14,601,600 license plates**

25. How many ways can six books be arranged on a shelf if one of the books is a dictionary and it must be on an end? **240 ways**

26. For a particular model of truck, a truck dealer offers 5 versions of that model, 16 body colors, and 8 truck cab colors. How many different possibilities are available for that model? **640**

In this text, when referring to a deck of cards, we mean a standard deck of 52 cards.

27. Suppose five cards are drawn from a standard deck of cards. Three are red and two are black.

  a. How many possibilities are there for this hand? **10,140,000**

  b. Suppose exactly one of the black cards is a face card. Now how many possibilities are there? *A face card is a jack, queen, or king.* **1,872,000**

Critical Thinking

28. See students' work; the problem should involve finding numbers whose product is 2340.

28. Write a problem that uses the fundamental counting principle and has an outcome of 2340. Explain in your own words how you went about finding a problem to fit the criteria.

Applications and Problem Solving

29. 210 combinations

29. Golf A golf club manufacturer makes irons with 7 different shaft lengths, 3 different grips, 5 different lies, and 2 different club head materials. How many different combinations are offered?

Practice Masters, p. 84

 NAME_____ DATE_____

Practice

Student Edition
Pages 708–713

The Counting Principle

Solve.

1. A briefcase lock has 3 rotating cylinders, each containing 10 digits. How many numerical codes are possible? **1000**

2. A golf club manufacturer makes irons with 7 different shaft lengths, 3 different grips, 5 different lies, and 2 different club head materials. How many different combinations are offered? **210**

3. There are five different routes that a commuter can take from her home to the office. In how many ways can she make a round trip if she uses a different route coming than going? **20**

4. In how many ways can the 4 call letters of a radio station be arranged if the first letter must be W or K and no letters repeat? **27,600**

5. How many 7-digit phone numbers can be formed if the first digit cannot be 0 or 1? **8,000,000**

6. How many 7-digit phone numbers can be formed if the first digit cannot be 0 or 1 and if no digit can be repeated? **483,840**

30. Linguistics An employee of the U.S. Public Health Service has organized a list of 30 words from which impressive-sounding 3-word phrases can be formed. If you choose one word at random from each of these three columns, you can make a distinctive phrase.

Column 1	Column 2	Column 3
balanced	digital	capability
compatible	incremental	concept
functional	logistical	contingency
integrated	management	flexibility
optional	monitored	hardware
parallel	organizational	mobility
responsive	policy	options
synchronized	reciprocal	programming
systematized	third-generation	projection
total	transitional	time-phase

a. How many different 3-word phrases can be made using this list? **1000**

b. How many different 3-word phrases could be made if each column had only five words in it? **125**

c. How many different 3-word phrases could be made if each column had sixteen words in it? **4096**

d. Write a sentence using the 3-word phrase that you think sounds most impressive. **Answers will vary.**

31. Dining Antonio's Italian Cuisine offers an Early Bird Special for customers who dine before 6:30 P.M. This offer includes an appetizer, a soup, and an entree, all for $6.95. There are 4 choices of appetizers, 3 soups, and 8 entrees. How many different meals are available under this offer? **96 meals**

32. Solve a Simpler Problem How many 5-digit numbers exist between 65,000 and 69,999 if each number has no repeated digits? **1344**

33. Communication When determining call letters for a radio station, the first letter must be either W or K. If no letters repeat, how many ways can the 4 call letters of a station be arranged? **27,600 ways**

Mixed Review

34. Expand $(2m - 3)^6$. (Lesson 11-8)

35. Solve $\ln 9.5 = \ln (e^{0.2x})$. (Lesson 10-5) **11.26**

34. $64m^6 - 576m^5 + 2160m^4 - 4320m^3 + 4860m^2 - 2916m + 729$

36. Money The average American household income is $36,000. Of this average, $11,160 is spent on housing, $6480 on transportation, $5400 on food, $3240 on personal insurance and pensions, $2160 on clothing and services, $1800 on health care, and $5760 on miscellaneous expenses. Make a circle graph to display this information. (Lesson 9-5) **See margin.**

37. Graph $f(x) = x^6$. (Lesson 8-3) **See margin.**

38. $\left(0, 2\frac{1}{2}\right)$

38. Electronics The headlights on a car contain parabolic reflectors. A special lightbulb with two filaments is used to produce the high and low beams. The filament placed at the focus produces the high beam, and the low beam is produced by the filament placed off the focus. If the equation of the parabola that is the cross section of the reflector is $y = \frac{1}{10}x^2$, where should the filament for the high beam be placed? (Lesson 7-2)

39. Simplify $\dfrac{\sqrt{3} + n\sqrt{6}}{4 - \sqrt{n}}$. (Lesson 5-6) $\dfrac{4\sqrt{3} + 4n\sqrt{6} + \sqrt{3n} + n\sqrt{6n}}{16 - n}$

Lesson 12-1 The Counting Principle **717**

Extension ▬▬▬

Reasoning Ask students how they would represent the arrangement of x different items. $x(x-1)(x-2) \ldots (1)$ or $x!$

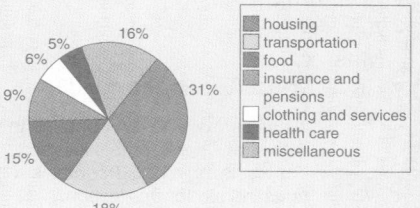

4 ASSESS

Closing Activity
Modeling Toss a coin and then roll a die. Record each outcome and then count the number of different possible outcomes. **12**

Additional Answers

36.

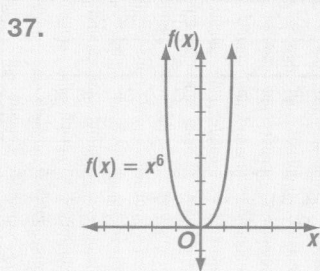

housing
transportation
food
insurance and pensions
clothing and services
health care
miscellaneous

37.

$f(x) = x^6$

Enrichment Masters, p. 84

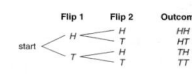

12-1 NAME _____ DATE _____
Enrichment Student Edition Pages 708-713

Tree Diagrams and the Power Rule

If you flip a coin once, there are two possible outcomes: heads showing (H) or tails showing (T). The tree diagram to the right shows the four (2^2) possible outcomes if you flip a coin twice.

Example 1: Draw a tree diagram to show all the possible outcomes for flipping a coin three times. List the outcomes.

There are eight (2^3) possible outcomes. With each extra flip, the number of outcomes doubles. With 4 flips, there would be sixteen (2^4) outcomes.

Example 2: In a cup there are a red, a blue, and a yellow marble. How many possible outcomes are there if you draw one marble at random, replace it, and then draw another?

There are nine (3^2) possible outcomes.

The Power Rule for the number of outcomes states that if an experiment is repeated n times, and if there are b possible outcomes each time, there are b^n total possible outcomes.

Find the total number of possible outcomes for each experiment. Use tree diagrams to help you.

1. flipping a coin 5 times 2^5
2. doing the marble experiment 6 times 3^6
3. flipping a coin 8 times 2^8
4. rolling a 6-sided die 2 times 6^2
5. rolling a 6-sided die 3 times 6^3
6. rolling a 4-sided die 2 times 4^2
7. rolling a 4-sided die 3 times 4^3
8. rolling a 12-sided die 2 times 12^2

Chapter 12 **717**

NCTM Standards: 1–4, 12

Instructional Resources

- Study Guide Master 12-2
- Practice Master 12-2
- Enrichment Master 12-2
- Assessment and Evaluation Masters, p. 324
- Real-World Applications, 31

 Transparency 12-2A contains the 5-Minute Check for this lesson; **Transparency 12-2B** contains a teaching aid for this lesson.

Recommended Pacing	
Standard Pacing	Day 2 of 12
Honors Pacing	Day 2 of 10
Block Scheduling*	Day 1 of 6 (along with Lesson 12-1)

 *For more information on pacing and possible lesson plans, refer to the *Block Scheduling Booklet*.

1 FOCUS

 5-Minute Check
(over Lesson 12-1)

1. How many 3-digit numbers can be formed from the digits 1, 3, 5, 7, and 9 if repetitions are allowed?
$5 \cdot 5 \cdot 5 = 125$

2. How many different combinations of 3-person groups can be formed using 13 people? (No one is in more than one group.)
$13 \cdot 12 \cdot 11 = 1716$

3. If the first letter of a radio station's name must be *W* or *K*, how many combinations of 4 letters are possible? Assume that each letter of the alphabet can occur only once in each station's name.
27,600

Permutations

 **What** YOU'LL LEARN

- To solve problems involving linear and circular permutations.

Why IT'S IMPORTANT

You can use permutations to solve problems involving retailing and cheerleading.

F Y I

Kinepolis in Brussels, Belgium, is the world's largest theater complex with 24 screens and a total seating capacity of 7000.

APPLICATION
Entertainment

Have you ever wondered why certain movies are shown at one theater but not at another? The selection of movies depends on what movies the film buyer purchases from a film distributor. The film buyer views all of the movies and then looks at the theaters in his or her area. The movies are selected based upon such things as the size and location of the theater, the clientele that frequents the theater, the type of movie, and the amount of money the movie will generate.

Suppose a film buyer has 11 films for an 8-screen theater. Since the screens are in rooms with different seating capacities, the film buyer must decide on which screens to show the movies, based on expected ticket sales. How many different arrangements are there for the 8 screens to show the 11 movies?

One way to organize this problem is to make a *decision chart*. Ask yourself, "How many decisions do I need to make in this problem?" In this case, the theater has 8 movie screens, so there are eight decisions to be made, a decision for each screen.

$$\underset{\substack{\text{1st} \\ \text{Screen}}}{\underline{11}} \quad \underset{\substack{\text{2nd} \\ \text{Screen}}}{\underline{10}} \quad \underset{\substack{\text{3rd} \\ \text{Screen}}}{\underline{9}} \quad \underset{\substack{\text{4th} \\ \text{Screen}}}{\underline{8}} \quad \underset{\substack{\text{5th} \\ \text{Screen}}}{\underline{7}} \quad \underset{\substack{\text{6th} \\ \text{Screen}}}{\underline{6}} \quad \underset{\substack{\text{7th} \\ \text{Screen}}}{\underline{5}} \quad \underset{\substack{\text{8th} \\ \text{Screen}}}{\underline{4}}$$

After one of the 11 movies is chosen for the first screen, there are only 10 movie choices left for the second screen, and so on, until the eighth screen is filled. The number of choices for each movie screen is affected by the choice of the previous screen, so these are dependent events. There are $11 \cdot 10 \cdot 9 \cdot 8 \cdot 7 \cdot 6 \cdot 5 \cdot 4$ or 6,652,800 movie arrangements possible.

The eight movie screens in the example above are in a certain order. When a group of objects or people are arranged in a certain order, the arrangement is called a **permutation.** In a permutation, the *order* of the objects is very important. The arrangement of objects in a line is called a **linear permutation**.

Notice that $11 \cdot 10 \cdot 9 \cdot 8 \cdot 7 \cdot 6 \cdot 5 \cdot 4$ is the product of the first 8 factors of 11!. We can write an equivalent expression in terms of 11!.

$$11 \cdot 10 \cdot 9 \cdot 8 \cdot 7 \cdot 6 \cdot 5 \cdot 4 = 11 \cdot 10 \cdot 9 \cdot 8 \cdot 7 \cdot 6 \cdot 5 \cdot 4 \cdot \frac{3 \cdot 2 \cdot 1}{3 \cdot 2 \cdot 1}$$

$$= \frac{11 \cdot 10 \cdot 9 \cdot 8 \cdot 7 \cdot 6 \cdot 5 \cdot 4 \cdot 3 \cdot 2 \cdot 1}{3 \cdot 2 \cdot 1} \text{ or } \frac{11!}{3!}$$

Notice that the denominator of $\frac{11!}{3!}$ is the same as $(11 - 8)!$.

Sleepless in Seattle

Aladdin

F Y I

The top five movies of all time and their revenues as of April, 1994, are as follows.

1. *E.T.,* $228.2 million
2. *Jurassic Park,* $208.0 million
3. *Star Wars,* $193.8 million
4. *Return of the Jedi,* $169.2 million
5. *Batman,* $150.5 million

The number of ways to arrange 11 things taken 8 at a time is written as $P(11, 8)$. Thus, $P(n, r)$ is read, "the permutation of n objects taken r at a time" and is defined in the following manner.

Definition of $P(n, r)$	The number of permutations of n objects taken r at a time is defined as follows. $$P(n, r) = \frac{n!}{(n - r)!}$$

Example **A group of 5 teens went to the movie theater. They found a row with 7 empty seats. How many different ways can the teens be seated in the row?**

You must find the number of permutations of 7 seats, taken 5 at a time.

$$P(n, r) = \frac{n!}{(n - r)!}$$

$$P(7, 5) = \frac{7!}{(7 - 5)!} \qquad n = 7, r = 5$$

$$= \frac{7 \cdot 6 \cdot 5 \cdot 4 \cdot 3 \cdot 2 \cdot 1}{2 \cdot 1} \text{ or } 2520$$

There are 2520 ways five teens can be seated in a row of 7 seats.

TECHNOLOGY Tips

You can use a graphing calculator to find permutations. The nPr function can be found by pressing [MATH] [◄] 2.

In Example 1, you may have noticed that the factors of $(n - r)!$ are contained in $n!$. Instead of writing all the factors of each term, you could also have evaluated the expression in the following way.

$$\frac{7!}{(7 - 5)!} = \frac{7 \cdot 6 \cdot 5 \cdot 4 \cdot 3 \cdot 2!}{2!} \qquad \frac{2!}{2!} = 1$$

$$= 7 \cdot 6 \cdot 5 \cdot 4 \cdot 3 \text{ or } 2520$$

Example **2** **APPLICATION Retailing**

A manager of Camelot Music is reducing some of the prices of CDs for a special promotion. She has 5 pop/rock CDs, 4 rap CDs, and 4 jazz CDs that she wants to arrange on a shelf for this sale. How many ways can these CDs be arranged on a shelf if they are ordered according to type?

First consider how many different ways each type of CD can be arranged.

The pop/rock CDs can be arranged in $P(5, 5)$ or 5! different ways.

The rap CDs can be arranged in $P(4, 4)$ or 4! different ways.

The jazz CDs can be arranged in $P(4, 4)$ or 4! different ways.

Remember, by definition, $0! = 1$.

(continued on the next page)

Motivating the Lesson

Situational Problem List or have students name all the schools that are in your district's league for athletic events. Ask students to name the different possible combinations for first- and second-place teams in the league if each team begins the season with an equal chance to be first or second.

2 TEACH

Teaching Tip When defining $P(n, r)$, point out to students that it is sometimes written $_nP_r$.

Technology Tip
Remind students that $_nP_r$ is not a list operation. The order of keystrokes to compute

$_4P_3$ is 4 [MATH] [◄] 2 3 [ENTER].

In-Class Examples

For Example 1
How many ways can 3 books be placed on a shelf if they are chosen from a selection of 8 different books? 336

For Example 2
How many ways can 2 geometry, 4 geography, 5 history, and 3 physics books be arranged on a shelf by subject? 829,440

Teaching Tip Example 2 assumes that each of the various types of CDs is different.

Now consider how many ways the 3 types can be arranged. There are 3 types of CDs, so $P(3, 3) = 3!$ ways.

The total number of ways the CDs can be arranged is the product of these four permutations.

$$5! \cdot 4! \cdot 4! \cdot 3! = 414,720$$

There are 414,720 ways to arrange the CDs according to type.

The Hawaiian language is made up of only 12 letters, the vowels a, e, i, o, u and the consonants h, k, l, m, n, p, and w. The five letters in the word *aloha* can be arranged in $P(5, 5)$ or 5! ways. However, some of these 5! or 120 arrangements look the same because there are two *a*'s. If you label the *a*'s as a_1 and a_2, then a_1loha_2 is different from a_2loha_1. However, without subscripts, the two arrangements look the same. To account for this in the final count of possible permutations, divide $P(5, 5)$ or 120 by the number of arrangements of *a*.

The two *a*'s can be arranged in $P(2, 2)$ or 2! ways.

$$\frac{P(5, 5)}{P(2,2)} = \frac{5!}{2!}$$
$$= \frac{5 \cdot 4 \cdot 3 \cdot 2!}{2!} \text{ or } 60$$

Thus, there are 60 ways to arrange the letters in *aloha*.

When some objects are alike, use the rule below to find the number of permutations of those objects.

Permutations with Repetitions	The number of permutations of n objects of which p are alike and q are alike is $\frac{n!}{p!q!}$.

This rule can be extended for any number of objects that are repeated.

Example **How many different ways can the letters of the word *PERPENDICULAR* be arranged?**

The first and fourth letter, P, are the same.

The second and fifth letter, E, are the same.

The third and last letter, R, are the same.

So, you need to find the permutations of 13 letters, of which 3 sets of letters are the same. You must divide 13! by 2! 3 times.

$$\frac{13!}{2!2!2!} = \frac{13 \cdot 12 \cdot 11 \cdot 10 \cdot 9 \cdot 8 \cdot 7 \cdot 6 \cdot 5 \cdot 4 \cdot 3 \cdot 2!}{2!2!2!} \text{ or } 778,377,600$$

There are 778,377,600 ways to arrange the letters.

Sometimes in a permutation the arrangement of objects is in a circle. This is called a **circular permutation**.

Example **4** The disk jockey at station WXYZ is setting up some of the music she will be playing during her shift. She is loading a CD tray with 6 different compact discs. How many different ways can these discs be arranged on the tray?

Each tray is a circle. Let a represent the first disc, let b represent the second disc, and so on. Three possible arrangements of the compact discs are shown below.

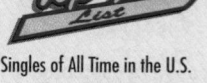

Singles of All Time in the U.S.

1. *White Christmas*, Bing Crosby, 1942

2. *I Want to Hold Your Hand*, Beatles, 1964

3. *Hound Dog/Don't Be Cruel*, Elvis Presley, 1956

4. *It's Now or Never*, Elvis Presley, 1960

5. *I Will Always Love You*, Whitney Houston, 1992

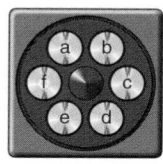 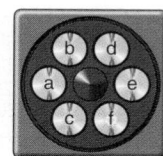 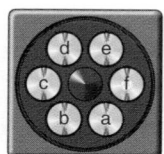

How does the arrangement change as the first tray is turned? Which arrangement is *really* different from the other two?

When 6 different objects are placed in a line, there are 6! or 720 arrangements of the 6 objects taken 6 at a time. However, when the 6 objects are arranged in a circle, some of the arrangements are alike. These arrangements fall into groups of 6. Once an arrangement is determined, the other five members of the group are formed by rotating the circle. Then you can rearrange the items and another group of 6 is formed. Thus, the total number of *really* different arrangements of 6 objects around a circle is $\frac{1}{6}$ of the total number of arrangements in a line.

$$\frac{1}{6} \cdot 6! = \frac{6 \cdot 5 \cdot 4 \cdot 3 \cdot 2 \cdot 1}{6}$$
$$= 5 \cdot 4 \cdot 3 \cdot 2 \cdot 1$$
$$= 5! \text{ or } 120 \qquad \textit{Note that } 5! = (6-1)!.$$

There are $(6 - 1)!$ or 120 possible arrangements of the discs.

When n objects are arranged in a circle, use the following rule to find the number of permutations of those objects.

Circular Permutations	If n distinct objects are arranged in a circle, then there are $\frac{n!}{n}$ or $(n - 1)!$ permutations of the objects around the circle.

Suppose n objects are in a circular arrangement, but the position of the objects is related to a fixed point. Rotating the circle will relate a different object to the fixed point and will make a new arrangement of the objects. Because of this fixed point, the permutations are now considered linear. The number of permutations for a circular permutation with a fixed point is $n!$.

In-Class Example

For Example 4

a. Eight toppings for pizza are placed on a revolving tray. How many ways can these toppings be arranged? **5040**

b. How many ways can 3 men and 3 women be seated alternately at a round table? **12**

Teaching Tip Remind students that circular arrangements are reflections only when the objects can actually be turned over. Therefore, the arrangement described in Example 4 could not be a reflection.

The three top-grossing concerts as of December, 1993, are as follows.

1. Michael Jackson; $12,543,400; 5 days; Mexico City

2. Bette Midler; $11,119,320; 5 weeks; New York City

3. Madonna; $8,927,703; 3 days; Mexico City

Teaching Tip Show students how the formula used in Example 5 is determined. For a linear permutation, $P(n, r) = \frac{n!}{(n-r)!}$.

If $r = n$, then $P(n, n) = \frac{n!}{(n-n)!}$.

By definition, $0! = 1$.

So $P(n, n) = n!$.

In-Class Example

For Example 5
There are four people seated at a round table. One of them is seated at a stationary computer terminal. How many arrangements are possible? **24**

Teaching Tip Emphasize that the permutations are linear if circular arrangements are in relation to a fixed point.

3 PRACTICE/APPLY

Check for Understanding
Exercises 1–13 are designed to help you assess your students' understanding through reading, writing, speaking, and modeling. You should work through Exercises 1–6 with your students and then monitor their work on Exercises 7–13.

Error Analysis
Order of operations is important when simplifying $(n - r)!$.
Example: $(5 - 3)! \neq 5! - 3!$ and $5! - 3! \neq 2!$

Additional Answers
4. In a circular permutation, there is no reference point for the exact beginning of the arrangement.
5. Denise; the number of linear permutations is 8! or 40,320, and the number of circular permutations is 7! or 5040.

Example  **5**

APPLICATION
Construction

A cul-de-sac is a street closed at one end.

Let each circle represent an empty cul-de-sac ready to be developed into 5 different lots with each lot having a different home design. Let the labeled points represent the 5 home designs. Let the arrow represent the home nearest the opening to the cul-de-sac. How many arrangements are possible?

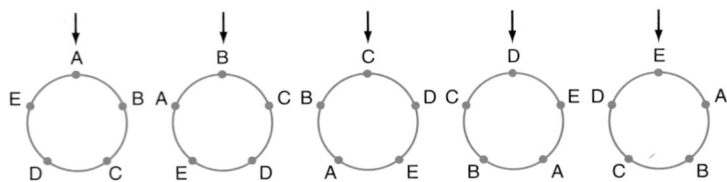

These arrangements can be considered different because in each one, a different house sits next to the cul-de-sac opening. Thus, there are $P(5, 5)$ or 5! arrangements relative to a fixed point.

$$5! = 5 \cdot 4 \cdot 3 \cdot 2 \cdot 1 \text{ or } 120$$

There are 120 possible arrangements.

Suppose three keys are placed on a key ring. How many different arrangements are possible? Using the formula for circular permutations, it appears that there are at most $(3 - 1)!$ or 2 different arrangements of keys on the ring. But what happens if the first key ring arrangement is turned over?

When the key ring is turned over, the first arrangement becomes the second arrangement. Then there is really only one arrangement of the three keys. These two arrangements are **reflections** of each other. As a result, there are only half as many arrangements when reflections are possible.

$$\frac{(3 - 1)!}{2} = \frac{2 \cdot 1}{2} \text{ or } 1$$

Reflections also occur in linear arrangements. Suppose five juniors are being inducted into the National Honor Society. Sitting on one side of the gym are Marisa, Brandon, Tyree, Cheryl, and Haley, in order from left to right. However, an observer on the opposite side of the gym sees the order from left to right as Haley, Cheryl, Tyree, Brandon, and Marisa. If you were asked how many possible arrangements of the students there were for these students, your answer would be half of 5! or 60 arrangements.

CHECK FOR UNDERSTANDING

Communicating Mathematics

Study the lesson. Then complete the following. 4–5. See margin.

1. **Explain** what 6! means. $6 \cdot 5 \cdot 4 \cdot 3 \cdot 2 \cdot 1$

2. **Discuss** the important characteristic that a counting problem has to have in order to classify it as a permutations problem. Order is important.

3. There are five different letters and each letter is used once.

3. **Explain** why 5! gives the correct solution to the possible number of ways to arrange the letters in the word *VIDEO*.

4. **Explain** the difference between a linear permutation and a circular permutation.

5. **You Decide** Brad says there are *twice* as many ways for 8 people to stand in a line than there are for them to stand around in a circle. Denise says there are *eight times* as many ways. Who is correct? Explain your answer.

722 *Chapter 12 Investigating Discrete Mathematics and Probability*

Reteaching

Using Cooperative Learning
Separate the class into groups. Give each group an expression used to find a permutation. First, have them make up their own word problem that uses that expression to find the answer.

Then have them solve it and see if it makes sense. Example: $\frac{(5 - 1)!}{2}$

They would describe a circular permutation that is also a reflection. 12

MODELING MATHEMATICS

6. **Model** the meaning of $P(4, 4)$ using colored counters or candies. What is its value? **24**

Guided Practice

How many different ways can the letters of each word be arranged?

7. MATH **24**   8. FUN **6**

9. SEE **3**   10. PENCIL **720**

Determine whether each arrangement is *linear* or *circular*. Then determine if it is also a *reflection* and find the number of arrangements.

11. linear, not reflection; 362,880

12. circular, not reflection; 120

13b. $\dfrac{52}{\text{winner}} \dfrac{51}{\text{1st}} \dfrac{50}{\text{2nd}} \dfrac{49}{\text{3rd}}$

11. batting order of a baseball team with 9 players

12. a group of 6 children playing Ring Around The Rosy

13. **Pageants** The Miss Teen USA pageant has fifty-two contestants. The judges choose the next Miss Teen USA and her three runners-up.
   a. Is order important? Why? **See margin.**
   b. Make a decision chart for this problem.
   c. In how many different ways can the next Miss Teen USA and her three runners-up be chosen? **6,497,400 ways**

EXERCISES

Practice

How many different ways can the letters of each word be arranged? **25. 453,600**

 A

14. LEVEL **30**   15. FLORIDA **5040**   16. POP **3**

17. PARALLEL **3360**   18. ALASKA **120**   19. FREE **12**

20. PEGGY **60**   21. STUDY **120**   22. MISSISSIPPI **34,650**

23. ALGEBRA **2520**   24. ESSENTIAL **90,720**   25. REPETITION

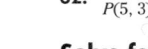

Determine whether each arrangement is linear or circular. Then determine if it is also a reflection and find the number of arrangements.

26. ten beads on a necklace with a clasp

27. a basketball huddle of 5 players **circular, not reflection; 24**

28. six nickels in a circle on a table **circular, not reflection; 120**

29. eight pizza toppings placed on a revolving tray

30. seven shoppers in line at a checkout counter

31. six charms on a bracelet with no clasp **circular, reflection; 60**

B

26. linear, reflection; 1,814,400

29. circular, not reflection; 5040

30. linear, not reflection; 5040

Evaluate each expression.

32. $\dfrac{P(6, 4)}{P(5, 3)}$ **6**   33. $\dfrac{P(6, 3)P(4, 2)}{P(5, 2)}$ **72**   34. $\dfrac{P(12, 6)}{P(12, 3)P(8, 2)}$ **9**

Solve for n.

C

35. $P(n, 4) = 40[P(n - 1, 2)]$ **8**   36. $P(n, 4) = 3[P(n, 3)]$ **6**

37. $n[P(5, 3)] = P(7, 5)$ **42**   38. $208P(n, 2) = P(16, 4)$ **15**

Assignment Guide

Core: 15–39 odd, 40, 41, 43, 45, 47–55
Enriched: 14–40 even, 41–55

For **Extra Practice,** see p. 904.

The red A, B, and C flags, printed only in the Teacher's Wraparound Edition, indicate the level of difficulty of the exercises.

Additional Answer

13a. Order is important since each place winner receives a different cash prize and awards.

Study Guide Masters, p. 85

NAME_____ DATE_____

12-2 Student Editic
Study Guide Pages 714–72

Permutations

An arrangement of things in a certain order is called a **permutation.** In a permutation, the *order* is important. The arrangement of n objects in a line is called a **linear permutation.** The number of linear permutations of n objects taken r at a time is denoted by the symbol $P(n, r)$. If all of the objects are clearly distinguishable, then changing even one object in a permutation leads to a different permutation. The value of $P(n, r)$ is given by the formula

$$P(n, r) = \frac{n!}{(n - r)!}$$

If not all the objects are distinguishable, that fact must be taken into account in counting the permutations. For example, if p of the objects are indistinguishable and another q of the objects are also indistinguishable, then the number of distinguishable linear permutations of the n objects is $\frac{n!}{p!q!}$.

Example: Five people line up for a photo. Among them are two sets of dressed-alike identical twins. How many of the possible lineups would be distinguishable by the photographer?
   The number of distinguishable lineups is $\frac{5!}{2!2!}$, or 30.

If n distinct objects are arranged in a circle, they form a **circular permutation.** There are only $(n - 1)!$ circular permutations of n objects. If n objects are in a circular arrangement, but the position of the objects is related to a fixed point, then there are $n!$ permutations. Because of the fixed point, the permutations are now considered linear.

How many different ways can the letters of each word be arranged?

1. MONDAY 2. MOM 3. STEREO
   720   3   360
Solve.

4. How many ways can 8 members of a family be seated side-by-side in a movie theater if the father is seated on the aisle? 5040
5. How many ways can 3 books be placed on a shelf if chosen from a selection of 7 different books? 210
6. The bride and groom and 8 members of the bridal party are seated around a round table. The bride and groom have specific seats. In how many ways can the bridal party be seated around the table? 40,320
7. How many ways can 6 charms be placed on a bracelet that has no clasp? 60
8. How many ways can 6 charms be placed on a bracelet if there is a clasp? 360
9. How many ways can 8 campers be seated around a campfire? 5040

39. Geometry How many ways can 6 points be labeled *A* through *F* on the circle at the right, relative to its *x*-intercept? **720 ways**

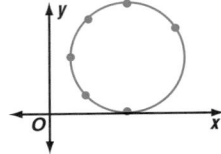

Critical Thinking

40. According to the writers of the CD-ROM game *Trivial Pursuit*, you can play chess 25×10^{120} times without repeating the same total moves. Explain how you could get that result. List all the factors you need to consider. You may want to draw a diagram to help explain your thinking.

40. See students' work.

Applications and Problem Solving

41. Cheerleading Seven football cheerleaders printed large letters on cards that spell out their school's mascot, COUGARS. Each card has one letter on it and each cheerleader is supposed to hold up one card. At half-time they realize that someone has mixed up the cards. How many ways are there to arrange the cards? **5040 ways**

42. Emergency Service The table at the right shows common medical emergency telephone numbers for six countries. How many other 3-digit emergency telephone numbers are possible if any digit can be repeated? **994**

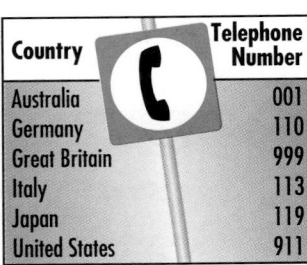

Country	Telephone Number
Australia	001
Germany	110
Great Britain	999
Italy	113
Japan	119
United States	911

Source: *Health, 1994*

43. Photography A photographer is taking a picture of a bride and a groom together with 6 attendants. How many ways can he arrange the 8 people in a line if the bride and groom stand in the middle? **1440 ways**

Where U.S. Consumers Buy PCs

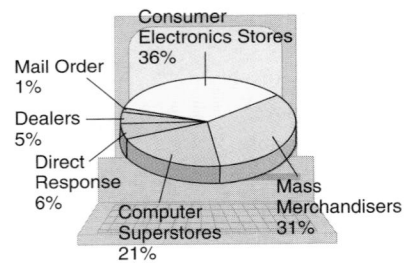

Consumer Electronics Stores 36%

Mail Order 1%

Dealers 5%

Direct Response 6%

Computer Superstores 21%

Mass Merchandisers 31%

44. Statistics Look at the circle graph at the left.
  a. How many different arrangements of the wedges are possible? **120 arrangements**
  b. How many different arrangements are possible if the largest section of the graph stays in the same place? **120 arrangements**

45. Electricity Eight switches are connected on a circuit so that if any one or more of the switches are closed, the light will go on. How many combinations of open and closed switches exist that will permit the light to go on? **255 combinations**

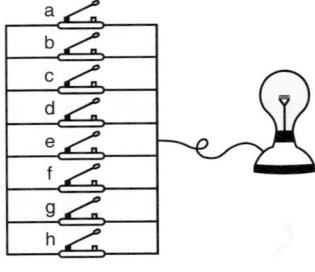

Tech Prep

EMS Worker Students who are interested in emergency medical services may wish to do further research on the information provided in Exercise 42 and explore the potential growth of this career. For more information on tech prep, see the *Teacher's Handbook.*

Practice Masters, p. 85

NAME _____ DATE _____

Student Edition Pages 714–721

12-2 Practice

Permutations

How many different ways can the letters of each word be arranged?

1. CANADA **120**

2. ILLINI **60**

3. ANNUALLY **5040**

4. MEMBERS **1260**

Evaluate each expression.

5. $\frac{8!}{6!}$ **56**

6. $P(8, 6)$ **20,160**

7. $\frac{P(7, 5)}{P(4, 3)}$ **105**

8. $\frac{P(6, 5)P(4, 4)}{P(5, 1)P(9, 2)}$ **48**

9. $\frac{P(8, 3)}{7!}$ $\frac{1}{15}$

10. $\frac{P(7, 4) \cdot P(5, 3)}{P(6, 5)}$ **70**

Solve.

11. A photographer is taking a picture of a bride and groom together with 6 attendants. How many ways can he arrange the 8 people in a line if the bridge and groom stand in the middle? **1440**

12. How many ways can 3 identical pen sets and 5 identical watches be given to 8 graduates if each receives one item? **56**

13. How many ways can 4 charms be arranged on a bracelet that has no clasp? **3**

14. How many ways can 4 charms be arranged on a bracelet that has a clasp? **12**

15. How many ways can 5 men and 5 women be seated alternately at a round table? **1152**

16. How many ways can Laura and her 6 friends be seated around a table if Laura sits at the head of the table? **720**

46. Puzzles Refer to the puzzle below.

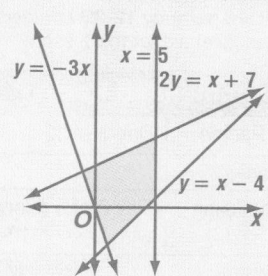

a. How many ways are there to arrange the letters in each of the first two scrambled words? **120 ways**

b. How many ways are there to arrange the letters in each of the last two scrambled words? **720 ways; 360 ways**

c. Unscramble each of the words to find the letters in the circles. How many ways are there to arrange these letters? **60 ways**

d. Unscramble the circled letters to find the answer to the riddle. **ORDER**

e. How many different seating arrangements are possible for the jurors? **12! or 479,001,600 arrangements**

Mixed Review

47. How many ways can you have 50¢ if you have at least one quarter? (Lesson 12–1) **13 ways**

48. Find the sum of $\frac{2}{3} + \frac{1}{3} + \frac{1}{6} + \cdots$. (Lesson 11–5) $\frac{4}{3}$

49. Biology An amoeba divides into two amoebas once every hour. How long would it take for a single amoeba to become a colony of 4096 amoebas? (Lesson 10–2) **12 hours**

50. If y varies inversely as x, and $y = -8$ when $x = 1.5$, find x when $y = -3$. (Lesson 9–2) **4**

51. State the number of possible positive real zeros, negative real zeros, and imaginary zeros of $f(x) = 3x^5 - 8x^2 + 1$. (Lesson 8–4) **2 or 0; 1; 2 or 4**

52. Animals The fastest-recorded physical action of any living thing is the wing beat of the common midge. This tiny insect normally beats its wings at a rate of 133,000 times per minute. How many times would the midge beat its wings in an hour at this rate? Write your answer in scientific notation. (Lesson 5–1) 7.98×10^6

53. Find $\begin{bmatrix} 3 & -1 \\ 2 & 5 \end{bmatrix} \cdot \begin{bmatrix} 4 & -1 & -2 \\ -3 & 5 & 4 \end{bmatrix}$. (Lesson 4–3) $\begin{bmatrix} 15 & -8 & -10 \\ -7 & 23 & 16 \end{bmatrix}$

54. Graph the system of inequalities and name the vertices of the polygon formed. Then find the maximum and minimum values of $f(x, y) = 4x - 3y$ for the region. (Lesson 3–5)

$x \le 5$

$y \ge -3x$

$2y \le x + 7$

$y \ge x - 4$ **(1, −3), (−1, 3), (5, 6), (5, 1); 17; −13; See margin for graph.**

55. Write a mathematical expression for the verbal expression *the theater can hold no more than 400 people.* (Lesson 1–6) $p \le 400$

Extension

Communication Have students verbalize a solution process for the following problem. Then have them solve it.

The reserve tennis team has four fewer players than does the varsity team. Two players from each team are chosen, in order, to play a match. The number of arrangements of varsity players is three times the number of arrangements of reserve players. How many players are on each team?

$P(n, 2) = 3[P(n - 4, 2)]$; **10 varsity, 6 reserve players**

4 ASSESS

Closing Activity

Writing Have students write a short paragraph explaining in their own words the difference between a linear and a circular permutation.

Chapter 12, Quiz A (Lessons 12-1 and 12-2), is available in the *Assessment and Evaluation Masters,* p. 324.

Additional Answer

54.

Enrichment Masters, p. 85

12-2

NAME _____ DATE _____

Enrichment

Student Edition
Pages 714–721

Street Networks: Finding All Possible Routes

A section of a city is laid out in square blocks. Going north from the intersection of First Avenue and First Street, the avenues are 1st, 2nd, 3rd, and so on. Going east, the streets are numbered in the same way.

Factorials can be used to find the number, $r(e, n)$, of different routes between two intersections. The formula is shown at the right. The number of streets going east is e; the number of avenues going north is n.

$$r(e, n) = \frac{[(e - 1) + (n - 1)]!}{(e - 1)!\,(n - 1)!}$$

The following problems examine the possible routes from one location to another. Assume that you never use a route that is unnecessarily long. Assume that $e \ge 1$ and $n \ge 1$.

Solve each problem.

1. List all the possible routes from 1st Street and 1st Avenue to 4th Street and 3rd Avenue. Use ordered pairs to show the routes, with street numbers first, and avenue numbers second. For example, each route starts at (1, 1) and ends at (4, 3).

(1, 1) − (2, 1) − (3, 1) − (4, 1) − (4, 2) − (4, 3)
(1, 1) − (2, 1) − (3, 1) − (3, 2) − (4, 2) − (4, 3)
(1, 1) − (2, 1) − (3, 1) − (3, 2) − (3, 3) − (4, 3)
(1, 1) − (2, 1) − (2, 2) − (3, 2) − (4, 2) − (4, 3)
(1, 1) − (2, 1) − (2, 2) − (3, 2) − (3, 3) − (4, 3)
(1, 1) − (2, 1) − (2, 2) − (2, 3) − (3, 3) − (4, 3)
(1, 1) − (1, 2) − (2, 2) − (3, 2) − (4, 2) − (4, 3)
(1, 1) − (1, 2) − (2, 2) − (3, 2) − (3, 3) − (4, 3)
(1, 1) − (1, 2) − (2, 2) − (2, 3) − (3, 3) − (4, 3)
(1, 1) − (1, 2) − (1, 3) − (2, 3) − (3, 3) − (4, 3)

2. Use the formula to compute the number of routes from (1, 1) to (4, 3). There are 4 streets going east and 3 avenues going north. $\frac{(3 + 2)!}{3!2!} = 10$

3. Find the number of routes from 1st Street and 1st Avenue to 7th Street and 6th Avenue. $\frac{(6 + 5)!}{6!5!} = 462$

NCTM Standards: 1–4, 12

Instructional Resources

- Study Guide Master 12-3
- Practice Master 12-3
- Enrichment Master 12-3
- Graphing Calculator Masters, p. 12

Transparency 12-3A contains the 5-Minute Check for this lesson; **Transparency 12-3B** contains a teaching aid for this lesson.

Recommended Pacing	
Standard Pacing	Day 3 of 12
Honors Pacing	Day 3 of 10
Block Scheduling*	Day 2 of 6 (along with Lesson 12-4)

*For more information on pacing and possible lesson plans, refer to the *Block Scheduling Booklet*.

1 FOCUS

5-Minute Check
(over Lesson 12-2)

1. How may different ways can the letters of the word *PEOPLE* be arranged?
$\frac{6!}{2!2!} = 180$

2. Evaluate $\frac{P(9, 5) \cdot P(6, 3)}{P(4, 4)}$. 75,600

3. How many ways can 8 books be arranged on a shelf?
40,320

4. How many ways can 6 people be seated relative to each other at a round table?
120

5. How many ways can 6 people be arranged around a circular table if 2 people must be seated next to each other? 48

12-3

Combinations

What YOU'LL LEARN

- To solve problems involving combinations.

Why IT'S IMPORTANT

You can use combinations to solve problems involving social studies and the lottery.

APPLICATION
Lottery

How would you like to win $27 million? That's how much the Virginia state lottery was worth in 1992 when a group of Australian investors tried to buy every combination of numbers— all 7.1 million of them! The investors won by buying 5.6 million sets of numbers, one of which was the winner. For each ticket, they chose 6 numbers out of 44. The order of the numbers selected was not important, only the set of the numbers themselves. An arrangement, or listing, in which order is not important, is called a **combination.** *You will verify the number of combinations in Exercise 44.*

Let's look at a simpler combination. Suppose a lottery was held in which each person chose three numbers from the numbers 0–9 and the order did not matter. Since order is not important, we are counting combinations, *not* permutations, of 10 objects taken 3 at a time. The combination of 10 objects taken 3 at a time is written as $C(10, 3)$. You already know how to count $P(10, 3)$.

$$P(10, 3) = \frac{10!}{(10 - 3)!}$$
$$= 10 \cdot 9 \cdot 8 \text{ or } 720$$

But these permutations are not all different combinations. This group includes (1, 4, 8), (1, 8, 4), (4, 1, 8), (4, 8, 1), (8, 1, 4), and (8, 4, 1). Since these are all the same combination, we are counting this combination, and all others as well, 3! or 6 times when we calculate $P(10, 3)$. Thus, combinations should be counted as follows.

$$C(10, 3) = \frac{P(10, 3)}{3!}$$
$$= \frac{10!}{(10 - 3)! \cdot 3!} \qquad P(10, 3) = \frac{10!}{(10 - 3)!}$$
$$= \frac{10!}{7! \cdot 3!} \text{ or } 120$$

The three numbers can be chosen from the 10 numbers in 120 ways.

Notice that 7! and $(10 - 3)!$ are equivalent. This suggests the following definition.

Definition of $C(n, r)$	The number of combinations of *n* distinct objects taken *r* at a time is defined as follows. $$C(n, r) = \frac{n!}{(n - r)!r!}$$

726 Chapter 12 *Investigating Discrete Mathematics and Probability*

The basic difference between a permutation and a combination is that order is considered in a permutation and order is *not* considered in a combination.

Example 1

The principal at Cobb County High School wants to start a peer mediation group to work with discipline problems. He needs to narrow down his choice to six students from a group of nine students. How many ways can a group of six be selected?

In this case, order does not matter. The combination of nine objects or people taken six at a time is written as $C(9, 6)$.

$$C(9, 6) = \frac{9!}{(9 - 6)! \cdot 6!} \qquad C(n, r) = \frac{n!}{(n - r)! r!}$$

$$= \frac{9!}{3! \cdot 6!} \text{ or } 84$$

The six peer mediation members can be chosen from the nine students in 84 ways.

TECHNOLOGY Tips

You can use a graphing calculator to find combinations. The nCr function can be found by pressing [MATH] ◄ 3.

Example 2

A basket contains 4 acorn squash, 5 gourds, and 8 pumpkins. How many ways can 2 acorn squash, 1 gourd, and 2 pumpkins be chosen?

This involves the product of three combinations, one for each type of item.

$C(4, 2)$ Two of 4 acorn squash will be chosen.
$C(5, 1)$ One of 5 gourds will be chosen.
$C(8, 2)$ Two of 8 pumpkins will be chosen.

We can multiply the combinations because of the fundamental counting principle.

$$C(4, 2) \cdot C(5, 1) \cdot C(8, 2) = \frac{4!}{(4 - 2)! 2!} \cdot \frac{5!}{(5 - 1)! 1!} \cdot \frac{8!}{(8 - 2)! 2!}$$

$$= \frac{4!}{2! 2!} \cdot \frac{5!}{4! 1!} \cdot \frac{8!}{6! 2!}$$

$$= \frac{4 \cdot 3 \cdot 2!}{2 \cdot 2!} \cdot \frac{5 \cdot 4!}{4!} \cdot \frac{8 \cdot 7 \cdot 6!}{6! \cdot 2}$$

$$= 3 \cdot 5 \cdot 8 \cdot 7 \text{ or } 840$$

You can also use a scientific calculator to evaluate the expression.

Enter: 4 [x!] [×] 5 [x!] [×] 8 [x!] [÷] [(]
2 [x!] [×] 2 [x!] [×] 4 [x!] [×]
6 [x!] [×] 2 [x!] [)] [=] *840*

There are 840 different ways to choose the items.

Motivating the Lesson

Hands-On Activity Ask one student to choose three students from the class to be on a relay team with him or her. Ask the same student to select three other students from the class to work with him or her on a class project. Elicit student responses as to why order could be important in the first choice and is not important in the second choice.

Teaching Tip When defining $C(n, r)$, point out to students that it is sometimes written as $_nC_r$.

Technology Tip Remind students that $_nC_r$ is not a list operation. The order of keystrokes to compute $_5C_3$ is

5 [MATH] [◄] 3 3 [ENTER].

2 TEACH

In-Class Examples

For Example 1
How many committees of 5 students can be selected from a class of 25? **53,130**

For Example 2
A box contains 12 black and 8 green marbles. How many ways can 3 black and 2 green marbles be chosen? **6160**

Teaching Tip Emphasize that dividing by $r!$ in solving for $C(n, r)$ eliminates the importance of order. Otherwise, the formula would be the same as that for linear permutations.

Teaching Tip In Example 2, point out that $\frac{4!}{2! 2!} = \frac{4 \cdot 3}{2}$ and $\frac{8!}{6! 2!} = \frac{8 \cdot 7}{2}$. Then ask students to identify a pattern.

In-Class Examples

For Example 3
Given 7 distinct points in a plane, how many line segments will be drawn if every pair of points is connected? **21**

For Example 4
From a deck of 52 cards, how many 5-card hands can be selected to meet the following conditions?

a. has at least 3 aces **4704**
b. has exactly 3 aces **4512**

Teaching Tip In Example 4, combinations may be used to select the suits rather than $P(4, 2)$. There are $C(4, 1)$ or 4 ways to first choose the suit that will have 3 cards. Then there are $C(3, 1)$ or 3 ways to choose the suit that will have 2 cards. So $4 \cdot 3 = 12$, which equals $P(4, 2)$.

There are over 350 variations of card games for one player, called solitaire games. In most of these games, success depends mostly on the initial arrangement of the cards.

3 PRACTICE/APPLY

Check for Understanding
Exercises 1–14 are designed to help you assess your students' understanding through reading, writing, speaking, and modeling. You should work through Exercises 1–5 with your students and then monitor their work on Exercises 6–14.

Error Analysis
Have students simplify factorials in steps in order to understand the properties of factorials.

Additional Answer

1. A permutation is an arrangement in which the order is important. Order is not important in a combination.

Example ③ **Find the total number of diagonals that can be drawn in an octagon.**

Geometry

Each diagonal has two endpoints. Suppose one has endpoints *B* and *G*. Since segments *BG* and *GB* are the same, order is not important. The combination of 8 points taken 2 at a time gives the total number of segments connecting any two points.

$C(8, 2) = \frac{8!}{6!2!}$ or 28

However, 28 is not our answer. Since eight of the segments connecting the points are sides of the octagon, you must subtract 8 from 28, the number of combinations.

Thus, the total number of diagonals in an octagon is $28 - 8$ or 20.

Some applications can involve *both* permutations and combinations. The example below involves the use of a standard deck of 52 playing cards. Remember, there are four suits, each suit containing 13 cards.

Example ④ **Eight cards are drawn from a standard deck of 52 cards. How many 8-card hands having 5 cards of one suit and 3 cards of another suit can be formed?**

Cards and card games probably originated in China between the 7th and 10th centuries. They were brought to Europe by Venetian explorers in the 13th century. The 52-card modern deck derives from the French in the 15th century.

First consider how many ways 2 suits can be chosen from 4 suits. Since a different number of cards is being selected from each suit, order is important. Then consider the combinations possible with each suit.

$P(4, 2)$ — Select 2 suits from 4 suits.
$C(13, 5)$ — Select 5 cards from 13 cards in one suit.
$C(13, 3)$ — Select 3 cards from 13 cards in the other suit.

$P(4, 2) \cdot C(13, 5) \cdot C(13, 3) = \frac{4!}{2!} \cdot \frac{13!}{8!5!} \cdot \frac{13!}{10!3!}$
$= 12 \cdot 1287 \cdot 286$ or 4,416,984

There are 4,416,984 eight-card hands having 5 cards of one suit and 3 cards of another.

CHECK FOR UNDERSTANDING

Communicating Mathematics

Study the lesson. Then complete the following.   1, 3. See margin.

1. **Describe** the difference between a permutation and a combination.

2. **Write** an expression to represent the possible number of starting teams of five basketball players that can be formed from 11 players. $C(11, 5)$

4. Find the product of the two combinations, $C(4, 3)$ and $C(5, 2)$.

3. **Draw** a diagram to verify that the answer for Example 3 is 20 diagonals.

4. **Explain** how you would find out how many committees of 3 men and 2 women can be formed from a group of 4 men and 5 women.

728   Chapter 12   *Investigating Discrete Mathematics and Probability*

Additional Answer

3.

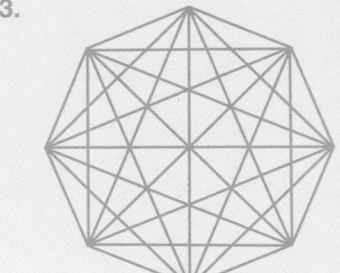

Reteaching

Using Discussion Orally give students problems involving combinations or permutations. Have students write down the expression that would be used to solve that problem and then discuss why it is one or the other. Discuss ways to distinguish between the two types of problems.

MATH JOURNAL

5. Your principal announces that everyone should buy a permutation lock for their lockers. Your friend leans over to you and says, "Doesn't she mean a combination lock?" How would you answer your friend? **The principal is mathematically correct because the order is important.**

Guided Practice

Determine whether each situation involves a permutation or a combination.

6. choosing a class president, vice president, and secretary   **permutation**

7. four tennis players from a group of nine   **combination**

8. eight toppings for ice cream   **combination**

Evaluate each expression.

9. $C(4, 2)$ **6**

10. $C(7, 2)$ **21**

11. $C(3, 2) \cdot C(8, 3)$ **168**

12. $C(8, 5) \cdot C(7, 3)$ **1960**

Solve each problem.   **13. 840 bouquets**

13. Floral Design   A bucket at DeSantis Florists contains 8 red tulips, 5 white daisies, and 4 yellow tulips. How many bouquets could be created so that each bouquet has 2 red tulips, 1 white daisy, and 2 yellow tulips?

14. Volleyball   How many starting volleyball teams of 6 members can be formed from a bench of 12 talented players?   **924 teams**

EXERCISES

Practice

Determine whether each situation involves a permutation or a combination.

15. a classroom seating chart   **permutation**

16. finding the diagonals of a polygon   **combination**

17. the batting order of the Pittsburgh Pirates   **permutation**

18. 10 books on a library shelf   **combination**

19. a hand of five cards from a deck of 52 cards   **combination**

20. a seven-person committee from your class   **combination**

21. first, second, and third chairs for six clarinets in a band   **permutation**

22. six outfits chosen from fourteen outfits to be modeled   **combination**

Evaluate each expression.

23. $C(5, 2)$ **10**

24. $C(10, 5)$ **252**

25. $C(8, 4)$ **70**

26. $C(24, 21)$ **2024**

27. $C(12, 7)$ **792**

28. $C(10, 4)$ **210**

29. $C(12, 4) \cdot C(8, 3)$ **27,720**

30. $C(9,3) \cdot C(6, 2)$ **1260**

31. $C(10, 4) \cdot C(5, 3)$ **2100**

32. $C(8,2) \cdot C(5,1) \cdot C(4, 2)$ **840**

INTEGRATION
Geometry

33. Suppose there are 8 points in a plane such that no three points are collinear. How many distinct triangles could be formed with 3 of these points as vertices?   **56 triangles**

34. A circle has nine randomly-placed points. In how many different ways can you form each polygon listed below?

a. triangle   **84**   **b.** octagon   **9**   **c.** pentagon   **126**

d. quadrilateral   **126**   **e.** decagon   **none**   **f.** hexagon   **84**

Assignment Guide

Core: 15–45 odd, 47–54
Enriched: 16–38 even, 39–54

For **Extra Practice,** see p. 904.

The red A, B, and C flags, printed only in the Teacher's Wraparound Edition, indicate the level of difficulty of the exercises.

Study Guide Masters, p. 86

12-3

NAME_____   DATE_____

Study Guide

Student Edition
Pages 722–727

Combinations

A **combination** is a selection of objects where the order is not important. (Remember that order *is* important in a permutation.) The number of combinations of n objects taken r at a time is denoted by the symbol $C(n, r)$. To find $C(n, r)$, use the following formula:

$$C(n, r) = \frac{n!}{(n - r)!r!}$$

Example: From a group of 8 men and 6 women, how many committees of 4 men and 3 women can be formed? Order is not considered.

$$C(8, 4) \cdot C(6, 3) = \frac{8!}{(8 - 4)!4!} \cdot \frac{6!}{(6 - 3)!3!}$$

$$= \frac{8 \cdot 7 \cdot 6 \cdot 5 \cdot 4 \cdot 3 \cdot 2 \cdot 1}{4 \cdot 3 \cdot 2 \cdot 1 \cdot 4 \cdot 3 \cdot 2 \cdot 1} \cdot \frac{6 \cdot 5 \cdot 4 \cdot 3 \cdot 2 \cdot 1}{3 \cdot 2 \cdot 1 \cdot 3 \cdot 2 \cdot 1}$$

$$= 70 \cdot 20 \text{ or } 1400$$

Determine whether each situation involves a permutation or a combination.

1. arrangement of 10 books on a shelf
permutation

2. selection of a committee of 3 from 10 people
combination

3. a hand of 6 cards from a deck of 52 cards
combination

4. arrangement of 8 people around a circular table
permutation

5. a subset of 12 elements contained in a set of 26
combination

6. a guest list of 3 friends that your family has said you can invite to dinner
combination

Solve.

7. There are 15 different books. How many groups of 6 books can be selected?
455

8. From a group of 10 men and 12 women, how many committees of 5 men and 6 women can be formed?
232,848

9. How many tennis teams of 6 players can be formed from 14 players without regard to position played?
3003

10. From a standard deck of 52 cards, how many ways can 5 cards be drawn?
2,598,960

Additional Answer

39. $C(n, r) = \dfrac{n!}{(n-r)!r!}$ or

$\dfrac{n!}{(n-r)!} \cdot \dfrac{1}{r!}$; $P(n, r) = \dfrac{n!}{(n-r)!}$

By substituting, $C(n, r) =$

$P(n, r) \cdot \dfrac{1}{r!}$ or $\dfrac{P(n, r)}{r!}$.

Solve for n.

35. $C(n, 5) = C(n, 7)$ 12

36. $C(11, 8) = C(11, n)$ 3 or 8

37. $C(14, 3) = C(n, 11)$ 14

38. $C(n, 7) = C(n, 2)$ 9

Critical Thinking

39. Prove $C(n, r) = \dfrac{P(n, r)}{r!}$.   **See margin.**

Applications and Problem Solving

40. School   The biology class is preparing for its final exam. From a class of 22 girls and 16 boys, how many study groups of 2 girls and 3 boys can be formed?   **129,360 study groups**

41. Committees   A five-member recycling committee is being formed from a group of 8 freshmen and 10 sophomores. How many committees can be formed given each condition?
a. all freshmen   56
b. all sophomores   252
c. 1 freshman, 4 sophomores   1680
d. 3 freshmen, 2 sophomores   2520

42. Solve a Simpler Problem   Ten points are marked on a circle. How many line segments can be drawn between any two of the points?   **45 line segments**

43. Business   A box of Anthony Thomas candy contains 9 dark chocolate creams, 6 milk chocolate creams, and 4 milk chocolates with nuts. How many ways can 5 candies be selected to meet each condition?   **d. 2808**
a. all milk chocolate creams   6
b. all nuts   0
c. all dark chocolate creams   126
d. 2 of one kind, 3 of another
e. 2 nuts, 2 milk chocolate creams, 1 dark chocolate cream   810

44. $\dfrac{44!}{(44-6)!6!}$ or

7,059,052 combinations

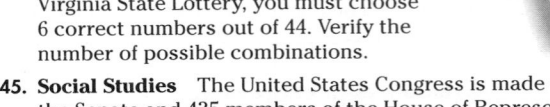

44. Lottery   Refer to the application at the beginning of the lesson. To win the Virginia State Lottery, you must choose 6 correct numbers out of 44. Verify the number of possible combinations.

45. Social Studies   The United States Congress is made up of 100 members of the Senate and 435 members of the House of Representatives. How many five-member senatorial committees are possible?   **75,287,520 senatorial committees**

46. World Cultures   *Hanafuda* is a popular card game invented in Japan in the eighteenth century. The deck is made up of 12 suits, with each suit having four cards depicting a plant related to one of the 12 months of the year. How many 7-card hands can be formed so that 3 are from one suit and 4 are from another?
$P(12, 2) \cdot C(4, 3) \cdot C(4, 4) = 528$ ways

Month	Plant
January	Pine tree
February	Plum tree
March	Cherry tree
April	Wisteria
May	Iris
June	Peony
July	Bush clover
August	Pampas grass
September	Chrysanthemum
October	Maple
November	Willow
December	Paulownia tree

Practice Masters, p. 86

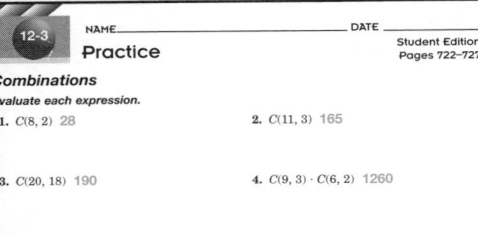

12-3   NAME_____ DATE _____
Practice   Student Edition Pages 722–727

Combinations
Evaluate each expression.
1. $C(8, 2)$ 28
2. $C(11, 3)$ 165
3. $C(20, 18)$ 190
4. $C(9, 3) \cdot C(6, 2)$ 1260

Solve for x.
5. $C(x, 7) = C(x, 2)$ 9
6. $C(11, 2) = C(x, 9)$ 11

Solve.
7. How many 4-person bobsled teams can be chosen from a group of 9 athletes?   126
8. From a dessert cart in a fine restaurant, customers are allowed to pick 3 desserts from the 10 that are displayed. How many combinations are possible?   120

9. How many diagonals does a polygon with 12 sides have?   54
10. How many 5-sided polygons can be formed by joining any 5 of 11 points located on a circle?   462

An urn contains 8 white, 6 blue, and 9 red balls. How many ways can 6 balls be selected to meet each condition?
11. All balls are red.   84
12. Three are blue, 2 are white, and 1 is red.   5040

13. Two are blue, and 4 are red.   1890
14. Exactly 4 balls are white.   7350

Extension

Reasoning   Find the value of *n* in each problem.
$C(3, 0) + C(3, 1) = C(n, 1)$ 4
$C(5, 1) + C(5, 2) = C(n, 2)$ 6
$C(4, 3) + C(4, 4) = C(n, 4)$ 5
$C(6, 2) + C(6, 3) = C(n, 3)$ 7
Then write a formula for the general relationship shown in the problems.
$C(n, r) + C(n, r + 1) = C(n + 1, r + 1)$

47. Community Service As a community project, the members of the Spanish Club at Lakota High School are preparing circular vegetable trays to be delivered to homebound senior citizens in their neighborhood. Each tray is made up of 5 items: broccoli, carrots, celery, green peppers, and cucumbers. How many different ways can these items be arranged on a tray if each item must fit in its own section? (Lesson 12–2) **120**

48. Find $\sum_{s=1}^{4} 2s\left(-\frac{1}{2}\right)^2.$ (Lesson 11–4) **5**

49. Finance Graham's grandparents started a savings account for him when he was born. They invested $100 in an account with 8% annual interest compounded annually. (Lesson 10–1)

   a. Write an exponential equation to express the amount of money in the account on Graham's nth birthday. $y = 100(1.08)^n$

   b. How much is in the account on his 16th birthday? **$342.59**

50. $x^2 + 9x + 14 = 0$

50. Write a quadratic equation that has roots -2, -7. (Lesson 6–5)

51. 1.20×10^{25} molecules

51. Chemistry The mole is a standard unit of measure in chemistry. One mole of any compound contains 6.02×10^{23} molecules. How many molecules are in 19.9 moles of ammonia? (Lesson 5–1)

52. Graph the system of equations and state its solution. (Lesson 3–1)

$x + y = 1$

$3x - 2y = -7$ **$(-1, 2)$; See margin for graph.**

53. $m = \frac{3}{4}$; $b = \frac{5}{2}$

53. Find the slope and y-intercept of the graph of $3x - 4y = -10$. (Lesson 2–4)

54. Solve $|x + 4| = 5$. (Lesson 1–5) **-9, 1**

Mathematics and SOCIETY

"Fowl" Advertising

The article below appeared in *Teacher Magazine* in March, 1995.

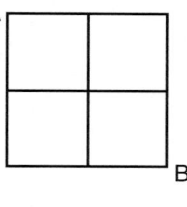

A NATIONAL RESTAURANT CHAIN THAT boasts about its tasty chicken is eating crow after a high school mathematics class cried foul over a television ad. The ad shows football star Joe Montana standing at the counter at a Boston Chicken restaurant puzzling over side-dish choices; an announcer says that more than 3,000 combinations can be created by choosing three of the . . . 16 side-dish offerings. But Bob Swaim, a math teacher at Souderton Area High School near Philadelphia, and his class did the math and found that the correct number was 816. "We goofed," says . . . a spokesman for Boston Chicken. "Apparently we didn't listen to our high school math teachers." The company has, however, listened to Swaim and corrected its ads. For their part, the students were awarded free meals and $500 to expand the math menu at Souderton. ∎

2–4. See students' work.

1. How do you think the students got the number 816? **See margin.**

2. When you hear celebrities, media persons, or people in authority quote numbers or statistics, do you assume they must be correct? What factors might be preventing you from listening more critically and raising more questions?

3. Why do you think advertisers often use famous people and celebrities in ads for their products?

4. Have you ever bought a product because of a celebrity who helped to advertise it? Why or why not?

Mathematics and SOCIETY

The diagram below represents a simple street map. The goal is to get from point A to point B. Without backtracking, how many paths are there from A to B? Have students draw a tree of paths. **11**

Answer for Mathematics and Society

1. $C(16, 3) + C(16, 2) \cdot C(2, 1) + C(16, 1) = 560 + 240 + 16$ or **816**

4 ASSESS

Closing Activity

Speaking Have students compare and contrast linear permutations and combinations.

Additional Answer

52.

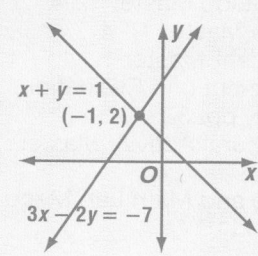

$x + y = 1$
$(-1, 2)$
$3x - 2y = -7$

Enrichment Masters, p. 86

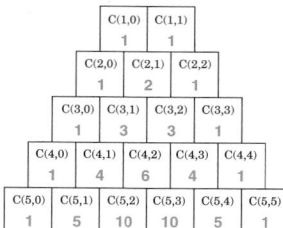

12-3   NAME _____ DATE _____
Student Edition Pages 722–727
Enrichment

Combinations and Pascal's Triangle

Pascal's triangle is a special array of numbers invented by Blaise Pascal (1623–1662). The values in Pascal's triangle can be found using the combinations shown below.

1. Evaluate the expression in each cell of the triangle.

2. The pattern shows the relationship between $C(n, r)$ and Pascal's triangle. In general, it is true that $C(n, r) + C(n, r + 1) = C(n + 1, r + 1)$. Complete the proof of this property. In each step, the denominator has been given.

12-4 Probability

Instructional Resources

- Study Guide Master 12-4
- Practice Master 12-4
- Enrichment Master 12-4
- Assessment and Evaluation Masters, pp. 323–324
- Multicultural Activity Masters, p. 23
- Science and Math Lab Manual, pp. 111–116

 Transparency 12-4A contains the 5-Minute Check for this lesson; **Transparency 12-4B** contains a teaching aid for this lesson.

Recommended Pacing

Standard Pacing	Day 4 of 12
Honors Pacing	Day 4 of 10
Block Scheduling*	Day 2 of 6 (along with Lesson 12-3)

 *For more information on pacing and possible lesson plans, refer to the *Block Scheduling Booklet.*

1 FOCUS

 ### 5-Minute Check
(over Lesson 12-3)

Determine whether each situation represents a permutation or a combination.

1. a batting order in baseball
   permutation
2. a committee of 4 men and 5 women, chosen from 8 men and 7 women **combination**
3. Evaluate $C(6, 2) \cdot C(4, 3)$. **60**
4. How many different combinations of committees of 4 men and 3 women can be formed from a group of 7 men and 8 women?
   $35 \cdot 56 = 1960$
5. How many diagonals does a convex octagon have? **20**

What YOU'LL LEARN

- To find the probability of an event, and
- to determine the odds of success and failure of an event.

Why IT'S IMPORTANT

You can use probability to solve problems involving darts, genetics, and music.

APPLICATION
Earthquakes

On January 17, 1994, an earthquake registering 6.7 on the Richter scale struck Northridge in the densely-populated San Fernando Valley of Los Angeles. The earthquake, which lasted only 40 seconds, left 20,000 people homeless and caused approximately $20 billion in damages. Geologists say there is an 86% chance that a quake of even greater magnitude will strike the southern part of California sometime in the next three decades. What are the chances that such an earthquake will hit within 15 years? within 5 years? We can use **probability** to measure the chances of an event occurring.

Mathematicians often use coin tossing and dice rolling to illustrate probability. When you toss a coin, there are only two possible outcomes— heads or tails. A desired outcome is called a **success**. Any other outcome is called a **failure**.

Probability of Success and of Failure	If an event can succeed in *s* ways and fail in *f* ways, then the probabilities of success, $P(s)$, and of failure, $P(f)$, are as follows. $$P(s) = \frac{s}{s+f} \qquad P(f) = \frac{f}{f+s}$$

What does the sum of s and f represent?

If an event cannot fail, it has a probability of 1. If an event cannot succeed, it has a probability of 0. The probability of an event occurring is always between 0 and 1, inclusive. In fact, the sum of $P(s)$ and $P(f)$ is always equal to 1. Thus, they are called **complements**. So if $P(s) = \frac{1}{5}$, then $P(f) = 1 - \frac{1}{5}$ or $\frac{4}{5}$. This property is often used in finding the probability of events.

Example **A bag of M&M's® contains 12 red, 11 yellow, 5 green, 6 orange, 5 blue, and 16 brown candies. What is the probability that if you choose an M&M from the bag without looking, or *at random*, you will choose a yellow M&M?**

The term at random means that an outcome is chosen without any preference.

The probability of choosing a yellow M&M is written $P(yellow)$.

There are 11 ways to choose a yellow M&M, and there are $12 + 5 + 6 + 5 + 16$ or 44 ways *not* to choose a yellow M&M. So, $s = 11$ and $f = 44$.

Like any ratio, probability can be expressed as a fraction, decimal, or percent.

$$P(yellow) = \frac{s}{s+f} \qquad \textit{Replace s with 11 and f with 44.}$$
$$= \frac{11}{11 + 44}$$
$$= \frac{11}{55} \text{ or } \frac{1}{5}$$

The probability of selecting a yellow M&M is $\frac{1}{5}$ or 20%.

Alternative Learning Styles

Visual Circle graphs are excellent aids in visualizing probabilities. Answers to many problems and examples can be converted to circle graphs. Example 1 can be represented by the circle graph at the right.

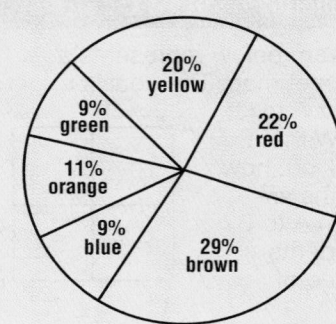

Many people enjoy playing games where players of equal skill have the same chance of winning.

MODELING MATHEMATICS

Games of Chance

A *fair game* is one in which each player has an equal chance of winning. In an *unfair game*, players do *not* have an equal chance of winning. In the game *Scissors, Paper, Stone*, the winner is decided by the following rules.

- scissors cut paper
- paper wraps stone
- stone breaks scissors

If both players pick the same object, the round is a draw.

Your Turn

a. Play 27 rounds of *Scissors, Paper, Stone* with a partner. Record the number of times each player wins.   **See students' work.**

b. How many different outcomes are possible?   **9**

g. $\frac{1}{9}, \frac{2}{3}, \frac{2}{9}$

c. How many ways can you win?   **3 ways**

d. How many ways can your partner win?   **3 ways**

e. Is *Scissors, Paper, Stone* a fair game? Explain.
Yes; each player has an equally likely chance of winning.

h. No; the outcomes are not equally likely.

In a different version of *Scissors, Paper, Stone*, there are 3 players. If all 3 players match, player A gets a point; if 2 players match, player B gets a point; and if none of the players match, player C gets a point.

f. Play 27 rounds of this version of *Scissors, Paper, Stone* with two other people. Record the number of times each player wins.   **See students' work.**

g. What is the probability that A will win? B? C?

h. Is this a fair game? Explain.

The counting methods you used in finding permutations and combinations are often used in determining probability.

Example **2** Suppose Miguel draws 5 cards from a standard deck of 52 cards. What is the probability that his hand contains 2 cards of one suit and 3 cards of another suit?

First, find how many 5-card hands meet these conditions.

$P(4, 2)$ Select 2 suits among 4. Order is important since different numbers of cards are to come from each suit.

$C(13, 2)$ Select 2 cards from a suit containing 13 cards.

$C(13, 3)$ Select 3 cards from the other suit.

Now use the counting principle.

$P(4, 2) \cdot C(13, 2) \cdot C(13, 3) = \frac{4!}{2!} \cdot \frac{13!}{11!2!} \cdot \frac{13!}{10!3!}$ or 267,696

So, the number of successes is 267,696.

Now find the total number of possible 5-card hands.

$C(52, 5) = \frac{52!}{47!5!}$ or 2,598,960

There are 2,598,960 ways to choose a 5-card hand, so $s + f = 2,598,960$.

$\frac{s}{s+f} = \frac{267,696}{2,598,960}$ or about 0.103   *Use a calculator.*

The probability of drawing a 5-card hand with 2 cards of one suit and 3 cards of another suit is about 10%.

Lesson 12–4 Probability **733**

GLENCOE Technology

Interactive Mathematics Tools Software

This multimedia software provides an interactive lesson by observing the probability of an event in several examples. A **Computer Journal** gives students an opportunity to write about what they have learned.

For Windows & Macintosh

Motivating the Lesson
Hands-On Activity Toss a coin. Without revealing the result, ask students how likely the result is to be heads. Have students explain their reasoning.

2 TEACH

MODELING MATHEMATICS Students can use a simple table to model the two-person version of the game.

Player B / Player A	scissors	paper	stone
scissors	draw	A	B
paper	B	draw	A
stone	A	B	draw

In-Class Examples

For Example 1
A bag contains 6 white, 3 blue, and 7 green marbles. If one marble is chosen at random, what is the probability of each event?

a. Marble is white. $\frac{3}{8}$

b. Marble is not green. $\frac{9}{16}$

For Example 2
Suppose three letters are selected from the word *arrangements*. Find the probability of randomly selecting three consonants.
$\frac{14}{55} \approx 0.255$

Teaching Tip Emphasize that the terms *success* and *failure* refer only to whether a specific outcome happens or not and have no further meaning in this context. The terms can be confusing when a success refers to what normally may be considered a failure, such as a team losing a ball game.

Teaching Tip The terms *odds* and *probability* are frequently used incorrectly as interchangeable terms. Be sure students know the difference between odds and probability.

In-Class Examples

For Example 3
Find the odds of the following events if two distinguishable dice are tossed.

a. dice total 7 1:5 or 1 to 5

b. at least one 2 appears 11:25 or 11 to 25

For Example 4
Three stuffed animals are to be chosen randomly from a group of 3 bears, 6 tigers, and 4 lions. Find the odds of each selection.

a. 1 bear, 1 tiger, and 1 lion 6:143

b. 3 bears 1:286

Teaching Tip In Example 4, point out that $C(6, 2)$ is the number of successes and $C(5, 2)$ is the total number of trials. The combination concept is merely a way to compute the successes and the total numbers of trials.

Color blindness is also called *daltonism*. The red-green deficiency is referred to as *dichromatic vision*. A rare form where the individual sees only shades of gray is called *achromatic vision*.

Another way to measure the chance of an event occurring is with **odds**. The odds of an event can be expressed as the ratio of successes to failures.

Definition of Odds	The odds of the successful outcome of an event can be expressed as the ratio of the number of ways it can succeed to the number of ways it can fail. **Odds in favor** = number of successes : number of failures **Odds against** = number of failures : number of successes

Example 3

Genetics

About 8 million people in the United States have the red/green form of color blindness, which can neither be cured nor corrected.

Color blindness is the genetic inability to distinguish between certain colors. The most common form is a red-green deficiency, in which a person sees all colors in tones of yellow and blue. Eight out of 100 males and 1 out of 1000 females have some form of color blindness.
a. What are the odds of a male being color-blind?
b. What are the odds of a female being color-blind?

Color blindness test

a. Eight out of 100 males are color-blind. So the number of successes (being color-blind) is 8. The number of males who are not color-blind is 100 − 8 or 92. So the number of failures is 92.

odds of a male being color-blind = $s{:}f$
= 8:92 or 2:23

The odds of a male being color-blind are 2 to 23.

b. One out of 1000 females is color-blind. So the number of successes is 1. The number of females who are not color-blind is 1000 − 1 or 999. So the number of failures is 999.

odds of a female being color-blind = $s{:}f$
= 1:999

The odds of a female being color-blind are 1 to 999.

Sometimes you may have to use permutations and combinations when finding odds.

Example 4

A committee to organize the school prom has 6 seniors and 5 juniors. If a subcommittee of 4 students is selected at random to choose the music for the prom, what are the odds that it will contain 2 seniors and 2 juniors?

Since a committee is being formed, order is not important. Use combinations to find the odds.

There are $C(6, 2)$ ways to choose 2 seniors from 6 seniors. There are $C(5, 2)$ ways to choose 2 juniors from 5 juniors. Use the counting principle to find the number of successes (a senior or a junior).

$$C(6, 2) \cdot C(5, 2) = \frac{6!}{4!2!} \cdot \frac{5!}{3!2!} \text{ or } 150$$

So, the number of successes is 150.

Alternative Teaching Strategies

Reading Algebra Students must be careful when using the terms *outcome*, *event*, *experiment*, and *sample space*. Encourage them to define each term and clarify the distinction between *event* and *outcome*.

Now find the number of possible subcommittees of 4 people out of a group of 11 people.

$$C(11, 4) = \frac{11!}{7!4!} \text{ or } 330$$

The number of 4-person subcommittees that do not meet the conditions is $330 - 150$ or 180. Thus, the odds of selecting a subcommittee of 2 juniors and 2 seniors are 150:180 or 5:6.

CHECK FOR UNDERSTANDING

Communicating Mathematics

1. The chance that an event will happen.
2. No; the probability of an event can never be greater than 1.
5. Neither is right. The probability for both is $\frac{3}{8}$.

Study the lesson. Then complete the following.   3. 1:5

1. **Define** the term *probability*.
2. **Explain** whether or not $P(s)$ can equal $\frac{5}{4}$.
3. **State** the odds of getting a 4 when rolling a die.
4. **Determine** the odds that an event will *not* occur if the odds that the event *will* occur are 2:5.   5:2
5. **You Decide** LaToya says that if she tosses three coins, she can get exactly two heads. Donovan bets he could do something even harder—get exactly two heads if he tosses 4 coins. LaToya argues that it is *easier* to get two heads out of four. Who is right? Explain how you reached your conclusion.

6. **Assess Yourself** Describe an event in your life that has a probability of 1 and an event that has a probability of 0.   Answers will vary.

Guided Practice

State the odds of an event occurring, given the probability of the event.

7. $\frac{3}{4}$ 3:1   8. $\frac{2}{9}$ 2:7

State the probability of an event occurring, given the odds of the event.

9. 6:5 $\frac{6}{11}$ 10. 1:1 $\frac{1}{2}$

11. The probability of Cathy earning a college scholarship is $\frac{4}{5}$. What are the odds that she will *not* earn a scholarship?   1:4

12. $\frac{1}{10}$

12. **Genealogy** The odds that an American is of English ancestry are 1:9. What is the probability that an American is of English ancestry?

Suppose you select 2 letters at random from the word *Pacific*. Find each probability.

13. $\frac{1}{7}$ 14. $\frac{2}{7}$ 15. $\frac{4}{7}$

13. P(2 vowels)   14. P(2 consonants)   15. P(1 vowel, 1 consonant)

16. **Genetics** Find the probability of a couple having a left-handed child, given the following odds.

16a. $\frac{2}{3}$ 16b. $\frac{1}{7}$ 16c. $\frac{1}{17}$

   a. If both parents are left-handed, the odds are 2 to 1.
   b. If only one parent is left-handed, the odds are 1 to 6.
   c. If neither parent is left-handed, the odds are 1 to 16.

Reteaching

Using Alternative Methods An alternate solution to finding $P(s)$ involves finding $P(f)$ and then subtracting the result from 1.

Check for Understanding
Exercises 1–16 are designed to help you assess your students' understanding through reading, writing, speaking, and modeling. You should work through Exercises 1–6 with your students and then monitor their work on Exercises 7–16.

Error Analysis
Odds = $\frac{s}{f}$; $P(s) = \frac{s}{(s + f)}$;
$P(f) = \frac{f}{(s + f)}$.

When converting odds to probability, one must add the numerator and denominator to get the new denominator. When converting from probability to odds, one must subtract the numerator from the denominator to get either the new numerator or denominator, whichever the case may be.

Assignment Guide

Core: 17–47 odd, 49–57
Enriched: 18–40 even, 42–57
All: Self Test, 1–10

For **Extra Practice,** see p. 904.

The red A, B, and C flags, printed only in the Teacher's Wraparound Edition, indicate the level of difficulty of the exercises.

Study Guide Masters, p. 87

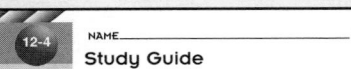

12-4	NAME_____ DATE_____

Study Guide Student Edition Pages 728–734

Probability

When a die is tossed, only six outcomes are possible. The die will show 1, 2, 3, 4, 5, or 6. The desired outcome is called a **success.** Any other outcome is called a **failure.** Probabilities and odds give you a way of gauging the chance of success or failure.

Probability of Success and Failure

Definition	Example
If an event can succeed in s ways and fail in f ways, then the **probability of success,** $P(s)$, and the **probability of failure,** $P(f)$, are as follows. $P(s) = \frac{s}{s+f}$ and $P(f) = \frac{f}{s+f}$	A bag contains 3 red marbles and 5 green marbles. If one marble is chosen at random, what is the probability that it will be red? P(red marble) = $\frac{s}{s+f}$ Drawing a red marble is a success. Drawing a green marble is a failure. $= \frac{3}{3+5}$ $= \frac{3}{8}$ The probability of selecting a red marble is $\frac{3}{8}$ or 0.375.

Odds

Definition	Example
The **odds** of the successful outcome of an event is expressed as the ratio of the number of ways it can succeed to the number of ways it can fail. Odds is the ratio of s to f or $\frac{s}{f}$.	What are the odds of drawing a 5 from a standard deck of 52 cards? Odds = $\frac{4}{48}$ A 5 can appear 4 ways. Other numbers can appear in 48 ways. The odds of getting a 5 are 4 to 48 (or 1 to 12).

One bag of candy gummy fish contains 15 red gummy fish, 10 yellow gummy fish, and 6 green gummy fish. Find the probability of each selection.

1. picking a red gummy fish
$\frac{15}{31}$

2. not picking a yellow gummy fish
$\frac{21}{31}$

3. picking a green gummy fish
$\frac{6}{31}$

4. not picking a red gummy fish
$\frac{16}{31}$

Solve.

5. In a bag there are 5 math questions and 4 science questions. Ardie picks a question from the bag. What are the odds of not picking a science question?
$\frac{5}{4}$

6. What are the odds that a person chosen at random got a passing grade on an algebra test if the scores were 3 A's, 4 B's, 10 C's, 2 D's, and 2 F's?
$\frac{19}{2}$

736 Chapter 12

EXERCISES

Practice

State the odds of an event occurring, given the probability of the event.

A

17. $\frac{1}{2}$ 1:1

18. $\frac{3}{8}$ 3:5

19. $\frac{11}{12}$ 11:1

20. $\frac{4}{7}$ 4:3

21. $\frac{1}{5}$ 1:4

22. $\frac{4}{11}$ 4:7

State the probability of an event occurring, given the odds of the event.

23. 6:1 $\frac{6}{7}$

24. 3:7 $\frac{3}{10}$

25. 5:6 $\frac{5}{11}$

26. 9:8 $\frac{9}{17}$

27. 1:8 $\frac{1}{9}$

28. 7:9 $\frac{7}{16}$

29a. $\frac{1}{4}$ 29b. $\frac{2}{5}$

29. A bag of Jelly-Belly® jelly beans contains 40 Polynesian Punch and 120 Blueberry jelly beans.

   a. If you draw one jelly bean out of the bag, find the probability that it is Polynesian Punch.

   b. If you add 40 Polynesian Punch jelly beans to the original bag and draw out a bean, what is the probability that it is Polynesian Punch?

   c. How many Polynesian Punch jelly beans do you need to add to the original bag to double the original probability of drawing a Polynesian Punch jelly bean? Explain.   **80 jelly beans**

Alma has 4 gray kittens and 7 white kittens. She randomly picks up 2 to give to her nieces. Find the probability of each selection. Then find the odds of that selection.

30. $\frac{6}{55}$, 6:49

B

30. P(2 gray kittens)

31. P(2 white kittens)

32. P(1 of each color)

31. $\frac{21}{55}$, 21:34

Sonia is moving and all of her CDs are mixed up in a box. Twelve CDs are rock, eight are jazz, and five are classical. If she reaches in the box and selects three at random, find each probability.

32. $\frac{28}{55}$, 28:27

33. P(all jazz) $\frac{14}{575}$

34. P(all rock) $\frac{11}{115}$

35. P(1 classical, 2 jazz) $\frac{7}{115}$

36. P(2 classical, 1 rock) $\frac{6}{115}$

37. P(1 classical, 1 jazz, 1 rock) $\frac{24}{115}$

38. P(2 jazz, 1 reggae)   **0**

INTEGRATION

Geometry

C

39. A square target 15 cm on a side, like the one shown at the right, contains 40 non-overlapping circles each 2 cm in diameter. Find the probability that a dart thrown at random hits one of the circles. $\frac{40\pi}{225}$ **or about 56%**

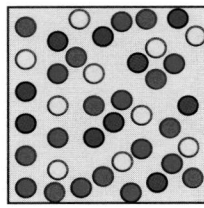

40b. $\frac{1}{36}$ 40c. $\frac{5}{12}$

40. A red, blue, and green die are rolled. The number on each die represents a side length of a triangle. So, 4, 2, 4 would represent an isosceles triangle.

   a. How many combinations can be rolled?   **216 combinations**

   b. What is the probability that you could build an equilateral triangle?

   c. What is the probability that you could build a nonequilateral isosceles triangle?

736 Chapter 12   Investigating Discrete Mathematics and Probability

Classroom Vignette

"An extension of Exercise 40 is to model the possible lengths of the sides of a triangle with different-colored pipe cleaners or straws. Have students determine the probability that a roll of the three dice will give lengths that form any triangle—equilateral, isosceles, or scalene."

Cindy Boyd
Abilene High School
Abilene, Texas

41. Find the probability that a point, chosen at random, belongs to the shaded region of the figure at the right. Write your answer in terms of π. $\dfrac{\pi - 1}{\pi}$

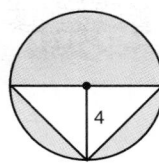

Critical Thinking

42. $\dfrac{2}{11}$; $k = 8, 10$

are factorable

Applications and Problem Solving

44. 1 person

42. What is the probability that $x^2 + kx + 16$ will factor if $0 \le k \le 10$ and k is an integer chosen at random?

43. Two octahedral, or eight-sided dice are rolled. What is the probability that the sum of the numbers on the dice equals 9? $\dfrac{1}{8}$

44. Music   In the summer of 1994, 250,000 people attended the Woodstock 25th-Anniversary Concert in Saugerties, New York. Approximately 5000 were treated for injuries, which was less than the insurance companies covering the concert had anticipated. Out of 50 randomly selected concert-goers, how many would you expect were treated for injuries?

45. Geography   A state is chosen at random from the 50 states. Find each probability.

45a. $\dfrac{1}{10}$

45c. $\dfrac{21}{50}$

46. $\dfrac{1}{13{,}983{,}816}$

47. $\dfrac{3}{16}$

a. P(next to the Pacific Ocean)
b. P(has at least one representative in the House of Representatives)   **1**
c. P(has at least five neighboring states)
d. P(has three U.S. senators)   **0**

46. Finance   The state of Florida has a Lotto drawing in which 6 numbers out of 49 are drawn at random. The proceeds from the lottery help to finance education in the state. What is the probability that you will win one of the weekly Lotto drawings if you buy one ticket?

47. Genetics   Guinea pigs have genes that can produce four types of fur: black short (BBSS, BBSs, BbSS, or BbSs), black long (BBss or Bbss), white short (bbSS or bbSs), or white long (bbss). Use the Punnett square below to find the probability that two parents with black short fur (both with BbSs fur genes) will produce an offspring that has white short fur.

	BS	**Bs**	**bS**	**bs**
BS	BBSS	BBSs	BbSS	BbSs
Bs	BBSs	BBss	BbSs	Bbss
bS	BbSS	BbSs	bbSS	bbSs
bs	BbSs	Bbss	bbSs	bbss

Tech Prep

Genetics Lab Technician Students who are interested in genetics may wish to do further research on the statistics given in Exercise 47 and explore the potential growth of this career. For more information on tech prep, see the *Teacher's Handbook*.

Extension

Problem Solving If two of the following statements are selected at random, what is P(both true)?   **0**

- $P(5, 2) + P(5, 3) = P(6, 3)$ false
- $C(5, 2) + C(5, 3) = C(6, 3)$ true
- The letters from the word *odds* can form 24 four-letter patterns.   false

Practice Masters, p. 87

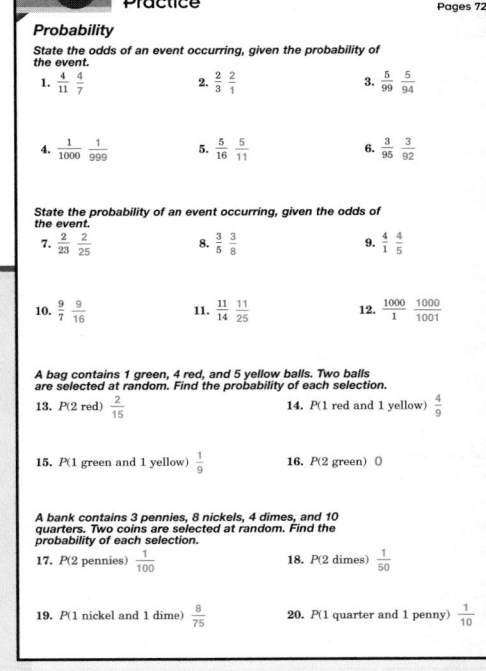

12-4   NAME _____   DATE _____
Practice   Student Editi
Pages 728–7

Probability

State the odds of an event occurring, given the probability of the event.

1. $\dfrac{4}{11}$ $\dfrac{4}{7}$ **2.** $\dfrac{2}{3}$ $\dfrac{2}{1}$ **3.** $\dfrac{5}{99}$ $\dfrac{5}{94}$

4. $\dfrac{1}{1000}$ $\dfrac{1}{999}$ **5.** $\dfrac{5}{16}$ $\dfrac{5}{11}$ **6.** $\dfrac{3}{95}$ $\dfrac{3}{92}$

State the probability of an event occurring, given the odds of the event.

7. $\dfrac{2}{23}$ $\dfrac{2}{25}$ **8.** $\dfrac{3}{5}$ $\dfrac{3}{8}$ **9.** $\dfrac{4}{1}$ $\dfrac{4}{5}$

10. $\dfrac{9}{7}$ $\dfrac{9}{16}$ **11.** $\dfrac{11}{14}$ $\dfrac{11}{25}$ **12.** $\dfrac{1000}{1}$ $\dfrac{1000}{1001}$

A bag contains 1 green, 4 red, and 5 yellow balls. Two balls are selected at random. Find the probability of each selection.

13. P(2 red) $\dfrac{2}{15}$ **14.** P(1 red and 1 yellow) $\dfrac{4}{9}$

15. P(1 green and 1 yellow) $\dfrac{1}{9}$ **16.** P(2 green)   0

A bank contains 3 pennies, 8 nickels, 4 dimes, and 10 quarters. Two coins are selected at random. Find the probability of each selection.

17. P(2 pennies) $\dfrac{1}{100}$ **18.** P(2 dimes) $\dfrac{1}{50}$

19. P(1 nickel and 1 dime) $\dfrac{8}{75}$ **20.** P(1 quarter and 1 penny) $\dfrac{1}{10}$

Closing Activity

Modeling Have students use models to show that $P(s) + P(f) = 1$.

Chapter 12, Quiz B (Lessons 12-3 and 12-4), is available in the *Assessment and Evaluation Masters,* p. 324.

Mid-Chapter Test (Lessons 12-1 through 12-4) is available in the *Assessment and Evaluation Masters,* p. 323.

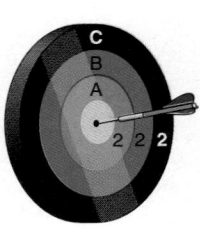

48. Darts According to the *Guinness Book of World Records*, John Lowe won a record prize of £102,000, or approximately $178,500, for his performance in a darts event in England on October 13, 1984. A dart, thrown at random, hits the dart board shown at the right. Find each probability. (*Hint:* What is the area of each ring?)

48a. $\frac{3}{16}$ 48b. $\frac{5}{16}$ 48c. $\frac{7}{16}$

a. $P(A)$ **b.** $P(B)$ **c.** $P(C)$

Mixed Review

49. Music The Groveport Community Children's Chorus now has six altos and eight sopranos. For the songs they are performing at the spring concert, they need two alto soloists and two soprano soloists. How many ways can these four soloists be selected at random?   (Lesson 12–3)   **420**

50. How many ways can 5 books be placed on a shelf?   (Lesson 12-2)   **120**

51. $\frac{1}{9}, \frac{1}{3}, 1$

51. Find the missing terms of __?__, __?__, __?__, 3, 9, 27.   (Lesson 11–3)

52. Approximate the real zeros of $g(x) = x^4 - 4x^2 + 3$ to the nearest tenth.   (Lesson 8–3)   **1, −1, 1.7, −1.7**

53. $f(m) = 4m^2 - 20m + 25$

53. Write $f(m) = (2m - 5)^2$ in quadratic form.   (Lesson 6–1)

54. Simplify $\sqrt[4]{5} + 6\sqrt[4]{5} - 2\sqrt[4]{5}$.   (Lesson 5–6)   **$5\sqrt[4]{5}$**

55. Which of the points, $(0, 0)$, $(1, 2)$, or $(-3, 1)$, satisfy the inequality $x + 2y \le 7$?   (Lesson 2–7)   **(0, 0), (1, 2), (−3, 1)**

56. Find the slope of a line that is perpendicular to the line whose equation is $x = 4y + 7$.   (Lesson 2–3)   **−4**

57. Solve $2 \le \frac{x}{3} + 5 \le 13$.   (Lesson 1–7)   **$-9 \le x \le 24$**

SELF TEST

1. At the Burger Bungalow, you can order your hamburger with or without cheese, with or without onions or pickles, and either rare, medium, or well-done.   (Lesson 12–1)
   a. What type of pictorial representation could you use to calculate the number of choices?
   b. How many different hamburgers are possible?

2. For a particular model of car, a dealer offers 6 versions of that model, 18 body colors, and 7 upholstery colors. How many different possibilities are available for that model?   (Lesson 12–1)

3. Five algebra and four geometry books are to be arranged on a shelf. How many ways can they be arranged if all the algebra books must be together?   (Lesson 12–2)

4. **Government**   How many ways can the 100 United States senators seat themselves in a 100-seat auditorium if there are no restrictions? Write your answer in factorial form.   (Lesson 12–2)

Determine whether each situation involves a permutation or combination.   (Lesson 12–3)

5. 8 guests seated around a table for dinner

6. a hand of 5 cards from a standard deck of cards

Evaluate each expression.   (Lessons 12–2 and 12–3)

7. $P(12, 3)$ 8. $C(8, 3)$

9. How many 6-person volleyball teams can be chosen from a group of 13 athletes?   (Lesson 12–3)

10. **Games**   In bridge, all 52 cards in a deck are dealt among four players. How many different hands are possible? Write your answer in factorial form.   (Lesson 12–3)

Enrichment Masters, p. 87

NAME_____   DATE _____

Student Edition
Pages 728–734

Enrichment

Geometric Probability

If a dart, thrown at random, hits the triangular board shown at the right, what is the chance that it will hit the shaded region? This chance, also called a probability, can be determined by comparing the area of the shaded region to the area of the board. This ratio indicates what fraction of the tosses should hit in the shaded region.

$$\frac{\text{area of shaded region}}{\text{area of triangular board}} = \frac{\frac{1}{2}(4 \times 6)}{\frac{1}{2}(8 \times 6)}$$
$$= \frac{12}{24} \text{ or } \frac{1}{2}$$

In general, if S is a subregion of some region R, then the probability, $P(S)$, that a point, chosen at random, belongs to subregion S is given by the following.

$$P(S) = \frac{\text{area of subregion } S}{\text{area of region } R}$$

Find the probability that a point, chosen at random, belongs to the shaded subregions of the following regions.

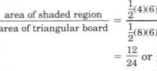

1. $\frac{1}{2}$ 2. $\frac{5}{9}$ 3. $\frac{\pi}{4}$

The dart board shown at the right has 5 concentric circles whose centers are also the center of the square board. Each side of the board is 38 cm, and the radii of the circles are 2 cm, 5 cm, 8 cm, 11 cm, and 14 cm. A dart hitting within one of the circular regions scores the number of points indicated on the board, while a hit anywhere else scores 0 points.

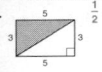

If a dart, thrown at random, hits the board, find the probability of scoring the indicated number of points.

4. 0 points $\frac{361 - 49\pi}{361}$ 5. 1 point $\frac{75\pi}{1444}$ 6. 2 points $\frac{57\pi}{1444}$

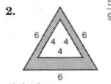 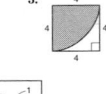 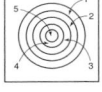

7. 3 points $\frac{39\pi}{1444}$ 8. 4 points $\frac{21\pi}{1444}$ 9. 5 points $\frac{\pi}{361}$

SELF TEST

The Self Test provides students with a brief review of the concepts and skills in Lessons 12-1 through 12-4. Lesson numbers are given to the right of exercises or instruction lines so students can review concepts not yet mastered.

12-5

Multiplying Probabilities

APPLICATION
Transportation

One study found that when an airplane is more than 80% full, there is a greater chance the flight will not depart on schedule because of the time it takes to stow all the carry-on bags. As a result, the flight may not arrive on schedule. A travel agent informs a customer making flight reservations that the probability that her flight to Nashville will arrive on schedule is 85%. Her flight to Denver is on a different airline and has an 80% chance of arriving on schedule. What is the probability that both her flights will arrive on schedule? *This problem will be solved in Example 1.*

If there are two events, as in the application above, you can find the probability of *both* events occurring if you know the probability of *each* event occurring. You can use an *area diagram* to model the probability of two events occurring at the same time.

What YOU'LL LEARN

• To find the probability of two or more independent or dependent events.

Why IT'S IMPORTANT

You can multiply probabilities to solve problems involving spelling and transportation.

MODELING MATHEMATICS

Area Diagrams

Suppose there are 1 red and 3 blue pens and 1 black and 2 yellow pencils in a drawer. The area diagram below represents the probabilities of choosing pairs of pens and pencils if one of each is chosen at random. For example, rectangle A represents drawing 1 blue pen and 1 yellow pencil.

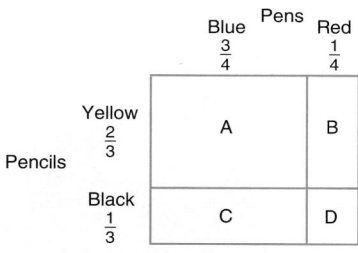

P(blue pen and yellow pencil)

$= P$(blue pen) $\cdot$ P(yellow pencil)

$= \dfrac{3}{4} \cdot \dfrac{2}{3}$ or $\dfrac{1}{2}$

Your Turn   a–b. See margin.

a. Find the probabilities of rectangles B, C, and D and explain what each area represents.

b. What is the length and width of the whole square? What is the area? Why does the area necessarily have to have this value?

c. Suppose you have a bouquet of roses and daisies: 1 lavender, 2 red, and 3 pink roses and 1 yellow and 3 white daisies. Make an area diagram that represents the probabilities of randomly selecting 1 rose and 1 daisy from the bouquet. Label the diagram and describe what each rectangle represents.   **See Solutions Manual.**

Since your first choice (a pen) does not affect your second choice (a pencil), these outcomes are *independent*.

Probability of Two Independent Events	**If two events *A* and *B* are independent, then the probability of both events occurring is found as follows.** $P(A \text{ and } B) = P(A) \cdot P(B)$

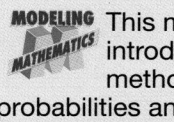

MODELING MATHEMATICS

This modeling exercise introduces students to a method for visualizing probabilities and conjunctions of probabilities. The method can be extended to the product of three probabilities by using a cube.

Answers for Modeling Mathematics

a. $\dfrac{1}{6}$, drawing a red pen and yellow pencil; $\dfrac{1}{4}$, drawing a blue pen and black pencil; $\dfrac{1}{12}$, drawing a red pen and a black pencil

b. 1 unit, 1 unit, 1 square unit; The sum of all the probabilities must equal 1.

12-5 LESSON NOTES

NCTM Standards: 1–4, 11

Instructional Resources

• Study Guide Master 12-5
• Practice Master 12-5
• Enrichment Master 12-5
• Modeling Mathematics Masters, pp. 55–57
• Tech Prep Applications Masters, p. 23

Transparency 12-5A contains the 5-Minute Check for this lesson; **Transparency 12-5B** contains a teaching aid for this lesson.

Recommended Pacing

Standard Pacing	Day 5 of 12
Honors Pacing	Day 5 of 10
Block Scheduling*	Day 3 of 6 (along with Lesson 12-6)

*For more information on pacing and possible lesson plans, refer to the *Block Scheduling Booklet*.

1 FOCUS

5-Minute Check
(over Lesson 12-4)

1. State the odds of an event given the probability is $\dfrac{8}{9}$.
8 to 1

2. State the probability of an event given the odds are 5 to 11. $\dfrac{5}{16}$

3. Two different-colored dice are tossed. How many distinct outcomes are possible? **36**

4. Two dice are tossed. What is the probability of a sum greater than 8? $\dfrac{5}{18}$

5. What are the odds of getting a 7 when tossing two dice?
1:5

Situational Problem Choose a topic and have students generate a list of independent events and a list of dependent events related to the topic. For example, if the topic is a basketball game, independent events might be making a foul shot and fouling another player. Dependent events might be the number of rebounds made and the number of baskets made.

2 TEACH

In-Class Examples

For Example 1
Suppose you spin the spinner below twice. Find the probability that you get *B* and then *C*. $\frac{1}{18}$

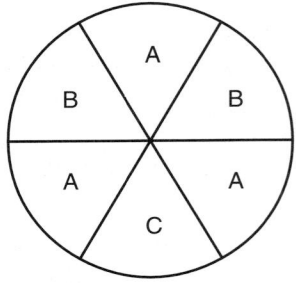

For Example 2
A bag contains 6 orange, 8 blue, and 4 yellow marbles. What is the probability of selecting 2 blue marbles in succession providing the marble drawn first is then replaced before the second is drawn? $\frac{16}{81}$

Teaching Tip Emphasize that "with replacement" is associated with independent events and "without replacement" is associated with dependent events.

Example **1** Refer to the application at the beginning of the lesson. The probability that the first flight arrives on schedule is 85% or $\frac{17}{20}$. The probability that the second flight arrives on schedule is 80% or $\frac{4}{5}$. What is the probability that both flights arrive on schedule?

APPLICATION
Transportation

The two events are independent since the outcome of one flight does not affect the outcome of the other flight. Let *A* be the event that the first flight arrives on schedule. Let *B* be the event that the second flight arrives on schedule.

$P(A \text{ and } B) = P(A) \cdot P(B)$

$= \frac{17}{20} \cdot \frac{4}{5} \text{ or } \frac{17}{25}$

The probability of both flights arriving on schedule is $\frac{17}{25}$ or 68%.

Example **2** Every Friday, the physical education classes go bowling at a local bowling alley. On one shelf at the bowling alley, there are 5 black and 3 green bowling balls. One student selects a bowling ball at random from the shelf and then puts it back because it is too heavy. A second student then selects a ball from the same shelf. What is the probability that each student picked a green bowling ball?

The events are independent since the first bowling ball is placed back on the shelf. The outcome of the second selection is not affected by the results of the first selection.

$P(\text{both green}) = P(\text{green}) \cdot P(\text{green})$
$= \frac{3}{8} \cdot \frac{3}{8} \text{ or } \frac{9}{64}$

The probability that both students selected a green bowling ball is $\frac{9}{64}$ or about 0.14. You can verify the result with a tree diagram.

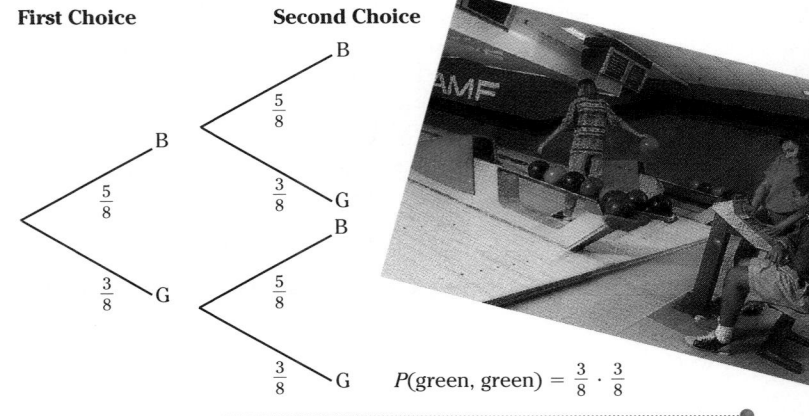

First Choice   **Second Choice**

$P(\text{green, green}) = \frac{3}{8} \cdot \frac{3}{8}$

In Example 2, what is the probability that both students selected a green bowling ball if the first selection is not put back on the shelf? These events are dependent because the outcome of the first event affects the second selection.

GLENCOE Technology

 Interactive Mathematics Tools Software

This multimedia software provides an interactive lesson by having students observe the differences in the probabilities of choosing marbles with and without replacement. A **Computer Journal** gives students an opportunity to write about what they have learned.

For Windows & Macintosh

Suppose the first selection is green.

first selection   *second selection*
$P(\text{green}) = \frac{3}{8}$ $P(\text{green}) = \frac{2}{7}$ *Notice that when the green bowling ball is removed, there is not only one less green ball but also one less ball on the shelf.*

$P(\text{both green}) = P(\text{green}) \cdot P(\text{green following green})$
$= \frac{3}{8} \cdot \frac{2}{7} \text{ or } \frac{3}{28}$

The probability that both students selected a green ball is $\frac{3}{28}$ or about 0.11.

Probability of Two Dependent Events	If two events A and B are dependent, then the probability of both events occurring is found as follows. $P(A \text{ and } B) = P(A) \cdot P(B \text{ following } A)$

Example 3

Mark has 2 quarters, and he needs 50¢ more to pay the turnpike toll. There are 4 dimes, 8 quarters, and 9 nickels in his glove compartment. If he reaches in and selects two coins at random without replacing the first one, find the probability of each event described below.

Because the first coin is not replaced, these events are dependent. Therefore, $P(A \text{ and } B) = P(A) \cdot P(B \text{ following } A)$. Let d represent the dime, q the quarter, and n the nickel.

a. a quarter, then a nickel

$P(q, \text{ then } n) = P(q) \cdot P(n \text{ following } q)$
$P(q, \text{ then } n) = \frac{8}{21} \cdot \frac{9}{20} \text{ or } \frac{6}{35}$

The probability is $\frac{6}{35}$ or about 0.17.

b. two quarters

$P(q, \text{ then } q) = P(q) \cdot P(q \text{ following } q)$
$P(q, \text{ then } q) = \frac{8}{21} \cdot \frac{7}{20} \text{ or } \frac{2}{15}$

The probability is $\frac{2}{15}$ or about 0.13.

Example 4

From a deck of 52 cards, 3 cards are randomly chosen. They are a 10, a jack, and another 10, in that order.

a. Find the probability of this event occurring if the cards are replaced after each selection.

When the cards are replaced, the events are independent.

$P(10, \text{ jack}, 10) = P(10) \cdot P(\text{jack}) \cdot P(10)$
$P(10, \text{ jack}, 10) = \frac{4}{52} \cdot \frac{4}{52} \cdot \frac{4}{52} \text{ or } \frac{1}{2197}$

The probability is $\frac{1}{2197}$ or about 0.0005.

b. Find the probability of the event occurring if the cards are not replaced. *Will this probability be greater or less than when the cards are replaced? Why?*

When the cards are not replaced, the events are dependent.

$P(10, \text{ jack}, 10) = P(10) \cdot P(\text{jack following } 10) \cdot P(10 \text{ following jack following } 10)$

$P(10, \text{ jack}, 10) = \frac{4}{52} \cdot \frac{4}{51} \cdot \frac{3}{50} \text{ or } \frac{2}{5525}$

The probability is $\frac{2}{5525}$ or about 0.0004.

Teaching Tip Be sure students understand that the difference in determining probability for dependent and independent events is that the second event has one less possibility for dependent events.

In-Class Examples

For Example 3
There are 3 quarters, 4 dimes, and 5 nickels in a purse. Suppose 3 coins are to be selected without replacement. Find the following probabilities.

a. selecting 3 quarters
$\frac{1}{220} \approx 0.005$

b. selecting a quarter, then a dime, then a nickel
$\frac{1}{22} \approx 0.045$

For Example 4
A green, a red, and a blue die are tossed. Find each probability.

a. Only the green die has a 5.
$\frac{25}{216} \approx 0.116$

b. All three dice have different numbers. $\frac{5}{9} \approx 0.556$

Check for Understanding

Exercises 1–12 are designed to help you assess your students' understanding through reading, writing, speaking, and modeling. You should work through Exercises 1–6 with your students and then monitor their work on Exercises 7–12.

Additional Answers

3. Events A and B are independent since the outcome of each die rolled does not affect the other.

5c. Sample answer: As the number of trials increases, the results become more reliable. However, you cannot be absolutely certain there are no black marbles in the bag without looking at the marbles.

6.

	First Choice	
	Black 5/8	Green 3/8
Second Choice Black 5/8	$\frac{25}{64}$	$\frac{15}{64}$
Green 3/8	$\frac{15}{64}$	$\frac{9}{64}$

//////// **CHECK FOR UNDERSTANDING**

Communicating Mathematics

1. Multiply their individual probabilities.

2. Events that are affected by previous choices.

4. See students' work.

Study the lesson. Then complete the following.

1. **Explain** how to find the probability of two independent events.

2. **Describe** what is meant by *dependent events*.

3. **Determine** whether events A and B are dependent or independent if a blue die and a red die are rolled and A is the event that the blue die shows 6, and B is the event that the red die shows an even number. Explain your answer. **See margin.**

4. **Write** an example of two real-life events that are dependent.

5. **Examine** the problem below and explain your conclusions. You are given a bag containing 10 marbles. **a. no**

   a. Ten times you draw a marble, record its color, and put it back. If you don't record any black marbles, can you conclude that there aren't any black marbles in the bag?

   b. If you do this 50 times and you don't record any black marbles, can you conclude that there aren't any black marbles in the bag? **no**

   c. How many times do you have to repeat the drawing and replacing of marbles to be absolutely certain that there aren't any black marbles in the bag? Explain. **See margin.**

MODELING MATHEMATICS

6. **Model** the problem in Example 2 using an area diagram. **See margin.**

Guided Practice

Determine if the events are *independent* or *dependent*. Then find the probability.

7. Minal has 7 blue pens, 3 black pens, and 2 red pens in her desk drawer. If she selects three pens at random with no replacement, what is the probability that she will first select a blue pen, then a black pen, and then another blue pen?

8. A green die and a red die are tossed. What is the probability that a 2 shows on the green die and a 6 shows on the red die?

9. José's wallet contains three $1 bills, four $5 bills, and two $10 bills. If three bills are selected in succession, find the probability of selecting one of each if:

   a. each bill is replaced. **independent,** $\frac{8}{243}$

   b. no bills are replaced. **dependent,** $\frac{1}{21}$

7. dependent, $\frac{21}{220}$

8. independent, $\frac{1}{36}$

There are 8 movie videos, 3 exercise videos, and 5 cartoon videos on the shelf. Suppose two videotapes are to be selected at random from the shelf. Find each probability.

10. P(selecting 2 movie videos), if no replacement occurs $\frac{7}{30}$

11. P(selecting 2 movie videos), if replacement occurs $\frac{1}{4}$

12. P(selecting an exercise video, then a cartoon video), if no replacement occurs $\frac{1}{16}$

Reteaching

Using Class Discussion Give students a problem in which to find the probability of the event occurring with replacement and then find the probability of the event occurring without replacement. Have them discuss the results and determine when the probability will be greater and when it will be less.

Practice

13. dependent, $\frac{3}{28}$

14. independent, $\frac{25}{81}$

15. independent, $\frac{81}{2401}$

16. $\frac{25}{49}$

17. $\frac{10}{21}$

22. $\frac{1}{10}$

23. $\frac{1}{5}$

24a. $\frac{1}{9}$; See margin for diagram.

24b–c. See margin.

24d. $\frac{1}{3}$ 24e. $\frac{1}{3}$

Determine if the events are *independent* or *dependent*. Then find the probability.

13. There are 3 glasses of diet cola and 5 glasses of regular cola on the counter. Susan drinks 2 of them at random. What is the probability that she drank 2 glasses of diet cola?

14. A bowl contains 4 peaches and 5 apricots. Monica randomly selects one, puts it back, and then randomly selects another. What is the probability that both selections were apricots?

15. When Tricia plays her video game, the odds are 3 to 4 that she will reach the highest level of the game. What is the probability that she will reach the highest level the next four games?

The Scrabble® tiles *A, B, G, I, M, R,* and *S* are placed face down in the lid of the game. If two tiles are chosen at random, find each probability.   19a. (2, 6), (6, 2), (4, 4), (3, 5), (5, 3)

16. *P*(selecting 2 consonants), if replacement occurs

17. *P*(selecting 2 consonants), if no replacement occurs

18. *P*(selecting the same letter twice), if no replacement occurs   0

19. Suppose you roll one red die and one green die and get a sum of 8.
   a. List the different ways in which this can occur.
   b. Suppose you know the sum is 8 but not the number on each die. Explain why the probability that you rolled two 4s would be $\frac{1}{5}$.

   (4, 4) is one of 5 possible outcomes when rolling a sum of 8.

Corinne takes her 3-year-old son into an antique shop. There are 4 statues, 3 picture frames, and 3 vases on a shelf. The 3-year-old accidentally knocks 2 items off the shelf and breaks them. Find each probability.

20. *P*(breaking 2 vases) $\frac{1}{15}$

21. *P*(breaking 2 statues) $\frac{2}{15}$

22. *P*(breaking a picture frame, then a vase)

23. *P*(breaking a picture frame and a vase)

24. Suppose you spin the spinner at the right two times.
   a. Sketch a tree diagram showing all of the possibilities and use it to find the probability of spinning a red and then a blue.
   b. Sketch an area diagram of the outcomes.
   c. Shade the region on your area diagram corresponding to getting the same color twice.
   d. What is the probability that you get the same color on both spins?
   e. If you know that you got the same color twice, what is the probability that the color was red?

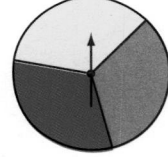

Assignment Guide

Core: 13–37 odd, 38, 39, 41–48
Enriched: 14–36 even, 38–48

For **Extra Practice,** see p. 905.

The red A, B, and C flags, printed only in the Teacher's Wraparound Edition, indicate the level of difficulty of the exercises.

Additional Answers

24a.

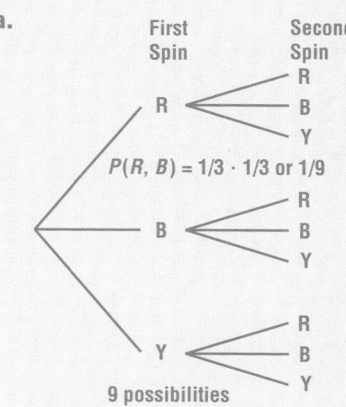

First Spin — Second Spin

R < R, B, Y

$P(R, B) = 1/3 \cdot 1/3$ or $1/9$

B < R, B, Y

Y < R, B, Y

9 possibilities

24b–c.

		First Spin		
		Blue 1/3	Yellow 1/3	Red 1/3
Second Spin	Blue 1/3	BB 1/9	BY 1/9	BR 1/9
	Yellow 1/3	YB 1/9	YY 1/9	YR 1/9
	Red 1/3	RB 1/9	RY 1/9	RR 1/9

Study Guide Masters, p. 88

12-5   NAME _____ DATE _____
Study Guide   Student Edition Pages 735–741

Multiplying Probabilities

To calculate the probability that event A *and* event B will occur, you need to know whether the events are independent or dependent.

Probability of Two Events	
Independent Events	**Example**
If two events A and B are independent, then the probability of both events occurring is found as follows. $P(A \text{ and } B) = P(A)P(B)$	A bag contains 5 red marbles and 4 white marbles. A marble is to be selected and replaced in the bag. A second selection is then made. What is the probability of selecting 2 red marbles? These events are independent because the first marble selected is replaced. The outcome is not affected by the results of the first selection. $P(\text{both reds}) = P(\text{red}) \cdot P(\text{red})$ $= \frac{5}{9} \cdot \frac{5}{9} = \frac{25}{81}$ The probability is $\frac{25}{81}$ or approximately 0.309.
Dependent Events	**Example**
If two events A and B are dependent, then the probability of both events occurring is found as follows. $P(A \text{ and } B) = P(A) \cdot P(B \text{ following } A)$	There are 7 dimes and 9 pennies in a wallet. Suppose two coins are to be selected at random, without replacing the first one. Find the probability of picking a penny and then a dime. Because the coins are not replaced, the events are dependent. Thus, $P(A \text{ and } B) = P(A) \cdot P(B \text{ following } A)$. $P(\text{penny and dime}) = P(\text{penny}) \cdot P(\text{dime following penny})$ $= \frac{9}{16} \cdot \frac{7}{15} = \frac{21}{80}$ The probability is $\frac{21}{80}$ or 0.2625.

Determine if each event is independent or dependent. Then find the probability.

1. A box contains 5 triangles, 6 circles, and 4 squares. If a figure is removed, replaced, and a second is picked, what is the probability that a triangle and then a circle will be picked?

   independent, $\frac{2}{15}$ or about 0.133

2. What is the probability of drawing two cards showing odd numbers from a set of cards that show the first 20 counting numbers if the first card is not replaced before the second is chosen?

   dependent, $\frac{9}{38}$ or about 0.237

3. A jar contains 7 lemon jawbreakers, 3 cherry jawbreakers, and 8 rainbow jawbreakers. What is the probability of selecting 2 lemon jawbreakers in succession providing the jawbreaker drawn first is then replaced before the second is drawn?

   independent, $\frac{49}{324}$ or about 0.151

4. There are 3 quarters, 4 dimes, and 7 nickels in a change purse. Suppose 3 coins are to be selected without replacement. What is the probability of selecting a quarter, then a dime, and then a nickel?

   dependent, $\frac{1}{26}$ or about 0.038

Two dice are rolled. Find each probability.

25. $P(2 \text{ and } 3)$ $\frac{1}{36}$

26. $P(\text{no } 6\text{s})$ $\frac{25}{36}$

27. $P(\text{two } 4\text{s})$ $\frac{1}{36}$

28. $P(1 \text{ and any number})$ $\frac{1}{6}$

29. $P(\text{two numbers alike})$ $\frac{1}{6}$

30. $P(\text{two different numbers})$ $\frac{5}{6}$

31a. $\frac{7}{170}$

31b. $\frac{168}{4913}$

31. A bag contains 7 red, 4 blue, and 6 yellow marbles. If 3 marbles are selected in succession, find the probability that all three are different colors if:

    a. no replacement occurs.   **b.** replacement occurs each time.

32a. $\frac{1}{28}$

32b. $\frac{15}{512}$

32. A box of chocolates contains 8 cherry cremes, 3 lemon cremes, and 5 marshmallow cremes. Arlene randomly chooses three chocolates. Find the probability that she will select one of each if:

    a. no chocolates are replaced.   **b.** each chocolate is replaced.

A standard deck of 52 cards contains 4 suits of 13 cards each. Find each probability if 13 cards are drawn and no replacement occurs.

33. $P(\text{all clubs})$ $\frac{1}{635,013,559,600}$

34. $P(\text{all black cards})$ $\frac{19}{1,160,054}$

35. $P(\text{all one suit})$ $\frac{1}{158,753,389,900}$

36. $P(\text{all face cards})$ 0

37. In a game using the spinners below, you are allowed to move around the game board if you get your color on *both* spinners.

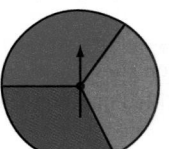 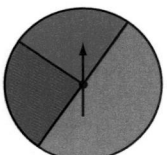

37a. $\frac{1}{12}$

37b. $\frac{1}{6}$

    a. Chet always chooses the color blue because that is his favorite color. Use an area model to find the probability that Chet can move his marker.

    b. Hoshi always chooses red. What is the probability that she can move?

    c. How many outcomes are there in which no one gets to move? Name them.   6 outcomes; GR, GB, BR, BG, RG, RB

Critical Thinking

38. On a recent *Today* show, two women were profiled who had known each other since childhood in England. After one of the women married, she moved to California with her husband, and the women lost contact for 50 years. Then one day, while standing in line at a restaurant in California, the women struck up a conversation and each of them realized that she was speaking to her long-lost friend. After listening to their story, Katie Couric, the host of *Today,* pointed out that the chances of this happening must be "one in a million." One of the women, however, said that she believed the chances were probably closer to "one in a billion." Describe the steps you would take to compute the odds of this occurring. Be sure to list all of the factors that would have to be considered. See students' work.

Practice Masters, p. 88

12-5

NAME_____ DATE _____

Student Edition
Pages 735–741

Practice

Multiplying Probabilities

There are 3 nickels, 2 dimes, and 5 quarters in a purse. Three coins are selected in succession at random.

1. Find the probability of selecting 1 nickel, 1 dime, and 1 quarter in that order without replacement. $\frac{1}{24}$

2. Find the probability of selecting 1 nickel, 1 dime, and 1 quarter in that order with replacement. $\frac{3}{100}$

3. Find the probability of selecting 1 nickel, 1 dime, and 1 quarter in any order with replacement. $\frac{9}{50}$

4. Find the probability of selecting 1 nickel, 1 dime, and 1 quarter in any order without replacement. $\frac{1}{4}$

A red, a green, and a yellow die are tossed. What is the probability that the following occurs?

5. All 3 dice show 4. $\frac{1}{216}$

6. None of the 3 dice shows 4. $\frac{125}{216}$

7. The red die shows an even number and the other 2 dice show different odd numbers. $\frac{1}{12}$

8. All 3 dice show the same number. $\frac{1}{36}$

From a standard deck of 52 cards, 2 cards are selected. What is the probability that the following occurs?

9. 2 black cards; selection without replacement. $\frac{25}{102}$

10. 2 black cards; selection with replacement. $\frac{1}{4}$

11. 1 red card and 1 spade in any order; selection without replacement. $\frac{13}{51}$

12. 1 red card and 1 spade in that order; selection without replacement. $\frac{13}{102}$

Cooperative Learning

Trade-A-Problem Separate students into groups of three. Each student should think up a conditional probability situation from the real world. The other students should check that it is a case of conditional probability. For more information on the trade-a-problem strategy, see *Cooperative Learning in the Mathematics Classroom,* one of the titles in the Glencoe Mathematics Professional Series, pages 25–26.

39a. $\frac{1}{12} \cdot \frac{1}{11} \cdot \frac{1}{10}$ or $\frac{1}{1320}$

39b. $\left(\frac{1}{12}\right)^5$ or $\frac{1}{248,832}$

39. Literature The following quote is from *The Mirror Crack'd*, which was written by Agatha Christie in 1962.

> "I think you're begging the question," said Haydock, "and I can see looming ahead one of those terrible exercises in probability where six men have white hats and six men have black hats and you have to work it out by mathematics how likely it is that the hats will get mixed up and in what proportion. If you start thinking about things like that, you would go round the bend. Let me assure you of that!"

a. If the twelve white and black hats are all mixed up and each man randomly chooses a hat, what is the probability that the first three men get their own hats?

b. Find the probability that the first five men get their own hats, if the hats are replaced after each selection.

40. Spelling In 1994, Ned Andrews won the 67th National Spelling Bee by spelling the word "antediluvian." Suppose Ned has a 93% chance of spelling any given word in a contest correctly.

a. What is the probability that he spells the first five words in a contest correctly? **0.7**

b. What is the probability that he spells the first three words correctly and then misspells the fourth and fifth words? **0.004**

c. If each contestant is given 30 words to spell, what is the probability that Ned will spell all of his words right? **0.11**

Mixed Review

41a. $\frac{1}{204}$

41b. $\frac{9}{340}$

41c. $\frac{6}{119}$

41. Probability A gumball machine contains 7 red gumballs, 8 orange gumballs, 9 purple gumballs, 7 white gumballs, and 5 yellow gumballs. Tyson had three quarters with which to buy three gumballs. Find each probability. (Lesson 12–4)

a. P(3 red gumballs)   **b.** P(2 white gumballs, 1 purple gumball)

c. P(1 purple gumball, 1 orange gumball, 1 yellow gumball)

42. Find the sum of $50 + 33 + 16 + \ldots + (-52)$. (Lesson 11–2) **−7**

43. Solve $\frac{1}{y+1} - \frac{3}{y-3} = 2$. (Lesson 9–5) **0, 1**

44. Solve $x^2 - 22x = -117$ by factoring. (Lesson 6–2) **9, 13**

45. Archaeology Since carbon-14 is present in all living organisms and decays at a predictable rate after death, archaeologists use the amount of carbon-14 left in a fossil to estimate the age of the fossil. This is commonly called *carbon dating*. The approximate number of milligrams A of carbon-14 left in a fossil after 5000 years can be found using the formula $A = A_0 (2.7)^{-\frac{3}{5}}$, where A_0 is the initial amount of carbon-14 in the organism. Find the amount of carbon-14 left in an organism that contained 500 milligrams of carbon-14. (Lesson 5–7) **276 milligrams**

47. $-\frac{7}{8}$

46. Graph the system of equations and state its solution. Then state whether the system is *consistent and independent*, *consistent and dependent*, or *inconsistent*. (Lesson 3–1)

$3x - y = 4$

$9x - 6 = 3y$ **No solution, inconsistent; see margin for graph.**

47. What is the slope of a line perpendicular to the line that passes through $(7, 4)$ and $(0, -4)$? (Lesson 2–3)

48. Find the value of $12a^2 + bc$ if $a = 3$, $b = 7$, and $c = -2$. (Lesson 1–1) **94**

Extension

Communication Have students verbalize the solution process for the following problem and then solve the problem.

How many people, selected at random, would have to be asked their birthdays in order for the probability of any two of them having the same birthday to be greater than $\frac{1}{2}$? Assume that 366 different birthdays are possible. **23**

4 ASSESS

Closing Activity

Writing Have students multiply probabilities to solve the problem presented in Example 2 and compare the result to that found by using combinations.

Additional Answer

46.

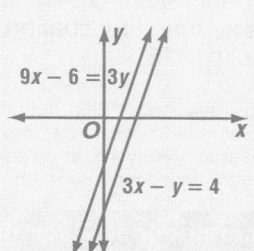

$9x - 6 = 3y$

$3x - y = 4$

Enrichment Masters, p. 88

12-5   NAME_____ DATE_____
Enrichment   Student Edition Pages 735–741

Probabilities in Genetics

Genes are the units which transmit hereditary traits. The possible forms which a gene may take, **dominant** and **recessive**, are called **alleles**. A particular trait is determined by two alleles, one from the female parent and one from the male parent. If an organism has the trait which is dominant, it may have either two dominant alleles or one dominant and one recessive allele. If the organism has the trait which is recessive, it must have two recessive alleles.

Example: Consider a plant in which tall stems, T, are dominant to short stems, t. What is the probability of obtaining a long-stemmed plant if two long-stemmed plants both with the genetic formula Tt are crossed?

A *Punnett square* is a chart used to determine the possible combinations of characteristics among offspring.

	T	t
T	TT	Tt
t	Tt	tt

  3 tall-stemmed
+ 1 short-stemmed
  4 total

Thus, the probability is $\frac{3}{4}$.

In a certain plant, red flowers, R, are dominant to white flowers, r. If a white-flowered plant, rr is crossed with a red-flowered plant, Rr, find the probability of each of the following.

1. white-flowered plant $\frac{1}{2}$ **2.** red-flowered plant $\frac{1}{2}$

In a certain plant, tall, T, is dominant to short, t, and green pods, G, are dominant to yellow pods, g. Plants with the genetic formulas TtGg and TTGg are crossed. Find the probability of each of the following.

3. tall plant with green pods $\frac{3}{4}$ **4.** tall plant with yellow pods $\frac{1}{4}$

Instructional Resources

- Study Guide Master 12-6
- Practice Master 12-6
- Enrichment Master 12-6
- Assessment and Evaluation Masters, p. 325

Transparency 12-6A contains the 5-Minute Check for this lesson; **Transparency 12-6B** contains a teaching aid for this lesson.

Recommended Pacing

Standard Pacing	Day 6 of 12
Honors Pacing	Day 6 of 10
Block Scheduling*	Day 3 of 6 (along with Lesson 12-5)

*For more information on pacing and possible lesson plans, refer to the *Block Scheduling Booklet*.

1 FOCUS

5-Minute Check
(over Lesson 12-5)

1. In a bag are 5 red and 3 blue marbles. Two marbles are selected without replacement. What is the probability of drawing a red and a blue marble in that order? $\frac{15}{56}$

2. Two books are selected from a group of 5 algebra and 3 geometry books. What is the probability that both of them are geometry books? $\frac{3}{28}$

3. A bag contains 3 black marbles and 6 white marbles. A marble is drawn and then replaced. A second drawing is made. What is the probability that a black marble will be drawn both times? $\frac{1}{9}$

12-6

Adding Probabilities

Meteorology

The Born Loser®

THE BORN LOSER reprinted by permission of Newspaper Enterprise Association, Inc.

What YOU'LL LEARN

- To find the probability of mutually exclusive or inclusive events.

Why IT'S IMPORTANT

You can add probabilities to solve problems involving meteorology and recycling.

CAREER CHOICES

A **meteorologist** studies air pressure, temperature, humidity, and wind velocity, and applies physical relationships to make short- and long-range weather forecasts.

A beginning job as a meteorologist requires a bachelor's degree with a major in meteorology or a closely related field with coursework in meteorology.

For more information, contact:

American Meteorological Society
45 Beacon St.
Boston, MA 02108

In the cartoon above, the forecaster predicted a 100% chance of rain for the weekend. Do you think this forecast is correct? Why or why not? *You will solve this problem in Exercise 4.*

When there are two events, it is important to understand how they are related before finding the probability of one or the other event occurring. Suppose you draw a card from a standard deck of 52 cards. What is the probability of drawing a jack or a queen? Since a card cannot be both a jack *and* a queen, the events are **mutually exclusive**. That is, the two events cannot occur at the same time. The probability of drawing a jack or a queen is found by adding their individual probabilities.

$$P(\text{drawing a jack or queen}) = P(\text{drawing a jack}) + P(\text{drawing a queen})$$
$$= \frac{4}{52} + \frac{4}{52}$$
$$= \frac{8}{52} \text{ or } \frac{2}{13}$$

The probability of drawing a jack or a queen is $\frac{2}{13}$.

Probability of Mutually Exclusive Events	If two events, **A** and **B**, are mutually exclusive, then the probability that either **A** or **B** occurs is the sum of their probabilities. $P(A \text{ or } B) = P(A) + P(B)$

What is the probability of drawing a queen or a diamond from a deck of cards? Since it is possible to draw a card that is both a queen and a diamond, these events are *not* mutually exclusive. They are called **inclusive** events. In this case, you must adjust the formula for mutually exclusive events much like you did to account for duplication in some permutations.

$P(\text{queen})$	$P(\text{diamond})$	$P(\text{diamond queen})$
$\frac{4}{52}$	$\frac{13}{52}$	$\frac{1}{52}$
1 queen in each suit	*diamonds*	*queen of diamonds*

CAREER CHOICES

Meteorologists gather their information from computer models, radars, weather balloons, and satellites. Dynamic meteorology deals with motion in the atmosphere and air flow. Synoptic meteorology deals with the weather.

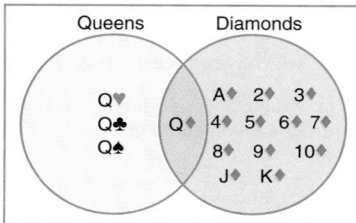

Queens   Diamonds

Q♥
Q♣   Q♦   A♦ 2♦ 3♦
Q♠   4♦ 5♦ 6♦ 7♦
              8♦ 9♦ 10♦
              J♦ K♦

The probability of drawing a queen is counted twice, once for a queen and once for a diamond. To find the correct probability, you must subtract P(queen of diamonds) from the sum of their individual probabilities.

P(queen or diamond) = P(queen) + P(diamond) − P(queen of diamonds)

$$= \frac{4}{52} + \frac{13}{52} - \frac{1}{52} \text{ or } \frac{4}{13}$$

The probability of drawing a queen or a diamond is $\frac{4}{13}$.

Probability of Inclusive Events	If two events, **A** and **B**, are inclusive, then the probability that either **A** or **B** occurs is the sum of their probabilities decreased by the probability of both occurring. **P(A or B) = P(A) + P(B) − P(A and B)**

Example ①

Jerome has 5 quarters, 4 dimes, and 6 nickels in his pocket. He takes one coin from his pocket at random. What is the probability that it is a quarter or a nickel?

These are mutually exclusive events since a coin cannot be a quarter *and* a nickel. Since P(quarter and nickel) = 0, find the sum of the individual probabilities.

P(quarter or nickel) = P(quarter) + P(nickel)

$$= \frac{5}{15} + \frac{6}{15} \text{ or } \frac{11}{15}$$

The probability of selecting a quarter or a nickel is $\frac{11}{15}$.

Example ②

APPLICATION
Recycling

F Y I

Every two weeks, Americans throw away enough glass bottles and jars to fill the twin towers of the World Trade Center in New York.

In 1973, Americans recycled only 15% of all aluminum cans. Today, 64% or 59.5 billion cans are recycled each year, many through curbside recycling. In one community, a survey of 300 people was conducted to determine how many would participate in a curbside recycling program. Of the people surveyed, 134 said they would recycle aluminum cans, and 108 said they would recycle glass. Of those people, 62 said they would recycle both. If a member of the community were selected at random, what is the probability that he or she would participate in a community recycling program by recycling aluminum *or* glass?

Since it is possible to recycle both aluminum and glass, these events are inclusive.

P(recycle aluminum) = $\frac{134}{300}$ P(recycle glass) = $\frac{108}{300}$

P(recycle aluminum and glass) = $\frac{62}{300}$

P(recycle aluminum or glass) = $\frac{134}{300} + \frac{108}{300} - \frac{62}{300}$ or $\frac{180}{300}$

The probability that a person chosen would recycle aluminum *or* glass is $\frac{180}{300}$ or $\frac{3}{5}$.

Motivating the Lesson

Questioning Ask students what is wrong with the statement, "Pedro made an A and a B on the test." Use student responses to develop an informal definition of mutually exclusive events.

2 TEACH

Teaching Tip Emphasize that mutually exclusive events cannot occur simultaneously. Another example would be the toss of a coin. A coin cannot show both heads and tails on the same toss.

In-Class Examples

For Example 1
A marble is selected from a bag containing 5 blue, 2 red, and 3 white marbles. What is the probability that it is a blue or a white marble? $\frac{4}{5}$

For Example 2
A letter is picked at random from the alphabet. What is the probability the letter is contained in the word *glass* or in the word *slower*? $\frac{4}{13}$

F Y I

Recycling, the recovery and reuse of waste materials, is becoming increasingly popular. Commonly recycled materials include aluminum, steel, glass, paper, plastic, motor oil, and automobile tires.

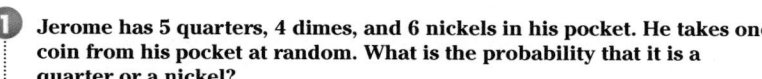

Alternative Teaching Strategies

Student Diversity Provide students with oral descriptions of inclusive situations or events and have students draw Venn diagrams illustrating those situations or events. For example, you might describe a neighborhood

meeting at which 4 of the attendees are male and 10 are female, 1 male and 4 females are teachers, and the other attendees are of different professions. Then have students diagram the relationships.

In-Class Example

For Example 3

A bag contains 7 red and 4 white marbles. Three marbles are selected. What is the probability that at least one is white? $\frac{26}{33} \approx 0.788$

---

3 PRACTICE/APPLY

Check for Understanding

Exercises 1–8 are designed to help you assess your students' understanding through reading, writing, speaking, and modeling. You should work through Exercises 1–4 with your students and then monitor their work on Exercises 5–8.

Additional Answers

1. **Mutually exclusive events cannot occur at the same time, whereas inclusive events can.**

2. **Sample answer: going to school, eating pizza, or watching TV.**

3.

Aluminum / Glass

Alum. and Glass

72 | 62 | 46

Example ③ There are 5 boys and 6 girls on the yearbook staff. A committee of 5 people is being selected at random to design the front cover of the book. What is the probability that the committee will have at least 3 boys?

At least 3 boys means that the committee may have 3, 4, or 5 boys. It is not possible to select a group of 3 boys, a group of 4 boys, and a group of 5 boys all in the same 5-member committee.

$P(\text{at least 3 boys}) = P(\text{3 boys}) + P(\text{4 boys}) + P(\text{5 boys})$

$$\begin{array}{ccccc}
& 3\text{ boys, 2 girls} & 4\text{ boys, 1 girl} & 5\text{ boys, 0 girls} \\
= & \dfrac{C(5, 3) \cdot C(6, 2)}{C(11, 5)} & + \dfrac{C(5, 4) \cdot C(6,1)}{C(11, 5)} & + \dfrac{C(5, 5) \cdot C(6, 0)}{C(11, 5)}
\end{array}$$

$$= \frac{150}{462} + \frac{30}{462} + \frac{1}{462} \text{ or } \frac{181}{462}$$

The probability of at least 3 boys on the committee is $\frac{181}{462}$ or about 0.392.

CHECK FOR UNDERSTANDING

Communicating Mathematics

Study the lesson. Then complete the following. 1–3. See margin.

1. **Describe** the difference between *mutually exclusive* and *inclusive* events.

2. **Write** an example of three inclusive events that could occur in everyday life.

3. **Draw** a Venn diagram to illustrate the events in Example 2.

MATH JOURNAL

4a. The events are not mutually exclusive.

4. Refer to the comic at the beginning of the lesson.

   a. Why is the forecaster's prediction incorrect?

   b. What do you need to know to find the correct probability of rain for the weekend? **probability of rain on both days**

Guided Practice

5a. mutually exclusive, $\frac{2}{13}$

5b. inclusive, $\frac{4}{13}$

6b. $\frac{35}{64}$

6c. $\frac{21}{64}$

6d. $\frac{1}{32}$

7. $\frac{8}{26}$

8. $\frac{17}{28}$

5. Determine if each event of drawing a card from a standard deck of cards is *mutually exclusive* or *inclusive*. Then find the probability.

   a. $P(5 \text{ or ace})$ b. $P(\text{jack or diamond})$

6. Six coins are dropped onto the floor. Find each probability. 6a. $\frac{11}{32}$

   a. $P(\text{at least 4 heads})$ b. $P(3 \text{ tails or 2 heads})$

   c. $P(4 \text{ tails or 1 head})$ d. $P(\text{all heads or all tails})$

7. The letters of the alphabet are placed in a bag. What is the probability of selecting a vowel or a letter from the word *equation*?

8. **School** The enrollment at Southburg High School is 1400. Suppose 550 students take French, 700 take algebra, and 400 take both French and algebra. What is the probability that a student selected at random takes French or algebra?

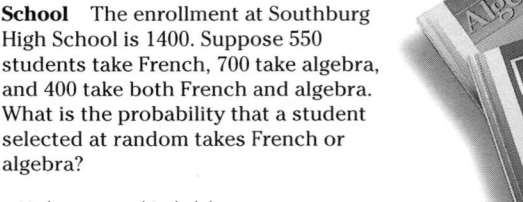 **Alternative Learning Styles**

Kinesthetic Organize in four corners of the classroom the following groups of students: Those with (1) dark shirt, dark pants; (2) dark shirt, light pants; (3) light shirt, dark pants; (4) light shirt, light pants. Then illustrate "those with dark pants" by moving the two groups together.

Reteaching

Using Comparison Have students give examples of mutually exclusive events and inclusive events. Discuss why each example is one or the other.

Practice

Determine if the events in Exercises 9–12 are *mutually exclusive* or *inclusive*. Then find each probability.

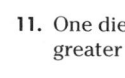

9. There are 3 physics books, 4 math books, and 2 history books on a shelf. If a book is randomly selected, what is the probability of selecting a physics book or a history book? **mutually exclusive, $\frac{5}{9}$**

10. A card is drawn from a deck of cards. What is the probability that it is a black card or a face card? **inclusive, $\frac{8}{13}$**

11. One die is tossed. What is the probability of tossing a 5 or a number greater than 3? **inclusive, $\frac{1}{2}$**

12. In the drama club, 7 of the 20 girls are seniors, and 4 of the 14 boys are seniors. What is the probability of randomly selecting a boy or a senior to represent the drama club at a national performing arts symposium? **inclusive, $\frac{21}{34}$**

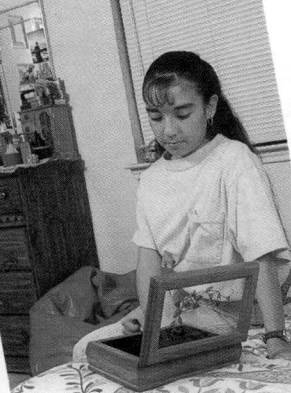

Juanita has 9 rings in her jewelry box. Five are gold and 4 are silver. If she randomly selects 3 rings to wear to a party, find each probability.

13. $P(\text{exactly 2 silver})$ $\frac{5}{14}$

14. $P(\text{all 3 gold or all 3 silver})$ $\frac{1}{6}$

15. $P(\text{at least 2 gold})$ $\frac{25}{42}$

16. $P(\text{at least 1 silver})$ $\frac{37}{24}$

Two cards are drawn from a standard deck of 52 cards. Find each probability.

18. $\frac{11}{221}$ 19. $\frac{188}{663}$

17. $P(\text{both kings or both black})$ $\frac{55}{221}$

18. $P(\text{both kings or both face cards})$

19. $P(\text{both face cards or both red})$

20. $P(\text{both either red or a king})$ $\frac{71}{221}$

Seven women and six men walk into a computer store at the same time. There are five salespeople available to help them. Find the probability that a salesperson will first help:

21. $P(\text{4 women, 1 man or 4 men, 1 woman})$ $\frac{35}{143}$

22. $P(\text{3 women, 2 men or 3 men, 2 women})$ $\frac{105}{143}$

23. $P(\text{all women or all men})$ $\frac{3}{143}$

24. $P(\text{at least 3 women})$ $\frac{84}{143}$

The numbers 1 through 30 are written on Ping-Pong™ balls and placed in one wire cage. The numbers 20 through 45 are also written on Ping-Pong™ balls and placed in a different wire cage. One ball is chosen at random from each spinning cage. Find each probability.

25. $P(\text{each is a 25})$ $\frac{1}{780}$

26. $P(\text{neither is a 20})$ $\frac{145}{156}$

27. $P(\text{at least one is a 30})$ $\frac{11}{156}$

28. $P(\text{each is greater than 15})$ $\frac{1}{2}$

Critical Thinking

29. Suppose there are three inclusive events, A, B, and C. List all the events you would need to consider in order to calculate $P(A \text{ or } B \text{ or } C)$ and describe how you would calculate the probability. **See margin.**

Lesson 12–6 Adding Probabilities   **749**

GLENCOE Technology

CD-ROM
Interaction

A multimedia simulation allows students to use counting principles and probability in an interactive game room. A blackline master activity with teacher's notes provides a follow-up to the CD-ROM simulation.

For Windows & Macintosh

Assignment Guide

Core: 9–33 odd, 34–40
Enriched: 10–28 even, 29–40

For **Extra Practice,** see p. 905.

The red A, B, and C flags, printed only in the Teacher's Wraparound Edition, indicate the level of difficulty of the exercises.

Additional Answer

29. $P(A)$, $P(B)$, $P(C)$, $P(A \text{ and } B)$, $P(B \text{ and } C)$, $P(A \text{ and } C)$, $P(A \text{ and } B \text{ and } C)$;
$P(A \text{ or } B \text{ or } C) = P(A) + P(B) + P(C) - P(A \text{ and } B) - P(B \text{ and } C) - P(A \text{ and } C) + P(A \text{ and } B \text{ and } C)$

Study Guide Masters, p. 89

NAME_____ DATE_____

12-6 **Study Guide**

Student Edition
Pages 742–747

Adding Probabilities

Events that cannot occur at the same time are called **mutually exclusive. Inclusive events** are not mutually exclusive. Therefore, the two events can occur at the same time.

Mutually Exclusive Events	Example
The probability of one or the other of two mutually exclusive events A and B occurring is the sum of their individual probabilities. $P(A \text{ or } B) = P(A) + P(B)$	What is the probability of drawing a jack or a king from a standard deck of 52 cards? $P(A \text{ or } B) = P(A) + P(B)$ There are 4 jacks in a deck of 52 or $\frac{4}{52} = \frac{1}{13}$. $= \frac{1}{13} + \frac{1}{13}$ There are 4 kings in a deck of 52 or $\frac{4}{52} = \frac{1}{13}$. $= \frac{2}{13}$ The probability of picking a jack or a king is $\frac{2}{13}$ or about 0.154.

Inclusive Events	Example
The probability of one or the other of two inclusive events A and B occurring is the sum of the individual probabilities decreased by the probability of both occurring. $P(A \text{ or } B) = P(A) + P(B) - P(A \text{ and } B)$	A card is selected from a standard deck of 52 cards. What is the probability that it is a red card or an ace? $P(\text{red or ace}) = P(\text{red}) + P(\text{ace}) - P(\text{red ace})$ $= \frac{26}{52} + \frac{4}{52} - \frac{2}{52}$ There are 2 red aces. Thus, these events are inclusive. $= \frac{28}{52}$ or $\frac{7}{13}$ The probability of selecting a red card or an ace is $\frac{7}{13}$.

State whether the events are inclusive or mutually exclusive. Then find the probability.

1. Three cards are selected from a standard deck of 52 cards. What is the probability of selecting a king, a queen, or a red card?

inclusive, $\frac{15}{26}$ or about 0.577

2. A bag contains 45 dyed eggs: 15 yellow, 12 green, and 18 red. What is the probability of selecting a green or a red egg?

mutually exclusive, $\frac{2}{3}$ or about 0.667

3. The letters from the words LOVE and LIVE are placed on cards and put in a box. What is the probability of selecting an L or O from the box?

inclusive, $\frac{3}{8}$ or 0.375

4. The letters of the alphabet are placed in a bag. What is the probability of selecting a vowel or the letters QUIZ?

inclusive, $\frac{7}{26}$ or about 0.269

30. Sample answer: Let *A* stand for a white counter in the bag in the beginning, *B* for a black counter, and *C* for the added white counter. After a white counter is taken, there are three equally possible situations:
1. *C* has been taken, leaving *A*.
2. *A* has been taken, leaving *C*.
3. *C* has been taken, leaving *B*.

Since a white counter remains in the bag for the first two cases and a black counter remains in the third case, the answer is $\frac{2}{3}$.

32a.

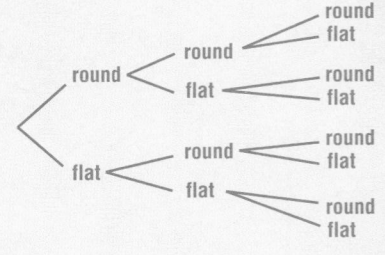

Practice Masters, p. 89

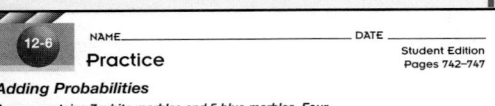

12-6	NAME_____ DATE_____
Practice	Student Edition Pages 742–747

Adding Probabilities

An urn contains 7 white marbles and 5 blue marbles. Four marbles are selected without replacement. What is the probability that the following occurs?

1. all white or all blue $\frac{8}{99}$ 2. exactly 3 white $\frac{35}{99}$

3. at least 3 white $\frac{14}{33}$ 4. exactly 3 white or exactly 3 blue $\frac{49}{99}$

Two cards are drawn from a standard deck of 52 cards. What is the probability that the following occurs?

5. 2 spades $\frac{1}{17}$ 6. 2 spades or 2 red cards $\frac{31}{102}$

7. 2 red cards or 2 jacks $\frac{55}{221}$ 8. 2 spades or 2 face cards $\frac{47}{442}$

Three dice are tossed. What is the probability that the following occurs?

9. only two 5s $\frac{5}{72}$ 10. at least two 5s $\frac{2}{27}$

11. three 5s $\frac{1}{216}$ 12. no 5s $\frac{125}{216}$

30. The problem below appeared in Lewis Carroll's book, *Pillow-Problems Thought Out During Sleepless Nights*.

> A bag contains one counter, known to be either white or black. A white counter is put in, the bag shaken, and a counter drawn out, which proves to be white. What is now the chance of drawing a white counter?

Analyze the problem and explain how you arrived at your answer. **See margin.**

Applications and Problem Solving

31. International Volunteers During the 1990s, approximately 6000 people volunteered to serve in the Peace Corps. If 1800 of the volunteers were women in their 20s, use the graph at the right to find the probability that a Peace Corps volunteer in the 1990s was either a woman or a person in his or her 20s. **96%**

Peace Corps Volunteers

Women	52%
In their 20s	74%
Single	93%
Holders of a bachelor's degree	96%

Source: Peace Corps

Totolospi

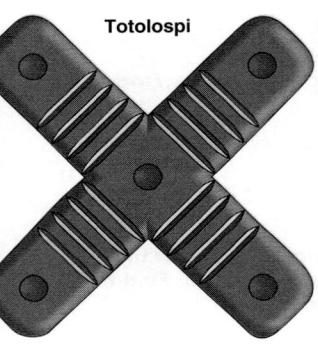

32. World Cultures *Totolospi* is a Hopi game of chance that is played by adults as well as children. The players use cane dice, which have both a flat side and a round side, and a counting board inscribed in stone, like the one shown at the left. When tossing 3 cane dice, if three round sides land up, the player advances 2 lines. If three flat sides land up, the player advances 1 line. If a combination is thrown, the player loses a turn. The winner is the first to reach the opposite end of the arm on which he or she is playing.

a. Draw a tree diagram showing all of the possibilities when throwing 3 cane dice. **See margin.**

b. Find each probability.
   P(advancing 2 lines)
   P(advancing 1 line)
   P(advancing at least 1 line)
   P(losing a turn)

32b. $\frac{1}{8}, \frac{1}{8}, \frac{1}{4}, \frac{3}{4}$

33. Tennis Fourteen-year-old Venus Williams learned to play tennis at a public park in Compton, California. She now competes in junior tennis tournaments all around the country. On each point in tennis, a player is allowed two serves. Suppose while playing tennis, Venus gets her first serve in, about 75% of the time. When she gets her first serve in, she wins the point about 80% of the time. If she misses her first serve, her second serve goes in, about 90% of the time. She wins the point on her second serve about 35% of the time.

a. Draw a tree diagram of the situation. **See margin.**

b. Find the probability that Venus Williams wins a point when she is serving. **67.9%**

c. If you know she won a point while serving, what is the probability that she made her first serve? **88.4%**

Additional Answer

33a.

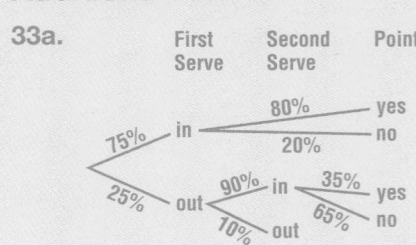

Mixed Review

34. Law Enforcement A law enforcement agency hired a technical researcher to find the following probabilities concerning drivers.

Probability of:	
A driver being intoxicated	0.02
An intoxicated driver: having an unimpeded trip having an accident being arrested having his case dismissed being convicted after arrest	0.99911 0.00045 0.00044 0.30 0.70
A driver not being intoxicated	0.98
An unintoxicated driver: having an unimpeded trip having an accident	0.99984 0.00016

Find the following probabilities. Round answers to seven decimal places. (Lesson 12–5)

a. P(being intoxicated and having an unimpeded trip) **0.0199822**

b. P(being unintoxicated and having an unimpeded trip) **0.9798432**

c. P(being intoxicated, arrested, and convicted) **0.00000616**

d. P(being intoxicated, arrested, and dismissed) **0.00000264**

35. Probability A gumball machine contains 7 red gumballs, 8 orange gumballs, 9 purple gumballs, 7 white gumballs, and 5 yellow gumballs. Tyson had three quarters with which to buy three gumballs. Find each probability. (Lesson 12–4)

35a. $\frac{1}{204}$

35b. $\frac{1}{119}$

35c. $\frac{3}{340}$

a. P(1 red gumball, then another red gumball, then another red gumball)

b. P(1 purple gumball, then 1 orange gumball, then 1 yellow gumball)

c. P(1 white gumball, then another white gumball, then 1 purple gumball)

36. Find the 57th term of the arithmetic sequence 6, 15, 24, 33, ... (Lesson 11–1) **510**

37. Simplify $\dfrac{\frac{3x+5}{3x+1}-2}{3+\frac{3x}{1-2x}}$. (Lesson 9–3) $\dfrac{1-2x}{3x+1}$

38. Find $f(2)$ for $f(x) = -3x^3 + 2$. (Lesson 8–1) **−22**

39. History The elliptical chamber in the United States Capitol building is 46 feet wide and 96 feet long. (Lesson 7–4)

39a. $\dfrac{x^2}{2304} + \dfrac{y^2}{529} = 1$

a. Write an equation to describe the shape of the room. Assume that it is centered at the origin and the major axis is horizontal.

b. John Quincy Adams discovered that he could overhear the conversations being held at the opposing party leader's desk if he stood in a certain spot in the elliptical chamber. Describe the position of the desk and how far Adams had to stand to overhear.
The desk is at one focus point; about 84 feet.

40. Solve $\begin{bmatrix} 3 & -5 \\ 5 & -7 \end{bmatrix} \cdot \begin{bmatrix} x \\ y \end{bmatrix} = \begin{bmatrix} 4 \\ 8 \end{bmatrix}$ by using inverse matrices. (Lesson 4–6) **(3, 1)**

Extension

Problem Solving One card is drawn from a standard deck of cards. What is the probability that it is a red card, a card from 2 through 6, or a card from 6 through 8? Encourage students to use a Venn diagram. $\frac{10}{13}$

---

4 ASSESS

Closing Activity

Speaking Have students explain the difference in finding $P(A \text{ and } B)$ and $P(A \text{ or } B)$.

Chapter 12, Quiz C (Lessons 12-5 and 12-6), is available in the *Assessment and Evaluation Masters,* p. 325.

Enrichment Masters, p. 89

12-6	NAME_____	DATE _____
	Enrichment	Student Edition Pages 742–747

Probability and Tic-Tac-Toe

What would be the chances of winning at tic-tac-toe if it were turned into a game of pure chance? To find out, the nine cells of the tic-tac-toe board are numbered from 1 to 9 and nine chips (also numbered from 1 to 9) are put into a bag. Player A draws a chip at random and enters an X in the corresponding cell. Player B does the same and enters an O.

To solve the problem, assume that both players draw all their chips without looking and all X and O entries are made at the same time. There are four possible outcomes: a draw, A wins, B wins, and either A or B can win.

There are 16 arrangements that result in a draw. Reflections and rotations must be counted as shown below.

```
O X O     X O X     O O X
X O X 4   O O X 4   X X O 8
X O X     X X O     O X X
```

There are 36 arrangements in which either player may win because both players have winning triples.

```
X X X     X X X     X O X     X X X     X X X     X X O
O O O 4   X O X 4   X X X 4   X X O 8   O O O 8   X X X 8
X O X     O O O     O O O     O O O     X X O     O O O
```

In these 36 cases, A's chances of winning are $\frac{13}{40}$.

1. Find the 12 arrangements in which B wins and A cannot.
```
O O X     O X O
X O X 8   X O X 4
X X O     X X O
```

2. Below are 12 of the arrangements in which A wins and B cannot. Write the numbers to show the reflections and rotations for each arrangement. What is the total number? **62**

```
O X O     X O X     X X X     X X X     X O O     X O O
X X X 1   O X O 1   X O O 4   O X O 4   X X X 4   X X O 4
O X O     X O X     X O O     O X O     O O X     O O X

X X O     X X X     X X X     X X X     X O O     X O O
O X X 4   O X O 8   X O O 8   X O O 8   X X X 8   O X O 8
O O X     O X O     O X O     O O X     O X O     X O X
```

3. There are $\frac{9!}{(5!4!)}$ different and equally probable distributions. Complete the chart to find the probability for a draw or for A or B to win.

Draw: $\frac{16}{126}$		$= \frac{8}{63}$
A wins: $\frac{62}{126}$	$+ \frac{13}{40}\left(\frac{36}{126}\right)$	$= \frac{737}{1260}$
B wins: $\frac{12}{126}$	$+ \frac{27}{40}\left(\frac{36}{126}\right)$	$= \frac{121}{420}$

Instructional Resources

- Study Guide Master 12-7
- Practice Master 12-7
- Enrichment Master 12-7
- Modeling Mathematics Masters, p. 72
- Multicultural Activity Masters, p. 24
- Real-World Applications, 32
- Tech Prep Applications Masters, p. 24

 Transparency 12-7A contains the 5-Minute Check for this lesson; **Transparency 12-7B** contains a teaching aid for this lesson.

Recommended Pacing	
Standard Pacing	Days 7 & 8 of 12
Honors Pacing	Day 7 of 10
Block Scheduling*	Day 4 of 6

 *For more information on pacing and possible lesson plans, refer to the *Block Scheduling Booklet.*

1 FOCUS

 5-Minute Check
(over Lesson 12-6)

1. A bag contains 6 red and 5 white marbles. Three are selected. What is the probability that exactly 2 white marbles are drawn?
$\frac{4}{11} \approx 0.363$

2. Find the probability of selecting 2 kings or 2 red cards from a deck of 52 cards.
$\frac{55}{221} \approx 0.249$

3. There are 8 red, 3 blue, and 12 black marbles in a bag. if 3 are selected, what is the probability that all are red or all are blue?
$\frac{57}{1771} \approx 0.032$

12-7

Binomial Experiments and Simulations

 **APPLICATION**
Basketball

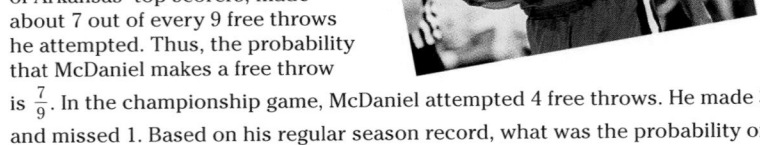

What YOU'LL LEARN

- To use binomial experiments to find probabilities, and
- to use simulation to solve various probability problems.

Why IT'S IMPORTANT

You can use binomial experiments to solve problems involving basketball and biology.

In 1995, Arkansas played UCLA for the NCAA championship. During the regular season, Clint McDaniel, one of Arkansas' top scorers, made about 7 out of every 9 free throws he attempted. Thus, the probability that McDaniel makes a free throw is $\frac{7}{9}$. In the championship game, McDaniel attempted 4 free throws. He made 3 and missed 1. Based on his regular season record, what was the probability of making 3 of 4?

Let S stand for scoring when he attempts a free throw. Let M stand for missing when he attempts a free throw.

The possible ways of scoring on 3 free throws and missing 1 free throw are shown at the right. This shows the combination of 4 things (free throws) taken three at a time (scores), or $C(4, 3)$.

M,	S,	S,	S
S,	M,	S,	S
S,	S,	M,	S
S,	S,	S,	M

LOOK BACK

You can refer to Lesson 11-8 for more information on binomial expansion.

The terms of the binomial expansion of $(S + M)^4$ can be used to find the probabilities of each combination of scores and misses.

$$(S + M)^4 = S^4 + 4S^3M + 6S^2M^2 + 4SM^3 + M^4$$

Coefficient	Term	Meaning
$C(4, 4) = 1$	S^4	1 way to score all 4 times
$C(4, 3) = 4$	$4S^3M$	4 ways to score 3 times and miss 1 time
$C(4, 2) = 6$	$6S^2M^2$	6 ways to score 2 times and miss 2 times
$C(4, 1) = 4$	$4SM^3$	4 ways to score 1 time and miss 3 times
$C(4, 0) = 1$	M^4	1 way to miss all 4 times

The probability that McDaniel scores on a free throw is $\frac{7}{9}$. So, the probability that he misses is $\frac{2}{9}$. To find the probability of scoring 3 out of 4 free throws, substitute $\frac{7}{9}$ for S and $\frac{2}{9}$ for M in the term $4S^3M$.

$$4S^3M = 4\left(\frac{7}{9}\right)^3\left(\frac{2}{9}\right)$$
$$= \frac{2744}{6561} \text{ or about } 0.418$$

So the probability of Clint McDaniel making 3 out of 4 free throws during the championship game was about 42%, given his regular season record.

Problems that can be solved using binomial expansion are called **binomial experiments**.

Conditions of a Binomial Experiment	A binomial experiment exists *if and only if* these conditions occur. • There are exactly two possible outcomes for any trial. • There is a fixed number of trials. • The trials are independent. • The probability of each trial is the same.

Example

Dwight forgot to read the newspaper to prepare for the social studies quiz on current events, so he had to guess on all five true/false questions on the quiz. What is the probability that he will get 3 answers right and 2 answers wrong?

There are only two possible outcomes for each question, right or wrong. There are five questions on the quiz, and they are independent. The probability of guessing an answer correctly is $\frac{1}{2}$. This problem meets all the conditions outlined above. Thus, it is a binomial experiment.

Let R represent guessing the answer correctly, and let W represent guessing the answer incorrectly. When $(R + W)^5$ is expanded, the term R^3W^2 represents 3 correct answers and 2 incorrect answers. The coefficient of R^3W^2 is $C(5, 3)$.

$P(\text{3 correct, 2 incorrect})$

$= C(5, 3)R^3W^2$ *Replace R with P(R) and W with P(W).*

$= \frac{5 \cdot 4}{2 \cdot 1}\left(\frac{1}{2}\right)^3\left(\frac{1}{2}\right)^2$ or $\frac{5}{16}$ *Both P(R) and P(W) equal $\frac{1}{2}$.*

Thus, the probability that Dwight will get 3 answers right and 2 answers wrong is $\frac{5}{16}$ or about 0.313.

Example ❷

APPLICATION
Consumerism

An article in *USA Today* reported that approximately 1 out of 6 cars sold in 1994 was green. Suppose a salesperson sells 7 cars per week. What is the probability that he or she sells at least 3 green cars in a week?

Explore   There are two possible outcomes for car color: green or not green. Since 1 out of 6 cars sold was green, the probability of selling a car that is green is $\frac{1}{6}$. The probability of selling a car that is *not* green is $\frac{5}{6}$.

Let G represent the probability that a car sold is green.

Let N represent the probability that a car sold is *not* green.

Plan   Look at the binomial expansion of $(G + N)^7$.

$(G + N)^7 = G^7 + 7G^6N + 21G^5N^2 + 35G^4N^3 + 35G^3N^4 + 21G^2N^5 + 7GN^6 + N^7$

The probability of selling at least 3 green cars equals the sum of the probabilities of selling 3, 4, 5, 6, or all 7 green cars.

(continued on the next page)

Lesson 12–7 Binomial Experiments and Simulations **753**

2 TEACH

Teaching Tip The binomial expansion on page 752 may be incorporated with combination notation. Thus, $(S + M)^4$ can be expanded as $C(4, 4)S^4 + C(4, 3)S^3M + C(4, 2)S^2M^2 + C(4, 1)SM^3 + C(4, 0)M^4$.

Teaching Tip On page 752, you may want to give students another example, such as the probability for scoring twice and missing twice, to be sure they understand how to use the binomial expansion.

In-Class Examples
For Example 1 A die is tossed 6 times. Find the probability that only one toss shows a 3. $\frac{3125}{7776} \approx 0.402$
For Example 2 Peggy guesses on all 10 questions of a true-false test. Find the probability that she gets exactly 8 correct. $\frac{45}{1024} \approx 0.044$

In-Class Examples

For Example 3
A family has five children. What is the probability that four of the children are girls and the other is a boy? $\frac{5}{32} = 0.15625$

Teaching Tip A simulation device does not have to have the exact number of choices as are in the problem if the choices for the device can be divided into that number of categories. For example, a deck of cards could be used for Example 3 if hearts represent white and all other suits represent green.

Teaching Tip Be sure students understand that the more simulated trials done, the more reliable the results. Computers can quickly run simulations for a large number of trials.

fabulous
FIRSTS

Florence R. Sabin was also the first woman elected President of the American Association of Anatomists (1924) and the first female member of the National Academy of Science (1925).

Solve P(at least 3 green cars)

$$= G^7 + 7G^6N + 21G^5N^2 + 35G^4N^3 + 35G^3N^4$$

$$= \left(\frac{1}{6}\right)^7 + 7\left(\frac{1}{6}\right)^6\left(\frac{5}{6}\right) + 21\left(\frac{1}{6}\right)^5\left(\frac{5}{6}\right)^2 + 35\left(\frac{1}{6}\right)^4\left(\frac{5}{6}\right)^3 + 35\left(\frac{1}{6}\right)^3\left(\frac{5}{6}\right)^4$$

$$= \frac{1}{279,936} + \frac{35}{279,936} + \frac{525}{279,936} + \frac{4375}{279,936} + \frac{21,875}{279,936} \text{ or } \frac{8937}{93,312}$$

The probability that the salesperson sells at least 3 cars is $\frac{8937}{93,312}$, or about 0.096.

Examine Check to see if the answer makes sense. The probability of selling 0, 1, or 2 green cars is 0.904 and $1 - 0.904$ is 0.096. Thus, the answer is correct.

Up to this point in this text, all of the probabilities we have found have been **theoretical probabilities.** They are determined using mathematical methods and provide an idea of what might happen in a given situation.

Experimental probability is determined by performing tests or experiments and observing the outcomes. One method for finding experimental probability is **simulation.** In a simulation, a device is used to model the event, and you observe how the model responds to the conditions listed in a given problem. This process saves long and difficult samplings.

Example **3**

Biology

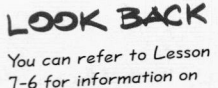
You can refer to Lesson 7-6 for information on simulation.

fabulous
FIRSTS

Florence R. Sabin
(1871–1953)

Florence Sabin became the first female member of the National Academy of Sciences in 1925 after being the first woman to graduate from the Johns Hopkins University School of Medicine in 1900.

While studying genetics, students in a biology class perform a lab experiment in which they each plant 4 corn seeds to determine the plants' gene combinations. The Punnett square at the right shows that green parent plants (Gg) produce green plants (GG and Gg) and albino, or white, plants (gg). What is the probability that at least one of a student's plants will be white?

		G	g
G		GG	Gg
g		Gg	gg

From the Punnett square, we know $P(\text{white}) = \frac{1}{4}$ and $P(\text{green}) = \frac{3}{4}$. We could spin a spinner like the one below four times to simulate the colors of four plants. The green section (G) represents the probability that a plant will be green. The white section (W) represents the probability that a plant will be white.

Now spin the spinner 4 times and record your results. Below are the results of 20 trials.

GGWG	GGGW	GWGW	GWWG	**GGGG**
GGGG	WGWW	GGGW	WGGG	GWGG
WWGG	**GGGG**	WGGG	GGWG	**GGGG**
GWGG	**GGGG**	**GGGG**	WGGG	WGGW

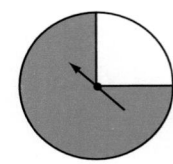

The trials in blue represent at least one white plant.

In our simulation, 14 of 20 trials yielded at least one W, or at least one white plant. Therefore, based on this simulation, the probability that at least one plant out of four will be white is $\frac{14}{20}$ or about 0.7.

GLENCOE *Technology*

 Interactive Mathematics Tools Software

This multimedia software provides an interactive lesson by computing probability using binomial expansions in the situation of basketball shooting averages. A **Computer Journal** gives students an opportunity to write about what they have learned.

For Windows & Macintosh

Other devices can be used to create simulations. For example, to find the probability that two out of three children are boys, you could toss three coins and let heads be one gender and tails be the other or roll three dice and let odd numbers be one gender and even numbers be the other. Another way to use the dice is to let the numbers 1, 2, and 3 represent boys and 4, 5, and 6 represent girls.

MODELING MATHEMATICS

Experimental vs. Theoretical Probability

Materials: individual-size packages of candy (M&M's®, Skittles®, or Reese's Pieces®)

Work in groups of four.

- Each person should open a bag of candy, but *not* look into the bag. Each should then remove one piece of candy from the bag. Record the color of the candy on a group chart and then put the candy back in the bag. (Don't eat the candy until this experiment is finished!)
- Repeat this task 20 times and record your findings.
- Determine the experimental probability of each color for your group. Then determine the experimental probability of each color for the entire class.
- Empty your bags and count the actual number of items of each color. Determine the theoretical probability of each color for your group. Then

determine the theoretical probability of each color for the entire class.

Your Turn

a. Compare the experimental to the theoretical probabilities. Which pair of probabilities were closer to each other: your individual probabilities, your group's probabilities, or your class's probabilities? Why do you think this is the case? **See margin.**

b. How different do you think the results would be if you dumped a large bag of candy into a bowl on each table and conducted the experiment again? **See students' work.**

CHECK FOR UNDERSTANDING

Communicating Mathematics

Study the lesson. Then complete the following.

1. **List** the conditions that must be satisfied for a problem to be classified as a binomial experiment. **See margin.**

2. **Draw** a tree diagram to answer the question in the application at the beginning of the lesson. **See Solutions Manual.**

3. Sample answer: coins, dice, spinners, random draws from a bag.

4. See students' work.

5. The results will be closer to the theoretical probability.

7. The theoretical probability is $\frac{11}{16}$.

3. **Name** some objects that could be used to simulate a given situation.

4. **Describe** a situation in which a simulation would not be useful.

5. **Explain** how increasing the number of trials in a simulation affects the results.

6. Refer to Example 3.

   a. Use binomial expansion to find the probability that at least one of a student's plants will be white. **about 68.4%**

   b. Compare your results with those obtained by simulation. **See students' work.**

7. **Model** the following problem using any type of device you choose and use simulation to find the probability. If a family has 4 children, what is the probability that at least 2 are boys?

Lesson 12–7 Binomial Experiments and Simulations **755**

Reteaching

Using Reasoning Have students develop four different experiments. None of these are to be binomial experiments. Experiment 1 will meet all but the first condition on page 753. Experiment 2 will meet all but the second condition, and so on.

Additional Answers

1. A binomial experiment exists if and only if these conditions occur.
   a. There are exactly 2 possible outcomes for any trial.
   b. There is a fixed number of trials.
   c. The trials are independent.
   d. The probability of each trial is the same.

 This activity illustrates the difference between experimental and theoretical probability. Point out to students that the probabilities that they compute from the experiment may be very different from the theoretical probability.

Answer for Modeling Mathematics

a. Sample answer: The class's probabilities should be closer to the theoretical probability since there is a greater number of trials. As the number of trials increases, the value of the experimental probability approaches the value of the theoretical probability.

3 PRACTICE/APPLY

Check for Understanding

Exercises 1–11 are designed to help you assess your students' understanding through reading, writing, speaking, and modeling. You should work through Exercises 1–7 with your students and then monitor their work on Exercises 8–11.

Study Guide Masters, p. 90

12-7

NAME_____ DATE_____

Study Guide

Student Edition Pages 748–753

Binomial Experiments and Simulations

Problems that can be solved using binomial expansion are called **binomial experiments**. A binomial experiment exists if and only if the following conditions occur.

1. There are exactly two possible outcomes for any trial.
2. There is a fixed number of trials.
3. The trials are independent.
4. The probability for a given outcome is the same for each trial.

Example: What is the probability that 4 coins show heads and 1 shows tails when 5 coins are tossed?

There are only two possible outcomes: heads (H) and tails (T). The tosses of 5 coins are independent events. When $(H + T)^5$ is expanded, the term containing H^4T^1, which represents 4 heads and 1 tail, is used to get the desired probabilities. The coefficient of H^4T^1 is $C(5, 4)$.

$P(4 \text{ heads}, 1 \text{ tail}) = C(5, 4) \; H^4T^1$ Replace H with $P(H)$ which is $\frac{1}{2}$.

$= \frac{5!}{4!1!} \left(\frac{1}{2}\right)^4 \left(\frac{1}{2}\right)^1$ or $\frac{5}{32}$ Replace T with $P(T)$ which is $\frac{1}{2}$.

The probability of 4 heads and 1 tail is $\frac{5}{32}$ or approximately 0.156.

Find each probability if a coin is tossed five times.

1. $P(2 \text{ heads})$
   $\frac{5}{16}$ or 0.3125

2. $P(\text{at least 2 heads})$
   $\frac{13}{16}$ or 0.8125

Mike guesses on all 10 questions of a true-false test. Find each probability.

3. Mike gets exactly 8 correct.
   $\frac{45}{1024}$ or 0.044

4. Mike gets at most 3 correct.
   $\frac{11}{64}$ or 0.172

5. A die is tossed 4 times. What is the probability of tossing exactly two sixes?
   $\frac{25}{216}$ or 0.116

6. A die is tossed 6 times. What is the probability of getting exactly one 3?
   $\frac{3125}{7776}$ or 0.402

Assignment Guide

Core: 13–33 odd, 34–39
Enriched: 12–30 even, 31–39

For **Extra Practice,** see p. 905.

The red A, B, and C flags, printed only in the Teacher's Wraparound Edition, indicate the level of difficulty of the exercises.

Guided Practice

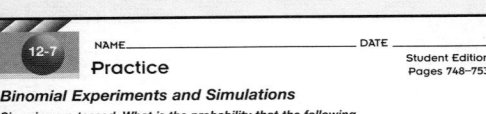

Determine whether each situation represents a binomial experiment. Solve those that represent a binomial experiment.

8. What is the probability of 1 head and 2 tails if Jordan tosses a coin 3 times?

9. What is the probability of Vanessa drawing 4 jacks from a deck of cards for each condition?
   a. She replaces the card each time.   **b.** She does not replace the card.

10. Four cans of root beer, 8 cans of diet cola, and 6 cans of orange soda are placed in a cooler. Two cans are randomly selected with replacement after the first selection. Find each probability.
    a. both diet   **b.** both root beer   **c.** both orange
    d. 1 diet, 1 root beer   **e.** 1 diet, 1 orange   **f.** 1 root beer, 1 orange
       not binomial   not binomial   not binomial

11. **Traffic Control**   The probability that a traffic light at Morse Road is green is $\frac{3}{5}$. What is the probability that exactly 4 of the next 7 cars will have to stop? $\frac{3024}{15,625} \approx 0.194$

8. binomial, $\frac{3}{8}$ 9a. binomial, $\frac{1}{28,561}$ 9b. not binomial

10a. $\frac{16}{81} \approx 0.198$ 10b. $\frac{4}{81} \approx 0.049$ 10c. $\frac{1}{9} \approx 0.111$

EXERCISES

Practice

12. $\frac{1}{16} \approx 0.063$

13. $\frac{3}{8} = 0.375$

14. $\frac{5}{16} \approx 0.313$

Find each probability if a coin is tossed four times.

12. P(all tails)   13. P(2 heads, 2 tails)   14. P(at least 3 tails)

Find each probability if a die is rolled five times.

15. P(only one 5)   16. P(at least three 5s)   17. P(no more than two 5s)
    $\frac{3125}{7776} \approx 0.402$ $\frac{276}{7776} \approx 0.035$ $\frac{625}{648} \approx 0.965$

As an apartment manager, Anne Lewis is responsible for showing prospective renters the different model apartments. When showing a model, the probability of pulling out the correct key from her set of apartment keys is $\frac{1}{4}$. If she shows 5 models in a day, find each probability.

18. $\frac{243}{1024} \approx 0.237$

19. $\frac{1}{64} \approx 0.016$

20. $\frac{1023}{1024} \approx 0.999$

21. $\frac{45}{512} \approx 0.088$

22. $\frac{105}{512} \approx 0.205$

23. $\frac{319}{512} \approx 0.623$

24. $\frac{1}{1024} \approx 0.001$

18. P(never the correct key)   19. P(correct at least 4 times)

20. P(no more than 4 times correct)   21. P(correct exactly 3 times)

Prisana guesses at all 10 true/false questions on her economics test. Find each probability.

22. P(6 correct)   23. P(at least half correct)   24. P(all wrong)

Luis Gonzalez of the Houston Astros has a batting average of 0.300 (meaning 300 hits in 1000 times at bat). Find each probability for the next 5 times at bat.

25. P(exactly 2 hits)   26. P(at least 2 hits)   27. P(at least 4 hits)
    ≈ 0.309 ≈ 0.472 ≈ 0.031

28. ≈ 0.213
29. ≈ 0.0000168
30. ≈ 0.562

If a thumbtack is dropped, the probability of its landing point up is 0.4. If 12 tacks are dropped, find each probability.

28. P(exactly 4 points up)   29. P(all points up)   30. P(at least 5 points up)

Practice Masters, p. 90

 12-7

NAME_____   DATE _____
Practice   Student Edition
                                Pages 748–753

Binomial Experiments and Simulations

Six coins are tossed. What is the probability that the following occurs?

1. 3 heads and 3 tails $\frac{5}{16}$ 2. at least 4 heads $\frac{11}{32}$

3. 2 heads or 5 tails $\frac{21}{64}$ 4. all heads or all tails $\frac{1}{32}$

The probability of Chris making a free throw is $\frac{2}{3}$. If she shoots five times, what is the probability of the following?

5. all missed $\frac{1}{243}$ 6. all made $\frac{32}{243}$

7. exactly 4 made $\frac{80}{243}$ 8. at least 3 made $\frac{64}{81}$

When Mary and Sam play a certain board game, the probability that Mary will win a game is $\frac{3}{4}$. If they play five games, find the probability of each event.

9. Sam wins only once. $\frac{405}{1024}$ 10. Mary wins exactly twice. $\frac{45}{512}$

11. Sam wins at least two games. $\frac{47}{128}$ 12. Mary wins at least three games. $\frac{509}{512}$

31. Football Luke Monroe is a quarterback on the football team at Jacksonville High School. In his freshman season, he has completed $\frac{2}{3}$ of his passes. Assume he will do the same in his sophomore year. Use a simulation to find the probability of completing at least 6 of 10 passes for an entire game if he has already completed 4 of 5 passes in the first half.
0.95

Applications and Problem Solving

32. World Cultures The Cayuga Indians played a game of chance called *Dish*, in which they used 6 smoothed and flattened peach stones blackened on one side by burning. They placed the peach stones in a wooden bowl and tossed them. The winner was the first person to get a prearranged number of points. The table below shows the points that were given for each toss. Assume that each face (black or neutral) has an equal chance of showing up.

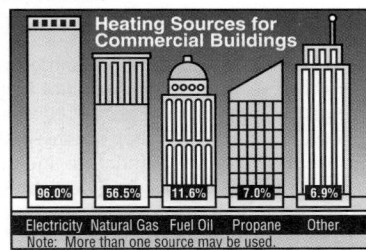

a. Copy and complete the table by finding the probability of each outcome.

b. Find the probability that a player gets at least 1 point for a toss. (*Hint:* Find P(at least 5 black) + P(at least 5 neutral).) $\frac{7}{32}$

Outcomes	Points	Probability
6 black	5	1/64
5 black, 1 neutral	1	6/64
4 black, 2 neutral	0	15/64
3 black, 3 neutral	0	20/64
2 black, 4 neutral	0	15/64
1 black, 5 neutral	1	6/64
6 neutral	5	1/64

Heating Sources for Commercial Buildings

Electricity	Natural Gas	Fuel Oil	Propane	Other
96.0%	56.5%	11.6%	7.0%	6.9%

Note: More than one source may be used.

Source: Energy Information Administration, 1992

33. Energy The graph at the left displays the various heating sources for commercial buildings. Find the probability that on a street with 6 commercial buildings, at least 1 is heated with propane.
about 0.353

Mixed Review

34. Probability There are 8 girls and 8 boys on the faculty advisory committee. Three are juniors. Find the probability of selecting a boy or a girl from the committee who is not a junior. (Lesson 12–6)

34. $\frac{13}{16}$

35. Use a calculator to find the common logarithm of 349.948, rounded to four decimal places. Then state the characteristic and the mantissa. (Lesson 10–4)

35. 2.5440; 2; 0.5440

36. Graph $y = \frac{-3x}{x-1}$. (Lesson 9–1) **See margin.**

37. Use the distance formula to find the distance between $(9, 6)$ and $(8, 0)$. (Lesson 7–1)

37. $\sqrt{37}$ units

38. Business Images Camera Shop can sell 21 KS-2 cameras a month at $120 each. The owner estimates that for each $5 decrease in price, they could sell three more of these cameras a month. The cameras cost the store $75 each. (Lesson 6–3)

a. If the store sells all of the cameras bought each month, what should they charge for a camera to maximize profit? **$115**

b. What is the maximum profit? **$960**

39. Find $\begin{bmatrix} -3 & 14 & 12 \\ -2 & -1 & 7 \end{bmatrix} + \begin{bmatrix} 1 & -5 & 10 \\ 22 & 13 & -8 \end{bmatrix}$. (Lesson 4–2) $\begin{bmatrix} -2 & 9 & 22 \\ 20 & 12 & -1 \end{bmatrix}$

Extension

Problem Solving A student is guessing the answers on a true-false test of 9 questions. He will pass the test if he answers 5 questions correctly. The teacher has graded 8 questions and notices that he must answer the last question correctly in order to pass. What is the probability that he will pass? $\frac{35}{256} \approx 0.137$

4 ASSESS

Closing Activity
Writing Have students list reasons that a simulation may be useful.

Additional Answer

36.
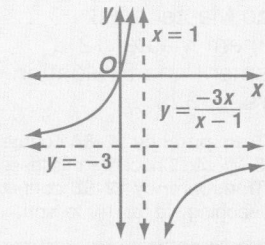

Enrichment Masters, p. 90

12-7 NAME _____ DATE _____
Enrichment Student Edition Pages 748–753

Conditional Probability

Suppose a pair of dice is thrown. It is known that the sum is greater than seven. Find the probability that the dice match.

The probability of an event given the occurrence of another event is called *conditional probability*. The conditional probability of event A, the dice match, given event B, their sum is greater than seven, is denoted $P(A/B)$.

There are 15 sums greater than seven and there are 36 possible pairs altogether.

There are three matching pairs greater than seven.

$$P(B) = \frac{15}{36} \qquad P(A \text{ and } B) = \frac{3}{36}$$

$$P(A/B) = \frac{P(A \text{ and } B)}{P(B)}$$

$$P(A/B) = \frac{\frac{3}{36}}{\frac{15}{36}} \text{ or } \frac{1}{5}$$

The conditional probability is $\frac{1}{5}$.

A card is drawn from a standard deck of 52 and is found to be red. Given that event, find each of the following probabilities.

1. P(heart) $\frac{1}{2}$
2. P(ace) $\frac{1}{13}$
3. P(face card) $\frac{3}{13}$
4. P(jack or ten) $\frac{2}{13}$
5. P(six of spades) 0
6. P(six of hearts) $\frac{1}{26}$

A sports survey taken at Stirers High School shows that 48% of the respondents liked soccer, 66% liked basketball, and 38% liked hockey. Also, 30% liked soccer and basketball, 22% liked basketball and hockey, and 28% liked soccer and hockey. Finally, 12% liked all three sports. Find each of the following probabilities.

7. The probability Meg likes soccer if she likes basketball. $\frac{30}{66}$ or $\frac{5}{11}$
8. The probability Biff likes basketball if he likes soccer. $\frac{30}{48}$ or $\frac{5}{8}$
9. The probability Muffy likes hockey if she likes basketball. $\frac{22}{66}$ or $\frac{1}{3}$
10. The probability Greg likes hockey and basketball if he likes soccer. $\frac{12}{48}$ or $\frac{1}{4}$

NCTM Standards: 1–4, 11–12

Instructional Resources

- Study Guide Master 12-8
- Practice Master 12-8
- Enrichment Master 12-8
- Assessment and Evaluation Masters, p. 325

Transparency 12-8A contains the 5-Minute Check for this lesson; **Transparency 12-8B** contains a teaching aid for this lesson.

Recommended Pacing	
Standard Pacing	Days 9 & 10 of 12
Honors Pacing	Day 8 of 10
Block Scheduling*	Day 5 of 6

*For more information on pacing and possible lesson plans, refer to the *Block Scheduling Booklet.*

1 FOCUS

5-Minute Check
(over Lesson 12-7)

Find each probability if a coin is tossed five times.

1. P(all heads) $\frac{1}{32}$

2. P(one head) $\frac{5}{32}$

3. P(four heads) $\frac{27}{32}$

4. P(no heads) $\frac{1}{32}$

Motivating the Lesson

Situational Problem Suppose you wanted to predict who will win the presidential election. It is the day before the vote. You sit down at your telephone to ask Americans how they will vote tomorrow. You can't call everyone. You decide that you have time to call 200 households. How would you decide which 200 households to call?

Sampling and Testing Hypotheses

What YOU'LL LEARN

- To determine an unbiased sample,
- to find margins of sampling error, and
- to test hypotheses by designing and conducting experiments.

Why IT'S IMPORTANT

Sampling and hypothesis testing are used to help analyze and describe data.

APPLICATION
Sports

Do you think that professional athletes, celebrities, and entertainers are overpaid, underpaid, or are paid just about the right amount? A survey taken by the Roper Starch marketing firm in May, 1994, of a group of 1996 men and women ages 18 and over found that 87% of the respondents said that they thought pro athletes were overpaid.

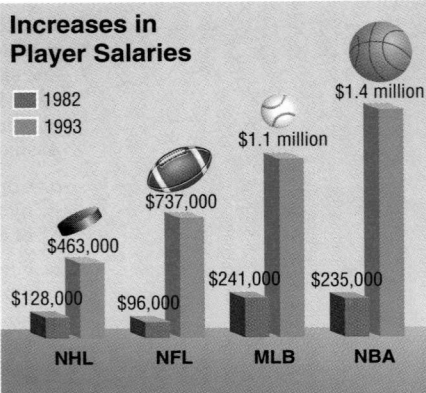

Increases in Player Salaries

- 1982
- 1993

NHL $128,000 / $463,000
NFL $96,000 / $737,000
MLB $241,000 / $1.1 million
NBA $235,000 / $1.4 million

Source: *USA TODAY* research

When opinion polling organizations or marketing firms want to find out how the public feels about some issue, they do not have the time or money to ask everyone. Instead, they obtain their results by asking a small portion of the people in the population in which they are interested. To be sure that the results are representative of the population and are unbiased, they need to make sure that this portion is a **random** or **unbiased sample** of the population. A sample of size n is random when every possible sample of size n has an equal chance to be selected.

Example 1 **Do you think that the following methods will produce a random sample?**

a. pointing with your pencil at a class list while your eyes are shut as a way to find a random sample of students in your class

This would probably not result in a random sample because you will tend to point toward the middle of the page. So, those at the beginning or end of the page will have less of a chance to be selected.

b. putting the names of all seniors in a hat, then drawing names from the hat to determine a random sample of seniors

This would result in a random sample because each senior will have an equal chance to be selected.

c. selecting one person whose last name begins with each letter of the alphabet to find a random sample of students in your grade

This would not result in a random sample because there are many more people with last names beginning with some letters than with others. For example, there are many more last names beginning with s or t than with q or z. Those people whose last names begin with s would have a smaller chance of being selected than those whose last names begin with q.

Alternative Learning Styles

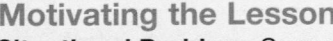

Auditory Refer to the most recent presidential election. Find an article that polled voters about their voting preferences. Read the article to students. Have them identify the probability concepts in the article, especially margin of error.

Suppose you take repeated random samples of a population. How close will the sample results be to the population results? It is reasonable to think that the sample data will not be exactly like the population data, but they should be similar. As the size of the sample increases, it more accurately reflects the population. If you sampled only three people and two prefer Brand A, you could say, "Two out of three people choose Brand A over any other brand," but you would not be giving a true picture of how the total population would respond. The **sampling error** is the difference between the sample results and the true population results.

Margin of Sampling Error	If the percentage of people in a sample responding in a certain way is *p* and the size of the sample is *n*, then 95% of the time, the percentage of the population responding in that same way will be within $p \pm ME$, where $$ME = 2\sqrt{\frac{p(1-p)}{n}}.$$ *ME* is called the *margin of sampling error*.

That is, the probability is 0.95 that $p \pm ME$ will contain the true population results.

Example ② In a *Washington Post* survey of 1003 randomly-selected adults published on May 26, 1995, 61% of those surveyed said they regret things they didn't do in their lives. What is the margin of error?

$$ME = 2\sqrt{\frac{p(1-p)}{n}}$$

$$= 2\sqrt{\frac{0.61(1-0.61)}{1003}} \quad p = 61\% \text{ or } 0.61; n = 1003$$

$$\approx 0.030802 \quad \text{Use a calculator.}$$

0.030802 would be reported as a 3% margin of error. This means that there is a 95% probability that the value of *p* in the population is between $61 - 3$ or 58% and $61 + 3$ or 64% and that 58% to 64% of adults regret things they didn't do in their lives.

Example ③

Sports

Refer to the application at the beginning of the lesson. In a survey taken in May, 1994, 87% of the people surveyed stated that they thought pro athletes were overpaid. This survey had a margin of error of 4%.

a. What does the 4% indicate about the results?

b. How many people were surveyed?

a. The 4% means that there is a 95% probability that the value of *p* in the population is between $87 - 4$ or 83% and $87 + 4$ or 91% and that 83% to 91% of the population believes that pro athletes are overpaid.

b.
$$ME = 2\sqrt{\frac{p(1-p)}{n}}$$

$$0.04 = 2\sqrt{\frac{0.87(1-0.87)}{n}} \quad ME = 0.04 \text{ and } p = 0.87$$

$$0.02 = \sqrt{\frac{0.87(0.13)}{n}} \quad \text{Divide each side by 2.}$$

$$0.0004 = \frac{0.87(0.13)}{n} \quad \text{Square each side.}$$

$$n = 282.75 \quad \text{Use a calculator.}$$

Since it is not possible for 0.75 of a person to exist, round down. Thus, there were about 282 people in the survey.

Lesson 12–8 Sampling and Testing Hypotheses **759**

 Alternative Learning Styles

Kinesthetic You might want to add an exercise where students do a simulation about something they expect to happen and describe the variability around the outcomes: Toss a ten-sided die 30 times to see how many times 1, 2, 3, and 4 occur. Repeat this working in a group so you have about 50 sets of 30 tosses. (This can simulate a population where 30% have a certain characteristic. Also look for the variability in the sampling process. How many with that characteristic would you expect to find? 0.4×30 or 12, but there will be a certain natural variation about the 12. The experiment will reveal the nature of that variation.)

2 TEACH

In-Class Examples

For Example 1
Will the following methods produce a random sample?

a. Determine what percent of Americans are Democrats by selecting 100 people at random from New York City.
no

b. Determine what percent of Americans are Democrats by selecting 2 people at random from each state. yes

For Example 2
Suppose 42% of those surveyed said they regret things they didn't do in their lives. What is the margin of error?
0.031

For Example 3
Suppose the margin of error had been reported as 2%.

a. What does the 2% indicate about the results? There is a 95% probability that 85% to 89% of the population believe that professional athletes are overpaid.

b. How many people were surveyed? 1131

Teaching Tip Point out to students that in the formula for the margin of sampling error, as *n*, the sample size, becomes larger, the value of *ME* becomes smaller.

Teaching Tip Point out that the formula is valid only if the samples are independent and the sample sizes are large.

MODELING MATHEMATICS Design an experiment to test the hypothesis that people can crawl faster than they can hop on one leg. Follow steps 1 through 4 as in the activity.

3 PRACTICE/APPLY

Check for Understanding

Exercises 1–8 are designed to help you assess your students' understanding through reading, writing, speaking, and modeling. You should work through Exercises 1–2 with your students and then monitor their work on Exercises 3–8.

Additional Answers

2. The margin of sampling error decreases when the size of the sample n increases. As n increases, $\frac{p(1-p)}{n}$ decreases.

5. There is a 95% probability that the value of p in the population is between $68 - 4$ or 64% and $68 + 4$ or 72% and that 64% to 72% of high school students are involved in extracurricular activities.

Study Guide Masters, p. 91

12-8 NAME_____ DATE_____
Student Edition
Pages 754–760

Study Guide

Sampling and Testing Hypotheses

A sample of size n is random when every possible sample of size n has an equal chance of being selected.

Example: Determine whether this situation represents a random sampling.

To determine how people in the U.S. feel about mass transit, we decide to stop people at a commuter train station and ask their opinion.

No; we would be questioning only people who actually use a mass-transit facility. The sample would not include people who prefer to ride a bike, drive a car, or walk.

The sampling error is the difference between the sample results and the true population results. If the percentage of people in a sample responding in a certain way is p and the size of the sample is n, then 95% of the time, the percentage of the population responding in that same way will be within $p \pm$ ME where ME $= 2\sqrt{\frac{p(1-p)}{n}}$.

Example: Find the margin of sampling error in this situation and explain what it indicates about the results.

A high-school counselor sent a letter to each member of the preceding year's graduating class of 172 members, asking how well he or she was doing in college. 83% said that they were "having a great year" or "doing well."

ME $= 2\sqrt{\frac{0.83(1-0.83)}{172}} = 2(0.01147) \approx 2.3\%$

This 2.3% means that there is a 95% probability that between 80.8% and 85.2% of the population believes they are "having a great year" or "doing well."

Determine whether this situation represents a random sampling. Write yes or no and explain.

1. Asking people in Phoenix, Arizona, to determine the average rainfall for the United States **No; it rains less in Phoenix than most places in the U.S.**
2. Obtaining a variety of tree types in North America from all of the U.S. National Forests **Yes; there are National Forests in about every state in the U.S.**

Find the margin of sampling error in Exercises 3 and 4. Explain what it indicates about the results.

3. A survey by the makers of Sneezarrest capsules claimed that in a poll of 200 doctors, 90% of the physicians surveyed preferred their product. **ME = 1.3% There is a 95% probability that 88.7–91.3% of the doctors preferred Sneezarrest.**
4. A study of 50,000 drivers in Indiana, Illinois, and Ohio showed that 68% preferred a speed limit of 75 mph over 65 mph on highways and country roads. **ME = 0.4% There is a 95% probability that 67.6–68.4% preferred a 75 mph speed limit on highways.**

A **hypothesis** is a statement to be tested. You can design an experiment to help you determine whether a hypothesis is true or false.

MODELING MATHEMATICS

Design an Experiment

Design an experiment to test the following hypothesis.
People react to sound and touch at the same rate.

Materials: meterstick   stopwatch   grid paper

Separate the class into two groups. You can measure reaction time by having someone drop a meterstick and then having someone else catch it between their fingers. The distance the stick falls will be directly proportional to their reaction time. Half of the class will investigate the time it takes to react when someone is told the stick has dropped. The other half will measure the time it takes to react when the catcher is alerted by a touch.

Step 1 Describe the variables that can be controlled.

Factors such as the length of the meterstick, the height from which it is dropped, the position of the person catching the stick, the number of practice runs, and whether to use one try or to take the average of several tries can be controlled.

Step 2 Describe the variables that should be randomized.

Factors such as whether boys or girls have a different reaction time should be randomized. Randomly assign boys and girls to each treatment.

Step 3 Conduct the experiment.

Conduct the experiment in each group and record the results. Organize the results so that they can be compared.

Step 4 Organize and summarize your results.

Based on the results of your experiment, do you think your hypothesis is true?

CHECK FOR UNDERSTANDING

Communicating Mathematics

Study the lesson. Then complete the following. 1. See students' work.

1. **Give** an example of a biased sample and a random sample.
2. **Explain** what happens to the margin of sampling error when the size of the sample n increases. Why does this happen? **See margin.**

Guided Practice

Determine whether each situation represents a random sampling. Write yes or no and explain.

3. collecting 1-digit numbers from license plates on cars on the interstate **yes**
4. surveying students in the advanced chemistry classes to determine the average time students in your school study each week **no**

Find the margin of sampling error in Exercises 5 and 6. Explain what it indicates about the results. **5–6. See margin for explanations.**

5. In a survey of 520 randomly-selected high school students, 68% of those surveyed stated that they were involved in extracurricular activities at their school. **4%**
6. In a survey of 1730 randomly-selected adults, 45% agreed that the results of call-in polls are believable. **2%**
7. **Media** According to a recent survey in *American Demographics,* 77% of Americans age 12 or older said they listen to the radio every day. Suppose the survey had a margin of error of 5%.
   a. What does the 5% indicate about the results? **See Solutions Manual.**
   b. How many people were surveyed? **283 people**

760 Chapter 12 *Investigating Discrete Mathematics and Probability*

Additional Answer

6. There is a 95% probability that the value of p in the population is between $45 - 2$ or 43% and $45 + 2$ or 47% and that 43% to 47% of adults believe that the results of call-in polls are believable.

Reteaching

Using Discussion Randomly select $\frac{1}{4}$ of the students in the class. How many are wearing blue? Predict the number of students in the room wearing blue. What might affect this prediction? How could students make the prediction more accurate? Keep track of the number of students wearing blue for one week. How closely does this match the prediction?

8. Design an experiment to test the following hypothesis. **See students' work.**
Students who eat breakfast regularly score higher on math tests than students who do not eat breakfast regularly.

EXERCISES

Practice

Determine whether each situation represents a random sampling. Write *yes* or *no* and explain.

9. yes

 A

9. obtaining a list of teenage girls' first names from your high school yearbook

10. yes

10. calling every twentieth person listed in the telephone book to determine which political candidate is favored

11. no

11. asking every tenth person coming out of a health spa how many times a week they exercise to determine how often people in the city exercise

12. finding the heights of all the boys in a freshman gym class to determine the average height of all the boys in your school   **no**

13. taking a poll during lunch to find how many students in your school would participate in a car wash fund-raiser   **yes**

Find the margin of sampling error in Exercises 14 and 15. Explain what it indicates about the results.   14–16. See margin for explanations.

 B

14. A poll conducted for the Robert Wood Johnson Foundation asked people to name the most serious problem facing the country. Forty-six percent of the randomly-selected people said crime. Find the margin of error if 800 people were randomly selected.   **4%**

15. Although skim milk has as much calcium as whole milk, only 33% of 2406 adults surveyed in *Shape* magazine said skim milk is a good calcium source.   **2%**

 C

16. According to *Vitality* magazine, in a recent survey of randomly-selected adults who smoked, 34% of those surveyed said they have tried to quit smoking. If this survey had a margin of error of 4%, how many people were surveyed?   **561 people**

Programming

17a. See students' work.

17. The graphing calculator program at the right creates a population of numbers with a mean of *M* and a standard deviation of *S*. It then draws a random sample of *N* data from the population and calculates the mean and standard deviation of that sample. You must enter *M*, *S*, and *N* when the program prompts you to do so. *It may take a little longer for the program to calculate a large sample.*

   a. Run the program for a population with a mean of 50 and a standard deviation of 5 for sample sizes of 5, 10, 50, 100, and 200. Record the data in a table.

```
PROGRAM: SAMPLE
: Prompt M, S, N
: 0→A:0→B
: For (K,1,N)
: 0→R
: For(L,1,12)
: rand+R→R
: End
: iPart (S*(R-6))+M→X
: A+X→A:B+X*X→B
: End
: B-A*A/N→B
: Disp "SAMPLE MEAN=",A/N
: Disp "SAMPLE S.D.=",
    √ (B/N)
: Stop
```

(continued on the next page)

Lesson 12-8 Sampling and Testing Hypotheses   **761**

Additional Answers

14. There is a 95% probability that the value of *p* in the population is between 46 − 4 or 42% and 46 + 4 or 50% and that 42% to 50% of the population believe that crime is the most serious problem facing the country.

15. There is a 95% probability that the value of *p* in the population is between 33 − 2 or 31% and 33 + 2 or 35% and that 31% to 35% of adults believe that skim milk is a good calcium source.

16. There is a 95% probability that the value of *p* in the population is between 34 − 4 or 30% and 34 + 4 or 38% and that 30% to 38% of adults who smoke have tried to quit smoking.

Assignment Guide

Core: 9–17 odd, 18, 19, 21–26
Enriched: 10–16 even, 17–26

For **Extra Practice,** see p. 906.

The red A, B, and C flags, printed only in the Teacher's Wraparound Edition, indicate the level of difficulty of the exercises.

Using the Programming Exercises The program given in Exercise 17 is for use with a TI-82 graphing calculator. For other programmable calculators, have students consult their owner's manual for commands similar to those presented here.

Practice Masters, p. 91

12-8   NAME_____   DATE_____
Practice   Student Edition
                                       Pages 754–760

Sampling and Testing Hypotheses

Determine whether each situation represents a random sampling. Write yes or no and explain.

1. You are calling every twentieth name in the telephone directory to determine if people own or rent their homes in your community.
   Yes; this is a random sample since most people in the community are listed in telephone directories.

2. A school's librarian was concerned because not many students were using the library. To find out why, she gave a questionnaire to every student entering the library.
   No; she is only polling the students who are coming to the library—not all of the students in the school.

3. Overall performance of tires is tested on highways.
   No; overall tire performance needs to be tested on all types of surface areas.

4. Presidential election results are predicted by polling people in every third home in different neighborhoods of your community.
   Yes; different neighborhoods will result in a good range of results.

Find the margin of sampling error in Exercises 5–7. Explain what it indicates about the results.

5. According to a poll of 500 teenagers, 43% said that they use a personal computer at home.
   ME = 4.4% There is a 95% probability that 38.6–47.4% of the students use a personal computer.

6. A survey of 605 people, ages 13–33, showed that 68% trust their parents more than their best friends to tell them the truth.
   ME = 3.8% There is a 95% probability that 64.2–71.8% of 13–33 year-olds trust their parents more than their best friends.

7. A study by the University of Illinois in 1995 showed a 10% increase in productivity of 75 employees who wore headsets and listened to the music of their choice while they were working.
   ME = 6.9% There is a 95% probability that there was a 3.1–16.9% increase in productivity of the employees who wore headsets and listened to music while they were working.

Chapter 12   **761**

Closing Activity

Modeling Select a tree and measure the lengths of 50 leaves. Determine how to select a random sample of leaves that will reflect the distribution of lengths of leaves on the entire tree.

Chapter 12, Quiz D (Lessons 12-7 and 12-8), is available in the *Assessment and Evaluation Masters*, p. 325.

Additional Answer

19a. There is a 95% probability that the value of *p* in the population is between 90 − 2 or 88% and 90 + 2 or 92% and that 88% to 92% of people registered to vote actually vote on election day.

Enrichment Masters, p. 91

NAME_____ DATE_____

Enrichment

Student Edition
Pages 754–760

12-8

The Harmonic Mean

The *harmonic mean*, H, is a useful measure of central tendency in special cases of averaging rates.

Example: Recently Kendra and Bill took a trip of 370 miles and shared the driving. Kendra drove two hours at a rate of 30 mph and then drove the next 100 miles on a freeway at 55 mph. Then Bill drove the next two hours at 30 mph and he drove the last 100 miles on a freeway at 55 mph. What was the average speed of each driver?

Kendra drove the same length of time on both portions of her driving, so her average speed is the mean of the two rates. Her average speed was $\frac{30 + 55}{2}$ or 42.5 mph.

On the other hand, Bill drove the same distance on both portions of his driving, but the two lengths of time varied. Actually, the time he drove was $\frac{100}{30} + \frac{100}{55}$, or approximately 5.15 hours. His average speed was $\frac{200}{5.15}$, or about 38.8 mph.

Bill's average speed may be found by using the formula for the harmonic mean as follows.

Let n = number of rates x_i where $1 \le i \le n$. $\quad H = \frac{n}{\sum \frac{1}{x_i}}$

We apply the formula to Bill's speeds. $\quad H = \frac{2}{\frac{1}{30} + \frac{1}{55}}$

$\qquad H \approx 38.8$ mph

The mean, also called the arithmetic mean, is used when equal times are involved. When equal distances are involved, the harmonic mean is used.

Find the harmonic mean of each set of data. Round each answer to the nearest hundredth.

1. {3, 4, 5, 6} 4.21   2. {5, 10, 15, 20, 25} 10.95

3. Bev, Phyllis, and Gordon competed in a 375-mile relay race. Bev drove 40 mph, Phyllis drove 50 mph, and Gordon drove 60 mph. If each drove 125 miles, find the average driving speed of the contestants. 48.65 mph

762 *Chapter 12*

17b–c. See students' work.

b. Find the average of the sample means and the average of the sample standard deviations. How closely do these averages match the population mean and standard deviation?

c. Look at the data for each of your samples. What conclusion can you draw about the size of the sample and how representative the sample is of the population?

Critical Thinking

18. Sample answer: The reported margin of error is too small, or the polls reach different populations.

18. The following excerpt appeared in *Chance* magazine in 1993.

> How big was Bill Clinton's lead on October 20, the day after the third presidential debate of the 1992 campaign? Nineteen points, reported NBC and *Wall Street Journal*. Fourteen points, said *U.S. News and World Report*. . . .And CNN gave us two answers—12 points in their poll done by the Gallup organization and 7 points in their poll conducted by Yankelovich-Clancy-Schulman. . . .News organizations report the results of their election surveys with a familiar caveat: The poll has a "margin of error," usually plus or minus three percentage points. If the survey were conducted repeatedly on the same population and if the only source of variability in the polls were random sampling, then in only 1 out of 20 tries would the results differ from those reported by more than 3%. . . .But they produced estimates of Clinton's lead that differed by as much as *12* percentage points.

List some possible explanations for the differences in these poll results.

Applications and Problem Solving

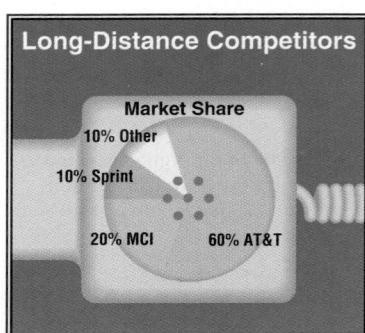

Long-Distance Competitors

Market Share
10% Other
10% Sprint
20% MCI
60% AT&T

Source: *USA TODAY* research

19. Politics To vote in a presidential election in most states, a person must be registered at least 30 days before election day. According to the postelection validation of registration and voting, about 90% of those people who were registered actually voted on election day. Suppose this postelection survey, which has been part of the National Election Study since 1964, had a margin of error of 2%.

a. What does the 2% indicate the results? See margin.

b. How many people were surveyed? 900 people

20. Consumerism A recent article in *USA Today* reported the percentage of telephone customers that use various long-distance companies. The data are shown at the left. Suppose 1500 telephone customers were randomly selected for the survey. Find the margin of error to the nearest tenth of a percent for each of the survey results.

a. AT&T 2.5%   **b.** MCI 2.1%   **c.** Sprint 1.5%

21. Design an experiment to test the following hypothesis.

People who exercise regularly fall asleep quicker at night than those who don't get regular exercise. See students' work.

Mixed Review

22. $\frac{1}{1024} \approx 0.001$

22. Probability Chris guessed at all ten questions on a true-false test. What is the probability that all of the guesses were correct? (Lesson 12–7)

23. Solve $2 \log_6 3 + 3 \log_6 2 = \log_6 x$. (Lesson 10–3) 72

24. Use synthetic substitution to find $f(3)$ and $f(-2)$ for all $f(x) = 2x^2 - 8x + 6$. (Lesson 8–2) 0, 30

25. Solve $x^2 \le 6$. (Lesson 6–7) $\{x | -\sqrt{6} \le x \le \sqrt{6}\}$

26. Solve $|m - 4| + 2 \ge 0$. (Lesson 1–7) all reals

Extension

Connections Quality control is a branch of applied statistics that measures and controls the quality of a manufactured product. Have students do library research on this valuable application of mathematics.

VOCABULARY

After completing this chapter, you should be able to define each term, property, or phrase and give an example or two of each.

Probability

binomial experiments (p. 753)
complements (p. 732)
experimental probability
 (p. 754)
failure (p. 732)
inclusive events (p. 747)
mutually exclusive events
 (p. 746)
odds (p. 734)
probability (p. 732)
simulation (p. 754)
success (p. 732)
theoretical probability (p. 754)

Geometry

area diagram (p. 739)

Problem Solving

solve a simpler problem
 (p. 712)

Statistics

hypothesis (p. 760)
random sample (p. 758)
sampling error (p. 759)
unbiased sample (p. 758)

Discrete Mathematics

circular permutation
 (p. 721)
combination (p. 726)
dependent events (p. 714)
fundamental counting
 principle (p. 713)
independent events (p. 713)
linear permutation (p. 718)
permutation (p. 718)
reflections (p. 722)

UNDERSTANDING AND USING THE VOCABULARY

Choose the letter of the term that best matches each statement or phrase.

1. two events whose outcomes may be the same   e

2. an illustration used to show the total number of possible outcomes   l

3. the number of possibilities of n objects, taken r at a time and defined as $C(n, r) = \frac{n!}{(n - r)!r!}$ b

4. the number of ways that n objects can be arranged in a circle and defined by $(n - 1)!$ a

5. a statement that a given population characteristic is true   d

6. the desired outcome of an event   k

7. a sample in which every member of the population has an equal chance to be selected   i

8. If one event can occur in m ways and another in n ways, then the number of ways that both can occur is $m \cdot n$.   c

9. the number of possibilities of n objects arranged in a line and defined by $P(n, r) = \frac{n!}{(n - r)!}$ f

10. two events in which the outcome can never be the same   g

11. the ratio of the number of ways an event can succeed to the number of ways it can fail   h

12. the difference between the sample result and the true population results   j

a. circular permutation
b. combination
c. fundamental counting principle
d. hypothesis
e. inclusive events
f. linear permutation
g. mutually exclusive events
h. odds
i. random sample
j. sampling error
k. success
l. tree diagram

Chapter 12 Highlights **763**

Using the CHAPTER HIGHLIGHTS

The Chapter Highlights begins with a listing of the new terms, properties, and phrases that were introduced in this chapter. Have students define each term and provide an example or two of it, if appropriate.

Assessment and Evaluation Masters, pp. 311–312

12 NAME_____ DATE_____
Chapter 12 Test, Form 1B

Write the letter for the correct answer in the blank at the right of each problem.

1. An ice cream store has 31 flavors of ice cream and 10 toppings. A regular sundae has one flavor of ice cream, one topping, and comes with or without whipped cream. How many different ice cream sundaes can be ordered?
A. 310   B. 372   C. 620   D. 82   1. __C__

2. A license plate has one letter (not I or O) followed by five digits. How many possible combinations are there?
A. 120   B. 2,400,000   C. 2,399,976   D. 100,000   2. __B__

3. What is the value of $P(10, 4)$?
A. 5040   B. 151,200   C. 30,240   D. 907,200   3. __A__

4. A clown has 7 balloons, each a different color. There are 5 children. How many ways can the clown give each child a balloon?
A. 120   B. 5040   C. 25,200   D. 2520   4. __D__

5. There are 5 different novels, 2 different science books, and 4 different history books on a shelf. How many ways can the books be arranged if all the novels are together?
A. 39,916,800   B. 332,640   C. 5040   D. 604,800   5. __D__

6. How many ways can 9 people be seated at a round table?
A. 5040   B. 20,160   C. 40,320   D. 362,880   6. __C__

7. How many ways can 8 charms be placed on a bracelet with a clasp?
A. 5040   B. 2560   C. 40,320   D. 20,160   7. __D__

8. What is the value of $C(13, 9)$?
A. 17,160   B. 715   C. 24   D. 117   8. __B__

9. A group has 6 men and 5 women. How many ways can a committee of 3 men and 2 women be formed?
A. 200   B. 462   C. 7200   D. 3,326,400   9. __A__

10. From a standard deck of 52 cards, 3 cards are dealt. What is the probability that 2 are of one suit and 1 is of another?
A. $\frac{3}{169}$ B. $\frac{2}{169}$ C. $\frac{12,168}{22,100}$ D. $\frac{3042}{22,100}$ 10. __C__

11. In a bag are 5 green, 7 blue, and 4 red marbles. Two are selected at random without replacement. What are the odds that both are red?
A. 1 to 20   B. 20 to 1   C. 1 to 19   D. 19 to 1   11. __A__

12 NAME_____ DATE_____
Chapter 12 Test, Form 1B (continued)

12. A red die and a blue die are tossed. What is the probability that the red die shows a six and the blue die shows an even number?
A. $\frac{1}{36}$ B. $\frac{1}{18}$ C. $\frac{1}{12}$ D. $\frac{2}{3}$ 12. __C__

13. Fifty tickets are numbered 1 to 50 and are placed in a box. Three tickets are drawn at random without replacement. What is the probability that their numbers are all greater than 35?
A. $\frac{27}{1000}$ B. $\frac{13}{560}$ C. $\frac{3}{10}$ D. $\frac{1}{7840}$ 13. __B__

14. In a bag are 4 yellow and 8 blue marbles. Three are selected at random without replacement. What is the probability that all three are yellow or all three are blue?
A. $\frac{3}{11}$ B. $\frac{30}{143}$ C. $\frac{28}{143}$ D. $\frac{60}{143}$ 14. __A__

15. From a standard deck of 52 cards, 2 cards are dealt. What is the probability that both are aces or both are black?
A. $\frac{331}{1326}$ B. $\frac{7}{13}$ C. $\frac{63}{221}$ D. $\frac{55}{221}$ 15. __D__

16. The probability that a loaded die will show six is $\frac{1}{3}$. What is the probability that 3 out of 8 tosses will show six?
A. $\frac{56}{6561}$ B. $\frac{7}{32}$ C. $\frac{1792}{6561}$ D. $\frac{1}{27}$ 16. __C__

17. A batter is now batting .300. (The probability of getting a hit is $\frac{3}{10}$.) In the next 4 at-bats, what is the probability of getting at least two hits?
A. $\frac{3483}{10,000}$ B. $\frac{16}{10,000}$ C. $\frac{9}{100}$ D. $\frac{1251}{10,000}$ 17. __A__

18. Which of the following tasks provides a random sample?
A. pulling a coin from your pocket to represent the average value of U.S. coins
B. choosing a book from a student's locker to sample his or her reading interest
C. choosing one student in the hall to represent the school's average shoe size
D. weighing one brownie from the school cafeteria to represent the weight of all brownies served   18. __B__

19. Out of 100 high school graduates surveyed, 60% said they planned to get additional education. Find the margin of error of this survey.
A. 5%   B. 10%   C. 0.05%   D. 0.10%   19. __B__

20. The formula for the margin of error is $ME = 2\sqrt{\frac{p(1-p)}{n}}$. What happens to the margin of error as the sample size decreases?
A. It does not change.   B. It decreases.
C. It increases.   D. all of the above   20. __C__

Bonus Simplify the expression $\frac{(2n-2)(n+1)!}{n^2(n!) - n!}$.   **Bonus** __D__
A. $2 - \frac{2}{n}$ B. $\frac{2}{n}$ C. $n!$ D. 2

Instructional Resources

Three multiple-choice tests and three free-response tests are provided in the *Assessment and Evaluation Masters*. Forms 1A and 2A are for honors pacing, and Forms 1B, 1C, 2B, and 2C are for average pacing. Chapter 12 Test, Form 1B is shown at the right. Chapter 12 Test, Form 2B is shown on the next page.

Skills and Concepts Encourage students to refer to the objectives and examples on the left as they complete the review exercises on the right.

Assessment and Evaluation Masters, pp. 317–318

12 NAME_____ DATE _____
    Chapter 12 Test, Form 2B

1. A store sells T-shirts in 7 colors, 5 designs, and 3 sizes.   1. _____ 105
   Find the number of different T-shirts available.

2. How many different 7-digit telephone numbers are possible   2. _____ 800,000
   if the first digit is not 9 or 0 and the last digit is 1?

3. Twelve runners are in a cross-country race. How many   3. _____ 1320
   different ways can they finish first, second, and third?

4. Find the value of P(7, 3).   4. _____ 210

5. How many ways can 4 birthday cards, 3 get-well cards, and   5. _____ 1728
   2 blank cards be arranged on a shelf if the cards are
   ordered according to type?

6. Eight children stand in a circle to play a game. How many   6. _____ 5040
   different ways can the children be arranged?

7. Find the value of n for which C(n, 3) = C(n, 6).   7. _____ 9

8. Five cheerleaders will be chosen from a group of 15   8. _____ 3003
   students. How many different cheerleading squads can
   be formed?

9. The odds of an event occurring are 4 to 7. What is the   9. _____ $\frac{4}{11}$
   probability that the event will occur?

10. A coin purse contains 4 pennies, 5 nickels, and 8 dimes.   10. _____ $\frac{7}{85}$
    Three coins are selected at random without replacement.
    Find the probability that all three coins are dimes.

12 NAME_____ DATE _____
    Chapter 12 Test, Form 2B (continued)

11. From a standard deck of 52 cards, 4 cards are dealt. What   11. _____ 46 to 787
    are the odds that all 4 cards are red?

12. What is the probability of getting 2 hearts if 2 cards are   12. _____ $\frac{1}{17}$
    drawn from a well-shuffled deck without replacement?

13. Three cards are drawn from a standard deck of 52 cards   13. _____ $\frac{2}{5525}$
    without replacement. Find the probability that the first
    card is a jack, and the second and third are aces.

14. From a group of 6 men and 8 women, a committee of 3 is   14. _____ $\frac{19}{91}$
    to be selected at random. Find the probability that all 3
    are men or all 3 are women.

15. How many different arrangements of charms are there for   15. _____ 12
    a bracelet that has 5 charms and no clasp?

16. Four coins are tossed. Find the probability that at least   16. _____ $\frac{11}{16}$
    2 show heads.

17. Suppose a couple wants to have 4 children. Assume the   17. _____ $\frac{11}{16}$
    probability of having a boy is $\frac{1}{2}$. What is the probability
    of having at least 2 boys?

18. Determine if the following situation represents a random   18. _____ No; library card
    sampling. Write yes or no and explain.   holders may not
    surveying persons with library cards to determine if a city   have opinions that
    should raise taxes to pay for a new library   are typical of the
                                                 community.

19. In a survey of customers in a supermarket, 40% expect to   19. _____ 13%
    use the express line. Sixty customers were sampled. What
    is the margin of error?

20. In a survey of small business owners, 65% said that they   20. _____ 185
    preferred company A to company B for overnight package
    delivery. The margin of error was 7%. What was the
    approximate sample size?

Bonus Find all values of k for which the equation   **Bonus** _____ 13
C(k + 1, 2) = 7C(k, k − 1) is true.

764 Chapter 12

SKILLS AND CONCEPTS

OBJECTIVES AND EXAMPLES

Upon completing this chapter, you should be able to:

- solve problems by using the fundamental counting principle (Lesson 12–1)

How many different license plates are possible with two letters followed by three digits?

The license plate consists of five separate symbols, chosen one at a time. There are 26 different possibilities for each letter. There are 10 different possibilities for each number. Thus, the number of license plates possible for this country is as follows.

$26 \cdot 26 \cdot 10 \cdot 10 \cdot 10 = 26^2 \cdot 10^3$ or $676,000$

- solve problems involving linear and circular permutations (Lesson 12–2)

Eleven keys are to be placed on a key ring. How many different ways can the keys be placed on the key ring if the key ring has a clasp?

Since there is a clasp, this is treated as a linear permutation. However, since the key ring can be turned over, it is still reflective. So, the number of arrangements will be half that of a linear permutation.

$\frac{11!}{2} = 19,958,400$ **20. 18 arrangements**

- solve problems involving combinations (Lesson 12–3)

A basket contains 3 apples, 6 oranges, 7 pears, and 9 peaches. How many ways can 1 apple, 2 oranges, 6 pears, and 2 peaches be selected?

This involves the product of four combinations, one for each type of fruit.

$C(3, 1) \cdot C(6, 2) \cdot C(7, 6) \cdot C(9, 2)$

$= \frac{3!}{(3-1)!1!} \cdot \frac{6!}{(6-2)!2!} \cdot \frac{7!}{(7-6)!6!} \cdot \frac{9!}{(9-2)!2!}$

$= 3 \cdot 15 \cdot 7 \cdot 36$ or $11,340$

There are 11,340 different ways to choose the fruit from the basket.

REVIEW EXERCISES

Use these exercises to review and prepare for the chapter test.

13. How many different batting orders does a girls' fast-pitch softball team of ten players have if it does not matter who bats last? **3,628,800**

14. The letters a, c, e, g, i, and k are used to form 6-letter passwords for a movie theater security system. How many passwords can be formed if the letters can be used more than once in any given password? **46,656 passwords**

15. Using all ten digits 0-9, how many 4-digit patterns can be formed if each number can only be used once? **5040 patterns**

How many different ways can the letters of each word be arranged? 17. 19,958,400

16. LINEAR **720**   17. PERMUTATION
18. CIRCULAR **10,080** 19. REFLECTIVE **604,800**

20. Four people are taking a road trip to Montreal, Canada. Two sit in the front seat and two sit in the back seat. Three of the people agree to share the driving. In how many different arrangements can the four people sit?

21. How many ways can 8 people be seated at a round table? **5040 ways**

22. A college basketball team has 13 players. In how many different ways can the coach choose the five starting players, assuming that each player can play any position? **1287 ways**

23. A pizza shop offers 8 different toppings How many different 2-topping pizzas can be made? **28 pizzas**

24. **Geometry** Find the number of diagonals in a polygon that has 16 sides. **104**

GLENCOE Technology

Test and Review Software

You may use this software, a combination of an item generator and item bank, to create your own tests or worksheets. Types of items include free response, multiple choice, short answer, and open ended.

For IBM & Macintosh

OBJECTIVES AND EXAMPLES

• find the probability of an event (Lesson 12–4)

A bag of golf tees contains 23 red, 19 blue, 16 yellow, 21 green, 11 orange, 19 white, and 17 black tees. What is the probability that if you choose a tee from the bag at random, you will choose a green tee?

There are 21 ways to choose a green tee and $23 + 19 + 16 + 11 + 19 + 17$ or 105 ways not to choose a green tee. So, s is 21 and f is 105.

$P(\text{green tee}) = \frac{s}{s + f}$

$= \frac{21}{21 + 105}$ or $\frac{1}{6}$

The probability is 1 out of 6 or about 16.7%.

• find the probability of two or more independent or dependent events (Lesson 12–5)

There are 3 dimes, 2 quarters, and 5 nickels in Robert's pocket. If he reaches in and selects three coins at random without replacing any of the coins, what is the probability that he will choose a dime, then a quarter, then a nickel?

Let d = dime, q = quarter, and n = nickel.

$P(d, \text{ then } q, \text{ then } n) = \frac{3}{10} \cdot \frac{2}{9} \cdot \frac{5}{8}$ or $\frac{1}{24}$

The probability is $\frac{1}{24}$ or about 4.2%.

• find the probability of mutually exclusive or inclusive events (Lesson 12–6)

Trish has four $1 bills and six $5 bills. She takes three bills from her wallet at random. What is the probability that Trish will pull at least two $1 bills from her wallet?

$P(\text{at least two \$1 bills})$

$= P(\text{two \$1, one \$5}) + P(\text{three \$1, no \$5})$

$= \frac{C(4, 2) \cdot C(6, 1)}{C(10, 3)} + \frac{C(4, 3) \cdot C(6, 0)}{C(10, 3)}$

$= \frac{\frac{4! \cdot 6!}{(4 - 2)!2!(6 - 1)!1!}}{\frac{10!}{(10 - 3)!3!}} + \frac{\frac{4! \cdot 6!}{(4 - 3)!3!(6 - 0)!0!}}{\frac{10!}{(10 - 3)!3!}}$

$= \frac{36}{120} + \frac{4}{120}$ or $\frac{1}{3}$

The probability is $\frac{1}{3}$ or about 0.333.

REVIEW EXERCISES

25. There are 5 girls and 4 boys on the Bruins student council. A committee of three is to be selected at random to study the council's plans for a vending machine. What is the probability that the three selected are all girls?

26. A sports cooler for the high school football team contains several types of colas: 14 regular, 6 cherry, 10 diet, 7 diet cherry, 8 caffeine-free, and some caffeine-free diet. You pick one of the colas without looking at the type of drink. The probability that it is a diet drink is $\frac{3}{7}$. How many caffeine-free diet colas are in the sports cooler?

25. $\frac{5}{42}$ **26.** 4 colas

27. $\frac{1}{7}$ **28.** $\frac{19}{1763}$

27. There are 28 pieces of paper, numbered 1 through 28, in a box. You pick a piece of paper, replace it, and then pick another piece of paper. What is the probability that the first number was greater than 14 and the second number was greater than 25 or less than 6?

28. For a state lottery game, plastic balls numbered 1 through 46 are placed in a drum. Six balls are drawn at random. What is the probability that all six are odd numbers, if no replacement occurs?

30. mutually exclusive, $\frac{5}{13}$ **31.** mutually exclusive, $\frac{1}{2}$ **32.** inclusive, $\frac{55}{221}$

Determine whether each event is *mutually exclusive* or *inclusive*. Then find the probability.   **29.** mutually exclusive, $\frac{1}{2}$

29. There are 10 algebra 1 books, 15 geometry books, 20 algebra 2 books, and 15 pre-calculus books on a shelf. If a book is randomly selected, what is the probability of selecting a geometry book or a pre-calculus book?

30. A card is drawn from a standard deck of cards. What is the probability the card will be a king or less than a six?

31. A die is rolled. What is the probability of rolling a 6 or a number less than 3?

32. Two cards are drawn from a standard deck of 52 cards. What is the probability that both are jacks or both are red?

Applications and Problem Solving Encourage students to work through the exercises in the Applications and Problem Solving section to strengthen their problem-solving skills.

OBJECTIVES AND EXAMPLES

- use binomial experiments to find probabilities (Lesson 12–7)

To practice for a jigsaw puzzle competition, Laura and Julian put together 4 jigsaw puzzles. The probability that Laura puts in the last piece is $\frac{3}{5}$, and the probability that Julian puts in the last piece is $\frac{2}{5}$. What is the probability that Laura will put in the last piece of at least two puzzles?

The probability equals the sum of the probabilities of putting in the last piece in 2, 3, or all 4 puzzles.

$P = L^4 + 4L^3W + 6L^2W^2$

$= \left(\frac{3}{5}\right)^4 + 4\left(\frac{3}{5}\right)^3\left(\frac{2}{5}\right) + 6\left(\frac{3}{5}\right)^2\left(\frac{2}{5}\right)^2$

$= \frac{81}{625} + \frac{216}{625} + \frac{216}{625}$ or 0.8208

The probability is 82.08%.

- find margins of sampling error (Lesson 12–8)

In a survey taken at a local high school, 75% of the student body stated that they thought school lunches should be free. This survey had a margin of error of 3%. How many people were surveyed?

$ME = 2\sqrt{\dfrac{p(1-p)}{n}}$

$0.03 = 2\sqrt{\dfrac{0.75(1-0.75)}{n}}$ *ME = 0.03 and p = 0.75*

$n = 833\frac{1}{3}$ *Use a calculator.*

Since it is not possible for $\frac{1}{3}$ of a person to exist, there were about 833 people in the survey.

REVIEW EXERCISES

33. Find the probability of getting 7 heads in 8 tosses of a coin. The probability of success (getting a head) in a single toss is $\frac{1}{2}$. Thus, the probability of failure (getting a tail) is $\frac{1}{2}$. $\frac{1}{32}$

34. Find the probability that a family with seven children will have exactly five boys. Assume that the probability of having a boy is $\frac{1}{2}$. $\frac{21}{128}$

35. A die is rolled twelve times. Find the probability of each of the following.

   a. a 3 twelve times

   b. exactly one 3 in twelve tries

   c. six 3s out of twelve tries

   35a. $\dfrac{1}{2,176,782,336}$ b. $\dfrac{585,937,500}{2,176,782,336}$

   c. $\dfrac{14,437,500}{2,176,782,336}$

36. In a poll asking people to name their most valued freedom, 51% of the randomly selected people said it was the freedom of speech. Find the margin of sampling error if 625 people were randomly selected.   **4%**

37. According to a recent survey of mothers with children who play sports, 63% of them would prefer that their children not play football. Suppose the margin of error is 4.5%. How many mothers were surveyed?   **460 mothers**

APPLICATIONS AND PROBLEM SOLVING

38. **Combination Lock**   You have forgotten the combination lock to your locker in the health club. There are 36 numbers on the lock, and the correct combination is R ☐ – L ☐ – R ☐. How many combinations may be necessary to try in order to open the lock? (*Hint:* Numbers such as 3-3-3 may be repeated.) (Lesson 12–1)   **46,656 combinations**

39. **Auto Manufacturing**   An auto manufacturer produces 9 models, each available in 7 different colors, with 5 different upholstery fabrics, and 4 different interior colors. How many varieties of automobiles are available? (Lesson 12–1)   **1260 varieties**

A practice test for Chapter 12 is provided on page 923.

ALTERNATIVE ASSESSMENT

COOPERATIVE LEARNING PROJECT

Probability   In this chapter, you learned ways of grouping objects by combinations and permutations. You learned how to find the probability of an event. And you learned how to predict events based on probability. Many examples were given of the ways probability is involved in our everyday lives. A lot of these examples come from the games we play.

YAHTZEE® is a game that involves the rolling of 5 six-sided dice and keeping score by how many dice show the same number. SCRABBLE® involves the random selection of wooden tiles. Each wooden tile has an inscribed letter that is assigned a point value. The object of the game is to make words and obtain high point values based on where the word is placed on the board. TRIVIAL PURSUIT® is another game played with dice. The object of this game is to roll two dice, move a game piece around the board and answer a trivia question on a given category based on where the game piece lands. As you might suspect, almost every game involves probability.

In this project, you will design and construct a game based on probability. All games have certain features in common. The object of the game is to win, so your game should have a starting point and an ending point. But not all games involve a playing board. Some games involve playing pieces, others do not. Some games are played with dice, others with spinners, and still others with marbles.

Follow these steps to design and construct your game.

- Brainstorm with your group to choose the features your game will have.
- Outline a plan you can follow.
- Use materials you can easily find. It's okay to borrow dice, spinners, marbles, and so on from other games. Be original; don't design your game so it looks like another game that already exists.
- Carry out your plan.
- Determine the probabilities of the events which will take place in your game.
- Write several paragraphs describing how you designed and play your game. Include how you constructed the game, the rules of the game, and how someone can win the game.

THINKING CRITICALLY

- Write a probability problem involving binomial expansion.
- Have your fellow students see if they can solve the problem. Make sure you can solve the problem yourself. Explain how and why you chose this problem.

PORTFOLIO

Select your favorite word problem from this chapter and place it in your portfolio with a note explaining why it is your favorite word problem.

SELF EVALUATION

We all have to cope with the unpredictability of life. When you plan a camping trip, you consider the possibility of bad weather. When you ride your bike, you consider the possibility of a flat tire. When you participate in sports, you consider the possibility of winning or losing. Understanding probability can help you make decisions. But, it does not guarantee you will always like the outcome of certain events. Adaptability to whatever events might come is just as important as understanding the probability of those same events.

Assess yourself. How adaptable are you? How do you react when the unpredictability of life "rains on your parade?" List two or three ways you can make a conscious effort to be more adaptable when you do not like the outcome of an event. Understand that knowing probability is important, but being adaptable to the unpredictability of life is equally important.

Chapter 12   Study Guide and Assessment **767**

Assessment and Evaluation Masters, pp. 322, 333

 12   NAME_____ DATE _____

Chapter 12 Performance Assessment

Instructions: *Demonstrate your knowledge by giving a clear, concise solution to each problem. Be sure to include all relevant drawings and justify your answers. You may show your solution in more than one way or investigate beyond the requirements of the problem.*

1. Mrs. Hong is in charge of assigning booths to exhibitors at the Lexington County Fair. There are 10 display areas. Each area has 6 booths arranged in a circle.
   a. If there are 60 exhibitors, how many combinations of 6 exhibitors are possible? Explain your reasoning.
   b. If there is a preferred position in a display area, find the number of different possible arrangements of the 6 exhibitors in each display area. Explain your reasoning.
   c. Give at least two reasons why exhibitors may prefer one position over another.
   d. If there are no preferred positions in a display area, find the number of possible arrangements of exhibitors in a display area. Explain why the answer differs from the answer to part b.

2. A new insurance salesperson is told that she has a probability of about $\frac{1}{10}$ of making a sale each time she makes a new contact. Repeat sales have a probability of $\frac{1}{2}$.
   a. What is the probability of her not making a sale each time she makes a new contact? Explain how you know.
   b. If two events are independent, how do you find the probability of both occurring?
   c. Find the probability of her making sales on her first 2 contacts. Explain your reasoning.
   d. Find the probability of selling a new contact and making a repeat sale the next time she contacts that customer. Justify your answer.
   e. On Wednesday the salesperson is making 2 contacts. One is a new contact and one is a previous customer. What is her probability of making a sale on Wednesday? Explain your reasoning.
   f. State the necessary conditions for a binomial experiment.
   g. If the insurance salesperson makes 5 new contacts, what is the probability of her making at least 1 sale?

Scoring Guide
Chapter 12
Performance Assessment

Level	Specific Criteria
3 Superior	• Shows thorough understanding of the concepts *combination permutations; probability of an event; probability of independent, dependent, and mutually exclusive events;* and *binomial experiments, and how they are related to each other.* • Uses appropriate strategies to solve problems. • Computations are correct. • Written explanations are exemplary. • Diagrams are accurate and appropriate. • Goes beyond requirements of problem.
2 Satisfactory, with Minor Flaws	• Shows understanding of the concepts *combinations; permutations; probability of an event; probability of independent, dependent, and mutually exclusive events;* and *binomial experiments, and how they are related to each other.* • Uses appropriate strategies to solve problems. • Computations are mostly correct. • Written explanations are effective. • Diagrams are mostly accurate and appropriate. • Satisfies all requirements of problem.
1 Nearly Satisfactory, with Serious Flaws	• Shows understanding of most of the concepts *combinations; permutations; probability of an event; probability of independent, dependent, and mutually exclusive events;* and *binomial experiments, and how they are related to each other.* • May not use appropriate strategies to solve problems. • Computations are mostly correct. • Written explanations are satisfactory. • Diagrams are mostly accurate and appropriate. • Satisfies most requirements of problem.
0 Unsatisfactory	• Shows little or no understanding of the concepts *combinations; permutations; probability of an event; probability of independent, and mutually exclusive events;* and *binomial experiments, and how they are related to each other.* • May not use appropriate strategies to solve problems. • Computations are incorrect or inappropriate. • Written explanations are not satisfactory. • Diagrams are not accurate or appropriate. • Does not satisfy requirements of problem.

 **Alternative Assessment**

The Alternative Assessment section provides students with the opportunity to assess their own work by thinking critically, working with others, keeping a portfolio, and honestly evaluating their own progress. For more information on alternative forms of assessment, see *Alternative Assessment in the Mathematics Classroom,* one of the titles in the Glencoe Mathematics Professional Series.

Performance Assessment

Performance Assessment tasks for this chapter are included in the *Assessment and Evaluation Masters.* A scoring guide is also provided.

NCTM Standards: 1–9

This Investigation is designed to be completed over several days or weeks. It may be considered optional. You may want to assign the Investigation and the follow-up activities to be completed at the same time.

Objective

Design a roller coaster to fit into a designated space, have a ride time of at least 2 minutes, and be safe.

Mathematical Overview

This Investigation will use the following mathematical skills and concepts from Chapters 13 and 14.

- changing radian measure to degree measure and vice versa
- identifying coterminal angles
- graphing and using trigonometric functions
- finding amplitude and period for sine and cosine functions
- verifying identities by using double- and half-angle formulas

Recommended Time		
Part	**Pages**	**Time**
Investigation	768–769	1 class period
Working on the Investigation	785, 810, 834, 859	20 minutes each
Closing the Investigation	868	1 class period

Instructional Resources

Investigations and Projects Masters, pp. 21–24

A recording sheet, teacher notes, and scoring guide are provided for each investigation in the *Investigations and Projects Masters.*

1 MOTIVATION

This Investigation uses common materials to create a design for a roller coaster. Students will follow certain specifications to find the best design. Ask them if they have ever been on a roller coaster. Discuss the role played by the PE, KE, gravity, and friction in the design of the coaster.

225-foot drop, Kennywood's Steel Phantom

MATERIALS NEEDED

drawing paper

file folder

heavy cardboard

masking tape

protractor

ruler

small toy car

straws

Roller coasters and other amusement park rides that make you scream with fear and excitement are designed to provide safe, quick rides for crowds of people, while maximizing the thrill for riders. The thrill comes from tall heights, sudden drops, high speeds, tight curves, and sensory effects (such as dark tunnels, special lighting, wind, and sounds).

As the coaster cars are pulled up the first hill by motors, potential energy *PE* (stored energy due to location) is gained by the cars. This motorized pull on the first hill is the only external energy applied to the cars so that they can complete the remainder of the ride. *PE* becomes kinetic energy *KE* (the energy of motion) as the cars "fall" down the hills, accel-

erated by gravity. Gravity is a vertical force, so a steep hill helps the cars gain speed.

To design a good roller coaster, you would want to maximize falling heights and include steep angles of fall. For the cars to be able to negotiate curves, certain factors must be considered, such as the speed of the cars as they approach a curve, the angle of the curve, and the banking needed to hold the cars on the track. You would also want to consider that friction during the ride constantly diminishes the potential and kinetic energy.

In this Investigation, your team of four engineers will be given the task of designing a roller coaster that will thrill the rider, fit into a designated land space, have a ride time of at least 2 minutes, and be safe.

Make an Investigation Folder in which you can store all of your work on this Investigation for future use.

768 *Investigation: Scream Machines!*

Cooperative Learning

This Investigation offers an excellent opportunity for using cooperative learning groups. For more information on cooperative learning strategies and group management, see *Cooperative Learning in the Mathematics Classroom,* one of the titles in the Glencoe Mathematics Professional Series.

 **TEKS** 1.b.

Six Flags Over Texas

1 Think about the shapes of roller coasters that you have ridden or have seen in magazines, books, or amusement park advertisements. Find pictures of the different types of coasters you wish to consider. Sketch how the supporting beams and trusses of each roller coaster appear.

2 Study the designs with your team. Based on the information you have gathered, decide upon a roller coaster design that your team could build using straws, tape, and strips of lightweight cardboard. Sketch a scale model of the coaster, labeling the height of each hill, the angle of each vertical drop, and the angle of curvature for each curve. Also label the angles for positioning the trusses to support the structure.

⋯⋯ **BUILD THE ROLLER COASTER**

3 Build a scale model of your coaster design using straws and masking tape as building materials to construct the supporting structure. Cut a file folder into strips for the lightweight cardboard needed for the track. Make sure the strips are wide enough to support a toy car. Use a piece of heavy cardboard measuring 2 feet by 2 feet to represent the land on which the coaster is anchored. Include a legend on the base of your model that states the scale factor.

Mean Streak, Cedar Point

4 Test your completed model by releasing a small toy car from the top of the first hill. Can the car run the entire track? If not, how should your design be altered so the car can complete the full ride?

5 Revise your model and retest the model with the car. Record your observations and corrective measures after each trial of the car.

You will continue working on this Investigation throughout Chapters 13 and 14.

Be sure to keep your tables, graphs, and other materials in your Investigation Folder.

Scream Machines! Investigation

Working on the Investigation
Lesson 13–2, p. 785
⋯⋯⋯⋯⋯
Working on the Investigation
Lesson 13–6, p. 810
⋯⋯⋯⋯⋯
Working on the Investigation
Lesson 14–1, p. 834
⋯⋯⋯⋯⋯
Working on the Investigation
Lesson 14–5, p. 859
⋯⋯⋯⋯⋯
Closing the Investigation
End of Chapter 14, p. 868
⋯⋯⋯⋯⋯

Investigation: Scream Machines! **769**

---

2 SETUP

You may wish to have a student read the first two paragraphs of the Investigation to provide background information about roller coasters. You may then wish to read the next three paragraphs, which introduce the activity. Discuss the activity with your students. Then separate the class into groups of four.

3 MANAGEMENT

Each group member should be responsible for a specific task.

Recorder Collects data.
Designer Sketches a scale model of the coaster.
Builder Makes a scale model of the coaster.
Tester Tests model and makes adjustments.

At the end of the activity, each member should turn in his or her respective equipment.

Sample Answers

Answers will vary as they are based on each design.

Investigations and Projects Masters, p. 24

13, 14

NAME_____ DATE_____

Investigation, Chapters 13 and 14 Student Edition Pages 768–769, 785, 810, 834, 859, 868

Scream Machines!

Work with your group to answer the following questions and add others to be considered.

- How can you calculate the kinetic energy of the roller coaster cars as they "fall" down the hills?
- How can you calculate the speed of the roller coaster cars as they move from the top of the first hill to the bottom of the last?
- How can you calculate the highest speed that cars can go around a curve without flying off the track?
- How can you calculate how much banking is needed to hold a car on the track?
- What equation will express the relationship between height of a fall, angle of the fall, and speed of the car as it comes out of the fall?
- How can you account for friction slowing down the cars?

Do research to find out what equations you will need to help you with the structural design of the roller coaster. Record the equations in the column on the left. To the right of the equation, list each variable it contains and give the definition of the variable.

Equation	Variable/Definition	Variable/Definition	Variable/Definition	Variable/Definition	Variable/Definition

Please keep this page and any other research in your Investigation folder.

Exploring Trigonometric Ratios

PREVIEWING THE CHAPTER

This chapter begins with right triangle trigonometry. Then students study coterminal angles and equivalent radian and degree measures. They find the values of the six trigonometric functions and of expressions involving the functions. Students apply problem-solving strategies to determine the number of possible solutions and solve the triangle if solutions do exist. Next, students solve triangles and problems using the law of sines and the law of cosines. Then the concept of the unit circle is used to define and use the trigonometric functions. The chapter concludes with a presentation of the inverse trigonometric functions.

Lesson (Pages)	Lesson Objectives	NCTM Standards	State/Local Objectives
13-1 (772–779)	Find values of trigonometric functions for acute angles. Solve problems involving right triangles.	1–7, 9	1.a.
13-2 (780–785)	Change radian measure to degree measure and vice versa. Identify coterminal angles.	1–5, 9	
13-3 (786–791)	Find values of trigonometric functions for general angles. Use trigonometric identities to find values of trigonometric functions.	1–6, 9	1.a.
13-4 (792–798)	Solve triangles by using the law of sines. Examine solutions.	1–7, 9	
13-5 (799–804)	Solve triangles by using the law of cosines.	1–7, 9	
13-6 (805–810)	Define and use the trigonometric functions based on the unit circle.	1–6, 9	1.a., 4.a.
13-7 (811–814)	Find values of expressions involving inverse trigonometric functions.	1–6, 9	1.a., 4.a., 4.c.

A complete, 1-page lesson plan is provided for each lesson in the *Lesson Planning Guide*. Answer keys for each lesson are available in the *Answer Key Masters*.

ORGANIZING THE CHAPTER

You may want to refer to the **Course Planning Calendar** on page T12 for detailed information on pacing.
PACING: Honors—9 days; **Block**—6 days

LESSON PLANNING CHART

| Lesson (Pages) | Materials/ Manipulatives | Extra Practice (Student Edition) | BLACKLINE MASTERS | | | | | | | | | | Real-World Applications | Interactive Mathematics Tools Software | Teaching Transparencies |
			Study Guide	Practice	Enrichment	Assessment and Evaluation	Modeling Mathematics	Multicultural Activity	Tech Prep Applications	Graphing Calculator	Science and Math Lab Manual			
13-1 (772–779)	graphing calculator astrolabe	p. 906	p. 92	p. 92	p. 92		pp. 58–60	p. 25			pp. 9–12		13-1	13-1A 13-1B
13-2 (780–785)	graphing calculator	p. 906	p. 93	p. 93	p. 93	p. 352								13-2A 13-2B
13-3 (786–791)	calculator graphing calculator	p. 907	p. 94	p. 94	p. 94					p. 13		33		13-3A 13-3B
13-4 (792–798)	picture of Leaning Tower of Pisa calculator	p. 907	p. 95	p. 95	p. 95	pp. 351, 352				p. 25		34	13-4	13-4A 13-4B
13-5 (799–804)		p. 907	p. 96	p. 96	p. 96				p. 26	p. 26				13-5A 13-5B
13-6 (805–810)	graphing calculator	p. 908	p. 97	p. 97	p. 97	p. 353	p. 73						13-6	13-6A 13-6B
13-7 (811–814)	calculator	p. 908	p. 98	p. 98	p. 98	p. 353								13-7A 13-7B
Study Guide/ Assessment (815–819)						pp. 337 –351, 354 –356								

ORGANIZING THE CHAPTER

OTHER CHAPTER RESOURCES

Student Edition
Investigation, pp. 768–769
Chapter Opener, pp. 770–771
Mathematics and Society, p. 804
Working on the Investigation,
 pp. 785, 810

Teacher's Classroom Resources
Investigations and Projects Masters,
 pp. 73–76

Technology
Teacher's Guide for Software
 Resources
Test and Review Software (IBM
 and Macintosh)
CD-ROM Interactions (Windows
 and Macintosh)

Professional Publications
Block Scheduling Booklet
Glencoe Mathematics Professional
 Series

OUTSIDE RESOURCES

Books/Periodicals
Gregory, John, *Geometry: Plane and Simple*,
 Creative Publications
Sloyer, Cliff, *Fantastiks of Mathematics*, Dale
 Seymour Publications

Software
Ballooning: Vectors From Here to There, Sunburst
Gliding, Sunburst

Videos/CD-ROMs
*Algebra Math Video Series: Verbal Problems/
 Intro to Trigonometry*, ETA
Sines and Cosines, Parts 1 and 2, NCTM

See the *Teacher's Guide for Software Resources* for software addresses.

ASSESSMENT RESOURCES

Student Edition
Math Journal, pp. 777, 808
Mixed Review, pp. 779, 785,
 791, 798, 804, 810, 814
Self Test, p. 798
Chapter Highlights, p. 815
Chapter Study Guide and
 Assessment, pp. 816–818
Alternative Assessment, p. 819
 Portfolio, p. 819

College Entrance Exam Practice,
 pp. 820–821

Teacher's Wraparound Edition
5-Minute Check, pp. 772, 780,
 786, 792, 799, 805, 811
Check for Understanding, pp. 777,
 783, 789, 796, 802, 808, 813
Closing Activity, pp. 779, 785,
 791, 798, 804, 810, 814
Cooperative Learning, pp. 773,
 781

Assessment and Evaluation Masters
Multiple-Choice Tests, Forms 1A
 (Honors), 1B (Average), 1C
 (Basic), pp. 337–342
Free-Response Tests, Forms 2A
 (Honors), 2B (Average), 2C
 (Basic), pp. 343–348
Calculator-Based Test, p. 349
Performance Assessment, p. 350
Mid-Chapter Test, p. 351
Quizzes A–D, pp. 352–353
Standardized Test Practice, p. 354
Cumulative Review, pp. 355–356

ENHANCING THE CHAPTER

Examples of some of the materials for enhancing Chapter 13 are shown below.

 **DIVERSITY**

Multicultural Activity Masters, pp. 25, 26

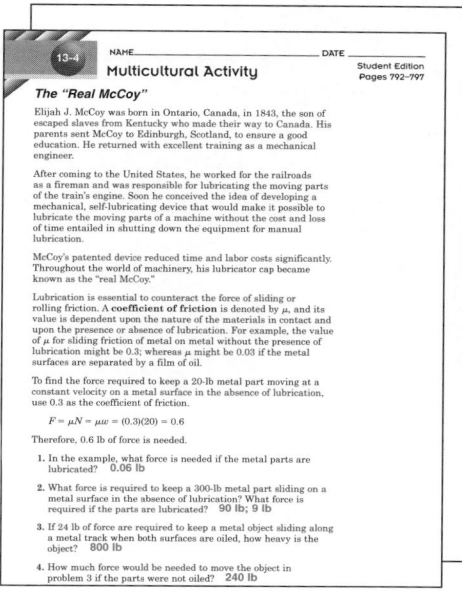

13-4 NAME _____ DATE _____
Student Edition Pages 792–797
Multicultural Activity

The "Real McCoy"

Elijah J. McCoy was born in Ontario, Canada, in 1843, the son of escaped slaves from Kentucky who made their way to Canada. His parents sent McCoy to Edinburgh, Scotland, to ensure a good education. He returned with excellent training as a mechanical engineer.

After coming to the United States, he worked for the railroads as a fireman and was responsible for lubricating the moving parts of the train's engine. Soon he conceived the idea of developing a mechanical, self-lubricating device that would make it possible to lubricate the moving parts of a machine without the cost and loss of time entailed in shutting down the equipment for manual lubrication.

McCoy's patented device reduced time and labor costs significantly. Throughout the world of machinery, his lubricator cap became known as the "real McCoy."

Lubrication is essential to counteract the force of sliding or rolling friction. A **coefficient of friction** is denoted by μ, and its value is dependent upon the nature of the materials in contact and upon the presence or absence of lubrication. For example, the value of μ for sliding friction of metal on metal without the presence of lubrication might be 0.3; whereas μ might be 0.03 if the metal surfaces are separated by a film of oil.

To find the force required to keep a 20-lb metal part moving at a constant velocity on a metal surface in the absence of lubrication, use 0.3 as the coefficient of friction.

$$F = \mu N = \mu w = (0.3)(20) = 0.6$$

Therefore, 0.6 lb of force is needed.

1. In the example, what force is needed if the metal parts are lubricated? **0.06 lb**

2. What force is required to keep a 300-lb metal part sliding on a metal surface in the absence of lubrication? What force is required if the parts are lubricated? **90 lb; 9 lb**

3. If 24 lb of force are required to keep a metal object sliding along a metal track when both surfaces are oiled, how heavy is the object? **800 lb**

4. How much force would be needed to move the object in problem 3 if the parts were not oiled? **240 lb**

 **APPLICATIONS**

Real-World Applications, 33, 34

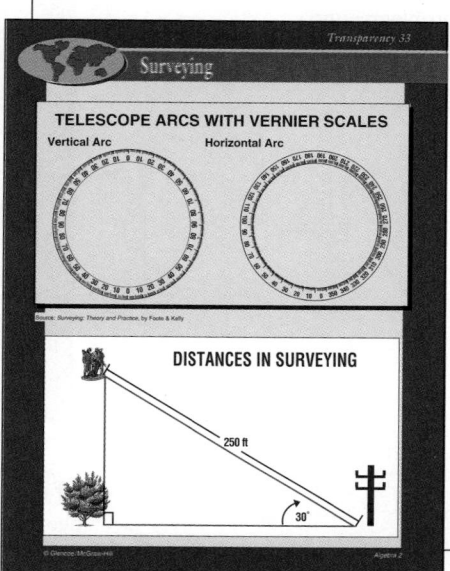

Transparency 33
Surveying

TELESCOPE ARCS WITH VERNIER SCALES
Vertical Arc   Horizontal Arc

Source: Surveying: Theory and Practice, by Foote & Kelly

DISTANCES IN SURVEYING

250 ft

30°

 **TECHNOLOGY**

Graphing Calculator Masters, p. 13

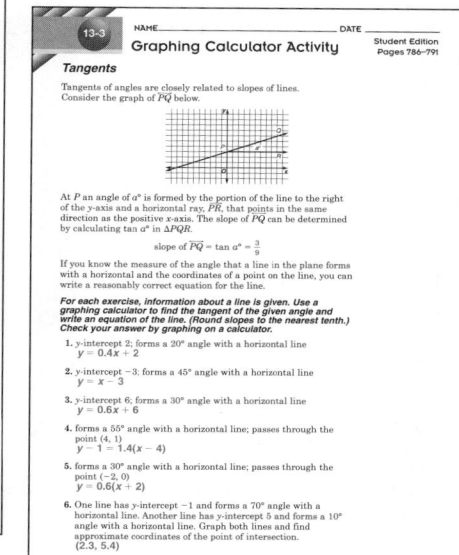

13-3 NAME _____ DATE _____
Student Edition Pages 786–791
Graphing Calculator Activity

Tangents

Tangents of angles are closely related to slopes of lines. Consider the graph of $\overline{PQ}$ below.

At P an angle of $a°$ is formed by the portion of the line to the right of the y-axis and a horizontal ray, $\overline{PR}$, that points in the same direction as the positive x-axis. The slope of $\overline{PQ}$ can be determined by calculating $\tan a°$ in $\triangle PQR$.

$$\text{slope of } \overline{PQ} = \tan a° = \frac{3}{9}$$

If you know the measure of the angle that a line in the plane forms with a horizontal and the coordinates of a point on the line, you can write a reasonably correct equation for the line.

For each exercise, information about a line is given. Use a graphing calculator to find the tangent of the given angle and write an equation of the line. (Round slopes to the nearest tenth.) Check your answer by graphing on a calculator.

1. y-intercept 2; forms a 20° angle with a horizontal line
   $y = 0.4x + 2$

2. y-intercept -3; forms a 45° angle with a horizontal line
   $y = x - 3$

3. y-intercept 6; forms a 30° angle with a horizontal line
   $y = 0.6x + 6$

4. forms a 55° angle with a horizontal line; passes through the point (4, 1)
   $y - 1 = 1.4(x - 4)$

5. forms a 30° angle with a horizontal line; passes through the point $(-2, 0)$
   $y = 0.6(x + 2)$

6. One line has y-intercept -1 and forms a 70° angle with a horizontal line. Another line has y-intercept 5 and forms a 10° angle with a horizontal line. Graph both lines and find approximate coordinates of the point of intersection.
   (2.3, 5.4)

 **TECH PREP**

Tech Prep Applications Masters, pp. 25, 26

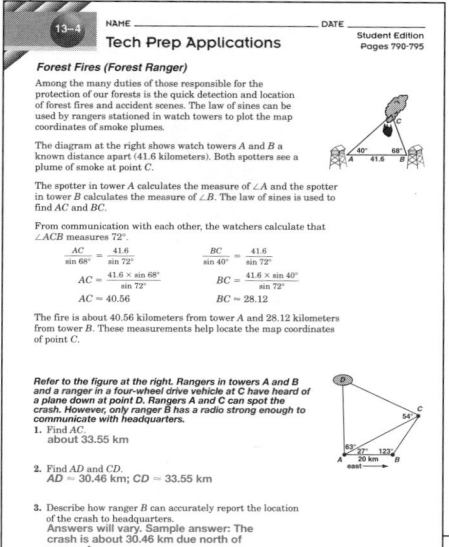

13-4 NAME _____ DATE _____
Student Edition Pages 790–795
Tech Prep Applications

Forest Fires (Forest Ranger)

Among the many duties of those responsible for the protection of our forests is the quick detection and location of forest fires and accident scenes. The law of sines can be used by rangers stationed in watch towers to plot the map coordinates of smoke plumes.

The diagram at the right shows watch towers A and B a known distance apart (41.6 kilometers). Both spotters see a plume of smoke at point C.

The spotter in tower A calculates the measure of $\angle A$ and the spotter in tower B calculates the measure of $\angle B$. The law of sines is used to find AC and BC.

From communication with each other, the watchers calculate that $\angle ACB$ measures 72°.

$$\frac{AC}{\sin 68°} = \frac{41.6}{\sin 72°} \qquad \frac{BC}{\sin 40°} = \frac{41.6}{\sin 72°}$$

$$AC = \frac{41.6 \times \sin 68°}{\sin 72°} \qquad BC = \frac{41.6 \times \sin 40°}{\sin 72°}$$

$$AC \approx 40.56 \qquad BC \approx 28.12$$

The fire is about 40.56 kilometers from tower A and 28.12 kilometers from tower B. These measurements help locate the map coordinates of point C.

Refer to the figure at the right. Rangers in towers A and B and a range in a four-wheel drive vehicle at C have heard of a plane down at point D. Rangers A and C can spot the crash. However, only ranger B has a radio strong enough to communicate with headquarters.

1. Find AC.
   about 33.55 km

2. Find AD and CD.
   $AD \approx 30.46$ km; $CD \approx 33.55$ km

3. Describe how ranger B can accurately report the location of the crash to headquarters.
   Answers will vary. Sample answer: The crash is about 30.46 km due north of ranger A.

 **CONNECTIONS**

Science and Math Lab Manual, pp. 9–12

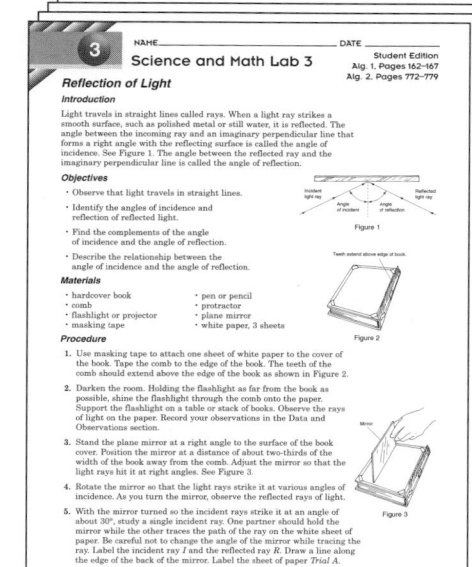

3 NAME _____ DATE _____
Student Edition Alg. 1, Pages 162–167
Alg. 2, Pages 772–779
Science and Math Lab 3

Reflection of Light

Introduction
Light travels in straight lines called rays. When a light ray strikes a smooth surface, such as polished metal or still water, it is reflected. The angle between the incoming ray and an imaginary perpendicular line that forms a right angle with the reflecting surface is called the angle of incidence. See Figure 1. The angle between the reflected ray and the imaginary perpendicular line is called the angle of reflection.

Objectives
• Observe that light travels in straight lines.
• Identify the angles of incidence and reflection of reflected light.
• Find the complements of the angle of incidence and the angle of reflection.
• Describe the relationship between the angle of incidence and the angle of reflection.

Materials
• hardcover book
• comb
• flashlight or projector
• masking tape
• pen or pencil
• protractor
• plane mirror
• white paper, 3 sheets

Procedure
1. Use masking tape to attach one sheet of white paper to the cover of the book. Tape the comb to the edge of the book. The teeth of the comb should extend above the edge of the book as shown in Figure 2.

2. Darken the room. Holding the flashlight as far from the book as possible, shine the flashlight through the comb onto the paper. Support the flashlight on a table or stack of books. Observe the rays of light on the paper. Record your observations in the Data and Observations section.

3. Stand the plane mirror at a right angle to the surface of the book cover. Position the mirror at a distance of about two-thirds of the width of the book away from the comb. Adjust the mirror so that the light rays hit it at right angles. See Figure 3.

4. Rotate the mirror so that the light rays strike at various angles of incidence. As you turn the mirror, observe the reflected rays of light.

5. With the mirror turned so the incident rays strike at an angle of about 30°, study a single incident ray. One partner should hold the mirror while the other traces the path of the ray on the white sheet of paper. Be careful not to change the angle of the mirror while tracing the ray. Label the incident ray I and the reflected ray R. Draw a line along the edge of the back of the mirror. Label the sheet of paper *Trial A*.

 **PROBLEM SOLVING**

Problem of the Week Cards, 33, 34

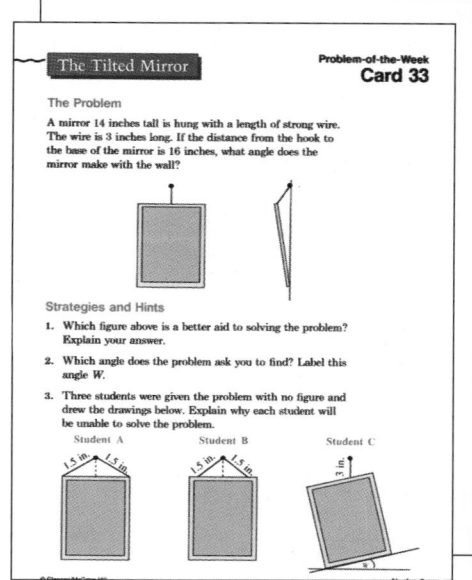

The Tilted Mirror
Problem-of-the-Week
Card 33

The Problem

A mirror 14 inches tall is hung with a length of strong wire. The wire is 3 inches long. If the distance from the hook to the base of the mirror is 16 inches, what angle does the mirror make with the wall?

Strategies and Hints

1. Which figure above is a better aid to solving the problem? Explain your answer.

2. Which angle does the problem ask you to find? Label this angle W.

3. Three students were given the problem with no figure and drew the drawings below. Explain why each student will be unable to solve the problem.

Student A   Student B   Student C

MAKING MATHEMATICS RELEVANT

This two-page introduction to the chapter provides students with an opportunity to explore contemporary topics and their applications to mathematics.

Background Information

The Sounds of Music The table below shows that more people are viewing teaching as a means of combining a love of music with working with children of all ages. Public school music teachers may teach band, orchestra, and various choirs and glee clubs as well as classes in music theory and history.

Number of Credentialed U.S. Public School Music Teachers

Year	Number
1992–93	104,644
1991–92	101,099
1990–91	101,347
1989–90	98,243
1988–89	94,253
1987–88	94,280
1986–87	87,088

CHAPTER 13

Exploring Trigonometric Functions

Objectives

In this chapter, you will:

- find values of trigonometric functions,
- solve problems by using right triangle trigonometry,
- examine solutions to problems, and
- solve triangles by using the law of sines and law of cosines.

The Sounds of Music

Type	Year Introduced
Record Player	1877
33-RPM Records	1948
45-RPM Records	1949
Transistor Radio	1957
Audio Cassette	1965
Walkman	1979
CDs	1982
CD Walkman	1986

Source: *Encyclopedia Brittanica,* 1994

Music has been an artistic expression of humans since the dawn of humanity. Every society, from the earliest bands of people spreading across the globe, to modern post-industrial countries, has created music to express its identity. Music is universal, important, and a very pleasurable activity, both for listening and for creating. How important is music in your life?

TIME *Line*

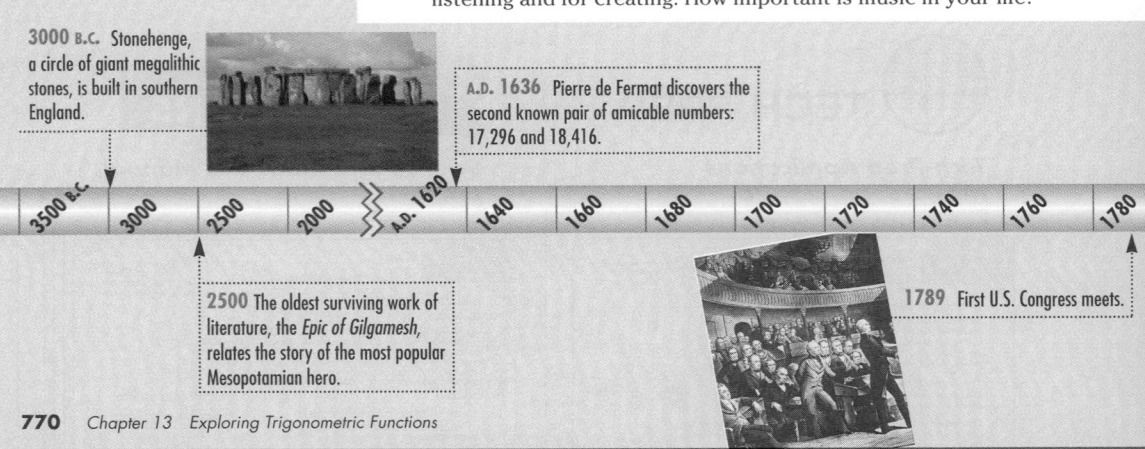

3000 B.C. Stonehenge, a circle of giant megalithic stones, is built in southern England.

A.D. 1636 Pierre de Fermat discovers the second known pair of amicable numbers: 17,296 and 18,416.

| 3500 B.C. | 3000 | 2500 | 2000 | A.D. 1620 | 1640 | 1660 | 1680 | 1700 | 1720 | 1740 | 1760 | 1780 |

2500 The oldest surviving work of literature, the *Epic of Gilgamesh,* relates the story of the most popular Mesopotamian hero.

1789 First U.S. Congress meets.

TIME *Line*

Stonehenge was an ancient synthesis of astronomy, mathematics, and architecture. Students might find it interesting to report on the mystery of Stonehenge.

inter**NET** CONNECTION

The Classical Guitar Home Page links to a beginner's page, guitar MIDI files, classical guitar pages, The Flamenco Guitar Home Page, and more.

World Wide Web
http://www.teleport.com/~jdimick/cg.html

One student who understands passion for music is **AnnaMaría Padilla**. She is only 16 years old, yet she is a student at the University of New Mexico earning a degree in business administration while also enrolled at Santa Fe Community College, studying for an associate of arts degree. She is a flamenco and classical guitarist who believes that teenagers should pursue their dreams with energy and enthusiasm. So strong is her conviction that she has recorded a CD and has written and published a book titled *Why Wait? Graduate!* that encourages students to pursue their educational goals. She hopes that, in sharing the secrets of her success, young people will see alternatives that they could also pursue.

You probably think of music as being sounds or notes. But did you know that music can also be represented mathematically? In fact, trigonometry can be used to connect music and physics, seemingly unrelated subjects.

Do research on the ways music, trigonometry, and physics are related. Devise a creative presentation to share your research with your classmates. Some possibilities include a poster, a video, or an experiment.

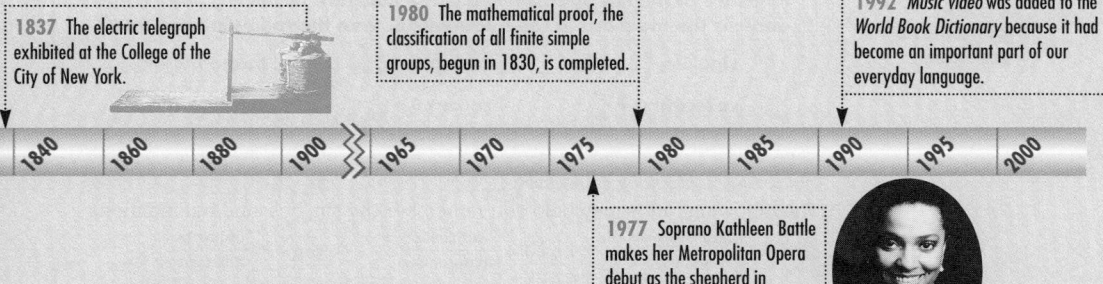

1837 The electric telegraph exhibited at the College of the City of New York.

1980 The mathematical proof, the classification of all finite simple groups, begun in 1830, is completed.

1992 *Music video* was added to the *World Book Dictionary* because it had become an important part of our everyday language.

1977 Soprano Kathleen Battle makes her Metropolitan Opera debut as the shepherd in *Tannhäuser.*

Chapter 13 **771**

Alternative Chapter Projects

Two other chapter projects are included in the *Investigations and Projects Masters*. In Chapter 13 Project A, pp. 73–74, students extend the topic in the chapter opener. In Chapter 13 Project B, pp. 75–76, students design and build a scale model of a building.

Anna María encourages students to discover their dreams and accept responsibility for their own education. "It is my belief that many of my peers are in need of alternatives. The school system is indisputably in trouble, causing numerous students to face dismal futures."

Chapter Project

Cooperative Learning
Xylophones and stringed instruments make excellent models of the relationship between mathematics and music. But all musical instruments exhibit these relationships. Try to set up groups so that each group has at least one student with an instrument.

Investigations and Projects Masters, p. 73

13 NAME_____ DATE_____
Chapter 13 Project A
Student Edition
Pages 772–814

A Golden Oldie

1. For this project, you will work in a small group to research the musical discoveries of the ancient Greek mathematician Pythagoras. Use reference books to find answers to the following questions.

   • What did Pythagoras notice when he plucked two strings whose lengths were in ratios of small whole numbers?

   • What is meant by the frequency of a musical tone?

   • How are the frequencies of two notes an octave apart related to one another mathematically?

2. Research several different groups of musical instruments to learn how they produce sound. Find out how each kind of instrument changes the frequency of its sounds and how mathematics is involved. You may want to ask the music teacher at your school to arrange demonstrations of different instruments.

3. Design an interactive museum exhibit about Pythagoras and his contributions to mathematics and the study of music. Try to use a variety of pictures, writing, and objects in your exhibit. Include some "hands-on" activities that will help people understand the relationship between music and mathematics.

4. Share your ideas for the museum exhibit with other groups.

NCTM Standards: 1–7, 9

Instructional Resources

- Study Guide Master 13-1
- Practice Master 13-1
- Enrichment Master 13-1
- Modeling Mathematics Masters, pp. 58–60
- Multicultural Activity Masters, p. 25
- Science and Math Lab Manual, pp. 9–12

 Transparency 13-1A contains the 5-Minute Check for this lesson; **Transparency 13-1B** contains a teaching aid for this lesson.

Recommended Pacing	
Honors Pacing	Day 1 of 9
Block Scheduling*	Day 1 of 6 (along with lesson 13-2)

 *For more information on pacing and possible lesson plans, refer to the *Block Scheduling Booklet*.

1 FOCUS

 ### 5-Minute Check
(over Chapter 12)

1. How many ways can 4 books be placed on a shelf from a selection of 10 books? **5040**
2. How many ways can 9 people be seated around a campfire? **40,320**
3. From a list of 18 books, how many groups of 6 can be selected? **18,564**
4. Four coins are tossed. What is the probability that they show 3 heads and 1 tail? $\frac{1}{4} = 0.25$
5. What is the probability of drawing a face card or a red card from a deck of 52 cards? $\frac{8}{13} \approx 0.615$

An Introduction to Trigonometry

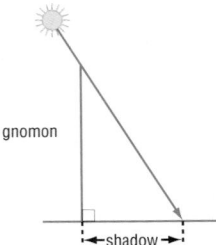

What YOU'LL LEARN

- To find values of trigonometric functions for acute angles, and
- to solve problems involving right triangles.

Why IT'S IMPORTANT

You can use trigonometry to solve problems involving surveying and literature.

 ### CONNECTION
Literature

"Where was the sun? Over the oak. Where was the shadow? Under the elm."

With these clues, Sherlock Holmes set out to solve a mystery in *The Musgrave Ritual*. Unfortunately, the elm had been struck by lightning ten years earlier, so Holmes was not able to measure the shadow directly. *You will solve the mystery in Exercise 50.*

Sherlock Holmes was not the first to use "shadow reckoning." The study of **trigonometry** probably began when early astronomers used the length of a shadow cast by a stick, called a *gnomon,* to determine the time of day. Egyptians relied on sundials as early as 1500 B.C., and there is evidence that astronomers in China, Mesopotamia, and India also understood that as the sun rises in the sky, it casts a unique shadow. In other words, the shadow is a function of the time of day.

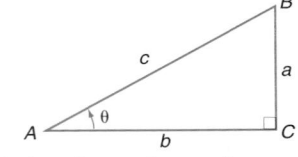

The word *trigonometry* was derived from two Greek words—*trigon* meaning triangle and *metra* meaning measurement. So, trigonometry began as the study of the relationships between the angles and sides of a right triangle.

Consider right triangle *ABC* shown below in which the measure of the acute angle *A* is identified with the Greek letter *theta,* θ.

The hypotenuse of the triangle is side $\overline{AB}$. Its length is *c* units.
The leg opposite ∠*A* is $\overline{BC}$. Its length is *a* units.
The leg adjacent to ∠*A* is $\overline{AC}$. Its length is *b* units.

Using these sides, you can define six **trigonometric functions—sine, cosine, tangent, secant, cosecant,** and **cotangent,** which are abbreviated as sin, cos, tan, sec, csc, and cot, respectively.

Trigonometric Functions	If θ is the measure of one acute angle in a right triangle, *a* is the measure of the leg opposite θ, *b* is the measure of the leg adjacent to θ, and *c* is the measure of the hypotenuse, then the following are true.

$$\text{sine } \theta = \frac{a}{c} \qquad \text{cosine } \theta = \frac{b}{c} \qquad \text{tangent } \theta = \frac{a}{b}$$

$$\text{cosecant } \theta = \frac{c}{a} \qquad \text{secant } \theta = \frac{c}{b} \qquad \text{cotangent } \theta = \frac{b}{a}$$

Notice that the sine, cosine, and tangent functions are reciprocals of the cosecant, secant, and cotangent functions, respectively.

The following ratios may help you remember the sin, cos, and tan functions.

$$\sin \theta = \frac{\text{opposite}}{\text{hypotenuse}} \qquad \cos \theta = \frac{\text{adjacent}}{\text{hypotenuse}} \qquad \tan \theta = \frac{\text{opposite}}{\text{adjacent}}$$

SOH-CAH-TOA is a mnemonic device for remembering the first letter of each word in the ratios. For example, SOH refers to s̲in-o̲pposite-h̲ypotenuse.

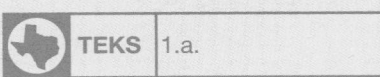 TEKS | 1.a.

The domain of each of these trigonometric functions is the set of all acute angles θ of a right triangle. The values of the functions depend only on the measure of θ and not on the size of the right triangle. For example, consider sin θ in the figure at the right.

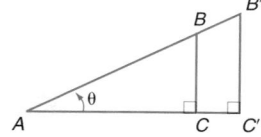

Using △ABC   *Using △AB'C'*

$$\sin \theta = \frac{BC}{AB} \qquad \sin \theta = \frac{B'C'}{AB'}$$

Notice that the triangles are similar because they are two right triangles that share a common angle, θ. Since they are similar, the ratios of corresponding sides are equal. That is, $\frac{BC}{AB} = \frac{B'C'}{AB'}$. Therefore, you will find the same value for sin θ regardless of which triangle you use.

Example **Find the values of the six trigonometric functions for angle θ. Round each value to four decimal places.**

For angle θ, the hypotenuse is $\overline{AB}$, the opposite leg is $\overline{BC}$, and the adjacent leg is $\overline{AC}$.

$$\sin \theta = \frac{5}{13} \text{ or } 0.3846 \qquad \csc \theta = \frac{13}{5} \text{ or } 2.6000$$

$$\cos \theta = \frac{12}{13} \text{ or } 0.9231 \qquad \sec \theta = \frac{13}{12} \text{ or } 1.0833$$

$$\tan \theta = \frac{5}{12} \text{ or } 0.4167 \qquad \cot \theta = \frac{12}{5} = 2.4000$$

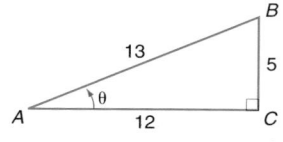

Example **Find tan A when $\cos A = \frac{2}{3}$. Round to four decimal places.**

Since $\cos A = \frac{2}{3}$, the measure of the leg adjacent to ∠A is 2, and the measure of the hypotenuse is 3. Draw and label a right triangle. Then use the Pythagorean theorem to find the measure of the leg opposite ∠A.

$\cos A = \frac{adjacent}{hypotenuse}$

$$a^2 + 2^2 = 3^2$$

$$a^2 = 5$$

$$a = \sqrt{5}$$

Now, find tan A.

$$\tan A = \frac{\sqrt{5}}{2} \qquad tan\ A = \frac{opposite}{adjacent}$$

$$\approx 1.1180$$

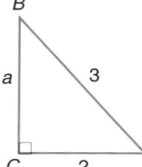

For convenience of notation, we refer to the angle with vertex A as angle A (∠A) and use A to stand for its measurement.

Angles that measure 30°, 45°, and 60° occur frequently in trigonometry. You can find the values of the trigonometric functions for these angles by using the special characteristics of a 45°–45° right triangle and a 30°–60° right triangle.

Cooperative Learning

Corners You may wish to have students work in cooperative groups. Have them cut several different right triangles from construction paper. Have them use metric rulers and protractors to measure a side and an acute angle or two sides. Then have them use trigonometric functions to find the measures of the other side(s) and angles. Confirm solutions by measuring. For more information on the corners strategy, see *Cooperative Learning in the Mathematics Classroom,* one of the titles in the Glencoe Mathematics Professional Series, page 17.

Motivating the Lesson
Hands-On Activity Using a stack of books and a notebook, model a ramp. By changing the angle of elevation, show students how all parts of a triangle are related. For example, discuss how the other angle and the sides may change if the angle of elevation is increased.

2 TEACH

In-Class Examples

For Example 1

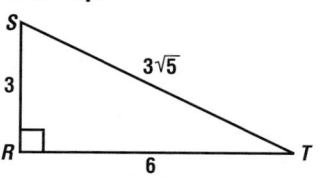

Use the triangle above to find each value and round to four decimal places.

a. $\cos S \quad \frac{\sqrt{5}}{5} \approx 0.4472$

b. $\tan T \quad \frac{1}{2} = 0.5000$

c. $\csc S \quad \frac{3\sqrt{5}}{6} \approx 1.1180$

For Example 2
Find tan M when $\cos M = \frac{10}{13}$. Round each value to four decimal places.

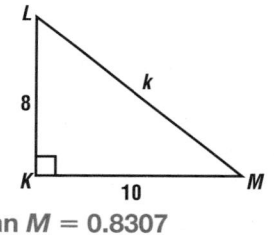

$\tan M = 0.8307$

Technology Tip
On the TI-82 graphing calculator, press ⬚SIN⬚ before entering the angle measure.

EXPLORATION

This Exploration gives students experience using their calculators for trigonometric applications. It also introduces students to the graph of the sine function.

To find the trigonometric values for a 45° angle, use an isosceles right triangle, $\triangle ABC$. Let the length of each leg be 1 unit. Use the Pythagorean theorem to find the length of the hypotenuse.

$$1^2 + 1^2 = c^2$$
$$2 = c^2$$
$$\sqrt{2} = c$$

The length of the hypotenuse is $\sqrt{2}$ units.

Therefore, the sine, cosine, and tangent values for 45° are as follows.

$$\sin 45° = \frac{1}{\sqrt{2}} \quad \text{or} \quad \frac{\sqrt{2}}{2} \qquad \cos 45° = \frac{1}{\sqrt{2}} \quad \text{or} \quad \frac{\sqrt{2}}{2} \qquad \tan 45° = \frac{1}{1} \quad \text{or} \quad 1$$

To find the trigonometric values for a 30° angle, use an equilateral triangle, $\triangle XYZ$. Let the length of each side be 2 units. The altitude $\overline{ZW}$ separates $\triangle XYZ$ into two 30°–60° right triangles. Since $\overline{ZW}$ is the perpendicular bisector of $\overline{XY}$, the length of $\overline{XW}$ is 1 unit. Find the length of altitude $\overline{ZW}$.

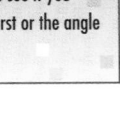

$$x^2 + 1^2 = 2^2 \qquad \textit{Pythagorean theorem}$$
$$x^2 = 3$$
$$x = \sqrt{3}$$

The length of altitude $\overline{ZW}$ is $\sqrt{3}$ units.

Therefore, the sine, cosine, and tangent values for 30° are as follows.

$$\sin 30° = \frac{1}{2} \qquad\qquad \cos 30° = \frac{\sqrt{3}}{2} \qquad\qquad \tan 30° = \frac{1}{\sqrt{3}} \text{ or } \frac{\sqrt{3}}{3}$$

To find the sine, cosine, and tangent for 60°, use $\triangle XWZ$ shown above.

$$\sin 60° = \frac{\sqrt{3}}{2} \qquad\qquad \cos 60° = \frac{1}{2} \qquad\qquad \tan 60° = \frac{\sqrt{3}}{1} \quad \text{or} \quad \sqrt{3}$$

TECHNOLOGY Tips

Consult the user's guide for your calculator to see if you press ⬚SIN⬚ first or the angle measure first.

Before hand-held calculators became accessible, students had to rely on "trig tables" to find the values of trigonometric functions for angles other than 30°, 45°, and 60°. Today, you can use the ⬚SIN⬚, ⬚COS⬚, and ⬚TAN⬚ keys on your calculator to find these values.

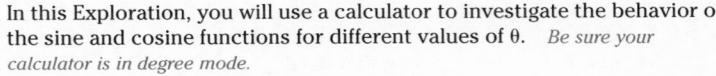

EXPLORATION — CALCULATORS

In this Exploration, you will use a calculator to investigate the behavior of the sine and cosine functions for different values of θ. *Be sure your calculator is in degree mode.*

Your Turn a–b. See students' work.

a. Choose five values of θ between 0° and 90° and evaluate sin θ for each of them. Write your answers as ordered pairs (θ, sin θ).

b. Graph the ordered pairs on a coordinate plane.

c. Use your graph to estimate the value of sin 0° and sin 90°. Check your answer with a calculator.   sin 0° = 0, sin 90° = 1

d. Explain how the value of sin θ changes as θ increases from 0° to 90°.

e. Repeat steps a–d using the cosine function.

d. Sample answer: sin θ increases from 0 to 1.

e. Sample answer: cos θ decreases from 1 to 0.

GLENCOE Technology

 Interactive Mathematics Tools Software

This multimedia software provides an interactive lesson that explores the relationship of the sine ratio to the length of the hypotenuse of the right triangle. A **Computer Journal** gives students an opportunity to write about what they have learned.

For Windows & Macintosh

You can also use the inverse capabilities of a calculator to find the measure of an angle when you know one of its trigonometric ratios. *You will learn more about inverses in Lesson 13–7.*

Example **3** **Find *x* if sin *x* = 0.7590. Round to the nearest degree.**

ENTER: 0.7590 SIN⁻¹   *49.37611923*   The SIN⁻¹ key may be a second function on your calculator.

Therefore, *x* is approximately 49°.

If you know the measure of any two sides of a right triangle or the measure of one side and one acute angle, you can determine the measures of all the sides and angles of the triangle. This process of finding the missing measures is known as **solving a triangle.**

Example **4** **Solve each triangle. Round measures of sides to the nearest tenth and measures of angles to the nearest degree.**
  a. △ ABC

You know the measures of the sides. You need to find *A* and *B*.

Find *A*. $\sin A = \frac{12}{15}$ $\sin A = \frac{opposite}{hypotenuse}$

$\sin A = 0.8$

Use a calculator and the $\sin^{-1}$ function to find the angle whose sine is 0.8.

0.8 SIN⁻¹   *53.130102*

To the nearest degree, A ≈ 53°.

Find *B*.   53° + B ≈ 90°   *Angles A and B are complementary.*

B ≈ 37°

Therefore, A ≈ 53° and B ≈ 37°.

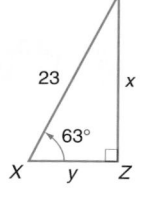

b. △ XYZ

You know the measure of the hypotenuse and one acute angle. You need to find *x*, *y*, and *Y*.

Find *x* and *y*. $\sin 63° = \frac{x}{23}$ $\cos 63° = \frac{y}{23}$

$0.8910 \approx \frac{x}{23}$ $0.4540 \approx \frac{y}{23}$

$x \approx 20.5$ $y \approx 10.4$

Find *Y*.   63° + Y = 90°

Y = 27°

Therefore, Y = 27°, x ≈ 20.5, and y ≈ 10.4.

Trigonometry has many practical applications in the real world. Among the most important is the ability to find distances or lengths that cannot be measured directly.

Lesson 13–1 An Introduction to Trigonometry **775**

GLOBAL CONNECTIONS

The gnomon dates from 3500 B.C. and the first Egyptian sundials from 1500 B.C. Next came the hemispherical sundial from Babylon about 300 B.C. More complex sundials like the hemicyclium, which uses conic sections, were created later by the Greeks.

In-Class Examples

For Example 3
Find *x* if cos *x* = 0.9659. Round to the nearest degree. **15°**

For Example 4
Solve each right triangle. Round measures of sides to the nearest tenth and measures of angles to the nearest degree.

a. $a = 5, b = 4, c = \sqrt{41}$
   A ≈ 51°, B ≈ 38°

b. A = 60°, b = 8
   B = 30°, c = 16, a = 13.9

Teaching Tip In Example 4, remind students that the acute angles in a right triangle are complementary.

Teaching Tip If the SIN key is a second function, be sure to press the 2nd key first.

GLOBAL CONNECTIONS

Sundials use a shadow falling on a calibrated scale to tell time. In some primitive regions of Egypt, sundials are still used to tell time.

Classroom Vignette

"I use the following mini-project after this section. 'Pretend you are the author of a math textbook and you need to write application problems that deal with trigonometric functions and right triangles. You must write five problems, draw any appropriate diagrams, and make a solution key.'"

Susan Creekmore
Marion High School
Marion, Arkansas

Susan Justus Creekmore

In-Class Examples

For Example 5
A car is traveling 750 meters along a ramp raised 4 degrees from the ground. How far did it rise during this distance?
$\approx$ 52.3 meters

For Example 6
Trevor is standing on top of a cliff 200 feet above a lake. The measurement of the angle of depression to a boat on the lake is 21°. How far is the boat from the base of the cliff to the nearest foot? $\approx$ 521 feet

Teaching Tip Make sure students understand the terminology used. You may want to review the concepts of alternate interior angles and congruent angles.

Teaching Tip Point out to students that this is a method of indirect measurement and is frequently used to measure items or distances too difficult to measure directly.

Example 5

APPLICATION
Surveying

Utah's Bryce Canyon National Park contains some of the most colorful rock formations on Earth. For over 60 million years, water and ice have worn the canyon rocks into unusual shapes in shades of red, copper, pink, and cream. Some parts of the canyon are 1000 feet deep.

To find the distance across Bryce Canyon at a particular point, a surveyor sets up a transit at point *C* and sights a rock formation across the canyon at point *B*. Then the surveyor turns the transit 90° and sights point *A* that is 100 feet away. Using the transit at point *A*, the surveyor determines that the measure of $\angle A$ is 84°. Find the distance across the canyon from *B* to *C*.

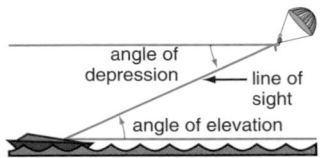

Let *a* represent the distance, in feet, from *B* to *C*.

$\tan 84° = \dfrac{a}{100}$ $\tan = \dfrac{opposite}{adjacent}$

$9.5144 \approx \dfrac{a}{100}$

$a \approx 951.44$

The distance across Bryce Canyon at this point is about 951 feet.

Some applications of trigonometry use an **angle of elevation** or **angle of depression**. In the figure at the right, the angle formed by the line of sight from the boat and a horizontal line is called an angle of elevation. The angle formed by the line of sight from the parasail and a horizontal line is called an angle of depression.

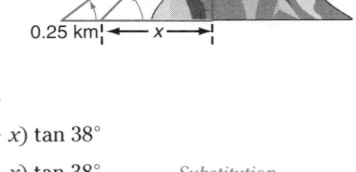

The line of sight is a transversal intersecting the two horizontal lines. The angle of elevation and the angle of depression are alternate interior angles. Since the horizontal lines are parallel, the angle of elevation and the angle of depression are congruent.

Example 6

APPLICATION
Geology

On May 18, 1980, Mount Saint Helens in Washington erupted. It was one of the largest recent volcanic eruptions in North America.

A geologist measured a 43° angle of elevation to the top of a volcano crater. After moving 0.25 kilometers farther away, the angle of elevation was 38°. How high is the top of the volcano crater?

The figure at the right shows two right triangles that share a common height. Let *h* represent the height of the crater in kilometers. Let *x* represent the side adjacent to the angle whose measure is 43°. Write a system of equations in two variables.

$\tan 43° = \dfrac{h}{x}$ $\tan 38° = \dfrac{h}{0.25 + x}$

$h = x \tan 43°$ $h = (0.25 + x) \tan 38°$

First, solve for *x*. $x \tan 43° = (0.25 + x) \tan 38°$ *Substitution*
$x \tan 43° = 0.25 \tan 38° + x \tan 38°$ *Distributive property*
$x \tan 43° - x \tan 38° = 0.25 \tan 38°$ *Subtract $x \tan 38°$ from each side.*
$x(\tan 43° - \tan 38°) = 0.25 \tan 38°$ *Distributive property*

Alternative Learning Styles

Kinesthetic Have students use an astrolabe or some other method to measure the angle of elevation for a tall object on the school grounds, such as a flagpole, tree, or building. Measure the distance from the astrolabe to the base of the object and determine the height of the object. Be sure to include the distance of the astrolabe from the ground.

F Y I

A volcano is one of many holes in Earth's crust. Earth's crust consists of many large solid plates floating on molten magma. The lava that flows out of a volcano is a glimpse of the inside of Earth, which is hot melted rock.

$$x = \frac{0.25 \tan 38°}{\tan 43° - \tan 38°}$$
$$x \approx 1.29$$

Now, find h. $h = x \tan 43°$
$$h \approx 1.29(0.9325)$$
$$h \approx 1.20$$

Therefore, the volcano crater is about 1.20 kilometers high.

CHECK FOR UNDERSTANDING

Communicating Mathematics

1. hyp, c; adj, b; opp, a

Study the lesson. Then complete the following.

1. **Identify** the hypotenuse, the leg adjacent to θ, and the leg opposite θ in the triangle at the right.

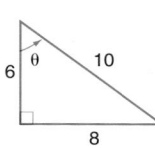

2. **Define** the word *trigonometry*.   triangle measure

3. **Evaluate** the six trigonometric functions of θ in the triangle at the right. Round your answers to four decimal places. **See margin.**

6   θ   10   8

4. **Draw and label** a figure that shows an angle of depression from a person on a Ferris wheel who is looking at a friend waiting in line. **See margin.**

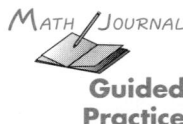

MATH JOURNAL

5. Write a paragraph explaining how you can use trigonometry to find the height of a flagpole. Include a drawing with your explanation. **See students' work.**

Guided Practice

8. $\sin 42° = \frac{x}{39}$, $x \approx 26.1$

9. $\tan x° = \frac{33}{15}$, $x \approx 66°$

12. $B = 27°$, $c \approx 10.9$, $b \approx 4.9$

13. $b = 5$, $A \approx 67°$, $B \approx 23°$

14. $a \approx 14.4$, $b \approx 10.5$, $B = 36°$

Suppose θ is an acute angle of a right triangle. For each function, find the values of the remaining five trigonometric functions of θ. Round to four decimal places.   6–7. See margin.

6. $\sin \theta = \frac{\sqrt{3}}{2}$

7. $\tan \theta = 2$

Write an equation involving sin, cos, or tan that can be used to find x. Then solve the equation. Round measures of sides to the nearest tenth and measures of angles to the nearest degree.

8.
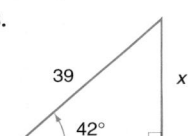
39   x 42°

9.
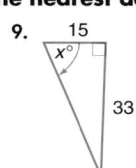
15   $x°$ 33

Find the value of x. Round to the nearest degree.

10. $\sin x = 0.7364$ **47°**

11. $\cos x = 0.9912$ **8°**

Solve each right triangle. Round measures of sides to the nearest tenth and measures of angles to the nearest degree.

12.
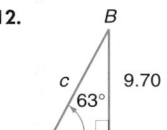
B c 9.70   63° A b C

13.
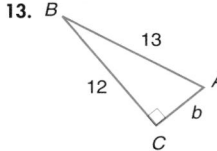
B 13   12 A b C

14.
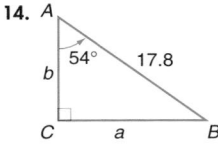
A 54°   17.8 b C a B

15. **Traveling**   In a sightseeing boat near the base of the Horseshoe Falls at Niagara Falls, a passenger estimates the angle of elevation to the top of the falls to be 30°. If the Horseshoe Falls are 173 feet high, what is the distance from the boat to the base of the falls?   about 300 feet

Lesson 13–1   An Introduction to Trigonometry   **777**

Reteaching

Using Discussion   Separate the class into groups. Give each group a word problem using right triangle trigonometry. Have them set up the diagram and the equation. Have the groups exchange problems in order for the new groups to see if they agree that the diagram and equation are correct.

Additional Answers

6. $\cos \theta = 0.5$
   $\tan \theta \approx 1.7321$
   $\csc \theta \approx 1.1547$
   $\sec \theta = 2$
   $\cot \theta \approx 0.5774$

7. $\sin \theta \approx 0.8944$
   $\cos \theta \approx 0.4472$
   $\csc \theta \approx 1.1180$
   $\sec \theta \approx 2.2361$
   $\cot \theta = 0.5$

3 PRACTICE/APPLY

Check for Understanding

Exercises 1–15 are designed to help you assess your students' understanding through reading, writing, speaking, and modeling. You should work through Exercises 1–5 with your students and then monitor their work on Exercises 6–15.

Error Analysis

Have students first check their diagrams before setting up an equation to solve. Incorrect labeling, such as using the c value for a leg and not for the hypotenuse, is a common mistake. Review rules for labeling a right triangle.

Additional Answers

3. $\sin \theta = 0.8$
   $\cos \theta = 0.6$
   $\tan \theta \approx 1.3333$
   $\csc \theta = 1.25$
   $\sec \theta \approx 1.6667$
   $\cot \theta = 0.75$

4.
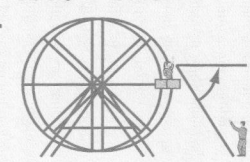

Study Guide Masters, p. 92

13-1   NAME_____   DATE_____
    Study Guide   Student Edition Pages 770–775

An Introduction to Trigonometry

Trigonometry can be used to find the missing measures of triangles. Refer to the diagram at the right. The **hypotenuse** of triangle ABC is side AB, and its length is c units. The side opposite angle A is side BC. Its length is a units. The side **adjacent** to angle A is side AC. Its length is b units.

Using the figure, trigonometric values can be defined in the following way.

$\sin A = \frac{\text{opposite side}}{\text{hypotenuse}} = \frac{a}{c}$ $\cos A = \frac{\text{adjacent side}}{\text{hypotenuse}} = \frac{b}{c}$ $\tan A = \frac{\text{opposite side}}{\text{adjacent side}} = \frac{a}{b}$

$\csc A = \frac{\text{hypotenuse}}{\text{opposite side}} = \frac{c}{a}$ $\sec A = \frac{\text{hypotenuse}}{\text{adjacent side}} = \frac{c}{b}$ $\cot A = \frac{\text{adjacent side}}{\text{opposite side}} = \frac{b}{a}$

Example: Find the sine, cosine, tangent, cosecant, secant, and cotangent of angle A rounded to four decimal places.

$\sin A = \frac{6}{10}$ or 0.6000 $\csc A = \frac{10}{6}$ or 1.6667

$\cos A = \frac{8}{10}$ or 0.8000 $\sec A = \frac{10}{8}$ or 1.2500

$\tan A = \frac{6}{8}$ or 0.7500 $\cot A = \frac{8}{6}$ or 1.3333

Solve. Round measures of sides and angles to the nearest tenth.

1. If $c = 21$ and $a = 15$, find b.   14.7

2. If $a = 32$ and $b = 15$, find A.   64.9°

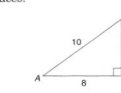

3. If $A = 32°$ and $c = 8$, find b.   6.8

4. If $a = 5$ and $b = 10$, find A, B, and c.   26.6°, 63.4°, 11.2

5. A 150-foot rope is tied from the top of a 100-foot-tall pole to a stake in the ground. What is the angle between the rope and the ground?   41.8°

6. A 6-foot-long pipe is propped on a 3-foot-tall packing crate that sits on level ground. One foot of the pipe extends above the top edge of the crate and the other end rests on the ground. What angle does the pipe form with the ground?   53.1°

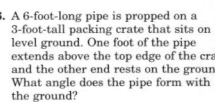

Chapter 13   **777**

Assignment Guide

Core: 17–53 odd, 55–64
Enriched: 16–46 even, 48–64

For **Extra Practice,** see p. 906.

The red A, B, and C flags, printed only in the Teacher's Wraparound Edition, indicate the level of difficulty of the exercises.

Additional Answers

16. $\sin\theta \approx 0.9231$; $\cos\theta \approx 0.3846$; $\cot\theta \approx 0.4167$; $\csc\theta \approx 1.0833$; $\sec\theta = 2.6$
17. $\sin\theta \approx 0.9682$; $\tan\theta \approx 3.8730$; $\csc\theta \approx 1.0328$; $\sec\theta = 4$; $\cot\theta \approx 0.2582$
18. $\sin\theta \approx 0.4472$; $\cos\theta \approx 0.8944$; $\tan\theta = 0.5$; $\csc\theta \approx 2.2361$; $\sec\theta \approx 1.1180$
19. $\sin\theta = 0.4$; $\cos\theta \approx 0.9165$; $\tan\theta \approx 0.4364$; $\sec\theta \approx 1.0911$; $\cot\theta \approx 2.2913$
20. $\sin\theta \approx 0.9428$; $\cos\theta \approx 0.3333$; $\tan\theta \approx 2.8284$; $\csc\theta \approx 1.0607$; $\cot\theta \approx 0.3536$
21. $\cos\theta \approx 0.8660$; $\tan\theta \approx 0.5774$; $\sec\theta \approx 1.1547$; $\csc\theta = 2$; $\cot\theta \approx 1.7321$

22. $\cos 23° = \dfrac{32}{x}$, $x \approx 34.8$

23. $\sin 54° = \dfrac{17.8}{x}$, $x \approx 22.0$

24. $\tan 17.5° = \dfrac{x}{23.7}$, $x \approx 7.5$

Practice Masters, p. 92

NAME_____ DATE_____

13-1 **Practice** Student Edition Pages 770–775

An Introduction to Trigonometry

Using the triangle shown, write an equation involving sin, cos, or tan that can be used to find the missing measure. Then solve the equation. Round measures of sides to the nearest tenth.

1. If $A = 20°$ and $c = 32$, find a.
   $\sin 20° = \dfrac{a}{32}$; 10.9

2. If $A = 49°$ and $a = 17$, find b.
   $\tan 49° = \dfrac{17}{b}$; 14.8

3. If $A = 27.3°$ and $a = 7$, find c.
   $\sin 27.3° = \dfrac{7}{c}$; 15.3

4. If $a = 19.2$ and $A = 63.4°$, find b.
   $\tan 63.4° = \dfrac{19.2}{b}$; 9.6

5. If $a = 28$ and $B = 41°$, find c.
   $\cos 41° = \dfrac{28}{c}$; 37.1

Solve each right triangle. Assume that C represents the right angle and c is the hypotenuse. Round measures of sides and angles to the nearest tenth.

6. $a = 12$, $A = 35°$
   $B = 55°$, $b = 17.1$, $c = 20.9$

7. $b = 25$, $B = 71°$
   $A = 19°$, $a = 8.6$, $c = 26.4$

8. $a = 4$, $b = 7$
   $A = 29.6°$, $B = 60.3°$, $c = 8.1$

9. $b = 52$, $c = 95$
   $a = 79.5$, $A = 56.8°$, $B = 33.2°$

Solve each problem. Round measures of lengths to the nearest tenth.

10. An airplane is directly above a beacon that is 10,000 feet from an airport control tower. The angle of depression from the plane to the base of the control tower is 6°. How high above the beacon is the plane?
    1051.0 feet

11. John views the top of a water tower at an angle of elevation of 36°. He walks 120 meters in a straight line toward the tower. Then he sights the top of the tower at an angle of elevation of 51°. How far is John from the base of the tower?
    171.5 meters

778 Chapter 13

Practice Suppose θ is an acute angle of a right triangle. For each function, find the values of the remaining five trigonometric functions of θ. Round to four decimal places.

16–27. See margin.

16. $\tan\theta = \dfrac{12}{5}$ 17. $\cos\theta = \dfrac{1}{4}$ 18. $\cot\theta = 2$

19. $\csc\theta = \dfrac{5}{2}$ 20. $\sec\theta = 3$ 21. $\sin\theta = 0.5$

Write an equation involving sin, cos, or tan that can be used to find **x**. Then solve the equation. Round measures of sides to the nearest tenth and measures of angles to the nearest degree.

22.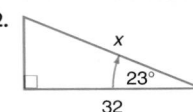
23.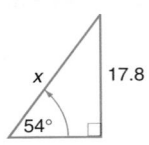
24.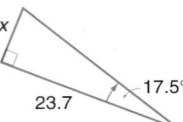

25.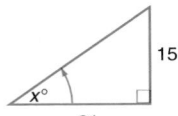
26.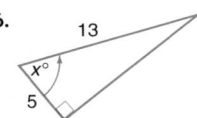
27.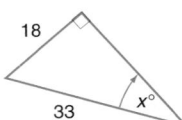

Find the value of **x**. Round to the nearest degree.

28. $\tan x = 0.5923$ **31°**   29. $\cos x = 0.5269$ **58°**   30. $\tan x = 0.2126$ **12°**
31. $\sin x = 0.9998$ **89°**   32. $\cos x = 0.9998$ **1°**   33. $\sin x = 0.5000$ **30°**

Solve each right triangle. Assume that **C** represents the right angle and **c** is the hypotenuse. Round measures of sides to the nearest tenth and measures of angles to the nearest degree.

34–45. See Solutions Manual.

34.
35.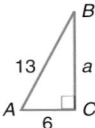
36.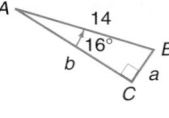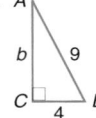

37. $B = 18°$, $a = \sqrt{15}$ 38. $A = 56°$, $c = 16$ 39. $A = 45°$, $c = 7\sqrt{2}$

40. $c = 25$, $A = 15°$ 41. $B = 30°$, $b = 11$ 42. $\tan A = \dfrac{7}{8}$, $a = 7$

43. $a = 7$, $A = 27°$ 44. $\tan B = \dfrac{8}{6}$, $b = 8$ 45. $\sin A = \dfrac{1}{3}$, $a = 5$

INTEGRATION
Geometry

46. In square $ABCD$ at the right, the midpoint of side $\overline{AD}$ is E. Find the values of x, y, and z to the nearest tenth of a degree. $x \approx 63.4°$, $y \approx 26.6°$, $z \approx 63.4°$

47. Isosceles triangle RST below at the right has base $\overline{TS}$ measuring 10 centimeters and base angles each measuring 39°. Find the length of the altitude $\overline{QR}$. **4.05 cm**

Critical Thinking

48. Describe a set of given conditions for which it would be impossible to solve a right triangle. **See margin.**

49. Explain why the sine and cosine of an acute angle are never greater than 1 but the tangent of an acute angle may be greater than 1. **See margin.**

Additional Answers

25. $\tan x° = \dfrac{15}{21}$, $x \approx 36°$

26. $\cos x° = \dfrac{5}{13}$, $x \approx 67°$

27. $\sin x° = \dfrac{18}{33}$, $x \approx 33°$

48. Sample answer: if you know two acute angles and no sides
49. Sample answer: The legs of a right triangle are never greater than the hypotenuse, but one leg may be greater than the other leg.

50. Literature Refer to the application at the beginning of the lesson. Sherlock Holmes needed to find the length of the shadow cast by the elm. He was able to determine that the elm tree was 64 feet tall before it was struck by lightning. At the appropriate time, Holmes used a 6-foot rod to cast a shadow. Its shadow was 9 feet. What was the length of the shadow of the elm? **96 feet**

51. Broadcasting Dolores and Bill are standing 100 feet apart and in a straight line with the WWV television tower. The angle of elevation from Bill to the tower is 30° and the angle of elevation from Dolores is 20°. Find the height of the television tower to the nearest foot. **99 feet**

52. Skiing The Aerial run in Snowbird, Utah, is 8395 feet long. Its vertical drop is 2900 feet. If the slope were constant, estimate the angle of elevation that the run makes with the horizontal. **20.2°**

53. History The Great Pyramid in Egypt has a square base, 230 meters on each side. The triangular faces of the pyramid make an angle of 51.8° with the base. Suppose you want to make a model of the pyramid for your history project. What measure should you use for the base angle of each triangle? **58.3°**

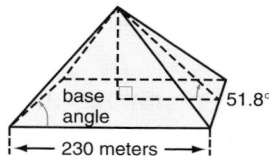

base angle — 51.8°
|← 230 meters →|

54. Aviation When an airplane is flying, the air pressure creates a force called the *lift,* which is perpendicular to the wings. If a plane banks for a turn, this lift is separated into a horizontal and vertical force. The horizontal force is what is responsible for the turn, and the measure of the vertical force is the plane's weight.

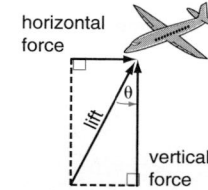

horizontal force

lift θ

vertical force

54a. 532,089 pounds, 181,985 pounds

a. Suppose a plane weighs 500,000 pounds. Find the measure of the lift and horizontal component for a banking angle, θ, of 20°.

b. If the maximum lift that the wings can sustain is 650,000 pounds, what is the maximum banking angle? **39.7°**

Mixed Review

55. no

56. $\frac{3840}{16,807} \approx 22.8\%$

55. Statistics Determine whether a sample of people attending a concert is a random sample for a survey of people's favorite performer. (Lesson 12–8)

56. Four of every 7 pitches thrown by Elias Ramos are strikes. What is the probability that 4 of the next 5 pitches will be strikes? (Lesson 12–7)

57. Probability State the probability of an event occurring given that the odds of the event are $\frac{5}{1}$. (Lesson 12–4) $\frac{5}{6}$

58. Expand the binomial $(r + s)^6$. (Lesson 11–8) **See margin.**

59. Find the nth term of a geometric sequence in which $a_1 = 4$, $n = 3$, and $r = 5$. (Lesson 11–3) **100**

60. Solve $\log_4(x + 2) + \log_4(x - 4) = 2$. (Lesson 10–3) **6**

61. Simplify $\left(x^{\sqrt{2}}\right)^{\sqrt{8}}$. (Lesson 10–1) x^4

62. Use the distance formula to find the distance between the points at (3, 3) and $\left(\sqrt{3}, \sqrt{3}\right)$. (Lesson 7–1) $2\sqrt{6 - 3\sqrt{3}}$ **or about 1.8 units**

63. Chemistry A chemist performed an experiment that yields 1.8×10^{24} molecules of ethanol. The mole is the standard unit of measure for the chemical quantity of a substance. There are 6.02×10^{23} molecules in a mole. How many moles of ethanol did the experiment yield? (Lesson 5–1) **about 0.299×10^1 or 2.99**

64. What property of real numbers is demonstrated by $x(a + b) = xa + xb$? (Lesson 1–2) **distributive property**

Lesson 13–1 An Introduction to Trigonometry **779**

Extension

Connections The Great Pyramid of Cheops in Egypt has a square base. This base is 230 meters on a side. The faces of the pyramid make an angle of 51°50' with the horizontal. How tall is the pyramid? **about 146 meters**

---

4 ASSESS

Closing Activity

Modeling Show students a set of complete blueprints for a building. Have them list areas of the blueprint where knowing angle measurements or side lengths of right triangles is important.

Additional Answer

58. $r^6 + 6r^5s + 15r^4s^2 + 20r^3s^3 + 15r^2s^4 + 6rs^5 + s^6$

Enrichment Masters, p. 92

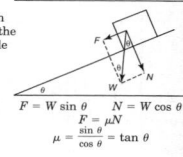

13-1 NAME_____ DATE_____
Enrichment
Student Edition
Pages 770–775

The Angle of Repose

Suppose you place a block of wood on an inclined plane, as shown at the right. If the angle, θ, at which the plane is inclined from the horizontal is very small, the block will not move. If you increase the angle, the block will eventually overcome the force of friction and start to slide down the plane.

At the instant the block begins to slide, the angle formed by the plane is called the angle of friction, or the angle of repose.

For situations in which the block and plane are smooth but unlubricated, the angle of repose depends *only* on the types of materials in the block and the plane. The angle is independent of the area of contact between the two surfaces and of the weight of the block.

The drawing at the right shows how to use vectors to find a coefficient of friction. This coefficient varies with different materials and is denoted by the Greek letter mu, μ.

$F = W \sin \theta$ $N = W \cos \theta$
$F = \mu N$
$\mu = \frac{\sin \theta}{\cos \theta} = \tan \theta$

Solve each problem.

1. A wooden chute is built so that wooden crates can slide down into the basement of a store. What angle should the chute make for the crates to slide down at a constant speed? 27°

Material	Coefficient of Friction μ
Wood on wood	0.5
Wood on stone	0.5
Rubber tire on dry concrete	1.0
Rubber tire on wet concrete	0.7

2. Will a 100-pound wooden crate slide down a stone ramp that makes an angle of 20° with the horizontal? Explain your answer.
No, the angle must be at least 27°.

3. If you increase the weight of the crate in Exercise 2 to 300 pounds, does it change your answer?
No, the weight does not affect the angle.

4. A car with rubber tires is being driven on dry concrete pavement. If the car tires spin without traction on a hill, how steep is the hill?
at least 45°

5. For Exercise 4, does it make a difference if it starts to rain? Explain your answer.
Yes, the street needs to be only 35° for the car tires to spin.

Angles and Angle Measure

NCTM Standards: 1–5, 9

Instructional Resources

- Study Guide Master 13-2
- Practice Master 13-2
- Enrichment Master 13-2
- Assessment and Evaluation Masters, p. 352

Transparency 13-2A contains the 5-Minute Check for this lesson; **Transparency 13-2B** contains a teaching aid for this lesson.

Recommended Pacing	
Honors Pacing	Day 2 of 9
Block Scheduling*	Day 1 of 6 (along with Lesson 13-1)

*For more information on pacing and possible lesson plans, refer to the *Block Scheduling Booklet.*

1 FOCUS

5-Minute Check
(over Lesson 13-1)

Solve each right triangle. Assume that *C* represents the right angle and *c* is the hypotenuse. Round measures of sides to the nearest tenth and measures of angles to the nearest degree.

1. $A = 50°$, $a = 11$
   $B = 40°$, $b = 9.2$, $c = 14.4$
2. $a = 15$, $c = 20$
   $A = 48°$, $B = 41°$, $b = 13.2$
3. $B = 31°$, $c = 12$
   $A = 59°$, $a = 10.3$, $b = 6.2$
4. The top of a staircase is 3.5 meters higher than the bottom. Viewed from the side, the horizontal length is 4.75 meters. Find the angle of depression from the top of the stairway to the bottom.
   36°23'

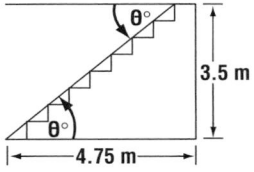

What YOU'LL LEARN

- To change radian measure to degree measure and vice versa, and
- to identify coterminal angles.

Why IT'S IMPORTANT

You can use angles to solve problems involving astronomy and geography.

CONNECTION
Geography

When French novelist Jules Verne wrote *Around the World in Eighty Days* in 1873, traveling that great distance in such a short time was unheard of. Do you think you could travel westward around the world in just one day? How fast would you have to travel to accomplish this? *A problem like this will be solved in Exercise 50.*

The answers to these questions depend on your position on Earth. Cartographers use a grid that contains circles through the poles, called *longitude* lines, and circles parallel to the equator, called *latitude* lines. In the figure at the right, point *P* is located by traveling north from point *Q* on the equator through a central angle of *a*° to a circle of latitude, and then west along that circle through an angle of *b*°.

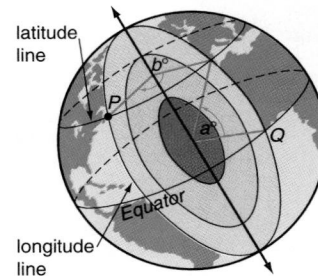

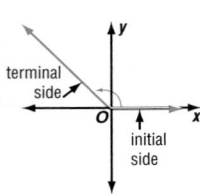

On a coordinate plane, an angle may be generated by the rotation of two rays that share a fixed endpoint at the origin. One ray, called the **initial side** of the angle, is fixed along the positive *x*-axis. The other ray, called the **terminal side** of the angle, can rotate about the center. An angle positioned so that its vertex is at the origin and its initial side is along the positive *x*-axis is said to be in **standard position.**

The measure of an angle is determined by the amount of rotation from the initial side to the terminal side. If the rotation is in a counterclockwise direction, the measure of the angle is positive. If the rotation is in a clockwise direction, the measure of the angle is negative.

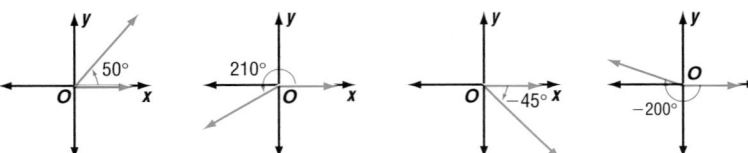

When terminal sides rotate, they may sometimes make one or more revolutions. An angle whose terminal side has made exactly one revolution has a measure of 360°.

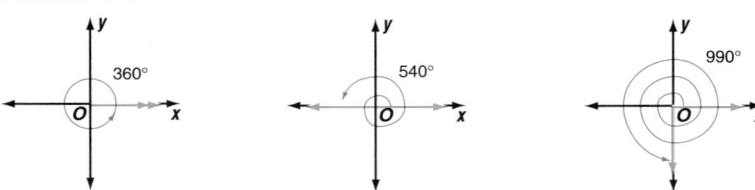

Example **1**

APPLICATION
Astronomy

Eratosthenes, an astronomer who lived in Greece in the third century B.C., is credited with providing the first accurate measure of Earth's circumference. He found that at noon on the day of the summer solstice, the sun was directly over the city of Syene. At the same time, in Alexandria, which is north of Syene, the sun was 7°12′ south of being directly overhead. If the distance between the two cities was 5000 stadia, find Eratosthenes' measure of the circumference of Earth.

The stadium (singular form of stadia) was an ancient unit of measurement equal to about 0.098 mile.

F Y I

Why are there 360° in one revolution instead of 100° or 1000°? The answer may lie in ancient Babylon where mathematicians developed a number system based on 60. For example, there were 60 bushels in a *mana* and 60 *mana* in a *talent*. Today, we further subdivide 1 degree into 60 minutes (60′) and 1 minute into 60 seconds (60″).

Since there are 360° in a full rotation around Earth, the following proportion can be written.

$$\frac{360°}{7°12′} = \frac{c}{5000}$$
$$(7°12′)c = (360°)5000$$
$$c = \frac{(360°)5000}{7°12′}$$
$$c = \frac{(360°)5000}{7.2°} \quad 7°12′ = \left(7\frac{12}{60}\right)° \text{ or } 7.2°$$
$$c = 250,000$$

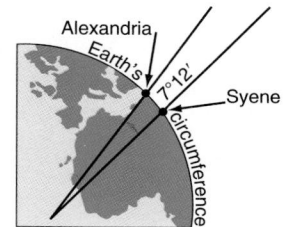

Alexandria
Earth's
7°12′
Syene
circumference

Eratosthenes' measure of Earth's circumference was 250,000 stadia or 24,500 miles. This is only 158 miles less than the currently accepted value.

As you have seen, the degree is commonly used in applications involving surveying and navigation. However, in the late 1800s, mathematicians began to see the need for another unit of measure, called a **radian**, that would simplify certain mathematical and physical formulas.

The definition of a radian is based on the concept of a **unit circle**, which is a circle of radius 1 unit with its center at the origin of a coordinate system. The radian measure of an angle is based on the length of an arc on the unit circle. In the figure at the right, θ is in standard position so that the rays of the angle intercept an arc with length 1 unit. The measure of this angle is defined to be 1 radian.

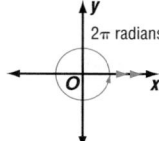

As with degrees, the measure of an angle in radians is positive if its rotation is counterclockwise. The measure is negative if the rotation is clockwise.

The circumference of any circle is $2\pi r$, where r is the radius measure. So the circumference of a unit circle is $2\pi(1)$ or 2π units. Therefore, an angle representing one complete revolution of the circle measures 2π radians.

Several common angles and their radian measure are shown below.

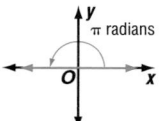
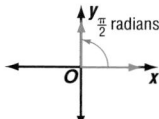
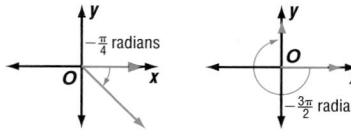

Motivating the Lesson
Hands-On Activity Have students play "Treasure Hunt" with a partner. Have each student draw a circle with a radius of 10 units on graph paper. On the circumference of that circle, locate three treasures. Guess the locations of the other students' treasures by using ordered pairs of whole numbers. A guess is a "find" if both coordinates are within 1 unit of the location.

2 TEACH

In-Class Example

For Example 1
On the planet Flippo, they have the Celebration of the Pink Moon. In Zorbo, a city on Flippo, the pink moon has risen to directly overhead and the festival begins. In Tango, a city 100 bleeps away, the moon is still 8°15′ from being directly overhead, so their celebration has not begun. Find an approximation (to the nearest bleep) for the circumference of Flippo. ≈ **4364 bleeps**

Teaching Tip You may want to mention that if the terminal side lies on one of the coordinate axes, the angle is called a *quadrantal angle.* For example, 270° and −180° are quadrantal angles.

F Y I

It is no coincidence that 360 is very close to the number of days in one year.

Cooperative Learning

Round Table Play another game of "Treasure Hunt" as described in Motivating the Lesson. Instead of two players, use two groups of two students each. Guess angle measures instead of coordinates, allowing use of calculators and protractors. A guess is correct if it is within 5° or 0.1 radian. Be sure students realize that there is more than one correct measure of an angle. For more information on the round table strategy, see *Cooperative Learning in the Mathematics Classroom,* one of the titles in the Glencoe Mathematics Professional Series, pages 21–22.

In-Class Examples

For Example 2
Change each degree measure
to radian measure.

a. $80°$ $\frac{4\pi}{9}$

b. $415°$ $\frac{83\pi}{36}$

c. $-160°$ $\frac{-8\pi}{9}$

For Example 3
Change each radian measure
to degree measure.

a. $\frac{9\pi}{5}$ $324°$

b. $\frac{-3\pi}{2}$ $270°$

c. $-1\frac{1}{4}$ $\frac{-225°}{\pi} \approx -71.6°$

Teaching Tip Note that the sum
of the absolute values of the
clockwise and counterclockwise
measures of an angle totals $360°$,
assuming there have been no
complete rotations in either
direction.

To find a relationship between degree measure and radian measure, consider one complete counterclockwise rotation. The degree measure is 360 while the radian measure of the same angle is 2π. Therefore, the following equation is true.

$$2\pi \text{ radians} = 360°$$

To change angle measures from radians to degrees or vice-versa, solve the equation above in terms of both units.

1 radian $\approx 57.3°$

$2\pi \text{ radians} = 360°$	$2\pi \text{ radians} = 360°$
$\dfrac{2\pi \text{ radians}}{2\pi} = \dfrac{360°}{2\pi}$	$\dfrac{2\pi \text{ radians}}{360} = \dfrac{360°}{360}$
$1 \text{ radian} = \dfrac{180°}{\pi}$	$\dfrac{\pi \text{ radians}}{180} = 1°$

If you know the degree measure of an angle and you need to find the radian measure, multiply the number of degrees by $\frac{\pi \text{ radians}}{180°}$.

Example ❷   Change each degree measure to radian measure.

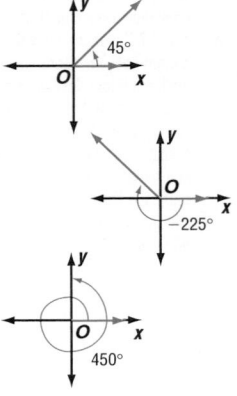

a. $45°$

$45° \left(\frac{\pi \text{ radians}}{180°} \right) = \frac{45\pi}{180}$ radians or $\frac{\pi}{4}$ radians

b. $-225°$

$-225° \left(\frac{\pi \text{ radians}}{180°} \right) = \frac{-225\pi}{180}$ radians or $-\frac{5\pi}{4}$ radians

c. $450°$

$450° \left(\frac{\pi \text{ radians}}{180°} \right) = \frac{450\pi}{180}$ radians or $\frac{5\pi}{2}$ radians

If you know the radian measure of an angle and you need to find the degree measure, multiply the number of radians by $\frac{180°}{\pi \text{ radians}}$.

Example ❸   Change each radian measure to degree measure.

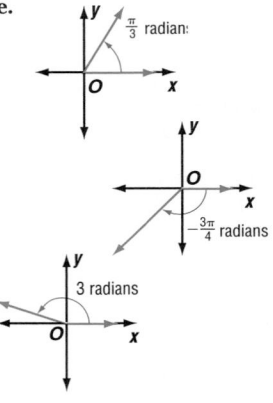

The word <u>radian</u> is usually omitted when angles are expressed in radian measure.

a. $\frac{\pi}{3}$ radians

$\frac{\pi}{3}$ radians $\left(\frac{180°}{\pi \text{ radians}} \right) = \left(\frac{180°\pi}{3\pi} \right)$ or $60°$

b. $-\frac{3\pi}{4}$ radians

$-\frac{3\pi}{4}$ radians $\left(\frac{180°}{\pi \text{ radians}} \right) = \left(\frac{540°\pi}{4\pi} \right)$ or $-135°$

c. 3 radians

3 radians $\left(\frac{180°}{\pi \text{ radians}} \right) = \left(\frac{540°}{\pi} \right)$ or about $172°$

Alternative Teaching Strategies

Reading Algebra Review the terms *intercept* and *arc* in relation to the unit circle.

If you graph a 390° angle and a 30° angle in standard position on the same coordinate plane, you will notice that the terminal side of the 390° angle is the same as the terminal side of the 30° angle. When two angles in standard position have the same terminal sides, they are called **coterminal angles**.

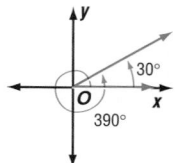

Every angle has infinitely many coterminal angles.

Notice that 390° − 30° = 360°. In degree measure, coterminal angles differ by an integral multiple of 360°. You can find an angle that is coterminal to a given angle by adding or subtracting a multiple of 360°. In radian measure, a coterminal angle is found by adding or subtracting a multiple of 2π.

Example **4** Find one positive and one negative angle that are coterminal with each angle.

a. **135°**

A positive angle is 135° + 360° or 495°.
A negative angle is 135° − 360° or −225°.

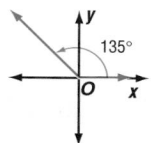

b. $\dfrac{11\pi}{4}$

A positive angle is $\dfrac{11\pi}{4} - 2\pi$ or $\dfrac{3\pi}{4}$.

A negative angle is $\dfrac{11\pi}{4} - 4\pi$ or $-\dfrac{5\pi}{4}$.

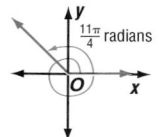

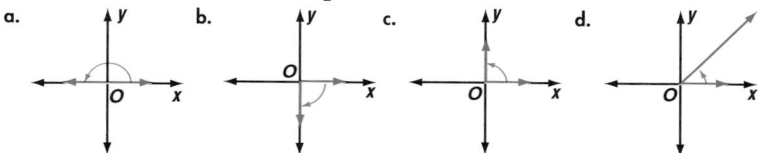

CHECK FOR UNDERSTANDING

Communicating Mathematics

1–2. See margin.

Study the lesson. Then complete the following.

1. **Describe** when an angle is in standard position.

2. **Draw** a unit circle and label an angle that measures 1 radian.

3. **Choose** the angle that measures $\dfrac{\pi}{2}$ radians. **c**

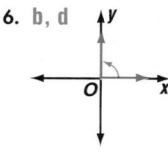

a. | b. | c. | d.

4. 360° is one complete revolution.

4. **Explain** why the measures of coterminal angles differ by a multiple of 360°.

5. **You Decide** Eduardo thinks that an angle of 20° is coterminal with an angle of 2000°. Toshi thinks the angles are not coterminal. Who is correct? Explain your reasoning. **Toshi; their difference is not a multiple of 360.**

Guided Practice

Match each angle with its measure. There may be more than one correct answer.

6. b, d | 7. a | 8. f, h | 9. g

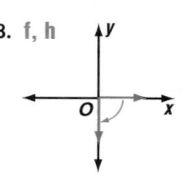
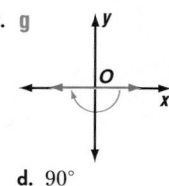

a. 270°   b. $\dfrac{\pi}{2}$ c. 2π   d. 90°

e. 180°   f. $-\dfrac{\pi}{2}$ g. −π   h. −90°

Lesson 13-2 Angles and Angle Measure **783**

Reteaching

Decision Making Separate the class into groups. Have each group write five degree measures of which some are equivalent and some are not. Have groups exchange papers and decide which pairs are equivalent and which pairs are not. Return to original groups to check and discuss.

Additional Answer

2.

In-Class Example

For Example 4
Find one positive and one negative angle that are coterminal with each angle.
a. 141° **501°, −219°**
b. $\dfrac{3\pi}{4}$ **$\dfrac{11\pi}{4}$, $\dfrac{-5\pi}{4}$**

Teaching Tip Encourage the use of diagrams and calculators when they would be helpful in solving the exercises.

3 PRACTICE/APPLY

Check for Understanding
Exercises 1–19 are designed to help you assess your students' understanding through reading, writing, speaking, and modeling. You should work through Exercises 1–5 with your students and then monitor their work on Exercises 6–19.

Additional Answer

1. when an angle has its vertex at the origin and its initial side along the positive x-axis

Study Guide Masters, p. 93

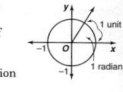

For **Extra Practice,** see p. 906.

The red A, B, and C flags, printed only in the Teacher's Wraparound Edition, indicate the level of difficulty of the exercises.

Additional Answers

47a. $a^2 + (-b)^2 = a^2 + b^2 = 1$
47b. $b^2 + a^2 = a^2 + b^2 = 1$
47c. $b^2 + (-a)^2 = a^2 + b^2 = 1$

Change each degree measure to radian measure.

10. $45°$ $\frac{\pi}{4}$ 11. $-120°$ $-\frac{2\pi}{3}$ 12. $540°$ 3π

Change each radian measure to degree measure.

13. $\frac{2\pi}{3}$ $120°$ 14. $-\frac{7\pi}{4}$ $-315°$ 15. 5 $\frac{900°}{\pi} \approx 286.48°$

Find one positive angle and one negative angle that are coterminal with each angle. 16–18. Sample answers are given.

16. $-60°$ $300°, -420°$ 17. $\frac{\pi}{4}$ $\frac{9\pi}{4}, -\frac{7\pi}{4}$ 18. $750°$ $390°, -330°$

19. **Time** Find both the degree and radian measures of the angle through which the hour hand on a clock rotates from 3:00 P.M. to 5:00 P.M.
$-60°, -\frac{\pi}{3}$

EXERCISES

Practice

Change each degree measure to radian measure.

20. $-90°$ $-\frac{\pi}{2}$ 21. $180°$ π 22. $135°$ $\frac{3\pi}{4}$

23. $1200°$ $\frac{20\pi}{3}$ 24. $-315°$ $-\frac{7\pi}{4}$ 25. $-800°$ $-\frac{40\pi}{9}$

26. $150°$ $\frac{5\pi}{6}$ 27. $540°$ 3π 28. $3600°$ 20π

Change each radian measure to degree measure.

29. π $180°$ 30. $-\frac{\pi}{2}$ $-90°$ 31. $-\frac{8\pi}{3}$ $-480°$

32. $\frac{3\pi}{4}$ $135°$ 33. 5π $900°$ 34. $\frac{5\pi}{2}$ $450°$

35. 7 $\frac{1260}{\pi} \approx 401.07°$ 36. 3.5 $\frac{630}{\pi} \approx 200.54°$ 37. -1.5 $-\frac{270}{\pi} \approx -85.94°$

Find one positive angle and one negative angle that are coterminal with each angle. 38–46. Sample answers are given.

38. $-120°$ $240°, -480°$ 39. $310°$ $670°, -50°$ 40. -5π $\pi, -3\pi$

41. $\frac{9\pi}{4}$ $\frac{\pi}{4}, -\frac{7\pi}{4}$ 42. $-450°$ $270°, -90°$ 43. $720°$ $360°, -360°$

44. $\frac{\pi}{8}$ $\frac{17\pi}{8}, -\frac{15\pi}{8}$ 45. $-900°$ $180°, -180°$ 46. $-\frac{8\pi}{3}$ $\frac{4\pi}{3}, -\frac{2\pi}{3}$

Critical Thinking

47. If (a, b) is on the unit circle with center at the origin, prove that each point is also on the unit circle. **a–c. See margin.**

   a. $(a, -b)$ b. (b, a) c. $(b, -a)$

Applications and Problem Solving

48. **Astronomy** Earth rotates on its axis once every 24 hours. **b. 8 h**
   a. How long does it take Earth to rotate through an angle of $300°$? **20 h**
   b. How long does it take Earth to rotate through an angle of $\frac{2\pi}{3}$ radians?

49. **Physics** When an object travels on a circular path like the one shown at the right, its *angular velocity,* ω, is the rate at which θ changes. Angular velocity is defined by the equation $\omega = \frac{\theta}{t}$, where θ is usually expressed in radians and t represents time. Find the angular velocity in radians per second of a point on a bicycle tire if it completes 2 revolutions in 3 seconds. $\frac{4\pi}{3}$ radians/second

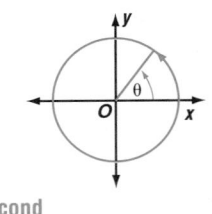

Practice Masters, p. 93

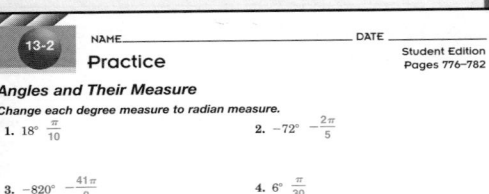

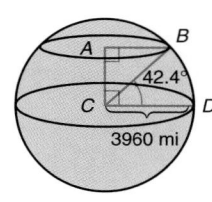
3960 mi

50. Geography Suppose a plane tried to circle Earth at the latitude of Boston, Massachusetts, in one day.

  a. Boston is located at 42.4°N latitude. In the figure at the right, the circle through point B represents the latitude line through Boston. Find the measure of $\angle ACB$.   **47.6°**

  b. Use $\triangle ABC$ to find the radius AB. (*Hint:* The radius of Earth is about 3960 miles.)   **2924 miles**

  c. What is the circumference of the latitude line passing through Boston?

50c. 18,374 miles

  d. Suppose a plane tried to circle Earth from Boston in one day. At what speed, in miles per hour, would it have to travel?   **766 miles per hour**

Mixed Review

51. Navigation The top of a lighthouse is 120 meters above sea level. From the top of the lighthouse, the measurement of the angle of depression to a boat on the ocean is 43°. How far is the boat from the foot of the lighthouse? (Lesson 13–1) **128.7 meters**

52. $\frac{1}{18} \approx 0.0\overline{5}$

52. Probability Two dice are rolled. Find $P(3 \text{ and } 4)$. (Lesson 12–5)

53. Geometry Find the total number of diagonals that can be drawn in a decagon, shown at the right. (Lesson 12–3) **35**

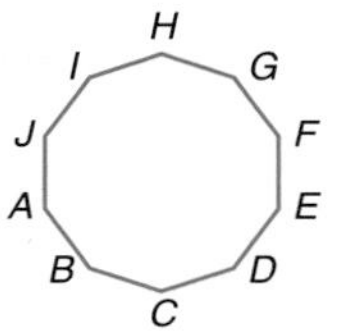

54. Find the sum of a geometric series for which $a_1 = 48$, $a_n = 3$, and $r = \frac{1}{2}$. (Lesson 11–4) **84**

55. Solve $\frac{7}{m-3} = \frac{m+4}{m-3}$. (Lesson 9–5) **no solution**

56. For the functions $g(x) = x - 1$ and $h(x) = x^2$, find $g[h(x)]$. (Lesson 8–7) $x^2 - 1$

57. $x^2 - 10x + 24 = 0$

57. Write a quadratic equation that has roots 6 and 4. (Lesson 6–5)

58. Use a matrix equation to solve the system of equations. (Lesson 4–6)

$$5x + 3y = -5 \quad (2, -5)$$
$$7x + 5y = -11$$

59. additive identity

59. What property is illustrated by $(11a + 3b) + 0 = (11a + 3b)$? (Lesson 1–2)

WORKING ON THE

Refer to the Investigation on pages 768–769.

Scream Machines!

The *Mean Streak* roller coaster at Cedar Point Amusement Park in Sandusky, Ohio, is one of the fastest and tallest wooden roller coasters in the world. Built in 1991, it is 5427 feet long. Its first hill is 161 feet high with a vertical drop of 155 feet and 52° angle of descent. It has banked curves and a course that crisscrosses the structure nine times. The 12 hills and valleys give you a ride that lasts about 2.5 minutes, reaching a top speed of 65 mph.

1 Make a sketch of the first hill of the *Mean Streak*. Label L_v as the vertical height of the hill and θ as the angle of descent. Let L_h represent the horizontal distance from the valley before the hill to the valley after the hill. Use a right triangle to find the value of L_h.

2 Discuss what determines the *Mean Streak's* top speed of 65 mph, and estimate where and how long a roller coaster would go at that speed.

Add the results of your work to your Investigation Folder.

---

4 ASSESS

Closing Activity

Modeling Have students use diagrams to model examples of the terms *arc, standard position, radian,* and *coterminal angles.*

Chapter 13, Quiz B (Lessons 13-1 and 13-2), is available in the *Assessment and Evaluation Masters,* p. 352.

Enrichment Masters, p. 93

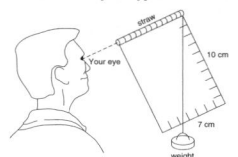

NAME_____ DATE_____

Student Edition
Pages 776–782

13-2 Enrichment

Making and Using a Hypsometer

A **hypsometer** is a device that can be used to measure the height of an object. To construct your own hypsometer, you will need a rectangular piece of heavy cardboard that is at least 7 cm by 10 cm, a straw, transparent tape, a string about 20 cm long, and a small weight that can be attached to the string.

Mark off 1-cm increments along one short side and one long side of the cardboard. Tape the straw to the other short side. Then attach the weight to one end of the string, and attach the other end of the string to one corner of the cardboard, as shown in the figure below. The diagram below shows how your hypsometer should look.

To use the hypsometer, you will need to measure the distance from the base of the object whose height you are finding to where you stand when you use the hypsometer.

Sight the top of the object through the straw. Note where the free-hanging string crosses the bottom scale. Then use similar triangles to find the height of the object.

1. Draw a diagram to illustrate how you can use similar triangles and the hypsometer to find the height of a tall object. See students' diagrams.

Use your hypsometer to find the height of each of the following.   See students' work.

2. your school's flagpole

3. a tree on your school's property

4. the highest point on the front wall of your school building

5. the goal posts on a football field

6. the hoop on a basketball court

Extension

Connections Have students research the different phases of the moon. For each phase, have them draw a diagram, labeling the measure of the angle formed. In each diagram, Earth is at the origin, the ray from Earth to the sun forms the initial side of an angle, and the ray from Earth to the moon forms the terminal side of the angle.

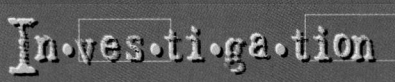

Working on the Investigation

The Investigation on pages 768–769 is designed to be a long-term project that is completed over several days or weeks. Encourage students to keep their materials in their Investigation Folder as they work on the Investigation.

NCTM Standards: 1–6, 9

Instructional Resources

- Study Guide Master 13-3
- Practice Master 13-3
- Enrichment Master 13-3
- Graphing Calculator Masters, p. 13
- Real-World Applications, 33

 Transparency 13-3A contains the 5-Minute Check for this lesson; **Transparency 13-3B** contains a teaching aid for this lesson.

Recommended Pacing

Honors Pacing	Day 3 of 9
Block Scheduling*	Day 2 of 6

 *For more information on pacing and possible lesson plans, refer to the *Block Scheduling Booklet*.

1 FOCUS

 ### 5-Minute Check
(over Lesson 13-2)

Change each degree measure to radian measure.

1. 280° $\frac{14\pi}{9}$

2. −225° $\frac{-5\pi}{4}$

Change each radian measure to degree measure.

3. $\frac{11\pi}{4}$ 495°

4. 3 $\frac{540°}{\pi} \approx 171.9°$

5. Are angles that measure 53° and −307° coterminal? **yes**

TEKS 1.a.

Trigonometric Functions of General Angles

What YOU'LL LEARN

- To find values of trigonometric functions for general angles, and
- to use trigonometric identities to find values of trigonometric functions.

Why IT'S IMPORTANT

You can use trigonometry to solve problems invoving basketball and optics.

APPLICATION
Optics

Rainbows that result from light passing through a prism are caused by the refraction of light. When the light passes from one medium into another, the light ray is bent and the rainbow results. In this case, the light passes from air into glass. According to Snell's law, the angle at which the light ray approaches the prism, called the *angle of incidence,* and the angle at which the light ray is bent, called the *angle of refraction,* are related by the formula 2 sin I = 3 sin r. Find the angle of refraction for this prism if the angle of incidence is 60°. *This problem will be solved in Example 5.*

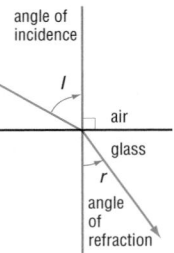

In Lesson 13–1, you found the values of trigonometric functions whose domains were the set of all acute angles of a right triangle. In this lesson, we will extend the domain to include angles of any measure.

Place an angle, θ, in standard position as shown at the right. The trigonometric functions of an angle in standard position may be defined in terms of the ordered pair for *any* point $P(x, y)$ on its terminal side and the distance r between that point and the origin. By the Pythagorean theorem, $r = \sqrt{x^2 + y^2}$.

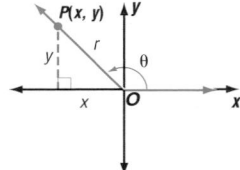

> **Trigonometric Functions of an Angle in Standard Position**
>
> For any angle in standard position with measure θ, a point $P(x, y)$ on its terminal side, and $r = \sqrt{x^2 + y^2}$, the trigonometric functions of θ are as follows.
>
> $\sin \theta = \dfrac{y}{r}$ $\qquad \cos \theta = \dfrac{x}{r}$ $\qquad \tan \theta = \dfrac{y}{x}$
>
> $\csc \theta = \dfrac{r}{y}$ $\qquad \sec \theta = \dfrac{r}{x}$ $\qquad \cot \theta = \dfrac{x}{y}$

Example The terminal side of an angle θ in standard position passes through $P(8, -15)$. Find the exact values of sin θ, cos θ, and tan θ.

You know $x = 8$ and $y = -15$. You need to find r.

$r = \sqrt{x^2 + y^2}$
$\quad = \sqrt{8^2 + (-15)^2}$
$\quad = \sqrt{289}$ or 17

Now, write the ratios.

$\sin \theta = \dfrac{y}{r}$ $\qquad \cos \theta = \dfrac{x}{r}$ $\qquad \tan \theta = \dfrac{y}{x}$

$\quad = \dfrac{-15}{17}$ $\qquad = \dfrac{8}{17}$ $\qquad = \dfrac{-15}{8}$

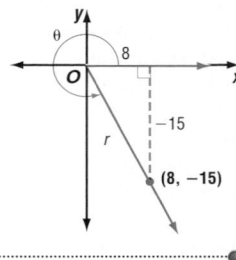

As illustrated in Example 1, the values of the trigonometric functions may be either positive or negative. Sometimes the value is 0 or it is undefined. Since r is always positive, the signs of the functions are determined by the signs of x and y. These signs are determined by the quadrant in which the terminal side of θ lies.

LOOK BACK

You can refer to Lesson 2-1 for information about quadrants.

The chart at the right summarizes the signs of the trigonometric functions for each quadrant. The domain of the sine and cosine functions is the set of real numbers, because $\sin \theta$ and $\cos \theta$ are defined for any angle θ. However, since division by zero is undefined, there are several angle measures that are excluded from the domain of the tangent, cotangent, secant, and cosecant functions. For example, angles like $90°$, π, or $-270°$ have their terminal sides on an axis where x or y is equal to zero. These angles are called **quadrantal angles**.

Function	Quadrant			
	I	II	III	IV
$\sin \theta$ or $\csc \theta$	+	+	−	−
$\cos \theta$ or $\sec \theta$	+	−	−	+
$\tan \theta$ or $\cot \theta$	+	−	+	−

Example 2

Find the values of the six trigonometric functions for an angle in standard position that measures $90°$.

Choose $P(0, 1)$ on the terminal side of the angle.
Therefore, $x = 0$, $y = 1$, and $r = 1$.

$\sin 90° = \frac{y}{r}$ or 1 \qquad $\cos 90° = \frac{x}{r}$ or 0

$\tan 90° = \frac{y}{x}$ \quad Since division by zero is undefined, $\tan 90°$ is undefined.

$\cot 90° = \frac{x}{y}$ or 0 \qquad $\csc 90° = \frac{r}{y}$ or 1

$\sec 90° = \frac{r}{x}$ \quad Since division by zero is undefined, $\sec 90°$ is undefined.

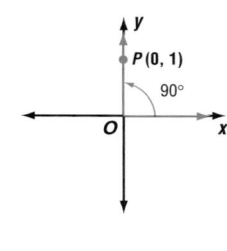

You can find the trigonometric functions of other special angles by using relationships from geometry. In a $30°$–$60°$ right triangle, the lengths of the sides are in the ratio $1:\sqrt{3}:2$. In a $45°$–$45°$ right triangle, the lengths of the sides are in the ratio $1:1:\sqrt{2}$.

Example 3

Find the exact value of each trigonometric function.
a. $\tan 300°$

Sketch the angle in standard position. Its terminal side lies in Quadrant IV. Notice the $30°$–$60°$ right triangle.

Choose $P(x, y)$ on the terminal side of the angle so that $r = 2$. It follows that $x = 1$ and $y = -\sqrt{3}$.
$\tan 300° = \frac{y}{x}$ or $-\sqrt{3}$. \quad $-\sqrt{3} \approx -1.7321$

Verify the values with a calculator.

b. $\sin \frac{3\pi}{4}$

The terminal side of the angle lies in Quadrant II. Notice the $45°$–$45°$ right triangle. Choose $P(x, y)$ so that $x = -1$ and $y = 1$. Therefore, $r = \sqrt{2}$.

$\sin \frac{3\pi}{4} = \frac{y}{r}$ or $\frac{\sqrt{2}}{2}$ \quad $\frac{\sqrt{2}}{2} \approx 0.7071$

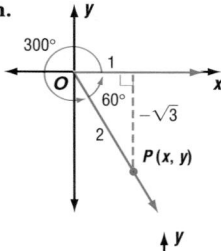

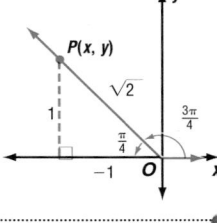

Alternative Learning Styles

Visual If a calculator designed to be used on an overhead projector is available, use it to demonstrate solving the example problems. Students can also be placed in cooperative groups based on similarities of calculators. Students can work together in these groups to solve the example problems.

Motivating the Lesson
Questioning Show students an empty box and tell them the area of its base, its width, and its height. Ask students to name what other information they can know about the box just by using the given information. Answers might include the volume of the box, its length, and its surface area. Emphasize that useful information can often be derived from other information. Compare this to the right triangles students have solved in previous lessons.

2 TEACH

In-Class Examples

For Example 1
The terminal side of an angle θ in standard position passes through $P(3, 4)$. Find $\sin \theta$, $\cos \theta$, and $\tan \theta$. $\frac{4}{5}, \frac{3}{5}, \frac{4}{3}$

For Example 2
Find the values of the six trigonometric functions for an angle in standard position that measures $180°$.
$\sin 180° = 0$
$\cot 180° = $ undefined
$\cos 180° = -1$
$\csc 180° = $ undefined
$\tan 180° = 0$
$\sec 180° = -1$

For Example 3
Find the exact value of each trigonometric function.

a. $\tan 240°$ \quad $\sqrt{3}$

b. $\sin \frac{2\pi}{3}$ \quad $\frac{\sqrt{3}}{2}$

Teaching Tip Remind students that the restrictions upon $\cos \theta$ and $\sin \theta$ are made so that the denominator is not zero. Thus the tan, sec, cot, and csc are not defined at those points.

This Exploration expands on the Exploration in Lesson 13-1. Students get an idea of what the sine and cosine functions look like for angles greater than 90°. The cyclic nature of these functions is also introduced.

In-Class Example

For Example 4

If $\sin \theta = -\frac{\sqrt{2}}{2}$ and $\cos \theta = -\frac{\sqrt{2}}{2}$, the terminal side of θ must lie in Quadrant III. Find the exact values of $\tan \theta$, $\csc \theta$, $\cot \theta$, and $\sec \theta$.

$1, -\sqrt{2}, 1, -\sqrt{2}$

TECHNOLOGY
Tips

Be sure your calculator is in degree mode.

c. sin θ increases until θ = 90, decreases until θ = 270, then increases until θ = 360.
d. The pattern in part c repeats.

In the Exploration in Lesson 13–1, you used a calculator to investigate the behavior of the sine and cosine functions for different values of θ between 0° and 90°. In the following Exploration, you will investigate the behavior of these functions between 0° and 360°.

EXPLORATION

As the value of θ increases from 0° to 90°, sin θ increases from 0 to 1 and cos θ decreases from 1 to 0. What happens for angle measures greater than 90°?

Your Turn a–b. See students' work.

a. Choose twenty values of θ between 0° and 360° and evaluate sin θ for each of them. Write your answers as the ordered pair (θ, sin θ).

b. Graph the ordered pairs on a coordinate plane.

c. Explain how the value of sin θ changes as θ increases from 0° to 360°.

d. Predict the behavior of sin θ from 360° to 720°.

e. Repeat steps a–d using the cosine function.   See students' work.

There are many relationships among the trigonometric functions that can be derived from their definitions. These **trigonometric identities** are true for *all* values of the variable(s) for which the expressions are defined. Consider the ratio $\frac{\sin \theta}{\cos \theta}$.

$$\frac{\sin \theta}{\cos \theta} = \frac{\frac{y}{r}}{\frac{x}{r}} \quad \sin \theta = \frac{y}{r}, \cos \theta = \frac{x}{r}$$

$$= \frac{y}{r} \cdot \frac{r}{x} \text{ or } \frac{y}{x} \quad \frac{y}{r} \div \frac{x}{r} = \frac{y}{r} \cdot \frac{r}{x}$$

By definition, $\tan \theta = \frac{y}{x}$. Therefore, $\frac{\sin \theta}{\cos \theta} = \tan \theta$. This and other trigonometric identities are defined as follows.

Trigonometric Identities

> **The following trigonometric identities hold for all values of θ except those for which any function is undefined.**
>
> $$\frac{\sin \theta}{\cos \theta} = \tan \theta \qquad \frac{\cos \theta}{\sin \theta} = \cot \theta$$
>
> *These are sometimes called the <u>quotient identities</u>.*
>
> $$\csc \theta = \frac{1}{\sin \theta} \qquad \sec \theta = \frac{1}{\cos \theta} \qquad \cot \theta = \frac{1}{\tan \theta}$$
>
> *These are sometimes called the <u>reciprocal identities</u>.*

If you know the values of the sine and cosine functions, you can use the trigonometric identities to find the values of all six trigonometric functions.

Example 4 If $\sin \theta = \frac{3}{5}$ and $\cos \theta = -\frac{4}{5}$, the terminal side of θ must lie in Quadrant II. Find the exact values of $\tan \theta$, $\csc \theta$, $\cot \theta$, and $\sec \theta$.

First, use the quotient identity to find tan θ.

$$\tan \theta = \frac{\sin \theta}{\cos \theta}$$

$$= \frac{\frac{3}{5}}{-\frac{4}{5}} \text{ or } -\frac{3}{4} \quad \frac{3}{5} \div \left(-\frac{4}{5}\right) = \frac{3}{5} \cdot \left(-\frac{5}{4}\right) \text{ or } -\frac{3}{4}$$

Use the reciprocal identities to find $\cot \theta$, $\sec \theta$, and $\csc \theta$.

$$\cot \theta = \frac{1}{\tan \theta} \quad \text{or} \quad -\frac{4}{3} \qquad \sec \theta = \frac{1}{\cos \theta} \quad \text{or} \quad -\frac{5}{4} \qquad \csc \theta = \frac{1}{\sin \theta} \quad \text{or} \quad \frac{5}{3}$$

In Lesson 13–1, you used trigonometric functions to solve problems dealing with surveying, navigation, and construction. Trigonometric functions also appear in formulas for optics, electronics, physics, and many other applications.

Example **5**

APPLICATION

Optics

Refer to the application at the beginning of the lesson.

a. The angle of incidence I and the angle of refraction r are related by the formula $2 \sin I = 3 \sin r$. Find the angle of refraction if $I = 60°$.

$$2 \sin I = 3 \sin r$$
$$2 \sin 60° = 3 \sin r \quad \text{Replace I with 60°.}$$
$$\frac{2 \sin 60°}{3} = \sin r$$
$$0.5774 \approx \sin r \quad \text{sin 60° ≈ 0.8660}$$
$$35.3° \approx r$$

The angle of refraction is about 35°.

b. The general form of Snell's law is $n = \frac{\sin I}{\sin r}$, where n is the index of refraction. Suppose a beam of light moves from a vacuum to glass. If the angle of refraction is 30° and the index of refraction is $\sqrt{2}$, what is the angle of incidence?

$$n = \frac{\sin I}{\sin r}$$
$$\sqrt{2} = \frac{\sin I}{\sin 30°} \quad \text{Replace r with 30° and n with } \sqrt{2}.$$
$$\sqrt{2} \sin 30° = \sin I \quad \text{sin 30° = 0.5}$$
$$0.7071 = \sin I$$
$$45° = I$$

The angle of incidence is 45°.

CHECK FOR UNDERSTANDING

Communicating Mathematics

2. trigonometric expressions that are equal for all values of θ

Study the lesson. Then complete the following.

1. **State** the quadrant or quadrants in which $\sin \theta$ and $\cos \theta$ are both positive. **I**

2. **Define** a trigonometric identity.

3. **Explain** why $\sec \theta = \frac{1}{\cos \theta}$. See margin.

4. **You Decide** Luisa thinks $\sin 13°$ is greater than $\sin 12°$. Henry thinks you can't tell unless you use a calculator or trig table. Who is correct? Explain your reasoning.   Luisa; $\sin \theta$ increases as θ goes from 0° to 90°.

5. Copy and complete the chart below that shows the value of $\sin \theta$, $\cos \theta$, and $\tan \theta$ for the quadrantal angles. A dash indicates that the function is undefined.

Function	0°	90°	180°	270°
$\sin \theta$	0	1	0	−1
$\cos \theta$	1	0	−1	0
$\tan \theta$	0	—	0	—

Lesson 13–3 Trigonometric Functions of General Angles **789**

Reteaching

Using Alternative Methods Have one student say a trigonometric function aloud and then point to another student to give the definition of that function. Continue this around the room until everyone has had a chance. Example: The student says "csc 45°" and then points to another student who should say, "$\frac{1}{\sin 45°}$."

In-Class Example

For Example 5
Find the angle of refraction if $I = 30°$. $r = 19.57°$

3 PRACTICE/APPLY

Check for Understanding
Exercises 1–16 are designed to help you assess your students' understanding through reading, writing, speaking, and modeling. You should work through Exercises 1–5 with your students and then monitor their work on Exercises 6–16.

Error Analysis
Have students especially watch the use of positive and negative signs. Have them draw pictures in order to determine the quadrant in which they are working.

Additional Answer

3. $\frac{1}{\cos \theta} = \frac{1}{\frac{x}{r}} = \frac{r}{x} = \sec \theta$

Study Guide Masters, p. 94

13-3   NAME_____ DATE _____
Student Edition
Study Guide   Pages 783–789

Trigonometric Functions of General Angles

Trigonometric identities are true for *all* values of the variable(s) for which the expressions are defined.

The following trigonometric identities hold for all values of θ except those for which any function is undefined.

$\tan \theta = \frac{\sin \theta}{\cos \theta}$ $\sec \theta = \frac{1}{\cos \theta}$

$\cot \theta = \frac{\cos \theta}{\sin \theta}$ $\csc \theta = \frac{1}{\sin \theta}$ $\cot \theta = \frac{1}{\tan \theta}$

Example: Find $\tan 150°$

$$\tan 150° = \frac{\sin 150°}{\cos 150°} \quad \text{Definition of tangent}$$
$$= \frac{\frac{1}{2}}{\frac{\sqrt{3}}{2}} \quad \text{Substitute values for sin 150° and cos 150°.}$$
$$= -\frac{1}{\sqrt{3}} \text{ or } -\frac{\sqrt{3}}{3}$$

Find the exact value of each trigonometric function.

1. $\tan(-510°)$ $\frac{\sqrt{3}}{3}$
2. $\csc \frac{11\pi}{4}$ $\sqrt{2}$
3. $\sin(-90°)$ -1

4. $\cot 1665°$ 1
5. $\cot 30°$ $\sqrt{3}$
6. $\tan 315°$ -1

7. $\csc \frac{\pi}{4}$ $\sqrt{2}$
8. $\tan \frac{4\pi}{3}$ $\sqrt{3}$
9. $\cot 1110°$ $\sqrt{3}$

10. $\cos 270°$ 0
11. $\csc(-45°)$ $-\sqrt{2}$
12. $\sin 30°$ $\frac{1}{2}$

13. $\sec 2\pi$ 1
14. $\cot(-30°)$ $-\sqrt{3}$
15. $\csc 3\pi$ undefined

Assignment Guide

Core: 17–55 odd, 56–65
Enriched: 18–52 even, 53–65

For **Extra Practice,** see p. 907.

The red A, B, and C flags, printed only in the Teacher's Wraparound Edition, indicate the level of difficulty of the exercises.

Additional Answers

9. $\sin \theta = -\dfrac{8\sqrt{65}}{65}$, $\cos \theta = \dfrac{\sqrt{65}}{65}$,

$\tan \theta = -8$

10. $\sin \theta = -\dfrac{4}{5}$, $\cos \theta = -\dfrac{3}{5}$,

$\tan \theta = \dfrac{4}{3}$

14. $\cos \theta = \dfrac{3}{5}$, $\tan \theta = -\dfrac{4}{3}$,

$\csc \theta = -\dfrac{5}{4}$, $\sec \theta = \dfrac{5}{3}$,

$\cot \theta = -\dfrac{3}{4}$

15. $\sin \theta = \dfrac{2\sqrt{5}}{5}$, $\cos \theta = \dfrac{\sqrt{5}}{5}$,

$\cot \theta = \dfrac{1}{2}$, $\csc \theta = \dfrac{\sqrt{5}}{2}$,

$\sec \theta = \sqrt{5}$

26. $\sin \theta = \dfrac{8}{17}$, $\cos \theta = -\dfrac{15}{17}$,

$\tan \theta = -\dfrac{8}{15}$

27. $\sin \theta = 0$, $\cos \theta = -1$,

$\tan \theta = 0$

Practice Masters, p. 94

NAME_____ DATE _____

Student Edition
Pages 783–789

Practice

Trigonometric Functions of General Angles

Find the exact value of each trigonometric function.

1. $\tan 135°$ -1
2. $\sec \dfrac{\pi}{6}$ $\dfrac{2\sqrt{3}}{3}$

3. $\csc -\dfrac{\pi}{6}$ -2
4. $\cot 210°$ $\sqrt{3}$

5. $\sec 210°$ $-\dfrac{2\sqrt{3}}{3}$
6. $\csc\left(-\dfrac{3}{4}\pi\right)$ $-\sqrt{2}$

7. $\tan \dfrac{5}{3}\pi$ $-\sqrt{3}$
8. $\cot(-405°)$ -1

9. $\csc(-390°)$ -2
10. $\sec 270°$ undefined

11. $\cot(-87\pi)$ undefined
12. $\tan \dfrac{13}{6}\pi$ $\dfrac{\sqrt{3}}{3}$

13. $\sec(-225°)$ $-\sqrt{2}$
14. $\csc 4\dfrac{2}{3}\pi$ $\dfrac{2\sqrt{3}}{3}$

15. $\tan(-720°)$ 0
16. $\cot(-90°)$ 0

17. $\sec 330°$ $\dfrac{2\sqrt{3}}{3}$
18. $\csc -\dfrac{11\pi}{6}$ 2

19. $\cot \dfrac{9\pi}{4}$ 1
20. $\tan -\dfrac{3\pi}{4}$ 1

Guided Practice

State whether the value of each function is *positive, negative, zero,* or *undefined.*

6. $\sin 200°$ $-$
7. $\cos \dfrac{\pi}{2}$ 0
8. $\tan \dfrac{\pi}{4}$ $+$

Find the exact values of sin θ, cos θ, and tan θ if the terminal side of θ in standard position contains the given point. 9–10. See margin.

9. $P(1, -8)$
10. $P(-3, -4)$

Find the exact value of each trigonometric function.

11. $\cos 120°$ $-\dfrac{1}{2}$
12. $\tan\left(-\dfrac{\pi}{3}\right)$ $-\sqrt{3}$
13. $\sin 225°$ $-\dfrac{\sqrt{2}}{2}$

Suppose θ is an angle in standard position whose terminal side lies in the given quadrant. For each function, find the exact values of the remaining five trigonometric functions of θ. 14–15. See margin.

14. $\sin \theta = -\dfrac{4}{5}$; Quadrant IV
15. $\tan \theta = 2$; Quadrant I

16. **Navigation** Ships and airplanes measure distance in nautical miles. The formula 1 nautical mile = $(6077 - 31 \cos 2\theta)$ feet, where θ is the latitude in degrees, can be used to find the approximate length of a nautical mile at a certain latitude. Find the length of a nautical mile where the latitude is 30°. **6061.5 feet**

EXERCISES

Practice

State whether the value of each function is *positive, negative, zero,* or *undefined.*

17. $\sin(-135°)$ $-$
18. $\cos 405°$ $+$
19. $\tan 315°$ $-$
20. $\sin 2\pi$ 0
21. $\cos \dfrac{\pi}{4}$ $+$
22. $\sin \dfrac{11\pi}{4}$ $+$
23. $\tan 90°$ **undefined**
24. $\cos 450°$ 0
25. $\sin(-45°)$ $-$

Find the exact values of sin θ, cos θ, and tan θ if the terminal side of θ in standard position contains the given point.

26–31. See margin.

26. $P(-15, 8)$
27. $P(-3, 0)$
28. $P(-\sqrt{2}, \sqrt{2})$
29. $P(5, -3)$
30. $P(0, 2)$
31. $P(4, 4)$

Find the exact value of each trigonometric function.

32. $\cos 150°$ $-\dfrac{\sqrt{3}}{2}$
33. $\cos \dfrac{11\pi}{3}$ $\dfrac{1}{2}$
34. $\tan 135°$ -1
35. $\sin 240°$ $-\dfrac{\sqrt{3}}{2}$
36. $\sin \dfrac{3\pi}{2}$ -1
37. $\cos(-60°)$ $\dfrac{1}{2}$
38. $\sin(-180°)$ 0
39. $\tan 405°$ 1
40. $\tan\left(-\dfrac{5\pi}{6}\right)$ $\dfrac{\sqrt{3}}{3}$

Suppose θ is an angle in standard position whose terminal side lies in the given quadrant. For each function, find the exact values of the remaining five trigonometric functions of θ.

41–46. See Solutions Manual.

41. $\cos \theta = -\dfrac{1}{2}$; Quadrant II
42. $\sec \theta = \sqrt{3}$; Quadrant IV
43. $\tan \theta = 3$; Quadrant III
44. $\sin \theta = -\dfrac{1}{5}$; Quadrant IV
45. $\cot \theta = -5$; Quadrant II
46. $\csc \theta = -3$; Quadrant IV

Additional Answers

28. $\sin \theta = \dfrac{\sqrt{2}}{2}$, $\cos \theta = -\dfrac{\sqrt{2}}{2}$, $\tan \theta = -1$

29. $\sin \theta = -\dfrac{3\sqrt{34}}{34}$, $\cos \theta = \dfrac{5\sqrt{34}}{34}$,

$\tan \theta = -\dfrac{3}{5}$

30. $\sin \theta = 1$, $\cos \theta = 0$, $\tan \theta$ undefined

31. $\sin \theta = \dfrac{\sqrt{2}}{2}$, $\cos \theta = \dfrac{\sqrt{2}}{2}$, $\tan \theta = 1$

48. $\cos \theta = -\frac{1}{3}$

$\sin \theta = \pm\frac{2\sqrt{2}}{3}$

49. $\sin \theta = \pm 1$

$\tan \theta =$ undefined

Critical Thinking

Applications and Problem Solving

54b. 45°; 2 × 45° or 90° yields the greatest value for sin 2θ.

Mixed Review

58. $\frac{18}{31} \approx 0.581$

59. $\frac{8}{9}$

64. $y = -\frac{4}{5}x + \frac{17}{5}$

---

47. If $\cos \theta = \frac{2}{3}$, find all possible values of sin θ. $\sin \theta = \pm\frac{\sqrt{5}}{3}$

48. If $\sec \theta = -3$, find all possible values of sin θ and cos θ.

49. If $\cos \theta = 0$, find all possible values of sin θ and tan θ.

Suppose θ is an angle in standard position with the given conditions. State the quadrant or quadrants in which the terminal side of θ lies. 52. III

50. sin θ > 0   I, II   **51.** sin θ > 0, cos θ < 0   II   **52.** tan θ > 0, cos θ < 0

53. If θ is any angle for which the functions are defined, prove $\cot \theta = \frac{\cos \theta}{\sin \theta}$. See margin.

54. Baseball   The formula $R = \frac{V_0^2 \sin 2\theta}{g}$ gives the distance of a baseball that is hit at an initial velocity of V_0 feet per second at an angle of θ with the ground. The variable g represents the acceleration due to gravity, which is 32 feet per second².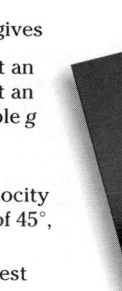
   a. If the ball was hit with an initial velocity of 100 feet per second at an angle of 45°, how far was it hit?   **312.5 feet**
   b. Which angle will result in the greatest distance? Explain your reasoning.

55. Basketball   The maximum height that a basketball reaches after being shot is given by the formula $H = \frac{V_0^2 \sin^2 \theta}{2g}$, where V_0 represents the initial velocity, θ represents the degree measure of the angle which the path of the basketball makes with the ground, and g represents the acceleration due to gravity, 32 feet per second². Find the maximum height reached by a free-throw if it is shot with an initial velocity of 25 feet per second at an angle of 65°.   **8 feet**

56. Change $\frac{5\pi}{6}$ radians to degrees.   (Lesson 13–2)   **150°**

57. Solve $\triangle ABC$ shown at the right if $c = 21$ and $b = 18$.
   (Lesson 13–1) $a \approx 10.8$, $A = 31°$, $B = 59°$

58. Probability   In homeroom, 3 of the 16 girls have red hair, and 2 of the 15 boys have red hair. What is the probability of selecting a boy or a red-haired person as homeroom representative to student council?
   (Lesson 12–6)

59. Find the sum of the infinite geometric series $\frac{4}{3} - \frac{2}{3} + \frac{1}{3} - \frac{1}{6} + \cdots$.
   (Lesson 11–5)

60. Name the next four terms of the arithmetic sequence 21, 15, 9, ...
   (Lesson 11–1)   **3, −3, −9, −15**

61. Chemistry   The pH of a solution is related to the number of gram atoms of hydrogen ions, H^+, by the formula $pH = \log_{10} \frac{1}{H^+}$. If the pH level of a lake is 5, how much more acidic is it than neutral water that has a pH of 7?
   (Lesson 10–3)   **100 times**

62. Simplify $\frac{w + 12}{4w - 16} - \frac{w + 4}{2w - 8}$.   (Lesson 9–4) $-\frac{1}{4}$

63. Write the polynomial function of least degree with integral coefficients whose zeros are 6 and $4 - 2i$.   (Lesson 8–4) $x^3 - 14x^2 + 68x - 120$

64. Find the slope-intercept form of the equation that passes through $(-2, 5)$ and $(3, 1)$ (Lesson 2–4)

65. Solve $-1.6m + 5 = -7.8$.   (Lesson 1–4)   **8**

Extension

Reasoning   Two angles with measures whose sum is 180° are called *supplementary angles*. Make a general statement about each of the following for a pair of supplementary angles.
1. difference of the sines
2. sum of the cosines
3. sum of the tangents
4. sum of the secants
All equal 0.

Tech Prep

Sports Manager   Students who are interested in sports may wish to do further research on the data given in Exercises 54 and 55 and explore the potential growth of this career. For more information on tech prep, see the *Teacher's Handbook*.

---

4 ASSESS

Closing Activity

Writing   Have students summarize the advantages of working with calculators when finding values involving trigonometric functions.

Additional Answer

53. $\frac{\cos \theta}{\sin \theta} = \frac{\frac{x}{r}}{\frac{y}{r}} = \frac{x}{r} \cdot \frac{r}{y} = \frac{x}{y} = \cot \theta$

Enrichment Masters, p. 94

13-3   NAME_____   DATE_____
Enrichment   Student Edition Pages 783–789

Areas of Polygons and Circles

A regular polygon has sides of equal length and angles of equal measure. A regular polygon can be inscribed in or circumscribed about a circle. For n-sided regular polygons, the following area formulas can be used.

Area of circle $A_c = \pi r^2$

Area of inscribed polygon $A_i = \frac{nr^2}{2} \times \sin \frac{360°}{n}$

Area of circumscribed polygon $A_c = nr^2 \times \tan \frac{180°}{n}$

Use a calculator to complete the chart below for a unit circle (a circle of radius 1).

	Number of Sides	Area of Inscribed Polygon	Area Circle minus Area of Polygon	Area of Circumscribed Polygon	Area of Polygon minus Area of Circle
	3	1.2990381	1.8425545	5.1961524	2.054597
1.	4	2	1.1415927	4	0.8584073
2.	8	2.8284271	0.3131655	3.3137085	0.1721158
3.	12	3	0.1415926	3.2153903	0.0737977
4.	20	3.0901699	0.0514227	3.1676888	0.0260961
5.	24	3.1058285	0.0357641	3.1596599	0.0180672
6.	28	3.1152931	0.0262996	3.1548423	0.0132496
7.	32	3.1214452	0.0201475	3.1517249	0.0101322
8.	1000	3.1415720	0.0000206	3.1416030	0.0000103

9. What number do the areas of the circumscribed and inscribed polygons seem to be approaching?   π

Instructional Resources

- Study Guide Master 13-4
- Practice Master 13-4
- Enrichment Master 13-4
- Assessment and Evaluation Masters, pp. 351–352
- Real-World Applications, 34
- Tech Prep Applications Masters, p. 25

Transparency 13-4A contains the 5-Minute Check for this lesson; **Transparency 13-4B** contains a teaching aid for this lesson.

Recommended Pacing

Honors Pacing	Day 4 of 9
Block Scheduling*	Day 3 of 6

*For more information on pacing and possible lesson plans, refer to the *Block Scheduling Booklet*.

1 FOCUS

5-Minute Check
(over Lesson 13-3)

Find the exact value of each trigonometric function.

1. $\cos 30°$ $\frac{\sqrt{3}}{2}$

2. $\sin\left(\frac{-5\pi}{3}\right)$ $\frac{\sqrt{3}}{2}$

3. $\sec 240°$ -2

4. $\tan(-300°)$ $\sqrt{3}$

5. $\csc \frac{4\pi}{3}$ $-\frac{2\sqrt{3}}{3}$

Motivating the Lesson

Situational Problem Show students a picture of a building that is at a right angle with the ground. Ask how the height can be found. Show students a picture of the Leaning Tower of Pisa. Ask students why the previous method of finding height could not be used for this building. Emphasize that not all useful triangles are right triangles.

Law of Sines

13-4

What YOU'LL LEARN

- To solve triangles by using the law of sines, and
- to examine solutions.

Why IT'S IMPORTANT

You can use the law of sines to solve problems involving forestry and aviation.

States with the most visitors per year, in millions
1. California; 6.2
2. New York; 5.4
3. Texas; 5.0
4. Florida; 3.9
5. Hawaii; 2.2

APPLICATION
Forestry

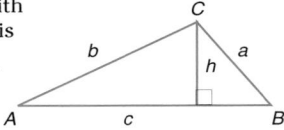

Yosemite National Park, located in California's Sierra Nevada mountains, is home to beautiful meadows, spectacular waterfalls, and jagged mountains. More than 30 kinds of trees and more than 1300 species of plants can be found in the park.

When drought conditions exist in the park, the Park Service often imposes restrictions on open fires. Suppose two forest rangers, 10 miles apart from each other on a straight service road, both sight an illegal campfire away from the road. Using their radios to communicate with each other, they determine that the fire is between them. The first ranger's line of sight to the fire makes an angle of 34° with the road, and the second ranger's line of sight to the fire makes a 67° angle with the road. How far is the fire from each ranger? What is the shortest distance from the road to the fire? *This problem will be solved in Example 3.*

In Lesson 13–1, you solved problems that involved acute angles of right triangles. It is also possible to use trigonometric functions to solve triangles that do not necessarily contain a right angle. You can even use trigonometric functions to find the area of triangles.

Consider $\triangle ABC$ with height h units and sides with lengths a units, b units, and c units. The area of this triangle is $\frac{1}{2} ch$. Note that $\sin A = \frac{h}{b}$ or $h = b \sin A$. By combining these equations, you can find a new formula for the area of the triangle.

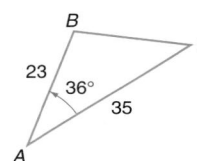

$$\text{Area} = \frac{1}{2} ch$$
$$= \frac{1}{2} c(b \sin A) \quad h = b \sin A$$

You can find two other formulas for the area of the triangle in a similar way.

$$\text{Area} = \frac{1}{2} bc \sin A = \frac{1}{2} ac \sin B = \frac{1}{2} ab \sin C$$

These formulas allow you to find the area of any triangle when you know the measures of two sides and the included angle.

Example   **Find the area of $\triangle ABC$ if $b = 35$, $c = 23$, and $A = 36°$.**

$\text{Area} = \frac{1}{2} bc \sin A$

$= \frac{1}{2}(35)(23)\sin 36°$ *sin 36° ≈ 0.5878*

≈ 236.59

To the nearest whole unit, the area is 237 square units.

All of the area formulas above represent the area of the same triangle. So, the following must be true.

$$\frac{1}{2} bc \sin A = \frac{1}{2} ac \sin B = \frac{1}{2} ab \sin C$$

The **law of sines** is obtained by dividing each of the expressions above by $\frac{1}{2} abc$.

$$\frac{\sin A}{a} = \frac{\sin B}{b} = \frac{\sin C}{c}$$

Listed below is the income each state derived from tourism in 1993.

California	$42.5 billion
Florida	$28.6 billion
Texas	$20.2 billion
New York	$19.9 billion
Hawaii	$ 5.8 billion

Law of Sines	Let △ABC be any triangle with a, b, and c representing the measures of sides opposite angles with measurements A, B, and C, respectively. Then, $$\frac{\sin A}{a} = \frac{\sin B}{b} = \frac{\sin C}{c}.$$

You can apply the law of sines to a triangle if you know
- the measures of two angles and the measure of any side, or
- the measures of two sides and the angle opposite one of the sides.

Example 2

Use the law of sines to solve the triangle below. Round measures of sides to the nearest tenth.

You are given the measures of two angles and a side. First, find the measure of the third angle, ∠C.

$$40° + 60° + C = 180°$$
$$C = 80°$$

Now, use the law of sines to find b and c.

$$\frac{\sin A}{a} = \frac{\sin B}{b}$$
$$\frac{\sin 40°}{20} = \frac{\sin 60°}{b}$$
$$b = \frac{20 \sin 60°}{\sin 40°}$$
$$b \approx 26.9$$

$$\frac{\sin A}{a} = \frac{\sin C}{c}$$
$$\frac{\sin 40°}{20} = \frac{\sin 80°}{c}$$
$$c = \frac{20 \sin 80°}{\sin 40°}$$
$$c \approx 30.6$$

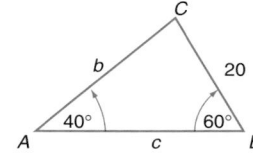

Therefore, b ≈ 26.9, c ≈ 30.6, and C = 80°.

Example 3

APPLICATION

Forestry

Refer to the application at the beginning of the lesson.
a. How far is the fire from each ranger?
b. What is the shortest distance from the road to the fire?

First, draw a diagram. You are given the measure of two angles and a side. Find the measure of the third angle, angle C.

$$34° + 67° + C = 180°$$
$$C = 79°$$

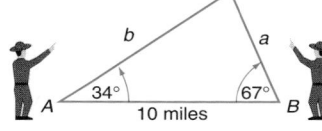

a. Use the law of sines to find a and b, the distance from each ranger to the fire.

$$\frac{\sin 79°}{10} = \frac{\sin 34°}{a}$$
$$a \approx \frac{10 \sin 34°}{\sin 79°}$$
$$a \approx 5.7$$

$$\frac{\sin 79°}{10} = \frac{\sin 67°}{b}$$
$$b \approx \frac{10 \sin 67°}{\sin 79°}$$
$$b \approx 9.4$$

Therefore, the fire is 9.4 miles from Ranger A and 5.7 miles from Ranger B.

b. The shortest distance from the road to the fire is from point D, which is on the perpendicular from C to the road. Let h represent the measure of segment CD.

$$\sin 34° = \frac{h}{9.4}$$
$$h \approx 5.3$$

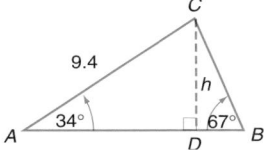

The shortest distance from the road to the fire is about 5.3 miles.

GLENCOE *Technology*

 Interactive Mathematics Tools Software

This multimedia software provides an interactive lesson by using the law of sines to solve real-life distance problems. A **Computer Journal** gives students an opportunity to write about what they have learned.

For Windows & Macintosh

In-Class Examples

For Example 1
Find the area of each triangle described below.
a. a = 7, c = 11, B = 36°
≈ 23 sq. units
b. a = 83, b = 79, C = 92°42'
≈ 3274.9 sq. units

For Example 2
Use the law of sines to solve the triangle described. Round measures of sides to the nearest tenth and measures of angles to the nearest degree.
a = 16, b = 10, A = 70°
B = 36°, C = 73°, c = 16.2

For Example 3
A surveyor measures a fence 440 meters long. She takes bearings of a landmark C from A and B and finds that A = 48° and B = 75°. Find the distance from A to C to the nearest meter.
about 507 meters

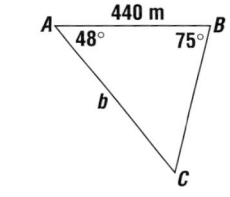

In-Class Example

For Example 4
Use the law of sines to solve the triangle described: $A = 50°$, $a = 12$, $b = 8$. Round measures of sides to the nearest tenth and measures of angles to the nearest degree.
$B = 30°$, $C = 99°$, $c = 15.5$

Teaching Tip Encourage the use of diagrams and calculators where needed to solve the problems.

Example **4** **Use the law of sines to solve the triangle below. Round to the nearest tenth.**

You are given the measures of two sides and the angle opposite one of them. First, find the measure of the angle opposite the other given side, $\angle B$.

$$\frac{\sin A}{a} = \frac{\sin B}{b}$$

$$\frac{\sin 42°}{63} = \frac{\sin B}{57}$$

$$\sin B = \frac{57 \sin 42°}{63}$$

$$\sin B \approx 0.6054$$

$$B \approx 37.3°$$

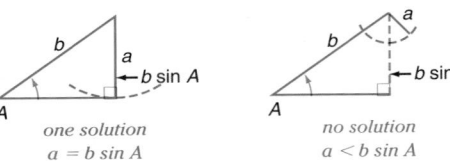

Next, find the measure of the third angle, $\angle C$.

$$37.3° + 42° + C = 180°$$

$$C \approx 100.7°$$

Then, find the measure of c.

$$\frac{\sin A}{a} = \frac{\sin C}{c}$$

$$\frac{\sin 42°}{63} = \frac{\sin 100.7°}{c}$$

$$c = \frac{63 \sin 100.7°}{\sin 42°}$$

$$c \approx 92.5$$

Therefore, $C \approx 100.7°$, $B \approx 37.3°$, and $c \approx 92.5$ units.

When solving a triangle, you must analyze the data to determine whether there is a solution or not. For example, if you are given the measures of two angles and a side, as in Examples 2 and 3, the triangle has a unique solution. However, if you are given the measures of two sides and the angle opposite one of them is given, a single solution may not exist. One of the following will be true.

- No triangle exists, and there is no solution.

- Exactly one triangle exists, and there is one unique solution.

- Two triangles exist, and there are two solutions.

Suppose you are given a, b, and A. First, consider the case where $A < 90°$. If $a < b$, there are three possibilities.

one solution
$a = b \sin A$

no solution
$a < b \sin A$

two solutions
$b > a > b \sin A$

If $a > b$, there is one unique solution.

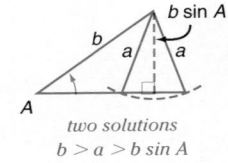

Consider the case where $A \geq 90°$. There are two possibilities.

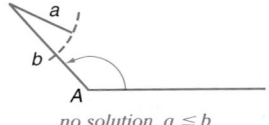

no solution, $a \leq b$

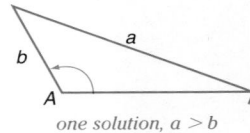

one solution, $a > b$

In Example 4, you were given the measures of two sides and the angle opposite one of them. When you solved the triangle, there was one unique solution. The following examples show triangles in which there are no solutions and two solutions.

Example **5** Solve each triangle described below.
  a. $A = 35°$, $b = 14$, and $a = 6$

Example 5

PROBLEM SOLVING

Examine the Solution

Angle A is less than $90°$. Find $b \sin A$ and compare with a.

$b \sin A = 14 \sin 35°$ *b sin A is the minimum*

$\quad\quad\quad = 14(0.5736)$ *distance from C to $\overline{AB}$.*

$\quad\quad\quad \approx 8.03$

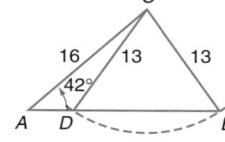

Since $6 < 8.03$, there is no solution.

b. $A = 42°$, $a = 13$, and $b = 16$.

$b \sin A = 16 \sin 42°$

$\quad\quad\quad \approx 16(0.6691)$

$\quad\quad\quad \approx 10.71$

Since $42° < 90°$ and $10.71 < 13 < 16$, there are two solutions. The two triangles to be solved are $\triangle ABC$ and $\triangle ADC$.

When two solutions exist, it is called the ambiguous case. Why?

Solve $\triangle ABC$.

First, use the law of sines to find B.

$\dfrac{\sin 42°}{13} = \dfrac{\sin B}{16}$ $\quad\quad \dfrac{\sin A}{a} = \dfrac{\sin B}{b}$

$\sin B = \dfrac{16 \sin 42°}{13}$

$\quad B \approx 55.4°$

Find $\angle ACB$.

$42° + 55.4° + \angle ACB \approx 180°$

$\quad\quad\quad\quad \angle ACB \approx 82.6°$

Find c.

$\dfrac{\sin 42°}{13} = \dfrac{\sin 82.6°}{c}$

$c \approx \dfrac{13 \sin 82.6°}{\sin 42°}$

$c \approx 19.3$

Therefore, $B \approx 55.4°$, $\angle ACB \approx 82.6°$, and $c \approx 19.3$.

Solve $\triangle ADC$.

First, find $\angle ADC$.

$\triangle DBC$ is isosceles, so the measures of the base angles are equal. Therefore, since $\angle B \approx 55.4°$, $\angle CDB \approx 55.4°$.

$\angle ADC$ is supplementary to $\angle CDB$, so $\angle ADC \approx 124.6°$.

Find $\angle ACD$.

$42° + 124.6° + \angle ACD \approx 180°$

$\quad\quad\quad\quad \angle ACD \approx 13.4°$

Then, use the law of sines to find the measure of segment AD in $\triangle ADC$.

$\dfrac{\sin 42°}{13} = \dfrac{\sin 13.4°}{AD}$

$AD \approx \dfrac{13 \sin 13.4°}{\sin 42°}$

$AD \approx 4.5$

Therefore, $AD \approx 4.5$, $\angle ACD \approx 13.4°$, and $\angle ADC \approx 124.6°$.

In-Class Example

For Example 5
Solve each triangle described below.
a. $A = 50°$, $a = 2$, $b = 10$
   Since $50° < 90°$ and $2 < 7.66$, no solution exists.
b. $A = 70°$, $a = 6$, $b = 11$
   Since $70° < 90°$ and $6 < 10.34$, no solution exists.
c. $A = 32°$, $a = 7$, $b = 11$
   Solution I: $B = 123°37'$, $C = 24°23'$, $c = 5.5$;
   Solution II: $B = 56°23'$, $C = 91°37'$, $c = 13.2$

Check for Understanding

Exercises 1–14 are designed to help you assess your students' understanding through reading, writing, speaking, and modeling. You should work through Exercises 1–5 with your students and then monitor their work on Exercises 6–14.

Error Analysis
To avoid incorrect assumptions, have students draw a triangle from the given data in approximate proportion.

Assignment Guide

Core: 15–41 odd, 42, 43, 45, 47–54
Enriched: 16–40 even, 42–54
All: Self Test, 1–10

For **Extra Practice,** see p. 907.

The red A, B, and C flags, printed only in the Teacher's Wraparound Edition, indicate the level of difficulty of the exercises.

Additional Answers
1. $\dfrac{\sin A}{a} = \dfrac{\sin B}{b} = \dfrac{\sin C}{c}$
3. if $A < 90°$ and $a < b \sin A$ or if $A > 90°$ and $a < b$

Study Guide Masters, p. 95

NAME _____ DATE _____
Student Edition Pages 790–795

13-4 **Study Guide**

Law of Sines

You can use any of the following formulas to find the area of any △ABC, including triangles that are not right triangles.

area = ½ab sin C
area = ½bc sin A
area = ½ac sin B

Example: Find the area of △ABC if a = 10, b = 14, and C = 40°.

area = ½ab sin C
= ½(10)(14)sin 40°
= 44.9951

To the nearest square unit, the area is 45 square units.

From the formulas above, we can deduce the **Law of Sines:**
sin A/a = sin B/b = sin C/c

The law of sines can be used to solve right triangles.

Example: If a = 12, b = 9, and A = 28°, find B.

sin A/a = sin B/b
sin 28°/12 = sin B/9
sin B = 9 sin 28°/12
sin B = 0.3521
B = 20.45°

Find the area of each triangle described below. Round answers to the nearest tenth.

1. a = 10, b = 10, c = 40°   2. a = 6, c = 14, B = 41°
   32.1 square units   27.6 square units

Solve each triangle described below. Round measures of sides and angles to the nearest tenth.

3. B = 71°, c = 8, b = 16   4. A = 40°, B = 14°, a = 52
   C = 28.2°, A = 80.8°, a = 16.7   b = 19.6, c = 65.5, C = 126°

CHECK FOR UNDERSTANDING

Communicating Mathematics

2. Sample answer: two sides and the angle opposite one of them

Study the lesson. Then complete the following.

1. **State** the law of sines.   See margin.
2. **Describe** a set of conditions for which the law of sines can be used.
3. **Explain** how you know when a triangle has no solution.   See margin.
4. **Draw** $\triangle ABC$ if $\angle ABC = 35°$, $BC = 8$, and $\angle BCA = 70°$.   See margin.
5. **Choose** a value for a so that the triangle at the right has one solution. $a > 10$

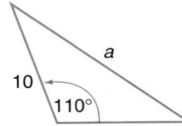

Guided Practice

Write an equation that can be used to find the area of each triangle. Then solve the equation. Round to the nearest tenth.

6. $A = \frac{1}{2}ab \sin C$, 133.6
7. $A = \frac{1}{2}bc \sin A$, 135.9

6.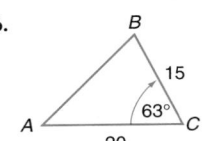
7.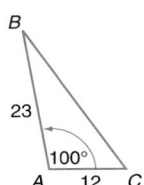

Solve each triangle. Round measures of sides to the nearest tenth and measures of angles to the nearest degree.

8. $A = 65°$, $B = 65°$, $c \approx 10.1$
9. $B = 80°$, $a \approx 13.1$, $c \approx 17.6$

8.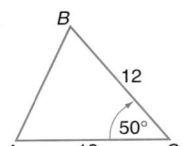
9.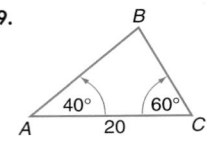
10. $a = 8$, $A = 49°$, $B = 57°$
    $C = 74°$, $c \approx 10.2$, $b \approx 8.9$

Determine whether each triangle has no solution, one solution, or two solutions. Then solve each triangle. Note that the triangles may not be drawn to scale.

11. two; $B \approx 51.6°$, $C \approx 92.4°$, $c \approx 10.2$; $B \approx 128.4°$, $C \approx 15.6°$, $c \approx 2.7$
12. no solution

11.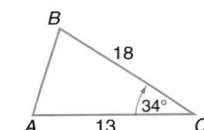
12.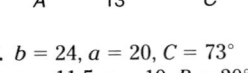
13.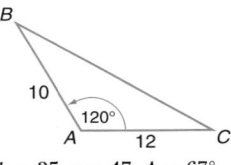
    $a = 64$, $c = 90$, $C = 98°$ one; $A \approx 44.8°$, $B \approx 37.2°$, $b \approx 55.0$

14. The longest side of a triangle is 67 inches. Two angles have measures of 47° and 55°. Solve the triangle. $B = 78°$, $a \approx 50.1$, $c \approx 56.1$

EXERCISES

Practice

15–20. See Solutions Manual.

Write an equation that can be used to find the area of each triangle. Then solve the equation. Round to the nearest tenth.

15.
16.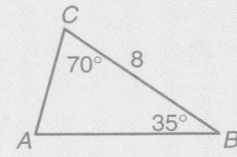

17. $b = 24$, $a = 20$, $C = 73°$
18. $b = 35$, $c = 47$, $A = 67°$
19. $a = 11.5$, $c = 19$, $B = 20°$
20. $a = 9.4$, $c = 13.5$, $B = 95°$

Reteaching

Using Discussion Working in groups, have each group work a problem to determine the number of solutions and, if a solution exists, to solve the triangle. Have one person from each group explain their answer to the class. No one in the group should know who is going to explain so that all the members must be sure they understand the group's solution.

Additional Answer

4.

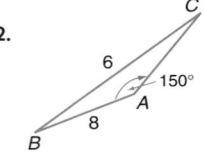

Solve each triangle. Round measures of sides and angles to the nearest tenth. 21–30. See margin.

21.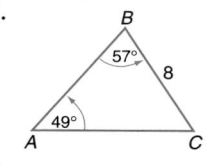

22.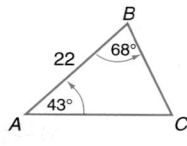

23.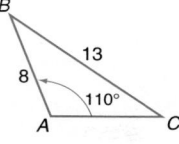

24.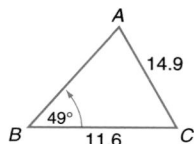

25.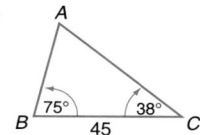

26.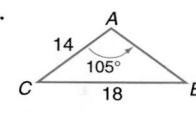

27. $A = 30°, C = 70°, c = 8$

28. $c = 17, b = 15, C = 64°$

29. $a = 14, b = 7.5, A = 103°$

30. $a = 23, A = 73°, C = 24°$

Determine whether each triangle has no solution, one solution, or two solutions. Then solve each triangle. Note that the triangles may not be drawn to scale. 31–39. See margin.

31.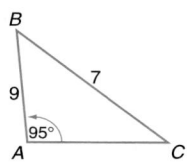

32. 33.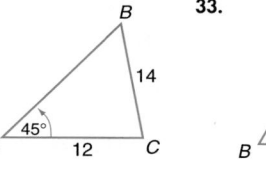

34. $a = 9, b = 20, A = 31°$

35. $a = 12, b = 14, A = 90°$

36. $a = 125, b = 150, A = 25°$

37. $A = 40°, b = 16, a = 10$

38. $a = 18, b = 20, A = 120°$

39. $A = 40°, b = 10, a = 8$

Geometry

40. An isosceles triangle has a base of 22 centimeters and exactly one angle measuring 36°. Find its perimeter. **93.2 cm**

41. The sides of a triangle measure 22, 13, and 8. Find the measure of the smallest angle. **There is no solution.**

Critical Thinking

42. Prove that the law of sines holds for right triangles. **See students' work.**

Applications and Problem Solving

43. **Aviation** A pilot takes off from Newport News, Virginia, and flies toward the Atlantic Ocean. After reaching point *C*, the plane develops mechanical difficulties, and the pilot needs to return either to Newport News or Norfolk, Virginia. How far is it to the nearer airport? **46.8 miles to Norfolk**

Lesson 13–4 Law of Sines **797**

Tech Prep

Aviation Maintenance Technician
Students who are interested in aviation may wish to do further research on the data provided in Exercise 43 and explore the potential growth of this career. For more information on tech prep, see the *Teacher's Handbook*.

Additional Answers

21. $C = 74°, b \approx 8.9, c \approx 10.2$
22. $C = 69°, b \approx 21.8, a \approx 16.1$
23. $C \approx 35.3°, B \approx 34.7°, b \approx 7.9$
24. $A \approx 36.0°, C \approx 95°, c \approx 19.7$
25. $A = 67°, b \approx 47.2, c \approx 30.1$
26. $B \approx 48.7°, C \approx 26.3°, c \approx 8.3$
27. $B = 80°, a \approx 4.3, b \approx 8.4$
28. $B \approx 52.5°, A \approx 63.5°, a \approx 16.9$
29. $B \approx 31.5°, C \approx 45.5°, c \approx 10.2$
30. $B = 83°, c \approx 9.8, b \approx 23.9$
31. no solution
32. one solution; $B \approx 37.3°$, $C \approx 97.7°, c \approx 19.6$
33. no solution
34. no solution
35. no solution
36. two solutions; $B \approx 30.5°$, $C \approx 124.5°, c \approx 243.8$; $B \approx 149.5°, C \approx 5.5°, c \approx 28.4$
37. no solution
38. no solution
39. two solutions; $B \approx 53.5°$, $C \approx 86.5°, c \approx 12.4$; $B \approx 126.5°, C \approx 13.5°, c \approx 2.9$

Practice Masters, p. 95

 NAME_____ DATE_____
13-4 **Practice**
Student Edition
Pages 790–795

Law of Sines

Find the area of each triangle described below. Round answers to the nearest tenth.

1. $a = 9, b = 11, C = 46°$
   35.6
2. $a = 12, c = 15, B = 58°$
   76.3
3. $b = 9, c = 9, A = 40°$
   26.0
4. $a = 12.6, b = 8.9, C = 32°$
   29.7
5. $a = 14.9, c = 18.6, B = 27°$
   62.9
6. $b = 19.4, c = 8.6, A = 34°$
   46.7
7. $a = 9, b = 7, C = 26.1°$
   13.9
8. $b = 12, c = 19, A = 46.4°$
   82.6
9. $a = 12, c = 14, B = 56.5°$
   70.0
10. $b = 12, c = 14, A = 17.4°$
   25.1

Solve each triangle described below. Round measures of sides and angles to the nearest tenth.

11. $A = 50°, B = 30°, c = 9$
    $C = 100°, a = 7.0, b = 4.6$
12. $a = 12, A = 56°, B = 38°$
    $C = 86°, b = 8.9, c = 14.4$
13. $a = 14, b = 18, A = 36.8°$
    $B = 50.4°, C = 92.8°, c = 23.3$
14. $b = 20, c = 25, C = 70.2°$
    $B = 48.8°, A = 61.0°, a = 23.2$
15. $a = 25, b = 30, A = 46.3°$
    $B = 60.2°, C = 73.5°, c = 33.2$
16. $a = 40, A = 80.2°, C = 14.2°$
    $B = 85.6°, b = 40.5, c = 10.0$
17. $A = 80°, C = 40°, c = 30$
    $B = 60°, a = 46.0, b = 40.4$
18. $c = 42, b = 56, C = 43.5°$
    $B = 66.6°, A = 69.9°, a = 57.3$
19. $b = 13, B = 46.6°, C = 112°$
    $A = 21.4°, a = 6.5, c = 16.6$
20. $A = 110°, a = 20, b = 8$
    $B = 22.1°, C = 47.9°, c = 15.8$

Closing Activity

Speaking Have students tell in their own words how to determine the number of solutions if they are given the measurements of two sides of a triangle and an angle opposite one of the given sides.

Additional Answer

47. $\sin 180° = 0$, $\cos 180° = -1$, $\tan 180° = 0$, $\csc 180°$ undefined, $\sec 180° = -1$, $\cot 180°$ undefined

Chapter 13, Quiz B (Lessons 13-3 and 13-4), is available in the *Assessment and Evaluation Masters,* p. 352.

Mid-Chapter Test (Lessons 13-1 through 13-4) is available in the *Assessment and Evaluation Masters,* p. 351.

Enrichment Masters, p. 95

13-4

NAME_____ DATE_____

Student Edition
Pages 790–795

Enrichment

Navigation

The bearing of a boat is an angle showing the direction the boat is heading. Often, the angle is measured from north, but it can be measured from any of the four compass directions. At the right, the bearing of the boat is 155°. Or, it can be described as 25° east of south (S25°E).

Example: A boat A sights the lighthouse B in the direction N65°E and the spire of a church C in the direction S75°E. According to the map, B is 7 miles from C in the direction N30°W. In order for A to avoid running aground, find the bearing it should keep to pass B at 4 miles distance.

In $\triangle ABC$, $\angle a = 180° - 65° - 75°$ or $40°$
$\angle C = 180° - 30° - (180° - 75°)$
$= 45°$
$a = 7$ miles

With the Law of Sines,
$AB = \dfrac{a \sin C}{\sin a} = \dfrac{7(\sin 45°)}{\sin 40°} = 7.7$ mi.

The ray for the correct bearing for A must be tangent at X to circle B with radius $BX = 4$. Thus $\triangle ABX$ is a right triangle.

Then $\sin \theta = \dfrac{BX}{AB} = \dfrac{4}{7.7} \approx 0.519$. Therefore, $\angle \theta = 31°18'$.

The bearing of A should be 65° − 31°18′ or 33°42′.

Solve the following.

1. Suppose the lighthouse B in the example is sighted at S30°W by a ship P due north of the church C. Find the bearing P should keep to pass B at 4 miles distance.   S64°51′W

2. In the fog, the lighthouse keeper determines by radar that a boat 18 miles away is heading to the shore. The direction of the boat from the lighthouse is S80°E. What bearing should the lighthouse keeper radio the boat to take to come ashore 4 miles south of the lighthouse?   S87.2°E

3. To avoid a rocky area along a shoreline, a ship at M travels 7 km to R, bearing 22°15′, then 8 km to P, bearing 68°30′, then 6 km to Q, bearing 109°15′. Find the distance from M to Q.   17.4 km

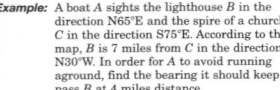

---

45. 4.9 and 10.4 miles

44. **Make a Drawing** Karen was given an assignment to draw and then construct a triangular model of three steel girders for her engineering class. Two of the girders measured 7 cm and 6 cm, and the angle opposite the 7 cm girder had to be 30°. Can she construct the triangle? If so, how long is the third girder?   **yes, 11.5 cm**

45. **Communication** A low-watt radio station has its transmitter on County Line Road, 10 miles from where it intersects with the interstate highway. If the radio station has a range of 7 miles, between what two distances from the intersection can cars on the interstate hear the radio station?

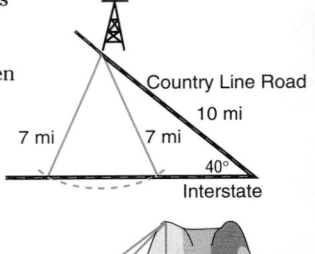

46. **Geology** A geologist measured a 43° angle of elevation to the top of a volcano crater. After moving 0.25 kilometers farther away, the angle of elevation was 38°.
   a. Use the law of sines to find the height of the top of the volcano crater.   **1.2 km**
   b. This problem was solved in Example 6 on page 776. Compare and contrast the method used there with the method you used here.

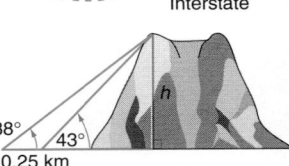

Mixed Review

46b. See students' work.

50. Yes; Sean has $3064.85 in his account.

52. $\dfrac{x^2}{32} + \dfrac{y^2}{36} = 1$

53. $(2x + 3)(x - 7)$

54. 24

47. Find the exact values of the six trigonometric functions for an angle in standard position that measures 180°. (Lesson 13–3)   **See margin.**

48. **Counting** How many ways can 6 different books be arranged on a shelf? (Lesson 12–2)   **720**

49. Find the sum of the first 50 terms of an arithmetic series where $a_1 = 5$ and $d = 25$. (Lesson 11–2)   **30,875**

50. **Finance** Use the formula $A = Pe^{rt}$ to determine whether Sean can buy a used car costing $2500 with the $1000 his grandparents invested for him 16 years ago at 7%. (Lesson 10–5)

51. Simplify $\dfrac{3x - 21}{x^2 - 49} \div \dfrac{3x}{x^2 + 7x}$.   **1**

52. Write the equation of the ellipse shown at the right. (Lesson 7–4)

53. Factor $2x^2 - 11x - 21$. (Lesson 5–4)

54. Evaluate the determinant of $\begin{bmatrix} 6 & 4 \\ -3 & 2 \end{bmatrix}$. (Lesson 4–4)

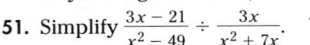

SELF TEST

1. Solve the right triangle shown at the right. (Lesson 13–1) $B = 41°$, $c \approx 9.3$, $b \approx 6.1$

Change each degree measure to radian measure. (Lesson 13–2)

2. 90° $\dfrac{\pi}{2}$

3. 150° $\dfrac{5\pi}{6}$

4. −135° $-\dfrac{3\pi}{4}$

Change each radian measure to degree measure. (Lesson 13–2)

5. $\dfrac{3\pi}{2}$ 270°

6. $-\dfrac{7\pi}{4}$ −315°

7. 2 $\approx 114.6°$

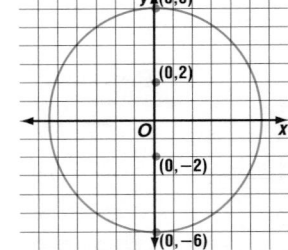

8. Find $\sin \theta$, $\cos \theta$, and $\tan \theta$ if the terminal side of θ in standard position contains $P(-2, 0)$. (Lesson 13–3) $\sin \theta = 0$, $\cos \theta = -1$, $\tan \theta = 0$

9. **Electronics** The power P in watts absorbed by an AC circuit is given by the formula $P = IV \cos \theta$, where I is the current in amps, V is the voltage, and θ is the measure of the phase angle. Find the power absorbed by a circuit if its current is 2 amps, its voltage is 120 volts, and its phase angle is 70°. (Lesson 13–3)   **82.1 watts**

10. Solve the triangle in which $A = 40°$, $b = 12$, and $a = 5$. (Lesson 13–4)   **no solution**

798   *Chapter 13   Exploring Trigonometric Functions*

Extension

Problem Solving Two buildings are 25 miles apart, with building B due east of building A. A shopping mall is under construction at N30°E of building A and N50°W of building B. Find the perpendicular distance from the mall to line AB. **about 10 miles**

SELF TEST

The Self Test provides students with a brief review of the concepts and skills in Lessons 13-1 through 13-4. Lesson numbers are given to the right of exercises or instruction lines so students can review concepts not yet mastered.

Law of Cosines

What YOU'LL LEARN

- To solve triangles by using the law of cosines.

Why IT'S IMPORTANT

You can use the law of cosines to solve problems involving paleontology and emergency medicine.

FYI

The movie *Jurassic Park* is the second biggest moneymaker in Hollywood history, earning $357 million. The only movie to make more money is *E.T. the Extra-Terrestrial* with $400 million.

Scene from *Jurassic Park*

APPLICATION
Paleontology

If *Jurassic Park* were a real place, it would be easy for scientists to study how dinosaurs move from place to place. But, since it's not, scientists are left to study the footprints made by dinosaurs millions of years ago. At dinosaur digs, anthropologists use *locomotor parameters,* which are numbers associated with physical motion.

The figure at the right shows footprints of a carnivorous dinosaur taken from the Glen Rose formation in Texas. The *pace* is the distance from the left footprint to the right footprint, and vice versa. The *stride* is the distance from left footprint to the next left footprint or the right footprint to the next right footprint. If an animal walks in such a way that the footprints are directly in line, the stride will be twice the pace. But usually, the footprints show a "zig-zag" pattern that can be described numerically by the *step angle,* θ. An efficient walker has a step angle that approaches 180°, meaning that the animal minimizes zig-zag motion while maximizing forward motion.

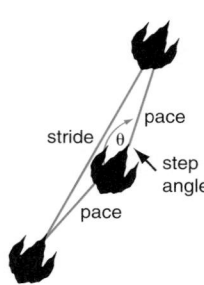

Anthropologists use trigonometry to determine the step angle. However, problems such as this, in which you know the measures of the sides of a triangle, cannot be solved using the law of sines. You can solve problems such as this by using the **law of cosines.**

To derive the law of cosines, consider $\triangle ABC$ with height h units and sides with lengths a units, b units, and c units. Suppose segment AD is x units long. Then segment DC is $b - x$ units long. What relationship exists between a, b, c, and A?

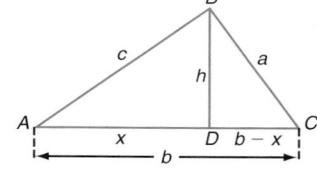

$a^2 = (b - x)^2 + h^2$ *Use the Pythagorean theorem for $\triangle DBC$.*

$a^2 = b^2 - 2bx + x^2 + h^2$ *Expand $(b - x)^2$.*

$a^2 = b^2 - 2bx + c^2$ *In $\triangle ADB$, $c^2 = x^2 + h^2$.*

$a^2 = b^2 - 2b(c \cos A) + c^2$ *$\cos A = \frac{x}{c}$, so $x = c \cos A$.*

$a^2 = b^2 + c^2 - 2bc \cos A$

The measure a is now defined in terms of the measures of the other two sides and angle A. You can find two other formulas relating the lengths of sides to the cosine of B and C in a similar way. All three formulas can be summarized as follows.

Lesson 13–5 Law of Cosines **799**

FYI

Warner Brothers produced the first sound films in the late 1920s.

13-5 LESSON NOTES

NCTM Standards: 1–7, 9

Instructional Resources

- Study Guide Master 13-5
- Practice Master 13-5
- Enrichment Master 13-5
- Multicultural Activity Masters, p. 26
- Tech Prep Applications Masters, p. 26

 Transparency 13-5A contains the 5-Minute Check for this lesson; **Transparency 13-5B** contains a teaching aid for this lesson.

Recommended Pacing

Honors Pacing	Day 5 of 9
Block Scheduling*	Day 4 of 6

 *For more information on pacing and possible lesson plans, refer to the *Block Scheduling Booklet*.

1 FOCUS

 5-Minute Check
(over Lesson 13-4)

Determine the number of possible solutions. If a solution exists, solve the triangle.

1. $a = 7$, $b = 6$, $A = 30°$
   1; $B = 25.37°$, $C = 124.63°$, $c = 11.52$
2. $b = 40$, $a = 32$, $A = 125.33°$
   No solutions exist
3. $a = 26$, $b = 29$, $A = 58°$
   2; $B = 71.07°$, $C = 50.93°$, $c = 3.8$; $B = 108.93°$, $C = 13.07°$, $c = 6.93$

Write an equation that can be used to find the area of each triangle described. Then solve the equation. Round to the nearest tenth.

4. $b = 19$, $c = 23$, $A = 15°$
   $\frac{1}{2} bc \sin A$, 56.6
5. $a = 98$, $c = 73$, $B = 8°$
   $\frac{1}{2} ac \sin B$, 497.8

Motivating the Lesson

Questioning A boy has built a two-sided ramp, with a different slope on each side. The top angle and the length of each side are known. Ask students to explain why the law of sines could not be used to solve this triangle.

2 TEACH

In-Class Examples

For Example 1
Find c if $a = 12$, $b = 16$, and $C = 29°$. $c = 8$

For Example 2
Solve each triangle. Round answers to the nearest tenth.

a. $A = 38°$, $b = 6$, $c = 10$
 $a = 6.4$, $B = 35.2°$,
 $C = 106.5°$
b. $a = 15$, $b = 16$, $C = 23°$
 $A = 68.2°$, $B = 88.3°$,
 $c = 6.3$

Teaching Tip Point out that each form of the law of cosines uses four different variables. If any three of these are known, the fourth can be found.

Teaching Tip Point out that both laws can be used together to solve a triangle.

Law of Cosines	Let $\triangle ABC$ be any triangle with a, b, and c representing the measures of sides, and opposite angles with measurement A, B, and C, respectively. Then the following equations are true. $$a^2 = b^2 + c^2 - 2bc \cos A$$ $$b^2 = a^2 + c^2 - 2ac \cos B$$ $$c^2 = a^2 + b^2 - 2ab \cos C$$

You can apply the law of cosines to a triangle if you know
• the measures of three sides, or
• the measures of two sides and the included angle.

Example **Find c if $a = 15$, $b = 18$, and $C = 34°$.**

You are given the measure of two sides and the included angle.
$$c^2 = a^2 + b^2 - 2ab \cos C$$
$$c^2 = 15^2 + 18^2 - 2(15)(18)\cos 34°$$
$$c^2 \approx 101.32$$
$$c \approx 10.07$$

Example **Solve each triangle. Round to the nearest tenth.**
a. $A = 47°$, $c = 27$, $b = 22$

You are given the measures of two sides and the included angle. First, determine a by using the law of cosines.
$$a^2 = b^2 + c^2 - 2bc \cos A$$
$$a^2 = 22^2 + 27^2 - 2(22)(27)\cos 47°$$
$$a^2 \approx 402.8$$
$$a \approx 20.1$$

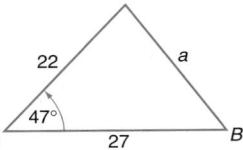

Next, use the law of sines to determine the measure of an angle.
$$\frac{\sin A}{a} = \frac{\sin B}{b}$$
$$\frac{\sin 47°}{20.1} \approx \frac{\sin B}{22} \qquad A = 47°, a \approx 20.1, b = 22$$
$$\sin B \approx \frac{22 \sin 47°}{20.1} \qquad \sin 47° \approx 0.7314$$
$$\sin B \approx 0.8005$$
$$B \approx 53.2°$$

Now, determine the measure of the third angle, $\angle C$.
$$47° + 53.2° + C \approx 180$$
$$C \approx 79.8°$$
Therefore, $a \approx 20.1$, $B \approx 53.2°$, and $C \approx 79.8°$.

b. $p = 29$, $q = 31$, $r = 48$

You are given the measures of three sides.
Use the law of cosines to find the measure of an angle.
$$p^2 = q^2 + r^2 - 2qr \cos P$$
$$29^2 = 31^2 + 48^2 - 2(31)(48)\cos P$$
$$2(31)(48)\cos P = 31^2 + 48^2 - 29^2$$
$$\cos P = \frac{31^2 + 48^2 - 29^2}{2(31)(48)}$$
$$\cos P \approx 0.8145$$
$$P \approx 35.5°$$

Alternative Learning Styles

Auditory In the initial classroom discussion, concentrate primarily on the development and use of the law of cosines. As you proceed through the examples, informally review the concepts learned in previous lessons in the chapter. Emphasize an integrated approach to problem solving that incorporates all skills in an approach that is both appropriate and efficient.

Use the law of sines to determine the measure of another angle.

$$\frac{\sin P}{p} = \frac{\sin Q}{q}$$

$$\frac{\sin 35.5°}{29} = \frac{\sin Q}{31}$$

$$\sin Q \approx \frac{31 \sin 35.5°}{29}$$

$$\sin Q \approx 0.6208$$

$$Q \approx 38.4°$$

Now find the measure of the third angle.

$$35.5° + 38.4° + R \approx 180°$$

$$R \approx 106.1°$$

Therefore, $P \approx 35.5°$, $Q \approx 38.4°$, and $R \approx 106.1°$.

Example ③

APPLICATION

Paleontology

fabulous

FIRSTS

**Mary Anning
(1799–1847)**

As a child, Mary Anning loved to explore the coast of England, looking for shells and fossils. When she was only 12, she became the first person to discover a nearly complete skeleton of an extinct reptile, Ichthyosaurus. Before this discovery, other scientists believed that animals like this may have existed, but lacked proof. Mary Anning provided that proof for them.

At the Glen Rose formation in Texas, an anthropologist measured the pace and stride of footprints made by a bipedal (two-footed), carnivorous (meat-eating) dinosaur and the hindfeet of a herbivorous (plant-eating) dinosaur. The data are shown at the right.

a. Find the step angle for each dinosaur.

b. What can you tell about the motion of each dinosaur from its step angle?

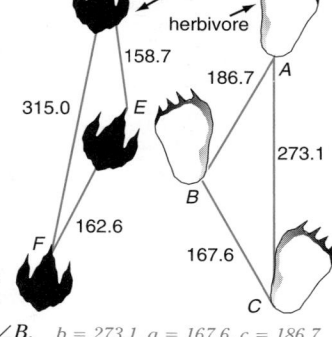

a. Find the step angle for the herbivore, $\angle B$.   *b = 273.1, a = 167.6, c = 186.7*

$$b^2 = a^2 + c^2 - 2ac \cos B \quad \text{Use the law of cosines.}$$

$$(273.1)^2 = (167.6)^2 + (186.7)^2 - 2(167.6)(186.7)\cos B$$

$$2(167.6)(186.7)\cos B = (167.6)^2 + (186.7)^2 - (273.1)^2$$

$$\cos B = \frac{(167.6)^2 + (186.7)^2 - (273.1)^2}{2(167.6)(186.7)}$$

$$\cos B \approx -0.1859$$

$$B \approx 100.7° \quad \textit{The step angle for the herbivore is 100.7°.}$$

Find the step angle for the carnivore, $\angle E$.   *e = 315.0, d = 162.6, f = 158.7*

$$e^2 = d^2 + f^2 - 2df \cos E \quad \text{Use the law of cosines.}$$

$$(315.0)^2 = (162.6)^2 + (158.7)^2 - 2(162.6)(158.7)\cos E$$

$$2(162.6)(158.7)\cos E = (162.6)^2 + (158.7)^2 - (315.0)^2$$

$$\cos E = \frac{(162.6)^2 + (158.7)^2 - (315.0)^2}{2(162.6)(158.7)}$$

$$\cos E \approx -0.9223$$

$$E \approx 157.3° \quad \textit{The step angle for the carnivore is 157.3°.}$$

b. Since the step angle for the carnivore is closer to 180°, it appears as though the carnivore made more forward progress with each step than the sauropod.   *Why do you suppose a step angle close to 180° was important for a carnivore?*

In-Class Example

For Example 3
The sides of a triangle measure 16 cm, 20 cm, and 32 cm. Find the measure of the largest angle.   **125.1°**

fabulous

FIRSTS

Paleontology is the study of life of the geologic past through the study of fossils. Paleontological research dates back to the early 1800s.

Check for Understanding

Exercises 1–11 are designed to help you assess your students' understanding through reading, writing, speaking, and modeling. You should work through Exercises 1–6 with your students and then monitor their work on Exercises 7–11.

Additional Answers

7. cosines; $c \approx 11.5$, $B \approx 81.6°$, $A \approx 56.4°$
8. sines; $a \approx 16.7$, $A \approx 80.8°$, $C \approx 28.2°$
9. sines; $b \approx 21.0$, $C \approx 44.3°$, $B \approx 101.7°$
10. cosines; $A \approx 47.7°$, $B \approx 62.6°$, $C \approx 69.7°$

Assignment Guide

Core: 13–33 odd, 34, 35, 37–45
Enriched: 12–32 even, 33–45

For **Extra Practice,** see p. 907.

The red A, B, and C flags, printed only in the Teacher's Wraparound Edition, indicate the level of difficulty of the exercises.

Study Guide Masters, p. 96

NAME _____ DATE _____

13-5

Study Guide

Student Edition
Pages 796–802

Law of Cosines

Law of Cosines
Let △ABC be any triangle with a, b, and c representing the measures of sides opposite angles with measurements A, B, and C, respectively. Then, the following equations are true. $a^2 = b^2 + c^2 - 2bc \cos A$ $b^2 = a^2 + c^2 - 2ac \cos B$ $c^2 = a^2 + b^2 - 2ab \cos C$

Use the law of cosines to solve a triangle in the following cases.
1. To find the length of the third side of any triangle if the lengths of two sides and the measurement of the included angle are given.
2. To find the measurement of an angle of a triangle if the lengths of three sides are given.

Example: A hiker walks 3 miles due east from his house. He then turns 45° and walks 2 miles northeast. How far will he have to walk to get home?

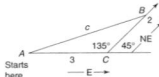

$c^2 = a^2 + b^2 - 2ab \cos C$
$c^2 = 2^2 + 3^2 - 2(2)(3) \cos 135°$
$c^2 = 4 + 9 - 12(-0.7071)$
$c^2 = 21.4852$
$c \approx 4.6$
He will have to walk about 4.6 miles.

Solve each triangle described below. Round measures of sides and angles to the nearest tenth.

1. $a = 14$, $c = 20$, $B = 38°$
   $b = 12.4$, $A \approx 43.9°$, $C = 98.1°$
2. $A = 60°$, $c = 17$, $b = 12$
   $a = 15.1$, $B \approx 43.4°$, $C = 76.6°$
3. $a = 4$, $b = 6$, $c = 3$
   $A = 36.3°$, $B = 117.3°$, $C = 26.4°$
4. $A = 20°$, $b = 100$, $c = 84$
   $a = 35.6$, $B = 73.7°$, $C = 86.3°$
5. A diver leaps 2.5 feet off the board and jackknifes 10 feet into the water at an angle of 20°. How far from the edge of the board does she enter the water?
   7.7 feet
6. Some children set up a tepee in the woods. The poles are 7 feet long, and the children want the distance between adjacent poles to be 4 feet at the base. How wide must the angle be between the poles?
   33.2°

802 Chapter 13

Communicating Mathematics

1. Sample answer: if you know the measure of three sides

2. $a^2 = 8^2 + 10^2 - 2 \cdot 8 \cdot 10 \cos 40°$

4. You do not know two parts of one ratio.

5. See students' work.

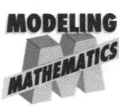

6. See students' work.

Study the lesson. Then complete the following.

1. **Describe** a set of conditions for which the law of cosines can be used.

2. **State** which form of the law of cosines you would use to find a in the triangle at the right.

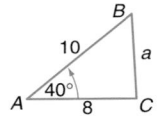

3. **Choose** the triangles that should be solved by beginning with the law of cosines. **a, c**

a. 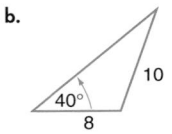   b.   c.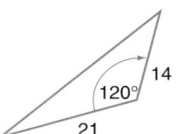

4. **Explain** why you cannot use the law of sines to solve a triangle if you are given $A = 80°$, $b = 20$, and $c = 55$.

5. **Make a chart** that summarizes the conditions necessary to use the law of sines and law of cosines.

6. Collect data from your classmates or members of the track team and determine their step angles. Compare and contrast the step angles when walking versus running. Collect data from your classmates' pets and compare and contrast the step angles of different kinds of pets.

7–10. See margin.

Determine whether each triangle can be solved by beginning with the law of sines or law of cosines. Then solve each triangle.

7.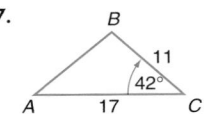

8.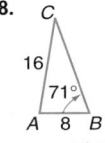

9. $a = 12$, $c = 15$, $A = 34°$

10. $a = 15$, $b = 18$, $c = 19$

11. The sides of a triangle are 6.8 cm, 8.4 cm, and 4.9 cm long. Find the measure of the smallest angle. **35.7°**

12–17. See margin.

Guided Practice A

Determine whether each triangle can be solved by beginning with the law of sines or law of cosines. Then solve each triangle.

12.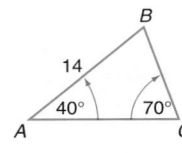

13.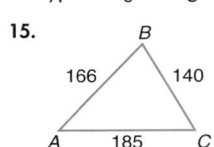

14.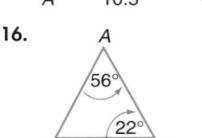

15.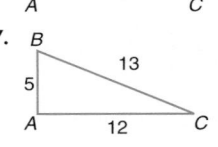

16.

17.

Additional Answers

12. cosines; $a \approx 4.5$, $B \approx 50.8°$, $C \approx 89.2°$
13. cosines; $c \approx 6.5$, $A \approx 76.1°$, $B \approx 68.9°$
14. sines; $a \approx 9.6$, $b \approx 14$, $B = 70°$
15. cosines; $A \approx 46.6°$, $B \approx 73.8°$, $C \approx 59.6°$
16. sines; $b \approx 14.4$, $c \approx 5.5$, $B \approx 102.0°$
17. cosines; $A = 90°$, $B \approx 67.4°$, $C \approx 22.6°$

Reteaching

Using Problem Solving Have students work the following problem. The distance between three cities, A, B, and C, are $AB = 120$ km, $AC = 50$ km, and $BC = 150$ km. C is due west of A. In what direction is B from A if B is north of the line through A and C? Have students find the other angle measures, too, in order to verify their answers.
28° E of N

18. $A = 35°, b = 16, c = 19$

19. $a = 20, c = 24, B = 47°$

20. $a = 21.5, b = 13, C = 38.3°$

21. $A = 40°, B = 59°, c = 14$

22. $a = 51, c = 61, B = 19°$

23. $a = 13.7, A = 25°, B = 78°$

24. $a = 15, b = 25, c = 40$

25. $a = 345, b = 648, c = 442$

26. $c = 10.3, a = 21.5, b = 16.7$

27. $A = 28°, b = 5, c = 4.9$

28. $A = 29°, b = 7.6, c = 14.1$

29. $a = 8, b = 24, c = 18$

INTEGRATION
Geometry

30. The sides of a parallelogram measure 55 cm and 71 cm. Find the length of each diagonal if the larger angle measures 106°.   **76.9 cm, 101.1 cm**

31. Circle Q at the right has a radius of 15 cm. Two radii $\overline{QA}$ and $\overline{QB}$ form an angle of 123°. Find the length of chord AB.   **26.4 cm**

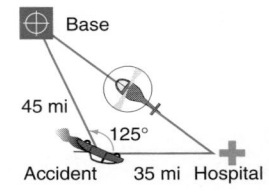

32. The sides of a triangle are 50 meters, 70 meters, and 85 meters. Find the measure of the angle opposite the shortest side.   **36°**

Programming

33. The graphing calculator program at the right finds the measure of a side of a triangle using the law of cosines. A is the measure of the missing side, B and C are the measures of the second and third sides, and θ is the measure of the angle opposite side A.

```
PROGRAM: Cosine
:Deg
:Disp "INPUT B"
:Input B
:Disp "INPUT C"
:Input C
:Disp "INPUT θ"
:Input θ
:√ (B² + C² − 2BC cosθ)→A
:Disp "A="
:Disp A
:End
```

Use the program at the right to find the measure of the missing side.

a. $B = 2, C = 4, \theta = 78°$ **4.08**

b. $B = 9, C = 19, \theta = 45°$ **14.15**

c. $B = 5.4, C = 6.9, \theta = 95°$ **9.12**

Critical Thinking

34. Explain how the Pythagorean theorem is a special case of the law of cosines.   **Since $\cos 90° = 0$, $c^2 = a^2 + b^2 - 2ab \cos C$ becomes $c^2 = a^2 + b^2$.**

Applications and Problem Solving

35. **Surveying**   Two sides of a triangular plot of land have lengths of 400 feet and 600 feet. The measure of the angle between those sides is 46.3°. Find the perimeter and area of the plot.   **1434 ft; 86,756.06 ft²**

36. 71.1 miles

36. **Emergency Medicine**   A medical rescue helicopter has flown 45 miles from its home base to pick up an accident victim and 35 miles from there to the hospital. The angle between the two legs of the trip was 125°. The pilot needs to know how far he is now from his home base so he can decide whether to refuel before returning. How far is the hospital from the helicopter's base?

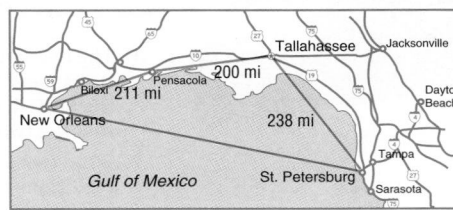

Base
45 mi
125°
Accident   35 mi Hospital

37. about 561 miles

37. **Geography**   Use the information in the map below to find the shortest distance from St. Petersburg, Florida, to New Orleans, Louisiana. The angle at Tallahassee, Florida, measures 125°, and the angle at Pensacola, Florida, measures 166°. (*Hint:* First find the distance from St. Petersburg to Pensacola.)

Tallahassee   Jacksonville
200 mi
Biloxi 211 mi   Pensacola   Dayton Beach
New Orleans   238 mi
Tampa
Gulf of Mexico   St. Petersburg
Sarasota

Extension

Problem Solving   Find the area of a regular octagon inscribed in a circle whose radius measures 6 millimeters.
about 101.8 mm²

Additional Answers

18. cosines; $a \approx 10.9$, $B \approx 57.3°$, $C \approx 87.7°$

19. cosines; $b \approx 17.9$, $A \approx 54.7°$, $C \approx 78.3°$

20. cosines; $c \approx 13.9$, $A \approx 106.2°$, $B \approx 35.5°$

21. sines; $C = 81°$, $a \approx 9.1$, $b \approx 12.2$

22. cosines; $b \approx 21.0$, $A \approx 90.0°$, $C \approx 71.0°$

23. sines; $b \approx 31.7$, $C \approx 77.0°$, $c \approx 31.6$

24. no solution

25. cosines; $A \approx 30.0°$, $B \approx 69.2°$, $C \approx 80.8°$

26. cosines; $A \approx 102.9°$, $B \approx 49.3°$, $C \approx 27.8°$

27. cosines; $a \approx 2.4$, $B \approx 78.0°$, $C \approx 74.0°$

28. cosines; $a \approx 8.3$, $B \approx 26.3°$, $C \approx 124.7°$

29. cosines; $A \approx 14.6°$, $B \approx 130.8°$, $C \approx 34.6°$

Using the Programming Exercises   The program given in Exercise 33 is for use with a TI-82 graphing calculator. For other programmable calculators, have students consult their owner's manual for commands similar to those presented here.

Practice Masters, p. 96

13-5   NAME_____   DATE_____
Practice   Student Edition
Pages 796–802

Law of Cosines

Solve each triangle described below. Round measures of sides and angles to the nearest tenth.

1. $a = 12, b = 7, C = 80°$
$c = 12.8, A = 67.4°,$
$B = 32.6°$

2. $a = 16, b = 20, C = 54°$
$c = 16.7, A = 50.7°,$
$B = 75.2°$

3. $A = 78.3°, b = 7, c = 11$
$a = 11.8, B = 35.5°,$
$C = 66.2°$

4. $B = 71°, c = 6, a = 11$
$b = 10.7, C = 32.0°,$
$A = 77°$

5. $a = 8, b = 6, c = 9$
$A = 60.6°, B = 40.8°,$
$C = 78.6°$

6. $a = 16.4, b = 21.1, c = 18.5$
$A = 48.4°, B = 74.2°,$
$C = 57.4°$

7. $a = 4, b = 5, c = 8$
$A = 24.1°, B = 30.7°,$
$C = 125.2°$

8. $a = 4, b = 3, c = 6$
$A = 36.3°, B = 26.4°,$
$C = 117.3°$

9. $A = 23°, b = 10, c = 12$
$a = 4.8, B = 54.5°,$
$C = 102.5°$

10. $C = 35°, b = 24, a = 18$
$c = 13.9, B = 82°,$
$A = 63.0°$

11. Two motorists start at the same point and travel in two straight courses. The courses diverge by 95°. If one is traveling at 50 mph and the other is traveling at 65 mph, how far apart will they be after 4 hours?
341.6 miles

12. In problem 11, when will the motorists be 400 miles apart?
4.7 hours

Closing Activity

Writing Have students write a short paragraph explaining how they would know whether to use the law of sines or the law of cosines to solve a problem.

Additional Answer

41.

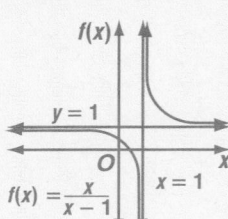

$f(x) = \dfrac{x}{x-1}$

with lines $y = 1$ and $x = 1$

Enrichment Masters, p. 96

13-5

NAME_____ DATE _____

Enrichment

Student Edition
Pages 796–802

The Law of Cosines and the Pythagorean Theorem

The law of cosines bears strong similarities to the Pythagorean theorem. According to the law of cosines, if two sides of a triangle have lengths a and b and if the angle between them has a measure of $x°$, then the length, y, of the third side of the triangle can be found by using the equation

$y^2 = a^2 + b^2 - 2ab \cos x°.$

Answer the following questions to clarify the relationship between the law of cosines and the Pythagorean theorem.

1. If the value of $x°$ becomes less and less, what number is $\cos x°$ close to? **1**

2. If the value of $x°$ is very close to zero but then increases, what happens to $\cos x°$ as $x°$ approaches 90°? **decreases, approaches 0**

3. If $x°$ equals 90°, what is the value of $\cos x°$? What does the equation of $y^2 = a^2 + b^2 - 2ab \cos x°$ simplify to if $x°$ equals 90°? **0, $y^2 = a^2 + b^2$**

4. What happens to the value of $\cos x°$ as $x°$ increases beyond 90° and approaches 180°? **decreases to −1**

5. Consider some particular value of a and b, say 7 for a and 19 for b. Use a graphing calculator to graph the equation you get by solving $y^2 = 7^2 + 19^2 - 2(7)(19) \cos x°$ for y. **See students' graphs.**

a. In view of the geometry of the situation, what range of values should you use for X? **X min = 0°; X max = 180°**

b. Display the graph and use the TRACE function. What do the maximum and minimum values appear to be for the function? **See students' graphs.**

c. How do the answers for Part b relate to the lengths 7 and 19? Are the maximum and minimum values from Part b ever actually attained in the geometric situation? **min = 19 − 7; max = 19 + 7; no**

---

38. Use the law of sines to solve the triangle at the right. (Lesson 13–4) $B \approx 42.3°$, $C \approx 92.7°$, $c \approx 117.3$

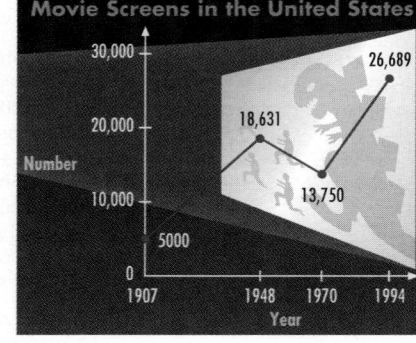

39. Change −45° to radians. (Lesson 13–2) $-\dfrac{\pi}{4}$

40. How many 7-letter patterns can be formed from the letters of the word BENZENE? (Lesson 12–2) **420**

41. Graph $f(x) = \dfrac{x}{x-1}$. (Lesson 9–1) **See margin.**

42. Geometry The volume of a rectangular solid is 72 cubic units. The width is twice the height and the length is 7 units more than the height. Find the dimensions of the solid. (Lesson 8–5) **4 units by 9 units by 2 units**

43. Solve $z^2 + 4z = 96$ by completing the square. (Lesson 6–3) **8, −12**

44. Simplify $(3 + \sqrt{2})(\sqrt{10} + \sqrt{5})$. (Lesson 5–6) **$4\sqrt{10} + 5\sqrt{5}$**

45. Entertainment More than 100 years ago, on December 28, 1895, the first motion picture was shown to a public audience. Many of the people who witnessed the film of a train pulling into a station were so afraid that they dove to the floor. By 1907, there were about 5000 nickelodeons in the United States. The admission price in 1907 was 5 cents. (Lesson 2–4)

45a. Sample answer: $y = 249x + 5000$

45b. Sample answer based on the equation in 45a: 28,157

a. The graph shows the increase in the number of movie screens in the United States from 1907 until 1994. Write an equation to represent this situation.

b. Predict the number of movie screens there will be in the year 2000.

The Channel Tunnel

The excerpt below appeared in an article in *Popular Science* in May, 1994.

> THIS IS THE CHANNEL TUNNEL. DREAMED of by Napoleon, futilely attempted 100 years ago, and built at a cost greater than most countries' gross national product, the 31-mile underwater rail link between England and continental Europe is finally in place. By 1996, the system will transport some 8 million car passengers and 4.5 million bus passengers each year . . . The owner, Eurotunnel, hopes to entice a large chunk of the tourist traffic that currently uses hovercrafts and ferries to cross the choppy waters of the English Channel . . . Commonly referred to as "The Chunnel," the Channel Tunnel is actually a complex of three parallel passageways, dipping as far as 148 feet below the seabed of the English Channel. ∎

1. The two long sections of tunnel were dug toward each other from the British and French sides until they finally met and were linked deep below the English Channel. What types of measurements were needed to ensure that the two sections would meet properly? **1–2. See margin.**

2. What types of hazards might Chunnel travelers be exposed to? How might the Chunnel designers have protected travelers against them?

Mathematics and SOCIETY

England and France were once joined together naturally. But 7000 years ago, when the last Ice Age ended, the melting ice flooded the lowlands, creating the English channel and making England an island.

Answers for Mathematics and Society

1. Sample answer: measurements of angles, directions, depths, and distances along each segment

2. Sample answer: flooding, water leakage, fire, inadequate ventilation

13-6

Circular Functions

What YOU'LL LEARN

- To define and use the trigonometric functions based on the unit circle.

Why IT'S IMPORTANT

You can use circular functions to solve problems involving music and entertainment.

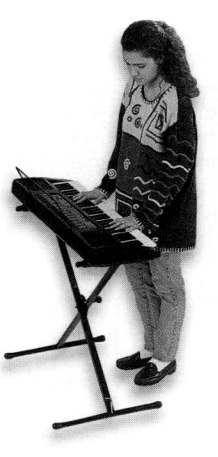

CONNECTION
Music

If you have taken piano lessons, you probably know that the musical scale includes the notes A-B-C-D-E-F-G. If you start at the A below middle C and play the seven white keys that are highlighted in the figure below, there is a one-to-one correspondence between the keys on the piano and the notes of the musical scale. That is, for each highlighted key, there is exactly one musical note or name. However, there are several keys on the piano that are named A, B, C, and so on. If you play all the white keys, there is a many-to-one correspondence between the keys on the piano and the notes of the scale.

Similarly, there is a many-to-one correspondence between angles in standard position and their trigonometric functions. For example, the figure at the right shows that $\sin 30° = \frac{1}{2}$ and $\sin 150° = \frac{1}{2}$. In this lesson, we will now further generalize the trigonometric functions by defining them in terms of the unit circle.

Consider an angle θ in standard position. The terminal side of the angle intersects the unit circle at a unique point, $P(x, y)$. Recall that $\sin \theta = \frac{y}{r}$ and $\cos \theta = \frac{x}{r}$. Since $P(x, y)$ is on the unit circle, $r = 1$. Therefore, $\sin \theta = y$ and $\cos \theta = x$.

Definition of Sine and Cosine	If the terminal side of an angle θ in standard position intersects the unit circle at $P(x, y)$, then $\cos \theta = x$ and $\sin \theta = y$.

Since there is exactly one point $P(x, y)$ for any angle θ, the relations $\cos \theta = x$ and $\sin \theta = y$ are functions of θ. Because they are both defined using a unit circle, they are often called **circular functions**.

Example ① Point $P(0.6, 0.8)$ is located on a unit circle. Find $\sin \theta$, $\cos \theta$, and $\tan \theta$.

$\sin \theta$ is the value of the y-coordinate.
$\sin \theta = 0.8$

$\cos \theta$ is the value of the x-coordinate.
$\cos \theta = 0.6$

$\tan \theta$ can be found by using the identity $\tan \theta = \frac{\sin \theta}{\cos \theta}$.

$\tan \theta = \frac{0.8}{0.6}$
≈ 1.3333

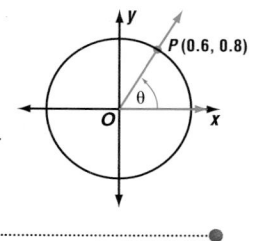

Lesson 13-6 Circular Functions **805**

TEKS 1.a., 4.a.

13-6 LESSON NOTES

NCTM Standards: 1–6, 9

Instructional Resources

- Study Guide Master 13-6
- Practice Master 13-6
- Enrichment Master 13-6
- Assessment and Evaluation Masters, p. 353
- Modeling Mathematics Masters, p. 73

Transparency 13-6A contains the 5-Minute Check for this lesson; **Transparency 13-6B** contains a teaching aid for this lesson.

Recommended Pacing	
Honors Pacing	Day 6 of 9
Block Scheduling*	Day 5 of 6 (along with Lesson 13-7)

*For more information on pacing and possible lesson plans, refer to the *Block Scheduling Booklet*.

1 FOCUS

5-Minute Check
(over Lesson 13-5)

Determine whether each triangle can be solved by beginning with the law of sines or the law of cosines. Then solve each triangle. Round measures of sides to the nearest tenth and measures of angles to the nearest degree.

1. $B = 20°$, $a = 120$, $c = 100$
   $b = 43.0$, $A = 107°$, $C = 53°$
2. $A = 78°$, $b = 2$, $c = 4$
   $a = 4.1$, $B = 29°$, $C = 73°$
3. $C = 30°$, $a = 15$, $b = 15$
   $c = 7.8$, $A = 75°$, $B = 75°$
4. $B = 15°$, $a = 12$, $c = 6$
   $b = 6.4$, $A = 151°$, $C = 14°$
5. $a = 6$, $b = 10$, $c = 6$
   $A = 34°$, $B = 113°$, $C = 34°$

Motivating the Lesson

Questioning Ask students how many of them have ever ridden a Ferris wheel. Ask them if they know how their location on a Ferris wheel relates to trigonometry.

In-Class Example

For Example 1
Point $P(0.39, 0.92)$ is located on a unit circle. Find $\sin \theta$, $\cos \theta$, and $\tan \theta$. **0.92, 0.39, 2.36**

Teaching Tip It may be helpful to have students draw reference triangles, similar to the one in Example 1, that represent cases in the third and fourth quadrants and thus have negative values. For example, a diagram could illustrate $\cos(-135°) = \cos(225°) = \cos(180° + 45°)$.

EXPLORATION

In this Exploration, students use a graphing calculator to examine the graphs of the sine and cosine functions.

In the Exploration below, you will investigate the behavior of the sine and cosine functions on the unit circle.

EXPLORATION
GRAPHING CALCULATORS

Press MODE and highlight Degree and Par. Then use the following range values to set up a viewing window: TMIN = 0, TMAX = 360, TSTEP = 15, XMIN = −2.4, XMAX = 2.35, XSCL = 0.5, YMIN = −1.5, YMAX = 1.55, YSCL = 0.5. Define the unit circle with the definition $X_{1T} = \cos T$ and $Y_{1T} = \sin T$. Press GRAPH .

Your Turn
a. Activate the TRACE function to move around the circle. What does T represent? What does the x-value represent? What does the y-value represent?
b. Determine the sine and cosine of the angles whose terminal sides lie at 0°, 90°, 270°, and 360°.
c. How does the sine function change as you move around the unit circle? How does the cosine function change?

In this chapter, you have found the values of trigonometric functions for acute angles of right triangles, for angles in standard position on a coordinate plane, and now for angles of a unit circle. You have found exact values by using characteristics of special right triangles, and you have found approximate values by using a calculator. And you have done all of this for angles measured in degrees and in radians. This information can be summarized in the chart below. For convenience, the decimal approximations are rounded to the nearest tenth.

degrees	0	30	45	60	90	120	135	150	180	210	225	240	270	300	315	330	360
radians	0	$\frac{\pi}{6}$	$\frac{\pi}{4}$	$\frac{\pi}{3}$	$\frac{\pi}{2}$	$\frac{2\pi}{3}$	$\frac{3\pi}{4}$	$\frac{5\pi}{6}$	π	$\frac{7\pi}{6}$	$\frac{5\pi}{4}$	$\frac{4\pi}{3}$	$\frac{3\pi}{2}$	$\frac{5\pi}{3}$	$\frac{7\pi}{4}$	$\frac{11\pi}{6}$	2π
$\sin \theta$	0	$\frac{1}{2}$	$\frac{\sqrt{2}}{2}$	$\frac{\sqrt{3}}{2}$	1	$\frac{\sqrt{3}}{2}$	$\frac{\sqrt{2}}{2}$	$\frac{1}{2}$	0	$-\frac{1}{2}$	$-\frac{\sqrt{2}}{2}$	$-\frac{\sqrt{3}}{2}$	−1	$-\frac{\sqrt{3}}{2}$	$-\frac{\sqrt{2}}{2}$	$-\frac{1}{2}$	0
nearest tenth	0	0.5	0.7	0.9	1	0.9	0.7	0.5	0	−0.5	−0.7	−0.9	−1	−0.9	−0.7	−0.5	0
$\cos \theta$	1	$\frac{\sqrt{3}}{2}$	$\frac{\sqrt{2}}{2}$	$\frac{1}{2}$	0	$-\frac{1}{2}$	$-\frac{\sqrt{2}}{2}$	$-\frac{\sqrt{3}}{2}$	−1	$-\frac{\sqrt{3}}{2}$	$-\frac{\sqrt{2}}{2}$	$-\frac{1}{2}$	0	$\frac{1}{2}$	$\frac{\sqrt{2}}{2}$	$\frac{\sqrt{3}}{2}$	1
nearest tenth	1	0.9	0.7	0.5	0	−0.5	−0.7	−0.9	−1	−0.9	−0.7	−0.5	0	0.5	0.7	0.9	1

You will learn more about the graphs of trigonometric functions in Chapter 14.

As is often the case, a graph may be a more effective way of presenting data. In the graphs below, the horizontal axis shows the values of θ, and the vertical axis shows the values of $\sin \theta$ or $\cos \theta$.

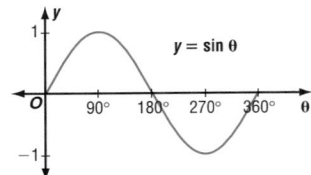

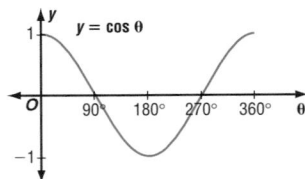

GLENCOE Technology

Interactive Mathematics Tools Software

This multimedia software provides an interactive lesson that compares the values of sine and cosine of an angle, as it relates to the unit circle. A **Computer Journal** gives students an opportunity to write about what they have learned.

For Windows & Macintosh

The following chart contains the same information as the earlier chart, but for angles from 360° to 720°. Compare the information in the two charts. As you can see, the values of sin θ and cos θ are the same for two angles that are coterminal.

degrees	360	390	405	420	450	480	495	510	540	570	585	600	630	660	675	690	720
radians	2π	$\frac{13\pi}{6}$	$\frac{9\pi}{4}$	$\frac{7\pi}{3}$	$\frac{5\pi}{2}$	$\frac{8\pi}{3}$	$\frac{11\pi}{4}$	$\frac{17\pi}{6}$	3π	$\frac{19\pi}{6}$	$\frac{13\pi}{4}$	$\frac{10\pi}{3}$	$\frac{7\pi}{2}$	$\frac{11\pi}{3}$	$\frac{15\pi}{4}$	$\frac{23\pi}{6}$	4π
sin θ	0	$\frac{1}{2}$	$\frac{\sqrt{2}}{2}$	$\frac{\sqrt{3}}{2}$	1	$\frac{\sqrt{3}}{2}$	$\frac{\sqrt{2}}{2}$	$\frac{1}{2}$	0	$-\frac{1}{2}$	$-\frac{\sqrt{2}}{2}$	$-\frac{\sqrt{3}}{2}$	-1	$-\frac{\sqrt{3}}{2}$	$-\frac{\sqrt{2}}{2}$	$-\frac{1}{2}$	0
nearest tenth	0	0.5	0.7	0.9	1	0.9	0.7	0.5	0	−0.5	−0.7	−0.9	−1	−0.9	−0.7	−0.5	0
cos θ	1	$\frac{\sqrt{3}}{2}$	$\frac{\sqrt{2}}{2}$	$\frac{1}{2}$	0	$-\frac{1}{2}$	$-\frac{\sqrt{2}}{2}$	$-\frac{\sqrt{3}}{2}$	-1	$-\frac{\sqrt{3}}{2}$	$-\frac{\sqrt{2}}{2}$	$-\frac{1}{2}$	0	$\frac{1}{2}$	$\frac{\sqrt{2}}{2}$	$\frac{\sqrt{3}}{2}$	1
nearest tenth	1	0.9	0.7	0.5	0	−0.5	−0.7	−0.9	−1	−0.9	−0.7	−0.5	0	0.5	0.7	0.9	1

Notice there is a many-to-one correspondence between the angles and their sine and cosine functions.

Every 360°, or 2π radians, represents one complete revolution of the terminal side. As you can see by comparing the two charts, for every 360° or 2π radians, the sine and cosine functions repeat their values. So, we can say that the sine and cosine functions are **periodic**. Each has a **period** of 360° or 2π radians.

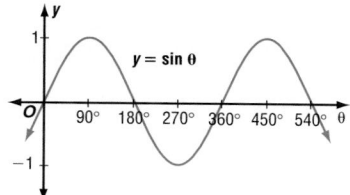

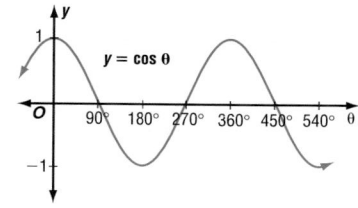

Definition of Periodic Function	A function is called periodic if there is a number *a* such that $f(x) = f(x + a)$ for all *x* in the domain of the function. The least positive value of *a* for which $f(x) = f(x + a)$ is called the period of the function.

When you look at the graph of a periodic function, you will see a repeating pattern: a shape that repeats over and over as you travel out the *x*-axis. The period is the distance along the *x*-axis from the beginning of the pattern to the point at which it begins again.

For the sine and cosine functions, cos (*x* + 360°) = cos *x*, and sin (*x* + 360°) = sin *x*. In radian measure, cos (*x* + 2π) = cos *x*, and sin (*x* + 2π) = sin *x*. Therefore, the period of the sine and cosine functions is 360° or 2π.

Example Find the exact value of each function.

a. 420°

$\sin 420° = \sin(60 + 360)°$

$= \sin 60°$

$= \frac{\sqrt{3}}{2}$

b. $\cos\left(-\frac{3\pi}{4}\right)$

$\cos\left(-\frac{3\pi}{4}\right) = \cos\left(-\frac{3\pi}{4} + 2\pi\right)$

$= \cos\left(\frac{5\pi}{4}\right)$

$= -\frac{\sqrt{2}}{2}$

Lesson 13–6 Circular Functions **807**

In-Class Example

For Example 2
Find the exact value of each function.

a. sin 570° $-\frac{1}{2}$

b. $\cos\left(-\frac{5\pi}{6}\right)$ $-\frac{\sqrt{3}}{2}$

Alternative Teaching Strategies

Student Diversity Review the idea of quadrants and the sign of *x* and *y* in each quadrant.

In-Class Example

For Example 3
An object vibrates producing a low-frequency wave of 22 cycles per second or 22 Hz. Identify the period of this function.

$\frac{1}{22}$ second

3 PRACTICE/APPLY

Check for Understanding

Exercises 1–10 are designed to help you assess your students' understanding through reading, writing, speaking, and modeling. You should work through Exercises 1–4 with your students and then monitor their work on Exercises 5–10.

Additional Answers

2. Sample answer: sin θ is positive until 180° and is negative until 360°.

3. Sample answer: Graphs have same shape but cross the *x*-axis at different points.

Study Guide Masters, p. 97

NAME_____ DATE_____

13-6

Student Edition
Pages 803–808

Study Guide

Circular Functions

If (x, y) is the point on the unit circle at which the terminal ray of an angle θ in standard position intersects the unit circle, then $\cos \theta = x$ and $\sin \theta = y$.

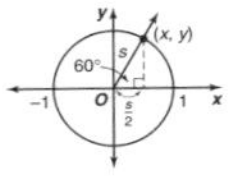

Example: Find cos 60°. Look at the diagram at the right. The dashed line segment cuts the *x*-axis and the terminal side of the angle to form a 30°–60° right triangle. The length of the radius of the circle is 1 unit. Thus,

$$s = 1 \text{ unit and } \frac{s}{2} = \frac{1}{2} \text{ unit.}$$

The *x*-coordinate of the point (x, y) is $\frac{1}{2}$.
Therefore, $\cos 60° = \frac{1}{2}$.

Every 360° or 2π radians through which the terminal side of an angle rotates corresponds to a complete rotation around the unit circle. When comparing the sine and cosine tables, you see that every 360° or 2π radians the sine and cosine functions repeat their values. The sine and cosine functions are therefore called **periodic functions**.

Periodic Function	
Definition	**Example**
A function is called **periodic** if there is a number *a* such that $f(x) = f(x + a)$ for all *x* in the domain of the function. The least positive value of *a* for which $f(x) = f(x + a)$ is called the **period** of the function.	Find the value of the function sin 570°. $\sin 570° = \sin (210 + 360)°$ $= \sin 210°$ $= -\frac{1}{2}$ 570 = 210 + 360 The sine function has a period of 360°. sin θ is negative in the third quadrant.

For each of the following, find the least positive angle measurement that is coterminal.

1. −90°   270°
2. 1000°   280°
3. $\frac{20\pi}{7}$ $\frac{6\pi}{7}$

Find the value of each function.

4. cos(−420)°   0.5
5. cos 2280°   −0.5
6. sin(−510)°   −0.5
7. sin 495° $\frac{\sqrt{2}}{2}$

8. $\cos\left(-2\frac{1}{2}\pi\right)$ 0
9. $\cos\left(\frac{11\pi}{4}\right)$ $-\frac{\sqrt{2}}{2}$
10. $\sin\left(\frac{5\pi}{3}\right)$ $-\frac{\sqrt{3}}{2}$
11. $\sin\left(-\frac{3\pi}{4}\right)$ $-\frac{\sqrt{2}}{2}$

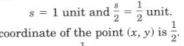

Many real-world situations have characteristics that can be described with periodic functions.

Example ③ When a string on a guitar is plucked, it is displaced from a fixed point in the middle of the string and vibrates back and forth, producing a musical tone. The exact tone depends on the frequency, or number of cycles per second, that the string vibrates. To produce an **A**, the frequency is 440 cycles per second, or 440 hertz (Hz).
  a. Identify the period of this function.
  b. Graph this situation.

  a. Since the string vibrates at a frequency of 440 Hz, the period is the time it takes to complete one cycle, or $\frac{1}{440}$ second.

  b. Let the horizontal axis represent the time in seconds. Let the vertical axis represent how far the fixed point on the string is displaced from its resting position.

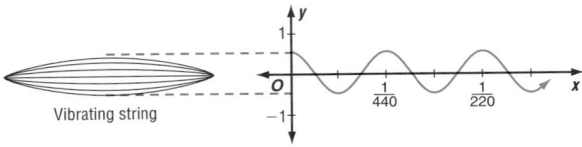

Vibrating string

CHECK FOR UNDERSTANDING

Communicating Mathematics

1. $\cos \theta = x, \sin \theta = y$

2–3. See margin.

MATH JOURNAL

Guided Practice

4. See students' work.

5. $\sin \theta = \frac{4}{5}$,

$\cos \theta = -\frac{3}{5}$,

$\tan \theta = -\frac{4}{3}$

6. $\sin \theta = -\frac{5}{13}$

$\cos \theta = -\frac{12}{13}$

$\tan \theta = \frac{5}{12}$

Study the lesson. Then complete the following.

1. **Define** the sine and cosine functions for the angle at the right.
2. **Look for a pattern** in the chart on page 806.
3. **Compare and contrast** the graphs of the sine and cosine functions on page 807.

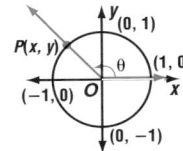

4. **Assess Yourself** Write a paragraph in which you state your understanding of trigonometry as it has developed from the acute angles of a right triangle to angles on a coordinate plane that intersect the unit circle.

Find sin θ, cos θ, and tan θ for each angle.

5. $P\left(-\frac{3}{5}, \frac{4}{5}\right)$

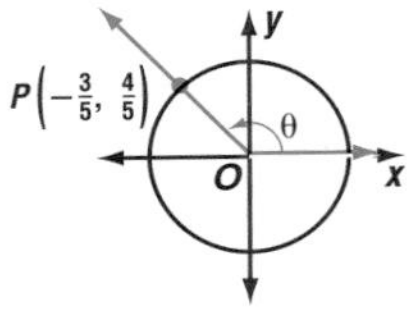

6. $P\left(-\frac{12}{13}, -\frac{5}{13}\right)$

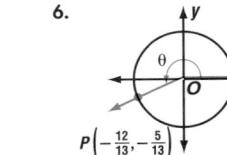

7. Determine the period of the function that is graphed below.   9

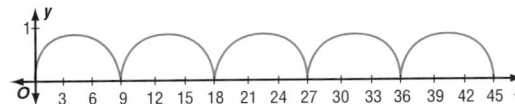

Find the value of each function.

8. $\cos\left(-\frac{3\pi}{4}\right)$ $-\frac{\sqrt{2}}{2}$

9. $\sin 660°$ $-\frac{\sqrt{3}}{2}$

10. **Music** Refer to the application at the beginning of the lesson. Determine whether the musical scale on a piano is a periodic function. If so, name the period.   yes; 7 white keys

808   *Chapter 13   Exploring Trigonometric Functions*

Reteaching

Using Models Give students an angle measure from each of the four quadrants that can be used in a 30°−60° or 45°−45° right triangle. Have them construct their own unit circle and diagram to find the sine and cosine value of that measure. Check these diagrams.

Practice

A

Find sin θ, cos θ, and tan θ for each angle.

11. sin θ = $\frac{\sqrt{2}}{2}$,

cos θ = $\frac{\sqrt{2}}{2}$, tan θ = 1

12. sin θ = $-\frac{12}{13}$,

cos θ = $\frac{5}{13}$,

tan θ = $-\frac{12}{5}$

13. sin θ = 0, cos θ = 1,

tan θ = 0

11.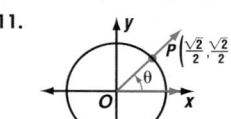
12.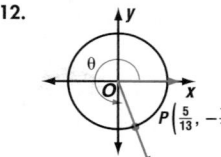
13.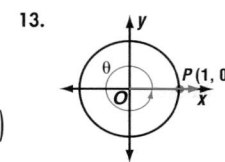

Determine the period of each function.

14.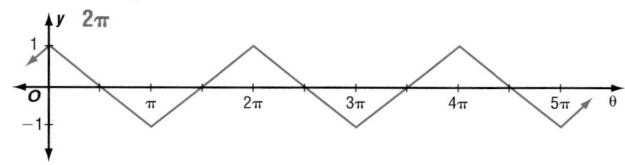
2π

B

15.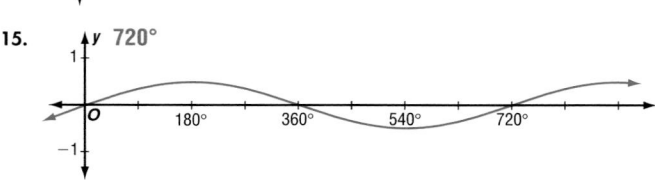
720°

16.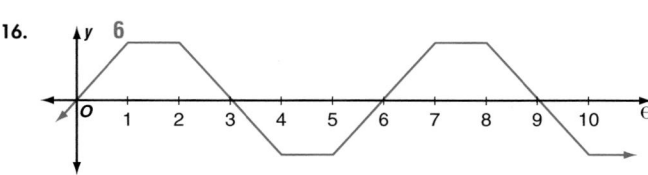
6

Find the exact value of each function.

17. sin 1020° $-\frac{\sqrt{3}}{2}$

18. cos (−450°)   0

19. sin (−180°)   0

20. sin $\left(-\frac{13\pi}{6}\right)$ $-\frac{1}{2}$

21. sin $\frac{3\pi}{2}$ −1

22. cos $\frac{9\pi}{2}$ 0

C

23. 4(sin 30°)(cos 60°)   1

24. $\frac{\sin 30° + \cos 60°}{2}$ $\frac{1}{2}$

25. $\frac{4 \sin 300° + 2 \cos 30°}{3}$ $-\frac{\sqrt{3}}{3}$

26. sin 30° + sin 60° $\frac{1 + \sqrt{3}}{2}$

27. $(\sin 60°)^2 + (\cos 60°)^2$ 1

28. 8(sin 120°)(cos 120°) $-2\sqrt{3}$

Graphing Calculator

29. Use a graphing calculator to graph the functions y = sin θ and y = 2 sin θ on the same screen. Predict the shape of the graph of y = 3 sin θ. Check by graphing.   **See students' work.**

Critical Thinking

30. Determine the domain and range of the functions y = sin θ, y = cos θ, and y = tan θ.   **See margin.**

Lesson 13–6   Circular Functions   **809**

Assignment Guide

Core: 11–29 odd, 30, 31, 33–39
Enriched: 12–28 even, 29–39

For **Extra Practice,** see p. 908.

The red A, B, and C flags, printed only in the Teacher's Wraparound Edition, indicate the level of difficulty of the exercises.

Additional Answer

30. sine: D = {all reals},
    R = {−1 ≤ x ≤ 1}
    cosine: D = {all reals},
    R = {−1 ≤ x ≤ 1}
    tangent: D = {all reals except
    90, 270, ...}, R = {all reals}

Practice Masters, p. 97

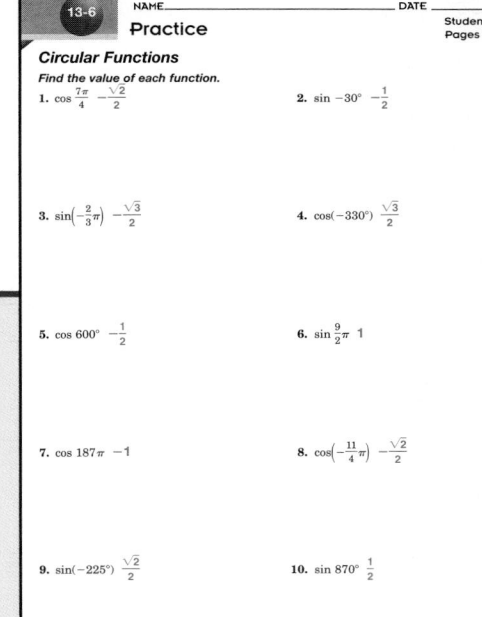

Closing Activity

Speaking To emphasize the general meaning of the term *periodic,* have students name several events in nature that are periodic. Examples might be changes in moon phases, seasons, or tides.

Chapter 13, Quiz C (Lessons 13-5 and 13-6), is available in the *Assessment and Evaluation Masters,* p. 353.

Additional Answers

31.

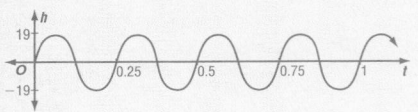

32.

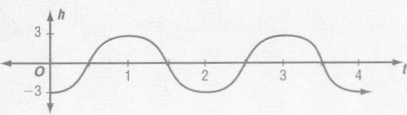

Enrichment Masters, p. 97

NAME_____ DATE _____

Student Edition
Pages 803–808

Enrichment

Polar Coordinates

Consider an angle in standard position with its vertex at a point O called the *pole.* Its initial side is on a coordinated axis called the *polar axis.* A point P on the terminal side of the angle is named by the *polar coordinates* (r, θ) where r is the directed distance of the point from O and θ is the measure of the angle.

Graphs in this system may be drawn on polar coordinate paper such as the kind shown at the right.

The polar coordinates of a point are not unique. For example, $(3, 30°)$ names point P as well as $(3, 390°)$. Another name for P is $(-3, 210°)$. Can you see why? The coordinates of the pole are $(0, \theta)$ where θ may be any angle.

Example: Draw the graph of the function $r = \cos \theta$. Make a table of convenient values for θ and r. Then plot the points.

θ	0°	30°	60°	90°	120°	150°	180°
r	1	$\frac{\sqrt{3}}{2}$	$\frac{1}{2}$	0	$-\frac{1}{2}$	$-\frac{\sqrt{3}}{2}$	-1

Since the period of the cosine function is 180°, values of r for $\theta > 180°$ are repeated.

Graph each function by making a table of values and plotting the values on polar coordinate paper.

1. $r = 4$
r = 4 for all values of θ. Graph should be a circle with radius 4 and center at the pole.

2. $r = 3 \sin \theta$
Graph is circle of radius $\frac{3}{2}$ with center at $\left(\frac{3}{2}, 90°\right)$.

3. $r = 3 \cos 2\theta$
Graph looks like flower with 4 petals, points of petals are at $(3, 0°)$, $(3, 90°)$, $(3, 180°)$, $(3, 270°)$. All petals meet at pole.

4. $r = 2(1 + \cos \theta)$
Graph is heart-shaped curve, symmetric with respect to polar axis.

Applications and Problem Solving

31–32. See margin.

Mixed Review

35. No; the figure is not self-similar.

31. **Entertainment** As you ride a Ferris wheel, the height that you are above the ground varies periodically. Consider the height of the center of the wheel to be the starting point. A particular wheel has a diameter of 38 feet and travels at a rate of 4 revolutions per minute. Make a graph in which the horizontal axis represents time and the vertical axis represents height in relation to the starting point.

32. **Physics** The motion of a weight on a spring varies periodically. Suppose you pull the weight down 3 inches from its equilibrium point and then release it. It bounces above the equilibrium point and then returns below the equilibrium point in 2 seconds. Graph the height of the spring as a function of time.

33. **Aviation** A pilot is flying from Chicago to Columbus, a distance of 300 miles. In order to avoid an area of thunderstorms, she alters her course by 15° and flies on this course for 75 miles. How far is she from Columbus? (Lesson 13–5) **about 228 miles**

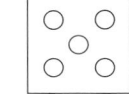

34. Find $\tan 135°$. (Lesson 13–3) **−1**

35. Determine whether the figure at the right is a fractal. Explain your reasoning. (Lesson 11–7)

36. Solve $4^x = 24$. (Lesson 10–6) **about 2.2925**

37. Solve $x^4 - 13x^2 + 36 = 0$. (Lesson 8–6) **−3, 3, −2, 2**

38. If $A = \begin{bmatrix} -3 & 5 \\ 1 & -4 \end{bmatrix}$, find A^{-1}. (Lesson 4–5) $\frac{1}{7}\begin{bmatrix} -4 & -5 \\ -1 & -3 \end{bmatrix}$

39. Use the elimination method to solve the system of equations. (Lesson 3–2)
$x + 2y = -2$ **(2, −2)**
$3x - 2y = 10$

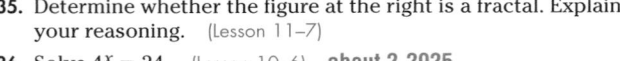

WORKING ON THE

In·ves·ti·ga·tion

Refer to the Investigaton on pages 768—769.

Scream Machines!

Select a picture of a roller coaster whose support structure is made of triangular shapes. Find a section of the structure that contains at least two different triangular shapes.

1 Make an enlarged scale drawing of the section you chose. Select one triangle and label its angles, A, B, and C, and its sides a, b, and c.

2 Use a ruler to measure the lengths of b and c. Use a protractor to measure $\angle A$. Include these measurements on your drawing.

3 Use the law of cosines and the law of sines to solve your triangle. Use a ruler and protractor

to check your calculations. If calculations do not agree with your measurements, try to explain why.

4 Repeat this activity with a different triangle in the section.

5 Do you think a knowledge of trigonometry would be helpful to a coaster designer? Explain why or why not.

Add the results of your work to your Investigation Folder.

Extension

Communication Have students write short paragraphs relating how each of the following topics might be represented by a sine function.

1. a water wheel
2. an animal population
3. a spring with a weight attached

In·ves·ti·ga·tion

Working on the Investigation

The Investigation on pages 768–769 is designed to be a long-term project that is completed over several days or weeks. Encourage students to keep their materials in their Investigation Folder as they work on the Investigation.

Inverse Trigonometric Functions

13-7 LESSON NOTES

NCTM Standards: 1–6, 9

Instructional Resources

- Study Guide Master 13-7
- Practice Master 13-7
- Enrichment Master 13-7
- Assessment and Evaluation Masters, p. 353

Transparency 13-7A contains the 5-Minute Check for this lesson; **Transparency 13-7B** contains a teaching aid for this lesson.

Recommended Pacing	
Honors Pacing	Day 7 of 9
Block Scheduling*	Day 5 of 6 (along with Lesson 13-6)

*For more information on pacing and possible lesson plans, refer to the *Block Scheduling Booklet*.

What YOU'LL LEARN

- To find values of expressions involving inverse trigonometric functions.

Why IT'S IMPORTANT

You can use inverse trigonometric functions to solve problems involving navigation and architecture.

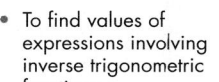
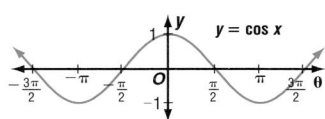
Architecture

Chinese-born architect I. M. Pei is well known for incorporating triangles into the design of his buildings. Among his famous designs are the glass pyramid entrance to the Louvre museum in Paris and the newly opened Rock and Roll Hall of Fame in Cleveland, Ohio.

Architects often use trigonometry when designing buildings. Sometimes the value of some trigonometric function for an angle is known and it is necessary to find the measure of the angle. The concept of inverse functions can be applied to find the inverse of trigonometric functions.

In Lesson 8–8, you learned that the inverse of a function is the relation in which all the values of x and y are reversed. The graphs of $y = \cos x$ and its inverse, $x = \cos y$, are shown below. Notice that the inverse is not a function, since it fails the vertical line test. None of the inverses of the trigonometric functions are functions.

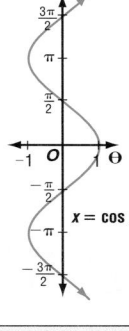

We must restrict the domain of the trigonometric functions so that the inverses are functions. The values in these restricted domains are called **principal values**. Capital letters are used to distinguish trigonometric functions with restricted domains from the usual trigonometric functions.

Definitions of the Cosine, Sine, and Tangent Functions	$y = \text{Cos } x$ if and only if $y = \cos x$ and $0 \le x \le \pi$. $y = \text{Sin } x$ if and only if $y = \sin x$ and $-\frac{\pi}{2} \le x \le \frac{\pi}{2}$. $y = \text{Tan } x$ if and only if $y = \tan x$ and $-\frac{\pi}{2} \le x \le \frac{\pi}{2}$.

The inverse of the Cosine function is called the **Arccosine function** and is symbolized by Cos^{-1} or **Arccos**.

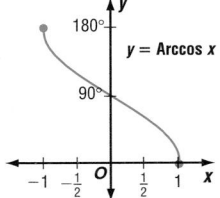

Definition of Inverse Cosine	Given $y = \text{Cos } x$, the inverse Cosine function is defined by the following equation. $y = \text{Cos}^{-1} x$ or $y = \text{Arccos } x$

The Arccosine function has the following characteristics.

- Its domain is the set of real numbers from -1 to 1.
- Its range is the set of angle measures from 0 to π, inclusive.
- $\text{Cos } x = y$ if and only if $\text{Cos}^{-1} y = x$.
- $[\text{Cos}^{-1} \circ \text{Cos}](x) = [\text{Cos} \circ \text{Cos}^{-1}](x) = x$. *Recall function composition from Lesson 8–7.*

Lesson 13–7 Inverse Trigonometric Functions **811**

GLENCOE *Technology*

CD-ROM Interaction

A multimedia simulation connects trigonometric functions with using a launcher to sink a disabled tanker. A blackline master activity with teacher's notes provides a follow-up to the CD-ROM simulation.

For Windows & Macintosh

TEKS | 1.a., 4.a., 4.c.

---

1 FOCUS

5-Minute Check
(over Lesson 13-6)

1. Point $P(0.47, 0.88)$ is located on a unit circle. Find $\sin \theta$, $\cos \theta$, and $\tan \theta$.
   0.88, 0.47, 1.87

Find the exact value of each function.

2. $\sin 840°$ $\dfrac{\sqrt{3}}{2}$

3. $\cos 1215°$ $-\dfrac{\sqrt{2}}{2}$

4. $\sin \dfrac{13\pi}{4}$ $\dfrac{\sqrt{2}}{2}$

5. $\cos \dfrac{9\pi}{2}$ **0**

Motivating the Lesson

Hands-On Activity Have students duplicate angles by tracing. Discuss other ways to duplicate a given triangle. Have students draw a triangle when given side measurements such as 6, 8, and 10 centimeters. Compare different students' triangles. Are the angle measurements the same? Discuss different ways to determine the angle measures.

Teaching Tip In Example 1, encourage students to rewrite the equation in the form of an inverse function.

Teaching Tip Be sure students realize that cos^{-1} and Arccos are synonymous and may be used interchangeably. This also is true for equivalent terms for other trigonometric functions.

In-Class Examples

For Example 1
Solve.

a. Cos $x = 1$ **0**

b. Sin $x = \dfrac{\sqrt{2}}{2}$ **45°**

c. Tan $x = 1$ **45°**

For Example 2
If the curve in Example 2 has a radius of 500 feet and the speed limit is 35 mph, at what angle should the curve be banked? **9.4°**

Study Guide Masters, p. 98

NAME_____ DATE _____
Student Edition
Pages 809–812

13-7
Study Guide

Inverse Trigonometric Functions

The inverse of a trigonometric function is not a function. However, for functions with properly restricted domains, the inverse is a function. The values in these restricted domains are called **principal values**. Capital letters are used to distinguish trigonometric functions with restricted domains from those with unrestricted domains.

Function	Restrictions	Inverse
$y = \text{Cos } x$	$0 \le x \le \pi$	$y = \text{Cos}^{-1} x$ or $y = \text{Arccos } x$
$y = \text{Sin } x$	$-\dfrac{\pi}{2} \le x \le \dfrac{\pi}{2}$	$y = \text{Sin}^{-1} x$ or $y = \text{Arcsin } x$
$y = \text{Tan } x$	$-\dfrac{\pi}{2} < x < \dfrac{\pi}{2}$	$y = \text{Tan}^{-1} x$ or $y = \text{Arctan } x$

Example: Find $\text{Cos}^{-1}\left(-\dfrac{\sqrt{3}}{2}\right)$.

Let $\theta = \text{Cos}^{-1}\left(-\dfrac{\sqrt{3}}{2}\right)$.

Then, $\text{Cos } \theta = -\dfrac{\sqrt{3}}{2}$ and $\theta = \dfrac{5\pi}{6}$.

Find each value.

1. $\cot(\text{Tan}^{-1} 2)$
$\dfrac{1}{2}$

2. $\text{Arctan}(-1)$
$-45°$

3. $\text{Cot}^{-1} 1$
$45°$

4. $\cos\left(\text{Sin}^{-1} -\dfrac{\sqrt{2}}{2}\right)$
$\dfrac{\sqrt{2}}{2}$

5. $\text{Sin}^{-1} -\dfrac{\sqrt{3}}{2}$
$-60°$

6. $\sin\left(\text{Arcsin} \dfrac{\sqrt{3}}{2}\right)$
$\dfrac{\sqrt{3}}{2}$

7. $\tan\left(\text{Arcsin} -\dfrac{5}{7}\right)$
$-\dfrac{5\sqrt{6}}{12}$

8. $\sin\left(\text{Tan}^{-1} \dfrac{5}{12}\right)$
$\dfrac{5}{13}$

9. $\sin[\text{Arctan} (-\sqrt{2})]$
$-\dfrac{\sqrt{6}}{3}$

10. $\text{Arccos}\left(-\dfrac{\sqrt{3}}{2}\right)$
$150°$

11. $\text{Arcsin}\left(\dfrac{\sqrt{2}}{2}\right)$
$45°$

12. $\text{Arccot} -\dfrac{\sqrt{3}}{3}$
$-60°$

The definitions of the Arcsine and Arctangent functions are similar to the definition of the Arccosine function.

Definition of Inverse Sine and Inverse Tangent	Given $y = \text{Sin } x$, the inverse Sine function is defined as follows. $y = \text{Sin}^{-1} x$ or $y = \text{Arcsin } x$ Given $y = \text{Tan } x$, the inverse Tangent function is defined as follows. $y = \text{Tan}^{-1} x$ or $y = \text{Arctan } x$

The expressions in each row of the table below are equivalent. You can use these expressions to rewrite and solve trigonometric equations.

$y = \text{Sin } x$	$x = \text{Sin}^{-1} y$ or $x = \text{Arcsin } y$
$y = \text{Cos } x$	$x = \text{Cos}^{-1} y$ or $x = \text{Arccos } y$
$y = \text{Tan } x$	$x = \text{Tan}^{-1} y$ or $x = \text{Arctan } y$

Example Solve Cos $x = \dfrac{1}{2}$.

If Cos $x = \dfrac{1}{2}$, then x is the least value whose cosine is $\dfrac{1}{2}$.

$x = \text{Arccos } \dfrac{1}{2}$ (1 ÷ 2) COS⁻¹   *60*

Therefore, $x = 60°$. *In radians, $x = \dfrac{\pi}{3}$.*

Many application problems involve finding the inverse of a trigonometric function.

Example

APPLICATION
Civil Engineering

Highway curves are usually banked, or tilted inward, so that cars can negotiate the curve more safely. The proper banking angle θ for a car making a turn of radius r feet at a velocity of v feet per second is given by the the equation $\tan \theta = \dfrac{v^2}{gr}$, where g is the acceleration due to gravity, 32 ft/s². An engineer is designing a curve with a radius of 1000 feet. If the speed limit on the curve will be 55 mph, at what angle should the curve be banked?

First, rewrite 55 miles per hour in feet per seconds.

$$\dfrac{55 \text{ miles}}{\text{hour}} \cdot \dfrac{5280 \text{ feet}}{\text{mile}} \cdot \dfrac{\text{hour}}{3600 \text{ seconds}} \approx 80.7 \text{ feet per second}$$

Now, use the equation $\tan \theta = \dfrac{v^2}{gr}$.

$$\tan \theta = \dfrac{80.7^2}{(32)(1000)}$$

$$\theta = \arctan \dfrac{80.7^2}{(32)(1000)}$$

Use a calculator to find θ.

80.7 x² ÷ (32 × 1000) = TAN⁻¹   *11.503467*

Therefore, the curve should be banked at an angle of 11.5°.

You can also use a calculator to find the value of a complicated trigonometric expression.

CAREER CHOICES

Architects combine knowledge of mathematics, science, and the arts to create safe, functional, and attractive buildings.

For more information, contact:

American Institute of Architects
1735 New York Avenue NW
Washington, DC 20006

CAREER CHOICES

Architects combine aesthetic and utilitarian needs to design buildings with varying levels of decoration and function.

Example 3

Use a scientific calculator to find $\tan\left(\text{Sin}^{-1}\left(\frac{5}{13}\right)\right)$.

$$\boxed{(}\ 5\ \boxed{\div}\ 13\ \boxed{)}\ \boxed{\text{SIN}^{-1}}\ \boxed{\text{TAN}}\qquad 0.4166667$$

Therefore, $\tan\left(\text{Sin}^{-1}\left(\frac{5}{13}\right)\right) \approx 0.4167$.

In-Class Example

For Example 3
Find each value.

a. $\sin\left(\text{Arccos }\frac{1}{2}\right)$ $\frac{\sqrt{3}}{2}$

b. $\text{Sin}^{-1}\left(\cos\frac{\pi}{3}\right)$ $30°$ or $\frac{\pi}{6}$

c. $\text{Arccos }(\sin \pi)$ $90°$ or $\frac{\pi}{2}$

d. $\tan\left(\text{Arcsin }\frac{24}{25}\right)$ $\frac{24}{7}$ or $3\frac{3}{7}$

Teaching Tip Remind students of the importance of the order of operations.

3 PRACTICE/APPLY

Check for Understanding
Exercises 1–14 are designed to help you assess your students' understanding through reading, writing, speaking, and modeling. You should work through Exercises 1–3 with your students and then monitor their work on Exercises 4–14.

Error Analysis
Make sure students use answers within the restricted domains defined on page 811. For $\text{Arcsin }\dfrac{\sqrt{2}}{2}$, the answer is $\frac{\pi}{4}$, not $\frac{3\pi}{4}$.

Practice Masters, p. 98

CHECK FOR UNDERSTANDING

Communicating Mathematics

Study the lesson. Then complete the following.

1. **Describe** how $y = \text{Sin } x$ and $y = \text{Arcsin } x$ are related. **See margin.**

2. **Explain** why the domains of the trigonometric functions must be restricted before finding the inverse functions. **See margin.**

3. **Explain** how you know when the domain of a trigonometric function is restricted. **Restricted domains are denoted with a capital letter.**

Guided Practice

Write each equation in the form of an inverse function.

4. $x = \sin \theta$ $\theta = \text{Arcsin } x$

5. $\tan y = -3$ $y = \text{Arctan } -3$

Solve each equation.

6. $x = \text{Arcsin } 0$ $0°$

7. $\text{Arctan } 1 = y$ $45°$

Find each value.

8. $\sin\left(\text{Cos}^{-1}\left(\frac{2}{3}\right)\right)$ $\frac{\sqrt{5}}{3}$

9. $\cos\left(\text{Cos}^{-1}\left(\frac{4}{5}\right)\right)$ $\frac{4}{5}$

10. $\cos\left(\text{Cos}^{-1}\left(\frac{1}{2}\right)\right)$ $\frac{1}{2}$

11. $\text{Tan}^{-1}(-1)$ $-45°$

12. $\text{Sin }\frac{\pi}{6}$ $\frac{1}{2}$

13. $\text{Sin}^{-1}(1)$ $90°$

14. **Architecture** The support for a roof will be shaped like two right triangles as shown at the right. Each right triangle will have one leg 8 feet long and a hypotenuse of 16 feet. Find θ.   **30°**

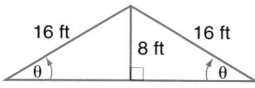

16 ft   8 ft   16 ft θ θ

EXERCISES

Practice

15. $b = \text{Arccos } a$
16. $y = \text{Arcsin } x$
17. $\alpha = \text{Arctan } \beta$
18. $\text{Arcsin }\frac{1}{2} = 30°$
19. $\text{Arccos } y = 45°$
20. $\text{Arctan }\left(-\frac{4}{3}\right) = x$

Write each equation in the form of an inverse function.

15. $a = \cos b$

16. $\sin y = x$

17. $\tan \alpha = \beta$

18. $\sin 30° = \frac{1}{2}$

19. $\cos 45° = y$

20. $-\frac{4}{3} = \tan x$

Solve each equation.

21. $x = \text{Cos}^{-1}(0)$ $90°$

22. $x = \text{Sin}^{-1}\left(\frac{1}{\sqrt{2}}\right)$ $45°$

23. $y = \text{Arctan }\frac{\sqrt{3}}{3}$ $30°$

24. $\text{Arctan } 0 = x$ $0°$

25. $\text{Sin}^{-1}\left(\frac{1}{2}\right) = y$ $30°$

26. $x = \text{Cos}^{-1}\left(\frac{\sqrt{2}}{2}\right)$ $45°$

Find each value.

27. $\text{Cos}^{-1}\left(-\frac{1}{2}\right)$ $120°$

28. $\sin\left(\text{Sin}^{-1}\left(\frac{1}{2}\right)\right)$ $\frac{1}{2}$

29. $\text{Sin}^{-1}\left(\cos\frac{\pi}{2}\right)$ $0°$

30. $\tan\left(\text{Cos}^{-1}\left(\frac{6}{7}\right)\right)$ $\frac{\sqrt{13}}{6}$

31. $\cot\left(\text{Sin}^{-1}\left(\frac{5}{6}\right)\right)$ $\frac{\sqrt{11}}{5}$

32. $\cot\left(\text{Sin}^{-1}\left(\frac{7}{9}\right)\right)$ $\frac{4\sqrt{2}}{7}$

Reteaching

Logical Thinking Compare inverse trigonometric functions with taking the root of a power. Both involve reversing a thought process or working backward.

Additional Answers

1. They are inverses of each other.
2. The trigonometric functions are not one-to-one functions.

13-7   NAME_____   DATE_____

Practice   Student Edition
Pages 809–81.

Inverse Trigonometric Functions

Find each value.

1. $\text{Cos}^{-1}\left(-\frac{\sqrt{3}}{2}\right)$ $150°$

2. $\text{Sin}^{-1}\left(-\frac{\sqrt{2}}{2}\right)$ $-45°$

3. $\text{Arctan}\left(-\frac{\sqrt{3}}{3}\right)$ $-30°$

4. $\text{Arccos } 1$ $0°$

5. $\sin\left(\text{Sin}^{-1}\frac{3}{8}\right)$ $\frac{3}{8}$

6. $\cos\left(\text{Sin}^{-1}-\frac{3}{5}\right)$ $\frac{4}{5}$

7. $\tan\left(\text{Cos}^{-1}-\frac{\sqrt{3}}{2}\right)$ $-\frac{\sqrt{3}}{3}$

8. $\sec\left(\text{Cos}^{-1}\frac{2}{9}\right)$ $\frac{9}{2}$

9. $\csc(\text{Arctan } -1)$ $-\sqrt{2}$

10. $\cot\left(\text{Arcsin }\frac{12}{13}\right)$ $\frac{5}{12}$

11. $\text{Sin}^{-1}\left(\cos\frac{\pi}{3}\right)$ $30°$

12. $\text{Cos}^{-1}\left(\tan\frac{3}{4}\pi\right)$ $180°$

13. $\sin\left(2\text{ Cos}^{-1}\frac{15}{17}\right)$ $\frac{240}{289}$

14. $\cos\left(2\text{ Sin}^{-1}\frac{\sqrt{3}}{2}\right)$ $-\frac{1}{2}$

15. $\sin\left(\text{Arctan }\frac{\sqrt{3}}{3}\right)$ $\frac{1}{2}$

16. $\text{Sin}^{-1}(\tan 45°)$ $\frac{\pi}{2}$ or $90°$

17. $\text{Cos}^{-1}\left(\text{Sin }\frac{\pi}{6}\right)$ $\frac{\pi}{3}$ or $60°$

18. $\sec\left(\text{Cos}^{-1}\frac{4}{5}\right)$ $\frac{5}{4}$

19. $\csc\left(\text{Sin}^{-1}\frac{9}{10}\right)$ $\frac{10}{9}$

20. $\cot(\text{Sin}^{-1} 0)$ undefined

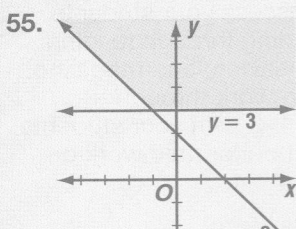

Assignment Guide

Core: 15–47 odd, 48–55
Enriched: 16–44 even, 45–55

For **Extra Practice,** see p. 908.

The red A, B, and C flags, printed only in the Teacher's Wraparound Edition, indicate the level of difficulty of the exercises.

4 ASSESS

Closing Activity

Speaking Have students name the inverse of the Tangent function three different ways. Tan^{-1}, Arctangent function, Arctan

Additional Answer

55.

Enrichment Masters, p. 98

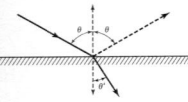

13-7

NAME_____ DATE_____

Enrichment

Student Edition
Pages 809–812

Snell's Law

Snell's Law describes what happens to a ray of light that passes from air into water or some other substance. In the figure, the ray starts at the left and makes an angle of incidence θ with the surface.

Part of the ray is reflected, creating an angle of reflection θ. The rest of the ray is bent, or refracted, as it passes through the other medium. This creates angle θ'.

The angle of incidence equals the angle of reflection.

The angles of incidence and refraction are related by Snell's Law:

$$\sin \theta = k \sin \theta'$$

The constant k is called the index of refraction.

k	Substance
1.33	Water
1.36	Ethyl alcohol
1.54	Rock salt and Quartz
1.46-1.96	Glass
2.42	Diamond

Use Snell's Law to solve the following. Round angle measures to the nearest tenth of a degree.

1. If the angle of incidence at which a ray of light strikes the surface of a window is 45° and $k = 1.6$, what is the measure of the angle of refraction? 26.2°

2. If the angle of incidence of a ray of light that strikes the surface of water is 50°, what is the angle of refraction? 35.2°

3. If the angle of refraction of a ray of light striking a quartz crystal is 24°, what is the angle of incidence? 38.8°

4. The angles of incidence and refraction for rays of light were measured five times for a certain substance. The measurements (one of which was in error) are shown in the table. Was the substance glass, quartz, or diamond? glass

θ	15°	30°	40°	60°	80°
θ'	9.7°	16.1°	21.2°	28.6°	33.2°

5. If the angle of incidence at which a ray of light strikes the surface of ethyl alcohol is 60°, what is the angle of refraction? 39.6°

814 *Chapter 13*

33. $\sin\left(\text{Arctan }\dfrac{\sqrt{3}}{3}\right)$ $\dfrac{1}{2}$ 34. $\cos\left(\text{Arcsin }\dfrac{3}{5}\right)$ $\dfrac{4}{5}$ 35. $\tan(\text{Arctan }3)$ 3

36. $\dfrac{\pi}{2}$ or 90°

36. $\text{Sin}^{-1}\left(\tan\dfrac{\pi}{4}\right)$ 37. $\text{Arctan }\sqrt{3}$ 60°   38. $\text{Arccos }\dfrac{\sqrt{3}}{2}$ 30°

40. $\dfrac{\sqrt{3}}{2}$

39. $\cos\left(\text{Tan}^{-1}\left(\sqrt{3}\right)\right)$ $\dfrac{1}{2}$ 40. $\cos\left[\text{Arcsin}\left(-\dfrac{1}{2}\right)\right]$ 41. $\cos(\text{Tan}^{-1}(1))$ $\dfrac{\sqrt{2}}{2}$

42. $\dfrac{\sqrt{2}}{2}$

42. $\cos\left[\text{Cos}^{-1}\left(\dfrac{\sqrt{2}}{2}\right) - \dfrac{\pi}{2}\right]$ 43. $\sin\left(2\text{ Sin}^{-1}\left(\dfrac{1}{2}\right)\right)$ $\dfrac{\sqrt{3}}{2}$ 44. $\sin\left(2\text{ Cos}^{-1}\left(\dfrac{3}{5}\right)\right)$ $\dfrac{24}{25}$

Critical Thinking

45. Prove that $[\text{Cos}^{-1} \circ \text{Cos}](x) = [\text{Cos} \circ \text{Cos}^{-1}](x) = x$. **See students' work.**

Applications and Problem Solving

46. 60° north of east

46. **Navigation** The *Western Princess* sailed due east 24 miles before turning north. When the *Princess* became disabled and radioed for help, the rescue boat needed to know the fastest route to her. The navigator of the *Princess* found that the fastest route for the rescue boat would be 48 miles. The cosine of the angle at which the rescue boat should sail is $\dfrac{1}{2}$. Find the angle at which the rescue boat should travel to aid the *Western Princess*.

47. **Optics** When light is polarized, all of the waves are traveling in parallel planes. You may have polarized sunglasses that eliminate glare by polarizing the light. Suppose vertically polarized light with intensity I_o strikes a polarizing filter with its axis at an angle of θ with the vertical. The intensity of the transmitted light I_t and θ are related by the equation $\cos \theta = \sqrt{\dfrac{I_t}{I_o}}$. If one fourth of the polarized light is transmitted through the lens, at what angle is the lens being held? **60°**

Mixed Review

48. Determine the period of the function shown at the right. (Lesson 13-6) π

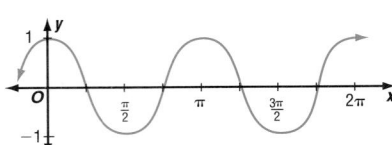

49. **Recreation** Isabel is flying a kite for which the angle of elevation is 70°. The string on the kite is 65 meters long. How far is the kite above the ground? (Lesson 13-1) **61.1 meters**

50. Write the expression $\displaystyle\sum_{k=1}^{10} (2 + k)$ in expanded form and find the sum.
(Lesson 11-1) $3 + 4 + 5 + 6 + 7 + 8 + 9 + 10 + 11 + 12; 75$

51. **Biology** Bacteria from a certain strain grows from 80 to 164 bacteria in 3 hours. Find k for the growth formula for this strain. (*Hint:* The exponential growth formula is $y = ne^{kt}$. (Lesson 10-7) **0.2392**

52. Find the center and radius of a circle whose equation is $(x - 4)^2 + (y - 9)^2 = 4$. (Lesson 7-3) **(4,9), 2**

53. Solve $x^2 - 7x = 0$ by factoring. (Lesson 6-2) **0, 7**

54. Find AA if $A = \begin{bmatrix} 2 & 7 \\ 0 & -1 \end{bmatrix}$. (Lesson 4-3) $\begin{bmatrix} 4 & 7 \\ 0 & 1 \end{bmatrix}$

55. Solve the system of inequalities by graphing. (Lesson 3-4) **See margin.**

$$x + y > 2$$
$$y > 3$$

814 *Chapter 13 Exploring Trigonometric Functions*

Extension

Problem Solving Find $\cos\left[\text{Cos}^{-1}\left(\dfrac{\sqrt{3}}{2}\right)\right] + \sin 2\left[\text{Tan}^{-1}\sqrt{3} + \text{Tan}^{-1}(-1)\right]$.

$\dfrac{1 + \sqrt{3}}{2}$

Using the
CHAPTER HIGHLIGHTS

The Chapter Highlights begins with a listing of the new terms, properties, and phrases that were introduced in this chapter. Have students define each term and provide an example or two of it, if appropriate.

VOCABULARY

After completing this chapter, you should be able to define each term, property, or phrase and give an example or two of each.

Geometry
angle of depression (p. 776)
angle of elevation (p. 776)
coterminal angles (p. 783)
initial side (p. 780)
standard position (p. 780)
terminal side (p. 780)

Trigonometry
circular functions (p. 805)
cosecant (p. 772)
cosine (p. 772, 805)
Cosine function (p. 811)
cotangent (p. 772)

inverse Cosine (Cos⁻¹ or Arccos) (p. 811)
inverse Sine (Sin⁻¹ or Arcsin) (p. 812)
inverse Tangent (Tan⁻¹ or Arctan) (p. 812)
law of cosines (p. 799)
law of sines (p. 792)
period (p. 807)
periodic function (p. 807)
principal values (p. 811)
quadrantal angles (p. 787)
quotient identities (p. 788)
radian (p. 781)
reciprocal identities (p. 788)

secant (p. 772)
sine (p. 772, 805)
Sine function (p. 811)
solving a triangle (p. 775)
tangent (p. 772)
Tangent function (p. 811)
trigonometric functions (p. 772)
trigonometric functions of an angle in standard position (p. 786)
trigonometric identities (p. 788)
trigonometry (p. 772)
unit circle (p. 781)

UNDERSTANDING AND USING THE VOCABULARY

State whether each sentence is *true* or *false*. If false, replace the underlined word(s) or number to make a true sentence.

1. When two angles in standard position have the same terminal side, they are called <u>quadrantal</u> angles. **false, coterminal**

2. The <u>law of sines</u> is used when the measure of two angles and the measure of any side are known. **true**

3. <u>Trigonometric</u> functions can be defined by using a unit circle. **true**

4. $\csc \theta = \dfrac{1}{\cos \theta}$ is a reciprocal identity. **false, sec θ**

5. A <u>radian</u> is the measure of an angle on the unit circle where the rays of the angle intercept an arc with length 1 unit. **true**

6. If the measures of three sides of a triangle are known, then the <u>law of sines</u> can be used to solve the triangle. **false, law of cosines**

7. The period of a function is the distance along the <u>x-axis</u> from the beginning of the pattern to the point at which it begins again. **true**

8. <u>60°</u> is a quadrantal angle. **false, an angle that has its terminal side on an axis where *x* or *y* is equal to zero**

9. $\cot \theta = \dfrac{\sin \theta}{\cos \theta}$ **false, tan θ**

10. In a coordinate plane, the <u>initial</u> side of an angle is the ray that rotates about the center. **false, terminal**

Instructional Resources

Three multiple-choice tests and three free-response tests are provided in the *Assessment and Evaluation Masters*. Forms 1A and 2A are for honors pacing, and Forms 1B, 1C, 2B, and 2C are for average pacing. Chapter 13 Test, Form 1B is shown at the right. Chapter 13 Test, Form 2B is shown on the next page.

Assessment and Evaluation Masters, pp. 339–340

13 NAME_____ DATE_____
Chapter 13 Test, Form 1B

Write the letter for the correct answer in the blank at the right of each problem.

For questions 1 and 2, refer to the diagram below.

1. What is the value of csc *A* to the nearest ten-thousandth?
   A. 2.1250   B. 1.1333
   C. 1.8750   D. 0.5333   1. __B__

2. What is the value of cot *B* to the nearest ten-thousandth?
   A. 2.1250   B. 1.1333
   C. 1.8750   D. 0.5333   2. __C__

3. Find the measure of ∠*A* to the nearest degree in the triangle at the right.
   A. 49°   B. 37°
   C. 41°   D. 53°   3. __C__

4. What is 100° expressed in radians?
   A. $\frac{5}{9}$ B. $\frac{5\pi}{9}$ C. $\frac{10}{9}$ D. $\frac{10\pi}{9}$ 4. __B__

5. What is $\frac{5\pi}{4}$ radians expressed in degrees?
   A. $\frac{225}{\pi}$ B. 225°   C. $\frac{112.5°}{\pi}$ D. 112.5°   5. __B__

6. What is the least positive angle measure that is coterminal with −400°?
   A. 40°   B. 80°   C. 320°   D. 400°   6. __C__

7. What is the value of $\cos\left(-\frac{\pi}{4}\right)$?
   A. $\frac{\sqrt{2}}{2}$ B. $-\frac{\sqrt{2}}{2}$ C. $\frac{\sqrt{3}}{2}$ D. $-\frac{\sqrt{3}}{2}$ 7. __A__

8. What is the value of 3 sin 120° cos 120°?
   A. $-\frac{3}{4}$ B. $-\frac{3\sqrt{3}}{4}$ C. $\frac{3}{4}$ D. $\frac{3\sqrt{3}}{4}$ 8. __B__

9. What is the value of cot 450°?
   A. 0   B. undefined   C. 1   D. −1   9. __A__

10. Suppose that *a* and *b* are the lengths of two sides of a triangle and *A* is the measure of the angle opposite the side with measure *a*. Which of the following sets of conditions is it impossible to satisfy?
    A. *A* < 90°, *a* > *b*   B. *A* < 90°, *b* sin *A* < *a* < *b*
    C. *A* ≥ 90°, *a* ≤ *b*   D. *A* ≥ 90°, *a* > *b*   10. __C__

11. Find the length of the longest side of a triangle with *A* = 40°, *B* = 60°, and *a* = 5.
    A. 6.43   B. 5   C. 6.74   D. 7.66   11. __D__

13 NAME_____ DATE_____
Chapter 13 Test, Form 1B (continued)

12. Find the measure of ∠*B* in a triangle where *C* = 30°, *c* = 22, and *b* = 42.
    A. 72°40′   B. 77°20′
    C. 72°40′ and 107°20′   D. no triangle possible   12. __C__

13. In △*ABC*, suppose you know *a*, *b*, and *c*. Which equation would you use to find the measure of ∠*A*?
    A. $\cos A = \frac{b^2 + c^2 + a^2}{2bc}$ B. $A = \frac{b^2 + c^2 - a^2}{2bc}$
    C. $\cos A = \frac{b^2 + c^2 - a^2}{2bc}$ D. $\cos A = \frac{b^2 + c^2 - a^2}{-2bc}$ 13. __C__

14. In △*ABC*, *C* = 60°, *a* = 12, and *b* = 5. Find *c* to the nearest hundredth.
    A. 109.00   B. 10.44   C. 11.79   D. 15.13   14. __B__

15. In △*ABC*, *a* = 15, *b* = 25, and *c* = 30. Find the measure of ∠*C* to the nearest tenth of a degree.
    A. 56.3°   B. 29.9°   C. 86.2°   D. 93.8°   15. __D__

16. Find the value of cos (−60°).
    A. $-\frac{1}{2}$ B. $\frac{1}{2}$ C. 0   D. 1   16. __D__

17. Find the value of sin 870°.
    A. $-\frac{1}{2}$ B. $\frac{1}{2}$ C. 0   D. 1   17. __B__

18. Find tan θ.
    A. −0.75   B. −0.8
    C. −1.39   D. 0.75   18. __A__

19. What is the measure of $\text{Sin}^{-1}\left(-\frac{1}{2}\right)$?
    A. −30°   B. 30°   C. 150°   D. 330°   19. __A__

20. What is the value of $\tan\left(\text{Tan}^{-1}\frac{1}{2}\right)$?
    A. −1   B. 1   C. $\frac{1}{2}$ D. $-\frac{1}{2}$ 20. __C__

Bonus Two cities are 10 miles apart. An object is seen hovering in the sky above the line joining the two cities. The angles of elevation of the object are 24° and 40°. What is the height of the object above the ground to the nearest tenth of a mile?
A. 2.9 mi   B. 4.5 mi   C. 7.2 mi   D. 9.5 mi   Bonus __A__

Skills and Concepts Encourage students to refer to the objectives and examples on the left as they complete the review exercises on the right.

Assessment and Evaluation Masters, pp. 345–346

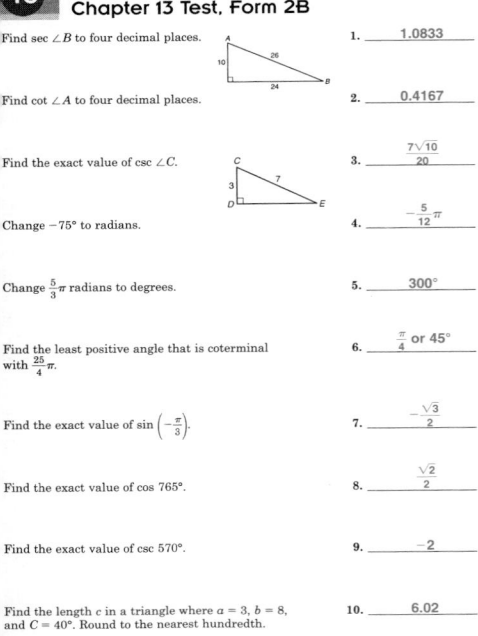

13 NAME_____ DATE _____

Chapter 13 Test, Form 2B

Find sec ∠B to four decimal places. 1. ____1.0833____

Find cot ∠A to four decimal places. 2. ____0.4167____

Find the exact value of csc ∠C. 3. ____$\frac{7\sqrt{10}}{20}$____

Change −75° to radians. 4. ____$-\frac{5}{12}\pi$____

Change $\frac{5}{3}\pi$ radians to degrees. 5. ____300°____

Find the least positive angle that is coterminal with $\frac{25}{4}\pi$. 6. ____$\frac{\pi}{4}$ or 45°____

Find the exact value of $\sin\left(-\frac{\pi}{3}\right)$. 7. ____$-\frac{\sqrt{3}}{2}$____

Find the exact value of cos 765°. 8. ____$\frac{\sqrt{2}}{2}$____

Find the exact value of csc 570°. 9. ____−2____

Find the length c in a triangle where $a = 3$, $b = 8$, and $C = 40°$. Round to the nearest hundredth. 10. ____6.02____

13 NAME_____ DATE _____

Chapter 13 Test, Form 2B (continued)

Determine whether each triangle has no solution, one solution, or two solutions. Then solve each triangle. Round lengths to the nearest hundredth and degree measures to the nearest tenth of a degree.

11. $a = 5$, $b = 14$, and $A = 29°$ 11. ____no solution____

12. $a = 9$, $b = 6$, and $B = 33°$ 12. ____two solutions—$A = 54.8°$; $C = 92.2°$; $c = 11.01$ or $A = 125.2°$; $C = 21.8°$; $c = 4.09$____

13. In △ABC, $a = 3$, $b = 4$, and $c = 6$. What is the measure of ∠A to the nearest tenth of a degree? 13. ____26.4°____

14. In △ABC, $a = 5$, $b = 7$, and $C = 114.6°$. Solve the triangle. Give answers to the nearest tenth. 14. ____$c = 10.2$; $A = 26.6°$; $B = 38.8°$____

15. In △ABC, $a = 12$, $b = 9$, and $c = 6$. Find the area of △ABC to the nearest square unit. 15. ____26____

16. Name two angles, one between 0° and 360° and another between 360° and 720°, that have the same sine as 45°. 16. ____135° and 405° or 135° and 495°____

17. Name two angles, one between 0 and 2π and another between 2π and 4π, that have the same cosine as $\frac{\pi}{3}$. 17. ____$\frac{5\pi}{3}$ and $\frac{7\pi}{3}$ or $\frac{5\pi}{3}$ and $\frac{11\pi}{3}$____

18. Determine the period of the function graphed below. 18. ____8π____

19. Solve $x = \text{Tan}^{-1}(-1)$. 19. ____−45°____

20. Find the value of $\sin\left(\text{Arctan}\,\frac{\sqrt{3}}{3}\right)$. 20. ____$\frac{1}{2}$____

Bonus From one point on the ground the angle of elevation to the top of a building is 35°, while 100 feet closer, the angle of elevation is 45°. Find the height of the building to the nearest foot. Bonus ____234 ft____

OBJECTIVES AND EXAMPLES

Upon completing this chapter, you should be able to:

• find values of trigonometric functions for acute angles (Lesson 13–1)

Find the values of the other five trigonometric functions if $\sin\theta = \frac{7}{8}$.

$\cos\theta = \frac{\sqrt{15}}{8}$ or 0.4841 $\sec\theta = \frac{8\sqrt{15}}{15}$ or 2.0656

$\tan\theta = \frac{7\sqrt{15}}{15}$ or 1.8074 $\cot\theta = \frac{\sqrt{15}}{7}$ or 0.5533

$\csc\theta = \frac{8}{7}$ or 1.1429

11–14. See margin.

• solve problems involving right triangles (Lesson 13–1)

Solve the right triangle in which $c = 14$ and $A = 42°$.

$\sin 42° = \frac{a}{14}$ $\cos 42° = \frac{b}{14}$

$14\sin 42° = a$ $14\cos 42° = b$

$9.4 \approx a$ $10.4 \approx b$

$B = 90° - 42°$ or 48°

$a \approx 9.4$, $b \approx 10.4$, $B = 48°$

• change radian measure to degree measure and vice versa (Lesson 13–2)

Change the degree measure 240° to radians.

$240° \cdot \frac{\pi\ \text{radians}}{180°} = \frac{240\,\pi}{180}$ radians or $\frac{4\pi}{3}$ radians

Change the radian measure $\frac{\pi}{12}$ to degrees.

$\frac{\pi}{12}$ radians $\cdot \frac{180°}{\pi\ \text{radians}} = \frac{180°\pi}{12\pi}$ or 15°

REVIEW EXERCISES

Use these exercises to review and prepare for the chapter test.

Suppose θ is an acute angle of a right triangle. For each function, find the values of the remaining five trigonometric functions of θ. Round to four decimal places.

11. $\cos\theta = \frac{2}{15}$ 12. $\tan\theta = 0.5$

13. $\sin\theta = \frac{3}{4}$ 14. $\sec\theta = 2\frac{1}{2}$

Find the value of x. Round to the nearest degree.

15. $\tan x = 0.2679$ **15°** 16. $\cos x = 0.8387$ **33°**

17. $\sin x = 0.9659$ **75°** 18. $\tan x = 1.0724$ **47°**

Solve each right triangle. Assume that C represents the right angle and c is the hypotenuse. Round measures of sides to the nearest tenth and measures of angles to the nearest degree.

19. $c = 16$, $a = 7$ $b \approx 14.4$, $A \approx 26°$, $B \approx 64°$
20. $A = 25°$, $c = 6$ $a \approx 2.5$, $b \approx 5.4$, $B = 65°$
21. $B = 45°$, $c = 12$ $A = 45°$, $a \approx 8.5$, $b \approx 8.5$
22. $B = 83°$, $b = \sqrt{31}$ $A = 7°$, $a \approx 0.7$, $c \approx 5.6$
23. $a = 9$, $B = 49°$ $A = 41°$, $b \approx 10.4$, $c \approx 13.7$
24. $\cos A = \frac{1}{4}$, $a = 4$ $A \approx 76°$, $B \approx 14°$, $b \approx 1.0$, $c \approx 4.1$

Change each degree measure to radian measure.

25. 255° $\frac{17\pi}{12}$ 26. −210° $-\frac{7\pi}{6}$
27. 65° $\frac{13\pi}{36}$ 28. 120° $\frac{2\pi}{3}$

Change each radian measure to degree measure.

29. $\frac{7\pi}{4}$ **315°**   30. $-\frac{5\pi}{12}$ **−75°**
31. -4π **−720°**   32. $\frac{5\pi}{3}$ **300°**

GLENCOE *Technology*

Test and Review Software

You may use this software, a combination of an item generator and item bank, to create your own tests or worksheets. Types of items include free response, multiple choice, short answer, and open ended.

For IBM & Macintosh

Additional Answers

11. $\sin \theta \approx 0.9911$
    $\tan \theta \approx 7.4330$
    $\csc \theta \approx 1.0090$
    $\sec \theta = 7.5000$
    $\cot \theta \approx 0.1345$
12. $\sin \theta \approx 0.4472$
    $\cos \theta \approx 0.8944$
    $\csc \theta \approx 2.2361$
    $\sec \theta \approx 1.1180$
    $\cot \theta = 2.000$
13. $\cos \theta \approx 0.6614$
    $\tan \theta \approx 1.1339$
    $\csc \theta \approx 1.3333$
    $\sec \theta \approx 1.5119$
    $\cot \theta \approx 0.8819$
14. $\sin \theta \approx 0.9165$
    $\cos \theta = 0.4000$
    $\tan \theta \approx 2.2913$
    $\csc \theta \approx 1.0911$
    $\cot \theta \approx 0.4364$

OBJECTIVES AND EXAMPLES	REVIEW EXERCISES

- find values of trigonometric functions for general angles   (Lesson 13–3)

Find the exact value of $\sin 120°$.

Sketch the angle in standard position. Its terminal side lies in Quadrant II. Notice the $30°-60°$ right triangle. Choose $P(x, y)$ on the terminal side of the angle so that $r = 2$.

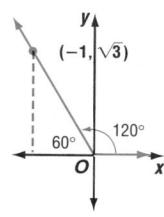

It follows that $x = -1$ and $y = \sqrt{3}$.

$\sin 120° = \dfrac{y}{r}$ or $\dfrac{\sqrt{3}}{2}$

Find the exact value of each trigonometric function.

33. $\cos 210°$ $-\dfrac{\sqrt{3}}{2}$ 34. $\tan 120°$ $-\sqrt{3}$

35. $\sin \dfrac{5}{4}\pi$ $-\dfrac{\sqrt{2}}{2}$ 36. $\cos 3\pi$ -1

37. $\sec (-30°)$ $\dfrac{2\sqrt{3}}{3}$ 38. $\cot \dfrac{7}{6}\pi$ $\sqrt{3}$

Find the exact values of $\sin \theta$, $\cos \theta$, and $\tan \theta$ if the terminal side of θ in standard position contains the given point.

39. $P(2, 5)$ 40. $P(15, -8)$

39. $\sin \theta = \dfrac{5\sqrt{29}}{29}$, $\cos \theta = \dfrac{2\sqrt{29}}{29}$, $\tan \theta = \dfrac{5}{2}$ 40. $\sin \theta = -\dfrac{8}{17}$, $\cos \theta = \dfrac{15}{17}$, $\tan \theta = -\dfrac{8}{15}$

- solve triangles by using the law of sines (Lesson 13–4)

Solve the triangle in which $A = 54°$, $C = 72°$, and $a = 20$.

$\dfrac{\sin 54°}{20} = \dfrac{\sin 72°}{c}$

$c = \dfrac{20 \sin 72°}{\sin 54°} \approx 23.5$

$B = 180 - (54 + 72)$ or $54°$

$\dfrac{\sin 54°}{b} = \dfrac{\sin 54°}{20}$

$b = 20$

Solve each triangle described. Round measures of sides to the nearest tenth and measures of angles to the nearest degree.

41. $A = 50°$, $b = 12$, $a = 10$
    $B = 67°$, $C = 63°$, $c = 11.7$
42. $B = 46°$, $C = 83°$, $b = 65$
    $A = 51°$, $a = 70.2$, $c = 89.7$
43. $A = 45°$, $B = 30°$, $b = 20$
    $C = 105°$, $a = 28.3$, $c = 38.6$
44. $A = 105°$, $a = 18$, $b = 14$
    $B = 49°$, $C = 26°$, $c = 8.3$

- examine solutions   (Lesson 13–4)

How many solutions does the triangle described by $A = 37°$, $a = 6$, and $b = 12$ have?

Angle A is less than $90°$.

Find $b \sin A$ and compare with a.

$b \sin A = 12 \sin 37°$

≈ 7.22

$a ? b \sin A$

$6 < 7.22$

Therefore, there is no solution.

Determine whether each triangle described has no solution, one solution, or two solutions. Then solve each triangle.

45. $a = 24$, $b = 36$, $A = 64°$ no solution
46. $a = 17$, $b = 21$, $A = 64°$ no solution
47. $b = 10$, $c = 15$, $C = 66°$ one solution
48. $A = 82°$, $a = 9$, $b = 12$ no solution
47. $B = 38°$, $A = 76°$, $a = 15.9$

Applications and Problem Solving Encourage students to work through the exercises in the Applications and Problem Solving section to strengthen their problem-solving skills.

OBJECTIVES AND EXAMPLES

• solve triangles by using the law of cosines (Lesson 13–5)

Solve the triangle in which $A = 62°$, $c = 12$, and $b = 15$.

$a^2 = b^2 + c^2 - 2bc \cos A$
$a^2 = (15)^2 + (12)^2 - 2(15)(12) \cos 62°$
$a^2 = 200$
$a \approx 14.1$
$\frac{\sin 62°}{14.1} \approx \frac{\sin C}{12}$
$\sin C \approx \frac{12 \sin 62°}{14.1}$ or about $48.7°$
$B \approx 180 - (62 + 48.7)$ or $69.3°$

• define and use the trigonometric functions based on the unit circle (Lesson 13–6)

Find the value of $\cos\left(-\frac{7}{4}\pi\right)$.

$\cos\left(-\frac{7}{4}\pi\right) = \cos\left(-\frac{7}{4}\pi + 2\pi\right)$
$= \cos\left(\frac{1}{4}\pi\right)$
$= \frac{\sqrt{2}}{2}$

• find values of expressions involving inverse trigonometric functions (Lesson 13–7)

Find $\text{Cos}^{-1}\left[\tan\left(-\frac{\pi}{6}\right)\right]$.

$\text{Cos}^{-1}\left[\tan\left(-\frac{\pi}{6}\right)\right] = \text{Cos}^{-1}\left(-\frac{\sqrt{3}}{3}\right)$
$A = \text{Cos}^{-1}\left(-\frac{\sqrt{3}}{3}\right)$
$\cos A = -\frac{\sqrt{3}}{3}$
$A \approx 125.3°$

REVIEW EXERCISES

Solve each triangle described. Round measures of sides to the nearest tenth and measures of angles to the nearest degree.

49. $C = 65°$, $a = 4$, $b = 7$
    $c \approx 6.4$, $A \approx 35°$, $B \approx 80°$
50. $b = 2$, $c = 5$, $A = 60°$
    $a \approx 4.4$, $B \approx 23°$, $C \approx 97°$
51. $a = 6$, $b = 7$, $C = 40°$
    $c \approx 4.5$, $A \approx 59°$, $B \approx 81°$
52. $B = 24°$, $a = 42$, $c = 6.5$
    $b \approx 36.2$, $A \approx 28°$, $C \approx 128°$
53. $a = 11$, $b = 13$, $c = 15$
    $A \approx 45°$, $B \approx 58°$, $C \approx 77°$

Find the exact value of each function.

54. $\sin(-150°)$ $-\frac{1}{2}$
55. $\cos 300°$ $\frac{1}{2}$
56. $(\sin 45°)(\sin 225°)$ $-\frac{1}{2}$
57. $\sin\frac{5}{4}\pi$ $-\frac{\sqrt{2}}{2}$
58. $(\sin 30°)^2 + (\cos 30°)^2$ 1
59. $\frac{4\cos 150° + 2\sin 300°}{3}$ $-\sqrt{3}$

Find each value.

60. $\text{Sin}^{-1}(-1)$ $-90°$
61. $\text{Cos}^{-1}\left(\frac{\sqrt{3}}{2}\right)$ $30°$
62. $\text{Tan}^{-1}\sqrt{3}$ $60°$
63. $\cos(\text{Sin}^{-1} 1)$ 0
64. $\tan\left(\text{Arcsin}\frac{3}{5}\right)$ $\frac{3}{4}$
65. $\cot\left(\text{Tan}^{-1}\frac{8}{15}\right)$ $\frac{15}{8}$

APPLICATIONS AND PROBLEM SOLVING

66. **Aviation** A pilot 3000 feet above the ocean notes the measurement of the angle of depression to a ship is 42°. How far is the plane from the ship? (Lesson 13–1)   **4483.43 ft**

A practice test for Chapter 13 is provided on page 924.

67. **Geography** Town and Rich streets meet to form a triangular region with the river bank as shown. Find the measure of the angle that is formed by the two streets. (Lesson 13–5)
55.75°

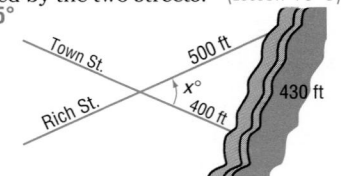

ALTERNATIVE ASSESSMENT

COOPERATIVE LEARNING PROJECT

Starfish Varieties   In this project, you will design your own varieties of starfish. A starfish is a spiny-skinned sea animal that has thick, armlike extensions on its body. Most species have five such "arms" and look somewhat like five-pointed stars. Research starfish to get an idea of the various differences in their size, shape, and color.

Design three different species of starfish of your own. Describe, make a drawing of, give a name to, and color these three species. Include the diameter, angle measure of the end of each extension, radius of each extension, and any other data that would be helpful in visualizing your starfish designs. Your data must be accurate and mathematically sound.

Incorporate these ideas in your project.

- Research starfish.
- Be creative in your designs.
- Write and solve trigonometric relationships involved in the designs.
- Draw a "blueprint" for each design.
- Draw a realistic picture with color for each design.
- Prepare a paragraph describing each design as well as naming it.

THINKING CRITICALLY

- When solving a right triangle, certain information needs to be known. Summarize the combinations of sides and angles of a right triangle that must be known in order to arrive at a solution.

- In which quadrant does $\angle B$ lie, given that $\tan B < 0$ and $\cot B < 0$?   **Since tangent and cotangent have the same sign in every quadrant, the quadrant cannot be determined.**

PORTFOLIO

Of the seven lessons in this chapter, pick the one with which you are still having trouble understanding. Describe this lesson and analyze your learning relative to the material. Answer questions like the following.

- What was the lesson about?
- What made sense to you in this lesson?
- What questions do you still have about this lesson?
- How could the methods used in this lesson be better explained?

Place this in your portfolio.

SELF EVALUATION

Comparing strategies and sharing ideas with other students enhances confidence in your abilities and thinking skills. Verbalizing draws out thoughts and questions from both people, which in turn helps to clarify your thinking.

Assess yourself. Do you test your ideas on other people? Do you allow your thoughts and skills to be processed by someone other than yourself before you determine a final solution? Do you present your ideas to another person in a way that makes you defend your thoughts and allows the situation to be fully explored? Describe a time when you used this process and the results you got.

Assessment and Evaluation Masters, pp. 350, 361

13   NAME_____   DATE_____

Chapter 13 Performance Assessment

Instructions: *Demonstrate your knowledge by giving a clear, concise solution to each problem. Be sure to include all relevant drawings and justify your answers. You may show your solution in more than one way or investigate beyond the requirements of the problem.*

1. Engineers and physicists frequently need to find the x- and y-components of forces.

   a. Find x- and y-components of F_1. Show your work.

   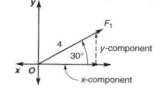

   b. Find x- and y-components of F_2. Show your work.

   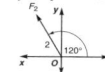

   c. Add the x-components and then the y-components of F_1 and F_2 to find the x- and y-components of $F_3 = F_1 + F_2$.

   d. Find the magnitude of F_3 and the angle formed by F_3 and the positive x-axis.

2. The developer of the Lake Murray subdivision wants to find the distances between the corner stakes of a property. The layout of the property and the known distances and angle measures are shown below.

   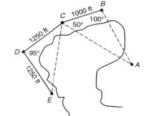

   a. Solve triangle ABC. Tell why you first chose to use the law of sines or cosines. Show your work.

   b. Solve triangle CDE. Tell why you first chose to use the law of sines or cosines. Show your work.

Scoring Guide
Chapter 13
Performance Assessment

Level	Specific Criteria
3 Superior	• Shows thorough understanding of the concepts *solving problems using right triangle trigonometry* and *solving triangles using the laws of sines and cosines.* • Uses appropriate strategies to solve problems. • Computations are correct. • Written explanations are exemplary. • Goes beyond requirements of problem.
2 Satisfactory, with Minor Flaws	• Shows understanding of the concepts *solving problems using right triangle trigonometry* and *solving triangles using the laws of sines and cosines.* • Uses appropriate strategies to solve problems. • Computations are mostly correct. • Written explanations are effective. • Satisfies all requirements of problem.
1 Nearly Satisfactory, with Serious Flaws	• Shows understanding of most of the concepts *solving problems using right triangle trigonometry* and *solving triangles using the laws of sines and cosines.* • May not use appropriate strategies to solve problems. • Computations are mostly correct. • Written explanations are satisfactory. • Satisfies most requirements of problem.
0 Unsatisfactory	• Shows little or no understanding of the concepts *solving problems using right triangle trigonometry* and *solving triangles using the laws of sines and cosines.* • May not use appropriate strategies to solve problems. • Computations are incorrect. • Written explanations are not satisfactory. • Does not satisfy requirements of problem.

 **Alternative Assessment**

The Alternative Assessment section provides students with the opportunity to assess their own work by thinking critically, working with others, keeping a portfolio, and honestly evaluating their own progress. For more information on alternative forms of assessment, see *Alternative Assessment in the Mathematics*

Classroom, one of the titles in the Glencoe Mathematics Professional Series.

 Performance Assessment

Performance Assessment tasks for this chapter are included in the *Assessment and Evaluation Masters.* A scoring guide is also provided.

Using the
COLLEGE ENTRANCE
EXAM PRACTICE

These two pages review the skills and concepts presented in Chapters 1–13. This review is formatted to reflect new trends in college entrance testing.

A more traditional cumulative review is provided in the *Assessment and Evaluation Masters*, pp. 355–356.

Assessment and Evaluation Masters, pp. 355–356

COLLEGE ENTRANCE EXAM PRACTICE

CHAPTERS 1–13

SECTION ONE: MULTIPLE CHOICE

There are eight multiple-choice questions in this section. After working each problem, write the letter of the correct answer on your paper.

1. When Tashia spins the spinner shown below, what is the probability that the result will be a number greater than 3 or an even number? **C**

   A. $\frac{1}{9}$

   B. $\frac{20}{81}$

   C. $\frac{2}{3}$

   D. 1

2. Solve $\sqrt{c + 4} = \sqrt{c + 20} - 2$. **D**

   A. 20

   B. -15

   C. -10

   D. 5

3. Takara insists she needs to go to the mall to buy more clothes. Her mother disagrees. "But I have only 5 shirts, 4 pairs of pants, and 2 pairs of shoes!" Takara's mother still feels she has enough clothes and tells her to list all possible outfits so that she can see for herself. How many different outfits should Takara be able to list? **A**

   A. 40 outfits

   B. 11 outfits

   C. 22 outfits

   D. 60 outfits

4. The Wildcats play 84 games this season. It is now midseason, and they have won 30 games. To win at least 60% of all their games, how many of the remaining games must they win? **A**

   A. 21 games

   B. 50 games

   C. 24 games

   D. 33 games

5. Points X and Y are on opposite sides of a valley. Point C is 60 kilometers from point X. Angle YXC is 108° and angle YCX is 35°. Find the width of the valley. **B**

   A. 63 km

   B. 57.2 km

   C. 37 km

   D. 45.2 km

6. The Worthington Public Library charges a fine of 5¢ per day for overdue books. What will the fine be on a book that is two weeks overdue? **D**

   A. 50¢

   B. 10¢

   C. 60¢

   D. 70¢

7. Michelle and her family took a vacation to Oregon. As Michelle observed Mount Hood from a distance, the sine of the angle at which she looked up was $\frac{40}{41}$. Find the tangent of this angle. **A**

   A. $\frac{40}{9}$

   B. $\frac{41}{9}$

   C. $\frac{9}{41}$

   D. $\frac{9}{40}$

8. Write $\frac{2}{3} + \frac{3}{5} + \frac{4}{7} + \frac{5}{9} + \dots + \frac{21}{41}$ using sigma notation. **B**

   A. $\displaystyle\sum_{n=2}^{20} \frac{n+1}{n+2}$

   B. $\displaystyle\sum_{n=1}^{20} \frac{n+1}{2n+1}$

   C. $\displaystyle\sum_{n=1}^{20} \frac{n+1}{n+2}$

   D. $\displaystyle\sum_{n=2}^{20} \frac{n+1}{2n+1}$

Standardized Test Practice Questions are also provided in the *Assessment and Evaluation Masters*, p. 354.

---

13 NAME_____ DATE_____
Chapter 13 Cumulative Review

1. What property of equality is illustrated by the following? If $39 = 3 \cdot 13$, then $3 \cdot 13 = 39$. (Lesson 1-2) — 1. symmetric property

2. Find the slope, x-intercept, and y-intercept of $8x + 3y = 24$. (Lesson 2-2) — 2. $-\frac{8}{3}$; 3; 8 See students' graphs.

3. Solve the system by graphing. (Lesson 3-4) $y \geq x - 2$, $y \geq -x + 3$ — 3.

4. Find the inverse of $\begin{bmatrix} -5 & 5 \\ 2 & -4 \end{bmatrix}$. (Lesson 4-4) — 4. $-\frac{1}{10}\begin{bmatrix} 4 & 5 \\ 2 & 5 \end{bmatrix}$

5. Use synthetic division to find $(4n^3 + 8n^2 - 9n + 9) \div (n + 3)$. (Lesson 5-3) — 5. $4n^2 - 4n + 3$

6. Simplify $(8 - 2i) - (5 - 4i)$. (Lesson 5-10) — 6. $3 + 2i$

7. Solve $c^2 - 4c + 3 = 0$ by completing the square. (Lesson 6-3) — 7. 3, 1

8. Solve $x^{\frac{2}{3}} - x^{\frac{1}{3}} - 2 = 0$. (Lesson 6-2) — 8. -1, 32

9. Write the equation $h(x) = 3(x + 2)^2 + 4$ in quadratic form. Identify the quadratic term, the linear term, and the constant term. (Lesson 7-2) — 9. $n(x) = 3x^2 + 12x + 16$; $3x^2$; $12x$; 16

10. Solve $x^2 - x \geq 20$. (Lesson 6-7) — 10. $\{x \mid x \leq -4 \text{ or } x \geq 5\}$

11. Write the equation of the parabola with vertex $(-5, -2)$ and focus $(-5, -1)$. (Lesson 7-2) — 11. $y = \frac{1}{4}(x + 5)^2 - 2$

12. State whether the graph of the equation $4(y + 2)^2 - (x - 1)^2 = 16$ is a circle, parabola, ellipse, or hyperbola. (Lesson 7-6) — 12. hyperbola

13. Find $p(3 - x)$ for $p(x) = 2x^2 + x - 2$. (Lesson 8-1) — 13. $2x^2 - 13x + 19$

14. Find all rational zeros of $f(x) = 2x^3 + 7x^2 - 42x - 72$. (Lesson 8-5) — 14. $-\frac{3}{2}$, 4, -6 See students' graphs.

15. Graph $y = \frac{5}{x + 2}$ and show the vertical and horizontal asymptotes. (Lesson 9-1) — 15.

16. A swimming pool can be drained in 12 hours by the use of an old pump. A new pump drains it in 8 hours. If both pumps are used, how long will it take to drain the pool? (Lesson 9-5) — 16. $4\frac{4}{5}$ hours

13 NAME_____ DATE_____
Chapter 13 Cumulative Review (continued)

17. If y varies inversely as x and $x = 6$ when $y = 32$, find y when $x = 15$. (Lesson 9-2) — 17. $\frac{64}{5}$

18. Simplify $\frac{27\sqrt{7}}{3\sqrt{2}}$. (Lesson 10-1) — 18. $3\sqrt[3]{7} - \sqrt{2}$

19. Evaluate $\log_5 125 + \log_5 5 - \log_5 625$. (Lesson 10-3) — 19. 0

20. Solve $x^{\frac{2}{3}} = 4$. (Lesson 10-6) — 20. ± 8

21. Find the sum of the arithmetic series if $a_1 = 10$, $n = 6$, and $d = 5$. (Lesson 11-2) — 21. 135

22. Express $0.\overline{24}$ as the ratio of two whole numbers. (Lesson 11-5) — 22. $\frac{8}{33}$

23. State the number of terms in the expansion of $(r + s)^4$. (Lesson 11-8) — 23. 5

24. Evaluate $C(10, 4)$. (Lesson 12-3) — 24. 210

25. There are 7 pennies, 4 nickels, and 5 dimes in a bag. Three coins are selected. Find the probability of getting 1 dime, 1 nickel, and 1 penny if each coin is replaced after being selected. (Lesson 12-5) — 25. $\frac{35}{1024}$

26. Seven coins are tossed. What is the probability of no heads occurring? (Lesson 12-7) — 26. $\frac{1}{128}$

For questions 27 and 28, refer to the data chart. (Lesson 6-8)

Item	1	2	3	4	5	6	7	8	9
Frequency	4	2	2	3	4	1	2	4	3

27. Find the standard deviation of the set of data. — 27. 2, 7

28. Find the range of the set of frequencies. — 28. 3

29. A set of test scores is normally distributed. The mean score is 75 with a standard deviation of 8. What percentage of the scores are between 75 and 99? (Lesson 6-9) — 29. 49.5%

30. Express $\frac{7\pi}{4}$ radians in degrees. (Lesson 13-1) — 30. 315°

31. Express the value of $\cos^{-1}\frac{\sqrt{2}}{2}$ in radians. (Lesson 13-4) — 31. $\frac{\pi}{4}$

32. For $\triangle ABC$, $a = 9$, $B = 49°$, and $C = 90$. Solve the triangle. (Lesson 13-6) — 32. $A = 41°$; $b = 10.35$; $c = 13.72$

33. In $\triangle ABC$, $a = 16$, $b = 7$, and $c = 12$. Solve the triangle. (Lesson 13-9) — 33. $A = 112° 1'$; $B = 23° 56'$; $C = 44° 3'$

SECTION TWO: SHORT ANSWER

This section contains seven questions for which you will provide short answers. Write your answer on your paper.

9. Calvin keeps his CD's in a carousel on top of his stereo. He has 6 jazz, 4 rock, and 2 classical CD's. How many different ways can he arrange those CD's on the carousel?   **39,916,800**

10. Naren bought 2 slices of pizza, two cartons of milk, and one chocolate chip cookie for lunch. He spent $2.05 on his lunch. Ted brought a sandwich from home and bought a carton of milk and 3 cookies for a total of 75¢. Sarah spent $0.95 on one slice of pizza and a carton of milk. What are the individual prices of a slice of pizza, a carton of milk, and a chocolate chip cookie?   **65¢, 30¢, 15¢**

11. Viho is practicing his free throws. He knows the rim of the basket is 10 feet above the floor. From the spot on the floor where he is standing, the angle of elevation to the rim is 33° 33'. Find the distance from Viho's feet to the rim.   **18.09 ft or 18 ft 1 in.**

12. Find all zeros of the function
$f(x) = 4x^4 - 35x^3 + 78x^2 + 28x - 165$.
$3, -\dfrac{5}{4}, \dfrac{7 \pm \sqrt{5}}{2}$

13. For breakfast, Mrs. Crocker baked a dozen blueberry muffins, six bran muffins, and eight banana-nut muffins and put them on a serving plate on the table. Her daughter, Betty, took two blueberry muffins to school with her. Then Mr. Crocker sat down to breakfast. What is the probability that he will eat a blueberry muffin and a bran muffin? $\dfrac{60}{552}$ or $\dfrac{5}{46}$

14. Find the vertices and foci of the hyperbola whose equation is $25x^2 - 4y^2 = 100$.
$(\pm 2, 0); (\pm\sqrt{29}, 0)$

15. Find the value of each of the trigonometric functions for angle A shown below.
See margin.

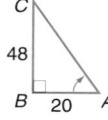

SECTION THREE: COMPARISON

This section contains five comparison problems which involve comparing two quantities, one in column A and one in column B. In certain questions, information related to one or both quantities is centered above them. All variables used represent real numbers.

Compare quantities A and B below.

- Write A if quantity A is greater.
- Write B if quantity B is greater.
- Write C if the two quantities are equal.
- Write D if there is not enough information to determine the relationship.

16. A   **17.** B   **18.** A   **19.** C   **20.** D

Column A	Column B
$-2x + 7y = -21$	

16. the y-intercept of the line parallel to the given line and containing $(-3, 4)$ | the y-intercept of the line perpendicular to the given line and containing $(-2, 9)$

the value of the missing side

17.
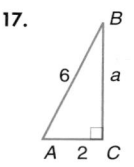
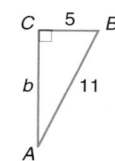

$\log_2 3 = 1.585; \log_2 7 = 2.807$

18. $\log_2 0.75$ | $\log_2 \dfrac{36}{49}$

19. the probability that a hockey team will win if the odds of winning are 8:3 | the odds of hitting a target if the probability of missing it is $\dfrac{11}{19}$

20. $\dfrac{a+3b}{7} = 3$
$11a - b = -7$ | $r + 11 = 8t$
$8(r - t) = 3$

Using Trigonometric Graphs and Identities

PREVIEWING THE CHAPTER

Students begin by drawing graphs of trigonometric functions. The use of graphing calculators is integrated to help students graph these functions. Students investigate the unit circle and apply this knowledge to derive the basic trigonometric identities. Then they use these identities to simplify and evaluate expressions. Next, students verify trigonometric identities using the sum and difference formulas and the half- and double-angle formulas. The chapter concludes with a lesson on solving trigonometric equations.

Lesson (Pages)	Lesson Objectives	NCTM Standards	State/Local Objectives
14-1A (824–825)	Use a graphing calculator to graph trigonometric functions.	1–4, 6, 8–9	
14-1 (826–834)	Graph trigonometric functions. Find the amplitude and period for variations of the sine and cosine functions.	1–6, 8–9	
14-2 (835–840)	Use trigonometric identities to simplify or evaluate expressions.	1–6, 8–9	
14-3A (841)	Use a graphing calculator to verify trigonometric identities.	1–6, 8–9	
14-3 (842–846)	Verify trigonometric identities. Solve problems by working backward.	1–6, 9	
14-4 (847–852)	Find values of sine and cosine involving sum and difference formulas. Verify identities by using the sum and difference formulas.	1–6, 9	
14-5 (853–859)	Find values of sine and cosine involving double and half angles. Verify identities by using double- and half-angle formulas.	1–6, 9	
14-6A (860)	Use a graphing calculator to solve trigonometric equations.	1–6, 8–9	
14-6 (861–867)	Solve trigonometric equations.	1–6, 9	2.a.

A complete, 1-page lesson plan is provided for each lesson in the *Lesson Planning Guide*. Answer keys for each lesson are available in the *Answer Key Masters*.

ORGANIZING THE CHAPTER

You may want to refer to the **Course Planning Calendar** on page T12 for detailed information on pacing.
PACING: Honors—11 days; **Block**—6 days

LESSON PLANNING CHART

Lesson (Pages)	Materials/ Manipulatives	Extra Practice (Student Edition)	Study Guide	Practice	Enrichment	Assessment and Evaluation	Modeling Mathematics	Multicultural Activity	Tech Prep Applications	Graphing Calculator	Science and Math Lab Manual	Real-World Applications	Interactive Mathematics Tools Software	Teaching Transparencies
14-1A (824–825)	graphing calculator									pp. 57, 58				
14-1 (826–834)	wave simulator or picture of waves graphing calculator	p. 908	p. 99	p. 99	p. 99			p. 27	p. 27	p. 14		35	14-1.1 14-1.2	14-1A 14-1B
14-2 (835–840)		p. 909	p.100	p. 100	p.100	p. 380		p. 28						14-2A 14-2B
14-3A (841)	graphing calculator									pp. 59, 60				
14-3 (842–846)		p. 909	p. 101	p. 101	p. 101	pp. 379, 380								14-3A 14-3B
14-4 (847–852)		p. 909	p.102	p. 102	p. 102									14-4A 14-4B
14-5 (853–859)		p. 910	p. 103	p. 103	p. 103	p. 381								14-5A 14-5B
14-6A (860)	graphing calculator									pp. 61, 62				
14-6 (861–867)	graphing calculator	p. 910	p.104	p. 104	p. 104	p. 381	p. 74		p. 28		pp. 117–120	36		14-6A 14-6B
Study Guide/ Assessment (869–873)						pp. 365–378, 382–384								

ORGANIZING THE CHAPTER

OTHER CHAPTER RESOURCES

Student Edition
Chapter Opener, pp. 822–823
Mathematics and Society, p. 867
Working on the Investigation,
   pp. 834, 859
Closing the Investigation, p. 868

Teacher's Classroom Resources
Investigations and Projects Masters,
   pp. 73–76

Technology
Teacher's Guide for Software
   Resources
Test and Review Software (IBM
   and Macintosh)
CD-ROM Interactions (Windows
   and Macintosh)

Professional Publications
Block Scheduling Booklet
Glencoe Mathematics Professional
   Series

OUTSIDE RESOURCES

Books/Periodicals
Moody, M., "Trig Skits," *The Mathematics Teacher,*
   December 1994
Ren, G., "Match Geometric Figures with
   Trigonometric Identities," *The Mathematics
   Teacher,* January 1995

Software
Graphing Equations, Sunburst
Mathgrapher, Queue

Videos/CD-ROMs
*Connecting the Past with the Future: Women in
   Mathematics and Science,* Dale Seymour
   Publications

See the *Teacher's Guide for Software Resources* for software addresses.

ASSESSMENT RESOURCES

Student Edition
Math Journal, pp. 832, 864
Mixed Review, pp. 834, 840,
   846, 852, 859, 867
Self Test, p. 846
Chapter Highlights, p. 869
Chapter Study Guide and
   Assessment, pp. 870–872
Alternative Assessment, p. 873
Portfolio, p. 873

Teacher's Wraparound Edition
5-Minute Check, pp. 826, 835,
   842, 847, 853, 861
Check for Understanding, pp. 831,
   839, 845, 850, 857, 864
Closing Activity, pp. 834, 840,
   846, 852, 859, 867
Cooperative Learning, pp. 848,
   854

Assessment and Evaluation Masters
Multiple-Choice Tests, Forms 1A
   (Honors), 1B (Average), 1C
   (Basic), pp. 365–370
Free-Response Tests, Forms 2A
   (Honors), 2B (Average), 2C
   (Basic), pp. 371–376
Calculator-Based Test, p. 377
Performance Assessment, p. 378
Mid-Chapter Test, p. 379
Quizzes A–D, pp. 380–381
Standardized Test Practice, p. 382
Cumulative Review, pp. 382–384

ENHANCING THE CHAPTER

Examples of some of the materials for enhancing Chapter 14 are shown below.

DIVERSITY

Multicultural Activity Masters, pp. 27, 28

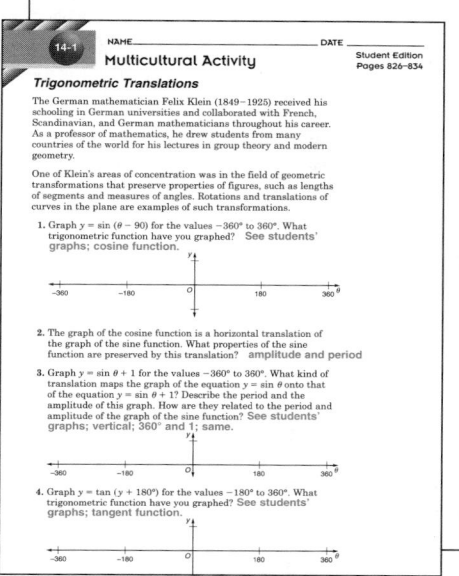

Trigonometric Translations

The German mathematician Felix Klein (1849–1925) received his schooling in German universities and collaborated with French, Scandinavian, and German mathematicians throughout his career. As a professor of mathematics, he drew students from many countries of the world for his lectures in group theory and modern geometry.

One of Klein's areas of concentration was in the field of geometric transformations that preserve properties of figures, such as lengths of segments and measures of angles. Rotations and translations of curves in the plane are examples of such transformations.

1. Graph $y = \sin(\theta - 90)$ for the values $-360°$ to $360°$. What trigonometric function have you graphed? See students' graphs; cosine function.

2. The graph of the cosine function is a horizontal translation of the graph of the sine function. What properties of the sine function are preserved by this translation? amplitude and period

3. What kind of translation maps the graph of the equation $y = \sin \theta$ onto that of the equation $y = \sin \theta + 1$? Describe the period and the amplitude of this graph. How are they related to the period and amplitude of the graph of the sine function? See students' graphs; vertical; 360° and 1; same.

4. Graph $y = \tan(y + 180°)$ for the values $-180°$ to 360°. What trigonometric function have you graphed? See students' graphs; tangent function.

APPLICATIONS

Real-World Applications, 35, 36

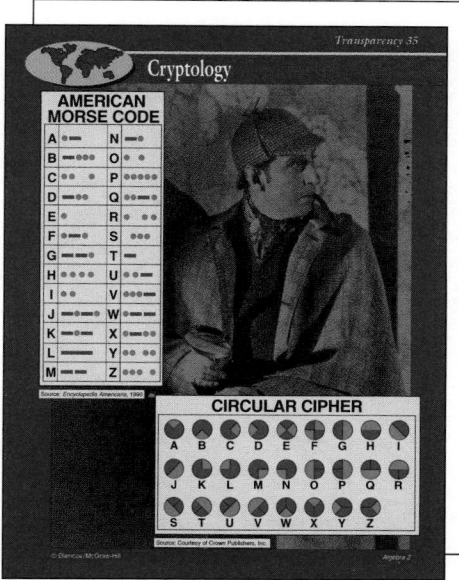

TECHNOLOGY

Graphing Calculator Masters, p. 14

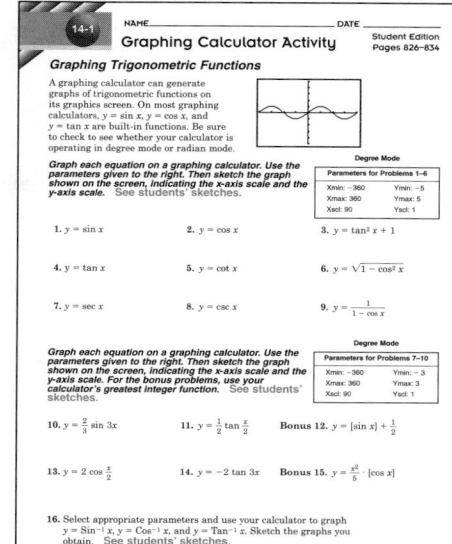

Graphing Trigonometric Functions

A graphing calculator can generate graphs of trigonometric functions on its graphics screen. On most graphing calculators, $y = \sin x$, $y = \cos x$, and $y = \tan x$ are built-in functions. Be sure to check to see whether your calculator is operating in degree mode or radian mode.

Graph each equation on a graphing calculator. Use the parameters given to the right. Then sketch the graph shown on the screen, indicating the x-axis scale and the y-axis scale. See students' sketches.

Degree Mode	
Parameters for Problems 1–6	
Xmin: −360	Ymin: −5
Xmax: 360	Ymax: 5
Xscl: 90	Yscl: 1

1. $y = \sin x$ 2. $y = \cos x$ 3. $y = \tan^2 x + 1$

4. $y = \tan x$ 5. $y = \cot x$ 6. $y = \sqrt{1 - \cos^2 x}$

7. $y = \sec x$ 8. $y = \csc x$ 9. $y = \dfrac{1}{1 - \cos x}$

Graph each equation on a graphing calculator. Use the parameters given to the right. Then sketch the graph shown on the screen, indicating the x-axis scale and the y-axis scale. For the bonus problems, use your calculator's greatest integer function. See students' sketches.

Degree Mode	
Parameters for Problems 7–10	
Xmin: −360	Ymin: −3
Xmax: 360	Ymax: 3
Xscl: 90	Yscl: 1

10. $y = \frac{2}{3} \sin 3x$ 11. $y = \frac{1}{2} \tan \frac{x}{2}$ Bonus 12. $y = [\sin x] + \frac{1}{2}$

13. $y = 2 \cos \frac{x}{2}$ 14. $y = -2 \tan 3x$ Bonus 15. $y = \frac{x^2}{5} - [\cos x]$

16. Select appropriate parameters and use your calculator to graph $y = \operatorname{Sin}^{-1} x$, $y = \operatorname{Cos}^{-1} x$, and $y = \operatorname{Tan}^{-1} x$. Sketch the graphs you obtain. See students' sketches.

TECH PREP

Tech Prep Applications Masters, pp. 27, 28

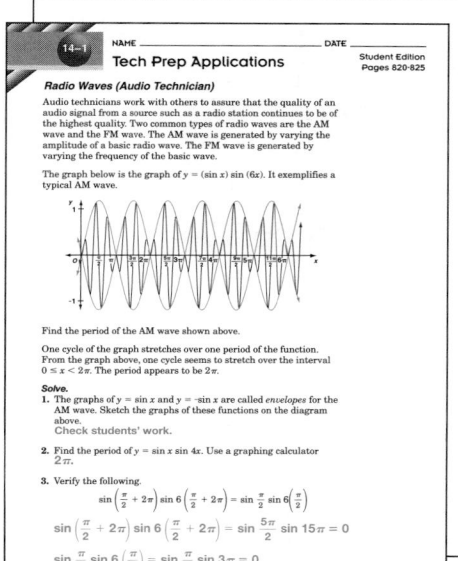

Radio Waves (Audio Technician)

Audio technicians work with others to assure that the quality of an audio signal from a source such as a radio station continues to be of the highest quality. Two common types of radio waves are the AM wave and the FM wave. The AM wave is generated by varying the amplitude of a basic radio wave. The FM wave is generated by varying the frequency of the basic wave.

The graph below is the graph of $y = (\sin x) \sin (6x)$. It exemplifies a typical AM wave.

Find the period of the AM wave shown above.

One cycle of the graph stretches over one period of the function. From the graph above, one cycle seems to stretch over the interval $0 \le x < 2\pi$. The period appears to be 2π.

Solve.

1. The graphs of $y = \sin x$ and $y = -\sin x$ are called *envelopes* for the AM wave. Sketch the graphs of these functions on the diagram above. Check students' work.

2. Find the period of $y = \sin x \sin 4x$. Use a graphing calculator. 2π.

3. Verify the following.

$$\sin\left(\frac{\pi}{2} + 2\pi\right) \sin 6\left(\frac{\pi}{2} + 2\pi\right) = \sin \frac{\pi}{2} \sin 6\left(\frac{\pi}{2}\right)$$

$$\sin\left(\frac{\pi}{2} + 2\pi\right) \sin 6\left(\frac{\pi}{2} + 2\pi\right) = \sin \frac{5\pi}{2} \sin 15\pi = 0$$

$$\sin \frac{\pi}{2} \sin 6\left(\frac{\pi}{2}\right) = \sin \frac{\pi}{2} \sin 3\pi = 0$$

CONNECTIONS

Science and Math Lab Manual, pp. 117–120

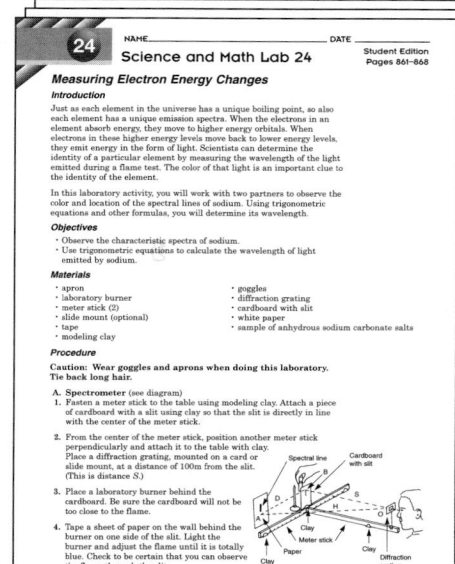

Measuring Electron Energy Changes

Introduction

Just as each element in the universe has a unique boiling point, so also each element has a unique emission spectra. When the electrons in an element absorb energy, they move to higher energy orbitals. When electrons in these higher energy levels move back to lower energy levels, they emit energy in the form of light. Scientists can determine the identity of a particular element by measuring the wavelength of the light emitted during a flame test. The color of that light is an important clue to the identity of the element.

In this laboratory activity, you will work with two partners to observe the color and location of the spectral lines of sodium. Using trigonometric equations and other formulas, you will determine its wavelength.

Objectives

· Observe the characteristic spectra of sodium.
· Use trigonometric equations to calculate the wavelength of light emitted by sodium.

Materials

· apron
· laboratory burner
· meter stick (2)
· slide mount (optional)
· tape
· modeling clay
· goggles
· diffraction grating
· cardboard with slit
· white paper
· sample of anhydrous sodium carbonate salts

Procedure

Caution: Wear goggles and aprons when doing this laboratory. Tie back long hair.

A. Spectrometer (see diagram)

1. Fasten a meter stick to the table using modeling clay. Attach a piece of cardboard with a slit using clay so that the slit is directly in line with the center of the meter stick.

2. From the center of the meter stick, position another meter stick perpendicularly and attach it to the table with clay. Place a diffraction grating, mounted on a card or slide mount, at a distance of 100m from the slit. (This is distance S.)

3. Place a laboratory burner behind the cardboard. Be sure the cardboard will not be too close to the flame.

4. Tape a sheet of paper on the wall behind the burner on one side of the slit. Light the burner and adjust the flame until it is totally blue. Check to be certain that you can observe the flame through the slit.

PROBLEM SOLVING

Problem of the Week Cards, 35, 36

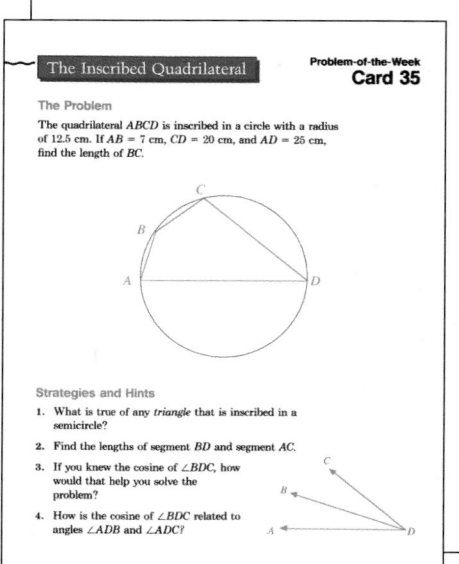

The Inscribed Quadrilateral

Problem-of-the-Week Card 35

The Problem

The quadrilateral $ABCD$ is inscribed in a circle with a radius of 12.5 cm. If $AB = 7$ cm, $CD = 20$ cm, and $AD = 25$ cm, find the length of BC.

Strategies and Hints

1. What is true of any *triangle* that is inscribed in a semicircle?

2. Find the lengths of segment BD and segment AC.

3. If you knew the cosine of $\angle BDC$, how would that help you solve the problem?

4. How is the cosine of $\angle BDC$ related to angles $\angle ADB$ and $\angle ADC$?

MAKING MATHEMATICS RELEVANT

This two-page introduction to the chapter provides students with an opportunity to explore contemporary topics and their applications to mathematics.

Background Information

Hearing Aids The first electrical hearing aid was invented by Millan Hutchinson in 1902. While we usually think of transistors being used in portable radios and similar equipment, the first commercial use of transistors was in the hearing aid, in 1952. Since 1952, hearing aids have become smaller and more effective.

CHAPTER

14

Using Trigonometric Graphs and Identities

Objectives

In this chapter, you will:

* graph trigonometric functions,
* use trigonometric identities,
* solve problems by working backward, and
* solve trigonometric equations.

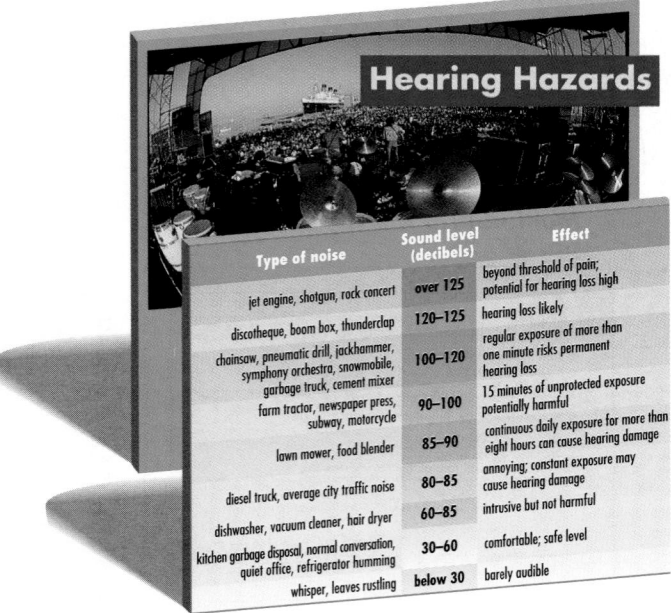

Hearing Hazards

Type of noise	Sound level (decibels)	Effect
jet engine, shotgun, rock concert	over 125	beyond threshold of pain; potential for hearing loss high
discotheque, boom box, thunderclap	120–125	hearing loss likely
chainsaw, pneumatic drill, jackhammer, symphony orchestra, snowmobile, garbage truck, cement mixer	100–120	regular exposure of more than one minute risks permanent hearing loss
farm tractor, newspaper press, subway, motorcycle	90–100	15 minutes of unprotected exposure potentially harmful
lawn mower, food blender	85–90	continuous daily exposure for more than eight hours can cause hearing damage
diesel truck, average city traffic noise	80–85	annoying; constant exposure may cause hearing damage
dishwasher, vacuum cleaner, hair dryer	60–85	intrusive but not harmful
kitchen garbage disposal, normal conversation, quiet office, refrigerator humming	30–60	comfortable; safe level
whisper, leaves rustling	below 30	barely audible

Source: National Institute on Deafness and Other Communication Disorders, National Institutes of Health, January 1990

Warning! Rock concerts may be hazardous to your hearing! There are many causes of deafness and people are affected in varying degrees. More than 24 million people in the United States suffer from some form of deafness, and nearly 2 million of them are profoundly deaf. The gap between hearing and hearing-impaired people has slowly narrowed. In 1988, students at Washington's Gallaudet College led a protest that pressured the institution into hiring its first deaf president.

TIME *Line*

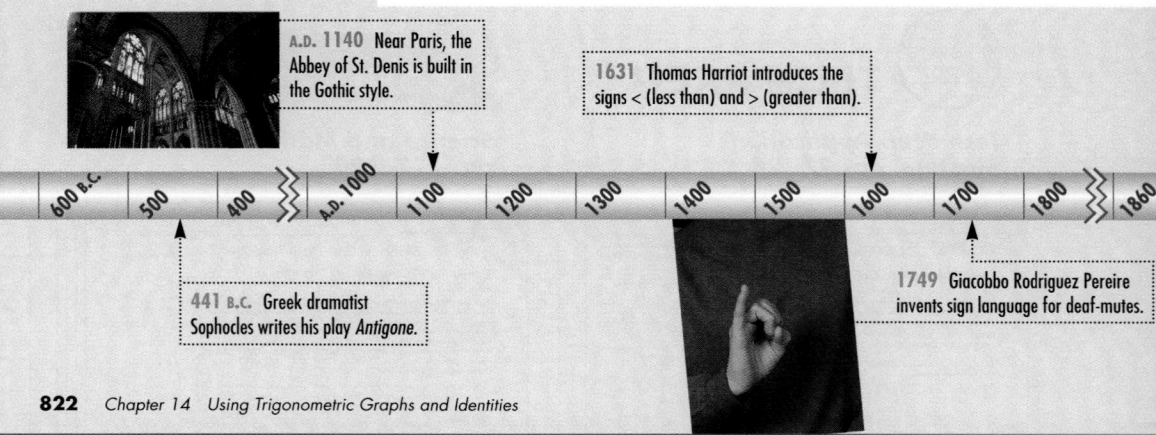

A.D. 1140 Near Paris, the Abbey of St. Denis is built in the Gothic style.

1631 Thomas Harriot introduces the signs < (less than) and > (greater than).

600 B.C. | 500 | 400 | A.D. 1000 | 1100 | 1200 | 1300 | 1400 | 1500 | 1600 | 1700 | 1800 | 1860

441 B.C. Greek dramatist Sophocles writes his play *Antigone*.

1749 Giacobbo Rodriguez Pereire invents sign language for deaf-mutes.

TIME *Line*

Students often assume that mathematics has always been written in symbols. Remind them that in Ancient Greece, mathematics was written in natural language and only slowly were symbols developed. Students might want to do a class presentation about the history of mathematical symbols.

*inter*NET
CONNECTION

This collection of resources about deaf culture, American Sign Language, and schools for the deaf is worth checking out.

World Wide Web
http://darwin.clas.virgina.edu/
~tms4s/deaf.html

Chapter Project

Write a report that includes a list of hearing-impaired people who have made important contributions in areas such as science, medicine, politics, and the arts. List their contributions and describe how they communicate with hearing people. Include a discussion of the relationship between the vibration made by sound waves and the graphs of trigonometric functions.

At 21, **Heather Whitestone** became the first disabled person to win the Miss America Pageant in 1995. For the talent portion of the contest, Heather danced to music she "heard" by feeling its vibrations. Although she has been almost completely deaf since she was 18 months old, having no hearing in one ear and only 5 percent in the other, she learned to talk. She also learned to read lips and took her own notes while attending Berry High School in Alabama. Heather overcame her obstacles and graduated from high school with a 3.6 GPA.

As Miss America, Heather became an inspiration to many. "When children see me speaking and see me dance," she said, "they will realize they have no excuse for not making their own dreams come true."

Heather tells her own story in her book, *Yes, You Can, Heather!: The Story of Heather Whitestone, Miss America*, written by Daphne Gray. Available in most libraries and bookstores, it makes for fascinating reading.

Chapter Project

Cooperative Learning Organize students into small groups based on common interests. Have the science group research contributions to science by hearing-impaired scientists. Do the same for the arts group, entertainment group, and so on. Finally, set up a math group to investigate the relationship between sound waves and trigonometric functions. Each group can do a class presentation with visual aids.

Investigations and Projects Masters, p. 77

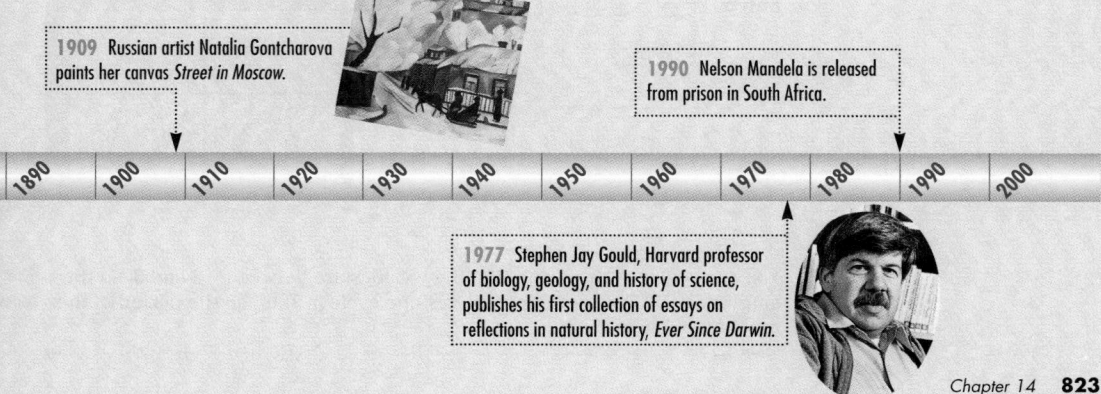

1909 Russian artist Natalia Gontcharova paints her canvas *Street in Moscow.*

1990 Nelson Mandela is released from prison in South Africa.

1890 1900 1910 1920 1930 1940 1950 1960 1970 1980 1990 2000

1977 Stephen Jay Gould, Harvard professor of biology, geology, and history of science, publishes his first collection of essays on reflections in natural history, *Ever Since Darwin.*

Chapter 14 **823**

Alternative Chapter Projects ▬

Two other chapter projects are included in the *Investigations and Projects Masters*. In Chapter 14 Project A, pp. 73–74, students extend the topic in the chapter opener. In Chapter 14 Project B, pp. 75–76, students research how mathematics is used in geology and geophysics.

---

14 | Chapter 14 Project A
NAME_____ DATE_____
Student Ed
Pages 824–

Now Hear This

1. For this project, you will work with a partner to learn about the science of hearing. Use reference books to find out how sound waves travel to the inner ear and then to the brain. As you do your research, also find answers to the following questions.

   • How are sound waves produced?

   • How are certain characteristics of sound, such as frequency and intensity, related to the graphs of trigonometric functions?

   • What is meant by the terms *hertz* and *decibel*?

   • Are there limits to the sounds that human beings can hear? If so, what are they?

2. Interview a doctor who specializes in hearing disorders to find out how loud sounds damage human hearing. What other factors can lead to loss of hearing? What recommendations does he or she have for protecting hearing and keeping the ears healthy?

3. Decide how you and your partner want to present the information you have gathered. For example, you might decide to create a multimedia encyclopedia article about hearing or a documentary for television or radio. Be sure to use charts, diagrams, graphs, and demonstrations to enhance your presentation.

4. Share your work with the rest of the class.

14–1A Graphing Technology
Trigonometric Functions

A Preview of Lesson 14–1

Objective
Use a graphing calculator to graph trigonometric functions.

Recommended Time
25 minutes

Instructional Resources
Graphing Calculator Masters, pp. 57 and 58

These masters provide keystroking instruction for this lesson for the TI-81 and Casio graphing calculators.

1 FOCUS

Motivating the Lesson
Have students graph $y = \sin x$ on their graphing calculators. Explain the definition of *period* to them. Ask them what they think would happen to the graph if they multiplied the function by 2 or if they multiplied it by $\frac{1}{2}$. Make a chart showing what your students think will happen to the graph.

2 TEACH

Teaching Tip Trigonometric functions are periodic functions because they repeat.

Graphing calculators can graph trigonometric functions in both degrees and radians. To select the appropriate angle measure, check the MODE menu of the calculator. In this lesson, only degrees will be used. Press $\boxed{\text{MODE}}$ and make sure that Degree is selected.

Example Graph $y = \sin x$ in the trigonometric window. Find the period and the amplitude.

In the trigonometric window, found by pressing $\boxed{\text{ZOOM}}$ 7, each tick mark on the x-axis represents 90°. Each tick mark on the y-axis represents one unit.

Enter: $\boxed{\text{Y=}}$ $\boxed{\text{SIN}}$ $\boxed{\text{X,T,}\theta}$
$\boxed{\text{ZOOM}}$ 7

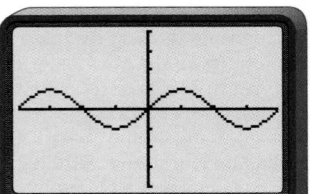

Notice that the y values of the graph are between -1 and 1. The **amplitude** of a periodic function is half the absolute value of the difference between the maximum and minimum values. So, the amplitude of this graph is $\frac{1}{2}|1 - (-1)|$ or 1. The graph completes one cycle in 360°, so the *period* of the function is 360°.

Graph the function using the *radian* setting. Compare and contrast the two graphs.

Example Graph $y = 3 \cos 2x$ in the trigonometric window. Find the period and amplitude.

Enter: $\boxed{\text{Y=}}$ 3 $\boxed{\text{COS}}$ 2 $\boxed{\text{X,T,}\theta}$
$\boxed{\text{ZOOM}}$ 7

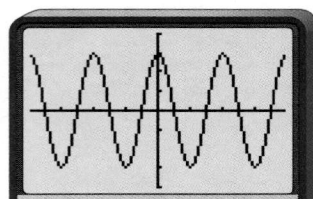

You can see from the graph that the y values are between -3 and 3, so the amplitude is 3. The graph completes one cycle in 180°, so the period of the function is 180°.

Example Graph $y = \cos x$ and $y = \cos (x + 90°)$ in the trigonometric window. Describe any similarities or differences between the two graphs.

Enter:

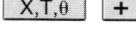

90 ⌐⌐ [ZOOM] 7

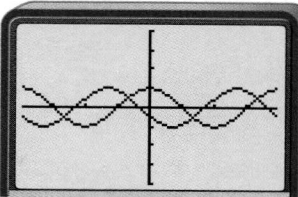

The graph of $y = \cos (x + 90°)$ has the same shape as the graph of $y = \cos x$ except that it is shifted 90° to the left. This is called a **phase shift** of 90°.

You can graph all six trigonometric functions with a graphing calculator. The graphs of $y = \csc x$ and $y = \cot x$ are all defined in terms of $\sin x$, $\cos x$, and $\tan x$. Example 4 illustrates how to obtain these graphs.

Example Graph $y = \sec x$ in the trigonometric window.

The vertical asymptotes may appear on the viewing screen, as shown at the right.

Recall that $\sec x = \dfrac{1}{\cos x}$.

Enter: [Y=] 1 [÷] [COS] [X,T,θ]

[ZOOM] 7

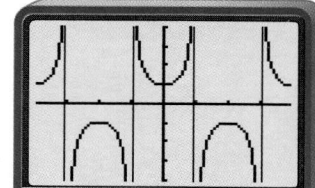

The graph has no amplitude. It takes 360° to complete one cycle. Therefore, the period is 360°. If you trace the graph, you will see that the function is undefined for $x = 90° + k \cdot 180°$, where k is any integer. *Why?*

EXERCISES

1–14. See Solutions Manual.

Graph each equation with a graphing calculator so that a complete graph is shown. Then sketch each graph on a sheet of paper.

1. $y = \tan x$

2. $y = \cos x$

3. $y = \cos (-x)$

4. $y = \csc x$

5. $y = \cot x$

6. $y = \tan (x - 180°)$

7. $y = \tan 5x$

8. $y = 3 \sec (-x)$

9. $y = 12 \sin (x + 45°)$

10. $y = \frac{1}{2} \csc (2x + 90°)$

11. $y = 3 \tan (90° - x)$

12. $y = 0.1 \sec (360° + 2x)$

13. $y = 0.5 \cot (x + 45°)$

14. $y = 3 \cos \frac{2}{3} x$

Lesson 14–1A Graphing Technology: Trigonometric Functions **825**

Using Technology

This lesson offers an excellent opportunity for using technology in your algebra classroom. For more information on using technology, see *Graphing Calculators in the Mathematics Classroom*, one of the titles in the Glencoe Mathematics Professional Series.

Teaching Tip If students are having difficulty with the meaning of the terminology in this section, graph the base function along with a function that alters it. This way they can see how the graph changed.

Teaching Tip Graph the functions $y = \cos x$ and $y = \sec x$ in the same viewing window of $[-360, 360]$ by $[-5, 5]$. Have students compare the two graphs. For example, they have the same period, they intersect whenever $y = 1$, and so on. Also have them notice that when y is zero for the $\cos x$, there is no value for $\sec x$. Ask them why. The denominator of $\sec x = \dfrac{1}{\cos x}$ would be zero and the function is undefined there. Also compare $\sin x$ with $\csc x$ and $\tan x$ with $\cot x$.

3 PRACTICE/APPLY

Assignment Guide

Core: 1–14
Enriched: 1–14

4 ASSESS

Observing students working with technology is an excellent method of assessment.

NCTM Standards: 1–6, 8–9

Instructional Resources

- Study Guide Master 14-1
- Practice Master 14-1
- Enrichment Master 14-1
- Graphing Calculator Masters, p. 14
- Multicultural Activity Masters, p. 27
- Real-World Applications, 35
- Tech Prep Applications Masters, p. 27

 Transparency 14-1A contains the 5-Minute Check for this lesson; **Transparency 14-1B** contains a teaching aid for this lesson.

Recommended Pacing	
Honors Pacing	Day 2 of 11
Block Scheduling*	Day 1 of 6

 *For more information on pacing and possible lesson plans, refer to the *Block Scheduling Booklet.*

1 FOCUS

 5-Minute Check
(over Chapter 13)

1. Find sin 570°. $-\frac{1}{2}$
2. Find the value of (sin 45°)(sin 225°). $-\frac{1}{2}$
3. Find tan(−120°). $\sqrt{3}$
4. Find $\sin^{-1}\left(\tan \frac{\pi}{4}\right)$. **90°**
5. Use a calculator to find x if tan x = 0.4286. **23°**

Motivating the Lesson

Hands-On Activity Show students a wave simulator or a picture of ocean waves. Ask students what the waves have in common. Use student responses to develop informal definitions of *period* and *amplitude.*

What YOU'LL LEARN

- To graph trigonometric functions, and
- to find the amplitude and period for variations of the sine and cosine functions.

Why IT'S IMPORTANT

You can graph trigonometric functions to solve problems involving zoology and music.

LOOK BACK

You can refer to Lesson 13-6 for information about periodic functions.

14-1

Graphing Trigonometric Functions

APPLICATION

Amusement Parks

The world's first Ferris wheel was built for the World's Columbian Exhibition in Chicago in 1892. The wheel was 250 feet in diameter and had 36 cars that could carry 40 passengers each. Suppose you are seated in a Ferris wheel with a diameter of 50 feet. While the wheel rotates, your vertical position varies between 0 and 25 feet above and below an imaginary horizontal plane that contains a horizontal line through the center of the wheel.

The diagram below illustrates your vertical position as a function of time for a Ferris wheel that makes 1 rotation every 30 seconds.

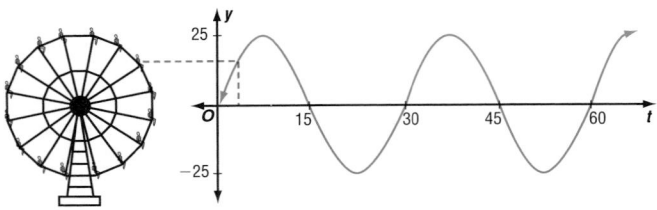

In each rotation, the wheel repeats the pattern that you see in the diagram. Recall that functions which have a graph that repeats a basic pattern are called *periodic functions.*

To find the period, start from any point on the graph and proceed to the right until the pattern begins to repeat. The simplest approach is to begin at the origin. Notice that at 30 the graph begins to repeat. Thus, the period of the function is 30 seconds.

To graph $y = \sin \theta$ or $y = \cos \theta$, use values of θ expressed either in degrees or radians. Ordered pairs for points on these graphs are of the form (θ, sin θ) and (θ°, cos θ).

θ	0°	30°	45°	60°	90°	120°	135°	150°	180°	210°	225°	240°	270°	300°	315°	330°	360°
sin θ	0	$\frac{1}{2}$	$\frac{\sqrt{2}}{2}$	$\frac{\sqrt{3}}{2}$	1	$\frac{\sqrt{3}}{2}$	$\frac{\sqrt{2}}{2}$	$\frac{1}{2}$	0	$-\frac{1}{2}$	$-\frac{\sqrt{2}}{2}$	$-\frac{\sqrt{3}}{2}$	−1	$-\frac{\sqrt{3}}{2}$	$-\frac{\sqrt{2}}{2}$	$-\frac{1}{2}$	0
nearest tenth	0	0.5	0.7	0.9	1	0.9	0.7	0.5	0	−0.5	−0.7	−0.9	−1	−0.9	−0.7	−0.5	0
cos θ	1	$\frac{\sqrt{3}}{2}$	$\frac{\sqrt{2}}{2}$	$\frac{1}{2}$	0	$-\frac{1}{2}$	$-\frac{\sqrt{2}}{2}$	$-\frac{\sqrt{3}}{2}$	−1	$-\frac{\sqrt{3}}{2}$	$-\frac{\sqrt{2}}{2}$	$-\frac{1}{2}$	0	$\frac{1}{2}$	$\frac{\sqrt{2}}{2}$	$\frac{\sqrt{3}}{2}$	1
nearest tenth	1	0.9	0.7	0.5	0	−0.5	−0.7	−0.9	−1	−0.9	−0.7	−0.5	0	0.5	0.7	0.9	1

GLENCOE Technology

 CD-ROM Interaction

A multimedia simulation links trigonometric functions with musical notes and sound waves. A blackline master activity with teacher's notes provides a follow-up to the CD-ROM simulation.

For Windows & Macintosh

F Y I

The largest Ferris wheel in the world, called the Cosmoclock 21 is in Yokohama, Japan. It is 344.5 feet high, 328 feet in diameter, and has 60 eight-seat gondolas.

After plotting several points, complete the graphs of $y = \sin \theta$ and $y = \cos \theta$ by connecting the points with a smooth, continuous curve.

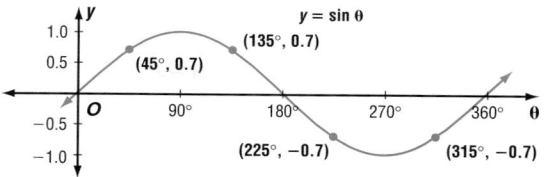

Negative values of θ would be represented to the left of zero.

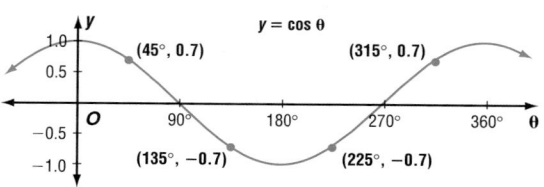

As you recall from your studies of the sine and cosine functions in Chapter 13, each of these functions has a *period* of 360° or 2π radians. That is, the graph of each function repeats itself every 360° or 2π radians. The following example illustrates a sine function that has a period of less than 360°.

Example ❶ **Graph $y = \sin 2\theta$. State the period.**

First, complete a table of values.

θ	0°	15°	30°	45°	60°	75°	90°	105°	120°	135°	150°	165°	180°
2θ	0°	30°	60°	90°	120°	150°	180°	210°	240°	270°	300°	330°	360°
$\sin 2\theta$	0	$\frac{1}{2}$	$\frac{\sqrt{3}}{2}$	1	$\frac{\sqrt{3}}{2}$	$\frac{1}{2}$	0	$-\frac{1}{2}$	$-\frac{\sqrt{3}}{2}$	-1	$-\frac{\sqrt{3}}{2}$	$-\frac{1}{2}$	0

Then plot the points for ordered pairs of the form (θ, y), and connect to form a curve.

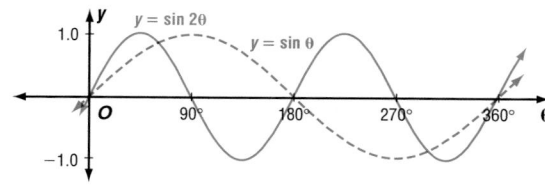

The graph of $y = \sin 2\theta$ repeats every 180° or π radians. Therefore, the period of $y = \sin 2\theta$ is 180° or π radians. *Notice that the period is $\frac{360°}{2}$ or $\frac{2\pi}{2}$.*

Lesson 14–1 Graphing Trigonometric Functions **827**

Teaching Tip For Example 1, remind students of common radian measure equivalents, $90° = \frac{\pi}{2}$, $180° = \pi$, and so on.

In-Class Example

For Example 1
Graph $y = \sin 3\theta$.
State the period.

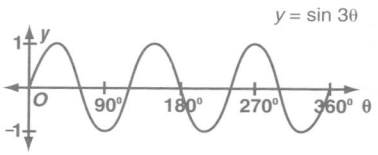

period = 135° or $\frac{3\pi}{2}$ radians

F Y I

What is the distance between each gondola? **17 feet**

Alternative Learning Styles

Visual There are many applications of graphs of trigonometric functions. For example, some animal populations vary periodically. Assume that 2.7 years after the start of a study, a fox population is at a minimum of 200 foxes and 2.4 years later reaches a maximum of 700 foxes. Have students sketch the graph and predict the population 7 years after the study started. **about 250 foxes**

Chapter 14 **827**

EXPLORATION

In this activity, students use graphing calculators to visualize the effect of changing b in the general function $y = \sin b\theta$.

In-Class Example

For Example 2

Graph $y = \frac{1}{3} \sin \theta$. State the amplitude.

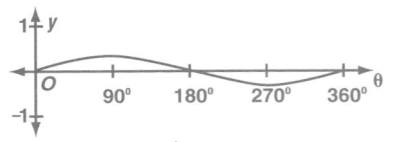

amplitude $= \frac{1}{3}$

The trigonometric function in Example 1 has a maximum value of 1 and a minimum value of -1. The **amplitude** of the graph of a periodic function is the absolute value of half the difference between its maximum value and its minimum value. So, in Example 1, the amplitude of the graph is $\left| \frac{1 - (-1)}{2} \right|$ or 1.

You can use a graphing calculator to compare the graphs of $y = \sin b\theta$ for various values of b.

EXPLORATION

GRAPHING CALCULATORS

Set MODE to degrees. Then use the viewing window $[0, 720]$ by $[-1.5, 1.5]$ with a scale factor of 45 for the x-axis and 0.5 for the y-axis.

Your Turn

a. Enter the function Y1 = sin X into the Y= list. Press [GRAPH]. How many times does the function reach a maximum point on screen? twice

d. The greater the value of b, the more frequently the curve repeats itself between 0° and 720°. Thus, the greater the value of b, the smaller the period.

b. Enter the function Y2 = sin 2X. Press [GRAPH]. How many times does the function reach its maximum point? 4 times

c. Enter the function Y3 = sin (X/2). How many times does the function reach its maximum point? once

d. Repeat the steps for several other values of b. What conclusion can you draw about the effect of b on the period of the function $y = \sin b\theta$?

Example **2**   **Graph $y = \frac{1}{2} \cos \theta$. State the amplitude.**

θ	0°	30°	60°	90°	120°	150°	180°	210°	240°	270°	300°	330°	360°
$\cos \theta$	1	$\frac{\sqrt{3}}{2}$	$\frac{1}{2}$	0	$-\frac{1}{2}$	$-\frac{\sqrt{3}}{2}$	-1	$-\frac{\sqrt{3}}{2}$	$-\frac{1}{2}$	0	$\frac{1}{2}$	$\frac{\sqrt{3}}{2}$	1
$\frac{1}{2} \cos \theta$	$\frac{1}{2}$	$\frac{\sqrt{3}}{4}$	$\frac{1}{4}$	0	$-\frac{1}{4}$	$-\frac{\sqrt{3}}{4}$	$-\frac{1}{2}$	$-\frac{\sqrt{3}}{4}$	$-\frac{1}{4}$	0	$\frac{1}{4}$	$\frac{\sqrt{3}}{4}$	$\frac{1}{2}$

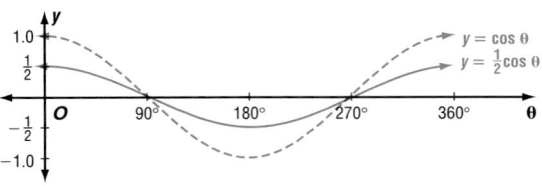

The amplitude of $y = \frac{1}{2} \cos \theta$ is $\frac{1}{2}$.   *Notice that the amplitude is $\left| \frac{1}{2} \right|$ or $\frac{1}{2}$.*

There are many applications of trigonometry in everyday life. One of these is the pitch of a pure musical tone that you hear when the tone travels through the air to reach your ear. When viewed on an oscilloscope, the tone produces the graph of a sine or cosine function. The louder the tone, the greater the amplitude of the function.

GLENCOE Technology

Interactive Mathematics Tools Software

This multimedia software provides interactive lessons by having students match the equation of a sine or cosine function with the graph of the function by manipulating the amplitude and period. **Computer Journals** give students an opportunity to write about what they have learned.

For Windows & Macintosh

Alternative Teaching Strategies

Student Diversity Attach a penlight to the spoke of a bicycle tire. Use a stationary video camera to film the light as a student walks the bicycle past the camera. View the tape and trace the path of the light on a piece of plastic placed over the TV screen. Compare this path to the sine and cosine functions. The tire is the unit circle. Discuss why there are limitations in the y values.

Example ③

APPLICATION

Physics

A pure tone is graphically viewed on an oscilloscope screen at various levels of loudness. At one of the levels, the screen displays a graph that can be modeled by the equation $y = -10 \sin 100\pi t$, where y is the pressure variation above or below the atmospheric pressure of air in dynes per square centimeter at time t in seconds.

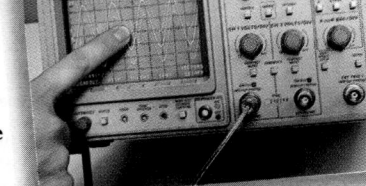

a. Graph the function and state the amplitude and period.

b. Find the pressure variation when $\frac{1}{16}$ second has elapsed.

a. Since the equation is expressed in terms of radians, use values of θ expressed in radians to complete a table of values and graph the function.

t seconds	0	0.001	0.002	0.003	0.004	0.005	0.006	0.008	0.01	0.012	0.014	0.016	0.018	0.02
$100\pi t$	0	0.1π	0.2π	0.3π	0.4π	0.5π	0.6π	0.8π	π	1.2π	1.4π	1.6π	1.8π	2π
$\sin 100\pi t$	0	0.31	0.59	0.81	0.95	1.0	0.95	0.59	0	−0.59	−0.95	−0.95	−0.59	0
$-10 \sin 100\pi t$	0	−3.1	−5.9	−8.1	−9.5	−10	−9.5	−5.9	0	5.9	9.5	9.5	5.9	0

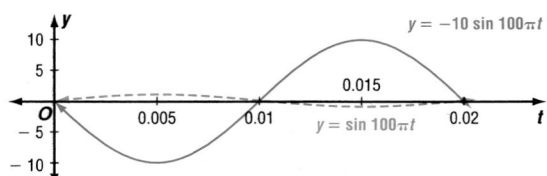

The amplitude of the graph is 10, and the period is 0.02 second.

Notice that the amplitude is $|-10|$ or 10 and the period is $\frac{2\pi}{|100\pi|} = \frac{1}{50}$ or 0.02.

b. Find y when $t = \frac{1}{16}$

$y = -10 \sin 100\pi t$

$\quad = -10 \sin 100\pi \left(\frac{1}{16}\right)$ *Replace t with $\frac{1}{16}$.*

$\quad = -10 \sin 6.25\pi$

$\quad = -10 \sin [3(2\pi) + 0.25\pi]$ *$\sin (2k\pi + \theta) = \sin \theta$*

$\quad = -10 \sin (0.25\pi)$

$\quad \approx -10(0.707)$ or -7.1

When $\frac{1}{16}$ second has elapsed, the pressure is about 7.1 dynes per square centimeter less than atmospheric pressure (about 1,000,000 dynes per square centimeter).

Lesson 14–1 Graphing Trigonometric Functions **829**

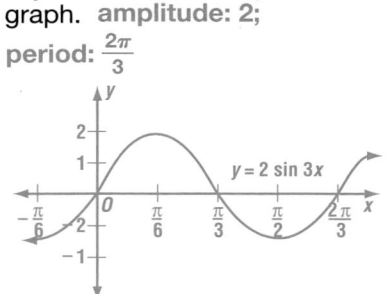

Teaching Tip For Example 3, the amplitude is the vertical measure between the horizontal axis and the maximum/minimum value of the function.

In-Class Example

For Example 3
Find the amplitude and period of $y = 2 \sin 3x$. Then draw the graph. **amplitude: 2;**

period: $\frac{2\pi}{3}$

These examples suggest the following generalizations.

Amplitudes and Periods	For functions of the form $y = a \sin b\theta$ and $y = a \cos b\theta$, the amplitude is $\lvert a \rvert$, and the period is $\frac{360°}{\lvert b \rvert}$ or $\frac{2\pi}{\lvert b \rvert}$.

The four remaining trigonometric functions—tangent, cotangent, secant, and cosecant—can also be graphed. Make a table of values for $y = \tan \theta$ and graph the function.

θ	0°	30°	45°	60°	90°	120°	135°	150°	180°	210°	225°	240°	270°	300°	315°	330°	360°
tan θ	0	$\frac{\sqrt{3}}{3}$	1	$\sqrt{3}$	nd	$-\sqrt{3}$	-1	$-\frac{\sqrt{3}}{3}$	0	$\frac{\sqrt{3}}{3}$	1	$\sqrt{3}$	nd	$-\sqrt{3}$	-1	$-\frac{\sqrt{3}}{3}$	0

nd = not defined

The tangent function is not defined for $90°, 270°, \ldots, 90° + k \cdot 180°$, where k is an integer. The graph is separated by vertical asymptotes, indicated by dashed lines. The x-intercepts of the asymptotes are the values for which $y = \tan \theta$ is not defined.

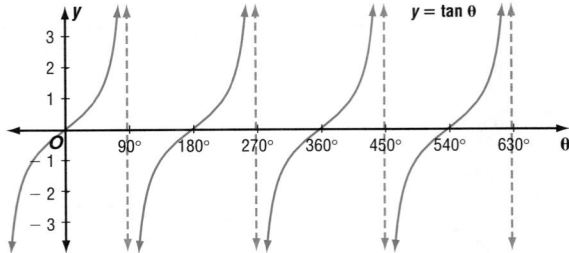

The period of the tangent function is $180°$ or π radians. Since the tangent function has no maximum or minimum value, it has no amplitude.

The graphs of the secant, cosecant, and cotangent functions are shown below. Compare them to the graphs of the cosine, sine, and tangent functions, which are shown in red.

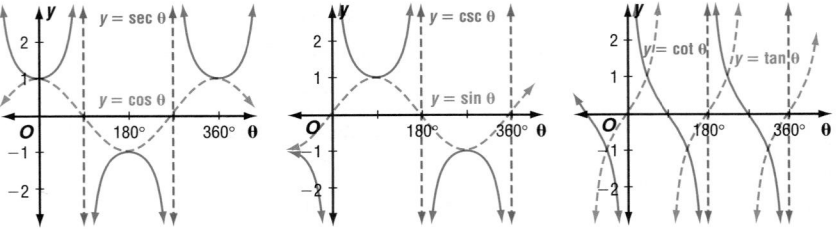

Notice that the period of the secant and cosecant functions is $360°$ or 2π radians. The period of the cotangent function is $180°$ or π radians. What are the amplitudes of the secant, cosecant, and cotangent functions?

Classroom Vignette

"I have students plot each of the six trigonometric functions on a different sheet of graph paper using a different color pen each time. Then, I give each student a large sheet of graph paper and ask them to graph all six trigonometric functions on one set of coordinate axes using the same color code as the first assignment."

Susan Justus Creekmore

Susan Creekmore
Marion High School
Marion, Arkansas

Example **4** **Graph** $y = -\frac{1}{2} \csc 2\theta$.

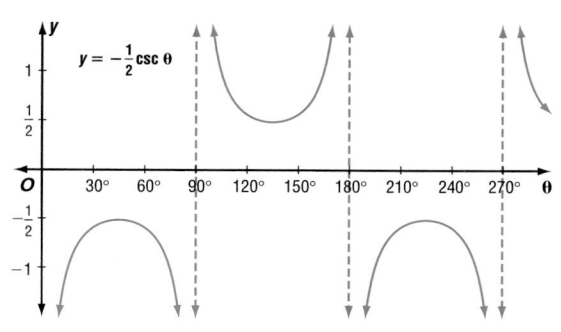

θ	0°	15°	30°	45°	60°	75°	90°	105°	120°	135°	150°	165°	180°
2θ	0°	30°	60°	90°	120°	150°	180°	210°	240°	270°	300°	330°	360°
$-\frac{1}{2}\csc 2\theta$	nd	-1	$-\frac{\sqrt{3}}{3}$	$-\frac{1}{2}$	$\frac{\sqrt{3}}{3}$	-1	nd	1	$\frac{\sqrt{3}}{3}$	$\frac{1}{2}$	$\frac{\sqrt{3}}{3}$	1	nd

nd = not defined

The period is $\frac{360°}{|2|}$ or 180°. This function has no maximum or minimum value when θ equals 0°, 90°, 180°, ... , $0° + k \cdot 90°$. Thus, it has no amplitude.

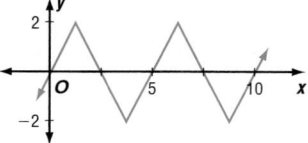

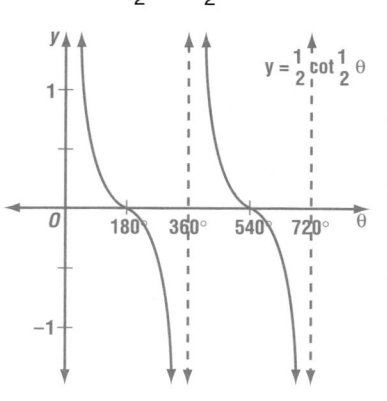

CHECK FOR UNDERSTANDING

Communicating Mathematics

1. The values of the function repeat in 180° intervals.

2. half the distance between the maximum and minimum values

Study the lesson. Then complete the following.

1. **Explain** what it means to say that the period of a function is 180°.

2. **Explain** what the amplitude of a sine or cosine function is.

3. Write your impressions of the function that is graphed at the right.

   a. Does it appear to have an amplitude? If so, what is it?   **yes; 2**

   b. Does it appear to be periodic? If so, what is the period?   **yes; 5**

   c. Does it appear to be a sine or cosine function? If so, what is a possible equation?   **no**

4. **You Decide**   Tina and Tanya were observing the graph of the equation $y = 10 \cos 524\pi t$ on the screen of an oscilloscope. They noticed that by rotating one of the dials, they were able to move the graph to the right until the y-intercept changed from 10 to 0. Neither the amplitude nor the period of the graph had changed. Tina concluded that the sine function could be used to describe the graph in its new position. Tanya believed that since the original curve was a cosine graph, only a cosine function could be used. Who was right?   **Tina; a possible equation is $y = 10 \sin 524\pi t$.**

Lesson 14-1   Graphing Trigonometric Functions   **831**

---

3 PRACTICE/APPLY

Check for Understanding
Exercises 1–17 are designed to help you assess your students' understanding through reading, writing, speaking, and modeling. You should work through Exercises 1–5 with your students and then monitor their work on Exercises 6–17.

Error Analysis
Students sometimes misinterpret the effect of b on the period of $y = a \sin (bx + c)$ as a direct variation. While the amplitude varies directly with a, the period varies inversely with b. $b \cdot p = k$, where p is the period and k is $2\pi \cdot p = \frac{2\pi}{b}$.

Reteaching

Using Technology Demonstrate the effects of a, b, and c in $y = a \sin (bx + c)$ and $y = a \cos (bx + c)$ using an overhead projection of the screen of a computer or graphing calculator.

Assignment Guide

Core: 19–45 odd, 46, 47, 49–57
Enriched: 18–44 even, 45–57

For **Extra Practice,** see p. 908.

The red A, B, and C flags, printed only in the Teacher's Wraparound Edition, indicate the level of difficulty of the exercises.

Additional Answer

5. Both functions have the same shape, period, and amplitude; they have different x- and y-intercepts, and the cosine function is translated to the right 90° on the x-axis.

Study Guide Masters, p. 99

NAME_____ DATE_____

Study Guide   Student Edition
Pages 826–834

Graphing Trigonometric Functions

The chart below shows useful information about common trigonometric functions. Study the chart.

Function	Period	Zeros	Max.	Min.
sine (sin)	360°	0°, 180°, 360°, ⋯	1	−1
cosine (cos)	360°	90°, 270°, ⋯	1	−1
tangent (tan)	180°	0°, 180°, ⋯	none	none
cotangent (cot)	180°	90°, 270°, ⋯	none	none
secant (sec)	360°	none	−1 (rel.)	1 (rel.)
cosecant (csc)	360°	none	−1 (rel.)	1 (rel.)

When graphing trigonometric functions, it helps to remember that for $y = a \sin b\theta$, $y = a \cos b\theta$, $|a|$ is the amplitude, and $\frac{360°}{|b|}$ is the period of the function.

Example: State the period and amplitude for $y = \frac{1}{2}\cos\frac{1}{2}\theta$.

amplitude $= \frac{1}{2}$ period $= \frac{360°}{\frac{1}{2}} = 720°$

State the amplitude (if it exists) and period for each function. Then graph each function.

1. $y = 2\cos\theta$ 2; 360° or 2π 2. $y = -3\sin\theta$ 3; 360° or 2π

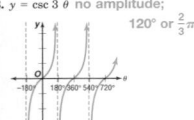   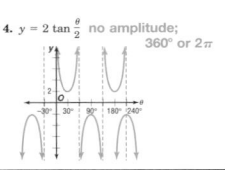

3. $y = \csc 3\theta$ no amplitude; 120° or $\frac{2}{3}\pi$ 4. $y = 2\tan\frac{\theta}{2}$ no amplitude; 360° or 2π

832 Chapter 14

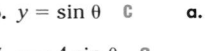 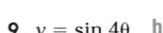

5. Write a paragraph describing ways in which the functions $y = a \sin b\theta$ and $y = a \cos b\theta$ are the same and ways in which they are different.
   See margin.

Guided Practice

Match the graphs on the right with the equations on the left.

6. $y = \sin\theta$ **c**   a. 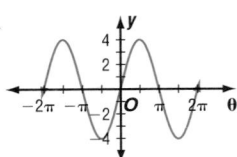   b.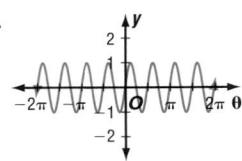

7. $y = 4\sin\theta$ **a**

8. $y = \cos 0.4\theta$ **d**

9. $y = \sin 4\theta$ **b**

c. 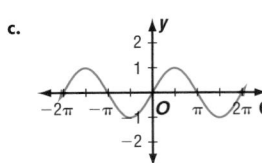   d.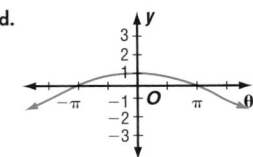

State the amplitude (if it exists) and the period of each function. Then graph each function. 10–15. See Solutions Manual for graphs.

10. $y = 3\cos\frac{1}{2}\theta$ 3, 720°   11. $y = 6\sin\frac{2}{3}\theta$ 6, 540°

12. $y = -2\sin\theta$ 2, 360°   13. $y = \sec 3\theta$ none, 120°

14. $y = 3\tan\theta$ none, 180°   15. $y = \cot 5\theta$ none, 36°

16. Which of the functions in Exercises 10–15 are defined for all real values of θ? **Exercises 10, 11, and 12**

17. **Music** When represented on an oscilloscope, the note A above middle C has a period of $\frac{1}{440}$. Which of the following can be an equation for an oscilloscope graph of this note? The amplitude of the graph is K. **c**

   a. $y = K\sin 220\pi t$ b. $y = K\sin 440\pi t$ c. $y = K\sin 880\pi t$

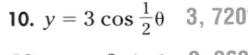

EXERCISES

Practice **Graph each function.** 18–35. See Solutions Manual.

18. $y = \frac{1}{2}\sin\theta$ 19. $y = 3\sin\theta$ 20. $y = \cos 3\theta$

21. $y = \sin 4\theta$ 22. $y = \cos 2\theta$ 23. $y = -3\sin\theta$

24. $y = \cot\theta$ 25. $y = \frac{2}{3}\cos\theta$ 26. $y = 3\sec\theta$

27. $y = \csc 2\theta$ 28. $y = \frac{1}{3}\sec\theta$ 29. $y = 4\sin\frac{1}{2}\theta$

30. $y = 4\cos\frac{3}{4}\theta$ 31. $y = 3\csc\frac{1}{2}\theta$ 32. $y = -\frac{1}{2}\cot 2\theta$

33. $2y = \tan\theta$ 34. $3y = 2\sin\frac{1}{2}\theta$ 35. $\frac{3}{4}y = \frac{2}{3}\sin\frac{3}{5}\theta$

832 Chapter 14 *Using Trigonometric Graphs and Identities*

Extension

Communication Have students research and write a short report on operation and uses of oscilloscopes.

Write an equation of the given sine or cosine function having the specified characteristics.

Function	Amplitude	Period	
36. sine	4	360°	$y = 4 \sin \theta$
37. cosine	0.6	720°	$y = 0.6 \cos \frac{1}{2}\theta$
38. sine	5	180°	$y = 5 \sin 2\theta$
39. cosine	$\frac{1}{3}$	90°	$y = \frac{1}{3} \cos 4\theta$
40. cosine	4.25	360°	$y = 4.25 \cos \theta$
41. sine	6.7	120°	$y = 6.7 \sin 3\theta$

Write an equation for the graph that is displayed.

42.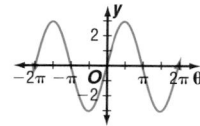

$y = 3 \sin \theta$

43.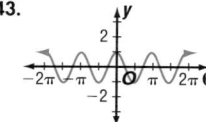

$y = \cos 2\theta$

44.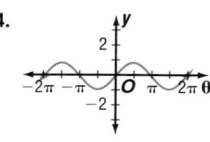

$y = \sin \frac{1}{2}\theta$

Graphing Calculator

45. Graph $Y_1 = \sin X$ in the viewing window $[0, 720]$ and $[-2, 2]$. Use scale factors of 45 for the x-axis and 0.5 for the y-axis. Then graph the following functions. *Be sure your calculator is in degree mode.* **a–d. See margin.**

 a. $Y_2 = 2 \sin X$ **b.** $Y_3 = -2 \sin X$ **c.** $Y_4 = -\frac{1}{2} \sin X$

 d. Examine your results from parts a–c. What conclusions can you draw about the effect of the constant a on the graph of the function $y = a \sin \theta$?

Critical Thinking

46. Suppose you were told that for a certain value of d, $y = \sin \theta$ and $y = \cos(\theta + d)$ have exactly the same graph. How would you find a value of d for which this true?   **See margin.**

Applications and Problem Solving

47. Zoology In predator-prey systems, the number of predators and the number of prey tend to vary in a periodic manner. In a certain region with coyotes as predators and rabbits as prey, the rabbit population R varied according to the equation $R = 1000 + 250 \sin \frac{1}{2}\pi t$, where t is the time in years since January 1, 1990.

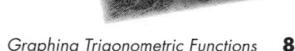

 a. Graph the function that describes the rabbit population at time t.   **See margin.**

 b. What was the rabbit population on January 1, 1990?   **1000**

 c. What is the maximum rabbit population? On what date was the maximum population first reached?   **1250; January 1, 1991**

 d. What is the minimum rabbit population? On what date was the minimum population first reached?   **750; January 1, 1993**

Additional Answers

46. By trial and error, using simple values for θ. For example, if $\theta = 0$, then $\sin \theta = 0 = \cos d$. Thus, a possible value for d is 90° since $\cos 90° = 0$. Next, use a calculator to check several values of θ in the equation $\sin \theta = \cos(\theta + 90°)$ to show that the conjecture is plausible.

47a.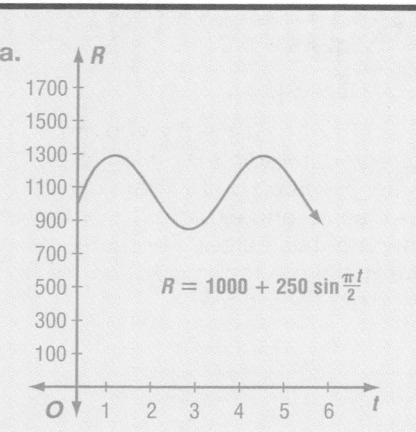

Additional Answers

45a.

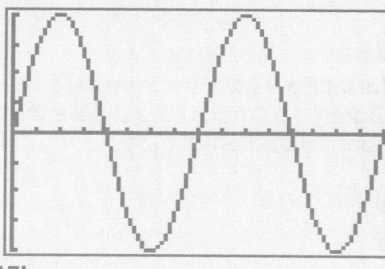

45b.

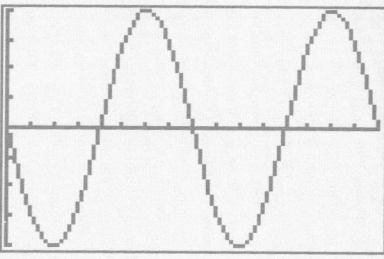

45c.

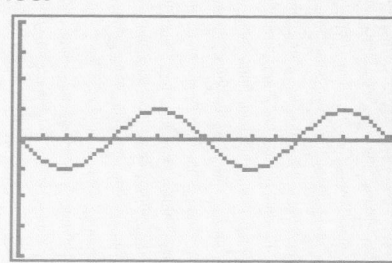

45d. The greater the absolute value of a, the greater the amplitude. If a is negative, then the curve is the same as would be obtained by reflecting the curve $y = -a \sin \theta$ about the x-axis.

Practice Masters, p. 99

14-1   NAME_____   DATE_____
Practice   Student Edition
Pages 826–834

Graphing Trigonometric Functions

State the amplitude (if it exists) and period of each function.

1. $y = -4 \sin \theta$ 4; 360° or 2π **2.** $y = \cos 5\theta$ 1; 72° or $\frac{2\pi}{5}$

3. $y = \frac{1}{2} \sin \frac{3}{8}\theta$ $\frac{1}{2}$; 960° or $\frac{16\pi}{3}$ **4.** $2y = -6 \cos 4\theta$ 3; 90° or $\frac{\pi}{2}$

Graph each function.

5. $y = \sec 5\theta$
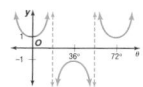

6. $y = \csc \frac{3}{4}\theta$
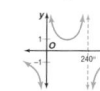

7. $y = \cot \frac{1}{2}\theta$
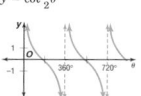

8. $y = \tan 10\theta$
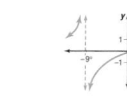

9. $y = 3 \csc 6\theta$
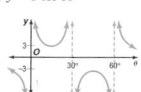

10. $y = \frac{1}{2} \sec 4\theta$
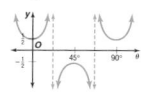

Chapter 14   **833**

Closing Activity

Modeling Have students use diagrams to model the difference in period and amplitude.

Additional Answer

54.

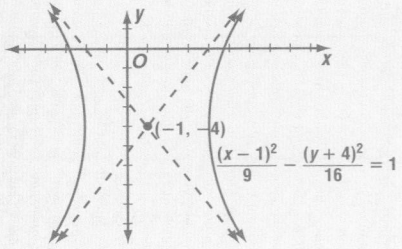

$$\frac{(x-1)^2}{9} - \frac{(y+4)^2}{16} = 1$$

(-1, -4)

Enrichment Masters, p. 99

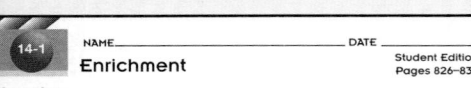

14-1

NAME_____ DATE_____

Enrichment

Student Edition
Pages 826–834

Blueprints

Interpreting blueprints requires the ability to select and use trigonometric functions and geometric properties. The figure below represents a plan for an improvement to a roof. The metal fitting shown makes a 30° angle with the horizontal. The vertices of the geometric shapes are *not* labeled in these plans. Relevant information must be selected and the appropriate function used to find the unknown measures.

Example: Find the unknown measures in the figure at the right.

The measures x and y are the legs of a right triangle. The measure of the hypotenuse is $\frac{15}{16}$ in. + $\frac{5}{16}$ in. or $\frac{20}{16}$ in.

$\frac{y}{\frac{20}{16}} = \cos 30°$

$\frac{x}{\frac{20}{16}} = \sin 30°$

$y = 1.08$ in. $x = 0.63$ in.

Roofing Improvement

Find the unknown measures of each of the following.

1. Chimney on roof
$y = 3.78'$
$x = 5.72'$
$\angle A = 40°$

2. Air vent
$\angle C = 63.43°$
$\angle D = 26.57°$

3. Elbow joint
$\angle A = 40°$
$\angle B = 50°$
$t = 9.63'$
$r = 4.87'$

---

48. Communications The carrier wave for a certain FM station can be modeled by an equation of the form $y = A \sin(10^7 \cdot 2\pi t)$, where t is the time in seconds. Determine the period of the carrier wave. $\frac{1}{10^7}$ **second**

Mixed Review

49. Trigonometry Find $\sin\left(\text{Cos}^{-1}\frac{15}{17}\right)$. (Lesson 13–7) $\frac{8}{17}$

50. Cosmotology Sandy Chung carries several colors of lipstick in a cosmetic bag in her purse. The probability of pulling out the color she wants without looking is $\frac{1}{3}$. If she uses lipstick 4 times a day, find the probability that she never pulls out the correct lipstick all day. (Lesson 12–7) $\frac{16}{81}$

51. Find the missing terms of the geometric sequence __?__, __?__, 9.5, 19, 38. (Lesson 11–3) **2.375, 4.75**

52. Use a calculator to find ln 56.9 rounded to four decimal places. (Lesson 10–5) **4.0413**

53. Solve $\frac{x-3}{2x} = \frac{x-2}{2x+1} - \frac{1}{2}$. (Lesson 9–5) $\pm\frac{\sqrt{6}}{2}$

54. Graph $\frac{(x-1)^2}{9} - \frac{(y+4)^2}{16} = 1$. (Lesson 7–5) **See margin.**

55. Express $\sqrt[3]{16a^5b^7}$ using rational exponents. (Lesson 5–7) $16^{\frac{1}{3}}a^{\frac{5}{3}}b^{\frac{7}{3}}$

56. Find the maximum and minimum values of the function $f(x, y) = x - y$ defined for the polygonal region having vertices with coordinates $(0, 0)$, $(0, 5)$, $(3, 4)$, and $(6, 0)$. (Lesson 3–5) **6, −5**

57. Write an expression to demonstrate the distributive property. (Lesson 1–2)
Sample answer: $a(b + c) = ab + ac$

WORKING ON THE

In·ves·ti·ga·tion

Refer to the Investigation on pages 768–769.

Scream Machines!

Review the meaning of potential energy *PE* and kinetic energy *KE*. When a car is at its maximum height, it has maximum *PE* and minimum *KE*. When it has just arrived at the bottom of the steepest slope, it has maximum *KE* and little *PE*. The formulas for calculating *PE* and *KE* are

$PE = w \cdot L_v$ and $KE = \frac{1}{2} \cdot \frac{w}{g}s^2$, where w is the weight of the car, L_v is its vertical height on the track, g is the acceleration of gravity (32 ft/s^2), and s is the speed of the cars in ft/s.

1 Sketch what you think the graph of the potential energy of a roller coaster car would be

from the beginning to the end of the ride. Let the horizontal axis represent time and the vertical axis represent the amount of energy.

2 Graph the amount of kinetic energy for the cars during the ride on the same coordinate plane with the graph of the potential energy. Discuss any similarities or differences in the shapes of the two graphs. How do these graphs compare to the graph of $y = \sin \theta$?

Add the results of your work to your Investigation Folder.

 Tech Prep

Broadcaster Students who are interested in radio may wish to do further research on the data given in Exercise 48 and explore the potential growth of this career. For more information on tech prep, see the *Teacher's Handbook*.

In·ves·ti·ga·tion

Working on the Investigation

The Investigation on pages 768–769 is designed to be a long-term project that is completed over several days or weeks. Encourage students to keep their materials in their Investigation Folder as they work on the Investigation.

Trigonometric Identities

What YOU'LL LEARN

• To use trigonometric identities to simplify or evaluate expressions.

Why IT'S IMPORTANT

You can use trigonometric identities to solve problems involving running and history.

F Y I

The 1996 Summer Olympics were the first where the paralympics, athletic games for paralyzed athletes, shared the same venues and were run by a unified organization. Over 4000 athletes competed for medals.

APPLICATION
Running

While practicing on a circular track, a runner notices that his body is not perpendicular to the ground. Instead, it leans away from a vertical position. The nonnegative acute angle θ that the runner's body makes with the vertical is called the **angle of incline** and is described by the equation $\tan \theta = \frac{v^2}{gR}$, where R is the radius of the track in meters, v is the speed of the runner in meters per second, and g is the acceleration due to gravity, 9.8 meters per second squared.

This is not the only equation that describes the angle of incline in terms of trigonometric functions. Another such equation is $\sin \theta = \cos \theta \cdot \frac{v^2}{gR}$, where $0 \le \theta < 90°$.

Are these two equations completely independent of one another or are they merely different versions of the same relationship? To answer this question, recall the following relationship that you learned in Chapter 13.

$$\tan \theta = \frac{\sin \theta}{\cos \theta}, \text{ if } \cos \theta \neq 0$$

This is an example of a **trigonometric identity,** an equation that is true for all values for which every expression in the equation is defined. You know that the above identity is true except for angle measures such as θ = 90°, 270°, 450°, ..., 90° + k · 180°. The cosine of each of these angles is 0, so none of the expressions tan 90°, tan 270°, tan 450°, and so on, are defined.

Now divide each side of the second formula, $\sin \theta = \cos \theta \cdot \frac{v^2}{gR}$, by cos θ, allowing only values of θ for which cos θ ≠ 0. The result is as follows.

$$\frac{\sin \theta}{\cos \theta} = \frac{\cos \theta}{\cos \theta} \cdot \frac{v^2}{gR}$$

$$\tan \theta = 1 \cdot \frac{v^2}{gR} \qquad \textit{Tangent identity}$$

$$\tan \theta = \frac{v^2}{gR}$$

Notice that this is the first angle of inclination formula. The two formulas are not independent. Each is a variation of the other.

Lesson 14–2 Trigonometric Identities **835**

F Y I

The Olympics in the year 2000 will be held in Sydney, Australia.

NCTM Standards: 1–6, 8–9

Instructional Resources

• Study Guide Master 14-2
• Practice Master 14-2
• Enrichment Master 14-2
• Assessment and Evaluation Masters, p. 380
• Multicultural Activity Masters, p. 28

Transparency 14-2A contains the 5-Minute Check for this lesson; **Transparency 14-2B** contains a teaching aid for this lesson.

Recommended Pacing	
Honors Pacing	Day 3 of 11
Block Scheduling*	Day 2 of 6

*For more information on pacing and possible lesson plans, refer to the *Block Scheduling Booklet*.

1 FOCUS

5-Minute Check
(over Lesson 14-1)

State the amplitude and period of each function.

1. $y = 4 \cos \frac{3\theta}{4}$ **4, $\frac{8\pi}{3}$**

2. $y = \sin 4\theta$ **1, $\frac{\pi}{2}$**

3. State the period of $\cot \frac{\theta}{3}$. **3π**

4. In which quadrants is the secant an increasing function? **I and II**

5. Graph $y = \sin 2\theta$.

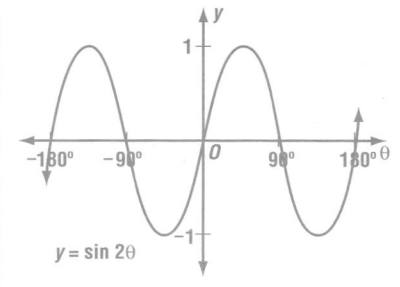

$y = \sin 2\theta$

Questioning Ask students what
the difference is between identical
and fraternal twins. From student
responses, develop the concept
that the term *identical*, and thus
identity, means that any
characteristic named is true for all
individuals classified as identical.

2 TEACH

In-Class Example

For Example 1
Show that
$\cot \theta + \tan \theta = \csc \theta \sec \theta$.

$$\cot \theta + \tan \theta = \frac{\cos \theta}{\sin \theta} + \frac{\sin \theta}{\cos \theta}$$

$$= \frac{\cos^2 \theta + \sin^2 \theta}{\sin \theta \cos \theta}$$

$$= \frac{1}{\sin \theta \cos \theta}$$

$$= \csc \theta \ \sec \theta$$

In Chapter 13, you also became familiar with other trigonometric identities, such as those below.

$$\cot \theta = \frac{\cos \theta}{\sin \theta} \qquad \sec \theta = \frac{1}{\cos \theta} \qquad \csc \theta = \frac{1}{\sin \theta}$$

To find another useful trigonometric identity, begin with the equation for the unit circle, $x^2 + y^2 = 1$. By substituting $\cos \theta$ for x and $\sin \theta$ for y, we have the following equation.

$$(\cos \theta)^2 + (\sin \theta)^2 = 1$$

This equation is usually written as follows.

$$\cos^2 \theta + \sin^2 \theta = 1$$

The equation $\cos^2 \theta + \sin^2 \theta = 1$ is an identity because it is true for all values of θ. Some other trigonometric identities are given below.

Basic Trigonometric Identities	**The following trigonometric identities hold true for all values of θ except those for which either side of the equation is undefined.** $\cos^2 \theta + \sin^2 \theta = 1$ $\tan^2 \theta + 1 = \sec^2 \theta$ $\cot^2 \theta + 1 = \csc^2 \theta$

The steps in the following example show the development of a basic trigonometric identity. The expression on one side of the equation is transformed into the exact form of the expression on the other side.

Example 1 Show that $1 + \cot^2 \theta = \csc^2 \theta$.

$$1 + \cot^2 \theta = \csc^2 \theta$$

$$1 + \left(\frac{\cos \theta}{\sin \theta}\right)^2 = \csc^2 \theta \qquad \textit{Definition of cot } \theta$$

$$1 + \frac{\cos^2 \theta}{\sin^2 \theta} = \csc^2 \theta$$

$$\frac{\sin^2 \theta}{\sin^2 \theta} + \frac{\cos^2 \theta}{\sin^2 \theta} = \csc^2 \theta \qquad 1 = \frac{\sin^2 \theta}{\sin^2 \theta}$$

$$\frac{\sin^2 \theta + \cos^2 \theta}{\sin^2 \theta} = \csc^2 \theta$$

$$\frac{1}{\sin^2 \theta} = \csc^2 \theta \qquad \sin^2 \theta + \cos^2 \theta = 1$$

$$\csc^2 \theta = \csc^2 \theta$$

Therefore, $1 + \cot^2 \theta = \csc^2 \theta$.

Alternative Learning Styles

Auditory While solving Example 1, have students name each step and its justification. Then ask students to show step-by-step that $\cot^2 \theta + 1 = \csc^2 \theta$. When simplifying expressions that contain trigonometric functions, question students to develop criteria for determining that an expression is simplified.

You can use trigonometric identities to find values of trigonometric functions. In the next example, β is the Greek letter beta.

Example **2** Find $\csc \beta$ if $\cot \beta = \frac{4}{5}$ and $180° \le \beta \le 270°$.

$\csc^2 \beta = 1 + \cot^2 \beta$ *Trigonometric identity*

$\csc^2 \beta = 1 + \left(\frac{4}{5}\right)^2$ *Substitute $\frac{4}{5}$ for $\cot \beta$.*

$\csc^2 \beta = \frac{41}{25}$

$\csc \beta = \pm \sqrt{\frac{41}{25}}$ *Take the square root of each side.*

$\csc \beta = \pm \frac{\sqrt{41}}{\sqrt{25}}$

$\csc \beta = -\frac{\sqrt{41}}{5}$ or about -1.2806 *$\csc \beta$ is negative for values of β between 180° and 270°.*

Example **3** If $\cot A = 4$, find $\sin A$. Assume that angle A is positive and acute.

$\csc^2 A = 1 + \cot^2 A$ *Trigonometric identity*

$\csc^2 A = 1 + (4)^2$

$\csc^2 A = 17$

$\frac{1}{\sin^2 A} = 17$ *$\csc A = \frac{1}{\sin A}$*

$\sin^2 A = \frac{1}{17}$

$\sin A = \frac{\sqrt{1}}{\sqrt{17}}$ *$\sin A$ is positive for positive acute angles.*

$\sin A = \frac{\sqrt{17}}{17}$ or about 0.2425

Trigonometric identities can also be used to simplify expressions containing trigonometric functions. Simplifying an expression that contains trigonometric functions means that the expression is written as a numerical value or in terms of a single trigonometric function, if possible.

Example **4** Simplify $\frac{1}{1 + \cos x} + \frac{1}{1 - \cos x}$.

$\frac{1}{1 + \cos x} + \frac{1}{1 - \cos x} = \frac{(1 - \cos x) + (1 + \cos x)}{(1 + \cos x)(1 - \cos x)}$

$= \frac{2}{1 - \cos^2 x}$

$= \frac{2}{\sin^2 x}$ *$\cos^2 x + \sin^2 x = 1$, so $1 - \cos^2 x = \sin^2 x$.*

$= 2 \cdot \frac{1}{\sin^2 x}$

$= 2 \csc^2 x$ *$\frac{1}{\sin x} = \csc x$*

In-Class Examples

For Example 2

Find $\cos \theta$ if $\sin \theta = \frac{2}{3}$ and $0° \le \theta \le 90°$. $\frac{\sqrt{5}}{3}$

For Example 3

If $\sin A = \frac{1}{2}$, find $\tan A$. Assume that angle A is obtuse. $-\frac{\sqrt{3}}{3}$

For Example 4

Simplify

$\left(\frac{\cos^3 \beta}{\sin \beta}\right) \tan \beta + \left(\frac{\sin^3 \beta}{\cos \beta}\right) \cot \beta$.   **1**

Alternative Teaching Strategies

Reading Algebra Have students refer to a physics text and look through the sections on waves, especially light and sound. They should focus on the meanings of *period* and *amplitude*.

In-Class Example

For Example 5

Suppose the sine of the angle of incline, θ, is $\frac{\sqrt{2}}{2}$ and the speed of the runner is 8 m/s. Find the radius of the circular arc.

4.6 meters

GLOBAL CONNECTIONS

Locations of the four Olympics at the beginning of this century are as follows.

1900	Paris, France
1904	St. Louis, U.S.
1908	London, England
1912	Stockholm, Sweden

Study Guide Masters, p. 100

14-2

NAME_____ DATE_____

Study Guide

Student Edition
Pages 835–840

Trigonometric Identities

An equation that is true for all values of the variables for which it is defined is called an **identity.**

Basic Trigonometric Identities

The following equations are trigonometric identities. They hold for all values of θ except those for which an expression in the equation is undefined.
$\sin^2 \theta + \cos^2 \theta = 1$
$1 + \tan^2 \theta = \sec^2 \theta$
$1 + \cot^2 \theta = \csc^2 \theta$

Example: If $\tan a = -\frac{3}{5}$, find $\cos a$ for values of a between 90° and 180°.

$\sec^2 a = 1 + \tan^2 a$ Trigonometric identity

$\sec^2 a = 1 + \left(-\frac{3}{5}\right)^2$

$\left(\frac{1}{\cos a}\right)^2 = \frac{34}{25}$ $\sec a = \frac{1}{\cos a}$

$\cos^2 a = \frac{25}{34}$

$\cos a = -\sqrt{\frac{25}{34}}$ cos a is negative for values of a between 90° and 180°.

$\cos a = \frac{-5\sqrt{34}}{34}$

Solve for values of θ between 0° and 90°.

1. If $\sin \theta = \frac{3}{7}$, find $\tan \theta$.
$\frac{3\sqrt{10}}{20}$

2. If $\cos \theta = \frac{\sqrt{3}}{2}$, find $\csc \theta$.
2

3. If $\sin \theta = \frac{3}{5}$, find $\cos \theta$.
$\frac{4}{5}$

4. If $\sin \theta = \frac{1}{3}$, find $\sec \theta$.
$\frac{3}{4}\sqrt{2}$

Simplify each expression.

5. $\frac{\tan \theta \csc \theta}{\sec \theta}$
1

6. $\frac{\cot^2 x - 1}{1 + \cot^2 x}$
$1 - 2 \sin^2 \theta$ (or $\cos^2 \theta - \sin^2 \theta$ or $2 \cos^2 \theta - 1$)

7. $\frac{\sin^3 \theta - \cot \theta \tan \theta}{\cot \theta \sin \theta}$
$-\cos \theta$

8. $\frac{\cos \theta}{\sec \theta - \tan \theta}$
$1 + \sin \theta$

Example **5**

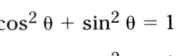 **Sports**

A portion of a race track has the shape of a circular arc with a radius of 16.7 meters. As a runner races along the arc, the sine of her angle of incline θ is found to be $\frac{1}{4}$. Find the speed of the runner.

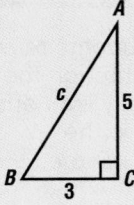

GLOBAL CONNECTIONS

Running games were organized in ancient Egypt as early as 3800 B.C. The first marathon race, which was 24 miles long, was held during the 1896 Olympic games in Athens.

Use the angle-of-incline formula given in the application at the beginning of the lesson,

$\tan \theta = \frac{v^2}{gR}$. The value of $\tan \theta$

can be found if $\cos \theta$ is also known. So, find $\cos \theta$ first.

$\cos^2 \theta + \sin^2 \theta = 1$

$\qquad \cos^2 \theta = 1 - \sin^2 \theta$

$\qquad \cos^2 \theta = 1 - \left(\frac{1}{4}\right)^2$

$\qquad \cos^2 \theta = 1 - \frac{1}{16}$

$\qquad \cos^2 \theta = \frac{15}{16}$

$\qquad \cos \theta = \frac{\sqrt{15}}{4}$ *Take the square root of each side.*
The cosine of an acute angle is positive.

Use $\cos \theta$ to find $\tan \theta$.

$\tan \theta = \frac{\sin \theta}{\cos \theta}$

$\qquad = \frac{\frac{1}{4}}{\frac{\sqrt{15}}{4}}$ *$\sin \theta = \frac{1}{4}$ and $\cos \theta = \frac{\sqrt{15}}{4}$*

$\qquad = \frac{1}{\sqrt{15}}$

$\qquad = \frac{\sqrt{15}}{15}$ or about 0.2582

Now substitute the value of $\tan \theta$ and the given values to solve the problem.

$\qquad \tan \theta = \frac{v^2}{gR}$ *$\tan \theta = 0.2582$, $g = 9.8$, and $R = 16.7$*

$\qquad 0.2582 = \frac{v^2}{9.8(16.7)}$

$\qquad 0.2582 = \frac{v^2}{163.66}$ *Multiply each side by 163.66.*

$\qquad 42.257 \approx v^2$

$\pm\sqrt{42.257} \approx v$

$\qquad \pm 6.5 \approx v$

Since her speed is positive, the speed of the runner is about 6.5 meters per second.

Reteaching

Using Graphics If $\cot B$ is given as $\frac{3}{5}$, then a first quadrant reference triangle can be drawn. So $c = \sqrt{34}$. Consideration of the sign of a given trigonometric function and the interval for B allows for all other trigonometric functions to be found.

Communicating Mathematics

Study the lesson. Then complete the following.   1–2. See margin.

1. **Describe** what the coordinates (x, y) represent on the unit circle.

2. **Explain** what it means to simplify an expression containing trigonometric functions.

3. **Determine** in which quadrant(s) the terminal side of angle β is if $\tan \beta = -\frac{4}{3}$. Explain why.   **II or IV, where only one of its components (sin or cos) is negative**

Guided Practice

Solve for values of θ between 0° and 90°.

4. If $\cot \theta = 2$, find $\tan \theta$. $\frac{1}{2}$

5. If $\sin \theta = \frac{4}{5}$, find $\cos \theta$. $\frac{3}{5}$

6. If $\cos \theta = \frac{2}{3}$, find $\sin \theta$. $\frac{\sqrt{5}}{3}$

7. If $\cos \theta = \frac{2}{3}$, find $\csc \theta$. $\frac{3\sqrt{5}}{5}$

8. Show that $\sin x \sec x = \tan x$ is an identity.   **See margin.**

Simplify each expression.   9. $\sin \theta \cos \theta$

9. $\tan \theta \cos^2 \theta$

10. $\csc^2 \theta - \cot^2 \theta$ **1**

11. $\frac{\cos x \csc x}{\tan x}$ $\cot^2 x$

12. **History**   Pythagoras is most famous for the theorem that bears his name. The identity $\cos^2 \theta + \sin^2 \theta = 1$ is an example of a *Pythagorean identity*. Why do you think that this identity is classified in this way?   **The functions $\cos \theta$ and $\sin \theta$ can be thought of as the lengths of the legs of a right triangle and the number 1 can be thought of as the measure of the corresponding hypotenuse.**

EXERCISES

Practice

Solve for values of θ between 90° and 180°.

 A

13. If $\cos \theta = -\frac{3}{5}$, find $\csc \theta$. $\frac{5}{4}$

14. If $\sin \theta = \frac{1}{2}$, find $\tan \theta$. $-\frac{\sqrt{3}}{3}$

15. If $\sin \theta = \frac{3}{5}$, find $\cos \theta$. $-\frac{4}{5}$

16. If $\tan \theta = -2$, find $\sec \theta$. $-\sqrt{5}$

Solve for values of θ between 180° and 270°.

17. If $\cos \theta = -\frac{3}{5}$, find $\csc \theta$. $-\frac{5}{4}$

18. If $\sec \theta = -3$, find $\tan \theta$. $2\sqrt{2}$

19. If $\cot \theta = \frac{1}{4}$, find $\csc \theta$. $-\frac{\sqrt{17}}{4}$

20. If $\sin \theta = -\frac{1}{2}$, find $\cos \theta$. $-\frac{\sqrt{3}}{2}$

Solve for values of θ between 270° and 360°.

 B

21. If $\cos \theta = \frac{5}{13}$, find $\sin \theta$. $-\frac{12}{13}$

22. If $\tan \theta = -1$, find $\sec \theta$. $\sqrt{2}$

23. If $\sec \theta = \frac{5}{3}$, find $\cos \theta$. $\frac{3}{5}$

24. If $\csc \theta = -\frac{5}{3}$, find $\cos \theta$. $\frac{4}{5}$

Lesson 14–2   Trigonometric Identities   **839**

Additional Answers

1. Given an angle in standard position whose measurement is θ and which intersects the circle at point (x, y), $x = \cos \theta$ and $y = \sin \theta$.

2. It means to write the expression as a numerical value or in terms of a single trigonometric function.

8. $\sin x \sec x \overset{?}{=} \tan x$

$\sin x \dfrac{1}{\cos x} \overset{?}{=} \tan x$

$\dfrac{\sin x}{\cos x} \overset{?}{=} \tan x$

$\tan x = \tan x$

---

3 PRACTICE/APPLY

Check for Understanding

Exercises 1–12 are designed to help you assess your students' understanding through reading, writing, speaking, and modeling. You should work through Exercises 1–3 with your students and then monitor their work on Exercises 4–12.

Error Analysis

Students may confuse the $\sin^2 A + \cos^2 A = 1$ from the unit circle and $x^2 + y^2 = r^2$ from the equation of a circle with center 0 and radius r. They may write $\sin^2 A + \cos^2 A = r^2$. But $\sin^2 A + \cos^2 A = 1$ for all circles with center 0. Substitute $r \cos A$ for x and $r \sin A$ for y.

Assignment Guide
Core: 13–43 odd, 45–52 **Enriched:** 14–40 even, 41–52

For **Extra Practice,** see p. 909.

The red A, B, and C flags, printed only in the Teacher's Wraparound Edition, indicate the level of difficulty of the exercises.

Practice Masters, p. 100

14-2   NAME_____   DATE_____
Practice   Student Edition Pages 835–840

Trigonometric Identities

Solve for values of θ between 0° and 90°.

1. If $\cos \theta = \frac{5}{13}$, find $\sin \theta$. $\frac{12}{13}$

2. If $\sec \theta = 2$, find $\tan \theta$. $\sqrt{3}$

3. If $\cot \theta = \frac{1}{2}$, find $\sin \theta$. $\frac{2\sqrt{5}}{5}$

4. If $\tan \theta = \frac{2}{5}$, find $\cot \theta$. $\frac{5}{2}$

Solve for values of θ between 180° and 270°.

5. If $\sin \theta = -\frac{15}{17}$, find $\sec \theta$. $-\frac{17}{8}$

6. If $\tan \theta = 4$, find $\sec \theta$. $-\sqrt{17}$

7. If $\csc \theta = -\frac{3}{2}$, find $\cot \theta$. $\frac{\sqrt{5}}{2}$

8. If $\sin \theta = -\frac{2}{9}$, find $\csc \theta$. $-\frac{9}{2}$

Solve for values of θ between 270° and 360°.

9. If $\cos \theta = \frac{3}{10}$, find $\cot \theta$. $-\frac{3\sqrt{91}}{91}$

10. If $\tan \theta = -\frac{1}{2}$, find $\sin \theta$. $-\frac{\sqrt{5}}{5}$

11. If $\csc \theta = -8$, find $\sec \theta$. $\frac{8\sqrt{7}}{21}$

12. If $\sec \theta = 3$, find $\cot \theta$. $-\frac{\sqrt{2}}{4}$

4 ASSESS

Closing Activity

Speaking Have students explain how trigonometric identities can be used to simplify an expression that contains trigonometric functions.

Chapter 14, Quiz A (Lessons 14-1 and 14-2), is available in the *Assessment and Evaluation Masters*, p. 380.

Additional Answers

42. The length of $\overline{AB}$ (the segment "touching" circle *O*) represents tan θ, and the length of $\overline{OB}$ (the segment "cutting" circle *O*) represents sec θ. Then, since *OA* = 1, the identity reflects the Pythagorean relationship between the lengths of the three sides of right triangle *OAB*.

45.

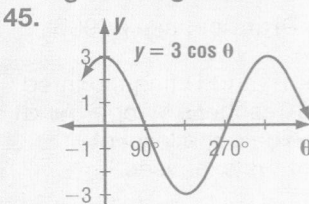

$y = 3 \cos \theta$

Enrichment Masters, p. 100

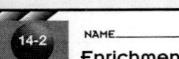

14-2 NAME_____ DATE_____ Student Edition Pages 835–840

Enrichment

Heron's Formula

Heron's formula can be used to find the area of a triangle if you know the lengths of the three sides. Consider any triangle *ABC*. Let *K* represent the area of △*ABC*. Then

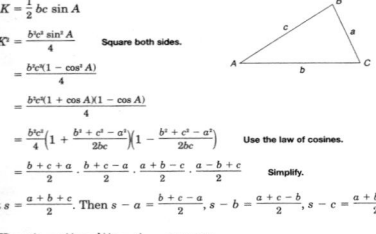

$K = \frac{1}{2} bc \sin A$

$K^2 = \frac{b^2c^2 \sin^2 A}{4}$ Square both sides.

$= \frac{b^2c^2(1 - \cos^2 A)}{4}$

$= \frac{b^2c^2(1 + \cos A)(1 - \cos A)}{4}$

$= \frac{b^2c^2}{4}\left(1 + \frac{b^2 + c^2 - a^2}{2bc}\right)\left(1 - \frac{b^2 + c^2 - a^2}{2bc}\right)$ Use the law of cosines.

$= \frac{b + c + a}{2} \cdot \frac{b + c - a}{2} \cdot \frac{a + b - c}{2} \cdot \frac{a - b + c}{2}$ Simplify.

Let $s = \frac{a + b + c}{2}$. Then $s - a = \frac{b + c - a}{2}, s - b = \frac{a + c - b}{2}, s - c = \frac{a + b - c}{2}$.

$K^2 = s(s - a)(s - b)(s - c)$ Substitute.

$K = \sqrt{s(s - a)(s - b)(s - c)}$

Heron's Formula | The area of △*ABC* is $\sqrt{s(s - a)(s - b)(s - c)}$, where $s = \frac{a + b + c}{2}$.

Use Heron's formula to find the area of △*ABC*.

1. $a = 3, b = 4.4, c = 7$ 4.1

2. $a = 8.2, b = 10.3, c = 9.5$ 36.8

3. $a = 31.3, b = 92.0, c = 67.9$ 782.9

4. $a = 0.54, b = 1.32, c = 0.78$ no such triangle

5. $a = 321, b = 178, c = 298$ 26,160.9

6. $a = 0.05, b = 0.08, c = 0.04$ 0.00082

7. $a = 21.5, b = 33.0, c = 41.7$ 351.6

8. $a = 2.08, b = 9.13, c = 8.99$ 9.3

840 *Chapter 14*

Simplify each expression.

25. $\csc \alpha \cos \alpha \tan \alpha$ **1**

26. $\cos \alpha \csc \alpha$ **cot α**

27. $\sec^2 \theta - 1$ **tan² θ**

28. $\sin x + \cos x \tan x$ **2 sin x**

29. $\frac{\tan \beta}{\sin \beta}$ **sec β**

30. $\frac{1 - \sin^2 \alpha}{\sin^2 \alpha}$ **cot² α**

31. $\tan \beta \cot \beta$ **1**

32. $\tan x \csc x$ **sec x**

33. $\sin \beta(1 + \cot^2 \beta)$ **csc β**

34. $\frac{1}{\sin^2 \theta} - \frac{\cos^2 \theta}{\sin^2 \theta}$ **1**

35. $\frac{\tan^2 \theta - \sin^2 \theta}{\tan^2 \theta \sin^2 \theta}$ **1**

36. $2(\csc^2 \theta - \cot^2 \theta)$ **2**

Show that each equation is an identity. **37–40. See Solutions Manual.**

37. $1 + \tan^2 \theta = \sec^2 \theta$

38. $1 + \cot^2 \theta = \csc^2 \theta$

39. $\sec \alpha - \cos \alpha = \sin \alpha \tan \alpha$

40. $\frac{\sec \theta}{\csc \theta} = \tan \theta$

Critical Thinking

41. If $\tan \beta = \frac{3}{4}$, find $\frac{\sin \beta \sec \beta}{\cot \beta}$. $\frac{9}{16}$

42. Refer to the diagram at the right to help you determine why tan² θ + 1 = sec² θ is a Pythagorean identity. It will help you to know that the words tangent and secant are based on the Latin words for "touch" and "cut," respectively.
See margin.

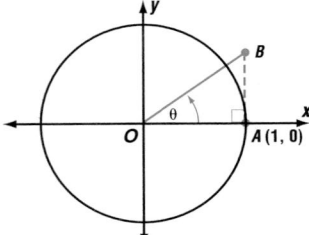

Applications and Problem Solving

43. **Running** Refer to the application at the beginning of the lesson. Find the measure of the angle of incline in Example 5. **about 14.5°**

44. **Amusement Parks** The angle-of-incline formula can be used for a person riding on a merry-go-round. Suppose the sine of the angle of incline of a person riding on an outside horse is $\frac{1}{5}$ and the diameter of the merry-go-round is 16 meters. Find the value of the angle of incline and the velocity of the merry-go-round.
about 11.5°; 4 m/s

45. See margin.   46. −0.5774

Mixed Review

45. **Trigonometry** Graph $y = 3 \cos \theta$. (Lesson 14–1)

46. **Trigonometry** Find tan (−390°). (Lesson 13–6)

47. Evaluate $C(12, 5)$. (Lesson 12–3) **792**

48. **Advertising** A store has 15 sofas, 12 lamps, and 10 tables for sale. How many different sofa-lamp-table combinations can be made for the sales brochure? (Lesson 12–1) **1800**

49. 18, 23, 28

49. Find the next three terms of the sequence 3, 8, 13, ... (Lesson 11–1)

50. Find all the roots of $x^3 + 3x^2 - 6x - 8 = 0$. (Lesson 8–4) **−4, −1, 2**

51. Solve $y^2 + 4y - 21 = 0$ by factoring. (Lesson 6–2) **3, −7**

52. Solve for *n* if $\begin{vmatrix} 4 & 3 & 6 \\ 2 & 2n & 7 \\ -4 & -3n & 3 \end{vmatrix} = -582$. (Lesson 4–4) **−4**

Extension

Problem Solving If $\cot \theta = \frac{4}{5}$ and θ is in the third quadrant, find

$$\frac{\cos \theta \csc \theta}{\tan \theta} \cdot \frac{(\csc \theta + 1)(\csc \theta - 1)}{\frac{1 - \cos^2 \theta}{1 - \sin^2 \theta}}.$$

$\frac{4096}{15,625}$

14–3A Graphing Technology
Verifying Trigonometric Identities

A Preview of Lesson 14–3

You can use a graphing calculator to determine whether an equation may be a trigonometric identity. To verify an identity, graph the expressions on each side of the equals sign as two separate functions. If the graphs of the two functions do not match, then the equation is not an identity. If the graphs do coincide, then the equation *may* be an identity. The equation must be verified algebraically to be sure that it is an identity.

Example **Use a graphing calculator to determine whether the equation $\sec^2 x - 1 = \sin^2 x \sec^2 x$ may be an identity.** *Be sure your calculator is in degree mode.*

Graph the equations $y = \sec^2 x - 1$ and $y = \sin^2 x \sec^2 x$ in the trigonometric window.

Remember that $\sec x = \frac{1}{\cos x}$.

Enter: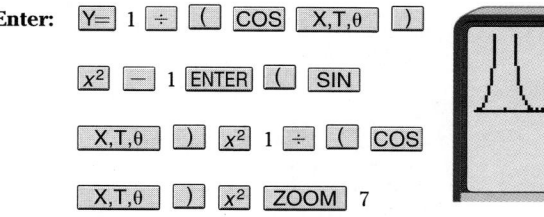

$\boxed{x^2}$ $\boxed{-}$ 1 $\boxed{\text{ENTER}}$ $\boxed{(}$ $\boxed{\text{SIN}}$

$\boxed{\text{X,T,}\theta}$ $\boxed{)}$ $\boxed{x^2}$ 1 $\boxed{\div}$ $\boxed{(}$ $\boxed{\text{COS}}$

$\boxed{\text{X,T,}\theta}$ $\boxed{)}$ $\boxed{x^2}$ $\boxed{\text{ZOOM}}$ 7

Since the graphs of the two functions coincide, the equation *may* be an identity.

EXERCISES

Use a graphing calculator to determine whether each equation may be an identity.

1. $(1 + \sin x)(1 - \sin x) = \cos^2 x$ **yes** **2.** $\cot x + \tan x = \csc x \cot x$ **no**

3. $\dfrac{\sec^2 x}{\tan x} = \sec x \csc x$ **yes** **4.** $\dfrac{1}{\sec x} + \dfrac{1}{\csc x} = 1$ **no**

5. $\sin(90° - x) = \cos x$ **yes** **6.** $\dfrac{1}{\sec x \tan x} = \csc x - \sin x$ **yes**

7. $\dfrac{\tan x}{1 + \tan x} = \dfrac{\sin x}{\sin x + \cos x}$ **yes** **8.** $\cot^2 x (\sec^2 x - 1) = 1$ **yes**

9. $\cos 2x = 1 - 2\sin^2 x$ **yes** **10.** $\dfrac{\csc(-x)}{\sec(-x)} = -\cot x$ **yes**

11. $\cos 3x + 1 = 2\cos^2 x$ **yes** **12.** $\dfrac{\csc^2 x}{\csc x - 1} = \dfrac{1 + \sin x}{\sin x}$ **no**

Lesson 14–3A Graphing Technology: Verifying Trigonometric Identities **841**

Using Technology
This lesson offers an excellent opportunity for using technology in your algebra classroom. For more information on using technology, see *Graphing Calculators in the Mathematics Classroom*, one of the titles in the Glencoe Mathematics Professional Series.

4 ASSESS

Observing students working with technology is an excellent method of assessment.

14-3A LESSON NOTES

NCTM Standards: 1–6, 8–9

Objective
Use a graphing calculator to verify trigonometric identities.

Recommended Time
15 minutes

Instructional Resources
Graphing Calculator Masters, pp. 59 and 60

These masters provide keystroking instruction for this lesson for the TI-81 and Casio graphing calculators.

1 FOCUS

Motivating the Lesson
Write the trigonometric identity $\cos^2 x + \sin^2 x = 1$ on the chalkboard or overhead. Ask students if this is a true statement. Then ask them how they can show whether it is true. Show students that they can graph both sides on a graphing calculator to see if the equation may be an identity.

2 TEACH

Teaching Tip Graphing two functions on a graphing calculator does not prove that they are identities because the two may be off by a very small fraction and you may not be able to tell this on your calculator.

3 PRACTICE/APPLY

Assignment Guide

Core: 1–12
Enriched: 1–12

NCTM Standards: 1–6, 9

Instructional Resources

- Study Guide Master 14-3
- Practice Master 14-3
- Enrichment Master 14-3
- Assessment and Evaluation Masters, pp. 379–380

 Transparency 14-3A contains the 5-Minute Check for this lesson; **Transparency 14-3B** contains a teaching aid for this lesson.

Recommended Pacing	
Honors Pacing	Day 5 of 11
Block Scheduling*	Day 3 of 6

 *For more information on pacing and possible lesson plans, refer to the *Block Scheduling Booklet*.

1 FOCUS

 ### 5-Minute Check
(over Lesson 14-2)

Simplify.

1. $\cos^2 \alpha + \tan^2 \alpha \cdot \cos^2 \alpha$ **1**
2. $\dfrac{(\cos \theta \cdot \csc \theta)}{\tan \theta}$ **$\cot^2 \theta$**
3. Find $\cos \beta$ if $\tan \beta = -\dfrac{3}{5}$ and $90° \le \beta \le 180°$. **$-\dfrac{5\sqrt{34}}{34}$**
4. Find $\sin \theta$ if $\tan \theta = \sqrt{7}$ and $180° \le \theta \le 270°$. **$-\dfrac{\sqrt{14}}{4}$**
5. In which quadrants is cosecant a decreasing function? **I and IV**

Motivating the Lesson

Questioning Ask students how many of them have ever used the phrase, "in other words." Ask them what it means. Point out that there is more than one way to say the same thing. Verifying trigonometric identities relates equal expressions in order to form a logical chain between two sides of an equation.

14-3

Verifying Trigonometric Identities

What YOU'LL LEARN

- To verify trigonometric identities, and
- to solve problems by working backward.

Why IT'S IMPORTANT

You can use trigonometric identities to solve problems involving physics.

APPLICATION
Physics

The device in the diagram at the right is called a *conical pendulum* because of the conical surface swept out by line segment $\overline{SP}$ as the weight rotates about the line. A formula for the relationship between the length L of the string and the angle θ that the string makes with the vertical line is given by the equation $L = \dfrac{g \sec \theta}{\omega^2}$ where g is the acceleration of gravity and ω (the Greek letter omega) is the angular velocity of the weight about the vertical line in radians per second. Is the equation $L = \dfrac{g \tan \theta}{\omega^2 \sin \theta}$ also an equation for the relationship between L and θ? *This problem will be solved in Example 3.*

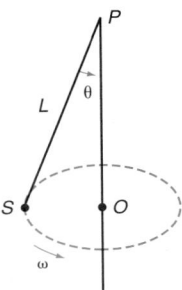

You can use the basic trigonometric identities and the definitions of the trigonometric functions to verify other identities. For example, suppose you wish to know whether $\tan \theta (\cot \theta + \tan \theta) = \sec^2 \theta$ is an identity. It is not sufficient to try some value of θ and conclude that the statement is true for all values of θ if it is true for that one. To verify that an equation is an identity, you must consider the general case.

Verifying an identity is like checking the solution of an equation. You do not know whether the expressions on the two sides of the equation are equal. That is what you are trying to verify. So, you must simplify one or both sides *separately* until they are the same. Often, it is easier to work with only one side of the equation. You may choose either side.

$$\tan \theta (\cot \theta + \tan \theta) \overset{?}{=} \sec^2 \theta \quad \textit{Simplify the left side only.}$$

$$\tan \theta \left(\frac{1}{\tan \theta} + \tan \theta\right) \overset{?}{=} \sec^2 \theta \quad \textit{cot } \theta = \frac{1}{\tan \theta}$$

$$1 + \tan^2 \theta \overset{?}{=} \sec^2 \theta \quad \textit{Distributive property}$$

$$\sec^2 \theta \overset{?}{=} \sec^2 \theta \quad \textit{1 + tan}^2 \theta = \sec^2 \theta$$

Thus, $\tan \theta (\cot \theta + \tan \theta) = \sec^2 \theta$ is an identity.

Example **1** **Verify that** $\dfrac{\sin^2 x}{1 - \cos x} = 1 + \cos x$ **is an identity.**

Notice that if the denominator, $1 - \cos x$, is multiplied by $1 + \cos x$, the result is $1 - \cos^2 x$, which equals $\sin^2 x$.

$$\dfrac{\sin^2 x}{1 - \cos x} \stackrel{?}{=} 1 + \cos x \qquad \textit{Multiply the numerator and denominator by } 1 + \cos x.$$

$$\dfrac{\sin^2 x}{1 - \cos x} \cdot \dfrac{1 + \cos x}{1 + \cos x} \stackrel{?}{=} 1 + \cos x \qquad \textit{Simplify.}$$

$$\dfrac{\sin^2 x (1 + \cos x)}{1 - \cos^2 x} \stackrel{?}{=} 1 + \cos x \qquad \textit{Simplify.}$$

$$\dfrac{\sin^2 x (1 + \cos x)}{\sin^2 x} \stackrel{?}{=} 1 + \cos x$$

$$1 + \cos x = 1 + \cos x$$

The identity could also be verified by working from the right side. The first step would be to multiply $1 + \cos x$ by $\dfrac{1 - \cos x}{1 - \cos x}$.

When you verify a trigonometric identity, you are really working backward. In Example 1, notice that the last step, $1 + \cos x = 1 + \cos x$, is actually the first step in the reasoning process. Since that step is clearly true, you can conclude that the next-to-last step is also true and write it with the symbol "$=$" instead of the symbol "$\stackrel{?}{=}$". Reason in the same manner to the step before that, continuing all the way back to the original equation, which now can be written without the "$\stackrel{?}{=}$" symbol: $\dfrac{\sin^2 x}{1 - \cos x} = 1 + \cos x$.

You can use the problem-solving strategy **work backward** to solve other types of problems.

Example **2** **Find the sum of the reciprocals of two numbers whose sum is 9 and whose product is 18.**

PROBLEM SOLVING

Work Backward

Let x and y be the numbers.

We could set up these equations.
$$x + y = 9$$
$$xy = 18$$

Solving this system of equations is complicated. Rather than using this approach, work backward. The desired outcome is $\dfrac{1}{x} + \dfrac{1}{y}$.

$$\dfrac{1}{x} + \dfrac{1}{y} = \dfrac{y}{xy} + \dfrac{x}{xy} \qquad \textit{The LCD is xy.}$$

$$= \dfrac{x + y}{xy}$$

Looking back to our two original equations, we can see that $x + y = 9$ and $xy = 18$. So, $\dfrac{x + y}{xy} = \dfrac{9}{18}$ or $\dfrac{1}{2}$. The sum of the reciprocals is $\dfrac{1}{2}$.

Alternative Learning Styles

Kinesthetic To help students learn the basic trigonometric identities, have them write each side of the identity on separate cards. Have students match the cards that go together.

2 TEACH

Teaching Tip Caution students that identities hold for all values of the variable except those for which either side of the equation is undefined.

In-Class Examples

For Example 1
Verify that $\tan \theta \sin \theta = \dfrac{1 - \cos^2 \theta}{\cos \theta}$ is an identity.

$$\tan \theta \sin \theta \stackrel{?}{=} \dfrac{\sin^2 \theta}{\cos \theta}$$

$$\tan \theta \sin \theta \stackrel{?}{=} \dfrac{\sin \theta}{\cos \theta} \cdot \dfrac{\sin \theta}{1}$$

$$\tan \theta \sin \theta = \tan \theta \sin \theta$$

For Example 2
Find the sum of the reciprocals of two numbers whose sum is 12 and whose product is 36.
$\dfrac{1}{3}$

Teaching Tip Emphasize that students should look for relationships among the given expressions to determine the best expression to use when substituting.

In-Class Examples

For Example 3

Verify that $\dfrac{\cos \theta}{\sec \theta + 1} + \dfrac{\cos \theta}{\sec \theta - 1} = 2 \cot^2 \theta$ is an identity.

$\dfrac{\cos \theta (\sec \theta - 1)}{(\sec \theta + 1)(\sec \theta - 1)} +$

$\dfrac{\cos \theta (\sec \theta + 1)}{(\sec \theta + 1)(\sec \theta - 1)} \stackrel{?}{=} 2 \cot^2 \theta$

$\dfrac{\cos \theta \sec \theta - \cos \theta}{\sec^2 \theta - 1} +$

$\dfrac{\cos \theta \sec \theta + \cos \theta}{\sec^2 \theta - 1} \stackrel{?}{=} 2 \cot^2 \theta$

$\dfrac{2 \cos \theta \sec \theta}{\tan^2 \theta} \stackrel{?}{=} 2 \cot^2 \theta$

$\dfrac{2 \cos \theta \cdot \dfrac{1}{\cos \theta}}{\tan^2 \theta} \stackrel{?}{=} 2 \cot^2 \theta$

$\dfrac{2}{\tan^2 \theta} \stackrel{?}{=} 2 \cot^2 \theta$

$2 \cot^2 \theta = 2 \cot^2 \theta$

For Example 4

Verify that $\csc x + 1 = \dfrac{\cot^2 x}{\csc x - 1}$ is an identity.

$\csc x + 1 \stackrel{?}{=} \dfrac{\cot^2 x(\csc x + 1)}{(\csc x - 1)(\csc x + 1)}$

$\csc x + 1 \stackrel{?}{=} \dfrac{\cot^2 x(\csc x + 1)}{(\csc^2 x - 1)}$

$\csc x + 1 \stackrel{?}{=} \dfrac{\cot^2 x(\csc x + 1)}{\cot^2 x}$

$\csc x + 1 = \csc x + 1$

Study Guide Masters, p. 101

14-3

NAME_____ DATE _____

Student Edition
Pages 842–846

Study Guide

Verifying Trigonometric Identities

The basic trigonometric identities along with the definitions of the trigonometric functions can be used to verify other identities. Verifying an identity is like checking the solution to an equation. To verify that the expressions on each side are equal, you must simplify one or both sides **separately** until they are the same.

Example: Verify $\tan^2 x - \sin^2 x = \tan^2 x \sin^2 x$.

$\tan^2 x - \sin^2 x \stackrel{?}{=} \tan^2 x \sin^2 x$

$\dfrac{\sin^2 x}{\cos^2 x} - \sin^2 x \stackrel{?}{=} \tan^2 x \sin^2 x \quad \tan x = \dfrac{\sin x}{\cos x}$

$\left(\dfrac{1}{\cos^2 x} - 1\right) \sin^2 x \stackrel{?}{=} \tan^2 x \sin^2 x \quad$ Distributive property

$(\sec^2 x - 1) \sin^2 x \stackrel{?}{=} \tan^2 x \sin^2 x \quad \sec x = \dfrac{1}{\cos x}$

$(\tan^2 x) \sin^2 x = \tan^2 x \sin^2 x \quad 1 + \tan^2 x = \sec^2 x$

Verify that each of the following is an identity.

1. $\tan \beta(\cot \beta + \tan \beta) = \sec^2 \beta$

$\tan \beta\left(\dfrac{1}{\tan \beta} + \tan \beta\right) \stackrel{?}{=} \sec^2 \beta$

$1 + \tan^2 \beta \stackrel{?}{=} \sec^2 \beta$

$\sec^2 \beta = \sec^2 \beta$

2. $\tan^2 \theta \cos^2 \theta = 1 - \cos^2 \theta$

$\left(\dfrac{\sin^2 \theta}{\cos^2 \theta}\right) \cos^2 \theta \stackrel{?}{=} 1 - \cos^2 \theta$

$\sin^2 \theta \stackrel{?}{=} 1 - \cos^2 \theta$

$1 - \cos^2 \theta = 1 - \cos^2 \theta$

3. $\csc x \sec x = \cot x + \tan x$

$\left(\dfrac{1}{\sin x}\right)\left(\dfrac{1}{\cos x}\right) \stackrel{?}{=} \dfrac{\cos x}{\sin x} + \dfrac{\sin x}{\cos x}$

$\dfrac{1}{\sin x \cos x} \stackrel{?}{=} \dfrac{\cos^2 x + \sin^2 x}{\sin x \cos x}$

$\dfrac{1}{\sin x \cos x} = \dfrac{1}{\sin x \cos x}$

4. $\cos^2 x + \tan^2 x \cos^2 x = 1$

$\cos^2 x + \left(\dfrac{\sin^2 x}{\cos^2 x}\right) \cos^2 x \stackrel{?}{=} 1$

$\cos^2 x + \sin^2 x \stackrel{?}{=} 1$

$1 = 1$

5. $\tan \theta \sin \theta = \dfrac{1 - \cos^2 \theta}{\cos \theta}$

$\tan \theta \sin \theta \stackrel{?}{=} \dfrac{\sin^2 \theta}{\cos \theta}$

$\tan \theta \sin \theta \stackrel{?}{=} \dfrac{\sin \theta}{\cos \theta} \cdot \sin \theta$

$\tan \theta \sin \theta = \tan \theta \sin \theta$

6. $\sin \alpha(\csc \alpha - \sin \alpha) = \cos^2 \alpha$

$\sin \alpha \csc \alpha - \sin^2 \alpha \stackrel{?}{=} \cos^2 \alpha$

$\sin \alpha\left(\dfrac{1}{\sin \alpha}\right) - \sin^2 \alpha \stackrel{?}{=} \cos^2 \alpha$

$1 - \sin^2 \alpha \stackrel{?}{=} \cos^2 \alpha$

$\cos^2 \alpha = \cos^2 \alpha$

844 Chapter 14

Example ③ Refer to the application at the beginning of the lesson.

Does $\dfrac{g \sec \theta}{\omega^2} = \dfrac{g \tan \theta}{\omega^2 \sin \theta}$?

APPLICATION

Physics

$\dfrac{g \sec \theta}{\omega^2} \stackrel{?}{=} \dfrac{g \tan \theta}{\omega^2 \sin \theta} \quad$ Simplify the right side.

$\dfrac{g \sec \theta}{\omega^2} \stackrel{?}{=} \dfrac{g \left(\dfrac{\sin \theta}{\cos \theta}\right)}{\omega^2 \sin \theta} \quad \tan \theta = \dfrac{\sin \theta}{\cos \theta}$

$\dfrac{g \sec \theta}{\omega^2} \stackrel{?}{=} \dfrac{g \left(\dfrac{1}{\cos \theta}\right)}{\omega^2 \cdot 1} \quad$ Divide the numerator and denominator of the right side by sin θ.

$\dfrac{g \sec \theta}{\omega^2} = \dfrac{g \sec \theta}{\omega^2} \quad \dfrac{1}{\cos \theta} = \sec \theta$

So, the formulas are equivalent.

The following suggestions may be helpful as you verify trigonometric identities.

- Start with the more complicated side of the equation. Transform the expression into the form of the simpler side.

   or

- Work with each side of the equation at the same time. Transform each expression separately into the same form.

- Substitute one or more basic trigonometric identities to simplify the expression.

- Try factoring or multiplying to simplify the expression.

- Multiply both the numerator and the denominator by the same trigonometric expression.

- If nothing else seems to work, write both sides of the identity in terms of sine and cosine only. Then simplify each side as much as possible.

Example ④ Verify that $1 - \tan^4 \beta = 2 \sec^2 \beta - \sec^4 \beta$ is an identity.

$1 - \tan^4 \beta \stackrel{?}{=} 2 \sec^2 \beta - \sec^4 \beta$

$(1 - \tan^2 \beta)(1 + \tan^2 \beta) \stackrel{?}{=} \sec^2 \beta (2 - \sec^2 \beta) \quad$ Factor each side.

$[1 - (\sec^2 \beta - 1)][\sec^2 \beta] \stackrel{?}{=} (2 - \sec^2 \beta)(\sec^2 \beta) \quad 1 + \tan^2 \beta = \sec^2 \beta$

$(2 - \sec^2 \beta)(\sec^2 \beta) = (2 - \sec^2 \beta)(\sec^2 \beta) \quad$ Simplify.

Thus, the identity is verified.

844 Chapter 14 Using Trigonometric Graphs and Identities

Reteaching ▬▬▬

Decision Making Have students verify some trigonometric identities by numerical substitution. For each value that the students pick for the angle, have them compute the values of both sides of the identity. To avoid roundoff errors, round results to two fewer places than used in the calculations. Stress that this verifies the identity only for the value chosen.

Communicating Mathematics

Study the lesson. Then complete the following.

1. **Describe** the various methods you can use to identify trigonometric identities.   See students' work.

2. **Verify** the identity in Example 3 by simplifying each side separately into the same trigonometric expression.   See margin.
3–8. See Solutions Manual.

Guided Practice

Verify that each of the following is an identity.

3. $\sin\theta\sec\theta\cot\theta = 1$

4. $\tan^2 x\cos^2 x = 1 - \cos^2 x$

5. $\csc y\sec y = \cot y + \tan y$

6. $\tan\alpha\sin\alpha\cos\alpha\csc^2\alpha = 1$

7. $\dfrac{\sec\beta + \csc\beta}{1 + \tan\beta} = \csc\beta$

8. $\dfrac{1 - 2\cos^2\beta}{\sin\beta\cos\beta} = \tan\beta - \cot\beta$

9. **Physics**   Philip is building a clock that will use a conical pendulum to keep time. If the pendulum rotates at an angular velocity of 8 radians per second, the clock will keep the correct time. Due to the shape of the clock, he wants the pendulum to swing outward at an angle of 40° from the vertical. How long should he make the pendulum, in centimeters? (*Hint:* The acceleration due to gravity is 980 cm/s².)   about 20 cm
10–29. See Solutions Manual.

EXERCISES

Practice

Verify that each of the following is an identity.

 10. $\sec^2 x - \tan^2 x = \tan x\cot x$

11. $\dfrac{1}{\sec^2\theta} + \dfrac{1}{\csc^2\theta} = 1$

12. $\tan^2\theta - \sin^2\theta = \tan^2\theta\sin^2\theta$

13. $\dfrac{\sec\alpha}{\sin\alpha} - \dfrac{\sin\alpha}{\cos\alpha} = \cot\alpha$

14. $\dfrac{\sin\alpha}{1 - \cos\alpha} + \dfrac{1 - \cos\alpha}{\sin\alpha} = 2\csc\alpha$

15. $\dfrac{\sin\theta}{\sec\theta} = \dfrac{1}{\tan\theta + \cot\theta}$

 16. $\dfrac{1 - \cos x}{\sin x} = \dfrac{\sin x}{1 + \cos x}$

17. $\dfrac{\sec\theta + 1}{\tan\theta} = \dfrac{\tan\theta}{\sec\theta - 1}$

18. $\dfrac{1 - \cos x}{1 + \cos x} = (\csc x - \cot x)^2$

19. $\cos^2 x + \tan^2 x\cos^2 x = 1$

20. $\dfrac{\cot\theta + \csc\theta}{\sin\theta + \tan\theta} = \cot\theta\csc\theta$

21. $\dfrac{1 + \tan^2\theta}{\csc^2\theta} = \tan^2\theta$

22. $\dfrac{1 + \sin x}{\sin x} = \dfrac{\cot^2 x}{\csc x - 1}$

23. $\dfrac{\cos y}{1 + \sin y} + \dfrac{\cos y}{1 - \sin y} = 2\sec y$

 24. $\cos^4\theta - \sin^4\theta = \cos^2\theta - \sin^2\theta$

25. $\cot x(\cot x + \tan x) = \csc^2 x$

26. $\dfrac{\tan^2 x}{\sec x - 1} = 1 + \dfrac{1}{\cos x}$

27. $\dfrac{1 + \tan\alpha}{1 + \cot\alpha} = \dfrac{\sin\alpha}{\cos\alpha}$

28. $\sin\theta + \cos\theta = \dfrac{1 + \tan\theta}{\sec\theta}$

29. $1 + \sec^2 x\sin^2 x = \sec^2 x$

Critical Thinking

30. Create a trigonometric identity. Explain the method you used to do this. Then trade with another student and verify each other's identities.   See students' work.

Applications and Problem Solving

31. **Work Backward**   After cashing her paycheck, Estrella paid her father back the $15 she had borrowed. She then spent half of the remaining money on clothes, and then spent half of what remained on a concert ticket. She bought a cassette tape for $7.45 and had $10.25 left. What was the amount of Estrella's paycheck? $85.80

Additional Answer

2. $\dfrac{g\sec\theta}{\omega^2} = \dfrac{g\dfrac{1}{\cos\theta}}{\omega^2}$

$= \dfrac{g}{\omega^2}\cdot\dfrac{1}{\cos\theta}$

$= \dfrac{g}{\omega^2\cos\theta}$

$\dfrac{g\tan\theta}{\omega^2\sin\theta} = \dfrac{g\dfrac{\sin\theta}{\cos\theta}}{\omega^2\sin\theta}$

$= \dfrac{g}{\omega^2}\cdot\dfrac{\sin\theta}{\cos\theta}\cdot\dfrac{1}{\sin\theta}$

$= \dfrac{g}{\omega^2\cos\theta}$

---

3 PRACTICE/APPLY

Check for Understanding
Exercises 1–9 are designed to help you assess your students' understanding through reading, writing, speaking, and modeling. You should work through Exercises 1–2 with your students and then monitor their work on Exercises 3–9.

Assignment Guide

Core: 11–29 odd, 30, 31, 33–38
Enriched: 10–28 even, 30–38
All: Self Test, 1–10

For **Extra Practice,** see p. 909.

The red A, B, and C flags, printed only in the Teacher's Wraparound Edition, indicate the level of difficulty of the exercises.

Practice Masters, p. 101

14-3 NAME_____ DATE_____
Practice   Student Edition Pages 842–846

Verifying Trigonometric Identities
Verify that each of the following is an identity.

1. $(1 + \sin\theta)(1 - \sin\theta) = \dfrac{1}{\sec^2\theta}$
$(1 + \sin\theta)(1 - \sin\theta) \overset{?}{=} \dfrac{1}{\sec^2\theta}$
$1 - \sin^2\theta \overset{?}{=} \cos^2\theta$
$\cos^2\theta = \cos^2\theta$

2. $\cos^2 x\cot^2 x = \cot^2 x - \cos^2 x$
$\cos^2 x\cot^2 x \overset{?}{=} \cot^2 x - \cos^2 x$
$\cos^2 x\cdot\dfrac{\cos^2 x}{\sin^2 x} \overset{?}{=} \dfrac{\cos^2 x}{\sin^2 x} - \dfrac{\cos^2 x\sin^2 x}{\sin^2 x}$
$\dfrac{\cos^4 x}{\sin^2 x} \overset{?}{=} \dfrac{\cos^2 x(1 - \sin^2 x)}{\sin^2 x}$
$\dfrac{\cos^4 x}{\sin^2 x} = \dfrac{\cos^4 x}{\sin^2 x}$

3. $\tan^4 w + 2\tan^2 w + 1 = \sec^4 w$
$\tan^4 w + 2\tan^2 w + 1 \overset{?}{=} \sec^4 w$
$(\tan^2 w + 1)^2 \overset{?}{=} \sec^4 w$
$(\sec^2 w)^2 \overset{?}{=} \sec^4 w$
$\sec^4 w = \sec^4 w$

4. $\sin^2 x(\csc^2 x + \sec^2 x) = \sec^2 x$
$\sin^2 x(\csc^2 x + \sec^2 x) \overset{?}{=} \sec^2 x$
$1 + \dfrac{\sin^2 x}{\cos^2 x} \overset{?}{=} \sec^2 x$
$1 + \tan^2 x \overset{?}{=} \sec^2 x$
$\sec^2 x = \sec^2 x$

5. $\dfrac{\sin x + \cos x}{1 - \sin x} = \dfrac{1 + \cot x}{\csc x - 1}$
$\dfrac{\sin x + \cos x}{1 - \sin x} \overset{?}{=} \dfrac{1 + \cot x}{\csc x - 1}$
$\dfrac{\frac{\sin x}{\sin x} + \frac{\cos x}{\sin x}}{\frac{1}{\sin x} - \frac{\sin x}{\sin x}} \overset{?}{=} \dfrac{1 + \cot x}{\csc x - 1}$
$\dfrac{1 + \cot x}{\csc x - 1} = \dfrac{1 + \cot x}{\csc x - 1}$

6. $\dfrac{1 - \tan x}{1 + \tan x} = \dfrac{\cot x - 1}{\cot x + 1}$
$\dfrac{1 - \tan x}{1 + \tan x} \overset{?}{=} \dfrac{\cot x - 1}{\cot x + 1}$
$\dfrac{\frac{1}{\tan x} - \frac{\tan x}{\tan x}}{\frac{1}{\tan x} + \frac{\tan x}{\tan x}} \overset{?}{=} \dfrac{\cot x - 1}{\cot x + 1}$
$\dfrac{\cot x - 1}{\cot x + 1} = \dfrac{\cot x - 1}{\cot x + 1}$

Closing Activity

Speaking Have students explain what is meant by verifying a trigonometric identity.

Chapter 14, Quiz B (Lesson 14-3), is available in the *Assessment and Evaluation Masters*, p. 380.

Mid-Chapter Test (Lessons 14-1 through 14-3) is available in the *Assessment and Evaluation Masters*, p. 379.

SELF TEST

The Self Test provides students with a brief review of the concepts and skills in Lessons 14-1 through 14-3. Lesson numbers are given to the right of exercises or instruction lines so students can review concepts not yet mastered.

Enrichment Masters, p. 101

14-3

NAME_____ DATE _____

Student Edition
Pages 842–846

Enrichment

Planetary Orbits

The orbit of a planet around the sun is an ellipse with the sun at one focus. Let the pole of a polar coordinate system be that focus and the polar axis be toward the other focus. The polar equation of an ellipse is $r = \frac{2ep}{1 - e\cos\theta}$. Since $2p = \frac{b^2}{c}$ and $b^2 = a^2 - c^2$, $2p = \frac{a^2 - c^2}{c} = \frac{a^2}{c}\left(1 - \frac{c^2}{a^2}\right)$.

Because $e = \frac{c}{a}$, $2p = a\left(\frac{a}{c}\right)\left(1 - \left(\frac{c}{a}\right)^2\right) = a\left(\frac{1}{e}\right)(1 - e^2)$.

Therefore $2ep = a(1 - e^2)$. Substituting into the polar equation of an ellipse yields an equation that is useful for finding distances from the planet to the sun.

$$r = \frac{a(1 - e^2)}{1 - e\cos\theta}$$

Note that e is the eccentricity of the orbit and a is the length of the semi-major axis of the ellipse. Also, a is the mean distance of the planet from the sun.

Example: The mean distance of Venus from the sun is 67.24 × 10⁶ miles and the eccentricity of its orbit is .006788. Find the minimum and maximum distances of Venus from the sun.
The minimum distance occurs when $\theta = \pi$.
$r = \frac{67.24 \times 10^6(1 - 0.006788^2)}{1 - 0.006788\cos\pi} = 66.78 \times 10^6$ miles
The maximum distance occurs when $\theta = 0$.
$r = \frac{67.24 \times 10^6(1 - 0.006788^2)}{1 - 0.006788\cos 0} = 67.70 \times 10^6$ miles

Complete each of the following.

1. The mean distance of Mars from the sun is 141.64 × 10⁶ miles and the eccentricity of its orbit is 0.093382. Find the minimum and maximum distances of Mars from the sun.
max. dist. = 15.49 × 10⁷ mi   min. dist. = 12.84 × 10⁷ mi

2. The minimum distance of Earth from the sun is 91.445 × 10⁶ miles and the eccentricity of its orbit is 0.016734. Find the mean and maximum distances of Earth from the sun.
max. dist. = 93.00 × 10⁶ mi   mean dist. = 91.47 × 10⁶ mi

32. Physics If a ball is hit or kicked from ground level, the maximum height it will reach is given by the formula $h = \frac{v_0^2 \sin^2\theta}{2g}$, where θ is the measure of the angle between the ground and the initial path of the ball, v_0 is its initial velocity in meters per second, and g is the acceleration due to gravity. The value of g is 9.8 m/s².

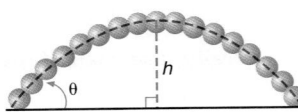

32a. See Solutions Manual.

32b. No, its maximum height will be about 66 meters.

a. Show that the formula $h = \frac{v_0^2 \tan^2\theta}{2g\sec^2\theta}$ is equivalent to the one given above.

b. If a baseball is hit with an initial velocity of 47 meters per second at an initial angle of 50° from the ground, find the maximum height the ball will reach, to see whether it will stay under the roof of the Astrodome, which is about 60 meters high.

c. For a given initial velocity, a ball's maximum horizontal range is attained when the angle of elevation is 45°. If a ball was thrown to a height of 50 meters and traveled as far horizontally as it possibly could, what was its initial velocity? **about 44 meters per second**

Mixed Review

33. Trigonometry Simplify $\frac{\sec\alpha}{\sin\alpha} - \frac{\sin\alpha}{\cos\alpha}$. (Lesson 14–2) **cot α**

34. Trigonometry Find the exact value of $\cos\frac{17\pi}{3}$. (Lesson 13–3) $\frac{1}{2}$

35. $\frac{1}{18}$

35. Probability Two dice are rolled. Find the probability of rolling a 3 and a 4. (Lesson 12–5)

36. Find the sum of the infinite geometric series, $12 + 6 + 3 + ...$, if it exists. (Lesson 11–5) **24**

37. Simplify $\left(x^2y^2\right)^2 x^3y^3$. (Lesson 5–1) x^7y^7

38. Suppose $h(x) = [3x - 1]$. Find $h(-2.1)$. (Lesson 2–6) **−8**

SELF TEST

State the amplitude (if it exists) and period of each function. (Lesson 14–1)

1. $y = \cos 4\theta$ $1; \frac{\pi}{2}$ or 90°   2. $y = 3\sin\theta$ $3; 2\pi$ or 360°   3. $y = 2\tan\frac{1}{5}\theta$ none; 5π or 900°

Graph each function. (Lesson 14–1) **4–5. See Solutions Manual.**

4. $y = \frac{1}{2}\cos\theta$ 5. $y = 5\sin\theta$

Solve for values between 90° and 270°. (Lesson 14–2)

6. If $\cot\theta = -\frac{2}{5}$, find $\csc\theta$. $\frac{\sqrt{29}}{5}$ 7. If $\cos\alpha = -\frac{1}{2}$, find $\tan\alpha$. $\pm\sqrt{3}$

Verify that each of the following is an identity. (Lesson 14–3) **8–9. See Solutions Manual.**   **10.** $\frac{4}{7}$

8. $\sec\theta - \tan\theta\sin\theta = \cos\theta$ 9. $(1 - \sin^2\theta)(1 + \tan^2\theta) = 1$

10. Work Backward If the sum of two numbers is 4 and the product of the numbers is 7, find the sum of the reciprocals of these numbers. (Lesson 14–3)

846   *Chapter 14 Using Trigonometric Graphs and Identities*

Extension

Problem Solving Verify that $\frac{\sec x - \tan x}{\frac{\cos x}{1 + \sin x}} = 1$ is an identity.

$$(\sec x - \tan x) \cdot \frac{1 + \sin x}{\cos x} \stackrel{?}{=} 1$$

$$\left(\frac{1}{\cos x} - \frac{\sin x}{\cos x}\right) \cdot \frac{1 + \sin x}{\cos x} \stackrel{?}{=} 1$$

$$\frac{1 - \sin x}{\cos x} \cdot \frac{1 + \sin x}{\cos x} \stackrel{?}{=} 1$$

$$\frac{1 - \sin^2 x}{\cos^2 x} \stackrel{?}{=} 1$$

$$\frac{\cos^2 x}{\cos^2 x} \stackrel{?}{=} 1$$

$$1 = 1$$

Sum and Difference of Angles Formulas

What YOU'LL LEARN

- To find values of sine and cosine involving sum and difference formulas, and
- to verify identities by using the sum and difference formulas.

Why IT'S IMPORTANT

You can use sum and difference of angles formulas to solve problems involving geology and physical science.

CONNECTION
Physical Science

In Earth's northern hemisphere, the day with the most hours of sunlight occurs around June 22, and the day with the fewest hours of sunlight occurs around December 22. Suppose that E is the amount of light energy reaching a square foot patch of ground when the sun is directly overhead. When the sun is not overhead, the amount of light will depend on the angle that a ray of sunlight makes with the horizon.

Aurora Borealis, or "Northern Lights"

On June 22, the maximum amount of light energy falling on a square foot of ground at a certain location is given by $E \sin (113.5° − \phi)$ where ϕ (the Greek letter phi) is the latitude of the location. How would the amount of light energy that you receive compare with the amount received by other parts of Earth? *This problem will be solved in Example 2.*

It is often helpful to use the formulas for the trigonometric values of the difference or sum of two angles such as $\sin (113.5° − \phi)$. For example, you could find $\sin 15°$ by evaluating $\sin (45° − 30°)$. It is important to realize that $\sin (\alpha − \beta)$ is not the same as $\sin \alpha − \sin \beta$. The following discussion will show how to evaluate expressions like $\sin (\alpha − \beta)$ or $\cos (\alpha + \beta)$.

The figure at the right shows two angles α and β in standard position on the unit circle.

Use the distance formula to find d, where $(x_1, y_1) = (\cos \beta, \sin \beta)$ and $(x_2, y_2) = (\cos \alpha, \sin \alpha)$.

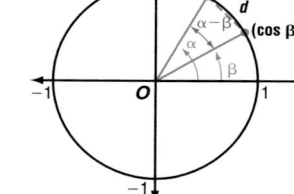

$d = \sqrt{(\cos \alpha − \cos \beta)^2 + (\sin \alpha − \sin \beta)^2}$

$d^2 = (\cos \alpha − \cos \beta)^2 + (\sin \alpha − \sin \beta)^2$

$d^2 = (\cos^2 \alpha − 2\cos \alpha \cos \beta + \cos^2 \beta) + (\sin^2 \alpha − 2 \sin \alpha \sin \beta + \sin^2 \beta)$

$d^2 = \cos^2 \alpha + \sin^2 \alpha + \cos^2 \beta + \sin^2 \beta − 2 \cos \alpha \cos \beta − 2 \sin \alpha \sin \beta$

$d^2 = 1 + 1 − 2 \cos \alpha \cos \beta − 2 \sin \alpha \sin \beta$ *$\sin^2 \alpha + \cos^2 \alpha = 1$ and $\sin^2 \beta + \cos^2 \beta = 1$*

$d^2 = 2 − 2 \cos \alpha \cos \beta − 2 \sin \alpha \sin \beta$

Lesson 14–4 Sum and Difference of Angles Formulas **847**

CAREER CHOICES

An **astronomer** uses the principles of physics and mathematics to learn about the nature of the universe, including the sun, moon, planets, stars, and galaxies.

A career in astronomy requires a doctoral degree.

For more information, contact:

American Astronomical Society, Educational Office
University of Texas
Department of Astronomy
Austin, TX 78712-1083

CAREER CHOICES

There are many careers within the space program, for example, aerospace engineers, pilots, exobiologists, geologists, and other specialists.

NCTM Standards: 1–6, 9

Instructional Resources

- Study Guide Master 14-4
- Practice Master 14-4
- Enrichment Master 14-4

Transparency 14-4A contains the 5-Minute Check for this lesson; **Transparency 14-4B** contains a teaching aid for this lesson.

Recommended Pacing	
Honors Pacing	Day 6 of 11
Block Scheduling*	Day 4 of 6 (along with Lesson 14-5)

*For more information on pacing and possible lesson plans, refer to the *Block Scheduling Booklet*.

1 FOCUS

5-Minute Check
(over Lesson 14-3)

True or False:

1. $\sin \theta \cdot \cot \theta = \cos \theta$ **true**
2. $1 + \tan^2 \theta = \cot^2 \theta$ **false**

Verify each identity.

3. $\tan^2 \beta \sin^2 \beta = \tan^2 \beta − \sin^2 \beta$

$\tan^2 \beta \sin^2 \beta$

$\overset{?}{=} \dfrac{\sin^2 \beta}{\cos^2 \beta} − \sin^2 \beta$

$\overset{?}{=} \sin^2 \beta \left(\dfrac{1}{\cos^2 \beta} − 1 \right)$

$\overset{?}{=} \sin^2 \beta (\sec^2 \beta − 1)$

$= \sin^2 \beta \tan^2 \beta$

4. $\cot^2 \alpha − \cot^2 \alpha \cdot \sec^2 \alpha = −1$

$\cot^2 \alpha (1 − \sec^2 \alpha) \overset{?}{=} −1$

$\cot^2 \alpha (−\tan^2 \alpha) \overset{?}{=} −1$

$\cot^2 \alpha − \left(\dfrac{1}{\cot^2 \alpha} \right) \overset{?}{=} −1$

$−1 = −1$

Motivating the Lesson
Situational Problem On a transparency, show a pizza drawn as a unit circle cut into 6 equal pieces. Ask students what must be done if seven students show up to eat the pizza and each student must have an equal share.

2 TEACH

Teaching Tip For Example 1, point out that any sum or difference equal to 105° can be used, such as 135° − 30°, but for convenience, choices should be made that use known sines and cosines.

In-Class Example

For Example 1
Find the exact value of each expression.

a. sin 15°
$\dfrac{\sqrt{6} - \sqrt{2}}{4}$

b. cos 300° $\dfrac{1}{2}$

Teaching Tip Students will find it helpful to memorize values of the sine and cosine function for 0°, 30°, 45°, 60°, 90°, 120°, 135°, 150°, and 180°.

Teaching Tip When using the formula for cos (α − β) to find a formula for cos (α + β), you may want to use the symmetry of the unit circle to illustrate these relationships.

Now find the value of d^2 when the angle having measure α − β is in standard position on the unit circle, as shown in the figure below.

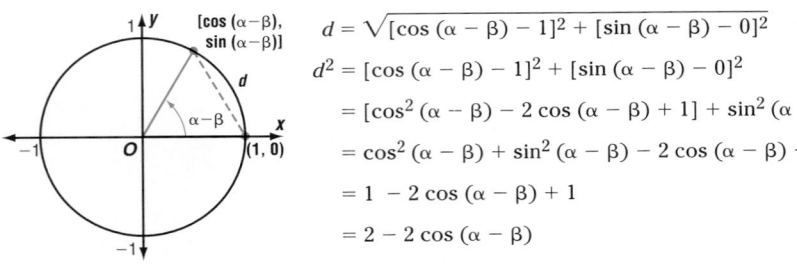

$$d = \sqrt{[\cos (\alpha - \beta) - 1]^2 + [\sin (\alpha - \beta) - 0]^2}$$

$$\begin{aligned}
d^2 &= [\cos (\alpha - \beta) - 1]^2 + [\sin (\alpha - \beta) - 0]^2 \\
&= [\cos^2 (\alpha - \beta) - 2 \cos (\alpha - \beta) + 1] + \sin^2 (\alpha - \beta) \\
&= \cos^2 (\alpha - \beta) + \sin^2 (\alpha - \beta) - 2 \cos (\alpha - \beta) + 1 \\
&= 1 - 2 \cos (\alpha - \beta) + 1 \\
&= 2 - 2 \cos (\alpha - \beta)
\end{aligned}$$

By equating the two expressions for d^2, you can find a formula for cos (α − β).

$$d^2 = d^2$$

$$2 - 2 \cos (\alpha - \beta) = 2 - 2 \cos \alpha \cos \beta - 2 \sin \alpha \sin \beta$$

$-1 + \cos (\alpha - \beta) = -1 + \cos \alpha \cos \beta + \sin \alpha \sin \beta$ *Divide each side by −2.*

$\cos (\alpha - \beta) = \cos \alpha \cos \beta + \sin \alpha \sin \beta$ *Add 1 to each side.*

Use the formula for cos (α − β) to find a formula for cos (α + β).

$$\begin{aligned}
\cos (\alpha + \beta) &= \cos [\alpha - (-\beta)] \\
&= \cos \alpha \cos (-\beta) + \sin \alpha \sin (-\beta) \\
&= \cos \alpha \cos \beta - \sin \alpha \sin \beta \quad \textit{cos } (-\beta) = \cos \beta; \sin (-\beta) = -\sin \beta
\end{aligned}$$

You can use a similar method to find formulas for sin (α + β) and sin (α − β).

Sum and Difference of Angles Formulas	**The following identities hold true for all values of α and β.** $\cos (\alpha \pm \beta) = \cos \alpha \cos \beta \mp \sin \alpha \sin \beta$ $\sin (\alpha \pm \beta) = \sin \alpha \cos \beta \pm \cos \alpha \sin \beta$

Notice the symbol ∓ in the formula for cos (α ± β). It means "minus or plus." In the cosine formula, when the sign on the left side of the equation is plus, the sign on the right side is minus; when the sign on the left side is minus, the sign on the right side is plus. The signs match each other in the sine formula.

The following examples show how to find exact values of trigonometric expressions by using the sum and difference formulas.

Example ❶ **Find the exact value of each expression.**
   a. sin 105°

Use the formula sin (α + β) = sin α cos β + cos α sin β.

$$\begin{aligned}
\sin 105° &= \sin (60° + 45°) \\
&= \sin 60° \cos 45° + \cos 60° \sin 45° \\
&= \frac{\sqrt{3}}{2} \cdot \frac{\sqrt{2}}{2} + \frac{1}{2} \cdot \frac{\sqrt{2}}{2} \\
&= \frac{\sqrt{6} + \sqrt{2}}{4} \text{ or about } 0.9659
\end{aligned}$$

 Cooperative Learning

Pairs Check Have students work with a partner to develop the formula for sin (a + b), discussing and justifying each step. Discuss with students development of the sum and difference of angle formulas for cos (a ± b) and sin (a − b) as they are illustrated on pages 847 and 848.

For more information on the pairs check strategy, see *Cooperative Learning in the Mathematics Classroom*, one of the titles in the Glencoe Mathematics Professional Series, pages 12–13.

b. cos (−120°)

Use the formula cos (α − β) = cos α cos β + sin α sin β.

cos (−120°) = cos (60° − 180°)

$$= \cos 60° \cos 180° + \sin 60° \sin 180°$$

$$= \frac{1}{2} \cdot (-1) + \frac{\sqrt{3}}{2} \cdot 0$$

$$= -\frac{1}{2}$$

Example ❷

APPLICATION

Physical Science

Refer to the application at the beginning of the lesson.
a. For what latitude will the light energy per square foot be greatest on June 22?
b. Suppose you live in Portland, Oregon (latitude: 45.5° N; longitude: 122.7° W). What is the maximum amount of light energy that a square foot of ground can receive on June 22 as a percent of that received at the latitude in part a?

a. Since the value of the sine function cannot be greater than 1, the given expression can be no greater than $E \cdot 1$ or E. The sine function equals 1 when 113.5° − φ = 90°; that is, when φ = 113.5° − 90°, or 23.5°. Thus, the greatest intensity of light energy on June 22 occurs at a latitude of 23.5° N.

b. *Explore*   Although information is provided about both the latitude and longitude of Portland, only the latitude is needed to solve the problem.

Plan   Use the difference formula for the sine.

sin (113.5° − φ)

$$= \sin 113.5° \cos φ − \cos 113.5° \sin φ$$

$$= 0.9171 \cos φ − (−0.3987) \sin φ$$

$$= 0.9171 \cos φ + 0.3987 \sin φ$$

Solve   The latitude of Portland is 45.5° N.

sin (113.5° − 45.5°)

$$= 0.9171 \cos 45.5° + 0.3987 \sin 45.5°$$

$$= 0.9171 \cdot 0.7010 + 0.3987 \cdot 0.7133$$

$$= 0.6429 + 0.2844$$

$$= 0.9273$$

In Portland, the maximum light energy per square foot is 0.9273E. Therefore, the light energy is about 93% of that found at a latitude of 23.5°.

Examine   Use a calculator to find sin (113.5° − 45.5°) or sin (68°). The answer is approximately 0.927 or 93%. Thus, the answer is correct.

In-Class Example

For Example 2

a. What latitude will receive the least light energy per square foot on June 22? **113.5°**

b. If you live in Columbus, Ohio (latitude: 40°N; longitude: 83°W), what is the maximum amount of light energy that a square foot of ground can receive on June 22 as a percent of that received at latitude 23.5°N? **96%**

In-Class Example

For Example 3
Verify that $\sin(270° + \theta) = -\cos \theta$ is an identity.
$\sin(270° + \theta) \stackrel{?}{=} \sin 270° \cos \theta + \cos 270° \sin \theta \stackrel{?}{=} -1 \cdot \cos \theta + 0 \cdot \sin \theta = -\cos \theta$

3 PRACTICE/APPLY

Check for Understanding

Exercises 1–10 are designed to help you assess your students' understanding through reading, writing, speaking, and modeling. You should work through Exercises 1–2 with your students and then monitor their work on Exercises 3–10.

Additional Answers

1. No; a counterexample is:
   $\cos(30° + 45°) = \cos 30° + \cos 45°$
   $= \dfrac{\sqrt{3}}{2} + \dfrac{\sqrt{2}}{2}$
   $= 1.5731.$
   Since a cosine value cannot be greater than 1, this statement must be false.
2. See students' work;
   $\dfrac{\sqrt{6} - \sqrt{2}}{4}$

Study Guide Masters, p. 102

14-4

NAME_____ DATE _____

Study Guide

Student Edition
Pages 847–852

Sum and Difference of Angles Formulas
It is often helpful to use formulas for the trigonometric values of the difference or sum of two angles.

Sum and Difference Angle Formulas
The following identities hold for all values of α and β.
$\cos(\alpha + \beta) = \cos \alpha \cos \beta - \sin \alpha \sin \beta$
$\cos(\alpha - \beta) = \cos \alpha \cos \beta + \sin \alpha \sin \beta$
$\sin(\alpha + \beta) = \sin \alpha \cos \beta + \cos \alpha \sin \beta$
$\sin(\alpha - \beta) = \sin \alpha \cos \beta - \cos \alpha \sin \beta$

Example: Evaluate sin 15°.
$\sin 15° = \sin(45° - 30°)$
$= \sin 45° \cos 30° - \cos 45° \sin 30°$ $\sin(\alpha - \beta) = \sin \alpha \cos \beta - \cos \alpha \sin \beta$
$= \dfrac{\sqrt{2}}{2} \cdot \dfrac{\sqrt{3}}{2} - \dfrac{\sqrt{2}}{2} \cdot \dfrac{1}{2}$
$= \dfrac{\sqrt{6} - \sqrt{2}}{4}$

Find the exact value of each expression.
1. $\cos 75°$ $\dfrac{\sqrt{6} - \sqrt{2}}{4}$
2. $\sin 255°$ $\dfrac{\sqrt{2} - \sqrt{6}}{4}$
3. $\cos(-15°)$ $\dfrac{\sqrt{6} + \sqrt{2}}{4}$
4. $\sin 75° - \sin 15°$ $\dfrac{\sqrt{2}}{2}$
5. $\sin 10° \cos 80° + \cos 10° \sin 80°$ 1
6. $\cos 20° \cos 40° - \sin 20° \sin 40°$ $\dfrac{1}{2}$
7. $\sin 60° \cos 15° - \cos 60° \sin 15°$ $\dfrac{\sqrt{2}}{2}$
8. $\cos 105° \cos 15° + \sin 105° \sin 15°$ 0

Verify that each of the following is an identity.
9. $\sin(90° - \theta) = \cos \theta$
   $\sin 90° \cos \theta - \cos 90° \sin \theta \stackrel{?}{=} \cos \theta$
   $1(\cos \theta) - 0(\sin \theta) \stackrel{?}{=} \cos \theta$
   $\cos \theta = \cos \theta$

10. $\sin(\theta + 270°) = -\cos \theta$
    $\sin \theta \cos 270° + \cos \theta \sin 270° \stackrel{?}{=} -\cos \theta$
    $\sin \theta(0) + \cos \theta(-1) \stackrel{?}{=} -\cos \theta$
    $-\cos \theta = -\cos \theta$

850 Chapter 14

You can also use the sum and difference formulas to verify identities.

Example 3 Verify that each of the following is an identity.

a. $\cos(90° - \theta) = \sin \theta$

$\cos(90° - \theta) \stackrel{?}{=} \sin \theta$
$\cos 90° \cos \theta + \sin 90° \sin \theta \stackrel{?}{=} \sin \theta$
$0 \cdot \cos \theta + 1 \cdot \sin \theta \stackrel{?}{=} \sin \theta$
$\sin \theta = \sin \theta$

b. $\cos(180° + \theta) = -\cos \theta$

$\cos(180° + \theta) \stackrel{?}{=} -\cos \theta$
$\cos 180° \cos \theta - \sin 180° \sin \theta \stackrel{?}{=} -\cos \theta$
$-1 \cdot \cos \theta - 0 \cdot \sin \theta \stackrel{?}{=} -\cos \theta$
$-\cos \theta = -\cos \theta$

CHECK FOR UNDERSTANDING

Communicating Mathematics

Study the lesson. Then complete the following. 1–2. See margin.

1. **Determine** whether the equation $\cos(x + y) = \cos x + \cos y$ is an identity.

2. **Describe** a method for finding the exact value of $\sin 15°$. Then find the value.

Guided Practice

Find the exact value of each expression.

3. $\cos 75°$ $\dfrac{\sqrt{6} - \sqrt{2}}{4}$

4. $\sin 165°$ $\dfrac{\sqrt{6} - \sqrt{2}}{4}$

5. $\cos 255°$ $\dfrac{\sqrt{2} - \sqrt{6}}{4}$

6. $\cos 80° \cos 20° + \sin 80° \sin 20°$ $\dfrac{1}{2}$

7–9. See Solutions Manual.

Verify that each of the following is an identity.

7. $\sin(270° - \theta) = -\cos \theta$

8. $\cos(90° + \theta) = -\sin \theta$

9. $\sin(x + 30°) + \cos(x + 60°) = \cos x$

10. Refer to Example 2. Another way to solve the problem would be to substitute 45.5° into the expression $\sin(113.5° - \theta)$ and find the value of $\sin 68°$ by using a calculator. When you do this, you obtain 0.9271838, or about 0.9272. This is slightly less than the result obtained in Example 2. Why is this so? When the difference formula is used, roundings occur in the intermediate steps. These produce small errors, which accumulate.

EXERCISES

Practice **Find the exact value of each expression.** 14–19. See margin.

11. $\sin 285°$ $\dfrac{-\sqrt{2} - \sqrt{6}}{4}$

12. $\sin 75°$ $\dfrac{\sqrt{6} + \sqrt{2}}{4}$

13. $\cos 195°$ $\dfrac{-\sqrt{6} - \sqrt{2}}{4}$

14. $\cos 105°$

15. $\cos 345°$

16. $\cos 165°$

17. $\sin 65° \cos 35° - \cos 65° \sin 35°$

18. $\sin 40° \cos 20° + \cos 40° \sin 20°$

19. $\cos 25° \cos 5° - \sin 25° \sin 5°$

850 Chapter 14 *Using Trigonometric Graphs and Identities*

Reteaching

Using Alternative Methods Using $\cos(A - B) = \cos A \cos B + \sin A \sin B$, which can be derived by analytic geometry, tell how to derive the other identities listed.

To Find:	Substitute:	In:
$\cos(A + B)$	$-B$ for B	$\cos(A - B)$
$\cos(90 - x)$	90 for A	$\cos(A - B)$
$\sin(90 - x)$	$90 - x = x$	$\cos(90 - x)$
$\sin(A - B)$	$A - B$ for x	$\cos(90 - x)$
$\sin(A + B)$	$-B$ for B	$\sin(A - B)$

Verify that each of the following is an identity.

20. $\cos(270° - \theta) = -\sin\theta$

21. $\sin(90° + \theta) = \cos\theta$

22. $\sin(180° + \theta) = -\sin\theta$

23. $\sin(90° - \theta) = \sin\theta$

24. $\sin(60° + \theta) + \sin(60° - \theta) = \sqrt{3}\cos\theta$

25. $\sin(x + y)\sin(x - y) = \sin^2 x - \sin^2 y$

26. $\sin\left(\theta + \frac{\pi}{3}\right) - \cos\left(\theta + \frac{\pi}{6}\right) = \sin\theta$

Use the identity $\tan(\alpha - \beta) = \dfrac{\tan\alpha - \tan\beta}{1 + \tan\alpha\tan\beta}$ to find the exact value of each expression.

27. $\tan(225° - 120°)$ $-2 - \sqrt{3}$

28. $\tan(315° - 120°)$ $2 - \sqrt{3}$

29. $\tan(30° + 30°)$ $\sqrt{3}$

30. $\tan 195°$ $2 - \sqrt{3}$

Graphing Calculator

Use a graphing calculator to determine the angle x that would make each equation true.

31. $\cos(\alpha + x) = -\sin x$ $90°$

32. $\sin(\alpha + x) = -\cos x$ $-90°$ or $270°$

33. $\tan(\alpha + x) = -\cot x$ $90°$

34. $\sin(\alpha + x) = -\sin x$ $180°$

Critical Thinking

35. Use the formulas for $\sin(\alpha + \beta)$ and $\cos(\alpha + \beta)$ to derive the formula for $\tan(\alpha + \beta)$. (*Hint:* Divide all terms of the expression by $\cos\alpha\cos\beta$.) See margin.

Applications and Problem Solving

36a. 0.7912 E

Key West, Florida

36. Physical Science Use the formula for $\sin(\alpha - \beta)$ to find the light energy that falls on a square foot of ground in each city on June 22. Express your answer in terms of E, the energy from an overhead sun. Check your answer by substituting directly into the expression $\sin(113.5° - \phi)$.

Anchorage, Alaska

a. Anchorage, Alaska (Latitude: 61.2° N)

b. Bangor, ME (Latitude: 44.8° N) 0.9317 E

c. Key West, FL (Latitude: 24.6° N) 0.9998 E

d. your community See students' work.

37. Physical Science On December 22, the maximum amount of light energy that falls on a square foot of ground at a certain location is given by $E\sin(113.5° + \phi)$, where ϕ is the latitude of the location. Use the sum formula for sines to find the light energy that falls on a square foot of ground at each location on December 22. Express your answer in terms of E, the energy from an overhead sun. Check your answer by substituting directly into the expression $\sin(113.5° + \phi)$.

a. Dallas, TX (Latitude: 32.8° N) 0.5549 E

b. Portland, OR (Latitude: 45.5° N) 0.3584 E

c. Equator (Latitude: 0.0° N) 0.9171 E

Lesson 14–4 Sum and Difference of Angles Formulas **851**

Additional Answer

35. $\tan(\alpha + \beta) = \dfrac{\sin(\alpha + \beta)}{\cos(\alpha + \beta)}$

$= \dfrac{\sin\alpha\cos\beta + \cos\alpha\sin\beta}{\cos\alpha\cos\beta - \sin\alpha\sin\beta}$

$= \dfrac{\dfrac{\sin\alpha\cos\beta}{\cos\alpha\cos\beta} + \dfrac{\cos\alpha\sin\beta}{\cos\alpha\cos\beta}}{\dfrac{\cos\alpha\cos\beta}{\cos\alpha\cos\beta} - \dfrac{\sin\alpha\sin\beta}{\cos\alpha\cos\beta}}$

$= \dfrac{\tan\alpha + \tan\beta}{1 - \tan\alpha\tan\beta}$

Assignment Guide

Core: 11–37 odd, 39–46
Enriched: 12–34 even, 35–46

For **Extra Practice,** see p. 909.

The red A, B, and C flags, printed only in the Teacher's Wraparound Edition, indicate the level of difficulty of the exercises.

Additional Answers

14. $\dfrac{\sqrt{2} - \sqrt{6}}{4}$

15. $\dfrac{\sqrt{6} + \sqrt{2}}{4}$

16. $\dfrac{-\sqrt{6} - \sqrt{2}}{4}$

17. $\dfrac{1}{2}$

18. $\dfrac{\sqrt{3}}{2}$

19. $\dfrac{\sqrt{3}}{2}$

Practice Masters, p. 102

14-4 NAME_____ DATE_____

Practice Student Edition Pages 847–852

Sum and Difference of Angles Formula

Find the exact value of each expression.

1. $\cos 75°$ $\dfrac{\sqrt{6} - \sqrt{2}}{4}$

2. $\cos 375°$ $\dfrac{\sqrt{6} + \sqrt{2}}{4}$

3. $\sin(-165°)$ $\dfrac{\sqrt{2} - \sqrt{6}}{4}$

4. $\sin(-105°)$ $\dfrac{-\sqrt{2} - \sqrt{6}}{4}$

5. $\sin 95°\cos 55° + \cos 95°\sin 55°$ $\dfrac{1}{2}$

6. $\cos 160°\cos 40° + \sin 160°\sin 40°$ $-\dfrac{1}{2}$

7. $\tan(135° + 120°)$ $2 + \sqrt{3}$

8. $\tan(315° - \theta)$ $\dfrac{\tan\theta + 1}{\tan\theta - 1}$

Verify that each of the following is an identity.

9. $\cos(180° - \theta) = -\cos\theta$
$\cos(180° - \theta)$
$= \cos 180°\cos\theta + \sin 180°\sin\theta$
$= (-1)\cos\theta + 0 \cdot \sin\theta$
$= -\cos\theta$

10. $\sin(360° + \theta) = \sin\theta$
$\sin(360° + \theta)$
$= \sin 360°\cos\theta + \cos 360°\sin\theta$
$= 0 \cdot \cos\theta + 1 \cdot \sin\theta$
$= \sin\theta$

11. $\sin(45° + \theta) - \sin(45° - \theta) = \sqrt{2}\sin\theta$
$\sin(45° + \theta) - \sin(45° - \theta)$
$= \sin 45°\cos\theta + \cos 45°\sin\theta -$
$\quad (\sin 45°\cos\theta - \cos 45°\sin\theta)$
$= 2 \cdot \cos 45°\sin\theta$
$= \sqrt{2}\sin\theta$

12. $\cos\left(x - \dfrac{\pi}{6}\right) + \sin\left(x - \dfrac{\pi}{3}\right) = \sin x$
$\cos\left(x - \dfrac{\pi}{6}\right) + \sin\left(x - \dfrac{\pi}{3}\right)$
$= \cos x\cos\dfrac{\pi}{6} + \sin x\sin\dfrac{\pi}{6} +$
$\quad \sin x\cos\dfrac{\pi}{3} - \cos x\sin\dfrac{\pi}{3}$
$= \dfrac{\sqrt{3}}{2}\cos x + \dfrac{1}{2}\sin x + \dfrac{1}{2}\sin x -$
$\quad \dfrac{\sqrt{3}}{2}\cos x$
$= \sin x$

4 ASSESS

Closing Activity
Speaking Have students explain the operation symbols used in the sum and difference of angle formulas.

Additional Answers

39. $\sin \theta \sec \theta \cot \theta \overset{?}{=} 1$

$\sin \theta \cdot \dfrac{1}{\cos \theta} \cdot \dfrac{\cos \theta}{\sin \theta} \overset{?}{=} 1$

$1 = 1$

43.

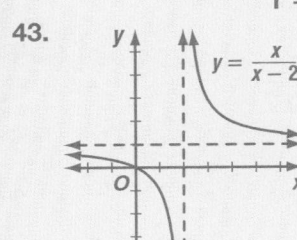

$y = \dfrac{x}{x-2}$

Enrichment Masters, p. 102

NAME_____ DATE_____

Student Edition
Pages 847–852

14-4 Enrichment

Translating Graphs of Trigonometric Functions

Three graphs are shown at the right:

$y = 3 \sin 2\theta$
$y = 3 \sin 2(\theta - 30°)$
$y + 4 = 3 \sin 2\theta$

Replacing θ with $(\theta - 30°)$ translates the graph to the right. Replacing y with $y + 4$ translates the graph 4 units down.

Example: Graph one cycle of
$y = 6 \cos (5\theta + 80°) + 2$.

Step 1 Transform the equation into the form $y - k = a \cos b(\theta - h)$.
$y - 2 = 6 \cos 5(\theta + 16°)$

Step 2 Sketch $y = 6 \cos 5\theta$.

Step 3 Translate $y = 6 \cos 5\theta$ to obtain the desired graph.

Sketch these graphs on the same coordinate system. See students' graphs.

1. $y = 3 \sin 2(\theta + 45°)$
2. $y - 1 = 3 \sin 2\theta$
3. $y + 5 = 3 \sin 2(\theta + 90°)$

Graph one cycle of each curve. See students' graphs.

4. $y = 2 \sin 4(\theta - 50°)$
5. $y = 5 \sin (3\theta + 90°)$

6. $y = 6 \cos (4\theta + 360°) + 3$
7. $y = 6 \cos 4\theta + 3$

8. The graphs for problems 6 and 7 should be the same. Use the sum formula for cosine of a sum to show that the equations are equivalent.
$\cos (4\theta + 360°) = (\cos 4\theta)(\cos 360°) - (\sin 4\theta)(\sin 360°)$
$= (\cos 4\theta)(1) - (\sin 4\theta)(0)$
$= \cos 4\theta$
So, $y = 6 \cos (4\theta + 360°) + 3$ and $y = 6 \cos 4\theta + 3$ are equivalent.

38. **Geology** Geologist Norma Ayala measures the angle between one side of a rectangular lot and the line from her position to the opposite corner of the lot as 30°. She then measures the angle between that line and the line to the point on the property where a river crosses the property as 45°. Dr. Ayala stands 100 yards from the opposite corner of the property. How far is she from the point at which the river crosses the property line?
$50\sqrt{6} - 50\sqrt{2}$ or about 51.8 yards

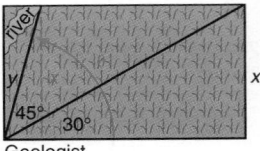
Geologist

Mixed Review

39. **Trigonometry** Verify that $\sin \theta \sec \theta \cot \theta = 1$ is an identity. (Lesson 14–3) **See margin.**

40. **Golf** Mr. Sanchez estimates that he hooked his last drive 18° to the left of where he intended and that the ball is now 200 yards from the tee. If the hole for which he was aiming is 180 yards from the tee, how far, to the nearest yard, is the ball from the hole? (Lesson 13–5) **63 yards**

41. **Probability** Two cards are drawn from a standard deck of cards. What is the probability of having drawn a black card or an ace? (Lesson 12–6)

41. $\dfrac{175}{221}$

42a. $\dfrac{0.50(0.08p)}{6} +$
$\dfrac{0.50(0.08p)}{4}$

42b. $\dfrac{0.2p}{12}$ or $\dfrac{p}{60}$

42c. $\dfrac{0.04p}{6}$ or $\dfrac{p}{150}$

42. **Business** At an annual board meeting of a small corporation, it was decided that 8% of the profits for the next year would be divided among the six managers of the corporation. There are two sales managers and four nonsales managers. Fifty percent of the amount would be split equally among all six managers. The other 50% would be split among the four nonsales managers. Let p represent the annual profits of the corporation. (Lesson 9–4)

a. Write an expression to represent the share of the profits each nonsales manager will receive.

b. Simplify this expression.

c. Write an expression in simplest form to represent the share of the profits each sales manager will receive.

43. Graph $f(x) = \dfrac{x}{x-2}$. (Lesson 9–1) **See margin.**

44. Use synthetic substitution to find $f(2)$ and $f(-1)$ if $f(x) = x^4 + x^3 + x^2 + x + 1$. (Lesson 8–2) **31, 1**

45. **Construction** A subdivision has 60 lots available. The builder knows from experience that she should plan to build at least three times as many ranch-style houses as colonial-style. If she will make a profit of $5000 on each colonial house and $4500 on each ranch, how many of each kind should she plan to build in this development? (Lesson 3–6)
15 colonial, 45 ranch

46. **Statistics** Choose a statistical graph— bar, line, circle, or pictograph— to represent the data shown in the table at the right. Then draw the graph. (Lesson 1–3)
See students' work.

Technology Used by Teens	
Item	**Percent**
cable TV	66
cellular telephone	35
computer	46
on-line service	17
VCR	96
video game player	77

Source: Chilton Research Services

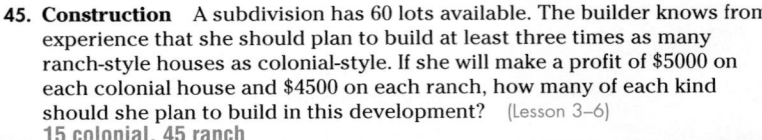

Extension

Communication Have students list for a partner the steps needed to solve the following problem, writing them if necessary, and then solve the problem.

Use the identity
$\tan (a - b) = \dfrac{\tan a - \tan b}{1 + \tan a \tan b}$
to find $\cot (a - b)$.

$\cot (a - b) = \dfrac{1 + \cot a \cot b}{\cot b - \cot a}$

Double-Angle and Half-Angle Formulas

What YOU'LL LEARN

- To find values of sine and cosine involving double and half angles, and
- to verify identities by using double- and half-angle formulas.

Why IT'S IMPORTANT

You can use double-angle and half-angle formulas to solve problems involving aviation and physics.

APPLICATION
Aviation

A plane that travels at the speed of sound (about 740 miles per hour) is said to be traveling at Mach 1. The Mach number, named after the Austrian physicist Ernst Mach (1838–1916), is defined as the ratio of the speed of the plane to the speed of sound. On October 14, 1947, Charles (Chuck) Yeager became the first person to fly an aircraft faster than Mach 1. In the process, his Bell X-1 rocket airplane created a sonic boom.

Chuck Yeager

When a plane travels at a Mach number greater than 1, a sonic boom is created by sound waves forming a cone that intersects the ground in the outline of a hyperbola. If θ is the measure of the angle at the vertex of the cone, then the Mach number is related to θ by the equation $\sin \frac{\theta}{2} = \frac{1}{M}$, provided that $M > 1$.

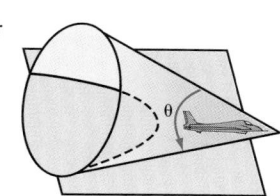

Suppose the measure of the cone's vertex angle is 45°. What is the speed of the plane? *This problem will be solved in Example 3.*

You can use the formula for $\sin(\alpha + \beta)$ to find the sine of twice an angle θ, $\sin 2\theta$, and the formula for $\cos(\alpha + \beta)$ to find the cosine of twice an angle θ, $\cos 2\theta$.

Let θ represent the measure of the angle.

$$\sin 2\theta = \sin(\theta + \theta)$$
$$= \sin\theta\cos\theta + \cos\theta\sin\theta$$
$$= 2\sin\theta\cos\theta$$
$$\cos 2\theta = \cos(\theta + \theta)$$
$$= \cos\theta\cos\theta - \sin\theta\sin\theta$$
$$= \cos^2\theta - \sin^2\theta$$

You can find alternate forms for $\cos 2\theta$ by making substitutions into the expression $\cos^2\theta - \sin^2\theta$.

$$\cos^2\theta - \sin^2\theta = (1 - \sin^2\theta) - \sin^2\theta \quad \text{Substitute } 1 - \sin^2\theta \text{ for } \cos^2\theta.$$
$$= 1 - 2\sin^2\theta$$
$$\cos^2\theta - \sin^2\theta = \cos^2\theta - (1 - \cos^2\theta) \quad \text{Substitute } 1 - \cos^2\theta \text{ for } \sin^2\theta.$$
$$= 2\cos^2\theta - 1$$

These formulas are called the **double-angle formulas.**

LOOK BACK

Refer to Lesson 7-5 for a review of hyperbolas.

fabulous
FIRSTS

Daniel H. "Chappie" James Jr. (1920–1978)

In 1975, Daniel H. James Jr. became the first African-American four-star general in the Air Force.

fabulous
FIRSTS

General James was born February 11, 1920, in Pensacola, Florida. He was widely known for his speeches on patriotism and Americanism.

14-5 LESSON NOTES

NCTM Standards: 1–6, 9

Instructional Resources

- Study Guide Master 14-5
- Practice Master 14-5
- Enrichment Master 14-5
- Assessment and Evaluation Masters, p. 381

Transparency 14-5A contains the 5-Minute Check for this lesson; **Transparency 14-5B** contains a teaching aid for this lesson.

Recommended Pacing	
Honors Pacing	Day 7 of 11
Block Scheduling*	Day 4 of 6 (along with Lesson 14-4)

*For more information on pacing and possible lesson plans, refer to the *Block Scheduling Booklet.*

1 FOCUS

5-Minute Check
(over Lesson 14-4)

Write each angle in terms of sums or differences of 30°, 45°, 60°, and 90° or their multiples.

1. $-165°$ $-135° - 30°$
2. $105°$ $45° + 60°$
3. Evaluate $\sin 195°$. $\dfrac{\sqrt{2} - \sqrt{6}}{4}$
4. Evaluate $\cos 285°$. $\dfrac{\sqrt{6} - \sqrt{2}}{4}$
5. Verify the identity $\cos(270° - \theta) = -\sin\theta$.
   $\cos 270° \cdot \cos\theta + \sin 270° \cdot \sin\theta = -\sin\theta$
   $0 - 1 \cdot \sin\theta = -\sin\theta$
   $-\sin\theta = -\sin\theta$

Motivating the Lesson
Hands-On Activity Have students fold a piece of paper in half. Discuss how they determined what was half. Repeat with a triangular paper by folding through one corner. Discuss how to determine half of an angle.

Teaching Tip Point out that the formula used to find $\cos 2\theta$ depends on what information is given in the problem.

In-Class Example

For Example 1

Suppose x is between $0°$ and $90°$ and $\sin x = \frac{1}{3}$. Find the exact value of $\sin 2x$. $\frac{4\sqrt{2}}{9}$

Double-Angle Formulas	The following identities hold true for all values of θ. $\sin 2\theta = 2 \sin \theta \cos \theta \qquad \cos 2\theta = \cos^2 \theta - \sin^2 \theta$ $\cos 2\theta = 1 - 2 \sin^2 \theta$ $\cos 2\theta = 2 \cos^2 \theta - 1$

Example Suppose x is between $90°$ and $180°$ and $\sin x = \frac{1}{2}$. Find the exact value of each expression.

a. $\cos 2x$

Use the identity $\cos 2x = 1 - 2 \sin^2 x$.

$$\cos 2x = 1 - 2 \sin^2 x$$
$$= 1 - 2\left(\frac{1}{2}\right)^2 \quad \textit{Substitute } \frac{1}{2} \textit{ for } \sin x.$$
$$= \frac{1}{2}$$

The value of $\cos 2x$ is $\frac{1}{2}$.

b. $\sin 2x$

Find the value of $\cos x$. Then use the identity $\sin 2x = 2 \sin x \cos x$.

$$\cos^2 x = 1 - \sin^2 x \quad \cos^2 x + \sin^2 x = 1$$
$$= 1 - \left(\frac{1}{2}\right)^2$$
$$= \frac{3}{4}$$
$$\cos x = -\frac{\sqrt{3}}{2} \quad \textit{cosine is negative in the second quadrant.}$$

$$\sin 2x = 2 \sin x \cos x$$
$$= 2\left(\frac{1}{2}\right)\left(-\frac{\sqrt{3}}{2}\right) \quad \textit{Substitute } \frac{1}{2} \textit{ for } \sin x \textit{ and } -\frac{\sqrt{3}}{2} \textit{ for } \cos x.$$
$$= -\frac{\sqrt{3}}{2}$$

The value of $\sin 2x$ is $-\frac{\sqrt{3}}{2}$.

You can also derive formulas to find the cosine and the sine of half a given angle. Let α represent the measure of this angle.

Find $\cos \frac{\alpha}{2}$.

$$2 \cos^2 \theta - 1 = \cos 2\theta$$
$$2 \cos^2 \frac{\alpha}{2} - 1 = \cos \alpha$$
$$\cos^2 \frac{\alpha}{2} = \frac{1 + \cos \alpha}{2}$$

Find $\sin \frac{\alpha}{2}$.

$$1 - 2 \sin^2 \theta = \cos 2\theta \quad \textit{Use double-angle formulas.}$$
$$1 - 2 \sin^2 \frac{\alpha}{2} = \cos \alpha \quad \textit{Substitute } \frac{\alpha}{2} \textit{ for } \theta \textit{ and } \alpha \textit{ for } 2\theta$$
$$\sin^2 \frac{\alpha}{2} = \frac{1 - \cos \alpha}{2} \quad \textit{Solve for the squared term.}$$

 Cooperative Learning

Co-op Co-op Have students work in pairs. One student should find $\cos 60°$ by using a double angle formula. The other student should find $\cos 60°$ by using a half-angle formula. They should compare results. For more information on the co-op co-op strategy, see *Cooperative Learning in the Mathematics Classroom,* one of the titles in the Glencoe Mathematics Professional Series, page 32.

$$\cos \frac{\alpha}{2} = \pm\sqrt{\frac{1 + \cos \alpha}{2}} \qquad \sin \frac{\alpha}{2} = \pm\sqrt{\frac{1 - \cos \alpha}{2}}$$ *Take the square root of each side.*

These are called the **half-angle formulas.** The signs are determined by the function of $\frac{\alpha}{2}$.

Half-Angle Formulas	**The following identities hold true for all values of α.** $\cos \frac{\alpha}{2} = \pm\sqrt{\frac{1 + \cos \alpha}{2}} \qquad \sin \frac{\alpha}{2} = \pm\sqrt{\frac{1 - \cos \alpha}{2}}$

In-Class Example

For Example 2
Suppose $\sin x = -\frac{2}{5}$ and x is between 270° and 360°. Find $\sin \frac{x}{2}$.

The solution is $\frac{\sqrt{50 - 10\sqrt{21}}}{10}$ since $\frac{x}{2}$ is in the second quadrant.

Teaching Tip Regarding the half-angle formulas, remind students that the sign of the solution is determined by the quadrant of the angle.

Example ② Suppose $\sin x = -\frac{9}{41}$ and x is between 270° and 360°. Find $\cos \frac{x}{2}$.

Since $\cos \frac{x}{2} = \pm\sqrt{\frac{1 + \cos x}{2}}$, we must find $\cos x$ first.

Use $\cos^2 x + \sin^2 x = 1$.

$$\cos^2 x + \sin^2 x = 1$$
$$\cos^2 x + \left(-\frac{9}{41}\right)^2 = 1 \qquad \textit{Replace } \sin x \textit{ with } -\frac{9}{41}.$$
$$\cos^2 x = 1 - \frac{81}{1681}$$
$$\cos^2 x = \frac{1600}{1681}$$
$$\cos x = \pm\frac{40}{41} \qquad \textit{Take the square root of each side.}$$

Since x is in the fourth quadrant, $\cos x = \frac{40}{41}$.

$$\cos \frac{x}{2} = \pm\sqrt{\frac{1 + \cos x}{2}} \qquad \textit{Half-angle formula}$$
$$= \pm\sqrt{\frac{1 + \frac{40}{41}}{2}} \qquad \textit{Replace } \cos x \textit{ with } \frac{40}{41}.$$
$$= \pm\sqrt{\frac{81}{82}} \textit{ or } \pm\frac{9\sqrt{82}}{82}$$

Since x is between 270° and 360°, $\frac{x}{2}$ is between 135° and 180°. Thus, $\cos \frac{x}{2}$ is negative and equals $-\frac{9\sqrt{82}}{82}$ or about -0.9939.

In-Class Examples

For Example 3
The range of a projected object is the distance that it travels from the point where it is released. In the absence of air resistance, a projectile released at an angle of elevation, θ, with an initial velocity of v_o has a range of $R = \dfrac{v_o^2}{g} \sin 2\theta$, where g is the acceleration due to gravity. Find the range of a projectile with an initial velocity of 15 feet per second if $\sin \theta = \dfrac{\sqrt{2}}{2}$ and $\cos \theta = \dfrac{\sqrt{2}}{2}$.

The acceleration due to gravity is 32 feet per second squared. **7.03125**

For Example 4
Verify that $\cos^2 2\theta = \cos^2 \theta \cos 2\theta - \sin^2 \theta \cos 2\theta$ is an identity.

$\cos^2 2\theta \overset{?}{=} \cos 2\theta \,(\cos^2 \theta - \sin^2 \theta)$

$\cos 2\theta \overset{?}{=} \cos^2 \theta - \sin^2 \theta$

$\cos 2\theta = \cos 2\theta$

Example ③

APPLICATION

Aviation

Refer to the application at the beginning of the lesson. A plane traveling at a supersonic speed sends out sound waves that form a cone with a vertex angle of 45°. Find the speed of the plane if Mach 1 is about 740 mph.

Use the equation $\sin \dfrac{\theta}{2} = \dfrac{1}{M}$ to find the Mach number. Then use the Mach number to find the speed.

The value of the left side of the Mach equation is found by using a half-angle identity. Since 45° is in the first quadrant, the negative solution is ignored.

$$\sin \dfrac{\theta}{2} = \sqrt{\dfrac{1 - \cos \theta}{2}}$$

$$= \sqrt{\dfrac{1 - \cos 45°}{2}} \qquad \textit{Replace } \theta \textit{ with } 45°.$$

$$= \sqrt{\dfrac{1 - \dfrac{\sqrt{2}}{2}}{2}}$$

$$= \sqrt{\dfrac{2 - \sqrt{2}}{4}}$$

$$= \dfrac{1}{2}\sqrt{2 - \sqrt{2}} \text{ or about } 0.3827$$

Substitute this value into the Mach equation.

$$0.3827 \approx \dfrac{1}{M}$$

$$0.3827M \approx 1$$

$$M \approx \dfrac{1}{0.3827} \text{ or about } 2.61$$

Multiply the Mach number by the speed of sound to get the speed of the plane.

$$s \approx 2.61 \cdot 740 \text{ mph or about } 1930 \text{ mph}$$

The speed of the plane is about 1930 miles per hour.

You can also use the double-angle and half-angle formulas to verify identities.

Example ④

Verify that $\cot x = \dfrac{\sin 2x}{1 - \cos 2x}$ is an identity.

$$\cot x = \dfrac{\sin 2x}{1 - \cos 2x}$$

$$= \dfrac{2 \sin x \cos x}{1 - (1 - 2 \sin^2 x)} \qquad \textit{Substitute } 2 \sin x \cos x \textit{ for } \sin 2x \textit{ and } 1 - 2 \sin^2 x \textit{ for } \cos 2x.$$

$$= \dfrac{2 \sin x \cos x}{2 \sin^2 x} \qquad \textit{Simplify.}$$

$$= \dfrac{\cos x}{\sin x}$$

$$= \cot x$$

Communicating Mathematics

Study the lesson. Then complete the following.

1. **Explain** how to find $\sin x$ if $2x$ is in the third quadrant.   See margin.

2. $\dfrac{\sqrt{82}}{82}$

2. Refer to Example 2. Find $\sin \dfrac{x}{2}$ if $\sin x = -\dfrac{9}{41}$ and x is between $270°$ and $360°$.

3. **You Decide**   Jack notices that $\sin 1° = 0.01745$, $\sin 2° = 0.03490$, and $\sin 4° = 0.0698$ and concludes that if you double an angle measure then you also double its sine. Minya says he is wrong and can give examples to prove it. Who is right? Explain.   Jack is right only for small angles such as those he tested. The pattern fails for angles with much greater measure. For example, $\sin 90° = 1$ and $\sin 180° = 0$.

Guided Practice

Find the exact values of $\sin 2x$, $\cos 2x$, $\sin \dfrac{x}{2}$, and $\cos \dfrac{x}{2}$ for each of the following.

4. $\sin x = \dfrac{5}{13}$; x is between $90°$ and $180°$. $-\dfrac{120}{169}, \dfrac{119}{169}, \dfrac{5\sqrt{26}}{26}, \dfrac{\sqrt{26}}{26}$

5. $\cos x = \dfrac{1}{5}$; x is in Quadrant IV. $-\dfrac{4\sqrt{6}}{25}, -\dfrac{23}{25}, \dfrac{\sqrt{10}}{5}, -\dfrac{\sqrt{15}}{5}$

Find the exact value of each expression by using the half-angle formulas.

6. $\cos \dfrac{\pi}{8}$ $\dfrac{\sqrt{2+\sqrt{2}}}{2}$

7. $\sin 22\dfrac{1}{2}°$ $\dfrac{\sqrt{2-\sqrt{2}}}{2}$

8–9. See Solutions Manual.

Verify that each of the following is an identity.

8. $(\sin x + \cos x)^2 = 1 + \sin 2x$

9. $\dfrac{1}{\sin x \cos x} - \dfrac{\cos x}{\sin x} = \tan x$

10. **Aviation**   Refer to the application at the beginning of the lesson. The Mach number for a certain plane traveling at supersonic speed is 1.4. Find the measure of the vertex angle of the cone formed by the sound waves that the plane sends out. $91°$

Practice

Find the exact values of $\sin 2x$, $\cos 2x$, $\sin \dfrac{x}{2}$, and $\cos \dfrac{x}{2}$ for each of the following.

 A

11. $\sin x = \dfrac{4}{5}$; x is between $90°$ and $180°$. $-\dfrac{24}{25}, -\dfrac{7}{25}, \dfrac{2\sqrt{5}}{5}, \dfrac{\sqrt{5}}{5}$

12. $\cos x = \dfrac{3}{5}$; x is in Quadrant I. $\dfrac{24}{25}, -\dfrac{7}{25}, \dfrac{\sqrt{5}}{5}, \dfrac{2\sqrt{5}}{5}$

13. $\cos x = -\dfrac{1}{3}$; x is between $180°$ and $270°$. $\dfrac{4\sqrt{2}}{9}, -\dfrac{7}{9}, \dfrac{\sqrt{6}}{3}, -\dfrac{\sqrt{3}}{3}$

14. $\cos x = -\dfrac{2}{3}$; x is in Quadrant III. $\dfrac{4\sqrt{5}}{9}, -\dfrac{1}{9}, \dfrac{\sqrt{30}}{6}, -\dfrac{\sqrt{6}}{6}$

Reteaching ▬▬▬▬▬

Using Technology To convince students of the validity of the formulas, have them find the value using a calculator or a table. You may wish to do the same for the double-angle formulas.

---

3 PRACTICE/APPLY

Check for Understanding

Exercises 1–10 are designed to help you assess your students' understanding through reading, writing, speaking, and modeling. You should work through Exercises 1–3 with your students and then monitor their work on Exercises 4–10.

Assignment Guide
Core: 11–31 odd, 32–37
Enriched: 12–28 even, 29–37

For **Extra Practice,** see p. 910.

The red A, B, and C flags, printed only in the Teacher's Wraparound Edition, indicate the level of difficulty of the exercises.

Additional Answer

1. x will be in Quadrant II. Use the double-angle formula for sine knowing that $\sin x$ will be positive.

Study Guide Masters, p. 103

14-5   NAME_____   DATE_____

Student Edition
Pages 853–859

Study Guide

Double-Angle and Half-Angle Formulas

Sometimes you want to find the cosine or sine of double an angle or half an angle. To do this you can use the following formulas.

Double-Angle Formulas
$\sin 2\theta = 2 \sin \theta \cos \theta$
$\cos 2\theta = \cos^2 \theta - \sin^2 \theta$
$\cos 2\theta = 1 - 2\sin^2 \theta$
$\cos 2\theta = 2\cos^2 \theta - 1$

Half-Angle Formulas
$\cos \dfrac{a}{2} = \pm\sqrt{\dfrac{1+\cos a}{2}}$
$\sin \dfrac{a}{2} = \pm\sqrt{\dfrac{1-\cos a}{2}}$

Example: Suppose x is between $90°$ and $180°$ and $\cos x = -\dfrac{3}{5}$.
Find $\cos \dfrac{x}{2}$.

Since x is in the second quadrant, $\dfrac{x}{2}$ is in the first quadrant and $\cos \dfrac{x}{2} > 0$.

$$\cos \dfrac{x}{2} = \sqrt{\dfrac{1+\cos x}{2}}$$
$$= \sqrt{\dfrac{1+\left(-\dfrac{3}{5}\right)}{2}}$$
$$= \sqrt{\dfrac{1}{5}} \text{ or } \dfrac{\sqrt{5}}{5}$$

Find the exact values of $\sin 2x$, $\cos 2x$, $\sin \dfrac{x}{2}$, and $\cos \dfrac{x}{2}$ for each of the following.

1. $\sin x = \dfrac{1}{4}$, x is in the first quadrant.
$\sin 2x = \dfrac{\sqrt{15}}{8}$, $\cos 2x = \dfrac{7}{8}$
$\sin \dfrac{x}{2} = \dfrac{\sqrt{8-2\sqrt{15}}}{4}$,
$\cos \dfrac{x}{2} = \dfrac{\sqrt{8+2\sqrt{15}}}{4}$

2. $\sin x = -\dfrac{1}{8}$, x is in the fourth quadrant.
$\sin 2x = -\dfrac{\sqrt{63}}{32}$, $\cos 2x = \dfrac{31}{32}$,
$\sin \dfrac{x}{2} = \dfrac{1}{4}\sqrt{8-\sqrt{63}}$,
$\cos \dfrac{x}{2} = \dfrac{1}{4}\sqrt{8+\sqrt{63}}$

3. $\cos x = -\dfrac{3}{5}$, x is in the third quadrant.
$\sin 2x = \dfrac{24}{25}$, $\cos 2x = -\dfrac{7}{25}$,
$\sin \dfrac{x}{2} = \dfrac{2}{5}\sqrt{5}$, $\cos \dfrac{x}{2} = -\dfrac{\sqrt{5}}{5}$

4. $\cos x = -\dfrac{4}{5}$, x is in the second quadrant.
$\sin 2x = -\dfrac{24}{25}$, $\cos 2x = \dfrac{7}{25}$,
$\sin \dfrac{x}{2} = \dfrac{3\sqrt{90}}{10}$, $\cos \dfrac{x}{2} = \dfrac{\sqrt{10}}{10}$

5. $\sin x = -\dfrac{3}{5}$, x is in the fourth quadrant.
$\sin 2x = -\dfrac{24}{25}$, $\cos 2x = \dfrac{7}{25}$,
$\sin \dfrac{x}{2} = \dfrac{\sqrt{10}}{10}$, $\cos \dfrac{x}{2} = -\dfrac{3\sqrt{10}}{10}$

6. $\cos x = -\dfrac{2}{3}$, x is in the second quadrant.
$\sin 2x = -\dfrac{4\sqrt{5}}{9}$, $\cos 2x = -\dfrac{1}{9}$,
$\sin \dfrac{x}{2} = \dfrac{\sqrt{30}}{6}$, $\cos \dfrac{x}{2} = \dfrac{\sqrt{6}}{6}$

Find the exact values of sin 2x, cos 2x, sin $\frac{x}{2}$, and cos $\frac{x}{2}$ for each of the following.

 B

15. sin $x = -\frac{3}{5}$; x is in Quadrant III. $\frac{24}{25}, \frac{7}{25}, \frac{3\sqrt{10}}{10} \cdot -\frac{\sqrt{10}}{10}$

16. sin $x = -\frac{3}{4}$; x is between 270° and 360°. $-\frac{3\sqrt{7}}{8}, -\frac{1}{8}, \frac{\sqrt{8 \pm 2\sqrt{7}}}{4}$

17. cos $x = -\frac{1}{3}$; x is in Quadrant II. $-\frac{4\sqrt{2}}{9}, -\frac{7}{9}, \frac{\sqrt{6}}{3}, \frac{\sqrt{3}}{3}$

18. sin $x = -\frac{1}{4}$; x is between 180° and 270°. $\frac{\sqrt{15}}{8}, \frac{7}{8}, \frac{\sqrt{8 \pm 2\sqrt{15}}}{4}$

Find the exact value of each expression by using the half-angle formulas.

19. $\frac{\sqrt{2+\sqrt{3}}}{2}$

20. $-\frac{\sqrt{2-\sqrt{3}}}{2}$

21. $\frac{\sqrt{2-\sqrt{2}}}{2}$

22. $\frac{\sqrt{2-\sqrt{3}}}{2}$

19. sin 105°

20. sin 195°

21. sin $\frac{7\pi}{8}$

22. cos $\frac{19\pi}{12}$

Verify that each of the following is an identity.   23–28. See Solutions Manual.

C

23. $\cos^2 2x + 4\sin^2 x \cos^2 x = 1$

24. $\sin^2 \theta = \frac{1}{2}(1 - \cos 2\theta)$

25. $\sin 2x = 2\cot x \sin^2 x$

26. $\sin^4 x - \cos^4 x = 2\sin^2 x - 1$

27. $2\cos^2 \frac{x}{2} = 1 + \cos x$

28. $\tan^2 \frac{x}{2} = \frac{1-\cos x}{1+\cos x}$

Critical Thinking

29. $\pm \dfrac{\sqrt{18 - 3\sqrt{18 - 6\sqrt{5}}}}{6}$

29. Explain the method that you would use to find sin x if sin 4x = $\frac{2}{3}$ and the terminal side of 4x lies in the second quadrant. Then find sin x. (*Hint:* Notice that the terminal sides of x and 2x do not necessarily lie in Quadrant I.)

Applications and Problem Solving

30. about 1480 miles per hour

30. **Aviation** A plane traveling at supersonic speed sends out sound waves that form a cone with a vertex angle of 60°. Find the speed of the plane.

31. **Physics** The index of refraction for a medium through which light is passing is the ratio of the velocity of light in free space to the velocity of light in the medium. For light passing through a medium such as glass or diamonds, the index of refraction n is given by the equation $n = \dfrac{\sin\left(\frac{\theta}{2} + \frac{\alpha}{2}\right)}{\sin \frac{\alpha}{2}}$, where α is the deviation angle and θ is the angle of the apex of the medium. If the medium is a zircon with an index of refraction of 1.9 and the angle of the apex of the diamond is 90°, determine the measure of the deviation angle.   61.3°

858   *Chapter 14 Using Trigonometric Graphs and Identities*

Practice Masters, p. 103

14-5   NAME _____ DATE _____

Practice   Student Edition Pages 853–859

Double-Angle and Half-Angle Formulas

Find the exact values of sin 2x, cos 2x, sin $\frac{x}{2}$, and cos $\frac{x}{2}$ for each of the following.

1. cos $x = \frac{5}{13}$, x is in the first quadrant.
$\frac{120}{169}, \frac{119}{169}, \frac{2\sqrt{13}}{13}, \frac{3\sqrt{13}}{13}$

2. cos $x = \frac{3}{7}$, x is in the fourth quadrant.
$\frac{12\sqrt{10}}{49}, \frac{31}{49}, \frac{\sqrt{14}}{7}, \frac{\sqrt{35}}{7}$

3. sin $x = \frac{40}{41}$, x is in the second quadrant.
$\frac{720}{1681}, \frac{1519}{1681}, \frac{5\sqrt{41}}{41}, \frac{4\sqrt{41}}{41}$

4. sin $x = -\frac{4}{5}$, x is in the third quadrant.
$\frac{24}{25}, -\frac{7}{25}, \frac{2\sqrt{5}}{5}, \frac{-\sqrt{5}}{5}$

5. sin $x = -\frac{7}{8}$, x is in the third quadrant.
$\frac{7\sqrt{15}}{32}, \frac{17}{32}, \frac{\sqrt{8+\sqrt{15}}}{4}, \frac{-\sqrt{8-\sqrt{15}}}{4}$

6. sin $x = \frac{9}{10}$, x is in the second quadrant.
$\frac{9\sqrt{19}}{50}, \frac{31}{50}, \frac{\sqrt{50+5\sqrt{19}}}{10}, \frac{\sqrt{50-5\sqrt{19}}}{10}$

Find the exact value of each expression using the half-angle formulas.

7. tan 105° $-2 - \sqrt{3}$

8. tan 15° $2 - \sqrt{3}$

9. cos $67\frac{1}{2}°$ $\frac{\sqrt{2-\sqrt{2}}}{2}$

10. $1 - 2\sin^2 15°$ $\frac{\sqrt{3}}{2}$

11. 8 sin (22.5°) cos (22.5°) $2\sqrt{2}$

12. sin $\left(-\frac{\pi}{8}\right)$ $\frac{-\sqrt{2-\sqrt{2}}}{2}$

Verify that each of the following is an identity.

13. $\sin 2\theta = \frac{2\tan\theta}{1+\tan^2\theta}$
$\sin 2\theta \stackrel{?}{=} \frac{2\tan\theta}{1+\tan^2\theta}$
$2\sin\theta\cos\theta \stackrel{?}{=} \frac{2\tan\theta}{\sec^2\theta}$
$2\sin\theta\cos\theta \stackrel{?}{=} \frac{2\sin\theta}{\cos\theta}\cdot\cos^2\theta$
$2\sin\theta\cos\theta = 2\sin\theta\cos\theta$

14. $\tan x + \cot x = 2\csc 2x$
$\tan x + \cot x \stackrel{?}{=} 2\csc 2x$
$\frac{\sin x}{\cos x} + \frac{\cos x}{\sin x} \stackrel{?}{=} \frac{2}{2\sin x\cos x}$
$\frac{\sin^2 x + \cos^2 x}{\cos x\sin x} \stackrel{?}{=} \frac{1}{\sin x\cos x}$
$\frac{1}{\cos x\sin x} = \frac{1}{\sin x\cos x}$

15. $\sin^2 \frac{x}{2} = \frac{\tan x - \sin x}{2\tan x}$
$\sin^2 \frac{x}{2} \stackrel{?}{=} \frac{\tan x - \sin x}{2\tan x}$
$\frac{1-\cos x}{2} \stackrel{?}{=} \frac{\frac{\tan x - \sin x}{\tan x}}{\frac{2\tan x}{\tan x}}$
$\frac{1-\cos x}{2} = \frac{1-\cos x}{2}$

16. $\sin 4\beta = 4\cos 2\beta\sin\beta\cos\beta$
$\sin 4\beta \stackrel{?}{=} 4\cos 2\beta\sin\beta\cos\beta$
$\sin 2(2\beta) \stackrel{?}{=} 4\cos 2\beta\sin\beta\cos\beta$
$2\sin 2\beta\cos 2\beta \stackrel{?}{=} 4\cos 2\beta\sin\beta\cos\beta$
$2\cdot 2\sin\beta\cos\beta\cdot\cos 2\beta \stackrel{?}{=} 4\cos 2\beta\sin\beta\cos\beta$
$4\cos 2\beta\sin\beta\cos\beta = 4\cos 2\beta\sin\beta\cos\beta$

858   Chapter 14

Tech Prep

Aviation Technician Students who are interested in aviation may wish to do further research on the information in Exercise 30 and explore the potential growth of this career. For more information on tech prep, see the *Teacher's Handbook.*

32. Geology A geologist stands on a ledge and finds that the angle of depression to a river's surface is 12°. The angle of depression to the riverbed below the surface is 13°. The geologist is 1500 feet from the river's surface. (Lesson 14–4)

a. Write an expression for the sine of the angle between the line from the geologist to the river's surface and the line from the geologist to the riverbed. **sin 1° = sin 13° cos 12° − cos 13° sin 12°**

b. How far above the riverbed is the surface of the water? **26.9 feet**

33. $b = 11.0$, $c = 12.2$, $C = 78$

33. Trigonometry Solve $\triangle ABC$. Round measures of sides and angles to the nearest tenth. (Lesson 13–4)

34. Environment Martel Johnson is an environmental research assistant. As part of her job, she makes video tapes of the countries she researches. On a circular carousel, she has six tapes of South America, four tapes of Africa, and two tapes of Australia. How many different ways can she arrange these tapes on the carousel? (Lesson 12–2) **39,916,800**

35. Use a calculator to find the antilogarithm of 0.2586, rounded to four decimal places. (Lesson 10–4) **1.814**

36. Find $\begin{bmatrix} 4 \\ -1 \\ 3 \end{bmatrix} \cdot \begin{bmatrix} 1 & 0 & 0 \\ 0 & 1 & 0 \\ 0 & 0 & 1 \end{bmatrix}$. (Lesson 4–3) **not defined**

37. Geometry The formula for the volume of a right circular cone is $V = \frac{1}{3}\pi r^2 h$, where r represents the radius of the circular base and h represents the height. Solve the formula for h. (Lesson 1–4) $h = \dfrac{3V}{\pi r^2}$

WORKING ON THE In·ves·ti·ga·tion

Refer to the Investigation on pages 768–769.

In the same way that a basketball is projected upward by the motion of your hands during a free-throw shot, a roller-coaster car is projected up the next hill by the energy accumulated going down the previous hill. The formula for the height of the car can be determined from the formula $h = (v_i \sin \theta)t - 0.5gt^2$, where h is the height of the object, v_i is the initial velocity, g is the acceleration due to gravity (32 ft/s²), and t is time (friction is ignored).

1 Suppose the first car of a roller coaster leaves the bottom of the first hill at an initial speed of 60 mph at an angle of 44° from the horizontal. Draw a sketch of this hill. Find the maximum height the coaster reaches on the next hill and at what time. Label your drawing.

2 Find the horizontal distance R the car travels as it follows the contour of the second hill if $R = (v_i \cos \theta)t$.

3 How would these formulas help in altering your roller coaster design? How might friction affect your calculations and plans?

Add the results of your work to your Investigation Folder.

Extension

Problem Solving Have students find the exact value of tan 15° using the half-angle formulas.

$2 - \sqrt{3}$ or $\sqrt{7 - 4\sqrt{3}}$

In·ves·ti·ga·tion

Working on the Investigation
The Investigation on pages 768–769 is designed to be a long-term project that is completed over several days or weeks. Encourage students to keep their materials in their Investigation Folder as they work on the Investigation.

---

4 ASSESS

Closing Activity
Modeling Have students use a diagram of a unit circle to model how to determine the quadrant of $2x$ or $\frac{x}{2}$ if the quadrant of x is known.

Chapter 14, Quiz C (Lessons 14-4 and 14-5), is in the *Assessment and Evaluation Masters*, p. 381.

Enrichment Masters, p. 103

14-5   NAME_____ DATE_____
Enrichment   Student Edition Pages 853–8

Identities for the Products of Sines and Cosines

By adding the identities for the sines of the sum and difference of the measures of two angles, a new identity is obtained.

$\sin(\alpha + \beta) = \sin \alpha \cos \beta + \cos \alpha \sin \beta$
$\sin(\alpha - \beta) = \sin \alpha \cos \beta - \cos \alpha \sin \beta$
(i) $\overline{\sin(\alpha + \beta) + \sin(\alpha - \beta) = 2 \sin \alpha \cos \beta}$

This new identity is useful for expressing certain products as sums.

Example: Write $\sin 3\theta \cos \theta$ as a sum.
In the identity let $\alpha = 3\theta$ and $\beta = \theta$ so that
$2 \sin 3\theta \cos \theta = \sin(3\theta + \theta) + \sin(3\theta - \theta)$. Thus,
$\sin 3\theta \cos \theta = \frac{1}{2}\sin 4\theta + \frac{1}{2}\sin 2\theta$.

By subtracting the identities for $\sin(\alpha + \beta)$ and $\sin(\alpha - \beta)$, a similar identity for expressing a product as a difference is obtained.

(ii) $\sin(\alpha + \beta) - \sin(\alpha - \beta) = 2 \cos \alpha \sin \beta$

Complete.

1. Use the identities for $\cos(\alpha + \beta)$ and $\cos(\alpha - \beta)$ to find identities for expressing the products $2 \cos \alpha \cos \beta$ and $2 \sin \alpha \sin \beta$ as a sum or difference.
$2 \cos \alpha \cos \beta = \cos(\alpha + \beta) + \cos(\alpha - \beta)$
$2 \sin \alpha \sin \beta = \cos(\alpha - \beta) - \cos(\alpha + \beta)$

2. Find the value of $\sin 105° \cos 75°$ without using tables.
$\frac{1}{2}[\sin(105° + 75°) + \sin(105° - 75°)]$;
$\frac{1}{2}[0 + \frac{1}{2}]; \frac{1}{2} \cdot \frac{1}{2} = \frac{1}{4}$

3. Express $\cos \theta \sin \frac{\theta}{2}$ as a difference.
$2 \cos \theta \sin \frac{\theta}{2} = \sin\left(\theta + \frac{\theta}{2}\right) - \sin\left(\theta - \frac{\theta}{2}\right)$
$\cos \theta \sin \frac{\theta}{2} = \frac{1}{2}\sin \frac{3\theta}{2} - \frac{1}{2}\sin \frac{\theta}{2}$

Solving Trigonometric Equations

A Preview of Lesson 14–6.

The coordinates of the points that make up the graph of a trigonometric function represent all of the values that satisfy the function. When you solve a trigonometric equation, you find all values of the variable that satisfy the equation. So, you can solve trigonometric equations by graphing the related trigonometric function and then finding the zeros of that function.

Example **Use a graphing calculator to solve $\sin x = 0.8$ if $0° \leq x < 360°$.**

To get the correct viewing window, be sure the calculator is in Degree mode.

Rewrite the equation as $\sin x - 0.8 = 0$. Then graph the function $f(x) = \sin x - 0.8$ and look for the zeros. Use the viewing window [0, 360] by [−2, 1] with a scale factor of 90 for the *x*-axis and 1 for the *y*-axis.

Enter:
[−] .8 [GRAPH]

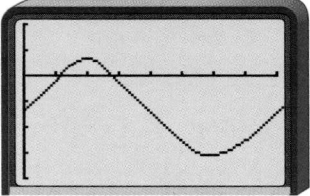

Based on the graph, you can see that there are two roots in the interval

$0° \leq x < 360°$. ZOOM in or use [2nd]

[CALC] root to approximate the solutions. The approximate solutions are 53.1° and 126.9°.

Example **Use a graphing calculator to solve $2 \cos x + 3 = 0$ if $0° \leq x < 360°$.**

The related function is $f(x) = 2 \cos x + 3$. Use the viewing window [0, 360] by [−3, 5] with a scale factor of 90 for the *x*-axis and 1 for the *y*-axis.

Enter:  2
[+] 3 [GRAPH]

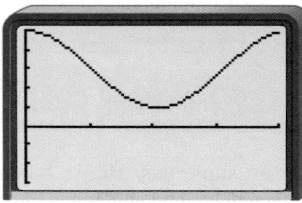

The function has no zeros. Thus, the related equation $2 \cos x + 3 = 0$ has no real solutions. *Note that $\cos x = -\frac{3}{2}$ and values of cosine are never less than −1.*

EXERCISES

Use a graphing calculator to solve each equation for the indicated values of x.

1. 11.5°, 168.5°
2. no solutions
3. 0°, 60°, 180°, 300°
4. 0°, 180°

1. $\sin x = 0.2$ if $0° \leq x < 360°$
2. $0.5 \cos x = 1.4$ if $-720° \leq x < 720°$
3. $\sin 2x = \sin x$ if $0° \leq x < 360°$
4. $\tan x = \sin x$ if $0° \leq x < 360°$
5. $3 \sin 2x - 5 \sin x = 1$ if $-360° \leq x < 360°$ −174.8°, −51.6°, 185.2°, 308.4°
6. $\tan^2 x \cos x + 5 \cos x = 0$ if $0° \leq x < 360°$ no solutions

---

NCTM Standards: 1–6, 8–9

Objective
Use a graphing calculator to solve trigonometric equations.

Recommended Time
15 minutes

Instructional Resources
Graphing Calculator Masters, pp. 61 and 62

These masters provide keystroking instruction for this lesson for the TI-81 and Casio graphing calculators.

1 FOCUS

Motivating the Lesson
Write the equation $3x^2 + 2x + 4 = 0$ on the chalkboard or overhead. Then substitute $\sin x$ for *x* to obtain the equation $3 \sin^2 x + 2 \sin x + 4 = 0$. Ask students if it is still a function. **yes** Can it be solved? **yes** If so, can it be solved by graphing? **yes** How?

2 TEACH

Teaching Tip Parentheses are needed around a trigonometric function only if you are raising it to a power. If you are multiplying the function, you do not need parentheses.

Teaching Tip It may be easier to redraw the graph in the original viewing window before zooming in to find the second zero.

3 PRACTICE/APPLY

Assignment Guide

Core: 1–6
Enriched: 1–6

4 ASSESS

Observing students working with technology is an excellent method of assessment.

Using Technology
This lesson offers an excellent opportunity for using technology in your algebra classroom. For more information on using technology, see *Graphing Calculators in the Mathematics Classroom,* one of the titles in the Glencoe Mathematics Professional Series.

Solving Trigonometric Equations

What YOU'LL LEARN

• To solve trigonometric equations.

Why IT'S IMPORTANT

You can use trigonometric equations to solve problems involving physical science.

CONNECTION

Physical Science

You know that the number of hours of daylight varies with the time of year. This variation can be approximated by a sine function. For example, in parts of northeast United States, the number of hours of daylight d may be represented by $d = 3 \sin \frac{2\pi}{365} t + 12$, where t is the number of days after March 21. On what days would you have $10\frac{1}{2}$ hours of daylight? *This problem will be solved in Example 6.*

These are called <u>conditional equations</u>.

Trigonometric identities are true for *all* values of the variable for which the equation is defined. However, most **trigonometric equations**, like most algebraic equations, are true for *some* but not *all* values of the variable.

Example **Solve $\sin^2 x + \cos 2x - \cos x = 0$ if $0° \leq x < 360°$.**

$$\sin^2 x + \cos 2x - \cos x = 0$$
$$\sin^2 x + (1 - 2\sin^2 x) - \cos x = 0 \quad \cos 2x = 1 - 2\sin^2 x$$
$$1 - \sin^2 x - \cos x = 0$$
$$\cos^2 x - \cos x = 0 \quad 1 - \sin^2 x = \cos^2 x$$
$$\cos x (\cos x - 1) = 0 \quad \text{Factor out } \cos x.$$

Now use the zero product property.
$$\cos x = 0 \qquad \text{or} \qquad \cos x - 1 = 0$$
$$x = 90° \text{ or } 270° \qquad \qquad \cos x = 1$$
$$x = 0°$$

The solutions are $0°$, $90°$, and $270°$.

Trigonometric equations are usually solved for values of the variable between $0°$ and $360°$ or 0 radians and 2π radians. There are solutions outside that interval. These other solutions differ by integral multiples of the period of the function.

Example **Solve $\cos \theta + 1 = 0$ for all values of θ if θ is measured in radians.**

$$\cos \theta + 1 = 0$$
$$\cos \theta = -1$$

Look at the graph of $y = \cos \theta$ to find solutions to $\cos \theta = -1$.

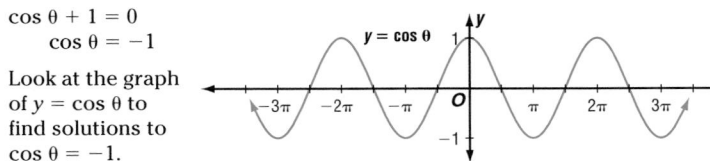

The solutions are $\pi, 3\pi, 5\pi$, and so on, and $-\pi, -3\pi, -5\pi$, and so on. The only solution in the interval 0 radians to 2π radians is π. The period of the cosine function is 2π radians. So the solutions can be written as $\pi + 2k\pi$, where k is any integer.

F Y I

Every year, the length of a day slightly increases. When dinosaurs were alive, a day was approximately 23 hours long.

F Y I

The average solar day is actually 23 hours, 56 minutes, 4 seconds long. It varies slightly during the year because Earth's orbiting speed varies.

NCTM Standards: 1–6, 9

Instructional Resources

• Study Guide Master 14-6
• Practice Master 14-6
• Enrichment Master 14-6
• Assessment and Evaluation Masters, p. 381
• Modeling Mathematics Masters, p. 74
• Real-World Applications, 36
• Science and Math Lab Manual, pp. 117–120
• Tech Prep Applications Masters, p. 28

 Transparency 14-6A contains the 5-Minute Check for this lesson; **Transparency 14-6B** contains a teaching aid for this lesson.

Recommended Pacing	
Honors Pacing	Day 9 of 11
Block Scheduling*	Day 5 of 6

 *For more information on pacing and possible lesson plans, refer to the *Block Scheduling Booklet*.

1 FOCUS

 5-Minute Check
(over Lesson 14-5)

1. x is a third quadrant angle. In which quadrant does the terminal side for $\frac{x}{2}$ lie? **II**

2. If $\sin x = \frac{4}{5}$ and x is in the second quadrant, find $\cos 2x$.
$-\frac{7}{25}$

3. If $\sin x = -\frac{3}{4}$ and x is in the third quadrant, find $\sin \frac{x}{2}$.
$\frac{-\sqrt{8 + 2\sqrt{7}}}{4}$

4. Find $\cos 165°$ using the half-angle formulas. $\frac{-\sqrt{2 + \sqrt{3}}}{2}$

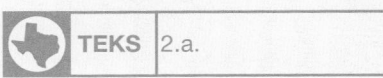 **TEKS** 2.a.

Motivating the Lesson

Hands-On Activity Shine a laser into a tank of cloudy water. Move the laser so that it shines in a straight line or at an angle. Discuss refraction. In physics, Snell's Law is used to study refraction. The law is $\frac{n_1}{n_2} = \frac{\sin \alpha_2}{\sin \alpha_1}$, where n is the index of refraction and α_1 and α_2 are the angles of incidence and refraction.

2 TEACH

Teaching Tip In Example 1, point out that x is limited because this problem deals with periodic functions. If x were not limited, there would be an infinite number of solutions.

In-Class Examples

For Example 1
Solve if $0° \le x < 360°$.

a. $4 \sin^2 x = 1$
30°, 150°, 210°, or 330°

b. $\sin x = -\sin x \cos x$
0° or 180°

For Example 2
Solve $\cos 2\theta - 1 = 0$ for all values of θ if θ is measured in degrees.
$0° + k \cdot 180°$, where k is any integer

For Example 3
Solve each equation for all values of x. Find values in degrees and in radians.

a. $2 \cos x = \sqrt{3}$ 330° + $k \cdot 360°$ or $\frac{11\pi}{6} + 2k\pi$; 30° + $k \cdot 360°$ or $\frac{\pi}{6} + 2k\pi$

b. $2 \cos^2 x - 1 = 0$ for any integer k: $x = 45° + k \cdot 90°$ or $\frac{\pi}{4} + \frac{k\pi}{2}$

For Example 4
Solve $2 \cos^2\theta - 3 \cos\theta - 2 = 0$ if $0 \le \theta < 2\pi$.
$\frac{2\pi}{3}, \frac{4\pi}{3}$

For Example 5
Solve $\cos \theta = 1 + \sin \theta$ if $0° \le \theta < 360°$. 0°, 270°

If an equation cannot be solved easily by factoring, try writing the expression in terms of only one trigonometric function.

Example ③ Solve $\sin^2 x - 1 = \cos^2 x$.

$\sin^2 x - 1 = \cos^2 x$

$\sin^2 x - 1 = 1 - \sin^2 x$ $\cos^2 x = 1 - \sin^2 x$

$2 \sin^2 x = 2$

$\sin^2 x = 1$ *Divide each side by 2.*

$\sin x = \pm 1$ *Take the square root of each side.*

$x = 90° + k \cdot 360°$ or $270° + k \cdot 360°$

The solutions are $90° + k \cdot 360°$ and $270° + k \cdot 360°$, where k is any integer.

Some trigonometric equations have *no solution*. In other words, there is no replacement for the variable that will make the sentence true. For example, the equation $\sin x = -3$ has no solution, since all values of $\sin x$ are between -1 and 1, inclusive. Thus, the solution set for $\sin x = -3$ is empty.

Example ④ Solve $2 \sin^2 \theta - 3 \sin \theta - 2 = 0$ if $0 \le \theta < 2\pi$.

$2 \sin^2 \theta - 3 \sin \theta - 2 = 0$

$(\sin \theta - 2)(2 \sin \theta + 1) = 0$

$\sin \theta - 2 = 0$ or $2 \sin \theta + 1 = 0$ *Factor*

$\sin \theta = 2$ $2 \sin \theta = -1$ *Zero product property*

$\sin \theta = -\frac{1}{2}$

There is no solution to $\sin \theta = 2$ since all values of $\sin \theta$ are between -1 and 1, inclusive.

$\theta = \frac{7\pi}{6}$ or $\frac{11\pi}{6}$

The solutions are $\frac{7\pi}{6}$ or $\frac{11\pi}{6}$.

> **LOOK BACK**
> Refer to Lesson 5-4 to review factoring trinomials.

Some algebraic operations, such as squaring, may result in answers that are *not* solutions of the original equation. So, it is necessary to check your solutions to trigonometric equations.

Example ⑤ Solve $\sin x = 1 + \cos x$ if $0° \le x < 360°$.

$\sin x = 1 + \cos x$

$\sin^2 x = (1 + \cos x)^2$ *Square each side of the equation.*

$1 - \cos^2 x = 1 + 2 \cos x + \cos^2 x$ $\sin^2 x = 1 - \cos^2 x$

$0 = 2 \cos x + 2 \cos^2 x$

$0 = 2 \cos x (1 + \cos x)$ *Factor.*

$2 \cos x = 0$ or $1 + \cos x = 0$ *Zero product property*

$\cos x = 0$ $\cos x = -1$

$x = 90°$ or $270°$ $x = 180°$

Check:

$$\sin x = 1 + \cos x \qquad\qquad \sin x = 1 + \cos x$$

$$\sin 90° \overset{?}{=} 1 + \cos 90° \qquad \sin 180° \overset{?}{=} 1 + \cos 180°$$

$$1 \overset{?}{=} 1 + 0 \qquad\qquad\qquad 0 \overset{?}{=} 1 + (-1)$$

$$1 = 1 \ \checkmark \qquad\qquad\qquad 0 = 0 \ \checkmark$$

$$\sin x = 1 + \cos x$$

$$\sin 270° \overset{?}{=} 1 + \cos 270°$$

$$-1 \overset{?}{=} 1 + 0$$

$$-1 \neq 1$$

The solutions are 90° and 180°.

You can use a graphing calculator to visualize the solution of a trigonometric equation as the intersection of two trigonometric graphs.

EXPLORATION
GRAPHING CALCULATORS

Set MODE to degrees. Then use the viewing window [0, 360] by [−2, 2] with a scale factor of 45 for the x-axis and 0.5 for the y-axis.

Your Turn

a. Graph the two sides of the equation of Example 5. Enter the functions
$Y1 = \cos X$ and $Y2 = 1 + \sin X$ into the Y = list. Then press GRAPH .
How many times do the two curves intersect? **2 times**

b. Use the TRACE function to find the intersection points of the graphs.
How are these points related to the results of Example 5?

c. Graph the function $y = \sin^2 x$ as Y1 and the function $y = \sin x - 0.5$ as
Y2. Then press GRAPH . What does the graph tell you about the
trigonometric equation $\sin^2 x = \sin x - \dfrac{1}{2}$?

b. The x-coordinates are the same as the two solutions in Example 5.

c. Since the two graphs do not intersect, the equation has no solution.

Example **6**

CONNECTION
Physical Science

Refer to the connection at the beginning of the lesson. In Hartford, Connecticut, the number of hours of daylight can be approximated by the equation $d = 3 \sin \dfrac{2\pi}{365}t + 12$. The angle measures are in radians, and leap years are not included.

On what days will you have $10\dfrac{1}{2}$ hours of daylight?

Explore   You know that $d = 10\dfrac{1}{2}$. You want to find the value of t.

Plan   Replace the known values into the formula and solve to find the number of days after March 21. Then use a calendar to find the actual dates.

(continued on the next page)

Remind students that if two equations are equal for at least one value of *x*, then their graphs will intersect in at least one point.

In-Class Example

For Example 6
On what days will Hartford, Connecticut, have 14 hours of sunlight? **May 2, August 11**

Check for Understanding

Exercises 1–12 are designed to help you assess your students' understanding through reading, writing, speaking, and modeling. You should work through Exercises 1–3 with your students and then monitor their work on Exercises 4–12.

Additional Answers

1. Sample answer: The function is periodic with two solutions in each of its infinite number of periods.

8. $0 + \frac{2k\pi}{3}$

9. $\frac{\pi}{2} + k\pi, \frac{2\pi}{3} + 2k\pi, \frac{4\pi}{3} + 2k\pi$

10. $\frac{\pi}{6} + 2k\pi, \frac{5\pi}{6} + 2k\pi$

11. $\frac{\pi}{3} + 2k\pi, \frac{5\pi}{3} + 2k\pi$

Top Five List

Longest Days in the Solar System*

1. Venus, 244 days
2. Mercury, 58 days, 14 hours
3. Sun, 25 days
4. Pluto, 6 days, 9 hours
5. Mars, 24 hours, 37 minutes.

*A day is a period of rotation, based on Earth day.

Solve

$$d = 3 \sin \frac{2\pi}{365}t + 12$$

$$10\tfrac{1}{2} = 3 \sin \frac{2\pi}{365}t + 12 \quad \textit{Replace d with } 10\tfrac{1}{2}.$$

$$-1.5 = 3 \sin \frac{2\pi}{365}t \quad \textit{Subtract 12 from each side.}$$

$$-\frac{1}{2} = \sin \frac{2\pi}{365}t \quad \textit{Divide each side by 3.}$$

$$\frac{2\pi}{365}t = \frac{7\pi}{6} \quad \text{or} \quad \frac{2\pi}{365}t = \frac{11\pi}{6}$$

$$t = \frac{7\pi}{6} \cdot \frac{365}{2\pi} \qquad t = \frac{11\pi}{6} \cdot \frac{365}{2\pi}$$

$$t \approx 213 \qquad t \approx 335$$

There will be $10\tfrac{1}{2}$ hours of daylight 213 days after March 21 and 335 days after March 21; that is, on October 20 and February 19.

Examine Check the solutions by substituting $t = 213$ and $t = 335$ into the original equation.

CHECK FOR UNDERSTANDING

Communicating Mathematics

Study the lesson. Then complete the following. 1. See margin.

1. **Explain** why the number of solutions to the equation $\sin x = -\frac{1}{2}$ is infinite.

2. **Explain** why the equation $\cos x = -2$ has no solutions. All values of cos x are between −1 and 1, inclusive.

 MATH JOURNAL

3. **Assess Yourself** How well do you understand the difference between an identity and a conditional equation? State whether the following sentence is true or false. "An identity is any equation that has an infinite number of solutions." Then explain your answer. False; an identity is an equation that is true for all values of the variable.

Guided Practice

Find all solutions if $0° \le \theta < 360°$.

4. $\cos^2 \theta = 1$ 0°, 180°

5. $\sin 2\theta = \frac{1}{2}$ 15°, 75°, 195°, 255°

6. $2 \cos^2 \theta + 2 = 5 \cos \theta$ 60°, 300°

7. $\sin \theta + \sin \theta \cos \theta = 0$ 0°, 180°

Solve each equation for all values of θ if θ is measured in radians.

8–11. See margin.

8. $\cos 2\theta = \cos \theta$

9. $\cos 2\theta + \cos \theta + 1 = 0$

10. $3 \sin^2 \theta - \cos^2 \theta = 0$

11. $4 \cos^2 \theta - 4 \cos \theta + 1 = 0$

Reteaching

Using Models A general approach to solving, or at least approximating, a solution to an equation is to "graph and squeeze." Graphing utilities and simple computer programs can reduce the tedium of repeated long calculations and precision graphing. The function must be continuous near its zeros.

Top Five List

Not only does Venus have the longest day, but one of the shortest years— 224 Earth days. This makes its day longer than its year!

12. Physical Science Using the results of Example 6, tell what days of the year have *at least* $10\frac{1}{2}$ hours of daylight. Explain how you know. **See margin.**

EXERCISES

Practice **A** ▶

Find all solutions if $0° \le x < 360°$. **13–18. See margin.**

13. $4\cos^2 x = 1$
14. $2\sin^2 x - 1 = 0$
15. $\sin 2x = 2\cos x$
16. $2\cos^2 x = \sin x + 1$
17. $4\sin^2 x - 4\sin x + 1 = 0$
18. $\sin 2x = \cos x$

Find all solutions if $0 \le \theta < 2\pi$. **19–24. See margin.**

19. $2\sin\theta = -1$
20. $2\cos\theta - 1 = 0$
21. $2\sin\theta = -\sqrt{3}$
22. $4\sin^2\theta = 1$
23. $2\sin^2\theta - \sin\theta = 1$
24. $2\sin^2\theta = -\sin\theta$

25–32. See margin.

B ▶

Solve each equation for all values of x if x is measured in degrees.

25. $\sin x = \cos x$
26. $\sin^2 x - 2\sin x - 3 = 0$
27. $\tan x = \sin x$
28. $\sin x = 1 + \cos x$
29. $3\cos 2x - 5\cos x = 1$
30. $\tan^2 x - \sqrt{3}\tan x = 0$
31. $\sin^2 x - \sin x = 0$
32. $\cos x \tan x - \sin^2 x = 0$

33–40. See margin.

C ▶

Solve each equation for all values of θ if θ is measured in radians.

33. $2\sin^2\theta - 3\sin\theta - 2 = 0$
34. $\cos 2\theta + 3\cos\theta - 1 = 0$
35. $2\sin^2\theta - \cos\theta - 1 = 0$
36. $\cos^2\theta - \frac{5}{2}\cos\theta - \frac{3}{2} = 0$
37. $\cos^2\theta - \frac{7}{2}\cos\theta - 2 = 0$
38. $2\cos^2\theta + 3\sin\theta - 3 = 0$
39. $\cos 2\theta = 1 - \sin\theta$
40. $\cos\theta = 3\cos\theta - 2$

Graphing Calculator

41. On a graphing calculator, set the mode to degrees. Use a viewing window of $[0, 360]$ by $[-2.5, 2.5]$ with a scale factor of 45 for the x-axis and 0.5 for the y-axis.

   a. Enter the functions $Y_1 = \sin 2X$ and $Y_2 = 2\cos X$ into the $Y=$ list. Then press GRAPH . How many times do the two curves intersect? For what values of x do they intersect? **two times; 90° and 270°**

   b. To which of Exercises 13–18 does the graph correspond? Does the graph agree with your answer to that exercise? **Exercise 15; yes**

   c. Repeat part a, but replace $2\cos X$ by $2\cos X \sin X$. What do you notice about the two curves? **They are the same.**

   d. What do parts a–c show you about the difference between an equation that is an identity and one that is not?

41d. If the equation is an identity then the two curves are identical. Otherwise, the curves intersect only at certain points.

Additional Answers

24. $0, \pi, \dfrac{7\pi}{6}, \dfrac{11\pi}{6}$

25. $45° + k \cdot 180°$

26. $270° + k \cdot 360°$

27. $0° + k \cdot 180°$

28. $90° + k \cdot 360°, 180° + k \cdot 360°$

29. $120° + k \cdot 360°, 240° + k \cdot 360°$

30. $0° + k \cdot 180°, 60° + k \cdot 180°$

31. $0° + k \cdot 180°, 90° + k \cdot 360°$

32. $0° + k \cdot 180°$

33. $\dfrac{7\pi}{6} + 2k\pi, \dfrac{11\pi}{6} + 2k\pi$

34. $\dfrac{\pi}{3} + 2k\pi, \dfrac{5\pi}{3} + 2k\pi$

35. $\pi + 2k\pi, \dfrac{\pi}{3} + 2k\pi, \dfrac{5\pi}{3} + 2k\pi$

36. $\dfrac{2\pi}{3} + 2k\pi, \dfrac{4\pi}{3} + 2k\pi$

37. $\dfrac{2\pi}{3} + 2k\pi, \dfrac{4\pi}{3} + 2k\pi$

38. $\dfrac{\pi}{6} + 2k\pi, \dfrac{5\pi}{6} + 2k\pi, \dfrac{\pi}{2} + 2k\pi$

39. $0 + k\pi, \dfrac{\pi}{6} + 2k\pi, \dfrac{5\pi}{6} + 2k\pi$

40. $0 + 2k\pi$

Assignment Guide

Core: 13–45 odd, 46–53
Enriched: 14–40 even, 41–53

For **Extra Practice,** see p. 910.

The red A, B, and C flags, printed only in the Teacher's Wraparound Edition, indicate the level of difficulty of the exercises.

Additional Answers

12. Every day from February 19 to October 20; explanations will vary. Sample explanation: Since the longest day of the year occurs around June 22, the days between February 19 and October 20 must increase in length until June 22 and then decrease in length until October 20.

13. 60°, 120°, 240°, 300°
14. 45°, 135°, 225°, 315°
15. 90°, 270°
16. 30°, 150°, 270°
17. 30°, 150°
18. 30°, 90°, 150°, 270°
19. $\dfrac{7\pi}{6}, \dfrac{11\pi}{6}$
20. $\dfrac{\pi}{3}, \dfrac{5\pi}{3}$
21. $\dfrac{4\pi}{3}, \dfrac{5\pi}{3}$
22. $\dfrac{\pi}{6}, \dfrac{5\pi}{6}, \dfrac{7\pi}{6}, \dfrac{11\pi}{6}$
23. $\dfrac{\pi}{2}, \dfrac{7\pi}{6}, \dfrac{11\pi}{6}$

Study Guide Masters, p. 104

14-6

NAME_____ DATE_____

Study Guide
Student Edition
Pages 861–86

Solving Trigonometric Equations

Trigonometric identities are true for *all* values of the variable for which both sides are defined. Most trigonometric equations are true for *some* but *not all* values of the variable. Usually trigonometric equations are solved for values of the variable between 0° and 360° or 0 radians and 2π radians.

Some trigonometric equations have *no solutions*. It is important to check your solutions because some algebraic operations may introduce answers that are *not* solutions to the original equation.

Example: Solve $\cos x = 1 - \sin x$ if $0° \le x < 360°$.
$\cos^2 x = (1 - \sin x)^2$
$1 - \sin^2 x = 1 - 2\sin x + \sin^2 x$
$0 = -2\sin x + 2\sin^2 x$
$0 = 2\sin x(\sin x - 1)$
$0 = 2\sin x(-1 + \sin x)$

$2\sin x = 0$ $-1 + \sin x = 0$
$\sin x = 0$ $\sin x = 1$
$x = 0°, 180°$ $x = 90°$

The solutions appear to be 0°, 90° and 180°. However, 180° does not satisfy the original equation. Thus, the solutions are 0° and 90°.

Find all solutions if $0° \le x < 360°$.

1. $\cot^2 x = 1$
   45°, 135°, 225°, 315°
2. $2\sin x - 1 = 0$
   30°, 150°
3. $3\sin^2 x - \cos^2 x = 0$
   30°, 150°, 210°, 330°
4. $2\cos^2 x + \cos x = 1$
   60°, 180°, 300°
5. $\sin^2 x \cos^2 x = 0$
   0°, 90°, 180°, 270°
6. $\cos 2x = \dfrac{\sqrt{3}}{2}$
   15°, 165°, 195°, 345°
7. $\sin\dfrac{x}{2} = 1$
   180°
8. $2\sin x - \sqrt{3} = 0$
   60°, 120°
9. $\tan x \sin x = \tan x$
   0°, 90°, 180°
10. $4\sin^2 x - 1 = 0$
    30°, 150°, 210°, 330°

Using the Programming Exercises The program given in Exercise 42 is for use with a TI-82 graphing calculator. For other programmable calculators, have students consult their owner's manual for commands similar to those presented here.

Programming

42. The graphing calculator program below finds solutions to $2\cos^2 x + 3\cos x - 2 = 0$ within a given interval. The interval is entered in degrees. The program is designed to pause after each solution is found. Press ENTER after each solution to continue. The program will indicate "Done" when finished. You can use this program to solve other trigonometric equations by simply changing the equation within the program.

```
PROGRAM:SOLN
: Disp "FIND THE SOLUTIONS    : Then
    OF"                        : Disp "ONE SOLUTION IS"
: Disp "2(cos x)² + 3cos       : Disp J
    (x)−2=0"                   : Disp "DEGREES"
: Disp                         : C+1 → C
: Disp "ENTER THE LEAST        : Pause
    VALUE TO BE TESTED"        : End
: Input A                      : End
: Disp "ENTER THE GREATEST     : If C=0
    VALUE TO BE TESTED"        : Then
: Input B                      : Disp "NO SOLUTIONS
: 0 → C                            BETWEEN"
: FOR(J,A,B)                   : Disp A
: J/57.2957795 → Y             : Disp "AND"
: (2(cos Y)²+3cos(Y)           : Disp B
    −2) → F                    : Disp "DEGREES"
: If abs (F)≤0.0000001         : End
```

Make the necessary changes in the program to solve each equation for values of x within the given interval.

a. $2\cos^2 x + 3\cos x - 2 = 0$ between 0° and 180° **60°**

b. $2\cos x - \sin 2x = 0$ between 0° and 360° **90°, 270°**

c. $2\sin^2 x + \sin x - 1 = 0$ between 180° and 240° **no solution**

d. $\sin x + \cos x \tan^2 x = 0$ between −360° and 0°

e. $\cos 2x + \sin x = 1$ between 0° and 720° **0°, 30°, 150°, 180°, 360°, 390°, 510°, 540°, 720°**

42d. −360°, −225°, −180°, −45°, 0°

Critical Thinking

43. Solve $\dfrac{\tan x - \sin x}{\tan x + \sin x} = \dfrac{\sec x - 1}{\sec x + 1}$ for all values of x if x is measured in radians.

all reals except $0 + \dfrac{k\pi}{2}$, where k is any integer

Applications and Problem Solving

44. **Physical Science** In New Orleans, Louisiana, the number of hours of daylight is approximately described by the equation $d = 2.3 \sin \dfrac{2\pi}{365}t + 11.7$, where t is the number of days after March 21 and the angle measures are in radians. On what days will you have 12.85 hours of daylight?
April 20 and August 20

45. **Physics** According to Snell's law, the angle at which light enters water α is related to the angle at which light travels in water β by the equation $\sin \alpha = 1.33 \sin \beta$. Is there any angle at which you could direct a beam of light at the surface of a pool so that the light is not bent? (*Hint:* If the light is not bent, what must be true about α and β?) **0°**

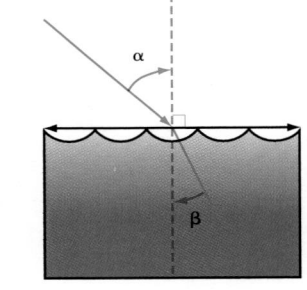

Extension

Connections Have students further research the field of optics and write a short report relating trigonometric functions to the use of refracted light in astronomy, gemology, or other areas.

Practice Masters, p. 104

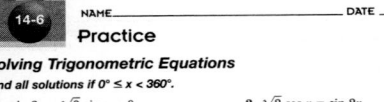

14-6 NAME_____ DATE_____
Student Edition
Pages 861–867

Practice

Solving Trigonometric Equations

Find all solutions if 0° ≤ x < 360°.

1. $\sin 2x - \sqrt{3}\sin x = 0$
   0°, 180°, 30°, 330°

2. $\sqrt{2}\cos x = \sin 2x$
   90°, 270°, 45°, 135°

Find all solutions if 0 ≤ x < 2π.

3. $\cos x + \cos(90 - x) = 0$
   $\frac{3}{4}\pi, \frac{7}{4}\pi$

4. $\tan^2 x + \sec x = 1$
   $0, \frac{2}{3}\pi, \frac{4}{3}\pi$

Solve each equation for all values of x if x is measured in degrees.

5. $\sin^2 x \cos x = \cos x$
   90° + 180n°

6. $\csc^2 x - 3\csc x + 2 = 0$
   30° + 360n°, 90° + 360n°, 150° + 360n°

7. $\frac{3}{1 + \cos x} = 4(1 - \cos x)$
   60° + 180n°, 120° + 180n°

8. $\sqrt{2}\cos^3 x = \cos^2 x$
   90° + 180n°, ± 45° + 360n°

Solve each equation for all values of θ if θ is measured in radians.

9. $\cos^2 \theta = \sin^2 \theta$
   $\frac{\pi}{4} + \frac{n\pi}{2}$

10. $\cot \theta = \cot^3 \theta$
    $\frac{\pi}{2} + n\pi, \frac{\pi}{4} + \frac{n\pi}{2}$

11. $\sqrt{2}\sin^2 \theta = \sin^2 \theta$
    $\frac{\pi}{4} + 2\pi n, \frac{3\pi}{4} + 2\pi n$

12. $\cos^2 \theta \sin \theta = \sin \theta$
    $0 + n\pi$

Mixed Review

46. Trigonometry If x is an angle whose terminal side lies in the second quadrant, in which quadrant does the terminal side for $\frac{x}{2}$ lie? (Lesson 14–5)

47. Trigonometry Find $\cos A$ when $\tan A = \frac{\sqrt{5}}{2}$. (Lesson 13–1) $\frac{2}{3}$

48. Probability A canister contains 20 pieces of candy: 5 pineapple flavored, 9 cherry flavored, and 6 lemon flavored. Two are selected at random. Find each probability. (Lesson 12–4)
  a. P(2 pineapple) **b.** P(1 pineapple and 1 lemon)

48a. $\frac{1}{19} \approx 0.053$

48b. $\frac{3}{19} \approx 0.158$

49. 24.576%

49. Cuisine A soufflé is a dish made from a sauce, egg yolks, beaten egg whites, and a flavoring of seafood, fruit, or vegetables. When it bakes, the batter rises dramatically and is very light and fluffy when done properly. However, soufflés often fall while baking. Dawn Depew is preparing soufflés for her parents' anniversary party. She averages 4 out of 5 soufflés baking correctly. If she prepares 6 soufflés for the party, what is the likelihood that exactly 4 of them will turn out all right? (Lesson 11–8)

50. Solve $2^{2x} = \frac{1}{8}$. (Lesson 10–1) $-\frac{3}{2}$

51. Solve $b^2 - \frac{3}{4}b + \frac{1}{8} = 0$ by completing the square. (Lesson 6–3) $\frac{1}{2}, \frac{1}{4}$

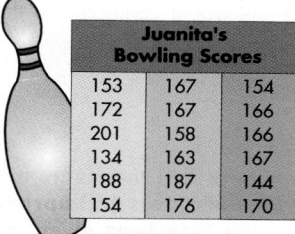

Juanita's Bowling Scores		
153	167	154
172	167	166
201	158	166
134	163	167
188	187	144
154	176	170

52. Bowling Juanita's bowling scores for each week of her summer bowling league are shown in the table at the left. (Lesson 4–8)
  a. Make a box-and-whisker plot of the data. **See margin.**
  b. Use the plot to describe the pattern in Juanita's bowling scores for the season. **She usually bowled between 154 and 172.**

53. Consumerism Ian can buy one piece of candy for 29¢. He has $6.09 that he can spend. Write an inequality to show how many pieces of candy Ian can buy. Then solve the inequality. (Lesson 2–7)
29x ≤ 609; x ≤ 21

Mathematics and SOCIETY

Fractal Drums

The excerpt below appeared in an article in *Science News* on September 17, 1994.

IT'S EASY TO DISTINGUISH THE SOUNDS OF different types of drums, even without seeing the instruments. What makes these sounds so readily identifiable is that each drum vibrates at characteristic frequencies. . . . The sounds of drums also suggest important questions in mathematics. . . . It turns out, for example, that different membrane shapes can sometimes generate identical spectra of frequencies.

A number of mathematicians and physicists are studying how the wiggliness of a drum's rim affects its sound, especially in cases where the boundary is so wrinkled . . . that it can be termed a fractal. . . . Such investigations may eventually furnish clues as to why fractals seem to abound in nature, from crazily indented coastlines to the intricate branching of air passages in the human lung. ∎

1. What could you do to a drum to change its vibration frequencies and therefore its sound? **1, 3. See margin.**

2. If you were blindfolded, could you identify some of the physical characteristics (such as softness, size, shape, weight) of the sources of sound that you hear? **See students' work.**

3. Given that drums of different shapes can produce identical frequency spectra, what would you say to a geophysicist who is trying to construct a model of Earth's interior from a study of underground seismic vibrations?

Answers for Mathematics and Society

1. Change the size, shape, tension, or material composition of the drumhead.

3. Sample answer: Tell the geophysicist to be very cautious in his or her assumptions and conclusions. Just because two or more underground structures produced identical frequency spectra does not mean that the structures are identical. The drum experiments indicate that identical spectra can, in fact, be produced by structures that are not identical.

---

4 ASSESS

Closing Activity

Writing Have students write a short paragraph explaining why it is necessary to check solutions to trigonometric equations.

Chapter 14, Quiz D (Lesson 14-6), is available in the *Assessment and Evaluation Masters*, p. 381.

Additional Answer

52a.

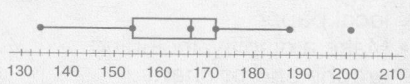

Mathematics and SOCIETY

Students might want to conduct a controlled scientific experiment. They can systematically vary certain factors that may or may not affect the sound of a drum. Use cylinders of varying circumferences, height, and lengths, and stretch a variety of materials over the top.

Enrichment Masters, p. 104

14-6 NAME _____ DATE _____
Enrichment Student Edition Pages 861–867

Alternating Current

The figure at the right represents an alternating current generator. A rectangular coil of wire is suspended between the poles of a magnet. As the coil of wire is rotated, it passes through the magnetic field and generates current.

As point X on the coil passes through the points A and C, its motion is along the direction of the magnetic field between the poles. Therefore, no current is generated. However, through points B and D, the motion of X is perpendicular to the magnetic field. This induces maximum current in the coil. Between A and B, B and C, C and D, and D and A, the current in the coil will have an intermediate value. Thus, the graph of the current of an alternating current generator is closely related to the sine curve.

The maximum current may have a positive or negative value.

The actual current, i, in a household current is given by $i = I_M \sin(120\pi t + \alpha)$ where I_M is the maximum value of the current, t is the elapsed time in seconds, and α is the angle determined by the position of the coil at time t.

Example: If $\alpha = \frac{\pi}{2}$, find a value of t for which $i = 0$.

If $i = 0$, then $I_M \sin(120\pi t + \alpha) = 0$. $i = I_M \sin(120\pi t + \alpha)$
Since $I_M \neq 0$, $\sin(120\pi t + \alpha) = 0$. If $ab = 0$ and $a \neq 0$, then $b = 0$.
Let $120\pi t + \alpha = s$. Thus, $\sin s = 0$.
$s = \pi$ because $\sin \pi = 0$.
$120\pi t + \alpha = \pi$ Substitute $120\pi t + \alpha$ for s.
$120\pi t + \frac{\pi}{2} = \pi$ Substitute $\frac{\pi}{2}$ for α.
$= \frac{1}{240}$ Solve for t.

This solution is the first positive value of t that satisfies the problem.

Using the equation for the actual current in a household circuit, $i = I_M \sin(120\pi t + \alpha)$, solve each problem. For each problem, find the first positive value of t.

1. If $\alpha = 0$, find a value of t for which $i = 0$. $t = \frac{1}{120}$

2. If $\alpha = 0$, find a value of t for which $i = +I_M$. $t = \frac{1}{240}$

3. If $\alpha = \frac{\pi}{2}$, find a value of t for which $i = -I_M$. $t = \frac{1}{120}$

4. If $\alpha = \frac{\pi}{4}$, find a value of t for which $i = 0$. $t = \frac{1}{160}$

Closing the Investigation

This activity provides students an opportunity to bring their work in the Investigation to a close. For each Investigation, students should present their findings to the class. Here are some ways students can display their work.

- Conduct and report on an interview or survey.
- Write a letter, proposal, or report.
- Write an article for the school or local paper.
- Make a display, including graphs and/or charts.
- Plan an activity.

Assessment

To assess students' understanding of the concepts and topics explored in the Investigation and its follow-up activities, you may wish to examine students' Investigation Folders.

The scoring guide provided in the *Investigations and Projects Masters,* p. 23, provides a means for you to score students' work on the Investigation.

Investigations and Projects Masters, p. 23

Scoring Guide
Chapters 13 and 14
Investigation

Level	Specific Criteria
3 Superior	• Shows thorough understanding of the concepts of *how to design and build a scale model, analyze data,* and *use trigonometric equations to find the solutions to structural problems.* • Uses appropriate strategies to solve problems. • Computations are correct. • Written explanations are exemplary. • Charts, graphs, and report are appropriate and sensible. • Goes beyond the requirements of some or all problems.
2 Satisfactory, with Minor Flaws	• Shows understanding of the concepts of *how to design and build a scale model, analyze data,* and *use trigonometric equations to find the solutions to structural problems.* • Uses appropriate strategies to solve problems. • Computations are mostly correct. • Written explanations are effective. • Charts, graphs, and report are appropriate and sensible. • Satisfies all requirements of problems.
1 Nearly Satisfactory, with Obvious Flaws	• Shows understanding of most of the concepts of *how to design and build a scale model, analyze data,* and *use trigonometric equations to find the solutions to structural problems.* • May not use appropriate strategies to solve problems. • Computations are mostly correct. • Written explanations are satisfactory. • Charts, graphs, and report are mostly appropriate and sensible. • Satisfies most requirements of problems.
0 Unsatisfactory	• Shows little or no understanding of the concepts of *how to design and build a scale model, analyze data,* and *use trigonometric equations to find the solutions to structural problems.* • May not use appropriate strategies to solve problems. • Computations are incorrect. • Written explanations are not satisfactory. • Charts, graphs, and report are not appropriate or sensible. • Does not satisfy the requirements of problems.

CLOSING THE
In·ves·ti·ga·tion

Refer to the Investigation on pages 768–769.

Amusement parks are a very competitive business. In order to attract large crowds, each park must have at least a ride or two that can be touted as the best, most thrilling, and most unusual. In recent years, some kind of roller coaster has remained at the top of the list of the most popular and exciting rides. As technology, engineering, and material manufacturing improve, progressive amusement parks constantly replace older rides with newer, more exciting ones.

Analyze

You have conducted experiments and organized your data in various ways. It is now time to analyze your findings and state your conclusions.

PORTFOLIO ASSESSMENT

You may want to keep your work on this Investigation in your portfolio.

1 Make a table to summarize your findings when building and revising your model of a roller coaster.

2 Make a list of things you would want to consider if you were to design and build the "best new roller coaster in the world." Include the type of roller coaster it would be.

3 Use your list to make a diagram showing how each item interrelates with others in the list. Include the mathematics you think you would need in considering each item.

4 List the types of specialists you would like to include on your team to build the coaster and how those specialists would contribute to the project.

Write

Amusement park owners and managers are always searching for new ideas to improve their rides. Suppose you have been given the opportunity to submit a proposal for a new roller coaster design that will fit into a 35-acre corner of Mathematica Amusement World. The ride should last at least 2 minutes. An old merry-go-round and a small Ferris wheel are to be removed from the site to make room for your new coaster.

5 Prepare a proposal for the design and building of your roller coaster. Include a scale drawing, the types of building materials, and the style of the ride.

6 Include a report on the rationale for your chosen design in which you address safety features, thrill factors, and unique features that will draw visitors to the amusement park. Also include why this one ride is better than the ones it is replacing.

7 Make sure you name the new roller coaster and tell how this name is reflected in the ride's design. Prepare a visual display to show how the name will appear at the ride's entrance.

VOCABULARY

After completing this chapter, you should be able to define each term, property, or phrase and give an example or two of each.

Trigonometry

amplitude   (p. 824, 828)

angle of incline   (p. 835)

conditional equation   (p. 861)

difference of angles formula   (p. 848)

double-angle formulas   (p. 853)

half-angle formulas   (p. 855)

phase shift   (p. 825)

sum of angles formula   (p. 848)

trigonometric equations   (p. 861)

trigonometric identity   (p. 835)

UNDERSTANDING AND USING THE VOCABULARY

Choose the letter that best matches each phrase.

1. $\cos (x + y) = \cos x \cos y - \sin x \sin y$ **h**

2. $\sin 2\theta = 2 \sin \theta \cos \theta$ **e**

3. the acute angle described by $\tan \theta = \dfrac{v^2}{gR}$ **b**

4. $\sin (x - y) = \sin x \cos y - \cos x \sin y$ **d**

5. the formula used to find $\cos 22\frac{1}{2}°$ **f**

6. an equation that is not true for all values of the variable   **c**

7. an equation that is true for all values for which every expression in the equation is defined   **i**

8. from one point on a graph until the pattern begins to repeat; a complete revolution   **g**

9. the absolute value of half the difference between the maximum value and the minimum value of a periodic function   **a**

a. amplitude
b. angle of incline
c. conditional equation
d. difference of angles formula
e. double-angle formula
f. half-angle formula
g. period
h. sum of angles formula
i. trigonometric identity

Using the CHAPTER HIGHLIGHTS

The Chapter Highlights begins with a listing of the new terms, properties, and phrases that were introduced in this chapter. Have students define each term and provide an example or two of it, if appropriate.

Assessment and Evaluation Masters, pp. 367–368

14 NAME_____ DATE_____

Chapter 14 Test, Form 1B

Write the letter for the correct answer in the blank at the right of each problem.

1. What is the amplitude of $y = -8 \cos 2\theta$?
   A. 2   B. -2   C. 8   D. -8   1. __C__

2. Find $\csc \beta$ if $\cot \beta = \frac{1}{3}$ and $180° \le \beta \le 270°$.
   A. $-\frac{2\sqrt{2}}{3}$ B. $\frac{2\sqrt{2}}{3}$ C. $\frac{\sqrt{10}}{3}$ D. $-\frac{\sqrt{10}}{3}$ 2. __D__

3. Find $\cos \frac{x}{2}$ if $\sin x = \frac{1}{4}$ and x is between 0° and 90°.
   A. $\frac{\sqrt{15}}{4}$ B. $-\frac{\sqrt{15}}{4}$ C. $\frac{1}{4}\sqrt{8 + 2\sqrt{15}}$ D. $\frac{1}{2}\sqrt{4 + \sqrt{15}}$ 3. __C__

4. What is the period of $y = \tan 3\theta$?
   A. $\frac{2\pi}{3}$ B. $\frac{\pi}{3}$ C. 3π D. 6π 4. __B__

5. Which equation is graphed at the right?
   A. $y = 4 \sec \frac{3}{2}x$ B. $y = 4 \csc \frac{3}{2}x$ C. $y = 4 \sec \frac{2}{3}x$ D. $y = 4 \csc \frac{2}{3}x$ 5. __D__

6. If $\cos \theta = -\frac{2}{3}$ and θ is between 90° and 180°, what is the value of $\sin \theta$?
   A. $-\frac{\sqrt{5}}{3}$ B. $\frac{\sqrt{5}}{3}$ C. $-\frac{\sqrt{13}}{3}$ D. $\frac{\sqrt{13}}{3}$ 6. __B__

7. If $\tan \theta = \frac{1}{4}$ and θ is between 180° and 270°, what is the value of $\sec \theta$?
   A. $\frac{\sqrt{15}}{4}$ B. $-\frac{\sqrt{15}}{4}$ C. $\frac{\sqrt{17}}{4}$ D. $-\frac{\sqrt{17}}{4}$ 7. __D__

8. What is the simplest form of $\frac{\sin^2 \theta + \cos^2 \theta}{\tan^2 \theta}$?
   A. $\cot^2 \theta$ B. $\sin^4 \theta + \sin^2 \theta$ C. $\cos^2 \theta + \cos^4 \theta$ D. $\csc^2 \theta$ 8. __A__

9. What is the value of $\sin 75° \cos 45° + \cos 75° \sin 45°$?
   A. $\frac{1}{2}$ B. $-\frac{1}{2}$ C. $\frac{\sqrt{3}}{2}$ D. $\frac{\sqrt{2}}{2}$ 9. __C__

10. What is the value of $\cos 75° \cos 45° - \sin 75° \sin 45°$?
   A. $-\frac{1}{2}$ B. $\frac{\sqrt{3}}{2}$ C. $\frac{\sqrt{2}}{2}$ D. undefined   10. __A__

14 NAME_____ DATE_____

Chapter 14 Test, Form 1B (continued)

11. What is the value of $\sin (-15°)$?
   A. $\frac{\sqrt{6} - \sqrt{2}}{4}$ B. $\frac{\sqrt{6} + \sqrt{2}}{4}$ C. $\frac{-\sqrt{6} + \sqrt{2}}{4}$ D. $\frac{-\sqrt{6} - \sqrt{2}}{4}$ 11. __C__

12. Find the value of $\sin 2x$ if $\sin x = -\frac{2}{3}$ and x is in the third quadrant.
   A. $-\frac{4\sqrt{5}}{9}$ B. $-\frac{4\sqrt{5}}{9}$ C. $\frac{1}{9}$ D. $\frac{4\sqrt{5}}{9}$ 12. __D__

13. Find the value of $\sin \frac{x}{2}$ if $\cos x = \frac{2}{3}$ and x is in the fourth quadrant.
   A. $\frac{1}{3}$ B. $-\frac{1}{3}$ C. $\frac{\sqrt{6}}{6}$ D. $-\frac{\sqrt{6}}{6}$ 13. __C__

14. Which expression is not equal to 1? Assume no expressions are undefined.
   A. $\sin^2 x + \cot^2 x \sin^2 x$ B. $\frac{\sin^2 x}{1 - \cos x} - \cos x$ C. $\csc^2 x + \cot^2 x$ D. none of these   14. __C__

15. If $0° \le x < 360°$, what are the solutions of $3 \sin x = 2 \cos^2 x$?
   A. 30°, 150°   B. 30°, 120°   C. 30°, 330°   D. 150°, 330°   15. __A__

16. What are all the solutions of $\cos 2x + \cos x - 2 = 0$?
   A. 0°, 360°   B. $0° + 360°n$ C. 0°, 180°, 360°   D. $0° + 180°n$ 16. __B__

17. Which of the following is not a solution of $\sin 2x = \cos x$?
   A. 270°   B. 90°   C. 330°   D. 750°   17. __C__

18. Find the sum of the reciprocals of two numbers whose sum is 10 and whose product is 16.
   A. $\frac{1}{2}$ B. $-\frac{1}{2}$ C. $\frac{3}{4}$ D. $\frac{5}{8}$ 18. __D__

19. Find the exact value of $\cos 375°$.
   A. $\frac{\sqrt{6} - \sqrt{2}}{4}$ B. $\frac{\sqrt{6} + \sqrt{2}}{4}$ C. $\frac{\sqrt{2} - \sqrt{6}}{4}$ D. $\frac{\sqrt{2} + \sqrt{6}}{4}$ 19. __B__

20. Which of the following is not a solution of $\sin^2 + \cos 2x - \cos x = 0$ if $0° \le x < 360°$?
   A. 270°   B. 90°   C. 0°   D. 30°   20. __D__

Bonus If $y = \frac{1}{2} \cos 4x$, find all values of x so that y is a maximum.
   A. $45n°$ B. $90n°$ C. $180n°$ D. $1440n°$ Bonus __B__

Instructional Resources

Three multiple-choice tests and three free-response tests are provided in the *Assessment and Evaluation Masters*. Forms 1A and 2A are for honors pacing, and Forms 1B, 1C, 2B, and 2C are for average pacing. Chapter 14 Test, Form 1B is shown at the right. Chapter 14 Test, Form 2B is shown on the next page.

Skills and Concepts Encourage students to refer to the objectives and examples on the left as they complete the review exercises on the right.

Assessment and Evaluation Masters, pp. 373–374

---

14 NAME_____ DATE_____

Chapter 14 Test, Form 2B

1. State the amplitude and period of $y = -3 \cos 2x$.   1. ____3; π____

2. State the amplitude and period of $y = \frac{1}{2} \sin \frac{\theta}{5}$.   2. ____$\frac{1}{2}$; 10π____

3. Graph $y = \frac{3}{2} \cos 2\theta$.   3. ___See students' graphs.___

4. Find $\sec \theta$ if $\sin \theta = \frac{6}{7}$ and θ is between 0° and 90°.   4. ____$\frac{7\sqrt{13}}{13}$____

5. Find $\csc \theta$ if $\cos \theta = -\frac{1}{3}$ and θ is between 90° and 180°.   5. ____$\frac{3\sqrt{2}}{4}$____

6. Find $\cot \theta$ if $\csc \theta = -\frac{5}{2}$ and θ is between 270° and 360°.   6. ____$-\frac{\sqrt{21}}{2}$____

7. Simplify $(\cos \theta + \sin \theta)^2 - 2 \cos \theta \sin \theta$.   7. ____1____

8. Simplify $\cos^2 x \sec^2 x - \cos^2 x - \sin^2 x$.   8. ____0____

9. Solve $\sin^2 x + \cos^2 x - \sin x = 0$ if $0° \le x \le 360°$.   9. ____90°____

10. Find the exact value of $\sin 195°$.   10. ____$\frac{\sqrt{2} - \sqrt{6}}{4}$____

---

14 NAME_____ DATE_____

Chapter 14 Test, Form 2B (continued)

11. Find the exact value of $\cos 285°$.   11. ____$\frac{\sqrt{6} - \sqrt{2}}{4}$____

12. If $\cos x = \frac{3}{7}$ and x is in the fourth quadrant, find the value of $\cos \frac{x}{2}$.   12. ____$\frac{\sqrt{35}}{7}$____

13. If $\sin x = -\frac{3}{5}$ and x is in the third quadrant, find the value of $\cos 2x$.   13. ____$\frac{7}{25}$____

14. Solve $\cot^2 \theta - \csc \theta - 1 = 0$ if $0° \le \theta \le 360°$.   14. ____30°, 150°, 270°____

15. Solve the equation $\cos 2\theta + \cos \theta = 0$ for all values of θ if θ is measured in degrees.   15. ____60° + 120n____

16. Simplify $\sin (30° + x) - \sin (30° - x) - \sqrt{3} \sin x$.   16. ____0____

17. Simplify $\frac{2 \cos 2\theta}{\sin 2\theta} - \cot \theta - \tan \theta$.   17. ____$-2 \tan \theta$____

18. Find the sum of the reciprocals of two numbers whose sum is 12 and whose product is 20.   18. ____$\frac{3}{5}$____

19. Find the exact value of $\sin 95° \cos 55° + \cos 95° \sin 55°$.   19. ____$\frac{1}{2}$____

20. Solve $\cos^2 \theta = \sin^2 \theta$ for all values of θ if θ is measured in radians.   20. ____$\frac{\pi}{4} + \frac{\pi n}{2}$____

Bonus Graph $y = \cos^{-1}(\cos x)$.   **Bonus** ___See students' graphs.___

870 Chapter 14

SKILLS AND CONCEPTS

OBJECTIVES AND EXAMPLES

Upon completing this chapter, you should be able to:

• graph trigonometric functions (Lesson 14–1)

Graph $y = 2 \cos \theta$.

amplitude $= |2|$ or 2

period $= \frac{360°}{|1|}$ or 360°

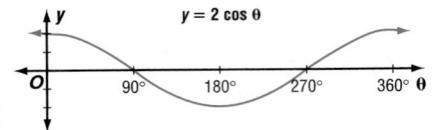
$y = 2 \cos \theta$

• use trigonometric identities to simplify or evaluate expressions (Lesson 14–2)

Simplify $\sin \theta \cot \theta \cos \theta$.

$\sin \theta \cot \theta \cos \theta = \frac{\sin \theta}{1} \cdot \frac{\cos \theta}{\sin \theta} \cdot \frac{\cos \theta}{1}$

$= \cos^2 \theta$

• verify trigonometric identities (Lesson 14–3)

Verify $\tan x + \cot x = \sec x \csc x$.

$\tan x + \cot x \overset{?}{=} \sec x \csc x$

$\frac{\sin x}{\cos x} + \frac{\cos x}{\sin x} \overset{?}{=} \sec x \csc x$

$\frac{\sin^2 x + \cos^2 x}{\cos x \sin x} \overset{?}{=} \sec x \csc x$

$\frac{1}{\cos x \sin x} \overset{?}{=} \sec x \csc x$

$\sec x \csc x = \sec x \csc x$

REVIEW EXERCISES

Use these exercises to review and prepare for the chapter test.

Graph each function. **10–15. See margin.**

10. $y = -\frac{1}{2} \cos \theta$

11. $y = 4 \sin 2\theta$

12. $y = \sin \frac{1}{2}\theta$

13. $y = 5 \sec \theta$

14. $y = \frac{1}{2} \csc \frac{2}{3}\theta$

15. $y = \tan 4\theta$

Solve for values of θ between 270° and 360°.

16. If $\csc \theta = \frac{-5}{3}$, find $\cot \theta$. $\frac{-4}{3}$

17. If $\sin \theta = -\frac{1}{2}$, find $\sec \theta$. $\frac{2\sqrt{3}}{3}$

Simplify each expression.

18. $\sin \alpha \csc \alpha - \cos^2 \alpha$ $\sin^2 \alpha$

19. $\cos^2 \theta \sec \theta \csc \theta$ $\cot \theta$

20. $\cos \beta + \sin \beta \tan \beta$ $\sec \beta$

21. $\sin \alpha (1 + \cot^2 \alpha)$ $\csc \alpha$

Verify that each of the following is an identity. **22–27. See Solutions Manual.**

22. $\frac{\sin \theta}{\tan \theta} + \frac{\cos \theta}{\cot \theta} = \cos \theta + \sin \theta$

23. $\frac{\sin \theta}{1 - \cos \theta} = \csc \theta + \cot \theta$

24. $\cot^2 \theta \sec^2 \theta = 1 + \cot^2 \theta$

25. $\sec x (\sec x - \cos x) = \tan^2 x$

26. $\frac{\cos x}{\csc x} - \frac{\sin x}{\cos x} = -\sin^2 x \tan x$

27. $\frac{\csc \theta + 1}{\cot \theta} = \frac{\cot \theta}{\csc \theta - 1}$

870 Chapter 14 Study Guide and Assessment

GLENCOE *Technology*

◉ **Test and Review Software**

You may use this software, a combination of an item generator and item bank, to create your own tests or worksheets. Types of items include free response, multiple choice, short answer, and open ended.

For IBM & Macintosh

OBJECTIVES AND EXAMPLES

● find values of sine and cosine involving sum and difference formulas   (Lesson 14–4)

Find the exact value of cos 75°.

$$\cos 75° = \cos (30° + 45°)$$
$$= \cos 30° \cos 45° - \sin 30° \sin 45°$$
$$= \frac{\sqrt{3}}{2} \cdot \frac{\sqrt{2}}{2} - \left(\frac{1}{2}\right) \cdot \frac{\sqrt{2}}{2}$$
$$= \frac{\sqrt{6}}{4} - \frac{\sqrt{2}}{4}$$
$$= \frac{\sqrt{6} - \sqrt{2}}{4}$$

REVIEW EXERCISES

Find the exact value of each expression.

28. cos 15° $\frac{\sqrt{6} + \sqrt{2}}{4}$

29. cos 285° $\frac{\sqrt{6} - \sqrt{2}}{4}$

30. sin 195° $\frac{\sqrt{2} - \sqrt{6}}{4}$

31. sin 255° $\frac{\sqrt{2} + \sqrt{6}}{-4}$

32. sin 165° $\frac{\sqrt{6} - \sqrt{2}}{4}$

33. cos (−210°) $\frac{-\sqrt{3}}{2}$

● verify identities using the sum and difference formulas

Verify that cos(θ − 90°) = sin θ.

$$\cos (\theta - 90°) \overset{?}{=} \sin \theta$$
$$\cos \theta \cos 90° + \sin \theta \sin 90° \overset{?}{=} \sin \theta$$
$$\cos \theta \cdot 0 + \sin \theta \cdot 1 \overset{?}{=} \sin \theta$$
$$\sin \theta = \sin \theta$$

Verify that each of the following is an identity.   34–35. See Solutions Manual.

34. cos (θ + 270°) = sin θ

35. cos (180° − α) = −cos α

36. $\frac{\sqrt{15}}{8}, \frac{7}{8}, \frac{\sqrt{8 - 2\sqrt{15}}}{4}, \frac{\sqrt{8 + 2\sqrt{15}}}{4}$
37. $\frac{120}{169}, \frac{119}{169}, \frac{5\sqrt{26}}{26}, -\frac{\sqrt{26}}{26}$

38. $\frac{-240}{289}, \frac{161}{289}, \frac{4\sqrt{17}}{17}, \frac{\sqrt{17}}{17}$
39. $-\frac{120}{169}, \frac{119}{169}, \frac{\sqrt{26}}{26}, \frac{-5\sqrt{26}}{26}$

● find values of sine and cosine involving double and half angles   (Lesson 14–5)

Suppose x is between 90° and 180° and $\cos x = -\frac{4}{5}$.

Find the exact value of sin 2x. Find the value of sin x. Then use the identity sin 2x = 2 sin x cos x.

$$\sin^2 x = 1 - \cos^2 x \qquad \sin 2x = 2 \sin x \cos x$$
$$= 1 - \left(-\frac{4}{5}\right)^2 \qquad = 2 \cdot \frac{3}{5} \cdot -\frac{4}{5}$$
$$= \frac{9}{25} \qquad \qquad \sin 2x = -\frac{24}{25}$$
$$\sin x = \frac{3}{5}$$

Find sin 2x, cos 2x, sin $\frac{x}{2}$, and cos $\frac{x}{2}$ for each of the following, given the two angle measures between which the terminal side of x lies.

36. $\sin x = \frac{1}{4}$; x is in Quadrant I

37. $\sin x = \frac{-5}{13}$, x is in Quadrant III

38. $\cos x = \frac{-15}{17}$, x is in Quadrant II

39. $\cos x = \frac{12}{13}$, x is in Quadrant IV

Additional Answers

10.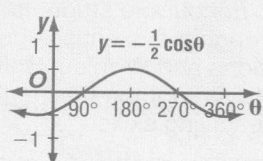

11.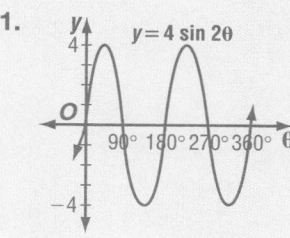

12.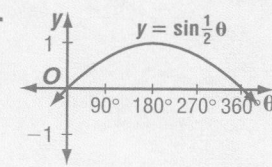

13.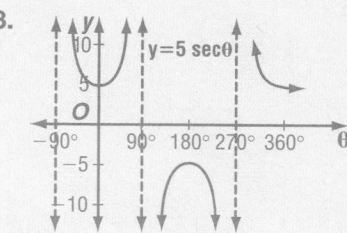

14.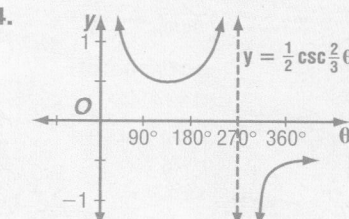

15.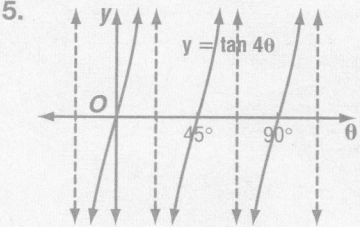

Applications and Problem Solving Encourage students to work through the exercises in the Applications and Problem Solving section to strengthen their problem-solving skills.

Additional Answers

40. $\sin^4\theta - \cos^4\theta \overset{?}{=} -\cos 2\theta$

$(\sin^2\theta + \cos^2\theta)$
$(\sin^2 - \cos^2\theta)$
$\overset{?}{=} -\cos 2\theta$
$1(\sin^2\theta - \sin^2\theta) \overset{?}{=} -\cos 2\theta$
$-(\cos^2\theta - \sin^2\theta) \overset{?}{=} -\cos 2\theta$
$-\cos 2\theta = -\cos 2\theta$

41. $\frac{1}{2}\sin 2x \overset{?}{=} \frac{\tan x}{1 + \tan^2 x}$

$\frac{1}{2}\sin 2x \overset{?}{=} \frac{\frac{\sin x}{\cos x}}{\sec^2 x}$

$\frac{1}{2}\sin 2x \overset{?}{=} \frac{\sin x}{\cos x} \cdot \cos^2 x$

$\frac{1}{2}\sin 2x \overset{?}{=} \frac{2\sin x \cos x}{2}$

$\frac{1}{2}\sin 2x = \frac{1}{2}\sin 2x$

42. $\frac{\sin 2\theta}{1 - \cos 2\theta} \overset{?}{=} \cot\theta$

$\frac{2\sin\theta\cos\theta}{1 - (1 - 2\sin^2\theta)} \overset{?}{=} \cot\theta$

$\frac{2\sin\theta\cos\theta}{2\sin^2\theta} \overset{?}{=} \cot\theta$

$\frac{\cos\theta}{\sin\theta} \overset{?}{=} \cot\theta$

$\cot\theta = \cot\theta$

OBJECTIVES AND EXAMPLES

• verify identities by using double- and half-angle formulas. (Lesson 14–5)

Verify that $\csc 2x = \dfrac{\sec x}{2\sin x}$.

$\csc 2x \overset{?}{=} \dfrac{\sec x}{2\sin x}$

$\dfrac{1}{\sin 2x} \overset{?}{=} \dfrac{\frac{1}{\cos x}}{2\sin x}$

$\dfrac{1}{\sin 2x} \overset{?}{=} \dfrac{1}{2\sin x \cos x}$

$\dfrac{1}{\sin 2x} = \dfrac{1}{\sin 2x}$

• solve trigonometric equations (Lesson 14–6)

Solve $\sin 2\theta + \sin\theta = 0$ if $0° \le \theta < 360°$.

$\sin 2\theta + \sin\theta = 0$

$2\sin\theta\cos\theta + \sin\theta = 0$

$\sin\theta\,(2\cos\theta + 1) = 0$

$\sin\theta = 0$ or $2\cos\theta + 1 = 0$

$\theta = 0°$ or $180°$ $\qquad \cos\theta = -\dfrac{1}{2}$

$\theta = 120°$ or $240°$

REVIEW EXERCISES

Verify that each of the following is an identity. 40–42. See margin.

40. $\sin^4\theta - \cos^4\theta = -\cos 2\theta$

41. $\dfrac{1}{2}\sin 2x = \dfrac{\tan x}{1 + \tan^2 x}$

42. $\dfrac{\sin 2\theta}{1 - \cos 2\theta} = \cot\theta$

Find all solutions if $0° \le \theta < 360°$.

43. $2\cos^2\theta + \sin^2\theta = 2\cos\theta$ $\quad 0°$

44. $\cos\theta = 1 - \sin\theta$ $\quad 0°, 90°$

45. $2\sin 2\theta = 1$ $\quad 15°, 75°, 195°, 255°$

Solve each equation for all values of x if x is measured in degrees.

46. $6\sin^2 x - 5\sin x - 4 = 0$

47. $2\cos^2 x = 3\sin x$ $\quad 30° + k \cdot 360°, 150° + k \cdot 360°$

48. $2\sin x \cos x = 1$ $\quad 45° + k \cdot 180°$

46. $210° + k \cdot 360°, 330° + k \cdot 360°$

APPLICATIONS AND PROBLEM SOLVING

49. Navigation When a plane is 320 miles from the runway, the angle of depression from the cockpit to the airport is 35°. At the same time, the angle of depression from the cockpit to the center of a lake located between the plane and the airport is 43°. How far is the center of the lake from the airport? (Lesson 14–4)
65.3 miles

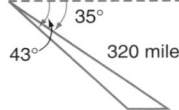

50. Music A tuning fork generates a wave represented by $\sin x + \cos x = y$. If $0 \le x < 2\pi$, what values of x satisfy the equation $\sin x + \cos x = \sqrt{2}$? (Lesson 14–6) $\quad \dfrac{\pi}{4}$

A practice test for Chapter 14 is provided on page 925.

ALTERNATIVE ASSESSMENT

COOPERATIVE LEARNING PROJECT

Tessellations   In this project, you will develop the idea of tessellations and design your own tessellations. A figure such as a regular hexagon, which can be used repeatedly to cover a surface without gaps or overlaps, is said to tile or *tessellate* the surface. The resulting pattern is called a *tessellation*.

Draw the first six regular polygons. For each one, trace additional copies around one of the vertices to determine if it tessellates. Which regular polygons tessellate and which ones do not tessellate? What conditions must the angles of a regular polygon satisfy in order for the polygon to tessellate?

Below is a convex pentagon. Will this pentagon tessellate? What sides will you try to match up in order to tessellate it? How many angles meet at vertex A for this tessellation? What is the number of degrees in each of these angles? How many angles meet at vertex D? What is the number of degrees in each of these angles?

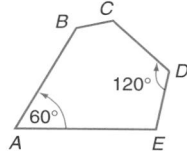

Can nonconvex polygons be tessellated? Can any of the three polygons below form a tessellation? If so, form a portion of that tessellation. Now, create and design a tessellation of your own.

Incorporate these ideas in your activity.

- Research tessellations.
- Experiment, and then verify conditions that need to be satisfied.
- Be creative in your design.
- Prepare a paragraph describing tessellations and their conditions.

THINKING CRITICALLY

- Explain how to derive a formula for cot $(A - B)$.
- Explain how you could use the identity tan $(A + B) = \dfrac{\tan A + \tan B}{1 - \tan A \tan B}$ to derive a formula for tan 2θ. Then derive it.

  Use cot $(A - B) = \dfrac{\cos (A - B)}{\sin(A - B)}$ or cot $(A - B) = \dfrac{1}{\tan(A - B)}$.

PORTFOLIO

Graphs can "show" a person information that is not easily understood otherwise. Graph the six trigonometric functions carefully. Compare and contrast these graphs. Classify each of them as discontinuous or continuous. Explain your reasoning for each classification. Place this in your portfolio.

SELF EVALUATION

You may be able to determine how a problem ends and then work in reverse toward the initial state to determine the steps in between.

Assess yourself. Do you work backward when solving problems? What must be known in order to use this strategy? Describe a problem in mathematics and in your daily life where you found this strategy to be helpful.

Assessment and Evaluation Masters, pp. 378, 389

NAME_____   DATE _____

14   Chapter 14 Performance Assessment

Instructions: *Demonstrate your knowledge by giving a clear, concise solution to each problem. Be sure to include all relevant drawings and justify your answers. You may show your solution in more than one way or investigate beyond the requirements of the problem.*

1. **a.** Write three functions of the form $y = a_1 \sin b_1\phi$, $y = a_2 \cos b_2\phi$, and $y = \tan b_3\phi$.

   b. Explain in your own words what is meant by the term *amplitude* of a periodic function.

   c. Give the amplitude of each function in part a.

   d. Explain what is meant by the term *period* of a periodic function.

   e. Find the period of the functions in part a. Show your work.

   f. Graph the functions in part a.

   g. Describe how the graphs of the sine and cosecant functions are related.

   h. Graph $y = 2 \csc 2\phi$.

2. The illuminance on a tabletop directly beneath a lamp is given by the formula $E = \frac{I}{d^2} \cos \phi$, where I represents the luminous intensity of the light in candles, d is the distance from the light to the table, and ϕ represents the angle the table is tilted from horizontal.

   a. Find the illuminance on the tabletop in foot candles when I is 250 cp, d is 4 ft, and ϕ is 30°.

   b. Find ϕ when E is 25 ft candles, I is 400 cp, and d is 2 ft.

Scoring Guide
Chapter 14
Performance Assessment

Level	Specific Criteria
3 Superior	• Shows thorough understanding of the concepts *amplitude and period of a periodic function, graphs of trigonometric functions,* and *solving trigonometric equations.* • Uses appropriate strategies to solve problems. • Computations are correct. • Written explanations are exemplary. • Graphs, diagram, and table are accurate and appropriate. • Goes beyond requirements of problem.
2 Satisfactory, with Minor Flaws	• Shows understanding of the concepts *amplitude and period of a periodic function, graphs of trigonometric functions,* and *solving trigonometric equations.* • Uses appropriate strategies to solve problems. • Computations are mostly correct. • Written explanations are effective. • Graphs, diagram, and table are mostly accurate and appropriate. • Satisfies all requirements of problem.
1 Nearly Satisfactory, with Serious Flaws	• Shows understanding of most of the concepts *amplitude and period of a periodic function, graphs of trigonometric functions,* and *solving trigonometric equations.* • May not use appropriate strategies to solve problems. • Computations are mostly correct. • Written explanations are satisfactory. • Graphs, diagram, and table are accurate and appropriate. • Satisfies most requirements of problem.
0 Unsatisfactory	• Shows little or no understanding of the concepts *amplitude and period of a periodic function, graphs of trigonometric functions,* and *solving trigonometric equations.* • May not use appropriate strategies to solve problems. • Computations are incorrect. • Written explanations are not satisfactory. • Graphs, diagram, and table are not accurate or appropriate. • Does not satisfy requirements of problem.

Alternative Assessment

The Alternative Assessment section provides students with the opportunity to assess their own work by thinking critically, working with others, keeping a portfolio, and honestly evaluating their own progress. For more information on alternative forms of assessment, see *Alternative Assessment in the Mathematics Classroom,* one of the titles in the Glencoe Mathematics Professional Series.

Performance Assessment

Performance Assessment tasks for this chapter are included in the *Assessment and Evaluation Masters.* A scoring guide is also provided.

APPENDIX

5.

```
        ×                        ×
        ×    ×          ×      × × ×
× × ××× ×    ××    ×  ××  ×××  ×××  ×××
────────────────────────────────────────
0  2  4  6  8 10 12 14 16 18 20 22 24 26 28 30
```

6.

Stem	Leaf
0	0 2 4 5 5 5 6 6 8
1	2 2 3 6 6 6 6 7 7 8 8
2	0 2 2 3 3 5 5 6 6 7 7
	7 9 9 9
3	0 0 1 $3|0 = 30°$

EXTRA PRACTICE

EXTRA PRACTICE

Lesson 1-1 Find the value of each expression.

1. $3(2^2 + 3)$ **21**
2. $2(3 + 8) - 3$ **19**
3. $5 + 3^2 - 16 + 4$ **2**
4. $(5 + 3) - 16 \div 4$ **4**
5. $4 + 8(4) \div 2 - 10$ **10**
6. $15 \div 3 \times 5 + 1$ **26**
7. $[(4 + 8)^2 \div 9] \cdot 5$ **80**
8. $5 + 8^2 \div 4 \cdot 3$ **53**
9. $5 \cdot 7 - 2(5 + 1) \div 3$ **31**
10. $3 + 7^2 - 16 \div 2$ **44**
11. $12 + 20 \div 4 - 5$ **12**
12. $[7 - (8 - 6)^2] - 1$ **2**
13. $\frac{1}{2}(3^2 + 5 \cdot 7) - 8$ **14**
14. $\frac{3 \cdot 5 + 3^2}{2^3}$ **3**
15. $\frac{6^2 + 4(2^4)}{28 + 9 \times 8}$ **1**

Evaluate each expression if $a = -0.5$, $b = 4$, $c = 5$, and $d = -3$.

16. $3b + 4d$ **0**
17. $ab^2 + c$ **−3**
18. $bc + d \div a$ **26**
19. $7ab - 3d$ **−5**
20. $ad + b^2 - c$ **12.5**
21. $d(b + d)^3$ **−3**
22. $\frac{4a + 3c}{3b}$ **$\frac{13}{12}$**
23. $\frac{3ab^2 - d^3}{a}$ **−6**
24. $\frac{5a + ad}{bc}$ **$-\frac{1}{20}$**

Lesson 1-2 Find the value of each expression. Then name the sets of numbers to which each value belongs. (Use N, W, Z, Q, I, and R.)

1. $4.1 + 8.2$
   12.3; Q, R
2. $-54 \div 6$
   −9; Z, Q, R
3. $\sqrt{36} - 3$
   3; N, W, Z, Q, R
4. $\sqrt{81 - 4}$
   $\sqrt{77}$, about 8.775; I, R

Name the property illustrated by each equation.   **5. commutative ($\times$)**

5. $(4 + 9a)2b = 2b(4 + 9a)$
6. $3\left(\frac{1}{3}\right) = 1$ **mult. inverse**
7. $a(3 - 2) = a \cdot 3 - a \cdot 2$ **dist.**
8. $3 + (-3) = 0$
   additive inverse
9. $(j + k) + 0 = (j + k)$
   additive identity
10. $(2a)b = 2(ab)$
    associative ($\times$)

Name the additive inverse and the multiplicative inverse of each number.

11. 3 **$-3; \frac{1}{3}$**
12. $-\frac{1}{8}$ **$\frac{1}{8}; -8$**
13. $\frac{2}{7}$ **$-\frac{2}{7}; \frac{7}{2}$**
14. 0.2 **$-0.2; 5$**

Simplify each expression.   **15. $27a - 2b$ 17. $-4x - 28y$**

15. $6(2a + 3b) + 5(3a - 4b)$
16. $7s + 9t + 2s - 7t$ **$9s + 2t$**
17. $4(3x - 5y) - 8(2x + y)$
18. $0.2(5m - 8) + 0.3(6 - 2m)$
    $0.4m + 0.2$
19. $\frac{1}{2}(7p + 3q) + \frac{3}{4}(6p - 4q)$
    $8p - \frac{3}{2}q$
20. $\frac{4}{5}(3v - 2w) - \frac{1}{5}(7v - 2w)$
    $v - \frac{6}{5}w$

Lesson 1-3 Find the median, mode, and mean for each set of data.

1. 4, 1, 2, 1, 1 **1; 1; 1.8**
2. 216, 399, 219, 179, 180, 399 **217.5; 399; 265.3**
3. 58, 52, 49, 60, 61, 56, 50, 61
   57; 61; 55.9
4. 25.5, 26.7, 20.9, 23.4, 26.8, 24.0, 25.7
   25.5; no mode; 24.7

The following high temperatures were recorded during a cold spell in Cleveland lasting thirty-eight days. Use this data for Exercises 5–9.

29°	26°	17°	12°	5°	4°	25°	17°	23°	18°	13°	6°	25°
20°	27°	22°	26°	30°	31°	2°	12°	27°	16°	27°	16°	30°
6°	16°	5°	0°	5°	29°	18°	16°	22°	29°	8°	23°	

5. Make a line plot of the temperatures. **See margin.**
6. Make a stem-and-leaf plot of the temperatures. **See margin.**
7. Find the median of the temperatures. **18**
8. Find the mode of the temperatures. **16**
9. Find the mean of the temperatures. **17.97**

Lesson 1-4 Write an algebraic expression to represent each verbal expression. 2. $12 - x^2$

1. twice the sum of a number and seven $2(x + 7)$
2. twelve decreased by the square of a number
3. the product of the square of a number and 6 $6x^2$
4. the product of 3 and a number decreased by 1
5. the sum of eight and four times a number $8 + 4x$
6. the square of the sum of a number and 11 $(x + 11)^2$ 4. $3(x - 1)$

Name the property illustrated by each statement.

7. If $5 \times 6 = 30$, then $30 = 5 \times 6$. symmetric (=)
8. If $x + (4 + 5) = 21$, then $x + 9 = 21$. subs. (=)
9. $4g + 99 = 4g + 99$ reflexive (=)
10. If $a + 1 = 6$, then $3(a + 1) = 3(6)$. mult. (=)
11. If $7x = 42$, then $7x - 5 = 42 - 5$. subtraction (=)
12. If $3 + 5 = 8$ and $8 = 2 \times 4$, then $3 + 5 = 2 \times 4$. transitive (=)

Solve each equation.

13. $5t + 8 = 88$ 16
14. $27 - x = -4$ 31
15. $17a = -8 + 9a$ -1
16. $6 = \frac{3x - 6}{3}$ 8
17. $\frac{3a + 3}{4} = \frac{5}{2}$ $\frac{7}{3}$
18. $\frac{3}{4}y = \frac{2}{3}y + 5$ 60
19. $-6 = 3.1s + 6.4$ -4
20. $8s - 3 = 5(2s + 1)$ -4
21. $0.4(p - 9) = 0.3(p + 4)$ 48
22. $2(m - 4) + 5 = 9$ 6
23. $5(a - 1) = 2(a + 5)$ 5
24. $4c - 3 = 7c + 18$ -7
25. $0.5z + 10 = z + 4$ 12
26. $3(k - 2) = k + 4$ 5
27. $4(y + 1) + 7 = y + 17$ 2
28. $\frac{2r - 3}{-7} = 5$ -16
29. $8q - \frac{q}{3} = 46$ 6
30. $\frac{1}{3}(3d - 1) = \frac{1}{2}(d + 2)$ $\frac{8}{3}$

Lesson 1-5 Evaluate each expression if $x = -5$, $y = 3$, and $z = -2.5$.

1. $|2x|$ 10
2. $|-3y|$ 9
3. $|2x + y|$ 7
4. $|y + 5z|$ 9.5
5. $-|x + z|$ -7.5
6. $8 - |5y - 3|$ -4
7. $2|x| - 4|2 + y|$ -10
8. $|x + y| - 6|z|$ -13

Solve each equation.

9. $|d + 1| = 7$ $-8, 6$
10. $|a - 6| = 10$ $-4, 16$
11. $2|x - 5| = 22$ $-6, 16$
12. $|t + 9| - 8 = 5$ $-22, 4$
13. $|p + 1| + 10 = 5$ no solution
14. $6|g - 3| = 42$ $-4, 10$
15. $2|y + 4| = 14$ $-11, 3$
16. $|3b - 10| = 2b$ 2, 10
17. $|3x + 7| + 4 = 0$ no solution
18. $|2c + 3| - 15 = 0$ $6, -9$
19. $7 - |m - 1| = 3$ $-3, 5$
20. $3 + |z + 5| = 10$ $-12, 2$
21. $4|h + 1| = 32$ $-9, 7$
22. $2|2x + 3| = 34$ $-10, 7$
23. $3|a - 5| - 4 = 14$ $-1, 11$
24. $2|2d - 7| + 1 = 35$ $-5, 12$
25. $|3t + 6| + 9 = 30$ $-9, 5$
26. $|d - 3| = 2d + 9$ -2
27. $|4y - 5| + 4 = 7y + 8$ $\frac{1}{11}$
28. $|2b + 4| - 3 = 6b + 1$ 0
29. $|5t| + 2 = 3t + 18$ $-2, 8$

Lesson 1-6 Solve each inequality. Graph the solution set. 1–21. See margin.

1. $2z + 5 \le 7$
2. $3r - 8 > 7$
3. $-3x > 6$
4. $0.75b < 3$
5. $2(3f + 5) \ge 28$
6. $-33 > 5g + 7$
7. $-3(y - 2) \ge -9$
8. $7a + 5 > 4a - 7$
9. $5(b - 3) \le b - 7$
10. $3(2x - 5) < 5(x - 4)$
11. $2(4m - 1) + 3(m + 4) \ge 6m$
12. $8(2c - 1) > 11c + 22$
13. $5y - 4(2y + 1) \le 2(0.5 - 2y)$
14. $2(d + 4) - 5 \ge 5(d + 3)$
15. $8 - 3t < 4(3 - t)$
16. $-x \ge \frac{x + 4}{7}$
17. $\frac{a + 8}{4} \le \frac{7 + a}{3}$
18. $-y < \frac{y + 8}{3}$
19. $2 + 4(d - 2) \le 3 - (d - 1)$
20. $5(x - 1) - 4x \ge 3(3 - x)$
21. $6s - (4s + 7) > 5 - s$

Define a variable and write an inequality for each problem. Then solve.

22. The product of 7 and a number is greater than 42. $7x > 42; \{x \mid x > 6\}$
23. Twice a number decreased by 3 is no more than 11. $2x - 3 \le 11; \{x \mid x \le 7\}$
24. The opposite of four times a number is greater than or equal to 16. $-4x \ge 16; \{x \mid x \le -4\}$
25. Fifty-four is less than the product of 18 and a number. $54 < 18x; \{x \mid x > 3\}$
26. Thirty decreased by a number is less than twice the number plus three. $30 - x < 2x + 3; \{x \mid x > 9\}$

Additional Answers for Lesson 1-6

1. $\{z \mid z \le 1\}$

2. $\{r \mid r > 5\}$
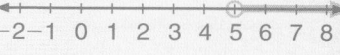

3. $\{x \mid x < -2\}$
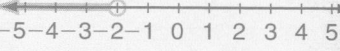

4. $\{b \mid b < 4\}$

5. $\{f \mid f \ge 3\}$

6. $\{g \mid g < -8\}$
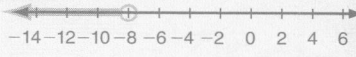

7. $\{y \mid y \le 5\}$

8. $\{a \mid a > -4\}$

9. $\{b \mid b \le 2\}$

10. $\{x \mid x < -5\}$

11. $\{m \mid m \ge -2\}$

12. $\{c \mid c > 6\}$

13. $\{y \mid y \le 5\}$

14. $\{d \mid d \le -4\}$

15. $\{t \mid t < 4\}$

16. $\left\{x \mid x \le -\frac{1}{2}\right\}$

17. $\{a \mid a \ge -4\}$

18. $\{y \mid y > -2\}$
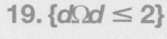

19. $\{d \mid d \le 2\}$

20. $\{x \mid x \ge 3.5\}$
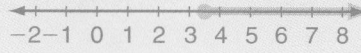

21. $\{s \mid s > 4\}$
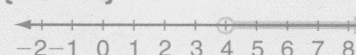

877

Additional Answers for Lesson 1-7

1.
$-10\!-\!8\!-\!6\!-\!4\!-\!2\ 0\ 2\ 4\ 6\ 8\ 10$

2.
$-10\!-\!8\!-\!6\!-\!4\!-\!2\ 0\ 2\ 4\ 6\ 8\ 10$

3.
$-10\!-\!8\!-\!6\!-\!4\!-\!2\ 0\ 2\ 4\ 6\ 8\ 10$

4. $\{a \mid -4 < a < -2\}$
$-8\!-\!7\!-\!6\!-\!5\!-\!4\!-\!3\!-\!2\!-\!1\ 0\ 1\ 2$

5. $\{t \mid t < 3 \text{ or } t > 5\}$
$-2\!-\!1\ 0\ 1\ 2\ 3\ 4\ 5\ 6\ 7\ 8$

6. $\{x \mid x \le -3 \text{ or } x \ge 3\}$
$-5\!-\!4\!-\!3\!-\!2\!-\!1\ 0\ 1\ 2\ 3\ 4\ 5$

7. $\{p \mid -2 \le p \le 2\}$
$-5\!-\!4\!-\!3\!-\!2\!-\!1\ 0\ 1\ 2\ 3\ 4\ 5$

8. $\{y \mid 1 < y < 4\}$
$-2\!-\!1\ 0\ 1\ 2\ 3\ 4\ 5\ 6\ 7\ 8$

9. $\{d \mid d \le -3 \text{ or } d \ge -1\}$
$-8\!-\!7\!-\!6\!-\!5\!-\!4\!-\!3\!-\!2\!-\!1\ 0\ 1\ 2$

10. $\{n \mid -2 < n < 3\}$
$-5\!-\!4\!-\!3\!-\!2\!-\!1\ 0\ 1\ 2\ 3\ 4\ 5$

11. $\{s \mid -1 \le s \le 7\}$
$-2\!-\!1\ 0\ 1\ 2\ 3\ 4\ 5\ 6\ 7\ 8$

12. all real numbers
$-5\!-\!4\!-\!3\!-\!2\!-\!1\ 0\ 1\ 2\ 3\ 4\ 5$

13. $\{x \mid -1 < x < 1.5\}$
$-5\!-\!4\!-\!3\!-\!2\!-\!1\ 0\ 1\ 2\ 3\ 4\ 5$

14. $\{v \mid v < -5 \text{ or } v > 1\}$
$-7\!-\!6\!-\!5\!-\!4\!-\!3\!-\!2\!-\!1\ 0\ 1\ 2\ 3$

15. $\{x \mid 1 < x < 4\}$
$-2\!-\!1\ 0\ 1\ 2\ 3\ 4\ 5\ 6\ 7\ 8$

16. $\{m \mid m < 3 \text{ or } m > 6\}$
$-2\!-\!1\ 0\ 1\ 2\ 3\ 4\ 5\ 6\ 7\ 8$

17. all reals
$-5\!-\!4\!-\!3\!-\!2\!-\!1\ 0\ 1\ 2\ 3\ 4\ 5$

18. $\{t \mid t \le -2 \text{ or } t \ge 2.5\}$
$-5\!-\!4\!-\!3\!-\!2\!-\!1\ 0\ 1\ 2\ 3\ 4\ 5$

Lesson 1-7 State an absolute value inequality for each of the following. Then graph each solution set. **1–3. See margin for graphs.**

1. all numbers between -5.5 and 5.5 $|x| < 5.5$ **2.** all number less than -9 and greater than 9 $|x| > 9$

3. all numbers greater than or equal to -6 and less than or equal to 6 $|x| \le 6$

Solve each inequality. Graph each solution set. **4–24. See margin.**

4. $|a + 3| < 1$ **5.** $|t - 4| > 1$ **6.** $|7x| \ge 21$

7. $|8p| \le 16$ **8.** $|2y - 5| < 3$ **9.** $|3d + 6| \ge 3$

10. $2 < n + 4 < 7$ **11.** $-3 \le s - 2 \le 5$ **12.** $|7d| \ge -42$

13. $|4x - 1| < 5$ **14.** $|6v + 12| > 18$ **15.** $7 < 4x + 3 < 19$

16. $3m - 2 < 7$ or $2m + 1 > 13$ **17.** $|z + 2| \ge z$ **18.** $5t + 3 \le -7$ or $4t - 2 \ge 8$

19. $12 + |2q| < 0$ **20.** $|2r + 4| < 6$ **21.** $|5w - 3| \ge 9$

22. $|3h| + 15 < 0$ **23.** $|5n| - 16 \ge 4$ **24.** $4x + 7 < 5$ or $2x - 4 > 12$

Lesson 2-1 State the domain and range of each relation. Then graph the relation and identify whether it is a function or not. For each function, state whether it is discrete or continuous.

1. $\{(1, 2), (2, 3), (3, 4), (4, 5)\}$ **2.** $\{(0, 3), (0, 2), (0, 1), (0, 0)\}$

3. $y = x^2$ **4.** $y = -2x$ **5.** $x = y + 1$ **6.** $x = |y|$

1–6. See Solutions Manual.

A function g includes the ordered pairs $(1, 2)$, $(2, 4)$, $(3, 6)$, and $(4, 8)$. State whether g will still be a function if each ordered pair given below is also included in g. Write *yes* or *no*.

7. $(1, 3)$ no   **8.** $(-1, 3)$ yes   **9.** $(-1, -3)$ yes   **10.** $(1, -3)$ no

Find each value if $f(x) = \frac{1}{2}(x + 7)$ and $g(x) = (x + 1)^2 - \frac{2}{x}$.

11. $f(2)$ $\frac{9}{2}$ **12.** $f(-4)$ $\frac{3}{2}$ **13.** $f\left(\frac{1}{2}\right)$ $\frac{15}{4}$ **14.** $f(a + 2)$ $\frac{a + 9}{2}$

15. $g(4)$ $\frac{49}{2}$ **16.** $g(-2)$ 2   **17.** $g\left(\frac{1}{2}\right)$ $-\frac{7}{4}$ **18.** $g(b - 1)$ $b^2 - \frac{2}{b - 1}$

Lesson 2-2 State whether each equation is linear. Write *yes* or *no*.

1. $\frac{x}{2} - y = 7$ yes   **2.** $x(y + 5) = 0$ no   **3.** $g(x) = \frac{2}{x - 3}$ no

4. $x = 3 + y$ yes   **5.** $f(x) = 7$ yes   **6.** $\frac{3}{x} - \frac{1}{4} = \frac{4}{3}$ no

Write each equation in standard form where A, B, and C are integers whose greatest common factor is 1. Identify A, B, and C.

7. $x + 7 = y$
$x - y = -7$; 1, -1, -7

8. $5x - 7y = \frac{1}{2}$
$10x - 14y = 1$; 10, -14, 1

9. $y = \frac{2}{3}x + 8$
$2x - 3y = -24$; 2, -3, -24

Find the x-intercept and the y-intercept of the graph of each equation.

10. $0.05x + 0.02y = 4$ 80; 200   **11.** $x = 3y$ 0; 0   **12.** $x = 7$ 7; none

Graph each equation. **13–21. See Solutions Manual.**

13. $2y = 3x$ **14.** $y = x - 4$ **15.** $2x + y = 6$

16. $3x - 2y = -12$ **17.** $0.2x - 0.5y = 1$ **18.** $5x = 20$

19. $3y + 7 = 12$ **20.** $\frac{x}{2} - \frac{y}{5} = \frac{1}{3}$ **21.** $\frac{3}{4}y - x = 1$

878   *Extra Practice*

19. $\varnothing$
$-5\!-\!4\!-\!3\!-\!2\!-\!1\ 0\ 1\ 2\ 3\ 4\ 5$

20. $\{r \mid -5 < r < 1\}$
$-7\!-\!6\!-\!5\!-\!4\!-\!3\!-\!2\!-\!1\ 0\ 1\ 2\ 3$

21. $\{w \mid w \le -1.2 \text{ or } w \ge 2.4\}$
$-5\!-\!4\!-\!3\!-\!2\!-\!1\ 0\ 1\ 2\ 3\ 4\ 5$

22. $\varnothing$
$-5\!-\!4\!-\!3\!-\!2\!-\!1\ 0\ 1\ 2\ 3\ 4\ 5$

23. $\{n \mid n \le -4 \text{ or } n \ge 4\}$
$-5\!-\!4\!-\!3\!-\!2\!-\!1\ 0\ 1\ 2\ 3\ 4\ 5$

24. $\{x \mid x < -0.5 \text{ or } x > 8\}$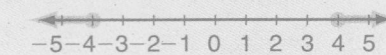
$-1\ 0\ 1\ 2\ 3\ 4\ 5\ 6\ 7\ 8\ 9$

Lesson 2-3 Find the slope of the line that passes through each pair of points. Then determine whether the line rises to the right, falls to the right, is horizontal or vertical.

1. $(0, 3), (5, 0)$ $-\frac{3}{5}$; falls
2. $(2, 3), (5, 7)$ $\frac{4}{3}$; rises
3. $(2, 8), (2, -8)$ undefined; vertical

Find the slope of the graph of each equation.

4. $2x + y = 8$ -2
5. $x - 5y = -15$ $\frac{1}{5}$
6. $y = 7$ 0

Determine the value of a so that a line through the points with the given coordinates has the given slope.

7. $(5, 0), (a, 9)$; slope $= 3$ 8
8. $(a, 8), (2, -8)$; slope $= \frac{4}{3}$ 14
9. $(a, 3), (7, 7)$; slope undefined 7
10. $(0, 3), (5, a)$; slope $= -5$ -22
11. $\left(\frac{1}{4}, a\right), \left(\frac{1}{2}, \frac{3}{4}\right)$; slope $= -\frac{1}{8}$ $\frac{25}{32}$
12. $(3.6, 1.2), (4.8, a)$; slope $= -1$ 0

Lesson 2-4 State the slope and y-intercept of the graph of each equation.

1. $y = 3x + 2$ $3; 2$
2. $y = 0.12x - 3.75$ $0.12; -3.75$
3. $-y = 6x + 4$ $-6; -4$
4. $6y = 3x - 9$ $\frac{1}{2}, -\frac{3}{2}$
5. $2 - 5x = 5y$ $-1; \frac{2}{5}$
6. $6y + 42 = 5x$ $\frac{5}{6}; -7$

Write an equation in slope-intercept form that satisfies each condition. 8. $y = -0.3x + 6.4$

7. slope $= \frac{5}{8}$, passes through origin $y = \frac{5}{8}x$
8. slope $= -0.3$, passes through $(-2, 7)$
9. passes through $(5, 3)$ and $(-5, -3)$ $y = \frac{3}{5}x$
10. x-intercept $= 2$, y-intercept $= 7$ $y = -\frac{7}{2}x + 7$
11. passes through $(7, 1)$, parallel to the graph of $y = \frac{5}{3}x - 2$ $y = \frac{5}{3}x - \frac{32}{3}$
12. passes through $(7, 1)$, perpendicular to the graph of $y = \frac{5}{3}x - 2$ $y = -\frac{3}{5}x + \frac{26}{5}$
13. passes through $(0, 5)$, perpendicular to the line that passes through $(7, 8)$ and $(2, 4)$ $y = -\frac{5}{4}x + 5$

Lesson 2-5

1. The table below shows the charges for telephone calls of various lengths of time.

Minutes	1	2	3	4	5	6	7	8	9
Cost	$0.20	$0.36	$0.52	$0.68	$0.84	$1.00	$1.16	$1.32	$1.48

   a. Draw a scatter plot to show how minutes m and cost c are related. See margin.
   b. Write a prediction equation that relates the cost of a telephone call and the number of minutes of the call. $c = 0.16m + 0.04$
   c. Using your equation find the approximate cost of a call that lasts 15 minutes. $2.44

2. The table below is information from an investor who charted three stocks for several months.

Month	0	1	2	3	4	5	6	7	8
Stock A	$31.72	$32.03	$32.65	$32.55	$33.26	$33.89	$34.39	$34.64	$34.83
Stock B	$13.20	$13.14	$13.42	$13.84	$13.88	$14.21	$14.61	$14.74	$14.91
Stock C	$14.37	$14.43	$14.65	$14.98	$15.49	$15.86	$16.25	$16.96	?

   a. Draw three scatter plots to show how the month m and the price p of each stock are related. a–b. See margin.
   b. Write a prediction equation that relates the month with the price of each stock.
   c. Use your equation for stock C to find the approximate price of the stock in the eighth month. about $17.05

Additional Answers for Lesson 2-5

1a.
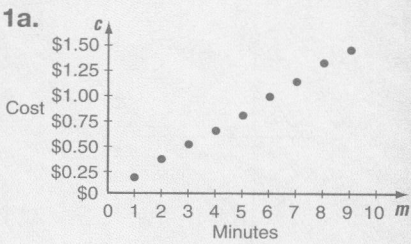

2a. Stock A
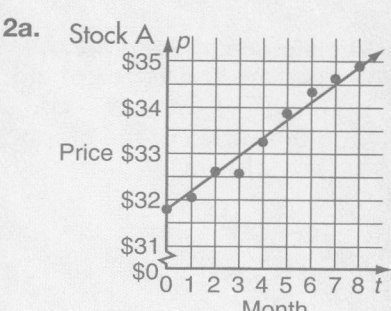

Stock B
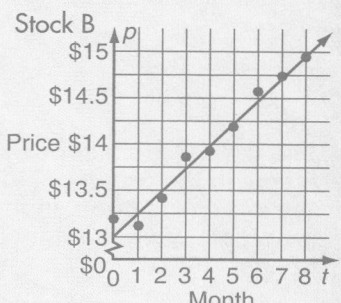

Stock C
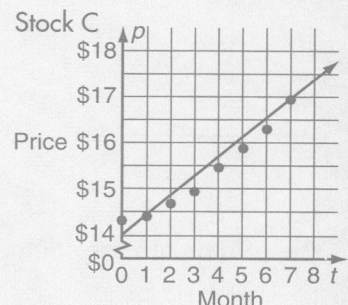

2b. Sample answers:
   Stock A: $p = 0.42m + 31.66$
   Stock B: $p = 0.23m + 13.04$
   Stock C: $p = 0.35m + 14.25$

15.

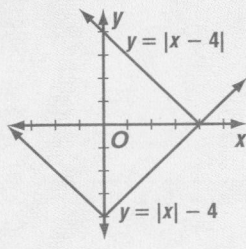

The shapes of the graphs are similar. The vertex of the graph of $|x| - 4$ is $(0, -4)$ and the vertex of the graph of $|x - 4|$ is $(4, 0)$.

16.

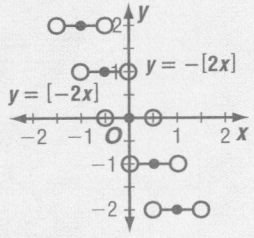

The graphs are a series of steps. In the graph of $[-2x]$, the left end is open. In the graph of $-[2x]$, the right is open.

17.

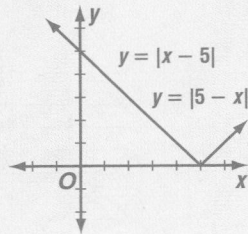

The graphs are the same.

18.

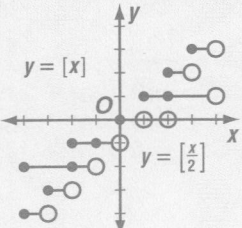

The graphs are a series of steps. The intervals for $y = \left[\frac{x}{2}\right]$ are twice the intervals for $y = [x]$.

EXTRA PRACTICE

Lesson 2-6 If $g(x) = \left[-\frac{x}{3}\right] - 2$, find each value.

1. $g(6)$ -4
2. $g(-6)$ 0
3. $g(-3)$ -1
4. $g(10)$ -6
5. $g\left(\frac{2}{3}\right)$ -3
6. $g(-25.5)$ 6
7. $g\left(\frac{9}{2}\right)$ -4
8. $g(23.7)$ -10

Identify each function as C for constant, D for direct variation, A for absolute value, or G for greatest integer function. Then graph each function. 9–14. See Solutions Manual for graphs.

9. $f(x) = -2x + 5$ **D**
10. $f(x) = \frac{17}{4}$ **C**
11. $h(x) = |x| - 4$ **A**
12. $g(x) = -2[x + 5]$ **G**
13. $g(x) = \frac{x}{2}$ **D**
14. $h(x) = |-2x| - 8$ **A**

Graph each pair of equations on the same coordinate plane. Discuss the similarities and differences in the two graphs. 15–18. See margin.

15. $y = |x| - 4$ and $y = |x - 4|$
16. $y = [-2x]$ and $y = -[2x]$
17. $y = |x - 5|$ and $y = |5 - x|$
18. $y = [x]$ and $y = \left[\frac{x}{2}\right]$

Lesson 2-7 Graph each inequality. 1–21. See Solutions Manual.

1. $y \geq x - 15$
2. $y \leq -3x - 1$
3. $4y \leq 2x - 3y + 8$
4. $3x > y$
5. $5x + 3 < 18$
6. $x + 2 \geq y - 7$
7. $7 > y - 7$
8. $2x < 5 - y$
9. $y > \frac{1}{5}x - 8$
10. $2y - 5x \leq 8$
11. $-2x + 5 \leq 3y$
12. $3x + 2y \geq 0$
13. $x - 3 < 5$
14. $y > 5x - 3$
15. $3x + 4y < 9$
16. $|x| \leq y + 3$
17. $\frac{y}{2} \leq x - 1$
18. $2x - 3y \leq 18$
19. $-y < \frac{2x}{3} + 5$
20. $-y \geq 8 - x$
21. $|y| < 7$

1–12. See Solutions Manual for graphs.
8. $\{(x, y) | 2x + 3y = 5\}$; consis., dep.   11. $\{(x, y) | 9x - 5 = 7y\}$; consis., dep.

Lesson 3-1 Graph each system of equations and state its solution. Also, state whether the system is consistent and independent, consistent and dependent, or inconsistent.

1. $x - y = 2$ no solutions;
   $2x - 2y = 10$ inconsistent
2. $x + 3y = 18$ $(3, 5)$; consis.,
   $-x + 2y = 7$ independent
3. $2x + 6y = 6$ $\{(x, y) | 2x + 6y = 6\}$;
   $\frac{1}{3}x + y = 1$ consis., dep.
4. $x + 3y = 0$ no solutions;
   $2x + 6y = 5$ inconsistent
5. $2x - y = 7$ $(5, 3)$; consis.,
   $\frac{2}{5}x - \frac{4}{3}y = -2$ dependent
6. $y = \frac{1}{3}x + 1$ $(0, 1)$; consis.,
   $y = 4x + 1$ independent
7. $\frac{3}{4}x - y = 0$ $(8, 6)$; consis.,
   $\frac{y}{3} + \frac{x}{2} = 6$ independent
8. $2x + 3y = 5$
   $-6x - 9y = -15$
9. $y = \frac{x}{2}$ no solutions;
   $2y = x + 4$ inconsistent
10. $\frac{2}{3}x = \frac{5}{3}y$ $\{(x, y) | 2x - 5y = 0\}$;
    $2x - 5y = 0$ cons., dep.
11. $9x - 5 = 7y$
    $4\frac{1}{2}x - 3\frac{1}{2}y = 2\frac{1}{2}$
12. $x - 2y = 4$ $(0, -2)$; consis.,
    $y = x - 2$ independent

Lesson 3-2 Solve each system of equations. Use either substitution or elimination.

1. $7x + y = 9$
$5x - y = 15$ **(2, −5)**

2. $2x + 3y = 10$
$x + 6y = 32$ **(−4, 6)**

3. $x = 4y - 10$
$5x + 3y = -4$ **(−2, 2)**

4. $r + 5s = -17$
$2r - 6s = -2$ **(−7, −2)**

5. $2x - 3y = 7$
$3x + 6y = 42$ **(8, 3)**

6. $2a + 5b = -13$
$3a - 4b = 38$ **(6, −5)**

7. $6p + 8q = 20$
$5p - 4q = -26$ **(−2, 4)**

8. $\frac{5}{2}x + \frac{1}{3}y = 13$
$\frac{1}{2}x - y = -7$ **(4, 9)**

9. $\frac{2}{7}c - \frac{4}{3}d = 16$
$\frac{4}{7}c + \frac{8}{3}d = -16$ **(14, −9)**

10. $3x - 4y = -27$
$2x + y = -7$ **(−5, 3)**

11. $3c + 4d = -1$
$6c - 2d = 3$ $\left(\frac{1}{3}, -\frac{1}{2}\right)$

12. $5x + 3y = -4$
$7x - y = 36$ **(4, −8)**

13. $x = 2y - 1$
$4x - 3y = 21$ **(9, 5)**

14. $3m + 4n = 28$
$5m - 3n = -21$ **(0, 7)**

15. $7x - y = 35$
$y = 5x - 19$ **(8, 21)**

Lesson 3-3 Find the value of each determinant.

1. $\begin{vmatrix} 7 & 6 \\ 2 & 5 \end{vmatrix}$ **23**

2. $\begin{vmatrix} -4 & 5 \\ 6 & 2 \end{vmatrix}$ **−38**

3. $\begin{vmatrix} 5 & 1 \\ 7 & -2 \end{vmatrix}$ **−17**

Use Cramer's rule to solve each system of equations.

4. $5x - 3y = 19$
$7x + 2y = 8$ **(2, −3)**

5. $4p - 3q = 22$
$2p + 8q = 30$ **(7, 2)**

6. $-x + y = 5$
$2x + 4y = 38$ **(3, 8)**

7. $2a - 3b = 7$
$5a + 7b = -55$ **(−4, −5)**

8. $2m + 6n = -6$
$4m + 3n = -18$ $\left(-5, \frac{2}{3}\right)$

9. $8r + 3s = 5$
$6r - 2s = -9$ $\left(-\frac{1}{2}, 3\right)$

10. $\frac{1}{3}x - \frac{1}{2}y = -8$
$\frac{3}{5}x + \frac{5}{6}y = -4$ **(−15, 6)**

11. $\frac{1}{4}c + \frac{2}{3}d = 6$
$\frac{3}{4}c - \frac{5}{3}d = -4$ **(8, 6)**

12. $0.3a + 1.6b = 0.44$
$0.4a + 2.5b = 0.66$ **(0.4, 0.2)**

13. $\frac{2}{3}m - \frac{5}{3}n = -\frac{1}{3}$
$\frac{5}{9}m + \frac{7}{6}n = 1$ $\left(\frac{3}{4}, \frac{1}{2}\right)$

14. $3y = 4x + 28$
$5x + 7y = 8$ **(−4, 4)**

15. $4.5x = 3y$
$2(x - 4y) = -20$ **(2, 3)**

Lesson 3-4 Solve each system of inequalities by graphing. **1–15. See Solutions Manual.**

1. $x \le 5$
$y \ge -3$

2. $x + y \le 2$
$y - x \le 4$

3. $x + y < 5$
$x < 2$

4. $y + x < 2$
$y \ge x$

5. $y < 3$
$y - x \ge -1$

6. $y \le x + 4$
$x + y \ge 1$

7. $y < \frac{1}{3}x + 5$
$y < 2x + 1$

8. $y + x \ge 1$
$y - x \ge -1$

9. $|x| > 2$
$|y| \le 5$

10. $|x - 2| \le 3$
$4y - 2x \ge 6$

11. $4x + 3y \ge 12$
$2y - x \ge 1$

12. $y \le -1$
$3x - 2y \ge 6$

13. $y > 1$
$y < -3x + 3$
$y > -3x + 1$

14. $y \ge -\frac{1}{2}x + 1$
$y \le -3x + 5$
$y \le 2x + 2$

15. $2x + 5y < 25$
$y < 3x - 2$
$5x - 7y < 14$

1. max: $f(6, 1) = 11$
   min: $f(-3, 2) = -8$
2. max: $f(1, 3) = 16$
   min: $f(2, -2) = -8$
3. max: $f(-3, 2) = 14$
   min: $f(6, 1) = -23$
4. max: $f(-3, 2) = 9$
   min: $f(2, -2) = -8$
5. max: $f(6, 1) = 17$
   min: $f(-3, 2) = -11$
6. max: $f(-3, 2) = 10$
   min: $f(6, 1) = -10$

7.

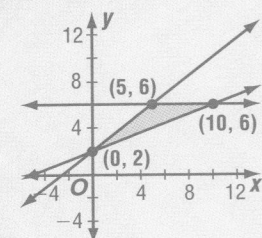

vertices: (0, 2), (5, 6), (10, 6)
max: $f(10, 6) = 16$
min: $f(0, 2) = 2$

8.

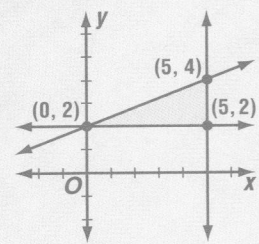

vertices: (0, 2), (5, 4), (5, 2)
max: $f(5, 4) = 19$
min: $f(0, 2) = 2$

9.

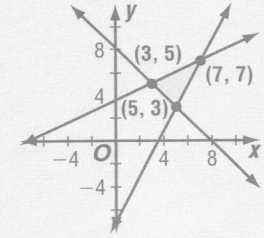

vertices: (3, 5), (7, 7), (5, 3)
max: $f(5, 3) = 3$
min: $f(3, 5) = -11$

10.

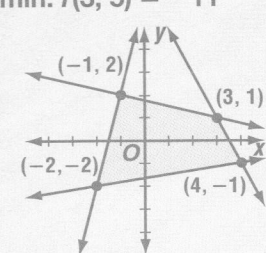

vertices: (-1, 2), (3, 1),
(4, -1), (-2, -2)
max: $f(4, -1) = 9$
min: $f(-1, 2) = -4$

882

Lesson 3-5 A feasible region has vertices at $(-3, 2)$, $(1, 3)$, $(6, 1)$, and $(2, -2)$. Find the maximum and minimum values of each function. **1–6. See margin.**

1. $f(x, y) = 2x - y$
2. $f(x, y) = x + 5y$
3. $f(x, y) = y - 4x$
4. $f(x, y) = -x + 3y$
5. $f(x, y) = 3x - y$
6. $f(x, y) = 2y - 2x$

Graph each system of inequalities. Name the coordinates of the vertices of the feasible region. Find the maximum and minimum values of the given function for this region. **7–12. See margin.**

7. $4x - 5y \geq -10$
   $y \leq 6$
   $2x - 5y \leq -10$
   $f(x, y) = x + y$

8. $x \leq 5$
   $y \geq 2$
   $2x - 5y \geq -10$
   $f(x, y) = 3x + y$

9. $x - 2y \geq -7$
   $x + y \geq 8$
   $2x - y \leq 7$
   $f(x, y) = 3x - 4y$

10. $y \leq 4x + 6$
    $x + 4y \leq 7$
    $2x + y \leq 7$
    $x - 6y \leq 10$
    $f(x, y) = 2x - y$

11. $y \geq 0$
    $y \leq 5$
    $y \leq -x + 7$
    $5x + 3y \geq 20$
    $f(x, y) = x + 2y$

12. $y \geq 0$
    $3x - 2y \geq 0$
    $x + 3y \leq 11$
    $2x + 3y \leq 16$
    $f(x, y) = 4x + y$

Lesson 3-6

1. **Manufacturing** A shoe manufacturer makes outdoor and indoor soccer shoes. There is a two-step manufacturing process for both kinds of shoes. Each pair of outdoor shoes requires 2 hours of processing in step one, 1 hour in step two, and produces a profit of $20 for the company. Indoor shoes require 1 hour of processing in step one, 3 hours in step two, and produce a profit of $15 for each pair. The company has 40 hours of labor per day available for step one and 60 hours of labor per day available for step two.

   a. If x represents the number of pairs of outdoor shoes and y the number of indoor shoes produced per day, write a system of inequalities that represents the number of pairs of outdoor and indoor soccer shoes that can be produced in one day. $x \geq 0$, $y \geq 0$, $2x + y \leq 40$, $x + 3y \leq 60$

   b. Draw the graph showing the feasible region. **See margin.**

   c. Write an expression for the profit per day. $20x + 15y$

   d. How many of each kind of shoe should be produced each day to have the maximum profit? What is the maximum profit? **12 outdoor pairs, 16 indoor pairs; $480**

2. **Manufacturing** A toy manufacturer makes a $3 profit on yo-yos and a $3 profit on tops. Department A requires 3 hours to make parts for 100 yo-yos and 4 hours to make parts for 100 tops. Department B needs 5 hours to make parts for 100 yo-yos and 2 hours to make parts for 100 tops. Department A has 450 hours available and department B has 400 hours available.

   a. How many yo-yos and tops should be made to maximize the profit? **5000 yo-yos, 7500 tops**

   b. What is the maximum profit the company can make from these two products? **$37,500**

Lesson 3-7 For each system of equations, an ordered triple is given. Determine whether or not it is a solution of the system.

1. $4x + 2y - 6z = -38$
   $5x - 4y + z = -18$ **yes**
   $x + 3y + 7z = 38$; $(-3, 2, 5)$

2. $u + 3v + w = 14$
   $2u - v + 3w = -9$ **no**
   $4u - 5v - 2w = -2$; $(1, 5, -2)$

3. $x + y = -6$
   $x + z = -2$ **no**
   $y + z = 2$; $(-4, -2, 2)$

Solve each system of equations.

4. $5a = 5$
   $6b - 3c = 15$
   $2a + 7c = -5$ $(1, 2, -1)$

5. $s + 2t = 5$
   $7r - 3s + t = 20$
   $2t = 8$ $(1, -3, 4)$

6. $2u - 3v = 13$
   $3v + w = -3$
   $4u - w = 2$ $(2, -3, 6)$

7. $4a + 2b - c = 5$
   $2a + b - 5c = -11$
   $a - 2b + 3c = 6$ $(1, 2, 3)$

8. $x + 2y - z = 1$
   $x + 3y + 2z = 7$
   $2x + 6y + z = 8$ $(3, 0, 2)$

9. $2x + y - z = 7$
   $3x - y + 2z = 15$
   $x - 4y + z = 2$ $(4, 1, 2)$

11.

vertices: (1, 5), (2, 5), (7, 0), (4, 0)
max: $f(2, 5) = 12$
min: $f(4, 0) = 4$

12.

vertices: (2, 3), (5, 2), (8, 0), (0, 0)
max: $f(8, 0) = 32$
min: $f(0, 0) = 0$

Lesson 4-1 Perform the indicated operations.

1. $\frac{3}{2}[8\ 4\ 3]$ $\left[12\ 6\ \frac{9}{2}\right]$

2. $-10\begin{bmatrix} 1.26 & 8.95 \\ 2.47 & -3.62 \end{bmatrix}$ $\begin{bmatrix} -12.6 & -89.5 \\ -24.7 & 36.2 \end{bmatrix}$

3. $-5\begin{bmatrix} 7.5 \\ -3.8 \end{bmatrix}$ $\begin{bmatrix} -37.5 \\ 19 \end{bmatrix}$

Solve for the variables. 4. $x = 5$, $y = 5$, $z = -15$ 6. $w = 3$, $x = 0$, $y = -1$, $z = -2$

4. $[2x\ \ 3y\ \ -z] = [2y\ \ -z\ \ 15]$

5. $\begin{bmatrix} x + y \\ 4x - 3y \end{bmatrix} = \begin{bmatrix} 1 \\ 11 \end{bmatrix}$ $x = 2$, $y = -1$

6. $-2\begin{bmatrix} w + 5 & x - z \\ 3y & 8 \end{bmatrix} = \begin{bmatrix} -16 & -4 \\ 6 & 2x + 8z \end{bmatrix}$

7. $y\begin{bmatrix} 2 & x \\ 5 & 1 \end{bmatrix} = \begin{bmatrix} 4 & -10 \\ 10 & 2z \end{bmatrix}$ $x = -5$, $y = 2$, $z = 1$

8. $\begin{bmatrix} 2x \\ -y \\ 3z \end{bmatrix} = \begin{bmatrix} 16 \\ 18 \\ -21 \end{bmatrix}$ $x = 8$, $y = -18$, $z = -7$

9. $\begin{bmatrix} x - 3y \\ 4y - 3x \end{bmatrix} = -5\begin{bmatrix} 2 \\ x \end{bmatrix}$ $x = -4$, $y = 2$

10. $\begin{bmatrix} x^2 + 1 & 5 - y \\ x + y & y - 4 \end{bmatrix} = \begin{bmatrix} 2 & x \\ 5 & 2 \end{bmatrix}$ $x = -1$, $y = 6$

11. $\begin{bmatrix} x + y & 3 \\ y & 6 \end{bmatrix} = \begin{bmatrix} 0 & 2y - x \\ z^2 & 4 - 2x \end{bmatrix}$ $x = -1$, $y = 1$, $z = \pm 1$

Lesson 4-2 Perform the indicated operations.

1. $\begin{bmatrix} 3 & 5 \\ -7 & 2 \end{bmatrix} + \begin{bmatrix} -2 & 6 \\ 8 & -1 \end{bmatrix}$ $\begin{bmatrix} 1 & 11 \\ 1 & 1 \end{bmatrix}$

2. $\begin{bmatrix} 45 & 36 \\ 18 & 63 \end{bmatrix} - 9\begin{bmatrix} 5 & 4 \\ 2 & 7 \end{bmatrix}$ $\begin{bmatrix} 0 & 0 \\ 0 & 0 \end{bmatrix}$

3. $4[-8\ 2\ 9] - 3[2\ -7\ 6]$ $[-38\ 29\ 18]$

4. $\frac{4}{5}\begin{bmatrix} -5 \\ 6 \\ 8 \end{bmatrix} + \frac{1}{4}\begin{bmatrix} 9 \\ -6 \\ 12 \end{bmatrix} - \frac{1}{2}\begin{bmatrix} 5 \\ 4 \\ 7 \end{bmatrix}$ $\begin{bmatrix} -4.25 \\ 1.3 \\ 5.9 \end{bmatrix}$

5. $\begin{bmatrix} -3 & 6 & -9 \\ 4 & -3 & 0 \\ 8 & -2 & 3 \end{bmatrix} - \begin{bmatrix} 1 & 5 & 7 \\ 5 & 2 & -6 \\ 3 & 0 & -2 \end{bmatrix}$ $\begin{bmatrix} -4 & 1 & -16 \\ -1 & -5 & 6 \\ 5 & -2 & 5 \end{bmatrix}$

6. $5\begin{bmatrix} 3 & 1 & 0 \\ 0 & 0 & 2 \\ 1 & -1 & -1 \end{bmatrix} - 3\begin{bmatrix} 2 & 0 & 3 \\ 1 & 1 & 2 \\ 2 & 1 & -1 \end{bmatrix}$ $\begin{bmatrix} 9 & 5 & -9 \\ -3 & -3 & 4 \\ -1 & -8 & -2 \end{bmatrix}$

7. $5\begin{bmatrix} 6 & -2 \\ 5 & 4 \end{bmatrix} - 2\begin{bmatrix} 6 & -2 \\ 5 & 4 \end{bmatrix} + 4\begin{bmatrix} 7 & -6 \\ -4 & 2 \end{bmatrix}$ $\begin{bmatrix} 46 & -30 \\ -1 & 20 \end{bmatrix}$

8. $1.3\begin{bmatrix} 3.7 & 4.8 \\ -5.4 & 9.5 \end{bmatrix} + 4.1\begin{bmatrix} 6.4 & -1.9 \\ -3.7 & -2.8 \end{bmatrix} - 6.2\begin{bmatrix} -0.8 & 5.1 \\ 3.2 & 7.4 \end{bmatrix}$ $\begin{bmatrix} 36.01 & -33.17 \\ -42.03 & -45.01 \end{bmatrix}$

Lesson 4-3 Find the dimensions of each matrix product. 2. not defined   3. not defined

1. $A_{4\times3} \cdot B_{3\times4}$ 4×4

2. $R_{2\times5} \cdot S_{2\times5}$

3. $G_{2\times5} \cdot H_{2\times3}$

4. $M_{3\times8} \cdot N_{8\times2}$ 3×2

5. $X_{4\times3} \cdot Y_{2\times6}$
   not defined

6. $J_{5\times3} \cdot K_{3\times6}$
   5×6

7. $C_{m\times n} \cdot D_{n\times p}$
   $m \times p$

8. $X_{2\times9} \cdot Y_{9\times7}$
   2×7

Perform the indicated operations, if possible.

9. $[7\ 2] \cdot \begin{bmatrix} -3 \\ 5 \end{bmatrix}$ $[-11]$

10. $\begin{bmatrix} 2 & -4 \\ 0 & 5 \end{bmatrix} \cdot \begin{bmatrix} 1 & 3 \\ -2 & -1 \end{bmatrix}$ $\begin{bmatrix} 10 & 10 \\ -10 & -5 \end{bmatrix}$

11. $\begin{bmatrix} 1 & 3 \\ -2 & -1 \end{bmatrix} \cdot \begin{bmatrix} 2 & -4 \\ 0 & 5 \end{bmatrix}$ $\begin{bmatrix} 2 & 11 \\ -4 & 3 \end{bmatrix}$

12. $\begin{bmatrix} 3 & 2 \\ 5 & 2 \end{bmatrix} \cdot \begin{bmatrix} -8 \\ 15 \end{bmatrix}$ $\begin{bmatrix} 6 \\ -10 \end{bmatrix}$

13. $\begin{bmatrix} -1 \\ 2 \\ 1 \end{bmatrix} \cdot \begin{bmatrix} 7 & 6 & 1 \\ 2 & -4 & 0 \end{bmatrix}$ not defined

14. $\begin{bmatrix} 0 & 1 & -2 \\ 5 & 3 & -4 \\ -1 & 0 & 0 \end{bmatrix} \cdot \begin{bmatrix} 1 & -3 & 0 \\ 2 & 0 & -1 \\ 0 & 1 & -2 \end{bmatrix}$ $\begin{bmatrix} 2 & -2 & 3 \\ 11 & -19 & 5 \\ -1 & 3 & 0 \end{bmatrix}$

15. $\begin{bmatrix} 3 & -2 \\ 4 & 5 \end{bmatrix} \cdot \begin{bmatrix} 1 & 0 \\ 0 & 1 \end{bmatrix}$ $\begin{bmatrix} 3 & -2 \\ 4 & 5 \end{bmatrix}$

16. $\begin{bmatrix} 3 & -2 \\ 4 & -5 \end{bmatrix} \cdot \begin{bmatrix} \frac{5}{7} & -\frac{2}{7} \\ \frac{4}{7} & -\frac{3}{7} \end{bmatrix}$ $\begin{bmatrix} 1 & 0 \\ 0 & 1 \end{bmatrix}$

Extra Practice **883**

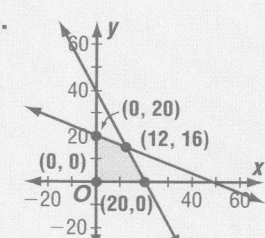

Additional Answers for Lesson 4-6

1. $\begin{bmatrix} 5 & 3 \\ 2 & -1 \end{bmatrix} \cdot \begin{bmatrix} x \\ y \end{bmatrix} = \begin{bmatrix} 6 \\ 9 \end{bmatrix}$

2. $\begin{bmatrix} 3 & 4 \\ 2 & -3 \end{bmatrix} \cdot \begin{bmatrix} x \\ y \end{bmatrix} = \begin{bmatrix} -8 \\ 6 \end{bmatrix}$

3. $\begin{bmatrix} 1 & 3 \\ 4 & -1 \end{bmatrix} \cdot \begin{bmatrix} x \\ y \end{bmatrix} = \begin{bmatrix} 1 \\ -22 \end{bmatrix}$

4. $\begin{bmatrix} 4 & -3 \\ 5 & -2 \end{bmatrix} \cdot \begin{bmatrix} x \\ y \end{bmatrix} = \begin{bmatrix} -1 \\ 39 \end{bmatrix}$

EXTRA PRACTICE

Lesson 4-4 Determine whether each matrix has a determinant. Write *yes* or *no*. If *yes*, find the value of the determinant.

1. $[3 \ 5]$ **no**

2. $\begin{bmatrix} 1 & -5 \\ 3 & 4 \end{bmatrix}$ **yes; 19**

3. $\begin{bmatrix} -1 & 6 & 1 \\ 0 & 5 & 1 \\ -5 & 2 & 3 \end{bmatrix}$ **yes; −18**

4. $\begin{bmatrix} 2 & 0 \\ 0 & 0 \\ 0 & 2 \end{bmatrix}$ **no**

Evaluate each determinant using expansion of minors.

5. $\begin{vmatrix} 2 & -3 & 5 \\ 1 & -2 & -7 \\ -1 & 4 & -3 \end{vmatrix}$ **48**

6. $\begin{vmatrix} 0 & -1 & 2 \\ -2 & 1 & 0 \\ 2 & 0 & -1 \end{vmatrix}$ **−2**

7. $\begin{vmatrix} 4 & 3 & -2 \\ 2 & 5 & -8 \\ 6 & 4 & -1 \end{vmatrix}$ **14**

8. $\begin{vmatrix} -3 & 0 & 2 \\ 1 & -2 & -1 \\ 0 & 5 & 0 \end{vmatrix}$ **−5**

Evaluate each determinant using diagonals.

9. $\begin{vmatrix} 3 & 2 & -1 \\ 2 & 3 & 0 \\ -1 & 0 & 3 \end{vmatrix}$ **12**

10. $\begin{vmatrix} 1 & 0 & 0 \\ 0 & 1 & 0 \\ 0 & 0 & 1 \end{vmatrix}$ **1**

11. $\begin{vmatrix} 4 & 3 & -2 \\ 2 & 5 & -8 \\ 6 & 4 & -1 \end{vmatrix}$ **14**

12. $\begin{vmatrix} 6 & 12 & 15 \\ 9 & 3 & 14 \\ 5 & 6 & 3 \end{vmatrix}$ **651**

Use a determinant to find the area of the triangle with the given vertices.

13. $(2, 3), (5, 6), (0, 0)$
1.5 units²

14. $(-5, -8), (2, 7), (6, -3)$
65 units²

15. $(-2, 2), (2, 2), (2, -2)$
8 units²

2. $\begin{bmatrix} \frac{1}{3} & \frac{1}{6} \\ 0 & -\frac{1}{4} \end{bmatrix}$

Lesson 4-5 Find the inverse of each matrix, if it exists. If it does not exist, explain why.

1. $\begin{bmatrix} 2 & 3 \\ 1 & 1 \end{bmatrix}$ $\begin{bmatrix} -1 & 3 \\ 1 & -2 \end{bmatrix}$

2. $\begin{bmatrix} 3 & 2 \\ 0 & -4 \end{bmatrix}$

3. $[3 \ 8]$ **not square**

4. $\begin{bmatrix} 3 & -6 \\ 2 & -4 \end{bmatrix}$ **det = 0**

5. $\begin{bmatrix} 2 & 4 \\ 2 & 3 \end{bmatrix}$ $\begin{bmatrix} -1.5 & 2 \\ 1 & -1 \end{bmatrix}$

6. $\begin{bmatrix} 8 & 5 \\ 6 & 4 \end{bmatrix}$ $\begin{bmatrix} 2 & -2.5 \\ -3 & 4 \end{bmatrix}$

7. $\begin{bmatrix} 10 & 3 \\ 5 & 2 \end{bmatrix}$ $\begin{bmatrix} 0.4 & -0.6 \\ -1 & 2 \end{bmatrix}$

8. $\begin{bmatrix} -3 & 4 \\ -4 & 8 \end{bmatrix}$ $\begin{bmatrix} -1 & \frac{1}{2} \\ -\frac{1}{2} & \frac{3}{8} \end{bmatrix}$

Determine whether each statement is *true* or *false*.

9. $\begin{bmatrix} -7 & -6 \\ 8 & 7 \end{bmatrix} \cdot \begin{bmatrix} -7 & -6 \\ 8 & 7 \end{bmatrix} = I$
true

10. $\begin{bmatrix} -3 & 4 \\ 2 & -2 \end{bmatrix} \cdot \begin{bmatrix} -2 & -2 \\ -4 & -3 \end{bmatrix} = I$
false

11. $\begin{bmatrix} 1 & 0 \\ 0 & 1 \end{bmatrix} \cdot \begin{bmatrix} -3 & 7 \\ 1 & 8 \end{bmatrix} = \begin{bmatrix} -3 & 7 \\ 1 & 8 \end{bmatrix}$
true

Lesson 4-6 Write a matrix equation for each system. **1–4. See margin.**

1. $5x + 3y = 6$
$2x - y = 9$

2. $3x + 4y = -8$
$2x - 3y = 6$

3. $x + 3y = 1$
$4x - y = -22$

4. $4x - 3y = -1$
$5x - 2y = 39$

Matrix M^{-1} is the inverse of the coefficient matrix. Use M^{-1} to solve each matrix equation.

5. $\begin{bmatrix} 3 & 4 \\ 2 & -5 \end{bmatrix} \cdot \begin{bmatrix} x \\ y \end{bmatrix} = \begin{bmatrix} 33 \\ -1 \end{bmatrix}$ $M^{-1} = \frac{1}{23}\begin{bmatrix} 5 & 4 \\ 2 & -3 \end{bmatrix}$
(7, 3)

6. $\begin{bmatrix} 1 & 2 & -1 \\ -2 & 3 & 1 \\ 1 & 1 & 3 \end{bmatrix} \cdot \begin{bmatrix} x \\ y \\ z \end{bmatrix} = \begin{bmatrix} 6 \\ 1 \\ 8 \end{bmatrix}$ $M^{-1} = \frac{1}{27}\begin{bmatrix} 8 & -7 & 5 \\ 7 & 4 & 1 \\ -5 & 1 & 7 \end{bmatrix}$
(3, 2, 1)

Solve each matrix equation or system of equation using inverse matrices. **7. (8000, 10,000)**

7. $\begin{bmatrix} 1 & 1 \\ 0.1 & -0.08 \end{bmatrix} \cdot \begin{bmatrix} x \\ y \end{bmatrix} = \begin{bmatrix} 18,000 \\ 0 \end{bmatrix}$

8. $\begin{bmatrix} -1 & 1 \\ 7 & -6 \end{bmatrix} \cdot \begin{bmatrix} x \\ y \end{bmatrix} = \begin{bmatrix} 0 \\ 3 \end{bmatrix}$ **(3, 3)**

9. $5x - y = 7$
$8x + 2y = 4$ **(1, −2)**

10. $3x + y = 4$
$2x + 2y = 3$ $\left(\frac{5}{4}, \frac{1}{4}\right)$

11. $6x + 5y = 7$
$3x - 10y = -4$ $\left(\frac{2}{3}, \frac{3}{5}\right)$

12. $3x - 5y = 1$
$x + 3y = 5$ **(2, 1)**

Lesson 4-7 Write an augmented matrix for each system of equations. Then solve each system.

1. $y = 2x + 3$
$y = 4x - 1$
1–4. See margin.

2. $3x + 4y = -6$
$5x - 3y = 19$

3. $3x + 2y + 4z = 9$
$2x + 5y - 2z = -7$
$4x + y - 3z = -3$

4. $x + 2y - 3z = 12$
$5x - 3y + z = -11$
$2x + y + 4z = -5$

Describe the solution for the system of equations represented by each reduced augmented matrix.

5. $\begin{bmatrix} -2 & 0 & | & -12 \\ 0 & 4 & | & -48 \end{bmatrix}$
(6, −12)

6. $\begin{bmatrix} 1 & 2 & 0 & | & 9 \\ 0 & 3 & 1 & | & 6 \\ 0 & 0 & 0 & | & 0 \end{bmatrix}$
(9 − 2y, y, 6 − 3y)

7. $\begin{bmatrix} 0 & 0 & 0 & | & -2 \\ 0 & 3 & 0 & | & 6 \\ 0 & 0 & 4 & | & 1 \end{bmatrix}$
no solution

Solve each system of equations using augmented matrices.

8. $2x = 3y - 31$
$3x + 5y = 1$ **(−8, 5)**

9. $6y = 4x - 9$
$3x = 7y - 2$ **(7.5, 3.5)**

10. $7x + 5y = 27$
$5x - 5y = 5$ $\left(\frac{8}{3}, \frac{5}{3}\right)$

11. $4x + 2y = 0$
$3x + 5y = 7$ **(−1, 2)**

12. $2x - 3y + 4z = -15$
$5x - y - 3z = 8$
$3x - 2y + 5z = -5$
(3, 7, 0)

13. $2x - y - 4z = -8$
$4x + y + 3z = 6$
$6x - z = -2$
no solution

14. $x - 4y + 2z = 4$
$2x + 3y + 2z = -5$
$2x - 5y + z = 2$
(−2, −1, 1)

15. $3x - 2y - 4z = 13$
$2x + 3y + 3z = 4$
$2x - 2y - 5z = 5$
(5, −5, 3)

Lesson 4-8 Use the box-and-whisker plot to answer each question.

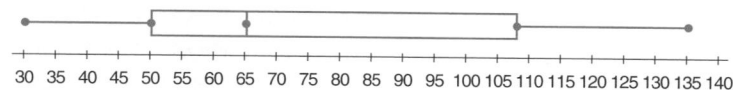

30 35 40 45 50 55 60 65 70 75 80 85 90 95 100 105 110 115 120 125 130 135 140

1. What is the range of the data? **105**

2. What percent of the data is greater than 65? **50%**

3. What percent of the data is less than 50? **25%**

4. What percent of the data is greater than 30 but less than 135? **100%**

Find the range, quartiles, interquartile range, and outliers for each set of data. Then make a box-and-whisker plot for each set of data. **5–9. See margin.**

5. {24, 19, 24, 22, 13, 20, 17, 24 20, 23, 24, 20, 17, 18, 20, 16, 17, 20, 10, 21, 20, 22, 23, 20, 13, 23}

6. {15, 9, 15, 11, 10, 9, 12, 13, 12, 11, 13, 12, 14, 12, 13, 10, 6, 12, 11, 8, 15, 14, 3, 5, 7, 8, 6, 12, 14}

7. {97, 83, 73, 33, 89, 67, 89, 73, 28, 55, 89, 80, 38, 84, 83, 89, 81, 88, 87, 76, 36, 72, 91, 73, 70, 47}

8. {30.4, 18.9, 11.1, 8.2, 5.5, 5.2, 13.6, 13.2, 8.8, 5.4, 6.2, 8.7}

9. {679, 565, 805, 556, 718, 625, 553, 2064, 496, 1033}

Lesson 5-1 Simplify. Assume that no variable equals 0. **2.** $(-3)^5 = -243$

1. $x^7 x^3 x$ x^{11}

2. $(-3)^4 (-3)$

3. $\frac{t^{12}}{t}$ t^{11}

4. $\frac{6^5}{6^3}$ $6^2 = 36$

5. $(m^3)^8$ m^{24}

6. -3^4 -81

7. $\left(\frac{x}{5}\right)^2$ $\frac{x^2}{25}$

8. $(-2y^5)^2$ $4y^{10}$

9. $3x^0$ **3**

10. $\frac{5^6 a^{x+y}}{5^4 a^{x-y}}$ $25a^{2y}$

11. ab^{-1} $\frac{a}{b}$

12. $\frac{b^{-4}}{b^{-5}}$ b

13. $(y^{-5})^{-7}$ y^{35}

14. $(5x^2 y^{-3})^4$ $\frac{625x^8}{y^{12}}$

15. $\frac{1}{x^{-3}}$ x^3

16. $\frac{2^{-1} xy^2}{2^3 y^8}$ $\frac{x}{16y^6}$

Evaluate. Express each answer in both scientific and decimal notation. **17–19. See margin.**

17. $(8.95 \times 10^9)(1.82 \times 10^7)$

18. $(-3.1 \times 10^5)(7.9 \times 10^{-8})$

19. $\frac{(2.38 \times 10^{13})(7.56 \times 10^{-5})}{(4.2 \times 10^{18})}$

Additional Answers for Lesson 4-7

1. $\begin{bmatrix} -2 & 1 & | & 3 \\ -4 & 1 & | & -1 \end{bmatrix}$; **(2, 7)**

2. $\begin{bmatrix} 3 & 4 & | & -6 \\ 5 & -3 & | & 19 \end{bmatrix}$; **(2, −3)**

3. $\begin{bmatrix} 3 & 2 & 4 & | & 9 \\ 2 & 5 & -2 & | & -7 \\ 4 & 1 & -3 & | & -3 \end{bmatrix}$; **(1, −1, 2)**

4. $\begin{bmatrix} 1 & 2 & -3 & | & 12 \\ 5 & -3 & 1 & | & -11 \\ 2 & 1 & 4 & | & -5 \end{bmatrix}$; **(0, 3, −2)**

Additional Answers for Lesson 4-8

5. 14; 17, 20, 23; 6; none

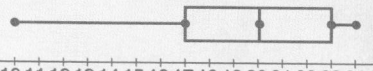

9 10 11 12 13 14 15 16 17 18 19 20 21 22 23 24 25

6. 12; 8.5, 12, 13; 4.5; none

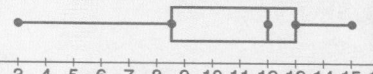

2 3 4 5 6 7 8 9 10 11 12 13 14 15 16

7. 69; 67, 78, 88, 21; 28, 33

20 25 30 35 40 45 50 55 60 65 70 75 80 85 90 95 100

8. 25.2; 5.85, 8.75, 13.4; 7.55; 30.4

4 6 8 10 12 14 16 18 20 22 24 26 28 30 32

9. 1568; 556, 652, 805; 249; 2064

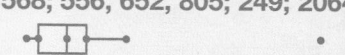

200 400 600 800 1000 1200 1400 1600 1800 2000 2200

Additional Answers for Lesson 5-1

17. $1.63 \times 10^{17} =$ 163,000,000,000,000,000

18. $-2.449 \times 10^{-2} = -0.02449$

19. $4.284 \times 10^{-10} =$ 0.0000000004284

885

Additional Answers for Lesson 5-2

6. $2x^3 - 2x^2 + 5x - 7y^2$
7. $9x^2 - x + 3$
8. $-11x^2 + 2x + 36$
9. $5x^2 + 12x + 10$
10. $20a^3b - 15a^2b^2$
11. $28u^3w^2 - 35u^2 + 1$
12. $12x^9 + 4x^8 - 4x^6 - 28x^5$
13. $35x^8 - 20x^7 + 10x^6 - 45x^4$
14. $8x^2 + 2x - 21$
15. $-6x^2 + 7x + 5$
16. $2x^3 + 5x^2 + 2x - 21$
17. $12x^3 - 26x^2 + 7x + 5$
18. $4x^2 - 25$
19. $9x^2 - 49$
20. $x^2 - 16$
21. $25 - 4w^2$
22. $9a^8 - 25$
23. $16x^2 - 100$
24. $9x^2 + 42x + 49$
25. $25x^2 - 20x + 4$
26. $x^2 + 14x + 49$
27. $t^2 - 10t + 25$
28. $49b^2 - 11.2b + 0.64$
29. $25x^2 - 30x^5 + 9x^8$

Additional Answers for Lesson 5-3

5. $5c^3 + 2c^2d - \frac{1}{5}$
6. $4f^{15} + 5f^6 - 2f^3$
7. $3m^4 + 5n^5 - m^2$
8. $8g^2 - 5g + 3$
9. $p^{14} + p^7 - 1$
10. $5x^2 - 2xy + y^2$
16. $6a^3 + 2a^2 - a + 5 + \frac{3}{a-4}$
17. $q^3 + 3 - \frac{7}{q+8}$
18. $3v^2 + 4v - 1 + \frac{2}{5v-4}$
19. $5y^2 + 4 - \frac{3}{2y^2-1}$
20. $5s^2 - 4s + 4 - \frac{11}{s+1}$
21. $x^2 + 11x - 34 + \frac{60}{x+2}$
22. $t^3 + t - 1$
23. $z^3 + z^2 + 3z + 1$
24. $3r^3 - 9r^2 + 7r - 6$
25. $2b^2 - 5b - 3$

EXTRA PRACTICE

Lesson 5-2 Determine whether each expression is a polynomial. Write *yes* or *no*. Then state the degree of each polynomial.

1. $5r^3 + 7r^2s - 3rs^2$ yes; 3
2. $\frac{xy}{3}$ yes; 2
3. $\frac{a^2}{b}$ no
4. $2 + \frac{7}{w}$ no
5. 15 yes; 0

Simplify. 6–29. See margin.

6. $4x^3 + 5x - 7x^2 - 2x^3 + 5x^2 - 7y^2$
7. $(2x^2 - 3x + 11) + (7x^2 + 2x - 8)$
8. $(-3x^2 + 7x + 23) + (-8x^2 - 5x + 13)$
9. $(-3x^2 + 7x + 23) - (-8x^2 - 5x + 13)$
10. $5a^2b(4a - 3b)$
11. $\frac{7u}{w}\left(4u^2w^3 - 5uw + \frac{w}{7u}\right)$
12. $-4x^5(-3x^4 - x^3 + x + 7)$
13. $-5x^4(9 - 2x^2 + 4x^3 - 7x^4)$
14. $(2x - 3)(4x + 7)$
15. $(3x - 5)(-2x - 1)$
16. $(2x - 3)(x^2 + 4x + 7)$
17. $(3x - 5)(4x^2 - 2x - 1)$
18. $(2x + 5)(2x - 5)$
19. $(3x - 7)(3x + 7)$
20. $(x + 4)(x - 4)$
21. $(5 + 2w)(5 - 2w)$
22. $(3a^4 - 5)(3a^4 + 5)$
23. $(-4x - 10)(-4x + 10)$
24. $(3x + 7)^2$
25. $(5x - 2)^2$
26. $(x + 7)^2$
27. $(t - 5)^2$
28. $(7b - 0.8)^2$
29. $(5x - 3x^4)^2$

Lesson 5-3 **Simplify.** 5–10. See margin.

1. $\frac{18r^3s^2 + 36r^2s^3}{9r^2s^2}$ $2r + 4s$
2. $\frac{15v^3w^2 - 5v^4w^3}{-5v^4w^3}$ $-\frac{3}{vw}$
3. $\frac{x^2 - x + 1}{x}$ $x - 1 + \frac{1}{x}$
4. $(5hb + 5hc) \div (b + c)$ $5h$
5. $(25c^4d + 10c^3d^2 - cd) \div 5cd$
6. $(16f^{18} + 20f^9 - 8f^6) \div 4f^3$
7. $(33m^5 + 55mn^5 - 11m^3)(11m)^{-1}$
8. $(8g^3 + 19g^2 - 12g + 9) \div (g + 3)$
9. $(p^{21} + 3p^{14} + p^7 - 2)(p^7 + 2)^{-1}$
10. $(15x^3 + 19x^2y - 7xy^2 + 5y^3) \div (3x + 5y)$
11. $(n^3 + 125) \div (n + 5)$ $n^2 - 5n + 25$
12. $(10z^3 - 90z) \div (2z - 6)$ $5z^2 + 15z$
13. $(8k^2 - 56k + 98) \div (2k - 7)$ $4k - 14$
14. $(2r^2 + 5r - 3) \div (r + 3)$ $2r - 1$
15. $(6y^2 + 7y - 3)(2y + 3)^{-1}$ $3y - 1$

Use synthetic division to find each quotient. 16–25. See margin.

16. $(6a^4 - 22a^3 - 9a^2 + 9a - 17) \div (a - 4)$
17. $(q^4 + 8q^3 + 3q + 17) \div (q + 8)$
18. $(15v^3 + 8v^2 - 21v + 6) \div (5v - 4)$
19. $(10y^4 + 3y^2 - 7)(2y^2 - 1)^{-1}$
20. $(5s^3 + s^2 - 7) \div (s + 1)$
21. $(x^3 + 13x^2 - 12x - 8)(x + 2)^{-1}$
22. $(t^4 - 2t^3 + t^2 - 3t + 2) \div (t - 2)$
23. $(z^4 - 3z^3 - z^2 - 11z - 4) \div (z - 4)$
24. $(3r^4 - 6r^3 - 2r^2 + r - 6) \div (r + 1)$
25. $(2b^3 - 11b^2 + 12b + 9) \div (b - 3)$

Lesson 5-4 Factor completely. If the polynomial is not factorable, write *prime*. 1–29. See margin.

1. $14a^3b^3c - 21a^2b^4c + 7a^2b^3c$
2. $10ax - 2xy - 15ab + 3by$
3. $x^2 + x - 42$
4. $2x^2 + 5x + 3$
5. $6x^2 + 71x - 12$
6. $6x^4 - 12x^3 + 3x^2$
7. $x^2(x + 3) + 2(x + 3)$
8. $x^2 - 6x + 2$
9. $2x^3 + 6x^2 + x + 3$
10. $x^2 - 2x - 15$
11. $6x^2 + 23x + 20$
12. $24x^2 - 76x + 40$
13. $6p^2 - 13pq - 28q^2$
14. $2x^2 - 6x + 3$
15. $x^2 + 49 - 14x$
16. $9x^2 - 64$
17. $9 - t^{10}$
18. $x^2 + 16$
19. $a^4 - 81b^4$
20. $3a^3 + 12a^2 - 63a$
21. $x^3 - 8x^2 + 15x$
22. $x^2 + 6x + 9$
23. $18x^3 - 8x$
24. $3x^2 - 42x + 40$
25. $2x^2 + 4x - 1$
26. $35ac - 3bd - 7ad + 15bc$
27. $5h^2 - 10hj + h - 2j$
28. $16r^2 - 24r + 9$
29. $3a^2 + 6a + 9y$

Additional Answers for Lesson 5-4

1. $7a^2b^3c(2a - 3b + 1)$
2. $(5a - y)(2x - 3b)$
3. $(x + 7)(x - 6)$
4. $(2x + 3)(x + 1)$
5. $(6x - 1)(x + 12)$
6. $3x^2(2x^2 - 4x + 1)$
7. $(x + 3)(x^2 + 2)$
8. prime
9. $(2x^2 + 1)(x + 3)$
10. $(x - 5)(x + 3)$
11. $(2x + 5)(3x + 4)$
12. $4(2x - 5)(3x - 2)$
13. $(2p - 7q)(3p + 4q)$
14. prime
15. $(x - 7)^2$
16. $(3x + 8)(3x - 8)$
17. $(3 + t^5)(3 - t^5)$
18. prime
19. $(a^2 + 9b^2)(a + 3b)$ $(a - 3b)$
20. $3a(a + 7)(a - 3)$
21. $x(x - 5)(x - 3)$
22. $(x + 3)^2$
23. $2x(3x + 2)(3x - 2)$
24. prime
25. prime
26. $(7a + 3b)(5c - d)$
27. $(5h + 1)(h - 2j)$
28. $(4r - 3)^2$
29. $3(a^2 + 2a + 3y)$

Lesson 5-5 Use a calculator to approximate each value to three decimal places.

1. $\sqrt{289}$ 17

2. $\sqrt[4]{0.0625}$ 0.5

3. $\sqrt[3]{-343}$ -7

4. $\sqrt{7832}$ 88.499

5. $\sqrt[10]{32^4}$ 4

6. $\sqrt[3]{49}$ 3.659

7. $\sqrt[5]{5}$ 1.380

8. $-\sqrt[4]{25}$ -2.236

Simplify. 11. no real roots 16. $p^5q^3rs^4$ 18. $-(2x^2-y)^2$ 20. $\pm 4m^3n$

9. $\sqrt{\left(-\frac{2}{3}\right)^4}$ $\frac{4}{9}$

10. $\sqrt[5]{-32}$ -2

11. $-\sqrt{-144}$

12. $\sqrt[4]{a^{16}b^8}$ a^4b^2

13. $\sqrt{9h^{22}}$ $3|h^{11}|$

14. $\pm\sqrt[4]{81x^4}$ $\pm 3x$

15. $\sqrt[5]{\frac{1}{100000}}$ $\frac{1}{10}$

16. $\sqrt[5]{p^{25}q^{15}r^5s^{20}}$

17. $\sqrt[3]{-d^6}$ $-d^2$

18. $-\sqrt[4]{(2x^2-y)^8}$

19. $\sqrt[5]{0}$ 0

20. $\pm\sqrt{16m^6n^2}$

21. $\sqrt[3]{(2x-y)^3}$
   $2x-y$

22. $\sqrt[4]{(r+s)^4}$
   $|r+s|$

23. $\sqrt{9a^2+6a+1}$
   $|3a+1|$

24. $\sqrt{4y^2+12y+9}$
   $|2y+3|$

5. $49|xy|\sqrt[4]{xy^2}$
8. $13\sqrt[3]{4}$
10. $\sqrt[3]{6}-\sqrt{6}$
11. $2\sqrt{10}-5\sqrt{2}$
12. $5\sqrt{6}+4\sqrt{21}$

Lesson 5-6 **Simplify.** 13. $-3-3\sqrt{7}$ 14. $15+3\sqrt{2}+5\sqrt{3}+\sqrt{6}$

1. $\sqrt{75}$ $5\sqrt{3}$

2. $7\sqrt{12}$ $14\sqrt{3}$

3. $\sqrt[3]{81}$ $3\sqrt[3]{3}$

4. $\sqrt{5r^5}$ $r^2\sqrt{5r}$

5. $\sqrt[4]{7^8x^5y^6}$

6. $3\sqrt{5}+6\sqrt{5}$ $9\sqrt{5}$

7. $\sqrt{18}-\sqrt{50}$ $-2\sqrt{2}$

8. $4\sqrt[3]{32}+\sqrt[3]{500}$

9. $\sqrt{12}\sqrt{27}$ 18

10. $\sqrt[3]{6}-\sqrt{6}$

11. $\sqrt{10}(2-\sqrt{5})$

12. $\sqrt{3}(5\sqrt{2}+4\sqrt{7})$

13. $(1-\sqrt{7})(4+\sqrt{7})$

14. $(5+\sqrt{2})(3+\sqrt{3})$

15. $(2+\sqrt{5})(2-\sqrt{5})$

16. $(x-\sqrt{3y})(x+\sqrt{3y})$

17. $(8+\sqrt{11})^2$

18. $(5z-2\sqrt{7})^2$

19. $\sqrt{\frac{3m^3}{24n^5}}$ $\frac{m\sqrt{2mn}}{4n^3}$

20. $\frac{\sqrt{18}}{\sqrt{32}}$ $\frac{3}{4}$

21. $2\sqrt[3]{\frac{r^5}{2s^2t}}$ $\frac{r\sqrt[3]{4r^2st^2}}{st}$

22. $\sqrt{\frac{2}{3}}-\sqrt{\frac{3}{8}}$ $\frac{\sqrt{6}}{12}$

23. $\frac{5}{3-\sqrt{10}}$ $-15-5\sqrt{10}$

24. $\frac{x+\sqrt{5}}{x-\sqrt{5}}$

15. -1 16. x^2-3y 17. $75+16\sqrt{11}$ 18. $25z^2+28-20z\sqrt{7}$ 24. $\frac{x^2+5+2x\sqrt{5}}{x^2-5}$

Lesson 5-7 **Evaluate.**

1. $2401^{\frac{1}{4}}$ 7

2. $27^{\frac{4}{3}}$ 81

3. $(-32)^{\frac{2}{5}}$ 4

4. $-81^{\frac{3}{4}}$ -27

5. $(-125)^{-\frac{2}{3}}$ $\frac{1}{25}$

6. $7^{\frac{5}{2}}\cdot 7^{\frac{1}{2}}$ 343

7. $8^{-\frac{2}{3}}\cdot 64^{\frac{1}{6}}$ $\frac{1}{2}$

8. $\left(\frac{48}{1875}\right)^{-\frac{5}{4}}$ $\frac{3125}{32}$

Express in simplest radical form.

9. $7^{\frac{5}{9}}$ $\sqrt[9]{7^5}$

10. $32^{\frac{2}{3}}$ $8\sqrt[3]{2}$

11. $k^{\frac{8}{5}}$ $k\sqrt[5]{k^3}$

12. $x^{\frac{2}{5}}\cdot x^{\frac{5}{8}}$ $x\sqrt[40]{x}$

13. $m^{\frac{2}{5}}\cdot n^{\frac{4}{5}}$ $\sqrt[5]{m^2n^4}$

14. $\left(p^{\frac{5}{4}}q^{\frac{7}{2}}\right)^{\frac{8}{3}}$ $p^3q^9\sqrt[3]{pq}$

15. $3^{\frac{9}{2}}c^{\frac{3}{2}}$ $81c\sqrt{3c}$

16. $\frac{7^{\frac{3}{4}}}{7^{\frac{5}{3}}}$ $\frac{\sqrt[12]{7}}{7}$

Simplify.

17. $\frac{\frac{1}{t^9}}{t^{\frac{9}{5}}}$ $\frac{t^{\frac{1}{5}}}{t^2}$

18. $a^{-\frac{8}{7}}$ $\frac{a^{\frac{6}{7}}}{a^2}$

19. $\frac{y^{\frac{1}{2}}}{x^{\frac{1}{2}}+y^{\frac{1}{2}}}$ $\frac{x^{\frac{1}{2}}y^{\frac{1}{2}}-y}{x-y}$

20. $(a+b)^{-\frac{3}{4}}$ $\frac{(a+b)^{\frac{1}{4}}}{a+b}$

21. $\frac{r}{r^{\frac{7}{5}}}$ $\frac{r^{\frac{3}{5}}}{r}$

22. $\frac{8}{5^{\frac{1}{2}}+3^{\frac{1}{2}}}$ $4\left(5^{\frac{1}{2}}-3^{\frac{1}{2}}\right)$

23. $\frac{v^{\frac{11}{7}}-v^{\frac{4}{7}}}{v^{\frac{4}{7}}}$ $v-1$

24. $\left(z^{\frac{5}{3}}\cdot z^{-\frac{9}{2}}\right)^{-\frac{12}{17}}$ z^2

Extra Practice **887**

Additional Answers for Lesson 6-1

1. $4x^2$; $-3x$; 8
2. $2r^2$; 0; 1
3. z^2; $6x$; 4
4. m^2; 0; -9
5. $4a^2$; $-16a$; 0
6. $5y^2$; $3y$; 0
7. $9w^2$; $20w$; 25
8. $-6x^2$; $7x$; 2
9. $9x^2$; 0; 0

16.

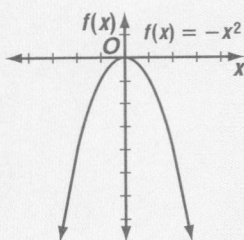

$(0, 0)$; $x = 0$

17.

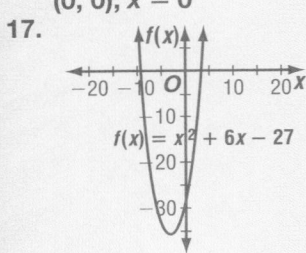

$(-3, -36)$; $x = -3$

18.

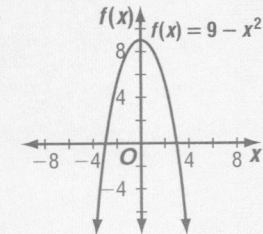

$(0, 9)$; $x = 0$

19.

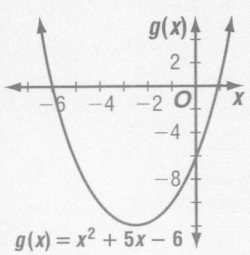

$(-2.5, -12.25)$; $x = -2.5$

20.

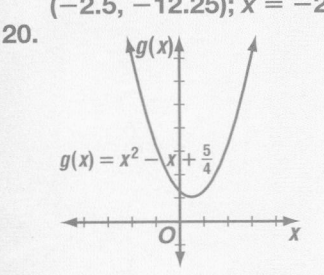

$(0.5, 1)$; $x = 0.5$

888

EXTRA PRACTICE

Lesson 5-8 Solve each equation. Be sure to check for extraneous solutions.   9. ± 2

1. $\sqrt{x} = 16$ 256
2. $\sqrt{z + 3} = 7$ 46
3. $\sqrt[4]{a + 5} = 1$ -4
4. $5\sqrt{s} - 8 = 3$ $\frac{121}{25}$
5. $\sqrt[4]{m + 7} + 11 = 9$
6. $d + \sqrt{d^2 - 8} = 4$ 3
7. $g\sqrt{7} + 8 = g$
8. $\sqrt{x - 8} = \sqrt{13 + x}$
9. $\sqrt{3x + 10} = 1 + \sqrt{2x + 5}$
10. $\sqrt{3 - x} = \sqrt{11} - \sqrt{x}$
11. $(3x + 8)^{\frac{1}{2}} = 2$ $-\frac{4}{3}$
12. $\sqrt{3n - 1} = \sqrt{4 - 2n}$ 1
13. $8w + 3 = 4 - w\sqrt{5}$
14. $\sqrt{5y + 4} = 8$ 12
15. $2 - 4\sqrt{21 - 6c} = 6$
16. $\sqrt{3x + 25} + \sqrt{10 - 2x} = 0$
17. $\sqrt{2c + 3} - 7 = 0$ 23
18. $\sqrt{3z - 5} - 3 = 1$ 7
19. $\sqrt{5y + 1} + 6 = 10$ 3
20. $\sqrt{3f + 1} - 2 = 6$ 21
21. $\sqrt{y - 5} - \sqrt{y} = 1$

5, 8, 10, 15, 16, 21. no real solution   7. $\dfrac{-4 - 4\sqrt{7}}{3}$ 13. $\dfrac{8 - \sqrt{5}}{59}$

Lesson 5-9 Simplify.   11. $6 + 14i$

1. $\sqrt{-289}$ $17i$
2. $\sqrt{-\frac{25}{121}}$ $\frac{5}{11}i$
3. $\sqrt{-625b^8}$ $25b^4i$
4. $\sqrt{-\frac{28f^6}{27g^5}}$ $\frac{2|f^3|}{3g^2}i\sqrt{\frac{7}{3g}}$
5. $(7i)^2$ -49
6. $(6i)(-2i)(11i)$ $132i$
7. $(\sqrt{-8})(\sqrt{-12})$ $-4\sqrt{6}$
8. $-i^{22}$ 1
9. $i^{17} \cdot i^{11} \cdot i^{26}$ -1
10. $3\sqrt{-24} - 7\sqrt{-96}$ $-22i\sqrt{6}$
11. $(14 - 5i) + (-8 + 19i)$
12. $(7i) - (2 + 3i)$ $-2 + 4i$
13. $(2 + 2i) - (5 + i)$ $-3 + i$
14. $(7 + 3i)(7 - 3i)$ 58
15. $(8 - 2i)(5 + i)$ $42 - 2i$
16. $(6 + 8i)^2$ $-28 + 96i$
17. $(15 - 3i)(15 + 3i)$ 234
18. $(9 + 5i)^2 + (15 - 3i)^2$ 272

Solve each equation.

19. $x^2 + 8 = 3$ $\pm i\sqrt{5}$
20. $\frac{4x^2}{49} + 6 = 3$ $\pm\frac{7i}{2}\sqrt{3}$
21. $8x^2 + 5 = 1$ $\pm\frac{i\sqrt{2}}{2}$
22. $12 - 9x^2 = 38$ $\pm\frac{i\sqrt{26}}{3}$

Lesson 5-10 Find the conjugate of each number.

1. $3 + i$ $3 - i$
2. $\sqrt{2} - 3i$ $\sqrt{2} + 3i$
3. $-8 + 7i$ $-8 - 7i$
4. $-i\sqrt{5}$ $i\sqrt{5}$

Find the product of each complex number and its conjugate.

5. $7i$ 49
6. $3 - i$ 10
7. $5 + 3i$ 34
8. $3 - 4i$ 25

Simplify.

9. $\frac{2 + i}{i}$ $1 - 2i$
10. $\frac{8 + 5i}{4i}$ $\frac{5}{4} - 2i$
11. $\frac{3 - 7i}{5 + 4i}$ $\frac{-13 - 47i}{41}$
12. $\frac{2 + 10i}{6 - i}$ $\frac{2 + 62i}{37}$
13. $\frac{9 + 12i}{8 + 3i}$ $\frac{108 + 69i}{73}$
14. $\frac{3}{6 - 2i}$ $\frac{9 + 3i}{20}$
15. $\frac{5i}{3 + 4i}$ $\frac{4 + 3i}{5}$
16. $\frac{5 + 3i}{1 + i}$ $4 - i$
17. $\frac{5}{\sqrt{3} + 2i}$ $\frac{5\sqrt{3} - 10i}{7}$
18. $\frac{3i}{1 + i\sqrt{2}}$ $\sqrt{2} + i$
19. $\frac{2 - i\sqrt{3}}{2 + i\sqrt{3}}$ $\frac{1 - 4i\sqrt{3}}{7}$
20. $\frac{1}{\sqrt{5} + i}$ $\frac{\sqrt{5} - i}{6}$

Find the multiplicative inverse of each complex number.

21. $5 + 2i$ $\frac{5 - 2i}{29}$
22. $\frac{7i}{3 - 4i}$ $\frac{3i + 4}{-7}$
23. $\frac{3 - i}{4 + i}$ $\frac{11 + 7i}{10}$
24. $\frac{1 + i}{1 - i}$ $-i$

21.

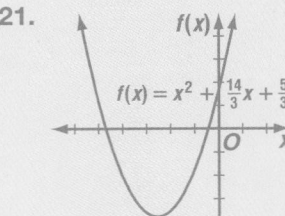

$\left(-\frac{7}{3}, -\frac{34}{9}\right)$; $x = -\frac{7}{3}$

Lesson 6-1 Identify the quadratic term, the linear term, and the constant term in each function.

1. $f(x) = 4x^2 - 3x + 8$ **2.** $g(r) = 2r^2 + 1$ **3.** $f(z) = (z + 3)^2 - 5$

4. $f(m) = m^2 - 9$ **5.** $g(a) = (2a - 4)^2 - 16$ **6.** $f(y) = 5y^2 + 3y$

7. $h(w) = (3w + 5)^2 - 10w$ **8.** $f(x) = 2 + 7x - 6x^2$ **9.** $f(x) = 9x^2$

1–9. See margin.

Use the related graph of each equation to determine its solutions.

10. $x^2 - 5x + 6 = 0$ **2, 3**   **11.** $x^2 + 2x + 1 = 0$ **−1**   **12.** $x^2 - 2x - 8 = 0$ **−2, 4**

13. $x^2 + x - 6 = 0$ **−3, 2**   **14.** $4x^2 - 9 = 0$ $-\frac{3}{2}, \frac{3}{2}$ **15.** $2x^2 + 7x - 4 = 0$ $\frac{1}{2}, -4$

Graph each function. Name the vertex and the axis of symmetry.   16–21. See margin.

16. $f(x) = -x^2$ **17.** $f(x) = x^2 + 6x - 27$ **18.** $f(x) = 9 - x^2$

19. $g(x) = x^2 + 5x - 6$ **20.** $g(x) = x^2 - x + \frac{5}{4}$ **21.** $f(x) = x^2 + \frac{14}{3}x + \frac{5}{3}$

Lesson 6-2 Solve each equation.

1. $(x + 5)(x - 3) = 0$ **−5, 3**   **2.** $(y - 2)(3y + 2) = 0$ $2, -\frac{2}{3}$ **3.** $s(2s - 1) = 0$ $0, \frac{1}{2}$

Solve each equation by factoring.

4. $x^2 + 7x + 10 = 0$ **−5, −2**   **5.** $x^2 - 4x - 21 = 0$ **7, −3**   **6.** $b^2 = 49$ **7, −7**

7. $3z^3 = 75z$ **0, 5, −5**   **8.** $2m^2 + 7m = 9$ $-\frac{9}{2}, 1$ **9.** $7x(x - 1) = 30(x + 1)$ $-\frac{5}{7}, 6$

Solve each equation by graphing or by factoring.   10–27. See margin.

10. $8x^2 = 48 - 40x$ **11.** $5x^2 = 20x$ **12.** $12d^2 - 71d - 6 = 0$

13. $16x^2 - 64 = 0$ **14.** $5x^2 - 45x + 90 = 0$ **15.** $24x^2 - 15 = 2x$

16. $x^2 = 72 - x$ **17.** $2x^2 + 5x + 3 = 0$ **18.** $4p^2 + 9 = 12p$

19. $2x^2 - 8x = 0$ **20.** $8b^2 + 10b = 3$ **21.** $12p^2 - 5p = 3$

22. $a^2 + 8a + 12 = 0$ **23.** $x^2 + 9x + 14 = 0$ **24.** $9g^2 + 1 = 6g$

25. $2x^2 = 6x$ **26.** $8b^2 + 10b = 3$ **27.** $g^2 - 4g = 21$

$6t^2 + 7t = 3$

Lesson 6-3 Find the value of c that makes each trinomial a perfect square.

1. $x^2 - 12x + c$ **36**   **2.** $y^2 + 20y + c$ **100**   **3.** $m^2 - 11m + c$ $\frac{121}{4}$

4. $g^2 - \frac{2}{3}g + c$ $\frac{1}{9}$ **5.** $z^2 + 30z + c$ **225**   **6.** $t^2 - 0.5t + c$ **0.0625**

7. $x^2 + \frac{3}{8}x + c$ $\frac{9}{256}$ **8.** $w^2 + 16w + c$ **64**   **9.** $a^2 - 3a + c$ $\frac{9}{4}$

Find the exact solution for each equation by completing the square.   10–30. See margin.

10. $x^2 + 3x - 4 = 0$ **11.** $x^2 + 5x = 0$ **12.** $x^2 + 2x - 63 = 0$

13. $3x^2 - 16x - 35 = 0$ **14.** $x^2 + 7x + 13 = 0$ **15.** $5x^2 - 8x + 2 = 0$

16. $x^2 - 6x + 11 = 0$ **17.** $x^2 - 12x + 36 = 0$ **18.** $8x^2 + 13x - 4 = 0$

19. $3x^2 + 5x + 6 = 0$ **20.** $x^2 + 14x - 1 = 0$ **21.** $4x^2 - 32x + 15 = 0$

22. $3x^2 - 11x - 4 = 0$ **23.** $x^2 + 8x - 84 = 0$ **24.** $x^2 - 7x + 5 = 0$

25. $t^2 + 3t - 8 = 0$ **26.** $a^2 - 5a - 10 = 0$ **27.** $3z^2 - 12z + 4 = 0$

28. $x^2 + 20x + 75 = 0$ **29.** $x^2 - 5x - 24 = 0$ **30.** $2t^2 + t - 21 = 0$

Additional Answers for Lesson 6-2

10. 1, −6
11. 0, 4
12. 6, $-\frac{1}{12}$
13. 2, −2
14. 3, 6
15. $-\frac{3}{4}, \frac{5}{6}$
16. −9, 8
17. −1, $-\frac{3}{2}$
18. $\frac{3}{2}$
19. 0, 4
20. $\frac{1}{4}, -\frac{3}{2}$
21. $\frac{3}{4}, -\frac{1}{3}$
22. −2, −6
23. −7, −2
24. $\frac{1}{3}$
25. 0, 3
26. $\frac{1}{3}, -\frac{3}{2}$
27. 7, −3

Additional Answers for Lesson 6-3

10. −4, 1
11. −5, 0
12. −9, 7
13. $-\frac{5}{3}$, 7
14. $\frac{-7 \pm i\sqrt{3}}{2}$
15. $\frac{4 \pm \sqrt{6}}{5}$
16. $3 \pm i\sqrt{2}$
17. 6
18. $\frac{-13 \pm 3\sqrt{33}}{16}$
19. $\frac{-5 \pm i\sqrt{47}}{6}$
20. $-7 \pm 5\sqrt{2}$
21. $-\frac{1}{2}, -\frac{15}{2}$
22. $-\frac{1}{3}$, 4
23. 6, −14
24. $\frac{7 \pm \sqrt{29}}{2}$
25. $\frac{-3 \pm \sqrt{41}}{2}$
26. $\frac{5 \pm \sqrt{65}}{2}$
27. $2 \pm \frac{2\sqrt{6}}{3}$
28. −5, −15
29. −3, 8
30. $-\frac{7}{2}$, 3

889

Additional Answers for Lesson 6-4

1. -3; 2 Im; $\dfrac{-7 \pm i\sqrt{3}}{2}$

2. 540; 2 R I; $\dfrac{-1 \pm \sqrt{15}}{2}$; $-2.44, 1.44$

3. -55; 2 Im; $\dfrac{5 \pm i\sqrt{55}}{10}$

4. 2880; 2 R I; $\dfrac{8 \pm 3\sqrt{5}}{4}$; 0.32, 3.68

5. 0; 1 R Q; $-\dfrac{7}{3}$

6. 208; 2 R I; $\dfrac{4 \pm \sqrt{13}}{2}$; 0.20, 3.80

7. 49; 2 R Q; $3, -\dfrac{1}{2}$

8. 0; 1 R Q; 9

9. 240; 2 R I; $\pm \dfrac{\sqrt{15}}{6}$; 0.65, -0.65

10. 784; 2 R Q; $\pm \dfrac{7}{2}$

11. 0; 1 R Q; 5

12. 4228; 2 R I; $\dfrac{-5 \pm \sqrt{1057}}{24}$; $-1.56, 1.15$

13. -140; 2 Im; $\dfrac{1 \pm i\sqrt{35}}{9}$

14. 49; 2 R Q; $0, \dfrac{7}{8}$

15. 3321; 2 R I; $\dfrac{1 \pm \sqrt{41}}{4}$; $-1.35, 1.85$

16. 0; 1 R Q; 2

17. 16; 2 R Q; $-\dfrac{3}{2}, -\dfrac{1}{2}$

18. 16; 2 R Q; $-\dfrac{3}{2}, -\dfrac{5}{2}$

19. -16; 2 Im; $3 \pm 2i$

20. 11,664; 2 R Q; 0, 36

21. -3; 2 Im; $\dfrac{1 \pm i\sqrt{3}}{2}$

22. -100; 2 Im; $-2 \pm 5i$

23. 41; 2 R I; $\dfrac{-3 \pm \sqrt{41}}{8}$; 0.43, -1.18

24. 97; 2 R I; $\dfrac{-5 \pm \sqrt{97}}{4}$; 1.21, -3.71

25. 0; 1 R Q; 4

26. 16; 2 RQ; $\dfrac{4}{7}, 0$

27. -4; 2 Im; $\dfrac{-3 \pm i}{2}$

28. 0; 1 R Q; $\dfrac{5}{3}$

29. -8; 2 Im; $\dfrac{2 \pm i\sqrt{2}}{3}$

30. -15; 2 Im; $\dfrac{-3 \pm i\sqrt{15}}{4}$

Additional Answers for Lesson 6-5

9. $\dfrac{3 \pm \sqrt{105}}{8}$

10. $\pm \dfrac{25}{2}$

11. $\dfrac{2}{9}$

12. $\dfrac{7 \pm \sqrt{37}}{2}$

EXTRA PRACTICE

Lesson 6-4 Find the value of the discriminant and describe the nature of the roots (real, complex, rational, irrational) of each quadratic equation. Then solve the equation. Express irrational roots as exact and approximate to the nearest hundredth. 1–30. See margin.

1. $x^2 + 7x + 13 = 0$
2. $6x^2 + 6x - 21 = 0$
3. $5x^2 - 5x + 4 = 0$
4. $16x^2 - 64x + 19 = 0$
5. $9x^2 + 42x + 49 = 0$
6. $4x^2 - 16x + 3 = 0$
7. $2x^2 = 5x + 3$
8. $x^2 + 81 = 18x$
9. $18x^2 = 6x^2 + 5$
10. $4x^2 = 49$
11. $3x^2 - 30x + 75 = 0$
12. $24x^2 + 10x = 43$
13. $9x^2 + 4 = 2x$
14. $7x = 8x^2$
15. $18x^2 = 9x + 45$
16. $y^2 - 4y + 4 = 0$
17. $4x^2 + 8x + 3 = 0$
18. $4y^2 + 16y + 15 = 0$
19. $y^2 - 6y + 13 = 0$
20. $3m^2 = 108m$
21. $x^2 - x + 1 = 0$
22. $n^2 + 4n + 29 = 0$
23. $4a^2 + 3a - 2 = 0$
24. $2x^2 + 5x = 9$
25. $n^2 = 8n - 16$
26. $7b^2 = 4b$
27. $2y^2 + 6y + 5 = 0$
28. $9a^2 - 30a + 25 = 0$
29. $3x^2 - 4x + 2 = 0$
30. $2x^2 + 3x + 3 = 0$

1. $x^2 - 2x - 63 = 0$ 2. $3x^2 - 11x + 6 = 0$ 3. $x^2 - 4x - 1 = 0$ 4. $9x^2 + 30x + 7 = 0$

Lesson 6-5 Write a quadratic equation that has the given roots.

1. $9, -7$
2. $\dfrac{2}{3}, 3$
3. $2 \pm \sqrt{5}$
4. $\dfrac{-5 \pm 3\sqrt{2}}{3}$
5. $17, 17$
6. $\dfrac{-6 \pm 2i\sqrt{3}}{5}$
7. $0, 8$
8. $\pm \dfrac{\sqrt{6}}{4}$

$x^2 - 34x + 289 = 0$ $25x^2 + 60x + 48 = 0$ $x^2 - 8x = 0$ $8x^2 - 3 = 0$

Solve each equation. Check by using the sum and product of the roots. 9–22. See margin.

9. $4x^2 - 3x - 6 = 0$
10. $4x^2 = 625$
11. $81x^2 + 4 = 36x$
12. $x^2 - 7x + 3 = 0$
13. $7x^2 + 3x + 1 = 3$
14. $6x^2 = 13x$
15. $5x^2 + 18x = 0$
16. $x^2 - 8x + 5 = 0$
17. $3x^2 - 16x - 12 = 0$
18. $9n^2 - 1 = 0$
19. $2x^2 - 7x = 15$
20. $15c^2 - 2c - 8 = 0$
21. $7s^2 + 5s - 1 = 0$
22. $12x^2 + 19x + 4 = 0$
23. $x^2 + x - 6 = 0$ $-3, 2$
24. $m^2 + 5m + 6 = 0$ $-3, -2$
25. $s^2 + 5s - 24 = 0$ $-8, 3$
26. $a^2 - 9a + 20 = 0$ 5, 4
27. $x^2 - 12x - 45 = 0$ $-3, 15$
28. $2m^2 - 10m + 9 = 0$ $\dfrac{5 \pm \sqrt{7}}{2}$
29. $3s^2 - 11 = 0$ $\dfrac{\pm\sqrt{33}}{3}$

1–21. See margin.

Lesson 6-6 Write each equation in the form $y = a(x - h)^2 + k$ if not already in that form. Then name the vertex, axis of symmetry, and direction of opening for the graph of each quadratic function.

1. $f(x) = -9(x - 7)^2 + 3$
2. $f(x) = (x + 6)^2 - 1$
3. $f(x) = 2(x - 8)^2 - 5$
4. $f(x) = -(x + 1)^2 + 7$
5. $f(x) = -x^2 + 10x - 3$
6. $f(x) = -2x^2 + 16x + 7$
7. $f(x) = 3x^2 + 9x + 8$
8. $f(x) = 8x^2 - 3x + 1$
9. $f(x) = \dfrac{3}{4}x^2 - 6x - 5$
10. $f(x) = x^2 - 2x + 4$
11. $f(x) = -3x^2 + 18x$
12. $f(x) = -2x^2 - 40x + 10$
13. $f(x) = 2x^2 - 8x + 9$
14. $f(x) = \dfrac{1}{3}x^2 + 2x + 7$
15. $f(x) = x^2 + 6x + 9$
16. $f(x) = x^2 + 3x + 6$
17. $f(x) = 2x^2 + 8x + 9$
18. $f(x) = x^2 - 8x + 9$
19. $f(x) = -x^2 - 10x + 10$
20. $f(x) = -\dfrac{2}{3}x^2 + 4x - 3$
21. $f(x) = -2x^2 - 8x - 1$

Write an equation for the parabola that passes through the given points. 23–30. See margin.

22. $(-1, 5), (2, -4), (5, 5)$
23. $(-3, 1), (-2, -1), (-1, -7)$
24. $(-5, -3), (-1, 5), (0, 9.5)$
25. $(0, -8), (2, -2), (4, -8)$
26. $(3, 0), (0, -9), (5, -4)$
27. $(-5, 5), (0, 0), (5, 5)$
28. $(0, -5), (-1, -7), (-4, -1)$
29. $(1, 5), (4, -4), (0, 0)$
30. $(1, 1.2), (0, 0.8), (-2, 3.6)$

890   Extra Practice

13. $\dfrac{-3 \pm \sqrt{65}}{14}$

14. $\dfrac{13}{6}, 0$

15. $0, -\dfrac{18}{5}$

16. $4 \pm \sqrt{11}$

17. $6, -\dfrac{2}{3}$

18. $\pm \dfrac{1}{3}$

19. $5, -\dfrac{3}{2}$

20. $\dfrac{4}{5}, -\dfrac{2}{3}$

21. $\dfrac{-5 \pm \sqrt{53}}{14}$

22. $-\dfrac{1}{4}, -\dfrac{4}{3}$

Lesson 6-7 Graph each inequality. 1–9. See Solutions Manual.

1. $y \le 5x^2 + 3x - 2$
2. $y \ge \frac{1}{2}x^2 - 4x$
3. $y > -3x^2 + 2$
4. $y \ge -x^2 - x + 3$
5. $y \le \frac{3}{8}x^2 + 2x - 1$
6. $y \le -5x^2 + 2x - 3$
7. $y > 4x^2 + x$
8. $y \ge -x^2 - 7$
9. $y < -\frac{2}{3}x^2 + x + 6$

Solve each inequality. 10–21. See margin.

10. $(x + 1)(x - 1) < 0$
11. $(2x + 3)(5x - 1) \ge 0$
12. $x^2 - 2x - 8 \le 0$
13. $-x^2 - 5x - 6 > 0$
14. $-3x^2 \ge 5$
15. $20x^2 + 9x + 1 < 0$
16. $2x^2 \ge 5x + 12$
17. $x^2 + 3x + 4 > 0$
18. $2x - x^2 \le -15$
19. $13x - 28x^2 + 6 < 0$
20. $3x^2 \le 36$
21. $x - x^2 \ge 1$

Lesson 6-8 Find the mean and standard deviation to the nearest hundredth for each set of data.

1. {86, 71, 74, 65, 45, 42, 76} 65.57; 15.15
2. {16, 20, 15, 14, 24, 23, 25, 10, 19} 18.44; 5.73
3. {18, 24, 16, 24, 22, 24, 22, 22, 24, 13, 17, 18, 16, 20, 16, 7, 22, 5, 4, 24} 17.9; 6.21
4. {364, 305, 217, 331, 305, 311, 352, 319, 272, 238, 311, 226, 220, 226, 215, 160, 123, 4, 24, 238, 99}
   4. 231.43; 98.74
5. {55, 50, 50, 55, 65, 50, 45, 35, 50, 40, 70, 40, 70, 50, 90, 30, 35, 55, 55, 40, 75, 35, 40, 45, 65, 50, 60}
   51.85; 13.75

6.

Stem	Leaf
130	1 1 3 9
131	7 7
132	1 2 3 5 6 7 7
133	0 0 1 3
134	1 3 4 4 5 6 8 9
135	0 1 1 1 4 5 8 9
136	1 3 5

130|3 = 13.03 13.37; 0.18

7.

Stem	Leaf
0	7 8
1	0 1 1 2 3 3 4 4 5 5 6 6 7 7 9 9
2	0 0 1 1 1 2 2 3 3 3 4 5

2|1 = 21 17.07; 4.94

Lesson 6-9

1. The diameters of metal fittings made by a machine are normally distributed. The mean diameter is 7.5 centimeters, and the standard deviation is 0.5 centimeters.
   a. What percentage of the fittings have diameters between 7.0 and 8.0 centimeters? 68%
   b. What percentage of the fittings have diameters between 7.5 and 8.0 centimeters? 34%
   c. What percentage of the fittings have diameters greater than 6.5 centimeters? 97.5%
   d. Of 100 fittings, how many will have a diameter between 6.0 and 8.5 centimeters? 97

2. The number of hours of television watched weekly by 3000 families is normally distributed. The mean is 22 hours and the standard deviation is 7.5 hours.
   a. How many families watch at least 22 hours of television per week? 1500
   b. How many families watch television between 7 and 29.5 hours per week? 2445
   c. What percent of the 3000 families watch more than 37 hours of television a week? 2.5%

3. The scores on a college entrance exam are normally distributed. The mean score is 510, and the standard deviation is 80. b. 34,000
   a. Of the 50,000 people who took the exam, how many scored above 510? 25,000
   b. Of the 50,000 people who took the exam, how many scored between 430 and 590?
   c. What percent of the people who took the exam scored below 670? 97.5%
   d. A student must score above 750 on the college entrance exam to qualify for a full scholarship at Carleton University. What percentage of the people who took the exam will qualify? 0.5%

Additional Answers for Lesson 6-6

1. (7, 3); $x = 7$; down
2. (−6, −1); $x = -6$; up
3. (8, −5); $x = 8$; up
4. (−1, 7); $x = -1$; down
5. $f(x) = -(x - 5)^2 + 22$; (5, 22); $x = 5$; down
6. $f(x) = -2(x - 4)^2 + 39$; (4, 39); $x = 4$; down
7. $f(x) = 3\left(x + \frac{3}{2}\right)^2 + \frac{5}{4}$; $\left(-\frac{3}{2}, \frac{5}{4}\right)$; $x = -\frac{3}{2}$; up
8. $f(x) = 8\left(x - \frac{3}{16}\right)^2 + \frac{23}{32}$; $\left(\frac{3}{16}, \frac{23}{32}\right)$; $x = \frac{3}{16}$; up
9. $f(x) = \frac{3}{4}(x - 4)^2 - 17$; (4, −17); $x = 4$; up
10. $f(x) = (x - 1)^2 + 3$; (1, 3); $x = 1$; up
11. $f(x) = -3(x - 3)^2 + 27$; (3, 27); $x = 3$; down
12. $f(x) = -2(x + 10)^2 + 210$; (−10, 210); $x = -10$; down
13. $f(x) = 2(x - 2)^2 + 1$; (2, 1); $x = 2$; up
14. $f(x) = \frac{1}{3}(x + 3)^2 + 4$; (−3, 4); $x = -3$; up
15. $f(x) = (x + 3)^2$; (−3, 0); $x = -3$; up
16. $f(x) = \left(x + \frac{3}{2}\right)^2 + \frac{15}{4}$; $\left(-\frac{3}{2}, \frac{15}{4}\right)$; $x = -\frac{3}{2}$; up
17. $f(x) = 2(x + 2)^2 + 1$; (−2, 1); $x = -2$; up
18. $f(x) = (x - 4)^2 - 7$; (4, −7); $x = 4$; up
19. $f(x) = -(x + 5)^2 + 35$; (−5, 35); $x = -5$; down
20. $f(x) = -\frac{2}{3}(x - 3)^2 + 3$; (3, 3); $x = 3$; down
21. $f(x) = -2(x + 2)^2 + 7$; (−2, 7); $x = -2$; down
22. $f(x) = (x - 2)^2 - 4$
23. $f(x) = -2(x + 3)^2 + 1$
24. $f(x) = \frac{1}{2}(x + 5)^2 - 3$
25. $f(x) = -\frac{3}{2}(x - 2)^2 - 2$
26. $f(x) = -(x - 3)^2$
27. $f(x) = \frac{1}{5}x^2$
28. $f(x) = x^2 + 3x - 5$
29. $f(x) = -2x^2 + 7x$
30. $f(x) = \frac{3}{5}x^2 - \frac{1}{5}x + \frac{4}{5}$

Additional Answers for Lesson 6-7

10. $\{x\Omega{-}1 < x < 1\}$
11. $\left\{x\Omega x \le -\frac{3}{2} \text{ or } x \ge \frac{1}{5}\right\}$
12. $\{x\Omega{-}2 \le x \le 4\}$
13. $\{x\Omega{-}3 < x < -2\}$
14. $\varnothing$
15. $\left\{x\Omega{-}\frac{1}{4} \le x \le -\frac{1}{5}\right\}$
16. $\left\{x\Omega x \le -\frac{3}{2} \text{ or } x \ge 4\right\}$
17. {all real numbers}
18. $\{x\Omega x \le -3 \text{ or } x \ge 5\}$
19. $\left\{x\Omega x < -\frac{2}{7} \text{ or } x > \frac{3}{4}\right\}$
20. $\left\{x\Omega{-}2\sqrt{3} \le x \le 2\sqrt{3}\right\}$
21. $\varnothing$

891

1. $(x - 3)^2 + (y - 2)^2 = 25$
2. $(x + 5)^2 + (y - 8)^2 = 9$
3. $(x - 1)^2 + (y + 6)^2 = \frac{4}{9}$
4. $x^2 + (y - 7)^2 = 6$
5. $(x - \sqrt{2})^2 + (y - 4)^2 = 81$
6. $(x + 8)^2 + (y + \sqrt{10})^2 = 121$
7. $(x - 0.8)^2 + (y - 0.5)^2 = 0.04$
8. $(x + 9)^2 + y^2 = \frac{25}{49}$
9. $(x - 4)^2 + (y - 1)^2 = 16$

EXTRA PRACTICE

Lesson 7-1   Use the distance formula to find the distance between each pair of points.

1. $(5, 7), (3, 19)$ $2\sqrt{37}$

2. $(-2, -1), (5, 3)$ $\sqrt{65}$

3. $(-3, 15), (7, -8)$ $\sqrt{629}$

4. $(6, -3), (-4, -9)$ $2\sqrt{34}$

5. $(3.89, -0.38), (4.04, -0.18)$ **0.25**

6. $(5\sqrt{3}, 2\sqrt{2}), (-11\sqrt{3}, -4\sqrt{2})$ $2\sqrt{210}$

Find the midpoint of each line segment whose endpoints are given.   9. $(-17.5, -25)$

7. $(7, -3), (-11, 13)$ $(-2, 5)$

8. $(16, 29), (-7, 2)$ $(4.5, 15.5)$

9. $(43, -18), (-78, -32)$

10. $(-7.54, 3.42), (4.89, -9.28)$ $(-1.325, -2.93)$

11. $(-8, 4.19), (0.34, 20)$ $(-3.83, 12.095)$

12. $(684, -239), (528, -735)$ $(606, -487)$

14. −18 or 30   15. −10 or 40   16. 0 or −14

Find the value of p so that each pair of points is 25 units apart.

13. $(p, 3), (8, 27)$ **15 or 1**

14. $(5, p), (-2, 6)$

15. $(15, -8), (p, -8)$

16. $(-17, -7), (7, p)$

17. $(8, p), (-3, -5)$ about −27.45 or about 17.45

18. $(p, -16), (25, 13)$ no real solution

19. $(-6.8, p), (3.7, -8.9)$ about 13.79 or about −31.59

20. $(p, -28), (-29, -35)$ −5 or −53

Given the coordinates of an endpoint of $\overline{AB}$ and its midpoint M, find the coordinates of the other endpoint.

21. $A(5, -16), M(-13, 2)$

   $B(-31, 20)$

22. $M(7.3, 2.8), B(-8.9, -3.4)$

   $A(23.5, 9)$

23. $M\left(\frac{5}{8}, \frac{7}{12}\right), A\left(\frac{2}{3}, \frac{5}{4}\right)$

   $B\left(\frac{7}{12}, -\frac{1}{12}\right)$

Lesson 7-2   Name the vertex, axis of symmetry, focus, directrix, and direction of opening of the parabola with the given equation. Then find the length of the latus rectum and graph the parabola.

1. $y + \frac{3}{4} = x^2$

2. $\frac{y}{5} = (x + 2)^2$

3. $4(y + 2) = 3(x - 1)^2$

4. $5x + 3y^2 = 15$

5. $y = 2x^2 - 8x + 7$

6. $x = 2y^2 - 8y + 7$

7. $3(x - 8)^2 = 5(y + 3)$

8. $x = 3(y + 4)^2 + 1$

9. $8y + 5x^2 + 15x + 9 = 0$

10. $x = -\frac{1}{5}y^2 + \frac{8}{5}y - 7$

11. $6x = y^2 - 6y + 39$

12. $-8y = x^2$

13. $(x + 3)^2 = \frac{1}{4}(y - 2)$

14. $y = x^2 - 6x + 33$

15. $y = x^2 + 4x + 1$

16. $4(x - 2) = (y + 3)^2$

17. $(y - 8)^2 = -4(x - 4)$

18. $6x = y^2 + 4y + 4$

1–18. See Solutions Manual.

1–9. See margin.

Lesson 7-3   Write an equation for each circle whose center and radius are given.

1. center $(3, 2), r = 5$ units

2. center $(-5, 8), r = 3$ units

3. center $(1, -6), r = \frac{2}{3}$ units

4. center $(0, 7), r = \sqrt{6}$ units

5. center $(\sqrt{2}, 4), r = 9$ units

6. center $(-8, -\sqrt{10}), r = 11$ units

7. center $(0.8, 0.5), r = 0.2$ units

8. center $(-9, 0), r = \frac{5}{7}$ units

9. center $(4, 1), r = 4$ units

10–20. See Solutions Manual.

Find the center and radius of each circle whose equation is given. Then draw the graph.

10. $x^2 + y^2 = 36$

11. $(x - 5)^2 + (y + 4)^2 = 1$

12. $x^2 + 3x + y^2 - 5y = \frac{1}{2}$

13. $x^2 + y^2 = 14x - 24$

14. $x^2 + y^2 = 2(y - x)$

15. $x^2 + 10x + (y - \sqrt{3})^2 = 11$

16. $x^2 + y^2 = 4x + 9$

17. $x^2 + y^2 + 12x - 10y + 45 = 0$

18. $x^2 + y^2 - 6x + 4y = 156$

19. $x^2 + y^2 - 2(\sqrt{5}x - \sqrt{7}y) = 1$

20. $16(x^2 + y^2) - 8(3x + 5y) + 33 = 0$

Lesson 7-4 Find the coordinates of the center and foci, and the lengths of the major and minor axes for each ellipse whose equation is given. Then draw the graph. **1–20. See Solutions Manual.**

1. $\frac{x^2}{36} + \frac{y^2}{81} = 1$

2. $\frac{x^2}{121} + \frac{(y-5)^2}{16} = 1$

3. $\frac{(x+2)^2}{12} + \frac{(y+1)^2}{16} = 1$

4. $\frac{(x-5)^2}{25} + \frac{(y+3)^2}{75} = 1$

5. $\frac{x^2}{9} + \frac{y^2}{36} = 1$

6. $\frac{(x-8)^2}{4} + \frac{(y+8)^2}{1} = 1$

7. $\frac{(x+2)^2}{36} + \frac{(y-4)^2}{40} = 1$

8. $\frac{(x+8)^2}{121} + \frac{(y-7)^2}{64} = 1$

9. $\frac{(x-4)^2}{16} + \frac{(y+1)^2}{9} = 1$

10. $8x^2 + 2y^2 = 32$

11. $7x^2 + 3y^2 = 84$

12. $9x^2 + 16y^2 = 144$

13. $169x^2 - 338x + 169 + 25y^2 = 4225$

14. $x^2 + 4y^2 + 8x - 64y + 236 = 0$

15. $4x^2 + 5y^2 = 4(6x + 5y + 111)$

16. $169x^2 + y^2 + 2366x = 4y - 8116$

17. $2x^2 + y^2 - 4x + 8y - 6 = 0$

18. $4x^2 + 9y^2 + 24x - 90y = -225$

19. $9x^2 + 10y^2 + 54x + 20y = -1$

20. $9x^2 + 16y^2 - 54x + 64y + 1 = 0$

Lesson 7-5 Find the coordinates of the vertices and foci and the slopes of the asymptotes for each hyperbola whose equation is given. Then draw the graph. **1–20. See Solutions Manual.**

1. $\frac{y^2}{25} - \frac{x^2}{9} = 1$

2. $\frac{x^2}{4} - \frac{y^2}{9} = 1$

3. $\frac{x^2}{81} - \frac{y^2}{36} = 1$

4. $\frac{x^2}{9} - \frac{y^2}{16} = 1$

5. $\frac{y^2}{100} - \frac{x^2}{144} = 1$

6. $\frac{x^2}{16} - \frac{y^2}{4} = 1$

7. $\frac{(x-4)^2}{64} - \frac{(y+1)^2}{16} = 1$

8. $\frac{(y-7)^2}{2.25} - \frac{(x-3)^2}{4} = 1$

9. $(x+5)^2 - \frac{(y+3)^2}{48} = 1$

10. $x^2 - 9y^2 = 36$

11. $4x^2 - 9y^2 = 36$

12. $49x^2 - 16y^2 = 784$

13. $144x^2 + 1152x - 25y^2 - 100y = 1396$

14. $576y^2 = 49x^2 + 490x + 29449$

15. $23.04y^2 - 46.08y - 1.96x^2 - 3.92x = 24.0784$

16. $25(y+5)^2 - 20(x-1)^2 = 500$

17. $16x^2 - y^2 + 96x + 8y + 112 = 0$

18. $y^2 - 4x^2 - 2y - 16x + 1 = 0$

19. $(y-1)^2 - 4(x-2)^2 = 168$

20. $3x^2 - 12y^2 + 45x + 60y = -60$

Lesson 7-6 Write each equation in standard form. State whether the graph of the equation is a *parabola*, a *circle*, an *ellipse*, or a *hyperbola*. Then graph the equation. **1–20. See Solutions Manual.**

1. $9x^2 - 36x + 36 = 4y^2 + 24y + 72$

2. $x^2 + 4x + 2y^2 + 16y + 32 = 0$

3. $x^2 + 6x + y^2 - 6y + 9 = 0$

4. $9y^2 = 25x^2 + 400x + 1825$

5. $2y^2 + 12y - x + 6 = 0$

6. $x^2 + y^2 = 10x + 2y + 23$

7. $3x^2 + y = 12x - 17$

8. $9x^2 - 18x + 16y^2 + 160y = -265$

9. $x^2 + 10x + 5 = 4y^2 + 16$

10. $\frac{(y-5)^2}{4} - (x+1)^2 = 4$

11. $9x^2 + 49y^2 = 441$

12. $4x^2 - y^2 = 4$

13. $x^2 + 4x + y^2 - 8y = 2$

14. $(x+3)^2 = 8(y+2)$

15. $9x^2 + 9y^2 = 9$

16. $y - x^2 = x + 3$

17. $2x^2 - 13y^2 + 5 = 0$

18. $16(x-3)^2 + 81(y+4)^2 = 1296$

19. $4x^2 - y^2 = 16$

20. $x^2 + 5y^2 = 16$

10.

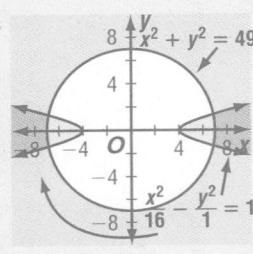

11.

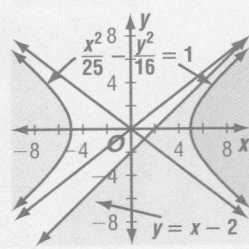

12.

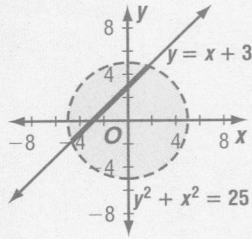

13.

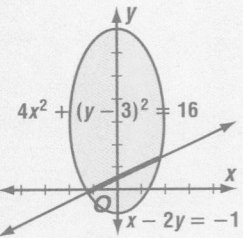

1. $(x^3 - x^2 + x + 6) =$
   $(x^2 - 3x + 7)(x + 2) -8$; no
2. $(5x^3 - 17x^2 + 6x + 2) =$
   $(5x^2 - 2x)(x - 3) + 2$; no
3. $(2x^3 - 4x^2 + 3x - 6) =$
   $(2x^2 + 4x + 19)(x - 4) +$
   70; no
4. $(x^3 - 8) = (x^2 + 2x + 4)$
   $(x - 2) + 0$; yes
5. $(x^2 + 6x - 3) = (x + 5)$
   $(x + 1) - 8$; no
6. $(x^4 + x^3 + x^2 + x + 1) =$
   $(x^3 + x)(x + 1) + 1$; no

EXTRA PRACTICE

Lesson 7-7 Solve each system of equations algebraically. Check your solutions with a graphing calculator. 3. $(\pm\sqrt{15}, 2), (\pm\sqrt{111}, 10)$

1. $4y = x^2 - 4$
   $x^2 + y^2 = 9$ $(\pm 2\sqrt{2}, 1)$

2. $x = y^2$
   $(x + 3)^2 + y^2 = 53$ $(4, \pm 2)$

3. $\frac{x^2}{3} - \frac{(y + 2)^2}{4} = 1$
   $x^2 = y^2 + 11$

4. $\frac{(x - 1)^2}{5} + \frac{y^2}{2} = 1$
   $y = x + 1$

5. $x^2 + y^2 = 13$
   $x^2 - y^2 = -5$ $(\pm 2, \pm 3)$

6. $\frac{x^2}{25} - \frac{y^2}{5} = 1$
   $y = x^2 - 4$ no solution

7. $x^2 + y = 0$
   $x + y = -2$ $(-1, -1), (2, -4)$

8. $x^2 - 9y^2 = 36$
   $x = y$ no solution

9. $5x^2 + y^2 = 30$
   $y^2 - 16 = 9x^2$ $(\pm 1, \pm 5)$

4. $\left(\frac{-3 + \sqrt{30}}{7}, \frac{4 + \sqrt{30}}{7}\right), \left(\frac{-3 - \sqrt{30}}{7}, \frac{4 - \sqrt{30}}{7}\right)$

Solve each system of inequalities by graphing. 10–13. See margin.

10. $\frac{x^2}{16} - \frac{y^2}{1} \geq 1$
    $x^2 + y^2 \geq 49$

11. $\frac{x^2}{25} - \frac{y^2}{16} \geq 1$
    $y \leq x - 2$

12. $y = x + 3$
    $x^2 + y^2 < 25$

13. $4x^2 + (y - 3)^2 \leq 16$
    $x - 2y = -1$

Lesson 8-1 Find $p(5)$ and $p(-1)$ for each function. 2. $-54; -12$ 3. $3165; 9$

1. $p(x) = 7x - 3$ $32; -10$
2. $p(x) = -3x^2 + 5x - 4$
3. $p(x) = 5x^4 + 2x^2 - 2x$
4. $p(x) = -13x^3 + 5x^2 - 3x + 2$
   $-1513; 23$
5. $p(x) = x^6 - 2$ $15,623; -1$
6. $p(x) = \frac{2}{3}x^2 + 5x$ $\frac{125}{3}; -\frac{13}{3}$

Find $g(a - 2)$ for each function.

7. $g(x) = 7x - 3$
   $7a - 17$
8. $g(x) = 3x + 5$
   $3a - 1$
9. $g(x) = -(x + 2)^2 + 8$
   $-a^2 + 8$
10. $g(x) = -2x^3 + 5x$
    $-2a^3 + 12a^2 - 19a + 6$

Find $-3[f(x)]$ for each function.

11. $f(x) = 4x^2 + 3x - 7$
    $-12x^2 - 9x + 21$
12. $f(x) = \frac{x}{6} - \frac{2x^3}{9} + 1$
    $\frac{2x^3}{3} - \frac{x}{2} - 3$
13. $f(x) = 5(x^2 + 2x)$
    $-15x^2 - 30x$
14. $f(x) = 8 - x$
    $3x - 24$

Lesson 8-2 Divide using synthetic division and write your answer in the form *dividend = quotient · divisor + remainder*. Is the binomial a factor of the polynomial?

1. $(x^3 - x^2 + x + 6) \div (x + 2)$
2. $(5x^3 - 17x^2 + 6x + 2) \div (x - 3)$
3. $(2x^3 - 4x^2 + 3x - 6) \div (x - 4)$
4. $(x^3 - 8) \div (x - 2)$
5. $(x^2 + 6x - 3) \div (x + 1)$
6. $(x^4 + x^3 + x^2 + x + 1) \div (x + 1)$
1–6. See margin.

Use synthetic substitution to find $g(3)$ and $g(-2)$ for each function.

7. $g(x) = 3x^5 - 5x^3 + 2x - 8$ $592; -68$
8. $g(x) = -2x^4 + 7x^3 + 8x^2 - 3x + 5$ $95; -45$
9. $g(x) = 10x^3 + 2$ $272; -78$
10. $g(x) = x^5 + x^4 + x^3 + x^2 + x + 1$ $364; -21$

Given a polynomial and one of its factors, find the remaining factors of the polynomial. Some factors may not be binomials. 12. $(3x^2 + 8x - 5)(2x + 3)$ 13. $(x^2 + 3x + 9)(x + 5)$ 14. $(x - 6)(x - 4)$

11. $(x^3 - 8x^2 + x + 42); (x - 7)$ $(x - 3)(x + 2)$
12. $(6x^4 + 13x^3 - 36x^2 - 43x + 30); (x - 2)$
13. $(x^4 + 5x^3 - 27x - 135); (x - 3)$
14. $(2x^3 - 15x^2 - 2x + 120); (2x + 5)$

Lesson 8-3 Approximate the real zeros of each function to the nearest tenth.

1. $f(x) = x^3 - 3x^2 + 8x - 7$ 1.2
2. $f(x) = 2x^5 + 3x^4 - 8x^2 + x + 4$ -0.7
3. $f(x) = x^4 - 5x^3 + 6x^2 - x - 2$ $-0.4, 3.4$
4. $f(x) = 2x^6 + 5x^4 - 3x^2 - 5$ ± 1.0
5. $f(x) = -x^3 - 8x^2 + 3x - 7$ -8.5
6. $f(x) = -x^4 - 3x^3 + 5x$ $0, 1.1$
7. $f(x) = x^5 - 7x^4 - 3x^3 + 2x^2 - 4x + 9$
   $-1.3, 0.9, 7.4$
8. $f(x) = x^4 - 5x^3 + x^2 - x - 3$ $-0.7, 4.9$

Graph each function.   9–16. See Solutions Manual.

9. $f(x) = \dfrac{x^3}{20} + \dfrac{x^2}{40} - 3x + \dfrac{1}{2}$
10. $f(x) = -\dfrac{x^4}{20} - \dfrac{x^3}{2} + \dfrac{3x^2}{4} + 11x + \dfrac{5}{4}$
11. $f(x) = x^4 - 128x^2 + 960$
12. $f(x) = -x^5 + x^4 - 208x^2 + 145x + 9$
13. $f(x) = x^5 - 452x^3 - 183x + 25$
14. $f(x) = 5x^3 - 27x^2 - 37x + 54$
15. $f(x) = 2x^4 - 7x^3 - 19x^2 + 22x + 78$
16. $f(x) = -x^3 + 8x^2 + 12x - 16$

Lesson 8-4 State the number of positive real zeros, negative real zeros, and imaginary zeros for each function.   1. 3 or 1; 3 or 1; 2, 4 or 6   6. 0; 6, 4, 2, or 0; 0, 2, 4, or 6

1. $f(x) = 5x^8 - x^6 + 7x^4 - 8x^2 - 3$
2. $f(x) = 6x^5 - 7x^2 + 5$ 2 or 0; 1; 2 or 4
3. $f(x) = -2x^6 - 5x^5 + 8x^2 - 3x + 1$ 3 or 1; 1; 2 or 4
4. $f(x) = 4x^3 + x^2 - 38x + 56$ 2 or 0; 1; 0 or 2
5. $f(x) = 3x^8 - 15x^5 - 7x^4 - 8x^3 - 3$ 1; 3 or 1; 4 or 6
6. $f(x) = -x^6 - 8x^5 - 5x^4 - 11x^3 - 2x^2 - 5x - 1$
7. $f(x) = 3x^4 - 5x^3 + 2x^2 - 7x + 5$
   4, 2, or 0; 0; 0, 2, or 4
8. $f(x) = x^5 - x^4 + 7x^3 - 25x^2 + 8x - 13$
   5, 3, or 1; 0; 0, 2, or 4

Given a function and one of its zeros, find all of the zeros of the function.

9. $f(x) = x^3 - 7x^2 + 16x - 10; 3 - i$ $3 + i, 1$
10. $f(x) = x^3 - 4x^2 + 6x - 4; 2$ $1 \pm i$
11. $f(x) = x^3 - 16x^2 + 79x - 114; 5 - \sqrt{6}$ $5 + \sqrt{6}, 6$
12. $f(x) = -3x^3 + 6x^2 + 5x - 8; 1$ $\dfrac{3 \pm \sqrt{105}}{6}$
13. $f(x) = 45x^4 - 222x^3 + 209x^2 - 138x - 104; \dfrac{2}{3} + i$ $\dfrac{2}{3} - i, 4, -\dfrac{2}{5}$
14. $f(x) = 4x^4 + 36x^3 + 57x^2 + 225x + 200; -\dfrac{5}{2}i$ $\dfrac{5}{2}i, -8, -1$
15. $f(x) = -x^4 + 6x^3 - 19x^2 + 42x - 10; 1 + 3i$ $1 - 3i, 2 \pm \sqrt{3}$

Lesson 8-5 List all possible rational zeros for each function.   1–4. See margin.

1. $f(x) = 3x^5 - 7x^3 - 8x + 6$
2. $f(x) = 4x^3 + 2x^2 - 5x + 8$
3. $f(x) = 6x^9 - 7$
4. $f(x) = 12x^4 + 3x^2 - 8x - 100$

Find all the rational zeros for each function.

5. $f(x) = x^4 + 3x^3 - 7x^2 - 27x - 18$ $\pm 3, -1, -2$
6. $f(x) = 6x^4 - 31x^3 - 119x^2 + 214x + 560$
7. $f(x) = 20x^4 - 16x^3 + 11x^2 - 12x - 3$
8. $f(x) = 2x^4 - 30x^3 + 117x^2 - 75x + 280$ 7, 8
9. $f(x) = 3x^5 - 17x^4 + 33x^3 - 19x^2 - 31x + 21$ 3
10. $f(x) = 2x^6 - 12x^5 + 17x^4 + 6x^3 - 10x^2 + 6x - 9$
11. $f(x) = 48x^5 + 16x^4 - 24x^3 - 8x^2 + 3x + 1$
12. $f(x) = x^5 - x^4 + x^3 + 3x^2 - x$ 0

6. $-\dfrac{5}{2}, -2, \dfrac{8}{3}, 7$ 7. $1, -\dfrac{1}{5}$ 10. $3, \pm 1$ 11. $\pm\dfrac{1}{2}, -\dfrac{1}{3}$

Find all the zeros of each function.   13–16. See margin.

13. $f(x) = 90x^4 - 99x^3 - 64x^2 + 36x + 16$
14. $f(x) = 2x^4 - 13x^3 - 34x^2 + 65x + 120$
15. $f(x) = 6x^4 + 5x^3 - 8x^2 - 45x - 14$
16. $f(x) = 4x^4 + 19x^2 - 63$

Additional Answers for Lesson 8-5

1. $\pm 1, \pm\dfrac{1}{3}, \pm\dfrac{2}{3}, \pm 2, \pm 6$

2. $\pm 1, \pm 2, \pm 4, \pm 8, \pm\dfrac{1}{2}, \pm\dfrac{1}{4}$

3. $\pm 1, \pm 7, \pm\dfrac{1}{6}, \pm\dfrac{7}{6}, \pm\dfrac{1}{2}, \pm\dfrac{7}{2},$
 $\pm\dfrac{1}{3}, \pm\dfrac{7}{3}$

4. $\pm 1, \pm 2, \pm 4, \pm 5, \pm 10, \pm 20,$
 $\pm 25, \pm 50, \pm 100, \pm\dfrac{1}{2}, \pm\dfrac{5}{2},$
 $\pm\dfrac{25}{2}, \pm\dfrac{1}{3}, \pm\dfrac{2}{3}, \pm\dfrac{4}{3}, \pm\dfrac{5}{3}, \pm\dfrac{10}{3},$
 $\pm\dfrac{20}{3}, \pm\dfrac{25}{3}, \pm\dfrac{50}{3}, \pm\dfrac{100}{3}, \pm\dfrac{1}{4},$
 $\pm\dfrac{5}{4}, \pm\dfrac{25}{4}, \pm\dfrac{1}{6}, \pm\dfrac{5}{6}, \pm\dfrac{25}{6}, \pm\dfrac{1}{12},$
 $\pm\dfrac{5}{12}, \pm\dfrac{25}{12}$

13. $\dfrac{4}{3}, -\dfrac{2}{5}, -\dfrac{1}{2}, \dfrac{2}{3}$

14. $8, -\dfrac{3}{2}, \sqrt{5}, -\sqrt{5}$

15. $2, -\dfrac{1}{3}, \dfrac{-5 + i\sqrt{31}}{4}, \dfrac{-5 - i\sqrt{31}}{4}$

16. $\dfrac{3}{2}, -\dfrac{3}{2}, i\sqrt{7}, -i\sqrt{7}$

1. $5\left(x^5\right)^2 - 6\left(x^5\right) - 3 = 0$

2. $3\left(\sqrt{r}\right)^2 + 2\left(\sqrt{r}\right) - 7 = 0$

3. impossible; $\left(z^3\right)^2 \neq z^9$

4. impossible; $\left(y^4\right)^2 \neq y^6$

5. $\left(x^{\frac{1}{2}}\right)^2 - 10\left(x^{\frac{1}{2}}\right) + 25 = 0$

6. $\left(x^{\frac{2}{3}}\right)^2 - 7\left(x^{\frac{2}{3}}\right) + 12 = 0$

7. $\left(y^{\frac{1}{4}}\right)^2 - 10\left(y^{\frac{1}{4}}\right) + 16 = 0$

8. $\left(r^{\frac{1}{3}}\right)^2 - 5\left(r^{\frac{1}{3}}\right) + 6 = 0$

9. $\left(x^{\frac{1}{4}}\right)^2 + 7\left(x^{\frac{1}{4}}\right) + 12 = 0$

10. $-\dfrac{3}{2}, \dfrac{3 \pm 3i\sqrt{3}}{4}$

11. $1, -\dfrac{64}{125}$

12. $\pm i, \pm \dfrac{\sqrt{10}}{2}$

13. $0, 0, 0, \pm \dfrac{\sqrt{21}}{3}$

14. $0, -2, -8$

15. $\pm 1, \pm\sqrt{2}$

16. $5, \dfrac{-5 \pm 5i\sqrt{3}}{2}$

17. $64, 1$

18. $8, 1000$

19. $27, 125$

20. $25, 36$

21. $\sqrt[3]{16}$

22. $8, \dfrac{64}{27}$

23. $\dfrac{4}{9}$

24. $16, 256$

896

Lesson 8-6 Write each equation in quadratic form if possible. If not, explain why not.

1. $5x^{10} - 6x^5 = 3$

2. $3r + 2\sqrt{r} - 7 = 0$

3. $z^9 = 8z^3$

4. $2y^6 + 3y^4 = 10$

5. $x - 10x^{\frac{1}{2}} + 25 = 0$

6. $x^{\frac{4}{3}} - 7x^{\frac{2}{3}} + 12 = 0$

7. $y^{\frac{1}{2}} - 10y^{\frac{1}{4}} + 16 = 0$

8. $r^{\frac{2}{3}} - 5r^{\frac{1}{3}} + 6 = 0$

9. $x^{\frac{1}{2}} + 7x^{\frac{1}{4}} + 12 = 0$

1–9. See margin.

Solve each equation.

10. $8x^3 + 27 = 0$

11. $5\sqrt[3]{z^2} - \sqrt[3]{z} = 4$

12. $2m^4 = 3m^2 + 5$

13. $3b^5 = 7b^3$

14. $x^3 + 10x^2 + 16x = 0$

15. $y^4 - 3y^2 + 2 = 0$

16. $a^3 = 125$

17. $m - 9\sqrt{m} + 8 = 0$

18. $r^{\frac{2}{3}} - 12r^{\frac{1}{3}} + 20 = 0$

19. $x^{\frac{2}{3}} - 8x^{\frac{1}{3}} + 15 = 0$

20. $m - 11m^{\frac{1}{2}} + 30 = 0$

21. $y^3 - 8y^{\frac{3}{2}} + 16 = 0$

22. $3g^{\frac{2}{3}} - 10g^{\frac{1}{3}} + 8 = 0$

23. $3m + m^{\frac{1}{2}} - 2 = 0$

24. $x^{\frac{1}{2}} - 6x^{\frac{1}{4}} + 8 = 0$

10–24. See margin.

Lesson 8-7 Find $[f \circ g](-4)$ and $[g \circ f](-4)$.

1. $f(x) = 3x + 5$
   $g(x) = x - 3$ $-16; -10$

2. $f(x) = \sqrt{x}$
   $g(x) = x^2$ $4; -4$

3. $f(x) = 2x^2 - 5x + 8$
   $g(x) = \dfrac{x - 8}{3}$ $60; \dfrac{52}{3}$

4. $f(x) = \{(-4, 2), (0, 5), (3, 7)\}$
   $g(x) = \{(-4, 0), (-3, 8), (2, 3)\}$
   $5; 3$

5. $f(x) = \{(3, 2), (1, -7), (-4, 0)\}$
   $g(x) = \{(-4, 1), (0, 11)\}$
   $-7; 11$

6. $f(x) = x^2 + 1$
   $g(x) = x + 1$
   $10; 18$

Find $g[h(x)]$ and $h[g(x)]$.

7. $g(x) = 8 - 2x$
   $h(x) = 3x$
   $8 - 6x; 24 - 6x$

8. $g(x) = x^2 - 7$
   $h(x) = 3x + 2$
   $9x^2 + 12x - 3; 3x^2 - 19$

9. $g(x) = 2x + 7$
   $h(x) = \dfrac{x - 7}{2}$
   $x; x$

10. $g(x) = |2x + 3|$
    $h(x) = 5 - 3x$
    $|13 - 6x|; 5 - 3|2x + 3|$

If $f(x) = x^2$, $g(x) = 3x$, and $h(x) = x - 1$, find each value.

11. $g[f(1)]$ 3

12. $[f \circ h](3)$ 4

13. $[h \circ f](3)$ 8

14. $[g \circ f](-2)$ 12

15. $g[h(-20]$ -63

16. $f[h(-3)]$ 16

17. $g[f(x)]$ $3x^2$

18. $[f \circ (g \circ h)](x)$
    $9x^2 - 18x + 9$

Lesson 8-8 Find the inverse of each relation and determine whether the inverse is a function.

1. $\{(-2, 7), (3, 0), (5, -8)\}$
   $\{(7, -2), (0, 3), (-8, 5)\}$; yes

2. $\{(-3, 9), (-2, 4), (3, 9), (-1, 1)\}$
   $\{(9, -3), (4, -2), (9, 3), (1, -1)\}$; no

3. $\{(1, 5), (2, 3), (4, 3), (-1, 5)\}$
   $\{(5, 1), (3, 2), (3, 4), (5, -1)\}$; no

Find the inverse of each function. Then graph the function and its inverse.

4. $f(x) = x - 5$

5. $y = 2x + 8$

6. $g(x) = 2x^2 - 3$

7. $h(x) = \dfrac{x}{5} + 1$

8. $y = -2$

9. $g(x) = 5 - 2x$

10. $y = -x^2 + 2$

11. $h(x) = -\dfrac{2}{3}x$

4–11. See Solutions Manual.

Determine whether each pair of functions are inverse functions. Write *yes* or *no*.

12. $f(x) = \dfrac{2x - 3}{5}$
    $g(x) = \dfrac{3x - 5}{3}$ no

13. $f(x) = 5x - 6$
    $g(x) = \dfrac{x + 6}{5}$ yes

14. $f(x) = 6 - 3x$
    $g(x) = 2 - \dfrac{1}{3}x$ yes

15. $f(x) = 3x - 7$
    $g(x) = \dfrac{1}{3}x + 7$ no

Lesson 9-1 State the equations of the vertical and horizontal asymptotes for each rational function. **3.** $x = -1$, $x = 8$, $y = 0$

1. $f(x) = \frac{1}{x + 4}$ $x = -4$, $y = 0$

2. $f(x) = \frac{x - 2}{x + 3}$ $x = -3$, $y = 1$

3. $f(x) = \frac{5}{(x + 1)(x - 8)}$

4. $f(x) = \frac{x}{x + 2}$ $x = -2$, $y = 1$

5. $f(x) = \frac{x^2 - 4}{x + 2}$ $x = -2$, none

6. $f(x) = \frac{-4}{x}$ $x = 0$, $y = 0$

Graph each rational function.   7–15. See margin.

7. $f(x) = \frac{1}{x - 5}$

8. $f(x) = \frac{3x}{x + 1}$

9. $f(x) = \frac{x^2 - 9}{x - 3}$

10. $f(x) = \frac{x}{x - 6}$

11. $f(x) = \frac{1}{(x - 3)^2}$

12. $f(x) = \frac{2}{(x + 3)(x - 4)}$

13. $f(x) = \frac{x + 4}{x^2 - 1}$

14. $f(x) = \frac{x + 2}{x + 3}$

15. $f(x) = \frac{4}{x}$

Lesson 9-2 State whether each equation represents a direct, inverse, or joint variation. Then name the constant of variation.

1. $xy = 10$ inverse, 10

2. $x = 6y$ direct, $\frac{1}{6}$

3. $\frac{x}{7} = y$ direct, $\frac{1}{7}$

4. $\frac{x}{y} = -6$ direct, $-\frac{1}{6}$

5. $10x = y$ direct, 10

6. $x = \frac{2}{y}$ inverse, 2

7. $A = \ell w$ joint, 1

8. $\frac{1}{4}b = -\frac{3}{5}c$ direct, $-\frac{5}{12}$

9. $D = rt$ joint, 1

Write an equation for each statement. Then solve the equation.

10. If y varies directly as x and $y = 16$ when $x = 4$, find y when $x = 12$. $y = 4x$, 48

11. If x varies inversely as y and $x = 12$ when $y = -3$, find x when $y = -18$. $xy = -36$, 2

12. If m varies directly as w and $m = -15$ when $w = 2.5$, find m when $w = 12.5$. $m = -6w$, -75

13. If y varies jointly as x and z and $y = 10$ when $z = 4$ and $x = 5$, find y when $x = 4$ and $z = 2$. $y = \frac{1}{2}xz$, 4

14. If y varies inversely as x and $y = \frac{1}{4}$ when $x = 24$, find y when $x = \frac{3}{4}$. $xy = 6$, 8

15. If y varies jointly as x and z and $y = 45$ when $x = 9$ and $z = 15$, find y when $x = 25$ and $z = 12$. $y = \frac{1}{3}xz$, 100

Lesson 9-3 Simplify each expression.   **11.** $\frac{(x + y)(x^2 + y^2)}{(x^2 - xy + y^2)(x^2 + xy + y^2)}$

1. $\frac{3x^3}{-2} \cdot \frac{-4}{9x}$ $\frac{2x^2}{3}$

2. $\frac{21x^2}{-5} \cdot \frac{10}{7x^3}$ $\frac{-6}{x}$

3. $\frac{2u^2}{3} \div \frac{6u^3}{5}$ $\frac{5}{9u}$

4. $\frac{15x^3}{14} \div \frac{18x}{7}$ $\frac{5x^2}{12}$

5. $\frac{xy^2}{2} \cdot \frac{x^2}{2y} \cdot \frac{2}{x^2y}$ $\frac{x}{2}$

6. $axy \div \frac{ax}{y} \div \frac{ay}{x}$ $\frac{xy}{a}$

7. $\frac{9u^2}{28v} \div \frac{27u^2}{8v^2} \div \frac{4u^2}{21}$ $\frac{v}{2u^2}$

8. $\frac{x^2 - 4}{4x^2 - 1} \cdot \frac{2x - 1}{x + 2}$ $\frac{x - 2}{2x + 1}$

9. $\frac{x^2 - 1}{2x^2 - x - 1} \div \frac{x^2 - 4}{2x^2 - 3x - 2}$ $\frac{x + 1}{x + 2}$

10. $\frac{2x^2 + x - 1}{2x^2 + 3x - 2} \div \frac{x^2 - 2x + 1}{x^2 + x - 2}$ $\frac{x + 1}{x - 1}$

11. $\frac{\dfrac{x^4 - y^4}{x^3 + y^3}}{\dfrac{x^3 - y^3}{x + y}}$

14.

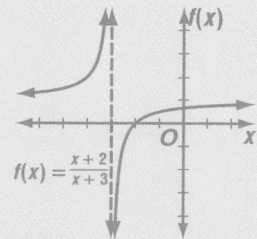

$f(x) = \frac{x + 2}{x + 3}$

15.

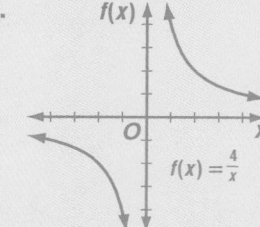

$f(x) = \frac{4}{x}$

Additional Answers for Lesson 9-1

7.

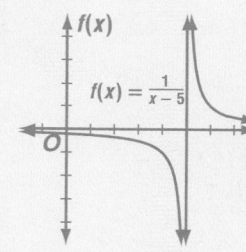

$f(x) = \frac{1}{x - 5}$

8.

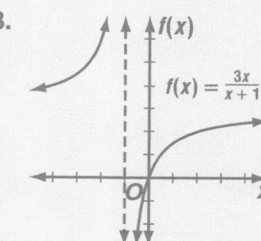

$f(x) = \frac{3x}{x + 1}$

9.

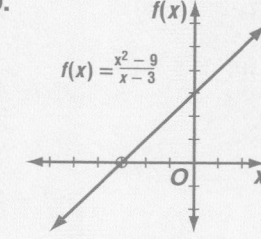

$f(x) = \frac{x^2 - 9}{x - 3}$

10.

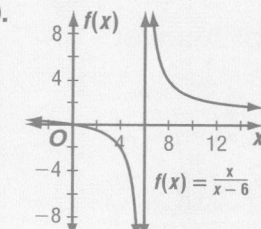

$f(x) = \frac{x}{x - 6}$

11.

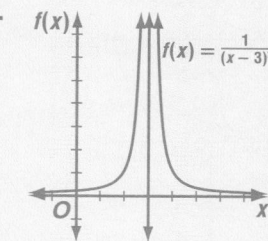

$f(x) = \frac{1}{(x - 3)^2}$

12.

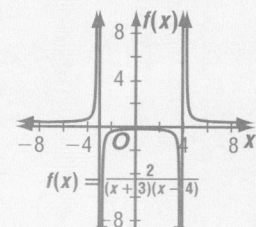

$f(x) = \frac{2}{(x + 3)(x - 4)}$

13.

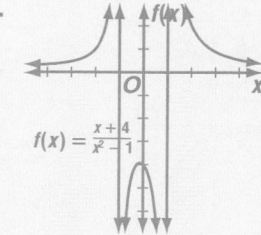

$f(x) = \frac{x + 4}{x^2 - 1}$

Additional Answers for Lesson 9-4

6. $\dfrac{(2u + 3v)^2}{12u^2v^2}$

7. $\dfrac{2}{(x - 1)(x + 1)}$

8. $-\dfrac{2}{(x - 1)^2(x + 1)}$

9. $\dfrac{21x^3 + 26y^3}{39x^2y^2}$

10. $\dfrac{y^2 - 2y + 2}{y - 1}$

11. $\dfrac{9m^2 + 4m + 1}{3m + 1}$

12. $\dfrac{-x}{x - y}$

13. $\dfrac{4m}{n(2m - 3n)^2}$

14. $\dfrac{5x}{(x + 3a)(x + 2a)(x - 2a)}$

15. $\dfrac{a + 14}{(a + 2)^2(a - 2)}$

16. $-\dfrac{10}{3(z - 1)(z + 4)}$

17. $\dfrac{xy}{(x + y)^2}$

18. $\dfrac{x - 1}{x + 1}$

Additional Answers for Lesson 10-1

25.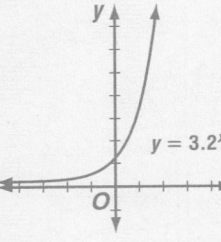
$y = 3.2^x$

26.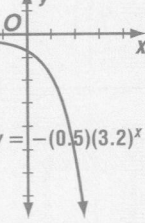
$y = -(0.5)(3.2)^x$

27.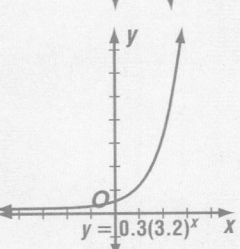
$y = 0.3(3.2)^x$

28.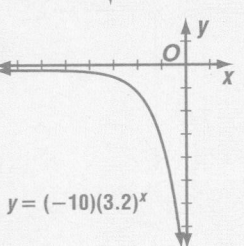
$y = (-10)(3.2)^x$

898

EXTRA PRACTICE

Lesson 9-4 Simplify each expression. 6–18. See margin.

1. $\dfrac{12}{7d} - \dfrac{3}{14d}$ $\dfrac{3}{2d}$

2. $\dfrac{x + 1}{x} - \dfrac{x - 1}{x^2}$ $\dfrac{x^2 + 1}{x^2}$

3. $\dfrac{2x + 1}{4x^2} - \dfrac{x + 3}{6x}$ $\dfrac{-2x^2 + 3}{12x^2}$

4. $\dfrac{5}{x} - \dfrac{3}{x + 5}$ $\dfrac{2x + 25}{x(x + 5)}$

5. $\dfrac{x}{x - 1} + \dfrac{1}{1 - x}$ 1

6. $\dfrac{1}{3v^2} + \dfrac{1}{uv} + \dfrac{3}{4u^2}$

7. $\dfrac{1}{x^2 - x} + \dfrac{1}{x^2 + x}$

8. $\dfrac{1}{x^2 - 1} - \dfrac{1}{(x - 1)^2}$

9. $\dfrac{7x}{13y^2} + \dfrac{4y}{6x^2}$

10. $y - 1 + \dfrac{1}{y - 1}$

11. $3m + 1 - \dfrac{2m}{3m + 1}$

12. $\dfrac{3x}{x - y} + \dfrac{4x}{y - x}$

13. $\dfrac{6}{4m^2 - 12mn + 9n^2} + \dfrac{2}{2mn - 3n^2}$

14. $\dfrac{3}{x^2 + 5ax + 6a^2} + \dfrac{2}{x^2 - 4a^2}$

15. $\dfrac{4}{a^2 - 4} - \dfrac{3}{a^2 + 4a + 4}$

16. $\dfrac{4}{3 - 3z^2} - \dfrac{2}{z^2 + 5z + 4}$

17. $\dfrac{\frac{1}{x + y}}{\frac{1}{x} + \frac{1}{y}}$

18. $\dfrac{1 - \frac{1}{x + 1}}{1 + \frac{1}{x - 1}}$

Lesson 9-5 Solve each equation. Check your solutions.

1. $\dfrac{5}{x} + \dfrac{3}{5} = \dfrac{2}{x}$ -5

2. $\dfrac{1}{2 + 3x} + \dfrac{2}{2 - 3x} = 0$ -2

3. $\dfrac{x - 2}{x} = \dfrac{x - 4}{x - 6}$ 3

4. $\dfrac{1}{x} + \dfrac{x}{x + 2} = 1$ 2

5. $\dfrac{1}{x + 1} + \dfrac{1}{x - 1} = \dfrac{2}{x^2 - 1}$ $\varnothing$

6. $\dfrac{2}{x} + \dfrac{1}{x - 2} = 1$ $1, 4$

7. $\dfrac{1}{x - 3} + \dfrac{1}{x + 5} = \dfrac{x + 1}{x - 3}$ $-3, -1$

8. $\dfrac{4}{x^2 - 2x - 3} = \dfrac{-x}{3 - x} - \dfrac{1}{x + 1}$ 1

9. $\dfrac{x}{x + 1} + \dfrac{3}{x - 3} + 1 = 0$ $0, 1$

10. $\dfrac{3x}{x^2 + 2x - 8} = \dfrac{1}{x - 2} + \dfrac{x}{x + 4}$ $\varnothing$

11. $\dfrac{5x + 2}{x^2 - 4} = \dfrac{-5x}{2 - x} + \dfrac{2}{x + 2}$ $\dfrac{3}{5}$

12. $\dfrac{1}{x - 3} + \dfrac{2}{x^2 - 9} = \dfrac{5}{x + 3}$ 5

13. $\dfrac{1}{x^2 - 1} = \dfrac{2}{x^2 + x - 2}$ 0

14. $\dfrac{12}{x^2 - 16} - \dfrac{24}{x - 4} = 3$ $-6, -2$

15. $\dfrac{4}{x - 2} - \dfrac{x + 6}{x + 1} = 1$ $\dfrac{1 \pm \sqrt{145}}{4}$

Lesson 10-1 Simplify each expression. 3. $x^{2\sqrt{3}} + 2x^{\sqrt{3} + \sqrt{5}} + x^{2\sqrt{5}}$

1. $\left(4^{\sqrt{2}}\right)\left(4^{\sqrt{8}}\right)$ $64^{\sqrt{2}}$

2. $\left(5^{\sqrt{5}}\right)^{\sqrt{45}}$ 5^{15}

3. $\left(x^{\sqrt{3}} + x^{\sqrt{5}}\right)^2$

4. $\left(w^{\sqrt{6}}\right)^{\sqrt{3}}$ $w^{3\sqrt{2}}$

5. $27^{\sqrt{5}} \div 3^{\sqrt{5}}$ $9^{\sqrt{5}}$

6. $8^{2\sqrt{3}} \times 4^{\sqrt{3}}$ $256^{\sqrt{3}}$

7. $5\left(2^{\sqrt{7}}\right)\left(4^{-\sqrt{7}}\right)$ $\dfrac{5}{2^{\sqrt{7}}}$

8. $\left(y^{\sqrt{x}}\right)^{\sqrt{x}}$ y^x

9. $5^{\sqrt{2}} \times 5^{\sqrt{3}}$ $5^{\sqrt{2} + \sqrt{3}}$

10. $\left(6^{\sqrt{5}}\right)^{\sqrt{2}}$ $6^{\sqrt{10}}$

11. $7^{\sqrt{3}} \times 7^{2\sqrt{3}}$ $7^{3\sqrt{3}}$

12. $\left(y^{\sqrt{3}}\right)^{\sqrt{27}}$ y^9

Solve each equation.

13. $3^x = \dfrac{1}{27}$ -3

14. $5^x = \sqrt{125}$ $\dfrac{3}{2}$

15. $8^{2 + x} = 2$ $-\dfrac{5}{3}$

16. $27^{2x - 1} = 3$ $\dfrac{2}{3}$

17. $4^{2x + 5} = 16^{x + 1}$ $\varnothing$

18. $49^{x - 2} = 7\sqrt{7}$ $\dfrac{11}{4}$

19. $6^{x + 1} = 36^{x - 1}$ 3

20. $10^{x - 1} = 100^{4 - x}$ 3

21. $\left(\dfrac{1}{5}\right)^{x - 3} = 125$ 0

22. $2^{x^2 + 1} = 32$ ± 2

23. $36^x = 6^{x^2 - 3}$ $3, -1$

24. $9^{x^2 - 2x} = 27^{x^2 + 1}$ $-1, -3$

Graph each equation. 25–28. See margin.

25. $y = 3.2^x$

26. $y = -(0.5)(3.2)^x$

27. $y = 0.3(3.2)^x$

28. $y = (-10)(3.2)^x$

Lesson 10-2   Evaluate each expression.

1. $\log_4 16$ 2
2. $\log_5 125$ 3
3. $\log_3 \frac{1}{9}$ -2
4. $\log_2 \frac{1}{8}$ -3

5. $\log_6 6\sqrt{6}$ $\frac{3}{2}$
6. $\log_8 4$ $\frac{2}{3}$
7. $\log_7 \sqrt{49}$ 1
8. $\log_{\frac{1}{2}} 8$ -3

Solve each equation for x.

9. $\log_8 x = 2$ 64
10. $\log_5 x = 3$ 125
11. $\log_{10} x = -\frac{1}{2}$ $\frac{\sqrt{10}}{10}$
12. $\log_{\frac{1}{9}} x = -\frac{1}{2}$ 3

13. $\log_x 5 = -\frac{1}{2}$ $\frac{1}{25}$
14. $\log_x 7 = 1$ 7
15. $\log_x 2 = 0$ $\varnothing$
16. $\log_5 (\log_3 x) = 0$ 3

17. $\log_4 (\log_3(\log_2 x)) = 0$ 8
18. $\log_2(x^2 - 9) = 4$ $5, -5$
19. $\log_b (x^2 + 7) = \frac{2}{3} \log_b 64$ $3, -3$

20. $\log_{10} (x - 1)^2 = \log_{10} 0.01$ 1.1, 0.9
21. $\log_{12} (7x - 3) = \log_{12} (5 - x^2)$ 1
22. $\log_9 (x^2 + 9x) = \log_9 10$ $1, -10$

Lesson 10-3   Use $\log_3 5 = 1.465$ and $\log_3 7 = 1.771$ to evaluate each expression.

1. $\log_3 \frac{7}{5}$ 0.306
2. $\log_3 245$ 5.007
3. $\log_3 35$ 3.236

Solve each equation.

4. $\log_2 x + \log_2 (x - 2) = \log_2 3$ 3
5. $\log_3 x = 2 \log_3 3 + \log_3 5$ 45

6. $\log_5 (x^2 + 7) = \frac{2}{3} \log_5 64$ $3, -3$
7. $\log_7 (3x + 5) - \log_7 (x - 5) = \log_7 8$ 9

8. $\log_2 (x^2 - 9) = 4$ $5, -5$
9. $\log_3 (x + 2) + \log_3 6 = 3$ $\frac{5}{2}$

10. $\log_6 x + \log_6 (x - 5) = 2$ 9
11. $\log_5 (x + 3) = \log_5 8 - \log_5 2$ 1

12. $2 \log_3 x - \log_3 (x - 2) = 2$ 6, 3
13. $\log_6 x = \frac{3}{2} \log_6 9 + \log_6 2$ 54

14. $\log_{10} (x + 6) + \log_{10} (x - 6) = 2$ $2\sqrt{34}$
15. $\frac{1}{2} \log_4 (x + 2) + \frac{1}{2} \log_4 (x - 2) = \frac{2}{3} \log_4 27$ $\sqrt{85}$

16. $\log_3 14 + \log_3 x = \log_3 42$ 3
17. $\log_{10} x = \frac{1}{2} \log_{10} 81$ 9

Lesson 10-4   Use a scientific calculator to find the logarithm for each number rounded to four decimal places. Then state the mantissa and characteristic.

1. 55.3   1.7427, 0.7427, 1
2. 0.067 $-1.1739, 0.8261, -2$
3. 334.8   2.5248, 0.5248, 2
4. 0.0008 $-3.0969, 0.9031, -4$

5. 3356.02   3.5258, 0.5258, 3
6. 0.365 $-0.4377, 0.5623, -1$
7. 99.64   1.9984, 0.9984, 1
8. 5.889   0.7700, 0.7700, 0

Use a scientific calculator to find the antilogarithm for each number rounded to four decimal places.

9. -2.6659 0.0022
10. 0.0865   1.2204
11. -1.6235 0.0238
12. 0.2554   1.8005

13. 0.6987   4.9969
14. 0.0045   1.0104
15. -3.0025 0.0010
16. 0.0006   1.0014

17. 0.2586   1.8138
18. 2.2249   167.8418
19. 1.0024   10.0554
20. -0.2586 0.5513

Lesson 10-5 Use a scientific calculator to find each value rounded to four decimal places.

1. ln 8.25 **2.1102**
2. ln 43.5 **3.7728**
3. ln 2.6243 **0.9648**
4. ln 0.04 **−3.2189**

5. antiln −0.1125 **0.8936**
6. antiln 1.006 **2.7346**
7. antiln −2.445 **0.0867**
8. antiln −1 **0.3679**

9. ln 43.988 **3.7839**
10. antiln −0.0115 **0.9886**
11. ln 0.0005 **−7.6009**
12. antiln 1.25 **3.4903**

Lesson 10-6 Approximate the value of each logarithm to three decimal places.

1. $\log_3 21$ **2.771**
2. $\log_4 62$ **2.977**
3. $\log_5 28$ **2.070**
4. $\log_2 25$ **4.644**

5. $\log_{12} 30$ **1.369**
6. $\log_4 63$ **2.989**
7. $\log_7 35$ **1.827**
8. $\log_6 100$ **2.570**

Use logarithms to solve each equation. Approximate the value of each solution to three decimal places.

9. $5^x \cdot 5^{-7x} = 5^{-18}$ **3**
10. $3^b = 19$ **2.680**
11. $6^x = 12$ **1.387**
12. $9^{2x+1} = 62.4$ **0.441**

13. $7^{3x-2} = 0.834$ **0.636**
14. $4 = 9^{2x-3}$ **1.815**
15. $6 = 15^{1-x}$ **0.338**
16. $1.76^x = 23.4$ **5.577**

17. $8 = 3 \times 5^x$ **0.609**
18. $3^x = 4 \times 2^x$ **3.419**
19. $2 \times 5^{x+1} = 5 \times 2^{x+2}$ **0.756**
20. $2^{6x-3} = 4 \times 2^{4x}$ **2.5**

Lesson 10-7

1. The number of bacteria B in a culture increases according to the equation $B = B_0 e^{kt}$. The culture starts with 400 bacteria and has 700 bacteria after 3 hours. How many bacteria will there be after 12 hours? **about 3750 bacteria**

2. Humberto deposited $785 in an account that pays $8\frac{3}{4}\%$ interest, compounded continuously. How long will it take until Humberto has $1000? **about 2.77 years**

3. A satellite has a radioactive-isotope power supply. The power output in watts is given by the equation $P = 50e^{(t/250)}$ where P is the power in watts and t is the time in days.
   a. How much power will be available at the end of one year? **about 215.3 watts**
   b. What is the half-life of the power supply? **about 173.3 days**
   c. The equipment aboard the satellite requires 10 watts of power to operate properly. What is the operational life of the satellite? **about 402.4 days**

4. A hard-boiled egg has a temperature of 98 degrees Celsius. If it is put into a sink that maintains a temperature of 18 degrees Celsius, its temperature x minutes later is given by $T(x) = 18 + 80\,e^{-0.28x}$. Hilda needs her egg to be exactly 30 degrees Celsius for decorating. How long should she leave it in the water? **about 6 min 47 s**

5. The number of people in the Denver suburban area has grown exponentially since 1950 according to the equation $P = P_0\,e^{kt}$. In 1950 there were 350,000 people, and in 1960, there were 705,300 people. How many people lived in the Denver suburban area in 1980? **about 2,866,747 people**

Lesson 11-1 Find the next four terms of each arithmetic sequence.

1. $9, 7, 5, ...$
$3, 1, -1, -3$

2. $3, 4.5, 6, ...$
$7.5, 9, 10.5, 12$

3. $40, 35, 30, ...$
$25, 20, 15, 10$

4. $2, 5, 8, ...$
$11, 14, 17, 20$

Find the nth term of each arithmetic sequence described.

5. $a_1 = 4, d = 5, n = 10$ 49

6. $a_1 = -30, d = -6, n = 5$ -54

7. $a_1 = \frac{3}{4}, d = -\frac{1}{4}, n = 72$ -17

8. $a_1 = -3, d = 32, n = 8$ 221

9. $a_1 = -\frac{1}{5}, d = \frac{3}{5}, n = 17$ $\frac{47}{5}$

10. $a_1 = 20, d = -3, n = 16$ -25

Write an equation for the nth term of each arithmetic sequence.

11. $3, 5, 7, 9, ...$ $a_n = 2n + 1$

12. $2, -1, -4, -7, ...$ $a_n = -3n + 5$

13. $20, 28, 36, 44, ...$ $a_n = 8n + 12$

Lesson 11-2 Find S_n for each arithmetic series described.

1. $a_1 = 3, a_n = 20, n = 6$ 69

2. $a_1 = 15, a_n = -12, n = 30$ 45

3. $a_1 = 90, a_n = -4, n = 10$ 430

4. $a_1 = 16, n = 12, a_n = 14$ 180

5. $a_1 = -80, n = 18, a_n = 120$ 360

6. $a_1 = -3, n = 14, a_n = -72$
-525

Find the sum of each arithmetic series.

7. $3 + 12 + 21 + 30 + ... + 57$ 210

8. $1 + 4 + 7 + 10 + ... + 31$ 176

9. $8 + 16 + 24 + ... + 80$ 440

Write the terms of each arithmetic series and find the sum.   **10–15. See margin.**

10. $\displaystyle\sum_{n=1}^{6} n + 2$

11. $\displaystyle\sum_{n=5}^{10} 2n - 5$

12. $\displaystyle\sum_{k=1}^{5} 40 - 2k$

13. $\displaystyle\sum_{k=8}^{12} 6 - 3k$

14. $\displaystyle\sum_{n=6}^{10} 2 + 3n$

15. $\displaystyle\sum_{n=1}^{4} 10n + 2$

Lesson 11-3 Find the next four terms of each geometric sequence.

1. $5, 15, 45, ...$
$135, 405, 1215, 3645$

2. $2, 10, 50, ...$
$250, 1250, 6250, 31{,}250$

3. $64, 16, 4, ...$
$1, \frac{1}{4}, \frac{1}{16}, \frac{1}{64}$

4. $-9, 27, -81, ...$
$243, -729, 2187, -6561$

Find the nth term of each geometric sequence described.

5. $a_1 = 5, r = 7, n = 6$ $84{,}035$

6. $a_1 = 200, r = -\frac{1}{2}, n = 10$ $-\frac{25}{64}$

7. $a_1 = 60, r = -2, n = 4$ -480

8. $a_1 = 300, r = \frac{1}{4}, n = 6$ $\frac{75}{256}$

9. $a_1 = 8, r = -2, n = 8$ -1024

10. $a_1 = 1, r = -1, n = 30$ -1

Find the value(s) of y that make each sequence geometric.   **13.** 67.5

11. $3, -6, 12, 2y - 12, ...$ -6

12. $2, -2, 2, 4y + 2, ...$ -1

13. $-10, 50, -250, 20y - 100, ...$

Extra Practice   **901**

Additional Answers for Lesson 11-2

10. $3 + 4 + 5 + 6 + 7 + 8 = 33$

11. $5 + 7 + 9 + 11 + 13 + 15 = 60$

12. $38 + 36 + 34 + 32 + 30 = 170$

13. $(-18) + (-21) + (-24) + (-27) + (-30) = -120$

14. $20 + 23 + 26 + 29 + 32 = 130$

15. $12 + 22 + 32 + 42 = 108$

16. $2 + 4 + 8 + 16 + 32 = 62$

17. $1 + \frac{1}{3} + \frac{1}{9} + \frac{1}{27} = \frac{40}{27}$

18. $2 + 10 + 50 + 250 = 312$

19. $3 + (-9) + 27 + (-81) = -60$

20. $1 + \frac{1}{2} + \frac{1}{4} + \frac{1}{8} + \frac{1}{16} + \frac{1}{32} = \frac{63}{32}$

21. $(-16) + 8 + (-4) + 2 + (-1) = -11$

Additional Answers for Lesson 11-6

1. 4, 9, 19, 39, 79, 159

2. 6, 13, 20, 27, 34, 41

3. 16, 21, 27, 34, 42, 51

4. $1, \frac{1}{3}, \frac{1}{6}, \frac{1}{10}, \frac{1}{15}, \frac{1}{21}$

EXTRA PRACTICE

Lesson 11-4 Find S_n for each geometric series described.

1. $a_1 = \frac{1}{81}, r = 3, n = 6$ $\frac{364}{81}$

2. $a_1 = 1, r = -2, n = 7$ 43

3. $a_1 = 5, r = 4, n = 5$ 1705

4. $a_1 = -27, r = -\frac{1}{3}, n = 6$ $-\frac{182}{9}$

5. $a_1 = 1000, r = \frac{1}{2}, n = 7$ $\frac{15{,}875}{8}$

6. $a_1 = 125, r = -\frac{2}{5}, n = 5$ $\frac{451}{5}$

Find the sum of each geometric series.

7. $a_1 = 10, r = 3, n = 6$ 3640

8. $r = -\frac{1}{5}, n = 5, a_1 = 1250$ 1042

9. $r = \frac{1}{3}, a_n = 5, a_1 = 1215$ 1820

10. $a_1 = 16, r = \frac{3}{2}, n = 5$ 211

11. $a_1 = 7, r = 2, n = 7$ 889

12. $r = -\frac{1}{2}, a_n = -\frac{3}{2}, n = 6$ 31.5

13. $a_1 = 16, r = -\frac{1}{2}, n = 10$ $\frac{341}{32}$

14. $a_1 = 243, r = -\frac{2}{3}, n = 5$ 165

15. $a_1 = 5, r = 3, n = 12$ 1,328,600

Write the terms of each geometric series and find the sum.   16–21. See margin.

16. $\sum_{k=1}^{5} 2^k$

17. $\sum_{n=0}^{3} 3^{-n}$

18. $\sum_{n=0}^{3} 2(5^n)$

19. $\sum_{k=2}^{5} -(-3)^{k-1}$

20. $\sum_{n=1}^{6} \left(\frac{1}{2}\right)^{n-1}$

21. $\sum_{n=0}^{4} 8\left(\frac{-1}{2}\right)^{n-1}$

Lesson 11-5 Find the sum of each infinite geometric series, if it exists.   2. does not exist

1. $54 + 18 + 6 + \ldots$ 81

2. $2 - 2 + 2 - 2 + \ldots$

3. $1000 - 200 + 40 - \ldots$ $833\frac{1}{3}$

4. $7 + 3 + \frac{9}{7} + \ldots$ $\frac{49}{4}$

5. $\frac{4}{5} + \frac{2}{25} + \frac{1}{125} + \ldots$ $\frac{8}{9}$

6. $49 + 14 + 4 \ldots$ $\frac{343}{5}$

7. $\frac{3}{4} + \frac{1}{2} + \frac{1}{3} + \ldots$ $\frac{9}{4}$

8. $1 - \frac{1}{4} + \frac{1}{16} - \ldots$ $\frac{4}{5}$

9. $12 - 4 + \frac{4}{3} - \ldots$ 9

10. $3 - 9 + 27 - \ldots$ does not exist

11. $3 - 2 + \frac{4}{3} - \ldots$ $\frac{9}{5}$

12. $10 - 1 + 0.1 - \ldots$ $\frac{100}{11}$

13. $\sum_{n=1}^{\infty} 3\left(\frac{1}{4}\right)^{n-1}$ 4

14. $\sum_{n=1}^{\infty} 5\left(-\frac{1}{10}\right)^{n-1}$ $\frac{50}{11}$

15. $\sum_{n=1}^{\infty} -\frac{2}{3}\left(-\frac{3}{4}\right)^{n-1}$ $-\frac{8}{21}$

Lesson 11-6 Find the first six terms of each sequence.   1–4. See margin.

1. $a_1 = 4, a_{n+1} = 2a_n + 1$

2. $a_1 = 6, a_{n+1} = a_n + 7$

3. $a_1 = 16, a_{n+1} = a_n + (n + 4)$

4. $a_1 = 1, a_{n+1} = \frac{n}{n+2} \cdot a_n$

Find the first three iterates of each function, using the given initial values.

5. $f(x) = 3x - 1, x_0 = 3$ 8, 23, 68

6. $f(x) = 2x^2 - 8, x_0 = -1$ -6, 64, 8184

7. $f(x) = 4x + 5, x_0 = 3$ 17, 73, 297

8. $f(x) = 3x^2 + 1, x_0 = 1$ 4, 49, 7204

9. $f(x) = x^2 + 4x + 4, x_0 = 1$ 9, 121, 15,129

10. $f(x) = x^2 + 9, x_0 = 2$ 13, 178, 31,693

Lesson 11-7 Draw the next stage of a fractal formed by replacing each segment with the pattern shown. 1–2. See margin.

1.

2.

3. Describe why lightning is an example of fractals found in nature. See margin.

Lesson 11-8 Use a calculator to evaluate each expression.

1. $6!$ 720

2. $4!$ 24

3. $\frac{13!}{6!}$ 8,648,640

4. $\frac{12!}{5!}$ 3,991,680

5. $\frac{10!}{3!\,7!}$ 120

6. $\frac{14!}{4!\,10!}$ 1001

7. $\frac{7!}{2!\,5!}$ 21

8. $\frac{9!}{8!}$ 9

Expand each binomial. 9–11. See margin.

9. $(x + y)^3$

10. $(2x - y)^4$

11. $(3r + 4s)^5$

Find the indicated term of each expression.

12. sixth term of $(x + 3)^8$ $13{,}608x^3$

13. fourth term of $(x - y)^9$ $-84x^6y^3$

14. fifth term of $(3x + 5y)^{10}$ $95{,}681{,}250x^6y^4$

15. sixth term of $(x + 4y)^7$ $21{,}504x^2y^5$

Lesson 12-1 Draw a tree diagram to illustrate all of the possibilities. 1–3. See margin.

1. tossing two pennies and rolling two number cubes

2. choosing a denim jacket that comes in dark blue, stone washed, or black that has buttons or snaps

3. ordering a large pizza with thin or thick crust and one topping of either pepperoni, sausage, or vegetables

State whether the events are *independent* or *dependent*.

4. A comedy video and an action video are selected from the video store. independent

5. The numbers 1–10 are written on pieces of paper and are placed in a hat. Three of them are selected one after the other without replacing any of the pieces of paper. dependent

Solve each problem.

6. On a bookshelf there are 10 different algebra books, 6 different geometry books, and 4 different calculus books. In how many ways can you choose 3 books, one of each kind? 240

7. In how many different ways can a 10-question true-false test be answered if each question must be answered? 1024

8. How many ways are there of selecting 3 cards, one after the other, from a deck of 26 cards if selected cards are not replaced? 15,600

9. A student council has 6 seniors, 5 juniors, and 1 sophomore as members. In how many ways can a 3-member council committee be formed that includes one member of each class? 30

10. How many license plates of 5 symbols can be made using a letter for the first symbol and digits for the remaining 4 symbols? 260,000

Additional Answers for Lesson 11-7

1.

2.

3. Lightning bolts break off into smaller and smaller parts that are of the same pattern and shape as the bigger lightning bolts.

Additional Answers for Lesson 11-8

9. $x^3 + 3x^2y + 3xy^2 + y^3$

10. $16x^4 - 32x^3y + 24x^2y^2 - 8xy^3 + y^4$

11. $243r^5 + 1620r^4s + 4320r^3s^2 + 5760r^2s^3 + 3840rs^4 + 1024s^5$

Additional Answers for Lesson 12-1

1.
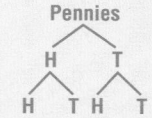

2.
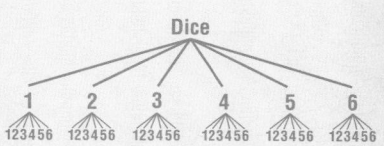

3.
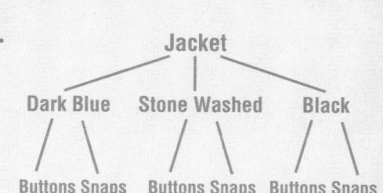

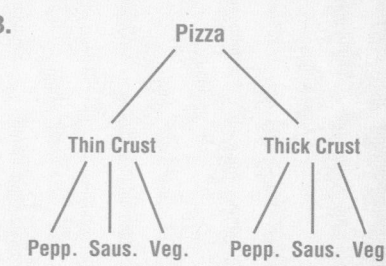

903

EXTRA PRACTICE

Lesson 12-2 How many ways can the letters of each word be arranged?

1. MONDAY **720**   2. EIGHT **120**   3. CINCINNATI **50,400**   4. INDIANA **630**

Evaluate each expression.

5. $\dfrac{P(5,3)}{P(3,2)}$ **10**

6. $\dfrac{P(5,2)\,P(4,3)}{P(6,3)}$ **4**

7. $\dfrac{P(10,6)}{P(12,2)\,P(7,2)}$ **27.$\overline{27}$**

Lesson 12-3 Determine whether each situation involves a permutation or a combination.

1. choosing a team of 9 players from a group of 20   **combination**

2. lining up in a cafeteria line   **permutation**

3. choosing 4 books from a list of 12 for a summer reading program   **combination**

4. arranging the order of songs on a compact disc   **permutation**

Evaluate each expression.

5. $C(8,6)$ **28**   6. $C(20,17)$ **1140**   7. $C(9,4) \cdot C(5,3)$ **1260**

8. $C(6,1) \cdot C(4,1) \cdot C(9,8)$ **216**   9. $C(10,5) \cdot C(8,4)$ **17,640**   10. $C(7,6) \cdot C(3,1)$ **21**

Solve each problem.

11. A standard bridge deck of cards consists of 4 suits (diamonds, clubs, hearts, and spades) of 13 cards each. How many 5-card hands can be dealt that includes 4 cards from the same suit and one card from a different suit?   **111,540**

12. At Hamburger Heaven, you can order hamburgers with cheese, onion, pickle, relish, mustard, lettuce, or tomato. How many different combinations of the "extras" can you order, choosing any three of them?   **35**

13. Students are required to answer any eight out of ten questions on a certain test. How many different combinations of eight questions can a student choose to answer?   **45**

Lesson 12-4 State the probability of an event occurring, given the odds of the event.

1. 5:9 $\dfrac{5}{14}$ 2. 4:8 $\dfrac{1}{3}$ 3. 3:10 $\dfrac{3}{13}$

4. 2:7 $\dfrac{2}{9}$ 5. 6:13 $\dfrac{6}{19}$ 6. 1:19 $\dfrac{1}{20}$

A jar contains 3 red, 4 green, and 5 orange marbles. Three marbles are drawn at random. Find the probability of each event.

7. P(all green) $\dfrac{1}{55}$ 8. P(1 red, 2 not red) $\dfrac{27}{55}$ 9. P(2 orange, 1 not orange) $\dfrac{7}{22}$

A bridge hand consists of 13 cards drawn at random from a 52-card bridge deck. Find the probability of each event.

10. P(4 kings) $\dfrac{11}{4165}$ 11. P(no aces) $\dfrac{6327}{20,825}$ 12. P(all red cards) $\dfrac{19}{1,160,054}$

Lesson 12-5 Find each probability.

1. The student council consists of 7 girls and 5 boys, of whom 3 girls and 3 boys are seniors. A 4-person dance committee is chosen.
   a. P(2 girls and 2 boys) $\frac{14}{33}$
   b. P(3 girls and 1 boy) $\frac{35}{99}$
   c. P(2 senior boys and 2 senior girls) $\frac{1}{55}$
   d. P(all seniors of whom at least 2 are girls) $\frac{4}{165}$

2. The probability that Leon will ask Frank to be his tennis partner is $\frac{1}{4}$, that Paula will ask Frank is $\frac{1}{3}$, and that Ray will ask Frank is $\frac{3}{4}$.
   a. P(Paula will ask and Leon will ask.) $\frac{1}{12}$
   b. P(Ray and Paula will ask, but Leon will not.) $\frac{3}{16}$
   c. P(At least two out of the three will ask.) $\frac{19}{48}$
   d. P(At least one out of the three will ask.) $\frac{7}{8}$

3. According to the weather reports, the probability of rain on a certain day is 70% in Yellow Falls and 50% in Copper Creek.
   a. P(It will rain in Yellow Falls, but not in Copper Creek.)   **35%**
   b. P(It will rain in both cities.)   **35%**
   c. P(It will rain in neither city.)   **15%**
   d. P(It will rain in at least one of the cities.)   **85%**

Lesson 12-6 Find each probability.   1. $\frac{3}{50}$

1. Two letters are chosen at random from the word GEESE and two are chosen at random from the word PLEASE. What is the probability that all four letters are Es or none of the letters is an E?

2. What is the probability of getting 8 or more questions correct on a 10-question true-false test if the questions are answered at random? $\frac{7}{128}$

3. Three dice are thrown.
   a. P(All three dice show the same number.) $\frac{1}{36}$
   b. P(Exactly 2 of the dice show the same number.) $\frac{5}{12}$

4. Two marbles are drawn at random from a bag containing 3 red, 5 blue, and 6 green marbles.
   a. P(at least 1 red marble) $\frac{36}{91}$
   b. P(at least one green marble) $\frac{9}{13}$
   c. P(2 marbles of the same color) $\frac{4}{13}$
   d. P(two marbles of different colors) $\frac{9}{13}$

Lesson 12-7 Find each probability.   1. $\frac{1}{4}$

1. A die is rolled and a coin is flipped. What is the probability that the number on the die is even and the coin shows heads?

2. Two marbles are to be drawn at random from a bag containing 8 red marbles and five green marbles. Use a tree diagram to determine the probability that one of the marbles will be red and one will be green.   **See margin.**

3. Ten percent of a batch of toothpaste is defective. Five tubes of toothpaste are selected at random from this batch.
   a. P(None are defective.)   **0.59**
   b. P(Exactly one is defective.)   **0.328**
   c. P(At least three are defective.)   **0.009**
   d. P(Less than three are defective.)   **0.991**

4. On a true-false test, Gil guessed on every problem. The test had 80 questions.
   a. P(Each question is right.) 8.27×10^{-25}
   b. P(Exactly 35 are right.)   **0.04789**

Additional Answer for Lesson 12-7

2.

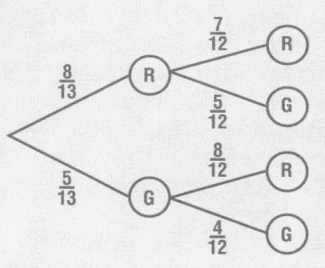

$\frac{20}{39}$

Additional Answers for Lesson 12-8

4. There is a 95% probability that between 70.2–73.8% of students choose oatmeal as their favorite breakfast meal.
5. There is a 95% probability that between 51.2–60.8% of people feel that they are impulse buyers at the supermarket.
6. There is a 95% probability that between 43.2–46.8% of women take the recommended daily allowance of calcium, as recommended by the NIH.

Additional Answers for Lesson 13-1

1. $\sin \theta = 0.8000$, $\tan \theta = 1.3333$, $\csc \theta = 1.2500$, $\sec \theta = 1.6667$, $\cot \theta = 0.7500$
2. $\sin \theta = 0.4706$, $\cos \theta = 0.8824$, $\csc \theta = 2.1250$, $\sec \theta = 1.1333$, $\cot \theta = 1.8750$
3. $\sin \theta = 0.9231$, $\cos \theta = 0.3846$, $\tan \theta = 2.4000$, $\csc \theta = 1.0833$, $\cot \theta = 0.4167$
4. $\sin \theta = 0.2800$, $\cos \theta = 0.9600$, $\tan \theta = 0.2917$, $\sec \theta = 1.0417$, $\cot \theta = 3.4286$
5. $\sin \theta = 0.7071$, $\cos \theta = 0.7071$, $\tan \theta = 1.0000$, $\csc \theta = 1.4142$, $\sec \theta = 1.4142$

18. $b = 6$, $A = 53.1°$, $B = 36.9°$
19. $c = 7.3$, $A = 15.9°$, $B = 74.1°$
20. $c = 23.7$, $A = 27.6°$, $B = 62.4°$
21. $A = 26°$, $a = 8.0$, $b = 16.4$
22. $A = 57°$, $b = 21.4$, $c = 39.3$
23. $A = 77°$, $a = 5.8$, $b = 1.3$
24. $B = 13°$, $a = 181.9$, $c = 186.7$
25. $B = 33°$, $a = 15.1$, $b = 9.8$
26. $B = 55°$, $b = 10.0$, $c = 12.2$
27. $A = 54°$, $a = 14.6$, $b = 10.6$
28. $A = 53.1°$, $B = 36.9°$, $a = 8.0$, $b = 6.0$
29. $A = 63.4°$, $B = 26.6°$, $a = 14$, $c = 15.7$

Lesson 12-8 Determine whether each situation represents a random sampling. Write *yes* or *no* and explain.

1. finding the most often prescribed pain reliever by asking all of the doctors at your local hospital   No; the doctors in one hospital in one town do not represent a good sample of all doctors in the country. The hospital might have a contract with the makers of a certain pain reliever.
2. taking a poll of the most popular baby girl names this year by studying birth announcements in newspapers from different cities across the country   Yes; this would be a random sampling because it is an unbiased and thorough representation.
3. polling people who frequent the neighborhood pizza parlor about their favorite restaurant in the city   No; by frequenting the pizza parlor, it is probably their favorite restaurant. This would not be a good random sample.

Find the margin of sampling error in each problem. Explain what it indicates about the results.

4. A poll conducted on the favorite breakfast choice of students in your school showed that 72% of the 2500 students asked indicated oatmeal as their favorite breakfast.   1.8%
5. Of the 420 people polled at the supermarket, 56% felt that they were easily swayed by the sample items in the aisles and purchased those items, even though they were not intending to when they arrived at the store.   4.8%
6. Of the 3000 women polled between the ages of 25 and 35, only 45% felt that they consume 1000 to 1500 mg of calcium daily, which is the recommended daily allowance by the National Institute of Health.   1.8%
4–6. See margin for explanations.

Lesson 13-1 Suppose θ is an acute angle of a right triangle. For each function, find the values of the remaining five trigonometric functions of θ. Round your answers to four decimal places.

1. $\cos \theta = \frac{3}{5}$ 2. $\tan \theta = \frac{8}{15}$ 3. $\sec \theta = \frac{13}{5}$ 4. $\csc \theta = \frac{25}{7}$ 5. $\cot \theta = 1$
1–5. See margin.

Find the value of x. Round your answers to the nearest degree.

6. $\tan x = 4.1436$ 76°   7. $\cos x = 0.3899$ 67°   8. $\sin x = 0.8045$ 54°   9. $\cos x = 0.0982$ 84°
10. $\sin x = 0.5950$ 37°   11. $\tan x = 0.1648$ 9°   12. $\tan x = 1.2763$ 52°   13. $\sin x = 0.2131$ 12°
14. $\cos x = 0.7878$ 38°   15. $\cos x = 0.4500$ 63°   16. $\sin x = 0.3657$ 21°   17. $\tan x = 2.8560$ 71°

Solve each right triangle. Assume that C represents the right angle and c is the hypotenuse. Round measures of sides and angles to the nearest tenth.   18–29. See margin.

18. $c = 10$, $a = 8$ 19. $a = 2$, $b = 7$ 20. $a = 11$, $b = 21$ 21. $B = 64°$, $c = 18.2$
22. $a = 33$, $B = 33°$ 23. $c = 6$, $B = 13°$ 24. $b = 42$, $A = 77°$ 25. $A = 57°$, $c = 18$
26. $A = 35°$, $a = 7$ 27. $B = 36°$, $c = 18$ 28. $\cos A = \frac{3}{5}$, $c = 10$ 29. $\tan B = \frac{1}{2}$, $b = 7$

Lesson 13-2 Change each degree measure to radian measure.

1. $60°$ $\frac{\pi}{3}$ 2. $270°$ $\frac{3\pi}{2}$ 3. $315°$ $\frac{7\pi}{4}$ 4. $150°$ $\frac{5\pi}{6}$ 5. $-135°$ $-\frac{3\pi}{4}$
6. $-315°$ $-\frac{7\pi}{4}$ 7. $45°$ $\frac{\pi}{4}$ 8. $80°$ $\frac{4\pi}{9}$ 9. $24°$ $\frac{2\pi}{15}$ 10. $-54°$ $-\frac{3\pi}{10}$

Change each radian measure to degree measure.

11. $-\pi$ $-180°$ 12. $\frac{9\pi}{4}$ $405°$ 13. $\frac{3\pi}{2}$ $270°$ 14. $-\frac{7\pi}{4}$ $-315°$ 15. $\frac{7\pi}{12}$ $105°$
16. $\frac{9\pi}{10}$ $162°$ 17. $-\frac{17\pi}{30}$ $-102°$ 18. 1 $\approx 57.30°$ 19. $-2\frac{1}{3}$ $\approx 133.69°$ 20. $6\frac{1}{2}$ $\approx 372.42°$
21–30. See margin for sample answers.
Find one positive angle and one negative angle that are coterminal with each angle.

21. $50°$ 22. $-75°$ 23. $125°$ 24. $-400°$ 25. $550°$
26. 3π 27. -2π 28. $\frac{2\pi}{3}$ 29. $\frac{12\pi}{5}$ 30. $-\frac{9\pi}{5}$

Additional Answers for Lesson 13-2

21. $410°$, $-310°$
22. $285°$, $-435°$
23. $485°$, $-235°$
24. $320°$, $-40°$
25. $190°$, $-170°$
26. π, $-\pi$
27. 2π, -4π
28. $\frac{8\pi}{3}$, $-\frac{4\pi}{3}$
29. $\frac{2\pi}{5}$, $-\frac{8\pi}{5}$
30. $\frac{\pi}{5}$, $-\frac{19\pi}{5}$

(Side margin, rotated: EXTRA PRACTICE)

Lesson 13-3 State whether the value of each function is *positive, negative, zero,* or *undefined.*

1. $\sin 145°$ +
2. $\cos 200°$ −
3. $\tan 180°$ 0
4. $\tan(-45°)$ −
5. $\cos 450°$ 0
6. $\tan\left(-\frac{3\pi}{2}\right)$ undefined
7. $\sin\frac{5\pi}{3}$ −
8. $\cos\left(-\frac{3\pi}{4}\right)$ −
9. $\tan\frac{6\pi}{5}$ +
10. $\sin\left(-\frac{\pi}{2}\right)$ −

Find the exact values of $\sin\theta$, $\cos\theta$, and $\tan\theta$ if the terminal side of θ in standard position contains the given point. 11–15. See margin.

11. $P(3, -4)$
12. $P(1, \sqrt{3})$
13. $P(0, -4)$
14. $P(-5, -5)$
15. $P(2.5, 0)$

Find the exact value of each trigonometric function.

16. $\cos 150°$ $-\frac{\sqrt{3}}{2}$
17. $\sin\left(-\frac{5\pi}{3}\right)$ $\frac{\sqrt{3}}{2}$
18. $\tan\frac{7\pi}{6}$ $\frac{\sqrt{3}}{3}$
19. $\tan(-300°)$ $\sqrt{3}$
20. $\cos\frac{7\pi}{4}$ $\frac{\sqrt{2}}{2}$

Suppose θ is an angle in standard position whose terminal side lies in the given quadrant. For each function, find the exact values of the remaining five trigonometric functions of θ.

21. $\cos\theta = -\frac{1}{3}$; Quadrant III
22. $\sec\theta = 2$; Quadrant IV
23. $\sin\theta = \frac{2}{3}$; Quadrant II
24. $\tan\theta = -4$; Quadrant IV
25. $\csc\theta = -5$; Quadrant III
26. $\cot\theta = -2$, Quadrant II
27. $\tan\theta = \frac{1}{3}$; Quadrant III
28. $\cos\theta = \frac{1}{4}$; Quadrant I
29. $\csc\theta = -\frac{5}{2}$; Quadrant IV
21–29. See margin.

Lesson 13-4 Write an equation that can be used to find the area of each triangle. Then solve the equation. Round your answer to the nearest tenth.

1. $a = 11, b = 13, C = 31°$ 36.8
2. $a = 15, b = 22, C = 90°$ 165
3. $a = 12, b = 12, C = 50°$ 55.2
4. $a = 6, c = 4, B = 52°$ 9.5
5. $b = 10, c = 17, A = 46°$ 61.1
6. $b = 4, c = 19, A = 73°$ 36.3
7. $a = 11, c = 5, B = 55°$ 22.5
8. $b = 8, c = 12, A = 75°$ 46.4
9. $a = 12, b = 9, C = 35°$ 31.0

Determine whether each triangle has no solution, one solution, or two solutions. Then solve each triangle. Round measures of sides and angles to the nearest tenth. 10–21. See margin.

10. $A = 40°, B = 60°, c = 20$
11. $B = 70°, C = 58°, a = 84$
12. $A = 40°, a = 5, b = 12$
13. $A = 58°, a = 26,$ and $b = 29$
14. $A = 38°, B = 63°, c = 15$
15. $a = 6, b = 8, A = 150°$
16. $a = 12, b = 19, A = 57°$
17. $a = 125, b = 150, A = 25°$
18. $a = 64, c = 90, C = 98°$
19. $A = 40°, B = 60°, c = 20$
20. $a = 33, b = 50, A = 132°$
21. $a = 83, b = 79, A = 45°$

Lesson 13-5 Determine whether each triangle can be solved by beginning with the law of sines or law of cosines. Then solve each triangle. 1–21. See Solutions Manual.

1. $A = 51°, b = 40, c = 45$
2. $a = 10, c = 8, A = 40°$
3. $a = 14, c = 21, B = 60°$
4. $a = 14, b = 15, c = 16$
5. $B = 41°, C = 52°, c = 27$
6. $a = 19, b = 24.3, c = 21.8$
7. $A = 112°, a = 32, c = 20$
8. $b = 8, c = 7, A = 28°$
9. $a = 5, b = 6, c = 7$
10. $C = 35°, a = 11, b = 10.5$
11. $a = 8, A = 49°, B = 58°$
12. $A = 42°, b = 120, c = 160$
13. $c = 14, A = 40°, C = 70°$
14. $a = 10, b = 16, c = 19$
15. $a = 20, c = 24, B = 47°$
16. $a = 10, c = 8, B = 100°$
17. $A = 40°, B = 45°, c = 4$
18. $a = 32, c = 20, A = 112°$
19. $c = 8, b = 16, B = 71°$
20. $b = 100, c = 84, A = 20°$
21. $b = 40, c = 49, B = 53°$

Additional Answers for Lesson 13-3

11. $\sin\theta = -\frac{4}{5}$, $\cos\theta = \frac{3}{5}$, $\tan\theta = -\frac{4}{3}$

12. $\sin\theta = \frac{\sqrt{3}}{2}$, $\cos\theta = \frac{1}{2}$, $\tan\theta = \sqrt{3}$

13. $\sin\theta = -1$, $\cos\theta = 0$; $\tan\theta$ is undefined

14. $\sin\theta = -\frac{\sqrt{2}}{2}$, $\cos = -\frac{\sqrt{2}}{2}$, $\tan\theta = 1$

15. $\sin\theta = 0$, $\cos\theta = 1$, $\tan\theta = 0$

21. $\sin\theta = -\frac{2\sqrt{2}}{3}$, $\tan\theta = 2\sqrt{2}$, $\csc\theta = -\frac{3\sqrt{2}}{4}$, $\sec\theta = -3$; $\cot\theta = \frac{\sqrt{2}}{4}$

22. $\sin\theta = -\frac{\sqrt{3}}{2}$, $\cos\theta = \frac{1}{2}$, $\tan\theta = -\sqrt{3}$, $\csc\theta = -\frac{2\sqrt{3}}{3}$, $\cot\theta = -\frac{\sqrt{3}}{3}$

23. $\cos\theta = -\frac{\sqrt{5}}{3}$, $\tan\theta = -\frac{2\sqrt{5}}{5}$, $\csc\theta = \frac{3}{2}$, $\sec\theta = -\frac{3\sqrt{5}}{5}$, $\cot\theta = -\frac{\sqrt{5}}{2}$

24. $\sin\theta = -\frac{4\sqrt{17}}{17}$, $\cos\theta = \frac{\sqrt{17}}{17}$, $\csc\theta = -\frac{\sqrt{17}}{4}$, $\sec\theta = \sqrt{17}$, $\cot\theta = -\frac{1}{4}$

25. $\sin\theta = -\frac{1}{5}$, $\cos\theta = -\frac{2\sqrt{6}}{5}$, $\tan\theta = \frac{\sqrt{6}}{12}$, $\sec\theta = -\frac{5\sqrt{6}}{12}$, $\cot\theta = 2\sqrt{6}$

26. $\sin\theta = \frac{\sqrt{5}}{5}$, $\cos\theta = -\frac{2\sqrt{5}}{5}$, $\tan\theta = -\frac{1}{2}$, $\csc\theta = \sqrt{5}$, $\sec\theta = -\frac{\sqrt{5}}{2}$

27. $\sin\theta = -\frac{\sqrt{10}}{10}$, $\cos\theta = -\frac{3\sqrt{10}}{10}$, $\csc\theta = -\sqrt{10}$, $\sec\theta = -\frac{\sqrt{10}}{3}$, $\cot\theta = 3$

28. $\sin\theta = \frac{\sqrt{15}}{4}$, $\tan\theta = \sqrt{15}$, $\csc\theta = \frac{4\sqrt{15}}{15}$, $\sec\theta = 4$, $\cot\theta = \frac{\sqrt{15}}{15}$

29. $\sin\theta = -\frac{2}{5}$, $\cos\theta = \frac{\sqrt{21}}{5}$, $\tan\theta = -\frac{2\sqrt{21}}{21}$, $\sec\theta = \frac{5\sqrt{21}}{21}$, $\cot\theta = -\frac{\sqrt{21}}{2}$

Additional Answers for Lesson 13-4

10. 1; $C = 80°, a = 13.1, b = 17.6$
11. 1; $A = 52°, b = 100.2, c = 90.4$
12. none
13. 2; $B = 71.0°, C = 51.0°, c = 23.8; B = 109.0°, C = 13.0°, c = 7.0$
14. 1; $C = 79°, a = 9.4, b = 13.6$
15. none
16. none
17. 2; $B = 30.5°, C = 124.5°, c = 243.7; B = 149.5°, C = 5.5°, c = 28.2$
18. 1; $A = 44.8°, B = 37.2°, b = 55.0$
19. 1; $C = 80°, a = 13.1, b = 17.6$
20. none
21. 1; $B = 42.3°, C = 92.7°, c = 117.2$

907

1.

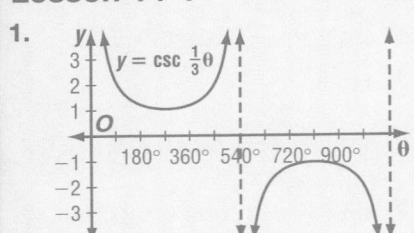

2.

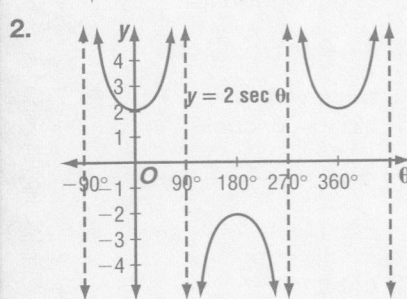

3.

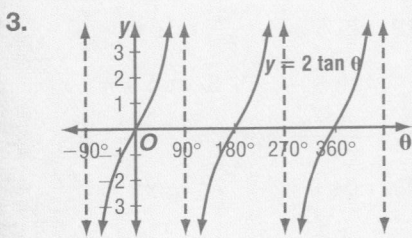

4.

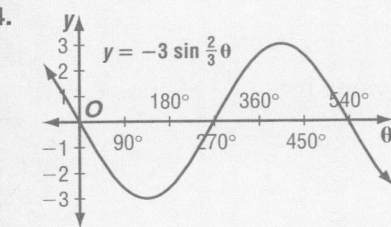

5.

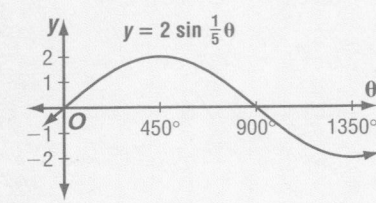

6.

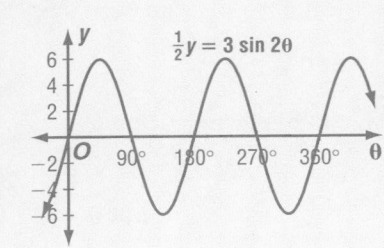

7.

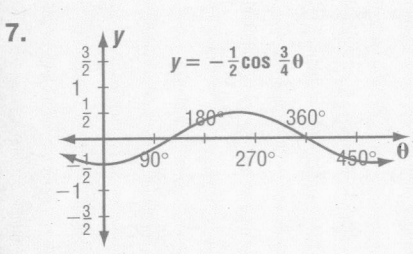

EXTRA PRACTICE

Lesson 13-6   Determine the period of each function.

1.

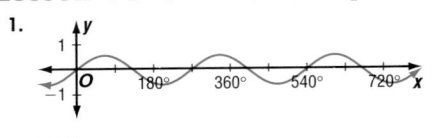

270°

2.

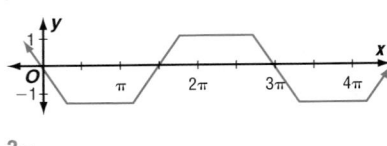

3π

Find the value of each function.

3. $\sin 210°$ $-\frac{1}{2}$

4. $\cos 150°$ $-\frac{\sqrt{3}}{2}$

5. $\cos(-135°)$ $-\frac{\sqrt{2}}{2}$

6. $\cos\frac{3\pi}{4}$ $-\frac{\sqrt{2}}{2}$

7. $\sin 570°$ $-\frac{1}{2}$

8. $\sin 390°$ $\frac{1}{2}$

9. $\sin\frac{4\pi}{3}$ $-\frac{\sqrt{3}}{2}$

10. $\cos\left(-\frac{7\pi}{3}\right)$ $\frac{1}{2}$

11. $\cos 30° + \cos 60°$
$\frac{1+\sqrt{3}}{2}$

12. $5(\sin 45°)(\cos 45°)$
$\frac{5}{2}$

13. $\frac{\sin 210° + \cos 240°}{2}$
$-\frac{1}{2}$

14. $\frac{6\cos 120° + 4\sin 150°}{5}$
$-\frac{1}{5}$

Lesson 13-7   Write each equation in the form of an inverse function.

1. $\sin m = n$
$\text{Arcsin } n = m$

2. $\tan 45° = 1$
$\text{Arctan } 1 = 45°$

3. $\cos x = \frac{3}{2}$
$\text{Arccos } \frac{3}{2} = x$

4. $\sin 65° = a$
$\text{Arcsin } a = 65°$

5. $\tan 60° = \sqrt{3}$
$\text{Arctan } \sqrt{3} = 60°$

Solve each equation.

6. $y = \text{Sin}^{-1}\frac{\sqrt{2}}{2}$
45°

7. $\text{Tan}^{-1} 1 = x$
45°

8. $a = \text{Arccos}\frac{\sqrt{3}}{2}$
30°

9. $\text{Arcsin } 0 = x$
0°

10. $y = \text{Cos}^{-1}\frac{1}{2}$
60°

Find each value.

11. $\text{Arccos}\left(-\frac{\sqrt{2}}{2}\right)$ 135°

12. $\text{Sin}^{-1} -1$ $-90°$

13. $\cos\left(\text{Arcsin}\frac{\sqrt{2}}{2}\right)$

14. $\tan\left(\text{Sin}^{-1}\left(\frac{5}{13}\right)\right)$ $\frac{5}{12}$

15. $\sin 2\left(\text{Arccos}\frac{1}{2}\right)$ $\frac{\sqrt{3}}{2}$

16. $\sin\left(\text{Arccos}\frac{15}{17}\right)$ $\frac{8}{17}$

17. $\sin\left(\text{Tan}^{-1}\frac{5}{12}\right)$ $\frac{5}{13}$

18. $\tan\left(\text{Arccos}\left(-\frac{\sqrt{3}}{2}\right)\right)$
$-\frac{\sqrt{3}}{3}$

13. $\frac{\sqrt{2}}{2}$

Lesson 14-1   Graph each function.   1–12. See margin.

1. $y = \csc\frac{1}{3}\theta$

2. $y = 2\sec\theta$

3. $y = 2\tan\theta$

4. $y = -3\sin\frac{2}{3}\theta$

5. $y = 2\sin\frac{1}{5}\theta$

6. $\frac{1}{2}y = 3\sin 2\theta$

7. $y = -\frac{1}{2}\cos\frac{3}{4}\theta$

8. $\frac{1}{2}y = 5\csc 3\theta$

9. $y = 2\cot 6\theta$

10. $y = \csc 6\theta$

11. $y = 3\tan\frac{1}{3}\theta$

12. $y = \frac{4}{3}\cot\frac{1}{2}\theta$

13–22. See margin.
Write an equation of the given sine or cosine function having the specific characteristics.

	Function	Amplitude	Period
13.	sine	3	360°
14.	sine	4.8	120°
15.	sine	0.45	60°
16.	sine	5	1080°
17.	sine	$\frac{1}{3}$	30°

	Function	Amplitude	Period
18.	cosine	0.8	360°
19.	cosine	5	60°
20.	cosine	$\frac{1}{4}$	90°
21.	cosine	3	720°
22.	cosine	6.5	120°

Lesson 14-2
Solve for values of θ between 0° and 90°.

1. If $\cos \theta = \frac{4}{5}$, find $\tan \theta$. $\frac{3}{4}$
2. If $\sin \theta = \frac{1}{2}$, find $\cos \theta$. $\frac{\sqrt{3}}{2}$
3. If $\sin \theta = \frac{3}{4}$, find $\sec \theta$. $\frac{4\sqrt{7}}{7}$
4. If $\tan \theta = 4$, find $\sin \theta$. $\frac{4\sqrt{17}}{17}$
5. If $\tan \theta = 4$, find $\cos \theta$. $\frac{\sqrt{17}}{17}$
6. If $\cot \theta = \frac{1}{4}$, find $\csc \theta$. $\frac{\sqrt{17}}{4}$

Solve for values of θ between 180° and 270°.

7. If $\sec \theta = -3$, find $\tan \theta$. $2\sqrt{2}$
8. If $\cos \theta = -\frac{3}{5}$, find $\csc \theta$. $-\frac{5}{4}$
9. If $\sin \theta = -\frac{1}{2}$, find $\cos \theta$. $-\frac{\sqrt{3}}{2}$
10. If $\cot \theta = \frac{1}{4}$, find $\csc \theta$. $-\frac{\sqrt{17}}{4}$
11. If $\cot \theta = \frac{3}{5}$, find $\csc \theta$. $-\frac{\sqrt{34}}{5}$
12. If $\tan \theta = 4$, find $\cos \theta$. $-\frac{\sqrt{17}}{17}$

Simplify each expression.

13. $\frac{\sin^2 \theta + \cos^2 \theta}{\sin^2 \theta}$ $\csc^2 \theta$
14. $\frac{1 + \tan^2 \theta}{1 + \cot^2 \theta}$ $\tan^2 \theta$
15. $\frac{1}{1 + \sin \theta} + \frac{1}{1 - \sin \theta}$ $2 \sec^2 \theta$
16. $\frac{1 - \sin^2 \theta}{\sin^2 \theta}$ $\cot^2 \theta$

17. $\csc^2 \theta - \cot^2 \theta$ 1
18. $\cos \theta \csc \theta$ $\cot \theta$
19. $\tan \theta \csc \theta$ $\sec \theta$
20. $\sin \theta \cot \theta$ $\cos \theta$

Lesson 14-3
Verify that each of the following is an identity.   1–21. See Solutions Manual.

1. $1 + \tan^2 \theta = \sec^2 \theta$
2. $\frac{\tan \theta}{\sin \theta} = \sec \theta$
3. $\frac{\tan \theta}{\cot \theta} = \tan^2 \theta$
4. $\frac{\cos^2 \theta}{1 - \sin \theta} = 1 + \sin \theta$
5. $1 - \cot^4 \theta = 2 \csc^2 \theta - \csc^4 \theta$
6. $\sin^4 \theta - \cos^4 \theta = \sin^2 \theta - \cos^2 \theta$
7. $\cos^2 \theta + \tan^2 \theta \cos^2 \theta = 1$
8. $\frac{\sec \theta}{\sin \theta} - \frac{\sin \theta}{\cos \theta} = \cot \theta$
9. $\frac{\cos \theta}{\sec \theta - 1} + \frac{\cos \theta}{\sec \theta + 1} = 2 \cot^2 \theta$
10. $\tan \theta + \cot \theta = \csc \theta \sec \theta$
11. $\frac{1 - \cos \theta}{\sin \theta} = \frac{\sin \theta}{1 + \cos \theta}$
12. $\cot^2 \theta + \sin^2 \theta = \csc^2 \theta - \cos^2 \theta$
13. $\sec \theta + \tan \theta = \frac{\cos \theta}{1 - \sin \theta}$
14. $\frac{\cot^2 \theta}{1 + \cot^2 \theta} = 1 - \sin^2 \theta$
15. $\frac{\tan \theta - \sin \theta}{\sec \theta} = \frac{\sin^3 \theta}{1 + \cos \theta}$
16. $\sin^2 \theta + \sin^2 \theta \tan^2 \theta = \tan^2 \theta$
17. $\frac{\sec \theta - 1}{\sec \theta + 1} + \frac{\cos \theta - 1}{\cos \theta + 1} = 0$
18. $1 + \sec^2 \theta \sin^2 \theta = \sec^2 \theta$
19. $\tan \theta + \frac{\cos \theta}{1 + \sin \theta} = \sec \theta$
20. $\frac{\tan \theta}{\sec \theta + 1} = \frac{1 - \cos \theta}{\sin \theta}$
21. $\csc \theta - \frac{\sin \theta}{1 + \cos \theta} = \cot \theta$

Lesson 14-4
Find the exact value of each expression.

1. $\sin 195°$ $\frac{\sqrt{2} - \sqrt{6}}{4}$
2. $\cos 285°$ $\frac{\sqrt{6} - \sqrt{2}}{4}$
3. $\sin 255°$ $\frac{-\sqrt{6} - \sqrt{2}}{4}$
4. $\sin 105°$ $\frac{\sqrt{2} + \sqrt{6}}{4}$
5. $\cos 15°$ $\frac{\sqrt{6} + \sqrt{2}}{4}$
6. $\sin 15°$ $\frac{\sqrt{6} - \sqrt{2}}{4}$
7. $\cos 375°$ $\frac{\sqrt{6} + \sqrt{2}}{4}$
8. $\sin 165°$ $\frac{\sqrt{6} - \sqrt{2}}{4}$

Verify that each of the following is an identity.   9–13. See Solutions Manual.

9. $\sin (270° - \theta) = -\cos \theta$
10. $\cos (90° + \theta) = -\sin \theta$
11. $\sin \left(\frac{\pi}{2} + x \right) = \cos x$
12. $\sin (x + 30°) + \cos (x + 60°) = \cos x$
13. $\cos (30° - x) + \cos (30° + x) = \sqrt{3} \cos x$

14. $-2 - \sqrt{3}$ 15. $2 + \sqrt{3}$

Use the identity $\tan(\alpha + \beta) = \frac{\tan \alpha + \tan \beta}{1 - \tan \alpha \tan \beta}$ **to find the exact value of each expression.**

14. $\tan (60° + 45°)$
15. $\tan (135° + 120°)$
16. $\tan 165°$ $\sqrt{3} - 2$
17. $\tan 255$ $2 + \sqrt{3}$

Additional Answers for Lesson 14-1

8. 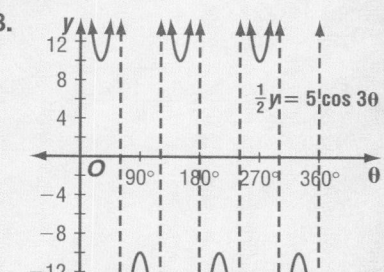 $\frac{1}{2}y = 5 \cos 3\theta$

9. 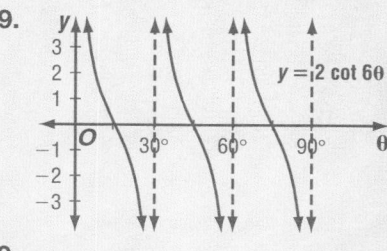 $y = 2 \cot 6\theta$

10. 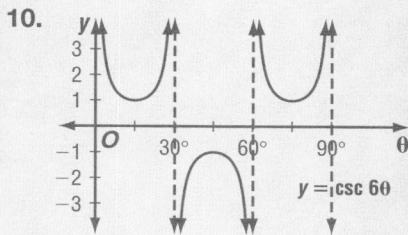 $y = \csc 6\theta$

11. 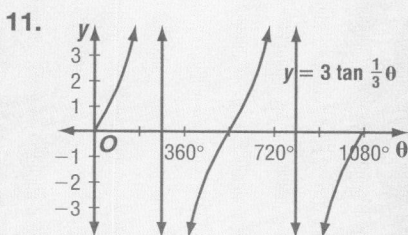 $y = 3 \tan \frac{1}{3}\theta$

12. 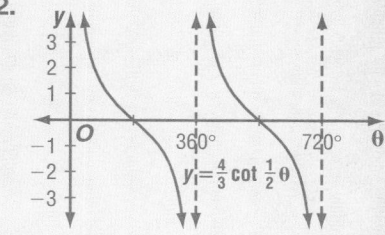 $y = \frac{4}{3} \cot \frac{1}{2}\theta$

13. $y = 3 \sin \theta$
14. $y = 4.8 \sin 3\theta$
15. $y = 0.45 \sin 6\theta$
16. $y = 5 \sin \frac{1}{3}\theta$
17. $y = \frac{1}{3} \sin 12\theta$
18. $y = 0.8 \cos \theta$
19. $y = 5 \cos 6\theta$
20. $y = \frac{1}{4} \cos 4\theta$
21. $y = 3 \cos \frac{1}{2}\theta$
22. $y = 6.5 \cos 3\theta$

Additional Answers for Lesson 14-5

1. $\frac{336}{625}, -\frac{527}{625}, \frac{3}{5}, \frac{4}{5}$

2. $\frac{4\sqrt{21}}{25}, \frac{17}{25}, \frac{\sqrt{50-10\sqrt{21}}}{10},$
   $\frac{\sqrt{50+10\sqrt{21}}}{10}$

3. $\frac{3\sqrt{7}}{32}, -\frac{31}{32}, \frac{3}{4}, -\frac{\sqrt{7}}{4}$

4. $-\frac{120}{169}, \frac{119}{169}, \frac{\sqrt{26}}{26}, -\frac{5\sqrt{26}}{26}$

5. $-\frac{\sqrt{35}}{18}, -\frac{17}{18}, \frac{\sqrt{21}}{6}, \frac{\sqrt{15}}{6}$

6. $-\frac{17\sqrt{35}}{162}, \frac{127}{162}, \frac{\sqrt{35}}{6}, \frac{1}{6}$

Lesson 14-5 Find the exact values of $\sin 2x$, $\cos 2x$, $\sin \frac{x}{2}$, and $\cos \frac{x}{2}$ for each of the following, given the two measures between which the terminal side of x lies. **1–6. See margin.**

1. $\cos x = \frac{7}{25}$; x is between $0°$ and $90°$

2. $\sin x = \frac{2}{5}$; x is between $0°$ and $90°$

3. $\cos x = -\frac{1}{8}$; x is between $180°$ and $270°$

4. $\sin x = -\frac{5}{13}$; x is between $270°$ and $360°$

5. $\sin x = \frac{\sqrt{35}}{6}$; x is between $90°$ and $180°$

6. $\cos x = -\frac{17}{18}$; x is between $90°$ and $180°$

Find the exact value of each expression by using the half-angle formulas.

7. $\sin 15°$ $\frac{\sqrt{2-\sqrt{3}}}{2}$

8. $\cos 75°$ $\frac{\sqrt{2-\sqrt{3}}}{2}$

9. $\sin \frac{\pi}{8}$ $\frac{\sqrt{2-\sqrt{2}}}{2}$

10. $\cos \frac{13\pi}{12}$ $-\frac{\sqrt{2+\sqrt{3}}}{2}$

Verify that each of the following is an identity. **11–19. See Solutions Manual.**

11. $\frac{\sin 2x}{2\sin^2 x} = \cot x$

12. $1 + \cos 2x = \frac{2}{1+\tan^2 x}$

13. $\csc x \sec x = 2 \csc 2x$

14. $\frac{1-\tan^2 x}{1+\tan^2 x} = \cos 2x$

15. $\sin 2x (\cot x + \tan x) = 2$

16. $\sin^2 x = \frac{1}{2}(1 - \cos 2x)$

17. $\frac{\cos x + \sin x}{\cos x - \sin x} = \frac{1 + \sin 2x}{\cos 2x}$

18. $\frac{\sin \frac{x}{2}}{\cos \frac{x}{2}} = \frac{\sin x}{1 + \cos x}$

19. $\cot x = \frac{\sin 2x}{1 - \cos 2x}$

Lesson 14-6 Find all solutions if $0° \le x < 360°$. **2. $120°, 150°, 300°, 330°$**   **3. $30°, 150°$**

1. $\cos x = -\frac{\sqrt{3}}{2}$ $150°, 210°$

2. $\sin 2x = -\frac{\sqrt{3}}{2}$

3. $\cos 2x = 8 - 15 \sin x$

4. $\sin x + \cos x = 1$ $0°, 90°$

5. $2 \sin^2 x + \sin x = 0$
   $0°, 180°, 210°, 330°$

6. $\sin 2x = \cos x$
   $30°, 90°, 150°, 270°$

Find all solutions if $0 \le \theta < 2\pi$. **8. $0, \frac{\pi}{4}, \frac{\pi}{2}, \frac{3\pi}{4}, \pi, \frac{5\pi}{4}, \frac{3\pi}{2}, \frac{7\pi}{4}$**   **9. $0, \pi, \frac{7\pi}{6}, \frac{11\pi}{6}$**

7. $\tan \theta = 1$ $\frac{\pi}{4}, \frac{5\pi}{4}$

8. $\cos 8\theta = 1$

9. $\sin \theta + 1 = \cos 2\theta$

10. $8 \sin \theta \cos \theta = 2\sqrt{3}$
    $\frac{\pi}{6}, \frac{\pi}{3}, \frac{7\pi}{6}, \frac{4\pi}{3}$

11. $\cos \theta = 1 + \sin \theta$
    $0, \frac{3\pi}{2}$

12. $2 \cos^2 \theta = \cos \theta$
    $\frac{\pi}{3}, \frac{\pi}{2}, \frac{3\pi}{2}, \frac{5\pi}{3}$

14. $90° + 180k°, 30° + 360k°, 150° + 360k°$

Solve each equation for all values for x if x is measured in degrees.

13. $2 \sin^2 x - 1 = 0$ $45° + 90k°$

14. $\cos x - 2 \cos x \sin x = 0$

15. $\cos 2x \sin x = 1$ $270° + 360k°$

16. $(\tan x - 1)(2 \cos x + 1) = 0$

17. $2 \cos^2 x = 0.5$

18. $\sin x \tan x - \tan x = 0$

16. $45° + 180k°, 120° + 360k°, 240 + 360k°$ 17. $60° + 360k°, 120° + 360k°, 240° + 360k°, 300° + 360k°$

18. $180k°, 90° + 360k°$ **22. $2k\pi, \frac{\pi}{3} + 2k\pi, \frac{5\pi}{3} + 2k\pi$**   **23. $k\pi, \frac{\pi}{6} + k\pi$**   **24. $\frac{2\pi}{3} + k\pi, \frac{5\pi}{6} + k\pi$**

Solve each equation for all values of θ if θ is measured in radians.

19. $\cos 2\theta \sin \theta = 1$ $\frac{3\pi}{2} + 2k\pi$

20. $\sin \frac{\theta}{2} + \cos \frac{\theta}{2} = \sqrt{2}$ $\frac{\pi}{2} + 2k\pi$

21. $\cos 2\theta + 4 \cos \theta = -3$
    $\pi + 2k\pi$

22. $\sin \frac{\theta}{2} + \cos \theta = 1$

23. $3 \tan^2 \theta - \sqrt{3} \tan \theta = 0$

24. $4 \sin \theta \cos \theta = -\sqrt{3}$

CHAPTER 1 TEST

Name the property illustrated by each equation or statement.   2. symmetric (=)

1. $(7 \cdot s) \cdot t = 7 \cdot (s \cdot t)$ associative ($\times$)

2. If $(r + s)t = rt + st$, then $rt + st = (r + s)t$.

3. $\left(3 \cdot \frac{1}{3}\right) \cdot 7 = \left(3 \cdot \frac{1}{3}\right) \cdot 7$ reflexive (=)

4. $(6 - 2)a - 3b = 4a - 3b$ substitution (=)

5. $(7 \cdot s) \cdot t = t \cdot (7 \cdot s)$ commutative ($\times$)

6. If $5(3) + 7 = 15 + 7$ and $15 + 7 = 22$, then $5(3) + 7 = 22$.   transitive (=)

Find the value of each expression.

7. $[2 + 3^3 - 4] \div 2$ 12.5

8. $(2 + 3)^3 - 4 \div 2$ 123

9. $(4^5 - 4^2) + 4^3$ 1072

10. $[5(17 - 2) \div 3] - 2^4$ 9

Evaluate each expression if $a = -9$, $b = \frac{2}{3}$, $c = 8$, and $d = -6$.

11. $\frac{db + 4c}{a}$ $-\frac{28}{9}$

12. $\frac{a}{b^2} + c$ -12.25

13. $2b(4a + a^2)$ 60

14. $\frac{4a + 3c}{3b}$ -6

Name the sets of numbers to which each number belongs. Use N, W, Z, Q, I, and R.

15. $\sqrt{17}$ I, R

16. 0.86 Q, R

17. $\sqrt{64}$ N, W, Z, Q, R

18. $-10 \div 2$ Z, Q, R

Solve each equation.

19. $5t - 3 = -2t + 10$ $\frac{13}{7}$

20. $2x - 7 - (x - 5) = 0$ 2

21. $5m - (5 + 4m) = (3 + m) - 8$ all reals

22. $|8w + 2| + 2 = 0$ no solution

23. $12 \left| \frac{1}{2}y + 3 \right| = 6$ $-5, -7$

24. $2|2y - 6| + 4 = 8$ 2, 4

Solve each inequality. Graph each solution set.   25–30. See Solutions Manual for graphs.

25. $4 > b + 1$ $\{b \mid b < 3\}$

26. $3q + 7 \geq 13$ $\{q \mid q \geq 2\}$

27. $5(3x - 5) + x < 2(4x - 1) + 1$ $\{x \mid x < 3\}$

28. $|9y - 4| + 8 > 4$ all reals

29. $-12 < 7s - 5 \leq 9$ $\{s \mid -1 < s \leq 2\}$

30. $|5 + k| \leq 8$ $\{k \mid -13 \leq k \leq 3\}$

31. **Employment**   The back-to-back stem-and-leaf plot below shows the median weekly incomes of male and female workers in various occupations. Find the median, mode, and mean of the male workers' incomes and of the female workers' incomes.

Males	Stem	Females
	2	0 1 4 4
5 6	.	6 7 9
0	3	1
7	.	5 6
0 2 2 3	4	1 4
5 8	.	9
1	5	
	.	
	6	
6 7	.	$2 \mid 4 = 240$

Define a variable, write an equation, and solve the problem.

32. **Statistics**   To receive a B in his English class, Dale must earn at least 400 points on five tests. He scored 87, 89, 76, and 77 on his first four tests. What must he score on the last test to receive a B in the class?   Let s = score on last test; $s + 87 + 89 + 76 + 77 = 400$; 71

33. **Car Rental**   A salesman rented a car that could get 35 miles per gallon. He paid $19.50 a day for the car plus $0.18 per mile. He rented the car for 1 day and paid $33. How many miles did he travel?   Let m = miles traveled; $19.50 + 0.18m = 33$; 75 miles

31. males — 420, 420, 432.3; females — 290, 240, 313.1

Graph each relation. State the domain and the range. Is the relation a function?

1. $\{(-4, -81), (-2, 21), (0, 51), (2, 33), (4, -9)\}$ $D = \{-4, -2, 0, 2, 4\}$; $R = \{-81, 21, 51, 33, -9\}$; yes
2. $\{(-5, 0), (-3, 1), (-1, 2), (-3, 3), (-5, 4)\}$ $D = \{-5, -3, -1\}$; $R = \{0, 1, 2, 3, 4\}$; no
1–2. See Solutions Manual for graphs.

Find values of functions for the given elements of the domain.

3. Find $f(-3)$ if $f(x) = 2x^2 - 3x + 5$.   **32**

4. Find $f(5)$ if $f(x) = 11x^3 - x + 1$.   **1371**

5. Find $f(3.7)$ if $f(x) = 7 - x^2$.   **−6.69**

6. Find $f(0)$ if $f(x) = x - 3x^2$.   **0**

Graph each equation or inequality.   7–18. See Solutions Manual.

7. $-2x + 5 \le 3y$

8. $4x - y + 2 = 0$

9. $x = -4$

10. $y = 2x - 5$

11. $y \le 10$

12. $x > 6$

13. $-8x + 4y \ge 32$

14. $f(x) = [3x] + 3$

15. $y < 4|x - 1|$

16. $f(x) = 3x - 1$

17. $g(x) = -\frac{1}{2}x$

18. $y = \frac{3}{5}x - 4$

Find the slope of the line that passes through each pair of points.

19. $(8, -4)$ and $(6, 1)$ $-\frac{5}{2}$

20. $(-2, 5)$ and $(4, 5)$ **0**

21. $(5, 7)$ and $(4, -6)$ **13**

22. $(4, 5)$ and $(4, -3)$ **undefined**

23. $(-5, -4)$ and $(5, 2)$ $\frac{3}{5}$

24. $(-3, -5)$ and $(9, -1)$ $\frac{1}{3}$

Write an equation in slope-intercept form that satisfies each condition.

25. slope $= -5$, y-intercept $= 11$ $y = -5x + 11$

26. slope $= \frac{2}{3}$, passes through $(-6, 15)$ $y = \frac{2}{3}x + 19$

27. passes through $(-3, 7)$ and $(7, -8)$ $y = -\frac{3}{2}x + \frac{5}{2}$

28. x-intercept $= 9$, y-intercept $= -4$ $y = \frac{4}{9}x - 4$

29. passes through $(4, -2)$ and the origin $y = -\frac{1}{2}x$

30. parallel to $6x - y = 7$, passes through $(-2, 8)$ $y = 6x + 20$

31. perpendicular to $x + 3y = 7$, passes through $(5, 2)$ $y = 3x - 13$

The table below shows the expected number of people in the U.S. that are age 100 and over.

Year	1994	1996	1998	2000	2002	2004
Number of People	50,000	56,000	65,000	75,000	94,000	110,000

Source: U.S. Census Bureau

32. See Solutions Manual.

32. Draw a scatter plot of the data to show the relationship. Let x represent the years since 1990.

33. Find a prediction equation to show how time and the number of people aged 100 and over are related.   Sample answer: $y = 6000x + 20,000$

CHAPTER 3 TEST

Graph each system of equations and state its solution. 1–3. See Solutions Manual for graphs.

1. $-4x + y = -5$
   $2x + y = 7$ **(2, 3)**

2. $x + y = -8$
   $-3x + 2y = 9$ **(−5, −3)**

3. $-6x + 3y = 33$
   $-4x + y = 16$ **(−2.5, 6)**

Solve each system of equations. Use either the substitution or the elimination method.

4. $3x - 2y = 8$
   $y = 6x + 11$ $\left(-\dfrac{10}{3}, -9\right)$

5. $2y = 5x - 1$
   $x + y = -1$ $\left(-\dfrac{1}{7}, -\dfrac{6}{7}\right)$

6. $-7x + 6y = 42$
   $3x + 4y = 28$ **(0, 7)**

Find the value of each second-order determinant.

7. $\begin{vmatrix} -4 & 3 \\ 5 & -2 \end{vmatrix}$ -7

8. $\begin{vmatrix} 1 & -6 \\ 8 & 7 \end{vmatrix}$ 55

9. $\begin{vmatrix} 0 & -4 \\ 2 & 11 \end{vmatrix}$ 8

Use Cramer's rule to solve each system of equations.

10. $4x + 5y = 60$
    $5x + 4y = -20$ $\left(-\dfrac{340}{9}, \dfrac{380}{9}\right)$

11. $6x + y = 15$
    $x - 4y = -16$ **(1.76, 4.44)**

12. $3x - 8y = 23$
    $5x + y = 24$ **(5, −1)**

Solve each system of inequalities by graphing. 13–15. See Solutions Manual.

13. $y \geq x - 3$
    $y \geq -x + 1$

14. $x + 2y \geq 7$
    $3x - 4y < 12$

15. $|x| > 5$
    $x + y < 6$

Graph each system of inequalities. Name the coordinates of the vertices of the feasible region. Find the maximum and the minimum values of the given function for this region. 16–17. See Solutions Manual for graphs.

16. $y \leq 5$
    $y \geq -3$
    $4x + y \leq 5$
    $-2x + y \leq 5$
    $f(x, y) = 4x - 3y$

    vertices: (0, 5), (−4, −3), (2, −3)
    max: $f(2, -3) = 17$;
    min: $f(0, 5) = -15$

17. $x \geq -10$
    $y \geq -6$
    $y \leq 1$
    $\dfrac{3}{4}x + y \leq -2$
    $y \geq \dfrac{1}{2}x - 5$
    $f(x, y) = 2x + y$

    vertices: (−10, 1), (−4, 1),
    (2.4, −3.8), (−2, −6), (−10, −6)
    max: $f(2.4, -3.8) = 1$
    min: $f(-10, -6) = -26$

A sporting goods manufacturer makes a $5 profit on soccer balls and a $4 profit on volleyballs. Department S requires 2 hours to make 75 soccer balls and 3 hours to make 60 volleyballs. Department V needs 3 hours to make 75 soccer balls and 2 hours to make 60 volleyballs. Department S has 500 hours available and Department V has 450 hours available. 18. 11,250 soccer balls and 0 volleyballs

18. How many soccer balls and volleyballs should be made to maximize the profit?

19. What is the maximum profit the company can make from these two products? **$56,250**

Solve each system of equations. 22. (0.25, 0.5, 0.75)

20. $x + y + z = -1$
    $2x + 4y + z = 1$
    $x + 2y - 3z = -3$ **(−4, 2, 1)**

21. $x + z = 7$
    $2y - z = -3$
    $-x - 3y + 2z = 11$ **(−2, 3, 9)**

22. $x - y + z = 0.5$
    $-x - y + z = 0$
    $7x - y + 4z = 4.25$

Carla, Beth, and Heidi went on a shopping spree to get ready for college. Carla bought 3 shirts, 4 pairs of pants, and 2 pairs of shoes costing her a total of $149.79. Beth came away with 5 shirts, 3 pairs of pants, and 3 pairs of shoes totaling $183.19. Heidi, not to be outdone, bought 6 shirts, 5 pairs of pants and a pair of shoes. Her total bill came to $181.14. Assume that all the shirts cost the same price, all the pants cost the same price, and all the shoes cost the same price.

23. How much money did each girl pay for a shirt? **$12.95**

24. How much money did each girl pay for a pair of pants? **$15.99**

25. How much money did each girl pay for a pair of shoes? **$23.49**

Perform the indicated operations, if possible.

1. $\begin{bmatrix} 1 & 2 \\ -4 & 3 \\ 5 & 2 \end{bmatrix} \cdot \begin{bmatrix} 5 \\ 4 \end{bmatrix}$ $\begin{bmatrix} 13 \\ -8 \\ 33 \end{bmatrix}$

2. $\begin{bmatrix} 2 & -4 & 1 \\ 3 & 8 & -2 \end{bmatrix} - 2\begin{bmatrix} 1 & 2 & -4 \\ -2 & 3 & 7 \end{bmatrix}$ $\begin{bmatrix} 0 & -8 & 9 \\ 7 & 2 & -16 \end{bmatrix}$

3. $\begin{bmatrix} -0.5 & 0.7 \\ 0.2 & -0.6 \end{bmatrix} + \begin{bmatrix} 3.4 \\ 2.1 \end{bmatrix}$ not possible

4. $-4\begin{bmatrix} -5 & 7 \\ 2 & -6 \end{bmatrix} + 0.5\begin{bmatrix} -2 & 8 \\ 2 & -4 \end{bmatrix}$ $\begin{bmatrix} 19 & -24 \\ -7 & 22 \end{bmatrix}$

5. $\begin{bmatrix} -5 & 7 \\ 2 & -6 \end{bmatrix} \cdot \begin{bmatrix} 2 & -4 & 1 \\ 3 & 8 & -2 \end{bmatrix}$ $\begin{bmatrix} 11 & 76 & -19 \\ -14 & -56 & 14 \end{bmatrix}$

6. $\begin{bmatrix} 6 & 7 \\ -3 & -4 \end{bmatrix} \cdot \begin{bmatrix} -4 & 3 \\ -1 & -2 \\ 2 & 5 \end{bmatrix}$ not possible

8. yes, −57   9. no, not square   10. yes, −6

Determine whether each matrix has a determinant. Write *yes* or *no*. If *yes*, find the value of the determinant. If *no*, explain why not.

7. $\begin{bmatrix} -1 & 4 \\ -6 & 3 \end{bmatrix}$ yes, 21

8. $\begin{bmatrix} -2 & 0 & 5 \\ -3 & 4 & 0 \\ 1 & 3 & -1 \end{bmatrix}$

9. $\begin{bmatrix} 2 & -4 & 1 \\ 3 & 8 & -2 \end{bmatrix}$

10. $\begin{bmatrix} 5 & -3 & 2 \\ -6 & 1 & 3 \\ -1 & 4 & -7 \end{bmatrix}$

Find the inverse of each matrix, if it exists. If it does not exist, explain why not.

11. $\begin{bmatrix} -2 & 5 \\ 3 & 1 \end{bmatrix}$ $-\frac{1}{17}\begin{bmatrix} 1 & -5 \\ -3 & -2 \end{bmatrix}$

12. $\begin{bmatrix} -6 & -3 \\ 8 & 4 \end{bmatrix}$ det = 0

13. $\begin{bmatrix} 5 & -2 \\ 6 & 3 \end{bmatrix}$ $\frac{1}{27}\begin{bmatrix} 3 & 2 \\ -6 & 5 \end{bmatrix}$

14. $\begin{bmatrix} 35 \\ 23 \end{bmatrix}$ not square

Solve each matrix equation or system of equations.

15. $5a + 2b = -49$ $(-11, 3)$
    $2a + 9b = 5$

16. $6x - y = -15$ $(-2, 3)$
    $5x + 4 = -2y$

17. $2x - y + 3z = 1$
    $x - y + 4z = 0$ $(2, 6, 1)$
    $3x - 2y + z = -5$

18. $\begin{bmatrix} 1 & 8 \\ 2 & -6 \end{bmatrix} \cdot \begin{bmatrix} x \\ y \end{bmatrix} = \begin{bmatrix} -3 \\ -17 \end{bmatrix}$ $\left(-7, \frac{1}{2}\right)$

19. $\begin{bmatrix} 2 & 0 & 1 \\ 4 & 1 & 2 \\ 2 & 0 & 4 \end{bmatrix} \cdot \begin{bmatrix} a \\ b \\ c \end{bmatrix} = \begin{bmatrix} 10 \\ 19 \\ 22 \end{bmatrix}$ and $M^{-1} = \frac{1}{6}\begin{bmatrix} 4 & 0 & -1 \\ -12 & 6 & 0 \\ -2 & 0 & 2 \end{bmatrix}$ $(3, -1, 4)$

Find the range, quartiles, interquartile range, and outliers for each set of data.

20.
Stem	Leaf
0	1 1 8 8 9
1	4 5 5 7 7 7 9
2	1 4 4 5 8 8 8 8 9
3	0 1 3 6 6 7 8
4	4 5 6 9 $2\,|\,4 = 240$

480; 160, 265, 345; 185; no outliers

21. {100, 99, 93, 94, 96, 94, 95, 101, 109, 108, 104, 106, 125, 100, 104, 98, 19}
106; 94.5, 100, 105; 10.5; 19, 125

22. Judi is buying a pair of headphones to use with her stereo receiver. The prices of the 21 different types of stereo headphones sold at the Stereo Studio are $100, $150, $75, $79, $149, $120, $80, $70, $400, $190, $50, $80, $148, $40, $85, $60, $160, $90, $90, $125, and $120. Make a box-and-whisker plot of the data. See Solutions Manual.

24. $A'(8, -1)$, $C'(1, 0)$ 25. Sample answer: $A'(30, 15)$, $B'(5, 25)$, $C'(-5, 20)$

For Exercises 23–25, use $\triangle ABC$ whose vertices have coordinates $A(6, 3)$, $B(1, 5)$, and $C(-1, 4)$.

23. Use a determinant to find the area of $\triangle ABC$. $4\frac{1}{2}$ sq. units

24. Translate $\triangle ABC$ so that the coordinates of B' are $(3, 1)$. What are the coordinates of A' and C'?

25. Find the coordinates of the vertices of a similar triangle whose perimeter is five times that of $\triangle ABC$.

Simplify.

1. $(5b)^4(6c)^2$ $22{,}500b^4c^2$

2. $(13x - 1)(x + 3)$ $13x^2 + 38x - 3$

3. $(2h - 6)^3$
$8h^3 - 72h^2 + 216h - 216$

Evaluate. Express each answer in both scientific and decimal notation.

4. $(3.16 \times 10^3)(24 \times 10^2)$ 7.584×10^6; $7{,}584{,}000$

5. $\dfrac{7{,}200{,}000 \cdot 0.0011}{0.018}$ 4.4×10^5; $440{,}000$

Use synthetic division to find each quotient.

6. $(x^4 - x^3 - 10x^2 + 4x + 24) \div (x - 2)$
$x^3 + x^2 - 8x - 12$

7. $(2x^3 + 9x^2 - 2x + 7) \div (x + 2)$
$2x^2 + 5x - 12 + \dfrac{31}{x + 2}$

Factor completely. If the polynomial is not factorable, write *prime*.

8. $x^2 - 14x + 45$ $(x - 5)(x - 9)$

9. $2r^2 + 3pr - 2p^2$ $(2r - p)(r + 2p)$

10. $x^2 + 2\sqrt{3}x + 3$ $(x + \sqrt{3})^2$

Evaluate.

11. $\sqrt{175}$ $5\sqrt{7}$

12. $(5 + \sqrt{3})(7 - 2\sqrt{3})$ $29 - 3\sqrt{3}$

13. $3\sqrt{6} + 5\sqrt{54}$ $18\sqrt{6}$

14. $\dfrac{9}{5 - \sqrt{3}}$ $\dfrac{45 + 9\sqrt{3}}{22}$

15. $\left(9^{\frac{1}{2}} \cdot 9^{\frac{2}{3}}\right)^{\frac{1}{6}}$ $9^{\frac{7}{36}}$

16. $11^{\frac{1}{2}} \cdot 11^{\frac{7}{3}} \cdot 11^{\frac{1}{6}}$ 1331

Simplify.

17. $\sqrt[6]{256s^{11}t^{18}}$ $2st^3\sqrt[6]{4s^5}$

18. $v^{-\frac{7}{11}}$ $\dfrac{\sqrt[11]{v^4}}{v}$

19. $\dfrac{b^{\frac{1}{2}}}{b^{\frac{3}{2}} - b^{\frac{1}{2}}}$ $\dfrac{1}{b - 1}$

Solve each equation. Be sure to check for extraneous solutions.

20. $\sqrt{b + 15} = \sqrt{3b + 1}$ 7

21. $\sqrt{2x} = x - 4$ 8

22. $\sqrt[4]{y + 2} + 9 = 14$ 623

23. $\sqrt[3]{2w - 1} + 11 = 18$ 172

24. $\sqrt{4x + 28} = \sqrt{6x + 38}$ -5

25. $1 + \sqrt{x + 5} = \sqrt{2x + 5}$
$3 + 2\sqrt{7}$

Simplify each complex expression.

26. $(5 - 2i) - (8 - 11i)$ $-3 + 9i$

27. $(4 + 3i)(9 - 2i)$ $42 + 19i$

28. $(14 - 5i)^2$ $171 - 140i$

29. **Skydiving** The approximate time t in seconds that it takes an object to fall a distance d in feet is $t = \sqrt{\dfrac{d}{16}}$. A parachutist falls 11 seconds before the parachute opens. How far does the parachutist fall during this time period? **1936 feet**

30. **Soccer** A soccer field in a city park is rectangular. The length of the field is 120 yards and the width of the field is 60 yards. What is the distance from one corner flag to the opposite corner flag? $60\sqrt{5}$ yards

31. **Electricity** A circuit has a current of $(6 + 4j)$ amps and an impedance of $(3 - j)$ ohms. What will be the voltage of the circuit? $22 + 6j$

32. **Geometry** Hero of Alexandria, who lived sometime between 150 B.C. and A.D. 250, is credited with a formula for finding the area of any triangle with sides a, b, and c. The formula states that the area of a triangle is equal to $\sqrt{s(s - a)(s - b)(s - c)}$, with $s = \dfrac{1}{2}(a + b + c)$. If the sides of the triangle are 6, 9, and 12 feet, what is the area of the triangle? **26.14 ft²**

33. Write $4^{\frac{1}{4}}f^{\frac{3}{5}}g^{\frac{5}{8}}$ using a single radical. $\sqrt[40]{4^{10}f^{24}g^{25}}$

Solve each equation by graphing. 1–3. See Solutions Manual for graphs.

1. $x^2 + 3x - 40 = 0$ $-8, 5$ **2.** $4x^2 - 11x - 3 = 0$ $-\frac{1}{4}, 3$ **3.** $6x^2 - 216 = 0$ $-6, 6$

Solve each equation by factoring.

4. $-1.6x^2 - 3.2x + 18 = 0$ $-\frac{9}{2}, \frac{5}{2}$ **5.** $c^2 + c - 42 = 0$ $-7, 6$ **6.** $15x^2 + 16x - 7 = 0$ $-\frac{7}{5}, \frac{1}{3}$

Solve each equation by completing the square.

7. $b^2 + 8b - 48 = 0$ $-12, 4$ **8.** $h^2 + 12h + 11 = 0$ $-11, -1$ **9.** $x^2 - 9x - \frac{19}{4} = 0$ $-\frac{1}{2}, \frac{19}{2}$

Solve each equation by using the quadratic formula.

10. $3c^2 + 7c - 31 = 0$ $\dfrac{-7 \pm \sqrt{421}}{6}$ **11.** $10v^2 + 3v = 1$ $-\frac{1}{2}, \frac{1}{5}$ **12.** $-11x^2 - 174x + 221 = 0$ $-17, \frac{13}{11}$

Find the sum and the product of the roots for each quadratic equation.

13. $2x^2 + 8x - 3 = 0$ $-4, -\frac{3}{2}$ **14.** $5x^2 = 6$ $0, -\frac{6}{5}$ **15.** $4x^2 + 3x - 12 = 0$ $-\frac{3}{4}, -3$

Find a quadratic equation that has the given roots.

16. $-2, 5$ $x^2 - 3x - 10 = 0$ **17.** $-\frac{8}{3}, \frac{7}{3}$ $9x^2 + 3x - 56 = 0$ **18.** $3 + 4i, 3 - 4i$ $x^2 - 6x + 25 = 0$

Graph each equation. Name the vertex, the axis of symmetry, and the direction of opening for each graph.   19–21. See Solutions Manual.

19. $y = (x + 2)^2 - 3$ **20.** $f(x) = x^2 + 10x + 27$ **21.** $y = (x - 5)^2 - 6$

Graph each inequality.   22–24. See Solutions Manual.

22. $y \leq x^2 + 6x - 7$ **23.** $y > -2x^2 + 9$ **24.** $y \geq 3x^2 - 15x + 22$

Solve each inequality.   25. $\{x \mid x < -7 \text{ or } x > 5\}$ 26. $\{x \mid 0 \leq x \leq 11\}$ 27. $\left\{d \mid d \geq \dfrac{4\sqrt{3}}{3} \text{ or } d \leq -\dfrac{4\sqrt{3}}{3}\right\}$

25. $(x - 5)(x + 7) > 0$ **26.** $x^2 - 11x \leq 0$ **27.** $3d^2 \geq 16$

28. Family A class of 25 students took a survey of the number of brothers and sisters each student had in his or her family. The following is a list in response to this survey: 0, 0, 0, 1, 1, 1, 1, 1, 1, 2, 2, 2, 2, 2, 2, 2, 2, 2, 2, 3, 3, 3, 4, 5, 6.

   a. Find the mean of the number of siblings in this class. $\bar{x} = 2$

   b. Find the standard deviation for the number of siblings in this class.   1.41

   c. Make a histogram representing the number of siblings in this class.   See Solutions Manual.

29. Testing The scores on a standardized college entrance exam are normally distributed. The mean score is 525, and the standard deviation is 75.

   a. Of the estimated 65,000 students who took the exam, how many scored above 600?   10,400

   b. Of the estimated 65,000 students who took the exam, how many scored below 300?   325

   c. What percentage of the students who took the exam scored below 675?   97.5%

Find the distance between each pair of points with the given coordinates.

1. $(-6, 7), (3, 2)$ $\sqrt{106}$

2. $\left(\frac{1}{2}, \frac{5}{2}\right), \left(-\frac{3}{4}, -\frac{11}{4}\right)$ $\frac{\sqrt{466}}{4}$

3. $(8, -1), (8, -9)$ 8

Find the midpoint of each line segment if the coordinates of the endpoints are given.

4. $(7, 1), (-5, 9)$ $(1, 5)$

5. $\left(\frac{3}{8}, -1\right), \left(-\frac{8}{5}, 2\right)$ $\left(-\frac{49}{80}, \frac{1}{2}\right)$

6. $(-13, 0), (-1, -8)$ $(-7, -4)$

State whether the graph of each equation is a *parabola*, a *circle*, an *ellipse*, or a *hyperbola*. Then draw the graph. 7–18. See Solutions Manual for graphs.

7. $x^2 + 4y^2 = 25$ ellipse

8. $y = 4x^2 + 1$ parabola

9. $x^2 = 36 - y^2$ circle

10. $(x + 4)^2 = 7(y + 5)$ parabola

11. $4x^2 - 26y^2 + 10 = 0$ hyperbola

12. $25x^2 + 49y^2 = 1225$ ellipse

13. $-(y^2 - 24) = x^2 + 10x$ circle

14. $5x^2 - y^2 = 49$ hyperbola

15. $25(x - 1)^2 + 121(y + 6)^2 = 3025$ ellipse

16. $x^2 + 5x + y^2 - 9y = 7$ circle

17. $\frac{1}{3}x^2 - 4 = y$ parabola

18. $\frac{y^2}{9} - \frac{x^2}{25} = 1$ hyperbola

Solve each system of equations.

19. $x^2 + y^2 = 100$

$y = 2 - x$ $(-6, 8), (8, -6)$

20. $x^2 - y^2 - 12x + 12y = 36$

$x^2 + y^2 - 12x - 12y + 36 = 0$ $(0, 6), (12, 6)$

Solve each system of inequalities by graphing. 21–22. See Solutions Manual.

21. $x^2 + y^2 \leq 169$

$x^2 + y^2 \geq 121$

22. $x^2 + y^2 \leq 81$

$y \geq x - 1$

23. **Seismology** Three tracking stations have detected an earthquake in the local area. The first station is located at the origin on the county map, where each unit of the grid represents one square mile. The second and third stations are located at $(8, -8)$ and $(11, 10)$, respectively. The epicenter of the earthquake is 5 miles from the first tracking station, 13 miles from the second tracking station, and 10 miles from the third tracking station. What are the coordinates of the epicenter of the earthquake? Explain your answer. See Solutions Manual.

24. **Tunnels** The opening of a tunnel that goes through the Rocky Mountains is in the shape of a semi-elliptical arch. The arch is 60 feet wide and 40 feet high. Find a graph that models the arch. Then find the height of the arch both 6 feet and 12 feet from the edge of the tunnel. See Solutions Manual.

25. **Architecture** Two condominium apartment buildings that face each other have a front door awning that is shaped like a hyperbola. The equation of the hyperbola is $25x^2 - 81y^2 = 30,625$. Find the distance in meters between the two front door awnings at their closest point. 70 meters

Is the given binomial a factor of the given polynomial? Show by synthetic division and writing the answer in the form *dividend = quotient · divisor + remainder*.

1. $x^3 - x^2 - 5x - 3; x + 1$ yes; $x^3 - x^2 - 5x - 3 = (x^2 - 2x - 3)(x + 1) + 0$

2. $x^3 + 8x + 1; x + 2$ no; $x^3 + 8x + 1 = (x^2 - 2x + 12)(x + 2) - 23$

3. $x^4 + 2x^3 - 7x^2 - 8x + 12; x - 2$
   yes; $x^4 + 2x^3 - 7x^2 - 8x + 12 = (x^3 + 4x^2 + x - 6)(x - 2) + 0$

For each function, state the number of positive real zeros, negative real zeros, and complex zeros.   5. 3 or 1; 0; 0 or 2

4. $f(x) = x^3 - x^2 - 14x + 24$ 2 or 0; 1; 0 or 2

5. $f(x) = 2x^3 - x^2 + 16x - 5$

6. $f(x) = x^4 + x^3 - 9x^2 - 17x - 8$ 1; 3 or 1; 0 or 2

7. $f(x) = -7x^4 + 2x^3 + x^2 - 16$
   2 or 0; 2 or 0; 0 or 4

Approximate to the nearest tenth the real zeros of each function. Then use the functional values to graph the function.   8–11. See Solutions Manual for graphs. $-3.9, -2.3, 0$

8. $g(x) = x^3 + 6x^2 + 6x - 4$ $-4.4, -2, 0.4$

9. $h(x) = x^4 + 6x^3 + 8x^2 - x$

10. $f(x) = x^3 + 3x^2 - 2x + 1$ -3.6

11. $g(x) = x^4 - 2x^3 - 6x^2 + 8x + 5$
    $-2.1, -0.5, 1.7, 2.9$

Find all the rational zeros for each function. $-6, 4$

12. $g(x) = x^3 - 3x^2 - 53x - 9$ 9

13. $h(x) = x^4 + 2x^3 - 23x^2 + 2x - 24$

14. $f(x) = 6x^3 + 4x^2 - 14x + 4$ $-2, \frac{1}{3}, 1$

15. $f(x) = 10x^3 + 43x^2 + 36x - 9$
    $-3, -\frac{3}{2}, \frac{1}{5}$

Find all zeros of each function.   17. 3, $\dfrac{-7 \pm \sqrt{41}}{2}$

16. $g(x) = x^3 - 3x - 52$ 4, $-2 \pm 3i$

17. $f(x) = x^3 + 4x^2 - 19x - 6$

18. $h(x) = 4x^4 + 11x^3 + 10x^2 - 69x - 54$
    $2, -\frac{3}{4}, -2 \pm i\sqrt{5}$

19. $g(x) = x^4 - 9x^3 + 11x^2 - 19x - 40$
    $-1, 8, 1 \pm 2i$

Solve each equation.

20. $p^3 + 8p^2 = 18p$ $0, -4 \pm \sqrt{34}$

21. $16x^4 - x^2 = 0$ $0, \pm\frac{1}{4}$

22. $r^4 - 9r^2 + 18 = 0$ $\pm\sqrt{6}, \pm\sqrt{3}$

23. $p^{\frac{3}{2}} - 8 = 0$ 4

24. $2d + 3\sqrt{d} = 9$ $\frac{9}{4}$

25. $z^4 + 6z^3 + 8z^2 = 0$ $-2, -4, 0$

If $f(x) = 2x - 4$ and $g(x) = x^2 + 3$, find each value.

26. $g(x + h)$ $x^2 + 2xh + h^2 + 3$

27. $f[g(x)]$ $2x^2 + 2$

28. $g[f(x)]$ $4x^2 - 16x + 19$

29. $g[f(-3)]$ 103

Write the polynomial function of least degree with integral coefficients that has the given zeros.   33. $f(x) = x^4 - 7x^3 + 16x^2 - 18x + 8$

30. $-1, 3, i$ $f(x) = x^4 - 2x^3 - 2x^2 - 2x - 3$

31. $2, -i$ $f(x) = x^3 - 2x^2 + x - 2$

32. $-2, 1 + i$ $f(x) = x^3 - 2x + 4$

33. $1, 4, 1 - i$

CHAPTER 9 TEST

Simplify each expression.

1. $\dfrac{7ab}{9c} \cdot \dfrac{81c^2}{91a^2b}$ $\dfrac{9c}{13a}$

2. $\dfrac{4a}{5b} \cdot \dfrac{15b}{16a}$ $\dfrac{3}{4}$

3. $\dfrac{6}{x-5} + 7$ $\dfrac{7x-29}{x-5}$

4. $\dfrac{m+5}{2m+10}$ $\dfrac{1}{2}$

5. $\dfrac{7}{5a} - \dfrac{10}{3ab}$ $\dfrac{21b-50}{15ab}$

6. $\dfrac{4x}{x^2-x}$ $\dfrac{4}{x-1}$

7. $\dfrac{a^2-ab}{3a} \div \dfrac{a-b}{15b^2}$ $5b^2$

8. $\dfrac{z^2w-z^2}{z^3-z^3w}$ $-\dfrac{1}{z}$

9. $\dfrac{x^2-y^2}{y^2} \cdot \dfrac{y^3}{y-x}$ $-y(x+y)$

10. $\dfrac{4x^2y}{15a^3b^3} \div \dfrac{2xy^2}{5ab^3}$ $\dfrac{2x}{3a^2y}$

11. $\dfrac{x^2-2x+1}{y-5} \div \dfrac{x-1}{y^2-25}$ $(x-1)(y+5)$

12. $\dfrac{a^2-b^2}{2a} \div \dfrac{a-b}{6a}$ $3(a+b)$

13. $\dfrac{\dfrac{x^2-1}{x^2-3x-10}}{\dfrac{x^2+3x+2}{x^2-12x+35}}$ $\dfrac{(x-1)(x-7)}{(x+2)^2}$

14. $\dfrac{2x+2}{x^2+5x+6} \div \dfrac{3x+3}{x^2+2x-3}$ $\dfrac{2(x-1)}{3(x+2)}$

15. $\dfrac{x-2}{x-1} + \dfrac{6}{7x-7}$ $\dfrac{7x-8}{7(x-1)}$

16. $\dfrac{a^3-b^3}{a+b} \cdot \dfrac{a^2-b^2}{a^2+ab+b^2}$ $(a-b)^2$

17. $\dfrac{x}{x^2-9} + \dfrac{1}{2x+6}$ $\dfrac{3(x-1)}{2(x-3)(x+3)}$

18. $\dfrac{\dfrac{x^2-5x-14}{x^2+7x+12}}{\dfrac{3x-21}{x^2-16}}$ $\dfrac{(x+2)(x-4)}{3(x+3)}$

State the equations of the vertical and horizontal asymptotes for each rational function. Then graph each rational function.   19–21. See Solutions Manual for graphs.

19. $f(x) = \dfrac{-4}{x-3}$ $x=3,\ y=0$

20. $f(x) = \dfrac{x}{x+2}$ $x=-2,\ y=1$

21. $f(x) = \dfrac{2}{(x-2)(x+1)}$ $x=2,\ x=-1,\ y=0$

Solve each equation.

22. $8 - \dfrac{2-5x}{4} = \dfrac{4x+9}{3}$ 54

23. $\dfrac{9}{28} + \dfrac{3}{z+2} = \dfrac{3}{4}$ 5

24. $\dfrac{3}{x} + \dfrac{x}{x+2} = \dfrac{-2}{x+2}$ -3

25. $x + \dfrac{12}{x} - 8 = 0$ $2,\ 6$

26. $\dfrac{5}{6} - \dfrac{2m}{2m+3} = \dfrac{19}{6}$ $\dfrac{-21}{20}$

27. $\dfrac{x-3}{2x} = \dfrac{x-2}{2x+1} - \dfrac{1}{2}$ $\pm\dfrac{\sqrt{6}}{2}$

28. $\dfrac{2}{x-2} = 3 - \dfrac{x}{2-x}$ $\varnothing$

29. $r + \dfrac{r^2-5}{r^2-1} = \dfrac{r^2+r+2}{r+1}$ $3,\ -1$

30. Suppose y varies directly as x. If $y = 10$, then $x = -3$. Find y when $x = 20$. $-\dfrac{200}{3}$

31. Suppose y varies inversely as x. If $y = 9$, then $x = -\dfrac{2}{3}$. Find x when $y = -7$. $\dfrac{6}{7}$

32. Suppose g varies directly as w. If $g = 10$, then $w = -3$. Find w when $g = 4$. $-\dfrac{6}{5}$

33. Suppose y varies jointly as x and z. If $x = 10$ when $y = 250$ and $z = 5$, find x when $y = 2.5$ and $z = 4.5$. $\dfrac{1}{9}$

Write each equation in logarithmic form.

1. $6^4 = 1296$ $\log_6 1296 = 4$

2. $3^7 = 2187$ $\log_3 2187 = 7$

Write each equation in exponential form.

3. $\log_5 625 = 4$ $5^4 = 625$

4. $\log_8 16 = \frac{4}{3}$ $8^{\frac{4}{3}} = 16$

Use $\log_4 7 \approx 1.4037$ and $\log_4 3 \approx 0.7925$ to evaluate each expression.

5. $\log_4 21$ 2.1962

6. $\log_4 \frac{7}{12}$ -0.3888

Approximate the value of each logarithm to three decimal places.

7. $\log_{14} 24$ 1.204

8. $\log_3 50$ 3.561

Evaluate each expression.

9. $4^{\log_4 3}$ 3

10. $\log_{64} 8$ $\frac{1}{2}$

11. $\log_2 \frac{1}{256}$ -8

Simplify each expression.

12. $\left(3^{\sqrt{8}}\right)^{\sqrt{2}}$ 81

13. $81^{\sqrt{5}} \div 3^{\sqrt{5}}$ $3^{3\sqrt{5}}$

Solve each equation.

14. $2^{x-3} = \frac{1}{16}$ -1

15. $27^{2p+1} = 3^{4p-1}$ -2

16. $\log_2 128 = y$ 7

17. $\log_m 144 = -2$ $\frac{1}{12}$

18. $\log_3 x - 2\log_3 2 = 3\log_3 3$ 108

19. $\log_9 (x + 4) + \log_9 (x - 4) = 1$ 5

20. $\log_5 (8r - 7) = \log_5 (r^2 + 5)$ 2, 6

21. $\log_3 3^{(4x-1)} = 15$ 4

22. $\log_2 3 + \log_2 7 = \log_2 x$ 21

23. $\log_5 x = -2$ $\frac{1}{25}$

Find each value rounded to four decimal places.

24. $\ln 9.6$ 2.2618

25. $\log 535$ 2.7284

26. antilog 6.3337   2,156,254.407

27. antiln 0.4055   1.5001

Use logarithms to solve each equation.

28. $7.6^{x-1} = 431$ 3.9910

29. $\log_4 37 = x$ 2.6047

30. $3^x = 5^{x-1}$ 3.1507

31. $4^{2x-3} = 9^{x+3}$ 18.6848

32. **Biology**   A certain culture of bacteria will grow from 500 to 4000 bacteria in 1.5 hours. Find the constant k for the growth formula. (Use $y = ne^{kt}$.)   1.3863

33. **Finance**   Suppose a pilgrim ancestor of Jenny Chambers deposited $10 in a savings account at Provident Savings Bank. The annual interest rate was 4% compounded continuously. The account is now worth $75,000. How long ago was the account started? (Use $A = Pe^{rt}$.)   223 years

CHAPTER 11 TEST

1. Find the pattern and complete the sequence 3, 3, 6, 18, 72, __?__ , __?__ , __?__. 360, 2160, 15,120

2. Find the sixth term of the geometric sequence if $a_1 = 5$ and $r = -2$. -160

3. How many integers between 26 and 415 are multiples of 9? 44

4. Find the sum of the arithmetic series if $a_1 = 7$, $n = 31$, and $a_n = 127$. 2077

5. Find the next four terms of the arithmetic sequence 42, 37, 32, ... 27, 22, 17, 12

6. Find the 27th term of an arithmetic sequence if $a_1 = 2$ and $d = 6$. 158

7. Find the next two terms of the geometric sequence $\frac{1}{81}, \frac{1}{27}, \frac{1}{9}, ...$ $\frac{1}{3}$, 1

8. Find the sum of the geometric series if $a_1 = 125$, $r = \frac{2}{5}$, and $n = 4$. 203

9. Find the three arithmetic means between -4 and 16. 1, 6, 11

10. Find the two geometric means between 7 and 189. 21, 63

Find each sum.

11. $\sum_{k=3}^{15} (14 - 2k)$ -52

12. $\sum_{n=1}^{\infty} \frac{1}{3}(-2)^{n-1}$ no sum

13. Find the sum of the series $91 + 85 + 79 + ... + (-29)$. 651

14. Find the sum of the series $12 - 6 + 3 - \frac{3}{2} + ...$ 8

15. Expand $(2s - 3t)^5$. $32s^5 - 240s^4t + 720s^3t^2 - 1080s^2t^3 + 810st^4 - 243t^5$

16. Find the third term of $(x + y)^8$. $28x^6y^2$

17. **Design** A landscaper is designing a wall of white brick and red brick. The pattern starts with 20 red bricks on the bottom row. Each row above it contains 3 fewer red bricks than the preceding row. If the top row contains no red bricks, how many rows are there and how many red bricks were used?
8 rows, 77 bricks

18. **Business** Olsen's Electronics invested in computer equipment worth $900,000. The equipment depreciates at the rate of 25% per year of the previous year's value. What will be the value of the equipment at the end of four years?
$284,766

19. **Physics** In the first three seconds after liftoff, a rocket rises 40 feet, 60 feet, and 80 feet, respectively. If it continues to rise at this rate, how many feet will it rise in the 10th second? 220 feet

20. **Recreation** One minute after it is released, a gas-filled balloon has risen 100 feet. In each succeeding minute, the balloon rises only 50% as far as it rose in the previous minute. How far will the balloon rise in 5 minutes? 193.75 feet

Evaluate each expression.

1. $P(7, 3)$ **210**

2. $C(7, 3)$ **35**

3. $P(13, 5)$ **154,440**

4. $C(13, 5)$ **1287**

Solve each problem.

5. How many ways can 9 bowling balls be arranged on the upper rack of a bowling ball rack?
362,880 ways

6. From 11 skirts, 9 blouses, 3 belts, and 7 pairs of shoes, how many different outfits can be made?
2079 outfits

7. How many ways can the letters of the word *probability* be arranged? **9,979,200 ways**

8. How many different soccer teams consisting of 11 players can be formed from 18 players?
31,824 teams

9. In a row of 10 parking spaces in a parking lot, how many ways can 4 cars park? **5040 ways**

10. How many ways can 6 people be seated at a round table, if it does not matter who sits next to whom? **120 ways**

11. A number is drawn at random from a hat that contains all the numbers from 1 to 100. What is the probability that the number is less than sixteen? $\frac{3}{20}$

12. Eleven points are equally spaced on a circle. How many pentagons can be formed using these points, five at a time, as vertices? **462 pentagons**

13. A shipment of ten television sets contains 3 defective sets. How many ways can a hospital purchase 4 of these sets and receive at least 2 of the defective sets? **70 ways**

14. Two cards are drawn in succession from a standard deck of 52 cards without replacement. What is the probability that both cards are greater than 2 and less than 9? $\frac{46}{221}$

15. In a high school graduating class of 100 students, 52 studied mathematics, 58 studied Spanish, 54 studied computers, 22 studied both mathematics and computers, 25 studied both mathematics and Spanish, 7 studied computers and neither Spanish nor mathematics, 10 studied all three subjects, and 8 did not take any of the three. If a student is selected at random, what is the probability that he took mathematics only? $\frac{3}{20}$

16. While shooting arrows, William Tell can hit an apple 9 out of 10 times. What is the probability that he will hit it exactly 4 out of 7 times? $\frac{45,927}{2,000,000}$

17. Ten people are going on a camping trip in 3 cars that hold 5, 2, and 4 passengers, respectively. How many ways is it possible to transport the 10 people to their camp site? **6930 ways**

18. From a box containing 5 white golf balls and 3 red golf balls, 3 golf balls are drawn in succession, each being replaced in the box before the next draw is made. What is the probability that all 3 golf balls are the same color? $\frac{19}{64}$

19. In a ten-question multiple-choice test with four choices for each question, a student who was not prepared guesses on each item. Find the probability that the student gets

a. six questions right. $\frac{8505}{524,288}$

b. at least eight correct. $\frac{109}{262,144}$

c. fewer than eight correct. $\frac{262,035}{262,144}$

20. In a *USA Today*/CNN/Gallup Poll survey of 1208 randomly selected adults published on July 26, 1995, 47% of those surveyed approved of President Clinton's handling of the economy. What is the margin of error? Round your answer to the nearest tenth. **2.9%**

CHAPTER 13 TEST

Change each degree measure to radian measure and each radian measure to degree measure.

1. $275°$ $\dfrac{55\pi}{36}$

2. $-\dfrac{\pi}{6}$ $-30°$

3. $\dfrac{11}{2}\pi$ $990°$

4. $330°$ $\dfrac{11\pi}{6}$

5. $-600°$ $-\dfrac{10\pi}{3}$

6. $-\dfrac{7\pi}{4}$ $-315°$

Solve each right triangle. Round measures of sides to the nearest tenth and measures of angles to the nearest degree.

7. $a = 7, A = 49°$ $b = 6.1, c = 9.3, B = 41°$

8. $B = 75°, b = 6$ $a = 1.6, c = 6.2, A = 15°$

9. $A = 22°, c = 8$ $a = 3.0, b = 7.4, B = 68°$

10. $a = 7, c = 16$ $b = 14.4, A = 26°, B = 64°$

Find the exact value of each expression.

11. $\cos(-120°)$ $-\dfrac{1}{2}$

12. $\sin\dfrac{7}{4}\pi$ $-\dfrac{\sqrt{2}}{2}$

13. $\tan 135°$ -1

14. $\cot 300°$ $-\dfrac{\sqrt{3}}{3}$

15. $\sec\left(-\dfrac{7}{6}\pi\right)$ $-\dfrac{2\sqrt{3}}{3}$

16. $\csc\dfrac{5\pi}{6}$ 2

17. $\sin^{-1}\left(-\dfrac{\sqrt{3}}{2}\right)$ $-60°$

18. $\text{Arctan } 1$ $45°$

19. $\cos^{-1}(\sin -60°)$ $150°$

20. Determine the number of possible solutions for a triangle in which $A = 40°$, $b = 10$, and $a = 14$. If a solution exists, solve the triangle. $1; B = 27.3°, C = 112.7°, c = 20.1$

21. Suppose θ is an angle in standard position whose terminal side lies in Quadrant II. Find the exact values of the remaining five trigonometric functions of θ for $\cos\theta = -\dfrac{\sqrt{3}}{2}$. $\sin\theta = \dfrac{1}{2}, \tan\theta = -\dfrac{\sqrt{3}}{3}, \cot\theta = -\sqrt{3}, \sec\theta = -\dfrac{2\sqrt{3}}{3}, \csc\theta = 2$

22. **Geology** From the top of a cliff, a geologist spots a dry riverbed. The measurement of the angle of depression to the riverbed is $70°$. The cliff is 50 meters high. How far is the riverbed from the base of the cliff? 18.2 m

23. **Fire Fighting** A firefighter needs to use a 14-meter ladder to enter a window that is 13.5 meters above the ground. At what angle to the ground should the ladder be placed in order to reach the window? $74.6°$

24. **Broadcasting** A 40-foot television antenna stands on top of a building. From a point on the ground, the angles of elevation to the top and the bottom of the antenna measure $56°$ and $42°$, respectively. How tall is the building? 61.87 ft

25. **Geometry** A triangular lot faces two streets that meet at an angle measuring $85°$, as shown at the right. The sides of the lot facing the streets are each 160 feet in length. Find the perimeter of the lot. 536.19 ft

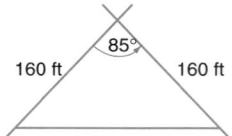

160 ft   85°   160 ft

Graph each function.   1–2. See Solutions Manual for graphs.

1. $y = 2 \sin 2x$

2. $y = 2 \cos \frac{1}{5}\theta$

Solve each of the following for values of θ between 180° and 270°.

3. If $\sin \theta = -\frac{1}{2}$, find $\tan \theta$. $\frac{\sqrt{3}}{3}$

4. If $\cot \theta = \frac{3}{4}$, find $\sec \theta$. $-\frac{5}{3}$

Verify that each of the following is an identity.   5–8. See Solutions Manual.

5. $(\sin x - \cos x)^2 = 1 - \sin 2x$

6. $\frac{\cos x}{1 - \sin^2 x} = \sec x$

7. $\frac{\sec x}{\sin x} - \frac{\sin x}{\cos x} = \cot x$

8. $\frac{1 + \tan^2 \theta}{\cos^2 \theta} = \sec^4 \theta$

Evaluate each expression.

9. $\cos 165°$ $\frac{-\sqrt{2} - \sqrt{6}}{4}$

10. $\sin 255°$ $\frac{-\sqrt{2} - \sqrt{6}}{4}$

11. $2 \sin 75° \cos 75°$ $\frac{1}{2}$

12. $(1 - \cos^2 \theta) \cot^2 \theta$ $\cos^2 \theta$

13. $\sin \beta (\cos \beta + \sin \beta \tan \beta)$ $\tan \beta$

14. $\sin \alpha \cot \alpha$ $\cos \alpha$

15. If x is in Quadrant II and $\cos x = -\frac{1}{6}$, find $\sin 2x$ and $\cos \frac{x}{2}$. $\frac{-\sqrt{35}}{18}, \frac{\sqrt{15}}{6}$

16. If x is in Quadrant I and $\cos x = \frac{3}{4}$, find $\sin \frac{x}{2}$ and $\cos 2x$. $\frac{\sqrt{2}}{4}, \frac{1}{8}$

17. If x is in Quadrant III and $\tan x = \frac{5}{12}$, find $\tan 2x$ and $\tan \frac{x}{2}$. $\frac{120}{119}, -5$

Solve each equation for $0° \le x < 360°$ if x is measured in degrees.

18. $\sec x = 1 + \tan x$ $0°$

19. $\cos 2x = \cos x$ $0°, 120°, 240°$

20. $\cos 2x + \sin x = 1$ $0°, 30°, 150°, 180°$

21. $\sin x = \tan x$ $0°, 180°$

22. $2 \sin x \cos x - \sin x = 0$ $0°, 60°\ 180°, 300°$

23. $\sin x + \sin x \cos x = 0$ $0°, 180°$

24. Golf   A golf ball leaves the club with an initial velocity of 100 feet per second. he distance the ball travels is found by the formula $d = \frac{v_0^2}{g} \sin 2\theta$, where v_0 is the initial velocity, g is the acceleration due to gravity, and θ is the measurement of the angle that the path of the ball makes with the ground. The acceleration due to gravity is 32 feet per second squared.

a. Find the distance the ball travels if the angle between the path of the ball and the ground measures 60°.   270.6 ft

b. Find the distance the ball travels if the angle between the path of the ball and the ground measures 45°.   312.5 ft

25. Football   The approximate distance s in meters that an object will travel if given an initial linear speed v_0 at an angle of elevation θ is given by the formula $s = \frac{v_0^2 \sin \theta \cos \theta}{5}$ where v_0 is in meters per second. At what angle must a football be thrown at 20 m/s in order to travel 20 meters? (Disregard the height of the person throwing the ball.)   15°, 75°

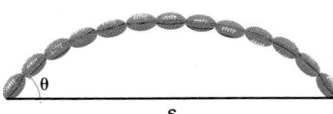

s

GLOSSARY

A

absolute value (37)   The absolute value of a number is the number of units it is from zero on the number line.

absolute value function (104)   A function described by $y = |x|$ or $f(x) = |x|$.

addition of matrices (195)   If A and B are two $m \times n$ matrices, then $A + B$ is the $m \times n$ matrix in which each element is the sum of the corresponding elements of A and B.

$$\begin{bmatrix} a & b & c \\ d & e & f \\ g & h & i \end{bmatrix} + \begin{bmatrix} j & k & l \\ m & n & o \\ p & q & r \end{bmatrix} = \begin{bmatrix} a+j & b+k & c+l \\ d+m & e+n & f+o \\ g+p & h+q & i+r \end{bmatrix}$$

addition property of equality (28)   For any numbers a, b, and c, if $a = b$, then $a + c = b + c$.

addition property of inequality (43)   For any numbers a, b, and c:

1. if $a > b$, then $a + c > b + c$;

2. if $a < b$, then $a + c < b + c$.

algebraic expressions (8)   An expression that contains at least one variable.

amplitude (824, 828)   The amplitude of the graph of a periodic function is the absolute value of half the difference between its maximum value and its minimum value.

angle of depression (776)   The angle formed by a horizontal line and the line of sight to an object at a lower level.

angle of elevation (776)   The angle formed by a horizontal line and the line of sight to an object at a higher level.

angle of incline (835)   The nonnegative acute angle formed by a vertical line and the line of an object's orientation.

antilogarithm (618)   If $\log x = a$, then $x = \text{antilog } a$.

Arcosine function (811)   The inverse of the Cosine function, symbolized by Cos^{-1} or Arccos.

arithmetic means (650)   The terms between any two nonconsecutive terms of an arithmetic sequence.

arithmetic sequence (648)   A sequence in which each term after the first is found by adding a constant, called the common difference d to the previous term.

arithmetic series (656)   The indicated sum of the terms of an arithmetic sequence.

associative properties (14)   The way three or more numbers are grouped, or associated, does not change their sum or product. That is, for all real numbers a, b, and c, $(a + b) + c = a + (b + c)$ and $(a \cdot b) \cdot c = a \cdot (b \cdot c)$.

asymptotes (441, 550)   Lines that a curve approaches.

augmented matrix (226)   The augmented matrix of a system of equations contains the coefficient matrix of the system with an extra column consisting of the constant terms of the system.

axis of symmetry (335)   The line about which a figure is symmetric.

B

back-to-back stem-and-leaf plot (20)   A back-to-back stem-and-leaf plot is used to compare two sets of data. The same stem is used for the leaves of both plots.

bell curve (393)   A symmetric curve that is the general shape of the graph of a normal distribution, which indicates that the frequencies are concentrated around the center portion of the distribution.

best-fit line (95)   A line drawn on a scatter plot to approximate the linear relationship for a set of data points.

binomial (261)   A polynomial with two unlike terms.

binomial experiments (753)   A binomial experiment exists if and only if there are exactly two possible outcomes for any trial, there is a fixed number of trials, the trials are independent, and the probability of each trial is the same.

binomial theorem (696)   If n is a positive integer, then $(a + b)^n = 1a^n b^0 + \frac{n}{1} a^{n-1} b^1 + \frac{n(n-1)}{1 \cdot 2} a^{n-2} b^2 + \ldots + 1a^0 b^n$.

boundary (378)   A line or curve that separates a graph into two parts.

box-and-whisker plot (237)   A pictorial representation of the variability of a set of data that summarizes the data set using its quartiles and extreme values.

Cartesian coordinate plane (64)   Composed of the x-axis and the y-axis which meet at the origin and is divided into four quadrants.

center of a circle (423)   The point from which all points on a circle are equidistant.

center of a hyperbola (441)   The intersection of the conjugate and transverse axes of a hyperbola.

center of an ellipse (432)   The intersection of the major and minor axes of an ellipse.

change of base formula (594, 628)   For all positive numbers a, b, and n, where $a \neq 1$ and $b \neq 1$, $\log_a n = \dfrac{\log_b n}{\log_b a}$.

characteristic (618)   The integer used to express a base 10 logarithm as the sum of an integer and a positive decimal.

circle (423)   The set of all points in a plane that are equidistant from a given point in the plane.

circular functions (805)   The six basic trigonometric functions defined using a unit circle.

circular permutation (721)   If n distinct objects are arranged in a circle, then there are $\dfrac{n!}{n}$ or $(n-1)!$ permutations of the objects around the circle.

coding matrix (212)   A message, where each letter corresponds to a numerical element in a matrix, can be converted to a code by multiplying the matrix by a coding matrix.

coefficient (255)   The numerical factor of a monomial.

column matrix (187)   A matrix that has only one column.

combination (726)   An arrangement, or listing, in which order is not important. The number of combinations of n distinct objects taken r at a time is $C(n, r) = \dfrac{n!}{(n-r)!r!}$.

common difference (649)   The number d added to find the next term of an arithmetic sequence.

common logarithms (617)   Logarithms to the base 10.

common ratio (662)   The number by which each term, after the first, in a geometric sequence is multiplied to obtain the next term.

commutative properties (14)   The order in which two numbers are added or multiplied does not change their sum or product. That is, for all real numbers a and b, $a + b = b + a$ and $a \cdot b = b \cdot a$.

complements (732)   Two events are complements of each other if the sum of their probabilities is 1.

completing the square (347)   A process used to create a perfect square trinomial.

complex conjugates (317)   Complex numbers of the form $a + bi$ and $a - bi$.

complex conjugate theorem (504)   Suppose a and b are real numbers with $b \neq 0$. If $a + bi$ is a zero of a polynomial function, then $a - bi$ is also a zero of the function.

complex fraction (565)   A fraction whose numerator and/or denominator contains a fraction.

complex numbers (311)   Any number that can be written in the form $a + bi$, where a and b are real numbers and i is the imaginary unit; a is called the real part, and bi is called the imaginary part.

composition of functions (520)   Suppose f and g are functions such that the range of g is a subset of the domain of f. Then the composite function $f \circ g$ can be described by the equation $[f \circ g](x) = f[g(x)]$.

compound inequality (49)   Two inequalities combined by the words *and* or *or*.

concentric circles (426)   Circles with the same center, but not necessarily the same radius.

conic section (415)   Any figure that can be formed by slicing a double cone with a plane.

conjugate axis (441)   The line segment that is perpendicular to the transverse axis at the center of a hyperbola and is an axis of symmetry of the hyperbola.

conjugate pair (506)   If a polynomial function has two imaginary roots of the form $a + bi$ and $a - bi$, these numbers form a conjugate pair.

conjugates (292)   Binomials in the form $a\sqrt{b} + c\sqrt{d}$ and $a\sqrt{b} - c\sqrt{d}$ where a, b, c, and d are rational numbers.

consistent system (127)   A system of equations that has at least one solution.

constant function (74)   A linear function of the form $f(x) = b$, for which the slope is zero.

constant of variation (556)   The constant k in either of the equations $y = kx$ or $y = \frac{k}{x}$.

constants (255)   Monomials that contain no variables.

constant term (334)   In a quadratic function described by $f(x) = ax^2 + bx + c$, c is the constant term.

constraints (153)   The inequalities in a system of inequalities whose graphs form the boundaries of the graph of the system's solution.

continuity (548)   A graph of a function that can be traced with a pencil that never leaves the paper is said to have continuity.

continuous function (67)   A continuous function can be graphed with a line or a smooth curve and has a domain with an infinite number of elements.

coordinate matrix (189)   A matrix containing the coordinates of the vertices of a geometric figure.

coordinate system (64)   Composed of two perpendicular number lines intersecting at their zero points creating a coordinate plane upon which ordered pairs may be graphed.

cosine (805)   If the terminal side of an angle θ in standard position intersects the unit circle at $P(x, y)$, then $\cos \theta = x$.

Cosine (811) $y = \text{Cos } x$ if and only if $y = \cos x$ and $0 \leq < x \leq \pi$.

coterminal angles (783)   Two angles in standard position having the same terminal side are called coterminal angles.

Cramer's rule (141)   A method that uses determinants to solve a system of linear equations.

D

degree   1. (255)   The degree of a nonzero monomial is the sum of the exponents of its variables.   **2.** (261)   The degree of a polynomial is the degree of the monomial with the greatest degree.

dependent events (714)   The outcome of a dependent event is affected by the outcome of another event.

dependent system (128)   A system of equations that has an infinite number of solutions.

dependent variable (73)   A variable whose value depends upon, or is affected by, the value of another variable.

depressed polynomial (487)   When you divide a polynomial by one of its binomial factors, the quotient is called a depressed polynomial.

Descartes' rule of signs (505)   If $P(x)$ is a polynomial whose terms are arranged in descending powers of the variable,

- the number of positive real zeros of $y = P(x)$ is the same as the number of changes in sign of the coefficients of the terms, or is less than this by an even number, and

- the number of negative real zeros of $y = P(x)$ is the same as the number of changes in sign of the coefficients of the terms of $P(-x)$, or is less than this by an even number.

determinant (141, 205)   A square array of numbers or expressions enclosed between two parallel vertical bars.

dilation (190)   A transformation in which a figure is enlarged or reduced.

dimensions (187)   In a matrix consisting of n rows and m columns, the matrix is said to have dimension $n \times m$ (read "n by m").

direct variation   1. (103)   A linear function described by $y = mx$ or $f(x) = mx$, where $m \neq 0$.   **2.** (556)   A type of variation where y varies directly as x if there is some constant k such that $y = kx$.

discrete function (65)   A function whose graph consists of points that are not connected.

discrete mathematics (188)   A branch of mathematics that deals with finite or discontinuous quantities.

discriminant (356)   For a quadratic equation $ax^2 + bz + c = 0$, the expression $b^2 - 4ac$ under the radical in the quadratic formula.

distance formula (409)   The distance between two points with coordinates (x_1, y_1) and (x_2, y_2) is given by $d = \sqrt{(x_2 - x_1)^2 + (y_2 - y_1)^2}$.

distributive properties (14)   For all real numbers a, b, and c, $a(b + c) = ab + ac$ and $(b + c)a = ba + ca$.

dividing rational expressions (563)   For all rational expressions $\frac{a}{b}$ and $\frac{c}{d}$, $\frac{a}{b} \div \frac{c}{d} = \frac{a}{b} \cdot \frac{d}{c} = \frac{ad}{bc}$, if $b \neq 0$, $c \neq 0$, and $d \neq 0$.

division property of equality (28)   For any real numbers a, b, and c, if $a = b$ and $c \neq 0$, then $\frac{a}{c} = \frac{b}{c}$.

division property of inequality (44)   For any real numbers a, b, and c:

1. if c is positive and $a < b$, then $\frac{a}{c} < \frac{b}{c}$;

2. if c is positive and $a > b$, then $\frac{a}{c} > \frac{b}{c}$;

3. if c is negative and $a < b$, then $\frac{a}{c} > \frac{b}{c}$;

4. if c is negative and $a > b$, then $\frac{a}{c} < \frac{b}{c}$.

domain (65)   The set of all first coordinates from the ordered pairs of a relation.

double-angle formulas (853)   The following identities hold true for all values of θ.

$\sin 2\theta = 2 \sin \theta \cos \theta$

$\cos 2\theta = \cos^2 \theta - \sin^2 \theta$

$\cos 2\theta = 1 - 2 \sin^2 \theta$

$\cos 2\theta = 2 \cos^2 \theta - 1$

E

element   1. (141)   A number or variable written within a determinant.   **2.** (186)   Each value in a matrix.

ellipse (431)   The set of all points in a plane such that the sum of the distances from the foci is constant.

empty set (40)   The set having no members, symbolized by { } or $\varnothing$.

equal matrices (188)   Two matrices are considered to be equal if they have the same dimensions and if each element of one matrix is equal to the corresponding element of the other matrix.

equation (27)   A sentence that states that two mathematical expressions are equal.

expansion by minors (205)   A method used to find the value of any third- or higher-order determinant by using determinants of lower order.

experimental probability (754)   A probability determined by performing tests or experiments and observing the outcomes.

exponential equations (626)   An equation in which variables occur in exponents.

exponential function (594, 597)   An equation of the form $y = a \cdot b^x$, where $a \neq 0$, $b > 0$, and $b \neq 1$, is called an exponential function with base b.

exponential growth (622)   Exponential growth occurs when a quantity increases exponentially.

exponential growth rate (626)   The positive constant k in the growth equation $P(t) = P_0 e^{kt}$ is called the exponential growth rate.

extraneous solutions (305)   Solutions that do not satisfy the original equation.

extreme values (304)   Data values that vary greatly from the central group of data values.

F

factorials (697)   If n is a positive integer, the expression $n!$ is defined as $n! = n(n - 1)(n - 2)(n - 3) \cdots 2 \cdot 1$. By definition, $0! = 1$.

factoring (341)   A method used to solve a quadratic equation that requires using the zero product property.

factors (274)   Numbers, variables, monomials, or polynomials multiplied to obtain a product.

factor theorem (487)   The binomial $x - a$ is a factor of the polynomial $f(x)$ if and only if $f(a) = 0$.

failure (732)   Any outcome other than the desired outcome of an event.

family of graphs (83)   A group of graphs that displays one or more similar characteristics.

feasible region (153)   The area of intersection of the graphs of inequalities in a system of inequalities in which every constraint is met.

Fibonacci sequence (683)   A special sequence often found in nature that is named after its discoverer, Leonardo Fibonacci.

fixed points (526)   The points at which the graph of a function $g(x)$ intersects the graph of the line $f(x) = x$.

FOIL method (263)   An application of the distributive property used to multiply two binomials. The product is the sum of the products of the first, outer, inner and last terms.

formula (9)   A mathematical sentence that expresses a general relationship between certain quantities.

fractal (318, 688)   A geometric figure that has self-similarity, is created using a recursive process, and is infinite in structure.

fractal geometry (688)   A new branch of mathematics that provides models of designs in nature.

frequency distribution (392)   Shows how data are spread out over the range of values.

function (65)   A special type of relation in which each element of the domain is paired with exactly one element of the range.

fundamental counting principle (713)   If event M can occur in m ways and is followed by an event N that can occur in n ways, then the event M followed by the event N can occur in $m \cdot n$ ways.

fundamental theorem of algebra (503)   Every polynomial equation with degree greater than zero has at least one root in the set of complex numbers.

general formula for growth and decay (631)   The formula is $y = ne^{kt}$, where y is the final amount, n is the initial amount, k is a constant, and t is the time.

geometric means (665)   The terms between any two nonconsecutive terms in a geometric sequence.

geometric sequence (662)   A sequence in which each term after the first is found by multiplying the previous term by a constant called the common ratio, r.

geometric series (670)   The indicated sum of the terms of a geometric series.

graphical iteration (526)   Graphical iterations produce a visual representation of the process of iteration.

greatest integer function (104)   A type of step function described by $f(x) = [x]$ where $[x]$ is the greatest integer *not* greater than x.

guess and check (342)   A problem-solving strategy in which several values or combinations of values are tried in order to find a solution to a problem.

half-angle formulas (855)   The following identities hold true for all values of α.

$$\cos \frac{\alpha}{2} = \pm \sqrt{\frac{1 + \cos \alpha}{2}}$$

$$\sin \frac{\alpha}{2} = \pm \sqrt{\frac{1 - \cos \alpha}{2}}$$

histogram (392)   A bar graph that displays a frequency distribution.

hyperbola (440)   The set of all points P in a plane such that the absolute value of the difference of the distances from P to two given points, called the foci, is constant.

hypotenuse (9)   The side opposite the right angle in a right triangle.

hypothesis (760)   A statement that is to be tested in an experiment.

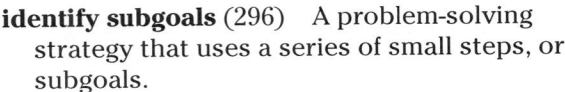

identify subgoals (296)   A problem-solving strategy that uses a series of small steps, or subgoals.

identity function (103)   A linear function described by $y = x$ or $f(x) = x$.

identity matrix (213)   Any square matrix A that, when multiplied by another matrix B of the same dimensions, equals that same matrix B.

identity properties (14)   If a is a real number, then $a + 0 = a = 0 + a$ and $a \cdot 1 = a = 1 \cdot a$.

imaginary unit (310)   The imaginary unit i is defined by $i = \sqrt{-1}$.

inclusive events (746)   Two events are inclusive if the outcomes of the events may be the same.

inconsistent system (128)   A system of equations that has no solution.

independent events (713)   The outcome of an independent event is not affected by the outcome of another event.

independent system (127)   A system of equations that has exactly one solution.

independent variable (73)   The variable whose value does not depend upon, nor is affected by, the value of another variable.

index of summation (658)   The variable defined below the Σ in sigma notation.

infinite geometric series (676)   The indicated sum of the terms of an infinite geometric sequence.

initial side (780)   One of two rays forming an angle on a coordinate plane that is fixed along the positive x-axis.

integral zero theorem (509)   If the coefficients of a polynomial function are integers such that $a_0 = 1$ and $a_n \neq 0$, any rational zeros of the function must be factors of a_n.

interquartile range (236)   The difference between the upper and lower quartile of a set of data.

intersection (49)   The graph of a compound inequality containing the word *and* is the intersection of the graphs of the two inequalities.

inverse Cosine (811)   Given $y = \cos x$, the inverse Cosine function is defined by $y = \cos^{-1} x$ or $y = \text{Arccos } x$.

inverse functions (528)   Two functions f and g are inverse functions if and only if both their compositions are the identity function. That is, $[f \circ g](x) = x$ and $[g \circ f](x) = x$.

inverse of a matrix (213)   The matrix by which another matrix is multiplied to produce the identity matrix.

inverse properties (14)   If a is a real number, then $a + (-a) = 0 = (-a) + a$ and $a \cdot \frac{1}{a} = 1 = \frac{1}{a} \cdot a$, if $a \neq 0$.

inverse relation (531)   Two relations are inverse relations if and only if whenever one relation contains the element (a, b), the other relation contains the element (b, a).

inverse Sine (812)   Given $y = \sin x$, the inverse Sine function is defined by $y = \sin^{-1} x$ or $y = \text{Arcsin } x$.

inverse Tangent (812)   Given $y = \tan x$, the inverse Tangent function is defined by $y = \tan^{-1} x$ or $y = \text{Arctan } x$.

inverse variation (557)   A type of variation where y varies inversely as x if there is some constant k such that $xy = k$ or $y = \frac{k}{x}$.

irrational number (13)   Irrational numbers are real numbers that cannot be written as terminating or repeating decimals.

iterate   **1.** (318)   To repeat a process or function over and over.   **2.** (526)   Each result of the iteration process is called an iterate.

iteration (522)   The process of finding the value of a function for a given number in the domain and generating a sequence of values by using each output as the next input value.

J

joint variation (558)   A type of variation where y varies jointly as x and z if there is some number k such that $y = kxz$, where $x \neq 0$ and $z \neq 0$.

L

latus rectum (417)   The line segment through the focus of a parabola and perpendicular to the axis of symmetry.

law of cosines (799)   For any triangle ABC with a, b, and c representing the measures of sides, and opposite angles with measurement A, B, and C, respectively, the following equations are true.

$$a^2 = b^2 + c^2 - 2bc \cos A$$
$$b^2 = a^2 + c^2 - 2ac \cos B$$
$$c^2 = a^2 + b^2 - 2ab \cos C$$

law of sines (793)   Let $\triangle ABC$ be any triangle with a, b, and c representing the measures of sides opposite angles with measurements A, B, and C, respectively. Then, $\frac{\sin A}{a} = \frac{\sin B}{b} = \frac{\sin C}{c}$.

leading coefficient (480)   The coefficient of the term with the highest degree.

legs (9)   The two sides of a right triangle that form the right angle.

like radical expressions (291)   Two or more radical expressions are called like radical expressions if both the indices and the radicands are alike.

like terms (261)   Two or more monomials that are the same or differ only by their numerical coefficients.

linear equation (73)   An equation whose graph is a line.

linear function (74)   A function is linear if it can be defined by $f(x) = mx + b$, where m and b are real numbers.

linear permutation (718)   The arrangement of things in a line.

linear programming (155)   A method for finding the maximum or minimum value of a function in two variables subject to given constraints on the variables.

linear term (334)   In a quadratic function described by $f(x) = ax^2 + bx + c$, bx is the linear term.

line plot (19)   Displays statistical data on a number line so that patterns and variability in data can be determined.

list possibilities (38)   A problem-solving strategy used to find all possible solutions to a problem.

location principle (494)   Suppose $y = f(x)$ represents a polynomial function and a and b are two numbers such that $f(a) < 0$ and $f(b) > 0$. Then the function has at least one real zero between a and b.

logarithm (605)   Suppose $b > 0$ and $b \neq 1$. For $n > 0$, there is a number p such that $\log_b n = p$ if and only if $b^p = n$.

logarithmic function (594, 607)   A function of the form $y = \log_b x$, where $b > 0$ and $b \neq 1$.

look for a pattern (80)   A problem-solving strategy often involving the use of tables to organize information so that a pattern may be determined.

lower extreme (236)   The least value in a set of data.

lower quartile (236)   The median of the lower half of a set of data.

major axis (432)   The longer of the two line segments that form the axes of symmetry for an ellipse.

mantissa (618)   The logarithm of a number between 1 and 10.

mapping (65)   A mapping shows how each member of the domain of a relation is paired with each member of the range.

matrix (186)   A rectangular array of variables or constants in horizontal rows and vertical columns, usually enclosed in brackets.

matrix equation (219)   An equation of the form $AX = C$, where A is the coefficient matrix for a system of linear equations, X is the column matrix consisting of the variables of the system, and C is the column matrix consisting of the constant terms of the system.

matrix logic (187)   A problem-solving strategy where information is organized using a matrix and possibilities are eliminated one by one until a solution is eventually found.

mean (21)   The sum of all the values in a set of data divided by the number of values.

measure of central tendency (21)   A number that represents the center or middle of a set of data.

median (21)   The middle value of a set of data. If there are two middle values, the median is the mean of those values.

midpoint formula (410)   If a line segment has endpoints at (x_1, y_1) and (x_2, y_2), then the midpoint of the line segment has coordinates $\left(\dfrac{x_1 + x_2}{2}, \dfrac{y_1 + y_2}{2}\right)$.

minor (205)   The determinant formed when the row and column containing an element of the given determinant are deleted.

minor axis (432)   The shorter of the two line segments that form the axes of symmetry for an ellipse.

mode (21)   The most frequent value in a set of data.

monomials (255)   An expression that is a number, a variable, or the product of a number and one or more variables.

multiplication property of equality (28)   For any real numbers a, b, and c, if $a = b$, then $a \cdot c = b \cdot c$.

multiplication property of inequality (44)   For any real numbers a, b, and c:

1. if c is positive and $a < b$, then $ac < bc$;
2. if c is positive and $a > b$, then $ac > bc$;
3. if c is negative and $a < b$, then $ac > bc$;
4. if c is negative and $a > b$, then $ac < bc$.

multiplying matrices (199)   The product of $A_{m \times n}$ and $B_{n \times r}$ is $(AB)_{m \times r}$. The element in the ith row and the jth column of AB is the sum of the products of the corresponding elements in the ith row of A and the jth column of B.

multiplying rational expressions (563)   For all rational expressions $\dfrac{a}{b}$ and $\dfrac{c}{d}$, $\dfrac{a}{b} \cdot \dfrac{c}{d} = \dfrac{ac}{bd}$, if $b \neq 0$ and $d \neq 0$.

mutually exclusive events (746)   Two events are mutually exclusive if their outcomes can never be the same.

natural logarithms (622)   Natural logarithms are logarithms to the base e.

normal distribution (393)   A data distribution that gives a bell-shaped, symmetric graph. About 68% of the values are within one standard deviation from the mean. About 95% of the values are within two standard deviations from the mean. About 99% of the values are within three standard deviations from the mean.

nth root (282)   For any real numbers a and b, and any positive integer n, if $a^n = b$, then a is an nth root of b.

O

octants (172)   Three mutually perpendicular planes separate space into eight regions, each called an octant.

odds (734)   The odds of a successful outcome of an event can be expressed as the ratio of the number of ways it can succeed to the number of ways it can fail.

open sentence (27)   A mathematical sentence that contains variables that are to be replaced with numerical values.

ordered pairs (64)   Points in a plane can be located by using ordered pairs of real numbers. An ordered pair consists of the coordinates of the point.

ordered triple (166)   The solution of a system of equations in three variables.

order of operations (7)   To evaluate a numerical expression, the order of operations must be followed. First, simplify the expressions inside grouping symbols. Evaluate all powers. Do all multiplications and divisions from left to right. Finally, do all additions and subtractions from left to right.

organize data (580)   A problem-solving strategy using diagrams, tables, and charts to arrange and evaluate data in order to determine a solution.

origin (64)   The point (0, 0) at which the axes of a coordinate plane intersect.

outlier (237)   Any value in the set of data that is at least 1.5 interquartile ranges beyond the upper and lower quartile.

P

parabola   1. (332, 335)   The general shape of the graph of a quadratic function.   **2.** (415) The set of all points in a plane that are the same distance from a given point called the focus and a given line called the directrix.

parallel lines (83)   In a plane, lines with the same slope are parallel. All vertical lines are parallel, and all horizontal lines are parallel.

parent graph (83)   The graph of the simplest polynomial of the form $f(x) = x^n$ in a family of graphs.

partial sum (676)   In an infinite series, S_n is called a partial sum because it is the sum of a certain number of terms and not the sum of the entire series.

Pascal's triangle (695)   The pyramid formation of the coefficients of binomial expansion.

periodic function (807)   A function is called periodic if there is a positive number a such that $f(x) = f(x + a)$ for all x in the domain of the function. The least positive value of a for which $f(x) = f(x + a)$ is called the period of the function.

permutation (718)   An arrangement of things in a certain order.

perpendicular lines (83)   In a plane, two oblique lines are perpendicular if and only if the product of their slopes is -1. Any vertical line is perpendicular to any horizontal line.

point discontinuity (548)   Point discontinuity occurs for values of x that make the denominator of a rational function zero and visually appears as breaks in the continuity of the graph of the rational function.

point-slope form (89)   The point-slope form of the equation of a line is $y - y_1 = m(x - x_1)$, where (x_1, y_1) are the coordinates of a point on the line and m is the slope of the line.

polynomial (261)   A monomial or the sum of monomials.

polynomial function (479)   A function that can be described by an equation of the form $P(x) = a_0 x^n + a_1 x^{n-1} + ... + a_{n-2} x^2 + a_{n-1} x + a_n$, where the coefficients $a_0, a_1, a_2, ..., a_n$ are real numbers, a_0 is not zero, and n is a nonnegative integer.

polynomial in one variable (478)   A polynomial in one variable x is an expression of the form $a_0 x^n + a_1 x^{n-1} + ... + a_{n-2} x^2 + a_{n-1} x + a_n$, where the coefficients $a_0, a_1, a_2, ..., a_n$ represent real numbers, a_0 is not zero, and n represents a nonnegative integer.

power (255)   An expression in the form x^n.

power property of logarithms (613)   For any real number p and positive numbers m and b, where $b \neq 1$, $\log_b m^p = p \cdot \log_b m$.

prediction equation (95)   The equation of the best-fit line suggested by the data points of a scatter plot. It may be used to estimate, or predict, one of the variables given the other.

prime number (274)   A whole number greater than 1 whose only factors are 1 and itself.

principal root (282)   The principal root is the nonnegative root. If there is a negative root but no nonnegative root, the principal root is the negative root.

principal values (811)   The values in the restricted domains of the functions Cosine, Sine, and Tangent are principal values.

probability (732)   If an event can succeed in s ways and fail in f ways, then the probabilities of success, $P(s)$, and of failure, $P(f)$, are $P(s) = \frac{s}{s+f}$ and $P(f) = \frac{f}{f+s}$.

probability matrix (200)   A probability matrix used in situations involving chance.

problem-solving plan (30)   A four-step plan used to solve problems that requires one to explore the problem, plan the solution, solve the problem, and examine the solution.

problem-solving strategies (38)   Various strategies that are used alone or in combination with each other to solve problems.

product property of logarithms (611)   For all positive numbers m, n, and b, where $b \neq 1$, $\log_b mn = \log_b m + \log_b n$.

property of equality for exponential functions (599)   Suppose b is a positive number other than 1. Then $b^{x_1} = b^{x_2}$ if and only if $x_1 = x_2$.

property of equality for logarithmic functions (608)   Suppose $b > 0$ and $b \neq 1$. Then $\log_b x_1 = \log_b x_2$ if and only if $x_1 = x_2$.

pure imaginary number (310)   A complex number of the form bi, where b is real and $b \neq 0$ and i is the imaginary unit.

Pythagorean theorem (9)   The Pythagorean theorem states that in a right triangle, if a and b are the measures of the legs and c is the measure of the hypotenuse, then $c^2 = a^2 + b^2$.

quadrantal angles (787)   Angles that have their terminal sides on an axis where x or y is equal to zero.

quadrants (64)   The four regions into which two perpendicular number lines separate the plane.

quadratic equation (336)   An equation that can be written in the form $ax^2 + bx + c = 0$, where $a \neq 0$.

quadratic form (515)   For any numbers a, b, and c, except $a = 0$, an equation that can be written as $a[f(x)]^2 + b[f(x)] + c = 0$, where $f(x)$ is some expression in x, is in quadratic form.

quadratic formula (354)   The solutions of a quadratic equation of the form $ax^2 + bx + c$, where $a \neq 0$, are given by the quadratic formula, which is $x = \frac{-b \pm \sqrt{b^2 - 4ac}}{2a}$.

quadratic function (332, 334)   A function described by an equation that can be written in the form $f(x) = ax^2 + bx + c$, where $a \neq 0$.

quadratic inequality (378)   An inequality described by $y < ax^2 + bx + c$, where $a \neq 0$.

quadratic term (334)   In a quadratic function described by $f(x) = ax^2 + bx + c$, the term ax^2.

quartiles (236)   The values in a set of data that separate the data into four sections, each containing 25% of the data.

quotient property of logarithms (612)   For all positive numbers m, n, and b, where $b \neq 1$, $\log_b \frac{m}{n} = \log_b m - \log_b n$.

radian (781)   The measure of an angle that intercepts an arc whose length is one unit.

radical equations (305)   Equations that contain radical expressions with variables in the radicand.

radius (423)   Any line segment whose endpoints are the center of a circle and a point on the circle.

random sample (758)   A sample in which every member of the population has an equal chance to be selected.

range   1. (65)   The set of all second coordinates from the ordered pairs of a relation.   **2.** (235) The difference between the greatest and least values in a set of data.

rational algebraic expressions (562)   An algebraic expression can be expressed as the quotient of two polynomials where the denominator does not equal zero.

rational equation (576)   An equation that contains one or more rational expressions.

rational exponent (298)   For any nonzero number b, and any integers m and n, with $n > 1$, $b^{\frac{m}{n}} = \sqrt[n]{b^m} = \left(\sqrt[n]{b}\right)^m$, except when $b > 0$ and n is even.

rational function (550)   An equation of the form $f(x) = \frac{p(x)}{q(x)}$, where $p(x)$ and $q(x)$ are polynomial functions and $q(x) \neq 0$.

rationalizing the denominator (290)   A process used to eliminate radicals from a denominator or fractions from a radicand.

rational number (13)   A number that can be expressed as a ratio $\frac{m}{n}$, where m and n are integers and n is not zero.

rational zero theorem (509)   Let $f(x) = a_0 x^n + a_1 x^{n-1} + ... + a_{n-1} x + a_n$ represent a polynomial function with integral coefficients ($a \neq 0$). If $\frac{p}{q}$ is a rational number in simplest form and is a zero of $y = f(x)$, then p is a factor of a_n and q is a factor of a_0.

real numbers (13)   The set of irrational numbers together with the set of rational numbers.

recursive formula (683)   A recursive formula has two parts: the value(s) of the first term(s), and a recursion equation that shows how to find each term from the term(s) before it.

reduced matrix (227)   The solution matrix that results when row operations are performed on an augmented matrix to solve a system of linear equations.

reducing a matrix (227)   The process of performing row operations on an augmented matrix to get the desired solution matrix.

reflections (722)   A reflection occurs when an arrangement of objects can be seen from two different views without changing the arrangement.

reflexive property of equality (28)   For any real number a, $a = a$.

relation (65)   A set of ordered pairs.

relative maximum (494)   A point on the graph of a function is called a relative maximum if no other nearby points have a greater y-coordinate.

relative minimum (494)   A point on the graph of a function is called a relative minimum if no other nearby points have a lesser y-coordinate.

remainder theorem (485)   If a polynomial $f(x)$ is divided by $x - a$, the remainder is the constant $f(a)$, and $f(x) = q(x) \cdot (x - a) + f(a)$, where $q(x)$ is a polynomial with degree one less than the degree of $f(x)$.

root (332, 336)   A solution of an equation.

rotation (201)   A transformation in which a figure is moved around a center point.

row matrix (187)   A matrix that has only one row.

row operations (226)   Operations performed on rows of an augmented matrix to find the solution to a system of linear equations.

sampling error (759)   The difference between the sample results and the true population results.

scalar multiplication (188)   Multiplication of each element of a matrix is multiplied by the same constant.

scatter plot (95)   A scatter plot visually shows the nature of a relationship that is determined both by the shape and closeness of the data.

scientific notation (254)   A number is in scientific notation when it is in the form $a \times 10^n$, where $1 \leq a < 10$ and n is an integer.

second-order determinant (141)   A determinant that has two rows and two columns. Its value can be found by calculating the difference of the products of the two diagonals.

self-similarity (689)   A characteristic of an object in which replicas of an entire shape or object are embedded over and over again inside the object in different sizes.

sequence (649)   A list of numbers in a specific order.

series (656)   The indicated sum of the terms of a sequence.

sigma notation (658)   Notation that uses the Σ symbol to indicate a sum of a series.

simplify (255)   To simplify an expression containing powers means to rewrite the expression without parentheses or negative exponents.

simulation (754)   A method for finding experimental probability in which a device is used to model the event and observations are made of how the model responds to the conditions listed in a given problem.

sine (805)   If the terminal side of an angle θ in standard position intersects the unit circle at $P(x, y)$, then $\sin \theta = y$.

Sine (811) $y = \mathrm{Sin}\, x$ if and only if $y = \sin x$ and $-\frac{\pi}{2} \leq x \leq \frac{\pi}{2}$.

skewed distribution (395)   A distribution curve that is not symmetric.

slope (82)   The slope of the line that passes through points (x_1, y_1) and (x_2, y_2) is given by $m = \dfrac{y_2 - y_1}{x_2 - x_1}$, where $x_1 \neq x_2$. The slope of a line described by $f(x) = mx + b$ is m.

slope-intercept form (88)   The slope-intercept form of the equation of a line is $y = mx + b$, where m is the slope and b is the y-intercept.

solution (28)   A value that can replace a variable in an equation to make the equation true.

solve a simpler problem (156, 712)   A problem-solving strategy in which a simpler, similar problem is solved to determine the concepts that can be used in solving a more complex problem.

solving a right triangle (775)   The process of finding the measures of all sides and angles of a right triangle.

square matrix (187)   A matrix that has the same number of rows and columns.

square root (281)   For any real numbers a and b, if $a^2 = b$, then a is a square root of b.

square root function (535)   A function that involves a square root.

standard deviation (384)   From a set of data with n values, where x_1 represents the first term and x_n represents the nth term, if $\bar{x}$ represents the mean, then the standard deviation is SD or
$$\sigma_{\bar{x}} = \sqrt{\dfrac{(x_1 - \bar{x})^2 + (x_2 - \bar{x})^2 + \ldots + (x_n - \bar{x})^2}{n}}.$$

standard form (73)   The standard form of a linear equation is $Ax + By = C$, where A, B, and C are real numbers and A and B are not both zero.

standard position (780)   An angle positioned so that its vertex is at the origin and its initial side is along the positive x-axis is said to be in standard position.

stem-and-leaf plot (19)   A compact way to display data in which each item is separated into two parts. The stem consists of the digits in the greatest common place value. The leaves contain the other digits of each item of data.

step functions (103)   A function whose graph is a series of disjoint lines or steps.

substitution property of equality (28)   If $a = b$, then a may be replaced by b.

subtraction property of equality (28)   For any numbers a, b, and c, if $a = b$, then $a - c = b - c$.

subtraction property of inequality (43)   For any numbers a, b, and c:
1. if $a > b$, then $a - c > b - c$;
2. if $a < b$, then $a - c < b - c$.

success (732)   A desired outcome of an event.

sum of a geometric series (671)   The sum S_n of the first n terms of a geometric series is given by $S_n = \dfrac{a_1 - a_1 r^n}{1 - r}$ or $S_n = \dfrac{a_1(1 - r^n)}{1 - r}$, where $r \neq 1$.

sum of an arithmetic series (657)   The sum S_n of the first n terms of an arithmetic series is given by $S_n = \dfrac{n}{2}(a_1 + a_n)$, where n is a positive integer.

sum of an infinite geometric series (677)   The sum S of an infinite geometric series where $-1 < r < 1$ is given by $S = \dfrac{a_1}{1 - r}$.

symmetric property of equality (28)   For all real numbers a and b, if $a = b$, then $b = a$.

synthetic division (269)   A simpler method than long division used to divide a polynomial by a binomial.

synthetic substitution (486)   The process of using synthetic division to find the value of a function.

system of equations (126)   A set of equations with the same variables.

system of inequalities (148)   A set of inequalities with the same variables.

T

tangent (425)   A line that intersects a circle in exactly one point is said to be tangent to the circle.

Tangent (811) $y = \text{Tan } x$ if and only if $y = \tan x$ and $-\dfrac{\pi}{2} \leq x \leq \dfrac{\pi}{2}$.

term (648)   Each number in a sequence.

terminal side (780)   One of two rays forming an angle on a coordinate plane that rotates about the origin.

terms (261)   The monomials that make up a polynomial.

theoretical probability (754)   Theoretical probability is determined using mathematical methods to provide an idea of what outcomes might occur in a given situation.

transformations (190)   Functions that map points of a graph onto its image.

transition matrix (200)   A matrix that contains information about the transition from one event to another.

transitive property of equality (28)   For all real numbers a, b, and c, if $a = b$ and $b = c$, then $a = c$.

translation (195)   A transformation in which a figure is moved from one location to another on the coordinate plane without changing its size, shape, or orientation.

translation matrix (196)   A matrix that represents the number of units a figure is moved vertically or horizontally from its original position.

transverse axis (441)   One of two line segments that form the axes of symmetry for a hyperbola whose endpoints are the vertices of a hyperbola.

trichotomy property (43)   For any two real numbers, a and b, exactly one of the following statements is true: $a < b$, $a = b$, or $a > b$.

trigonometric equations (861)   An equation involving one or more trigonometric functions which is true for some, but not all, values of the variable.

trigonometric functions (772)   If θ is the measure of one acute angle in a right triangle, a is the measure of the leg opposite θ, b is the measure of the leg adjacent to θ, and c is the measure of the hypotenuse, then

$$\text{sine } \theta = \frac{a}{c} \qquad \text{cosine } \theta = \frac{b}{c}$$
$$\text{tangent } \theta = \frac{a}{b} \qquad \text{cosecant } \theta = \frac{c}{a}$$
$$\text{secant } \theta = \frac{c}{b} \qquad \text{cotangent } \theta = \frac{b}{a}$$

trigonometric identities (788, 835)   A trigonometric equation that is true for all values of the variables.

trigonometry (772)   The study of the relationships between the angles and sides of right triangles.

trinomial (261)   A polynomial with three unlike terms.

unbounded (155)   A function is unbounded if a polygonal region is not formed by the constraints of a system of inequalities.

union (50)   The graph of a compound inequality containing the word *or* is the union of the graphs of the two inequalities.

unit circle (781)   In the coordinate plane, the circle with a radius of one unit and center at the origin.

upper extreme (236)   The greatest value in a set of data.

upper quartile (236)   The median of the upper half of a set of data.

use a simulation (452)   A problem-solving strategy that uses models, or simulations, of mathematical situations that are difficult to solve directly.

variables (27)   Letters used to represent numbers that are not known.

vertex   1. (335)   The point at which a parabola and its axis of symmetry intersect.   **2.** (441) The point on each branch of a hyperbola that is nearest the center of the hyperbola.

vertical line test (65)   If every vertical line drawn on the graph of a relation passes through no more than one point of the graph, then the relation is a function.

work backward (528)   A problem-solving strategy using inverse operations to determine an original value.

x-axis (64)   The horizontal number line that helps to form the coordinate plane.

x-intercept (75)   The x-coordinate of the point at which a graph crosses the x-axis.

y-axis (64)   The vertical number line that helps to form the coordinate plane.

y-intercept (75)   The y-coordinate of the point at which a graph crosses the y-axis.

zero (335)   For any function $f(x)$, if $f(a) = 0$, then a is a zero of the function.

zero product property (341)   For any real numbers a and b, if $ab = 0$, then either $a = 0$, $b = 0$, or both.

SPANISH GLOSSARY

A
---

absolute value/valor absoluto (37)   El valor absoluto de un número equivale al número de unidades que dicho número dista de cero en la recta numérica.

absolute value function/función valor absoluto (104) Función descrita por y = $|x|$ o por $f(x) = |x|$.

addition of matrices/suma de matrices (195)   Si A y B son dos matrices de tipo $m \times n$, entonces $A + B$ es la matriz en que cada elemento es la suma de los elementos correspondientes de A y B.

$$\begin{bmatrix} a & b & c \\ d & e & f \\ g & h & i \end{bmatrix} + \begin{bmatrix} j & k & l \\ m & n & o \\ p & q & r \end{bmatrix} = \begin{bmatrix} a+j & b+k & c+l \\ d+m & e+n & f+o \\ g+p & h+q & i+r \end{bmatrix}$$

addition property of equality/propiedad de adición de la igualdad (28)   Para cualquiera de los números a, b y c, si $a = b$, entonces $a + c = b + c$.

addition property of inequality/propiedad de adición de la desigualdad (43)   Para cualquiera de los números a, b y c:
1. si $a > b$, entonces $a + c > b + c$;
2. si $a < b$, entonces $a + c < b + c$.

algebraic expressions/expresiones algebraicas (8) Una expresión que contiene por lo menos una variable.

amplitude/amplitud (824, 828)   La amplitud de la gráfica de una función periódica es el valor absoluto de la mitad de la diferencia entre su valor máximo y su valor mínimo.

angle of depression/ángulo de depresión (776)   El ángulo formado por una recta horizontal y la línea de visión hasta un objeto a un nivel más bajo.

angle of elevation/ángulo de elevación (776)   El ángulo formado por una recta horizontal y la línea de visión hasta un objeto a un nivel más alto.

angle of incline/ángulo de inclinación (835)   El ángulo agudo no negativo formado por una recta vertical y la línea de orientación de un objeto.

antilogarithm/antilogaritmo (618)   Si log $x = a$, entonces, $x =$ antilog a.

Arcosine function/función arco coseno (811)   La inversa a la función coseno, simbolizada por Cos^{-1} o Arc cos.

arithmetic mean/media aritmética (650)   Los términos entre dos términos no consecutivos de una secuencia aritmética.

arithmetic sequence/secuencia aritmética (648) Secuencia en que cada término después del primero se halla sumando una constante, llamada diferencia común d, al término previo.

arithmetic series/serie aritmética (656)   La suma indicada de los términos de una secuencia aritmética.

associative properties/propiedades asociativas (14) La forma en que tres o más números están agrupados, o asociados, no cambia el resultado de su suma o de su producto. Es decir, para todo número real a, b, y c, $(a + b) + c = a + (b + c)$ y $(a \cdot b) \cdot c = a \cdot (b \cdot c)$.

asymptotes/asíntotas (441, 550)   Curva que se aproxima a unas rectas.

augmented matrix/matriz aumentada (226)   La matriz aumentada de un sistema de ecuaciones contiene la matriz coeficiente del sistema junto con una columna adicional de los términos constantes del sistema.

axis of symmetry/eje de simetría (335)   La línea a partir de la cual una figura es simétrica.

B
---

back-to-back stem-and-leaf plot/diagrama de tallo y hojas consecutivo (20)   Un diagrama de tallo y hojas consecutivo se usa para comparar dos conjuntos de datos. El mismo tallo se usa para las hojas de ambos diagramas.

bell curve/curva acampanada (393)   Una curva simétrica que tiene la misma forma general que la gráfica de una distribución normal, la cual indica que las frecuencias están concentradas alrededor del centro de la distribución.

best-fit line/línea de mejor ajuste (95)   Una línea que se dibuja en un diagrama de dispersión para aproximar la relación lineal del conjunto de puntos de los datos.

binomial/binomio (261)   Un polinomio con dos términos desemejantes.

binomial experiments/experimentos binómicos (753) Existe un experimento binómico si y solo si para cualquier prueba hay exactamente dos resultados posibles, hay un número determinado de pruebas, las pruebas son independientes y la probabilidad de cada prueba es la misma.

binomial theorem/teorema binómico (696)   Si n es un entero positivo, entonces, $(a + b)^n = 1a^nb^0 + \frac{n}{1}a^{n-1}b^1 + \frac{n(n-1)}{1 \cdot 2}a^{n-2}b^2 + ... + 1a^0b^n$.

boundary/frontera (378)   Una línea o curva que separa una gráfica en dos partes.

box-and-whisker plot/diagrama de caja y patillas (237) Una representación gráfica de la variabilidad de un conjunto de datos que resume el conjunto de datos usando sus valores cuartiles y extremos.

Cartesian coordinate plane/plano de coordenadas cartesianas (64) Plano compuesto del eje x y del eje y, los cuales se cruzan en un punto llamado origen. Está dividido en cuatro cuadrantes.

center of a circle/centro del círculo (423) El punto respecto al cual todos los puntos en un círculo están equidistantes.

center of a hyperbola/centro de la hipérbola (441) La intersección de los ejes conjugado y transversal de una hipérbola.

center of an ellipse/centro de la elipse (432) La intersección de los ejes principales y secundarios de una elipse.

change of base formula/cambio de fórmula de base (594, 628) Para todo número positivo a, b y n, en que $a \neq 1$ y $b \neq 1$, $\log_a n = \dfrac{\log_b n}{\log_b a}$.

characteristic/característica (618) El entero que se usa para expresar un logaritmo de base 10 como la suma de un entero y un decimal positivo.

circle/círculo (423) En un plano, el conjunto de todos los puntos que están equidistantes de un punto dado en el plano.

circular functions/funciones circulares (805) Las seis funciones trigonométricas básicas definidas usando un círculo unidad.

circular permutation/permutación circular (721) Si n número de objetos distintos se arreglan en forma de círculo, entonces hay $\dfrac{n!}{n}$ o $(n-1)!$ permutaciones de los objetos alrededor del círculo.

coding matrix/matriz de codificación (212) Un mensaje en el cual cada letra corresponde a un elemento numérico en una matriz, y el cual puede ser convertido en código multiplicando la matriz por una matriz de cifrado.

coefficient/coeficiente (255) El factor numérico de un monomio.

column matrix/matriz de columna (187) Una matriz que tiene solo una columna.

combination/combinación (726) Una disposición, o arreglo, en el cual el orden no es importante. El número de combinaciones de n objetos distintos tomados r número de veces a la vez es $C(n, r) = \dfrac{n!}{(n-r)!r!}$.

common difference/diferencia común (649) El número d que se añade para hallar el próximo término de una secuencia aritmética.

common logarithms/logaritmos comunes (617) Logaritmos de base 10.

common ratio/proporción común (662) El número por el cual se multiplica cada término después del primero, para obtener el segundo en una secuencia geométrica.

commutative properties/propiedades conmutativas (14) El orden en que se suman o multiplican dos números no cambia el resultado de su suma o de su producto. Es decir, para todos los números reales a y b, $a + b = b + a$ y $a \cdot b = b \cdot a$.

complements/complementos (732) Dos eventos son complementos uno del otro si la suma de sus probabilidades es 1.

completing the square/completando el cuadrado (347) Un proceso que se usa para crear un cuadrado perfecto trinómico.

complex conjugates/complejos conjugados (317) Números complejos de la forma $a + bi$ y $a - bi$.

complex conjugate theorem/teorema del conjugado complejo (504) Suponiendo que a y b son números reales, en que $b \neq 0$, si $a + bi$ es un cero de una función polinómica, entonces $a - bi$ es también un cero de la función.

complex fraction/fracción compleja (565) Una fracción cuyo numerador y/o denominador contiene una fracción.

complex numbers/números complejos (311) Cualquier número que se puede escribir en la forma $a + bi$, en que a y b son números reales e i es la unidad imaginaria; a se denomina la parte real y bi la parte imaginaria.

composition of functions/composición de funciones (520) Suponiendo que f y g son funciones tales que la amplitud de g es un subconjunto del dominio de f, entonces la función compuesta $[f \circ g](x) = f[g(x)]$.

compound inequality/desigualdad compuesta (49) Dos desigualdades combinadas con las conjunciones y u o.

concentric circles/círculos concéntricos (426) Círculos con el mismo centro, pero no necesariamente el mismo radio.

conic section/sección cónica (415) Cualquier figura formada de la división de un cono doble con un plano.

conjugate axis/eje conjugado (441) El segmento de recta perpendicular al eje transversal en el centro de una hipérbola y que es un eje de simetría de la hipérbola.

conjugate pair/par conjugado (506) Si una función polinómica tiene dos raíces imaginarias de la forma $a + bi$ y $a - bi$, estos números forman un par conjugado.

conjugates/conjugados (292) Binomios de la forma $a\sqrt{b} + c\sqrt{d}$ y $a\sqrt{b} - c\sqrt{d}$ en que a, b, c y d son números racionales.

Spanish Glossary

consistent system/sistema consistente (127)   Un sistema de ecuaciones que tiene por lo menos una solución.

constant function/función constante (74)   Una función lineal de la forma $f(x) = b$, para la cual la pendiente es cero.

constant of variation/constante de variación (556)   La constante k en cualquiera de las ecuaciones $y = kx$ o $y = \frac{k}{x}$.

constants/constantes (255)   Monomios que no contienen variables.

constant term/término constante (334)   En una función cuadrática descrita por $f(x) = ax^2 + bx + c$, el término constante es c.

constraints/restricciones (153)   Las desigualdades en un sistema de desigualdades cuyas gráficas forman las fronteras de la gráfica de la solución del sistema.

continuity/continuidad (548)   Una función que puede ser graficada sin que el lápiz deje el papel se dice que tiene continuidad.

continuous function/función continua (67)   Una función continua se puede trazar con una línea o una curva continua y tiene un dominio con un número infinito de elementos.

coordinate matrix/matriz de coordenadas (189)   Una matriz que contiene las coordenadas de los vértices de una figura geométrica.

coordinate system/sistema de coordenadas (64)   Compuesto de dos rectas numéricas perpendiculares que se intersecan en sus orígenes creando un plano de coordenadas sobre el cual se pueden trazar pares ordenados.

cosine/coseno (805)   Si el lado final de un ángulo θ en posición estándar interseca el círculo unidad en $P(x, y)$, entonces $\cos \theta = x$.

Cosine/coseno (811) $y = \cos x$, si y solo si $y = \cos x$ y $0 \le x \le \pi$.

coterminal angles/ángulos confinantes (783)   Dos ángulos en posición estándar y que comparten el mismo lado final se llaman ángulos confinantes.

Cramer's rule/regla de Cramer (141)   Un método que usa determinantes para resolver un sistema de dos ecuaciones lineales.

D

degree/grado   **1.** (255) El grado de un monomio no nulo es la suma de los exponentes de sus variables. **2.** (261) El grado de un polinomio es el grado del monomio con el grado más alto.

dependent events/eventos dependientes (714)   El resultado de un evento dependiente se ve afectado por el resultado de otro evento.

dependent systems/sistemas dependientes (128)   Un sistema de ecuaciones con un número infinito de soluciones.

dependent variable/variable dependiente (73)   Una variable cuyo valor depende de, o es afectado por el valor de otra variable.

depressed polynomial/polinomio reducido (487)   Cuando uno divide un polinomio entre uno de sus factores binómicos, el cociente se llama polinomio reducido.

Descartes' rule of signs/regla de signos de Descartes (505)   Si $P(x)$ es un polinomio cuyos términos se dan en potencias descendientes de la variable,

- el número de ceros reales positivos de $y = P(x)$ es el mismo que el número de cambios de signo de los coeficientes de los términos, o es menos que esto por un número par, y

- el número de ceros reales negativos de $y = P(x)$, es el mismo que el número de cambios de signo de los coeficientes de los términos de $P(-x)$, o es menos que esto por un número par.

determinant/determinante (141, 205)   Un arreglo cuadrado de números o expresiones encerradas por dos barras verticales paralelas.

dilation/dilatación (190)   Una transformación en la cual se amplía o reduce una figura.

dimensions/dimensiones (187)   En una matriz consistente de n hileras y m columnas, se dice que la matriz tiene dimensión $n \times m$ (lo cual se lee "n por m").

direct variation/variación directa   **1.** (103) Una función lineal descrita por $y = mx$ o $f(x) = mx$, en que $m \ne 0$. **2.** (556) Un tipo de variación en que y varía directamente con x si existe alguna constante k, tal que $y = kx$.

discrete function/función discreta (65)   Una función cuya gráfica consiste de puntos que no están conectados.

discrete mathematics/matemeaticas discretas (188)   Una rama de las matemáticas que estudia cantidades finitas o interrumpidas.

discriminant/discriminante (356)   Para una expresión cuadrática $ax^2 + bx + c = 0$, la expresión $b^2 - 4ac$ bajo el signo radical en la fórmula cuadrática.

distance formula/fórmula de distancia (409)   La distancia entre dos puntos con coordenadas (x_1, y_1) y (x_2, y_2) es dada por $d = \sqrt{(x_2 - x_1)^2 + (y_2 - y_1)^2}$.

distributive properties/propiedades distributivas (14)   Para todos los números reales a, b y c, $a(b + c) = ab + ac$ y $(b + c)a = ba + ca$.

dividing rational expressions/división de expresiones racionales (563)   Para todas las expresiones racionales $\frac{a}{b}$ y $\frac{c}{d}$, $\frac{a}{b} \div \frac{c}{d} = \frac{a}{b} \cdot \frac{d}{c} = \frac{ad}{bc}$, si $b \ne 0$, $c \ne 0$ y $d \ne 0$.

division property of equality/propiedad de división de la igualdad (28)   Para cualquiera de los números reales *a*, *b* y *c*, si *a* = *b* y *c* ≠ 0, entonces $\frac{a}{c} = \frac{b}{c}$.

division property of inequality/propiedad de división de la desigualdad (44)   Para cualquiera de los números reales *a*, *b* y *c*:

  1. si *c* es positivo y *a* < *b*, entonces $\frac{a}{c} < \frac{b}{c}$;

  2. si *c* es positivo y *a* > *b*, entonces $\frac{a}{c} > \frac{b}{c}$;

  3. si *c* es negativo y *a* < *b*, entonces $\frac{a}{c} > \frac{b}{c}$;

  4. si *c* es negativo y *a* > *b*, entonces $\frac{a}{c} < \frac{b}{c}$.

domain/dominio (65)   El conjunto de todas las primeras coordenadas de los pares ordenados de una relación.

double-angle formulas/fórmulas de doble ángulo (853)   Las siguientes identidades son válidas para todos los valores de θ.

$$\sin 2\theta = 2 \sin \theta \cos \theta$$
$$\cos 2\theta = \cos^2 \theta - \sin^2 \theta$$
$$\cos 2\theta = 1 - 2 \sin^2 \theta$$
$$\cos 2\theta = 2 \cos^2 \theta - 1$$

element/elemento   1. (141) Un número o variable escrito dentro de una determinante.   **2.** (186) Cada valor en una matriz.

ellipse/elipse (431)   El conjunto de todos los puntos en un plano de manera que la suma de las distancias desde los focos es constante.

empty set/conjunto vacío (40)   El conjunto sin ningún elemento, representado con { } o Ø.

equal matrices/matrices idénticas (188)   Se considera que dos matrices son idénticas si poseen las mismas dimensiones y si cada elemento de una matriz es igual al elemento correspondiente de la otra matriz.

equation/ecuación (27)   Un enunciado matemático que dice que dos expresiones matemáticas son iguales.

expansion by minors/expansión de menores (205)   Un método que se usa para hallar el valor de cualquier determinante de tercer orden o más alta mediante el uso de determinantes de orden más bajo.

experimental probability/probabilidad experimental (754)   Una probabilidad que se determina llevando a cabo pruebas o experimentos y observando los resultados.

exponential equation/ecuación exponencial (626)   Una ecuación en que las variables ocurren en forma de exponentes.

exponential function/función exponencial (594, 597)   Una ecuación de la forma $y = a \cdot b^x$, en que $a \neq 0$ y $b \neq 1$, se llama una función exponencial de base *b*.

exponential growth/crecimiento exponencial (622)   El crecimiento exponencial ocurre cuando una cantidad aumenta exponencialmente.

exponential growth rate/tasa de crecimiento exponencial (626)   La constante positiva *k* en la ecuación de crecimiento $P(t) = P_0 e^{kt}$ se llama la tasa de crecimiento exponencial.

extraneous solutions/soluciones extrenuas (305)   Soluciones que no satisfacen la ecuación original.

extreme values/valores extremos (305)   Datos que varían ampliamente de los valores centrales del grupo.

factorial/factorial (697)   Si *n* es un número positivo, la expresión *n*! se define como $n! = n(n-1)(n-2) \cdot (n-3) \cdots 2 \cdot 1$. Por definición, 0! = 1.

factoring/factorización (341)   Un método que se usa para resolver una ecuación cuadrática que requiere el uso de la propiedad del producto de cero.

factors/factores (274)   Números, variables, monomios o polinomios multiplicados para obtener un producto.

factor theorem/teorema del factor (487)   El binomio $x - a$ es un factor del polinomio $f(x)$, si y solo si $f(a) = 0$.

failure/fracaso (732)   Cualquier resultado que no es el resultado deseado de un evento.

family of graphs/familia de gráficas (83)   Un grupo de gráficas que despliegan una o más características semejantes.

feasible region/región factible (153)   El área de intersección de las gráficas de desigualdades en un sistema de desigualdades en que se cumple cada restricción.

Fibonacci sequence/sucesión de Fibonacci (683)   Una sucesión especial que a menudo se encuentra en la naturaleza y la cual fue nombrada en honor a su descubridor, Leonardo Fibonnaci.

fixed points/puntos fijos (526)   Los puntos en donde la gráfica de una función $g(x)$ intersecan la gráfica de la recta $f(x) = x$.

FOIL method/método FOIL (263)   Una aplicación de la propiedad distribuitiva que se usa para multiplicar dos binomios. El producto es la suma de los productos de los términos: primero, exterior, interior y último.

formula/fórmula (9)   Una representación matemática que expresa una relación general entre ciertas cantidades.

fractal/fractal (318, 688)   Una figura geométrica que posee similaridad propia, se crea usando un proceso recursivo y es infinita en estructura.

fractal geometry/geometría fractal (688)   Una nueva rama de las matemáticas que provee modelos de diseños en la naturaleza.

frequency distribution/distribución de frecuencias (392)   Muestra cómo los datos están esparcidos sobre una gama de valores.

function/función (65)   Un tipo especial de relación en que cada elemento del dominio se parea exactamente con un elemento de la amplitud.

fundamental counting principle/principio fundamental de contar (713)   Si el evento M puede ocurrir de m maneras y es seguido por un evento N que ocurre de n maneras, entonces el evento M seguido del evento N puede ocurrir en $m \cdot n$ maneras.

fundamental theorem of algebra/teorema fundamental de álgebra (503)   Cada ecuación polinómica con grado mayor de cero tiene por lo menos una raíz en el conjunto de números complejos.

general formula for growth and decay/formula general para crecimiento y disminución (631)   La fórmula es $y = ne^{kt}$, en que y es la cantidad final, n es la cantidad inicial, k es una constante y t es el tiempo.

geometric means/medias geométricas (665)   Los términos entre cualquier par de términos no consecutivos en una secuencia geométrica.

geometric sequence/sucesión geométrica (662)   Una sucesión en que cada término después del primero se halla multiplicando el término previo por una constante llamada razón común, r.

geometric series/serie geométrica (670)   La suma indicada de los términos en una serie geométrica.

graphical iteration/iteración gráfica (526)   Las iteraciones gráficas producen una representación visual del proceso de iteración.

greatest integer function/función del entero mayor (104)   Un tipo de función escalón descrita por $f(x) = [x]$ en que $[x]$ es el entero mayor, pero *no* mayor que x.

guess and check/conjetura y cotejo (342)   Una estrategia para resolver problemas en la cual se prueban varios valores o combinaciones de valores para hallar una solución al problema.

half-angle formulas/fórmulas de semiángulos (855)   Las siguientes identidades son válidas para todos los valores de α.

$$\cos \frac{\alpha}{2} = \pm \sqrt{\frac{1 + \cos \alpha}{2}}$$

$$\sin \frac{\alpha}{2} = \pm \sqrt{\frac{1 - \cos \alpha}{2}}$$

histogram/histograma (392)   Una gráfica de barras que despliega una distribución de frecuencia.

hyperbola/hipérbola (440)   El conjunto de todos los puntos P en un plano tal que el valor absoluto de la diferencia de las distancias desde P hasta dos puntos dados, llamados focos, es constante.

hypotenuse/hipotenusa (9)   El lado opuesto al ángulo recto en un triángulo rectángulo.

hypothesis/hipótesis (760)   Un enunciado que se prueba en un experimento.

identify subgoals/identificación de submetas (296)   Una estrategia para resolver problemas que utiliza una serie de pasos menores o submetas.

identity function/función identidad (103)   Una función lineal descrita por $y = x$ o $f(x) = x$.

identity matrix/matriz identidad (213)   Cualquier matriz cuadrada A que cuando se multiplica por otra matriz B de la misma dimensión, equivale a esa misma matriz B.

identity properties/propiedades de identidad (14)   Si a es un número real, entonces $a + 0 = a = 0 + a$ y $a \cdot 1 = a = 1 \cdot a$.

imaginary unit/unidad imaginaria (310)   La unidad imaginaria i está definida por $i = \sqrt{-1}$.

inclusive events/eventos inclusivos (746)   Dos eventos son inclusivos si los resultados de los eventos pueden ser los mismos.

inconsistent system/sistema inconsistente (128)   Un sistema de ecuaciones que no tiene solución.

independent events/eventos independientes (713)   El resultado de un evento independiente no se ve afectado por el resultado de otro evento.

independent system/sistema independiente (127)   Un sistema de ecuaciones que tiene exactamente una solución.

independent variable/variable independiente (73)   La variable cuyo valor no depende de, ni es afectado por el valor de otra variable.

index of summation/índice de adición (658)   La variable definida debajo del símbolo Σ en la notación sigma.

infinite geometric series/serie geométrica infinita (676)   La suma indicada de los términos de una sucesión geométrica infinita.

initial side/lado inicial (780)   Uno de los dos rayos que forman un ángulo en un plano de coordenadas fijo a lo largo del eje positivo x.

integral zero theorem/teorema del cero integrado (509)   Si los coeficientes de una función polinómica son números enteros, de modo que $a_0 = 1$ y $a_n \neq 0$, cualquiera de los ceros racionales de la función deben ser factores de a_n.

interquartile range/amplitud intercuartílica (236) La diferencia entre el cuartil superior y el inferior de un conjunto de datos.

intersection/intersección (49) La gráfica de una desigualdad compuesta que contiene la palabra *y* es la intersección de las gráficas de las dos desigualdades.

inverse Cosine/coseno inverso (811) Dado $y = \cos x$, la función del coseno inverso la define $y = \cos^{-1} x$ o $y = \text{arc cos } x$.

inverse functions/funciones inversas (528) Dos funciones f y g son funciones inversas si y solo si las composiciones de ambas son la función identidad. Es decir, $[f \circ g](x) = x$ y $[g \circ f](x) = x$.

inverse of a matrix/inverso de una matriz (213) La matriz por la cual se multiplica otra matriz para producir la matriz identidad.

inverse properties/propiedades del inverso (14) Si a es un número real, entonces $a + (-a) = 0 = (-a) + a$ y $a \cdot \frac{1}{a} = 1 = \frac{1}{a} \cdot a$, si $a \neq 0$.

inverse relation/relación inversa (531) Dos relaciones son inversas si y solo si siempre que una relación contenga el elmento (a, b), la otra relación contiene el elemento (b, a).

inverse Sine/seno inverso (812) Dado que $y = \text{seno } x$, la función seno inversa está definida por $y = \text{sen}^{-1} x$ o $y = \text{arc sen } x$.

inverse Tangent/tangente inversa (812) Dado $y = \text{Tan } x$, la función tangente inversa está definida por $y = \text{Tan}^{-1} x$ o $y = \text{arc tan } x$.

inverse variation/variación inversa (557) Un tipo de variación en la cual y varía inversamente con x si existe alguna constante k, de modo que $xy = k$ o $y = \frac{k}{x}$.

irrational number/número irracional (13) Los números irracionales son números reales que no se pueden escribir como decimales periódicos.

iterate/iterar **1.** (318) Cuando un proceso o función se repite una y otra vez. **2.** (526) Cada resultado de un proceso de iteración se llama iteración.

iteration/iteración (522) El proceso mediante el cual se determina el valor de una función para cierto número del dominio y se genera una sucesión de valores usando cada valor de salida como el próximo valor de entrada.

J

joint variation/variación conjunta (558) Un tipo de variación en el cual y varía conjuntamente con x y z, se existe algún número, k de modo que $y = kxz$, en que $x \neq 0$ y $z \neq 0$.

L

latus rectum/lado recto (417) El segmento de recta a través del foco de una parábola y perpendicular al eje de simetría.

law of cosines/ley de los cosenos (799) Para cualquier triángulo ABC con a, b y c representando las medidas de los lados, y con ángulos opuestos cuyas medidas son A, B y C, respectivamente, las siguientes ecuaciones son ciertas:

$$a^2 = b^2 + c^2 - 2bc \cos A$$
$$b^2 = a^2 + c^2 - 2ac \cos B$$
$$c^2 = a^2 + b^2 - 2ab \cos C.$$

law of sines/ley de los senos (793) Sea $\triangle ABC$ cualquier triángulo con a, b y c representando las medidas de los lados, y ángulos opuestos con medidas A, B y C, respectivamente. Entonces, $\frac{\sin A}{a} = \frac{\sin B}{b} = \frac{\sin C}{c}$.

leading coefficient/coeficiente guía (480) El coeficiente del término con el grado más alto.

legs/catetos (9) Los dos lados de un triángulo rectángulo, los cuales forman el ángulo recto.

like radical expressions/expresiones radicales semejantes (291) Dos o más expresiones radicales se denominan expresiones radicales semejantes si tanto los índices como los radicandos de ambas son iguales.

like terms/términos semejantes (261) Dos o más monomios que son iguales o que difieren solo en sus coeficientes numéricos.

linear equation/ecuación lineal (73) Una ecuación cuya gráfica es una recta.

linear function/función lineal (74) Se dice que una función es lineal si se puede definir por $f(x) = mx + b$, en la cual m y b son números reales.

linear permutation/permutación lineal (718) El despliegue de cosas en una recta.

linear programming/programación lineal (155) Un método para hallar el valor máximo o mínimo de una función en dos variables sujeto a restricciones dadas en las variables.

linear term/término lineal (334) En una función cuadrática descrita por $f(x) = ax^2 + bx + c$, bx es el término lineal.

line plot/esquema lineal (19) Despliega datos estadísticos sobre una recta numérica, de modo que se puedan determinar los patrones y las variabilidades en los datos.

list possibilities/listado de posibilidades (38) Una estrategia para resolver problemas que se usa para hallar todas las soluciones posibles a un problema.

location principle/principio de ubicación (494) Suponiendo que $y = f(x)$ representa una función polinómica y que a y b son dos números tales que $f(a) < 0$ y $f(b) > 0$, entonces, la función tiene por lo menos un cero real entre a y b.

logarithm/logaritmo (605) Suponiendo que $b > 0$ y $b \neq 1$, para $n > 0$, existe un número p, tal que $\log_b n = p$ si y solo si $b^p = n$.

logarithmic function/función logarítmica (594, 607) Una función de la forma $y = \log_b x$, en que $b > 0$ y $b \neq 1$.

look for a pattern/busca un patrón (80) Una estrategia para resolver problemas que a menudo involucra el uso de tablas para organizar la información y determinar un patrón.

lower extreme/extremo bajo (236) El valor menor en un conjunto de datos.

lower quartile/cuartil inferior (236) La mediana de la mitad inferior de un conjunto de datos.

major axis/eje mayor (432) El segmento de recta más largo de los dos segmentos que forman los ejes de simetría de una elipse.

mantissa/mantisa (618) El logaritmo de un número entre 1 y 10.

mapping/apareo (65) Un apareo muestra como cada miembro del dominio de una relación se aparea con cada miembro de la amplitud.

matrix/matriz (186) Una red rectangular de variables o constantes en hileras horizontales y columnas verticales, que por lo general se encierran en corchetes.

matrix equation/ecuación matricial (219) Una ecuación de la forma $AX = C$, en que A es la matriz coeficiente para un sistema de ecuaciones lineales, X es la matriz de columna que consiste de las variables del sistema y C es la matriz de columna que consiste de los términos constantes del sistema.

matrix logic/lógica matricial (187) Una estrategia para resolver problemas en la cual la información se organiza en una matriz y se eliminan una por una las posibilidades hasta hallar una solución.

mean/media (21) La suma de todos los valores en un conjunto de datos dividida entre el número de valores.

measure of central tendency/medida de tendencia central (21) Un número que representa el centro o la mitad de un conjunto de datos.

median/mediana (21) El valor del medio de un conjunto de datos. Si existen dos valores de medio, la mediana es la media de los números.

midpoint formula/fórmula de punto medio (410) Si un segmento de recta tiene extremos en (x_1, y_1) y (x_2, y_2), entonces el punto medio del segmento de recta tiene coordenadas $\left(\dfrac{x_1 + x_2}{2}, \dfrac{y_1 + y_2}{2}\right)$.

minor/menor (205) La determinante formada cuando se eliminan la hilera y la columna que contienen un elemento de la determinante dada.

minor axis/eje menor (432) El más corto de los dos segmentos de recta que forman los ejes de simetría de una elipse.

mode/modal (21) El valor más frecuente en un conjunto de datos.

monomials/monomios (255) Una expresión que consiste de un número, una variable o el producto de un número y una o más variables.

multiplication property of equality/propiedad de igualdad de la multiplicación (28) Para cualquiera de los números reales a, b y c, si $a = b$, entonces $a \cdot c = b \cdot c$.

multiplication property of inequality/propiedad de multiplicación de la desigualdad (44) Para cualquiera de los números reales a, b y c:

1. Si c es positivo y $a < b$, entonces $ac < bc$;
2. Si c es positivo y $a > b$, entonces $ac > bc$;
3. Si c es negativo y $a < b$, entonces $ac > bc$;
4. Si c es negativo y $a > b$, entonces $ac < bc$.

multiplying matrices/multiplicación de matrices (199) El producto de $A_{m \times n}$ y $B_{n \times r}$ es $(AB)_{m \times r}$. El elemento en la i–esima hilera y la j–esima columna de AB es la suma de los productos de los elementos correspondientes en la i–esima hilera de A y la j–esima columna de B.

multiplying rational expressions/multiplicación de expresiones racionales (563) Para todas las expresiones racionales $\frac{a}{b}$ y $\frac{c}{d}$, $\frac{a}{b} \cdot \frac{c}{d} = \frac{ac}{bd}$, si $b \neq 0$ y $d \neq 0$.

mutually exclusive events/eventos mutuamente exclusivos (746) Dos eventos son mutuamente exclusivos si sus resultados nunca pueden ser iguales.

natural logarithm/logaritmo natural (622) Los logaritmos naturales son los logaritmos de base e.

normal distribution/distribución normal (393) Una distribución que resulta en una gráfica simétrica acampanada. Cerca del 68% de los valores se hallan dentro de una desviación estándar de la media. Cerca del 95% de los valores se hallan dentro de dos desviaciones estándares de la media. Cerca del 99% de los valores se hallan dentro de tres desviaciones estándares de la media.

nth root/enésima raíz (282) Para cualquiera de los números reales a y b y cualquier número entero positivo n, si $a^n = b$, entonces a es una enésima raíz de b.

octants/octantes (172) Tres planos mutuamente perpendiculares separan el espacio en ocho regiones, cada una de ellas llamada una octante.

odds/posibilidades (734) Las posibilidades de que un evento tenga un resultado exitoso se pueden expresar como el cociente de la proporción del número de formas en que el evento puede tener éxito dividido entre el número de formas en que puede fracasar.

open sentence/operación abierta (27)   Un enunciado matemático que contiene variables que serán reemplazadas con valores numéricos.

ordered pairs/pares ordenados (64)   Los puntos en un plano se pueden ubicar mediante el uso de pares ordenados de números reales. Un par ordenado consiste de las coordenadas del punto.

ordered triple/triple ordenado (166)   La solución de un sistema de ecuaciones en tres variables.

order of operations/orden de operaciones (7)   Para evaluar una expresión numérica, se debe seguir el orden de operaciones. Primero, simplifica las expresiones dentro de los símbolos de agrupación. Evalúa todas las potencias. Realiza todas las multiplicaciones y las divisiones de izquierda a derecha. Finalmente, realiza todas las sumas y las restas de izquierda a derecha.

organize data/organizar datos (580)   Una estrategia para resolver problemas usando diagramas, tablas y esquemas para ordenar y evaluar datos y así poder hallar una solución.

origin/origen (64)   El punto (0, 0) en donde se intersecan los ejes del plano de coordenadas.

outlier/valor atípico (237)   Cualquier valor en un conjunto de datos que se encuentra por lo menos a 1.5 amplitudes intercuartílicas más allá del cuartillo superior y del inferior.

parabola/parábola 1. (332, 335) La forma generalizada de la gráfica de una función cuadrática. **2.** (415) El conjunto de todos los puntos en un plano que se encuentran a la misma distancia de un punto dado llamado el foco y de una recta dada llamada la directriz.

parallel lines/rectas paralelas (83)   En un plano, las rectas que tienen la misma pendiente son paralelas. Todas las rectas verticales son paralelas y todas las rectas horizontales son paralelas.

parent graph/gráfica madre (83)   La gráfica del polinomio más simple de forma $f(x) = x^n$ en una familia de gráficas.

partial sum/suma parcial (676)   En una serie infinita, S_n se llama una suma parcial porque es la suma de cierto número de términos y no la suma de la serie completa.

Pascal's triangle/triángulo de Pascal (695)   La formación en pirámide de los coeficientes de una expansión binómica.

periodic function/función periódica (807)   Una función es periódica si existe un número positivo a tal que $f(x) = f(x + a)$ para toda x en el dominio de la función. El menor valor positivo de a para el cual $f(x) = f(x + a)$ se llama el período de la función.

permutation/permutación (718)   Una disposición de cosas en cierto orden.

perpendicular lines/rectas perpendiculares (83)   En un plano, dos líneas oblicuas son perpendiculares si y solo si el producto de sus pendientes es -1. Cualquier recta vertical es perpendicular a cualquier recta horizontal.

point discontinuity/punto de discontinuidad (548)   El punto de discontinuidad ocurre para los valores de x que hacen que el denominador de una función racional sea cero y aparece a la vista como interrupciones en la continuidad gráfica de la función racional.

point-slope form/forma de punto–pendiente (89)   La forma de punto–pendiente de la ecuación de una recta es $y - y_1 = m(x - x_1)$, en la cual (x_1, y_1) son las coordenadas de un punto sobre la recta y m es la pendiente de la recta.

polynomial/polinomio (261)   Un monomio o la suma de monomios.

polynomial function/función polinómica (479)   Una función que se puede describir con una ecuación de la forma $P(x) = a_0 x^n + a_1 x^{n-1} + \ldots + a_{n-2} x^2 + a_{n-1} x + a_n$, en la cual los coeficientes $a_0, a_1, a_2, \ldots a_n$, son números reales, a_0 no es cero y n es un número entero no negativo.

polynomial in one variable/polinomio en una variable (478)   Un polinomio en una variable x es una expresión de la forma $a_0 x^n + a_1 x^{n-1} + \ldots + a_{n-2} x^2 + a_{n-1} x + a_n$, en la cual los coeficientes a_0, $a_1, a_2, \ldots a_n$, representan números reales, a_0 no es cero y n representa un número entero no negativo.

power/potencia (255)   Una expresión de la forma x^n.

power property of logarithms/propiedad de potencia de logaritmos (613)   Para cualquier número real p y números positivos m y b, en que $b \neq 1$, $\log_b m^p = p \cdot \log_b m$.

prediction equation/ecuación de predicción (95)   La ecuación de la línea de mejor ajuste sugerida por los puntos de una gráfica de dispersión. Se puede usar para estimar, o predecir, una de las variables a partir de otra dada.

prime number/número primo (274)   Un número entero mayor que 1 cuyos únicos factores son 1 y el número mismo.

principal root/raíz principal (282)   La raíz principal es la raíz no negativa. Si hay una raíz negativa, pero no hay ninguna raíz no negativa, la raíz principal es la raíz negativa.

principal values/valores principales (811)   Los valores de los dominios restringidos de las funciones del coseno, del seno y de la tangente son valores principales.

probability/probabilidad (732)   Si un evento puede suceder de s maneras y puede fracasar de f maneras, entonces las probabilidades de éxito $P(s)$, y de fracaso $P(f)$, son $P(s) = \frac{s}{s + f}$ y $P(f) = \frac{f}{f + s}$.

probability matrix/matriz de probabilidad (200)   Una matriz de probabilidad se usa en situaciones que involucran el azar.

problem solving plan/plan para solucionar problemas (30)   Un plan de cuatro pasos que se usa para solucionar problemas y el cual requiere que uno explore el problema, planifique la solución, resuelva el problema y examine la solución.

problem solving strategies/estrategias para resolver problemas (38)   Varias estrategias que se usan solas o en combinación para resolver problemas.

product property of logarithms/propiedad de producto de logaritmos (611)   Para todos los números positivos m, n y b, en que $b \neq 1$, $\log_b mn = \log_b m + \log_b n$.

property of equality for exponential functions/ propiedad de igualdad para las funciones exponenciales (599)   Suponiendo que b es un número positivo diferente de 1, entonces $b^{x_1} = b^{x_2}$ si y solo si $x_1 = x_2$.

property of equality of logarithmic functions/ propiedad de igualdad de funciones logarítmicas (608)   Suponiendo que $b > 0$ y $b \neq 1$, entonces $\log_b x_1 = \log_b x_2$, si y solo si $x_1 = x_2$.

pure imaginary numbers/números imaginarios puros (310)   Un número complejo de la forma bi, en que b es real y $b \neq 0$, e i es la unidad imaginaria.

Pythagorean theorem/teorema de Pitágoras (9)   El teorema de Pitágoras enuncia que en un triángulo rectángulo, si a y b son las medidas de los catetos y c es la medida de la hipotenusa, entonces, $c^2 = a^2 + b^2$.

quadrantal angles/ángulos de cuadrantes (787)   Ángulos cuyos lados finales están sobre un eje en el cual x o y es igual a cero.

quadrants/cuadrantes (64)   Las cuatro regiones en que dos rectas numéricas perpendiculares separan el plano.

quadratic equation/ecuación cuadrática (336)   Una ecuación que puede ser escrita en la forma $ax^2 + bx + c = 0$, en la cual $a \neq 0$.

quadratic form/forma cuadrática (515)   Para cualquiera de los números a, b y c, excepto $a = 0$, una ecuación que se puede escribir como $a[f(x)]^2 + b[f(x)] + c = 0$, en que $f(x)$ es una expresión en x, está en forma cuadrática.

quadratic formula/fórmula cuadrática (354)   Las soluciones de una ecuación cuadrática de la forma $ax^2 + bx + c = 0$, en la cual $a \neq 0$ son dadas por la fórmula cuadrática que es $x = \dfrac{-b \pm \sqrt{b^2 - 4ac}}{2a}$.

quadratic function/función cuadrática (332, 334)   Una función descrita por una ecuación que se puede escribir en la forma $f(x) = ax^2 + bx + c = 0$, en la cual $a \neq 0$.

quadratic inequality/desigualdad cuadrática (378)   Una desigualdad descrita por $y < ax^2 + bx + c = 0$, en la cual $a \neq 0$.

quadratic term/término cuadrático (334)   En una función cuadrática descrita por $f(x) = ax^2 + bx + c = 0$, el término ax^2.

quartiles/cuartiles (236)   Los valores en un conjunto de datos que separan los datos en cuatro secciones, cada una de las cuales contiene el 25% de los datos.

quotient property of logarithms/propiedad de cociente de logaritmos (612)   Para todos los números positivos m, n y b, en que $b \neq 1$, $\log_b \dfrac{m}{n} = \log_b m - \log_b n$.

R

radian/radián (781)   La medida de un ángulo que interseca un arco cuya longitud es de una unidad.

radical equations/ecuaciones radicales (305)   Ecuaciones que contienen expresiones radicales con variables en el radicando.

radius/radio (423)   Cualquier segmento de recta cuyos extremos son el centro de un círculo y un punto en el círculo.

random sample/muestra al azar (758)   Una muestra en que cada miembro de la población tiene la misma posibilidad de ser seleccionado.

range/amplitud   **1.** (65) El conjunto de todas las segundas coordenadas de los pares ordenados de una relación.   **2.** (235) La diferencia entre los valores mayor y menor en un conjunto de datos.

rational algebraic expressions/expresiones algebraicas racionales (562)   Una expresión algebraica puede ser expresada como el cociente de dos polinomios en los que el denominador no es igual a cero.

rational equation/ecuación racional (576)   Una ecuación que contiene una o más expresiones racionales.

rational exponent/exponente racional (298)   Para cualquier número no cero b y cualquiera de los números enteros m y n, en que $n > 1$, $b^{\frac{m}{n}} = \sqrt[n]{b^m} = \left(\sqrt[n]{b}\right)^m$, excepto cuando $b > 0$ y n es un número par.

rational function/función racional (550)   Una ecuación en la forma $f(x) = \dfrac{p(x)}{q(x)}$, en que $p(x)$ y $q(x)$ son funciones polinómicas y $q(x) \neq 0$.

rationalizing the denominator/racionalizar el denominador (290)   Un proceso que se usa para eliminar radicales de un denominador o fracciones de un radicando.

rational number/número racional (13)   Un número que se puede expresar como una proporción $\dfrac{m}{n}$, en la cual m y n son enteros y n no es cero.

rational zero theorem/teorema del cero racional (509) Daja que $f(x) = a_0 x^n + a_1 x^{n-1} + \ldots + a_{n-1} x + a_n$ represente una función polinómica con coeficientes integrales ($a \neq 0$). Si $\frac{p}{q}$ es un número racional en forma reducida y es un cero de $y = f(x)$, entonces p es un factor de a_n y q es un factor de a_0.

real numbers/números reales (13) El conjunto de números irracionales junto con el conjunto de números racionales.

recursive formula/fórmula recursiva (683) Una fórmula recursiva consta de dos partes: el valor o valores del primer término y una ecuación recursiva que muestra cómo hallar cada término a partir del término anterior.

reduced matrix/matriz reducida (227) La matriz que resulta después de efectuar operaciones en las hileras de una matriz aumentada para resolver un sistema de ecuaciones lineales.

reducing a matrix/reducir una matriz (227) El proceso de efectuar operaciones en las hileras de una matriz aumentada para obtener la matriz solución deseada.

reflections/reflexiones (722) Una reflexión ocurre cuando se puede ver una disposición de objetos desde dos vistas diferentes sin cambiar la disposición.

reflexive property of equality/propiedad reflexiva de la igualdad (28) Para cualquier número real a, $a = a$.

relation (65) Un conjunto de pares ordenados.

relative maximum/máximo relativo (494) Un punto en la gráfica de una función se llama máximo relativo si ningún otro punto cercano posee una coordenada y mayor.

relative minimum/mínimo relativo (494) Un punto en la gráfica de una función se llama mínimo relativo si ningún otro punto cercano posee una coordenada y menor.

remainder theorem/teorema del residuo (485) Si un polinomio $f(x)$ se divide entre $x - a$, el residuo es la constante $f(a)$ y $f(x) = q(x) \cdot (x - a) + f(a)$, en que $q(x)$ es un polinomio con un grado menor que el grado de $f(x)$.

root/raíz (332, 336) Una solución de una ecuación.

rotation/rotación (201) Una transformación en la cual se mueve una figura alrededor de un punto central.

row matrix/matriz horizontal (187) Una matriz que solo tiene una hilera.

row operations/operaciones horizontales (226) Operaciones que se efectúan en las hileras de una matriz aumentada para hallar la solución a un sistema de ecuaciones lineales.

sampling error/error del muestreo (759) La diferencia entre los resultados de la muestra y los resultados verdaderos de la población.

scalar multiplication/multiplicación escalar (188) Multiplicación de cada elemento de la matriz por la mizma constante.

scatter plot/diagrama de dispersión (95) Un diagrama de dispersión muestra visualmente la naturaleza de una relación, determinada tanto por la forma como por la proximidad de los datos.

scientific notation/notación científica (254) Un número está en notación científica cuando está en la forma de $a \times 10^n$, en que $1 \leq a < 10$ y n es un número entero.

second order determinant/determinante de segundo orden (141) Una determinante que tiene dos hileras y dos columnas. Su valor se puede hallar calculando la diferencia de los productos de las dos diagonales.

self-similarity/autosemejanza (689) Una característica de un objeto en el cual las replicas de una forma u objeto completo son incrustadas repetidamente dentro del objeto, en diferentes tamaños.

sequence/sucesión (649) Una lista de números en un orden específico.

series/serie (656) La suma indicada de los términos de una secuencia.

sigma notation/notación sigma (658) Notación que usa el símbolo Σ para indicar la suma de una serie.

simplify/simplificar (255) La simplificación de una expresión que contiene potencias significa el escribir de nuevo la expresión sin paréntesis o exponentes negativos.

simulation/simulación (754) Un método para hallar la probabilidad experimental en el cual se utiliza un dispositivo para modelar el evento y se hacen observaciones de la forma en que el modelo responde a las condiciones enumeradas en un problema dado.

sine/seno (805) Si el lado final de un ángulo θ en posición estándar interseca el círculo unidad en $P(x, y)$, entonces sen $\theta = y$.

Sine/seno (811) $y = \operatorname{sen} x$, si y solo si $y = \operatorname{sen} x$ y $-\frac{\pi}{2} \geq x \leq \frac{\pi}{2}$.

skewed distribution/distribución asimétrica (395) Una curva de distribución que no es simétrica.

slope/pendiente (82) La pendiente de la recta que pasa por los puntos (x_1, y_1) y (x_2, y_2) está dada por $m = \frac{y_2 - y_1}{x_2 - x_1}$, en que $x_2 \neq x_2$. La pendiente de una recta descrita por $f(x) = mx + b$ es m.

slope-intercept form/forma de pendiente—intersección (88) La forma de pendiente–intersección de la ecuación de una recta es $y = mx + b$, en la cual m es la pendiente y b es la intersección con el eje y.

solution/solución (28)   Un valor que puede reemplazar una variable en una ecuación para satisfacer la ecuación.

solve a simpler problem/resuelve un problema más simple (156, 712)   Una estrategia para resolver problemas en la cual se resuelve un problema similar más simple para determinar los conceptos que se pueden usar en la solución de un problema más complejo.

solving a right triangle/solución de un triángulo rectángulo (775)   El proceso de hallar las medidas de todos los lados y angulos de un triángulo rectángulo.

square matrix/matriz cuadrada (187)   Una matriz con el mismo número de hileras y columnas.

square root/raíz cuadrada (281)   Para cualquiera de los números reales a y b, si $a^2 = b$, entonces a es una raíz cuadrada de b.

square root function/función de raíz cuadrada (535)   Una función que involucra una raíz cuadrada.

standard deviation/desviación estándar (384)   De un conjunto de datos con n valores, en el que x_1 representa el primer término y x_n representa el *ené*simo término, si $\overline{x}$ representa la media, entonces la desviación estándar es SD o

$$\sigma_x = \sqrt{\frac{(x_1 - x)^2 + (x_2 - x)^2 + \ldots + (x_n - x)^2}{n}}.$$

standard form/forma estándar (73)   La forma estándar de una ecuación lineal es $Ax + By = C$, en la cual A, B y C son números reales y A y B no son cero.

standard position/posición estándar (780)   Se dice que un ángulo se encuentra en posición estándar si está colocado en una posición tal que su vértice está en el origen y su lado inicial está a lo largo del eje x positivo.

stem-and-leaf plot/gráfica de tallo y hojas (19)   Una forma compacta de exhibir datos en la cual cada artículo está separado en dos partes. El tallo consiste de los dígitos en el mayor valor de posición común. Las hojas contienen los otros dígitos de cada artículo de los datos.

step fuction/función escalón (103)   Una función cuya gráfica es una serie de rectas o escalones desunidos.

substitution property of equality/propiedad de sustitución de la igualdad (28)   Si $a = b$, entonces, a se puede reemplazar por b.

subtraction property of equality/propiedad de sustracción de la igualdad (28)   Para cualquiera de los números a, b y c, si $a = b$, entonces $a - c = b - c$.

subtraction property of inequality/propiedad de sustracción de la desigualdad (43)   Para cualquiera de los números a, b y c:
1. si $a > b$, entonces $a - c > b - c$;
2. si $a < b$, entonces $a - c < b - c$.

success/éxito (732)   El resultado deseado de un evento.

sum of geometric series/suma de la serie geométrica (671)   La suma S_n de los primeros términos n de una serie geométrica está dada por $S_n = \dfrac{a_1 - a_1 r^n}{1 - r}$ o $S_n = \dfrac{a_1(1 - r^n)}{1 - r}$, en que $r \neq 1$.

sum of arithmetic series/suma de una serie aritmética (657)   La suma S_n de los primeros términos n de una serie aritmética es dada por $S_n = \dfrac{n}{2}(a_1 + a_n)$, en que n es un número entero positivo.

sum of an infinite geometric series/suma de una serie geométrica infinita (677)   La suma S de una serie geométrica infinita en que $-1 < r < 1$ está dada por $S = \dfrac{a_1}{1 - r}$.

symmetric property of equality/propiedad simétrica de la igualdad (28)   Para todos los números reales a y b, si $a = b$, entonces $b = a$.

synthetic division/división sintética (269)   Un método más sencillo que la división larga, el cual se usa para dividir un polinomio entre un binomio.

synthetic substitution/sustitución sintética (486)   El proceso de usar división sintética para hallar el valor de una función.

system of equations/sistema de ecuaciones (126)   Un conjunto de ecuaciones con las mismas variables.

system of inequalities/sistema de desigualdades (148)   Un conjunto de desigualdades con las mismas variables.

T

tangent/tangente (425)   Una recta que interseca a un círculo en exactamente un punto se dice que es tangente al círculo.

Tangent/tangente (811) $y = \tan x$ si y solo si $y = \tan x$ y $-\dfrac{\pi}{2} \leq x \leq \dfrac{\pi}{2}$.

term/término (648)   Cada número en una secuencia.

terminal side/lado final (780)   Uno de los dos rayos que forman un ángulo en un plano de coordenadas que gira alrededor del origen.

terms/términos (261)   Los monomios que componen un polinomio.

theoretical probability/probabilidad teórica (754)   La probabilidad teórica se determina usando métodos matemáticos para proveer una idea de los resultados que pueden ocurrir en una situación dada.

transformations/transformaciones (190)   Funciones que relacionan puntos de una gráfica con su imagen.

transition matrix/matriz de transición (200)   Una matriz que contiene información sobre la transición de un evento a otro.

transitive property of equality/propiedad transitiva de la igualdad (28)   Para todos los números reales a, b y c, si $a = b$ y $b = c$, entonces $a = c$.

translation/traslación (195)   Una transformación en la cual una figura se mueve desde una ubicación a otra en el plano de coordenadas, sin cambiar su tamaño, forma u orientación.

translation matrix/matriz de traslación (196)   Una matriz que representa el número de unidades que una figura se mueve vertical u horizontalmente a partir de su posición original.

transverse axis/eje transversal (441)   Uno de los dos segmentos de recta que forman el eje de simetría de una parábola cuyos extremos son los vértices de una hipérbola.

trichotomy property/propiedad tricotomática (43)   Para cualquiera de los números reales, a y b, exactamente uno de los siguientes enunciados es válido: $a < b$, $a = b$ o $a > b$.

trigonometric equations/ecuaciones trigonométricas (861)   Una ecuación que involucra una o más funciones trigonométricas la cual es válida para algunos, pero no todos, los valores de la variable.

trigonometric functions/funciones trigonométricas (772)   Si θ es la medida de un ángulo agudo en un triángulo rectángulo, a es la medida del cateto opuesto a θ, b es la medida del cateto adyacente a θ y c es la medida de la hipotenusa, entonces

$$\text{seno } \theta = \frac{a}{c} \qquad \text{coseno } \theta = \frac{b}{c}$$
$$\text{tangente } \theta = \frac{a}{b} \qquad \text{cosecante } \theta = \frac{c}{a}$$
$$\text{secante } \theta = \frac{c}{b} \qquad \text{cotangente } \theta = \frac{b}{a}$$

trigonometric identities/identidades trigonométricas (788)   Una ecuación trigonométrica que es válida para todos los valores de las variables.

trigonometry/trigonometría (772)   El estudio de las relaciones entre los ángulos y los lados de los triángulos rectángulos.

trinomial/trinomio (261)   Un polinomio con tres términos no semejantes.

unbounded/no acotado (155)   Una función es no acotada si no se forma una región poligonal por las restricciones de un sistema de desigualdades.

union/unión (50)   La gráfica de una desigualdad compuesta que contiene la palabra o es la unión de las gráficas de las dos desigualdades.

unit circle/círculo unidad (781)   En el plano coordenado, el círculo cuyo radio mide una unidad y cuyo centro se encuentra en el origen.

upper extreme/extremo superior (236)   El mayor valor en un conjunto de datos.

upper quartile/cuartil superior (236)   La mediana de la mitad superior de un conjunto de datos.

use a simulation/usa una simulación (452)   Una estrategia para resolver problemas que usa modelos, o simulaciones, de situaciones matemáticas que son difíciles de resolver directamente.

variables/variables (27)   Letras usadas para representar números desconocidos.

vertex/vértice   **1.** (335) El punto en que se intersecan una parábola y su eje de simetría.   **2.** (441) El punto de cada rama de una hipérbola que está más cercano al centro de la hipérbola.

vertical line test/prueba de recta vertical (65)   Si cada recta vertical dibujada en la gráfica de una relación pasa por un solo punto de la gráfica, entonces la relación es una función.

work backward/trabaja al revés (528)   Una estrategia para resolver problemas que usa operaciones inversas para determinar un valor original.

x-axis/eje x (64)   La recta numérica horizontal que ayuda a formar el plano de coordenadas.

x-intercept/intersección con el eje x (75)   La coordenada x del punto sobre el cual una gráfica cruza el eje x.

y-axis/eje y (64)   La recta numérica vertical que ayuda a formar el plano de coordenadas.

y-intercept/intersección con el eje y (75)   La coordenada y del punto sobre el cual una gráfica cruza el eje y.

zero/cero (335)   Para cualquier función $f(x)$, si $f(a) = 0$, entonces a es un cero de la función.

zero product property/propiedad del producto cero (341)   Para cualquiera de los números reales a y b, si $ab = 0$, entonces $a = 0$, $b = 0$, o ambos.

SELECTED ANSWERS

CHAPTER 1 ANALYZING EQUATIONS AND INEQUALITIES

Page 6 Lesson 1–1A
1. 9.17 **3.** 8,998,924.67 **5.** 72 **7.** 40.88 **9.** 10, 0, −17.78, −20.56, 26.67

Pages 10–12 Lesson 1–1
7. 54 **9.** 47 **11.** 9 **13.** 28 **15.** 37°C **17.** $A = (a + 6)$
$(a − 6)$ in^2 **19.** 19 **21.** −3 **23.** 6 **25.** 7 **27.** $−\frac{17}{6}, −2.8\overline{3}$
29. −49 **31.** 32 **33.** 9.1 **35.** −9 **37.** −0.75 **39.** 15
41. −1.875 **43.** 19.25 **45.** 117 **47.** 37.5 **49.** $292.50
51. $3555.89 **53a.** 528 **53b.** 52.5 **53c.** 28.8 **55a.** $S = 22a^2 + 24a$ **55b.** 448 square units **55c.** 994.48 square units **57a.** 2, 3, 5, 7, 11, 13, 17, 19, 23, 29, 31, 37, 41, 43, 47, 53, 57, 59, 61, 67, 71, 73, 79, 83 **57b.** Answers will vary; sample answers are 3, 7, 31. **57c.** 496, 8128

Pages 16–18 Lesson 1–2
7. −1; R, Q, Z **9.** 7.550; R, I **11.** true
13. additive inverse **15.** $−7, \frac{1}{7}$ **17.** $20c + 4d$ **19.** $36.00
21. −7; R, Q, Z **23.** −42; R, Q, Z **25.** −1; R, Q, Z
27. $2\frac{1}{4}$; R, Q **29.** $\frac{1}{2}$; R, Q **31.** $\sqrt{67}$; R, I **33.** true
35. true **37.** true **39.** commutative (+) **41.** additive inverse **43.** commutative (×) **45.** multiplicative inverse
47. −0.2; 5 **49.** 1;−1 **51.** $3\frac{5}{7}; \frac{7}{26}$ **53.** $32c − 46d$
55. $\frac{11}{6}x − \frac{7}{4}y$ **57.** $4.4m − 2.9n$ **59a.** no **59b.** yes
59c. This method works because the difference between a number and the number whose digits are reversed is 9.
61. 0.09 **63.** 22 **65.** −3.5 **67.** 1440 times **69.** $737
71. 22

Pages 23–26 Lesson 1–3
7. 8; no mode; 7.8

9a.

Stem	Leaf
2	2 3 4 4 7 8 8 9 9
3	1 1 3 4 4 4 9
4	1 *3|1 = 31,000*

9b. about $30,059 **9c.** $29,000 **9d.** $34,000 **11.** 34; no mode; 35.4 **13.** 65; 50 and 65; about 63.8 **15.** 12.9; no mode; 12.975 **17.** 43; 43; about 47.29 **19.** 71; 71 and 88; 73 **21a.** Mean; it is higher. **21b.** Mode; it is lower and is what most employees make. It reflects the most representative worker. **23a.** The graphs of the data look different because a different scale is used in each graph.
23b. Sample answer: Graph A might be used by an employer to show an employee she cannot get a big raise. It appears that sales are steady but not rising drastically enough to warrant a big raise. **23c.** Sample answer: Graph B might be used by a company owner to show a prospective buyer. It looks like there is a dramatic rise in sales.

25a.

Employed	Stem	Unemployed
	0	2 2 2 3 3 3 4 4 6 6
	1	2
	2	
0 4 8	3	
6	4	
3 4 7	5	
4	6	
	7	
0 8	8	
	9	
	10	
	11	
	12	
	13	
4	14	*1|2 = 1,200,000*

25b. Answers will vary. Sample answers: The number of employed people in these states is much higher than the number of unemployed people. **25c.** Divide the number of unemployed people by the total number of employed and unemployed people.

25d.

California	7.7%
Florida	6.5%
Illinois	6.2%
Massachusetts	6.4%
Michigan	5.1%
New Jersey	6.7%
New York	6.5%
North Carolina	5.0%
Ohio	4.9%
Pennsylvania	6.0%
Texas	5.9%

27. $20,390; no mode; $46,867.08; The median is most representative of the data since there is such a wide range of costs.

29a.

29b. 79.5; 91; 77.58
29c.

29d. They each increase by 5 since the temperature increased by 5 degrees; different. **29e.** All points on the original line plot would be shifted 5 to the right to obtain the new line plot. **31.** $−10a + 6$ **33.** −7 **35.** 419.5°C

Pages 31–34 Lesson 1–4
7. $5x − 3$ **9.** multiplication (=) **11.** −5 **13.** −13
15. −21 **17.** $\frac{3V}{\pi r^2} = h$ **19.** $14 − x^2$ **21.** $4(n + n^2)$
23. $7 + 3n$ **25.** reflexive (=) **27.** addition (=)
29. subtraction (=) **31.** 2 **33.** 2 **35.** $\frac{1}{12}$ **37.** −4
39. $−\frac{409}{13}$ **41.** −16 **43.** 2 **45.** 19 **47.** $\frac{35}{2}$ **49.** $\frac{z}{x} − 2$
51. $\frac{5a − 9}{6}$ **53.** $\frac{Fr^2}{Gm}$ **55.** $30x + 15(5x) = 420$;

SELECTED ANSWERS

Selected Answers

four adult tickets; twenty student tickets **57.** $2x + 18 = 32$; \$7 **59.** the product of twice a number and the sum of the number and four added to twice the sum of the number and six **61.** Yes; the last day's trip will take him only 10.2 hours, which will bring the driver's total time to 64.95 hours. **63.** 7920 miles **65.** 217.5; 399; about 265.3

67.

January	Stem	July
1	1	
1 2 6	2	
0 5	3	
1 1 4	4	
1 3 7	5	6
	6	5
	7	0 3 3 5 8 9
$5\lvert 3\rvert = 35°$	8	1 2 3 6

69. $15a - 19$ **71.** additive identity **73.** \$17,400 **75.** -4

Page 34 Self Test
1. -5 **3.** -1; R, Q, Z **5.** $\sqrt{41}$, 6.403; R, I **7.** -4 **9.** 2

Page 36 Lesson 1–5A
1. 0.75 **3.** -30.83 **5.** 3.67 **7.** $-2, 8$ **9.** $44, -24$

Pages 40–42 Lesson 1–5
7. 5 **9.** $13, -23$ **11.** $18, -6$ **13.** $42, -48$
15a. $\lvert x - 16 \rvert = 0.2$ **15b.** $x = 16.2, x = 15.8$ **17.** 5 **19.** 1
21. -1.6 **23.** -6.6 **25.** $20, -14$ **27.** $31, -53$ **29.** $20, -2$
31. $14, -8$ **33.** no solution **35.** $5, -\frac{19}{3}$ **37.** $\frac{11}{8}, -\frac{25}{24}$
39. no solution **41.** 4 **43a.** $-2.4, 2.4$ **43b.** $-1.7, 0, 1.7$
43c. $-0.7, 2$ **43d.** $-2.2, -0.6, 2.2$ **45a.** $\lvert x - 697 \rvert = 5$
45b. $x = 702$ or $x = 692$ **47.** TAW, TAX, TAY, TBW, TBX, TBY, TCW, TCX, TCY, UAW, UAX, UAY, UBW, UBX, UBY, UCW, UCX, UCY, VAW, VAX, VAY, VBW, VBX, VBY, VCW, VCX, VCY **49.** $-\frac{15}{2}$ **51.** $p + 5$ **53.** 143; 141; about 143.7
55. -24; Z, Q, R

Pages 47–48 Lesson 1–6
5. $\{a \mid a \geq 1.75\}$

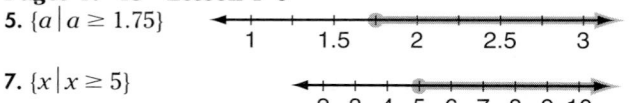

7. $\{x \mid x \geq 5\}$
9. $\{d \mid d \leq 20\}$
11. $\varnothing$ **13.** $n + 15 \geq 27$
15. $\{r \mid r < -5\}$
17. $\{x \mid x < 1.94\}$
19. $\{x \mid x \geq 5\}$
21. $\left\{x \mid x \geq \frac{5}{8}\right\}$
23. $\{x \mid x > 2.25\}$
25. $\{z \mid z \leq 5\}$
27. $\left\{m \mid m > \frac{4}{9}\right\}$

29. $\{b \mid b > 2\}$
31. $\{x \mid x \leq 1.66\}$
33. $\varnothing$
35. $\left\{x \mid x \leq -\frac{1}{2}\right\}$
37. $\left\{w \mid w \leq \frac{4}{3}\right\}$
39. $\frac{3}{4}x - 25 \geq 8$ **41.** $57 > 0.5x$ **43.** $62 < -6x$

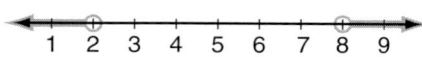
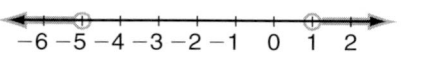

45. $\{r \mid r < 0.4375\}$ **47.** $\{s \mid s > -3\}$ **49a.** $750 < x < 990$
49b. 990 Calories **51.** $15, -7$ **53.** 11.2 **55.** about 6.309
57. distributive **59.** 0.6 amperes

Pages 52–54 Lesson 1–7
5. $\lvert x \rvert < 18$ **7.** $\lvert x \rvert < 4$
9. $\{x < 2 \text{ or } x > 8\}$
11. $\{x \mid x > 1 \text{ or } x < -5\}$
13. $\{x \mid x < -18 \text{ or } x > 10\}$
15. $\lvert x \rvert < 7$
17. $\lvert x \rvert > 11$
19. $\lvert x \rvert < 8$
21. $\lvert x \rvert < 3$ **23.** $\lvert x \rvert \geq 4$ **25.** $\lvert x + 1 \rvert > 2$
27. $\left\{x \mid -\frac{5}{4} \leq x \leq \frac{5}{4}\right\}$
29. $\{x \mid x < -5 \text{ or } x > 5\}$
31. $\left\{x \mid x \geq \frac{7}{3} \text{ or } x \leq -\frac{7}{3}\right\}$
33. $\left\{x \mid x > \frac{1}{2} \text{ or } x < -\frac{1}{2}\right\}$
35. $\varnothing$ **37.** $\left\{x \mid x < -4 \text{ or } x > -\frac{10}{3}\right\}$

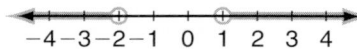

39. all reals **41.** $\varnothing$
43. $\{x \mid x < -2 \text{ or } x \geq 1\}$
45. $\{x \mid -1 \leq x \leq 1\}$ **47a.** $\lvert x - 58{,}000 \rvert \leq 18{,}000$
49. $\{x \mid x < 6\}$

51. $|x| < -8$ **53.** $1, \frac{5}{3}$ **55a.** $(0.50)6 + (0.35)x = 10$
55b. 20 **57.** 20.7; 21.6 and 20.7; 21.03

Page 55 Chapter 1 Highlights
1. j **3.** f **5.** b **7.** l **9.** c **11.** i

Pages 56–58 Chapter 1 Study Guide and Assessment
13. 2 **15.** 41 **17.** 4 **19.** -8, Z, Q, R **21.** $\sqrt{5}$, I, R
23. 54.978, I, R **25.** multiplicative inverse **27.** $2a - 4b$
29. 25; no mode; 40.8 **31.** 6.1; 6.1; 6.0 **33.** -21 **35.** 2
37. -20 **39.** 6 **41.** $\frac{A - p}{pr}$ **43.** $\frac{3a^2 - 1}{2c}$ **45.** 17, -7
47. 11, 25 **49.** no solution **51.** $-11, -1$ **53.** $\{z \mid z > 4\}$
55. $\{t \mid t \le 11\}$ **57.** $\{y \mid y > -35\}$
59. $\{z \mid z \ge 6\}$

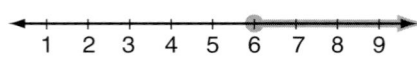

61. $\{x \mid 3 < x < 6\}$

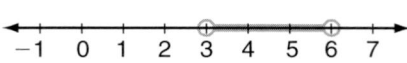

63. $\left\{y \mid \frac{5}{3} < y \le 5\right\}$

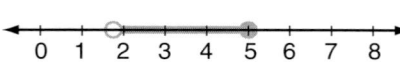

65. $\{x \mid -5 \le x \le -1\}$

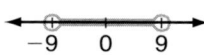

67. $\varnothing$ **69.** $\{x \mid -9 < x < 9\}$

71. 30 cm by 45 cm **73.** 97¢ **75.** 3777, none, 4330.4

952 *Selected Answers*

**CHAPTER 2 GRAPHING LINEAR RELATIONS
AND FUNCTIONS**

Pages 68–71 Lesson 2–1
7. function **9.** not a function
11. function; discrete **13.** not a function

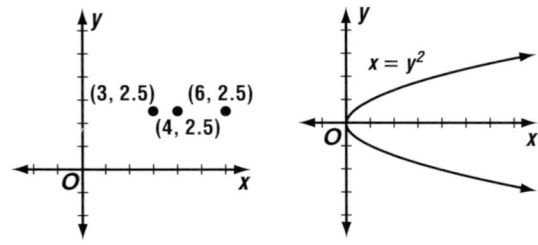

15. -7 **17.** not a function **19.** not a function
21. not a function **23.** not a function
25. D = {4, 6, 3}, **27.** D = {3, 4, 5, 6},
R = {5}; function; discrete R = {3, 4, 5, 6};
function; discrete

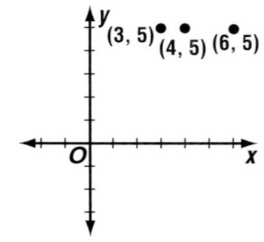 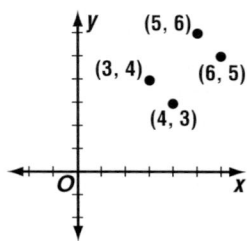

29. D = {all reals},
R = {all reals}; function;
continuous

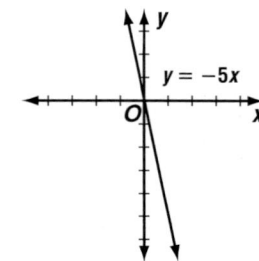

31. no **33.** yes **35.** 6 **37.** -3 **39.** $25n^2 - 5n$ **41.** -12
43. Sample answer: $f(x) = 2.5x$

45. **47.**

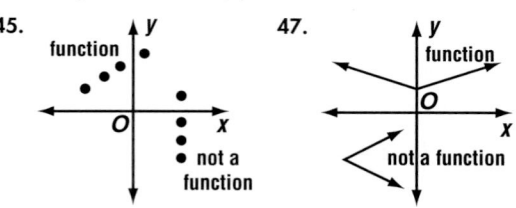

49. all real numbers except 3 and -3 **51a.** D = {year},
R = {stock price}

51.

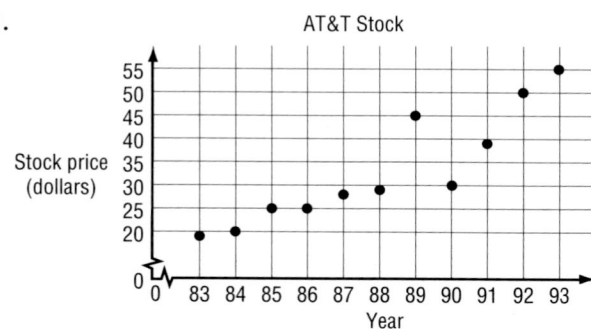

51c. yes **51d.** Sample answer: Yes; even when it dropped in value, it rose even higher. **53.** D = {−3 ≤ x ≤ 3}, R = {−3 ≤ y ≤ 3}; no **55.** {y | −8 < y < 6} **57.** x < 5.1 **59a.** $2.85 **59b.** $29.82 **61.** $x + 2x^2 - 7$ **63.** $31a + 10b$

Page 72   Lesson 2–2A

1.
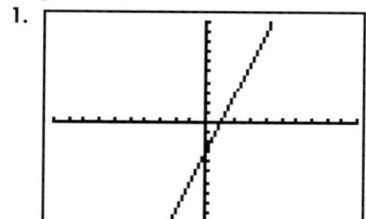

3.
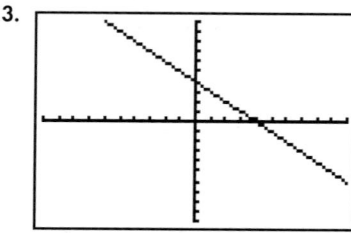

5.
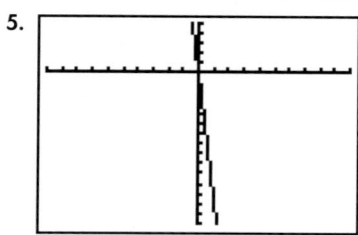

7.
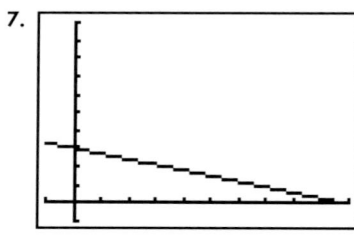

9.
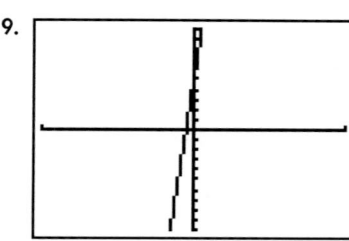

Pages 76–78   Lesson 2–2
7. yes **9.** $2x − 5y = 3$; 2, −5, 3 **11.** y:9, x:$\frac{3}{2}$

13. y:−2, x:2 **15.**
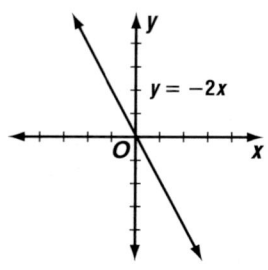

17. $71.80 **19.** no **21.** yes **23.** $12x − y = 0$; 12, −1, 0

25. $2x − y = 5$; 2, −1, 5 **27.** $y = 40$; 0, 1, 40 **29.** y:0, x:0
31. y:none, x:8 **33.** y:5, x:3

35.
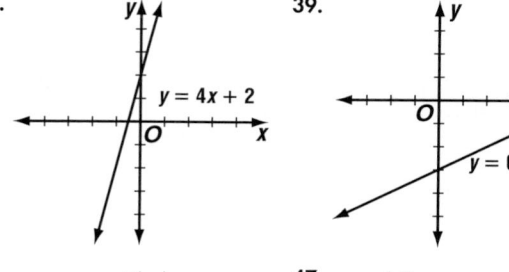

39.
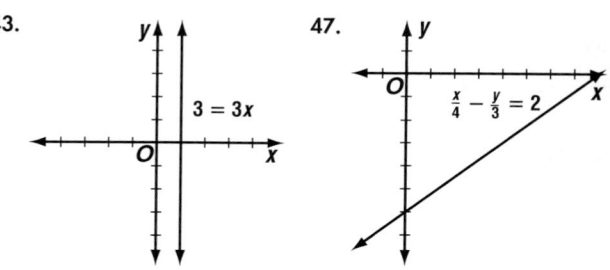

43.
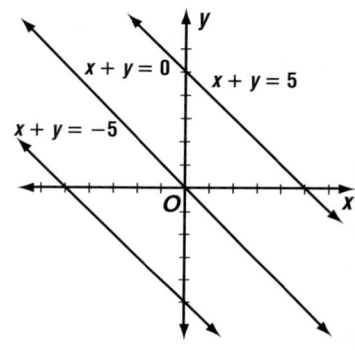

47.

49a. same slope, different y-intercepts, look parallel
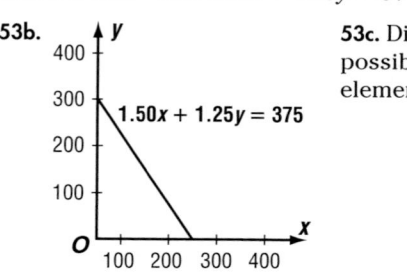

49b. Sample answer: $x + y = 2$ **51a.** $d(t) = 2380t$
51b. 119 feet **53a.** $1.50x + 1.25y = 375$

53b.
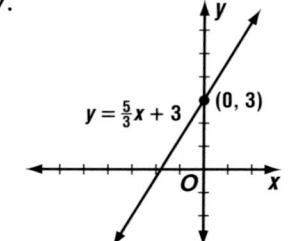

53c. Discrete; it is possible to list the elements of the domain.

53d. yes **55.** true for all x **57.** 0, $-\frac{10}{3}$ **59.** 90 or higher
61. $3s + 14$

Page 79   Lesson 2–2B
1. 1.5 **3.** 5 **5.** 0 **7.** 11.5 **9.** 0.7

Pages 84–87   Lesson 2–3
7. 1 **9.** 0; horizontal **11.** 1; rises **13.** −1 **15.** $\frac{3}{4}$, $-\frac{4}{3}$

17.
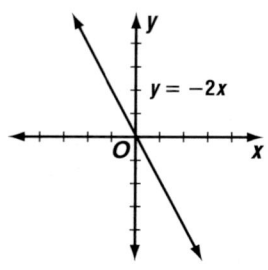

SELECTED ANSWERS

Selected Answers

19. 13; rises   **21.** 0; horizontal   **23.** undefined; vertical
25. undefined   **27.** $-\frac{2}{3}$ **29.** 0   **31.** 9   **33.** 1

35. 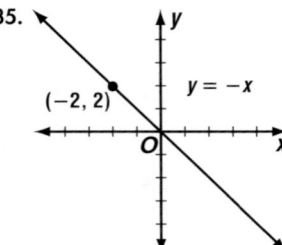   **37.**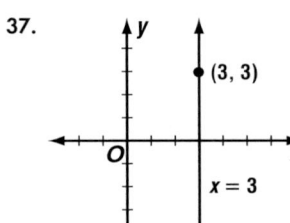

39. 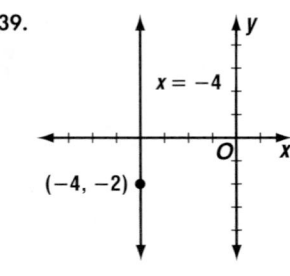   **41.**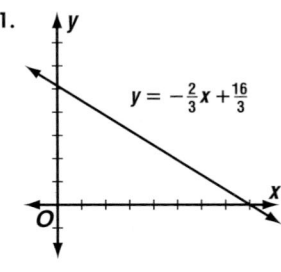

43. No; the product of the slopes is not -1.
45a. Graphs have the same y-intercept and slope is positive; as slope increases, the line gets steeper.
45b. Graphs have the same y-intercept and slope is negative; as the absolute value of the slope increases, the line gets steeper.   **47.** -1 **49a.** 36   **49b.** 36
51. $2x + y = 4$ **53.** $-1 < x < 3$ **55.** 1, -9
57. 91; 99; no mode   **59.** 9

Page 87   Self Test
1a. D = {0, 5, 10, 15, 20, 25, 30, 35, 40}R = {30, 27, 16, 9, 4, 1, -2, -4, -5}

1b.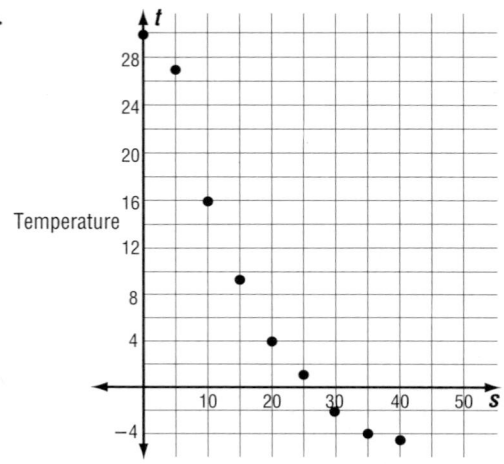

3. $6x + y = 4$ **5.**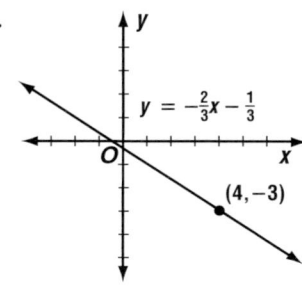

Page 91–94   Lesson 2–5
7. $y = 7x - 3$ **9.** $y = -\frac{1}{3}x + 4$ **11.** $m = 2; b, 3$
13. $y = \frac{5}{4}x + 7$ **15.** $y = \frac{1}{3}x - 2$ **17.** $y = -\frac{5}{2}x + 16$
19. $y = -x - 2$ **21.** $m = -\frac{2}{3}; b, -4$ **23.** $m = -0.3; b, -6$
25. $m = -\frac{3}{5}; b, 6$ **27.** $y = \frac{4}{5}x$ **29.** $y = -\frac{5}{3}x + \frac{29}{3}$
31. $y = -0.5x - 2$ **33.** $y = -\frac{4}{5}x + \frac{17}{5}$ **35.** $y = \frac{3}{2}x$
37. $y = \frac{3}{4}x - \frac{1}{4}$ **39.** $y = \frac{2}{3}x + \frac{10}{3}$ **41.** $y = -x - 4$ **43.** 7
45. 4   **47.** The lines are parallel with different y-intercepts.   **49.** The lines are the same.   **51.** 8.6 billion hours   **53.** $y = 8.33x$ **55a.** $y = 1.45x + 3.2$ **55b.** 16.25 million   **55c.** The slope is the average increase in subscribers; the y-intercept is the number of subscribers in 1990.   **57.** no   **59.** no solution   **61.** 1   **63.** $5.42; $5.00; $5.00   **65.** 272.16

Pages 98–100   Lesson 2–5
7. 173 lb   **9a.**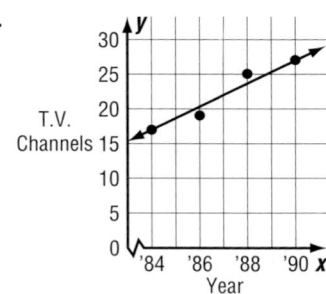

9b. $m = \frac{5}{3}$; y-intercept, 17   **9c.** about 42

11a.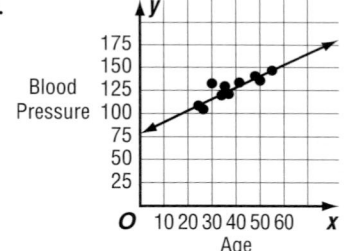

11b. Sample answer: $y = \frac{4}{3}x + 76$ **11c.** Sample answer based on the equation for 10b: 148
13a. Sample answer: $y = -50x + 226$

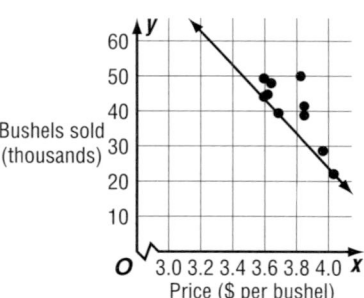

13b. 31,000 bushels   **13c.** $4.01   **15.** $y = -\frac{1}{3}x + 4$, $y = 3x - 6, y = 3$ **17.** $\{x \mid x < -7 \text{ or } x > -1\}$ **19.** $4x + 8$

Page 102   Lesson 2–5B

1.

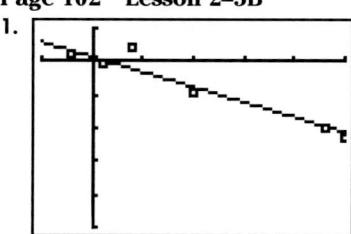

3a. $23,878.56

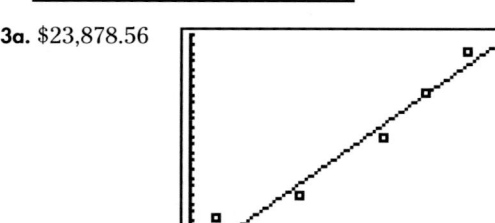

3b. $35,014.52

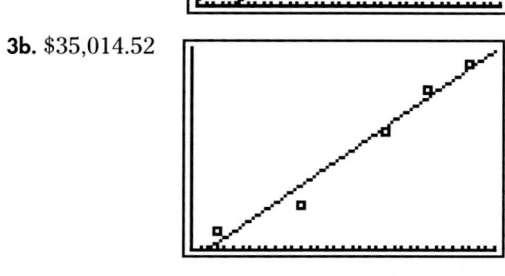

3c. The women's average income has increased at a greater rate than the men's; however, the men's average income was greater than the women's in 1950 and remains greater in 1990.

Pages 106–108   Lesson 2–6

7. G

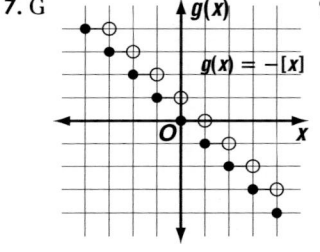

9. C

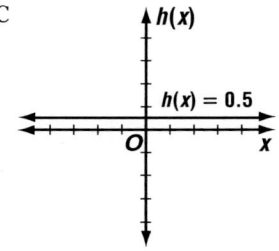

11. 10   **13.** 7   **15.** −2

17. D

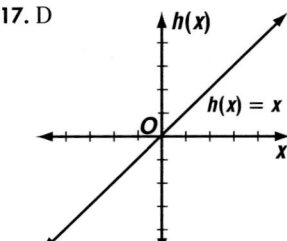

19. C

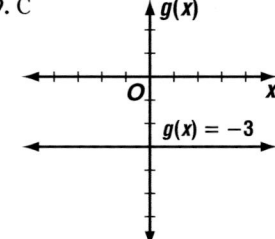

23. D

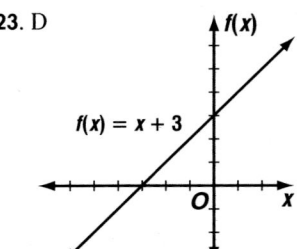

25. G

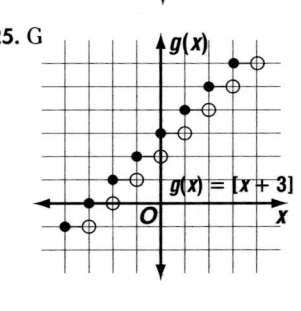

29. same graph translated 4 units right

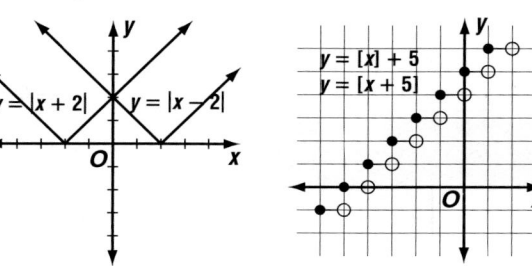

33. Graphs are the same.

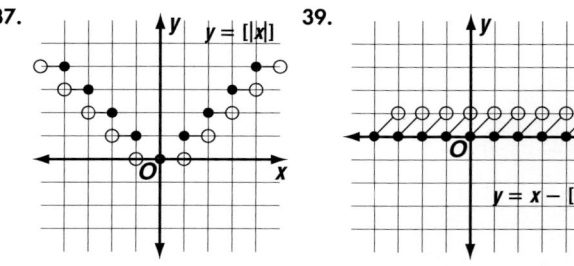

37.

39.

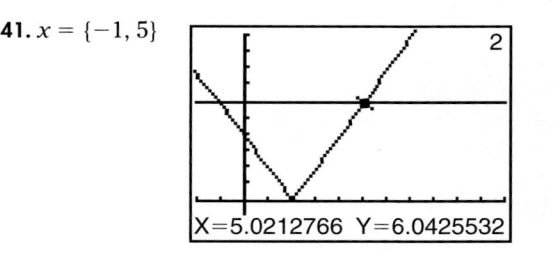

41. $x = \{-1, 5\}$

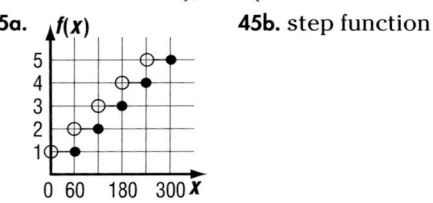

43. $y = |x|$: D = {all real numbers}, R = {all positive real numbers and zero}; $x = |y|$: D = all positive real numbers and zero}, R = {all real numbers}

45a.

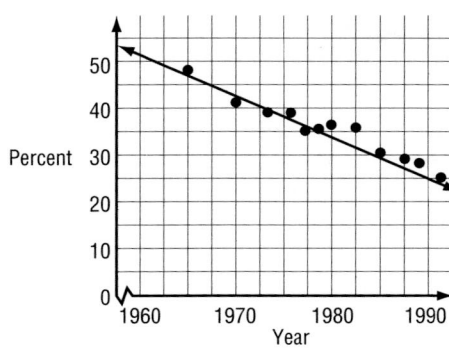

45b. step function

47a. Sample answer: $y = -0.72x + 1460$

47b. 20%   **49.**

$y = -\frac{1}{2}x + 3$

(0, 3)

SELECTED ANSWERS

Selected Answers

51. 6   **53a.** 51   **53b.** 1   **53c.** 16   **53d.** 5 or 11

Page 109   Lesson 2–7A

1.
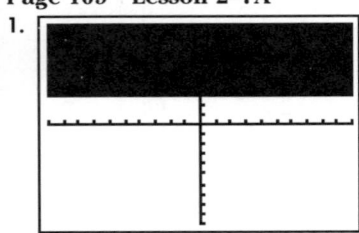

3.
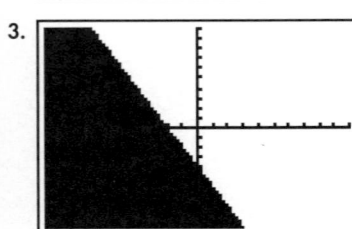

5.
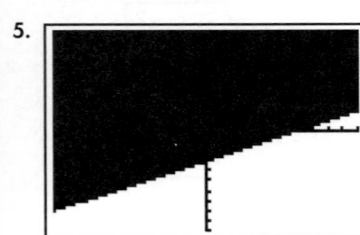

7.
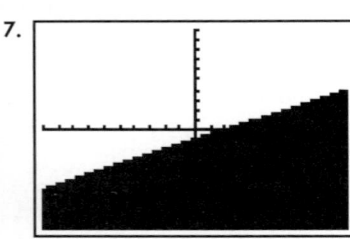

9.
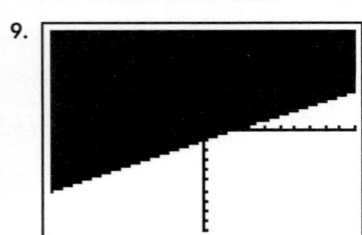

Pages 113–114   Lesson 2–7
5. $(0, 0)$, $(3, -4)$ **7.** $(3, -4)$

9.
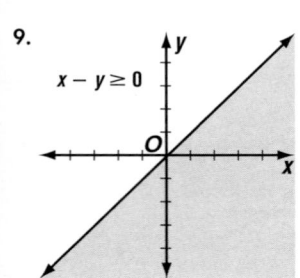
$x - y \geq 0$

11.
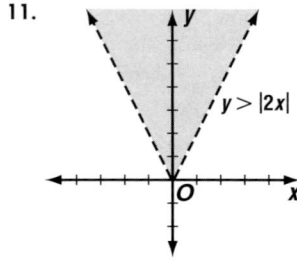
$y > |2x|$

13.
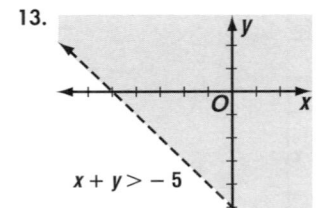
$x + y > -5$

17.
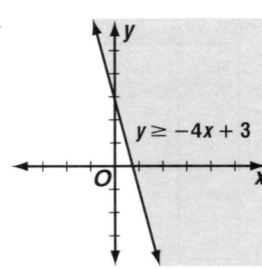
$y \geq -4x + 3$

21.
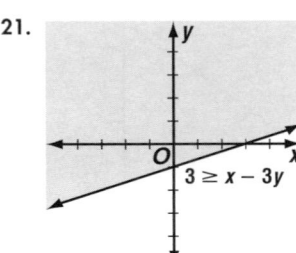
$3 \geq x - 3y$

25. $x < -2$
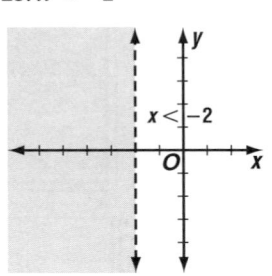
$x < -2$

27.
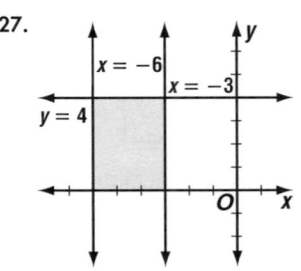
$x = -6$ $x = -3$ $y = 4$

29.
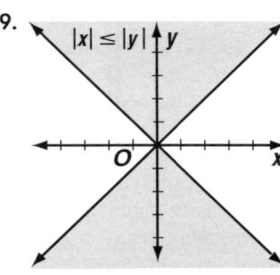
$|x| \leq |y|$

31.
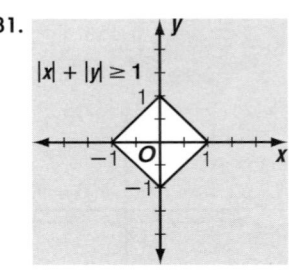
$|x| + |y| \geq 1$

33.
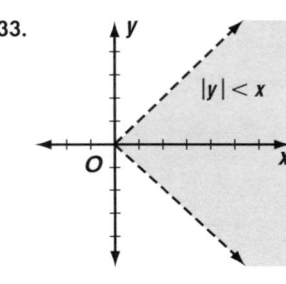
$|y| < x$

35a. $5x + 4y \geq 2500$

35b.
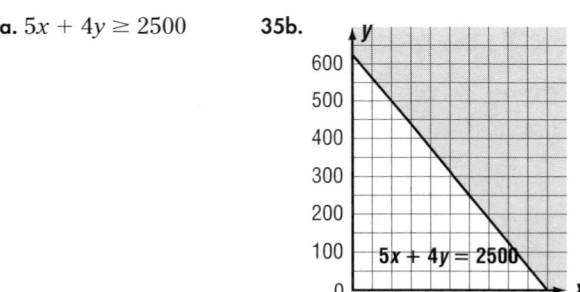
$5x + 4y = 2500$

35c. yes   **37a.** $m + v \geq 1200$

37b.
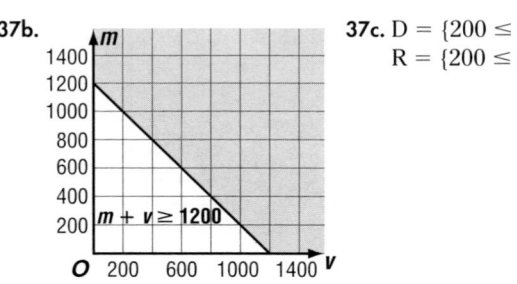
$m + v \geq 1200$

37c. D = $\{200 \leq m \leq 800\}$,
R = $\{200 \leq v \leq 800\}$

956   *Selected Answers*

39a.

39b. $y = 1333x$
39c. $10,664

41.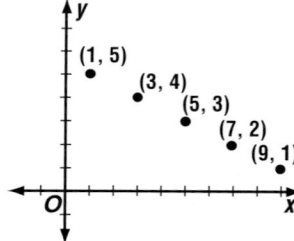

43. (7, 2)

41a.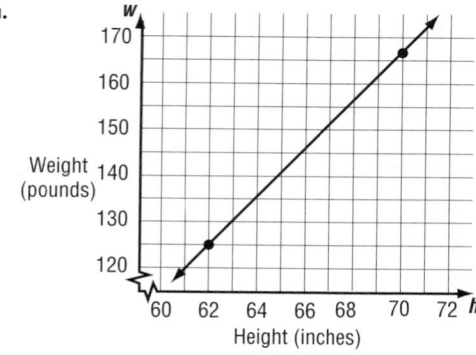

41b. $w = 5.25h - 200.5$ **41c.** 203.75 pounds **41d.** about 67.75 inches tall

43. G **45.** D

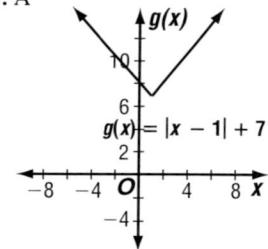 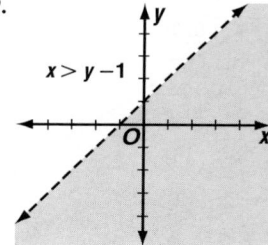

47. A **49.**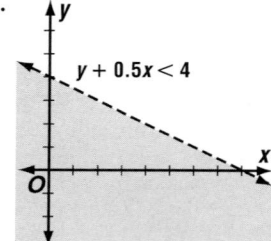

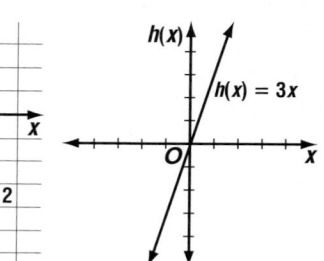

Page 115 Chapter 2 Highlights
1. prediction equation **3.** constant function **5.** absolute value function **7.** parallel lines **9.** perpendicular lines **11.** slope

51.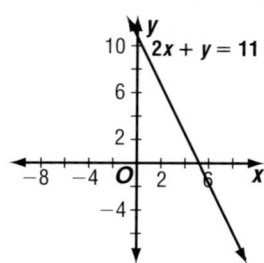

53. $117.20

Page 116–118 Chapter 2 Study Guide and Assessment
13. D = {1, 3, 5, 7, 9}
R = {1, 2, 3, 4, 5}; yes

15. D = {all reals},
R = {all reals}; yes

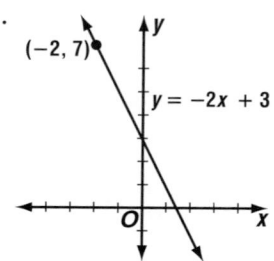 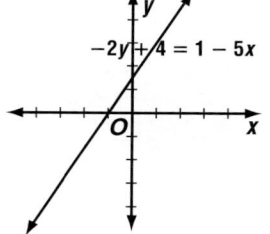

17. −3 **19.** $16v^2 - 10v - 9$

21. yes

23. no **25.** $5x + 2y = -4$ **27.** $5x + y = -20$
29. $x - y = 9$ **31.** $-\frac{3}{11}$ **33.** $y = \frac{3}{4}x + \frac{27}{2}$
35. $y = -\frac{5}{3}x - 3$ **37.** $y = -3x + 5$ **39.** $y = -\frac{3}{4}x + \frac{17}{4}$

CHAPTER 3 SOLVING SYSTEMS OF LINEAR EQUATIONS AND INEQUALITIES

Page 125 Lesson 3–1A
1. (2, 4) **3.** (1, 2) **5.** (3.40, −2.58) **7.** (−0.03, 1.03)

Pages 129–132 Lesson 3–1
7. 0; inconsistent

9. $y = 5x - 3$; consistent, dependent

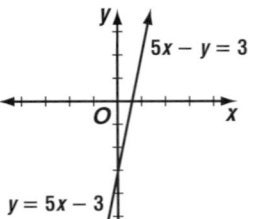

11. no solution; inconsistent

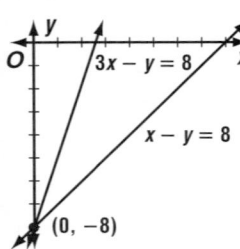

13. a **15.** 1; consistent, independent; $(-3, 0)$
17. 1; consistent; independent; $(-1, 3)$

19. $(0, -8)$; consistent, independent

23. $x + 2y = 4$; consistent, dependent

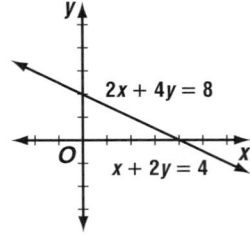

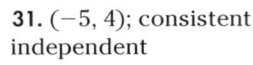

27. $(-9, 3)$; consistent, independent

31. $(-5, 4)$; consistent, independent

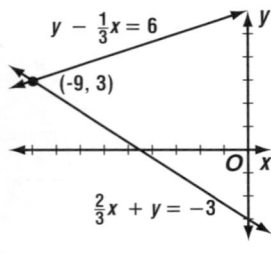

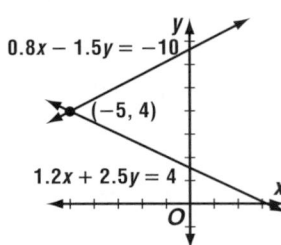

33. $m = \frac{5}{2}, n = -\frac{3}{2}$ **35.** $m = \frac{3}{2}, n \neq 4$ **37.** $(-6, 3)$

39. $(2, -3)$ **41.** $(-5.56, -12.00)$ **43a.** $\frac{a}{d} = \frac{b}{e} = \frac{c}{f}$

43b. $\frac{a}{d} \neq \frac{b}{e}$ **43c.** $\frac{a}{d} = \frac{b}{e} \neq \frac{c}{f}$ **45.** 3 field goals and
4 points after **47a.** butter **47b.** about 1957 **47c.** Yes,
the consumption of margarine has decreased in recent
years.

49.

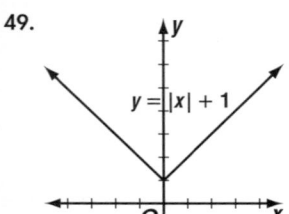

51a. Sample answer:
$y = -0.003x + 47$
51b. about 38%

53.

55. $3x - y = 9$

958 *Selected Answers*

Pages 137–140 Lesson 3–2
7. $(-5, 4)$ **9.** $(-3, 5)$ **11.** $2x + 3y = -15$ **13.** $\left(\frac{10}{3}, \frac{8}{3}\right)$
15. $(3, -2)$ **17.** $(6, 2)$ **19.** $\left(-3, \frac{1}{2}\right)$ **21.** $(-9, 1)$
23. $(8, -5)$ **25.** $(9, 8)$ **27.** $\left(\frac{1}{2}, -\frac{1}{2}\right)$ **29.** no solution
31. $(-7, 2)$ **33.** $(8, -3)$ **35.** $(12, -10)$ **37.** $(-5, 4)$
39. $(1, 4), (-2, -1), (5, 2)$ **41a.** $(9, 1)$ **41b.** $(6, -1)$
41c. $(4, -28)$ **41d.** $(10, 25)$ **43.** 210 cups of hot
chocolate, 85 cups of coffee **45a.** $p = 17.99 + 0.43d$
45b. $p = 3.67 + 0.95d$ **45c.** during the year 2265
47. Sample answer: 20¢ a mile or $15 plus 10¢ a mile
49. step function **51a.** Sample answer: $y = \frac{7}{8}x + 8$
51b. about 42¢ **53.** 9 **55.** 14.45; 13; no mode

Pages 144–146 Lesson 3–3
5. -3 **7.** $-\frac{6}{5}$ **9.** $(2, -1)$ **11.** $\left(-\frac{17}{23}, -\frac{16}{23}\right)$ **13.** -46
15. -29 **17.** -29 **19.** 0 **21.** 22.79 **23.** $(6, 3)$
25. $\left(\frac{2}{3}, -1\right)$ **27.** $\left(-\frac{3}{4}, 3\right)$ **29.** $(3, 10)$ **31.** $\left(\frac{2}{3}, \frac{5}{6}\right)$
33. $(2, -3)$ **35.** In both cases, the denominator is 0. If the
numerator is also 0, there is an infinite number of
solutions. If the numerator is not 0, there are no
solutions. **37.** 28.2 min **39.** $(-1, 2)$

41. $(-1, 3)$; consistent
and independent

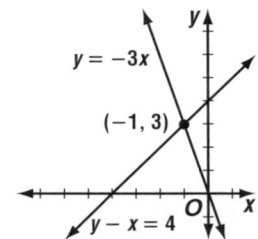

43. Sample answer: $y = -x + 2$ **45.** 120 units^2

Page 147 Lesson 3–4A
1.

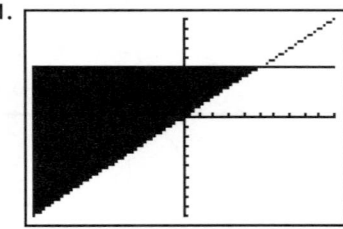

3.

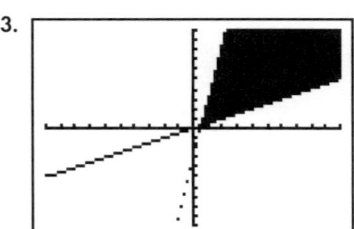

5.

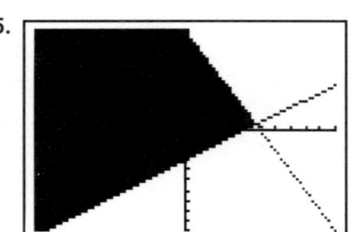

7.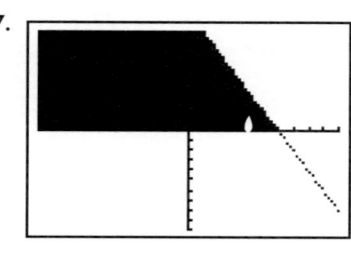

9.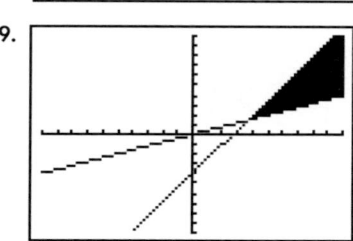

Pages 150–152   Lesson 3–4

7. c

9.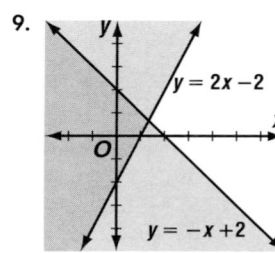

11.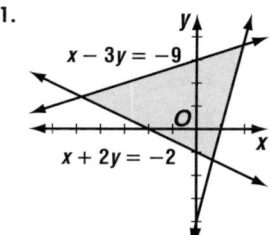

13.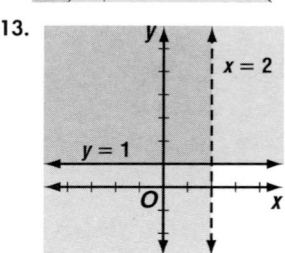

17.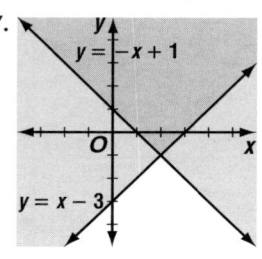

21.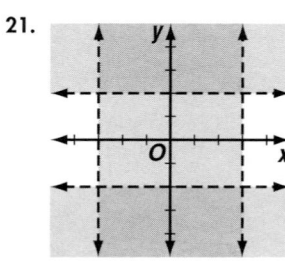

25.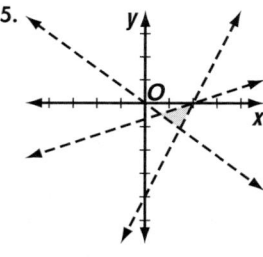

29. Sample answer: $x + y \le 4$, $x - y \le 4$, $y \ge -1$
31. 42 square units
33. $s \ge 7$ and $s + a \le 16$ **35.** $(-4, -4)$

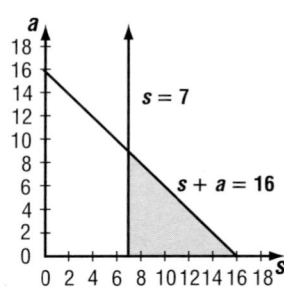

37. no solution   **39.** $3

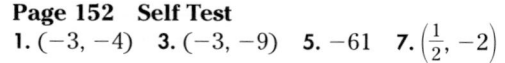

Page 152   Self Test

1. $(-3, -4)$ **3.** $(-3, -9)$ **5.** -61 **7.** $\left(\frac{1}{2}, -2\right)$

9.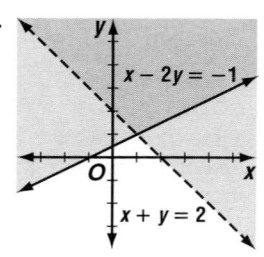

Pages 157–159   Lesson 3–5

5. max: $f(4, 1) = 15$ min: $f(-3, 2) = 14$

7. vertices: $(0, 2)$, $(4, 3)$, $\left(\frac{7}{3}, -\frac{1}{3}\right)$;
max: $f(4, 3) = 25$;
min: $f(0, 2) = 6$

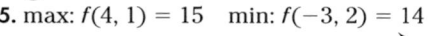

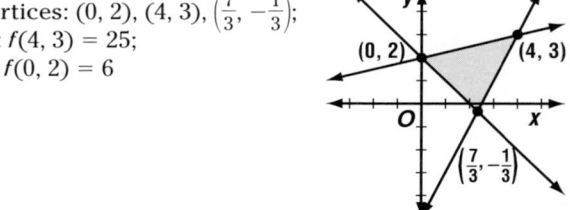

9a. Gauss used the strategy of solving a simpler problem as in Example 3.   **9b.** 2,001,000   **11.** max: $f(3, 5) = 19$
min: $f(-1, -2) = -7$ **13.** max: $f(-1, -2) = 4$
min: $f(3, 5) = -11$

15. vertices: $(1, 0)$, $(3, 0)$, $(1, 4)$;
max: $f(3, 0) = 9$;
min: $f(1, 0) = 3$

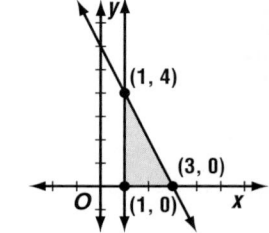

17. vertices: $(0, 1)$,
$(1, 3)$, $(6, 3)$, $(10, 1)$;
max: $f(10, 1) = 31$;
min: $f(0, 1) = 1$

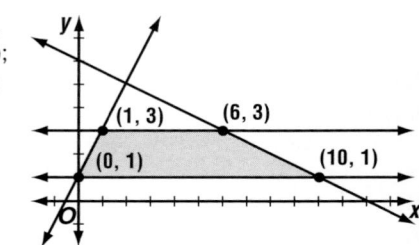

19. vertices: (0, 2), (4, 3), (2, 0); max: $f(4, 3) = 13$; min: $f(2, 0) = 2$

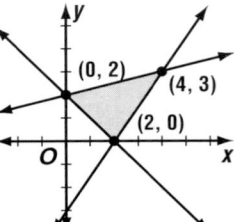

21. vertices: (2, 1), (4, 1), (4, 4), (2, 3); max: $f(4, 1) = 1$; min: $f(4, 4) = -8$

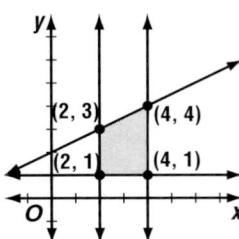

23. vertices: (5, 0), (0, 0), (0, 2), (2, 4), (5, 1); max: $f(5, 0) = 25$; min: $f(0, 2) = -6$ **25.** vertices: $(-4.08, -2)$, $(-1.58, 1)$, $(-0.4, 1)$, $(-0.4, -2)$; max: $f(-0.4, 1) = 0.4$; min: $f(-4.08, -2) = -20.32$
27. $164 **29.** Sample answer: No, he could only increase his income by $100. **31.** 120 telephone lines **33.** $(5, -3)$
35. no **37.** $54 - 32b$

Pages 162–164 Lesson 3–6
5a. $w \geq 0, d \geq 0, 8w + 5d \leq 80, 2w + 5d \leq 50$

5b.

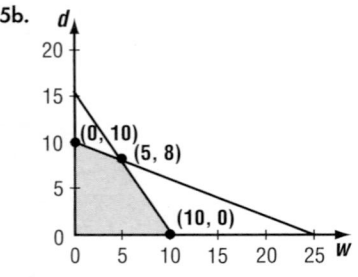

5c. $f(w, d) = 17w + 29d$ **5d.** 5 Wallbangers and 8 Dingbats; $317 **7a.** $20 **7b.** No, the vertex at (10, 30) still produces the least cost. **9a.** $a \geq 0, b \geq 0, 4a + b \leq 32, a + 6b \leq 54$ **9b.** 14 gal **11a.** 72 **11b.** Sample answer: Take a speed-reading course so that she can read and answer the multiple-choice questions in less time.

13. vertices: (0, 3), (0, 6), (2, 5), (1, 3); max: $f(1, 3) = -3$; min: $f(0, 6) = -12$

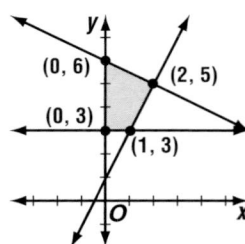

15. 55 mph **17.** $|x| < 4$

Pages 169–171 Lesson 3–7
3. yes **5.** (4, 1, 6) **7.** (1, 4, 9) **9.** Sample answer: $x + y + z = -9, x + y - z = 1, x - y + z = -13$ **11.** no
13. $(-2, 5, -4)$ **15.** (0, 1, 2) **17.** (4, -3, 1) **19.** $(-2, 3, 6)$
21. $\left(\frac{2}{3}, \frac{1}{2}, -\frac{1}{3}\right)$ **23.** $\left(\frac{1}{2}, \frac{1}{3}, \frac{1}{4}\right)$ **25.** 15, 3, -6 **27.** 16, 7, -5
29. 1-year, $2500; 2-year, $3500; 3-year, $9000

31. 3-pointers, 4; 2-pointers, 9; free throws, 5 **33.** a
35a. $y = 0.25x + 20; y = 0.25x + 35$ **35b.** parallel
35c. $15 **37.** $12, -\frac{12}{5}$

Page 173 Lesson 3–7B
1.

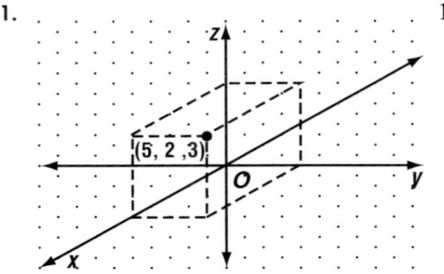

1

3.

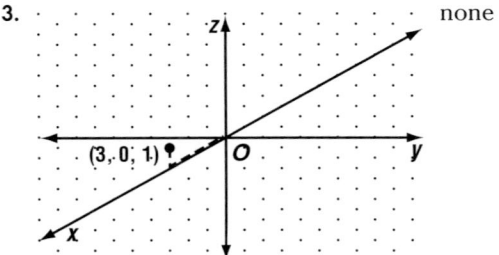

5. (1, 0, 0), (0, 4, 0), (0, 0, 2)

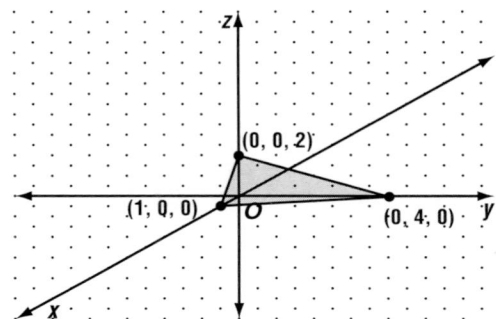

7. $(1, 0, 0), (0, -3, 0), \left(0, 0, \frac{1}{2}\right)$

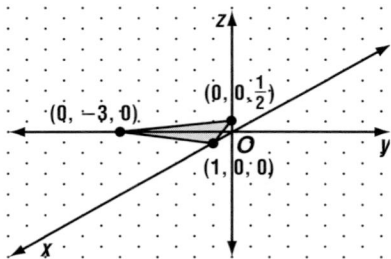

9. $(-3, 0, 0)$, none, $(0, 0, 2)$

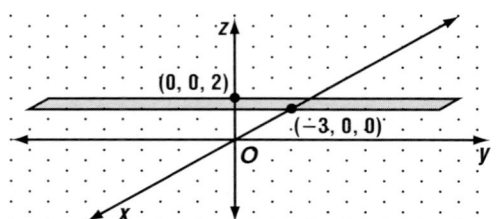

11. Sample answer: $5x - 5y + 2z = 10$ **13.** Two-dimensional graphs are divided into quadrants and three-dimensional graphs are divided into octants.

Page 175   Chapter 3   Highlights
1. c   **3.** f   **5.** a   **7.** i   **9.** d   **11.** k

Pages 176–178   Chapter 3   Study Guide and Assessment
13. no solution; inconsistent   **15.** $20y - 13x = 10$; consistent, dependent

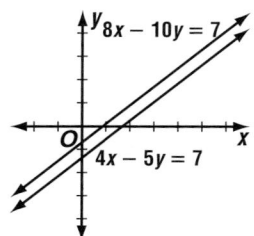

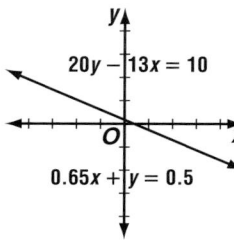

17. $(17.4, -13.6)$ **19.** $(-6, 2)$ **21.** $(3, 2)$ **23.** $\left(\frac{1}{2}, \frac{1}{2}\right)$

25. $\left(2, \frac{13}{8}\right)$ **27.** $\left(-\frac{3}{7}, -\frac{3}{7}\right)$ **29.**

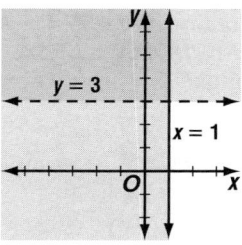

31. 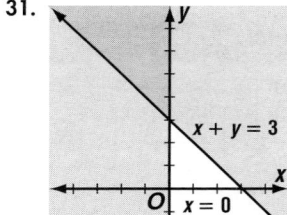   **33.**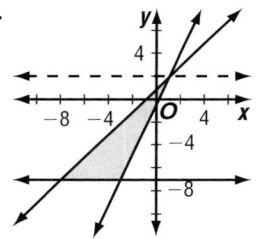

35. vertices: $(0, 5)$, $(3, 4)$, $(4, 0)$, $(0, 0)$; max: $f(3, 4) = 17$; min: $f(0, 0) = 0$

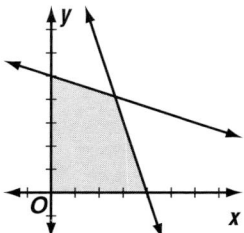

37. $(1, 2, 3)$ **39.** $(3, -1, 5)$ **41.** burger: \$1.89, fries: \$0.99, cola: \$0.79

CHAPTER 4   USING MATRICES

Page 185   Lesson 4–1A
1. $\begin{bmatrix} -1 & -4 \\ 3 & -6 \\ -7 & 2 \end{bmatrix}$ **3.** -10 **5.** $\begin{bmatrix} -.5 & -.5 & .5 \\ .4 & 1 & -.2 \\ .4 & 0 & -.2 \end{bmatrix}$

7. $\begin{bmatrix} 47 & 2 \\ -28 & 44 \end{bmatrix}$ **9.** $\begin{bmatrix} 32 & 14 & 41 \\ -4 & 5 & -10 \end{bmatrix}$ **11.** $\varnothing$

13. $\begin{bmatrix} .020715619 & 9.416195857\text{E-4} \\ .0131826742 & .0221280603 \end{bmatrix}$ **15.** $\begin{bmatrix} 2153 & 182 \\ -2548 & 1880 \end{bmatrix}$

17. $\begin{bmatrix} 277 & 130 \\ -89 & 34 \end{bmatrix}$

Pages 191–193   Lesson 4–1
7. $[-14 \ \ -6 \ \ 2]$ **9.** $x = 2.5$, $y = 1$, $z = 3$

11. $S = \begin{matrix} \text{turkey} \\ \text{ham} \\ \text{roast beef} \end{matrix} \begin{matrix} \text{plain} & \text{cheese} \\ \begin{bmatrix} 15 & 12 \\ 8 & 10 \\ 8 & 11 \end{bmatrix} \end{matrix}$ **13.** $\begin{bmatrix} 15 & -6 & 21 \\ -9 & 24 & 12 \end{bmatrix}$

15. $\left[2 \ \ -\frac{5}{3} \right]$ **17.** $\begin{bmatrix} -6.5 & 0 & -25.5 \\ -2 & -5 & -12.5 \end{bmatrix}$ **19.** $x = 3$, $y = -\frac{1}{3}$

21. $x = 3$, $y = -5$, $z = 6$ **23.** $x = \pm5$, $y = 9$, $z = 6$

25. $(0, 0)$, $(0, 3)$, $(1.25, 0)$ **27.** The perimeter is one-half the original perimeter; the triangle is rotated 180°.

29. $x = 3$, $y = 5$, $m = 10$, $r = 2$ **31.** no

33.

	male	female
exercise walking	21%	38%
swimming	27%	28%
bicycle riding	25%	22%
camping	23%	18%
bowling	20%	18%
fishing	25%	11%
exer. with equip.	17%	17%
basketball	18%	6%
aerobic exercising	5%	19%
golf	17%	5%

35. 100 adult, 50 student   **37.** 0   **39a.** 30; 26; about 30.4   **39b.** They are all located in the Southwestern U.S.

Pages 197–198   Lesson 4–2
5. $\begin{bmatrix} 1 & 10 \\ -7 & 5 \end{bmatrix}$ **7.** $[21 \ \ -2]$ **9a.**

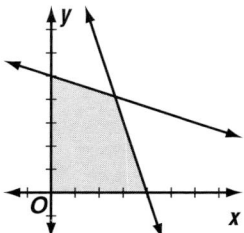

9b. $\begin{bmatrix} 3 & 3 & 3 \\ -7 & -7 & -7 \end{bmatrix}$ **9c.** $\begin{bmatrix} 1 & 6 & 8 \\ -5 & -2 & -9 \end{bmatrix}$ **11.** $[4 \ \ 20 \ \ 1]$

13. $\begin{bmatrix} -4 & -15 \\ 1.5 & -2 \end{bmatrix}$ **15.** $\begin{bmatrix} -19 & -6 \\ 20 & -11 \\ -20 & 34 \end{bmatrix}$

17a. $\begin{bmatrix} 4 & 4 & 4 & 4 \\ -2 & -2 & -2 & -2 \end{bmatrix}$

17b. $B'(10, -1)$, $T'(1, -7)$, $U'(7, 3)$ **19.** $x = 2$, $y = 7$, $z = -2$ **21a.** Sample answer: No; births and deaths are opposite occurrences.   **21b.** Yes; $B - D$ represents the population increase for 1992.   **21c.** Find $0.99D$.

17a. $\begin{bmatrix} 4 & 4 & 4 & 4 \\ -2 & -2 & -2 & -2 \end{bmatrix}$

17b. $B'(10, -1)$, $T'(1, -7)$, $U'(7, 3)$ **19.** $x = 2$, $y = 7$, $z = -2$ **21a.** Sample answer: No; births and deaths are opposite occurrences.   **21b.** Yes; $B - D$ represents the population increase for 1992.   **21c.** Find $0.99D$.

23. $\begin{bmatrix} -28 & 20 & -44 \\ 8 & -16 & 36 \end{bmatrix}$

25. 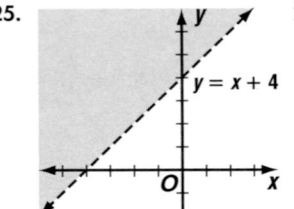   **27.** 12

$y = x + 4$

Pages 202–204   Lesson 4-3

7. 3×2 **9.** $\begin{bmatrix} -39 \\ 18 \end{bmatrix}$ **11.** $A'(-2, -5)$, $B'(-4, 3)$, $C'(4, 1)$;

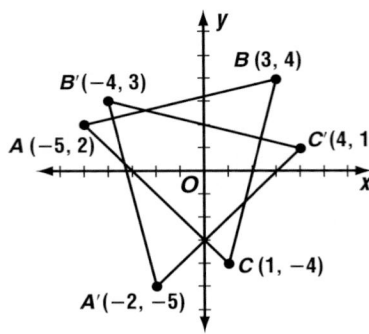

$B (3, 4)$
$B'(-4, 3)$
$A (-5, 2)$
$C'(4, 1)$
$C (1, -4)$
$A'(-2, -5)$

13. not defined   **15.** 3×1 **17.** not defined

19. $\begin{bmatrix} 1 & -25 & 2 \\ 29 & 1 & -30 \end{bmatrix}$ **21.** not possible to evaluate

23. $\begin{bmatrix} 0 & 64 & -40 \\ 9 & 11 & -11 \\ -3 & 39 & -23 \end{bmatrix}$ **25.** No; multiplication is not commutative.   **27.** not defined   **29.** $\begin{bmatrix} -39 & 9 \\ 5 & 16 \end{bmatrix}$

31. rotates $180°$ **33.** reflects over y-axis   **35.** $w = 1$, $x = 0$, $y = 0$, $z = 1$; the original matrix   **37.** about 39%
39a. \$22,800   **39b.** sold, \$22,735.50; lost, \$62.50

41. $\begin{bmatrix} -12 & 6 \\ 30 & -42 \end{bmatrix}$ **43.** $(-9, -7)$ **45.** $(8, 0)$ and $(0, -2)$

Pages 208–211   Lesson 4-4

5. no   **7.** yes, 1   **9.** 45   **11.** yes, 0   **13.** no   **15.** yes, -13 **17.** 16 units^2 **19.** -28 **21.** 0   **23.** -141 **25.** 11 units^2
27. $x = -6$ **29.** 29 units^2 **31.** $x = 22$

33. Sample answer: $\begin{bmatrix} 1 & 1 & 1 \\ 1 & 1 & 1 \\ 1 & 1 & 1 \end{bmatrix}$ **35.** about 68 mi^2

37. $x = 1$, $y = 3$, $z = 5$ **39.** $(4, 1)$ **41.** about 5.7

Page 211   Self Test

1. Sue - Lou; Elisa - Mateo; Tamara - Bob   **3.** $\begin{bmatrix} 4 & -0.5 \\ 0 & -1.5 \end{bmatrix}$

5. $\begin{bmatrix} -15 & 6 \\ 19 & 43 \\ -6 & -24 \end{bmatrix}$ **7.** $\begin{bmatrix} -15 & 6 \\ 19 & 43 \\ -6 & -24 \end{bmatrix}$ **9.** -119

Pages 216–218   Lesson 4-5

7. not square   **9.** $-\dfrac{1}{27}\begin{bmatrix} 4 & -1 \\ -7 & -5 \end{bmatrix}$ **11.** $\dfrac{1}{5}\begin{bmatrix} 1 & 0 \\ 0 & 5 \end{bmatrix}$

13. det $= 0$ **15.** $\dfrac{1}{34}\begin{bmatrix} 7 & 3 \\ -2 & 4 \end{bmatrix}$ **17.** $\dfrac{1}{32}\begin{bmatrix} 1 & 5 \\ -6 & 2 \end{bmatrix}$

19. $-\dfrac{1}{12}\begin{bmatrix} 6 & 0 \\ -5 & -2 \end{bmatrix}$ **21.** true
23. true   **25.** true   **27.** true

29. true   **31.** Let $\begin{bmatrix} a & b \\ c & d \end{bmatrix}$ represent A and let $\begin{bmatrix} 1 & 0 \\ 0 & 1 \end{bmatrix}$

$\begin{bmatrix} 1 & 0 \\ 0 & 1 \end{bmatrix} = \begin{bmatrix} a & b \\ c & d \end{bmatrix}$ represent I. $\begin{bmatrix} a & b \\ c & d \end{bmatrix}$.

$\begin{bmatrix} 1 & 0 \\ 0 & 1 \end{bmatrix} \cdot \begin{bmatrix} a & b \\ c & d \end{bmatrix} = \begin{bmatrix} a & b \\ c & d \end{bmatrix}$

Therefore, $A \cdot I = I \cdot A = A$.   **33a.** ALLATSIX   **33b.** MEET ME AT THE MALL AT SIX   **35.** 6, 8, 10 units   **37.** 7   **39.** no solution

Pages 223–225   Lesson 4-6

5. $\begin{bmatrix} 4 & -7 \\ 3 & 5 \end{bmatrix} \cdot \begin{bmatrix} x \\ y \end{bmatrix} = \begin{bmatrix} 2 \\ 9 \end{bmatrix}$ **7.** $\begin{bmatrix} -3 & 1 \\ 1 & 2 \end{bmatrix} \cdot \begin{bmatrix} x \\ y \end{bmatrix} = \begin{bmatrix} 0 \\ -21 \end{bmatrix}$

9. $\left(-1, \dfrac{9}{2}\right)$ **11.** infinitely many   **13.** $\begin{bmatrix} 3 & -7 \\ 6 & 5 \end{bmatrix} \cdot \begin{bmatrix} m \\ n \end{bmatrix} = \begin{bmatrix} -43 \\ -10 \end{bmatrix}$ **15.** $\begin{bmatrix} -1 & -1 \\ 2 & -1 \end{bmatrix} \cdot \begin{bmatrix} x \\ y \end{bmatrix} = \begin{bmatrix} 0 \\ 0 \end{bmatrix}$ **17.** $\begin{bmatrix} 2 & -3 \\ 4 & -1 \end{bmatrix} \cdot \begin{bmatrix} x \\ y \end{bmatrix} = \begin{bmatrix} 0 \\ 5 \end{bmatrix}$ **19.** $\left(\dfrac{2}{9}, -\dfrac{4}{3}\right)$ (-3, 5)   **21.** $\left(\dfrac{1}{2}, \dfrac{1}{3}\right)$ **23.** $\left(\dfrac{5}{3}, \dfrac{3}{2}\right)$

27. $(0, -4)$

29. no solution

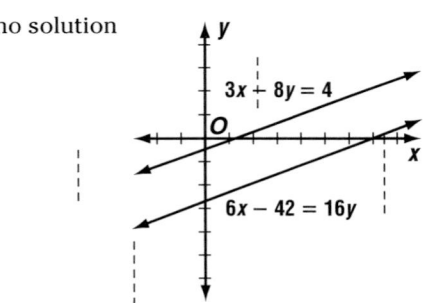

$3x + 8y = 4$
$6x - 42 = 16y$

31. $(2.5, 3)$ **33.** 80 mL of 60%; 120 mL of 40%   **35.** true
37. $y < 0$ or $x < 0$ **39.** 7.82 tons per square inch

Pages 229–231   Lesson 4-7

7. $\begin{aligned} 3x - 5y &= 25 \\ 2x + 4y &= 24 \end{aligned}$ **9.** $\begin{bmatrix} 4 & -7 & -19 \\ 3 & 2 & 22 \end{bmatrix}$ **11.** no solution

Pages 240–244   Lesson 4–8

7a. 20   **7b.** 26   **7c.** 25%   **7d.** 21 and 28   **9.** range = 19; $Q_1 = 25$; $Q_2 = 32.5$; $Q_3 = 38$; IR = 13; no outliers

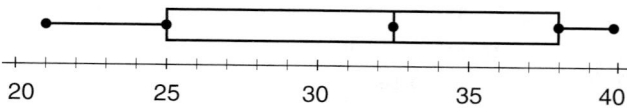

11a. 50%   **11b.** 75%   **11c.** 50%   **11d.** The least value and lower quartile are same number.

13. range = 43; $Q_1 = 31$; $Q_2 = 46$; $Q_3 = 59$; IR = 28; no outliers

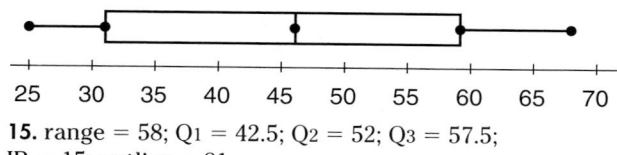

15. range = 58; $Q_1 = 42.5$; $Q_2 = 52$; $Q_3 = 57.5$; IR = 15; outlier = 81

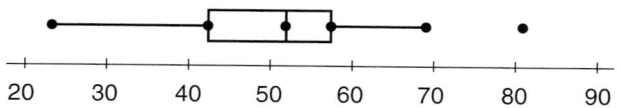

17. range = 2.7; $Q_1 = 13.95$; $Q_2 = 14.9$; $Q_3 = 15.85$; IR = 2; no outliers

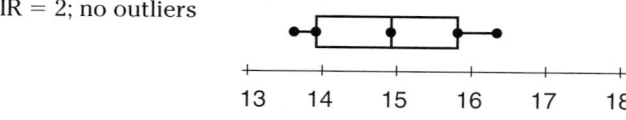

19a. Springfield   S.F.

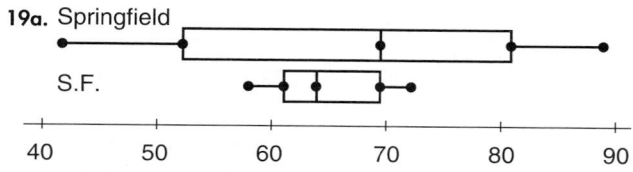

19b. The median average high temperature for San Francisco is 63.5°; the median average high temperature for Springfield is 69.5°.   **21.** Sample answer: {1, 4, 4, 4, 5, 5, 5, 6, 6, 15}

23a.

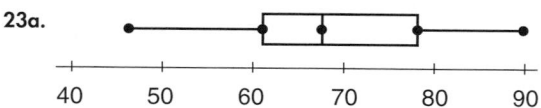

23b. Stem-and-leaf: advantage—all data are shown; disadvantage—difficult to see how data are dispersed. Box-and-whisker: advantage—easy to see range, median, and so on; disadvantage—data are lost.

25a.

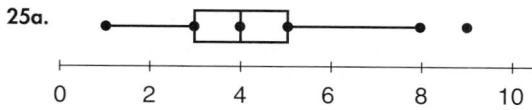

27b. Median is the same, box is longer.   **27c.** plain air-popped popcorn, Skittles   **29.** [−54, 6]   **31.** $\frac{2}{3}$ **33.** $1440

Page 245   Chapter 4   Highlights
1. identity matrix   **3.** scalar multiplication
5. determinant   **7.** dimensions   **9.** equal matrices

Pages 246–248   Chapter 4   Study Guide and Assessment

11. $\begin{bmatrix} 24 & -9 & 6 \\ 12 & 3 & 21 \end{bmatrix}$ **13.** $\begin{bmatrix} 2\frac{1}{2} & -4 \end{bmatrix}$ **15.** $\begin{bmatrix} 5.2 & 20.4 \\ -8 & -14.8 \\ -11.2 & 18 \end{bmatrix}$

17. $x = -5, y = -1$ **19.** $x = -1, y = 0$ **21.** $\begin{bmatrix} -3 & 0 \\ -2 & -6 \end{bmatrix}$

23. $\begin{bmatrix} 1 & -2 \\ -14 & 9 \end{bmatrix}$ **25.** $[-18]$ **27.** not possible to evaluate

29. -52 **31.** -36 **33.** -35 **35.** $\frac{1}{2}\begin{bmatrix} 7 & -6 \\ -9 & 8 \end{bmatrix}$

37. $\frac{1}{12}\begin{bmatrix} -1 & 2 \\ 3 & 6 \end{bmatrix}$ **39.** not possible   **41.** (2, 1)   **43.** (−1, 2)

45. (4, 2)   **47.** $\left(-\frac{1}{2}, 1, 6\right)$ **49.** 90; 25, 50, 75; 50; no outliers

51. 170; 1025, 1075, 1125; 100; no outliers   **53.** batteries, $74; spark plugs, $58; wiper blades, $48

CHAPTER 5   EXPLORING POLYNOMIALS AND RADICAL EXPRESSIONS

Pages 259–260   Lesson 5–1

5. $\frac{3w}{z^4}$ **7.** $81a^4$ **9.** $-8x^2$ **11.** $4s^2t^3$ **13.** $\frac{8}{b^3c^3}$

15. 3.86×10^5 **17.** 5×10^0; 5   **19.** b^8 **21.** m^9 **23.** an

25. ab **27.** $18r^5s^5$ **29.** $10m^3n^3$ **31.** $-\frac{2}{3}m^3n^7$ **33.** $-108x^4$

35. $-15m^4n^3p^2$ **37.** $\frac{-1}{4y^4}$ **39.** $-\frac{m^4n^9}{3}$ **41.** $\frac{a^4}{16b^4}$ **43.** $2a^4b^2$

45. 4   **47.** 7.865×10^8 **49.** 1.25×10^{-3} **51.** 3.331×10^{-2}

53. 4.02×10^{-5}; 0.0000402   **55.** 9.025×10^7; 90,250,000

57. 3.1×10^8; 310,000,000   **59.** 6   **61.** 3   **63.** $-\frac{21}{2}$ **65.** x^{10}

67. about 1.53×10^4 seconds or 4.25 hours

69. $\begin{bmatrix} 1 & 0 & 0 \\ 0 & 1 & 0 \\ 0 & 0 & 1 \end{bmatrix}$ **71.** 1, 5, 10   **73.**

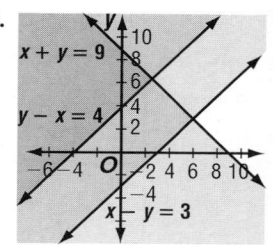

75. $y = 4x - 6$ **77.**

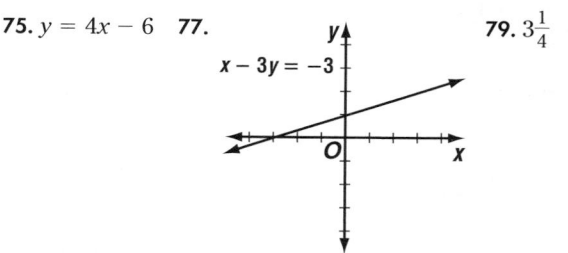

79. $3\frac{1}{4}$

Pages 264–266   Lesson 5–2

7. yes, 3   **9.** $11x + y$ **11.** $6xy + 18y$ **13.** $x^2 + 9x + 18$

15. $9m^2 - 1$ **17a.** $(4a - 2c)$ yd   **17b.** $(a^2 + 3ac + 2c^2)$ yd²

19. yes, 3   **21.** yes, 7   **23.** yes, 6   **25.** $3z^2 - 2z - 21$

27. $10m^2 + 5m - 15$ **29.** $r^2 - r + 6$ **31.** $4gf^2 - 4fbh$

33. $15m^3n^3 - 30m^4n^3 + 15m^5n^6$ **35.** $-2x^2 - 3xy - 6y^2$

37. $(28m - 12n)$ ft   **39.** $q^2 - 2q - 35$ **41.** $25 - r^2$

43. $6y^2 + 5y - 56$ **45.** $g^2 - 2 + \frac{1}{g^4}$ **47.** $y^2 - 6xy + 9x^2$

49. $4p^2 + 4pq^3 + q^6$ **51.** $(10y^2 + 6y)$ ft²   **53.** $\frac{9xy^2}{2}$ m²

55. $x^3 - y^3$ **57.** $x^4 + x^2 - 20$ **59.** $y^4 - 2x^2y^2 + x^4$

61a. $(a + b + c)^2$, $a^2 + 2ab + b^2 + 2ac + 2bc + c^2$

61b. $4a + 4b + 4c$ **63a.** $\frac{10x + 14}{9x - 2}$ **63b.** about 18.5°

65. 9 out of 16, RR; 6 out of 16, Rr; 1 out of 16, rr.

67. $(2, 1, -1)$ **69.** $\begin{bmatrix} -14 & -15 \\ 4 & 20 \end{bmatrix}$ **71.** $(12, 2)$ **73.** $(0, 0)$, $(-1, -3)$ **75.** 42.778, 42, 39

Pages 270–273   Lesson 5–3
5. $5y - 4 + 7x$ **7.** $a - 12$ **9.** $a^2 - ab + b^2$ **11.** $3x^3 - 9x^2 + 7x - 6$ **13.** $2x + 5$ **15.** $2xy - 7x^2$ **17.** $4s^2 + 3rs - 5r$ **19.** $-a^2b + a - \frac{2}{b}$ **21.** $x - 15$ **23.** $g + 5$
25. $3t^2 - 2t + 3$ **27.** $5y^2 - 4y + 4 - \frac{11}{y+1}$ **29.** $2y + 7 + \frac{5}{y-3}$ **31.** $x^2 + 3x + 9$ **33.** $3d^2 + 2d + 3 - \frac{2}{3d-2}$
35. $2c^2 + c + 5 + \frac{6}{c-2}$ **37.** $-w^2$ **39.** $2m^3 + m^2 + 3m - 1 + \frac{5}{m-3}$ **41.** $y^4 - 2y^3 + 4y^2 - 8y + 16$ **43.** $y = 2b^2 - b - 1 + \frac{4}{b+1}$ **45.** $r^3 - 9r^2 + 27r - 28$ and $r - 3$ **47.** $\frac{1}{8}$ in.
49. $a^2 - 2ab + b^2$ **51.** $(-1, 2, -3)$ **53.** 18   **55.** 5
57. $-6, 20$

Pages 278–280   Lesson 5–4
7. $-5x(3x + 1)$ **9.** $x(x + y + 3)$ **11.** $(y - 5)(y + 2)$
13. $3(h - 4)(h + 4)$ **15.** $(g + 20)(g^2 - 20g + 400)$
17. yes, $2y^2 + y - 1$ or $(2y - 1)(y + 1)$ **19.** $2a^2b(5a - 6b)$
21. prime   **23.** $(y - 10)(y - 2)$ **25.** $(y + 6)(y + 1)$
27. $(x^2 + y)(x^2 - y)$ **29.** $3(n + 8)(n - 1)$ **31.** $3(a - 3b)(a + 3b)$ **33.** $(x + 7)(x - 2)$ **35.** $5(x^2 + 3x - 2)$
37. $3(a + 3)(a + 5)$ **39.** prime   **41.** $(2a - 5b)(2x + 7y)$
43. $(9y + 7)(9y - 7)$ **45.** $2x^2(x + 1)^2$ **47.** $(y^2 + 4)(y + 2)(y - 2)$ **49.** $(8a + 3)(a + b + c)$ **51.** $(x + 3y)(3x + 5)(x - 1)$ **53.** $\frac{n - 7}{n + 3}$

55. correct

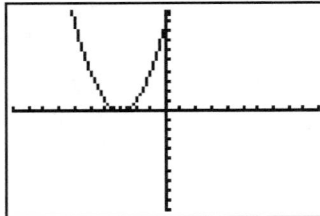

57. incorrect; $(x + 2)(x^2 - 2x + 4)$

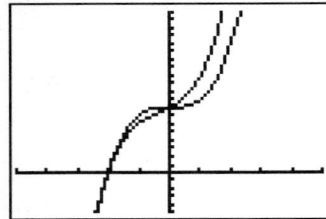

59. incorrect; $(2x + 1)(x - 3)$ **61a.** $(x^2 + 2xy + y^2)$ units^2
61b. 961 units^2

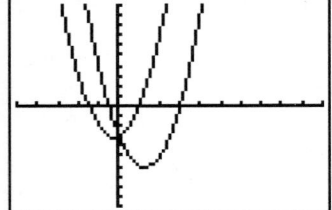

63. $t^2 - 2t + 1$ **65.** 2.592×10^{10} km   **67.** $\begin{bmatrix} 0 & -4 \\ -7 & \end{bmatrix}$

69. $(7, -2)$ **71.** $y = \frac{3}{2}x - 1$ **73.** distributive

Pages 285–287   Lesson 5–5
7. -2.844 **9.** 3   **11.** -2 **13.** m **15.** $-5|x^3|$ **17.** $|3m - 2n|$ **19.** -5 **21.** -12 **23.** 0.9   **25.** 5   **27.** 18.574   **29.** 4
31. 14   **33.** 3   **35.** $\frac{1}{2}$ **37.** 10   **39.** -0.5 **41.** y **43.** $-|x|$
45. $6|g^3|$ **47.** $m^2n^3z^4$ **49.** $-3a^3b^4$ **51.** $s + t$
53. $-|x + 1|$ **55.** $\pm|s - t|$ **57.** no real roots
59. $x = 0, y = 0$ **61.** about 127.3 feet   **63.** $25b^2$
65. $xy^3 + y + \frac{1}{x}$ **67.** 4   **69.** max: $f(-3, -3) = 3$; min: $f(0, 5) = -10$ **71.**

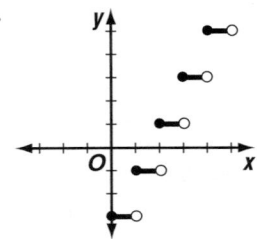

73a. 11.0, 3.3;10.1, 1.9   **73b.** 5.8, 3.0; 8.0, 3.8   **73c.** Sample answer: Teens have more leisure time than adults.

Page 287   Self Test
1. 9.3×10^7 miles   **3.** $-108x^8y^3$ **5.** $n^3 - n^2 - 5n + 2$
7. $m^2 - 3 - \frac{19}{m-4}$ **9.** $8(r - 2s^2)(r^2 + 2rs^2 + 4s^4)$
11. $|2n + 3|$

Pages 293–295   Lesson 5–6
9. $4\sqrt{5}$ **11.** $4x^2y$ **13.** $-42\sqrt{15}$ **15.** $\sqrt[3]{9}$
17. $\left|\frac{y}{y-3}\right|\sqrt{y-3}$ **19.** $15\sqrt[3]{5} - 6\sqrt[3]{3}$ **21.** $49 - 11y$
23. $4\sqrt{2}$ **25.** $2\sqrt[3]{2}$ **27.** $2\sqrt[3]{4}$ **29.** $y\sqrt{y}$ **31.** $\sqrt{3}$
33. $3xy^2\sqrt{10x}$ **35.** $-60\sqrt{30}$ **37.** $48\sqrt{7}$ **39.** 0
41. $-42\sqrt{2} - 15\sqrt{14}$ **43.** $3\sqrt[3]{2x}$ **45.** 34   **47.** $8 - 2\sqrt{15}$
49. $5\sqrt{2}$ **51.** $\frac{a^2\sqrt{b}}{b^2}$ **53.** $\frac{16\sqrt{10}}{5}$ **55.** $\frac{5\sqrt{6} - 3\sqrt{2}}{22}$
57. $\frac{\sqrt{x^2 - 1}}{x - 1}$ **59.** $|x| + x^2 + x^4$ **61.** $2y^2\sqrt{70}$ in.
63. when x and y are not negative   **65a.** Akikta: 58.09, Francisco: 56.91   **65b.** Akikta   **67.** 80 ft/s or about 55 mph   **69.** $(a + b)(1 + 3a - 3b)$ **71.** $-6x^3 - 4x^2y + 13xy^2$ **73.** $\begin{bmatrix} 4 & 3 \\ 1 & 3 \end{bmatrix}$ **75.** $(2, 3)$ **77.** 9   **79.** -63

Pages 300–302   Lesson 5–7
7. $27^{\frac{1}{4}}$ **9.** $16^{\frac{1}{3}}a^{\frac{5}{3}}b^{\frac{7}{3}}$ **11.** $\frac{1}{2}$ **13.** 2   **15.** $xy^2z\sqrt[6]{x^3y^2z^3}$
17. $\frac{x^{\frac{3}{5x}}}{5x}$ **19.** $\frac{c(a - 4b)^{\frac{1}{2}}}{a - 4b}$ **21.** $y^{\frac{2}{3}}$ **23a.** $\frac{1}{2}$ **23b.** $\frac{3}{5}$ **23c.** $\frac{1}{3}$
25. $\frac{1}{10}$ **27.** $81^{\frac{13}{6}}$ or $9^{\frac{13}{3}}$ or $3^{\frac{26}{3}}$ **29.** $\frac{1}{16}$ **31.** 8   **33.** $4 \cdot 6^{\frac{1}{3}}$
35. $\frac{8 \cdot 3^{\frac{1}{2}}}{3}$ **37.** $m\sqrt{2}$ **39.** $\frac{w^{\frac{4}{5}}}{w}$ **41.** $\frac{x^{\frac{1}{6}}}{x}$ **43.** $\frac{b^{\frac{5}{12}}}{8b}$
45. $\frac{x^2y + 3}{x}$ **47.** $\frac{pqr^{\frac{2}{3}}}{r}$ **49.** $\frac{b^{\frac{2}{3}}}{b} - b^{\frac{1}{3}}$ **51.** $11mn^3$
53. $a - a^{\frac{1}{3}}b^{\frac{2}{3}}$ **55.** $\sqrt[6]{r^3s^2}$ **57.** $13\sqrt[6]{13}$ **59.** $\sqrt{3}$
61. 0.010000001   **63.** 3.51   **65.** 1.12   **67a.** 831 vibrations per second   **67b.** 247 vibrations per second   **69.** $4x - 20$
71. $(ab - 3)(a^2b^2 + 3ab + 9)$ **73.** $(2, -4)$ **75.** 1, 2, 3
77. 83   **79.** $\{x \mid 3 < x < 6\}$

Pages 307–309   Lesson 5–8
5. -7 **7.** 13   **9.** 7   **11.** $0 \le n < 4$ **13.** $r = \pm\sqrt{y^2 - s^2}$

15. 64 **17.** $-\dfrac{7\sqrt{5}}{30}$ **19.** 13 **21.** 4 **23.** no solution **25.** $\dfrac{54}{4}$

27. $x \le -\dfrac{57}{5}$ **29.** $\dfrac{-15 - 5\sqrt{3}}{6}$ **31.** 9 **33.** $k \ge 0$ **35.** 5.41

37. no solution **39.** 3 **41.** $a \ge 5$ **43.** $\ell = g \cdot \dfrac{T^2}{4\pi^2}$

45. $p = \dfrac{m^6 g^2}{r}$ **47a.** $h = \dfrac{\sqrt{S^2 - r^4\pi^2}}{}$ **47b.** about 13.4

49. Yes, $\sqrt[k]{\sqrt[m]{b}} = \left(b^{\frac{1}{m}}\right)^{\frac{1}{k}} = b^{\frac{1}{km}} = \sqrt[km]{b}$ **51.** about 282 feet

53. $t = \dfrac{2\pi r\sqrt{GMr}}{}$ **55.** $5^{\frac{3}{7}}$ **57.** $|x + 5|$ **59.** y^{10} **61.** 34

63a. $y = 0.05x + 15$ **63b.** \$17.10

Pages 314–316   Lesson 5–9
7. $7i|mn|\sqrt{2}$ **9.** $-180\sqrt{3}$ **11.** 1 **13.** $5 + 5i$ **15.** 13

17.
$$5x^2 + 40 = 0$$
$$5(-2i\sqrt{2})^2 + 40 = 0$$
$$40i^2 + 40 = 0$$
$$40(-1) + 40 = 0$$
$$0 = 0$$

19. $\pm 4i$ **21.** $\dfrac{2}{3}i$ **23.** $10k^2 i$ **25.** $\dfrac{3i|x|}{5y^4}\sqrt{x}$ **27.** $-60i$

29. $-11\sqrt{2}$ **31.** -12 **33.** $4i\sqrt{3}$ **35.** i **37.** -1

39. $7 + 2i$ **41.** 2 **43.** $15 - i\sqrt{3} - i\sqrt{5}$ **45.** $14 + 5i$

47. 7 **49.** $-2 + 36i$ **51.** $\pm 2i\sqrt{2}$ **53.** $\pm 2i\sqrt{3}$ **55.** $\pm i\dfrac{\sqrt{5}}{2}$

57. $148 - 222i$ **59.** $20 + 15i$ **61.** 2, 3 **63.** $\dfrac{67}{11}, \dfrac{19}{11}$

65a. $y = -6x^2 - 30$, $y = 5x^2 + 40$, $y = 3x^2 + 18$, $y = 7x^2 + 84$
65b.

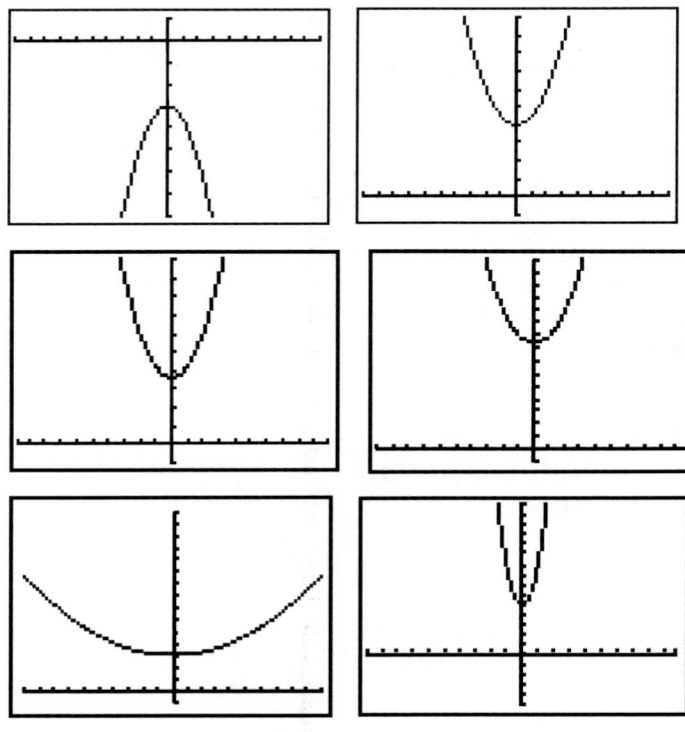

65c. Answers may vary. Sample answers: None of the graphs intercept the x-axis. All of the graphs are parabolas. **65d.** Since none of the graphs intercept the x-axis, none of the functions have real roots. This is confirmed by the solutions that are all imaginary.

67.
$$x^2 - 4x + 13 = 0$$
$$(2 - 3i)^2 - 4(2 - 3i) + 13 \stackrel{?}{=} 0$$
$$(4 - 12i + 9i^2) - 8 + 12i + 13 \stackrel{?}{=} 0$$
$$4 - 9 - 8 + 13 \stackrel{?}{=} 0$$
$$0 = 0$$
Yes, $2 - 3i$, because solutions involving imaginary numbers come in conjugate pairs.

69a.
$$AB = D \cdot (AB)$$
$$\begin{bmatrix} 0 & 1 \\ 1 & 0 \end{bmatrix} \cdot \begin{bmatrix} 0 & -i \\ i & 0 \end{bmatrix} \stackrel{?}{=} \begin{bmatrix} -1 & 0 \\ 0 & -1 \end{bmatrix} \cdot \left(\begin{bmatrix} 0 & -i \\ i & 0 \end{bmatrix} \cdot \begin{bmatrix} 0 & 1 \\ 1 & 0 \end{bmatrix} \right)$$
$$\begin{bmatrix} i & 0 \\ 0 & -i \end{bmatrix} \stackrel{?}{=} \begin{bmatrix} -1 & 0 \\ 0 & -1 \end{bmatrix} \cdot \begin{bmatrix} -i & 0 \\ 0 & i \end{bmatrix}$$
$$\begin{bmatrix} i & 0 \\ 0 & -i \end{bmatrix} \stackrel{?}{=} \begin{bmatrix} i & 0 \\ 0 & -i \end{bmatrix}$$

69b.
$$CB = D \cdot (BC)$$
$$\begin{bmatrix} 1 & 0 \\ 0 & -1 \end{bmatrix} \cdot \begin{bmatrix} 0 & -i \\ i & 0 \end{bmatrix} \stackrel{?}{=} \begin{bmatrix} -1 & 0 \\ 0 & -1 \end{bmatrix} \cdot \left(\begin{bmatrix} 0 & -i \\ i & 0 \end{bmatrix} \cdot \begin{bmatrix} 1 & 0 \\ 0 & -1 \end{bmatrix} \right)$$
$$\begin{bmatrix} 0 & -i \\ -i & 0 \end{bmatrix} \stackrel{?}{=} \begin{bmatrix} -1 & 0 \\ 0 & -1 \end{bmatrix} \cdot \begin{bmatrix} 0 & i \\ i & 0 \end{bmatrix}$$
$$\begin{bmatrix} 0 & -i \\ -i & 0 \end{bmatrix} = \begin{bmatrix} 0 & -i \\ -i & 0 \end{bmatrix}$$

71. $\dfrac{6(11 + 2\sqrt{3})}{109}$ **73.** 3.06 seconds **75.** $(2, 5, 4)$ **77.** sofa, \$1180; loveseat, \$590; table, \$330 **79.** $5x - 6y = 30$ **81.** 19

Pages 319–321   Lesson 5–10
5. $-7i$ **7.** 100 **9.** $\dfrac{7i}{2}$ **11.** $2 - i$ **13.** $\dfrac{5 + i}{2}$

15. $\left(\dfrac{7 + 3i}{1}\right)\left(\dfrac{7 - 3i}{58}\right) = \dfrac{58}{58} = 1$ **17.** $12 - i$ **19.** $10 + 4i$

21. $6 - i\sqrt{7}$ **23.** 29 **25.** 2 **27.** 68 **29.** $\dfrac{7 - 3i}{2}$ **31.** $\dfrac{3 + 6i}{5}$

33. $\dfrac{9 - 6i}{26}$ **35.** $\dfrac{1 + i}{2}$ **37.** i **39.** $\dfrac{-3 - 21i}{10}$ **41.** $\dfrac{3 + i\sqrt{2}}{11}$

43. $\dfrac{6 + 5i}{61}$ **45.** $\dfrac{x - yi}{x^2 + y^2}$ **47.** $2 - 6i, -94 - 72i$ **49.** $\dfrac{2 - 3i\sqrt{5}}{7}$

51. $\dfrac{-1 - i}{2}$ **53.** $\dfrac{16 + 63i}{50}$ **55.** $\overline{z \cdot w} = \overline{(a + bi) \cdot (c + di)}$
$$= \overline{ac + adi + bci - bd}$$
$$= \overline{(ac - bd) + (ad + bc)i}$$
$$= (ac - bd) - (ad + bc)i$$
$$= ac - adi - bd - bci$$
$$= ac - adi + bdi^2 - bci$$
$$= a(c - di) - bi(-di + c)$$
$$= (a - bi)(c - di)$$
$$= \bar{z} \cdot \bar{w}$$

57a. $\dfrac{159 + 95j}{17}$ **57b.** $\dfrac{-37 + 134j}{5}$ **57c.** $\dfrac{25 - 25j}{2}$
57d. $\dfrac{1310 - 920j}{41}$ **59.** $(1 + i, -1 + 2i), (-1 + 2i, -4 - 4i)$, $(-4 - 4i, -1 + 32i), (-1 + 32i, -1024 - 64i)$

61. $\dfrac{7\sqrt{2} - 14}{2}$ **63.** 36 inches **65.** $\left(\dfrac{1}{4}, 6, -\dfrac{1}{6}\right)$

67. Yes; each element of the domain is paired with exactly one element of the range. **69.** $-\dfrac{11}{3}$

Pages 323   Chapter 5   Highlights
1. scientific notation **3.** rationalizing the denominator
5. irrational numbers **7.** coefficient **9.** extraneous solution **11.** square root **13.** degree of a polynomial
15. fractals

SELECTED ANSWERS

Selected Answers

17. $\frac{1}{r^3}$ **19.** $8xy^4$ **21.** $-\frac{3}{2}$ **23.** $170,000,100; 1.7 \times 10^8$
25. $900; 9 \times 10^2$ **27.** $4x^2 + 22x - 34$ **29.** $d^2 - 2d - 15$
31. $4a^4 + 24a^2 + 36$ **33.** $8b^3 - 36b^2c + 54bc^2 - 27c^3$
35. $10x^3 - 5x^2 + 9x - 9$ **37.** $5x^2 + 3x + 1$ **39.** $2(5a^2 - 1)$
$(a - 2)$ **41.** $(s + 8)(s^2 - 8s + 64)$ **43.** ± 16 **45.** no real
roots   **47.** $\pm(x^4 - 3)$ **49.** $2m^2$ **51.** $2\sqrt{2}$ **53.** $-5\sqrt{3}$

55. $20 + 8\sqrt{6}$ **57.** $\frac{3 - \sqrt{5}}{4}$ **59.** $\frac{1}{9}$ **61.** $\frac{9}{4}$ **63.** $\frac{xyz^{\frac{2}{3}}}{z}$

65. 343 **67.** $-\sqrt{3}$ **69.** $1, 3$ **71.** 8 **73.** $16i$ **75.** $-65 -$
$10i$ **77.** $12\sqrt{ab}$ **79.** i **81.** 7 **83.** $\frac{7 - 24i}{25}$ **85.** $\frac{-1 + 2i\sqrt{2}}{3}$

87. No, she is not telling the truth. She was going approximately 49 mph.

CHAPTER 6   EXPLORING QUADRATIC FUNCTIONS AND INEQUALITIES

Page 333   Lesson 6–1A
1. Sample answer: Xmin $= -10$, Xmax $= 10$,   Ymin $=$
-10, Ymax $= 40$ **3.** Sample Answer: Xmin $= -50$,
Xmax $= 10$,   Ymin $= -2000$, Ymax $= 500$ **5.** Sample
Answer: Xmin $= -10$, Xmax $= 10$,   Ymin $= -80$, Ymax $=$
5 **7.** no solution   **9.** $-3.14, -38.53$

Pages 338–340   Lesson 6–1
7. $x^2; x; -4$ **9.** $(2, 0), x = 2$

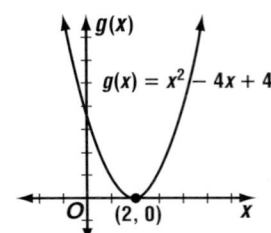

$g(x) = x^2 - 4x + 4$

11. $(-3, 0), x = -3$ **13.** 2

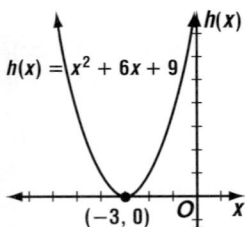

$h(x) = x^2 + 6x + 9$

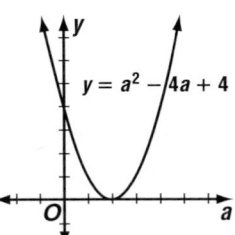

$y = a^2 - 4a + 4$

15. Between $x = 6$ and $x = 9$; since the value of y is
negative at $x = 6$ and positive at $x = 9$, the graph must
cross the x-axis between 6 and 9.   **17.** $3n^2; 0; -1$
19. $z^2; 3z; 0$ **21.** $9t^2; 6t; -7$ **23.** -4
25. $(0, 0), x = 0$ **27.** $(4\frac{1}{2}, -11\frac{1}{4}), x = 4\frac{1}{2}$

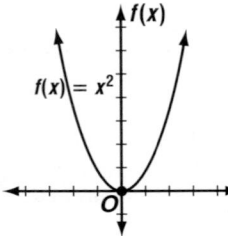

$f(x) = x^2$

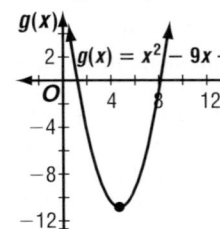

$g(x) = x^2 - 9x + 9$

29. $(0, -9), x = 0$

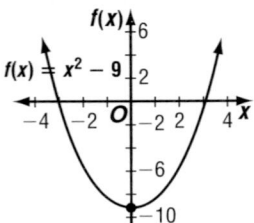

$f(x) = x^2 - 9$

31. $(-10, -7), x = -10$

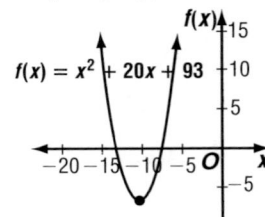

$f(x) = x^2 + 20x + 93$

33. $(-1\frac{1}{2}, -3\frac{1}{5}), x = -1\frac{1}{2}$

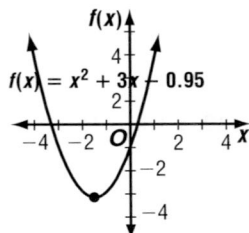

$f(x) = x^2 + 3x - 0.95$

35. $6, -4$

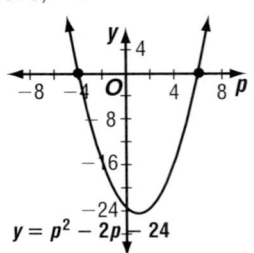

$y = p^2 - 2p - 24$

37. -2

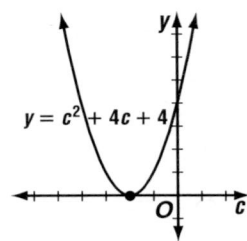

$y = c^2 + 4c + 4$

39. $-1.5, 3$

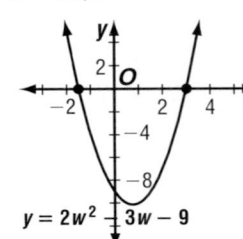

$y = 2w^2 + 3w - 9$

41. $-4, \frac{3}{2}$

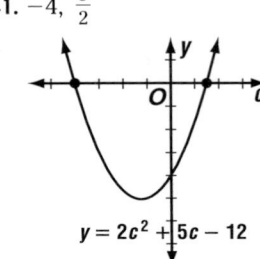

$y = 2c^2 + 5c - 12$

43a. There are no roots because the graph does not
touch the x-axis.   **43b.** Sample answer: There cannot be
any negative prime numbers since the graph has no
negative y values.

45a.

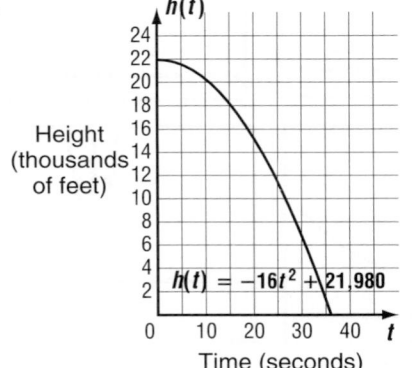

$h(t) = -16t^2 + 21,980$

Height (thousands of feet) vs. Time (seconds)

45b. about 37 seconds   **47.** 7 **49.** -57 **51.** $y = -3x -$
$16, 3x + y = -16$ **53.** 21
Pages 344–345   Lesson 6–2
5. $-\frac{7}{3}, -5$ **7.** 8 **9.** $2, -\frac{7}{3}$ **11.** $-4, -1$ **13.** $-3, 3$

15. $4, -3$ **17.** 6 **19.** $4, -1$ **21.** $-\frac{1}{6}, \frac{1}{3}$ **23.** $-\frac{4}{3}$ **25.** $5, -8$

27. $-\frac{1}{4}, 3$ **29.** $-\frac{3}{4}, -\frac{4}{3}$ **31.** $0, 3, -3$ **33.** $0, -\frac{6}{7}, \frac{2}{5}$

35. $y = 0.25(x + 8)(x - 4)$ or $y = 0.25x^2 + x - 8$

37a. about 45 minutes **37b.** 0.76 hour

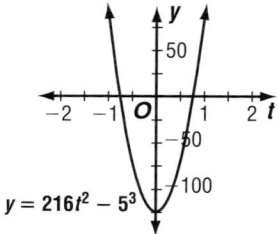

39. 8 chords **41.** $\pm 4i$ **43.** $\frac{1}{8}\begin{bmatrix} 6 & 2 \\ 3 & 4 \end{bmatrix}$ **45.** $\frac{4-27n}{5}$

Pages 350–352 Lesson 6–3

7. $\frac{49}{4}$ **9.** $\frac{5}{3}, -\frac{1}{4}$ **11.** $\frac{7 \pm \sqrt{33}}{2}$ **13.** $-1 \pm i\sqrt{5}$ **15.** 1

17. 400 **19.** 2500 **21.** $-6, 3$ **23.** $4 \pm \sqrt{5}$ **25.** $-\frac{9}{2}$

27. $-2 \pm i\sqrt{7}$ **29.** $\frac{-7 \pm i\sqrt{35}}{6}$ **31.** $\frac{3 \pm \sqrt{89}}{2}$ **33.** $\frac{7}{3}, -\frac{5}{4}$

35. $\frac{-b \pm \sqrt{b^2 - 4ac}}{2a}$ **37a.** ± 16 **37b.** 49 **37c.** 9 **37d.** 25

37e. ± 4 **37f.** 25

39a.

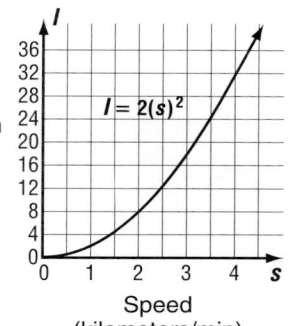

Collision Impact

Speed (kilometers/min)

39b. 2; 8; 32 **39c.** The impact of the collision quadruples.

41a. 40 ft **41b.** 49 ft **41c.** 3.5 s **43.** $5mn^2 \cdot \sqrt[4]{m}$

45.

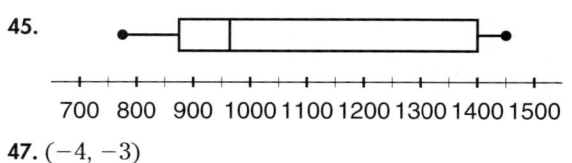

700 800 900 1000 1100 1200 1300 1400 1500

47. $(-4, -3)$

Pages 357–358 Lesson 6–4

7. $3, -5, -2; 49$ **9.** $1, 5, 7; -3$ **11.** $576; 2$ R, Q; $6, -6$

13. $-15; 2$ C; $\frac{-5 \pm i\sqrt{15}}{2}$ **15a.** 2 roots, $-1 \pm \sqrt{6}$ (1.4 and -3.4) **15b.** 1.4 and -3.4 **17.** $0; 1$ R, Q; 3 **19.** $49;$

2 R, Q; $-2, \frac{1}{3}$ **21.** $73; 2$ R, I; $\frac{-11 \pm \sqrt{73}}{6}; -0.41, -3.26$

23. $36; 2$ R, Q; $0, 6$ **25.** $-116; 2$ C; $\frac{4 \pm i\sqrt{29}}{5}$ **27.** $225; 2$ R,

Q; $7, -\frac{1}{2}$ **29.** $-31; 2$ C; $\frac{9 \pm i\sqrt{31}}{8}$

31a.

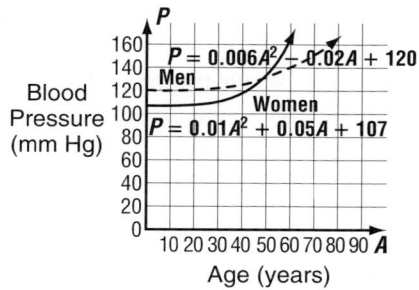

Blood Pressure (mm Hg)

Age (years)

The graph representing the normal blood pressure of women is more narrow than the graph of men's blood pressure. Initially, women's blood pressure is lower than men's, but it increases at a faster rate.

31b. 121 mm Hg **31c.** 50 years **33.** 1 **35.** $|x + 3|$

37. $(-19, -29)$

Page 358 Self Test

1. $-3, -1$ **3.** $4, -9$

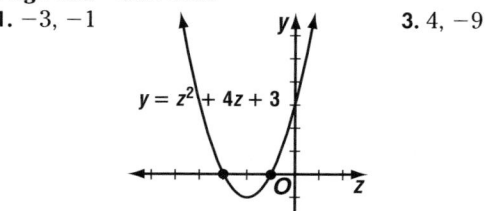

$y = z^2 + 4z + 3$

5. $-11, 5$ **7.** $56, 2$ real, irrational roots **9.** $\frac{9}{2}, 8$

Pages 362–364 Lesson 6–5

5. $12, 22$ **7.** $0, 25$ **9.** $x^2 - 8x + 11 = 0$ **11.** $3x^2 + 19x - 14 = 0$ **13.** $7, -7$ **15.** $\frac{9}{4}, -\frac{9}{4}$ **17.** $x^2 + 3x - 54 = 0$

19. $8x^2 - 21x + 10 = 0$ **21.** $25x^2 - 4 = 0$ **23.** $3x^2 + 14x + 8 = 0$ **25.** $x^2 - 8x + 13 = 0$ **27.** $16x^2 + 16x + 29 = 0$ **29.** $-4, -\frac{3}{2}$ **31.** $0, 8$ **33.** $\frac{1}{2}, -\frac{2}{3}$ **35.** $4 \pm \sqrt{34}$

37. $9, -\frac{5}{4}$ **39a.** $12x^2 - 48x + 13 = 0$ **39b.** $42x^2 - 7x + 10 = 0$ **41.** -6 **43.** 88.2 m/s **45.** $7, -5$

47. $(-4, -21); x = -4$ **49.** $(2x - 3)(2x + 3)$ **51.** $\frac{21}{8}$

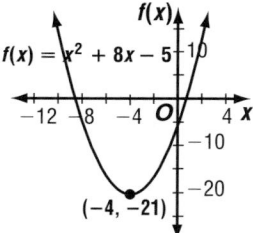

$f(x) = x^2 + 8x - 5$

$(-4, -21)$

Page 366 Lesson 6–6A

1. The value of k determines the vertical position of the graph. As you change the k, the graph will slide up or down the coordinate plane. Examples will vary. **3.** Both graphs have the same shape and vertex, but the first graph opens upward and the second graph opens downward. Examples will vary. **5.** Both graphs have the same shape, but the graph of $y = (x - 8)^2$ is 8 units to the right of the graph of $y = x^2$. **7.** Both graphs have the same shape, but the graph of $y = x^2 - 11$ is 11 units below the graph of $y = x^2$. **9.** The graph of $y = -2x^2$ opens downward and is more narrow than the graph of $y = x^2$. **11.** Both graphs have the same shape, but the graph of $y = -\frac{1}{3}x^2 + 2$ is 2 units above the graph of

$y = -\frac{1}{3}x^2$.   **13.** Both graphs have the same shape, but the graph of $y = (x + 2)^2 - 4$ is 5 units below the graph of $y = (x + 2)^2 + 1$.   **15.** The graph of $y = \frac{1}{2}(x - 4)^2 - 5$ is 8 units below and is wider than the graph of $y = 2(x - 4)^2 + 3$.

Pages 372–375   Lesson 6–6
7. $(0, -6)$, $x = 0$, up   **9.** $f(x) = -3(x - 2)^2 + 12$; $(2, 12)$, $x = 2$, down   **11.** $y = -\frac{1}{2}(x + 2)^2 - 3$ **13.** $y = 3x^2 - 4x + 7$ **15.**

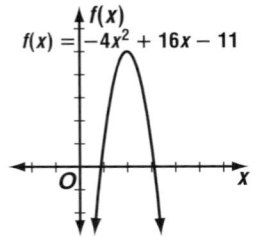
$f(x) = -4x^2 + 16x - 11$

17. $f(x) = 3x^2 - 5$

19. $(-11, -6)$, $x = -11$, down   **21.** $\left(\frac{1}{2}, \frac{1}{4}\right)$, $x = \frac{1}{2}$, up
23. $f(x) = -(x + 2)^2 + 12$; $(-2, 12)$, $x = -2$, down
25. $f(x) = -6(x - 2)^2 + 24$; $(2, 24)$, $x = 2$, down
27. $f(x) = -2(x + 5)^2$; $(-5, 0)$, $x = -5$, down
29. $f(x) = \frac{1}{3}(x - 6)^2 + 3$; $(6, 3)$, $x = 6$, up
31. $y = -\frac{3}{4}(x - 4)^2 + 1$ **33.** $y = \frac{1}{3}x^2 + 5$
35. $y = -3(x - 5)^2 + 4$ **37.** $y = \frac{1}{2}x^2 - 2x - 1$
39. $y = \frac{25}{3}x^2 + \frac{73}{3}x + 6$

41.
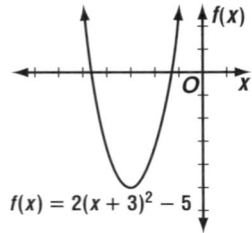
$f(x) = 2(x + 3)^2 - 5$

43.
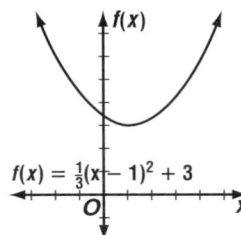
$f(x) = \frac{1}{3}(x - 1)^2 + 3$

45.
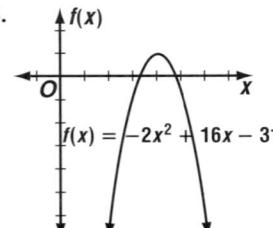
$f(x) = -2x^2 + 16x - 31$

47.
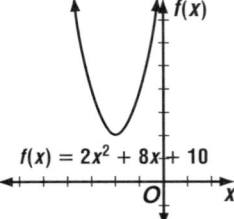
$f(x) = 2x^2 + 8x + 10$

49.
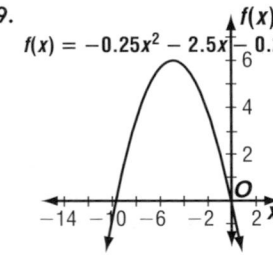
$f(x) = -0.25x^2 - 2.5x - 0.25$

51. $f(x) = -2(x - 2)^2 + 9$

53. $h = -\frac{b}{2a}$, $k = \frac{4ac - b^2}{4a}$ or $c - \frac{b^2}{4a}$

55a. Since the domain is the number of dots on a side, it is the set of integers greater than 0. Likewise, since the range is the total number of dots, it is also the set of integers greater than 0.

55b. $f(x) = \frac{1}{2}x(x + 1)$ **55c.** 0

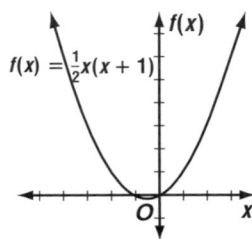
$f(x) = \frac{1}{2}x(x + 1)$

57. 5 ft   **59.** $(1, 4)$, $x = 1$

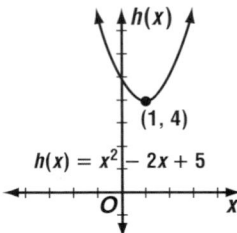
$(1, 4)$
$h(x) = x^2 - 2x + 5$

61. $3x^2 - 10x - 8$ **63.** $\begin{bmatrix} 6 & 0 & -24 \\ 14 & -\frac{2}{3} & -8 \end{bmatrix}$ **65.** $3x + 4y = -8$

Page 377   Lesson 6–7A
1.
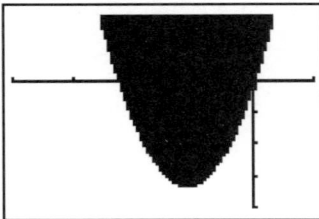

3.
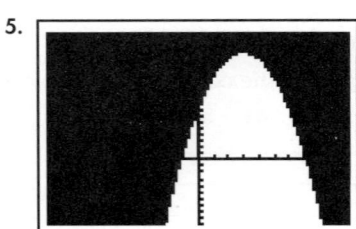

5.
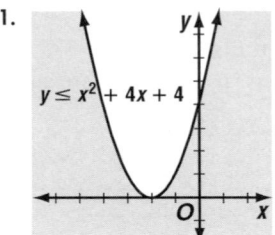

7. $\{x \mid x < -7 \text{ or } x > 3\}$ **9.** $\{x \mid x \leq -0.5 \text{ or } x \geq 0\}$
11. $\{x \mid -0.42 < x < 9.42\}$ **13.** $w \geq 3.66$, $\ell \geq 7.66$

Pages 381–383   Lesson 6–7
7. yes   **9.** no

11.
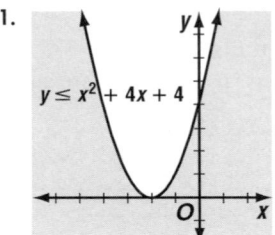
$y \leq x^2 + 4x + 4$

13.
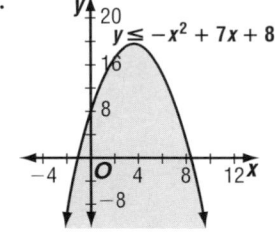
$y \leq -x^2 + 7x + 8$

15. $-2 \le x \le 6$ **17.** $x = 5$ **19.** $\{n \mid n \ge 2.5 \text{ or } n \le -3.8\}$
21. {all reals} **23.** $\left\{b \mid -\frac{3}{2} < b < 2\right\}$ **25.** $0 \le w \le 5$
27.

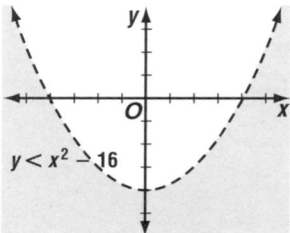

$y < x^2 - 16$

29.

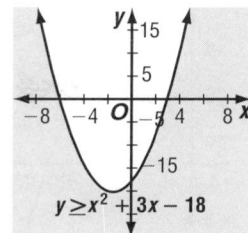

$y \ge x^2 + 3x - 18$

31.

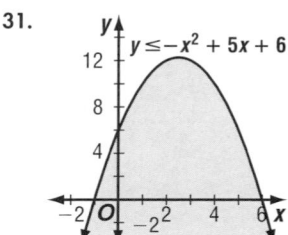

$y \le -x^2 + 5x + 6$

33.

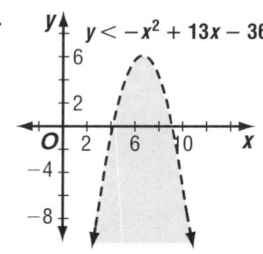

$y < -x^2 + 13x - 36$

35.

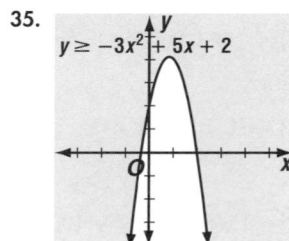

$y \ge -3x^2 + 5x + 2$

37.

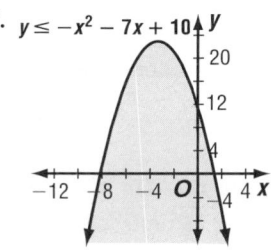

$y \le -x^2 - 7x + 10$

39. $\{x \mid x < -3 \text{ or } x > 6\}$ **41.** $\{q \mid q \le -6 \text{ or } q \ge 4\}$
43. $\left\{x \mid -4 \le x \le \frac{3}{2}\right\}$ **45.** $\{w \mid w \le 0 \text{ or } w \ge 2\}$
47. $\left\{g \mid -\frac{1}{2} < g < 3\right\}$ **49.** $\left\{n \mid -\sqrt{3} \le n \le \sqrt{3}\right\}$
51. $\left\{t \mid \frac{-1 - \sqrt{10}}{2} \le t \le \frac{-1 + \sqrt{10}}{2}\right\}$ **53.** $\{x \mid x \le -4 \text{ or } -2 \le x \le 8\}$ **55.** $\{x \mid x \le -3 \text{ or } -2 \le x \le 1 \text{ or } x \ge 2\}$ **57a.** No, the maximum height of the ball is 66 feet. **57b.** 78 feet per second **59.** 1 decrease of $0.20
61a. $f(x) = -\frac{2}{315}(x - 315)^2 + 630$ **61b.** 630 ft
61c. See students' work for comparisons.

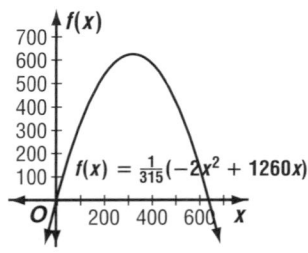

$f(x) = \frac{1}{315}(-2x^2 + 1260x)$

63. $\frac{6 \pm \sqrt{146}}{11}$ **65.** $33 + 20\sqrt{2}$ **67.** $-15a^2 + 14a - 3$
69. $(4, -2)$ **71.** all reals

Pages 389–391 Lesson 6–8
5. 50; 36.3 **7.** 58.18; 20.6 **9a.** 2.24 **9b.** small
9c. Answers will vary. **11.** 350; 50 **13.** 369.30; 194.14
15. 57.4; 9.1 **17.** 3.9; 0.55 **19.** 67.57; 19.68 **21.** 0; no variation from the mean **23a.** 79.52; 5.16 **23b.** 0.78; 0.47
25. 18.22¢; 3.99¢ **25b.** 20.47¢; 4.43¢ **27.** 250 ft

29. $\begin{bmatrix} 3 & 4 & \vdots & 22 \\ 7 & -1 & \vdots & 10 \end{bmatrix}, (2, 4)$

Pages 395–398 Lesson 6–9
5a. normally distributed

5b.

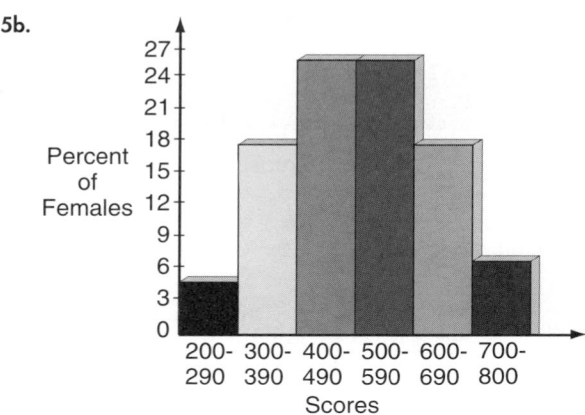

7a. 6800 tires **7b.** 250 tires **7c.** 1600 tires **7d.** 81.5%
9. normally distributed

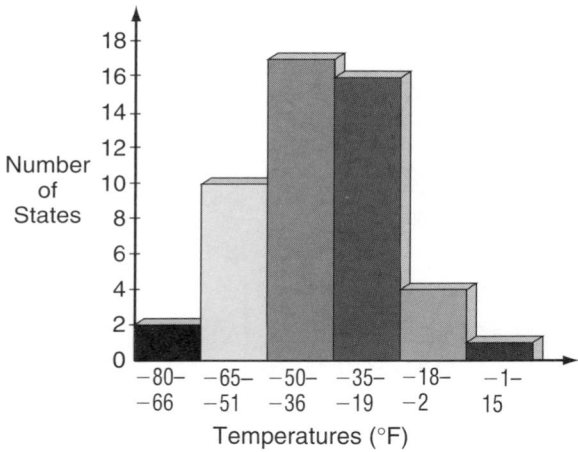

11a. 50% **11b.** 50% **11c.** 95% **13a.** 500 rods
13b. 815 rods **13c.** 16% **13d.** 84% **15.** Sample answer: The statistician was using standard deviations.
17a. 80.75; 4.94

17b.

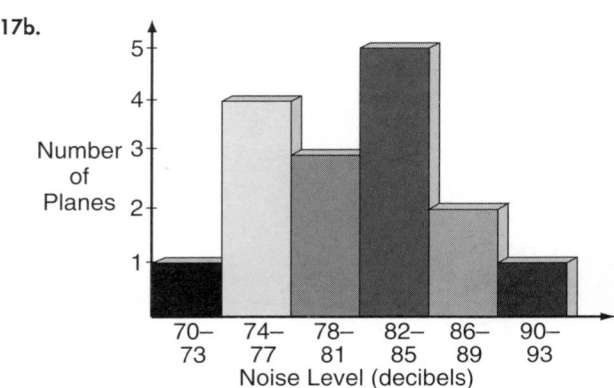

17c. Sample answer: The data do not appear to be normally distributed since they are not symmetrical about the mean.

19a.

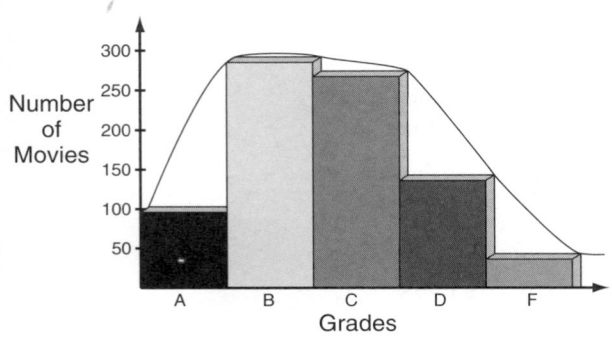

19b. no, positively skewed   **21a.** $y = 0.4(x - 7.5)^2 + 9.5$
21b. \$194.40   **21c.** \$312   **23.** $-3x^2 - 28x - 32$

Page 399   Chapter 6   Highlights
1. f   **3.** a   **5.** i   **7.** d   **9.** g

Pages 400–402   Chapter 6   Study Guide and Assessment
11. $-10, 4$ **13.** $-2, 10$

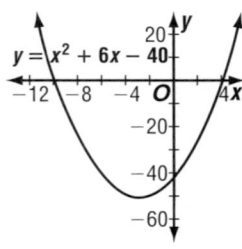 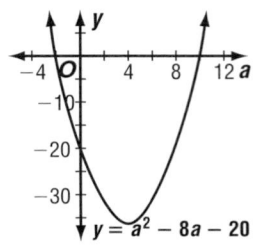

15. $-7, -5$

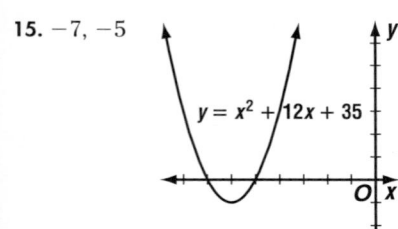

17. $-4, 8$ **19.** $-4, 4$ **21.** $-25, -4$ **23.** $-\frac{4}{5}, 0, \frac{9}{5}$

25. $-\frac{1}{2} \pm \frac{\sqrt{205}}{10}$ **27.** $3 \pm \sqrt{5}$ **29.** $2 \pm \sqrt{11}$ **31.** $-1 \pm i\sqrt{6}$ **33.** $\frac{5}{2} \pm \frac{i\sqrt{11}}{2}$ **35.** $-\frac{7}{6} \pm \frac{\sqrt{73}}{6}$ **37.** $x^2 - x - 42 = 0$ **39.** $2x^2 + 21x + 52 = 0$ **41.** $8x^2 - 22x - 105 = 0$
43. $(-2, 3)$, $x = -2$,   **45.** $f(x) = 5\left(x - \frac{7}{2}\right)^2 - \frac{13}{4}$;
down $\left(\frac{7}{2}, -\frac{13}{4}\right)$, $x = \frac{7}{2}$, up

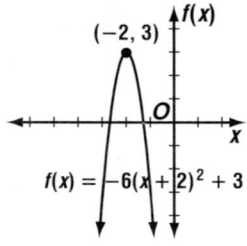 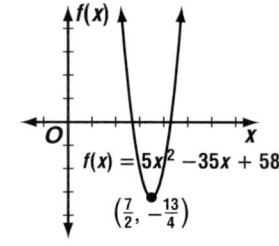

47. $f(x) = -\frac{1}{3}(x - 12)^2 + 48$;   **49.**
$(12, 48)$, $x = 12$, down

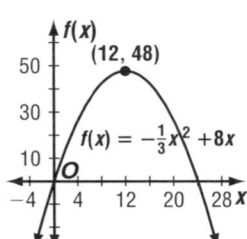 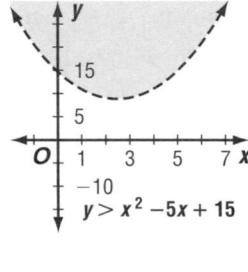

51.   **53.**

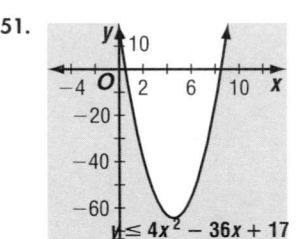 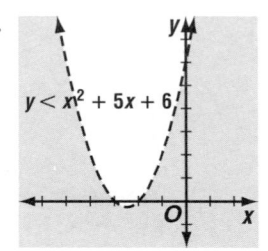

55. $\bar{x} = 157.5$, $\sigma = 23.98$ **57.** $\bar{x} = 315$, $\sigma = 18.47$
59a. 68%   **59b.** 2%   **59c.** 4 students   **59d.** 0.5%
59e. 20 students   **61.** 10 seconds

CHAPTER 7   ANALYZING CONIC SECTIONS

Pages 411–414   Lesson 7–1
5. $\sqrt{2.61}$ units   **7.** $\left(\frac{5}{2}, \frac{9}{4}\right)$ **9.** $AB = 2\sqrt{5}$, $BC = 2\sqrt{10}$,
$AC = 2\sqrt{5}$ **11.** 13 units   **13.** $3\sqrt{17}$ units   **15.** 16 units
17. $\sqrt{65}$ units   **19.** $(12, 5)$ **21.** $(-4, -2)$ **23.** $(0.075, -1)$ **25.** -1 or -13 **27.** about 12.8 or -6.8 **29.** $(-1, 1)$
31. $(-4.3, 2.8)$ **33a.** $y = -\frac{2}{5}x - 2$ **33b.** $\sqrt{29}$ units

33c. $\left(-\frac{5}{2}, -1\right)$ **35.** $\sqrt{65} + 2\sqrt{2} + \sqrt{122} + \sqrt{277}$ units

37a. $2\sqrt{58}$ and $6\sqrt{2}$ units   **37b.** $(9, 5)$ **39a.** 5 units
39b. about 18.97 miles
39c. : ClrHome
       : Disp "X1 ="
       : Input A
       : Disp "Y1 ="
       : Input B
       : Disp "X2 ="
       : Input C
       : Disp "Y2 ="
       : Input D
       : (A + C)/2 → X
       : (B + D)/2 → Y
       : Disp "X VALUE OF MIDPOINT IS"
       : Disp X
       : Disp "Y VALUE OF MIDPOINT IS"
       : Disp Y

39d. $(3.5, -1.5)$ **41a.** about 300 miles   **41b.** about 1.6 hours   **43a.** Sample answer: Draw several lines across the U.S. One should go from the northeast corner to the southwest corner, another should go from the southeast corner to the northwest corner, another should go across the middle of the U.S. from east to west, etc. Find the centers of these lines. Find a point that represents all of the points.   **43d.** Sample answer: Cut out Alaska and Hawaii and place them next to continental U.S. Follow the procedure described in Exercise 43a.   **43f.** Sample

answer: Because certain sections of the U.S. are more populated, the geographical and population centers differ.   **45.** $t - 5 + \frac{12}{t+2}$ **47.** $(11, 2, 24)$
49. 15 inches by 28 inches   **51.** 21

Pages 419–422   Lesson 7–2
5. $y = 2(x - 3)^2 - 12$ **7.** $x = 3\left(y + \frac{5}{6}\right)^2 - 11\frac{1}{12}$
9. $(3, -4)$; $\left(3, -3\frac{3}{4}\right)$; $x = 3$;   **11.** $\left(1\frac{1}{3}, \frac{2}{3}\right)$; $\left(1\frac{1}{3}, \frac{3}{4}\right)$; $x = 1\frac{1}{3}$;
$y = -4\frac{1}{4}$; up; 1 unit $y = \frac{7}{12}$; up; $\frac{1}{3}$ unit

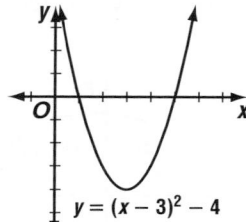
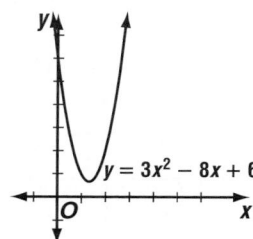

13. $y = -2x^2 + 3$ **15.** $x = -\frac{1}{8}(y + 1)^2 + 5$

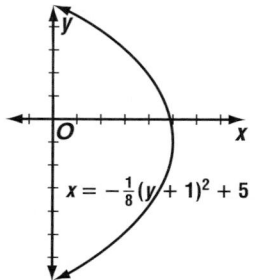

19. $(2, -3)$; $(3, -3)$; $y = -3$;
$x = 1$; right; 4 units

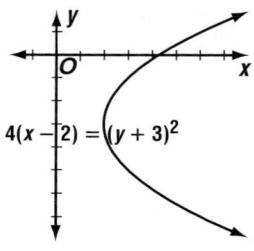

23. $\left(1\frac{1}{4}, -6\frac{7}{8}\right)$; $\left(1\frac{1}{4}, -7\right)$;
$x = 1\frac{1}{4}$; $y = -6\frac{3}{4}$;
down; $\frac{1}{2}$ unit

27. $(123, -18)$; $\left(122\frac{1}{4}, -18\right)$; $y = -18$;
$x = 123\frac{3}{4}$; left;

3 units

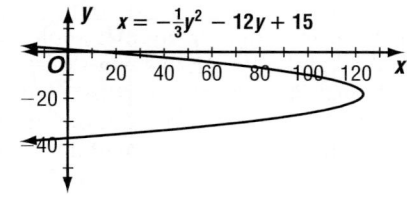

31. $x = 2(y - 2)^2 + 1$
33. $y = \frac{1}{8}(x + 3)^2 - 4$ **35.** $y = -\frac{1}{18}(x - 4)^2 + \frac{3}{2}$

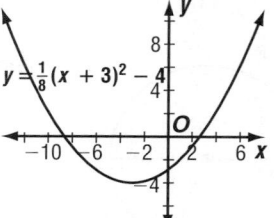
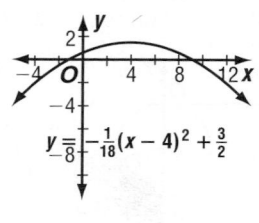

37. $x = \frac{1}{12}(y - 0)^2 + 1$ **39.** $x = -\frac{1}{24}(y - 6)^2 + 8$

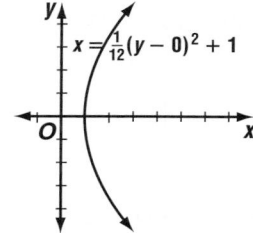
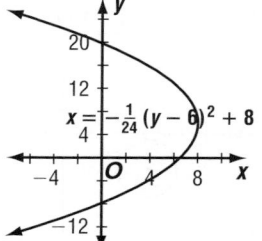

41. $y = \frac{1}{16}(x - 1)^2 + 7$ **43.** $x = \frac{1}{4}(y - 3)^2 + 4$

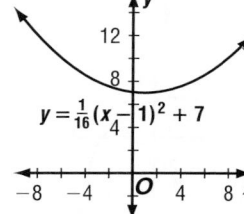
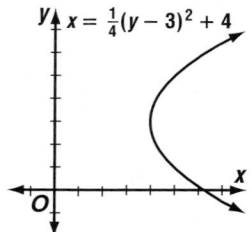

45a. 4 and 12   **45b.** $4 < x < 12$ **45c.** $x < 4$ or $x > 12$
47. 3 units   **49.** $y = -\frac{1}{26,200}x^2 + 6550$ **51.** $2\frac{5}{32}$ inches
53. $-7 \pm \sqrt{61}$ **55.** $201,600$; 2.016×10^5 **57.** 5
59. $d \geq -105$

Pages 426–429   Lesson 7–3
7. $(x + 12)^2 + y^2 = 23$ **9.** $(4, 1)$; 3 units

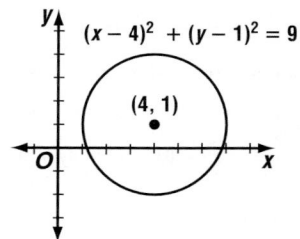

11. $(4, 0)$; $\frac{4}{5}$ units   **13.** $(-4, 3)$; 5 units

15. $(x - 3)^2 + (y + 1)^2 = 9$ **17.** $(x + 1)^2 + (y + 5)^2 = 4$

19. $(x + 8)^2 + (y - 7)^2 = \frac{1}{4}$

21. $(x - 0.5)^2 + (y - 0.7)^2 = 182.25$

23. $(0, -2)$; 2 units **27.** $(3, 0)$; 4 units

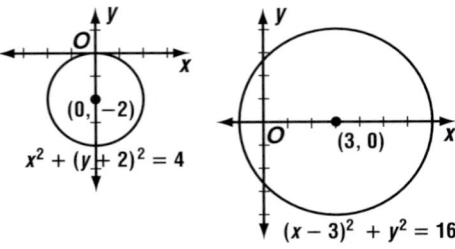

$x^2 + (y + 2)^2 = 4$

$(x - 3)^2 + y^2 = 16$

31. $(-7, -3)$, $2\sqrt{2}$ units **35.** $\left(0, -\frac{9}{2}\right)$, $\sqrt{19}$ units

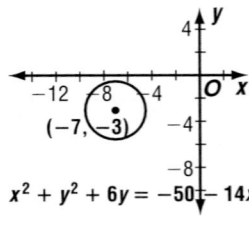

$x^2 + y^2 + 6y = -50 - 14x$

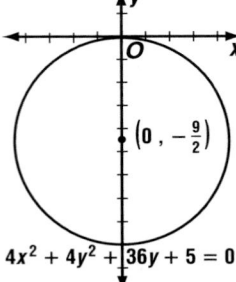

$4x^2 + 4y^2 + 36y + 5 = 0$

39. $(-1, -2)$, $\sqrt{14}$ units

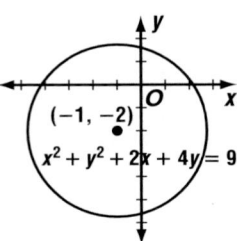

$x^2 + y^2 + 2x + 4y = 9$

41. $(x - 2)^2 + (y + 1)^2 = 4$ **43.** $(x + 3)^2 + (y + 2)^2 = 1$
45. $(x + \sqrt{13})^2 + (y - 42)^2 = 1777$ **47.** $(x + 8)^2 + (y + 7)^2 = 64$ **49.** $(x + 3)^2 + (y + 6)^2 = 9$

51. $y = 0$

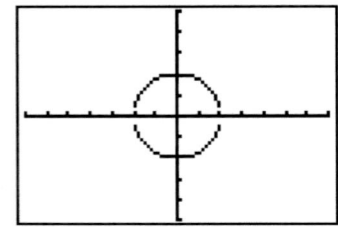

$x^2 + 6x + y^2 + 4y + 9 = 0$

53. $y = \sqrt{4 - x^2}$, $y = -\sqrt{4 - x^2}$

55. circles with a radius of 8 and centers on the graph of $x = 3$ **57a.** $x^2 + y^2 = 841,000,000$

972 *Selected Answers*

57b.

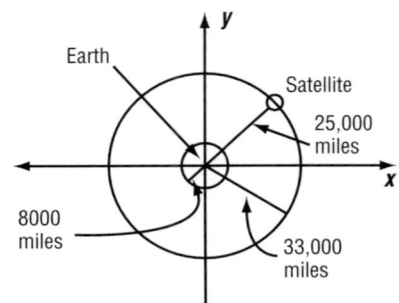

59. $x = \frac{1}{6}y^2$ **61.** $\frac{12 + 3i}{17}$ **63.** 4, -1 **65.** 16, 36 **67.** 120

Page 430 Lesson 7–4A

1.

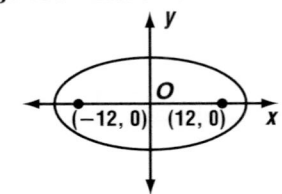

3.

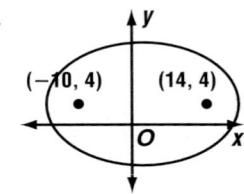

Pages 436–439 Lesson 7–4

7. $(4, -6)$, horizontal **9.** $\frac{(x - 1)^2}{30} + \frac{(y + 1)^2}{5} = 1$

11. $(1, -2)$; $(-3, -2)$, $(5, -2)$; $4\sqrt{5}$; 4 **13.** $(4, -2)$; $(4 \pm 2\sqrt{6}, -2)$; 10; 2

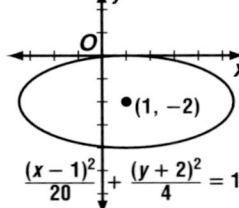

$\frac{(x - 1)^2}{20} + \frac{(y + 2)^2}{4} = 1$

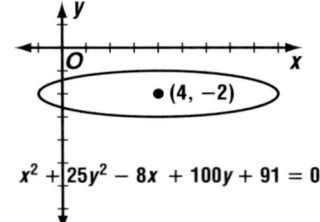

$x^2 + 25y^2 - 8x + 100y + 91 = 0$

15. $\frac{x^2}{36} + \frac{y^2}{100} = 1$ **17.** $\frac{(x - 5)^2}{64} + \frac{(y - 4)^2}{9} = 1$
19. $(0, 0)$; $(0, \pm \sqrt{5})$; $2\sqrt{10}$; $2\sqrt{5}$ **23.** $(0, 0)$; $(\pm 3\sqrt{5}, 0)$; 18; 12

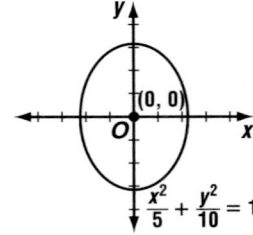

$\frac{x^2}{5} + \frac{y^2}{10} = 1$

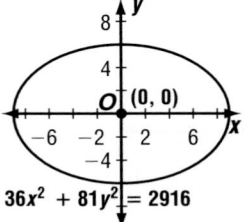

$36x^2 + 81y^2 = 2916$

27. $(-3, 1)$; $(-3, 5)$, $(-3, -3)$; $4\sqrt{6}$; $4\sqrt{2}$ **31.** $(1, -2)$; $(1 \pm \sqrt{7}, -2)$; 8; 6

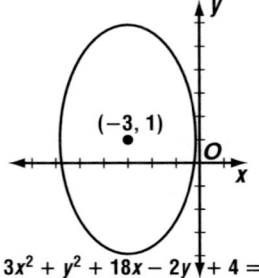

$3x^2 + y^2 + 18x - 2y + 4 = 0$

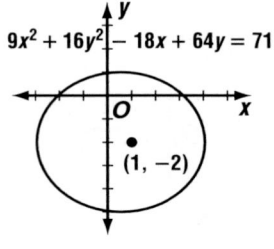

$9x^2 + 16y^2 - 18x + 64y = 71$

33. $\frac{(x-1)^2}{81} + \frac{(y-2)^2}{56} = 1$ **35.** $\frac{x^2}{169} + \frac{y^2}{25} = 1$ **37.** $\frac{(x-2)^2}{4} +$ $\frac{(y-4)^2}{64} = 1$ **39.** As k increases, the length of the major axis increases, but the minor axis length stays the same. **41.** $20\sqrt{3}$ cm or about 34.6 cm **43.** about $\frac{x^2}{2.02 \times 10^{16}} +$ $\frac{y^2}{2.00 \times 10^{16}} = 1$

45a.

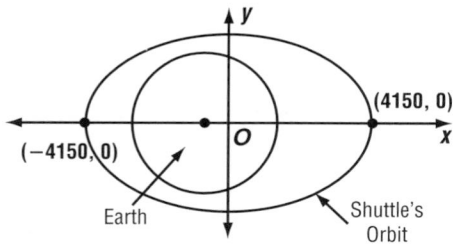

45b. $\frac{x^2}{17,222,500} + \frac{y^2}{17,200,000} = 1$

47.

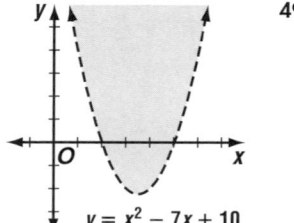

$y = x^2 - 7x + 10$

49. 6.25×10^{-11}

51. $(4.27, -5.11)$ **53.** $19°F$; $16°F$; about $18.5°F$

Page 439 Self Test
1. 13 units **3.** $\left(\frac{3}{2}, 6\right)$

5. $(0, 0)$; $\left(\frac{3}{2}, 0\right)$; $y = 0$; $x = -\frac{3}{2}$; right; 6

7. $(0, 4)$, 7 units

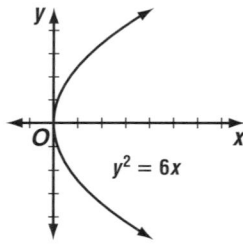

$y^2 = 6x$

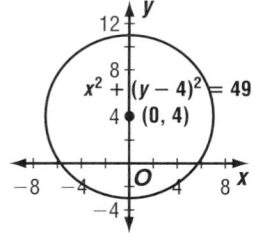

$x^2 + (y-4)^2 = 49$
$(0, 4)$

9. $\frac{(x-1)^2}{5} + \frac{(y-2.5)^2}{10} = 1$

Pages 445–447 Lesson 7–5
5. hyperbola **7.** hyperbola **9.** $\frac{(y+3)^2}{24} - \frac{(x-1)^2}{8} = 1$

11. $(\pm 6, 0)$; $(\pm\sqrt{37}, 0)$; $\pm\frac{1}{6}$ **13.** $(4 \pm 2\sqrt{5}, -2)$; $(4 \pm 3\sqrt{5}, -2)$; $\pm\frac{\sqrt{5}}{2}$

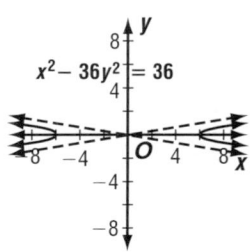

$x^2 - 36y^2 = 36$

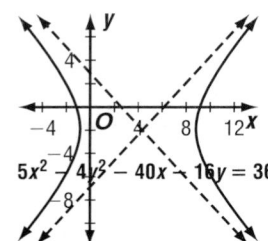

$5x^2 - 4y^2 - 40x - 16y = 36$

15. $\frac{x^2}{1} - \frac{y^2}{16} = 1$ **17.** $\frac{(y+5.5)^2}{6.25} - \frac{x^2}{6} = 1$

19. $(\pm 9, 0)$; $(\pm\sqrt{130}, 0)$; $\pm\frac{7}{9}$ **23.** $(\pm\sqrt{2}, 0)$; $(\pm\sqrt{3}, 0)$; $\pm\frac{\sqrt{2}}{2}$

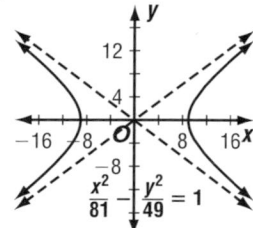

$\frac{x^2}{81} - \frac{y^2}{49} = 1$

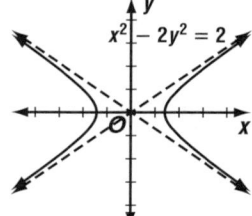

$x^2 - 2y^2 = 2$

27. $(-2, 0)$, $(-2, 8)$; $(-2, -1)$, $(-2, 9)$; $\pm\frac{4}{3}$ **31.** $(-5, 2)$, $(-1, 2)$; $(-3 \pm \sqrt{5}, 2)$; $\pm\frac{1}{2}$

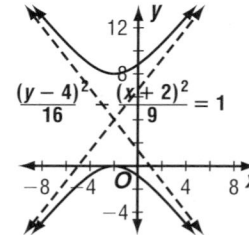

$\frac{(y-4)^2}{16} - \frac{(x+2)^2}{9} = 1$

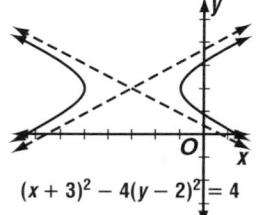

$(x+3)^2 - 4(y-2)^2 = 4$

35. $\frac{(x-2)^2}{49} - \frac{(y+3)^2}{4} = 1$ **37.** $\frac{x^2}{25} - \frac{y^2}{36} = 1$

39.

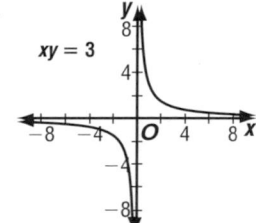

$xy = 3$

41.

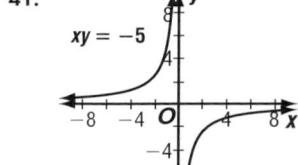

$xy = -5$

43. One branch is always in the first quadrant and the other is always in the third quadrant. As the value of c increases, the vertices move away from the origin.
45. The graph becomes the x- and y-axes.

47.

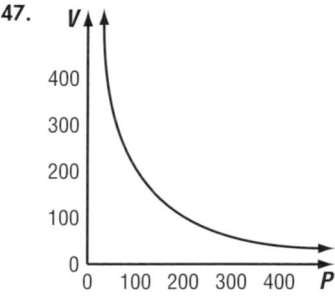

49. $\frac{(x-1)^2}{25} + \frac{(y-4)^2}{9} = 1$ **51.** $-7, \frac{3}{2}$

53.

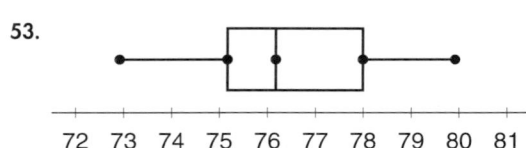

72 73 74 75 76 77 78 79 80 81

55. -12 **57.** $2x + 17y$

SELECTED ANSWERS

Selected Answers

Page 449   Lesson 7–6A

1. parabola

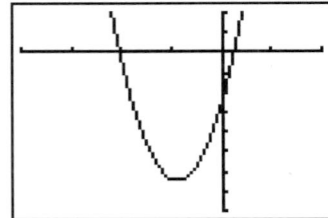

3. ellipse

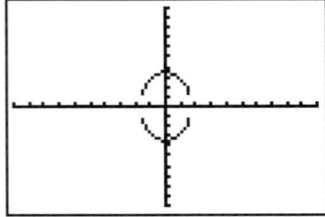

5. ellipse

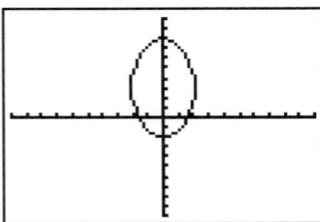

7. ellipse

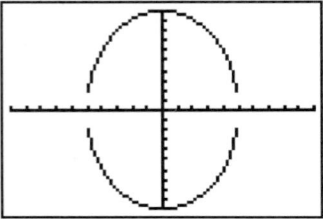

9. parabola

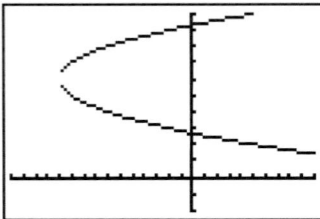

Pages 453–455   Lesson 7–6

5. circle   **7.** hyperbola

9. $y = \left(x + \frac{3}{2}\right)^2 - \frac{5}{4}$; parabola

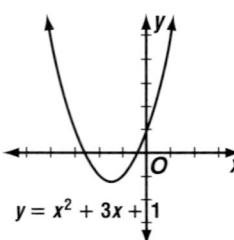

11. $\left(x - \frac{1}{2}\right)^2 + y^2 = \left(\frac{3}{2}\right)^2$; circle

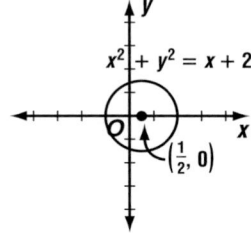

13. $y = -\left(x - \frac{1}{2}\right)^2 + \frac{9}{4}$

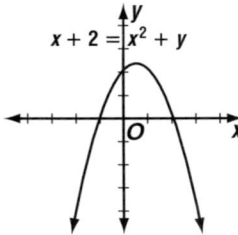

15. $y = \frac{1}{8}x^2$; parabola

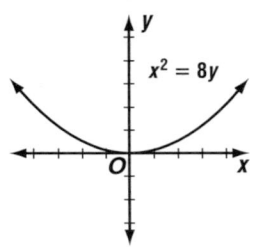

19. $y = (x - 2)^2 - 4$; parabola

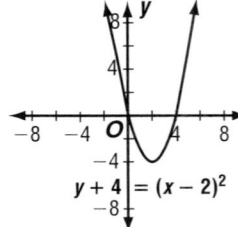

23. $y = -(x + 4)^2 - 7$; parabola

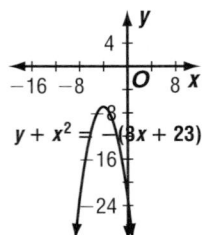

27. $\dfrac{(x - 3)^2}{25} + \dfrac{(y - 1)^2}{9} = 1$; ellipse

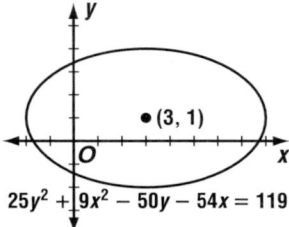

31. $\dfrac{(x - 2)^2}{5} + \dfrac{(y + 1)^2}{6} = 1$; hyperbola

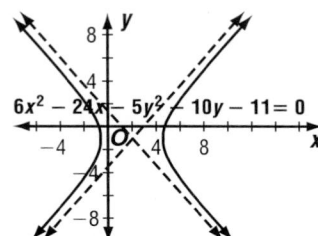

33. isolated point

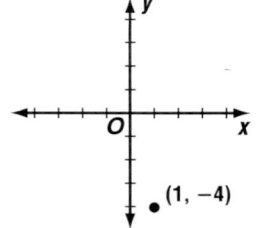

35a. ellipse   **35b.** hyperbola   **35c.** circle   **35d.** parabola
37. $y = \pm\frac{1}{8}x^2$ **41.** quadratic, $4x^2$; linear, $-8x$; constant, -2 **43.** -27 **45.**

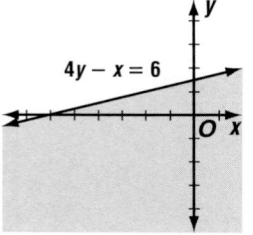

Page 457   Lesson 7–6B
1. The points are equidistant from the focus and the directrix.   3. Each branch of the hyperbola becomes more narrow, and the vertices become farther apart. Each branch of the hyperbola becomes wider, and the vertices become closer.

Page 459   Lesson 7–7A
1. $(\pm 1.68, 3.63)$ 3. $(0, -1), (\pm 1.36, 0.85)$
5. $(\pm 2.98, \pm 0.93)$ 7. $(0, 5), (4, 3)$

Pages 464–467   Lesson 7–7
7. ellipse, hyperbola; $\left(\frac{\pm\sqrt{39}}{2}, \frac{\pm\sqrt{3}}{2}\right)$;   9. parabola, hyperbola; no solution   11. $(\pm 1, 5), (\pm 1, \pm 5)$

13. 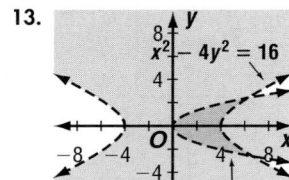   15. $(\pm 3\sqrt{3}, 6)$ 17. no solution

19. $(\pm 8, 0)$ 21. $(\pm 4, \pm 3)$ 23. $(5, \pm 2), (-1, \pm 4)$
25. $\left(\sqrt{5}, \sqrt{5}\right), \left(-\sqrt{5}, -\sqrt{5}\right)$ 27. $\left(-1 + \sqrt{17}, 1 + \sqrt{17}\right),$ $\left(-1 - \sqrt{17}, 1 - \sqrt{17}\right)$ 29. no solution
31. $\left(\pm\sqrt{6}, \pm\sqrt{5}\right)$

33. 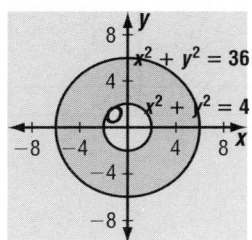   35.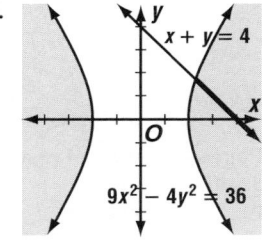

37. 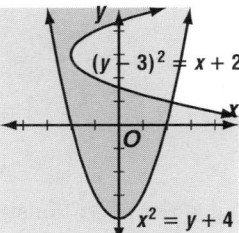   39. $y = -x - 1,$ $x = (y - 1)^2 - 4$

41. $y = -2x^2, x^2 + y^2 = 5$ 43. $x^2 + y^2 \geq 25, x^2 + y^2 \leq 100$
45. impossible   47. $x^2 + y^2 = 36, \frac{(x + 2)^2}{16} - \frac{y^2}{4} = 1$
49. $x^2 + y^2 = 81, \frac{x^2}{4} + \frac{y^2}{100} = 1$ 51a. $(-2, -2), \left(0, \sqrt{2}\right)$
51b. $(0, 1)$ 53. $(40, 30)$ 55. 1.3 57. $5b - 4 + 7a$
59. $(2, 3)$

61a.
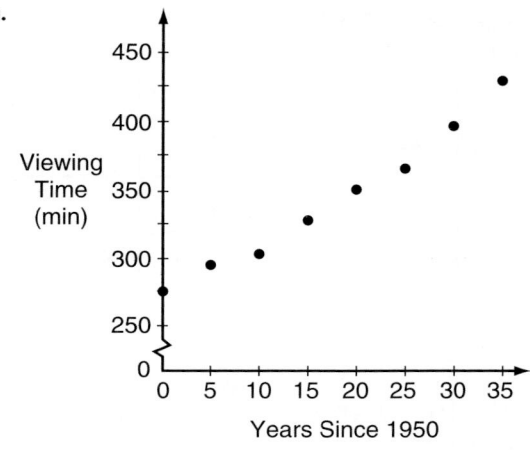

Sample answer: $y = 4.4x - 8305$ 61b. Sample answer: 8 h 15 min   63. $-\frac{19}{2}$

Page 469   Chapter 7   Highlights
1. true   3. true   5. true   7. false; A parabola is the set of all points that are the same distance from a given point called the focus and a given line called the directrix.
9. false; The conjugate axis is the line segment perpendicular to the transverse axis.   11. false; A hyperbola is the set of all points in a plane such that the absolute value of the difference of the distances from any point on the hyperbola to two given points is constant.
13. false; The midpoint formula is given by the following: $\left(\frac{x_1 + x_2}{2}, \frac{y_1 + y_2}{2}\right)$.   15. true

Pages 470–472   Chapter 7   Study Guide and Assessment
17. $\sqrt{290}$ 19. $\sqrt{61}$ 21. $\left(\frac{5}{2}, 4\right)$ 23. $(4a, -4b)$
25. $(1, 1); (1, 4); x = 1;$ 27. $(4, -2); (4, -4);$
$y = -2;$ up; 12 units $x = 4; y = 0;$ down; 8 units

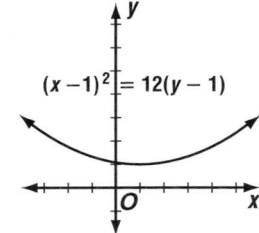   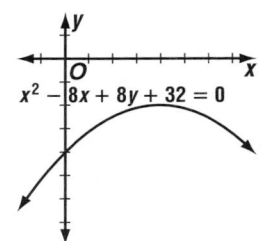

29. $(0, 0)$; 13 units   31. $(3, -8)$; 15 units

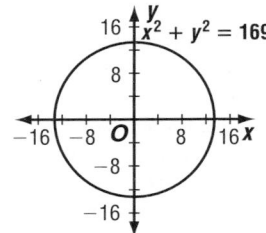   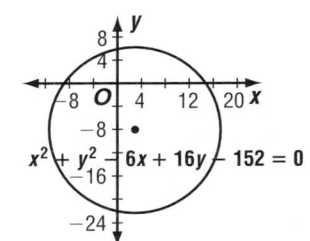

SELECTED ANSWERS

Selected Answers

33. $(0, 0)$; $(0, \pm\sqrt{33})$; 14; 8   **35.** $(0, 0)$; $(\pm\sqrt{39}, 0)$; 16; 10

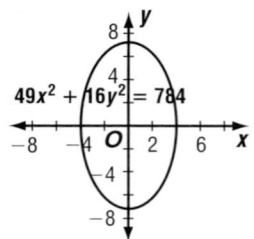

$49x^2 + 16y^2 = 784$

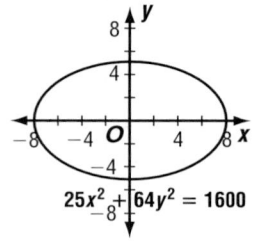

$25x^2 + 64y^2 = 1600$

37. $(0, \pm2)$; $(0, \pm\sqrt{13})$; $\pm\frac{2}{3}$ **39.** $(0, \pm4)$; $(0, \pm5)$; $\pm\frac{4}{3}$

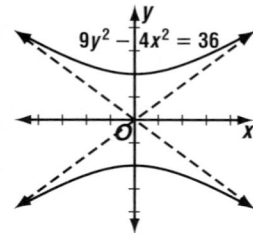

$9y^2 - 4x^2 = 36$

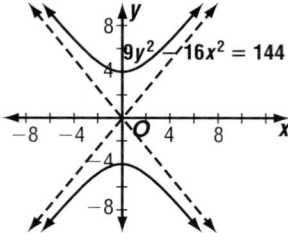

$9y^2 - 16x^2 = 144$

41. ellipse   **43.** parabola   **45.** circle   **47.** $(4, 1)$
49. 75 miles   **51.** $(x - 9)^2 + (y - 23)^2 = 2025$

CHAPTER 8   EXPLORING POLYNOMIAL FUNCTIONS

Pages 482-484   Lesson 8-1
7. 3   **9.** 5   **11.** quintic, 5, 5   **13.** quartic, 4, 4   **15.** a
17. c   **19.** 12, -12 **21.** $2x + 2h - 3$ **23.** 15.625 units
25. odd, 2   **27.** 21, -4 **29.** 37, -13 **31.** $-28, 37$ **33.** $x + h + 2$ **35.** $5x^2 + 10xh + 5h^2$ **37.** $3x^2 + 6xh + 3h^2 + 7$
39. $4x^2 + 20$ **41.** $x^3 + \frac{x^2}{4} - 8$ **43.** $f(x) = x^4 - 9x^3 + 27x^2 - 31x + 12$

45a.

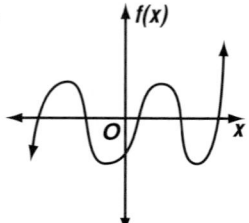

45b.

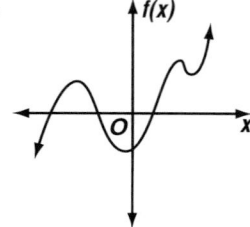

45c.

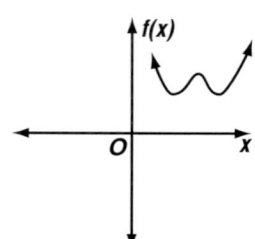

47. $3a^2 - 2a + 10$

49. $4x + 30$ **51.** $2x^2 + 18x + 60$ **53.** There is no real number x that can make the equation $0 = x^4 + x^2 + 1$ true.   **55.** 109 lumens   **57.** Approximately $(13.6, 21)$ or $(13.6, -21)$; that is, the epicenter could have been 13.6 miles east and 21 miles north or south of the first station.   **59.** $-20, 20$ **61.** 1.6×10^6; 1.7×10^6
63. $\begin{bmatrix} -6 & -12 \\ 9 & 7 \end{bmatrix}$ **65.** $(4, -28)$

Pages 489–490   Lesson 8-2
7. $(x^4 - 16) = (x^3 + 2x^2 + 4x + 8)(x - 2) + 0$; yes
9. $-4, -1$ **11.** $x - 3, x - 1$ **13.** $x - 1$; $x^2 + 2x + 3$
15. $x + 1, x + 3$ **17.** $(x^3 - 2x^2 - 5x + 6) = (x^2 + x - 2)(x - 3) + 0$; yes   **19.** $(x^3 + 27) = (x^2 - 3x + 9)(x + 3) + 0$; yes   **21.** $(6x^3 + 9x^2 - 6x + 2) = (6x^2 - 3x)(x + 2) + 2$; no   **23.** $(4x^4 - 2x^2 + x + 1) = (4x^3 + 4x^2 + 2x + 3)(x - 1) + 4$; no.   **25.** $-2, 16$ **27.** $-23, -2$ **29.** 62, 11   **31.** $x - 1, x + 2$ **33.** $2x + 1, x - 4$ **35.** $x - 2, x^2 + 2x + 4$ **37.** $2x - 3, 2x + 3, 4x^2 + 9$ **39.** $(x + 4)(x + 1)^3$
41. 8   **43.** 1, 4   **45a.** 7.5, 8, 7.5   **45b.** 0; The elevator is stopping or is stopped.   **47.** \$65,892   **49.** yes
51. $2x^2 - 3x - 2$ **53.** $(1, 2)$

Page 492   Lesson 8–3A
1. $[-10, 10]$ by $[-5, 25]$, 3   **3.** $[-15, 10]$ by $[-175, 75]$, 2

5. $-0.41, 2.41$

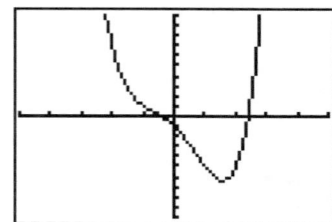

7. -0.78

9. $-2.38, -0.45, 0.11$

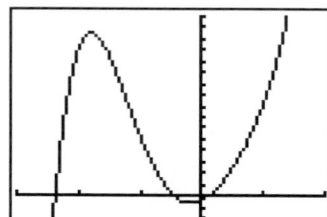

Pages 497–499   Lesson 8–3
5. -0.8
7.

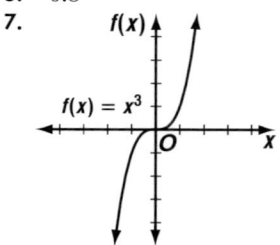

$f(x) = x^3$

9.

$f(x) = -3x^3 + 20x^2 - 36x + 16$

11. odd; 1 min, 1 max   **13.** even; 0 min, 1 max   **15.** -1.3
17. 1.4   **19.** $-2.6, 1.1$ **21.** $-0.3, 1.4, 4.3$

23.
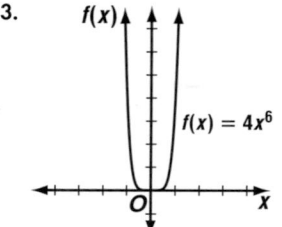
$f(x) = 4x^6$

25.
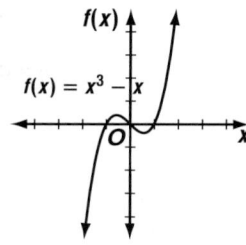
$f(x) = x^3 - x$

27.
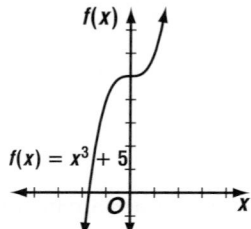
$f(x) = x^3 + 5$

29.
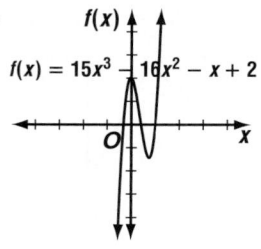
$f(x) = 15x^3 - 16x^2 - x + 2$

31.
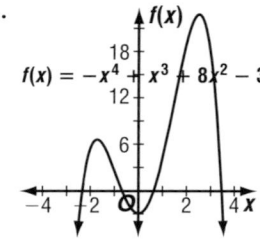
$f(x) = -x^4 + x^3 + 8x^2 - 3$

33. $-3.6, -1.6, -0.7, 0.6, 1.3$
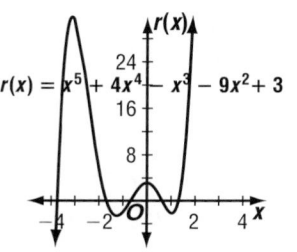
$r(x) = x^5 + 4x^4 - x^3 - 9x^2 + 3$

35. $-0.7, 1.0, 2.7$
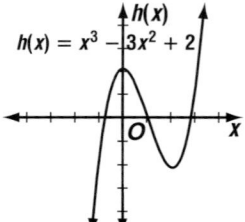
$h(x) = x^3 - 3x^2 + 2$

37. $-1.9, -0.1$
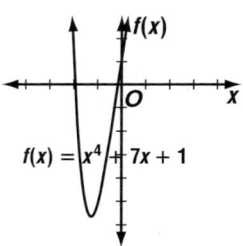
$f(x) = x^4 + 7x + 1$

39a.
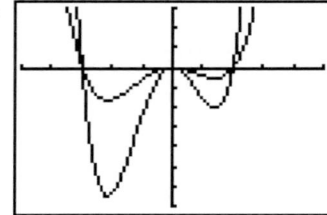

39b. The second graph is a vertical stretch of the first.
41. Sample answer: The ends of an even-degree function both point up or down and the ends of an odd-degree function point in opposite directions.   **43.** radius = 4.2 m, height = 21.2 m   **45.** 12 cm^3 **47.** $(3, -11), x = 3$
49. $\pm i\sqrt{6}$

51.
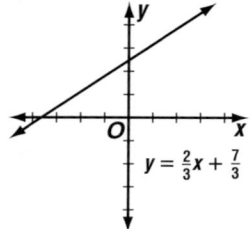
$y = \frac{2}{3}x + \frac{7}{3}$

Page 501   Lesson 8–3B
1. Sample answer: [0, 15], Xscl=3; [0, 11,000], Yscl=1000
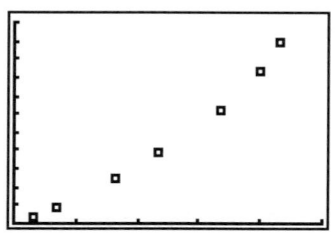

Pages 506–508   Lesson 8–4
7. $f(-x) = 6x^4 + 3x^3 + 5x^2 + x + 2$ **9.** 2 or 0; 1; 0 or 2
11. $4, 1 + i, 1 - i$ **13.** $5i, -5i, -7$ **15.** $f(x) = x^3 - 2x^2 - 19x + 20$ **17.** $\ell = 8$ in., $w = 5$ in., $h = 3$ in.   **19.** 1; 3 or 1; 2 or 0   **21.** 1; 1; 2   **23.** 3 or 1; 1; 10 or 12   **25.** 5, 3, or 1; 5, 3, or 1; 0, 2, 4, 6, or 8   **27.** 2, $1 + i, 1 - i$
29. $2i, -2i, \frac{i}{2}, -\frac{i}{2}$ **31.** $\frac{1}{2}, 4 + 5i, 4 - 5i$
33. $3 - 2i, 3 + 2i, -1, 1$ **35.** $y = x^3 - 2x^2 - 5x + 6$
37. $y = x^4 + 7x^2 - 144$ **39.** $y = x^5 - x^4 + 13x^3 - 13x^2 + 36x - 36$ **41.** 1

43a. $-22.3, -4.2, 0, 3.2$
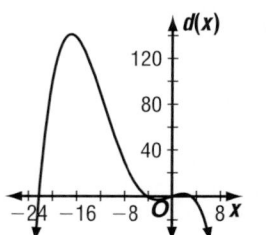
43b. 3.2

45.
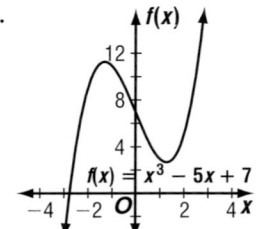
$f(x) = x^3 - 5x + 7$
47. $x^2 + 2x - 15$

49.
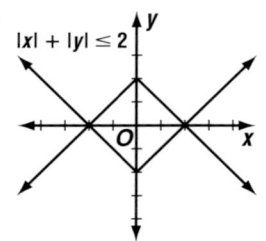
$|x| + |y| \le 2$
51. $\frac{19}{11}$

Page 508   Self Test
1. $4a^6 - 3a^4 + 2a^2 - 5$ **3.** $x + 6, x - 2$

SELECTED ANSWERS

Selected Answers

5.

$$g(x) = x^5 - 5$$

7. 2 or 0; 1; 2 or 0   **9.** even, 4

5. 4, staircase out

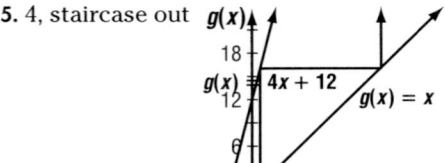

$$g(x) = 4x + 12$$ $$g(x) = x$$

7. -2, spiral out   **9.** $\frac{1}{4}$, staircase in

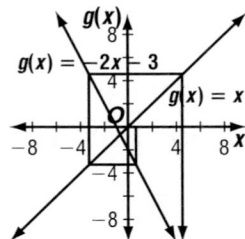

$$g(x) = -2x - 3$$ $$g(x) = x$$

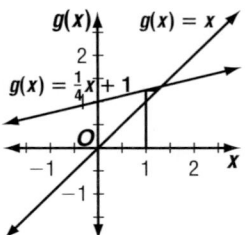

$$g(x) = x$$ $$g(x) = \frac{1}{4}x + 1$$

11. Sample answer: Functions whose slopes are positive form staircase paths, functions whose slopes are negative form spiral paths.

Pages 512–514   Lesson 8–5

7. $\pm 1, \pm 2, \pm 3, \pm 6$ **9.** $-2, -4, 7$ **11.** $0, 3$ **13.** $3,$ $\frac{2}{3}, -\frac{2}{3}, \frac{-3 \pm \sqrt{13}}{2}$ **15.** 12 cm by 8 cm by 4 cm   **17.** $\pm 1, \pm 2,$ $\pm 5, \pm 10$ **19.** $\pm 1, \pm \frac{1}{3}, \pm 3$ **21.** $\pm 1, \pm \frac{1}{3}, \pm \frac{1}{9}, \pm 3, \pm 9, \pm 27$

23. $-6, -5, 10$ **25.** $3, 3, -\frac{1}{2}$ **27.** $-2, -4$ **29.** $2, -2, 3,$ -3 **31.** $-7, 1, 3$ **33.** $-\frac{1}{2}, \frac{1}{3}, \frac{1}{2}, \frac{3}{4}$ **35.** $-2, \frac{4}{3}, \frac{-3 \pm i}{2}$

37. $-1, -2, 5, i, -i$ **39a.** \$59   **39b.** They are the same.

41a. 16 regions   **41b.** 8 points

43. $x = \frac{1}{7}y^2$ **45.** $T = \frac{2\pi \sqrt{mrF_c}}{F_c}$ **47.** $(3, -1)$ **49.** 4 feet

Pages 517–519   Lesson 8–6

5. $x(2x^2 + 7x - 8)$ **7.** $-y(y^4 - y^2 + 100)$ **9.** $(x - 9)(x^2 + 9x + 81)$ **11.** $(a^4)^2 + 10(a^4) - 16 = 0$ **13.** $0, -4, -3$ **15.** $3.8, -7, 0$ **17.** $(x^4)^2 + 10(x^4) + 13.2 = 0$ **19.** $84(n^2)^2 - 62(n^2) = 0$ **21.** impossible

23. $-2, 0, 5$ **25.** $11, \frac{-11 \pm 11i\sqrt{3}}{2}$ **27.** 400   **29.** 125, 64   **31.** $0, 1.4, -1.4$ **33.** $3.2, -4.7, 0$ **35.** $x^3 + x^2 - 6x = 0$ **37.** $a = 0.885; b = 3.185$ **39a.** 317.29 miles   **39b.** 119 pounds   **41.** 5 or -1 **43.** 4 seconds   **45.** $(-6, -8)$

Pages 523–525   Lesson 8–7

9. $5, 5$ **11.** $8x - 4, 8x - 1$ **13.** 9   **15.** $x^2 + 2$ **17.** $6, 12, 24, 48$ **19.** $-3, -3$ **21.** $16, 22$ **23.** $9, 12$ **25.** $x + 11, x + 11$ **27.** $x^2 - 2, x^2 - 4x + 4$ **29.** $x^3 + 1,$ $x^3 + 3x^2 + 3x + 1$ **31.** 7   **33.** 8   **35.** -9 **37.** $4x^2$ **39.** $16x^2 - 32x + 16$ **41.** $6, 18, 54, 162$ **43.** $0.2, 0.4, 1.2,$ 4.8 **45.** $25, 104, 425, 1716$ **47.** $f \circ g$ does not exist; $g \circ f =$ $\{(3, 6), (4, 4), (6, 6), (7, 8)\}$ **49.** 244   **51a.** $r(x) = x - 5,$ $p(x) = x - 0.25x$ **51b.** \$23.50; taking the discount first   **51c.** \$24.75; taking the rebate first   **53.** $(x^3)^2 + 3(x^3) - 10 = 0$ **55.** $11.09'; 0.097'$

57. $\begin{bmatrix} 10 & 17 & -4 & -5 \\ -28 & 3 & 48 & -9 \\ -13 & 1 & 22 & -4 \end{bmatrix}$ **59.** b   **61.** $9a + 10b$

Page 527   Lesson 8–7B

1. $1, 5, 25$ **3.** $4.6, 1.16, 2.54$

Pages 532–534   Lesson 8–8

7. $\{(2, 3), (2, 4)\}$, no

9. $y^{-1} = \frac{x}{7}$ **11.** $f^{-1}(x) = x + 6$

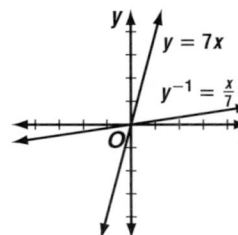

$$y = 7x$$ $$y^{-1} = \frac{x}{7}$$

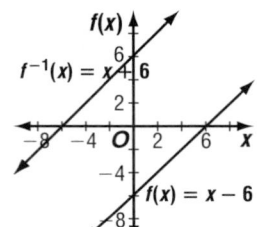

$$f^{-1}(x) = x + 6$$ $$f(x) = x - 6$$

13. no   **15.** $\{(4, 2), (1, -3), (8, 2)\}$, yes   **17.** $\{(3, 1), (-1, 1), (-3, 1), (1, 1)\}$, yes

19. $x = 6$ **23.** $f^{-1}(x) = -x$

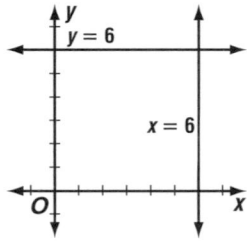

$$y = 6$$ $$x = 6$$

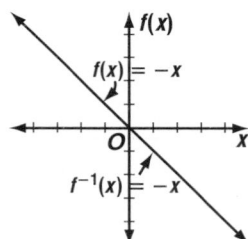

$$f(x) = -x$$ $$f^{-1}(x) = -x$$

27. $f^{-1}(x) = \frac{3x + 1}{2}$ **29.** $y^{-1} = \pm\sqrt{x} + 4$

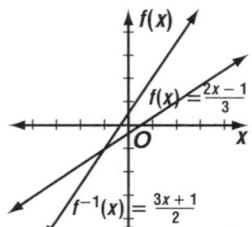

$$f(x) = \frac{2x - 1}{3}$$ $$f^{-1}(x) = \frac{3x + 1}{2}$$

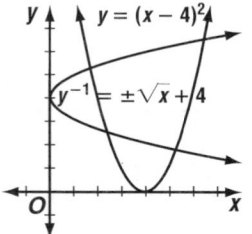

$$y = (x - 4)^2$$ $$y^{-1} = \pm\sqrt{x} + 4$$

31. yes **33.** no
35. yes   **37.** no

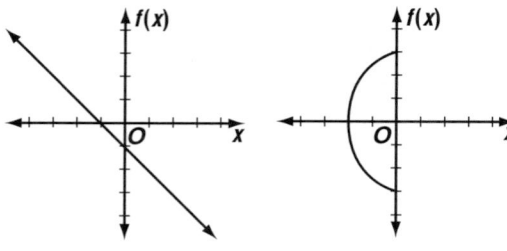

39. Sample answer: $f(x) = x$ and $f^{-1}(x) = x$ or $f(x) = -x$ and $f^{-1}(x) = -x$. **41.** 12 **43.** 288°K **45.** 300 ft, 2.5 seconds **47.** $\begin{bmatrix} 5 & -3 \\ 7 & 3 \end{bmatrix}$ **49.** D = {−11, 0, 1, 3, 9, 12}, R = {−6, −4, −3, 0, 1, 7, 8}; no

Page 537–538   Lesson 8–8B

5.
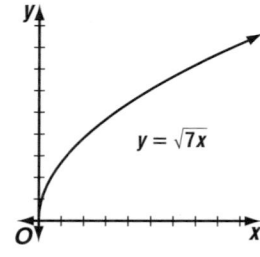
$y = \sqrt{7x}$
D: $x \geq 0$; R: $y \geq 0$

9.
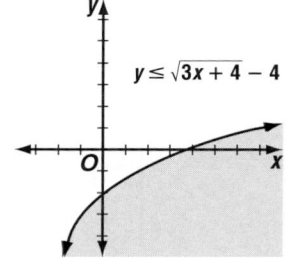
$y \leq \sqrt{3x + 4} - 4$

13.
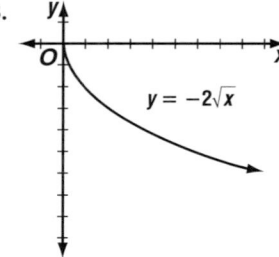
$y = -2\sqrt{x}$
D: $x \geq 0$; R: $y \leq 0$

17.
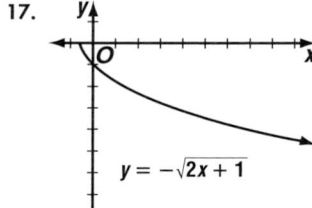
$y = -\sqrt{2x + 1}$
D: $x \geq -\frac{1}{2}$; R: $y \leq 0$

21.
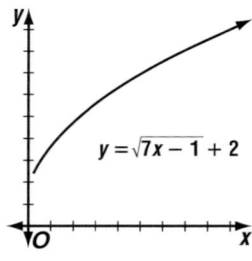
$y = \sqrt{7x - 1} + 2$
D: $x \geq \frac{1}{7}$; R: $y \geq 2$

25.
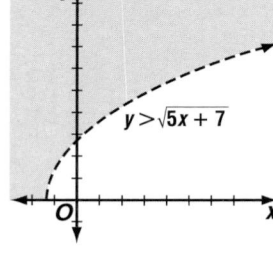
$y > \sqrt{5x + 7}$

29a.

If:	$h > 0$	$h < 0$	$k > 0$	$k < 0$
$a > 0$	h is minimum value in domain.	$-h$ is minimum value in domain.	k is minimum value in range.	
$a < 0$			k is maximum value in range.	

29b. $y = -2\sqrt{x}$ is a little wider than $y = \sqrt{x}$, and falls downward to the right. $y = \sqrt{x - 4}$ begins at (4, 0). $y = \sqrt{x + 3}$ begins at (0, 3). $y = 3\sqrt{x - 1} + 5$ is wider than $y = \sqrt{x}$, and begins at (1, 5).

Page 539   Chapter 8   Highlights
1. h **3.** a **5.** g **7.** f

Pages 540–542   Chapter 8   Study Guide and Assessment
9. $-6, x + h - 2$ **11.** $-21, 6x + 6h + 3$ **13.** $20, x^2 + 2xh + h^2 - x - h$ **15.** $4, -1$ **17.** $20, -20$ **19.** $x + 2, x + 2$ **21.** $x - 1, x - 2$

25. -2.0

27. $-1.9, 0.3, 1.4$

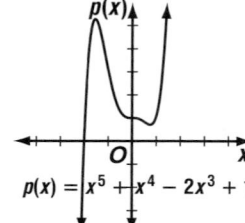
$p(x) = x^5 + x^4 - 2x^3 + 1$

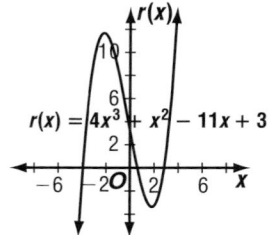
$r(x) = 4x^3 + x^2 - 11x + 3$

29. 3 or 1; 1; 2 or 0 **31.** 0; 0 or 2; 4 or 2 **33.** 2 or 0; 2 or 0; 4, 2, or 0 **35.** $-1, -1$ **37.** $-3, 5, \frac{1}{2}$ **39.** $\frac{5}{3}, -3, 0$ **41.** $4, -2 \pm 2i\sqrt{3}$ **43.** $2, -2$ **45.** $6x + 1, 6x + 7$ **47.** $-2x^2 - 1, 4x^2 - 4x + 2$ **49.** $x^3 - 2, x^3 - 6x^2 + 12x - 8$
53. $g^{-1}(x) = 3x - 6$ **55.** $y^{-1} = \pm\sqrt{x}$

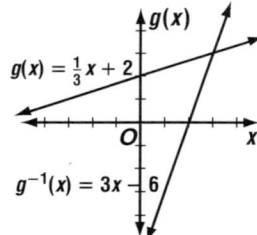
$g(x) = \frac{1}{3}x + 2$
$g^{-1}(x) = 3x - 6$

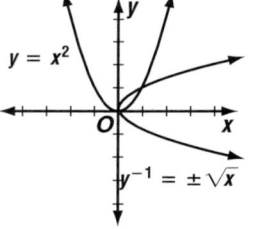
$y = x^2$
$y^{-1} = \pm\sqrt{x}$

57a. $A = 1000(1 + r)^6 + 1000(1 + r)^5 + 1000(1 + r)^4 + 1200(1 + r)^3 + 1200(1 + r)^2 + 2000(1 + r)$ **57b.** $8916.76
59. $7.50

CHAPTER 9   EXPLORING RATIONAL EXPRESSIONS

Page 549   Lesson 9–1A
1. $x = 4$

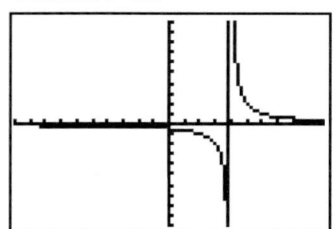

5. $x = 4$

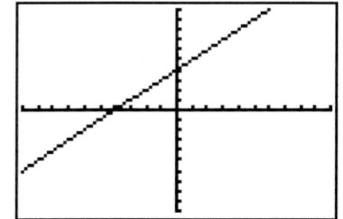

9. $y = 4$

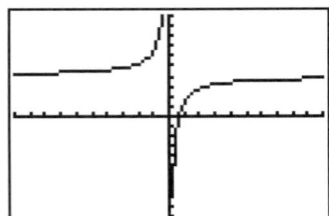

Pages 553–555   Lesson 9–1

5. $x = 1, x = -3, y = 0$ **7.**

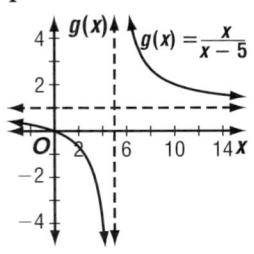

9.

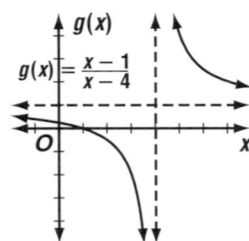

11.

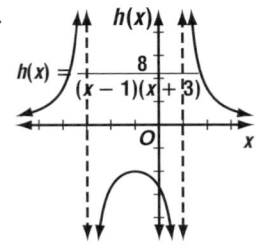

13. $x = 4, y = 1$ **15.** $x = 1, x = -5, y = 0$
17. $x = 3, y = 1$

19.

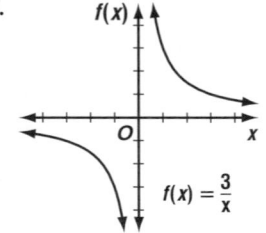

21.

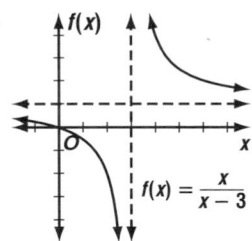

23.

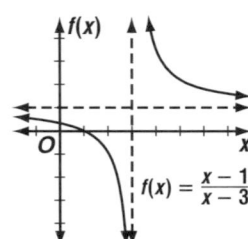

25.

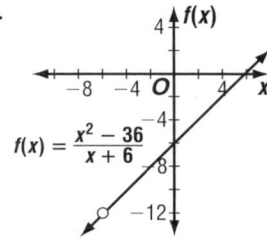

27.

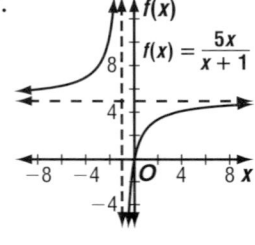

29.

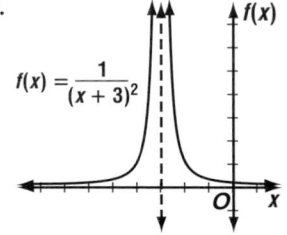

31.

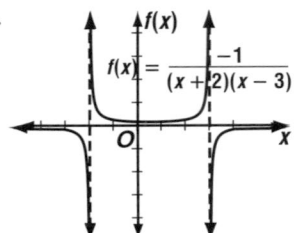

33.

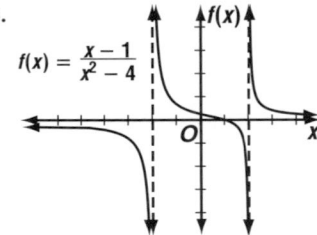

35a. 100 mg   **35b.** The graph has a vertical asymptote at
$y = -12$ and a horizontal asymptote at $C = 1$.

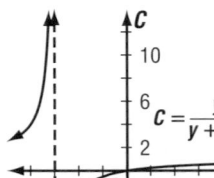

37. no   **39.** $\frac{y^2}{34} - \frac{x^2}{6} = 1$

41. 0; 1 R, Q; 5   **43.** $x:4; y:-6$

Pages 559–561   Lesson 9–2

5. inverse, -5 **7.** direct, $\frac{1}{3}$ **9.** $y = 5x, 60$ **11a.** $I = \frac{k}{d^2}$

11b.

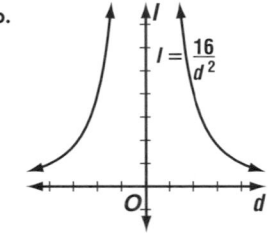

11c. The sound will be
heard $\frac{1}{4}$ as intensely.

13. direct, $-\frac{1}{7}$ **15.** inverse, 1   **17.** direct, $-\frac{4}{3}$
19. $rt = -54, 4.91$ **21.** $xy = 50, 1.25$ **23.** 38 meters
25. $\frac{22}{5}$ **27.** 4   **29a.** directly   **29b.** 2π **31a.** $P = 0.43d$
31b. 25.8 psi   **31c.** about 150 ft

31d.

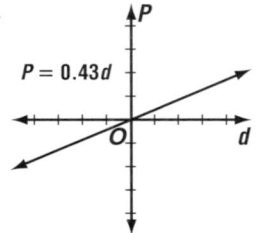

33a. like one third of a month

33b. like 5 weeks   **33c.** like 1 hour   **35.** 1500 BTU/h
37. x, x **39.** $\frac{(x+2)^2}{16} + \frac{(y-3)^2}{36} = 1$ **41.** 175 passengers

Pages 565–568   Lesson 9–3

5. $6x, \dfrac{5y}{2x}$ **7.** $c+5, \dfrac{1}{2}$ **9.** $\dfrac{3a^2}{2bc}$ **11.** 3   **13.** $\dfrac{4}{3}$ **15.** $\dfrac{2y(y-2)}{3(y+2)}$

17. $\dfrac{9x}{4y^4}$ **19.** $\dfrac{5}{x+1}$ **21.** y **23.** $\dfrac{3c}{20b}$ **25.** $\dfrac{xz}{8y}$ **27.** $\dfrac{10x}{3y^2}$ **29.** $\dfrac{b^3}{xy^2}$

31. $\dfrac{4}{5xyz^2}$ **33.** $\dfrac{6}{5(x-1)}$ **35.** $\dfrac{2x^2}{3(x+1)^2}$ **37.** $\dfrac{5(x-3)}{2(x+1)}$

39. $\dfrac{3(m+n)}{m^2+n^2}$ **41.** $\dfrac{4}{3}$ **43.** $4x^2+6x+2$ square feet

45. $21\frac{1}{3}$ m^3 **47.** $x^2+2xh+h^2-\frac{1}{2}x+\frac{1}{2}h$ **49a.** 8.8

49b. 5.9   **49c.** 6.7   **49d.** Fitright Shoes   **51.** -8

Page 568   Self Test

1. $x=4, y=0$ **3.**

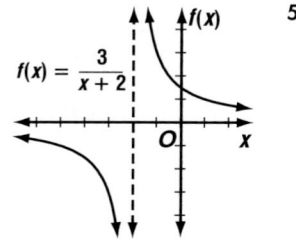

5. 22

7. $2560   **9.** $\dfrac{7}{2}$

Pages 573–575   Lesson 9–4

5. $70x^2y^2$ **7.** $\dfrac{6+8b}{ab}$ **9.** $\dfrac{2x+3}{x+1}$ **11.** $\dfrac{5x+16}{(x+2)^2}$ **13.** $\dfrac{q+p}{pq}$

15. $4w-12$ **17.** $x^2(x-y)(x+y)$ **19.** $2(x-5)(x+3)$

21. $\dfrac{6x+7}{x+2}$ **23.** $\dfrac{y+3}{y-4}$ **25.** $\dfrac{y^2-6y+10}{y-3}$ **27.** $\dfrac{x(x-9)}{(x+3)(x-3)}$

29. $\dfrac{3m-10}{(m-5)(m+4)}$ **31.** $\dfrac{-4x^2-5x-2}{(x+1)^2}$ **33.** $\dfrac{-12x+21xy-4y}{6x^2y}$

35. $\dfrac{4x^2-2x-14}{x^2-4}$ **37.** $\dfrac{2x^2+x-4}{(x-1)(x-2)}$ **39.** $\dfrac{1}{x+1}$

41. Sample answer: 2, 4; LCM = 4, GCF = 2; $4\times2=8$

43a.

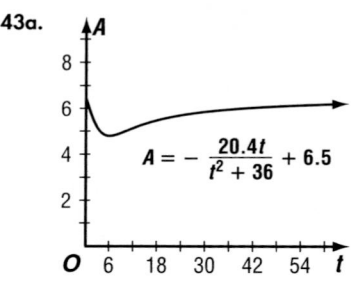

43b. 5.8

43c. It quickly drops below normal and then slowly rises back to normal.   **43d.** after 6 minutes   **45.** $-\dfrac{1}{2}, \dfrac{3}{2}, \dfrac{7}{2}$

47. $y=-\frac{1}{6}(x-11)^2+\frac{1}{2}$ **49.** $-1, 3$

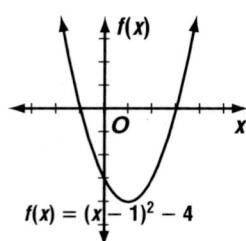

51. $x=24y+18$

Pages 581–583   Lesson 9–5

7. $(m-4)(m-2); 4, 2; 6$ **9.** $\dfrac{21}{5}$ **11.** $x>5$ **13.** 4; none; $\dfrac{1}{2}$

15. $m^2; 0; \dfrac{3}{2}$ **17.** $(a-6)(a-2); 6, 2; 6.94, 1.73$ **19.** 2

21. $y\le-6$ **23.** $-12, 1$ **25.** $-6, \dfrac{3}{2}$ **27.** -1 **29.** $\varnothing$

31. $\dfrac{b}{bc+1}$ **33a.** $\dfrac{x+11}{x+20}\ge 0.70$ **33b.** $x\ge 10$

33c. Selena needs at least 10 consecutive free throws.

35. 56.67 mph   **37.** 32   **39.** 0; 1; 2   **41.** $\sqrt{4.58}$ units

43. about 7 in. $\times$ 7 in. $\times$ 7 in.

Page 585   Chapter 9   Highlights

1. false, point discontinuity   **3.** true   **5.** false, asymptote

7. false, $x=-2$

Pages 586–588   Chapter 9   Study Guide and Assessment

9. $x=2; y=0$

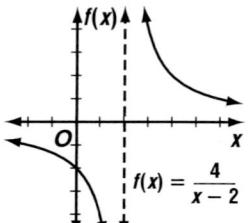

11. $x=0; y=0$

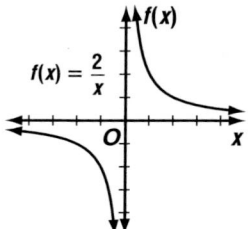

13. $x=3, x=-1; y=0$

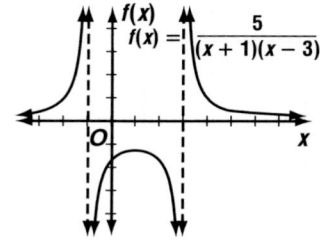

15. $xy=22.5; -37.5$ **17.** $y=\dfrac{9}{14}x; 98$

19. $y=\dfrac{25}{8}xz; 0.192$ **21.** $y-2$ **23.** $\dfrac{a}{5x^2}$ **25.** $\dfrac{x-2}{x+2}$

27. $\dfrac{2}{n-3}$ **29.** $\dfrac{28a-27b}{12ab}$ **31.** $\dfrac{7}{5(x+1)}$ **33.** $\dfrac{18}{y-2}$

35. $\dfrac{3(3m^2-14m+27)}{(m+3)(m-3)^2}$ **37.** 31   **39.** 0   **41a.** $I=\dfrac{6}{R}$ **41b.** 6

43. 42 lb/in^2

CHAPTER 10   EXPLORING EXPONENTIAL AND LOGARITHMIC FUNCTIONS

Page 595   Lesson 10–1A

1.

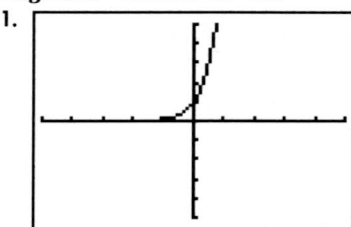

3.

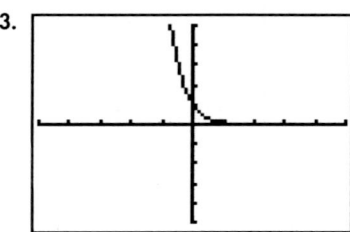

5.

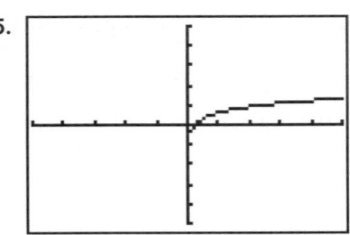

7. 1.50 **9.** 8.06 **11.** $-0.77, 2, 4$ **13.** 1.70 **15.** 1.73

Pages 600–602 Lesson 10-1
7. 4.7 **9.** $5^{4\sqrt{2}}$ **11.** $3^{2\sqrt{5}}$ **13.** -2 **15.** $n \le -2$ **17.** 16 cells
19. 0.7 **21.** 0.5 **23.** 0.5 **25.** $4^{3\sqrt{2}}$ **27.** y^6 **29.** $2^{5\sqrt{7}}$
31. a^{10} **33.** 4 **35.** -1 **37.** $\frac{1}{9}$ **39.** $\frac{3}{5}$ **41.** 6 **43.** $n < -3$
45. 12 **47.** $-3, 5$ **49.**

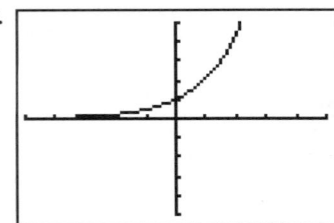

51.

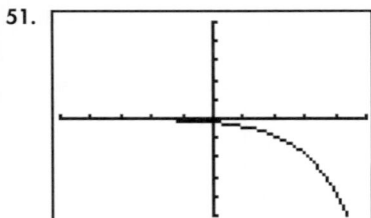

53a. 2, 4, 8, 16 **53b.** $y = 2^x$ **53c.** $y = 0.003(2)^x$
53d. about 3,221,225.47 in. **55a.** about 14.7 psi
55b. about 14.0 psi **55c.** about 11.4 psi
55d. about 16.0 psi
55e.

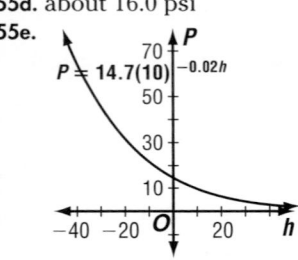

$P = 14.7(10)^{-0.02h}$

They represent the atmospheric pressure for places below sea level.

57a. $d = 1.30h^{\frac{3}{2}}$ **57b.** about 997 cm **59.** 0; 2 or 0; 2 or 4

61. 36 mi **63.** $\frac{3 + 4i}{25}$ **65.** $\begin{bmatrix} -15 & 6 \\ 19 & 43 \\ -6 & -24 \end{bmatrix}$ **67.** no

Page 604 Lesson 10-1B
1.

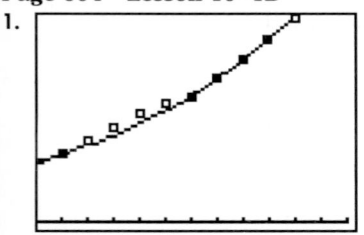

3. about 90.088 **5.** Louisiana Purchase

Pages 608–610 Lesson 10-2
7. $\log_2 32 = 5$ **9.** $5^3 = 125$ **11.** $10^{-3} = 0.001$ **13.** $\frac{1}{2}$
15. $\frac{1}{49}$ **17.** -3 **19.** ± 8 **21.** 10^3 or 1000 times stronger
23. 2 **25.** -4 **27.** $\frac{1}{2}$ **29.** 243 **31.** 32 **33.** 3 **35.** 125
37. 1000 **39.** 2 **41.** $x < \frac{1}{2}$ **43.** 0.5 **45.** 10 **47.** 1

49.

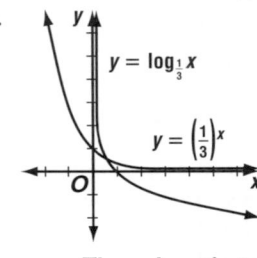

$y = \log_{\frac{1}{3}} x$

$y = \left(\frac{1}{3}\right)^x$

51. In the graphs of $y = \log_{10} x$ and $y = \log_5 x$, the value of y increases as the value of x increases. In the graphs of $y = \log_{\frac{1}{3}} x$ and $y = \log_{\frac{1}{2}} x$, the value of y decreases as the value of x increases. The value of y in the graph of $y = \log_5 x$ increases more as x increases than in the graph of $y = \log_{10} x$. The graphs of $y = \log_{\frac{1}{3}} x$ and $y = \log_{\frac{1}{2}} x$ are reflections of $y = \log_{10} x$ over the x-axis. All of the graphs cross the x-axis at 1.

53. $\log_4 16 \overset{?}{=} 2 \log_4 4$ **55.** $\log_{10} [\log_3 (\log_4 64)] \overset{?}{=} 0$

$\quad\quad 2 \overset{?}{=} 2(1) \quad\quad\quad\quad \log_{10} [\log_3 (3)] \overset{?}{=} 0$

$\quad\quad 2 = 2 \quad\quad\quad\quad\quad\quad \log_{10} [1] \overset{?}{=} 0$

$\quad\quad\quad\quad\quad\quad\quad\quad\quad\quad\quad\quad 0 = 0$

57. about 1.26 times greater **59.** $11^{4\sqrt{5}}$ **61.** $f \circ g$ does not exist; $g \circ f = \{(2, 5), (-1, -1), (3, 2)\}$ **63.** $x^2 - 36$

65. about 3.54 s **67.**

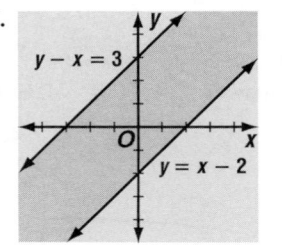

$y - x = 3$

$y = x - 2$

69. $x < -8$

Pages 614–616 Lesson 10-3
5. $2 \log_4 x + \log_4 y$ **7.** $\log_5 a + \log_5 c - \log_5 b$ **9.** 1.222
11. -0.415 **13.** 4 **15.** 6 **17.** 1.262 **19.** 1.1402
21. -0.3690 **23.** 4.2620 **25.** -0.2288 **27.** 7 **29.** 14
31. 4 **33.** 4 **35.** 12 **37.** 6 **39.** $\frac{x^4}{2}$ **41.** $\frac{1}{2}(n + 1)$

43. $\log_b \frac{x}{y^3}$ **45a.** $\text{pH} = 6.1 + \log_{10} B - \log_{10} C$ **45b.** a
very weak base **45c.** 7.197 **47.** 5 **49.** $2a^3 + 5a^2 + 8a + 5$ **51.** no **53.** $x(x + 7)(x - 5)$

Pages 619–621 Lesson 10-4
5. 2 **7.** 1.1367; 0.1367; 1 **9.** 2.8662 **11.** about 1.58 **13.** 3
15. 0.8129 **17.** 0.8129 **19.** 2.9544; 0.9544; 2 **21.** 0.8046;
0.8046; 0 **23.** -3.1549; 0.8451; -4 **25.** 141.0912
27. 0.0153 **29.** 0.0014 **31a.** about 316,227,766 times
31b. about 19,952,623 times **31c.** about 93.7% **33.** 72

35. $y = 3(x - 4)^2 - 1$ **37.** $\begin{bmatrix} 28 \\ -16 \\ 3 \end{bmatrix}$

Page 621 Self Test
1. -2 **3.** 4 **5.** $\frac{1}{2}$ **7.** 8 **9.** 2.7786; 0.7786; 2

Pages 623–625 Lesson 10-5
5. -3.1011 **7.** 1.2961 **9.** 0.2066 **11.** 2.0732 **13.** 4.0483

15. 1.0000 **17.** −5.2983 **19.** −4.6052 **21.** 1.0000
23. 0.8940 **25.** 2.7319 **27.** 4.7115
29.

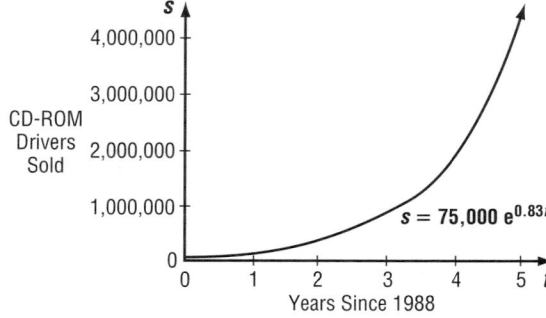

31. The graphs of $y = \ln x$ and $y = e^x$ are reflections of each other along the line $x = y$. **33a.** about 2.7167
33b. about 2.7183 **33c.** the second one
33d. about 0.06% **35a.** about 1,587,209,679 drives
35b.

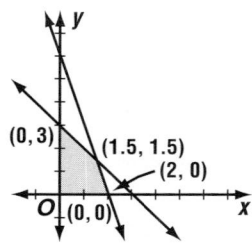

Sample answer: Both graphs show the sales increasing more and more each year. **37a.** 1.8882 **37b.** −2.2518
37c. 3603.2965 **37d.** 0.0006 **39.** $(x + 1)(x − 1)$
$(x^3 + x^2 + x + 1)$ **41.** 10 in. by 12 in.
43. vertices: (0, 0), (0, 3), (2, 0),
(1.5, 1.5), max: $f(0, 3) = 12$,
min: $f(0, 0) = 0$

Pages 628–630 Lesson 10–6
5. 1.833 **7.** 1.159 **9.** 3.483 **11.** −7.638 **13.** 1.723
15. 4.395 **17.** 1.295 **19.** 1.732 **21.** 2.191 **23.** −0.412
25. 2.558 **27.** 2.548 **29.** 4.836 **31.** 0.779 **33.** ±1.915
35. 0 **37.** 11.567 **39.** 8.849 **41.** 0.587 **43.** 0.205
45. 2.125 **47.** about 23 years **49.** 0.0023 **51.** ±2, ±1
53. $\{x \mid x > − 2 \text{ or } x < −9\}$ **55.** $x = 2, y = 3$
57. $3x + 2y = 24$

Pages 633–636 Lesson 10–7
3a. about 92.3 megahertz **3b.** about 9.4 cm from the left
side **5a.** about −0.00043 **5b.** $y = ne^{−0.00043t}$ **5c.** about
2.33 grams **5d.** in about 3224 years **5e.** Never; the
amount left will always be half of the amount that existed
1620 years ago. **7.** about 8.1 days **9a.** about $y =$
$546,488e^{0.0070t}$ **9b.** about 674,190 people **9c.** Sample
answer: If the economy of a city is doing well, more
people than expected may move into the area. If the
economy is not doing well, people may lose their jobs
and move out of the area. **11.** No; the bone is only about
19,000 years old and dinosaurs died out 63,000,000 years
ago. **13a.** about $t = 1.0208n^{0.7776}$ **13b.** about 2.4 min;
about 3.6 min **15a.** 11 payments **15b.** 16 payments

15c. 48 payments **15d.** 60 payments **15e.** 81 payments
15f. 157 payments **17.** about 2.45 **19a.** about 2.8 s
19b. about 4.7 s **19c.** about 6.2 s **19d.** No, the formula is
not a direct variation. **21.** 128 cm²

Page 637 Chapter 10 Highlights
1. h **3.** b **5.** a **7.** g

Pages 638–640 Chapter 10 Study Guide and Assessment
9. x^{10} **11.** $8^{3\sqrt{3}}$ **13.** $−\frac{7}{4}$ **15.** −2 **17.** $\log_5 \frac{1}{25} = −2$
19. $\log_4 8 = \frac{3}{2}$ **21.** $8^{\frac{1}{3}} = 2$ **23.** $6^0 = 1$ **25.** −3 **27.** 2

29. 2 **31.** 4 **33.** 3 **35.** no solution **37.** 1.7712
39. 1.2547 **41.** 3 **43.** 6 **45.** 1.6680 **47.** −2.3298
49. 562.3413 **51.** 0.2710 **53.** 0.8329 **55.** 3.9120
57. 7.2102 **59.** 0.6132 **61.** 1.683 **63.** 1.090 **65.** 2.131
67. 5.7286 **69.** ±2.2452 **71.** −1.8928 **73.** 3.2838
75. about 12.8 psi **77.** 5.05 days

CHAPTER 11 INVESTIGATING SEQUENCES AND SERIES

Page 647 Lesson 11–1A
1. 117 **3.** 12.112 **5.** 48

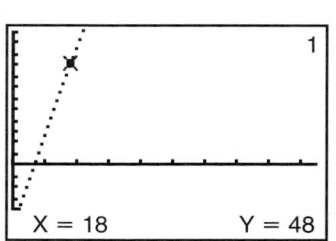

7. −126

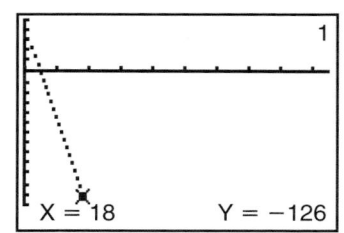

9. 144.49,
143.32, 142.15

Pages 652–655 Lesson 11–1
5. 24, 28, 32, 36 **7.** 5, 8, 11, 14, 17 **9.** −112 **11.** 15
13a. 56, 68, 80 **13b.** **15.** $88

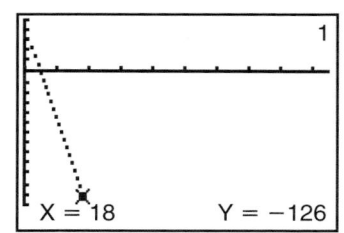

17. 10, 3, −4, −11 **19.** 4.2, 8.2, 12.2, 16.2 **21.** 41,
46, 51, 56, 61 **23.** $\frac{5}{8}$, 1, $\frac{11}{8}$, $\frac{14}{8}$, $\frac{17}{8}$ **25.** −175 **27.** $−12\frac{1}{12}$
29. 340 **31.** 19 **33.** 27 **35.** 173

37. 70, 85, 100

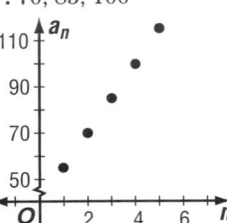

39. −8, −2, 1, 7

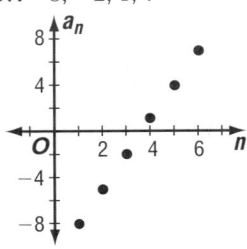

41. 3   **43.** 5   **45.** $a_n = 9n - 2$ **47a.** 35   **47b.** $a_n = 4n + 3$

49. 3, 347   **51.** 46

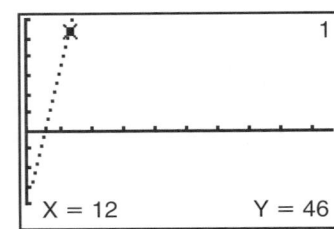

53. 17

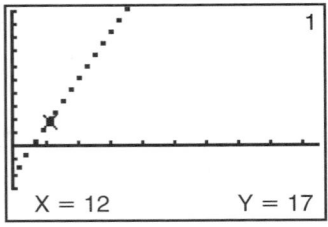

55. 50

57. 37.5 in.   **59a.** The bottom right box is divided into 4 parts.

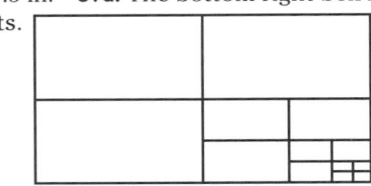

59b. 9   **59c.** 19, 29   **59d.** 499   **59e.** $10n - 1$ **61.** about 1.3863   **63.** $\dfrac{y^3 - w^2y - y + w^2}{w^2 - y^2}$ **65.** parabola   **67.** (9, 0); $x = 9$; downward   **69.** $\dfrac{1}{7}\begin{bmatrix} -4 & -5 \\ -1 & -3 \end{bmatrix}$ **71.** all reals

Pages 660–661   Lesson 11–2
5. 6, 1.4 11.6, 5   **7.** 30, −18, −78, 7   **9.** 230   **11.** 552
13. 260   **15a.** 1,001,000   **15b.** 166,833   **17.** 663   **19.** 2646
21. −140   **23.** 182   **25.** 225   **27.** 119   **29.** 735   **31.** −204
33. 92 + 97 + 102 + 107 + 112; 510   **35.** 17, 26, 35
37. −12, −9, −6   **39.** $\sum_{n=1}^{12} \frac{1}{5}n$; $\frac{78}{5}$ **41.** 3649   **43.** 12 days
45. 780 ft   **47.** −2.8824   **49.** even; 2
51. $f(x) = x^2 + 4x - 2$; x^2; $4x$; −2

Pages 667–669   Lesson 11–3
7. yes, −5   **9.** yes, $\frac{2}{3}$ **11.** 2, −4   **13.** 56   **15.** $\frac{15}{64}$ **17.** 635
19. 192, 256   **21.** 48, 32   **23.** −1, $\frac{1}{4}$ **25.** 243, 81, 27, 9, 3
27. 729   **29.** 243   **31.** 1   **33.** 78,125   **35.** −8748

37. ±18, 36, ±72

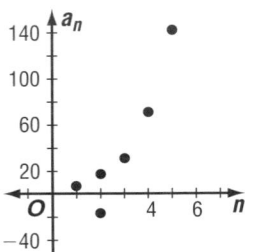

39. 16, 8, 4, 2

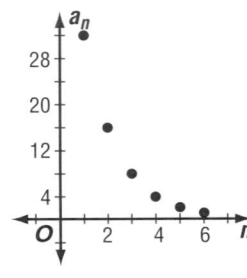

41. 25   **43.** $-\frac{4}{3}$ **45.** $a_n = 2^n$ **47.** $a_n = \frac{4}{25}(-5)^{n-1}$
49. 2, 4, 8, 16, 32   **51.** 243, 81, 27, 9, 3, 1, $\frac{1}{3}$, $\frac{1}{9}$

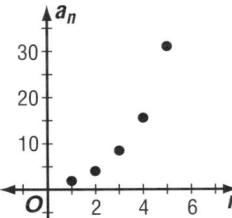
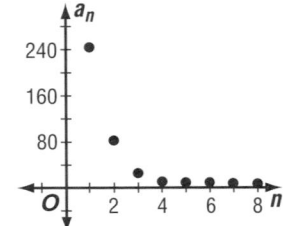

53. Sample answer: In a geometric sequence, each subsequent term can be found by multiplying the preceding term by r. So the nth term of a sequence a_n would equal $a_{n-1}r$. Each term of the sequence can be expressed in terms of the first term. The second term is $a_1 \cdot r$, the third term is $a_1 \cdot r \cdot r$ or a_1r^2, the fourth term is $a_1 \cdot r \cdot r \cdot r$ or a_1r^3, and so on. Notice each term is a product of a_1 and $n-1$ factors of r. So the nth term would be a_1r^{n-1}. Since $a_{n-1}r$ and a_1r^{n-1} both describe the nth term, they are equivalent.   **55.** 262.144 lb   **57a.** 307 mg/L   **57b.** 29 tiers   **57c.** at most 47 tiers   **59.** 9   **61.** 64
63. $x = \frac{1}{18}(y + 7)^2 + \frac{5}{2}$ **65.** $13 - 13i$
67. O'Hare, 31.2 million; Heathrow, 24 million

Pages 673–675   Lesson 11–4
5. 6, −3, −162, 4   **7.** 4, 3, 324, 5   **9.** 732   **11.** 81,915
13. $147\frac{7}{9}$ **15.** $81 + 27 + 9 + 3 + 1 + \frac{1}{3} + \frac{1}{9}$; $121\frac{4}{9}$
17. 1441   **19.** 1,328,600   **21.** 244   **23.** 1111   **25.** 300
27. 7.875   **29.** 1040.984   **31.** 144   **33.** 2101   **35.** 5 + 10 + 20 + 40 + 80 + 160 + 320 + 640 + 1280; 2555
37. 2 − 6 + 18 − 54 + 162 − 486; −364   **39.** 5   **41.** 243
43. $\sum_{n=1}^{12} 243\left(\frac{2}{3}\right)^{n-1}$, 723.38   **45.** −1,048,575   **47a.** $10.23, $10,485.75   **47b.** The amount you have to put away each day exceeds the funds available to anyone.
49. $\frac{1}{24}$, $\frac{1}{4}$ **51.** 3   **53.** $\left(\frac{3}{2}, -4\right)$; about 6.2 units   **55.** 11

Page 675   Self Test
1. 46   **3.** 816   **5.** 30, 36, 42   **7.** 100

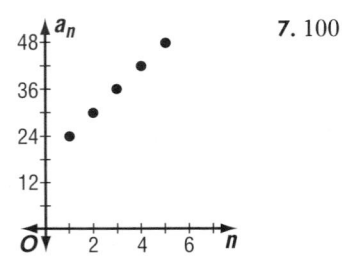

9. $\pm 6, 12, \pm 24$ **11.** -364

Pages 680–682   Lesson 11–5

7. $36, \frac{2}{3}; 108$ **9.** $6, -\frac{2}{3}; \frac{18}{5}$ **11.** $16, \frac{3}{2};$ none   **13.** $\frac{5}{9}$

15. $\frac{175}{999}$ **17.** 14   **19.** 45   **21.** 45   **23.** 3   **25.** $\frac{54}{5}$ **27.** 5

29. 144   **31.** -15 **33.** $\frac{1}{9}$ **35.** $\frac{82}{99}$ **37.** $\frac{41}{90}$ **39.** 1

41. $\sum_{n=1}^{\infty} 3(9)^{n-1}$, does not exist   **43.** 27, 18, 12   **45.** 24,

$16\frac{1}{2}, 11\frac{11}{32}, 7\frac{409}{512}$ **47.** Yes, it is possible to have infinite arithmetic series, but a sum does not exist since the sum increases with each term, or decreases with each

term if d is negative.   **49.** 50 ft   **51.** $\sum_{n=1}^{6} (-3)^{n-1}$

53. $\frac{3y^2 + 10y + 5}{2(y-5)(y+3)}$ **55a.** 340 items   **55b.** 475 items

55c. 495 items   **55d.** 170 items   **55e.** 237.5 items

57. $(4, 12, -3)$ **59.** $y = \frac{3}{4}x - 4$

Pages 686–687   Lesson 11–6

5. 1, 2, 5, 14, 41, 122   **7.** 3, 11, 123   **9.** $-7.2, -22.4, -52.8,$ $-113.6, -235.2$ **11.** 9, 14, 24, 44, 84, 164   **13.** 13, 18, 23, 28, 33, 38   **15.** $1, \frac{1}{2}, \frac{1}{3}, \frac{1}{4}, \frac{1}{5}, \frac{1}{6}$ **17.** 16, 142, 1276

19. $-7, -16, -43$ **21.** $-1, -1, -1$ **23.** 19, 71, 279, 1111, 4439   **25.** $-3, -17, -73, -297, -1193$ **27.** 67   **29.** 0.33, 0.333, 0.3333, ...; The values approach $\frac{1}{3}$.

31a. 1, 3, 6, 10, 15   **31b.** $a_{n+1} = a_n + (n+1)$ **31c.** 3240

33. 27   **35.** $\frac{(y-0.5)^2}{1} - \frac{(x-3)^2}{11.25} = 1$

37a.   Numbers of Job-Related Injuries

```
 x   x xxx x x  xxx                              x
                                                 x
 +-+-+-+-+-+-+-+-+-+-+-+-+-+-+-+-+-+-+-+-+-+
 10    15    20    25    30    35    40
```

37b.

Stem	Leaf
1	0 3 5 6 7 9
2	1 3 4 5
3	9 9 $2\,|\,1 = 21$

37c. 20; 39; 21.75

Pages 692–694   Lesson 11–7

5a. $a_1 = 1, a_{n+1} = 3a_n$ **5b.** 81

7.

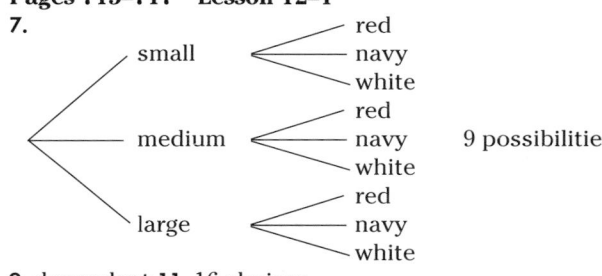

9a.

Stage 3   Stage 4

9b. $a_1 = 1, a_{n+1} = 8a_n$ **9c.** 32,768   **9d.** $a_1 = 81,$ $a_{n+1} = \frac{8}{9} a_n$ **9e.** The area approaches zero.   **11.** Sample answer: Small changes produced unexpected results.
15. -2.8824 **17.** $5x + y = 26, 2x - 3y = 41$

Pages 699–701   Lesson 11–8

5. 40,320   **7.** 66   **9.** $t^6 + 12t^5 + 60t^4 + 160t^3 + 240t^2 + 192t + 64$ **11.** $56a^5b^3$ **13.** $(8x^3 - 36x^2 + 54x - 27)$ cm^3
15. 120   **17.** 72   **19.** 32,760   **21.** 210   **23.** $r^7 + 7r^6s + 21r^5s^2 + 35r^4s^3 + 35r^3s^4 + 21r^2s^5 + 7rs^6 + s^7$
25. $m^5 - 5m^4a + 10m^3a^2 - 10m^2a^3 + 5ma^4 - a^5$
27. $16b^4 - 32b^3x + 24b^2x^2 - 8bx^3 + x^4$ **29.** $81x^4 + 216x^3y + 216x^2y^2 + 96xy^3 + 16y^4$ **31.** $243 + 135m + 30m^2 + \frac{10m^3}{3} + \frac{5m^4}{27} + \frac{m^5}{243}$ **33.** $924x^6y^6$ **35.** $145,152x^6y^3$
37. 0.111477   **39.** $(k+3)!$ **41.** $\frac{7}{n-3}$ **43a.** eighth

43b. 22nd power   **43c.** $319,770a^{14}b^8$ **45.** 1, 2, 4, 8, 16; 512

47. about 13.6%   **49.** $\frac{3}{2}$ **51.** 0.2393   **53.** 42 lb/in^2

55. circle   **57.** $y = \frac{2}{3}x + \frac{10}{3}$

Page 703   Chapter 11   Highlights
1. k   **3.** l   **5.** d   **7.** b, e   **9.** c

Pages 704–706   Chapter 11   Study Guide and Assessment
11. 38   **13.** -11 **15.** 97   **17.** 12   **19.** 10   **21.** $-3, 1, 5$
23. 9, 3, 0, -6 **25.** 2322   **27.** 1155   **29.** 7, 10, 13, 16, 19, 22, 25, 28, 31, 34, 37, 40; 282   **31.** $\frac{64}{3}$ **33.** 56   **35.** $\pm 6, 12, \pm 34$

37. 4, 2, 1, $\frac{1}{2}$ **39.** $\pm 14, \pm 686, -4802$ **41.** $\frac{21}{8}$ **43.** $\frac{11}{16}$

45. 625   **47.** -61 **49.** 72   **51.** $-\frac{16}{13}$ **53.** 1, 1, 1   **55.** $-5,$ 19, 355   **57.** $x^3 + 3x^2y + 3xy^2 + y^3$ **59.** $243r^5 + 405r^4s + 270r^3s^2 + 90r^2s^3 + 15rs^4 + s^5$ **61.** $-13,107,200x^9$ **63.** 43

CHAPTER 12   INVESTIGATING DISCRETE MATHEMATICS AND PROBABILITY

Pages 715–717   Lesson 12–1
7.

```
              /--- red
      small <---- navy
    /         \--- white
   /          /--- red
  <-- medium <---- navy      9 possibilities
   \          \--- white
    \         /--- red
      large <---- navy
              \--- white
```

9. dependent   **11.** 16 choices

13.

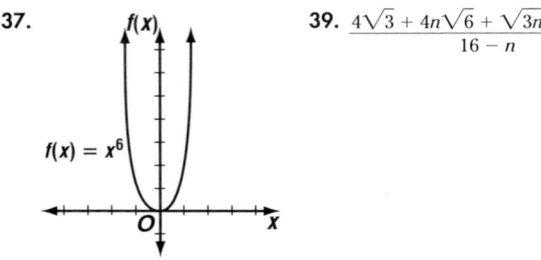

B — B — B
       — G
  — G — B
       — G
G — B — B
       — G
  — G — B
       — G

8 possibilities

15.

rare — ketchup
     — mayonnaise
     — cheese
     — onion
     — tomato
medium — ketchup
       — mayonnaise
       — cheese
       — onion
       — tomato
well — ketchup
     — mayonnaise
     — cheese
     — onion
     — tomato

15 possibilities **17.** dependent, if a person can hold only one office **19.** dependent **21.** 120 routes
23. 3125 passwords **25.** 240 ways **27a.** 10,140,000
27b. 1,872,000 **29.** 210 combinations **31.** 96 meals
33. 27,600 ways **35.** 11.26

37.

$f(x)$

$f(x) = x^6$

39. $\dfrac{4\sqrt{3} + 4n\sqrt{6} + \sqrt{3n} + n\sqrt{6n}}{16 - n}$

Pages 723–725 Lesson 12–2
7. 24 **9.** 3 **11.** linear, not reflection; 362,880 **13a.** Order
is important since each place winner receives a different
cash prize and awards. **13b.** $\dfrac{52}{\text{winner}}, \dfrac{51}{\text{1st}}, \dfrac{50}{\text{2nd}}, \dfrac{49}{\text{3rd}}$
13c. 6,497,400 ways **15.** 5040 **17.** 3360 **19.** 12 **21.** 120
23. 2520 **25.** 453,600 **27.** circular, not reflection; 24
29. circular, not reflection; 5040 **31.** circular, reflection;
60 **33.** 72 **35.** 8 **37.** 42 **39.** 720 ways **41.** 5040 ways
43. 1440 ways **45.** 255 combinations **47.** 13 ways
49. 12 hours **51.** 2 or 0; 1; 2 or 4 **53.** $\begin{bmatrix} 15 & -8 & -10 \\ -7 & 23 & 16 \end{bmatrix}$
55. $p \le 400$

Pages 729–731 Lesson 12–3
7. combination **9.** 6 **11.** 168 **13.** 840 bouquets
15. permutation **17.** permutation **19.** combination
21. permutation **23.** 10 **25.** 70 **27.** 792 **29.** 27,720
31. 2100 **33.** 56 triangles **35.** 12 **37.** 14
39. $C(n, r) = \dfrac{n!}{(n - r)!r!}$ or $\dfrac{n!}{(n - r)!} \cdot \dfrac{1}{r!}$; $P(n, r) = \dfrac{n!}{(n - r)!}$
By substituting, $C(n, r) = P(n, r) \cdot \dfrac{1}{r!}$ or $\dfrac{P(n, r)}{r!}$. **41a.** 56
41b. 252 **41c.** 1680 **41d.** 2520 **43a.** 6 **43b.** 0 **43c.** 126
43d. 2808 **43e.** 810 **45.** 75,287,520 senatorial
committees **47.** 120 **49a.** $y = 100(1.08)^n$ **49b.** $342.59

51. 1.20×10^{25} molecules **53.** $m = \dfrac{3}{4}; b = \dfrac{5}{2}$

Pages 735–738 Lesson 12–4
7. 3:1 **9.** $\dfrac{6}{11}$ **11.** 1:4 **13.** $\dfrac{1}{7}$ **15.** $\dfrac{4}{7}$ **17.** 1:1 **19.** 11:1
21. 1:4 **23.** $\dfrac{6}{7}$ **25.** $\dfrac{5}{11}$ **27.** $\dfrac{1}{9}$ **29a.** $\dfrac{1}{4}$ **29b.** $\dfrac{2}{5}$
29c. 80 jelly beans **31.** $\dfrac{21}{55}$, 21:34 **33.** $\dfrac{14}{575}$ **35.** $\dfrac{7}{115}$
37. $\dfrac{24}{115}$ **39.** $\dfrac{40\pi}{225}$ or about 56% **41.** $\dfrac{\pi - 1}{\pi}$ **43.** $\dfrac{1}{8}$ **45a.** $\dfrac{1}{10}$
45b. 1 **45c.** $\dfrac{21}{50}$ **45d.** 0 **47.** $\dfrac{3}{16}$ **49.** 420 **51.** $\dfrac{1}{9}, \dfrac{1}{3}, 1$
53. $f(m) = 4m^2 - 20m + 25$ **55.** (0, 0), (1, 2), (−3, 1)
57. $-9 \le x \le 24$

Page 738 Self Test
1a. tree diagram **1b.** 24 **3.** 14,400 ways **5.** permutation
7. 1320 **9.** 1716 teams

Pages 742–745 Lesson 12–5
7. dependent, $\dfrac{21}{220}$ **9a.** independent, $\dfrac{8}{243}$
9b. dependent, $\dfrac{1}{21}$ **11.** $\dfrac{1}{4}$ **13.** dependent, $\dfrac{3}{28}$
15. independent, $\dfrac{81}{2401}$ **17.** $\dfrac{10}{21}$ **19a.** (2, 6), (6, 2), (4, 4),
(3, 5), (5, 3) **19b.** (4, 4) is one of 5 possible outcomes
when rolling a sum of 8. **21.** $\dfrac{2}{15}$ **23.** $\dfrac{1}{5}$ **25.** $\dfrac{1}{36}$ **27.** $\dfrac{1}{36}$
29. $\dfrac{1}{6}$ **31a.** $\dfrac{7}{170}$ **31b.** $\dfrac{168}{4913}$ **33.** $\dfrac{1}{635,013,559,600}$
35. $\dfrac{1}{158,753,389,900}$ **37a.** $\dfrac{1}{12}$ **37b.** $\dfrac{1}{6}$ **37c.** 6 outcomes;
GR, GB, BR, BG, RG, RB **39a.** $\dfrac{1}{12} \cdot \dfrac{1}{11} \cdot \dfrac{1}{10}$ or $\dfrac{1}{1320}$
39b. $\left(\dfrac{1}{12}\right)^5$ or $\dfrac{1}{248,832}$ **41a.** $\dfrac{1}{204}$ **41b.** $\dfrac{9}{340}$ **41c.** $\dfrac{6}{119}$ **43.** 0, 1
45. 276 milligrams **47.** $-\dfrac{7}{8}$

Pages 748–751 Lesson 12–6
5a. mutually exclusive, $\dfrac{2}{13}$ **5b.** inclusive, $\dfrac{4}{13}$ **7.** $\dfrac{8}{26}$
9. mutually exclusive, $\dfrac{5}{9}$ **11.** inclusive, $\dfrac{1}{2}$ **13.** $\dfrac{5}{14}$
15. $\dfrac{25}{42}$ **17.** $\dfrac{55}{221}$ **19.** $\dfrac{188}{663}$ **21.** $\dfrac{35}{143}$ **23.** $\dfrac{3}{143}$ **25.** $\dfrac{1}{780}$
27. $\dfrac{11}{156}$ **29.** $P(A), P(B), P(C), P(A \text{ and } B), P(B \text{ and } C),$
$P(A \text{ and } C), P(A \text{ and } B \text{ and } C); P(A \text{ or } B \text{ or } C) = P(A) + P(B) + P(C) - P(A \text{ and } B) - P(B \text{ and } C) - P(A \text{ and } C) + P(A \text{ and } B \text{ and } C)$ **31.** 96%
33a.

	First Serve	Second Serve	Point

75% — in — 80% — yes
            — 20% — no
25% — out — 90% — in — 35% — yes
                       — 65% — no
            — 10% — out

33b. 67.9% **33c.** 88.4% **35a.** $\dfrac{1}{204}$ **35b.** $\dfrac{1}{119}$ **35c.** $\dfrac{3}{340}$
37. $\dfrac{1 - 2x}{3x + 1}$ **39a.** $\dfrac{x^2}{2304} + \dfrac{y^2}{529} = 1$ **39b.** The desk is at one
focus point; about 84 feet.

Pages 756–757   Lesson 12–7
9a. binomial, $\frac{1}{28,561}$ **9b.** not binomial   **11.** $\frac{3024}{15,625} \approx 0.194$

13. $\frac{3}{8} = 0.375$ **15.** $\frac{3125}{7776} \approx 0.402$ **17.** $\frac{625}{648} \approx 0.965$

19. $\frac{1}{64} \approx 0.016$ **21.** $\frac{45}{512} \approx 0.088$ **23.** $\frac{319}{512} \approx 0.623$

25. ≈ 0.309 **27.** ≈ 0.031 **29.** ≈ 0.0000168 **33.** about 0.353

35. 2.4330; 2; 0.5440   **37.** $\sqrt{37}$ units   **39.** $\begin{bmatrix} -2 & 9 & 22 \\ 20 & 12 & -1 \end{bmatrix}$

Pages 760–762   Lesson 12–8
3. yes   **5.** 4%; There is a 95% probability that the value of
p in the population is between $68 - 4$ or 64% and $68 + 4$
or 72% and that 64% to 72% of high school students are
involved in extracurricular activities.   **7a.** There is a 95%
probability that the value of p in the population is
between $77 - 5$ or 72% and $77 + 5$ or 82% and that 72%
to 82% of Americans age 12 or older listen to the radio
every day.   **7b.** 283 people   **9.** yes   **11.** no   **13.** yes
15. 2%; There is a 95% probability that the value of p in
the population is between $33 - 2$ or 31% and $33 + 2$ or
35% and that 33% to 35% of adults believe that skim milk
is a good calcium source.   **19a.** There is a 95% probability
that the value of p in the population is between $90 - 2$ or
88% and $90 + 2$ or 92% and that 88% to 92% of people
registered to vote actually vote on election day.
19b. 900 people   **23.** 72   **25.** $\{x \mid -\sqrt{6} \leq x \leq \sqrt{6}\}$

Page 763   Chapter 12   Highlights
1. e   **3.** b   **5.** d   **7.** i   **9.** f   **11.** h

**Pages 764–766   Chapter 12   Study Guide and
Assessment**
13. 3,628,800   **15.** 5040 patterns   **17.** 19,958,400
19. 604,800   **21.** 462 ways   **23.** 28 pizzas   **25.** $\frac{5}{42}$ **27.** $\frac{1}{7}$

29. mutually exclusive, $\frac{1}{2}$ **31.** mutually exclusive, $\frac{1}{2}$ **33.** $\frac{1}{32}$

35a. $\frac{1}{2,176,782,336}$ **35b.** $\frac{585,937,500}{2,176,782,336}$ **35c.** $\frac{14,437,500}{2,176,782,336}$

37. 460 mothers   **39.** 1260 varieties

**CHAPTER 13   EXPLORING TRIGONOMETRIC
FUNCTIONS**

Pages 777–779   Lesson 13–1
7. $\sin \theta \approx 0.8944$, $\cos \theta \approx 0.4472$, $\csc \theta \approx 1.1180$,
$\sec \theta \approx 2.2361$, $\cot \theta = 0.5$ **9.** $\tan x° = \frac{33}{15}$, $x \approx 66°$
11. 8°   **13.** $b = 5$, $A \approx 67°$, $B \approx 23°$ **15.** about 300 feet
17. $\sin \theta \approx 0.9682$, $\tan \theta \approx 3.8730$, $\csc \theta \approx 1.0328$,
$\sec \theta = 4$, $\cot \theta \approx 0.2582$ **19.** $\sin \theta = 0.4$, $\cos \theta \approx 0.9165$,
$\tan \theta \approx 0.4364$, $\sec \theta \approx 1.0911$, $\cot \theta \approx 2.2913$
21. $\cos \theta \approx 0.8660$, $\tan \theta \approx 0.5774$, $\sec \theta \approx 1.1547$,
$\csc \theta = 2$, $\cot \theta \approx 1.7321$ **23.** $\sin 54° = \frac{17.8}{x}$, $x \approx 22.0$

25. $\tan x° = \frac{15}{21}$, $x \approx 36°$ **27.** $\sin x° = \frac{18}{33}$, $x \approx 33°$
29. 58°   **31.** 89°   **33.** 30°   **35.** $a \approx 3.9$, $b \approx 13.5$, $B = 74°$
37. $b \approx 1.3$, $c \approx 4.1$, $A = 72°$ **39.** $B = 45°$, $a = 7$, $b = 7$
41. $a \approx 19.1°$, $c = 22$, $A = 60°$ **43.** $b \approx 13.7$, $c \approx 15.4$,
$B = 63°$ **45.** $b \approx 14.1$, $A \approx 19.5°$, $B \approx 70.5°$ **47.** 4.05 cm
49. Sample answer: The legs of a right triangle are never
greater than the hypotenuse, but one leg may be greater
than the other leg.   **51.** 99 feet   **53.** 58.3°   **55.** no   **57.** $\frac{5}{6}$
59. 100   **61.** x^4 **63.** about 2.99×10^1 or 2.99

Pages 783–785   Lesson 13–2
7. a   **9.** g   **11.** $-\frac{2\pi}{3}$ **13.** 120°   **15.** 286.48°   **17.** Sample
answer: $\frac{9\pi}{4}$, $-\frac{7\pi}{4}$ **19.** $-60°$, $-\frac{\pi}{3}$ **21.** π **23.** $\frac{20\pi}{3}$
25. $-\frac{40\pi}{9}$ **27.** 3π **29.** 180°   **31.** $-480°$ **33.** 900°
35. 401.07°   **37.** $-85.94°$ **39.** Sample answer: 670°, $-50°$
41. Sample answer: $\frac{\pi}{4}$, $-\frac{7\pi}{4}$ **43.** Sample answer: 360°,
$-360°$ **45.** Sample answer: 180°, $-180°$
47. $a^2 + (-b)^2 = a^2 + b^2 = 1$, $b^2 + a^2 = a^2 + b^2 = 1$,
$b^2 + (-a)^2 = a^2 + b^2 = 1$ **49.** $\frac{4\pi}{3}$ radians/second
51. 129 meters   **53.** 35   **55.** no solution
57. $x^2 - 10x + 24 = 0$ **59.** additive identity

Pages 790–791   Lesson 13–3
7. 0   **9.** $\sin \theta = -\frac{8\sqrt{65}}{65}$, $\cos \theta = \frac{\sqrt{65}}{65}$, $\tan \theta = -8$
11. $-\frac{1}{2}$ **13.** $-\frac{\sqrt{2}}{2}$ **15.** $\sin \theta = \frac{2\sqrt{5}}{5}$, $\cos \theta = \frac{\sqrt{5}}{5}$,
$\cot \theta = \frac{1}{2}$, $\csc \theta = \frac{\sqrt{5}}{2}$, $\sec \theta = \sqrt{5}$ **17.** $-$ **19.** $-$
21. $+$ **23.** undefined   **25.** $-$ **27.** $\sin \theta = 0$, $\cos \theta = -1$,
$\tan \theta = 0$ **29.** $\sin \theta = -\frac{3\sqrt{34}}{34}$, $\cos \theta = \frac{5\sqrt{34}}{34}$, $\tan \theta = -\frac{3}{5}$
31. $\sin \theta = \frac{\sqrt{2}}{2}$, $\cos \theta = \frac{\sqrt{2}}{2}$, $\tan \theta = 1$ **33.** $\frac{1}{2}$ **35.** $-\frac{\sqrt{3}}{2}$
37. $\frac{1}{2}$ **39.** 1   **41.** $\sin \theta = \frac{\sqrt{3}}{2}$, $\tan \theta = -\sqrt{3}$, $\csc \theta = \frac{2\sqrt{3}}{3}$,
$\sec \theta = -2$, $\cot \theta = -\frac{\sqrt{3}}{3}$ **43.** $\sin \theta = -\frac{3\sqrt{10}}{10}$,
$\cos \theta = -\frac{\sqrt{10}}{10}$, $\cot \theta = \frac{1}{3}$, $\csc \theta = -\frac{\sqrt{10}}{3}$,
$\sec \theta = -\sqrt{10}$ **45.** $\sin \theta = \frac{\sqrt{26}}{26}$, $\cos \theta = -\frac{5\sqrt{26}}{26}$,
$\tan \theta = -\frac{1}{5}$, $\csc \theta = \sqrt{26}$, $\sec \theta = -\frac{\sqrt{26}}{5}$
47. $\sin \theta = \pm\frac{\sqrt{5}}{3}$ **49.** $\sin \theta = \pm 1$, $\tan \theta = $ undefined
51. II   **53.** $\frac{\cos \theta}{\sin \theta} = \frac{\frac{x}{r}}{\frac{y}{r}} = \frac{x}{r} \cdot \frac{r}{y} = \frac{x}{y} = \cot \theta$ **55.** 8 feet
57. $a \approx 10.8$, $A = 31°$, $B = 59°$ **59.** $\frac{8}{9}$ **61.** 100 times
63. $x^3 - 14x^2 + 68x - 120$ **65.** 8

Pages 796–798 Lesson 13–4
7. $\frac{1}{2}bc \sin A$, 135.9   **9.** $B = 80°$, $a \approx 13.1$, $c \approx 17.6$
11. two; $B \approx 51.6°$, $C \approx 92.4°$, $c \approx 10.2$; $B \approx 128.4°$, $C \approx$
15.6°, $c \approx 2.7$ **13.** one; $A \approx 44.8°$, $B \approx 37.2°$, $b \approx 55.0$
15. $\frac{1}{2}ab \sin C$, 65.4   **17.** $\frac{1}{2}ab \sin C$, 229.5

19. $\frac{1}{2}ac \sin B$, 37.4   **21.** $C = 74°$, $b \approx 8.9$, $c \approx 10.2$

23. $B \approx 35.3°$, $A \approx 34.7°$, $a \approx 7.9$ **25.** $A = 67°$, $b \approx 47.2$,
$c \approx 30.1$ **27.** $B = 80°$, $a \approx 4.3$, $b \approx 8.4$ **29.** $B \approx 31.5°$,
$C \approx 45.5°$, $c \approx 10.3$ **31.** no solution   **33.** no solution
35. no solution   **37.** no solution   **39.** two solutions;
$B \approx 53.5°$, $C \approx 86.5°$, $c \approx 12.4$; $B \approx 126.5°$, $C \approx 13.5°$,
$c \approx 2.9$ **41.** There is no solution.   **43.** 46.8 miles to
Norfolk   **45.** 4.9 and 10.4 miles   **47.** $\sin 180° = 0$,
$\cos 180° = -1$, $\tan 180° = 0$, $\csc 180°$ undefined,
$\sec 180° = -1$, $\cot 180°$ undefined   **49.** 30,875   **51.** 1
53. $(2x + 3)(x - 7)$

SELECTED ANSWERS

Selected Answers

Page 798 Self Test

1. $B = 41°$, $c \approx 9.3$, $b \approx 6.1$ **3.** $\frac{5\pi}{6}$ **5.** $270°$ **7.** $114.6°$
9. 82.1 watts

Pages 802–804   Lesson 13–5

7. cosines; $c \approx 11.5$, $B \approx 81.6°$, $A \approx 56.4°$ **9.** sines; $b \approx$
21.0, $C \approx 44.3°$, $B \approx 101.7°$ **11.** $35.7°$ **13.** cosines; $c \approx$
6.5, $A \approx 76.1°$, $B \approx 68.9°$ **15.** cosines; $A \approx 46.6°$, $B \approx$
73.8°, $C \approx 59.6°$ **17.** cosines; $A = 90°$, $B \approx 67.4°$,
$C \approx 22.6°$ **19.** cosines; $b \approx 17.9$, $A \approx 54.7°$, $C \approx 78.3°$
21. sines; $C = 81°$, $a \approx 9.1$, $b \approx 12.2$ **23.** sines; $b \approx 31.7$,
$C \approx 77.0°$, $c \approx 31.6$ **25.** cosines; $A \approx 30.0°$, $B \approx 69.2°$, $C \approx$
80.8° **27.** cosines; $a \approx 2.4$, $B \approx 78.0°$, $C \approx 74.0°$
29. cosines; $A \approx 14.6°$, $B \approx 130.8°$, $C \approx 34.6°$ **31.** 26.4 cm
33a. 4.08 **33b.** 14.15 **33c.** 9.12 **35.** 1434 feet; 86,756.06
square feet **37.** about 561 miles **39.** $-\frac{\pi}{4}$
41.

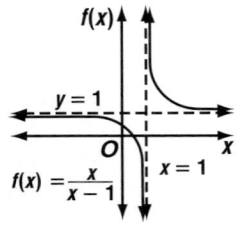

43. 8, -12 **45a.** Sample answer: $y = 249x + 5000$
45b. Sample answer based on equation in Exercise 45a:
28,157

Pages 808–810   Lesson 13–6

5. $\sin \theta = \frac{4}{5}$, $\cos \theta = -\frac{3}{5}$, $\tan \theta = -\frac{4}{3}$ **7.** 9 **9.** $-\frac{\sqrt{3}}{2}$

11. $\sin \theta = \frac{\sqrt{2}}{2}$, $\cos \theta = \frac{\sqrt{2}}{2}$, $\tan \theta = 1$ **13.** $\sin \theta = 0$,

$\cos \theta = 1$, $\tan \theta = 0$ **15.** $720°$ **17.** $-\frac{\sqrt{3}}{2}$ **19.** 0 **21.** -1

23. 1 **25.** $-\frac{\sqrt{3}}{3}$ **27.** 1
31.

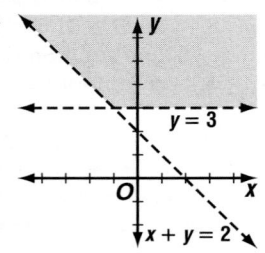

33. about 228 miles **35.** No; the figure is not self-similar.
37. $-3, 3, -2, 2$ **39.** $(2, -2)$

Pages 813–814   Lesson 13–7

5. $y = \text{Arctan} -3$ **7.** $45°$ **9.** $\frac{4}{5}$ **11.** $-45°$ **13.** $90°$

15. $b = \text{Arccos } a$ **17.** $\alpha = \text{Arctan } \beta$ **19.** $\text{Arccos } y = 45°$

21. $90°$ **23.** $30°$ **25.** $30°$ **27.** $120°$ **29.** $0°$ **31.** $\frac{\sqrt{11}}{5}$

33. $\frac{1}{2}$ **35.** 3 **37.** $60°$ **39.** $\frac{1}{2}$ **41.** $\frac{\sqrt{2}}{2}$ **43.** $\frac{\sqrt{3}}{2}$ **47.** $60°$
49. 61.1 meters **51.** 0.2392 **53.** 0, 7
55.

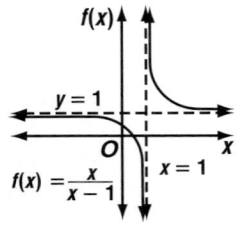

988 *Selected Answers*

Page 815   Chapter 13   Highlights
1. false, coterminal **3.** true **5.** true **7.** true **9.** false,
$\tan \theta$

**Pages 816–818   Chapter 13   Study Guide and
Assessment**
11. $\sin \theta \approx 0.9911$, $\tan \theta \approx 7.4330$, $\csc \theta \approx 1.0090$,
$\sec \theta = 7.5$, $\cot \theta \approx 0.1345$ **13.** $\cos \theta \approx 0.6614$,
$\tan \theta \approx 1.1339$, $\csc \theta \approx 1.3333$, $\sec \theta \approx 1.5119$,
$\cot \theta \approx 0.8819$ **15.** $15°$ **17.** $75°$ **19.** $b \approx 14.4$, $A \approx 26°$,
$B \approx 64°$ **21.** $A = 45°$, $a \approx 8.5$, $b \approx 8.5$ **23.** $A \approx 41°$,
$b \approx 10.4$, $c \approx 13.7$ **25.** $\frac{17\pi}{12}$ **27.** $\frac{13\pi}{36}$ **29.** $315°$ **31.** $-720°$
33. $-\frac{\sqrt{3}}{2}$ **35.** $-\frac{\sqrt{2}}{2}$ **37.** $\frac{2\sqrt{3}}{3}$ **39.** $\sin \theta = \frac{5\sqrt{29}}{29}$
41. $B = 67°$, $C = 63°$, $c = 11.7$ **43.** $C = 105°$, $a = 28.3$,
$c = 38.6$ **45.** no solution **47.** one solution; $B = 38°$,
$A = 76°$, $a = 15.9$ **49.** $c \approx 6.4$, $A \approx 35°$, $B \approx 80°$
51. $c \approx 4.5$, $A \approx 59°$, $B \approx 81°$ **53.** $A \approx 45°$, $B \approx 58°$,
$C \approx 77°$ **55.** $\frac{1}{2}$ **57.** $-\frac{\sqrt{2}}{2}$ **59.** $-\sqrt{3}$ **61.** $30°$ **63.** 0
65. $\frac{15}{8}$ **67.** $55.75°$

**CHAPTER 14   USING TRIGONOMETRIC GRAPHS
AND IDENTITIES**

Page 824   Lesson 14–1A
1.

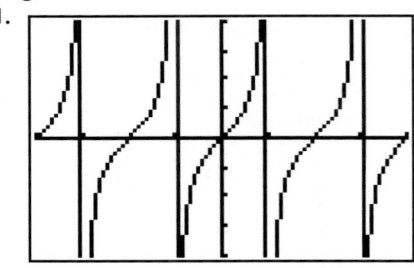

3.

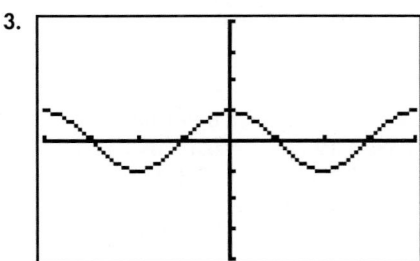

5.

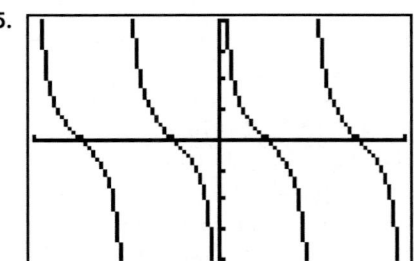

7.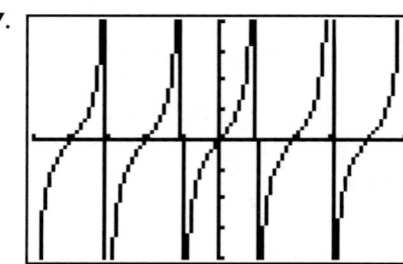

9.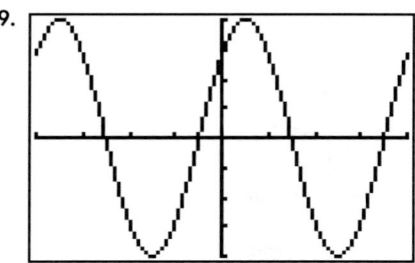

11.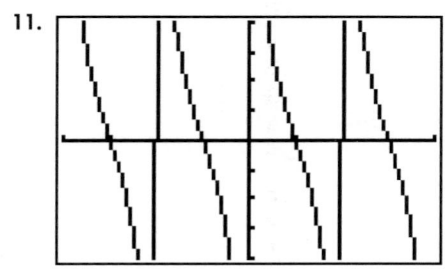

13.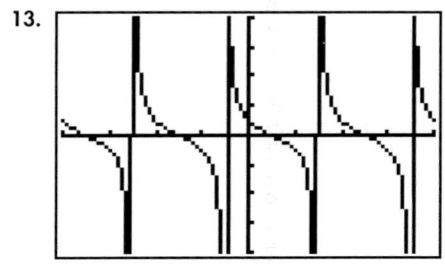

Pages 832–834 Lesson 14–1

7. a **9.** b **11.** 6, 540°

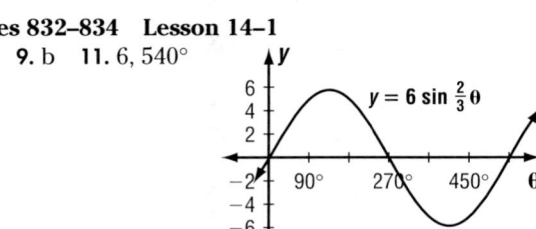

13. none, 120°

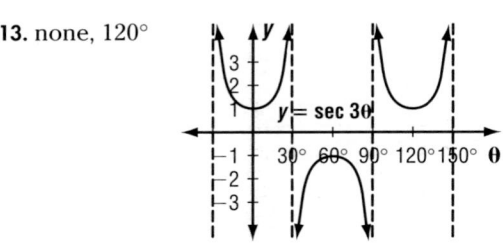

15. none, 36°

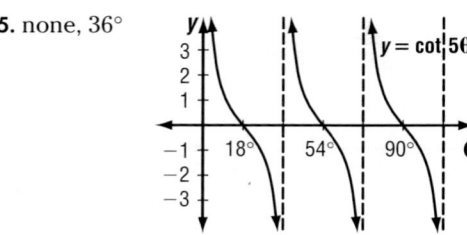

17. c **19.**

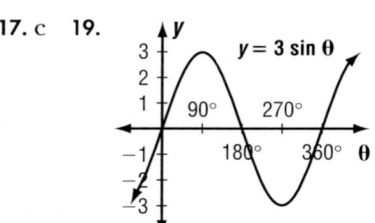

21. 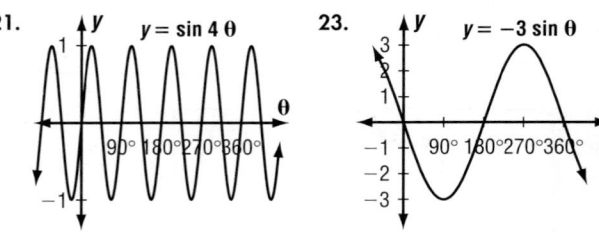 **23.**

25. 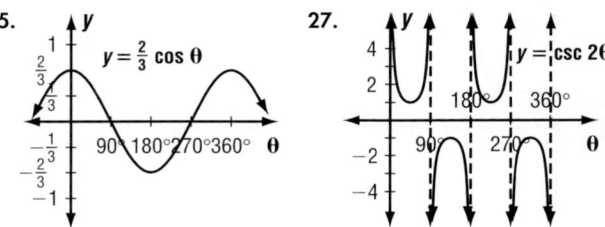 **27.**

29.

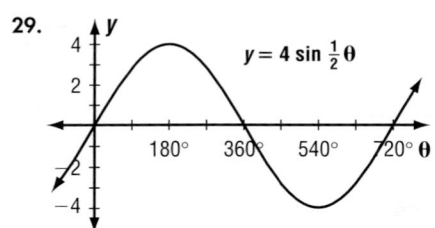

31.

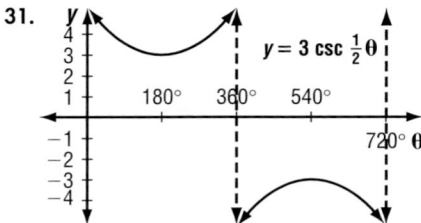

33.

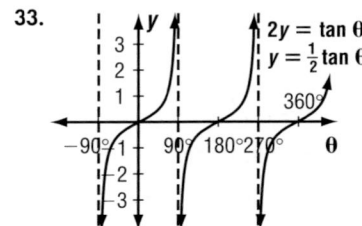

35.

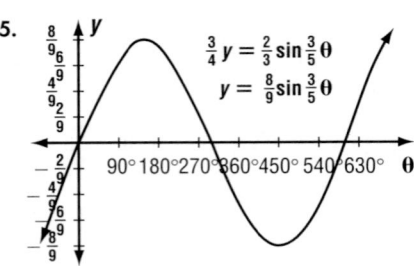

$\frac{3}{4}y = \frac{2}{3}\sin\frac{3}{5}\theta$

$y = \frac{8}{9}\sin\frac{3}{5}\theta$

37. $y = 0.6\cos\frac{1}{2}\theta$ **39.** $y = \frac{1}{3}\cos 4\theta$ **41.** $y = 6.7\sin 3\theta$

43. $y = \cos 2\theta$ **45a.**

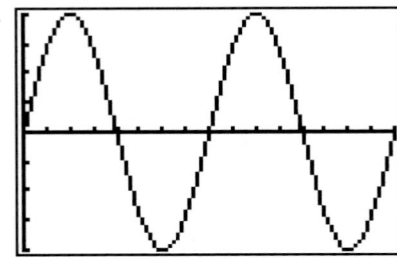

45b.

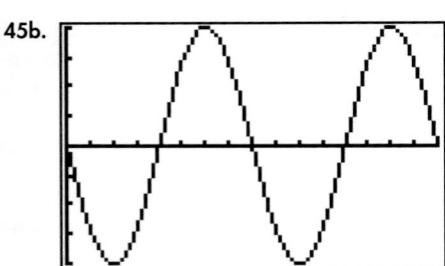

45c.

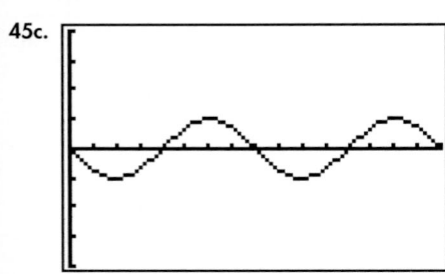

45d. The greater the absolute value of a, the greater the amplitude. If a is negative, then the curve is the same as would be obtained by reflecting the curve $y = -a\sin\theta$ about the x-axis.

47a.

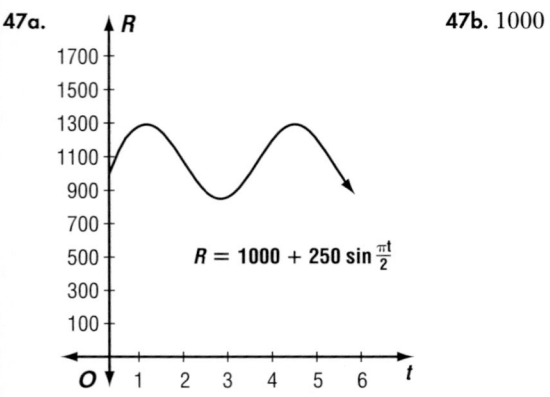

$R = 1000 + 250\sin\frac{\pi t}{2}$

47b. 1000

47c. 1250; January 1, 1991   **47d.** 750; January 1, 1993

49. $\frac{8}{17}$ **51.** 2.375, 4.75   **53.** $\pm\frac{\sqrt{6}}{2}$ **55.** $16^{\frac{1}{3}}a^{\frac{5}{3}}b^{\frac{7}{3}}$

57. Sample answer: $a(b + c) = ab + ac$

990   *Selected Answers*

Pages 839–840   Lesson 14–2

5. $\frac{3}{5}$ **7.** $\frac{3\sqrt{5}}{5}$ **9.** $\sin\theta\cos\theta$ **11.** $\cot^2 x$ **13.** $\frac{5}{4}$ **15.** $-\frac{4}{5}$

17. $-\frac{5}{4}$ **19.** $-\frac{\sqrt{17}}{4}$ **21.** $-\frac{12}{13}$ **23.** $\frac{3}{5}$ **25.** 1   **27.** $\tan^2\theta$

29. $\sec\beta$ **31.** 1   **33.** $\csc\beta$ **35.** 1

37. $1 + \tan^2\theta = 1 + \frac{\sin^2\theta}{\cos^2\theta}$

$\quad = \frac{\cos^2\theta}{\cos^2\theta} + \frac{\sin^2\theta}{\cos^2\theta}$

$\quad = \frac{\cos^2\theta + \sin^2\theta}{\cos^2\theta}$

$\quad = \frac{1}{\cos^2\theta}$

$\quad = \sec^2\theta$

39. $\sec\alpha - \cos\alpha = \frac{1}{\cos\alpha} - \cos\alpha$

$\quad = \frac{1}{\cos\alpha} - \frac{\cos^2\alpha}{\cos\alpha}$

$\quad = \frac{1 - \cos^2\alpha}{\cos\alpha}$

$\quad = \frac{\sin^2\alpha}{\cos\alpha}$

$\quad = \sin\alpha \cdot \frac{\sin\alpha}{\cos\alpha}$

$\quad = \sin\alpha \cdot \tan\alpha$

41. $\frac{9}{16}$ **43.** about $14.5°$ **45.**

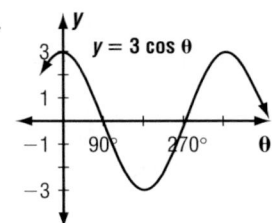

$y = 3\cos\theta$

47. 792   **49.** 18, 23, 28   **51.** 3, -7

Page 841   Lesson 14–3A

1. yes   **3.** yes   **5.** yes   **7.** no   **9.** yes   **11.** yes

Pages 845–846   Lesson 14–3

3. $\sin\theta\sec\theta\cot\theta \overset{?}{} 1$

$\sin\theta \cdot \frac{1}{\cos\theta} \cdot \frac{\cos\theta}{\sin\theta} \overset{?}{} 1$

$\qquad\qquad 1 = 1$

5. $\csc y\sec y \overset{?}{} \cot y + \tan y$

$\csc y\sec y \overset{?}{} \frac{\cos y}{\sin y} + \frac{\sin y}{\cos y}$

$\csc y\sec y \overset{?}{} \frac{\sin^2 y + \cos^2 y}{\sin y\cos y}$

$\csc y\sec y \overset{?}{} \frac{1}{\sin y\cos y}$

$\csc y\sec y \overset{?}{} \csc y\sec y$

7. $\dfrac{\frac{1}{\cos\beta} + \frac{1}{\sin\beta}}{1 + \frac{\sin\beta}{\cos\beta}} \overset{?}{=} \csc\beta$

$\dfrac{\frac{\sin\beta + \cos\beta}{\sin\beta\cos\beta}}{\frac{\sin\beta + \cos\beta}{\cos\beta}} \overset{?}{=} \csc\beta$

$\frac{\sin\beta + \cos\beta}{\sin\beta\cos\beta} \cdot \frac{\cos\beta}{\sin\beta + \cos\beta} \overset{?}{} \csc\beta$

$\frac{\cos\beta}{\sin\beta\cos\beta} \overset{?}{} \csc\beta$

$\frac{1}{\sin\beta} \overset{?}{} \csc\beta$

$\csc\beta = \csc\beta$

9. about 20 cm   **11.** $\cos^2\theta + \sin^2\theta \overset{?}{=} 1$
$$1 = 1$$

13.
$$\frac{\frac{1}{\cos\alpha}}{\sin\alpha} - \frac{\sin\alpha}{\cos\alpha} \overset{?}{=} \cot\alpha$$
$$\frac{1}{\sin\alpha\cos\alpha} - \frac{\sin^2\alpha}{\sin\alpha\cos\alpha} \overset{?}{=} \cot\alpha$$
$$\frac{1 - \sin^2\alpha}{\sin\alpha\cos\alpha} \overset{?}{=} \cot\alpha$$
$$\frac{\cos^2\alpha}{\sin\alpha\cos\alpha} \overset{?}{=} \cot\alpha$$
$$\frac{\cos\alpha}{\sin\alpha} \overset{?}{=} \cot\alpha$$
$$\cot\alpha = \cot\alpha$$

15.
$$\frac{\sin\theta}{\sec\theta} \overset{?}{=} \frac{1}{\frac{\sin\theta}{\cos\theta} + \frac{\cos\theta}{\sin\theta}}$$
$$\frac{\sin\theta}{\sec\theta} \overset{?}{=} \frac{1}{\frac{\sin^2\theta + \cos^2\theta}{\sin\theta\cos\theta}}$$
$$\frac{\sin\theta}{\sec\theta} \overset{?}{=} \frac{\sin\theta\cos\theta}{\sin^2\theta + \cos^2\theta}$$
$$\frac{\sin\theta}{\sec\theta} \overset{?}{=} \frac{\sin\theta\cos\theta}{1}$$
$$\frac{\sin\theta}{\sec\theta} = \frac{\sin\theta}{\sec\theta}$$

17.
$$\frac{\sec\theta + 1}{\tan\theta} \overset{?}{=} \frac{\tan\theta}{\sec\theta - 1} \cdot \frac{\sec\theta + 1}{\sec\theta + 1}$$
$$\frac{\sec\theta + 1}{\tan\theta} \overset{?}{=} \frac{\tan\theta \cdot (\sec\theta + 1)}{\sec^2\theta - 1}$$
$$\frac{\sec\theta + 1}{\tan\theta} \overset{?}{=} \frac{\tan\theta \cdot (\sec\theta + 1)}{\tan^2\theta}$$
$$\frac{\sec\theta + 1}{\tan\theta} = \frac{\sec\theta + 1}{\tan\theta}$$

19. $\cos^2 x + \tan^2 x \cos^2 x \overset{?}{=} 1$
$$\cos^2 x + \frac{\sin^2 x}{\cos^2 x} \cdot \cos^2 x \overset{?}{=} 1$$
$$\cos^2 x + \sin^2 x \overset{?}{=} 1$$
$$1 = 1$$

21.
$$\frac{1 + \tan^2\theta}{\csc^2\theta} \overset{?}{=} \tan^2\theta$$
$$\frac{\sec^2\theta}{\csc^2\theta} \overset{?}{=} \tan^2\theta$$
$$\frac{\frac{1}{\cos^2\theta}}{\frac{1}{\sin^2\theta}} \overset{?}{=} \tan^2\theta$$
$$\frac{1}{\cos^2\theta} \cdot \sin^2\theta \overset{?}{=} \tan^2\theta$$
$$\tan^2\theta = \tan^2\theta$$

23.
$$\frac{\cos y}{1 + \sin y} \cdot \frac{1 - \sin y}{1 - \sin y} + \frac{\cos y}{1 - \sin y} \cdot \frac{1 + \sin y}{1 + \sin y} \overset{?}{=} 2\sec y$$
$$\frac{\cos y(1 - \sin y) + \cos y(1 + \sin y)}{(1 + \sin y)(1 - \sin y)} \overset{?}{=} 2\sec y$$
$$\frac{\cos y - \sin y\cos y + \cos y + \sin y\cos y}{1 - \sin^2 y} \overset{?}{=} 2\sec y$$
$$\frac{2\cos y}{\cos^2 y} \overset{?}{=} 2\sec y$$
$$\frac{2}{\cos y} \overset{?}{=} 2\sec y$$
$$2\sec y = 2\sec y$$

25. $\cot x(\cot x + \tan x) \overset{?}{=} \csc^2 x$
$$\cot^2 x + \cot x\tan x \overset{?}{=} \csc^2 x$$
$$\csc^2 x - 1 + \frac{\sin x}{\cos x} \cdot \frac{\cos x}{\sin x} \overset{?}{=} \csc^2 x$$
$$\csc^2 x - 1 + 1 \overset{?}{=} \csc^2 x$$
$$\csc^2 x = \csc^2 x$$

27.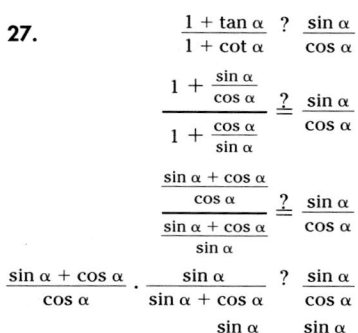
$$\frac{1 + \tan\alpha}{1 + \cot\alpha} \overset{?}{=} \frac{\sin\alpha}{\cos\alpha}$$
$$\frac{1 + \frac{\sin\alpha}{\cos\alpha}}{1 + \frac{\cos\alpha}{\sin\alpha}} \overset{?}{=} \frac{\sin\alpha}{\cos\alpha}$$
$$\frac{\frac{\sin\alpha + \cos\alpha}{\cos\alpha}}{\frac{\sin\alpha + \cos\alpha}{\sin\alpha}} \overset{?}{=} \frac{\sin\alpha}{\cos\alpha}$$
$$\frac{\sin\alpha + \cos\alpha}{\cos\alpha} \cdot \frac{\sin\alpha}{\sin\alpha + \cos\alpha} \overset{?}{=} \frac{\sin\alpha}{\cos\alpha}$$
$$\frac{\sin\alpha}{\cos\alpha} = \frac{\sin\alpha}{\cos\alpha}$$

29. $1 + \sec^2 x\sin^2 x \overset{?}{=} \sec^2 x$
$$1 + \frac{1}{\cos^2 x} \cdot \sin^2 x \overset{?}{=} \sec^2 x$$
$$1 + \tan^2 x \overset{?}{=} \sec^2 x$$
$$\sec^2 x = \sec^2 x$$

31. \$85.80   **33.** $\cot\alpha$ **35.** $\frac{1}{36}$ **37.** $x^7 y^7$

Page 846   Self Test
1. $1; \frac{\pi}{2}$ or $90°$ **3.** none; 5π or $900°$

5.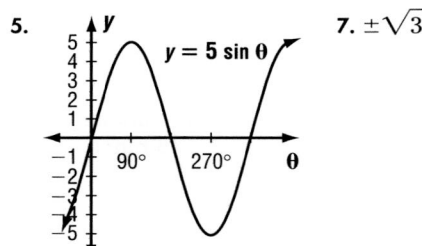
   7. $\pm\sqrt{3}$

9. $(1 - \sin^2\theta)(1 + \tan^2\theta) \overset{?}{=} 1$
$$\cos^2\theta\left(1 + \frac{\sin^2\theta}{\cos^2\theta}\right) \overset{?}{=} 1$$
$$\cos^2\theta + \sin^2\theta \overset{?}{=} 1$$
$$1 = 1$$

Pages 850–852   Lesson 14–4
3. $\dfrac{\sqrt{6} - \sqrt{2}}{4}$ **5.** $\dfrac{\sqrt{2} - \sqrt{6}}{4}$

7. $\sin(270° - \theta) \overset{?}{=} \sin 270°\cos\theta - \cos 270°\sin\theta$
$$\overset{?}{=} -1\cos\theta - 0$$
$$\overset{?}{=} -\cos\theta$$

9. $\sin(x + 30°) + \cos(x + 60°)$
$$\overset{?}{=} \sin x\cos 30° + \cos x\sin 30° + \cos x\cos 60° - \sin x\sin 60°$$
$$\overset{?}{=} \frac{\sqrt{3}}{2}\sin x + \frac{1}{2}\cos x + \frac{1}{2}\cos x - \frac{\sqrt{3}}{2}\sin x$$
$$\overset{?}{=} \frac{1}{2}\cos x + \frac{1}{2}\cos x$$
$$= \cos x$$

11. $\dfrac{-\sqrt{2}-\sqrt{6}}{4}$ **13.** $\dfrac{-\sqrt{6}-\sqrt{2}}{4}$ **15.** $\dfrac{\sqrt{6}+\sqrt{2}}{4}$ **17.** $\dfrac{1}{2}$

19. $\dfrac{\sqrt{3}}{2}$

21. $\sin(90° + \theta) \overset{?}{=} \sin 90° \cos \theta + \cos 90° \sin \theta$

$\overset{?}{=} 1 \cdot \cos \theta + 0$

$= \cos \theta$

23. $\sin(90° - \theta) \overset{?}{=} \sin 90° \cos \theta - \cos 90° \sin \theta$

$= 1 \cdot \cos \theta - 0 \cdot \sin \theta$

$= \cos \theta$

25. $\sin(x + y) \sin(x - y)$

$\overset{?}{=} (\sin x \cos y + \cos x \sin y)(\sin x \cos y - \cos x \sin y)$

$\overset{?}{=} \sin^2 x \cos^2 y - \cos^2 x \sin^2 y$

$\overset{?}{=} \sin^2 x(1 - \sin^2 y) - (1 - \sin^2 x)\sin^2 y$

$\overset{?}{=} \sin^2 x - \sin^2 x \sin^2 y - \sin^2 y + \sin^2 x \sin^2 y$

$= \sin^2 x - \sin^2 y$

27. $-2 - \sqrt{3}$ **29.** $\sqrt{3}$ **31.** $90°$ **33.** $90°$

35. $\tan(\alpha + \beta) = \dfrac{\sin(\alpha + \beta)}{\cos(\alpha + \beta)}$

$= \dfrac{\sin \alpha \cos \beta + \cos \alpha \sin \beta}{\cos \alpha \cos \beta - \sin \alpha \sin \beta}$

$= \dfrac{\dfrac{\sin \alpha \cos \beta}{\cos \alpha \cos \beta} + \dfrac{\cos \alpha \sin \beta}{\cos \alpha \cos \beta}}{\dfrac{\cos \alpha \cos \beta}{\cos \alpha \cos \beta} - \dfrac{\sin \alpha \sin \beta}{\cos \alpha \cos \beta}}$

$= \dfrac{\tan \alpha + \tan \beta}{1 - \tan \alpha \tan \beta}$

37a. 0.5549 E   **37b.** 0.3584 E   **37c.** 0.9171 E

39. $\sin \theta \sec \theta \cot \theta \overset{?}{=} 1$

$\sin \theta \cdot \dfrac{1}{\cos \theta} \cdot \dfrac{\cos \theta}{\sin \theta} \overset{?}{=} 1$

$1 \overset{?}{=} 1$

41. $\dfrac{175}{221}$ **43.**

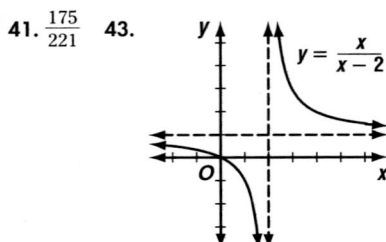

$y = \dfrac{x}{x - 2}$

45. 15 colonial, 45 ranch

Pages 857–859   Lesson 14–5

5. $-\dfrac{4\sqrt{6}}{25}, \dfrac{23}{25}, \dfrac{\sqrt{10}}{5}, -\dfrac{\sqrt{15}}{5}$ **7.** $\dfrac{\sqrt{2-\sqrt{2}}}{2}$

9. $\dfrac{1}{\sin x \cos x} - \dfrac{\cos x}{\sin x} \overset{?}{=} \tan x$

$\dfrac{1 - \cos^2 x}{\sin x \cos x} \overset{?}{=} \tan x$

$\dfrac{\sin^2 x}{\sin x \cos x} \overset{?}{=} \tan x$

$\tan x = \tan x$

11. $-\dfrac{24}{25}, -\dfrac{7}{25}, \dfrac{2\sqrt{5}}{5}, \dfrac{\sqrt{5}}{5}$ **13.** $\dfrac{4\sqrt{2}}{9}, -\dfrac{7}{9}, \dfrac{\sqrt{6}}{3}, -\dfrac{\sqrt{3}}{3}$

15. $\dfrac{24}{25}, \dfrac{7}{25}, \dfrac{3\sqrt{10}}{10}, -\dfrac{\sqrt{10}}{10}$ **17.** $-\dfrac{4\sqrt{2}}{9}, -\dfrac{7}{9}, \dfrac{\sqrt{6}}{3}, -\dfrac{\sqrt{3}}{3}$

19. $\dfrac{\sqrt{2+\sqrt{3}}}{2}$ **21.** $\dfrac{\sqrt{2-\sqrt{2}}}{2}$

23. $\cos^2 2x + 4 \sin^2 x \cos^2 x \overset{?}{=} 1$

$\cos^2 2x + \sin^2 2x \overset{?}{=} 1$

$1 = 1$

25. $\sin 2x \overset{?}{=} 2 \cot x \sin^2 x$

$2 \sin x \cos x \overset{?}{=} 2 \dfrac{\cos x}{\sin x} \cdot \sin^2 x$

$2 \sin x \cos x = 2 \sin x \cos x$

27. $2 \cos^2 \dfrac{x}{2} \overset{?}{=} 1 + \cos x$

$2\left(\pm\sqrt{\dfrac{1 + \cos x}{2}}\right)^2 \overset{?}{=} 1 + \cos x$

$2\left(\dfrac{1 + \cos x}{2}\right) \overset{?}{=} 1 + \cos x$

$1 + \cos x = 1 + \cos x$

29. $\pm \dfrac{\sqrt{18 - 3\sqrt{18 - 6\sqrt{5}}}}{6}$ **31.** $61.3°$

33. $b = 11.0, c = 12.2, C = 78$ **35.** 1.814   **37.** $h = \dfrac{3V}{\pi r^2}$

Page 860   Lesson 14–6A
1. $11.5°, 168.5°$ **3.** $0°, 60°, 180°, 300°$ **5.** $-170°, -51.6°,$
$185.2°, 308.4°$

Pages 864–867   Lesson 14–6
5. $15°, 75°, 195°, 255°$ **7.** $0°, 180°$ **9.** $\dfrac{\pi}{2} + k\pi, \dfrac{2\pi}{3} + 2k\pi,$

$\dfrac{4\pi}{3} + 2k\pi$ **11.** $\dfrac{\pi}{3} + 2k\pi, \dfrac{5\pi}{3} + 2k\pi$ **13.** $60°, 120°, 240°,$

$300°$ **15.** $90°, 270°$ **17.** $30°, 150°$ **19.** $\dfrac{7\pi}{6}, \dfrac{11\pi}{6}$ **21.** $\dfrac{4\pi}{3}, \dfrac{5\pi}{3}$

23. $\dfrac{\pi}{2}, \dfrac{7\pi}{6}, \dfrac{11\pi}{6}$ **25.** $45° + k \cdot 180°$ **27.** $0° + k \cdot 180°$

29. $120° + k \cdot 360°, 240° + k \cdot 360°$ **31.** $0° + k \cdot 180°,$

$90° + k \cdot 360°$ **33.** $\dfrac{7\pi}{6} + 2k\pi, \dfrac{11\pi}{6} + 2k\pi$

35. $\pi + 2k\pi, \dfrac{\pi}{3} + 2k\pi, \dfrac{5\pi}{3} + 2k\pi$ **37.** $\dfrac{2\pi}{3} + 2k\pi, \dfrac{4\pi}{3} + 2k\pi$

39. $0 + k\pi, \dfrac{\pi}{6} + 2k\pi, \dfrac{5\pi}{6} + 2k\pi$

41a. two times; $90°$ and $270°$ **41b.** Exercise 15; yes
41c. They are the same.   **41d.** If the equation is an
identity then the two curves are identical. Otherwise, the
curves intersect only at certain points.   **43.** All reals
except $0 + \dfrac{k\pi}{2}$, where k is any integer   **45.** $0°$ **47.** $\dfrac{2}{3}$

49. 24.576% **51.** $\dfrac{1}{2}, \dfrac{1}{4}$ **53.** $29x \le 609; x \le 21$

Page 869   Chapter 14   Highlights
1. g   **3.** b   **5.** e   **7.** i   **9.** a

**Pages 870–872   Chapter 14   Study Guide and
Assessment**
11.

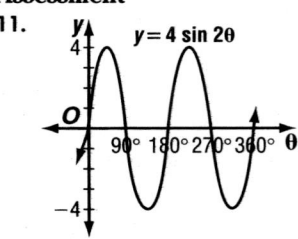

$y = 4 \sin 2\theta$

13.

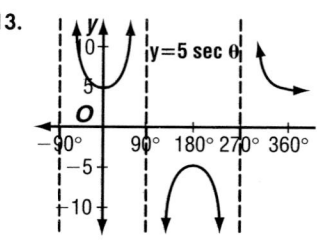

15.

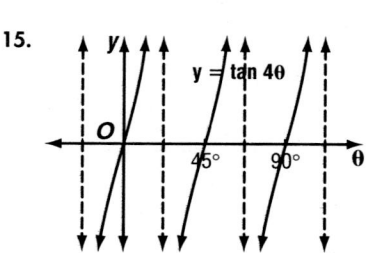

17. $\dfrac{2\sqrt{3}}{3}$

43. $0°$ **45.** $15°, 75°, 195°, 255°$ **47.** $30°, 210°$ **49.** 65.3 miles

19. $\cot\theta$ **21.** $\csc\alpha$

23.
$$\dfrac{\sin\theta}{1-\cos\theta} \overset{?}{} \dfrac{1}{\sin\theta}+\dfrac{\cos\theta}{\sin\theta}$$
$$\dfrac{\sin\theta}{1-\cos\theta} \overset{?}{} \dfrac{1+\cos\theta}{\sin\theta}\cdot\dfrac{1-\cos\theta}{1-\cos\theta}$$
$$\dfrac{\sin\theta}{1-\cos\theta} \overset{?}{} \dfrac{1-\cos^2\theta}{\sin\theta(1-\cos\theta)}$$
$$\dfrac{\sin\theta}{1-\cos\theta} \overset{?}{} \dfrac{\sin^2\theta}{\sin\theta(1-\cos\theta)}$$
$$\dfrac{\sin\theta}{1-\cos\theta} = \dfrac{\sin\theta}{1-\cos\theta}$$

25.
$$\sec x\,(\sec x-\cos x) \overset{?}{} \tan^2 x$$
$$\sec^2 x-\sec x\cos x \overset{?}{} \tan^2 x$$
$$\sec^2 x-1 \overset{?}{} \tan^2 x$$
$$\tan^2 x = \tan^2 x$$

27.
$$\dfrac{\csc\theta+1}{\cot\theta} \overset{?}{} \dfrac{\cot\theta}{\csc\theta-1}\cdot\dfrac{\csc\theta+1}{\csc\theta+1}$$
$$\dfrac{\csc\theta+1}{\cot\theta} \overset{?}{} \dfrac{\cot\theta(\csc\theta+1)}{\csc^2\theta}$$
$$\dfrac{\csc\theta+1}{\cot\theta} \overset{?}{} \dfrac{\cot\theta(\csc\theta+1)}{\cot^2\theta}$$
$$\dfrac{\csc\theta+1}{\cot\theta} = \dfrac{\csc\theta+1}{\cot\theta}$$

29. $\dfrac{\sqrt{6}-\sqrt{2}}{4}$ **31.** $\dfrac{\sqrt{2}+\sqrt{6}}{-4}$ **33.** $-\dfrac{\sqrt{3}}{2}$

35.
$$\cos(180°-\alpha) = \cos 180°\cos\alpha+\sin\alpha\sin 180°$$
$$= -1\cdot\cos\alpha+\sin\alpha\cdot 0$$
$$= -\cos\alpha$$

37. $\dfrac{120}{169}, \dfrac{119}{169}, \dfrac{5\sqrt{26}}{26}, -\dfrac{\sqrt{26}}{26}$ **39.** $-\dfrac{120}{169}, \dfrac{119}{169}, \dfrac{\sqrt{26}}{26}, -\dfrac{5\sqrt{26}}{26}$

41.
$$\tfrac{1}{2}\sin 2x \overset{?}{} \dfrac{\tan x}{1+\tan^2 x}$$
$$\tfrac{1}{2}\sin 2x \overset{?}{} \dfrac{\frac{\sin x}{\cos x}}{\sec^2 x}$$
$$\tfrac{1}{2}\sin 2x \overset{?}{} \dfrac{\sin x}{\cos x}\cdot\cos^2 x$$
$$\tfrac{1}{2}\sin 2x \overset{?}{} \dfrac{2\sin x\cos x}{2}$$
$$\tfrac{1}{2}\sin 2x = \tfrac{1}{2}\sin 2x$$

SELECTED ANSWERS

Selected Answers

Cover Pete Saloutos/The Stock Market, (l inset)Kunio Owaki/The Stock Market, (r inset)Matt Meadows; **iii** (t)Ron Batzdorff/Universal City Studios/Shooting Star, (b)National Portrait Gallery, Smithsonian Instituion/Art Resource, NY; **viii** (l)Chris Slagerman, (r)Michael Springer/Gamma-Liaison; **ix** (t)John Daniel/Allsport USA, (b)Jonathon Daniel/Allsport USA; **x** (l)Steve Lissau, (r)Walt Disney Studios/Shooting Star, (br)UPI/Bettmann; **xi** (t)H. Armstrong Roberts (b)Ed Bock/The Stock Market; **xii** (t)Wayne Shields/Valan Photos, (b)Shattil/Rozinski; **xiii** (t)Terje Rakke/The Image Bank, (b)NASA; **xiv** (t)Giraudon/Art Resource, NY, (c)CNRI/Science Photo Library/Photo Researchers, (b)Frank Abbeloos/Gamma-Liaison; **xv** (t)S. Kermani/Gamma-Liaison (b)Deborah Davis/PhotoEdit; **xvi** (t)Buddy Mays/FPG International, (b)Photofest; **xvii** (t)Bruce Byers/FPG International, (b)Bill Miles/The Stock Market; **xix** (t)Tony Quinn Photography, (bl)Lee Balgeman, (br)Charles Krebs/The Stock Market; **4** (t)John Elk III/Stock Boston, (b)Culver Pictures; **5** (tl)J.D. Cuban/Allsport USA, (tr)Chris Cole/Allsport USA, (c)The Bettmann Archive, (bl)Don Mason/The Stock Market, (br)H.P. Merten/The Stock Market; **7** Chris Slagerman; **8** Morton & White Photographic; **9** (l)The Bettmann Archive, (r)Frederic Stein/FPG International; **10** Per Eide/The Image Bank; **12** Jose L. Pelaez/The Stock Market; **15** Morton & White Photographic; **16** Doug Martin; **17** (t)Rob Tringali Jr./Sportschrome, (b)AP/Wide World Photos; **19** Aaron Haupt; **20** (t)Halebian/Gamma-Liaison, (b)Kunio Owaki/The Stock Market; **21** (t)Richard Hutchings/Photo Researchers, (b)Aaron Haupt; **22** (t)Craig Tuttle/The Stock Market, (b)Al Behrman/AP/Wide World Photos; **24** The Bettmann Archive; **25** (t)Jim Patrico/David R. Frazier Photolibrary, (b)Jim Steinberg/Photo Researchers; **26** (t)David Pollack/The Stock Market, (b)Steven Gottlieb/FPG International; **27** The Bettmann Archive; **31** Richard Pasley/Stock Boston; **32** Franco D'Ambrosio/Everett Collection; **33** (t)John M. Roberts/The Stock Market, (bl)Michael Schneps/The Image Bank, (br)Don Smith/Sports Photo Master; **34** Rick Weber; **37** (t)David Lawrence/The Stock Market, (b)Aaron Haupt; **38** Bob Daemmrich; **39** Howard M. Paul/Emergency! Stock; **41** Suzanne Murphy-Larronde/FPG International; **42** Peter Steiner/The Stock Market; **43** (t)Bob Daemmrich/Stock Boston, (b)Michael A. Keller Studios Ltd./The Stock Market; **46** Gary Bistram/The Image Bank; **48** (l)Doug Martin, (r)Thierry Cariou/The Stock Market; **49** Morton & White Photographic; **51** (t)Universal City Studios/Photofest, (b)Lucasfilm Ltd./Paramount Pictures, courtesy Kobal Collection; **52** Michael Furman/The Stock Market; **53** Marvy!/The Stock Market; **54** Jose L. Pelaez/The Stock Market; **58** Donna McLaughlin/The Stock Market; **59** Frank Moscati/The Stock Market; **60** (l)Geoff Butler, (r)UPI/Bettmann; **61** Animals Animals/Zig Leszczynski; **62** (t)Stephen Simpson/FPG International, (b)Animals Animals/Breck P. Kent; **63** (t)Jerry Jacka Photography, (c)Dick Dietrich/FPG International, (bl)FPG International, (bc)Yuri Dojc/The Image Bank, (br)First Image; **64** (t)Ron Thomas/FPG International, (b)courtesy University of AZ/George Kew International; **65** Lou Florence/David R. Frazier Photolibrary; **66** Robert A. Jureit/The Stock Market; **70** First Image; **71** Donald C. Johnson/The Stock Market; **75** Geoff Butler; **77** (l)Carl Roessler/FPG International, (r)Frank S. Balthis; **78** Richard Foreman/Everett Collection; **80** (l)The Bettmann Archive, (r)David Madison; **81** The Bettmann Archive; **86** (t)Ulf Sjostedt/FPG International, (b)FPG International; **88** Rick Weber; **90** (t)Charles E. Zirkle, (b)KS Studio; **91** Morton & White Photographic; **92** Marcus Brooke/FPG International; **93** John Youger; **94** Steve Lissau; **95** NASA; **97** (t)Michael Paris/Shooting Star, (b)Everett Collection; **99** (t)Telegraph Colour Library/FPG International, (b)Joseph DiCello; **100** Tom Bean/The Stock Market; **101** Arthur Tilley/FPG International; **104** Morton & White Photographic; **106** Gerald French/FPG International; **107** (l)Doug Martin, (r)Morton & White Photographic; **110** Geoff Butler; **112** Kenji Kerins; **113** Morton & White Photographic; **114** Vladimir Pcholkin/FPG International; **118** Geoff Butler; **119** (t)Etienne de Malglaive/Liaison International, (b)Animals Animals/Raymond A. Mendez; **122** (t)ATC Productions/The Stock Market, (c)Ancient Art & Architecture Collection, (b)The Bettmann Archive; **123** (tl)courtesy William Morrow & Co., Inc., (tr)Roger Tully/Tony Stone Images, (bl)Paul L. Ruben Archives, (br)The Bettmann Archive; **126** (t)Aaron Haupt, (b)Tom Tracy/Photo Researchers; **128** Mark D. Phillips/Photo Researchers; **132** David Cannon/Allsport USA; **133, 135** Aaron Haupt; **139** Glencoe photo; **140** Richard Hutchings; **145** John G. Davenport/Shooting Star; **146** courtesy Peter Shor; **148** NASA; **150** Ralph Morse, Life Magazine/Time Inc.; **151** Doris DeWitt/Tony Stone Images; **153** Mitch Kezar/Tony Stone Images; **154** Willard Clay/Tony Stone Images; **157** The Bettmann Archive; **158** (l)Kenji Kerins, (r)Stephen Wade/Allsport USA; **160** Aaron Haupt; **161** Geoff Butler; **162** Ken

Levine/Allsport USA; **163** Alan Carey; **165** Geoff Butler; **168** First Image; **170** Larry Hamill; **171** Jonathon Daniel/Allsport USA; **174** (t)Glencoe photo, (b)William J. Weber; **179, 180** First Image; **181** (t)Rick Weber, (b)H. Abernathy/H. Armstrong Roberts; **182** (t)Fred Ward/Black Star, (c)Geoff Butler, (b)Mak-I Photo Design; **183** (tl)courtesy Judy Hehs, (tr)David R. Frazier Photolibrary, (c)Dennis Brack/Black Star, (b)Alan Becker/The Image Bank; **186** (t)First Image, (b)courtesy Marietta College; **187** (t)Cheryl Blair, (bl)Steve Lissau, (br)Tim Courlas; **188** Ken Frick; **191** Geoff Butler; **192** courtesy Gloria P. Mondragon; **194** (t)Robert A. Jureit/The Stock Market, (b)Andrew Holbrooke/The Stock Market; **195** Mark E. Gibson; **197** Aaron Haupt; **198** Matt Meadows; **199** Geoff Butler; **200** (t)David M. Dennis, (b)Kenji Kerins; **203** Mark E. Gibson; **204** King/Zefa/H. Armstrong Roberts; **205** John M. Roberts/The Stock Market; **208** Trent Steffler/David R. Frazier Photolibrary; **210** George Holton/Photo Researchers; **211** Mark E. Gibson; **212** (t)Ron Lowery/The Stock Market, (b)National Archives; **216** courtesy Rebecca Marier; **218** Michael Simpson/FPG International; **219, 222** Mark Steinmetz/Amanita Pictures; **225** Matt Meadows; **226** Aaron Haupt; **228** R. Kord/H. Armstrong Roberts; **231** Geoff Butler; **235** Matt Meadows; **236** Doug Pensinger/Allsport USA; **239** (tl)H. Armstrong Roberts, (tr)courtesy Angela Wimberly, (b)Manfred Gottschalk/Tom Stack & Associates; **241** H. Armstrong Roberts; **243** (t)Jim Stratford/Black Star, (b)Steve Lissau; **244** Aaron Haupt; **252** (t)Geoff Butler, (c)Scala/Art Resource, NY, (bl)J. Snyder/The Stock Market, (br)Culver Pictures; **253** (tl)courtesy David Bray, (tr)Aaron Haupt, (c)Carol Halebian/Gamma-Liaison, (b)Morton & White Photographic from Dover Publications, Inc.; **258** Aaron Haupt; **260** UPI/Bettmann; **261** Mark E. Gibson; **265** Aaron Haupt; **266** David L. Perry; **267** Chisholm Rich & Associates/The Stock Market; **270** Ed Bock/The Stock Market; **272** Everett Collection; **280** Viviane Moos/The Stock Market; **281** John Paul/FSP/Gamma-Liaison; **284** Tony Freeman/PhotoEdit; **286** Reuters/Bettmann Newsphotos; **287** Stewart/Allsport USA; **288** Tony Freeman/PhotoEdit; **291** Rick Weber; **294** (l)Yann Guichaouva/Allsport USA, (r)Rick Weber; **295** (t)UPI/Bettmann, (b)Geoff Butler; **296** National Portrait Gallery, Smithsonian Institution/Art Resource, NY; **297** Everett Collection; **301** (l)Barry Seidman/The Stock Market, (r)Wernher Krutein/Gamma-Liaison; **303** Larry Hamill; **304** Alan Oddie/PhotoEdit; **308** Comnet/Westlight; **309** Kaku Kurita/Gamma-Liaison; **313** UPI/Bettmann; **316** Mehau Kulyk/Science Photo Library/Photo Researchers, (b inset)The Bettmann Archive; **317** Tibor Bognar/The Stock Market; **318 321** Digital Art/Westlight; **322** The Bettmann Archive; **327** (l)Doug Martin, (r)Glencoe photo; **328** David Ball/The Stock Market; **329** (t)Peter Beck/The Stock Market, (b)David Young-Wolff/PhotoEdit; **330** (t)David Young-Wolff/PhotoEdit, (b)Morton & White Photographic; **331** (t)Jesse Frohman, (c)Massimo Mastrorillo/The Stock Market, (bl)Presse Sports, (bc)reprinted with permission of Texas Instruments, (br)The Bettmann Archive; **334** (t)Ron Batzdorff/Universal City Studios/Shooting Star, (b)Raven/Explorer/Photo Researchers; **337** Doug Martin; **341** (t)Simon Bruty/Allsport USA, (b)Richard Martin/Allsport USA; **342** ©1995 Sotheby's, Inc.; **345** J. Barry O'Rourke/The Stock Market; **346** (l)Lee Snider, (r)Rick Weber; **349** Mark E. Gibson; **350** Aaron Haupt; **352** Vandystadt/Allsport USA; **353** Wes Thompson/The Stock Market; **355** Mark E. Gibson; **358** courtesy Bryan Starr; **361** Dave Lawrence/The Stock Market, (b)Warren Morgan/Westlight; **364** Kennon Cooke/Valan Photos; **367** Maggie Steber; **368** J. Pat Carter/Gamma-Liaison; **370** Buddy Mays/FPG International; **371** Bill Ross/Westlight; **374** The Kobal Collection; **377** First Image; **378** E.H. Wallop/The Stock Market; **382** Bob Mullenix; **383** T. Kitchin/Tom Stack & Associates; **384** J. Barry O'Rourke/The Stock Market; **386** Tim Defrisco/Allsport USA; **387** Wayne Shiels/Valan Photos; **388** C.W. Norris/Valan Photos; **389** Geoff Butler; **390** John Eastcott & Yva Momatiuk/Valan Photos; **391** Aaron Haupt; **392** (l)Mario Elie Dunks/Allsport USA, (r)Al Bello/Allsport USA; **393** Myrleen Ferguson/PhotoEdit; **394** Richard Dunoff/The Stock Market; **395** Chuck Savage/The Stock Market; **396** (l)Aaron Haupt, (r)Bob Daemmrich Photography; **397** Joe Towers/The Stock Market; **398** Doug Martin; **403** Rick Weber; **406** (t)Jon Bradley/Tony Stone Images, (c)The Bettmann Archive, (b)Glencoe photo; **407** (tl)National Geographic Society Image Collection, (tr)Everett Collection, (cl)The Bettmann Archive, (cr)courtesy Math Association of America, (b)Morton & White Photographic; **408** Paul Vandevelder/Gamma-Liaison; **412** Mark E. Gibson; **413** James Blank/FPG International; **414** Bob Newland/courtesy Belle Fourche Chamber of Commerce; **415** David R. Frazier Photolibrary; **418** (l)Hank Morgan/Science Source/Photo Researchers, (r)Arthur Tilley/FPG International; **419** Morton & White Photographic; **421** (t)C. Moore/

PHOTO CREDITS

Westlight, (b)Tom Tracy/FPG International; **423** Robert Landau/ Westlight; **424** Ron Watts/Westlight; **427** Shattil/Rozinski; **428** (l)Ted Rice, (r)Lawrence Manning/Westlight; **429** Mary Lou Uttermohlen; **431** Peter Pearson/Tony Stone Images; **434** NASA/Science Source/Photo Researchers; **438** Jeff Kaufman/FPG International; **440** R. Stockton/H. Armstrong Roberts; **447** David W. Hamilton/The Image Bank; **449** First Image; **450** Herman Kokojan/Black Star; **451** Dallas & John Heaton/Westlight; **452** A. Tovy/H. Armstrong Roberts; **454** (t)David Austen/FPG International, (b)First Image; **455** Doug Martin; **460** (l)Wadsworth Laboratories/Photo Unit NY State Dept. of Health, (r)Geoff Butler; **463** Geoff Butler; **466** (l)Photofest, (r)Gamma-Liaison; **467** Francois Gohier/Photo Researchers; **468** Steven Gottleib/FPG International; **472** David Lissy/FPG International; **473** (l)Doug Martin, (r)Harald Sund/The Image Bank; **476** (t)Aaron Haupt, (cl)First Image, (cr)Earl Young/FPG International, (b)Jerry Cooke/Photo Researchers; **477** (tl)Andy Freeberg/Time Magazine, (tr)Rick Weber, (c)Bridgeman/ Art Resource, NY, (b)courtesy The National Inventors Hall of Fame; **478** (l)Wolfpro, (r)Bill Watterson/Universal Press Syndicate; **482** Dallas & John Heaton/Westlight; **484** (t) Prisma/Westlight, (c)E.R. Degginger/Photo Researchers, (b)First Image; **485** David Stoecklein/ F-Stock; **488** George Haling/Photo Researchers; **490** Vic Bider/ PhotoEdit; **493** Morton & White Photographic; **495** Alfred Gescheidt/ The Image Bank; **497** Glencoe photo; **498** Dick Luria/Science Source/ Photo Researchers; **500** Vicki Silbert/PhotoEdit; **501** Ben Simmons/ The Stock Market; **502** (t)Bill Bachman/PhotoEdit, (b)First Image; **507** Geoff Butler; **509** (t)Jose Fuste Rage/The Stock Market, (b)AP/Wide World Photos; **514** (t)Geoff Butler, (b)Mak-I Photo Design; **517** J. Messerschmidt/The Stock Market; **519** (t)NASA/The Stock Market, (b)Thomas Del Brase/The Stock Market; **520** CNRI/Science Photo Library/Photo Researchers; **525** (t)Kenji Kerins, (c)NASA, (b)Morton & White Photographic; **528** David Ball/The Stock Market; **532** Tim Courlas; **534** Aaron Haupt; **535** Comstock, Inc.; **546** (t)David Young-Wolff/PhotoEdit, (c)Culver Pictures, (b)National Audobon Society Collections/Science Photo Library/Photo Researchers; **547** (tl)James A. Sugar, (tr)Jeff Greenberg/PhotoEdit, (c)courtesy Motorcycle Heritage Museum, (bl)NASA, (br)The Stock Market; **550** The Bettmann Archive; **552** Mark Steinmetz/Amanita Pictures; **554** Doug Martin; **556** David R. Frazier Photolibrary; **557** Bob Jones/Gamma-Liaison; **559** Bonnie Kamin/PhotoEdit; **560** Steven M. Barnett/Gamma-Liaison; **561** David R. Frazier Photolibrary; **567** (t)Aaron Haupt, (b)Jon Feingersh/The Stock Market; **569** First Image; **570** KS Studio; **572** "Men of Mark: Eminent, Progressive and Rising" by Rev. William J. Simmons, D.D, Arno Press and The New York Times, 1968; **573** Frank Abbeloos/Gamma-Liaison; **574** Morton & White Photographic; **576** (t)Tom McCarthy/PhotoEdit, (b)Mike Powell/Allsport USA; **579** (t)Raphael Gaillarde/Gamma-Liaison, (b)David Noble/FPG International; **580, 581, 582** David R. Frazier Photolibrary; **583** Robert Brenner/PhotoEdit; **584** Doug Martin; **588** Steve Grohe/The Stock Market; **589** Morton & White Photographic; **590** Dave Nagel/Gamma-Liaison; **591** First Image; **592** (t)Rick Reinhard/Impact Visuals, (c)Fujifotos/The Image Works, (b)Eric Sanford/f/Stock; **593** (t)Lori Grinker/Contact Press Images, (cl)NE State Historical Society, (cr)David Young-Wolff/PhotoEdit, (bl br)First Image; **596** Warner Bros./Everett Collection; **598** (t)David R. Frazier Photolibrary, (b)Stephen Green-Armytage/The Stock Market; **600** Oliver Meckes/Ottawa/Photo Researchers; **601** Harry Engels/Photo Researchers; **602** Dave Brown/The Stock Market; **603** First Image; **604** Geopress/H. Armstrong Roberts; **605** S. Kermani/Gamma-Liaison; **606** The Bettmann Archive; **608** First Image; **609** Alon Reininger/Contact Press/The Stock Market; **610** The Bettmann Archive; **611** Morton & White Photographic; **612** David R. Frazier Photolibrary; **614** Morton & White Photographic; **615** (l)Fisk University Library, (r)David R. Frazier Photolibrary; **617** (t)William Stevens/Gamma-Liaison, (bl)David R. Frazier Photolibrary, (br)Jeff Zaruba/The Stock Market; **619** Fotex/H. Kuehn/Shooting Star; **620** (t)David Nunuk/Science Photo Library/Photo Researchers, (c)First Image, (b)Aaron Haupt; **622** First Image; **624** (t)Rick Weber, (b)Kevin Galvin/The Stock Market; **625, 626** First Image; **631** (t)David R. Frazier Photolibrary, (c)Mark E. Gibson/The Stock Market, (b)FPG International; **632** Robin Prange/The Stock Market; **633** David R. Frazier Photolibrary; **634** (l)Mike Penney/David R. Frazier Photolibrary, (r)First Image; **635** Rick Weber; **636** (l)Joe Mahoney/AP/Wide World Photos, (r)Lee Balterman/FPG Internationl; **641** FPG International; **644** (t)First Image, (c)Telegraph Colour Library/FPG International, (b)Erich Lessing/Art Resource, NY; **645** (tl)Lou Coopey, (b)Aaron Haupt, (others)First Image; **648** Morton & White Photographic; **649** Aaron Haupt; **650** (l)courtesy WSBC Radio, (r)Matt Meadows; **652** John Kelly/The Image Bank; **654** Kenji Kerins; **656** Richard Hutchings/ PhotoEdit; **658** Charles O'Rear/Westlight; **661** Aaron Haupt; **662** The Walt Disney Company/Everett Collection; **667** from Rumpelstiltskin by Jacob & Wilhelm Grimm, illustrated by Bernadette Watts, published by North-South Books Inc., New York. 1993 by NordSud Verlag, Gossau Zurich, Switzerland; **668** (l)Kunio Owaki/The Stock Market, (r)Ed Bock/The Stock Market; **670** Lawrence Migdale; **671** Chris Jones/The Stock Market; **673** Bob Daemmrich; **675** Don Mason/The Stock Market; **677** Morton & White Photographic; **678** Larry Hamill; **680** Nick Nicholson/The Image Bank; **681** (t)Globus Brothers/The Stock Market, (b)Kenji Kerins; **683** Grant Faint/The Image Bank; **685** Jon Feingersh/The Stock Market; **686** Morton & White Photographic; **687** Robert W. Ginn/PhotoEdit; **688** (l)Marc Romanelli/The Image Bank, (c)Ray Ellis/Photo Researchers, (r)First Image; **690** Zefa-Sauer/The Stock Market; **692** Craig Hammell/The Stock Market; **693** (t)Geospace/Science Photo Library/Photo Researchers, (b)Cordon Art B.V.; **694** Deborah Davis/PhotoEdit; **695** Gianni Cigolini/The Image Bank; **698** Aaron Haupt; **700** David W. Hamilton/The Image Bank; **701** Thomas Zimmerman BFF/FPG International; **702** Blaine Harrington III/The Stock Market; **707** William Weber; **710** (t)Rod Joslin, (b)The Science Museum/Science & Society Picture Library; **711** (tl)courtesy Jim McHugh, (tr)Scott Cunningham, (bl)The Bettmann Archive, (bc)UPI/Everett Collection, (br)Tony Duffy/Allsport USA; **712** FPG International; **713** (l)Nino Mascardi/The Image Bank, (r)First Image; **714** PEANUTS reprinted by permission of United FeatureSyndicate, Inc.; **715** (l)Bob Daemmrich, (r)StudiOhio; **716** Latent Image; **718** (t)Bruce Byers/FPG International, (bl)McBroom/Tristar Pictures/Shooting Star, (br)Walt Disney Studios/Shooting Star; **719** Geoff Butler; **722** Aaron Haupt; **723** (t)Morton & White Photographic, (b)Geoff Butler; **724** Geoff Butler; **726** First Image; **727** Geoff Butler; **728** Aaron Haupt; **729** (t)William D. Popejoy, (b)James N. Westwater; **730** Geoff Butler; **731** David R. Frazier Photolibrary; **732** Ron Watts/Westlight; **733** Aaron Haupt; **734** First Image; **735** John Gajda/FPG International; **736** First Image; **738** Geoff Butler; **739** Aaron Haupt; **740** Geoff Butler; **741** Gail Meese/ Meese Photo Research; **742** (t)Geoff Butler, (b)Aaron Haupt; **743** (t)Geoff Butler, (b)Frederick McKinney/FPG International; **744** courtesy Denis Stone; **746** THE BORN LOSER reprinted by permission of Newspaper Enterprse Association, Inc.; **747** Ken Frick; **748** Morton & White Photographic; **749** Bob Daemmrich; **751** Billy Barnes/FPG International, Otto Greule/Allsport USA; **752** AP/Wide World Photos; **754** (t)Kunio Owaki/The Stock Market, (b)The Bettmann Archive; **756** Greg Davis/The Stock Market; **757** Canadian Museum of Civilization; **760, 761** Aaron Haupt; **768** Mak-I Photo Design; **768** courtesy Kennywood; **769** (t)courtesy Six Flags Amusement Park, (b)Cedar Point Photo by Dan Feicht; **770** (t)Mary Lou Uttermohlen, (c)J. Ciganovic/FPG International, (b)Mercury Archives/The Image Bank; **771** (tl)courtesy Anna Maria Padilla, (tr)Ted Horowitz/The Stock Market, (b)The Bettmann Archive, (c)Everett Collection; **772** (t)Photofest, (b)Morton & White Photographic; **776** John Meehan/Photo Researchers; **777** Cralle/The Image Bank; **779** Kenneth Redding/The Image Bank; **780** Frank L. Psaute; **781** Terje Rakke/The Image Bank; **784** Morton & White Photographic; **786** Geoffrey Clifford/The Stock Market; **789** Francisco Hidalgo/The Image Bank; **790** Bill Miles/The Stock Market; **791** Jim Erickson/The Stock Market; **792** M.L. Sinibaldi/The Stock Market; **793** J.B. Diedrich/The Stock Market; **797** James Blank/The Stock Market; **798** David Ball/The Stock Market; **799** (l)Universal City Studios/Photofest, (r)Universal City Studios/The Kobal Collection; **801** (l)The Natural History Museum, London, (r)Tom Bean/The Stock Market; **802** Alan Carey; **804** (t)Kenji Kerins, (b)Anne van der Vaeren/The Image Bank; **805** Morton & White Photographic; **808** Bob Daemmrich; **810** Stephen Marks/The Stock Market; **811** Tom Craig/FPG International; **814** KS Studio; **819** Joe DiChello; **822** (t)Veryl Oakland/Retna, (bl)Alan Hipwell/FPG International, (br)First Image; **823** (tl)Mark Sennet/Onyx, (tr)Morton & White Photographic, (c)Joe Wrinn/Harvard University Office of News & Public Affairs, (bl)SuperStock, (br)Mark Reinstein/FPG International; **826** Mercury Archives/The Image Bank; **829** (l)Morton & White Photographic, (r)Peter Aprahamian/Science Photo Library/Photo Researchers; **830** Kenji Kerins; **833** (tl)Gerard Vandystadt/Allsport USA, (tr)Ralph A. Clevenger/Westlight, (b)Alvin E. Staffan; **838** Dallas & John Heaton/Westlight; **840** (t)Pete Saloutos/The Stock Market, (b)Charles Krebs/The Stock Market; **842** Aaron Haupt; **845** First Image; **846** Tony Quinn Photography; **847** Paul McCormick/The Image Bank; **849** H. Richard Johnston/FPG International; **850** Kenji Kerins; **851** (t)Paul McCormick/The Image Bank, (b)David Noble/FPG International; **852** Larry Lee/Westlight; **853** (t)The Bettmann Archive, (b)USDOD; **856** Hank Delespin/The Image Bank; **858** Rick Gayle/The Stock Market; **861** First Image; **863** Steve Proehl/The Image Bank; **864** Telegraph Colour Library/FPG International; **865** Zefa-Kalt/The Stock Market; **866** Aaron Haupt; **867** Morton & White Photographic; **868** Lee Balgeman; **875** (tl)Kennon Cooke/Valan Photos, (tr)David Lawrence/The Stock Market, (bl)Zefa©Kalt/The Stock Market, (br)Larry Hamill.

Photo Credits **995**

City planning
for playground, 568
for population growth and new schools, 601
for subway, 139

Civics and government, 20–21, 71

Civil engineering, 359, 361–362, 579–580, 812

Climate. *See* Meteorology

Colleges
endowments, 168
entrance exams for, 75–76, 114, 120–121
saving for, 542, 589
selecting, 186

Combination locks, 766

Committees, 730, 748

Communication, 88, 90, 93, 171, 204, 421, 472, 561, 602, 635, 712, 713, 717, 762, 798, 834

Community service, 177, 182, 183, 266, 645, 731

Computers
CD-ROM drives, 624
depreciation of, 634
graphing software, 570–571
in home, 252, 253
Internet, 476, 477
nanoseconds, 439
on-line services, 93
Pentium chip, 515
places to purchase, 724
programming, 143
quantum, 146
spreadsheets, 337
viruses, 492

Conservation
of energy, 561
of wilderness, 414

Construction
of brick wall, 582
of foundation of office building, 661
painting, 629, 661
planning housing developments, 722, 852
of roads, 359, 361–362, 812
safety in, 303
of tunnels, 579–580, 804

Consumerism
auto rentals, 112, 139, 159, 171
auto sales, 753–754
average income, 15–16
catalog sales of shoes, 34
delayed payment plans, 118
food purchases, 15–16, 54, 131, 165, 170, 178, 191, 198, 199, 225, 231, 867
gasoline prices, 54
holiday gifts, 48
jeans prices, 21–22
loans, 71, 686
long-distance service, 762
monthly payments, 641, 652, 686
moving van rentals, 133, 134–135
photography, 131, 146
price comparisons, 131, 170
sale prices, 537
spending patterns, 384, 717
store displays, 675

video camera prices, 352
See also Sales

Contests, 42

Cooking, 635, 867

Cosmetology, 834

Cryptology, 212, 216, 218

Cultures
African-American harvest festival *(Kwanzaa),* 656
ancient, 86
Cayuga Indian game of chance *(Dish),* 757
Cherokee Indians, 367
Easter Island, 210
Hindu, 531
Hopi game of chance *(Totolospi),* 750
Japanese card game *(Hanafuda),* 730

Currency conversions, 76, 527

Decision making, 186

Decorating, 316

Demographics. *See* Population statistics

Design, 495, 510, 729

Diet. *See* Food; Health

Discounting, 528

Driving. *See* Automobiles

Earthquakes, 423, 424, 466, 485, 503, 605, 606, 608, 609, 610, 620, 621, 732. *See also Seismology.*

Ecology
recycling programs, 211, 244, 547, 730, 747
wasteful photocopying, 358
See also Environment

Economics
currency conversions, 76, 527
household income, 132
housing expenses, 132
inflation, 686
spending patterns, 384, 717
taxes, 260
See also Finance

Education
endowments, 168
nursing salaries, 54
SAT test scores, 75–76, 114, 393, 395
teacher salaries, 19–20, 23–24
time needed for exam, 161, 164
See also Colleges; School

Elastic potential, 630

Electrical engineering, 321, 340

Electricity
battery terminals, 321
circuits, 315, 694
conductors, 569
current, 48
impedance, 313, 317, 318, 340

power, 798
resistance, 569, 574, 588
switches, 724

Electronics, 694, 717, 798

Employment, 24, 102, 118, 158, 701. *See also* Business and work

Energy
cellular, 616
conservation of, 561
geothermal, 77
heating sources, 757
solar, 309, 418
wind, 483

Engineering
aerospace, 285, 308, 326, 363, 402, 428, 467, 500, 522, 560, 661, 681
automotive, 294
civil, 359, 361–362, 579–580, 812
electrical, 321, 340
plastics, 489
tunnels, 579–580, 804

Entertainment
amusement parks, 826, 840
animation, 662
CDs, 87, 110, 542, 719–720
cheerleading, 724
concerts, 308
Ferris wheel, 810, 826, 827
films, 51–52, 78, 334, 374, 398, 662, 718, 804
lottery, 726, 730, 737
magic, 267, 375
music, 301, 309, 330, 331, 501, 737, 738, 770, 771, 805, 808, 832
pageants, 723
radio, 633, 634, 648, 650, 717, 760, 798, 834
roller coasters, 768–769, 785, 834, 859, 868
state fair, 178
television, 98, 421, 467, 602, 779
theater, 32, 113, 193, 661
top income earners, 97
See also Games; Sports

Environment
acid rain, 609
air pollution, 101–102, 301
conservation of wilderness, 414
Earth Day commemorative globes, 583
energy conservation, 561
global warming, 101–102
protection of, 546, 547
recycling programs, 547, 730, 747
research tapes, 859
wasteful photocopying, 358
See also Ecology

Exercise 7, 145, 500, 576.
See also Sports

Farming, 59, 99, 153–154, 158, 387–388, 522, 632
aquatic, 669

Finance
credit cards, 528
financial planning, 542

Marketing, 504

Medicine
anesthesia, 394
disease control, 596
dosages of, 12, 394, 499, 554
emergency service, 724, 803
kidney stones, 438
measuring cardiac output, 509
pH of blood, 615
radioactive iodine, 634, 668
veterinary, 163
Young's Rule, 554
See also Health

Meteorology
acid rain, 609
careers in, 746
precipitation, 99, 193, 609, 673, 746
severe weather, 194, 197
sun's intensity, 371
temperature, 10, 25, 33, 242, 374
thunderstorms, 194, 197, 345
volume of water from melting snow, 556
windchill factor, 87

Microhydrotechnology, 317

Mirrors
hyperbolic, 463
parabolic, 418

Museums, 431, 438

Nature
patterns in, 683
shapes in, 688

Navigation, 440, 785, 790, 814

News media, 235, 238

Newspapers
declines in circulation of, 644
subscriptions to, 152

Noise level, 397

Number puzzle, 531

Nutrition. *See* Food; Health

Oceanography, 58, 225

Optics, 786, 789, 814

Orbits
of comets, 454, 467
of planets, 434, 454, 467, 574
of satellites, 308, 428, 467, 681
of spacecraft around Earth, 421, 438

Packaging, 32, 160–161, 504, 543

Paleontology, 631, 634, 799, 801

Parabolic mirrors, 418

Parabolic reflectors, 421, 717

Personal finance. *See* Finance

Pharmacy. *See* Medicine

Photography, 131, 146, 273, 414, 572, 573, 625, 724, 757

Physical fitness. *See* Exercise; Sports

Physics and physical science, 73, 280, 286, 294, 316, 335, 344, 349, 351, 352, 355, 402, 497, 516, 537, 588, 609, 610, 624, 636, 654, 658, 676, 678, 681, 687, 771, 784, 810, 829, 842, 844, 845, 846, 847, 849, 851, 858, 861, 863–864, 865, 866

Physiology, 398, 510. *See also* Human body

Playgrounds, 568, 681

Politics, 20–21, 145, 762

Pollution, 101–102, 301

Population statistics
on American Indians, 62
on Asian- and Pacific-Islander Americans, 243
births and deaths on Atlantic Seaboard, 198
census, 26, 62
for cities, 239, 510, 601, 634
on deer, 92
life expectancy, 447
on population growth, 64, 139, 601, 604, 626, 627, 629, 634
on rabbits in Australia, 598–599
for South American cities, 510
for states, 64, 139
on wildebeests, 478, 479

Postal service
number of different stamps, 622, 623
rates, 49, 104, 140

Prices
comparing, 131, 170
of gasoline, 54
of jeans, 21–22
per pound, 165
sale, 537
of video cameras, 352
wholesale, 542

Profits
dividing, 852
estimating, 253, 378

Puzzles, 531, 725

Pyramids, 86, 511, 779

Quality control, 389, 395

Quantum mechanics, 316

Radio broadcasting, 633, 634, 648, 650, 717, 760, 798, 834

Rainbows, 786

Real estate, 634, 635, 669

Records, world, 339

Recreation. *See* Entertainment; Games; Sports

Relativity, 560

Retail sales. *See* Sales

Safety
of air traffic, 428, 472
of automobile traffic, 98, 350, 555, 756
in construction, 303

Salary. *See* Income

Sales
advertising, 26, 466, 731, 840
of automobiles, 753–754
bonuses, 526
catalog, 34
of CD-ROM drives, 624
commissions, 537, 669
discounts, 528
of food, 15–16, 54, 131, 165, 170, 178, 191, 198, 199, 225, 231, 867
of hot drinks, 138, 389
of jeans, 21–22, 390
markups, 542
of newspapers, 152, 644
of paint, 163
retail, 163, 225, 492, 682, 719–720
sale prices, 537
of shoes, 34, 378
of sporting goods, 195
store displays, 675
of stuffed animals, 219, 222
tracking, 188
wholesale prices, 542

Satellites, 308, 428, 467, 681

School
city planning for, 601
class enrollment, 748
committees, 730, 748
competitions, 406, 407
epidemics, 204, 272
food costs, 178
grades, 23
peer mediation group, 727
prom, 734–735
schedule of classes, 715
student expenditures, 22
study groups, 730
tests, 23, 46, 58, 75–76, 78, 114, 204, 242, 715, 753
time management, 151
time needed for exam, 161, 164
yearbook staff, 748
See also Colleges

Science, 93, 95, 254

Seismology, 423, 424, 466, 485, 503, 605, 606, 608, 609, 610, 620, 621, 732. *See also* Earthquakes

Shopping
for CDs, 110, 542, 719–720
at malls, 25
See also Consumerism; Sales

Snell's law, 789, 866

Social studies, 730

Sociology, 239

Solar energy, 309, 418

Sonar, 77

INDEX

Index

fractal trees, 688
games of chance, 733
geometric series, 672, 673
graphing equations in three variables, 172–173
head vs. height, 96
inverses of functions, 534, 535
iteration, 529–530
locating foci of ellipses, 434, 436
logarithmic functions, 608
multiplying binomials, 262, 264
parabolas, 419
permutations, 723
rational functions, 552
rotations, 201, 202
special sequences, 684
step angles, 802
systems of equations, 134, 137
volume, 66

Monomials, 255–260

Multiple, least common, 569, 574

Multiplication
  of binomials, 262–263, 264, 276
  of complex numbers, 313
  identity matrix for, 213–218, 220
  of matrices, 188, 199–204
  of polynomials, 262–263, 276
  of powers, 255–256
  of rational expressions, 562–568
  of roots of quadratic equations, 359–364
  scalar, 188

Multiplication properties
  of equality, 28–29
  for inequalities, 44

Multiplicative inverse property, 14–15, 213–216

Mutually exclusive events, probability of, 746

Napier, John, 618
Natural logarithms, 622–625
Natural numbers, 13–14
Negative exponents, 254
Nichomachus of Gerusa, 4

Normal distribution, 392–398, 403

Notation
  factorial, 696–697
  functional, 154
  scientific, 254–255, 258
  set-builder, 45
  summation, 658–659, 673, 697–698
  nth root, 282–283, 289, 306
  nth term
    of arithmetic sequence, 649–651
    of geometric sequence, 663, 672

Null (empty) set, 40, 128, 149

Number(s)
  complex, 310–321
  integers, 13–14
  irrational, 13–14, 283, 304
  natural, 13–14
  perfect, 12
  prime, 274, 339, 583
  pure imaginary, 310, 313, 315
  rational, 13–14
  real, 13–18, 281–287
  triangular, 374
  whole, 13–14

Number line, 19, 37

Number theory
  fractions, 588
  perfect number, 12
  prime numbers, 274, 339, 583
  pure imaginary numbers, 310, 313, 315
  triangular numbers, 374

Numbered Heads Together, *see Cooperative Learning*

Octagon, 728
Octant, 172, 198
Odds, 734–738, 744, 781
Open sentences, 27, 73
Ordered pairs, 64–71
Ordered triple, 166–167
Order of operations, 7–8
Organizing the Chapter, 4b, 4c, 62b, 62c, 122b, 122c, 182b, 182c, 252b, 252c, 330b, 330c, 406b, 406c, 476b, 476c, 546b, 546c, 592b, 592c, 644b, 644c, 710b, 710c, 770b, 770c, 822b, 822c
Origin, 64
Outside Resources, 4c, 62c, 122c, 182c, 252c, 330c, 406c, 476c, 546c, 592c, 644c, 710c, 770c, 822c
Outliers, 237–238

Pairs Check, *see Cooperative Learning*

Parabolas, 67, 332, 335, 415–422
  in analyzing graphs of quadratic functions, 367–375
  defined, 415
  directrix of, 415

families of, 365–366
focus of, 415
in graphing and solving quadratic inequalities, 376–383
latus rectum, 417
models of, 416, 456
parent graph, 365–366
vertex of, 335

Parabolic curve, 375
Parabolic mirrors, 418
Parabolic reflectors, 421
Parallel lines, 83
Parallelograms
  area of, 264, 265, 560, 562, 564, 567
  length of diagonals in, 803
  perimeter of, 30, 264
  vertices of, 137, 138, 143

Parent graphs
  absolute value, 105
  exponential, 598–602
  linear, 83–87
  logarithmic, 605–610
  polynomial, 482
  quadratic, 365–366
  rational, 548–549
  square root, 535–538

Partial sum, 676–677
Pascal, Blaise, 546, 695
Pascal's triangle, 695–696
Patterns, 80–81, 86, 316, 340, 484, 516, 601, 616, 648, 654, 687, 701
Pendulum, 294, 296–297, 344, 678
  conical, 842, 845
Pentagon, 642, 653

People in the News
  Marc Andreessen, 477
  Amy Banna, 183
  Cheryl Beno, 63
  Tammy Bird, 711
  David Bray, 253
  Sarah Chang, 331
  Lynnea Fajardo, 645
  Chris Galeczka, 407
  AnnaMaria Padilla, 771
  Melissa Poe, 547
  Matt Seto, 123
  Celesly Shabi, 63
  Neil Willenson, 593
  Eldrick "Tiger" Woods, 5

Perfect numbers, 12
Perfect square trinomials, 274, 347, 351
Performance Assessment, 59, 119, 179, 249, 327, 403, 473, 543, 589, 641, 707, 767, 819, 873

Performance Assessment Tasks
  architectural geometry, 473
  area and volume, 327

Perimeter
  of parallelogram, 30, 264
  of pentagon, 642
  of quadrilateral, 654
  of rectangle, 58, 264, 278, 293, 383, 414
  of square, 42, 48, 264, 279, 521, 681, 778
  of triangle, 32, 48, 131, 190, 191, 218, 231, 264, 412, 521, 690, 797

Period, 807, 827, 830

Index

Index

Index